BUYING
MOVIE POSTERS

As a potential seller of movie posters, your prime objective is to realize the most amount of money possible. Assuming this to be true, you have a very important decision to make.

"How do I choose a buyer for my posters?"

This is certainly not an easy task. The pages of this price guide are filled with ads from a wide variety of poster dealers. The majority of these dealers are fine and reputable individuals with a genuine love of movies and movie posters. However, you should be aware that there are a few unscrupulous dealers who make a living preying on the unwary and unknowledgeable poster collector.

If you are considering selling you should keep the following facts in mind!

1. We have the financial ability to buy your posters! We will pay you cash on the spot, no time payments, no I.O.U's, no promises and no "we'll take it on consignment" options.

2. We pay more than any other poster dealer! We learned a long time ago that in order to get the best, you must pay the best. Our regularly advertised buy prices appear in each and every issue of MCW.

If you have movie posters for sale, you owe it to yourself to contact Metropolis.

Call TOLL-FREE:
1-800-229-METRO
STEPHEN FISHLER

873 Broadway, Suite 201 • New York, NY 10003
(212) 260-4147 • Fax: (212) 260-4304

Warren's MOVIE POSTER PRICE GUIDE

Fourth Edition

**The Complete Guide for Collectors of Original Movie Advertising Posters
Including a Comprehensive Index and Price Guide
Spanning the Years 1900 to Date**

by
Jon R. Warren

ISBN 0-9634319-3-5

© 1997 by Jon R. Warren

AMERICAN COLLECTORS EXCHANGE

A Warren Ventures Corp. Company

Chattanooga, TN

51995

9 789634 319351

$19.95

Warren's Movie Poster Price Guide
4th Edition
Published by American Collectors Exchange
A Warren Ventures Corp. Company
2401 Broad Street
Chattanooga, TN 37408
(423) 265-5515

FOURTH EDITION

Library of Congress Card Number:
92-075822

ISBN:
0-9634319-3-5

WARNING: Check listings, fake titles, incorrect years and stars, and other unique information are purposely included throughout the text of this book in order to protect our copyright.

LIMIT OF LIABILITY/DISCLAIMER OF WARRANTY

DEDICATION
To my wife Margaret, whose smile makes the hardest days easy; and to my children: Elizabeth (10), Susannah (7), and Jonathan (3)—no words can express my love for you all.

ADDITIONAL COPIES OF THIS BOOK
May be ordered for $19.95 plus $5 shipping by writing American Collectors Exchange, P. O. Box 2512, Chattanooga, TN 37409
Credit Card orders call 1 (423) 265-5515. FAX orders can be filled by FAXing to 1 (423) 265-5506
Wholesale prices may be obtained by calling 1 (423) 265-5515
Information on other books from American Collectors Exchange may be obtained by writing to the above address.

ABOUT THE AUTHOR

Jon and Margaret Warren

Jon Warren has been a collector of one thing or another since childhood. Stamps and coins were his first forray into collecting, then comic books, blues and jazz records, classic guitars, movie posters, vintage paperbacks, and...name it, he's probably collected it.

He began selling collectibles through mail-order at a very early age and by age 14 was selling rare United States commemorative stamps to collectors around the world. He started into the collectibles business as a full-time occupation in 1976, at age 17. In 1983, while on a road trip in search of rare blues records, he stumbled upon a collector in Houston, Texas who was selling movie posters. Fascinated by the beauty of these Hollywood icons, Jon began searching small-town theaters in hopes of a "poster find". The first edition of *Warren's Movie Poster Price Guide* was published in 1985.

"Of all the collectibles I've ever searched for, movie posters are my favorite and are by far the hardest to find. Most theaters simply threw them away. Someday I hope the general public will appreciate how beautiful and scarce these Hollywood advertising pieces truly are."

Warren is the author or editor of several other collector guides, including *The Official Price Guide To Paperback Books* (House of Collectibles, 1991), *The Overstreet Comic Book Update* (Overstreet, 1982 - 1992), *Posters At Auction* (ACEX, 1994), *The Wizard Comic Book Annual* (Wizard Press, 1994), *Wizard: The Guide To Comics* (Wizard Press), *Inquest: The Guide to Magic The Gathering Collectible Cards* (Wizard Press, 1996), and *Toyfare: The Guide to Collectible Action Figures* (Wizard Press, 1997).

About collecting and the rising costs associated with the collecting endeavor, Jon says, "People should remember that price guides are not bibles—they're intended as a general guide to values. Too many people use price guides as the ending point in a negotiation, rather than as the starting point. The final and real price is what one collector is willing to pay to another at that given time. Also, I think it's very important for collectors to focus on collecting for the love of the collection, not for any speculative future value the collection may (or may not) achieve."

Jon resides on Lookout Mountain in Chattanooga, Tennessee with his wife, Margaret, and their three children, Elizabeth, Susannah, and Jonathan. He is 38 years old.

ACKNOWLEDGEMENTS

A book of this scope would not be possible without the help of many people. The ongoing research represented in these pages is the result of cooperation among people who love the hobby. I take credit for compiling the data in a cohesive form—but special credit goes to everyone who took time to contribute information. Of course, in any attempt of such encyclopedic proportions there are errors. I am solely responsible for these. I hope readers will point me to the errors which inevitably occur.

Special thanks go to my wife, Margaret, for being so understanding during all the late nights spent at the office; to Wade Sain, Walter Irwin, Colette Hite and many others who helped with the day-to-day drudgery of data entry and proofing while compiling this edition. I'd also like to thank my Board of Advisors, and to all those who sent in corrections and letters of comment. And, last but by no means least, I'd like to thank everyone who has bought a copy of this book, GO OUT AND SPREAD THE GOSPEL OF MOVIE POSTERS!

BOARD OF ADVISORS

If you are new to movie posters, I'd recommend any of these people as a source of valuable info and guidance. All are knowledgable, honest, and respectable individuals who share a love of this hobby.

Morris Everett of Last Moving Picture Company in Cleveland, Ohio. Morris is among the most knowledgeable people in the hobby and has the collecting goal of owning one piece on every film ever made (Good Luck!). Morris is one of the true gentlemen in our hobby.

Ed Greguire owns Movie Art of Santa Rosa in Santa Rosa, California. He is a leading collector and dealer in western and serial movie posters. I'm greatful to have Ed as a contributor for our western prices.

John Hazelton sells movie posters to collectors around the world through his operation in Mineola, New York. John was particularly indispensable in contributing prices for western posters and for pricing posters with significant value.

Bruce Hershenson is in the top echelon of poster experts. Bruce organizes the annual movie poster auction for the prestigious Christie's auction house. He also issues several catalogs per year. I thank Bruce for contributing a vast amount of time in proofing and pricing poster rarities for this year's edition.

John Hodson is a well-known collector of western movie posters. As enthusiastic a collector as you will ever meet, I'm very thankful for the gracious contribution of time and energy John gave on this year's book.

Sean Linkenback specializes in Japanese monster posters from his business in Atlanta, Georgia. If it has anything to do with Godzilla, Gamera, Mothra or any of the other classic Japanese monsters, Sean is the man to talk to. Thanks, Sean, for all your help on Japanese posters this year.

Kirby McDaniel operates MovieArt in Austin, Texas. Kirby loves big posters (three sheets, six sheets, 24 sheets) and has an extensive knowledge of beautiful poster design. Thanks to Kirby for his and Channing Thomson's article on re-release posters in this year's book.

Mahtab Moayeri owns and operates the Movie Poster Web Page. Not only is Mahtab a lovely lady, she is one who loves to share her extensive knowledge of movie posters. She was instrumental in providing pricing information for modern posters (1960s and up) for this year's edition.

Peter G. Murphy is a major collector of serial posters. He was a big help in pricing serial posters this year. Thanks Peter!

John Sawyer is a dealer and collector of modern release posters. He, like Mahtab, was a major help in pricing modern movie posters.

Guy Steele operates Stage and Screen in Dallas, Texas and sets up at shows around the country. I'd like to thank Guy for his help on pricing in this year's Guide.

Channing Thomson operates his movie poster business from San Francisco, California. He co-wrote the article on re-release posters in this year's book, as well as contributing a major amount of time in pricing the poster market.

Gary Vaughn operates Cinemonde in Nashville, Tennessee. Gary is another of the true gentlemen in the hobby and has been a long-time friend and advisor. Thanks for everything, Gary.

Dan Welsh operates Stone Litho in Stone Mountain (Atlanta), Georgia. I'm greatly indebted to Dan for going above and beyond the call of duty in pricing data for this year's edition. Dan is one of the most trustworthy people in the hobby, and knows more about movie posters than most people ever will.

Table of Contents

INTRODUCTION

Welcome to the Fourth edition of *Warren's Movie Poster Price Guide*. If this is the first guide to movie poster collecting you've ever bought, I hope you get as much enjoyment from reading it as I have had compiling it. There's so much to learn in this hobby, and so many avenues for the collector to follow, I hope in its own way this book helps you reach your collecting goals.

Over the years, I've come to appreciate movie posters like no other area of collectibles I've been involved in. After all, what's more American than movies, what field has more American Icons, and what better represents these idols of Hollywood than the advertising posters produced to market them? My answer: Nothing!

I've devoted over ten years to building the database of title listings, and of learning the hobby so that I can share my knowledge with you. Why do it? Because I believe that collecting movie posters must become a national pastime and that through the pages of this guide I can do my small share to help spread the word.

Enjoy, and tell a friend about movie posters!

ABOUT THIS BOOK

I want this book to appeal to every level of collector. Although my colleagues in the movie poster field will probably read it just to see if I have a clue what I'm talking about, I'd like to think I have something to offer all collectors—from the new beginner to the oldtimer.

Over 80,000 prices are listed in this book. Obviously, actual sales could not be found to arrive at every price shown. Our expert advisors must sometimes make "educated guesses" when helping us compile prices. Even when interpreting listings of advertised selling prices, one must make a guess as to whether the poster actually sold, what condition it was in, etc. Armed with this guide as a "crash-course" in poster collecting, it is up to the collector or dealer to learn the intricacies of the marketplace. Only dedication, hours of study, and years of experience can do that. The goal of this book is to start the collector on his/her way while avoiding expensive mistakes. Invest your time before you invest your money.

There are numerous cases throughout this book where no documented sales exist. How can you price a poster when one has never been known to sell or, in some cases, even exist? This is difficult, but not impossible. All we can do is ask dealers the question, "What If?".

ALPHABETICAL ARRANGEMENT OF LISTINGS

After skipping articles "A", "AN', and "THE" at the beginning of a title, alphabetization is word by word, not letter by letter. So "An Affair To Remember" is listed under "Affair", and "A Day At The Races" is listed under "Day"; "Day Of The Trumpet" comes before "Day Of Triumph" because we include the article "The" in alphabetizing when it occurs as an interior part of the title. "And Now Tomorrow" appears under "And" because the word "And" is not an article. Using the one-word-at-a-time approach, all titles using the word "In", including "In Which We Serve", are used up before we go on to titles beginning "Incredible", "Inspector", "Intolerance". Compressions such as "Dr." or "St." will be found before titles starting with "Drive" or "Stand" but after titles starting with "Doctor" or "Squeal". Numeric titles such as "2001", or "5000 Faces" will be found mixed alphabetically as though the number were spelled out.

Because of our computer, titles with commas or dashes in the title are sometimes mis-sorted - we are working on a fix for this - until we solve this problem, titles like "Go, Baby, Go" are somehow listed after titles like "Go To Bed". Aren't computers great not?

ADDITIONS AND CORRECTIONS PLEASE HELP!

No book of this type is ever complete. Indeed, the database will continue to evolve and expand along with the hobby. I'm certain many errors have slipped through the cracks—please don't hesitate to bring them to my attention. Corrections and additions will be forthcoming in future editions. Information regarding actual sales is especially important, since it is reasonably certain that the growth of the hobby will hinge, to some degree, on the acceptance of the information contained in this book. You can participate in the evolution of movie poster collecting by adding to the knowledge base and submitting your input for future editions. Your help will be appreciated.

If you can supply an additional checklist from your personal collection, or if you have additional information regarding any of the listings, please forward the information directly to me. A handy form is included on the last page of this book.

ABOUT MOVIE POSTERS

Movie posters, unlike collectibles such as comic books or baseball cards, were never intended to be owned by the general public. In fact, movie posters carry a frightening warning that "this poster is leased, not sold." The warning is intended as a loud bark, not a vicious bite. No one has ever gone to jail for owning an original movie poster. The warning's intent is to instruct the theater owner to return posters to the studio's film exchange when finished with the film. It isn't "against the law" to own an original movie poster.

For the large supplies of original movie posters that found their way into the collector's market we can thank the theater owners who ingored these notices (thank God!). Few owners wanted to take the time to package and return posters at their own expense, so many of them simply stored huge stacks of them in basements or storage rooms. Eventually, the sheer size of the mass of posters would force the owners to do something about the storage problem, so they'd either give them away, sell them, or as too often was the case, simply throw them away.

The fact that posters were not produced for the mass-market makes them one of an elite group of very scarce collectibles. Even today, they are produced in very small quantities. Indeed, this is precisely why the fine art market has become interested in this growing field.. In many cases, posters are one-of-a-kind originals.

Movie posters had a simple purpose: to advertise upcoming films at the local theater. They were intended to be used over and over again, shipped from one theater to the next, until they fell apart from over-use. The print runs were only of sufficient number to supply the theaters that would be showing the film. During the 1930s there may have been as few as 3,000 theaters nationwide, so it is a safe bet that under 10,000 one sheets were printed for any given film during the 1930s. Even for a film such as *Rocky* or *Jaws*, only enough posters were printed to supply the theaters. Fewer than 25,000 theaters were in business as of 1980, so you get the idea.

Why has collecting movie posters become such a big deal? One reason is the universal appeal that posters have. Everyone loves films; and movie posters are the physical incarnation of these films. Movie stars are America's royalty. When we think of the great American icons of the last 75 years, we conjure images of Marilyn Monroe, James Dean, John Wayne, Elvis Presley, Clark Cable, Jack Nicholson, and so on. Hollywood is one of the great American creations—as imbedded in our culture as sports and jazz music. But gumcards and jazz records were produced in the millions. Movie posters are inherently scarce, like a limited-edition print. Therefore, movie posters are virtually unmatched as icons of American culture.

THE EARLY DAYS OF FANDOM

Original movie posters have interested collectors for many years. These collectors were mostly men (but now we are seeing a healthy interest from women, too) who were big movie fans. Many had worked in the exhibition business, as ad men, theater owners, projectionists, or distributors. They had a nostalgic fondness for this material and a knowledge of where posters could be found. They formed the nexus of poster collecting. Some acquired posters in bulk and re-warehoused them. Others simply approached the exchanges and asked if they might buy this or that. They began to trade with each other. Soon they were getting together at shows and conventions, trading in both posters and actual films. The early conventions happened in the late '60s, but by the '70s, film and poster conventions were common in the big cities. Stores specializing in movie posters, books and memorabilia began to spring up across the country. Collector tradezines, like *The Big Reel* and *Film Collector's World* sprang up, and it was through publications like these that collectors began to know each other, correspond and trade. The moment the first movie poster was sold for a profit, the movie poster dealer was born. The mail-order dealer became the chief outlet for much of the trading that was done for many years. Some of the dealers who were there in the beginning are still in business. In the late 1980s, auctions of film posters began. When the major auctioneers like Christie's and Sotheby's have made time in their schedules for film poster auctions, it indicates a wider acceptance of these posters as legitimate collectibles. A record of auction prices realized is published by the auction houses themselves and in such publications as *Posters At Auction*, also published by American Collectors Exchange.

COLLECTING HOLLYWOOD

There are about as many different ways to collect posters as there are poster collectors. We have completists who want one copy of every poster ever released, collectors of certain stars (from Bogart to Schwartzenegger), collectors of appealing graphics or famous American illustrators, collectors of certain film studios, cartoon collectors, horror collectors, Academy award collectors, sports collectors, collectors of certain artists, collectors of landmark (four-star) films, genre collectors (such as comedy, science fiction, mystery, western, etc.), and since the hot growth of the last few years, we have speculators and investors coming into the market.

Regardless of how you start your collection, follow an old collector's adage: Spend your time before you spend your money.

Each individual collector is possessed by a different collecting bug. If you are a new collector, you may decide to build a collection of posters of your favorite star, or you may like a particular genre. The best motivation for pursuing any collecting goal is to pick something you *like* and collect it with a passion.

I don't recommend that a new collector be motivated by a desire to make money. By collecting an area that you enjoy, your first reward will always be pride of ownership. If your collection rises in value, consider it an added plus. Regardless of which direction you go, follow an old collector's adage: Spend your time before you spend your money. This means that you should learn as much as you can about the hobby before you blindly drop cash down some empty hole. Along the way, you should be collecting knowledge as much as you are collecting posters.

HOW TO START YOUR COLLECTION

Once you have decided what to collect, you will want to make your first acquisition. In big cities such as New York or Los Angeles there are stores that specialize in vintage posters. If you are lucky enough to be in such a city, I would recommend that you go with haste to such a vintage poster shop. Yard sales, flea markets, estate sales, etc. are all potential sources if you have the time and patience. But, patience is the word. You will burn a lot of gas before you find some good vintage posters. Posters are very rare and were not intended for the general public, so finds at yard sales are few and far between unless you happen upon the widow of a deceased theater owner. But there is nothing greater than the thrill of the treasure hunt, and someday you too could walk into a poster bonanza... hundreds or maybe thousands of early film posters, with multiple copies of *Dracula* and *Frankenstein* one-sheets...asking the old theater owner his price while holding your breath...the stuff that dreams are made of!

ABOUT PRICES IN THIS BOOK

Prices shown are average retail values for **original release One Sheet movie posters of unless otherwise noted.**

Please be aware that **prices vary widely** from region to region. Movie poster prices are constantly changing. Current price estimates are the result of thousands of hours of research, with the help of a nationwide network of knowledgeable dealers and collectors including consultants from the major auction houses.

This guide shows a price range, with the low end being the estimated value of the poster in average (VG) used condition and the high end being the value of the poster in excellent (EX) unused or slightly-used condition. Posters in superb like-new condition are worth 25% above the high end of the range. Posters in less-than-average or worn condition will fetch anywhere from 25% to 75% of the low end of the range depending upon the amount of damage.

The price range also can be used as a wholesale/retail range, with the top price being the retail value of a poster in excellent condition, and the low range being the dealer price, or wholesale value of the poster in excellent condition.

This price guide is intended as a *guide* to the collector, and not the final authority. Use these prices as a guide, and learn the exceptions to the rule which may not be reflected in the prices shown (such as the difference in value between *Snow White* styles A, B and C).

The price range also can be used as a wholesale/retail range, with the top price being the retail value of a poster in excellent condition, and the low range being the dealer price, or wholesale value of the poster in excellent condition.

Prices are an average of retail prices being charged across the nation.

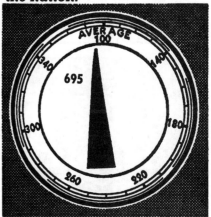

This price guide is intended as a guide to the collector, and not the final authority. Use these prices as a guide, and learn the exceptions to the rule which may not be reflected in the prices shown (such as the difference in value between Snow White styles A, B and C).

ONE SHEET

HALF SHEET

VALUING POSTERS OTHER THAN ONE SHEETS

ONE SHEET (1S). 27"x41" Priced as shown in the guide.
THREE SHEET (3S). 41"x81" 100-150% of one sheet price;
PRE-1950 Warner Bros.: 200% or more of one sheet price.
SIX SHEET (6S). 81"x81" Usually about the same as a three sheet, although in many cases of classic films prior to 1940 no known six sheets exist. In these cases, establishing a relative value is impossible.
HALF SHEET (HS). 28"x22" PRE-1950: 30-50% of one sheet price.
PRE-1950 Warner Bros.: 100% or more of one sheet price.
POST 1950: 75-100% of one sheet price.
INSERT (INS). 14"x36" PRE-1950: 30-50% of one sheet price.
PRE-1950 Warner Bros.: 100% or more of one sheet price.
POST 1950: 75-100% of one sheet price.
LOBBY CARD (LC). 14"x11" 10-25% (depending on scene) of one sheet price. Dead Cards (one without any significant image): 5% or less of one sheet price. Many collectors value a dead card at 10%-25% of a good scene card.
TITLE CARD (TC). 14"x11" 20-30% of one sheet price; Pre-1950 Warner Bros.: 40% of one sheet price.
JUMBO LOBBY CARD (JLC). 17"x14" 20-30% of one sheet price.
WINDOW CARD (WC). 14"x22" (approximately 14"x17" when the top banner is trimmed away). Relative Value: 20% of one sheet price.
JUMBO WINDOW CARD (JWC). 22"x28" 25-30% of one sheet price.
MIDGET WINDOW CARD (MWC). 8"x14" 20-25% of one sheet price.

WHAT IS A MOVIE POSTER?

It's an advertising poster created by the movie studio that created the film and usually distributed to theater owners through the National Screen Service (NSS). **Only an authentic, hung-in-the-window-at-the-theater poster is considered a *real* movie poster.** As I said earlier, true movie posters are produced in very limited quantities because only enough are produced to provide an adequate supply to theaters. Unlike commercially-produced posters, theater advertising posters are not intended for the mass market (never were).

Other promotional posters, such as video posters, fast-food promo posters, and other non-theater posters are not what we are talking about when we talk about movie posters. The posters sold in stores such as Walmart or Spencer Gifts are *not* real movie posters.

The values shown in this price guide are for true theater advertising posters.

After the mid-1940s, almost all movie posters had NSS release dates on the bottom right-hand corner border (exceptions to this include small, independent film posters and posters for films that weren't released through National Screen Service). But don't automatically pass on a poster that doesn't have a NSS date—because many modern film distributors no longer use National Screen.

Various sizes have been produced through the years. Here are descriptions and dimensions of most of the standard sizes (dimensions are width x height).

ONE SHEET (1S) 27"x41" A poster on light paper stock. The one sheet poster is the standard poster you see hanging at the movie theater. It is the most-collected of the various poster types. Prices listed in this book are for the one sheet.

Many studios issued several styles of one sheets. Factors in determining value of various styles are artistic/graphic appeal, rarity, and demand. For example, the one sheet from *Top Hat* showing Astaire and Rogers dancing is much more desirable and valuable than a second style that simply shows close-up head shots of the two stars. A photographic style one sheet is never as valuable or desirable as a stone litho or artist-drawn one sheet from the same film.

Most posters after 1945 were printed using a "photolithography" process. Prior to 1945 many posters, especially one sheets and larger sizes, were printed using a "stone lithography" process. Today, stone lithography is nearly a lost art. Stone lithos are highly-prized by collectors because of the fine art process involved and because of the striking beauty of the result.

For many movies released prior to 1940, *no posters are known to exist*. In such cases, the guide price is an estimate of what the poster *could* be worth should one be discovered. Again, this approach to pricing takes into consideration the value of certain stars and classic films and their desirability relative to other film posters known to exist. Admittedly, a vast amount of leeway is left to the collector fortunate enough to unearth a previously-unknown poster from a great film or featuring a great star. But until such a poster is put on the auction block and made available to the market, we can offer nothing more than an estimate of its value. However, our appraisal is based on consultation with major dealers and collectors and a consensus of opinion.

THREE SHEET (3S) 41"x81" A large poster in two or three sections. It's widely believed by poster experts that less than 2,000 three sheets were produced during the 1930's for a new film release.

SIX SHEET (6S) 81"x81" The name is a misnomer because the poster is generally in three or four sections that, when put together, form the poster dimensions shown above. Six sheet and larger posters are rare and are seldom found for films prior to 1950.

HALF SHEET (HS) 28"x22" On a heavier paper stock than the one sheet. Sometimes the graphics on the half sheet are the most appealing of any size, such as with the posters released by MGM and RKO during the 1930s.

INSERT (IN) 14"x36" A tall, narrow poster usually printed on heavier stock, although later studio inserts could be on light paper stock. Inserts are sometimes graphically more attractive than the one sheet, and in those cases should be priced higher.

LOBBY CARD (LC) 14"x11" A poster printed on heavier stock featuring a scene from the film advertised. Usually there were 8 cards to a complete lobby set, although sets of 4, 10 or 12 were sometimes produced. **Image appeal, more than anything else, determines the lobby card value.** Each card in the set has a different value based on the scene and how desirable that scene is to collectors. Deciding on the price of a set where no market value exists is more of an art than anything else. Experience and verified sales help. Some basic rules: Value is proportionate to the graphic appeal of the scene—which can mean anything from the "sex-appeal" of the scene, to how well you can see a monster, to how important the scene is to the movie (the "letter of transit" card in the *Casablanca* set is a good example of an "important" scene

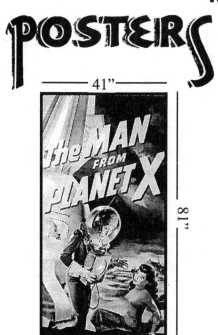

THREE SHEET

SIX SHEET

INSERT

POSTERS

LOBBY CARD

TITLE CARD
Note that the title is prominently
displayed on title cards.

WINDOW CARD

card) to how much of a closeup the photo is. Naturally, cards with close ups of the key stars are more valuable than distant shots or a card not showing any of the stars (known as a "dead card"). Silent lobby cards do not fit into the relative value formula except when dealing with a classic title. Common lobby cards from minor silent films generally sell for from $10-$35 each.

TITLE CARD (TC) 14"x11" Usually there is one card in a set of 8 that displays the title and top stars prominently in the graphics. The title card is the most desirable card in a set. In a sale or trade, title cards should be noted as such, otherwise it can be assumed that an 11x14" is a scene card.

JUMBO LOBBY CARD (JLC) 17"x14" A special oversize lobby card usually printed on a heavier or glossier stock and featuring a scene from the film advertised. Like other lobby cards, the value is proportionate to the graphic appeal of the scene. Naturally, close ups of the key stars are preferable to distant shots or cards that don't include any of the stars.

WINDOW CARD (WC) 14"x22" (approximately 14"x17" when the top banner is trimmed away). A heavy, almost cardboard poster of original studio release. A 4" blank border at the top was used by theatres to print show dates and locations. Often these blank borders have been trimmed away. The value of a trimmed window card in excellent condition is 50% that of an untrimmed window card in the same condition.

JUMBO WINDOW CARD (JWC) 22"x28" A vertically-oriented, larger version of a window card with a blank space at the top for theater imprint. Printed on a heavy stock of cheap paper and difficult to store because of bulky size. Damaged examples are therefore common.

MIDGET WINDOW CARD (MWC) 8"x14" Also known as a "mini window card" these heavy paper cards of studio release were displayed around the town where the movie was being shown. They are smaller than the standard window card and much rarer.

OTHER SIZES

Argentine One Sheet (29"x43")
Australian Insert or Daybill (14"x36")
Banner (American, heavier stock or cloth)
British Quad (30"x40")
Bus Stop Poster (45"x70")
French (24"x33", 47"x63", 63"x94", 94"x126", Door Panel 31"x94")
German (23"x32", 37"x55")
Italian (13"x28", 27"x39", 39"x55", 55"x78")
Spanish One Sheet (28"x39")
Subway Poster (30"x45")
40"x30" (American, heavy stock, silkscreen, valued at 75% of one sheet
    price)
24 Sheet (American, light stock, billboard size, rarely offered for sale).
Two Sheet or 40x60 (American, silkscreen process on heavy stock, valued at
    75-100% of the one sheet price.)

NON-POSTER STUDIO PROMOTIONAL ITEMS

PRESSBOOK (PB). Various Sizes The studios released publicity promotional books, sometimes call "campaign books", to theater owners and newspapers publicizing the films. These magazine format publications ran the gamut from full color, glossy, 100+ page "deluxe" books to small 8 page pamphlets. They usually showed black-and-white or color photos of the various styles of posters that could be ordered; and it is this feature that many collectors find most valuable. Pressbooks for common/unimportant titles are pretty worthless. But a campaign book for *The Wizard Of Oz* has sold for $5,000, a pressbook for *King Kong* has sold for several thousand, a pressbook to *Day The Earth Stood Still* has sold for $500, and most deluxe pressbooks for major films are quite valuable in their own right. It would take a separate guide to price the pressbook market, but for our purposes the collector should be aware that pressbooks can often have considerable value, especially for important films. It would be very difficult to give a general range to use to estimate the value of pressbooks relative to the one sheet price because there are so many different types of pressbooks. Many of the dealers we spoke to stated that they use 5 to 10% of the one sheet price as a rule-of-thumb for the pressbook. Others suggested that a deluxe pressbook should be worth about the same as a good lobby scene card. We leave it to the individual collector's knowledge, experience, and taste to determine a reasonable value.

IDENTIFYING AND DATING POSTERS

In most cases, identifying which poster you have is simple. In 90% of all cases, the title is prominently splashed across the artwork and the date of the poster is included in the copyright or NSS information found in the lower border area. Sometimes the release date can be determined by a code in the bottom right corner. The numbers 43/217 for example, would indicate that the year of release was 1943, while the number 217 is believed to be the printer's file identifier (i.e., the 217 would indicate that this poster was the 217th movie poster printed in 1943). If there is no date listed at all, which is more common than one would expect, then you must resort to comparing the stars to those listed in this book to determine a year of release. If that fails, do a search of the listings in this book for one that matches the poster you have.

Prior to the National Screen Service (NSS), most studios did not date their posters. So how do you know the date of the poster you have? Here's a rundown by studio of some of the points that will help you identify and date your posters.

The NSS took over the distribution of movie posters for most of the larger studios in 1941. Small companies still distributed their own posters, often undated. Prior to 1941, studios used various dating methods to date their posters, or worse, didn't date their posters at all. The dates in this book can be used to learn the dates of most titles, but this section will help you with other identifying points.

COLUMBIA—Prior to 1945, Columbia distributed its own posters, Usually with a copyright date. We have seen undated 1930s re-releases insome cases, but most always the posters are dated. IF you find a 1932 Columbia release that is dated 1938, you can rest assured that it is a re-release.

MGM—Prior to 1941, produced and distributed their own posters. Posters have been seen both dated and undated from films prior to 1941. Make sure the copyright date matches the original year of release. If not, the poster is probably a re-release.

MONOGRAM—Early 1930s posters are undated, but can be identified by the early Monogram logo. Copyright dates began to appear sometime in the

POSTERS

8"

14"

MIDGET WINDOW CARD

Dimensions vary

PRESSBOOK

63"

47"

FRENCH TWO PANEL

late 1930s. Beginning in the mid-1940s, National Screen Service (NSS) took over and used their dating nomenclature.

PARAMOUNT—Distributed its posters until 1941, when the NSS took over. Copyright dates were in roman numerals. Make sure the roman numeral date matches the original year of release. Re-releases are not idicated, however, the roman numeral dates don't match the original year of release, thus indicating a re-release.

REPUBLIC—Undated prior to 1941. Watch out for undated "stock" posters that are re-releases yet are not noted as such. In the late 1930s, re-releases were indicated with the words "A Re-release".

RKO—Prior to 1942, RKO distributed its posters without a date or copyright. You have to be familiar with poster images to be able to discern whether a 1930s King Kong poster is original or a 1938 re-release. The same applies with any other RKO title from the 1930s. Be careful.

FOX/20TH CENTURY FOX—Dated and distributed their own materials until 1946. Posters were always dated with roman numerals and had a copyright notice. Re-releases were always indicated.

UNITED ARTISTS—NSS took over in 1946. Always indicated a copyright and a date prior to NSS. Beware of Artlee re-releases from the 1920s and early 1930s. Otherwise, without a copyright date the poster is probably a re-release by Astor Pictures, Masterpiece Productions, or Producers Releasing Corp. (PRC).

UNIVERSAL—Prior to NSS takeover in 1946, Universal usually dated and and applied copyright "Universal Pictures" on posters. Re-releases were produced by "Realart" beinning in the late 1940s and continuing into the 1950s.

WARNER BROTHERS—NSS took over poster production in 1946. All Vitagraph/Warner material prior to 1946 had roman numeral dates. Early-to-late 1930s posters were released by Vitagraph and had roman numeral dates. Warner Brothers copyright began showing up in late 1930s. If you have a poster whose original release year was in the early 1930s but yet has a Warner Brothers copyright notice it is a re-release.

These are the major companies; we will update and expand this section in future editions as information becomes available.

SOME TERMINOLOGY

Advance—Same thing as teaser poster. A poster that was issued prior to the release of a film to promote the upcoming film, often with a line of text that advertises the release date. Sometimes the advance poster is of a different design than the regular release, in some cases making it more valuable.

Counterfeit— A fraudulent poster produced for the purpose of ripping off collectors. Known counterfeits exist for many posters, including *Rebel Without A Cause*, *Goldfinger*, *Yellow Submarine* lobby cards, and others. Collectors should be careful and get a second opinion if they have any doubt about a poster's authenticity. If in doubt about a poster, look at the printing. Is it grainy? Look at the pinholes. Do they appear to have been printed on the poster? Is it much smaller or larger than the standard size?

Duotone—A poster or lobby card which is printed in only two colors, usually black and brown, green, blue, or red. Warner Brothers one sheets from the 30s and 40s were often duotone, as were many Serial posters and lobby cards.

1980s Transamerica releases—Beware of United Artists titles from the 1960s and 1970s, especially James Bond titles, with United Artists/A Transamerica Company as the logo. They are easy to spot because of the large "T" next to the United Artists logo. These are 1980 re-releases although they have the original release year copyright dates.

Foreign Release Posters—Nearly all American films were also released overseas. Usually the title and cast names are in English but the rest is in another language. Sometimes even the title is in the other language. These posters often have beautiful graphics and are appealing to many collectors. They are also much more affordable than many of the classic American posters, selling at a fraction of the price of an original American release poster.

Monotone—A poster or lobby card printed in one color, such as brown, blue or green on white stock. Examples include Universal, Warner Brothers, and Columbia reissue material of the late 40s to mid-50s.

Original Foreign Release Posters—The United States did not have a monopoly on producing great films. There are original German films such as *Metropolis, The Blue Angel, The Golem, Nosferatu, The Cabinet Of Dr. Caligari*, etc., that are classics equal to or surpassing anything done in American cinema. Original posters from the original country of release for classic films such as these are very valuable. Some limited listings can be found in this book.

Other Company Posters—These are posters used by the theaters which were not authorized for production by the original studio. These posters are often graphically dull, and are rarely of the quality of the original studio release posters. Their value is usually less than the original studio posters, and many collectors shun them except in the case of rare titles.

Re-release—Re-release (sometimes called re-issue) posters are not fakes or reproductions; they are original posters from a later studio redistribution of a film. As such, a re-release poster is an **original poster** for that release. Popular movies have been re-distributed (or re-released) many times over the years (*King Kong* and *Gone With The Wind* are good examples). Each time a new release was distributed new posters were created. The letter **"R"** can usually be found in front of the release year in the tiny print on the lower right-hand border of the poster on most re-release posters printed after 1942. Prior to that time, re-releases were often designated with text on the poster that read "An MGM Re-Release" or some other text to that effect. In a some cases, like the 1938 *King Kong* re-release, no indication of any kind is given to show that the poster is a re-release. So, when in doubt, always get the advice of an expert.

Reproductions—Mass-market full color reproductions of classic movie posters have been popular in gift shops for years. **Portal Publications** of California has been one of the largest producers. Usually they are produced in odd sizes, like 26" x 32" (a non-standard size for original posters). Reproductions such as these have little or no collector value.

Teaser—Same thing as an advance poster. A poster that was issued prior to the release of a film to promote the upcoming film, often with a line of text that advertises the release date.

PUBLICATIONS OF INTEREST

As you progress in poster sophistication, you will begin to gnaw for something more; to search for the fraternity of people just like you—addicted and loving it. There is an organized network of fans/collectors, and most of us subscribe to three publications: *The Big Reel, Collecting Hollywood,* and *Movie Collectors World.*

The publishers of this book publish *Collecting Hollywood.* A sample copy of any of these magazines may be obtained by sending $5 per copy to American Collectors Exchange, P. O. Box 2512, Chattanooga, TN 37409.

MAIL-ORDER DEALERS SPECIALIZING IN MOVIE POSTERS

Eventually you will want to fill in those "impossible to find" titles missing from your collection. At that point you should consider buying posters from a reputable mail-order poster dealer. There is a booming business in selling collectible movie posters via catalogs sent through the mail. These catalogs run the gamut from hand-scrawled, mimeographed-sheets to well-produced, professionally typeset catalogs with color photos. Some are fixed-price catalogs, where you simply send in an order and wait for your posters. Others are mail-order auction catalogs, where you place bids and hope you are the highest bidder. This book features an ad section filled with numerous ads for poster dealers who offer catalogs. It is our policy to accept ads from reputable dealers only. In this way we hope to help collectors avoid any kind of mail fraud. When buying through the mail, don't be afraid to ask for references, photos, or anything that will prove the reliability of the person with whom you are dealing. Reputable dealers are happy to accomodate collectors in every way possible, and always offer a "satisfaction guaranteed" return policy if you are unhappy with any of your purchases.

FREQUENTLY-ASKED QUESTIONS

What if I have a poster that's not listed in your price guide?

Although my goal is to make this book as comprehensive as possible, there are still many titles missing from my database. Don't assume that because I don't list a title that it is rare or more valuable. Literally thousands of movie titles from the silent era are still missing from my database, as well as lots of titles from the modern era (1970 to date). If you have a title that I don't have listed, please drop me a note.

The guide only give values for one sheet posters, what if I want to know the value of other size posters and lobby cards?

See our section on pricing other posters. We chose to focus the scope of this book on one sheet posters because they are the standard poster and have been produced since the earliest days of movies. No other poster size has been around as long. In fact, today the one sheet remains the primary poster size produced for theaters.

Why do you sometimes list posters for less than what they have sold for at auction, isn't the auction price the best guide to a poster's value?

No. In fact, auction prices are more often than not misleading. The price a poster fetches at auction represents what someone was willing to pay at that point in time. Frequently, during the excitement of the bidding process, a buyer will bid more than he should have. The prices listed in this price guide reflect an average of what our board advisors, made up of experts from various regions of the country, reported as the average retail price.

What are double-sided posters?

Starting sometime in 1991, all the major studios began producing their posters with two sides, to accomodate the new lightbox displays they installed in the cineplexes. So, if the film was released in 1991 or after, it should have a double-sided poster associated with it. BUT, we have seen major studio releases from early 1991 that were not double-sided, so consider 1991 a switchover year. Smaller studios and independent releases continued to use single-sided posters but also sometimes used double-sided posters. If you have a major studio release, such as a Disney film or Warner Brothers, and it is not double-sided, then you probably have a second printing.

Why are some one sheets smaller than 27" x 41"?

Depending on the width of the roll of paper on which they were printed, one sheets can vary from 39-1/2 to 41-1/2 inches in length.

Why can't I find lobby card sets for modern films?

Studios stopped producing lobby card sets for the American market sometime in the mid-1980s. It's still possible to find lobby card sets for American films, but you'll have to find a dealer in International releases of American films. After the mid-1980s, the only lobby card sets produced were for International releases.

BOOKS OF INTEREST

All of the publications listed below should be on every collector's bookshelf.

Academy Award Movie Posters by Bruce Hershenson, 1996. OVER 300 COLOR PHOTOS! Order from American Collectors Exchange, $20 each ppd

Christies Auction Catalogs. Order from American Collectors Exchange, $20 each ppd

Sotheby's Auction Catalogs

Camden House Auction Catalogs. Order from American Collectors Exchange, $20 each ppd

Reel Art by Stephen Robello and Richard Allen. 1988 Abbeville Press

50 Years Of Movie Posters by John Kobal. 1973 Bounty Books

Cartoon Movie Posters by Bruce Hershenson, 1996. OVER 300 COLOR PHOTOS! Order from American Collectors Exchange, $20 each ppd

Color Collectors Guide #1 by Archival Photography. 1989

Cowboy Movie Posters by Bruce Hershenson, 1996. OVER 300 COLOR PHOTOS! Order from American Collectors Exchange, $20 each ppd

Crime Movie Posters by Bruce Hershenson, 1997. OVER 300 COLOR PHOTOS! Order from American Collectors Exchange, $20 each ppd

A Separate Cinema by John Kisch and Edward Mapp. 1993 Noonday Press

Graven Images by Ronald V. Borst. 1992 Grove Press

Sports Movie Posters by Bruce Hershenson, 1997. OVER 300 COLOR PHOTOS! Order from American Collectors Exchange, $20 each ppd

The Disney Poster: From Mickey Mouse To Aladdin. 1993 Hyperion

Yesterday's Tomorrows by Bruce Lanier Wright. 1993 Taylor Publishing

WHAT ABOUT POSTER RESTORATION?

Here are a few tips and comments about restoration by collectors and dealers.

Steve Bourgeouis, Oregon. *"Everybody uses restoration at some time or another, both the top collectors and the small ones. I don't have any problem with owning a restored poster, as long as it's done well."*

BOOK SHELF

You can order these books directly from American Collectors Exchange. Use your credit card and call (423) 265-5515 or mail your check or money order to P. O. Box 2512, Chattanooga, TN 37409

Academy Award Posters Over 300 color photos $20 ppd

Christies Auction Catalogs 1990-1996 Over 250 color photos in each. $20 each ppd.

Cartoon Movie Posters Over 300 color photos $20 ppd

Crime Movie Posters Over 300 color photos $20 ppd

Sports Movie Posters Over 300 color photos $20 ppd

Lynn Naron, Seattle. *"When you're looking for a restorer talk to some of the better dealers and experienced collectors and ask them who they've used and how good they are in comparison. Feel free to ask restorers for references. Any good one can give you several top names... Paperbacking and linenbacking is certainly worth the price. Posters look so much better in this protected state."*

Ken Porter, Los Angeles. *"Some of the work done by the support staff of many restorers simply is not up to standard. I've seen painting done so poorly it looks like kindergartners had worked on them with water colors."*

Deke Richards, Washington. *"I've tried a number of restorers and I haven't always been satisfied with their work. Everyone makes mistakes, but many improve, so you shouldn't rule out giving someone a second chance. If you really want to save a poster, and you really like it, then go for it, have it restored."*

Jim Sanchez, San Francisco. *"Forty percent of the posters today don't need any kind of backing or restoration. I believe that you shouldn't fool with posters that aren't in need of serious repairs. I'm not a big proponent of linenbacking or chemicals really. Watch out for restorers who over-paint with air brushes!"*

Dan Strebin, California. *"We should try to save as many of these posters as we can. Once movie posters and lobby cards become accepted as pieces of history, which they will, they will get absorbed into museums. Until that time I honestly feel like we collectors are the future museums."*

Bruce Webster, Oklahoma. *"Everyone uses pretty much the same methods and materials, but the real difference in quality is in the artistry touching it."*

CHOOSING A RESTORER

There are three primary factors to consider when choosing a restorer for your poster.

1.   **Quality** - If you have an extremely valuable piece, it is wise to do a little reference research before you send off your poster. You obviously will want the best person available for the job. Some restorers are better at certain types of repairs than others. There are also people who specialize in various sizes of memorabilia. Most restorers can do a solid linen-backing job; however, paper-backing is said to be a little trickier, and paper replacement and painting requires a skilled hand. A professional restorer will often refer you to someone else if the job warrants it.

2.   **Price** - Prices vary among restorers. There are a handful of museum conservation studios around the country, but they charge astronomical amounts of money (usually at least 3 or 4 times more than the a typical movie poster restorer) and they do it by the hour in most cases. You need to ask yourself: "How much money can I afford to put into the piece, and is it worth it?"

3.   **Turn-around time** - Some restorers have a heavier workload than others. Some of the finer restorers take a great deal of time to finish a job. You may have to wait up to a year to get a certain piece back. If the job is simple, however, there are restorers who can really get out the work in a hurry.

Store your posters in a cool, dry place. Preferably in a room that is air-conditioned and de-humidifed.

When displaying posters, keep them out of direct sunlight and any ultraviolet lighting.

HOW TO PRESERVE AND STORE YOUR PAPER COLLECTIBLES

By William M. Cole, P.E.

Movie Poster collecting today is for both fun and profit. Yet, the poster you thought was going to increase in value year after year could suddenly turn yellow after only a few months, rendering it worthless. What happened? What could have been done to prevent the yellowing? This article will discuss how paper is made, what materials are best suited for long term storage, and the guidelines for proper preservation.

Bill Cole is a Registered Professional Engineer and President of Bill Cole Enterprises, Inc., a company involved in the design and production of materials for the archival storage of paper collectibles. Questions may be addressed to P.O. Box 60, Randolph, MA 02368-0060.

How paper is made

Paper has plant fibers that have been reduced to a pulp, suspended in water and then matted into sheets. The fibers consist largely of cellulose, a strong, lightweight and somewhat durable material; cotton is an example of almost pure cellulose fiber. Although cotton and other kinds of fiber have been used in papermaking over the years, most paper products today are made from wood pulp.

Wood pulps come in two basic varieties: groundwood and chemical wood. In the first process, whole logs are shredded and mechanically beaten. In the second, the fibers are prepared by digesting wood chips in chemical cookers. Because groundwood is the cheaper of the two, it is the primary component in such inexpensive papers as newsprint, which is used in many newspapers, magazines, and yes, movie posters. Chemically purified pulps are used in more expensive applications, such as stationery and some magazines and hardcover books.

Since groundwood pulp is made from whole wood fiber, the resulting paper does not consist of pure cellulose. As much as one-third of its content may consist of non-cellulosic materials such as lignin, a complex woody acid. In chemical pulps, however, the lignin and other impurities are removed during the cooking process.

Deterioration of paper

The primary causes of paper deterioration are oxidation and acid hydrolysis. Oxidation attacks cellulose molecules with oxygen from the air, causing darkening and increased acidity. In addition, the lignin in groundwood paper breaks down quickly under the influence of oxygen and ultraviolet light. Light-induced oxidation of lignin is what turns newspapers yellow after a few days' exposure to sunlight. (Light can also cause some printing inks to fade.)

In acid hydrolysis, the cellulose fibers are cut by a reaction involving heat and acids, resulting in paper that turns brown and brittle. The sources of acidity include lignin itself, air pollution, and reaction by-products from the oxidation of paper. Another major source is alum, which is often used with rosin to prepare the paper surface for accepting printing inks. Alum eventually releases sulfuric acid in paper.

Acidity and alkalinity are measured in units of pH, with 0 the most acidic and 14 the most alkaline. (Neutral pH is 7..00) Because the scale is based on powers of 10, a pH of 4.5 is actually 200 times more acidic than a pH of 6.5. Fresh newsprint typically carries a pH of 4.5 or less, while older more deteriorated paper on the verge of crumbling, may run as low as pH 3.0. Although some modern papers are made acid free, most paper collectibles are acidic and need special treatment to lengthen their lives.

According to the US Library of Congress, the preferred material for preserving valuable documents is uncoated archival quality polyester film, such as Mylar type D by DuPont Co. or equivalent material Melinex 516 by ICI Corp.

Other factors which contribute to the destruction of paper include extremes of temperature and humidity, insects, rodents, mold and improper handling and storage.

Guidelines for preservation

First and foremost, keep your paper collectibles cool dark and dry. Store posters and other items in an air conditioned room, if possible, and regularly monitor the humidity. Excess humidity should be controlled with a dehumidifier. Storage materials such as envelopes, sleeves and boxes, should be of archival quality to prevent contamination of their contents.

Polyethylene and Polypropylene

For years collectors have stored their posters, lobby cards, and other material in polyethylene bags, PVC sheets and plastic wraps. Although such products may be useful in keeping away dirt, grease and vermin, many plastic sleeves contain plasticizers and other additives which can migrate into paper and cause premature aging. Both polyethylene and polypropylene contain solvents and additives in their manufacture to assure clarity and increase the flexibility in the plastic. Polyethylene when uncoated without any solvents is a good moisture barrier but has a high gas transmission rate, and eventually shrinks and loses its shape under warmer conditions.

In recent years polypropylene bags have been sold "archival quality". This, unfortunately, is untrue. Only uncoated and untreated material is suitable for archival protection. Currently, the only way to seal polypropylene is to add a substance called PVDC (Polyvinyl Dichloride which is a relative of PVC) to allow the material to be heat sealed. Therefore, once you add the harmful additive, the sleeve now becomes non-archival and should not be used for long term storage.

Mylar

According to the US Library of Congress, the preferred material for preserving valuable documents is uncoated archival quality polyester film, such as Mylar type D by DuPont Co. or equivalent material Melinex 516 by ICI Corp. Mylar is an exceptionally strong transparent film that resists moisture, pollutants, oils and acids. With a life expectancy of hundreds of years, Mylar will outlast most other plastics. In addition, the brilliance and clarity of Mylar enhances the appearance of any paper collectible.

Acid Free Boards and Boxes

Because ordinary cardboard is itself acidic, longterm storage in cardboard boxes may be hazardous to your collection, and is a leading cause of premature deterioration of paper collectibles. For proper storage, only acid free boards that meet the US Government's MINIMUM requirements are acceptable. These requirements have been defined as boards having a 3% calcium carbonate buffer throughout and a minimum pH of 8.5. Anything less will hasten your collection's aging. Many advertisers claim that their boards are "acid-free at time of manufacture." In reality, these products spray coated with an alkaline substance making them acid free for only a short time. Boards termed "acid-free at time of manufacture" do not offer sufficient protection or storage for anything other than short term (3 - 5 years). True acid-free boards have been impregnated with a calcium buffer resulting in an acid-free, alkaline pH content of 8.5 throughout.

Another way to extend the longevity of your collectibles is to decidify them before storage. Decidifying sprays and sollutions are now available for home use. By impregnating the paper with an alkaline reserve, you can neutralize existing acids and inhibit oxidation, future acidity and staining due to certain fungi. However, it is best left to the professionals to decidify your paper collectibles. Decidification with proper storage conditions will add centuries to the lifetime of paper.

In summary, we recommend the following guidelines for the maximum protection of your collectibles: Decidify the paper; store in Mylar sleeves with acid-free boards and cartons; and keep the collection cool, dry and dark. Periodic inspections and pH and humidity tests are also recommended. By following these simple guidelines, you can be assured of a collection that not only will increase in value, but will also last for many years to come.

HOW TO GRADE POSTERS

All organized hobbies, inluding fine art, coins, andstamps (fields where individual rarities have sold in the millions of dollars), recognize that a piece in top condition is more valuable than one in poor condition. Poster collecting is no different in this regard. Although definitions and terms used to describe the various grades of posters are not yet standardized, some of the more commonly-used grades are given below, with explanations.

MINT (M)—Never used. Signs of aging may be present; but, overall a superb piece that appears to be like new. To receive this grade, the poster may have only the slightest traces of wear. No pinholes, no trace of browning or brittleness may be present, very tiny amounts of wear at the borders or folds. No crease of any kind is acceptable on lobby cards. Window cards may have printed theatre banners. Since it was a policy prior to 1985 to ship and store posters by folding them, it is very nearly impossible to find unfolded posters prior to this time. Therefore, don't consider a folded poster that is otherwise unused to be defective in grade.

NEAR MINT (NM)—Superb. Unused or very carefully used, but with some minor storage defect, minor tear, one pinhole in each corner, or some other very minor flaw on an otherwise unused poster. One set of clean pinholes or staple holes in each corner could be present in this grade.

EXCELLENT (EX)—An above-average poster with minimal signs of use. Bright and clean. Could be NEVER-USED or SLIGHTLY USED depending upon catalog description. Poster has no major defects but could have an accumulation of several minor ones, such as a small (1/8" or less) border chip. No creases on lobby cards, but normal/minor creases on one-sheets and larger posters is to be expected. A few small pinholes or minor border tears could be present. Aging on older pieces to be expected. Paper could be slightly yellowed, but not brown. Minimal or slight restoration could be present if professionally done. Signs of wear and use could be present, including folds or creases (except on lobby cards), possibly a minor border tear, or pin-holes in the border. Not soiled; clean and bright. No tape repairs allowed in this grade,. Window cards may have written or printed banners. The image area of the poster should be clean and undamaged.

VERY GOOD (VG)—Average ; USED. The typical used poster in average condition. A sound example, although with wear and defects to be expected of an item that was intended to be used and re-used. Unusual problems should be described. The poster can have slight browning of paper but not brittleness or flaking; it may also have a small amount of writing in some unobtrusive portion of the poster. Minor border repair, edge tears, stains, or other signs of average use could be present. Eye appeal of the image area should be nice.

Minor soiling could be present. Larger paper could have minor fold tears (length of which should be described); also normal folds, creases, minor fold tears, possible repaired tears. Professional major restoration is acceptable in this grade. Corner creases can be present, but numerous creases affecting the image should be described. The poster should be complete and if not, major problems should be described (such as paper replacement). In every case, paper replacement and major color touchup and restoration should be described in detail. Tape anywhere on the poster should be mentioned and described. Small pen markings on the front can be present if noted, but not if large, heavy, or if affecting the eye appeal of the image. Heavy waterstains eliminate the poster from this grade. However, a minor dampstain on an unobtrusive part of the poster could be allowed. Sun-fading on the poster should be described, and if significant, should prevent the example from being in this grade. Heavy insect or rodent damage is not allowable in this grade. No amateur color touchup with colored markers is allowable.

GOOD—Means heavily worn ; USED AND ABUSED. Heavily used, with significant signs of use that affect the overall eye appeal of the piece. Small pieces may be missing from the borders. Image area will usually have minor defects that may impinge upon the graphics. Could have tape, writing, or tears. Numerous pinholes and resulting tears could be present. Complete, but graphics are face-worn.

POOR—Destroyed. A worn, torn, damaged example. Crumpled and worn corners. Tape, countless pinholes, waterstains, writing, brittleness, pieces or chips missing, heavily soiled etc., to be expected in this grade. Pieces could be missing that render the example incomplete. Typically a filler-copy only.

OTHER TERMS:

NEW—Same shape it was in when it arrived at the theater. Older releases will have normal signs of aging but no signs of use.

FOLDED—Means factory-folded; posters were folded at the factory prior to 1990. This is the way they are supposed to be. Don't expect posters to be rolled prior to 1990, they weren't made that way. In some rare cases, rolled examples may exist that were not folded due to an overrun at the printing plant.

NUF—Never-used, factory-folded. A poster that was never used in the theater, in other words, not hung for display. Posters described in this way will have signs of storage wear or other flaws, but no pinholes, tape, or other signs of use.

NUR—Never-used, rolled.

ROLLED—A poster that has not been folded. Arrives rolled up in a tube.

UF— Used, factory-folded.

UR—Used, rolled.

USED—Used as intended at the theater. Normal flaws from having been used in a theater and then carelessly stored away.

COLLECTING RE-RELEASE MOVIE POSTERS

by Channing Lyle Thomson and Kirby McDaniel

As you go about becoming a collector of original movie posters, you will eventually discover re-release posters. You will hear them mentioned with praise, scorn or most commonly, indifference. Each of these reactions is valid, but, as in any field of collecting, there are many golden opportunities to be found in this less-traveled area of movie paper collectibles.

First, it is important to distinguish exactly what a re-release poster is. Beginning with the talkies of the late 1920s (silents had quickly become anachronistic, with little commercial re-release potential at that point), it became obvious that many popular films could be released theatrically for the benefit of original fans, as well as newer generations unfamiliar with a classic film.

Re-releasing a film was invariably profitable for a studio, as they reissued only films which had already proven their boxoffice strength, and beyond the usual overhead of marketing (primarily newspaper, radio and posters in the 1930s and 1940s), and striking of prints, their investment was minimal. As a result, most studios had a regular program of reissues, re-releasing a number of titles each year, sometimes under the original studio banner, other times under secondary names.

Many films, such as *King Kong* and *Gone With the Wind* and the early Disney animated classics, became national standards in re-release, eagerly looked forward to by audiences.

This practice continued for years, affording both extra profit for studios and an opportunity for fans to see movies they'd either missed or simply been too young to see.

The first major dent in this re-release scheme was the introduction of television as the most accessible media format in the United States, and soon the world, supplanting simultaneously radio and films.

At first, Hollywood saw TV as the enemy and vowed to keep their product away from television. There was an unwritten, but strict agreement among major studios to not sell recent product (movies made after 1948 or so) to TV. As a result, for several years the only films visible on television were old B-westerns, second-tier studio product and British films. The lure of quick money, coupled with dwindling boxoffice receipts, soon forced the studios to sell their post-1948 inventory to TV. Most of them, as we shall see, made as much money as possible by quickly re-releasing famous titles one last time theatrically before doing so, however.

In 1960, 20th Century Fox said "enough." They struck a deal with NBC for a package of post-1948 'A ' films and on Sept. 23, 1961, NBC premiered the first of their *Saturday Night at the Movies*. broadcasting the Fox comedy *How To Marry A Millionaire*, starring Betty Grable, Lauren Bacall and, yes, Marilyn Monroe. Imagine, if you will, the thrill of seeing Marilyn Monroe, perhaps the biggest star of the decade, in your home, in living color (if you were lucky enough to have a color set), in a movie only eight years old, and for free!

Saturday Night at the Movies quickly jumped to the top of the ratings and other networks followed with their own "movie nights." Ratings meant cash, and the others studios slavishly followed Fox's lead and sold out their entire inventories to television.

Two other elements contributed to the decline of the theatrical re-release. First, in the mid-70s, cable television became increasingly popular with the so-called "pay-TV" channels, such as HBO and Showtime. These networks provided the cable-wired TV audience with a tremendous number of uncut films complete with

The collector must move beyond the general "wisdom" that only original release posters have any sort of collectible and/or artistic value.

their original theatrical nudity, violence, adult language and content. Cable TV satisfied the viewers tired of seeing the more "mature" films of the 1060s and 1970s cut-up and re-edited for content on over-the-air TV . This ability to program uncut movies diminished the small remaining re-release market, usually in repertory houses or universities.

Then, in the early 1980s, the videotape revolution really circumvented the traditional theatrical re-release. By this point, almost any film you wanted to see was now available on video tape at your local video store.

But theatrical re-releases were a significant part of studio output for many years, which begs the question: "Why create an entirely new poster for the re-release of a film?"

There are several answers to this question. First, a film that warranted re-release often did so because it had won several Academy Awards. The re-release poster might play up the coveted statuette on the poster or mention that the film was the winner of, say, as in the case of *Ben-Hur*, eleven Academy Awards.

Similarly, many films were re-released after receiving tremendous critical acclaim. A consequence of this type of release was the much-maligned "review" style poster, which features quotes from critics praising the film, usually at the sacrifice of artwork and other elements from the original. These posters, covered with wordy quotes, are less desirable that other types of re-release posters.

Perhaps the main reason for a brand new poster was changing times and the styles of artwork common to a particular era. Look at a poster of the 1930s, replete with beautiful, painterly artwork and compare it to the simplicity of design, color and style of the 1950s or 1960s and you will see a vast difference. In other words, artistic taste changes, advertising styles change and so on.

For example, a one sheet for *The Adventures of Robin Hood* (1938) may charmingly capture the design style of the late 1930s, but by the 1950s and 1960s, an era embracing the simplistic, stylish logo designs of Saul Bass and the pop-art culture of Andy Warhol, the poster from the 1930s would seem historically quaint but intrinsically out of fashion.

Another reason for a new poster design for a re-release is changes in actor's popularity, and subsequent changes in billing, that occurred over time. An example of this would be the original French poster for Jean Renoir's classic anti-war film, *Grand Illusion*. The original poster for the movie played up the participation of actress Dita Parlo (an icon most recently resurrected by pop star Madonna). But by the time of the lovely (and more collected) re-release poster, which features a heartrending image of a dove caught on a barbed-wire fence, Miss Parlo's popularity had waned and her name sunken to lower billing.

As you see, there are many reasons for the creation of a new poster design when a film is re-released. Consequently, there is an opportunity to collect these posters, many of which may be uniquely fulfilling to the collector interested in expanding the horizons of his collection. The collector must move beyond the general "wisdom" that only original release posters have any sort of collectible and/or artistic value.

There are many reasons to collect re-release movie posters. One of these is financial. If you are a fan of the films of Humphrey Bogart, an original poster of *Casablanca* can be prohibitively expensive (the one sheet has been offered at anywhere from $3,500 to $10,000). The re-release one sheet from 1956 is a relatively attractive poster, arguably better looking than the newspaper design, duotone original. Why not pay only a few hundred dollars and be nicely represented on the title and actor with the re-release one sheet?

Sometimes there may be features about the re-release poster that are attractive and unusual. For example, the 1949 re-release poster of *The Wizard of Oz* features a lovely image of Judy Garland as the MGM star, rather than the childlike Dorothy from Kansas.

Another benefit of re-release collecting is that often, the re-release one sheet is just plain better the original. The 1949 re-release poster of the baseball classic, *The Pride of the Yankees*, features a terrific image of Babe Ruth that adds luster and value to the re-release over the more standard star imagery found on the original release one sheet from 1942.

What constitutes a collectible re-release poster? Let's look at a few examples:

RKO

RKO originally released the relatively-early sound film *King Kong* in 1933, to great critical and commercial acclaim. By 1938, the studio sensed that a re-release of the horror classic had great financial potential, with little cost to them other than marketing. This reissue was a tremendous success, and set the stage for periodic re-releases of the film for the next twenty years. These releases occurred approximately every four to five years, in 1938, 1942, 1946-7, 1952 and 1956, with each release reaping additional financial rewards for the studio. New posters were created for each re-release, and all are highly-prized by collectors, although they vary in quality and degree of rarity. A full-color one sheet for the 1956 re-release recently sold for $800. On most re-release posters (but not, unfortunately, all), a small letter 'R', signifying re-release, appears before the National Screen Service year date and release number on the bottom right of the poster and also on the title and date stamp on the rear.

Other good examples of RKO re-release posters include *Bringing Up Baby*, the Astaire/Rogers musicals, the Val Lewton horror classics, and *Stage Door*. These films were re-released in the early to mid-1950s, not repeatedly as was Kong and a few other films. The one sheet posters to these classics vary in quality, but tend to be unique from the originals and quite interesting in design, color and concept.

Disney

Perhaps the studio which has profited the most from re-releasing its films is Walt Disney. The Disney animated classics have been almost continuously re-released since their inception, beginning with their first animated feature, *Snow White and the Seven Dwarfs* in 1937. It was re-released in 1943, 1951, 1967, 1987 and 1993. With each of these re-releases, the studio devised not only a new poster, but an entire new advertising campaign for the film, complete with Disney's true cash cow, merchandising. The posters for each release are very collectible, and individual collectors have their favorites. Disney has learned to cater to the collectible market; for instance they issued a special gold-laminated poster for *Snow White*'s 50th Anniversary re-release in 1987. Disney is currently following a canny policy of offering their classics on videotape, but only for limited periods, following which the film will be unavailable for a specified number of years, at the end of which there will be another theatrical re-release, followed by the inevitable video release, and so on, ad infinitum it seems.

20th Century-Fox

Movie poster collectors greatly value the posters created for the original releases of the 20th Century-Fox studios, particularly the mid-1930s through the mid-1949s. These films often warranted two different styles of one sheet: Very often one would be a striking offset print poster, sometimes featuring photographic material. The other style was usually a lovely stone lithograph, awash with dramatic, beautiful colors and imaginative artwork. These posters capture the collector's imagination for reasons of design, color and pure Hollywood glamour.

Unfortunately, the re-release posters from Fox, many from the late 1940s and early 1950s, are quite average, often using a duotone coloring, simple offset lithography and photographic imagery (some also mention that they are "A 20th Century-Fox Encore Hit".) A good example is the re-release poster for the Tyrone Power swashbuckler *The Black Swan*. The original release one sheet from 1942 features several of the positive attributes mentioned above. The re-release poster from 1952 is brown and white duotone, only slightly enlivened by a bit of red lettering of the title credits and a red scrim over a romantic photo of Power and Maureen O'Hara. This poster is only a lackluster reminder of the original film and the original release material. On the other hand, it is available for under $200, while the original release poster has sold for over $2,000.

MGM

MGM is a studio that found the art of re-release particularly worthwhile. Such classics as *Gone With the Wind* were re-released repeatedly and continued to be re-released even after their TV and cable debuts.

In the case of *GWTW*, there are many reasons to collect the re-release material. For example, the 1961 poster is interesting in that it reflects the centennial anniversary of the Civil War. The 1968 re-release describes the first rendering of the classic film in wide-screen (unfortunately cropped) and stereophonic sound. The artwork for the posters, beginning in 1967 and continuing through today, feature the famous Rhett and Scarlett embrace imagery (against a fiery Atlanta) that was unique to these later reissues (and now the most recognizable image from the film).

Many of the classic MGM films were re-released theatrically in 1962. Among these are the classic operettas of Jeanette McDonald and Nelson Eddy, *The Thin Man* and such major comedies as *Dinner at Eight* and *Father of the Bride*. The studio essentially raided the vault to squeeze every remaining drop of financial remuneration from the studio's existing product.

The posters from the 1962 re-releases can be quite lovely. Many are full-color, often available in 22" x 28" display size, as well as one sheets, with a handful reusing some of the original plate artwork from the first releases. There are, however, some duotone duds among these, so be sure to ask for a complete description when buying from a dealer.

The Films of Alfred Hitchcock

A number of director Alfred Hitchcock's films (especially the Paramount product of the 1950s) have been re-released several times since their initial openings.

Hitchcock's television series, *Alfred Hitchcock Presents*, appeared on network television (both NBC and CBS) from 1955 to 1965. The anthology series, introduced by Hitchcock, made him a household figure, as familiar, recognizable and popular as the Grace Kelly and Jimmy Stewarts who appeared in his films. As his image became etched in the American consciousness, something interesting began to happen with the re-release posters for his films—they now featured the director's unique silhouette and visage over the images of the stars.

The 1962 Paramount re-release of *Rear Window* shows a black-and-white head shot of Hitchcock asking you to "See it! If your nerves can stand it after Psycho!" The previous re-release one sheet, from 1959 (Paramount International) had not yet latched onto the director as a marketing device.

1966's re-release of MGM's *North by Northwest* featured a one sheet that is perhaps the most stylish, humorous and collectible of the Hitchcock re-release posters. On this graphic, Hitchcock's face is added to the dramatic rock wall portraiture of Mount Rushmore!

In 1983, Universal re-released Hitchcock's five significant Paramount films of the 1950s. The overall poster design for each of these was the same—essentially a stock image of Hitchcock, attached to the individual film's title and credits, plus a black-and-white photo from each film. Little imagination went into these designs other than to portray Hitchcock as a supreme cinematic auteur.

The year 1996 welcomed Robert A. Harris' 70MM Vista-Vision, DTS restoration release of the director's classic film *Vertigo*, from 1958. This release featured a poster that was nearly a duplication of the film's original Paramount one sheet, designed by Saul Bass. Perhaps based on the artistic merit and inspired design of the original, Universal decided to exactly replicate the familiar spiral design against a reddish-orange background. It seems the studio, in a mood of archival strategy, felt an impulse to celebrate the artistry of the original poster as well as the film. This was an extremely limited re-release, making this one sheet one of the most sought-after re-release posters in some time.

Interestingly enough, Warner Brothers re-released the 1950 Hitchcock classic *Strangers on a Train* in 1996 and managed to reproduce the original one sheet poster in newspaper advertising with only minor alterations.

The underlying message of these two releases would seem to be that the posters, as well as the films, warrant the memorialization brought about by an archival restoration.

Realart/Universal

During the late 1940s through the mid-50s, several companies specialized in re-releasing films originally produced and released by the major studios. Among these were Astor, Majestic, Realart and Dominant. The most popular of these, with respect to movie poster collecting, was Realart.

Realart gained access to the sound films produced by Universal Pictures from 1930 to 1946 (the year Universal merged with International) for re-release in the U.S. Among the films re-released were the classic Universal horror films, as well as the Maria Montez/Jon Hall and Sabu sarong-and-sword epics, and the comedy classics of W.C. Fields and the classic Abbott and Costello comedies.

During the early years, Realart tended to disguise the re-released nature of their product by subtle (and sometimes not-so-subtle) title changes. Later, the poster material, ranging from complete lobby card sets to full-color six sheets, included the company's familiar logo — two reels of film threading out into the name "Realart", underscored by the phrase "Realart Re-Release."

Naturally, Universal Pictures brings to mind the classic horror films of the 1930s and 1940s—among them *The Mummy, Frankenstein* and *The Wolf Man*. These films and their related spawn (e.g., *Ghost of Frankenstein* and *Abbott and Costello Meet Frankenstein*) were re-released by Realart. Colorful, exciting posters in various sizes assisted in the marketing effort. Note: In 1947, Universal itself re-released *Frankenstein* (re-release on sheet value approximately $7,000) and *Dracula* (re-release one sheet value from $10,000-$15,000).

For the average horror poster collector, original and early re-release material on these titles is prohibitively expensive—the original release one sheet for *Frankenstein* has sold at auction for $180,000. In March of 1997, the original release one sheet for *The Mummy* sold at Sotheby's in New York for over $430,000!

As you can see, the Realart re-releases are the only reasonable avenue for owning posters from these Universal horror classics. The Realart material is often colorful, completely different from the original posters' designs and, most importantly, stratospherically less expensive than the Universal originals. This is not to say that all Realart posters are fabulous and highly collectible. Some of these posters unfortunately feature what collectors have often referred to as "the laughing skull" — a black-and-white design of a skull that appears to be silly, childish and overused on some of the posters.

On the other hand, advanced horror poster collectors consider the Realart poster of *The Mummy* to be one of the strongest, most sought-after examples of a top re-release poster. This 1951 one sheet recently sold for $1,750. Bill Pirola, the well-known Bela Lugosi enthusiast, admires Realart's 36" x 14" insert for *The Raven*. These stylish, fun and colorful posters are a welcome addition to any collection and will prove to be a valuable and growing asset down the road.

Paramount, United Artists, Columbia and Warner Brothers

Paramount sporadically re-released many of its films, especially the Hope-Crosby Road pictures and the Cecil B. DeMille historical epics, with equally sporadic poster results. United Artists and Columbia re-released many of their films from the mid-1940s through the 1950s. There is little to call attention to these re-release posters.

Columbia's re-releases include some of their big films of the 1930s, like *Golden Boy*. Again, many of these feature unimpressive uses of duotone and photographic imagery. Price would be the main reason for collecting these re-release posters. Interestingly enough, 1961 brought re-release posters of the studio's 1956 hit *Picnic* that are full-color and contain completely different artwork from the original release posters.

Warner Brothers is a different case. In the mid-1950s, many of the classic Warner titles such as *To Have and Have Not, Casablanca* and *Jezebel* were re-released by a subsidiary company called Dominant Pictures. These so-called "Dominant" re-release posters are collected by poster enthusiasts for several reasons. Although many of the posters are duotone, some are well-designed and are not significantly less attractive than the often-maligned Warner Brothers originals of the 1940s (these originals often focused on standard issue, very 1940-ish design style with a great emphasis on black-and-white hand lettering and photo imagery). As an example, consider *Jezebel*. The original one sheet, while a stunning example of poster artwork, has reached astronomical price levels at auction ($10,000-$15,000). The re-release poster from 1956, while somewhat average-looking, can be acquired for a fraction of the price of the original.

The Present and the Future

The 1990s have ushered in an exciting era for re-release posters. Many major films, both foreign and domestic, are being restored and re-released theatrically before videotape release. Almost all of these posters have been sensational, featuring unique combinations of design, color, photography and star power. They also benefit from today's superior quality print technology and unfolded condition (sometimes with two-sided printing). Because these current re-releases tend to be limited to major cities and few venues, the printrun of the one sheet poster is also quite small, dramatically increasing their collectible value.

Among these re-releases have been such stellar works as *The Umbrellas of Cherbourg* (whose 1996 re-release poster shames the original release one sheet from 1964), *Spartacus, My Fair Lady, Lawrence of Arabia, The Star Wars Trilogy, El Cid, The Godfather, Giant, The Glenn Miller Story, A Star is Born*, etc.

Today's younger film audience is seeing many of these films preserved and presented in formats sometimes even superior to their original presentation, thanks to the developments of digital sound technology and re-strikings from original, restored negatives. The re-release one sheet posters for many of these historic re-releases are often stylish, well-designed and highly collectible. Of course, the practice of re-releasing films which have received great critical acclaim or that have won Academy Awards (or other, increasingly more influential awards, such as a Golden Globe) continues.

We are in a renaissance where tremendous care is being lavished upon our cinematic history and archive. The posters for these releases have managed to compete admirably with the superior quality of these restorations and respresent an important and growing arena for the collecting of original movie posters.

NOW Available in Smaller Quantities

Your Posters are Slowly Dying!!!
Don't Gamble with their Futures!!!

Preserve Your Movie Memorabilia with R-Kival™ Quality Mylar® D

Movie Poster Size Sleeves & Boards

Avoid protective sleeves made of polyethylene, polypropylene and polyvinyl chloride (PVC). Most of these plastics are coated with chemicals and contain additives that migrate into paper and cause premature aging. Even uncoated polypropylene emits gases that seep into paper. The only material which can actually preserve paper is uncoated, archival quality polyester film such as Mylar® D or Melinex® 516. BCE's Movie Gards™ are made entirely from Mylar® D. This exceptionally strong transparent film will resist moisture, pollutants, oils and acids, and has a life expectancy of hundreds of years.

4 Mil Mylar⁺ Movie-Gards™ for Movie Posters

CAT#	SIZE IN INCHES Plus 3/4" tab	TO FIT	PRICE EACH	wt. lbs.	PRICE PER 25	wt. lbs.	PRICE PER 50	wt. lbs.	PRICE PER 100	wt. lbs.	PRICE PER 500	wt. lbs.	PRICE PER 1,000	wt. lbs.
65	11 1/2" x 14 1/2"	Lobby Card			133.00	4	228.00	8	995.00	35	1,730.00	71		
71*	27 3/4" x 41 3/4"	One Sheet Size (w/o tab)	13.35	3	290.00	15	504.00	24	874.00	48	3,795.00	240	6,620.00	480
72*	14 3/4" x 36 3/4"	Insert Poster (w/o tab)	6.40	3	140.00	9	242.00	12	420.00	22	1,825.00	111	3,170.00	222
73*	28 3/4" x 22 3/4"	Half Sheet Poster (w/o tab)	7.50	3	165.00	10	286.00	14	496.00	27	2,150.00	135	3,740.00	270
74*	14 3/4" x 22 3/4"	Window Card Poster (w/o tab)	4.65	3	100.00	7	176.00	8	305.00	14	1,325.00	69	2,300.00	137

* Indicates no corner cut tab.

Note: In order to obtain the higher quantity discount, mix and match in increments of 50 only. All products are sold only in quantities, and multiples of quantities, shown on pricing chart.

Start with Mylar®
Movie Gards™

- Heavy-duty (4 mil thick) true archival protective sleeve

- Made entirely of crystal clear, archival Mylar® D

- Heat sealed with our exclusive Ultra-Weld™ for the strongest seams in the industry

Add an Acid-Free Backing Board
Time-X-Tenders™

- The original, true acid free, R-Kival™ backing boards

- Heavy weight, 42 mil thick

- 8.5 pH with a 3% calcium carbonate buffer throughout

42 Mil Acid Free Time-X-Tenders™ Backing Boards for Movie Posters

CAT #	SIZE	FOR USE WITH	PRICE PER 25	wt. lbs.	PRICE PER 50	wt. lbs.	PRICE PER 100	wt. lbs.	PRICE PER 500	wt. lbs.
35	11 1/4" x 14 1/4"	Lobby Cards	$21.00	4	$37.00	8	$61.00	16	$242.00	80
36	27 1/4" x 41 1/4"	One Sheet Size	190.00	30	345.00	60	575.00	120	2,300.00	600
37	14 1/4" x 36 1/4"	Insert Poster	66.00	15	118.00	30	196.00	60	782.00	300
38	28 1/4" x 22 1/4"	Half Sheet Poster	118.00	18	213.00	36	355.00	72	1,415.00	360
39	14 1/4" x 22 1/4"	Window Card Poster	59.00	16	107.00	32	177.00	64	710.00	320

Mix and match in increments of 50 only.

PAYMENT MUST ACCOMPANY ORDERS
MA residents add 5% sales tax
Minimum Order is $20.00 excluding freight
24 hour Toll Free Order Line
for Mastercard, Visa, or Discover Orders Only
1-800-225-8249
This is a recorded tape and does not relay product information or messages.
24 hour Toll Free FAX Line
for ordering only
1-800-FAX-BCE8

Combination Special
Get a set of 10 Mylar® Movie-Gards™
& 10 Acid-Free Time-X-Tenders™

Cat #	To Fit	Price per set	Wt. (lbs.)
6535	Lobby Cards	39.00	3
7136	One Sheet Size	279.00	13
7237	Insert Poster	83.00	7
7338	Half Sheet Poster	115.00	8
7439	Window Card Poster	66.50	5

GENERAL SHIPPING AND HANDLING CHART

TOTAL SHIPPING WEIGHT	IF YOUR ZIP CODE BEGINS WITH:				APO, FPO, AK,HI & ALL U.S. TER. via Parcel Post	ALL FOREIGN COUNTRIES via Parcel Post
	0,1	2,3 or 4	5,6 or 7	8,9		
0-2	5 75	6 75	7 25	7 75	7.00	12.50
3-5	7 25	7 75	8 25	8 75	9.50	14.50
6-10	8 75	10 00	10.50	11.50	16.75	29.25
11-15	10.00	11.50	12 25	14.25	22.00	37.75
16-20	11 50	13.50	14 50	17 75	25.50	48.75
21-25	14 00	15 25	17.75	19 25	28.50	65 50
26-30	15 25	17.00	19.75	22.00	29.00	75.00
31-35	17 50	19.75	22.00	25 75	30.00	84.50
36-40	18 50	20.50	23.25	26 25	33.00	94.50
41-45	19 50	22 50	25 75	29 50	34.00	103.75
46-50	21 00	25 00	27 75	32.50	35.00	116.50

Note: If weight is above 50 lbs add together additional amounts (Example 60 lbs in Zip 1 would be $21.00 plus $8 75 or $29 75total)

Bill Cole Enterprises, Inc.
P.O. Box 60, DEPT. MPG, Randolph, MA 02368-0600
(617) 986-2653   Fax (617) 986-2656
e-mail: BCEmylar@internetmci.com
web site: http://www. neponset.com/bcemylar

Time-X-Tenders™, Movie Gards™ Ultra-Weld™, and R-Kival™ are trademarks of Bill Cole Enterprises, Inc. All references to Mylar⁺ refer to archival quality polyester film such as Mylar™ type D by Dupont Co., or equivalent material such as Melinex® 516 by ICI Corp.

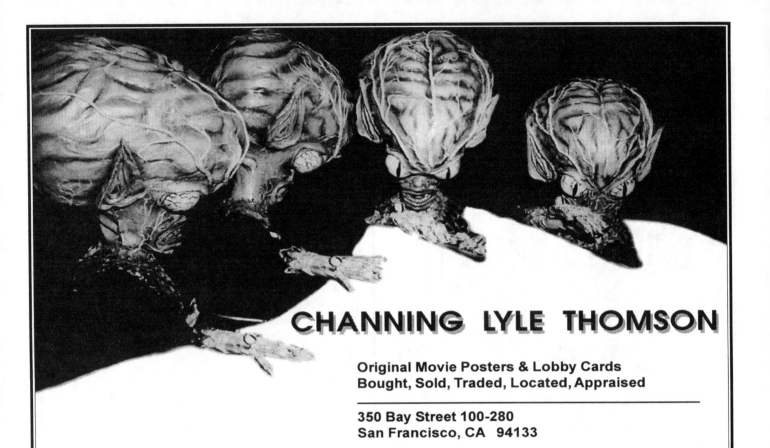

I'm here to help...

I'm available to help you paddle through the river of confusion that often can be the movie poster marketplace. As author of this price guide, and editor of *Collecting Hollywood* magazine, I have a unique responsibility in ensuring that newcomers to this hobby are treated fairly. I will, to the best of my ability, help you in any way I can to decide the best way to attain your goals, whether you are buying or selling.

Preparing to make a major purchase? I can give you sales history information to help you make an informed purchasing decision. I can also tell you whether or not we have ever had any complaints against the person you are buying from. However, if you are looking for investment advice, I won't be able to help you very much. I discourage people from buying collectibles of any kind as an investment.

Found a collection? Then you need to know your options. I'll be happy to explain the options you have for liquidating a collection you have inheritaed or, through good fortune, found.

Should you consign to the auction houses? Sometimes yes, sometimes no. I'll provide you with a list of the auction houses and a history of how posters have performed at each one.

Should you sell to a dealer? It depends on your needs and on what you have. I can provide you with a list of at least five dealers who are reputable and are buying material of the type that you have.

Or consign to a dealer? Who are the best dealers for consignments? What's a fair commission rate?

Or sell them yourself? This is another option for someone willing to take the time. I can give you pointers on how to get started and where to advertise.

Jon R. Warren
2401 Broad Street • Chattanooga, TN 37408
phone: (423) 265-5515   FAX: (423) 265-5506   email: jonrwarren@aol.com

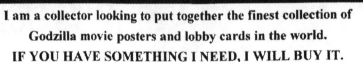

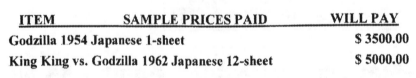

A BOUT DE SOUFFLE
(1959 - -) See BREATHLESS for prices

A LA CABARET
(1920S - Enterprise) Polly Moran, Joe Jackson
One Sheet: $250 - $600

A LA MODE
(1994 - Miramax) Jean Yanne, Ken Higelin, Florence Darel
One Sheet: $5 - $10   *French.*

A*P*E
(1976 - -) Rod Arrants, Alex Nicol
One Sheet: $5 - $10

AARON LOVES ANGELA
(1975 - Columbia) Kevin Hooks, Irene Cara
One Sheet: $5 - $10   *Black cast.*

AARON SLICK FROM PUNKIN' CRICK
(1952 - Paramount) Alan Young, Dinah Shore
One Sheet: $15 - $35

ABANDON SHIP
(1957 - Columbia) Tyrone Power, Mai Zetterling
One Sheet: $30 - $50

ABANDONED
(1949 - Universal) Dennis O'Keefe, Gale Storm
One Sheet: $50 - $100

ABAR, THE FIRST BLACK SUPERMAN
(1977 - -) Walter Smith, Tobar Mayo
One Sheet: $40 - $75   *Blaxploitation.*

ABBOTT AND COSTELLO GO TO MARS
(1953 - Universal) Bud Abbott, Lou Costello
One Sheet: $100 - $200

ABBOTT AND COSTELLO IN HOLLYWOOD
(1945 - MGM) Bud Abbott, Lou Costello
One Sheet: $200 - $400

ABBOTT AND COSTELLO IN THE FOREIGN LEGION
(1950 - Universal) Bud Abbott, Lou Costello
One Sheet: $100 - $200

ABBOTT AND COSTELLO IN THE NAVY
(1941 - Universal) Bud Abbott, Lou Costello
One Sheet: $200 - $400

ABBOTT AND COSTELLO MEET CAPTAIN KIDD
(1952 - Warner Bros.) Bud Abbott, Lou Costello, Charles Laughton
One Sheet: $100 - $200

ABBOTT AND COSTELLO MEET CAPTAIN KIDD
(1960R - RKO) Bud Abbott, Lou Costello, Charles Laughton
One Sheet: $15 - $35   *Re-release. Duotone.*

ABBOTT AND COSTELLO MEET DR. JEKYLL AND MR. HYDE
(1953 - Universal) Bud Abbott, Lou Costello, Boris Karloff
One Sheet: $200 - $400

ABBOTT AND COSTELLO MEET FRANKENSTEIN
(1949 - Universal) Bud Abbott, Lou Costello, Bela Lugosi, Lon Chaney
One Sheet: $800 - $1,500   *Graven Images, pg. 143.*

One Sheet

ABBOTT AND COSTELLO MEET FRANKENSTEIN
(1956R - Realart) Bud Abbott, Lou Costello, Bela Lugosi, Lon Chaney
One Sheet: $200 - $400   *Re-release.*

ABBOTT AND COSTELLO MEET THE INVISIBLE MAN
(1951 - Universal) Bud Abbott, Lou Costello
One Sheet: $150 - $300

ABBOTT AND COSTELLO MEET THE KEYSTONE KOPS
(1954 - Universal) Bud Abbott, Lou Costello
One Sheet: $50 - $100

ABBOTT AND COSTELLO MEET THE KILLER, BORIS KARLOFF
(1949 - Universal) Bud Abbott, Lou Costello, Boris Karloff
One Sheet: $200 - $400

ABBOTT AND COSTELLO MEET THE KILLER, BORIS KARLOFF
(1956R - Realart) Bud Abbott, Lou Costello, Boris Karloff
One Sheet: $75 - $150   *Re-release.*

ABBOTT AND COSTELLO MEET THE MUMMY
(1955 - Universal) Bud Abbott, Lou Costello
One Sheet: $125 - $250

One Sheet

ABBY
(1974 - -) William Marshall
One Sheet: $15 - $30   *Black cast.*

ABDICATION, THE
(1974 - Warner Bros.) Peter Finch, Liv Ullman
One Sheet: $3 - $5

ABDUCTION
(1975 - Black Pool) Judith Marie Bergan, David Pendleton
One Sheet: $3 - $5

ABDUCTORS, THE
(1957 - 20th Century Fox) Victor McLaglen, George Macready
One Sheet: $15 - $25

ABDUL THE BULBUL AMEER
(1941 - MGM) -
One Sheet: $250 - $600   *Cartoon. Full color stone litho. Cartoon Movie Posters #242.*

ABDUL THE DAMNED
(1938 - Columbia) Nils Asther
One Sheet: $100 - $200

ABDULLAH'S HAREM
(1956 - 20th Century Fox) George Ratoff, Kay Kendall
One Sheet: $15 - $35

ABE LINCOLN IN ILLINOIS
(1940 - RKO) Raymond Massey, Ruth Gordon
One Sheet: $75 - $150

ABIE'S IRISH ROSE
(1929 - Paramount) Nancy Carroll, Jean Herscholt
One Sheet: $200 - $400

ABIE'S IRISH ROSE
(1946 - United Artists) Michael Chekov, Joanne Dru
One Sheet: $40 - $75

ABILENE TOWN
(1946 - United Artists) Randolph Scott, Ann Dvorak
One Sheet: $50 - $100

ABILENE TRAIL
(1951 - Monogram) Whip Wilson, Andy Clyde
One Sheet: $30 - $50

ABOMINABLE DR. PHIBES
(1971 - AIP) Vincent Price, Joseph Cotten

One Sheet: $40 - $75

ABOMINABLE SNOWMAN OF THE HIMALAYAS, THE
(1957 - 20th Century Fox) Peter Cushing, Forrest Tucker
One Sheet: $30 - $60

ABOUT FACE
(1942 - United Artists) William Tracy, Joe Sawyer
One Sheet: $50 - $100

ABOUT FACE
(1952 - Warner Bros.) Gordon MacRae, Eddie Bracken
One Sheet: $15 - $30

ABOUT LAST NIGHT
(1985 - Tri-Star) Rob Lowe, Demi Moore, James Belushi
One Sheet: $7 - $15

ABOUT MRS. LESLIE
(1954 - Paramount) Shirley Booth, Robert Ryan
One Sheet: $30 - $50

ABOVE AND BEYOND
(1953 - MGM) Robert Taylor, Eleanor Parker
One Sheet: $15 - $35

ABOVE SUSPICION
(1943 - MGM) Joan Crawford, Fred MacMurray
One Sheet: $125 - $250

ABOVE THE CLOUDS
(1933 - Columbia) Robert Armstrong, Richard Cromwell
One Sheet: $150 - $300

ABOVE THE LAW
(1988 - Warner Bros.) Steven Seagal, Pam Grier, Sharon Stone
One Sheet: $7 - $15

ABOVE THE RIM
(1994 - New Line) Tupac Shakur, Duane Martin, Marlon Wayans
One Sheet: $5 - $10   *Sports (Basketball). Sports Movie Posters #103.*

ABOVE US THE WAVES
(1955 - Republic) John Mills, John Gregson
One Sheet: $20 - $40

ABRAHAM LINCOLN
(1930 - United Artists) Walter Huston, Una Merkel
One Sheet: $250 - $500

ABRAHAM LINCOLN
(1931R - Art Cinema) Walter Huston, Una Merkel
One Sheet: $75 - $150   *Re-release.*

ABROAD WITH TWO YANKS
(1944 - United Artists) William Bendix, Dennis O'Keefe
One Sheet: $75 - $150

ABSENCE OF MALICE
(1981 - Columbia) Paul Newman, Sally Field
One Sheet: $7 - $15

ABSENT MINDED PROFESSOR/SHAGGY DOG
(1967R - Disney) Fred MacMurray, Nancy Olsen, Jean Hagen
One Sheet: $10 - $20   *Double feature re-release poster.*

ABSENT-MINDED PROFESSOR, THE
(1961 - Buena Vista/Disney) Fred MacMurray, Nancy Olson
One Sheet: $20 - $40

ABSENT-MINDED PROFESSOR, THE
(1967R - Disney) Fred MacMurray, Nancy Olson
One Sheet: $10 - $20   *Re-release.*

ABSENT-MINDED PROFESSOR, THE
(1974R - Disney) Fred MacMurray, Nancy Olson
One Sheet: $15 - $25   *Re-release.*

ABSOLUTE BEGINNERS
(1986 - Virgin) Eddie O'Connell, Patsy Kensit, David Bowie
One Sheet: $7 - $15

ABSOLUTE POWER
(1997 - Columbia) Clint Eastwood, Gene Hackman
One Sheet: $5 - $10

ABSOLUTE QUIET
(1936 - MGM) Irene Hervey, Lionel Atwill
One Sheet: $100 - $200

ABSOLUTION
(1981 - Enterprise) Richard Burton
One Sheet: $50 - $10

ABSORBING JUNIOR
(1936 - Vitaphone) Shemp Howard, Johnnie Berkes
One Sheet: $200 - $400

ABUSED CONFIDENCE
(1938 - Columbia) Danniele Darrieux
One Sheet: $100 - $200

ABYSS, THE
(1989 - 20th Century Fox) Ed Harris, Mary Elizabeth Mastrantonio
One Sheet: $7 - $15   *Advance:$15-25.*

ABYSS, THE
(1993R - 20th Century Fox) Ed Harris, Mary Elizabeth Mastrantonio
One Sheet: $5 - $10   *Re-release. Special Edition.*

AC/DC: LET THERE BE ROCK
(1982 - -) AC/DC
One Sheet: $15 - $35   *Rock 'n' Roll.*

ACAPULGO GOLD
(1978 - Riddle) Marjoe Gortner, Randi Oakes
One Sheet: $5 - $10

ACCENT ON LOVE
(1941 - 20th Century Fox) George Montgomery, Osa Massen
One Sheet: $500 - $100

ACCENT ON YOUTH
(1935 - Paramount) Herbert Marshall, Sylvia Sydney
One Sheet: $350 - $750

ACCEPTABLE LEVELS
(1983 - Famous Players) Kay Adshead, Andy Rasleigh
One Sheet: $3 - $5   *British.*

ACCESS CODE
(1984 - -) Martin Landau, MacDonald Carey
One Sheet: $3 - $5

ACCIDENT
(1967 - Cinema 5) Dirk Bogarde, Stanley Baker
One Sheet: $3 - $5

ACCIDENT
(1983 - -) Terence Kelly, Fiona Reid
One Sheet: $3 - $5

ACCIDENTAL DEATH
(1963 - Allied Artists) John Carson, Jacqueline Ellis
One Sheet: $5 - $10

ACCIDENTAL TOURIST, THE
(1989 - Warner Bros.) William Hurt, Kathleen Turner
One Sheet: $5 - $10   *Academy Award Movie Posters #362.*

ACCIDENTS WILL HAPPEN
(1938 - Warner Bros.) Ronald Reagan, Gloria Blondell
One Sheet: $150 - $300

ACCOMPANIST, THE
(1993 - Sony Classics) Elena Sofonova
One Sheet: $3 - $5

ACCOMPLICE
(1946 - PRC) Richard Arlen, Veda Ann Borg
One Sheet: $50 - $100

ACCORDING TO MRS. HOYLE
(1951 - Monogram) Spring Byington, Anthony Caruso
One Sheet: $15 - $30

ACCOUNT RENDERED
(1957 - RFD) Griffith Jones, Honor Blackman
One Sheet: $7 - $15

ACCURSED, THE
(1958 - Allied Artists) Robert Bray, Donald Wolfit
One Sheet: $10 - $20

ACCUSED

(1937 - United Artists) Douglas Fairbanks Jr., Dolores Del Rio
One Sheet: $200 - $400

ACCUSED, THE
(1948 - Paramount) Loretta Young, Robert Cummings
One Sheet: $75 - $150

ACCUSED, THE
(1953 - -) Clifford Evans, Jean Lodge
One Sheet: $10 - $20

ACCUSED, THE
(1988 - -) Jodie Foster, Kelly McGillis
One Sheet: $10 - $20   *Academy Award: Best Actress (Foster). Academy Award Movie Posters #360.*

ACCUSED OF MURDER
(1956 - Republic) David Brian, Vera (Hruba) Ralston
One Sheet: $15 - $30

ACCUSING FINGER, THE
(1938 - Paramount) Paul Kelly, Robert Cummings
One Sheet: $125 - $250

ACE AND A JOKER, AN
(1918 - Fox) Mutt and Jeff
One Sheet: $3,500 - $5,000   *Cartoon. Full color stone litho. Cartoon Movie Posters #6.*

ACE DRUMMOND
(1936 - Universal) John King, Jean Rogers
One Sheet: $600 - $1,000   *Serial. 13 Chapters.*

ACE ELI AND RODGER OF THE SKIES
(1973 - 20th Century Fox) Cliff Robertson, Pamela Franklin
One Sheet: $3 - $5

ACE HIGH
(1969 - Paramount) Eli Wallach, Terrence Hill
One Sheet: $15 - $25

ACE IN THE HOLE
(1951 - Paramount) Kirk Douglas, Jan Sterling
One Sheet: $40 - $75   *AKA: BIG CARNIVAL.*

ACE OF ACES
(1933 - RKO) Richard Dix, Ralph Bellamy
One Sheet: $250 - $600

ACE OF HEARTS, THE
(1921 - Goldwyn) Lon Chaney, Leatrice Joy
One Sheet: $1,300 - $2,000

ACE OF SCOTLAND YARD, THE
(1929 - Universal) Crawford Kent, Florence Allen
One Sheet: $800 - $1,500   *Serial. 10 Chapters.*

ACE OF SPADES
(1925 - Adventure) William Desmond
One Sheet: $200 - $400   *Serial. 15 Chapters.*

ACE VENTURA: PET DETECTIVE
(1994 - Warner Bros.) Jim Carrey, Dan Marino
One Sheet: $7 - $15

ACE VENTURA: WHEN NATURE CALLS
(1995 - Warner Bros.) Jim Carrey
One Sheet: $5 - $12   *Price is for either style.*

One Sheet

ACES AND EIGHTS
(1936 - Syndicate) Tim McCoy, Jimmy Aubrey
One Sheet: $250 - $500

ACES HIGH
(1977 - EMI) Malcolm McDowell, Christopher Plummer, John Gielgud
One Sheet: $5 - $10

ACES: IRON EAGLE III
(1992 - New Line) Louis Gossett, Jr.
One Sheet: $3 - $5

ACES WILD
(1936 - Commodore) Harry Carey, Gertrude Messinger
One Sheet: $100 - $200

ACHE IN EVERY STAKE, AN
(1941 - Columbia) The Three Stooges (Curly)
One Sheet: $4,000 - $6,000   *Comedy short. Duotone.*

ACQUITTED
(1929 - Columbia) Lloyd Hughes, Margaret Livingston
One Sheet: $150 - $300

ACROSS 110TH STREET
(1972 - United Artists) Anthony Quinn, Yaphet Kotto
One Sheet: $7 - $15   *Blaxploitation. Blacks take on the mob.*

ACROSS MANCHURIA TO KOREA
(1920 - Paramount) -
One Sheet: $200 - $400   *From the Paramount Travel Pictures series.*

ACROSS THE BADLANDS
(1950 - Columbia) Charles Starrett, Smiley Burnette
One Sheet: $20 - $40

ACROSS THE BRIDGE
(1958 - Rank) Rod Steiger, Bernard Lee
One Sheet: $10 - $20

ACROSS THE CONTINENT
(1922 - Paramount) Wallace Reid, Mary MacLaren
One Sheet: $600 - $1,000

ACROSS THE FOOTLIGHTS
(1915 - Universal) Adele Lane, William Dowlan, Edward Sloman
One Sheet: $250 - $500

ACROSS THE GREAT DIVIDE
(1977 - Pacific International) Robert Logan, George "Buck" Flower
One Sheet: $5 - $10

ACROSS THE PACIFIC
(1942 - Warner Bros.) Humphrey Bogart, Mary Astor
One Sheet: $200 - $400

ACROSS THE PLAINS
(1939 - Monogram) Jack Randall, Joyce Bryant
One Sheet: $40 - $75

ACROSS THE RIO GRANDE
(1949 - Monogram) Jimmy Wakely, Lee White
One Sheet: $50 - $100

ACROSS THE RIVER
(1965 - Debema) Lou Gilber, Kay Doubleday
One Sheet: $5 - $10

ACROSS THE SIERRAS
(1941 - Columbia) Bill Elliot, Luana Walters
One Sheet: $50 - $100

ACROSS THE TRAIL
(1900 - -) Dir: Frank A. Mellen
One Sheet: $500 - $800

ACROSS THE WIDE MISSOURI
(1951 - MGM) Clark Gable, John Hodiak
One Sheet: $75 - $125

ACROSS TO SINGAPORE
(1928 - MGM) Joan Crawford, Ramon Novarro
One Sheet: $1,300 - $2,000

ACT, THE
(1984 - Film Ventures) Robert Ginty, Jill St. John
One Sheet: $3 - $5   *AKA: BLESS 'EM ALL.*

ACT OF LOVE
(1953 - United Artists) Kirk Douglas, Dany Robin
One Sheet: $15 - $30

ACT OF MURDER, AN
(1948 - Universal) Fredric March, Florence Eldridge
One Sheet: $75 - $150

ACT OF MURDER
(1965 - Warner Bros) John Carson, Anthony Bate
One Sheet: $7 - $15

ACT OF THE HEART
(1970 - Universal) Genevieve Bujold, Donald Sutherland
One Sheet: $5 - $10

ACT OF VENGEANCE
(1974 - AIP) Jo Ann Harris, Peter Brown
One Sheet: $5 - $10

ACT OF VIOLENCE
(1948 - MGM) Van Heflin, Janet Leigh, Robert Ryan
One Sheet: $75 - $150

ACT ONE
(1963 - Warner Bros.) George Hamilton, Jason Robards, Jr.
One Sheet: $15 - $30

ACTION
(1921 - Universal) Hoot Gibson, Francis Ford, Dir: John Ford
One Sheet: $300 - $700

ACTION FOR SLANDER
(1938 - United Artists) Clive Brook, Ann Todd
One Sheet: $75 - $150

ACTION IN ARABIA
(1944 - RKO) George Sanders, Virginia Bruce
One Sheet: $40 - $75

ACTION IN THE NORTH ATLANTIC
(1943 - Warner Bros.) Humphrey Bogart, Raymond Massey
One Sheet: $125 - $250   *Duotone.*

ACTION JACKSON
(1988 - Lorimar) Carl Weathers, Craig T. Nelson, Sharon Stone
One Sheet: $7 - $15

ACTION OF THE TIGER
(1957 - MGM) Van Johnson, Martine Carol
One Sheet: $15 - $25

ACTIVIST, THE
(1969 - Regional) Michael Smith, Leslie Gilbrum
One Sheet: $7 - $15

ACTOR'S ROMANCE, AN
(1913 - Selig) -
One Sheet: $250 - $500

ACTORS AND SIN
(1952 - United Artists) Edward G. Robinson, Marsha Hunt
One Sheet: $30 - $50

ACTRESS, THE
(1928 - MGM) Norma Shearer, Ralph Forbes
One Sheet: $500 - $800

ACTRESS, THE
(1953 - MGM) Spencer Tracy, Jean Simmons
One Sheet: $30 - $60

ADA
(1961 - MGM) Susan Hayward, Dean Martin
One Sheet: $20 - $40

ADAM AND EVA
(1923 - Paramount) Marion Davies
One Sheet: $600 - $1,000

ADAM AND EVALYN
(1949 - Universal International) Stewart Granger, Jean Simmons
One Sheet: $30 - $50

ADAM AND EVE
(1956 - Constelacion) Carlos Baena, Christiane Martel
One Sheet: $7 - $15   *Mexican.*

ADAM AND EVIL
(1927 - MGM) Lew Cody, Aileen Pringle
One Sheet: $150 - $300

ADAM AND SIX EVES
(1950S - -) -
One Sheet: $15 - $25

ADAM AT 6 A.M.
(1970 - National General) Michael Douglas, Lee Purcell
One Sheet: $3 - $5

ADAM HAD FOUR SONS
(1941 - Columbia) Warner Baxter, Ingrid Bergman
One Sheet: $75 - $150

ADAM'S RIB
(1938 - Cinelux) -
One Sheet: $30 - $50

ADAM'S RIB
(1949 - MGM) Spencer Tracy, Katharine Hepburn
One Sheet: $250 - $500

ADAM'S WOMAN
(1972 - Warner Bros.) Beau Bridges, Jane Merrow
One Sheet: $5 - $10

ADDAMS FAMILY, THE
(1991 - Paramount) Anjelica Huston, Raul Julia, Christopher Lloyd
One Sheet: $7 - $15   *Two Styles of Advance: $10-20.*

ADDAMS FAMILY VALUES
(1993 - Paramount) Angelica Huston, Raul Julia
One Sheet: $5 - $10

One Sheet (Advance)

ADDICTED TO LOVE
(1997 - Warner Bros.) Meg Ryan, Matthew Broderick
One Sheet: $3 - $5

ADDING MACHINE, THE
(1969 - Regional) Phyllis Diller, Milo O'Shea
One Sheet: $5 - $10

ADDRESS UNKNOWN
(1944 - Columbia) Paul Lukas, Mady Christians
One Sheet: $50 - $100

ADELE
(1919 - United Picture Theatres of America) Kitty Gordon, Mahlon Hamilton
One Sheet: $150 - $350

ADIOS
(1930 - First National) Mary Astor
One Sheet: $250 - $500

ADIOS AMIGO
(1975 - Atlas) Fred Williamson, Richard Pryor, James Brown
One Sheet: $10 - $20   *Black cast.*

ADIOS SABATA
(1971 - United Artists) Yul Brynner, Dean Reed
One Sheet: $10 - $20

ADMIRABLE CRICHTON, THE
(1957 - Columbia) Kenneth More, Sally Ann Howes
One Sheet: $10 - $20

ADMIRAL WAS A LADY, THE
(1950 - United Artists) Wanda Hendrix, Edmond O'Brien
One Sheet: $10 - $20

ADMIRALS ALL
(1935 - RKO) Wynne Gibson, Gordon Harker
One Sheet: $150 - $300

ADORABLE
(1933 - Fox) Janet Gaynor, Henry Garat
One Sheet: $200 - $400

ADORABLE CREATURES
(1956 - Continental) Martine Carol, Danielle
Darrieux
One Sheet: $20 - $40

ADORABLE JULIA
(1964 - See-Art) Lilli Palmer, Charles Boyer
One Sheet: $5 - $10

ADORABLE SAVAGE, THE
(1920 - Universal) Edith Roberts, Jack Perrin
One Sheet: $500 - $800

ADORATION
(1928 - Warner Bros.) Billie Dove
One Sheet: $250 - $500

ADRIFT
(1971 - MPO) Rade Markovic, Paula Pritchett
One Sheet: $3 - $5

A-DUCKING THEY DID GO
(1939 - Columbia) Three Stooges (Curly)
One Sheet: $7,500 - $12,000   *Comedy short.*
Duotone.

ADULTERESS, THE
(1976 - -) Tyne Daly, Eric Braeden
One Sheet: $5 - $10

ADVANCE TO THE REAR
(1964 - MGM) Glenn Ford, Stella Stevens
One Sheet: $10 - $20

ADVENTURE
(1945 - MGM) Clark Gable, Greer Garson
One Sheet: $125 - $250

One Sheet

ADVENTURE FOR TWO
(1945 - GFD) Laurence Olivier, Marjorie
Fielding
One Sheet: $125 - $250

ADVENTURE IN BALTIMORE
(1949 - RKO) Robert Young, Shirley Temple
One Sheet: $50 - $100

ADVENTURE IN BLACKMAIL
(1943 - English) Clive Brook, Judy Campbell
One Sheet: $100 - $200

ADVENTURE IN DIAMONDS
(1940 - Paramount) Isa Miranda, George Brent
One Sheet: $100 - $200

ADVENTURE IN IRAQ
(1943 - Warner Bros.) John Loder, Ruth Ford
One Sheet: $30 - $50

ADVENTURE IN MANHATTAN
(1936 - Columbia) Jean Arthur, Joel McCrea
One Sheet: $250 - $500

ADVENTURE IN MANHATTAN
(1948R - Columbia) Jean Arthur, Joel McCrea
One Sheet: $40 - $75   *Re-release.*

ADVENTURE IN SAHARA
(1938 - Columbia) Paul Kelly, Lorna Gray
One Sheet: $125 - $250

ADVENTURE IN WASHINGTON
(1941 - Columbia) Herbert Marshall, Virginia
Bruce
One Sheet: $75 - $125

ADVENTURE ISLAND
(1947 - Paramount) Rory Calhoun, Rhonda
Fleming
One Sheet: $40 - $75

ADVENTURE LIMITED
(1934 - Paramount) Harry Milton, Pearl Argyle
One Sheet: $100 - $200

**ADVENTURE OF THE MISSING REMBRANDT,
THE**
(1932 - First Anglo) -
One Sheet: $600 - $1,000

ADVENTURE'S END
(1937 - Universal) John Wayne, Diane Gibson
One Sheet: $300 - $700

ADVENTURE'S END
(1949R - Universal) John Wayne, Diane Gibson
One Sheet: $125 - $250   *Re-release.*

ADVENTURER, THE
(1917 - Art Dramas) Marian Swayne, Pell
Trenton
One Sheet: $150 - $350

ADVENTURER, THE
(1919 - Mutual) Charlie Chaplin, Edna
Purviance
One Sheet: $6,500 - $10,000

ADVENTURER, THE
(1970 - Paramount) Bekim Fehmiu, Ernest
Borgnine, Candice Bergen
One Sheet: $3 - $5

ADVENTURERS, THE
(1951 - Rank) Jack Hawkins, Peter Hammond
One Sheet: $7 - $15

ADVENTURERS, THE
(1970 - Paramount) Charles Aznavour, Ernest
Borgnine, Olivia de Havilland
One Sheet: $10 - $20

ADVENTURES IN BABYSITTING
(1987 - Buena Vista) Elisabeth Shue, Maia
Brewton
One Sheet: $10 - $20

ADVENTURES IN SILVERADO
(1948 - Columbia) William Bishop, Gloria Henry
One Sheet: $40 - $75

ADVENTURES OF A NEWSREEL CAMERAMAN
(1938 - 20th Century Fox) -
One Sheet: $250 - $500

ADVENTURES OF A ROOKIE, THE
(1943 - RKO) Wally Brown, Alan Carney
One Sheet: $40 - $75

ADVENTURES OF A YOUNG MAN
(1962 - 20th Century Fox) Richard Beymer,
Diane Baker, Paul Newman
One Sheet: $15 - $25

ADVENTURES OF BARON MUNCHAUSEN, THE
(1989 - Columbia) Eric Idle, Oliver Reed
One Sheet: $15 - $30   *Advance:$20-
40.*

**ADVENTURES OF BUCKAROO BANZAI:
ACROSS THE 8TH DIMENSION, THE**
(1984 - 20th Century Fox) Peter Weller, John
Lithgow
One Sheet: $15 - $30

ADVENTURES OF BUFFALO BILL
(1917 - Essanay) William Frederick Cody, Chief
Sitting Bull
One Sheet: $1,900 - $3,000

ADVENTURES OF BULLWHIP GRIFFIN, THE
(1967 - Buena Vista/Disney) Roddy McDowall,
Suzanne Pleshette
One Sheet: $10 - $20

ADVENTURES OF CAPTAIN AFRICA
(1955 - Columbia) John Hart, Rick Vallin
One Sheet: $40 - $75   *Serial. 15
Chapters.*

ADVENTURES OF CAPTAIN FABIAN, THE
(1951 - Republic) Erroll Flynn, Vincent Price
One Sheet: $40 - $75

ADVENTURES OF CAPTAIN MARVEL
(1941 - Republic) Tom Tyler, Frank Coghlan,
Jr.
One Sheet: $800 - $1,500   *Serial. 12
Chapters. One Sheet(Chapter One):$3500-5500.
Graven Images, pg. 138.*

ADVENTURES OF CASANOVA
(1948 - Eagle-Lion) Arturo DeCordova, Lucille
Bremer
One Sheet: $30 - $50

ADVENTURES OF CHICO
(1938 - Woodward) Dir: Stacy Woodard,

Horace Woodard
One Sheet: $50 - $100

ADVENTURES OF COLONEL BLIMP, THE
(1945 - G.C.F.) Anton Walbrook, Deborah Kerr
One Sheet: $150 - $300

ADVENTURES OF DON COYOTE, THE
(1947 - Comet) Richard Martin, Frances
Rafferty
One Sheet: $50 - $100

ADVENTURES OF DON JUAN, THE
(1949 - Warner Bros.) Errol Flynn, Viveca
Lindfors
One Sheet: $75 - $150

ADVENTURES OF FORD FAIRLANE
(1990 - 20th Century Fox) Andrew Dice Clay,
Wayne Newton
One Sheet: $5 - $10

ADVENTURES OF FRANK AND JESSE JAMES
(1948 - Republic) Clayton Moore, Steve Darrell
One Sheet: $75 - $150   *Serial.
Western. 13 Chapters.*

ADVENTURES OF FRANK AND JESSE JAMES
(1956R - Republic) Clayton Moore
One Sheet: $40 - $75   *Re-release.
Serial. Western.*

ADVENTURES OF FRANK MERRIWELL, THE
(1936 - Universal) Don Briggs, Jean Rogers
One Sheet: $200 - $400   *Serial. 12
Chapters. Stock full color One Sheet:$400-850.*

ADVENTURES OF FRONTIER FREEMONT, THE
(1976 - Sun Classics) Dan Haggerty, Denver
Pyle
One Sheet: $3 - $5

ADVENTURES OF GALLANT BESS
(1948 - Eagle-Lion) Cameron Mitchell, Audrey
Long
One Sheet: $30 - $50

ADVENTURES OF GERARD, THE
(1970 - United Artists) Peter McEnery, Claudia
Cardinale
One Sheet: $3 - $5

ADVENTURES OF HAJJI BABA, THE
(1954 - United Artists) John Derek, Elaine
Stewart
One Sheet: $15 - $25

ADVENTURES OF HUCK FINN, THE
(1993 - Buena Vista) Elijah Wood, Jason
Robards
One Sheet: $3 - $5

ADVENTURES OF HUCKLEBERRY FINN, THE
(1939 - MGM) Mickey Rooney, Walter Connelly
One Sheet: $125 - $250

ADVENTURES OF HUCKLEBERRY FINN, THE
(1960 - MGM) Tony Randall, Patty McCormack
One Sheet: $20 - $40

ADVENTURES OF HUCKLEBERRY FINN, THE
(1970R - MGM) Mickey Rooney, Walter
Connelly
One Sheet: $5 - $10   *Re-release.*

**ADVENTURES OF ICHABOD AND MR. TOAD,
THE**
(1949 - Disney/RKO) Voices of Basil Rathbone,
Bing Crosby
One Sheet: $125 - $250   *Cartoon.
Cartoon Movie Posters #378.*

ADVENTURES OF JANE, THE
(1949 - United Artists) Chrisabel Leighton-
Porter, Sebastian Cabot
One Sheet: $30 - $50

ADVENTURES OF JANE ARDEN, THE
(1939 - Warner Bros.) Rosella Towne, William
Gargan
One Sheet: $50 - $100

ADVENTURES OF KITTY O'DAY
(1945 - Monogram) Jean Parker, Peter
Cookson
One Sheet: $30 - $50

ADVENTURES OF MARCO POLO, THE
(1938 - MGM) Gary Cooper, Sigrid Gurie
One Sheet: $250 - $500

ADVENTURES OF MARCO POLO, THE
(1954R - MGM) Gary Cooper, Sigrid Gurie
One Sheet: $40 - $75   *Re-release.*

ADVENTURES OF MARK TWAIN
(1944 - Warner Bros.) Fredric March, Alexis
Smith
One Sheet: $30 - $50   *Duotone.*

ADVENTURES OF MARTIN EDEN
(1942 - Columbia) Glenn Ford, Claire Trevor
One Sheet: $50 - $100

ADVENTURES OF MILO AND OTIS, THE
(1989 - Columbia) Narrated by Dudley Moore
One Sheet: $3 - $5

ADVENTURES OF PC 49, THE
(1949 - Hammer) Hugh Latimer, Annette
Simmonds
One Sheet: $50 - $100   *British.*

ADVENTURES OF PINOCCHIO, THE
(1996 - New Line) Martin Landau, Jonathan
Taylor Thomas
One Sheet: $5 - $10

ADVENTURES OF POPEYE
(1935 - Paramount) Popeye
One Sheet: $1,900 - $3,000   *Cartoon.
Duotone. Cartoon Movie Posters #210.*

**ADVENTURES OF PRISCILLA QUEEN OF THE
DESERT, THE**
(1994 - Polygram) Terence Stamp, Hugo
Weaving
One Sheet: $7 - $15

ADVENTURES OF QUENTIN DURWARD, THE
(1955 - MGM) Robert Taylor, Kay Kendall
One Sheet: $30 - $50

ADVENTURES OF RED RYDER
(1940 - Republic) Don "Red" Barry, Noah Beery
One Sheet: $125 - $250   *Serial.
Western. 12 Chapters.*

ADVENTURES OF REX AND RINTY, THE
(1935 - Mascot) Rex, Rin-Tin-Tin, Jr., Kane
Richmond
One Sheet: $125 - $250   *Serial.
Western. 12 Chapters.*

ADVENTURES OF ROBIN HOOD, THE
(1938 - Warner Bros.) Errol Flynn, Olivia de
Havilland
One Sheet: $5,500 - $9,000

ADVENTURES OF ROBIN HOOD, THE
(1942R - Warner Bros.) Errol Flynn, Olivia
DeHavilland
One Sheet: $800 - $1,500   *Re-release.*

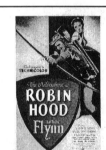

One Sheet

ADVENTURES OF ROBIN HOOD, THE
(1948R - Warner Bros.) Errol Flynn, Olivia
DeHavilland
One Sheet: $300 - $700   *Re-release.*

ADVENTURES OF ROBIN HOOD, THE
(1955R - Warner Bros.) Errol Flynn, Olivia
DeHavilland
One Sheet: $150 - $300   *Re-release.
One Sheet is red/brown duotone.*

ADVENTURES OF ROBIN HOOD, THE
(1976R - United Artists) Errol Flynn, Olivia
DeHavilland
One Sheet: $20 - $40   *Re-release.*

ADVENTURES OF ROBINSON CRUSOE
(1922 - Universal) Harry Myers
One Sheet: $250 - $500   *Serial. 18
Chapters.*

ADVENTURES OF ROBINSON CRUSOE, THE
(1954 - United Artists) Don O'Herlihy, Jaime
Fernandez

One Sheet: $10 - $20

ADVENTURES OF RUSTY
(1945 - Columbia) Ted Donaldson, Conrad Nagel
One Sheet: $40 - $75

ADVENTURES OF SADIE, THE
(1955 - 20th Century Fox) Joan Collins, George Cole
One Sheet: $30 - $50

ADVENTURES OF SHERLOCK HOLMES, THE
(1939 - 20th Century Fox) Basil Rathbone, Ida Lupino
One Sheet: $3,500 - $5,000

ADVENTURES OF SHERLOCK HOLMES' SMARTER BROTHER, THE
(1975 - 20th Century Fox) Gene Wilder, Madeline Kahn, Marty Feldman
One Sheet: $5 - $10

ADVENTURES OF SHORTY
(1917 - Sunnywest) Shorty Hamilton
One Sheet: $250 - $600   *Serial.*

ADVENTURES OF SIR GALAHAD, THE
(1949 - Columbia) George Reeves, Charles King
One Sheet: $50 - $100   *Serial. 15 Chapters.*

ADVENTURES OF SMILIN' JACK
(1943 - Universal) Tom Brown, Marjorie Lord
One Sheet: $50 - $100   *Serial. 13 Chapters. Full color stock one sheet:$300-$500.*

ADVENTURES OF SUPERMAN, THE
(1948 - -) See SUPERMAN

ADVENTURES OF TARTU
(1943 - MGM) Robert Donat, Valerie Hobson
One Sheet: $100 - $200

One Sheet

ADVENTURES OF TARZAN
(1921 - Numa) Elmo Lincoln
One Sheet: $3,500 - $5,000   *Serial. 15 Chapters.*

ADVENTURES OF THE FLYING CADETS
(1943 - Universal) Johnny Downs, Bobby Jordan
One Sheet: $75 - $125   *Serial. 13 Chapters.*

ADVENTURES OF THE GREAT MOUSE DETECTIVE, THE
(1986 - Disney) -
One Sheet: $10 - $20   *Cartoon.*

ADVENTURES OF THE LAST AMERICAN HERO
(1973 - 20th Century Fox) Jeff Bridges, Valerie Perrine
One Sheet: $5 - $10

ADVENTURES OF THE WILDERNESS FAMILY, THE
(1975 - Pacific-International) Robert Logan, Susan Shaw
One Sheet: $3 - $5

ADVENTURES OF TOM SAWYER, THE
(1938 - United Artists) Tommy Kelly, May Robson, Walter Brennan
One Sheet: $100 - $200

ADVENTURES OF TOM SAWYER, THE
(1945R - United Artists) Tommy Kelly, May Robson, Walter Brennan
One Sheet: $30 - $50   *Re-release.*

ADVENTURES OF TOM SAWYER, THE
(1966R - United Artists) Tommy Kelly, May

Robson, Walter Brennan
One Sheet: $5 - $10   *Re-release.*

ADVENTURESS, AN
(1920 - Republic) R. De Valentina (Rudolph Valentino)
One Sheet: $1,900 - $3,000

ADVENTURESS, THE
(1947 - GFD) Deborah Kerr, Trevor Howard
One Sheet: $40 - $75

ADVENTUROUS BLONDE
(1937 - Warner Bros.) Glenda Farrell, Barton MacLane
One Sheet: $75 - $150   *3rd in Torchy Blane series.*

ADVENTUROUS ROGUE
(1937 - United Artists) Bobby Nelson, Donald Reed
One Sheet: $75 - $150

ADVICE TO THE LOVELORN
(1933 - United Artists) Lee Tracy, Sally Blaine
One Sheet: $150 - $300

ADVISE AND CONSENT
(1962 - Columbia) Henry Fonda, Charles Laughton
One Sheet: $50 - $100   *Saul Bass art.*

AERIAL GUNNER
(1943 - Paramount) Chester Morris, Richard Arlen
One Sheet: $30 - $50

AESOP'S FABLES
(1931 - RKO Pathe) Animated by Paul Terry
One Sheet: $600 - $1,000   *Cartoon. Cartoon Movie Posters #72.*

AFFAIR IN HAVANA
(1957 - Allied Artists) John Cassavetes, Raymond Burr
One Sheet: $20 - $40

AFFAIR IN KAMAKURA
(1959 - -) Yujiro Ishihara, Masahiko Tsugawa
One Sheet: $50 - $100   *Japanese.*

AFFAIR IN MONTE CARLO
(1952 - Monogram) Merle Oberon, Richard Todd
One Sheet: $15 - $25

AFFAIR IN RENO
(1957 - Republic) John Lund, Doris Singleton
One Sheet: $15 - $30

AFFAIR IN TRINIDAD
(1952 - Columbia) Rita Hayworth, Glenn Ford
One Sheet: $250 - $500

AFFAIR OF SUSAN, THE
(1935 - Universal) Zasu Pitts, Hugh O'Connell
One Sheet: $150 - $300

AFFAIR OF THE SKIN, AN
(1964 - Zenith) Kevin McCarthy, Viveca Lindfors, Diana Sands
One Sheet: $10 - $20

AFFAIR TO REMEMBER, AN
(1957 - 20th Century Fox) Cary Grant, Deborah Kerr
One Sheet: $250 - $500

AFFAIR WITH A STRANGER
(1953 - RKO) Jean Simmons, Victor Mature
One Sheet: $30 - $50

AFFAIRS OF A GENTLEMAN
(1934 - Universal) Paul Lukas, Leila Hyams
One Sheet: $150 - $300

AFFAIRS OF A ROGUE, THE
(1949 - Columbia) Jean Pierre Aumont, Joan Hopkins
One Sheet: $30 - $60

AFFAIRS OF ANNABEL, THE
(1938 - RKO) Jack Oakie, Lucille Ball
One Sheet: $150 - $300

AFFAIRS OF CAPPY RICKS
(1937 - Republic) Walter Brennan, Mary Brian
One Sheet: $100 - $200

AFFAIRS OF CELLINI, THE
(1934 - 20th Century Fox) Fredric March, Constance Bennett
One Sheet: $250 - $500

AFFAIRS OF DOBIE GILLIS, THE
(1953 - MGM) Bobby Van, Debbie Reynolds
One Sheet: $30 - $50

AFFAIRS OF GERALDINE
(1946 - Republic) Jane Withers, James Lydon
One Sheet: $40 - $75

AFFAIRS OF MARTHA, THE
(1942 - MGM) Marsha Hunt, Richard Carlson
One Sheet: $50 - $100

AFFAIRS OF SUSAN, THE
(1945 - Paramount) Joan Fontaine, George Brent
One Sheet: $50 - $100

AFFECTIONATELY YOURS
(1941 - Warner Bros.) Merle Oberon, Rita Hayworth
One Sheet: $100 - $200

AFRAID TO TALK
(1932 - Universal) Eric Linden, Sidney Fox
One Sheet: $250 - $500

AFRAID TO TALK
(1938 - Universal) Robert Wilcox, Dorothea Kent
One Sheet: $125 - $250

AFRICA ABLAZE
(1962R - -) Robert Wilcox, Dorothea Kent
One Sheet: $7 - $15   *Re-release.*

AFRICA ADVENTURE
(1954 - RKO-Pathe) Robert C. Ruark
One Sheet: $15 - $25

AFRICA SCREAMS
(1949 - United Artists) Bud Abbott, Lou Costello
One Sheet: $100 - $200

AFRICA SPEAKS
(1930 - Columbia) -
One Sheet: $200 - $400

AFRICA SPEAKS
(194? - Sack Amusement) -
One Sheet: $50 - $100   *Black cast/ exploitation.*

AFRICA SQUAWKS
(1939 - 20th Century Fox) Terry-Toons
One Sheet: $100 - $200   *Cartoon.*

AFRICA TEXAS STYLE!
(1967 - Paramount) Hugh O'Brian, John Mills
One Sheet: $5 - $10

AFRICAN DIARY
(1945 - RKO/Disney) Goofy
One Sheet: $800 - $1,500   *Cartoon. The Disney Poster, pg. 75.*

AFRICAN ELEPHANT, THE
(1971 - National General) -
One Sheet: $5 - $10

AFRICAN FURY
(1952R - Lopert) Canada Lee, Charles Carson
One Sheet: $40 - $75   *Re-release. Aka: Cry, The Beloved Country. Separate Cinema, pg. 157.*

AFRICAN LION, THE
(1955 - Buena Vista/Disney) Documentary
One Sheet: $20 - $40

AFRICAN MANHUNT
(1954 - Republic) Myron Healy, Karen Booth
One Sheet: $20 - $40

AFRICAN QUEEN, THE
(1951 - United Artists) Humphrey Bogart, Katharine Hepburn
One Sheet: $500 - $800   *Academy Award: Best Actor. Academy Award Movie Posters #137.*

AFRICAN SAFARI
(1969 - Crown) -
One Sheet: $5 - $10

AFRICAN TREASURE
(1952 - Monogram) Johnny Sheffield, Laurette Luez
One Sheet: $30 - $50   *AKA: BOMBA AND THE AFRICAN TREASURE. From the Bomba, The Jungle Boy series.*

AFTER DARK MY SWEET
(1990 - Avenue) Jason Patric, Rachel Ward,

Bruce Dern
One Sheet: $7 - $15

AFTER HOURS
(1985 - Warner Bros.) Griffin Dunne, Rosanna Arquette
One Sheet: $5 - $10

AFTER MEIN KAMPF?
(1941 - -) -
One Sheet: $250 - $600   *War propaganda poster, black and white.*

AFTER MIDNIGHT
(1927 - MGM) Norma Shearer, Lawrence Gray
One Sheet: $250 - $600

AFTER MIDNIGHT
(1989 - -) Jullian McWhirter, Pamela Segall
One Sheet: $5 - $10

AFTER MIDNIGHT WITH BOSTON BLACKIE
(1943 - Columbia) Chester Morris, Richard Lane
One Sheet: $100 - $200

AFTER OFFICE HOURS
(1935 - MGM) Clark Gable, Constance Bennett
One Sheet: $800 - $1,500

AFTER SCHOOLDAYS
(1939 - Universal) Deanna Durbin
One Sheet: $150 - $300

AFTER THE BALL
(1933 - Fox) Basil Rathbone, Esther Ralston
One Sheet: $250 - $600

AFTER THE BALL
(1957 - IFD) Patricia Kirkwood, Laurence Harvey
One Sheet: $10 - $20

AFTER THE DANCE
(1935 - Columbia) Nancy Carroll, George Murphy
One Sheet: $125 - $250

AFTER THE FALL OF NEW YORK
(1983 - Almi) Michael Sopkiw, Valentine Monnier
One Sheet: $3 - $5

AFTER THE FOG
(1930 - Affiliated Exchange) Mary Philbin, Russell Simpson
One Sheet: $100 - $200

AFTER THE FOX
(1966 - United Artists) Peter Sellers, Victor Mature
One Sheet: $15 - $30   *Frazetta art.*

AFTER THE THIN MAN
(1936 - MGM) William Powell, Myrna Loy, James Stewart
One Sheet: $1,300 - $2,000

Mini Window Card

AFTER TOMORROW
(1932 - Fox) Charles Farrell, Marian Nixon
One Sheet: $250 - $500

AFTER TONIGHT
(1933 - RKO) Constance Bennett, Gilbert Roland
One Sheet: $600 - $1,000

AFTER YOU COMRADE
(1967 - Continental) Jamie Uys, Bob Courtney
One Sheet: $3 - $5

AFTER YOUR OWN HEART
(1921 - Fox) Tom Mix, Ora Carew
One Sheet: $600 - $1,000

AFTERMATH, THE
(1980 - -) Steve Barkett, Sid Haig
One Sheet: $3 - $5

AGAINST A CROOKED SKY
(1975 - Doty) Richard Boone, Stewart Petersen
One Sheet: $5 - $10

AGAINST ALL FLAGS
(1952 - Universal) Errol Flynn, Maureen O'Hara
One Sheet: $125 - $250

AGAINST ALL ODDS
(1924 - Fox) Buck Jones, Dolores Rousse
One Sheet: $600 - $1,000

AGAINST ALL ODDS
(1984 - Columbia) Rachel Ward, Jeff Bridges
One Sheet: $10 - $20

AGAINST THE LAW
(1934 - Columbia) Johnny Mack Brown
One Sheet: $150 - $300

AGAINST THE TIDE
(1937 - 20th Century Fox) Robert Cockran, Cathleen Nesbitt
One Sheet: $75 - $150

AGAINST THE WIND
(1948 - Eagle-Lion) Robert Beatty, Jack Warner, Simone Signoret
One Sheet: $15 - $30

AGATHA
(1979 - Warner Bros.) Dustin Hoffman, Vanessa Redgrave, Timothy Dalton
One Sheet: $7 - $15

AGE FOR LOVE, THE
(1931 - United Artists) Edward Everett Horton, Billie Dove
One Sheet: $150 - $300

AGE OF CONSENT, THE
(1932 - RKO) Eric Linden, Arline Judge
One Sheet: $150 - $300

AGE OF CONSENT, THE
(1970 - Columbia) James Mason, Helen Mirren
One Sheet: $5 - $10

AGE OF INDISCRETION
(1935 - MGM) Paul Lukas, Madge Evans, May Robson
One Sheet: $125 - $250

AGE OF INNOCENCE, THE
(1934 - RKO) Irenne Dunne, John Boles, Lionel Atwill
One Sheet: $500 - $800

AGE OF INNOCENCE
(1977 - Willoughby) Honor Blackman, David Warner
One Sheet: $5 - $10

AGE OF INNOCENCE, THE
(1993 - Columbia) Michelle Pfeiffer, Daniel Day-Lewis, Winona Ryder
One Sheet: $7 - $15

AGE OF PISCES
(1972 - -) Oliver Reed, Mark Damon
One Sheet: $5 - $10

AGENCY
(1981 - Farley) Robert Mitchum, Lee Majors
One Sheet: $5 - $10

AGENT 008
(1965 - Continental) Dirk Bogarde, Sylvia Koscina
One Sheet: $15 - $25

AGENT 38-24-36
(1964 - Seven Arts) Brigitte Bardot, Anthony Perkins
One Sheet: $40 - $75   *First Penelope Lightfeather film adventure.*

AGENT 8 3/4
(1965 - Rank) Dirk Bogarde, Robert Morley
One Sheet: $7 - $15

AGENT FOR H.A.R.M.
(1966 - Universal) Mark Richman, Wendell Corey
One Sheet: $5 - $10

AGES OF LULU, THE
(1994 - Academy Entertainment) Francesca Neri, Oscar Ladoire
One Sheet: $7 - $15   *Spanish.*

AGGIE APPLEBY MAKER OF MEN
(1933 - RKO) Betty Furness, William Gargan
One Sheet: $200 - $400

AGGRAVATIN' KID
(1946 - Universal) Buddy Messinger
One Sheet: $100 - $200

AGNES OF GOD
(1985 - Columbia) Jane Fonda, Anne Bancroft
One Sheet: $5 - $10

AGONY AND THE ECSTASY, THE
(1965 - 20th Century Fox) Charlton Heston, Rex Harrison
One Sheet: $30 - $60

AGONY OF LOVE
(1960S - -) -
One Sheet: $10 - $20

AGUIRRE, THE WRATH OF GOD
(1977 - New Yorker) Klaus Kinski, Dir: Werner Herzog
One Sheet: $30 - $50   *Photo style:$40-75.*

AH, QUELLE EQUIPE!
(1956 - Pathe) Sidney Bechet
One Sheet: $150 - $300   *French. Black cast. Separate Cinema, pg. 104.*

AH, WILDERNESS!
(1935 - MGM) Wallace Beery, Aline MacMahon
One Sheet: $125 - $250

A-HAUNTING WE WILL GO
(1942 - 20th Century Fox) Stan Laurel, Oliver Hardy
One Sheet: $250 - $500

Title Card

A-HUNTING WE WON'T GO
(1941 - Columbia) Color Rhapsodies, Fox & Crow
One Sheet: $250 - $500   *Cartoon. Full color semi-stock poster. Very early Fox & Crow.*

AIDA
(1954 - -) Sophia Loren, Lois Maxwell
One Sheet: $30 - $50

AIN'T MISBEHAVIN'
(1955 - Universal) Rory Calhoun, Piper Laurie, Mamie Van Doren
One Sheet: $40 - $75

AIR AMERICA
(1990 - TriStar) Mel Gibson, Robert Downey, Jr.
One Sheet: $5 - $10

AIR CADET
(1951 - Universal) Stephen McNally, Rock Hudson
One Sheet: $20 - $40

AIR CIRCUS, THE
(1928 - Fox) Louise Dressler, David Rollins, Dir: Howard Hawks
One Sheet: $500 - $800

AIR DEVILS
(1938 - Universal) Dick Purcell, Beryl Wallace
One Sheet: $100 - $200

AIR EAGLES
(1932 - Big Productions) Lloyd Hughes, Shirley Grey
One Sheet: $200 - $400

AIR FORCE
(1943 - Warner Bros.) Gig Young, John Garfield
One Sheet: $40 - $75   *One Sheet is*

all text.

AIR HAWKS
(1935 - Columbia) Ralph Bellamy, Wiley Post
One Sheet: $150 - $300

AIR HOSTESS
(1933 - Columbia) Evelyn Knapp, James Murray
One Sheet: $150 - $300

AIR HOSTESS, THE
(1937 - Columbia) Color Rhapsodies
One Sheet: $250 - $500   *Cartoon. Full color. Cartoon Movie Posters #40.*

AIR HOSTESS
(1949 - Columbia) Gloria Henry, Ross Ford
One Sheet: $20 - $40

AIR LEGION
(1929 - RKO) Ben Lyon, Martha Sleeper, Antonio Moreno
One Sheet: $600 - $1,000

AIR MAIL, THE
(1925 - Paramount) Warner Baxter, Billie Dove, Douglas Fairbanks, Jr.
One Sheet: $1,300 - $2,000

AIR MAIL
(1932 - Universal) Ralph Bellamy, Gloria Stuart
One Sheet: $150 - $300

AIR PATROL
(1962 - 20th Century Fox) Willard Parker, Merry Anders
One Sheet: $5 - $10

AIR POLICE
(1931 - Sono-Art World) Kenneth Harlan, Josephine Dunn
One Sheet: $150 - $350

AIR RAID WARDENS
(1943 - MGM) Laurel & Hardy, Edgar Kennedy
One Sheet: $250 - $500

AIR STRIKE
(1955 - Lippert) Richard Denning, Gloria Jean
One Sheet: $10 - $20

AIR TIGHT
(1925 - Educational) Bobby Vernon
One Sheet: $200 - $400

AIR UP THERE, THE
(1994 - Hollywood) Kevin Bacon, Charles Gitonga Maina
One Sheet: $7 - $15   *Sports (Basketball). Sports Movie Posters #104.*

AIRBORNE
(1962 - Diamond) Bobby Diamond, Robert Christian
One Sheet: $7 - $15

AIRBORNE
(1993 - Warner Bros.) Shane McDermott
One Sheet: $7 - $15   *Sports Movie Posters #309.*

AIRHEADS
(1994 - 20th Century Fox) Brendan Fraser, Steve Buscemi, Adam Sandler
One Sheet: $5 - $10

AIRMAIL MYSTERY, THE
(1932 - Universal) James Flavin, Lucile Browne
One Sheet: $350 - $750   *Serial. 12 Chapters.*

AIRPLANE!
(1980 - Paramount) Robert Hays, Julie Hagerty, Lloyd Bridges
One Sheet: $15 - $25

AIRPLANE II: THE SEQUEL
(1982 - Paramount) Robert Hays, Julie Hagerty, Lloyd Bridges
One Sheet: $3 - $5

AIRPORT
(1970 - Universal) Burt Lancaster, Helen Hayes, Dean Martin
One Sheet: $15 - $35   *Academy Award: Best Supporting Actress, Helen Hayes. Academy Award Movie Posters #263.*

AIRPORT '77
(1977 - Universal) Jack Lemmon, Lee Grant
One Sheet: $7 - $15

AIRPORT '79

(1979 - Universal) Alain Delon, Susan Blakely
One Sheet: $3 - $5   *AKA: CONCORDE, THE-AIRPORT '79 and AIRPORT '80: THE CONCORDE.*

AIRPORT 1975
(1974 - Universal) Charlton Heston, Karen Black
One Sheet: $7 - $15

AKA: CASSIUS CLAY
(1970 - United Artists) Mohammed Ali
One Sheet: $40 - $75   *Documentary. Sports (Boxing). Sports Movie Posters #155.*

AKIRA KUROSAWA'S DREAMS
(1990 - Warner Bros.) Akira Terao, Martin Scorsese
One Sheet: $15 - $25   *Japanese.*

AL CAPONE
(1959 - Allied Artists) Rod Steiger, Fay Spain
One Sheet: $30 - $50

AL JENNINGS OF OKLAHOMA
(1951 - Columbia) Dan Duryea, Gale Storm
One Sheet: $7 - $15

AL JENNINGS OF OKLAHOMA
(1957R - Columbia) Dan Duryea, Gale Storm
One Sheet: $7 - $15   *Re-release.*

ALADDIN
(1992 - Disney) -
One Sheet: $30 - $60   *Cartoon. Advance One Sheet:$30-$50. The Disney Poster, pg. 79.*

One Sheet

ALADDIN AND HIS LAMP
(1952 - Monogram) Patricia Medina, John Sands
One Sheet: $30 - $50

ALADDIN AND HIS MAGIC LAMP
(1968 - Childhood) -
One Sheet: $15 - $25   *Cartoon.*

ALADDIN AND HIS MAGIC LAMP
(1975 - Paramount) -
One Sheet: $5 - $10   *Cartoon.*

ALADDIN AND THE WONDERFUL LAMP
(1934 - Celebrity) Animation by Ub Iwerks
One Sheet: $800 - $1,500   *Cartoon. Cartoon Movie Poster #106.*

ALAKAZAM THE GREAT
(1961 - AIP) Toei Japanese Animation
One Sheet: $30 - $50   *Cartoon.*

ALAMO, THE
(1960 - United Artists) John Wayne, Richard Widmark, Dir: John Wayne
One Sheet: $150 - $300   *Cowboy Movie Posters #308.*

ALAMO, THE
(1967R - United Artists) John Wayne, Richard Widmark Dir: John Wayne
One Sheet: $40 - $75   *Re-release.*

ALASKA
(1944 - Monogram) Kent Taylor, Margaret Lindsay
One Sheet: $40 - $75

ALASKA
(1996 - Columbia) Charlton Heston, Thora Birch
One Sheet: $3 - $5

ALASKA HIGHWAY
(1943 - Paramount) Richard Arlen, Jean Parker
One Sheet: $50 - $100

ALASKA PASSAGE
(1958 - 20th Century Fox) Bill Williams, Nora Hayden
One Sheet: $10 - $20

ALASKA PATROL
(1948 - Burwood) Richard Travis, Helen Westcott
One Sheet: $20 - $40

ALASKA SEAS
(1954 - Paramount) Robert Ryan, Jan Sterling
One Sheet: $15 - $25

ALASKAN, THE
(1924 - Paramount) Thomas Meighan, Estelle Taylor
One Sheet: $250 - $600

ALASKAN ESKIMO
(1953 - RKO/Disney) -
One Sheet: $15 - $25

ALASKAN SAFARI
(1973 - American National) -
One Sheet: $3 - $5

ALBERT IN BLUNDERLAND
(1950 - MGM) -
One Sheet: $200 - $450   *Cartoon. Full color stone litho.*

ALBERT, R.N.
(1953 - Eros) Anthony Steel, Jack Warner
One Sheet: $15 - $25   *AKA: BREAK TO FREEDOM.*

ALBERT SCHWEITZER
(1957 - -) -
One Sheet: $15 - $25   *Documentary.*

ALBINO
(1980 - -) Christopher Lee, Sybil Danning
One Sheet: $5 - $10

ALBINO ALLIGATOR
(1996 - Miramax) Matt Dillon, Faye Dunaway, Gary Sinise
One Sheet: $15 - $25   *Billiards scene on one sheet.*

One Sheet

ALBUQUERQUE
(1948 - Paramount) Randolph Scott, Barbara Britton
One Sheet: $20 - $40

ALCATRAZ ISLAND
(1937 - First National) John Litel, Ann Sheridan
One Sheet: $100 - $200

ALCATRAZ ISLAND
(1950R - First National) John Litel, Ann Sheridan
One Sheet: $10 - $20   *Re-release.*

ALCATRAZ ISLAND
(1956R - -) John Litel, Ann Sheridan
One Sheet: $5 - $10   *Re-release.*

ALCHEMIST, THE
(1981 - -) Robert Ginty, Lucinda Dooling
One Sheet: $3 - $5

ALEX AND THE GYPSY
(1976 - 20th Century Fox) Jack Lemmon, Genevieve Bujold, James Woods
One Sheet: $3 - $5

ALEX IN WONDERLAND
(1970 - MGM) Donald Sutherland, Jeanne Moreau
One Sheet: $5 - $10

ALEXANDER HAMILTON
(1931 - Warner Bros.) George Arliss, Doris Kenyon
One Sheet: $150 - $300

ALEXANDER NEVSKY
(1938 - Mosfilm) Nikolai Cherkassov
One Sheet: $500 - $800   *Russian. Price is for 30 x 40.*

ALEXANDER THE GREAT
(1956 - United Artists) Richard Burton, Fredric March
One Sheet: $30 - $50

One Sheet

ALEXANDER'S RAGTIME BAND
(1938 - 20th Century Fox) Tyrone Power, Alice Faye
One Sheet: $1,300 - $2,000

ALEXANDER'S RAGTIME BAND
(1943R - 20th Century Fox) Tyrone Power, Alice Faye
One Sheet: $200 - $400   *Re-release.*

ALEXANDER'S RAGTIME BAND
(1947R - 20th Century Fox) Tyrone Power, Alice Faye
One Sheet: $100 - $200   *Re-release.*

ALF AND FAMILY
(1972 - Sherpix) Warren Mitchell, Randy Nichols
One Sheet: $5 - $10

ALF'S BABY
(1953 - Act) Jerry Desmonde, Pauline Stroud
One Sheet: $10 - $20

ALF'S BUTTON
(1921 - First National) Leslie Hensen, Alma Taylor
One Sheet: $1,900 - $3,000   *Graven Images, pg. 27.*

ALF'S BUTTON
(1930 - Gaumont) Tubby Eldin, Alf Goddard
One Sheet: $200 - $400

ALF'S BUTTON AFLOAT
(1938 - GFD) Bud Flanagan
One Sheet: $100 - $200

ALF'S CARPET
(1929 - British International) Janice Adair, Gerald Rawlinson
One Sheet: $250 - $500

ALFIE
(1966 - Paramount) Michael Caine, Shelley Winters
One Sheet: $15 - $35

ALFIE DARLING
(1975 - EMI) Alan Price, Joan Collins
One Sheet: $5 - $10

ALFRED THE GREAT
(1969 - MGM) David Hemmings, Michael York
One Sheet: $5 - $10

ALGIERS
(1938 - United Artists) Charles Boyer, Hedy Lamarr
One Sheet: $200 - $400

ALGIERS
(1953R - United Artists) Charles Boyer, Hedy Lamarr
One Sheet: $40 - $75   *Re-release.*

ALI BABA
(1936 - Celebrity) By Ub Iwerks
One Sheet: $900 - $1,600   *Cartoon. A ComiColor Cartoon. Cartoon Movie Posters #119.*

ALI BABA AND THE FORTY THIEVES
(1943 - Universal) Jon Hall, Maria Montez
One Sheet: $150 - $300

ALI BABA AND THE SEVEN MIRACLES OF THE WORLD
(1961 - AIP) -
One Sheet: $15 - $25

ALI BABA GOES TO TOWN
(1937 - 20th Century Fox) Eddie Cantor, June Lang
One Sheet: $250 - $500   *Style C(all text):$75-150.*

ALI BABA NIGHTS
(1953 - Lippert) George Robey, Anna May Wong
One Sheet: $20 - $40

ALI VS. FRAZIER
(1975 - Murray Poster Printing) Muhammed Ali, Joe Frazier
One Sheet: $75 - $150   *Sports (Boxing). Poster is red and black, with photo of Ali on left and Frazier on right. Under Ali's photo is thename "Cassius Clay", text begins "Direct From Ringside" on top line.*

ALI VS. MARCIANO
(1970 - -) Muhammad Ali, Rocky Marciano
One Sheet: $75 - $150   *Sports (Boxing).*

ALIAS A GENTLEMAN
(1948 - MGM) Wallace Beery, Tom Drake
One Sheet: $50 - $100

ALIAS BILLY THE KID
(1946 - Republic) Sunset Carson, Peggy Stewart
One Sheet: $30 - $60

ALIAS BOSTON BLACKIE
(1942 - Columbia) Chester Morris, Adele Mara
One Sheet: $75 - $125

ALIAS BULLDOG DRUMMOND
(1935 - Gaumont-British) Jack Hulbert, Fay Wray
One Sheet: $600 - $1,000   *AKA: BULLDOG JACK (British).*

ALIAS FRENCH GERTIE
(1930 - RKO) Bebe Daniels, Ben Lyon
One Sheet: $500 - $800

ALIAS JESSE JAMES
(1959 - United Artists) Bob Hope, Rhonda Fleming
One Sheet: $30 - $50

ALIAS JIMMY VALENTINE
(1928 - MGM) William Haines
One Sheet: $250 - $500

ALIAS JOHN LAW
(1935 - Supreme) Bob Steele, Roberta Gale
One Sheet: $200 - $400

ALIAS JOHN PRESTON
(1955 - Associated Artists) Alexander Knox, Betta St. John
One Sheet: $15 - $25

ALIAS JULIUS CEASAR
(1922 - First National) Charles Ray, Barbara Bedford
One Sheet: $350 - $750

ALIAS LADYFINGERS
(1921 - Metro) Bert Lytell, Ora Carew
One Sheet: $150 - $300   *AKA: LADYFINGERS.*

ALIAS MARY DOW
(1935 - Universal) Ray Milland, Sally Eilers, Henry O'Neill
One Sheet: $150 - $300

ALIAS MARY SMITH
(1932 - Mayfair) John Darrow, Gwen Lee
One Sheet: $200 - $400

ALIAS MR. TWILIGHT
(1946 - Columbia) Michael Duane, Trudy Marshall
One Sheet: $50 - $100

ALIAS NICK BEAL
(1949 - Paramount) Ray Milland, Audrey Totter
One Sheet: $40 - $75

ALIAS ST. NICK
(1935 - MGM) -
One Sheet: $250 - $500   *Cartoon.*

ALIAS THE BAD MAN
(1931 - Tiffany) Ken Maynard
One Sheet: $250 - $600

ALIAS THE CHAMP
(1949 - Republic) Gorgeous George, Robert Rockwell
One Sheet: $40 - $75   *Sports (Wrestling). Sports Movie Posters #s 340, 341, 342.*

One Sheet

ALIAS THE DEACON
(1940 - Universal) Bob Burns, Mischa Auer
One Sheet: $100 - $200

ALIAS THE DOCTOR
(1932 - First National) Norman Foster, Richard Barthelmess
One Sheet: $150 - $300

ALIAS THE LONE WOLF
(1927 - Columbia) Bert Lytell, Lois Wilson
One Sheet: $500 - $800

ALIAS THE NIGHT WIND
(1923 - Fox) William Russell
One Sheet: $200 - $400

ALIBI
(1929 - United Artists) Chester Morris, Mae Busch
One Sheet: $200 - $400

ALIBI
(1931 - Twickenham) Austin Trevor, Franklyn Dyall
One Sheet: $150 - $300

ALIBI
(1943 - Republic) Margaret Lockwood, Hugh Sinclair
One Sheet: $50 - $100

ALIBI BYE BYE
(1935 - Radio Pictures) Clark and McCullough
One Sheet: $250 - $500   *Comedy short.*

ALIBI BYE BYE
(1950R - RKO) Clark and McCullough
One Sheet: $50 - $100   *Re-release. Comedy short. Red and black duotone.*

ALIBI FOR MURDER
(1936 - Columbia) William Gargan, Marguerite Churchill
One Sheet: $150 - $350

ALIBI IKE
(1935 - Warner Bros.) Joe E. Brown, Olivia de Havilland
One Sheet: $150 - $300   *Sports Movie Posters #42.*

ALIBI INN
(1935 - MGM) Molly Lamont, Frederick Bradshaw
One Sheet: $200 - $400

ALICE
(1991 - Orion) Mia Farrow
One Sheet: $7 - $15

ALICE ADAMS
(1935 - RKO) Katharine Hepburn, Fred MacMurray
One Sheet: $800 - $1,500

ALICE DOESN'T LIVE HERE ANYMORE
(1974 - Warner Bros.) Ellen Burstyn, Harvey Keitel, Kris Kristofferson
One Sheet: $10 - $20   *Academy Award: Best Actress(Burstyn). Academy Award Movie Posters #281.*

ALICE IN THE JUNGLE
(1924 - By Walt Disney) Alice
One Sheet: $3,500 - $5,000 *Cartoon.*
Cartoon Movie Posters #21.

ALICE IN WONDERLAND
(1931 - -) Ruth Gilbert, Leslie King
One Sheet: $200 - $400

ALICE IN WONDERLAND
(1933 - Paramount) W. C. Fields, Charlotte
Henry, Cary Grant
One Sheet: $800 - $1,500

ALICE IN WONDERLAND
(1951 - RKO/Disney) -
One Sheet: $250 - $600 *Cartoon.*
Cartoon Movie Posters #381.

One Sheet

ALICE IN WONDERLAND
(1974R - Buena Vista/Disney) -
One Sheet: $30 - $50 *Re-release.*
Cartoon. Full color.

ALICE IN WONDERLAND
(1981R - Disney) -
One Sheet: $15 - $35 *Re-release.*
Cartoon.

ALICE, SWEET ALICE
(1978 - Allied Artists) Brooke Shields, Paula
Sheppard
One Sheet: $10 - $20

ALICE THE PEACEMAKER
(1924 - Walt Disney-Winkler Pictures) -
One Sheet: $13,000 - $20,000 *Cartoon.*
Cartoon Movie Posters #20.

ALICE'S ADVENTURES IN WONDERLAND
(1972 - AIP) Hywel Bennett, Fiona Fullerton
One Sheet: $7 - $15

ALICE'S RESTAURANT
(1969 - United Artists) Arlo Guthrie, Pat Quinn,
James Broderick
One Sheet: $30 - $60

ALIEN
(1979 - 20th Century Fox) Sigourney Weaver,
Tom Skerritt
One Sheet: $40 - $75 *Advance:$50-
100.*

ALIEN
(1994R - 20th Century Fox) Sigourney Weaver,
Tom Skerritt
One Sheet: $7 - $15 *Re-release.*

ALIEN 3
(1992 - 20th Century Fox) Sigourney Weaver
One Sheet: $5 - $10

ALIEN CONTAMINATION
(1982 - Cannon) Ian McCullough
One Sheet: $5 - $10

ALIEN FACTOR, THE
(1978 - -) Don Leifert
One Sheet: $5 - $10

ALIEN FROM L.A.
(1988 - -) Kathy Ireland, Linda Kerridge
One Sheet: $5 - $10

ALIEN NATION
(1988 - -) James Caan, Mandy Patinkin
One Sheet: $5 - $10

ALIEN RANGE
(1952R - United Artists) -
One Sheet: $5 - $10 *Re-release.*

ALIEN THUNDER

(1975 - Cinerama) Donald Sutherland, Chief
Dan George
One Sheet: $7 - $15

ALIEN ZONE
(1978 - -) Ivor Francis, Stefanie Auerbach
One Sheet: $3 - $5

ALIEN'S RETURN, THE
(1980 - -) Jan-Michael Vincent, Cybil Shepherd
One Sheet: $5 - $10

ALIENS
(1986 - 20th Century Fox) Sigourney Weaver,
Micheal Biehn
One Sheet: $20 - $40 *One
Sheet(Style B, Weaver with kid & eggs,
scarce):$60-125; One Sheet (Advance):$20-$40.*

ALIENS FROM ANOTHER PLANET
(1967 - -) James Darren, Robert Duvall
One Sheet: $15 - $25

ALIENS FROM SPACESHIP EARTH
(1977 - -) Lynda Day George, Donovan
One Sheet: $15 - $25

ALIMONY
(1924 - FBO) Warner Baxter, Grace Dermond
One Sheet: $200 - $400

ALIMONY
(1949 - Eagle-Lion) Martha Vickers, John Beal
One Sheet: $30 - $50

ALIMONY MADNESS
(1933 - Mayfair) Helen Chandler, Leon Waycoff
One Sheet: $75 - $150

ALIVE
(1993 - Buena Vista) Ethan Hawke, Vincent
Spano
One Sheet: $3 - $5

ALIVE AND KICKING
(1962 - Pathe) Sybil Thorndike, Kathleen
Harrison
One Sheet: $7 - $15

ALKALI IKE'S MISFORTUNES
(1913 - Essanay) Augustus Carney
One Sheet: $250 - $550 *Cowboy
Movie Posters #2.*

ALL ABOUT DOGS
(1940 - 20th Century Fox) Terry-toons
One Sheet: $75 - $150 *Cartoon. Full
color stone litho. Stock poster with inset title.*

ALL ABOUT EVE
(1950 - 20th Century Fox) Bette Davis, Anne
Baxter, Marilyn Monroe
One Sheet: $250 - $600 *Academy
Award: Best Picture, Best Direction(Mankiewicz).
Academy Award Movie Posters #126-#128 &
#132.*

Insert

ALL AMERICAN, THE
(1932 - Universal) Richard Arlen, Preston
Foster, Andy Devine
One Sheet: $150 - $300

ALL AMERICAN
(1953 - Universal) Tony Curtis, Lori Nelson,
Mamie Van Doren
One Sheet: $30 - $50 *Sports
(Football).*

ALL AMERICAN BOY
(1973 - Warner Bros.) Jon Voight, Anne Archer
One Sheet: $75 - $150

ALL AMERICAN CO-ED
(1941 - United Artists) Frances Langford,
Johnny Downs

One Sheet: $30 - $50

ALL AMERICAN SWEETHEART
(1937 - Columbia) Scott Colton, Patricia Farr
One Sheet: $75 - $150

ALL ASHORE
(1953 - Columbia) Mickey Rooney, Dick
Haymes
One Sheet: $15 - $30

ALL AT SEA
(1929 - MGM) Karl Dane, George K. Arthur,
Josephine Dunn
One Sheet: $250 - $500

ALL AT SEA
(1935 - 20th Century Fox) Tyrell Davis, Rex
Harrison
One Sheet: $150 - $300

ALL AT SEA
(1939 - British Lion) Sandy Powell
One Sheet: $75 - $150

ALL AT SEA
(1957 - MGM) Alec Guinness, Irene Browne
One Sheet: $15 - $30

ALL AT SEA
(1970 - Anvil) Gary Smith, Steven Mallett
One Sheet: $5 - $10

ALL BY MYSELF
(1943 - Universal) Patric Knowles, Evelyn
Ankers
One Sheet: $50 - $100

ALL CREATURES GREAT AND SMALL
(1975 - EMI) Anthony Hopkins, Simon Ward
One Sheet: $10 - $20

ALL DOGS GO TO HEAVEN
(1989 - United Artists) Voices of Burt Reynolds,
Loni Anderson
One Sheet: $7 - $15 *Cartoon.*

ALL DOGS GO TO HEAVEN 2
(1996 - MGM) Voices: Charlie Sheen, Dom
DeLuise
One Sheet: $5 - $10 *Cartoon.*

ALL FALL DOWN
(1962 - MGM) Eva Marie Saint, Warren Beatty
One Sheet: $20 - $40

ALL FOR MARY
(1956 - Rank) Nigel Patrick, Kathleen Harrison
One Sheet: $10 - $20

ALL GUMMED UP
(1947 - Columbia) The Three Stooges (Shemp)
One Sheet: $350 - $750 *Comedy short.
Duotone.*

ALL HANDS ON DECK
(1961 - 20th Century Fox) Pat Boone, Barbara
Eden
One Sheet: $15 - $25

ALL I DESIRE
(1953 - Universal) Barbara Stanwyck, Richard
Carlson
One Sheet: $40 - $75

ALL I WANT FOR CHRISTMAS
(1991 - Paramount) Leslie Nielsen, Harley Jane
Kozak
One Sheet: $5 - $10

ALL IN
(1936 - Gaumont) Ralph Lynn, Gina Malo
One Sheet: $125 - $250

ALL IN A NIGHT'S WORK
(1961 - Paramount) Dean Martin, Shirley
MacLaine
One Sheet: $10 - $20

ALL MEN ARE ENEMIES
(1934 - 20th Century Fox) Hugh Williams,
Helen Twelvetrees
One Sheet: $200 - $400

ALL MINE TO GIVE
(1957 - RKO) Glynis Johns, Cameron Mitchell
One Sheet: $7 - $15

ALL MY SONS
(1948 - Universal) Edward G. Robinson, Burt
Lancaster, Arlene Francis
One Sheet: $40 - $75

ALL NEAT IN BLACK STOCKINGS

(1969 - National General) Victor Henry, Susan
George
One Sheet: $7 - $15

ALL NIGHT
(1918 - Bluebird) Rudolpho di Valentina
(Rudolph Valentino), Carmel Myers
One Sheet: $1,300 - $2,000

ALL NIGHT LONG
(1924 - Pathecomedy) Harry Langdon
One Sheet: $250 - $600

ALL NIGHT LONG
(1961 - Rank) Patrick McGoohan, Marti
Stevens
One Sheet: $7 - $15

ALL NIGHT LONG
(1963 - -) -
One Sheet: $30 - $50 *Black cast.*

ALL NIGHT LONG
(1981 - Universal) Gene Hackman, Barbra
Streisand
One Sheet: $5 - $10

ALL OF A SUDDEN NORMA
(1919 - Exhibitors Mutual) Bessie Barriscale,
Jseph J. Dowling
One Sheet: $200 - $400

ALL OF ME
(1934 - Paramount) Fredric March, Miriam
Hopkins, George Raft
One Sheet: $250 - $500

Mini Window Card

ALL OF ME
(1984 - Universal) Steve Martin, Lily Tomlin
One Sheet: $5 - $10

ALL OUT FOR "V"
(1940 - 20th Century Fox) Terry-toons
One Sheet: $75 - $150 *Cartoon. Full
color stone litho. Stock poster with inset title.*

ALL OVER ME
(1997 - Fine Line) Alison Foland, Tara Subkoff,
Cole Hauser
One Sheet: $3 - $5

ALL OVER THE TOWN
(1949 - Rank) Norman Wooland, Sarah
Churchill
One Sheet: $40 - $75

ALL OVER TOWN
(1937 - Republic) Olson and Johnson
One Sheet: $75 - $150

ALL QUIET ON THE WESTERN FRONT
(1930 - Universal) Lew Ayres, Louis Wolheim
One Sheet: $4,000 - $6,000 *Academy
Award: Best Picture, Best Director (Lewis
Milestone). Academy Award Movie Posters #15 &
#17.*

ALL QUIET ON THE WESTERN FRONT
(1950R - Universal) Lew Ayres, Louis Wolheim
One Sheet: $100 - $200 *Re-release.*

ALL RIGHT, MY FRIEND
(1983 - Toho) Peter Fonda, Jinpachi Nezu
One Sheet: $5 - $10

ALL THAT GLITTERS
(1936 - GS Enterprises) Jack Hobbs, Moira
Lynd
One Sheet: $75 - $150

ALL THAT HEAVEN ALLOWS
(1955 - Universal) Jane Wyman, Rock Hudson
One Sheet: $40 - $75

ALL THAT JAZZ
(1979 - 20th Century Fox) Roy Scheider, Jessica Lange
One Sheet: $10 - $20

ALL THAT MONEY CAN BUY
(1941 - RKO) Edward Arnold, Walter Huston
One Sheet: $250 - $500   *Graven Images, pg. 121.*

ALL THE BROTHERS WERE VALIANT
(1953 - MGM) Robert Taylor, Stewart Granger
One Sheet: $20 - $40

ALL THE FINE YOUNG CANNIBALS
(1960 - MGM) Natalie Wood, Robert Wagner
One Sheet: $20 - $40

ALL THE GIRLS DO IT
(1950S - -) -
One Sheet: $15 - $30   *Sexploitation.*

ALL THE KING'S HORSES
(1935 - RKO) Mary Ellis, Carl Brisson
One Sheet: $100 - $200

ALL THE KING'S MEN
(1949 - Columbia) Broderick Crawford, John Ireland, Mercedes McCambridge
One Sheet: $100 - $200   *Academy Award: Best Picture, Best Actor(Crawford). Academy Award Movie Posters #121 & #125.*

ALL THE LOVING COUPLES
(1969 - U-M) Norman Alden, Gloria Manon, Scott Graham
One Sheet: $5 - $10

ALL THE MARBLES
(1981 - United Artists) Peter Falk, Vicki Frederick
One Sheet: $3 - $5

ALL THE PRESIDENT'S MEN
(1976 - Warner Bros.) Robert Redford, Dustin Hoffman, Jason Robards.
One Sheet: $15 - $35   *Academy Award: Best Supporting Actor(Robards). Academy Award Movie Posters #295.*

ALL THE RIGHT MOVES
(1983 - 20th Century Fox) Tom Cruise, Lea Thompson
One Sheet: $10 - $20   *Sports Movie Posters #211.*

One Sheet

ALL THE RIGHT NOISES
(1973 - 20th Century Fox) Tom Bell, Olivia Hussey
One Sheet: $5 - $10

ALL THE WAY
(1966R - Paramount) Frank Sinatra, Jeanette Gaynor
One Sheet: $7 - $15   *Re-release.*

ALL THE WAY BOYS
(1973 - Avco/Embassy) Terence Hill, Bud Spencer
One Sheet: $3 - $5

ALL THE WAY HOME
(1963 - Paramount) Jean Simmons, Robert Preston
One Sheet: $15 - $25

ALL THE WORLD'S A STOOGE
(1941 - Columbia) Three Stooges (Curly)
One Sheet: $4,000 - $6,000   *Comedy short. Duotone.*

ALL THE YOUNG MEN
(1960 - Columbia) Alan Ladd, Sidney Poitier
One Sheet: $15 - $35

ALL THE YOUNG WIVES
(1975 - United Films) Gerald Richards, Linda Cook
One Sheet: $5 - $10

ALL THESE WOMEN
(1964 - Janus) Jarl Kulle, George Funkquist
One Sheet: $5 - $10

ALL THINGS BRIGHT AND BEAUTIFUL
(1979 - World) John Alderson, Colin Blakely
One Sheet: $3 - $5

ALL THIS AND HEAVEN TOO
(1940 - Warner Bros.) Bette Davis, Charles Boyer
One Sheet: $250 - $500   *Duotone.*

ALL THIS AND WORLD WAR II
(1977 - 20th Century Fox) -
One Sheet: $5 - $10

ALL THROUGH THE NIGHT
(1942 - Warner Bros.) Humphrey Bogart, Conrad Veidt, Veronica Lake (C. Keane)
One Sheet: $250 - $600   *Duotone.*

One Sheet

ALL WET
(192? - Federated) Joe Rock
One Sheet: $125 - $250

ALL WOMAN
(1967 - Brenner) Robert Alda, Rebecca Sand
One Sheet: $7 - $15   *AKA: SCHIZO; ALL GIRL.*

ALL WOMEN HAVE SECRETS
(1939 - Paramount) Joseph Allen, Jeanne Cagney
One Sheet: $125 - $250

ALL WRONG
(1921 - William Fox) Clyde Cook
One Sheet: $250 - $600

ALL'S FAIR
(1942 - Educational) The Cabin Kids
One Sheet: $200 - $400   *Black cast. Separate Cinema, pg. 116.*

ALL-AMERICAN CHUMP
(1936 - MGM) Stuart Erwin, Betty Furness
One Sheet: $75 - $150

ALLAN QUARTERMAIN AND THE LOST CITY OF GOLD
(1987 - Cannon) Richard Chamberlain, Sharon Stone
One Sheet: $7 - $15

ALLEGHENY UPRISING
(1939 - RKO) John Wayne, Claire Trevor, Oliver Hardy
One Sheet: $700 - $1,200

ALLEGHENY UPRISING
(1952R - RKO) John Wayne, Claire Trevor, Oliver Hardy
One Sheet: $75 - $150   *Re-release.*

ALLEGHENY UPRISING
(1960R - RKO) John Wayne, Claire Trevor, Oliver Hardy
One Sheet: $40 - $75   *Re-release.*

ALLERGIC TO LOVE
(1944 - Universal) Noah Beery Jr., Martha O'Driscoll
One Sheet: $75 - $125

ALLEY CATS
(1950S - -) -
One Sheet: $10 - $20   *Sexploitation.*

ALLEZ OOP

(1934 - Educational) Buster Keaton, Dorothy Sebastian
One Sheet: $800 - $1,500

ALLIGATOR
(1980 - Group I) Robert Foster, Robin Riker
One Sheet: $5 - $10

ALLIGATOR NAMED DAISY, AN
(1957 - Rank) Donald Sinden, Diana Dors
One Sheet: $30 - $50

ALLIGATOR PEOPLE, THE
(1959 - 20th Century Fox) Beverly Garland, George Macready
One Sheet: $75 - $150

ALLOTMENT WIVES
(1945 - Monogram) Kay Francis, Paul Kelly
One Sheet: $40 - $75

ALL-STAR COMEDIES
(1950 - Columbia) -
One Sheet: $15 - $25

ALMOST A DIVORCE
(1931 - Dominions) Nelson Keys, Sydney Howard
One Sheet: $150 - $300

ALMOST A GENTLEMAN
(1938 - Butchers) Billy Bennett, Kathleen Harrison
One Sheet: $100 - $200

ALMOST A GENTLEMAN
(1939 - RKO) James Ellison, Helen Wood
One Sheet: $50 - $100

ALMOST A HONEYMOON
(1930 - British International) Clifford Mollison, Dorothy Watts
One Sheet: $200 - $400

ALMOST A HONEYMOON
(1938 - Pathe) Tommy Trinder, Linden Travers
One Sheet: $100 - $200

ALMOST A HUSBAND
(1919 - Goldwyn) Will Rogers, Peggy Wood
One Sheet: $600 - $1,000

ALMOST AN ANGEL
(1990 - Paramount) Paul Hogan
One Sheet: $5 - $10

ALMOST ANGELS
(1962 - Buena Vista/Disney) Peter Weck, Sean Scully
One Sheet: $7 - $15

ALMOST HUMAN
(1974 - Dania) Tomas Milian, Laura Beli
One Sheet: $5 - $10

ALMOST MARRIED
(1932 - Fox) Violet Heming, Ralph Bellamy
One Sheet: $200 - $400

ALMOST MARRIED
(1942 - Universal) Robert Paige, Jane Frazer
One Sheet: $75 - $125

ALMOST PERFECT AFFAIR, AN
(1979 - Paramount) Keith Carradine, Monica Vitti
One Sheet: $5 - $10

ALMOST SUMMER
(1978 - Universal) Bruno Kirby, Didi Conn
One Sheet: $3 - $5

ALMOST YOU
(1984 - Wescom) Brooke Adams, Griffin Dunne
One Sheet: $3 - $5

ALOHA
(1931 - Tiffany) Ben Lyon, Raquel Torres
One Sheet: $150 - $300

ALOHA, BOBBY AND ROSE
(1975 - Columbia) Paul LeMat, Dianne Hull
One Sheet: $7 - $15

ALOHA OE
(1915 - Triangle) Willard Mack, Enid Markey, Margaret Thompson
One Sheet: $500 - $800

ALOHA SUMMER
(1988 - -) Chris Makepeace, Yuji Okumoto
One Sheet: $3 - $5

ALOMA OF THE SOUTH SEAS

(1926 - Paramount) Gilda Gray, Percy Marmont, Warner Baxter
One Sheet: $500 - $800

ALOMA OF THE SOUTH SEAS
(1941 - Paramount) Dorothy Lamour, Jon Hall
One Sheet: $125 - $250

ALONE AGAINST ROME
(1963 - Medallion) Jeffries Lang
One Sheet: $5 - $10

ALONE IN THE DARK
(1982 - New Line/Masada) Jack Palance, Donald Pleasence
One Sheet: $7 - $15

ALONG CAME AUNTIE
(1926 - Pathe) Glenn Tryon
One Sheet: $150 - $300

ALONG CAME JONES
(1945 - RKO) Gary Cooper, Loretta Young
One Sheet: $500 - $800   *Norman Rockwell art on some styles. Cowboy Movie Posters #275.*

ALONG CAME LOVE
(1936 - Paramount) Irene Hervey, Charles Starrett
One Sheet: $100 - $200

ALONG CAME SALLY
(1934 - Gaumont) Cicely Courtneige, Sam Hardy
One Sheet: $150 - $300

ALONG CAME YOUTH
(1930 - Paramount Publix) Buddy Rogers, Stuart Erwin
One Sheet: $100 - $200

ALONG THE GREAT DIVIDE
(1951 - Warner Bros.) Kirk Douglas, Virginia Mayo
One Sheet: $30 - $50

ALONG THE GREAT DIVIDE
(1963R - Warner Bros.) Kirk Douglas, Virginia Mayo
One Sheet: $5 - $10   *Re-release.*

ALONG THE NAVAJO TRAIL
(1946 - Republic) Roy Rogers, George "Gabby" Hayes
One Sheet: $150 - $300

ALONG THE NAVAJO TRAIL
(1954R - Republic) Roy Rogers, George "Gabby" Hayes
One Sheet: $40 - $75   *Re-release.*

ALONG THE OREGON TRAIL
(1947 - Republic) Monte Hale, Adrian Booth
One Sheet: $50 - $100

ALONG THE RIO GRANDE
(1941 - RKO) Tim Holt, Ray Whitley
One Sheet: $50 - $100

ALONG THE SUNDOWN TRAIL
(1943 - PRC) Bill "Cowboy Rambler" Boyd, Art Davis, Lee Powell
One Sheet: $30 - $50

ALPHABET CITY
(1984 - Atlantic) Vincent Spano, Jami Gertz
One Sheet: $3 - $5

ALPHABET MURDERS, THE
(1966 - MGM) Tony Randall, Anita Ekberg
One Sheet: $7 - $15

ALPHABET PEOPLE, THE
(1959 - -) -
One Sheet: $5 - $10

ALPHAVILLE, A STRANGE CASE OF LEMMY CAUTION
(1965 - Pathe) Eddie Constantine, Anna Karina, Dir: Jean-Luc Godard
One Sheet: $150 - $300   *Graven Images, pg. 223.*

ALPINE ANTICS
(1928 - Universal) Oswald the Lucky Rabbit
One Sheet: $2,500 - $4,000   *Cartoon. Cartoon Movie Posters #27.*

ALPINE CLIMBERS
(1936 - RKO/Disney) Mickey Mouse
One Sheet: $10,000 - $15,000   *Cartoon. Cartoon Movie Posters #66.*

ALRAUNE
(1952 - Gloria) Erich Von Stroheim
One Sheet: $100 - $200   *German.*

ALTARS OF DESIRE
(1927 - MGM) Mae Murray. Conway Tearle
One Sheet: $250 - $500

ALTERED STATES
(1980 - Warner Bros.) William Hurt, Blair Brown
One Sheet: $10 - $20

ALVAREZ KELLY
(1966 - Columbia) William Holden, Richard
Widmark
One Sheet: $7 - $15   *Cowboy Movie Posters #318.*

ALWAYS
(1989 - Universal) Richard Dreyfuss, Holly
Hunter
One Sheet: $7 - $15

ALWAYS A BRIDE
(1940 - Warner Bros.) Rosemary Lane, George
Reeves
One Sheet: $40 - $75

ALWAYS A BRIDE
(1953 - Universal International) Peggy
Cummins, Terence Morgan
One Sheet: $30 - $50

ALWAYS A BRIDESMAID
(1943 - Universal) Andrews Sisters, Patric
Knowles
One Sheet: $100 - $200

ALWAYS AUDACIOUS
(1920 - Paramount) Wallace Reid, Margaret
Loomis
One Sheet: $125 - $250

ALWAYS GOODBYE
(1931 - Fox) Elissa Landi, Lewis Stone
One Sheet: $200 - $400

ALWAYS GOODBYE
(1938 - 20th Century Fox) Barbara Stanwyck,
Herbert Marshall
One Sheet: $150 - $350

ALWAYS IN MY HEART
(1942 - Warner Bros.) Kay Francis, Walter
Huston
One Sheet: $50 - $100

One Sheet

ALWAYS IN TROUBLE
(1938 - 20th Century Fox) Jane Withers, Jean
Rogers
One Sheet: $100 - $200

ALWAYS KICKIN'
(1939 - Paramount) Fleischer Studios
One Sheet: $600 - $1,000   *Cartoon.*

ALWAYS LEAVE THEM LAUGHING
(1949 - Warner Bros.) Milton Berle, Virginia
Mayo
One Sheet: $50 - $100

ALWAYS RIDIN' TO WIN
(1925 - Productions) Pete Morrison
One Sheet: $100 - $200

ALWAYS TOGETHER
(1948 - Warner Bros.) Robert Hutton, Joyce
Reynolds
One Sheet: $30 - $50

AM I GUILTY
(1940 - Supreme) Ralph Cooper, Sybil Lewis
One Sheet: $200 - $400   *Black cast.*

AMADEUS
(1984 - Orion) F. Murray Abraham, Tom Hulce
One Sheet: $30 - $50   *Academy
Award: Best Picture, Best Actor(Abraham), Best
Director(Forman). Duotone Review style: $10-20.
Academy Award Movie Posters#334-#336.*

AMARCORD
(1974 - Warner Bros.) Magali Noel, Bruno
Zanin, Dir: Federico Fellini
One Sheet: $20 - $40

AMARILLY OF CLOTHESLINE ALLEY
(1918 - Artcraft) Mary Pickford, William Scott
One Sheet: $1,900 - $3,000

AMATEUR, THE
(1982 - 20th Century Fox) John Savage,
Christopher Plummer
One Sheet: $3 - $5

AMATEUR, THE
(1995 - Sony Classics) Isabelle Huppert, Martin
Donovan
One Sheet: $5 - $10

AMATEUR ADVENTURESS, THE
(1919 - Metro) Emmy Whelen, Allen Sears
One Sheet: $800 - $1,500

AMATEUR CROOK
(1937 - Victory) Herman Brix, Joan Barclay
One Sheet: $75 - $125

AMATEUR DADDY
(1932 - Fox) Warner Baxter, Marian Nixon
One Sheet: $150 - $300

AMATEUR DETECTIVE, THE
(1925 - William Fox) Earle Foxe
One Sheet: $250 - $600

AMATEUR DEVIL, AN
(1921 - Paramount) Bryant Washburn
One Sheet: $500 - $800

AMATEUR GENTLEMAN, THE
(1936 - United Artists) Douglas Fairbanks, Jr.,
Elissa Landi
One Sheet: $250 - $500

AMAZING COLOSSAL MAN, THE
(1957 - AIP) Glenn Langan, Cathy Downs
One Sheet: $200 - $400   *Graven
Images, pg. 188.*

AMAZING COLOSSAL MAN/CAT GIRL
(1957 - AIP) -
One Sheet: $100 - $200   *Double
feature poster.*

AMAZING DOBERMANS, THE
(1976 - Golden) Fred Astaire, Barbara Eden
One Sheet: $15 - $25

AMAZING DR. CLITTERHOUSE, THE
(1938 - Warner Bros.) Edward G. Robinson,
Claire Trevor, Humphrey Bogart
One Sheet: $600 - $1,000

AMAZING GRACE
(1974 - United Artists) Moms Mabley, Stepin
Fetchit, Butterfly McQueen
One Sheet: $15 - $25   *Black cast.*

AMAZING GRACE AND CHUCK
(1987 - Tristar) Jamie Lee Curtis, Alex English,
Gregory Peck
One Sheet: $5 - $10

AMAZING MONSIEUR FABRE, THE
(1952 - Hartford) Pierre Fresnay, Elina L.
Bourdette
One Sheet: $10 - $20

AMAZING MR. BEECHAM, THE
(1950 - Eagle-Lion) Cecil Parker, David
Tomlinson
One Sheet: $15 - $25

AMAZING MR. BLUNDEN, THE
(1973 - Hemisphere) Diana Dors, Laurence
Naismith
One Sheet: $5 - $10

AMAZING MR. FORREST, THE
(1944 - PRC) Edward Everett Horton, Jack
Buchanan
One Sheet: $30 - $50

AMAZING MR. WILLIAMS, THE
(1939 - Columbia) Joan Blondell, Melvyn
Douglas
One Sheet: $75 - $125

AMAZING MR. X, THE
(1948 - Eagle-Lion) Turhan Bey, Lynn Bari
One Sheet: $30 - $50   *Duotone.*

AMAZING MRS. HOLLIDAY, THE
(1943 - Universal) Deanna Durbin, Edmond
O'Brien
One Sheet: $75 - $150

AMAZING TRANSPARENT MAN, THE
(1959 - AIP) Marguerite Chapman, Douglas
Kennedy; Dir: Edgar G. Ulmer
One Sheet: $75 - $125

AMAZING VAGABOND
(1929 - RKO) Bob Steele
One Sheet: $200 - $400

AMAZING WIFE, THE
(1919 - Universal) Mary MacLaren, Frank Mayo
One Sheet: $150 - $300

AMAZON HEADHUNTERS
(1932 - Principle) -
One Sheet: $100 - $200

AMAZON QUEST
(1949 - Film Classics) Tom Neal, Carole
Mathews
One Sheet: $30 - $50

AMAZON TRADER, THE
(1956 - Warner Bros.) John Sutton, Marie
Fernandez
One Sheet: $10 - $20

AMAZON WOMEN ON THE MOON
(1987 - -) Rosanna Arquette, Ralph Bellamy
One Sheet: $7 - $15

AMAZONS OF ROME
(1963 - United Artists) Jordan, Simo
One Sheet: $20 - $40

AMBASSADOR, THE
(1980 - Cannon) Robert Mitchum, Ellen Burstyn
One Sheet: $5 - $10

AMBASSADOR BILL
(1931 - Fox) Will Rogers
One Sheet: $200 - $400

One Sheet

AMBASSADOR BILL
(1936R - Fox) Will Rogers
One Sheet: $75 - $150   *Re-release.*

AMBASSADOR'S DAUGHTER, THE
(1956 - United Artists) Olivia de Havilland,
John Forsythe
One Sheet: $20 - $40

AMBLIN'
(1970 - Four Star) Dir: Stephen Spielberg
One Sheet: $30 - $50

AMBUSH
(1939 - Paramount) Gladys Swarthout, Lloyd
Nolan
One Sheet: $100 - $200

AMBUSH
(1949 - MGM) Robert Taylor, John Hodiak,
Arlene Dahl
One Sheet: $30 - $50

AMBUSH AT CIMARRON PASS
(1958 - 20th Century Fox) Scott Brady, Margi
Dean, Clint Eastwood
One Sheet: $40 - $75   *First film
mentioning Clint Eastwood in the credits (he's not
shown on the One Sheet).*

AMBUSH AT TOMAHAWK GAP
(1953 - Columbia) John Hodiak, John Derek

AMBUSH BAY
(1966 - United Artists) Hugh O'Brian, Mickey
Rooney
One Sheet: $7 - $15

AMBUSH TRAIL
(1946 - Pathe) Bob Steele, Syd Taylor
One Sheet: $50 - $100

AMBUSH VALLEY
(1936 - Reliable) Bob Custer, Victoria Vinton
One Sheet: $150 - $300

AMBUSHERS, THE
(1967 - Columbia) Dean Martin, Senta Berger
One Sheet: $15 - $30

AMERICA
(1924 - United Artists) Neil Hamilton, Carol
Dempster, Lionel Barrymore
One Sheet: $1,300 - $2,000   *Last of D.W.
Griffith's Silent Epics.*

AMERICA, AMERICA
(1964 - Warner Bros.) Stathis Giallelis, Frank
Wolff
One Sheet: $30 - $50

AMERICA'S ANSWER
(1942 - Division Of Films) -
One Sheet: $125 - $250   *Second
United States Official War Picture.*

AMERICAN ANTHEM
(1986 - -) Mitch Gaylord, Janet Jones
One Sheet: $3 - $5

AMERICAN BADGER, THE
(1921 - Pathe) -
One Sheet: $150 - $300   *From the
Adventures Of Bill And Bob series.*

AMERICAN BEAUTY
(1927 - First National) Billie Dove, Lloyd
Hughes
One Sheet: $250 - $500

AMERICAN BOYFRIENDS
(1989 - -) Margaret Langrick, John Wildman
One Sheet: $3 - $5

AMERICAN BUFFALO
(1995 - Samuel Goldwyn) Dustin Hoffman,
Dennis Franz
One Sheet: $5 - $10

AMERICAN DREAM, AN
(1966 - Warner Bros.) Stuart Whitman, Janet
Leigh
One Sheet: $7 - $15

AMERICAN DREAMER
(1984 - CBS) JoBeth Williams, Tom Conti
One Sheet: $3 - $5

AMERICAN EMPIRE
(1942 - United Artists) Richard Dix, Leo Carrillo
One Sheet: $75 - $150

AMERICAN ENTERTAINMENT COMPANY
(1900C - American Entertainment) -
One Sheet: $1,300 - $2,000   *Early stock
poster from turn of the century. Several versions
of the one sheet exist, price is for best style.*

AMERICAN FILM INSTITUTE
(1973 - -) Nar: Charlton Heston
One Sheet: $10 - $20   *Documentary.*

AMERICAN FLYERS
(1984 - Warner Bros.) Kevin Costner, David
Grant
One Sheet: $7 - $15

AMERICAN FRIEND, THE
(1977 - New Yorker) Dennis Hopper, Bruno
Ganz
One Sheet: $5 - $10

AMERICAN FRIENDS
(1993 - Castle Hill) Michael Palin, Trini
Alvarado
One Sheet: $3 - $5

AMERICAN GIGOLO
(1980 - Paramount) Richard Gere, Lauren
Hutton
One Sheet: $10 - $20

AMERICAN GOTHIC
(1988 - Pinetalk) Rod Stiger, Yvonne DeCarlo
One Sheet: $5 - $10

One Sheet: $10 - $20

AMERICAN GRAFFITI
(1973 - Universal) Richard Dreyfuss, Ronny Howard
One Sheet: $100 - $200

One Sheet

AMERICAN GRAFFITI
(1979R - Universal) Richard Dreyfuss, Ronny Howard
One Sheet: $15 - $35   *Re-release.*

AMERICAN GUERRILLA IN THE PHILLIPINES
(1950 - 20th Century Fox) Tyrone Power, Micheline Prelle
One Sheet: $30 - $50

AMERICAN HEART
(1993 - Triton) Jeff Bridges, Edward Furlong
One Sheet: $3 - $5

AMERICAN HOT WAX
(1978 - Paramount) Jay Leno, Chuck Berry
One Sheet: $15 - $30

AMERICAN IN PARIS, AN
(1951 - MGM) Gene Kelly, Leslie Caron
One Sheet: $250 - $600   *Academy Award: Best Picture. Academy Award Movie Posters #134.*

AMERICAN IN PARIS, AN
(1963R - MGM) Gene Kelly, Leslie Caron
One Sheet: $30 - $50   *Re-release.*

AMERICAN JUSTICE
(1986 - -) Jack Lucarelli, Gerald McRaney, Jameson Parker
One Sheet: $3 - $5   *AKA: JACKALS.*

AMERICAN KICKBOXER
(1991 - Cannon) John Barrett, Keith Vitali
One Sheet: $3 - $5   *Sports (Kick-Boxing). Sports Movie Posters #269.*

AMERICAN MADNESS
(1932 - Columbia) Walter Huston, Constance Cummings
One Sheet: $350 - $750

AMERICAN ME
(1992 - Universal) Edward James Olmos
One Sheet: $7 - $15

AMERICAN NIGHTMARE
(1984 - Mano) Lawrence Day, Michael Ironside
One Sheet: $5 - $10

AMERICAN NINJA
(1986 - Cannon) Michael Dudikoff, Steve James
One Sheet: $5 - $10

AMERICAN NINJA 2: THE CONFRONTATION
(1987 - -) Michael Dudikoff, Steve James
One Sheet: $3 - $5

AMERICAN NINJA 4: THE ANNIHILATION
(1991 - -) Michael Dudikoff, David Bradley
One Sheet: $2 - $3

AMERICAN NINJA III
(1989 - -) Steve James, David Bradley
One Sheet: $2 - $3

AMERICAN POP
(1981 - Columbia) Voices: Ron Thompson, Marya Small, Richard Moll
One Sheet: $10 - $20   *Cartoon.*

AMERICAN PRESIDENT, THE
(1995 - Columbia) Michael Douglas, Annette Bening
One Sheet: $5 - $10

AMERICAN PRISONER, THE
(1929 - British International) Carl Brisson, Madeleine Carroll
One Sheet: $150 - $350

AMERICAN ROMANCE, AN
(1944 - MGM) Brian Donlevy, Ann Richards
One Sheet: $100 - $200

AMERICAN SUCCESS COMPANY, THE
(1980 - Columbia) Jeff Bridges, Ned Beatty
One Sheet: $3 - $5

AMERICAN TABOO
(1984 - Lustgarten) Guy Horenstein
One Sheet: $5 - $10

AMERICAN TAIL, AN
(1986 - Universal) Voices of Dom DeLuise, Christopher Plummer
One Sheet: $7 - $15   *Cartoon.*

AMERICAN TRAGEDY, AN
(1931 - Paramount Publix) Phillip Holmes, Sylvia Sidney
One Sheet: $600 - $1,000

AMERICAN VENUS, THE
(1926 - Paramount) Esther Ralston, Ford Sterling
One Sheet: $500 - $800

AMERICAN WEREWOLF IN LONDON, AN
(1981 - Universal) David Naughton, Jenny Agutter
One Sheet: $10 - $20   *Sneak Preview Poster:$20-40.*

AMERICANA
(1981 - Sherwood) David Carradine
One Sheet: $5 - $10

AMERICANIZATION OF EMILY, THE
(1964 - MGM) James Garner, Julie Andrews
One Sheet: $15 - $25

AMERICANO, THE
(1923 - Tri-Stone) Douglas Fairbanks, Alma Rubens
One Sheet: $300 - $700

AMERICANO, THE
(1954 - RKO) Glenn Ford, Frank Lovejoy
One Sheet: $20 - $40

AMERICANS COME, THE
(1930 - Feature) -
One Sheet: $100 - $200

AMERICATHON
(1979 - United Artists) Harvey Korman, Fred Willard
One Sheet: $3 - $5

AMIN: THE RISE AND FALL
(1982 - Continental) Joseph Olita
One Sheet: $3 - $5

AMITYVILLE 3-D
(1983 - Orion) Tony Robert, Meg Ryan
One Sheet: $5 - $10

AMITYVILLE HORROR, THE
(1979 - AIP) James Brolin, Margot Kidder
One Sheet: $7 - $15

OneSheet

AMITYVILLE HORROR II: THE POSSESION
(1982 - Orion) Burt Young, Rutanya Alda
One Sheet: $3 - $5

AMONG HUMAN WOLVES
(1940 - Film Alliance) Basil Radford, Sylvia St. Claire
One Sheet: $50 - $100

AMONG THE LIVING
(1941 - Paramount) Albert Dekker, Susan Hayward
One Sheet: $150 - $350

AMONG THE MISSING
(1934 - Columbia) Henrietta Crosman, Richard Cromwell
One Sheet: $125 - $250

AMONG THOSE PRESENT
(1919 - Paramount) Ford Sterling
One Sheet: $200 - $400

AMONG VULTURES
(1964 - Rialto) Stewart Granger, Elke Sommer
One Sheet: $7 - $15

AMONGST FRIENDS
(1993 - Fine Line) Joseph Lindsey, Patrick McGraw
One Sheet: $3 - $5

AMOOZIN' BUT CONFOOZIN'
(1944 - Columbia) Li'l Abner
One Sheet: $800 - $1,500   *Cartoon. First Li'l Abner cartoon. Full color poster with scene inset.*

AMOROUS ADVENTURES OF DON QUIXOTE AND SANCHO PANZA, THE
(1976 - Burbank International) Hy Pyke, Corey John Fischer, Maria Aronoff
One Sheet: $7 - $15

AMOROUS ADVENTURES OF MOLL FLANDERS, THE
(1965 - Paramount) Kim Novak, Richard Johnson
One Sheet: $15 - $25

AMOROUS MR. PRAWN, THE
(1964 - BLC) Joan Greenwood, Cecil Parker
One Sheet: $7 - $15   *AKA: THE PLAYGIRL AND THE WAR MINISTER.*

AMOS AND ANDREW
(1992 - Columbia) Nicholas Cage, Samuel L. Jackson
One Sheet: $3 - $5

AMPHYTRION
(1937 - Globe) Henry Garat
One Sheet: $125 - $250

AMSTERDAM AFFAIR, THE
(1968 - Trio) William Marlowe, Catherine Von Schell
One Sheet: $5 - $10

AMSTERDAM KILL
(1978 - Columbia) Robert Mitchum, Richard Egan
One Sheet: $15 - $25

AMY
(1981 - Buena Vista) Jenny Agutter, Barry Newman, Nanette Fabray
One Sheet: $5 - $10

ANACONDA
(1997 - Columbia) Jennifer Lopez, Ice Cube, Jon Voight
One Sheet: $3 - $5

ANASTASIA
(1956 - 20th Century Fox) Ingrid Bergman, Yul Brynner, Helen Hayes
One Sheet: $75 - $150   *Academy Award: Best Actress(Bergman). Academy Award Movie Posters #171.*

ANATHAN
(1953 - Dalwa) A. Negishi, Dir: Joseph Von Sternberg
One Sheet: $15 - $25

ANATOMIST, THE
(1961 - British International) Alistair Sim, George Cole
One Sheet: $10 - $20

ANATOMY OF A MURDER
(1959 - Columbia) James Stewart, Lee Remick, Ben Gazzara
One Sheet: $125 - $250

ANATOMY OF A PSYCHO
(1950S - Unitel) Ronnie Burns, Pamela Lincoln
One Sheet: $20 - $40

ANATOMY OF LOVE
(1958 - Lux) Sophia Loren
One Sheet: $40 - $75

ANATOMY OF THE SYNDICATE
(1961 - Cinema Associates) -
One Sheet: $7 - $15

ANCHORS AWEIGH
(1945 - MGM) Gene Kelly, Frank Sinatra
One Sheet: $150 - $300

ANCHORS AWEIGH
(1955R - MGM) Gene Kelly, Frank Sinatra
One Sheet: $30 - $50   *Re-release.*

ANCHORS AWEIGH
(1969R - MGM) Gene Kelly, Frank Sinatra
One Sheet: $7 - $15   *Re-release.*

AND A NEW WALT DISNEY MICKEY MOUSE
(1932 - United Artists) Mickey Mouse
One Sheet: $13,000 - $20,000   *Cartoon. Lobby Card known to exist. Cartoon Movie Posters #59.*

AND BABY MAKES THREE
(1949 - Columbia) Robert Young, Barbara Hale
One Sheet: $30 - $50

AND GEORGE DID
(1926 - Stern Bros.) -
One Sheet: $150 - $300   *From the "Let George Do It" series.*

AND GOD CREATED WOMAN
(1956 - Cinemascope) Brigitte Bardot, Curt Jurgens
One Sheet: $100 - $200   *French(47x63, Cocinor):$300-500.*

AND GOD CREATED WOMAN
(1988 - Vestron) Rebecca DeMornay, Vincent Spano
One Sheet: $15 - $25

AND HOPE TO DIE
(1972 - 20th Century Fox) Robert Ryan, Jean-Louis Trintignant, Lea Massari
One Sheet: $5 - $10

AND JUSTICE FOR ALL
(1979 - Columbia) Al Pacino, Jack Warden, John Forsythe
One Sheet: $15 - $25

AND MILLIONS WILL DIE
(1973 - Columbia) Richard Basehart, Susan Strasberg
One Sheet: $3 - $5

AND NOW FOR SOMETHING COMPLETELY DIFFERENT
(1972 - Columbia) Graham Chapman, John Cleese, Monty Python
One Sheet: $15 - $30

AND NOW MIGUEL
(1966 - Universal) Guy Stockwell, Michael Ansara
One Sheet: $5 - $10

AND NOW THE SCREAMING STARTS
(1973 - Cinerama) Peter Cushing
One Sheet: $15 - $30

AND NOW TOMORROW
(1944 - Paramount) Loretta Young, Alan Ladd
One Sheet: $100 - $200

AND ONE WAS BEAUTIFUL
(1940 - MGM) Jean Muir, Laraine Day, Robert Cummings
One Sheet: $75 - $150

AND QUIET FLOW THE DON
(1960 - United Artists) Pyotr Glebov
One Sheet: $5 - $10

AND SO THEY WERE MARRIED
(1936 - Columbia) Melvyn Douglas, Mary Astor
One Sheet: $150 - $300

AND SO TO BED
(1965 - Medallion) Hildegrad Neff, Thomas Fritsch
One Sheet: $5 - $10   *German.*

AND SOON THE DARKNESS
(1971 - Levitt-Pickman) Pamela Franklin, Michele Dotrice
One Sheet: $10 - $20

AND SUDDEN DEATH
(1936 - Paramount) Randolph Scott, Frances Drake
One Sheet: $100 - $200

AND SUDDENLY IT'S MURDER
(1964 - Royal) Alberto Sordi, Silvana Mangano
One Sheet: $5 - $10

AND THE ANGELS SING
(1944 - Paramount) Fred MacMurray, Dorothy
Lamour
One Sheet: $75 - $125

One Sheet

AND THE SAME TO YOU
(1960 - Monarch) Brian Rix, Leo Franklyn
One Sheet: $5 - $10

AND THE SHIP SAILS ON
(1983 - Vides) Freddie Jones, Dir: Federico
Fellini
One Sheet: $15 - $25

AND THE VILLAIN STILL PURSUED HER
(1913 - Kalem) -
One Sheet: $200 - $400

AND THEN THERE WERE NONE
(1945 - 20th Century Fox) Barry Fitzgerald,
Walter Huston
One Sheet: $200 - $400

AND WOMEN SHALL WEEP
(1960 - RFD) Ruth Dunning, Max Butterfield
One Sheet: $10 - $20

ANDERSON TAPES, THE
(1971 - Columbia) Sean Connery, Dyan
Cannon
One Sheet: $5 - $10

ANDRE
(1994 - Paramount) Tina Majorino, Keith
Carradine
One Sheet: $5 - $10

ANDROCLES AND THE LION
(1952 - RKO) Alan Young, Jean Simmons
One Sheet: $30 - $50

ANDROID
(1982 - New World) Klaus Kinski, Brie Howard
One Sheet: $7 - $15

ANDROMEDA STRAIN, THE
(1971 - Universal) Arthur Hill, David Wayne
One Sheet: $7 - $15

ANDY
(1965 - Universal) Norman Alden
One Sheet: $5 - $10

ANDY CLYDE GETS SPRING CHICKEN
(1939 - Columbia) Andy Clyde
One Sheet: $75 - $150   *Comedy short.*
Duotone.

ANDY HARDY COMES HOME
(1958 - MGM) Mickey Rooney, Patricia Breslin
One Sheet: $30 - $60

ANDY HARDY GETS SPRING FEVER
(1939 - MGM) Mickey Rooney, Lewis Stone
One Sheet: $100 - $200

ANDY HARDY MEETS DEBUTANTE
(1940 - MGM) Mickey Rooney, Lewis Stone,
Judy Garland
One Sheet: $100 - $200

ANDY HARDY'S BLONDE TROUBLE
(1944 - MGM) Mickey Rooney, Lewis Stone
One Sheet: $75 - $150

ANDY HARDY'S DOUBLE LIFE
(1942 - MGM) Mickey Rooney, Lewis Stone,
Esther Williams (film debut)
One Sheet: $75 - $150

ANDY HARDY'S PRIVATE SECRETARY
(1941 - MGM) Mickey Rooney, Ann Rutherford
One Sheet: $75 - $150

ANDY WARHOL'S DRACULA
(1974 - Bryanston) Udo Kier, Joe Dallesandro
One Sheet: $20 - $40

ANDY WARHOL'S FRANKENSTEIN
(1974 - CBR) Joe Dallesandro, Udo Kier
One Sheet: $15 - $35   3-D.

ANGEL
(1937 - Paramount) Marlene Dietrich, Herbert
Marshall, Melvyn Douglas
One Sheet: $1,300 - $2,000

ANGEL
(1982 - Motion) Stephen Rea, Alan Devlin
One Sheet: $3 - $5

ANGEL
(1984 - New World) Donna Wilkes, Cliff
Gorman
One Sheet: $5 - $10

ANGEL 3: THE FINAL CHAPTER
(1988 - -) -
One Sheet: $5 - $10

ANGEL AND THE BADMAN
(1946 - Republic) John Wayne, Gail Russell
One Sheet: $800 - $1,500

One Sheet

ANGEL AND THE BADMAN
(1959R - Republic) John Wayne, Gail Russell
One Sheet: $75 - $150   *Re-release.*

ANGEL, ANGEL, DOWN WE GO
(1969 - AIP) Jennifer Jones, Roddy McDowall
One Sheet: $15 - $30   *AKA: CULT*
OF THE DAMNED.

ANGEL BABY
(1961 - Allied Artists) George Hamilton,
Mercedes McCambridge, Burt Reynolds
One Sheet: $10 - $20

ANGEL COMES TO BROOKLYN, AN
(1945 - Republic) Kay Dowd, Robert Duke
One Sheet: $50 - $100

ANGEL FACE
(1952 - RKO) Robert Mitchum, Jean Simmons
One Sheet: $125 - $250

ANGEL FROM TEXAS, AN
(1940 - Warner Bros.) Eddie Albert, Wayne
Morris, Ronald Reagan
One Sheet: $75 - $150

ANGEL HEART
(1987 - Tristar) Mickey Rourke, Robert DeNiro
One Sheet: $10 - $20

ANGEL IN EXILE
(1948 - Republic) John Carroll, Adele Mara
One Sheet: $30 - $50

ANGEL IN MY POCKET
(1969 - Universal) Andy Griffith, Jerry Van
Dyke
One Sheet: $15 - $25

ANGEL LEVINE, THE
(1970 - United Artists) Harry Belafonte, Zero
Mostel, Ida Kaminska
One Sheet: $15 - $25

ANGEL OF BROADWAY, THE
(1927 - Pathe) Leatrice Joy, Victor Varconi
One Sheet: $800 - $1,500

ANGEL OF H.E.A.T.
(1982 - -) Marilyn Chambers

One Sheet: $15 - $25

ANGEL ON MY SHOULDER
(1946 - United Artists) Paul Muni, Anne Baxter,
Claude Rains
One Sheet: $50 - $100

ANGEL ON THE AMAZON
(1948 - Republic) George Brent, Vera Ralston
One Sheet: $30 - $50

ANGEL UNCHAINED
(1970 - AIP) Don Stroud, Luke Askew
One Sheet: $30 - $50

ANGEL WHO PAWNED HER HARP, THE
(1956 - Associated Artists) Felix Aylmer, Diane
Cilento
One Sheet: $15 - $25

ANGEL WITH A TRUMPET
(1950 - London) Eileen Herlie, Oskar Werner,
Maria Schell
One Sheet: $15 - $30

ANGEL WORE RED, THE
(1960 - MGM) Ava Gardner, Dirk Bogarde
One Sheet: $15 - $30

ANGEL'S HOLIDAY
(1937 - 20th Century Fox) Jane Withers,
Robert Kent
One Sheet: $125 - $250

ANGELA
(1955 - 20th Century Fox) Dennis O'Keefe,
Rossano Brazzi
One Sheet: $10 - $20

ANGELA
(1977 - Montreal Travel) Sophia Loren, Steve
Railsback, John Huston
One Sheet: $5 - $10

ANGELA
(1996 - Tree Farm) Nurith Cohn, Charlotte
Blythe
One Sheet: $5 - $10

ANGELINA
(1935 - Fox) -
One Sheet: $100 - $200

ANGELO
(1951 - Scalera) Renato Baldini, Umberto
Spadaro
One Sheet: $30 - $50   *Italian.*
Duotone. Separate Cinema, pg. 149.

ANGELS ALLEY
(1948 - Monogram) Leo Gorcey, Huntz Hall
One Sheet: $40 - $75

ANGELS AND INSECTS
(1996 - Samuel Goldwyn) Mark Rylance, Patsy
Kensit
One Sheet: $5 - $10

ANGELS BRIGADE
(1980 - Arista) Sylvia Anderson, Lieu Chinh
One Sheet: $3 - $5

ANGELS DIE HARD
(1970 - New World) Tom Baker, William Smith
One Sheet: $15 - $30   *Biker film.*

ANGELS FROM HELL
(1968 - AIP) Tom Stern, Arlene Martel
One Sheet: $15 - $25   *Biker film.*

ANGELS HARD AS THEY COME
(1971 - New World) Scott Glenn, Gary Busey
One Sheet: $15 - $30   *Biker film.*

ANGELS IN DISGUISE
(1949 - Monogram) Leo Gorcey, Huntz Hall
One Sheet: $40 - $75

ANGELS IN THE OUTFIELD
(1951 - MGM) Paul Douglas, Janet Leigh
One Sheet: $75 - $150   *Sports*
(Baseball). Sports Movie Posters #63.

ANGELS IN THE OUTFIELD
(1994 - Buena Vista) Danny Glover, Tony
Danza, Christopher Lloyd
One Sheet: $5 - $10   *Sports*
(Baseball). Sports Movie Posters #86.

ANGELS OF DARKNESS
(1956 - Supra) Anthony Quinn, Linda Darnell
One Sheet: $15 - $25

ANGELS ONE FIVE

(1953 - Stratford) Jack Hawkins, John Gregson
One Sheet: $15 - $30

ANGELS OVER BROADWAY
(1940 - Columbia) Douglas Fairbanks Jr., Rita
Hayworth
One Sheet: $150 - $350

ANGELS WASH THEIR FACES, THE
(1939 - Warner Bros.) Ann Sheridan, Ronald
Reagan
One Sheet: $250 - $600

ANGELS WITH BROKEN WINGS
(1941 - Republic) Binnie Barnes, Gilbert
Roland
One Sheet: $50 - $100

ANGELS WITH DIRTY FACES
(1938 - Warner Bros.) James Cagney, Pat
O'Brien, Humphrey Bogart
One Sheet: $4,000 - $6,000

ANGELS WITH DIRTY FACES
(1956R - Warner Bros.) James Cagney, Pat
O'Brien, Humphrey Bogart
One Sheet: $50 - $100   *Re-release.*

ANGORA LOVE
(1929 - MGM) Laurel & Hardy
One Sheet: $3,500 - $5,000

ANGRY BREED, THE
(1969 - Commonwealth United) Jan Sterling,
James MacArthur
One Sheet: $5 - $10

ANGRY GOD, THE
(1948 - United Artists) Alicia Parla, Casimiro
Ortega
One Sheet: $40 - $75

ANGRY HILLS, THE
(1959 - MGM) Robert Mitchum, Elisabeth
Mueller
One Sheet: $75 - $125

ANGRY ISLAND
(1960 - Bentley) Kazuo Suzuki, Shigeo Tezuka
One Sheet: $7 - $15

ANGRY RED PLANET, THE
(1960 - AIP) Gerald Mohr, Les Tremayne
One Sheet: $75 - $125

ANGRY SILENCE, THE
(1960 - British Lion) Richard Attenborough,
Pier Angeli
One Sheet: $15 - $25

ANIMAL CRACKERS
(1930 - Paramount Publix) The Marx Brothers
One Sheet: $6,500 - $10,000

ANIMAL CRACKERS
(1974R - Universal) The Marx Brothers
One Sheet: $15 - $25   *Re-release.*

ANIMAL FARM
(1955 - RKO) Maurice Denham - voice
One Sheet: $150 - $300   *Cartoon.*

ANIMAL HOUSE
(1978 - Universal) John Belushi
One Sheet: $50 - $100   *One*
Sheet(Style A):$100-200.

One Sheet (Style B)

ANIMAL HOUSE
(1981R - Universal) John Belushi
One Sheet: $15 - $35   *Re-release.*

ANIMAL KINGDOM, THE
(1932 - RKO) Ann Harding, Leslie Howard
One Sheet: $200 - $400

ANIMAL WORLD, THE
(1956 - Warner Bros.) -
One Sheet: $50 - $100   *Documentary.*

Insert

ANIMALS, THE
(1971 - XYZ) Henry Silva, Keenan Wynn
One Sheet: $3 - $5

ANN CARVER'S PROFESSION
(1933 - Columbia) Fay Wray, Gene Raymond, Claire Dodd
One Sheet: $200 - $400

ANN VICKERS
(1933 - RKO) Irene Dunne, Walter Huston
One Sheet: $300 - $700

ANNA
(1951 - I.F.E.) Silvana Mangano, Raf Vallone
One Sheet: $15 - $25   *Italian.*

ANNA
(1987 - Magnus) Sally Kirkland, Paulina Porizkova
One Sheet: $3 - $5

ANNA AND THE KING OF SIAM
(1946 - 20th Century Fox) Irene Dunne, Rex Harrison
One Sheet: $125 - $250

ANNA CHRISTIE
(1923 - Associated First National) Blanche Sweet, George F. Marion
One Sheet: $600 - $1,000

ANNA CHRISTIE
(1930 - MGM) Greta Garbo, Charles Bickford, Marie Dressler
One Sheet: $3,500 - $5,000   *Garbo's first talkie.*

ANNA CHRISTIE
(1962R - MGM) Greta Garbo, Charles Bickford, Marie Dressler
One Sheet: $10 - $20   *Re-release.*

ANNA KARENINA
(1935 - MGM) Greta Garbo, Fredric March
One Sheet: $2,500 - $4,000

ANNA KARENINA
(1947 - 20th Century Fox) Vivien Leigh, Ralph Richardson
One Sheet: $150 - $350

ANNA LUCASTA
(1949 - Columbia) Paulette Goddard, William Bishop
One Sheet: $40 - $75

ANNA LUCASTA
(1958 - United Artists) Eartha Kitt, Sammy Davis Jr.
One Sheet: $50 - $100   *Black cast. Separate Cinema, pg. 87.*

ANNABEL TAKES A TOUR
(1938 - RKO) Jack Oakie, Lucille Ball
One Sheet: $125 - $250

ANNABELLE'S AFFAIRS
(1931 - Fox) Jeanette MacDonald, Victor McLaglen
One Sheet: $200 - $400

ANNAPOLIS
(1928 - Pathe) John Mack Brown, Jeanette Loff
One Sheet: $150 - $300

ANNAPOLIS FAREWELL
(1935 - Paramount) Sir Guy Standing, Rosalind Keith
One Sheet: $75 - $150

ANNAPOLIS SALUTE
(1937 - RKO) James Ellison, Marsha Hunt
One Sheet: $100 - $200

ANNAPOLIS STORY
(1955 - Allied Artists) John Derek, Diana Lynn
One Sheet: $20 - $40

ANNE AND EVE
(1970 - Chevron) Gio Petre, Marie Liljedhal
One Sheet: $7 - $15

ANNE FRANK REMEMBERED
(1996 - Sony Classics) Narrated: Kenneth Barnagh, Glenn Close
One Sheet: $10 - $20

ANNE OF GREEN GABLES
(1934 - RKO) Ann Shirley, Tom Brown
One Sheet: $250 - $600

ANNE OF THE INDIES
(1951 - 20th Century Fox) Jean Peters, Louis Jordan
One Sheet: $30 - $50

ANNE OF THE THOUSAND DAYS
(1970 - Universal) Richard Burton, Genevieve Bujold
One Sheet: $7 - $15

ANNE OF WINDY POPLARS
(1940 - RKO) Anne Shirley, James Ellison
One Sheet: $75 - $150

ANNE ONE HUNDRED
(1933 - Paramount) Betty Stockfield, Gyles Isham
One Sheet: $150 - $300

ANNIE
(1982 - Columbia) Albert Finney, Carol Burnett, Aileen Quinn
One Sheet: $3 - $5

ANNIE GET YOUR GUN
(1950 - MGM) Betty Hutton, Howard Keel
One Sheet: $100 - $200

ANNIE GET YOUR GUN
(1956R - MGM) Betty Hutton, Howard Keel
One Sheet: $30 - $50   *Re-release.*

ANNIE GET YOUR GUN
(1962R - MGM) Betty Hutton, Howard Keel
One Sheet: $10 - $20   *Re-release.*

ANNIE HALL
(1977 - United Artists) Woody Allen, Diane Keaton
One Sheet: $50 - $100   *Academy Award: Best Picture, Best Actress (Keaton),Best Director (Allen). Academy Award Movie Posters #297 & #299.*

ANNIE HALL
(1978R - United Artists) Woody Allen, Diane Kenton
One Sheet: $15 - $30

ANNIE LAURIE
(1936 - Butchers Film) Will Fyffe, Polly Ward
One Sheet: $75 - $150

ANNIE, LEAVE THE ROOM
(1935 - Universal) Eva Moore, Morton Selten
One Sheet: $150 - $300

ANNIE OAKLEY
(1935 - RKO) Barbara Stanwyck, Preston Foster
One Sheet: $600 - $1,000

ANNIE OAKLEY
(1952R - RKO) Barbara Stanwyck, Preston Foster
One Sheet: $50 - $100   *Re-release.*

ANNIHILATORS, THE
(1985 - New World) Christopher Stone, Andy Wood
One Sheet: $5 - $10

ANNIVERSARY, THE
(1968 - 20th Century Fox) Bette Davis, Christian Roberts
One Sheet: $20 - $40

ANONYMOUS VENETIAN, THE
(1971 - Allied Artists) Tony Musante
One Sheet: $3 - $5

ANOTHER 48 HOURS
(1990 - Paramount) Eddie Murphy, Nick Nolte

One Sheet: $5 - $10

ANOTHER COUNTRY
(1984 - Orion) Rupert Everett, Colin Firth
One Sheet: $3 - $5

ANOTHER DAWN
(1937 - Warner Bros.) Errol Flynn, Kay Francis
One Sheet: $200 - $400   *Duotone.*

ANOTHER DELIGHTFUL CARTOON FROLIC
(1950 - Columbia) Color Favorites
One Sheet: $100 - $200   *Cartoon. Full color stock re-release poster.*

ANOTHER FACE
(1935 - RKO) Walter Ford, Brian Donlevy
One Sheet: $100 - $200

ANOTHER FINE MESS
(1930 - MGM) Laurel & Hardy
One Sheet: $5,000 - $7,500

ANOTHER LANGUAGE
(1935 - MGM) Helen Hayes, Robert Montgomery
One Sheet: $250 - $600

One Sheet

ANOTHER MAN, ANOTHER CHANCE
(1977 - United Artists) James Caan, Genevieve Bujold
One Sheet: $5 - $10   *Cowboy Movie Posters #350.*

ANOTHER MAN'S POISON
(1952 - United Artists) Bette Davis, Anthony Steele
One Sheet: $125 - $250

ANOTHER MAN'S SHOES
(1922 - Universal) Herbert Rawlinson, Barbara Bedford
One Sheet: $200 - $400

ANOTHER NEW PARAMOUNT SCREEN SONG
(1929 - Paramount) With The Famous Bouncing Ball
One Sheet: $600 - $1,000   *Cartoon. Duotone. Cartoon Movie Posters #199.*

ANOTHER NEW POPEYE COMEDY
(1939 - Paramount) Popeye
One Sheet: $600 - $1,000   *Cartoon. Stock poster. Popeye socking the "O". Blue duotone. Cartoon Movie Posters #223.*

ANOTHER PART OF THE FOREST
(1948 - Universal) Fredric March, Dan Duryea
One Sheet: $40 - $75

ANOTHER SHORE
(1948 - General) Robert Beatty, Moira Lister
One Sheet: $15 - $25

ANOTHER SKY
(1960 - Harrison) Victoria Grayson, Catherine Lacey
One Sheet: $5 - $10

ANOTHER STAKEOUT
(1993 - Buena Vista) Richard Dreyfuss, Emilio Estevez
One Sheet: $3 - $5

ANOTHER THIN MAN
(1939 - MGM) Myrna Loy, William Powell, Ruth Hussey
One Sheet: $300 - $700

ANOTHER TIME, ANOTHER PLACE
(1958 - Paramount) Lana Turner, Barry Sullivan
One Sheet: $40 - $75

ANOTHER TIME, ANOTHER PLACE

(1983 - Umbrella) Phyllis Logan
One Sheet: $3 - $5

ANOTHER WOMAN
(1988 - Orion) Gena Rowlands, Mia Farrow
One Sheet: $3 - $5

ANOTHER YOU
(1991 - -) Gene Wilder, Richard Pryor, Vanessa Williams
One Sheet: $5 - $10

ANOUS LA LIBERTE
(1931 - Tobis) Henry Marchand, Raymond Cordy
One Sheet: $2,800 - $4,500   *French. Price is for French Two Panel.*

ANTARCTICA
(1984 - 20th Century Fox) Ken Takakura
One Sheet: $5 - $10

ANTHONY ADVERSE
(1936 - Warner Bros.) Fredric March, Olivia de Havilland, Gale Sondergaard
One Sheet: $200 - $400   *Academy Award Movie Posters #50.*

ANTHONY ADVERSE
(1948R - Warner Bros.) Fredric March, Olivia DeHavilland, Gale Sondergaard
One Sheet: $30 - $50   *Re-release.*

ANTHONY AND CLEOPATRA
(1973 - Rank) Charlton Heston, Hildegard Neil
One Sheet: $10 - $20

ANTICS
(1940S - Mudnaney) Laurel & Hardy
One Sheet: $50 - $100   *Indian release of an American film.*

ANTS IN THE PANTRY
(1936 - Columbia) The Three Stooges (Curly)
One Sheet: $10,000 - $16,000   *Comedy short. Duotone.*

ANVIL CHORUS, THE
(1922 - Hal Roach) Snub Pollard
One Sheet: $150 - $300

ANY DAY IN HOLLYWOOD
(1935 - -) Ben Turpin, All-Star Cameos
One Sheet: $250 - $500

ANY GUN CAN PLAY
(1969 - Golden Eagle) Edd Byrnes, Gilbert Roland
One Sheet: $5 - $10

ANY MAN'S WIFE
(1937 - Republic) Wynne Gibson, Warren Hull
One Sheet: $75 - $150

ANY NUMBER CAN PLAY
(1949 - MGM) Clark Gable, Alexis Smith
One Sheet: $75 - $150

ANY NUMBER CAN WIN
(1963 - MGM) Jean Gabin, Alain Delon
One Sheet: $5 - $10

ANY OLD PORT
(1931 - MGM) Laurel & Hardy
One Sheet: $2,800 - $4,500

ANY WEDNESDAY
(1966 - Warner Bros.) Jane Fonda, Jason Robards
One Sheet: $15 - $30

ANY WHICH WAY YOU CAN
(1980 - Warner Bros.) Clint Eastwood, Sondra Locke, Clyde
One Sheet: $20 - $40

ANY WIFE
(1922 - Fox) Pearl White, Holmes Herbert
One Sheet: $800 - $1,500

ANYBODY'S BLONDE
(1931 - Action) Dorothy Revier, Reed Howes
One Sheet: $125 - $250

ANYBODY'S WAR
(1930 - Paramount) The Two Black Crows (Moran and Mack)
One Sheet: $200 - $400

ANYBODY'S WOMAN
(1930 - Paramount Publix) Ruth Chatterton, Clive Brook, Paul Lukas
One Sheet: $200 - $400

ANYONE CAN PLAY
(1968 - Paramount) Ursula Andress, Virna Lisi, Claudine Auger
One Sheet: $5 - $10

ANYTHING CAN HAPPEN
(1952 - Paramount) Jose Ferrer, Kim Hunter
One Sheet: $15 - $25

ANYTHING FOR A THRILL
(1937 - Ambassador-Conn) Frankie Darro, June Gale
One Sheet: $50 - $100

ANYTHING GOES
(1936 - Paramount) Bing Crosby, Ethel Merman
One Sheet: $250 - $600

ANYTHING GOES
(1956 - Paramount) Bing Crosby, Donald O'Connor
One Sheet: $75 - $125

ANYTHING MIGHT HAPPEN
(1935 - Real Art) John Garrick, Judy Kelly
One Sheet: $75 - $150

ANYTHING ONCE!
(1917 - Bluebird) Franklyn Farnum, Claire Du Brey
One Sheet: $250 - $500

ANYTHING TO DECLARE?
(1939 - Butcher) Claude Hulbert
One Sheet: $75 - $150

ANZIO
(1968 - Columbia) Robert Mitchum, Peter Falk, Earl Holliman
One Sheet: $5 - $10

APACHE
(1954 - United Artists) Burt Lancaster, Jean Peters, Charles Buchinsky (Bronson)
One Sheet: $15 - $30

APACHE AMBUSH
(1955 - Columbia) Bill Williams, Richard Jaeckel
One Sheet: $15 - $25

APACHE CHIEF
(1949 - Lippert) Alan Curtis, Russell Hayden
One Sheet: $15 - $30

APACHE COUNTRY
(1952 - Columbia) Gene Autry, Pat Buttram
One Sheet: $50 - $100

APACHE DRUMS
(1951 - Universal) Stephen McNally, Coleen Gray
One Sheet: $15 - $25

APACHE GOLD
(1965 - Columbia) Lex Barker, Mario Adorf
One Sheet: $5 - $10

APACHE KID, THE
(1941 - Republic) Don "Red" Barry, Lynn Merrick
One Sheet: $40 - $75

Half Sheet (Style B)

APACHE RIFLES
(1964 - 20th Century Fox) Audie Murphy, Michael Dante
One Sheet: $30 - $50

APACHE ROSE
(1947 - Republic) Roy Rogers, Dale Evans
One Sheet: $125 - $250

APACHE ROSE
(1952R - Republic) Roy Rogers, Dale Evans
One Sheet: $75 - $125   *Re-release.*

APACHE TERRITORY
(1958 - Calhoun-Orsatti Enterprises) Rory Calhoun, Barbara Bates
One Sheet: $7 - $15

APACHE TRAIL
(1942 - MGM) Lloyd Nolan, Donna Reed
One Sheet: $40 - $75

APACHE UPRISING
(1966 - Paramount) Rory Calhoun, Corine Calvet
One Sheet: $7 - $15

APACHE WAR SMOKE
(1952 - MGM) Gilbert Roland, Glenda Farrell
One Sheet: $15 - $25

APACHE WARRIOR
(1957 - 20th Century Fox) Keith Larsen, Jim Davis
One Sheet: $15 - $25

APACHE WOMAN
(1955 - AIP) Lloyd Bridges, Joan Taylor, Dir:Roger Corman (his first)
One Sheet: $40 - $75

APANATCHI THE HALFBREED
(1973 - Hampton-International) Lex Barker
One Sheet: $7 - $15

APARTMENT, THE
(1960 - United Artists) Jack Lemmon, Shirley MacLaine
One Sheet: $50 - $100   *Academy Award: Best Picture, Best Director (Billy Wilder). The key is NOT Saul Bass art. Academy Award Movie Posters#194, #196 & #197.*

APARTMENT FOR PEGGY
(1948 - 20th Century Fox) Jeanne Crain, William Holden
One Sheet: $40 - $75

APARTMENT ZERO
(1988 -) Hart Bochner, Colin Firth
One Sheet: $5 - $10

APE, THE
(1940 - Monogram) Boris Karloff, Henry Hall
One Sheet: $200 - $400   *Graven Images, pg. 132.*

APE MAN, THE
(1943 - Monogram) Bela Lugosi, Wallace Ford
One Sheet: $600 - $1,000   *Graven Images, pg. 132.*

APE MAN, THE
(1949R - Monogram) Bela Lugosi, Wallace Ford
One Sheet: $75 - $150   *Re-release.*

APING HOLLYWOOD
(1920? - RCA Photophone) Tiffany Talking Chimps
One Sheet: $125 - $250

A-PLUMBING WE WILL GO
(1940 - Columbia) The Three Stooges (Curly)
One Sheet: $5,000 - $7,500   *Comedy short. Duotone.*

APOCALYPSE NOW
(1979 - United Artists) Marlon Brando, Robert Duvall, Martin Sheen
One Sheet: $30 - $50   *One Sheet (Review):$20-$30; One Sheet (Advance):$400 - $80.*

APOLLO 13
(1995 - Universal) Tom Hanks, Kevin Bacon, Bill Paxton
One Sheet: $7 - $15

APOLOGY FOR MURDER
(1945 - PRC) Anne Savage, Hugh Beaumont
One Sheet: $30 - $60

APOSTLE OF VENGEANCE, THE
(1916 - Triangle) William S. Hart, Nona Thomas
One Sheet: $1,900 - $3,000

APPALOOSA, THE
(1966 - Universal) Marlon Brando, Anjanette Comer
One Sheet: $15 - $35

APPLAUSE
(1929 - Paramount) Helen Morgan, Joan Peers
One Sheet: $150 - $350

APPLE DUMPLING GANG
(1975 - Buena Vista/Disney) Don Knotts, Tim Conway
One Sheet: $10 - $20

One Sheet

APPLE DUMPLING GANG RIDES AGAIN
(1979 - Buena Vista) Tim Conway, Don Knotts
One Sheet: $7 - $15

APPOINTMENT FOR LOVE
(1941 - Universal) Margaret Sullivan, Charles Boyer
One Sheet: $50 - $100

APPOINTMENT IN BERLIN
(1943 - Columbia) George Sanders, Marguerite Chapman
One Sheet: $50 - $100

APPOINTMENT IN HONDURAS
(1953 - RKO) Glenn Ford, Ann Sheridan
One Sheet: $40 - $75

APPOINTMENT IN LONDON
(1955 - Associated Artists) Dirk Bogarde, Dinah Sheridan
One Sheet: $15 - $25

APPOINTMENT IN LONDON
(1969 - MGM) Omar Sharif
One Sheet: $5 - $10

APPOINTMENT WITH A SHADOW
(1958 - Universal) George Nader, Joanna Moore
One Sheet: $15 - $25

APPOINTMENT WITH CRIME
(1945 - British National) William Hartnell, Robert Beatty
One Sheet: $30 - $50

APPOINTMENT WITH DANGER
(1951 - Paramount) Alan Ladd, Phyllis Calvert
One Sheet: $40 - $75

APPOINTMENT WITH DEATH
(1988 - Golan-Globus) Peter Ustinov, Lauren Bacall, Carrie Fisher
One Sheet: $5 - $10

APPOINTMENT WITH FEAR
(1985 - Galaxy Int.) Michael Wyle, Michele Little
One Sheet: $3 - $5

APPOINTMENT WITH MURDER
(1948 - Film Classics) John Calvert, Catherine Craig
One Sheet: $30 - $50

APPRENTICE TO MURDER
(1987 - New World) Donald Sutherland, Chad Lowe
One Sheet: $3 - $5

APPRENTICESHIP OF DUDDY KRAVITZ, THE
(1974 - Paramount) Richard Dreyfuss, Jack Warden
One Sheet: $3 - $5

APRIL FOLLY
(1920 - Paramount) Marion Davies
One Sheet: $300 - $700

APRIL FOOL'S DAY
(1986 - Paramount) Deborah Foreman, Griffin O'Neal
One Sheet: $5 - $10

APRIL FOOLS, THE
(1969 - National General) Jack Lemmon, Catherine Deneuve
One Sheet: $15 - $25

APRIL IN PARIS
(1952 - Warner Bros.) Doris Day, Ray Bolger
One Sheet: $30 - $50

APRIL LOVE
(1957 - 20th Century Fox) Pat Boone, Shirley Jones
One Sheet: $30 - $60

APRIL ROMANCE
(1936 - MGM) Richard Tauber, Jane Baxter
One Sheet: $100 - $200   *AKA: APRIL BLOSSOMS.*

APRIL SHOWERS
(1923 - Preferred) Kenneth Harlan, Colleen Moore
One Sheet: $500 - $800

APRIL SHOWERS
(1948 - Warner Bros.) Jack Carson, Ann Sothern
One Sheet: $30 - $50

AQUARELA DO BRASIL
(1955R - RKO/Disney) -
One Sheet: $75 - $150   *Cartoon. American re-release of "Saludos Amigo, 1943".*

ARAB, THE
(1924 - Goldwyn) Ramon Novarro, Alice Terry
One Sheet: $600 - $1,000

ARABELLA
(1969 - Universal) Virna Lisi, James Fox
One Sheet: $5 - $10

ARABESQUE
(1966 - Universal) Gregory Peck, Sophia Loren
One Sheet: $20 - $40

ARABIAN ADVENTURE
(1979 - Associated) Christopher Lee, Milo O'Shea
One Sheet: $15 - $35   *Alex Saviuk comic book art.*

ARABIAN LOVE
(1922 - Fox) John Gilbert, Barbara Bedford, Adolph Menjou
One Sheet: $500 - $800

ARABIAN NIGHTS
(1942 - Universal) Jon Hall, Maria Montez
One Sheet: $100 - $200

ARABIAN NIGHTS
(1950R - Realart) Jon Hall, Maria Montez, Sabu
One Sheet: $15 - $35   *Re-release.*

ARACHNOPHOBIA
(1990 - Touchstone) Julian Sands, John Goodman
One Sheet: $7 - $15

ARCH OF TRIUMPH, THE
(1948 - United Artists) Ingrid Bergman, Charles Boyer
One Sheet: $50 - $100

ARCTIC, THE
(1926 - Bray Productions) Dinky Doodle
One Sheet: $250 - $600   *Cartoon. Cartoon Movie Posters #11.*

ARCTIC FLIGHT
(1952 - Monogram) Wayne Morris, Lola Albright
One Sheet: $7 - $15

ARCTIC FURY
(1949 - Plymouth) Del Cambre, Eve Miller
One Sheet: $20 - $40

ARCTIC MANHUNT
(1949 - Universal) Mikel Conrad, Carol Thurston
One Sheet: $30 - $50

ARE HUSBANDS NECESSARY?
(1942 - Paramount) Ray Milland, Betty Field
One Sheet: $75 - $150

ARE THESE OUR CHILDREN?
(1931 - RKO) Eric Linden, Rochelle Hudson
One Sheet: $125 - $250

ARE THESE OUR PARENTS?
(1944 - Monogram) Helen Vinson, Lyle Talbot
One Sheet: $50 - $100

ARE WE CIVILIZED?
(1934 - Raspin) William Farnum, Anita Louise

One Sheet: $250 - $600

ARE YOU A MASON?
(1934 - Universal) Sonnie Hale, Robertson
Hare
One Sheet: $150 - $300

ARE YOU LISTENING?
(1932 - MGM) William Haynes, Karen Morley
One Sheet: $75 - $150

ARE YOU THERE?
(1930 - Fox) Beatrice Lillie, John Garrick
One Sheet: $125 - $250

ARE YOU WITH IT?
(1948 - Universal) Donald O'Connor, Olga San
Juan
One Sheet: $40 - $75

AREN'T MEN BEASTS?
(1937 - ABPC) Robertson Hare, June Clyde
One Sheet: $75 - $150

AREN'T WE ALL?
(1932 - Paramount British) Gertrude Lawrence,
Hugh Wakefield
One Sheet: $75 - $150

ARENA
(1953 - MGM) Gig Young, Jean Hagen
One Sheet: $20 - $40   *3-D.*

ARENA
(1973 - New World) Pam Grier
One Sheet: $10 - $20   *Blaxploitation.*

ARGENTINE LOVE
(1924 - Paramount) Bebe Daniels, Ricardo
Cortez
One Sheet: $600 - $1,000

ARGENTINE NIGHTS
(1940 - Universal) Ritz Brothers, Andrews
Sisters, George Reeves
One Sheet: $75 - $150

ARGYLE SECRETS, THE
(1948 - Eronel) William Gargan, Marjorie Lord
One Sheet: $30 - $50

ARIA
(1988 - -) John Hurt, Theresa Russell
One Sheet: $7 - $15

ARIANE
(1931 - Pathe Cinema) Elisabeth Bergner,
Rudolph Forster
One Sheet: $250 - $500

ARISE MY LOVE
(1940 - Paramount) Ray Milland, Claudette
Colbert
One Sheet: $100 - $200

One Sheet

ARISTOCATS
(1971 - Buena Vista/Disney) -
One Sheet: $30 - $50   *Cartoon.*

ARISTOCATS
(1973R - Disney) -
One Sheet: $15 - $25   *Cartoon. Re-release.*

ARISTOCATS
(1980R - Buena Vista/Disney) -
One Sheet: $15 - $25   *Re-release. Cartoon.*

ARISTOCATS
(1987R - Disney) -
One Sheet: $10 - $20   *Re-release. Cartoon.*

ARISTOCRACY

(1914 - Paramount) Tyrone Power, Marguerite
Skirvin, Edna Mayo
One Sheet: $1,300 - $2,000

ARIZONA
(1913 - All Star Feature) Cyril Scott
One Sheet: $250 - $600

ARIZONA
(1918 - Artcraft) Douglas Fairbanks
One Sheet: $500 - $800

ARIZONA
(1931 - Columbia) John Wayne, Laura La
Plante
One Sheet: $800 - $1,500   *AKA: MEN
ARE LIKE THAT.*

ARIZONA
(1940 - Columbia) William Holden, Jean Arthur
One Sheet: $100 - $200

Mini Window Card

ARIZONA BADMAN
(1935 - Kent) Reb Russell, Lois January
One Sheet: $100 - $200

ARIZONA BOUND
(1927 - Paramount) Gary Cooper, El Brendel
One Sheet: $1,600 - $2,500

ARIZONA BOUND
(1941 - Monogram) Buck Jones, Tim McCoy
One Sheet: $125 - $250

ARIZONA BUSHWHACKERS
(1968 - Paramount) Howard Keel, Scott Brady
One Sheet: $7 - $15

ARIZONA COWBOY
(1950 - Republic) Rex Allen, Gordon Jones
One Sheet: $75 - $150

ARIZONA CYCLONE
(1934 - Imperial) Wally Wales, Franklyn
Farnum
One Sheet: $125 - $250

ARIZONA CYCLONE
(1941 - Universal) Johnny Mack Brown
One Sheet: $75 - $125

ARIZONA DAYS
(1928 - Syndicate) Bob Custer, Peggy
Montgomery
One Sheet: $200 - $400

ARIZONA DAYS
(1937 - Grand National) Tex Ritter, Eleanor
Stewart
One Sheet: $125 - $250   *Cowboy
Movie Posters #220.*

ARIZONA FRONTIER
(1940 - Monogram) Tex Ritter
One Sheet: $100 - $200   *Jim Thorpe
pictured.*

ARIZONA GANG BUSTERS
(1940 - PRC) Tim McCoy
One Sheet: $50 - $100

ARIZONA GUNFIGHTER
(1937 - Republic) Bob Steele, Jean Carmen
One Sheet: $125 - $250

ARIZONA KID, THE
(1930 - Fox) Warner Baxter, Mona Maris, Carol
Lombard
One Sheet: $800 - $1,500   *Cisco Kid
series.*

ARIZONA KID, THE
(1939 - Republic) Roy Rogers, George "Gabby"
Hayes
One Sheet: $1,300 - $2,000   *Classic*

*Rogers one sheet graphics. Cowboy Movie
Posters #237.*

ARIZONA LEGION
(1939 - RKO) George O'Brien, Laraine Johnson
One Sheet: $75 - $150

ARIZONA MAHONEY
(1936 - Paramount) Buster Crabbe
One Sheet: $75 - $150

ARIZONA MANHUNT
(1951 - Republic) Michael Chapin, Eileen
Janssen
One Sheet: $15 - $25

ARIZONA NIGHTS
(1934 - Reliable) Jack Perrin, Ben Corbett
One Sheet: $100 - $200

ARIZONA RAIDERS, THE
(1936 - Paramount) Buster Crabbe
One Sheet: $100 - $200

ARIZONA RAIDERS
(1965 - Columbia) Audie Murphy, Michael
Dante
One Sheet: $15 - $30

ARIZONA RANGER, THE
(1948 - RKO) Tim Holt, Nan Leslie
One Sheet: $30 - $50

ARIZONA ROUND-UP
(1942 - Monogram) Tom Keene
One Sheet: $75 - $150

ARIZONA STAGECOACH
(1942 - Monogram) Ray Corrigan, John King,
Max Terhune
One Sheet: $30 - $60

ARIZONA TERRITORY
(1950 - Monogram) Whip Wilson, Andy Clyde
One Sheet: $40 - $75

ARIZONA TERROR
(1931 - Tiffany) Francis Natteford, Ken
Maynard
One Sheet: $350 - $750

ARIZONA TERRORS
(1942 - Republic) Don "Red" Barry, Lynn
Merrick
One Sheet: $40 - $75

ARIZONA TO BROADWAY
(1933 - Fox) James Dunn, Joan Bennett
One Sheet: $150 - $300

ARIZONA TRAIL
(1935 - Superior) Bill Patton, Edna Aslin
One Sheet: $100 - $200

ARIZONA TRAIL
(1943 - Universal) Tex Ritter, Fuzzy Knight
One Sheet: $50 - $100

ARIZONA WHIRLWIND
(1944 - Monogram) Ken Maynard, Hoot Gibson
One Sheet: $75 - $150

ARIZONA WILDCAT, THE
(1939 - 20th Century Fox) Jane Withers, Leo
Carrillo
One Sheet: $75 - $150

ARIZONIAN, THE
(1935 - RKO) Richard Dix
One Sheet: $100 - $200

ARIZONIAN, THE
(1951R - RKO) Richard Dix
One Sheet: $20 - $40   *Re-release.*

ARKANSAS JUDGE
(1941 - Republic) Weaver Bros. & Elviry, Roy
Rogers
One Sheet: $100 - $200   *Roy not
shown on posters.*

ARKANSAS SWING, THE
(1948 - Columbia) Gloria Henry, Stuart Hart,
Hoosier Hot Shots
One Sheet: $40 - $75   *Country
musical.*

ARKANSAS TRAVELER, THE
(1938 - Paramount) Bob Burns, Fay Bainter
One Sheet: $75 - $150

ARM OF THE LAW
(1932 - Monogram) Rex Bell, Marceline Day
One Sheet: $200 - $400

ARMCHAIR DETECTIVE, THE
(1952 - Meridian) Ernest Dudley, Sally Newton
One Sheet: $30 - $50

ARMED AND DANGEROUS
(1986 - Columbia) John Candy, Eugene Levy
One Sheet: $5 - $10

ARMED RESPONSE
(1986 - Cintel) David Carradine, Lee Van Cleef,
Mako
One Sheet: $3 - $5

ARMORED CAR
(1937 - Universal) Robert Wilcox, Judith
Barrett, Cesar Romero
One Sheet: $125 - $250

ARMORED CAR ROBBERY
(1950 - RKO) Charles McGraw, Robert Sterling
One Sheet: $30 - $50

ARMORED COMMAND
(1961 - Allied Artists) Howard Keel, Tina
Louise, Burt Reynolds
One Sheet: $7 - $15

ARMS AND THE MAN
(1932 - British International) Barry Jones, Anne
Grey
One Sheet: $125 - $250

ARMS AND THE WOMAN
(1916 - Gold Rooster) Mary Nash, Lumsden
Hare,
One Sheet: $600 - $1,000

ARMY BOUND
(1952 - Monogram) Stanley Clements, Karen
Sharpe
One Sheet: $15 - $25

ARMY GIRL
(1938 - Republic) Preston Foster, Madge
Evans
One Sheet: $50 - $100

ARMY OF DARKNESS
(1993 - Universal) Bruce Campbell, Embeth
Davidtz
One Sheet: $10 - $20

40 x 60

ARMY SURGEON
(1942 - RKO) James Ellison, Jane Wyatt
One Sheet: $75 - $150

ARMY WIVES
(1944 - Monogram) Elyse Knox, Rick Valen
One Sheet: $75 - $150

ARNELO AFFAIR, THE
(1947 - MGM) John Hodiak, George Murphy
One Sheet: $40 - $75

ARNOLD
(1973 - Cinerama) Stella Stevens, Roddy
McDowall
One Sheet: $5 - $10

AROUND THE CORNER
(1930 - Columbia) Charlie Murray, George
Sidney
One Sheet: $150 - $300

AROUND THE TOWN
(1938 - British Lion) Vic Oliver, Irene Ware
One Sheet: $75 - $150

AROUND THE WORLD
(1943 - RKO) Kay Kyser
One Sheet: $75 - $150

AROUND THE WORLD IN 80 DAYS
(1956 - United Artists) David Niven, Shirley

MacLaine
One Sheet: $75 - $150   *Academy
Award: Best Picture. One Sheet (Academy
Awards style):$30-$60. Academy Award Movie
Posters #167 &#168.*

AROUND THE WORLD IN 80 DAYS
(1968R - United Artists) David Niven, Shirley
McLaine
One Sheet: $20 - $40   *Re-release.*

AROUND THE WORLD IN A DAZE
(1963 - Columbia) The Three Stooges (Curly
Joe)
One Sheet: $50 - $100

AROUND THE WORLD UNDER THE SEA
(1966 - MGM) Lloyd Bridges, Shirley Eaton
One Sheet: $10 - $20

AROUND THE WORLD WITH FANNY HILL
(197? - Seaberg) Shirley Corrigan, Peter Bonke
One Sheet: $3 - $5

AROUSERS, THE
(1973 - New World) Tab Hunter, Cherie Latimer
One Sheet: $15 - $25   *AKA: SWEET
KILL; A KISS FROM EDDIE.*

ARRANGEMENT, THE
(1969 - Warner Bros.) Kirk Douglas, Faye
Dunaway, Deborah Kerr
One Sheet: $5 - $10

ARREST BULLDOG DRUMMOND
(1938 - Paramount) John Howard, Heather
Angel
One Sheet: $75 - $150

ARRIVAL, THE
(1996 - Orion) Charlie Sheen, Lindsay Crouse
One Sheet: $4 - $8

ARRIVEDERCI, BABY!
(1966 - Paramount) Tony Curtis, Rosanna
Schiaffino
One Sheet: $15 - $35   *Frazetta art.*

ARROW IN THE DUST
(1954 - Allied Artists) Sterling Hayden, Coleen
Gray
One Sheet: $15 - $25

ARROWHEAD
(1953 - Paramount) Charlton Heston, Jack
Palance
One Sheet: $30 - $60

ARROWSMITH
(1932 - Samuel Goldwyn) Ronald Colman,
Helen Hayes
One Sheet: $1,600 - $2,500

ARROWSMITH
(1944R - Film Classics) Ronald Colman, Helen
Hayes
One Sheet: $50 - $100   *Re-release.*

ARSENAL
(1929 - Vufku-Kino) Seymon Svashenko,
Amvroziy Buchma, Dir: Dovzhenko
One Sheet: $1,900 - $3,000   *Russian.
Classic silent film about the Bolshevik revolution.*

ARSENAL STADIUM MYSTERY, THE
(1939 - G & S (British)) Leslie Banks, Greta
Gynt
One Sheet: $125 - $250

ARSENE LUPIN
(1932 - MGM) John Barrymore, Lionel
Barrymore
One Sheet: $1,300 - $2,000

ARSENE LUPIN RETURNS
(1938 - MGM) Virginia Bruce, Melvyn Douglas,
Warren William
One Sheet: $100 - $200

ARSENIC AND OLD LACE
(1944 - Warner Bros.) Cary Grant, Josephine
Hull, Dir: Frank Capra
One Sheet: $250 - $500

ARSON FOR HIRE
(1958 - Allied Artists) Steve Brodie, Lyn
Thomas
One Sheet: $15 - $30

ARSON INC.
(1949 - Screen Guild) Robert Lowery, Ann
Gwynne
One Sheet: $30 - $50

ARSON RACKET SQUAD
(1938 - Republic) Bob Livingston, Rosalind
Keith
One Sheet: $75 - $150

ARSON SQUAD
(1945 - PRC) Frank Albertson, Robert
Armstrong
One Sheet: $30 - $50

ART IN THE RAW
(1933 - RKO) Edgar Kennedy, Franklin
Pangborn
One Sheet: $150 - $300

ART OF LOVE, THE
(1965 - Universal) James Garner, Elke Sommer
One Sheet: $15 - $30

ART OF SELF DEFENSE, THE
(1941 - RKO/Disney) Goofy
One Sheet: $800 - $1,500   *Cartoon. The
Disney Poster, pg. 65.*

ART OF SKIING, THE
(1941 - RKO/Disney) Goofy
One Sheet: $1,300 - $2,000   *Cartoon. The
Disney Poster, pg. 64.*

ARTFUL PENETRATION
(1950S - -)
One Sheet: $15 - $30   *Sexploitation.*

ARTHUR
(1981 - Orion) Dudley Moore, Liza Minnelli, Sir
John Gielgud
One Sheet: $15 - $25   *Academy
Award: Best Supporting Actor (Gielgud). Price is
for "bathtub style." One Sheet(in car style):$10-
$15. AcademyAward Movie Posters #322.*

ARTHUR 2: ON THE ROCKS
(1988 - Warner Bros.) Dudley Moore, Liza
Minnelli
One Sheet: $5 - $10

ARTHUR TAKES OVER
(1948 - 20th Century Fox) Lois Collier, Richard
Crane
One Sheet: $40 - $75

ARTICLE 99
(1992 - Orion) Ray Liotta
One Sheet: $3 - $5

ARTISTS AND MODELS
(1937 - Paramount) Jack Benny, Gail Patrick
One Sheet: $200 - $400

Mini Window Card

ARTISTS AND MODELS
(1955 - Paramount) Dean Martin, Jerry Lewis
One Sheet: $40 - $80

ARTISTS AND MODELS ABROAD
(1938 - Paramount) Jack Benny, Ida Lupino,
Louis Armstrong & Orch
One Sheet: $100 - $200

ARTURO'S ISLAND
(1962 - MGM) Reginald Kernan, Key Meersman
One Sheet: $3 - $5

ARYAN, THE
(1916 - Triangle) William S. Hart, Bessie Love
One Sheet: $1,300 - $2,000   *Cowboy
Movie Posters #9.*

AS GOOD AS MARRIED
(1937 - Universal) John Boles, Doris Nolan
One Sheet: $75 - $150

AS HUSBANDS GO
(1933 - Fox) Warner Baxter, Helen Vinson,
Warner Oland
One Sheet: $250 - $500

AS LONG AS THEY'RE HAPPY
(1957 - Rank) Jack Buchanan, Janette Scott
One Sheet: $15 - $25

AS LONG AS YOU'RE NEAR ME
(1956 - Warner Bros.) Maria Schell, O.W.
Fischer
One Sheet: $15 - $30   *German. AKA:
SOLANGE DU DA BIST.*

AS MAN DESIRES
(1925 - First National) Milton Sills, Viola Dana
One Sheet: $200 - $400

AS NO MAN HAS LOVED
(1925 - Fox) Edward Hearn, Pauline Starke
One Sheet: $500 - $800

AS THE DEVIL COMMANDS
(1932 - Columbia) Alan Dinehart, Mae Clarke
One Sheet: $100 - $200

AS THE EARTH TURNS
(1934 - Warner Bros.) Jean Muir, Donald
Woods
One Sheet: $150 - $350

AS THE SEA RAGES
(1960 - Columbia) Maria Schell, Cliff Robertson
One Sheet: $3 - $5

AS YOU DESIRE ME
(1932 - MGM) Greta Garbo, Melvyn Douglas
One Sheet: $4,000 - $6,000

AS YOU LIKE IT
(1937 - 20th Century Fox) Laurence Olivier,
Elisabeth Bergner
One Sheet: $600 - $1,000

AS YOU LIKE IT
(1948R - United Artists) Laurence Olivier,
Elisabeth Bergner
One Sheet: $10 - $20   *Re-release.
One Sheet(Duotone).*

AS YOU WERE
(1951 - Lippert) William Tracy, Joe Sawyer
One Sheet: $15 - $30

AS YOUNG AS WE ARE
(1958 - Paramount) Robert Harland, Pippa
Scott
One Sheet: $10 - $20

AS YOUNG AS YOU FEEL
(1951 - 20th Century Fox) Monty Woolley,
Thelma Ritter, Marilyn Monroe
One Sheet: $150 - $300

ASCENT OF THE MATTERHORN, THE
(1919 - Paramount) -
One Sheet: $250 - $600   *A Burlingham
Travel-Picture.*

ASH WEDNESDAY
(1973 - Paramount) Elizabeth Taylor, Henry
Fonda
One Sheet: $15 - $25

ASHANTI
(1979 - Columbia) Michael Caine, Peter
Ustinov
One Sheet: $5 - $10

ASHES
(1916 - Universal) Steadman, Courtleigh
One Sheet: $150 - $300

ASHES AND DIAMONDS
(1961 - Janus) Zbigniew Cybulski, Eva
Krzyzewska
One Sheet: $7 - $15   *Polish.*

ASHES OF VENGEANCE
(1923 - First National) Norma Talmadge,
Wallace Beery, Conway Tearle
One Sheet: $600 - $1,000

ASK A POLICEMAN
(1939 - MGM) Will Hay
One Sheet: $50 - $100

ASK ANY GIRL
(1959 - MGM) David Niven, Shirley MacLaine
One Sheet: $15 - $25

ASK BECCLES
(1933 - Paramount) Garry Marsh, Mary
Newland
One Sheet: $100 - $200

ASKING FOR TROUBLE

(1942 - British National) Carol Lynne, Mark
Lester
One Sheet: $40 - $75

ASLEEP AT THE SWITCH
(1923 - Pathecomedy) Ben Turpin
One Sheet: $250 - $600

ASPEN EXTREME
(1993 - Buena Vista) Paul Gross, Peter Berg
One Sheet: $5 - $10   *Sports (Snow
Skiing). Sports Movie Posters #314.*

ASPHALT JUNGLE, THE
(1950 - MGM) Marilyn Monroe, Sterling
Hayden, Louis Calhern
One Sheet: $250 - $500

ASPHALT JUNGLE, THE
(1954R - MGM) Marilyn Monroe, Sterling
Hayden, Louis Calhern
One Sheet: $150 - $300   *Re-release.*

ASPHYX, THE
(1972 - Paragon) Robert Stephens, Robert
Powell
One Sheet: $7 - $15   *AKA: SPIRIT
OF THE DEAD*

ASSAM GARDEN, THE
(1985 - Contemporary) Deborah Kerr, Madhur
Jaffrey
One Sheet: $7 - $15

ASSASSIN, THE
(1953 - United Artists) Richard Todd, Eva
Bartok
One Sheet: $10 - $20

ASSASSIN FOR HIRE
(1951 - Merton Park) Sydney Tafler
One Sheet: $7 - $15

ASSASSIN OF YOUTH
(1937 - McCarthy Films) Luana Walters
One Sheet: $75 - $150   *Quasi-
marijuana expose.*

ASSASSINATION
(1987 - Cannon) Charles Bronson, Jill Ireland
One Sheet: $3 - $5

ASSASSINATION BUREAU, THE
(1969 - Paramount) Oliver Reed, Diana Rigg
One Sheet: $7 - $15

One Sheet

ASSASSINATION OF TROTSKY, THE
(1972 - Cinerama) Richard Burton, Alain Delon,
Romy Schneider
One Sheet: $7 - $15

ASSASSINS
(1995 - Warner Bros.) Sylvester Stallone,
Antonio Banderas
One Sheet: $5 - $10

ASSAULT
(1971 - Rank) Suzy Kendall, Frank Finlay
One Sheet: $3 - $5   *AKA: IN THE
DEVIL'S GARDEN.*

ASSAULT OF THE KILLER BIMBOS
(1988 - -) Karen Nielsen, Debi Thibeault
One Sheet: $7 - $15

ASSAULT ON A QUEEN
(1966 - Paramount) Frank Sinatra, Virna Lisi
One Sheet: $15 - $35

ASSAULT ON AGATHON
(1976 - Nine Network) Nico Minardos, Nina Van
Pallandt
One Sheet: $3 - $5

ASSAULT ON PRECINCT 13

(1976 - Turtle) Austin Stoker, Darwin Joston
One Sheet: $10 - $20

ASSIGNED TO DANGER
(1948 - Eagle-Lion) Gene Raymond, Noreen Nash
One Sheet: $30 - $50

ASSIGNMENT - PARIS
(1952 - Columbia) Dana Andrews, Marta Toren
One Sheet: $10 - $20

ASSIGNMENT IN BRITTANY
(1943 - MGM) Jean-Pierre Aumont, Susan Peters
One Sheet: $30 - $50

ASSIGNMENT K
(1968 - Columbia) Stephen Boyd, Camilla Sparv
One Sheet: $5 - $10

ASSIGNMENT OUTERSPACE
(1962 - Four Crown) Archie Savage, Rik Von Nutter
One Sheet: $30 - $50

ASSIGNMENT TO KILL
(1969 - Warner Bros.) Patrick O'Neal, Joan Hackett, Herbert Lom
One Sheet: $5 - $10

ASSISTANT WIVES
(1927 - Pathecomedy) Charley Chase
One Sheet: $500 - $800

ASTONISHED HEART, THE
(1959 - Universal International) Noel Coward, Celia Johnson
One Sheet: $7 - $15

ASTOUNDING SHE-MONSTER, THE
(1958 - AIP) Robert Clarke, Kenneth Duncan, Marilyn Harvey
One Sheet: $250 - $600   *No Title Card.*

ASTRO-ZOMBIES
(1968 - Geneni) Wendell Corey, John Carradine
One Sheet: $50 - $100   *Unusual gore film.*

One Sheet

ASYLUM
(1972 - Cinerama) Peter Cushing, Britt Eckland
One Sheet: $15 - $25

ASYLUM OF SATAN
(1972 - -) Charles Kissinger, Carla Borelli
One Sheet: $7 - $15

AT BAR U RANCH
(1911 - NY Motion Pictures) -
One Sheet: $500 - $800

AT CLOSE RANGE
(1986 - Orion) Sean Penn, Christopher Walken
One Sheet: $3 - $5

AT DAWN WE DIE
(1943 - Republic) John Clements, Godfrey Tearle
One Sheet: $40 - $75

AT GUNPOINT
(1955 - Allied Artists) Fred MacMurray, Dorothy Malone
One Sheet: $15 - $25

AT LAST
(1977 - -) -
One Sheet: $7 - $15

AT LONG LAST LOVE
(1975 - Fox) Burt Reynolds, Cybill Shepherd
One Sheet: $10 - $20

AT SWORD'S POINT
(1952 - RKO) Cornel Wilde, Maureen O'Hara
One Sheet: $50 - $100

AT THE CIRCUS
(1939 - MGM) The Marx Brothers
One Sheet: $800 - $1,500

AT THE CIRCUS
(1943 - 20th Century Fox) Mighty Mouse
One Sheet: $250 - $500   *Cartoon. Full color stock poster with printed title. Huge image of Mighty Mouse on yellow background.*

AT THE CIRCUS
(1962R - MGM) The Marx Bros.
One Sheet: $15 - $25   *Re-release.*

AT THE EARTH'S CORE
(1976 - AIP) Doug McClure, Peter Cushing
One Sheet: $15 - $30

AT THE END OF THE WORLD
(1921 - Paramount) Betty Compson
One Sheet: $250 - $600

AT THE FRONT
(194? - Warner Bros.) -
One Sheet: $75 - $150   *Documentary. "Filmed Under Fire!".*

AT THE OLD STAGE DOOR
(1919 - Pathe) Harold Lloyd
One Sheet: $600 - $1,000

AT THE RIDGE
(1931 - Tiffany) Bob Steele, Al "Fuzzy" St. John
One Sheet: $250 - $500

AT THE STROKE OF NINE
(1957 - Grand National) Patricia Dainton
One Sheet: $10 - $20

AT WAR WITH THE ARMY
(1951 - United Artists) Dean Martin, Jerry Lewis
One Sheet: $40 - $75

AT WAR WITH THE ARMY
(1958R - United Artists) Dean Martin, Jerry Lewis
One Sheet: $15 - $25   *Re-release.*

ATHENA
(1954 - MGM) Jane Powell, Edmund Purdom, Debbie Reynolds
One Sheet: $30 - $50

ATLANTIC
(1930 - BIP) Madeleine Carroll
One Sheet: $75 - $150

ATLANTIC ADVENTURE
(1935 - Columbia) Lloyd Nolan, Nancy Carroll
One Sheet: $100 - $200

ATLANTIC CITY
(1944 - Republic) Constance Moore, Brad Taylor
One Sheet: $75 - $150

ATLANTIC CITY
(1981 - Paramount) Burt Lancaster, Susan Sarandon
One Sheet: $7 - $15   *AKA: ATLANTIC CITY, U.S.A.*

ATLANTIC CITY HONEYMOON
(1950 - Republic) -
One Sheet: $30 - $50

ATLANTIC CONVOY
(1942 - Columbia) John Beal, Virginia Field
One Sheet: $50 - $100

ATLANTIC FLIGHT
(1937 - Monogram) Dick Merrill, Paula Stone
One Sheet: $250 - $500

ATLANTIS
(1947 - -) Maria Montez
One Sheet: $50 - $100

ATLANTIS THE LOST CONTINENT
(1961 - MGM) Anthony Hall, Joyce Taylor
One Sheet: $40 - $80

ATLAS
(1961 - Filmgroup) Michael Forrest, Dir:Roger Corman
One Sheet: $30 - $50

ATLAS AGAINST THE CYCLOPS

(1963 - Medallion) Mitchell Gordan
One Sheet: $20 - $40

ATLAS AGAINST THE CZAR
(1964 - Medallion) Kirk Morris, Gloria Milland
One Sheet: $15 - $30

ATOM AGE VAMPIRE
(1961 - Topaz) Alberto Lupo, Susanne Loret
One Sheet: $40 - $75

ATOM MAN VS. SUPERMAN
(1950 - Columbia) Kirk Alyn, Lyle Talbot
One Sheet: $800 - $1,500   *Serial. 15 Chapters. Graven Images, pg. 182.*

ATOMIC BRAIN
(1964 - Emerson) Frank Gerstle, Erika Peters
One Sheet: $30 - $50   *AKA: MONSTROSITY.*

ATOMIC CITY, THE
(1952 - Paramount) Gene Barry, Lee Aaker
One Sheet: $50 - $100

ATOMIC KID, THE
(1954 - Republic) Mickey Rooney, Robert Strauss
One Sheet: $30 - $50

ATOMIC MAN, THE
(1956 - Allied Artists) Gene Nelson, Faith Domergue
One Sheet: $50 - $100

ATOMIC MONSTER, THE
(1953R - Realart) Lon Chaney, Jr.
One Sheet: $100 - $200   *Re-release of "THE MAN-MADE MONSTER", 1941.*

ATOMIC SUBMARINE, THE
(1960 - Allied Artists) Arthur Franz, Dick Foran, Joi Lansing
One Sheet: $50 - $100

Insert

ATONEMENT OF GOSTA BERLING
(1924 - -) Greta Garbo
One Sheet: $2,500 - $4,000   *Swedish.*

ATOR, THE FIGHTING EAGLE
(1983 - -) Miles O'Keeffe, Sabrina Siani
One Sheet: $3 - $5

ATOR, THE INVINCIBLE
(1984 - -) Miles O'Keeffe, Lisa Foster
One Sheet: $3 - $5

ATRAGON
(1965 - AIP) Tadao Takashima
One Sheet: $30 - $50   *Japanese poster:$300-$500.*

ATTA BOY!
(1926 - Pathe) Monty Banks, Mary Carr
One Sheet: $200 - $400

ATTA BOY'S LAST RACE
(1916 - Triangle) Dorothy Gish
One Sheet: $600 - $1,000   *Sports (Horse racing). AKA: THE BEST BET. Sports Movie Posters #237.*

ATTACK!
(1956 - United Artists) Jack Palance, Eddie Albert
One Sheet: $7 - $15

ATTACK OF THE 50 FOOT WOMAN
(1958 - Allied Artists) Allison Hayes, William Hudson
One Sheet: $800 - $1,500   *Graven Images, pg. 186.*

ATTACK OF THE 50 FOOT WOMAN
(1993 - -) Darryl Hannah

One Sheet: $7 - $15

ATTACK OF THE CRAB MONSTERS
(1957 - Allied Artists) Richard Garland, Pamela Duncan, Dir: Roger Corman
One Sheet: $350 - $750   *Graven Images, pg. 169.*

ATTACK OF THE CRAB MONSTERS/NOT OF THIS EARTH
(1957 - Allied Artists) Richard Garland/Paul Birch
One Sheet: $125 - $250   *Double feature poster.*

ATTACK OF THE GIANT LEECHES
(1959 - AIP) Ken Clark, Yvette Vickers
One Sheet: $150 - $300   *AKA: Demons Of The Swamp.*

ATTACK OF THE JUNGLE WOMEN
(1959 - Barjul Int.) William Phillips
One Sheet: $50 - $100

ATTACK OF THE KILLER TOMATOES
(1978 - Four Square) David Miller, Sharon Taylor
One Sheet: $50 - $100

ATTACK OF THE MAYAN MUMMY
(1963 - Medallion) Nina Knight, Richard Webb
One Sheet: $15 - $30

ATTACK OF THE MUSHROOM PEOPLE
(1964 - AIP) Akira Kubo, Kenji Sahara
One Sheet: $30 - $50

ATTACK OF THE PUPPET PEOPLE
(1958 - AIP) John Agar, John Hoyt
One Sheet: $125 - $250

ATTACK OF THE ROBOTS
(1967 - AIP) Eddie Constantine, Sophie Hardie
One Sheet: $30 - $50

ATTACK ON THE IRON COAST
(1968 - United Artists) Lloyd Bridges, Andrew Keir
One Sheet: $5 - $10

ATTEMPT TO KILL
(1966 - Allied Artists) Derek Farr, Tony Wright
One Sheet: $5 - $10

ATTIC, THE
(1979 - Atlantic) Carrie Snodgress, Ray Milland
One Sheet: $5 - $10

ATTILA
(1958 - Lux) Sophia Loren, Anthony Quinn
One Sheet: $30 - $50

ATTORNEY FOR THE DEFENSE
(1932 - Columbia) Edmund Lowe, Evelyn Brent
One Sheet: $600 - $1,000

AU REVOIR, LES ENFANTS
(1989 - Orion) Gaspard Manesse, Raphael Fejto
One Sheet: $15 - $25

AUCKLAND, THE METROPOLIS OF NEW ZEALAND
(1920 - Paramount) -
One Sheet: $200 - $400   *From the Paramount Travel Pictures series.*

AUDREY ROSE
(1977 - United Artists) Marsha Mason, Anthony Hopkins
One Sheet: $7 - $15

AUGUST WEEK-END
(1936 - Chesterfield) Valerie Hobson, Paul Harvey
One Sheet: $100 - $200

AULD LANG SYNE
(1929 - Famous Players) Harry Lauder, Pat Aherne
One Sheet: $200 - $400   *Silent film with 6 songs added.*

AULD LANG SYNE
(1937 - MGM) Andrew Cruickshank, Christine Adrian
One Sheet: $125 - $250

AUNT CLARA
(1954 - British Lion) Ronald Shiner, Margaret Rutherford
One Sheet: $10 - $20

AUNTIE MAME

(1958 - Warner Bros.) Rosalind Russell, Forrest Tucker
One Sheet: $40 - $75

AUSTIN POWERS: INTERNATIONAL MAN OF MYSTERY
(1997 - New Line) Michael Myers, Elizabeth Hurley
One Sheet: $7 - $15

AUTHOR! AUTHOR!
(1982 - 20th Century fox) Al Pacino, Dyan Cannon
One Sheet: $5 - $10

AUTOGRAPH HOUND, THE
(1939 - RKO/Disney) Donald Duck
One Sheet: $4,000 - $6,000   *Cartoon. Cartoon Movie Posters #157.*

AUTOPSY
(1977 - J. Brenner) Mimsy Farmer, Barry Primus
One Sheet: $5 - $10

AUTUMN CROCUS
(1934 - Auten) Ivor Novello, Fay Compton
One Sheet: $150 - $300

AUTUMN LEAVES
(1956 - Columbia) Joan Crawford, Cliff Robertson
One Sheet: $40 - $75

AUTUMN SONOTA
(1978 - New World) Ingrid Bergman, Liv Ullmann
One Sheet: $10 - $20

AVALANCHE
(1928 - Paramount) Jack Holt, Doris Hill
One Sheet: $300 - $700   *Cowboy Movie Posters #71.*

AVALANCHE
(1946 - PRC) Bruce Cabot, Veda Ann Borg
One Sheet: $15 - $25

AVALANCHE
(1978 - New World) Rock Hudson, Mia Farrow
One Sheet: $7 - $15

AVALANCHE EXPRESS
(1979 - 20th Century Fox) Robert Shaw, Lee Marvin, Linda Evans
One Sheet: $3 - $5

AVALON
(1990 - TriStar) Armin Mueller-Stahl, John Plowwright
One Sheet: $3 - $5

AVANTI!
(1972 - United Artists) Jack Lemmon, Juliette Mills
One Sheet: $5 - $10

AVENGER, THE
(1931 - Columbia) Buck Jones
One Sheet: $300 - $700

AVENGER, THE
(1933 - Monogram) Ralph Forbes, Adrienne Ames
One Sheet: $150 - $300

AVENGER, THE
(1965 - Medallion) Steve Reeves
One Sheet: $20 - $40

AVENGER, THE
(1966 - Estela) Franco Nero
One Sheet: $10 - $20

AVENGERS, THE
(1942 - Paramount) Ralph Richardson, Deborah Kerr
One Sheet: $50 - $100

AVENGERS, THE
(1950 - Republic) John Carroll, Adele Mara
One Sheet: $30 - $50

AVENGERS, THE
(1952R - Paramount) Ralph Richardson, Deborah Kerr
One Sheet: $15 - $30   *Re-release.*

AVENGING ANGEL
(1985 - New World) Betsy Russell, Rory Calhoun
One Sheet: $3 - $5

AVENGING ARROW, THE

(1921 - Pathe) -
One Sheet: $350 - $750   *Serial. 15 chapters.*

AVENGING CONSCIENCE, THE
(1914 - Mutual) Henry B. Walthall, Dir: D.W. Griffith
One Sheet: $800 - $1,500

AVENGING FORCE
(1986 - -) Michael Dudikoff, Steve James
One Sheet: $3 - $5

AVENGING HAND, THE
(1936 - Stafford) Noah Beery, Kathleen Kelly
One Sheet: $100 - $200

AVENGING RIDER, THE
(1942 - RKO) Tim Holt
One Sheet: $50 - $100

AVENGING WATERS, THE
(1936 - Columbia) Ken Maynard
One Sheet: $200 - $400

AVIATOR
(1929 - Warner Brothers) Edward Everett Horton
One Sheet: $200 - $400

AVIATOR
(1985 - MGM/UA) Christopher Reeve, Rosanna Arquette
One Sheet: $5 - $10

AWAKENING, THE
(1928 - United Artists) Vilma Banky
One Sheet: $300 - $700

AWAKENING, THE
(1938 - Cosmopolitan) Eric Elliott, Eve Gray
One Sheet: $75 - $150

AWAKENING, THE
(1980 - Warner Bros.) Susannah York, Jill Townsend
One Sheet: $3 - $5

AWAKENING OF JIM BURKE
(1935 - Columbia) Jack Holt, Florence Rice
One Sheet: $100 - $200

AWAKENINGS
(1991 - Columbia) Robin Williams, Robert De Niro
One Sheet: $7 - $15

AWAY ALL BOATS
(1956 - Universal) Jeff Chandler, Julie Adams, George Nader
One Sheet: $15 - $30

AWFUL DR. ORLOFF, THE
(1964 - Sigma III) Howard Vernon, Ricardo Valle
One Sheet: $15 - $25

AWFUL GOOF, THE
(1939 - Columbia) Charley Chase
One Sheet: $75 - $150   *Comedy short. Blue duotone.*

AWFUL TOOTH, THE
(1938 - MGM) Our Gang
One Sheet: $700 - $1,200

AWFUL TRUTH, THE
(1929 - Pathe) Ina Claire, Henry Daniell
One Sheet: $150 - $300

AWFUL TRUTH, THE
(1937 - Columbia) Irene Dunne, Cary Grant
One Sheet: $1,300 - $2,000   *Academy Award: Best Director (Leo McCarey). Academy Award Movie Posters #52.*

One Sheet

AWFULLY BIG ADVENTURE, AN
(1995 - Fine Line) Hugh Grant, Alan Rickman
One Sheet: $5 - $10

AZTEC MUMMY, THE
(1957 - Calderon) Ramon Gay
One Sheet: $30 - $50

BAB'S BURGLAR
(1917 - Paramount) Marguerite Clark
One Sheet: $200 - $400

BABAR! THE MOVIE
(1989 - New Line) -
One Sheet: $7 - $15   *Cartoon.*

BABBITT
(1934 - Warner Bros.) Guy Kibbee, Aline MacMahon
One Sheet: $600 - $1,000

BABE
(1981 - Big Apple) Bobbi Jackson, Samantha Fox, Veronica Hart
One Sheet: $75 - $125   *XXX. Classic Olivia art.*

BABE, THE
(1992 - Universal) John Goodman, Kelly McGillis
One Sheet: $7 - $15   *Sports (Baseball). Film about the life of Babe Ruth. Sports Movie Posters #83.*

BABE
(1995 - Universal) Maggie Szubanski, James Cromwell
One Sheet: $5 - $10

BABE COMES HOME
(1927 - First National) Babe Ruth
One Sheet: $25,000 - $40,000   *Sports (Baseball). Sports Movie Posters #s 36, 37.*

BABE RUTH STORY, THE
(1948 - Allied Artists) William Bendix, Claire Trevor, Babe Ruth (cameo)
One Sheet: $200 - $400   *Sports (Baseball). Sports Movie Posters #54.*

BABES AND BOOBS
(1918 - Vitagraph) Larry Semon
One Sheet: $200 - $400

BABES IN ARMS
(1939 - MGM) Mickey Rooney, Judy Garland
One Sheet: $250 - $500

BABES IN BAGDAD
(1952 - United Artists) Paulette Goddard, Gypsy Rose Lee
One Sheet: $30 - $50

BABES IN THE WOODS
(1932 - United Artists) Silly Symphony
One Sheet: $13,000 - $20,000   *Cartoon. Full color. The Disney Poster, pg. 13.*

BABES IN TOYLAND
(1934 - MGM) Stan Laurel, Oliver Hardy
One Sheet: $3,500 - $5,000   *Graven Images, pg. 97.*

BABES IN TOYLAND
(1961 - Buena Vista/Disney) Tommy Sands, Annette Funicello
One Sheet: $20 - $40

BABES ON BROADWAY
(1941 - MGM) Mickey Rooney, Judy Garland
One Sheet: $250 - $500

BABES ON SWING STREET
(1944 - Universal) Peggy Ryan, Ann Blyth
One Sheet: $50 - $100

BABETTE GOES TO WAR
(1960 - Columbia) Brigitte Bardot, Jacques Charrier
One Sheet: $30 - $60

BABETTE'S FEAST
(1987 - Orion) Stephane Audran, Bibi Andersson
One Sheet: $15 - $25

BABIES FOR SALE
(1940 - Columbia) Glenn Ford, Rochelle Hudson
One Sheet: $75 - $150

BABY, THE
(1973 - Scotia International) Anjanette Comer, Ruth Roman

One Sheet: $3 - $5

BABY AND THE BATTLESHIP, THE
(1957 - DCA) John Mills, Richard Attenborough
One Sheet: $7 - $15

BABY AND THE BOSS, THE
(1917 - Mutual) Marion Fairbanks, Helen Badgely, Boyd Marshall
One Sheet: $250 - $600

BABY BE GOOD
(1925 - Educational) Big Boy, Bonnie Barrett
One Sheet: $200 - $400

BABY BLUE MARINE
(1976 - Columbia) Jan-Michel Vincent, Glynnis O'Connor, Richard Gere
One Sheet: $7 - $15

BABY BOOM
(1987 - -) Diane Keaton, Harold Ramis
One Sheet: $3 - $5

BABY DOLL
(1956 - Warner Bros.) Karl Malden, Carroll Baker
One Sheet: $40 - $75

BABY FACE
(1933 - Warner Bros.) Barbara Stanwyck, George Brent, John Wayne
One Sheet: $2,200 - $3,500

BABY FACE HARRINGTON
(1935 - MGM) Una Merkel, Charles Butterworth
One Sheet: $100 - $200

BABY FACE MORGAN
(1942 - PRC) Mary Carlisle, Richard Cromwell
One Sheet: $40 - $75

BABY FACE NELSON
(1957 - United Artists) Mickey Rooney, Carolyn Jones
One Sheet: $40 - $75

BABY, IT'S YOU
(1983 - Paramount) Rosanna Arquette, Vincent Spano
One Sheet: $5 - $10

BABY LOVE
(1969 - Avco/Embassy) Ann Lynn, Keith Barron, Linda Hayden
One Sheet: $5 - $10

BABY MAKER, THE
(1970 - National General) Barbara Hershey, Scott Glenn
One Sheet: $5 - $10

BABY NEEDS A NEW PAIR OF SHOES
(1974 - -) Paul Harris, Reginald Farmer
One Sheet: $15 - $30   *Black cast.*

BABY PUSS
(1943 - MGM) Tom & Jerry
One Sheet: $600 - $1,000   *Cartoon. Full color stone litho. Cartoon Movie Posters #268.*

BABY: SECRET OF THE LOST LEGEND
(1985 - Touchstone) William Katt, Sean Young, Patrick McGoohan
One Sheet: $3 - $5

BABY SITTERS' JITTERS
(1951 - Columbia) The Three Stooges (Shemp)
One Sheet: $200 - $400   *Comedy short. Duotone.*

BABY TAKE A BOW
(1934 - Fox) Shirley Temple
One Sheet: $1,900 - $3,000   *Two styles one sheet exist, price is valid for either style.*

One Sheet

BABY THE RAIN MUST FALL
(1965 - Columbia) Lee Remick, Steve McQueen
One Sheet: $20 - $40

BABY WANTS A BOTTLESHIP
(1941 - Paramount) Popeye
One Sheet: $800 - $1,500   *Cartoon. Cartoon Movie Posters #224.*

BABYLON
(1980 - Diversity Music) Brinsley Forde
One Sheet: $7 - $15   *Reggae.*

BABYSITTER, THE
(1969 - Crown) Patricia Wymer, George E. Carey
One Sheet: $5 - $10

BABY-SITTERS CLUB, THE
(1995 - Columbia) Schuyler Fisk, Peter Horton
One Sheet: $3 - $5

BACHELOR AND THE BOBBY SOXER, THE
(1947 - RKO) Myrna Loy, Cary Grant, Shirley Temple
One Sheet: $100 - $200

BACHELOR AND THE BOBBY SOXER, THE
(1952R - RKO) Myrna Loy, Cary Grant, Shirley Temple
One Sheet: $15 - $30   *Re-release.*

BACHELOR APARTMENT
(1931 - RKO) Irene Dunne, Lowell Sherman
One Sheet: $150 - $300

BACHELOR BAIT
(1934 - RKO) Stuart Erwin, Rochelle Hudson
One Sheet: $75 - $150

BACHELOR DADDY
(1941 - Universal) Baby Sandy, Kathryn Adams
One Sheet: $75 - $150

BACHELOR DAZE
(1944 - Columbia) Slim Summerville
One Sheet: $50 - $100   *Comedy short. Duotone.*

BACHELOR FATHER, THE
(1931 - MGM) Marion Davies, Ralph Forbes
One Sheet: $250 - $500

BACHELOR FLAT
(1961 - 20th Century Fox) Tuesday Weld, Richard Beymer
One Sheet: $15 - $25

BACHELOR GIRL, THE
(1929 - Columbia) William Collier, Jr., Thelma Todd
One Sheet: $200 - $400

BACHELOR IN PARADISE
(1961 - MGM) Bob Hope, Lana Turner
One Sheet: $15 - $30

BACHELOR IN PARIS
(1953 - Lippert) Dennis Price, Anne Vernon
One Sheet: $15 - $25

BACHELOR MOTHER
(1933 - Hollywood) Evalyn Knapp, James Murray
One Sheet: $150 - $300

BACHELOR MOTHER
(1939 - RKO) Ginger Rogers, David Niven
One Sheet: $500 - $800

BACHELOR OF ARTS
(1934 - Fox) Tom Brown, Anita Louise
One Sheet: $150 - $350

BACHELOR OF HEARTS
(1958 - Rank) Hardy Kruger, Sylvia Syms
One Sheet: $10 - $20

BACHELOR PARTY
(1956 - United Artists) Don Murray, E. G. Marshall
One Sheet: $15 - $30

BACHELOR PARTY
(1984 - 20th Century Fox) Tom Hanks, Tawny Kitaen
One Sheet: $5 - $10

BACHELOR'S AFFAIRS
(1932 - Fox) Adolphe Menjou, Minna Gombell
One Sheet: $150 - $300

BACHELOR'S BABY

(1932 - Pathe) Ann Casson, William Freshman
One Sheet: $200 - $400

BACHELOR'S DAUGHTERS
(1946 - United Artists) Gail Russell, Claire Trevor
One Sheet: $40 - $75

BACHELOR'S FOLLY
(1932 - World Wide) -
One Sheet: $75 - $150

BACK DOOR TO HEAVEN
(1939 - Paramount) Aline McMahon, Jimmy Lydon, Wallace Ford
One Sheet: $75 - $125

BACK DOOR TO HELL
(1965 - 20th Century Fox) Jimmie Rodgers, Jack Nicholson
One Sheet: $15 - $30

BACK FROM ETERNITY
(1956 - RKO) Robert Ryan, Anita Ekberg
One Sheet: $30 - $60

BACK FROM THE DEAD
(1957 - 20th Century Fox) Arthur Franz, Peggie Castle
One Sheet: $30 - $50

BACK FROM THE FRONT
(1943 - Columbia) The Three Stooges (Curly)
One Sheet: $2,500 - $4,000   *Comedy short. Duotone.*

BACK HOME AND BROKE
(1922 - Paramount) Thomas Meighan
One Sheet: $125 - $250

BACK IN CIRCULATION
(1937 - Warner Bros.) Joan Blondell, Pat O'Brien, Margaret Lindsay
One Sheet: $75 - $125

BACK IN THE SADDLE
(1941 - Republic) Gene Autry, Smiley Burnette
One Sheet: $200 - $400

BACK IN THE U.S.S.R.
(1991 - 20th Century Fox) Frank Whaley, Natalya Negoda
One Sheet: $3 - $5

BACK OF THE MAN
(1917 - Triangle) Charles Ray, Dorothy Dalton
One Sheet: $250 - $600

BACK PAGE
(1933 - Pyramid) Peggy Shannon, Russell Hopton
One Sheet: $100 - $200

BACK PAY
(1930 - First National) Corrine Griffith, Grant Withers
One Sheet: $100 - $200

BACK ROADS
(1981 - CBS) Sally Field, Tommy Lee Jones
One Sheet: $5 - $10

BACK ROOM BOY
(1942 - General Film) Arthur Askey, Moore Marriott
One Sheet: $50 - $100

BACK STREET
(1932 - Universal) Irene Dunne, John Boles
One Sheet: $600 - $1,000

BACK STREET
(1941 - Universal) Margaret Sullavan, Charles Boyer
One Sheet: $250 - $500

BACK STREET
(1949R - Universal) Margaret Sullavan, Charles Boyer
One Sheet: $40 - $75   *Re-release.*

BACK STREET
(1961 - Universal) Susan Hayward, John Gavin
One Sheet: $20 - $40

BACK TO BATAAN
(1945 - RKO) John Wayne, Anthony Quinn
One Sheet: $200 - $400

BACK TO GOD'S COUNTRY
(1919 - First National) Nell Shipman
One Sheet: $500 - $800

BACK TO GOD'S COUNTRY

(1927 - Universal) Renee Adoree, Walter Long
One Sheet: $250 - $500

BACK TO GOD'S COUNTRY
(1953 - Universal) Rock Hudson, Steve Cochran
One Sheet: $30 - $50

BACK TO NATURE
(1936 - 20th Century Fox) Tony Martin, Spring Byington
One Sheet: $100 - $200

BACK TO SCHOOL
(1986 - Orion) Rodney Dangerfield, Sally Kellerman
One Sheet: $5 - $10

BACK TO THE BEACH
(1987 - Paramount) Frankie Avalon, Annette Funicello
One Sheet: $7 - $15

BACK TO THE FUTURE
(1985 - Universal) Michael J. Fox, Christopher Lloyd
One Sheet: $30 - $50

BACK TO THE FUTURE PART II
(1989 - Universal) Michael J. Fox, Christopher Lloyd
One Sheet: $10 - $20

BACK TO THE FUTURE PART III
(1990 - Universal) Michael J. Fox, Christopher Lloyd
One Sheet: $5 - $10

BACK TO THE SOIL
(1940 - 20th Century Fox) Terry-toons
One Sheet: $150 - $300   *Cartoon. Full color stone litho. Stock poster with inset title.*

BACK TO THE WOODS
(1937 - Columbia) The Three Stooges (Curly)
One Sheet: $8,500 - $14,000   *Comedy short. Duotone.*

BACK TRAIL
(1948 - Monogram) Johnny Mack Brown, Mildred Coles
One Sheet: $30 - $50

BACKBEAT
(1994 - Gramercy) Ian Hart, Stephen Dorff, Sheryl Lee
One Sheet: $5 - $10

BACKDRAFT
(1991 - Universal) Kurt Russell, Robert De Niro, Dir: Ron Howard
One Sheet: $10 - $20

BACKFIRE
(1950 - Warner Bros.) Virginia Mayo, Gordon MacRae
One Sheet: $30 - $50

BACKFIRE
(1961 - Allied Artists) Alfred Burke, Zena Marshall
One Sheet: $5 - $10

BACKFIRE
(1965 - Royal Films International) Jean-Paul Belmondo, Jean Seberg
One Sheet: $15 - $25

BACKGROUND TO DANGER
(1943 - Warner Bros.) George Raft, Peter Lorre, Sydney Greenstreet
One Sheet: $125 - $250

One Sheet

BACKGROUND TO DANGER
(1953 - Associated British) Valeria Hobson,

Philip Friend
One Sheet: $10 - $20   *AKA: EDGE OF DIVORCE.*

BACKLASH
(1946 - 20th Century Fox) Jean Rogers, Richard Travis
One Sheet: $40 - $75

BACKLASH
(1956 - Universal) Richard Widmark, Donna Reed
One Sheet: $7 - $15

BACKS TO NATURE
(1933 - MGM) Thelma Todd, Patsy Kelly
One Sheet: $100 - $200

BACKSTAGE
(1936 - Gaumont British) Ann Neagle, Arthur Tracy
One Sheet: $75 - $150

BACKSTAGE AT THE KIROV
(1983 - -) Kirov Ballet Troupe
One Sheet: $5 - $10

BACKTRACK
(1969 - Universal) Neville Brant, James Drury
One Sheet: $20 - $40   *TV-tie-in with the Virginian.*

BACKYARD
(1918 - Vitagraph) -
One Sheet: $250 - $500

BACON GRABBERS, THE
(1929 - -) Laurel & Hardy
One Sheet: $2,500 - $4,000

BAD (ANDY WARHOL'S)
(1977 - -) Carroll Baker, Perry King
One Sheet: $30 - $50

BAD AND THE BEAUTIFUL, THE
(1952 - MGM) Lana Turner, Kirk Douglas, Walter Pidgeon
One Sheet: $150 - $300   *Academy Award Movie Posters #147.*

BAD BASCOMB
(1946 - MGM) Wallace Beery, Margaret O'Brien
One Sheet: $75 - $125

BAD BEHAVIOUR
(1993 - October Films) Stephen Rea, Sinead Cusack
One Sheet: $3 - $5

BAD BLONDE
(1953 - Lippert) Barbara Payton, Frederick Valk
One Sheet: $40 - $75   *Sexploitation.*

BAD BOY
(1935 - 20th Century Fox) James Dunn, Louise Fazenda
One Sheet: $200 - $400   *Billiards.*

BAD BOY
(1938 - Radius) John Warwick, John Longden
One Sheet: $100 - $200   *AKA: BRANDED*

BAD BOY
(1939 - Atlas) Johnny Downs, Rosalind Keith
One Sheet: $75 - $150

BAD BOY
(1949 - Monogram) Lloyd Nolan, Jane Wyatt, Audie Murphy (film debut)
One Sheet: $40 - $75

BAD BOYS
(1983 - EMI) Sean Penn, Reni Santoni, Esai Morales
One Sheet: $7 - $15
Advance:$15-25.

BAD BOYS
(1995 - Columbia) Martin Lawrence, Will Smith
One Sheet: $5 - $12

BAD CHARLESTON CHARLIE
(1973 - International Cinema) Ross Magen, John Carradine
One Sheet: $5 - $10

BAD COMPANY
(1931 - RKO-Pathe) Ricardo Cortez, Helen Twelvetrees
One Sheet: $100 - $200

BAD COMPANY
(1972 - Paramount) Jeff Bridges, Barry Brown

One Sheet: $5 - $10

BAD COMPANY
(1995 - Buena Vista) Ellen Barkin, Laurence Fishburne
One Sheet: $3 - $5

BAD DAY AT BLACK ROCK
(1954 - MGM) Spencer Tracy, Anne Francis, Robert Ryan
One Sheet: $40 - $75

BAD DREAMS
(1988 - 20th Century Fox) Jennifer Rubin, Bruce Abbott
One Sheet: $3 - $5

BAD FOR EACH OTHER
(1953 - Lippert) Charlton Heston, Lizabeth Scott, Dianne Foster
One Sheet: $40 - $75

BAD GIRL
(1931 - Fox) James Dunn, Sally Eilers
One Sheet: $800 - $1,500   *Academy Award: Best Direction (Frank Borzage). Academy Award Movie Posters #24.*

BAD GIRLS
(1994 - Fox) Drew Barrymore, Andie McDowell
One Sheet: $5 - $12

One Sheet

BAD GUY
(1937 - MGM) Bruce Cabot, Virginia Grey
One Sheet: $75 - $150

BAD HOUSEKEEPING
(1937 - RKO) Edgar Kennedy
One Sheet: $100 - $200

BAD INFLUENCE
(1990 - Triumph) Rob Lowe, James Spader
One Sheet: $3 - $5

BAD LANDS, THE
(1925 - -) Harry Carey, Wilfred Lucas
One Sheet: $250 - $600

BAD LANDS
(1939 - RKO) Robert Barrat, Noah Beery Jr.
One Sheet: $75 - $150

BAD LIEUTENANT
(1992 - Aries) Harvey Keitel, Victor Argo
One Sheet: $5 - $10

BAD LITTLE ANGEL
(1939 - MGM) Virginia Weidler, Gene Reynolds
One Sheet: $75 - $150

BAD LORD BYRON, THE
(1949 - General) Dennis Price, Mai Zetterling
One Sheet: $30 - $50

BAD LUCK BLACKIE
(1949 - MGM) Tex Avery
One Sheet: $250 - $600   *Cartoon. Full color stone litho.*

BAD MAN, THE
(1930 - First National) Walter Huston
One Sheet: $350 - $750

BAD MAN, THE
(1941 - MGM) Wallace Beery, Lionel Barrymore, Laraine Day, Ronald Reagan
One Sheet: $200 - $400

BAD MAN FROM RED BUTTE
(1940 - Universal) Johnny Mack Brown, Bob Baker, Fuzzy Knight
One Sheet: $75 - $125

BAD MAN OF BRIMSTONE
(1937 - MGM) Wallace Beery, Virginia Bruce

One Sheet: $75 - $125

BAD MAN OF DEADWOOD
(1941 - Republic) Roy Rogers, Gabby Hayes
One Sheet: $200 - $400

BAD MAN'S RIVER
(1973 - Scotia) Lee Van Cleef, James Mason
One Sheet: $5 - $10

BAD MANNERS
(1984 - New World) Karen Black, Martin Mull
One Sheet: $3 - $5

BAD MEDICINE
(1985 - 20th Century Fox) Steve Guttenberg, Alan Arkin, Julie Hagerty
One Sheet: $3 - $5

BAD MEN OF ARIZONA
(1951R - Favorite Films) Buster Crabbe
One Sheet: $15 - $30

BAD MEN OF MISSOURI
(1941 - Warner Bros.) Dennis Morgan, Jane Wyman
One Sheet: $50 - $100

BAD MEN OF RIMROCK, THE
(1953 - Monogram) Harry Thomas, Denver Sherry
One Sheet: $10 - $20

BAD MEN OF THE BORDER
(1945 - Universal) Kirby Grant, Armida
One Sheet: $40 - $75

BAD MEN OF THE HILLS
(1942 - Columbia) Charles Starrett, Russell Hayden
One Sheet: $50 - $100

BAD MEN OF THUNDER GAP
(1943 - PRC) Dave O'Brien, Jim Newill
One Sheet: $20 - $40

BAD MEN OF TOMBSTONE
(1948 - Allied Artists) Barry Sullivan, Marjorie Reynolds
One Sheet: $20 - $40

BAD MOON
(1996 - Warner Bros.) Mariel Hemingway, Michael Pare
One Sheet: $5 - $10

One Sheet

BAD NEWS BEARS, THE
(1976 - Paramount) Walter Matthau, Tatum O'Neal, Vic Morrow
One Sheet: $15 - $25   *Jack Davis art. Sports Movie Posters #73.*

BAD NEWS BEARS GO TO JAPAN
(1978 - Paramount) Tony Curtis
One Sheet: $5 - $10

BAD NEWS BEARS IN BREAKING TRAINING, THE
(1977 - Paramount) William Devane, Clifton James
One Sheet: $7 - $15   *Jack Davis art.*

BAD ONE, THE
(1930 - United Artists) Dolores Del Rio, Edmund Lowe
One Sheet: $150 - $300

BAD SEED, THE
(1956 - Warner Bros.) Nancy Kelly, Patty McCormack
One Sheet: $40 - $75

BAD SISTER
(1931 - Universal) Conrad Nagel, Bette Davis,

Humphrey Bogart
One Sheet: $2,200 - $3,500   *At least one style of the one sheet pictures Davis, price is for Davis(style). Styles w/o Davis would be worth 1/3. Others should be valued based on the Davis image, if any.*

BAD SISTER
(1948 - Universal-International) Margaret Lockwood, Ian Hunter
One Sheet: $40 - $75

BAD TASTE
(1988 - -) Peter Jackson, Pete O'Herne
One Sheet: $3 - $5

BADGE 373
(1973 - Paramount) Robert Duvall, Verna Bloom
One Sheet: $5 - $10

BADGE OF HONOR
(1934 - Mayfair) Buster Crabbe, Gloria Shea
One Sheet: $100 - $200

BADGE OF MARSHAL BRENNAN, THE
(1957 - Allied Artists) Jim Davis, Arleen Whelan
One Sheet: $15 - $25

BADGER'S GREEN
(1934 - Paramount) Valerie Hobson, Bruce Lister
One Sheet: $125 - $250

BADGER'S GREEN
(1949 - General) Barbara Murray, Brian Nissen
One Sheet: $40 - $75

BADLANDERS, THE
(1957 - MGM) Alan Ladd, Ernest Borgnine
One Sheet: $15 - $35

BADLANDS
(1974 - Warner Bros.) Martin Sheen, Sissy Spacek
One Sheet: $10 - $20

BADLANDS OF DAKOTA
(1941 - Universal) Broderick Crawford, Robert Stack, Frances Farmer
One Sheet: $100 - $200

BADLANDS OF MONTANA
(1957 - 20th Century Fox) Rex Reason, Beverly Garland
One Sheet: $15 - $30

BADMAN'S COUNTRY
(1958 - Warner Bros.) George Montgomery, Buster Crabbe
One Sheet: $15 - $25

BADMAN'S GOLD
(1951 - Eagle-Lion) Johnny Carpenter, Alan Lockwood
One Sheet: $15 - $30

BADMAN'S TERRITORY
(1946 - RKO) Randolph Scott, Ann Richards, George "Gabby" Hayes
One Sheet: $75 - $125

BADMAN'S TERRITORY
(1954R - RKO) Randolph Scott, Ann Richards, George "Gabby" Hayes
One Sheet: $15 - $25   *Re-release.*

BAGDAD
(1949 - Universal) Maureen O'Hara, Paul Christian, Vincent Price
One Sheet: $50 - $100

BAGDAD CAFE
(1988 - Island) Jack Palance, Marianne Sagebrecht
One Sheet: $15 - $30

BAGGAGE BUSTER
(1941 - RKO/Disney) Goofy
One Sheet: $1,600 - $2,500   *Cartoon. The Disney Poster, pg. 63.*

BAH WILDERNESS
(1943 - MGM) Barney Bear
One Sheet: $300 - $700   *Cartoon. Full color stone litho. Cartoon Movie Posters #260.*

BAHAMA PASSAGE
(1941 - Paramount) Madeleine Carroll, Sterling Hayden
One Sheet: $100 - $200

BAIL OUT AT 43,000
(1957 - United Artists) John Payne, Karen

Steel
One Sheet: $15 - $30

BAIT, THE
(1921 - Paramount) Hope Hampton
One Sheet: $250 - $600

BAIT
(1950 - Adelphi) Diana Napier, John Bentley
One Sheet: $30 - $50

BAIT
(1954 - Columbia) Cleo Moore, Hugo Haas, John Agar
One Sheet: $40 - $75

BAKER'S HAWK
(1976 - Doty-Dayton) Clint Walker, Burl Ives
One Sheet: $5 - $10

BAL TABARIN
(1952 - Republic) Muriel Lawrence, William Ching
One Sheet: $30 - $50

BALALAIKA
(1939 - MGM) Nelson Eddy, Ilona Massey
One Sheet: $100 - $200

BALCONY, THE
(1963 - Continental) Shelley Winters, Peter Falk
One Sheet: $7 - $15

BALL AT SAVOY
(1936 - Stafford) Conrad Nagel, Marta Labarr
One Sheet: $100 - $200

BALL OF FIRE
(1941 - RKO) Gary Cooper, Barbara Stanwyck
One Sheet: $250 - $500

BALLAD OF A GUNFIGHTER
(1964 - Parade) Marty Robbins
One Sheet: $20 - $40   *Western. Based on his song "El Paso".*

BALLAD OF CABLE HOGUE, THE
(1970 - Warner Bros.) Jason Robards, Stella Stevens
One Sheet: $5 - $10

BALLAD OF GREGORIO CORTEZ, THE
(1983 - Embassy) Edward James Olmos, Tom Bower
One Sheet: $3 - $5

BALLAD OF JOSIE, THE
(1968 - Universal) Doris Day, Peter Graves
One Sheet: $30 - $50

BALLAD OF LITTLE JO, THE
(1993 - Fine Line) Eric Stoltz, David Chung
One Sheet: $3 - $5

BALLERINA
(1938 - Mayer) Jannine Charrat
One Sheet: $100 - $200   *Dancing (Ballet).*

BALLOON GOES UP, THE
(1942 - New Realm) Ethel Revnell, Gracie West
One Sheet: $50 - $100

BALLOONATIC
(1922 - -) Buster Keaton
One Sheet: $5,000 - $8,000

BALLOONLAND
(1935 - Celebrity) By Ub Iwerks
One Sheet: $600 - $1,000   *Cartoon. A ComiColor Cartoon. Cartoon Movie Posters #116.*

BALLYHOO BUSTER, THE
(1928 - -) Buffalo Bill, Jr., Peggy Shaw
One Sheet: $500 - $800

BALTIMORE BULLET, THE
(1980 - Avco/Embassy) James Coburn, Omar Sharif
One Sheet: $30 - $50   *Billiards.*

BALTO
(1995 - Universal) Voices of Kevin Bacon, Bob Hoskins, Dir: Simon Wells
One Sheet: $5 - $10   *Cartoon.*

BAMBI
(1942 - RKO/Disney) -
One Sheet: $1,300 - $2,000   *Cartoon. Window Card(best image of all posters):$2500-3500. Cartoon Movie Posters #362-#373. The Disney Poster, pg. 83.*

BAMBI
(1948R - RKO/Disney) -
One Sheet: $250 - $500 *Re-release. Cartoon.*

BAMBI
(1957R - Disney) -
One Sheet: $30 - $60 *Re-release. Cartoon.*

BAMBI
(1966R - Disney) -
One Sheet: $30 - $50 *Re-release. Cartoon.*

BAMBI
(1975R - Disney) -
One Sheet: $20 - $40 *Re-release. Cartoon.*

BAMBI
(1982R - Disney) -
One Sheet: $15 - $35 *Re-release. Cartoon.*

BAMBI
(1988R - Disney) -
One Sheet: $7 - $15 *Re-release. Cartoon.*

BAMBOLE
(1965 - Royal) Elke Sommer, Gina Lollabrigida
One Sheet: $7 - $15

BAMBOO BLONDE, THE
(1946 - RKO) Frances Langford, Russell Wade
One Sheet: $40 - $75

BAMBOO GODS AND IRON MEN
(1974 - -) James Iglehart, Shirley Washington
One Sheet: $15 - $25 *Blaxploitation martial arts film.*

BAMBOO PRISON, THE
(1954 - Columbia) Robert Francis, Brian Keith
One Sheet: $15 - $30

BAMBOO SAUCER, THE
(1968 - World Entertainment) Dan Duryea, John Ericson
One Sheet: $10 - $20

BANANA PEEL
(1965 - Pathe-Cont) Jeanne Moreau, Jean-Paul Belmondo
One Sheet: $15 - $25 *French.*

BANANA RIDGE
(1941 - Pathe) Robertson Hale, Isabel Jeans
One Sheet: $50 - $100

BANANAS
(1971 - United Artists) Woody Allen, Louise Lasser
One Sheet: $20 - $40

BAND OF ANGELS
(1955 - Warner Bros.) Clark Gable, Yvonne De Carlo
One Sheet: $40 - $75

BAND OF ASSASSINS
(1970 - TOHO) Toshiro Mifune
One Sheet: $15 - $30

BAND OF THE HAND
(1986 - -) Stephen Lang, Michael Carmine
One Sheet: $3 - $5

BAND OF THIEVES
(1962 - RFD) Acker Bilk, Jimmy Thompson
One Sheet: $7 - $15

BAND PLAYS ON, THE
(1934 - MGM) Robert Young
One Sheet: $125 - $250

BAND WAGON
(1940 - GFD) Arthur Askey, Richard Murdoch
One Sheet: $75 - $150

BAND WAGON
(1953 - MGM) Fred Astaire, Cyd Charisse
One Sheet: $200 - $400 *Dance musical.*

BAND WAGON, THE
(1968R - MGM) Fred Astaire, Cyd Charisse
One Sheet: $15 - $35 *Re-release. Dance musical.*

BANDIDO
(1956 - United Artists) Robert Mitchum, Ursula

Thiess
One Sheet: $50 - $100

BANDIDOS
(1973 - Stellar IV) Enrico Maria Salerno, Terry Thomas
One Sheet: $7 - $15

BANDIT KING OF TEXAS
(1949 - Republic) Allan "Rocky" Lane, Eddy Waller
One Sheet: $30 - $50

BANDIT OF SHERWOOD FOREST, THE
(1946 - Columbia) Cornel Wilde, Anita Louise
One Sheet: $75 - $125

BANDIT OF ZHOBE, THE
(1958 - Columbia) Victor Mature, Anthony Newley
One Sheet: $10 - $20

BANDIT QUEEN
(1950 - Lippert) Barbara Britton, Phillip Reed
One Sheet: $20 - $40

BANDIT RANGER
(1942 - RKO) Tim Holt
One Sheet: $40 - $75

BANDIT TRAIL, THE
(1941 - RKO) Tim Holt
One Sheet: $40 - $75

BANDIT'S BABY, THE
(192? - -) Fred Thomson
One Sheet: $150 - $300

BANDIT'S SON, THE
(1927 - FBO) Bob Steele, Tom Lingham, Anne Sheridan
One Sheet: $250 - $500

BANDITS AND BALLADS
(1939 - RKO) Ray Whitley, Ken Card
One Sheet: $75 - $150

BANDITS IN MILAN
(195? - -) Gian Maria Volonte
One Sheet: $15 - $30 *Indian.*

BANDITS OF CORSICA, THE
(1953 - United Artists) Richard Greene, Paula Raymond
One Sheet: $15 - $30

BANDITS OF DARK CANYON
(1948 - Republic) Allan "Rocky" Lane, Bob Steele
One Sheet: $40 - $75

BANDITS OF EL DORADO
(1949 - Columbia) Charles Starrett, Smiley Burnette
One Sheet: $30 - $50

BANDITS OF ORGOSOLO
(1964 - Pathe-Cont.) Michele Cossu, Peppaddu Cuccu
One Sheet: $15 - $25

BANDITS OF THE BADLANDS
(1945 - Republic) Sunset Carson, Peggy Stewart
One Sheet: $40 - $75

BANDITS OF THE WEST
(1953 - Republic) Allan "Rocky" Lane
One Sheet: $30 - $50

BANDOLERO!
(1968 - 20th Century Fox) James Stewart, Dean Martin, Raquel Welch, George Kennedy
One Sheet: $40 - $75 *Cowboy Movie Posters #324.*

BANG!
(1929 - Educational) Jimmie Adams
One Sheet: $150 - $300

BANG BANG KID, THE
(1968 - Ajay) Guy Madison, Tom Bosley
One Sheet: $5 - $10

BANG, BANG, YOU'RE DEAD
(1966 - AIP) Tony Randall, Senta Berger
One Sheet: $5 - $10

BANG THE DRUM SLOWLY
(1973 - Paramount) Robert De Niro, Michael Moriarity
One Sheet: $15 - $25 *Sports (Baseball). Sports Movie Posters #71.*

BANG! YOU'RE DEAD
(1954 - British Lion) Jack Warner, Veronica Hurst
One Sheet: $15 - $30

BANJO
(1947 - RKO) Sharyn Moffett, Jacqueline White, Banjo
One Sheet: $30 - $50

BANJO ON MY KNEE
(1936 - 20th Century Fox) Barbara Stanwyck, Joel McCrea
One Sheet: $150 - $300

Mini Window Card

BANJO ON MY KNEE
(1943R - 20th Century Fox) Barbara Stanwych, Joel McCrae
One Sheet: $30 - $50 *Re-release.*

BANK, THE
(1915 - Essanay) Charlie Chaplin, Edna Purviance
One Sheet: $6,500 - $10,000

BANK ALARM
(1937 - Grand National) Conrad Nagel, Eleanor Hunt
One Sheet: $100 - $200

BANK DICK, THE
(1940 - Universal) W. C. Fields, Una Merkel
One Sheet: $500 - $800

BANK DICK, THE
(1949R - Universal) W.C. Fields, Una Merkel
One Sheet: $100 - $200 *Re-release.*

BANK HOLIDAY
(1938 - GFD) John Lodge, Margaret Lockwood
One Sheet: $75 - $150

BANK MESSENGER MYSTERY, THE
(1936 - Hammer) George Mozart
One Sheet: $125 - $250

BANK RAIDERS, THE
(1958 - RFD) Peter Reynolds, Sandra Dorne
One Sheet: $15 - $25

BANK SHOT
(1974 - United Artists) George C. Scott, Joanna Cassidy
One Sheet: $10 - $20

BANNERLINE
(1951 - MGM) Sally Forrest, Keefe Brasselle
One Sheet: $15 - $30

BANNING
(1967 - Universal) Robert Wagner, Anjanette Comer, Jill St. John
One Sheet: $5 - $10

B.A.P.S.
(1997 - New Line) Halle Berry, Martin Landau, Natalie Desselle
One Sheet: $5 - $10

BAR 20
(1943 - United Artists) William Boyd, Andy Clyde
One Sheet: $150 - $300 *Last of the Bar 20 series.*

BAR 20 JUSTICE
(1938 - Paramount) William Boyd, George "Gabby" Hayes, Russell Hayden
One Sheet: $1,600 - $2,500 *Cowboy Movie Posters #s 217, 219.*

BAR 20 JUSTICE
(1943R - Western Classics) William Boyd, George "Gabby" Hayes, Russell Hayden

One Sheet: $125 - $250 *Re-release.*

BAR 20 RIDES AGAIN
(1935 - Paramount) William Boyd, Gabby Hayes
One Sheet: $600 - $1,000

BAR 20 RIDES AGAIN
(1943R - Western Classics) William Boyd, Gabby Hayes
One Sheet: $75 - $150 *Re-release.*

BAR GIRLS
(1995 - Orion) Nancy Allison Wolfe, Liza D'Agostino
One Sheet: $5 - $10

BAR L RANCH
(1930 - Big Four) Buffalo Bill, Jr., Wally Wales
One Sheet: $200 - $400 *Cowboy Movie Posters # 84.*

BAR MITZVAH
(1935 - Metro) Stephen Fishler, Betty Sain
One Sheet: $50 - $100

BAR NOTHIN'
(1921 - Fox) Buck Jones, Ruth Renick
One Sheet: $300 - $700

BARABBAS
(1962 - Columbia) Anthony Quinn, Silvana Mangano
One Sheet: $20 - $40

BARAKA
(1993 - Samuel Goldwyn) Documentary
One Sheet: $3 - $5

BARB WIRE
(1922 - Sunset) Jack Hoxie, Jean Porter
One Sheet: $600 - $1,000

BARB WIRE
(1996 - Gramercy) Pamela Anderson Lee
One Sheet: $5 - $12 *Based on the comic book series. Advance: $15-$20.*

BARBARELLA
(1968 - Paramount) Jane Fonda
One Sheet: $75 - $150 *One Sheet(Style B):$125-$250. Graven Images, pg. 223.*

One Sheet

BARBARELLA
(1977R - Paramount) Jane Fonda
One Sheet: $30 - $50 *Re-release. Boris art.*

BARBARIAN, THE
(1933 - MGM) Myrna Loy, Ramon Novarro
One Sheet: $250 - $500

BARBARIAN AND THE GEISHA, THE
(1958 - 20th Century Fox) John Wayne, Eiko Ando
One Sheet: $50 - $100

BARBARIAN QUEEN
(1985 - Concorde) Lana Clarkson, Latta Shea
One Sheet: $15 - $25 *Boris Vallejo art.*

BARBARIANS, THE
(1957 - Allied Artists) Pierre Cresoy, Helene Remy
One Sheet: $10 - $20

BARBARIANS, THE
(1987 - -) David Paul, Peter Paul
One Sheet: $5 - $10

BARBAROSA
(1982 - ITC) Willie Nelson, Gray Busey
One Sheet: $7 - $15 *Cowboy*

Movie Posters #356.

BARBARY COAST, THE
(1935 - United Artists) Joel McCrea, Miriam
Hopkins, Edward G. Robinson
One Sheet: $250 - $600

BARBARY COAST GENT
(1944 - MGM) Wallace Beery, Binnie Barnes
One Sheet: $30 - $50

BARBARY PIRATE
(1949 - Columbia) Donald Woods, Trudy
Marshall
One Sheet: $15 - $30

BARBED WIRE
(1927 - Paramount) Pola Negri, Clive Brook
One Sheet: $600 - $1,000

BARBED WIRE
(1952 - Columbia) Gene Autry
One Sheet: $50 - $100

BARBER OF STAMFORD HILL, THE
(1963 - British Lion) Meg Jenkins, John
Bennett
One Sheet: $5 - $10

BARDELYS THE MAGNIFICENT
(1926 - MGM) John Gilbert
One Sheet: $250 - $600

BARE KNUCKLES
(1921 - Fox) William Russell, Mary Thurman
One Sheet: $200 - $400

BARE KNUCKLES
(1978 - Intercontinental) Robert Viharo, Sherry
Jackson
One Sheet: $3 - $5

BAREFOOT BATTALION
(1956 - 20th Century Fox) Maria Costi
One Sheet: $15 - $25

BAREFOOT BOY
(1938 - Monogram) Jackie Moran, Claire
Windsor
One Sheet: $50 - $100

BAREFOOT CONTESSA, THE
(1954 - United Artists) Humphrey Bogart, Ava
Gardner, Edmond O'Brien
One Sheet: $100 - $200   *Academy
Award Movie Posters #158.*

BAREFOOT CONTESSA, THE
(1960R - United Artists) Humphrey Bogart, Ava
Gardner, Edmond O'Brien
One Sheet: $15 - $30   *Re-release.*

BAREFOOT EXECUTIVE, THE
(1971 - Buena Vista/Disney) Kurt Russell, Joe
Flynn
One Sheet: $15 - $30

Insert

BAREFOOT IN THE PARK
(1967 - Paramount) Robert Redford, Jane
Fonda
One Sheet: $30 - $50

BAREFOOT MAILMAN, THE
(1951 - Columbia) Robert Cummings, Terry
Moore
One Sheet: $30 - $50

BAREFOOT MAILMAN, THE
(1960R - Columbia) Robert Cummings, Terry
Moore
One Sheet: $7 - $15   *Re-release.*

BARELY PROPER
(1975 - -) Gideon, Heather Hughes
One Sheet: $5 - $10

BARFLY
(1987 - Cannon) Mickey Rourke, Faye
Dunaway
One Sheet: $15 - $25

BARGAIN, THE
(1914 - -) William S. Hart, Clara Williams
One Sheet: $1,900 - $3,000

BARGAIN, THE
(1923R - -) William S. Hart, Clara Williams
One Sheet: $150 - $300   *Re-release.*

BARGAIN, THE
(1931 - First National) Lewis Stone, Doris
Kenyon
One Sheet: $125 - $250

BARGEE, THE
(1964 - Warner-Pathe) Harry H. Corbett, Hugh
Griffith
One Sheet: $5 - $10

BARKER, THE
(1928 - Warner Bros.) Milton Sills, Betty
Compson
One Sheet: $250 - $500

BARKLEYS OF BROADWAY, THE
(1949 - MGM) Fred Astaire, Ginger Rogers
One Sheet: $200 - $400   *Dance
musical.*

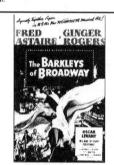

One Sheet

BARN DANCE
(1929 - Columbia) Mickey Mouse
One Sheet: $19,000 - $30,000   *Cartoon.
Cartoon Movie Posters #31.*

BARN OF THE NAKED DEAD
(1976 - Twin World) Andrew Prine
One Sheet: $15 - $25   *AKA:
TERROR CIRCUS.*

BARNACLE BILL
(1935 - Butcher) Archie Pitt, Joan Gardner
One Sheet: $150 - $300

BARNACLE BILL
(1941 - MGM) Wallace Beery, Marjorie Main,
Leo Carrillo
One Sheet: $125 - $250

BARNEY BEAR'S POLAR PEST
(1944 - MGM) Barney Bear
One Sheet: $500 - $800   *Cartoon.
Cartoon Movie Posters #257.*

BARNEY BEAR'S VICTORY GARDEN
(1942 - MGM) Barney Bear
One Sheet: $300 - $700   *Cartoon.
Cartoon Movie Posters #259.*

BARNEY GOOGLE AND SPARK PLUG
(1929 - FBO) -
One Sheet: $500 - $800

BARNEY'S HUNGRY COUSIN
(1953 - MGM) Barney Bear
One Sheet: $200 - $400   *Cartoon. Full
color stone litho.*

BARNSDALE'S MOVING PICTURES
(1905 - Barnsdale) -
One Sheet: $150 - $300

BARNUM WAS RIGHT
(1929 - Universal) Glenn Tryon, Merna
Kennedy
One Sheet: $250 - $600

BARNYARD FOLLIES
(1940 - Republic) Mary Lee, Rufe Davis
One Sheet: $75 - $125

BARNYARD OLYMPICS
(1932 - Columbia) Mickey Mouse
One Sheet: $16,000 - $25,000   *Cartoon.
Duotone. The Disney Poster, pg. 19.*

BARON, THE
(197? - -) Calvin Lockhart, Richard Lynch
One Sheet: $3 - $5

BARON BLOOD
(1972 - AIP) Elke Sommer, Joseph Cotten
One Sheet: $15 - $25

BARON OF ARIZONA, THE
(1950 - Lippert) Vincent Price, Ellen Drew
One Sheet: $30 - $50

BARONESS AND THE BUTLER, THE
(1938 - 20th Century Fox) Annabella, William
Powell
One Sheet: $150 - $300

BARQUERO
(1970 - United Artists) Lee Van Cleef, Warren
Oates
One Sheet: $7 - $15

BARRACUDA
(1978 - Republic) Wayne David Crawford,
Roberta Leighton
One Sheet: $5 - $10

BARRETTS OF WIMPOLE STREET, THE
(1934 - MGM) Norma Shearer, Fredric March
One Sheet: $800 - $1,500   *Price is for
either style.*

BARRETTS OF WIMPOLE STREET, THE
(1956 - MGM) Jennifer Jones, John Gielgud
One Sheet: $40 - $75

BARRICADE
(1939 - 20th Century Fox) Alice Faye, Warner
Baxter
One Sheet: $200 - $400

BARRICADE
(1950 - Warner Bros.) Dane Clark, Raymond
Massey
One Sheet: $15 - $25

BARRIER, THE
(1937 - Paramount) Leo Carillo, Jean Parker
One Sheet: $125 - $250

BARRIER BETWEEN
(1925 - Monopole) Catherine Countiss, William
H. Tooker
One Sheet: $150 - $300

BARRY LYNDON
(1975 - Warner Bros.) Ryan O'Neal, Marisa
Berenson, Dir: S. Kubrick
One Sheet: $15 - $35

BARS OF HATE
(1936 - Victory) Regis Toomey, Sheila Terry
One Sheet: $75 - $150

BARTLEBY
(1972 - Maron) Paul Scofield, John McEnery
One Sheet: $5 - $10

BARTON FINK
(1991 - 20th Century Fox) John Turturro
One Sheet: $7 - $15

BARTON MYSTERY, THE
(1932 - Paramount) Ursula Jeans, Ellis Jeffreys
One Sheet: $150 - $300

BAR-Z BAD MEN
(1937 - Republic) Johnny Mack Brown, Lois
January
One Sheet: $100 - $200

Six Sheet

BASHFUL BACHELOR, THE
(1942 - RKO) Lum and Abner, ZaSu Pitts
One Sheet: $50 - $100

BASHFUL BACHELOR, THE
(1950R - RKO) Lum & Abner, ZaSu Pitts
One Sheet: $15 - $35   *Re-release.*

BASHFUL ELEPHANT, THE
(1962 - Allied Artists) Molly Mack, Helmut
Schmid
One Sheet: $5 - $10

BASHFUL WHIRLWIND, THE
(1927 - Mustang) Edmund Cobb
One Sheet: $150 - $300

BASIC INSTINCT
(1992 - TriStar) Michael Douglas, Sharon
Stone
One Sheet: $7 - $15

BASIC TRAINING
(1986 - Movie Store) Ann Dusenberry, Rhonda
Shear
One Sheet: $3 - $5

BASIN STREET REVUE
(1955 - Studio Films) Nat King Cole, Sara
Vaughan, Lionel Hampton
One Sheet: $250 - $500   *Black cast.
Big Band. Count Basie and his Band, Amos
Milburn and his Band.*

BASKET CASE
(1982 - Analysis) Kevin Van Hentryck, Terri
Susan Smith
One Sheet: $10 - $20

BASKET CASE 2
(1990 - -) Ken Van Hentryk
One Sheet: $7 - $15

BASKETBALL DIARIES, THE
(1995 - New Line) Leonardo Di Caprio, Bruno
Kirby, Mark Wahlberg
One Sheet: $5 - $10

BASKETBALL FIX, THE
(1951 - Realart) John Ireland, Vanessa Brown
One Sheet: $50 - $100   *Sports
(Basketball).*

BASQUIAT
(1996 - Miramax) David Bowie, Gary Oldman,
Dennis Hopper
One Sheet: $7 - $15

BAT, THE
(1926 - United Artists) Andre de Beranger,
Charles Herzinger
One Sheet: $6,500 - $10,000   *Graven
Images, pg. 29.*

BAT, THE
(1959 - Allied Artists) Vincent Price, Agnes
Moorehead
One Sheet: $75 - $125

BAT, THE
(1970R - Allied Artists) Vincent Price, Agnes
Moorehead
One Sheet: $15 - $30   *Re-release.*

BAT 21
(1988 - -) Gene Hackman, Danny Glover
One Sheet: $3 - $5

BAT PEOPLE, THE
(1974 - AIP) Stewart Moss, Marianne
McAndrew
One Sheet: $10 - $20   *AKA: IT
LIVES BY NIGHT.*

BAT WHISPERS, THE
(1930 - United Artists) Chester Morris, Una
Merkel
One Sheet: $600 - $1,000   *Graven
Images, pg. 50.*

BAT WHISPERS, THE
(1933R - Atlantic) Chester Morris, Una Merkel
One Sheet: $200 - $400   *Re-release.*

BATAAN
(1943 - MGM) Robert Taylor, George Murphy
One Sheet: $50 - $100

BATH DAY
(1946 - RKO/Disney) Minnie Mouse, Figaro
One Sheet: $800 - $1,500   *Cartoon.*

BATHING BEAUTY
(1944 - MGM) Red Skelton, Esther Williams

One Sheet: $75 - $175   *Sports Movie Posters #'s 325, 326.*

BATMAN, THE
(1943 - Columbia) Lewis Wilson, Douglas Croft
One Sheet: $1,300 - $2,000   *Serial. 15 Chapters. Graven Images, pg. 138.*

BATMAN, THE
(1954R - Columbia) Lewis Wilson, Douglas Croft
One Sheet: $75 - $150   *Re-release. Serial. 15 chapters.*

BATMAN
(1966 - 20th Century Fox) Adam West, Burt Ward
One Sheet: $100 - $200   *Based on the television series.*

One Sheet

BATMAN
(1989 - Warner Bros.) Michael Keaton, Jack Nicholson
One Sheet: $10 - $20   *Advance (glossy paper):$15-25.*

BATMAN AND ROBIN
(1949 - Columbia) Robert Lowery, John Duncan
One Sheet: $600 - $1,000   *Serial. 15 Chapters. Graven Images, pg. 138.*

BATMAN AND ROBIN
(1966R - Columbia) Robert Lowery, John Duncan
One Sheet: $50 - $100   *Serial. Re-release of first 8 chapters of 1949 serial.*

BATMAN FOREVER
(1995 - Warner Bros.) Val Kilmer, Jim Carrey, Tommy Lee Jones
One Sheet: $10 - $20   *Jim Carrey (Riddler style): $15-$25. Val Kilmer (Batman style):$12-$15. Chris O'Donnell (Robin style): $12-$15. Tommy Lee Jones (Two Face style): $12-$15. Nicole Kidman style: $15-$25.*

BATMAN: MASK OF THE PHANTASM
(1993 - Warner Bros.) Voices of: Mark Hamill, Kevin Conroy
One Sheet: $10 - $20   *Cartoon.*

BATMAN RETURNS
(1992 - Warner Bros.) Michael Keaton, Danny DeVito, Michelle Pfeiffer
One Sheet: $10 - $20   *Characters Set:$80-125. Advance(Style A, B, C, or D):$10-15.*

BATS IN THE BELFRY
(1942 - MGM) -
One Sheet: $600 - $1,000   *Cartoon. Cartoon Movie Posters #247.*

BATTERIES NOT INCLUDED
(1987 - Universal) Hume Cronyn, Jessica Tandy
One Sheet: $3 - $5

BATTLE, THE
(1934 - United Artists) Charles Boyer, John Loder
One Sheet: $200 - $400

BATTLE AT APACHE PASS, THE
(1952 - Universal) John Lund, Jeff Chandler
One Sheet: $15 - $30

BATTLE AT BLOODY BEACH
(1961 - 20th Century Fox) Audie Murphy, Gary Crosby
One Sheet: $20 - $40

BATTLE BENEATH THE EARTH
(1968 - MGM) Kerwin Matthews, Viviane Ventura
One Sheet: $15 - $30

BATTLE BENEATH THE SEA
(1968 - MGM) Kerwin Mathews, Vivian Ventura
One Sheet: $15 - $30

BATTLE BEYOND THE STARS
(1980 - New World) Richard Thomas, Robert Vaughn
One Sheet: $5 - $10

BATTLE BEYOND THE SUN
(1963 - AIP) Edd Perry, Arla Powell
One Sheet: $50 - $100

BATTLE CIRCUS
(1953 - MGM) Humphrey Bogart, June Allyson
One Sheet: $50 - $100

BATTLE CRY
(1954 - Warner Bros.) Van Heflin, Aldo Ray
One Sheet: $10 - $20

BATTLE CRY OF CHINA
(1942 - -) WW II Documentary
One Sheet: $40 - $75

BATTLE CRY OF PEACE, THE
(1915 - Vitagraph) Charles Richman, L. Rogers Lytton
One Sheet: $700 - $1,200

BATTLE FLAME
(1959 - Allied Artists) Scott Brady, Robert Blake
One Sheet: $5 - $10

BATTLE FOR THE PLANET OF THE APES, THE
(1973 - 20th Century Fox) Roddy McDowall, Claude Akins
One Sheet: $15 - $35

One Sheet

BATTLE HELL
(1956 - DCA) Richard Todd, Akim Tamiroff
One Sheet: $15 - $30

BATTLE HYMN
(1957 - Universal) Rock Hudson, Martha Hyer
One Sheet: $30 - $50

BATTLE IN OUTER SPACE
(1960 - Columbia) Ryo Ikebe, Kyoko Anzai
One Sheet: $50 - $100

BATTLE OF ALGIERS, THE
(1968 - Magna) Yacef Saadi, Jean Martin
One Sheet: $10 - $20

BATTLE OF BLOOD ISLAND
(1960 - Film Group) Richard Devon, Ron Kennedy
One Sheet: $7 - $15

BATTLE OF BRITAIN, THE
(1969 - United Artists) Laurence Olivier, Ralph Richardson, Michael Caine
One Sheet: $10 - $20

BATTLE OF BROADWAY
(1938 - 20th Century Fox) Victor McLaglen, Louise Novick
One Sheet: $150 - $300

BATTLE OF EIDERBRUSH GULCH, THE
(1913 - AB) -
One Sheet: $250 - $600

BATTLE OF GALLIPOLI
(1931 - Capitol) Carl Harbord
One Sheet: $125 - $250   *AKA: TELL ENGLAND.*

BATTLE OF GREED
(1937 - Crescent) Tom Keene, Gwynne

BATTLE OF LOVE'S RETURN, THE
(1971 - Standard) Lloyd Kaufman
One Sheet: $5 - $10

BATTLE OF NERETVA, THE
(1971 - AIP) Yul Brynner, Orson Welles
One Sheet: $15 - $35

BATTLE OF PARIS, THE
(1929 - Paramount) Gertrude Lawrence, Charles Ruggles
One Sheet: $250 - $500

BATTLE OF ROGUE RIVER
(1954 - Columbia) George Montgomery, Richard Denning
One Sheet: $10 - $20

BATTLE OF RUSSIA, THE
(1943 - 20th Century Fox) -
One Sheet: $100 - $200   *Documentary.*

BATTLE OF THE AMAZONS
(1973 - AIP) Lincoln Tate, Lucretia Love
One Sheet: $10 - $20

BATTLE OF THE BULGE
(1966 - Warner Brothers) Henry Fonda, Robert Shaw
One Sheet: $15 - $30   *One Sheet (Cinerama style):$75-$150.*

BATTLE OF THE CENTURY, THE
(1927 - MGM) Laurel & Hardy
One Sheet: $3,500 - $5,000

BATTLE OF THE CORAL SEA
(1959 - Columbia) Cliff Robertson, Gia Scala
One Sheet: $5 - $10

BATTLE OF THE DRAG RACERS
(1966 - Warner Bros.) Road Runner, Speedy Gonzalez
One Sheet: $75 - $125   *Cartoon.*

BATTLE OF THE RIVER PLATE
(1956 - Rank) John Gregson, Peter Finch
One Sheet: $30 - $50   *AKA: PURSUIT OFTHE GRAF SPEE.*

BATTLE OF THE SEXES
(1914 - Mutual) Lillian Gish, Owen Moore, Dir: D. W. Griffith
One Sheet: $1,600 - $2,500

BATTLE OF THE SEXES
(1928 - United Artists) Jean Hersholt, Phyllis Haver, Dir: D.W. Griffith
One Sheet: $800 - $1,500

BATTLE OF THE SEXES
(1960 - Continental) Peter Sellers, Constance Cummings
One Sheet: $15 - $25

BATTLE OF THE VILLA FIORITA, THE
(1965 - Warner Bros.) Maureen O'Hara, Rossanno Brazzi
One Sheet: $5 - $10

BATTLE OF THE WORLDS
(1963 - Ultra) Claude Rains
One Sheet: $30 - $50

BATTLE STATIONS
(1955 - Columbia) John Lund, William Bendix
One Sheet: $7 - $15

BATTLE STRIPE
(1957 - -) Marlon Brando
One Sheet: $7 - $15   *Re-titled re-issue of "The Men".*

BATTLE TAXI
(1954 - United Artists) Sterling Hayden, Arthur Franz
One Sheet: $10 - $20

BATTLE ZONE
(1952 - Allied Artists) John Hodiak, Linda Christian
One Sheet: $10 - $20

BATTLEAXE, THE
(1962 - Danzinger) Jill Ireland, Francis Matthews
One Sheet: $7 - $15

BATTLEGROUND
(1949 - MGM) Van Johnson, John Hodiak, Ricardo Montalban

Shipman
One Sheet: $100 - $200

One Sheet: $50 - $100

BATTLES OF CHIEF PONTIAC
(1952 - Realart) Lon Chaney, Lex Barker
One Sheet: $15 - $30

BATTLESHIP POTEMKIN, THE
(1925 - -) Goskino, A. Antonov, Dir: Sergei Eisenstein
One Sheet: $600 - $1,000   *Russian. Original Title: Bronenosets Potemkin. Judged best film ever made in 1948, 1958. 1930's re-issueexists.*

BATTLESTAR GALACTICA
(1978 - Universal) Lorne Greene, Richard Hatch
One Sheet: $15 - $25

BATTLETRUCK
(1982 - -) See WARLORDS OF THE 21ST CENTURY for prices

BATTLING BUCKAROO
(1932 - Kent) Lane Chandler, Doris Hill
One Sheet: $125 - $250   *AKA: HIS LAST ADVENTURE.*

BATTLING BUTLER
(1926 - MGM) Buster Keaton, Sally O'Neil
One Sheet: $3,500 - $5,000   *Sports (Boxing). Sports Movie Posters #121.*

BATTLING MARSHALL
(1950 - Astor) Sunset Carson
One Sheet: $30 - $50

BATTLING WITH BUFFALO BILL
(1931 - Universal) Tom Tyler, Rex Bell
One Sheet: $300 - $700

BATTY BASEBALL
(1944 - MGM) -
One Sheet: $800 - $1,500   *Cartoon. Sports (Baseball). Cartoon Movie Posters #291. Sports Movie Posters #43.*

BAWDY ADVENTURES OF TOM JONES, THE
(1976 - Universal) Nicky Henson, Joan Collins
One Sheet: $5 - $10

BAXTER!
(1973 - National General) Scott Jacoby, Patricia Neal, Britt Eckland
One Sheet: $3 - $5

BAY BOY
(1984 - Orion) Kiefer Sutherland, Liv Ullmann
One Sheet: $3 - $5

BAY OF SAINT MICHEL, THE
(1963 - Rank) Keenan Wynn, Mai Zetterling
One Sheet: $5 - $10

BAYOU
(1957 - United Artists) Peter Graves, Lita Milan
One Sheet: $15 - $30

BE BIG
(1930 - -) Laurel & Hardy
One Sheet: $3,500 - $5,000

BE MINE TONIGHT
(1933 - Gaumont) Jan Kiepura, Sonnie Hale
One Sheet: $150 - $300

BE MY GUEST
(1965 - Three Kings) David Hemmings, Stephen Marriot

BE PATIENT, PATIENT
(1943 - Columbia) Fox & Crow
One Sheet: $350 - $750   *Cartoon. Full color poster with scene inset.*

BE YOURSELF
(1930 - United Artists) Fanny Brice, Robert Armstrong
One Sheet: $250 - $500

BEACH BALL
(1965 - Paramount) Edd Byrnes, Chris Noel, The Supremes
One Sheet: $30 - $50   *Rock 'n' Roll. Surfing.*

BEACH BLANKET BINGO
(1965 - AIP) Frankie Avalon, Annette Funicello
One Sheet: $50 - $100   *Rock 'n' Roll. Advance:$75-$125.*

BEACH GIRLS
(1982 - Crown) Debra Blee, Jeana Tomasina

One Sheet: $5 - $10

BEACH GIRLS AND THE MONSTER, THE
(1965 - U.S.) Jon Hall, Sue Casey, Walker
Edmiston
One Sheet: $40 - $75

BEACH PARTY
(1963 - AIP) Annette Funicello, Frankie Avalon
One Sheet: $75 - $150   *Rock 'n' Roll.*
Surfing. First Rock 'n' Roll surfing film.

Lobby Card

BEACH PICNIC
(1939 - RKO Radio Pictures) Donald Duck
One Sheet: $4,000 - $6,000   *Cartoon.*
Cartoon Movie Posters #155.

BEACH RED
(1967 - United Artists) Cornel Wilde, Rip Torn
One Sheet: $5 - $10

BEACHCOMBER, THE
(1939 - Paramount) Charles Laughton, Elsa
Lanchester
One Sheet: $125 - $250

BEACHCOMBER, THE
(1954 - United Artists) Glynis Johns, Robert
Newton
One Sheet: $15 - $25

BEACHES
(1988 - Buena Vista) Bette Midler, Barbara
Hershey
One Sheet: $15 - $25

BEACHHEAD
(1953 - United Artists) Tony Curtis, Frank
Lovejoy
One Sheet: $15 - $30

BEAR, THE
(1963 - Embassy) Renato Raschel
One Sheet: $15 - $25   *French.*

BEAR, THE
(1984 - -) Gary Busey, Cynthia Leake
One Sheet: $7 - $15   *Sports*
(Football). Tribute to Paul "Bear" Bryant.

BEAR, THE
(1989 - Tri-Star) Bart, Douce
One Sheet: $3 - $5

BEAR AND THE BEAVERS
(1942 - MGM) Barney Bear
One Sheet: $500 - $800   *Cartoon.*
Cartoon Movie Posters #254.

BEAR AND THE DOLL, THE
(1971 - Paramount) Brigitte Bardot, Jean Pierre
Cassel
One Sheet: $15 - $25

BEAR AND THE DOLL, THE
(1989 - -) -
One Sheet: $3 - $5

BEAR ISLAND
(1979 - Columbia) Donald Sutherland, Vanessa
Redgrave
One Sheet: $5 - $10

BEAR SHOOTERS
(1952R - Monogram) Little Rascals
One Sheet: $75 - $125   *Re-release.*

BEAR THAT COULDN'T SLEEP, THE
(1939 - MGM) Barney Bear
One Sheet: $700 - $1,200   *Cartoon.*
Cartoon Movie Posters #252.

BEARS AND BEES
(1932 - A Walt Disney Silly Symphony) Mickey
Mouse Presents

One Sheet: $10,000 - $15,000   *Cartoon.*
Cartoon Movie Posters #68.

BEARS AND I, THE
(1974 - Buena Vista) Patrick Wayne, Chief Dan
George
One Sheet: $5 - $10

BEAST, THE
(1916 - William Fox) George Walsh, Anna
Luther, Alan Hale
One Sheet: $250 - $500

BEAST, THE
(1988 - -) Jason Patric, Steven Bauer
One Sheet: $3 - $5

BEAST FROM 20,000 FATHOMS, THE
(1953 - Warner Bros.) Paul Christian, Paula
Raymond
One Sheet: $250 - $600   *Graven*
Images, pg. 164.

BEAST FROM THE HAUNTED CAVE
(1959 - Film Group) Michael Forest, Sheila
Carol
One Sheet: $100 - $200

BEAST IN THE CELLAR, THE
(1971 - Cannon) Beryl Reid, Flora Robson
One Sheet: $7 - $15

BEAST MUST DIE, THE
(1974 - Cinerama) Peter Cushing, Cal Lockhart
One Sheet: $15 - $30

BEAST OF BLOOD
(1970 - Hemisphere) John Ashley, Celeste
Yarnell
One Sheet: $15 - $30   *AKA:*
RETURN TO THE HORRORS OF BLOOD
ISLAND.

BEAST OF BLOOD/CURSE OF THE VAMPIRES
COMBO
(1970 - Hemisphere) -
One Sheet: $15 - $30   *Double*
feature poster. Full color.

BEAST OF BORNEO, THE
(1934 - DuWorld) -
One Sheet: $100 - $200

BEAST OF BUDAPEST, THE
(1957 - Allied Artists) Gerald Milton, John Hoyt
One Sheet: $10 - $20

BEAST OF HOLLOW MOUNTAIN, THE
(1956 - United Artists) Guy Madison, Patricia
Medina
One Sheet: $75 - $150

BEAST OF THE CITY, THE
(1932 - MGM) Walter Huston, Jean Harlow
One Sheet: $1,300 - $2,000

BEAST OF THE YELLOW NIGHT/CREATURE
WITH THE BLUE HAND
(1971 - New World) -
One Sheet: $15 - $30   *Double*
feature poster.

BEAST OF YUCCA FLATS, THE
(1961 - Crown) Douglas Mellor, Tor Johnson
One Sheet: $40 - $75

BEAST WITH A MILLION EYES, THE
(1955 - AIP) Paul Birch, Lorna Thayer
One Sheet: $250 - $600   *Graven*
Images, pg. 4.

BEAST WITH FIVE FINGERS, THE
(1947 - Warner Bros.) Robert Alda, Andrea
King, Peter Lorre
One Sheet: $150 - $300   *Graven*
Images, pg. 131.

BEAST WITHIN
(1982 - -) Ronny Cox, Bibi Besch
One Sheet: $3 - $5

BEASTMASTER, THE
(1982 - MGM) Marc Singer, Tanya Roberts, Rip
Torn
One Sheet: $7 - $15

BEASTS OF BERLIN
(1939 - PDC) Roland Drew, Steffi Duna
One Sheet: $125 - $250   *AKA:*
HITLERBEAST OF BERLIN.

BEASTS OF MARSEILLES, THE
(1959 - Lopert) Stephen Boyd, James
Robertson Justice

One Sheet: $15 - $30

BEASTS OF PARADISE
(1923 - Universal) Eileen Sedgwick
One Sheet: $150 - $300   *Serial. 15*
Chapters.

BEAT GENERATION, THE
(1959 - MGM) Steve Cochran, Mamie Van
Doren, Louis Armstrong
One Sheet: $75 - $125   *AKA: THIS*
REBEL AGE.

BEAT STREET
(1984 - Orion) Rae Dawn Chong, Guy Davis
One Sheet: $3 - $5

BEAT THE BAND
(1947 - RKO) Frances Langford, Ralph
Edwards, Gene Krupa
One Sheet: $30 - $60

BEAT THE DEVIL
(1953 - United Artists) Humphrey Bogart,
Jennifer Jones, Gina Lollobrigida
One Sheet: $75 - $150

BEATLES COME TO TOWN, THE
(196? - -) The Beatles
One Sheet: $200 - $400   *Rock 'n' Roll.*
Pre-American Tour Movie Clips.

BEATNIKS, THE
(1959 - Barjul International) Tony Travis, Peter
Breck
One Sheet: $40 - $75

BEATSVILLE
(1959 - Allied Artists) Gregg Palmer, Kathleen
Crowley
One Sheet: $40 - $75

BEAU BANDIT
(1930 - RKO) Rod LaRocque, Doris Kenyon
One Sheet: $200 - $400

BEAU BRUMMEL
(1924 - Warner Bros.) John Barrymore
One Sheet: $1,600 - $2,500

BEAU BRUMMEL
(1954 - MGM) Stewart Granger, Elizabeth
Taylor
One Sheet: $50 - $100

BEAU BRUMMEL
(1962R - MGM) Stewart Granger, Elizabeth
Taylor
One Sheet: $15 - $25   *Re-release.*

BEAU GESTE
(1927 - Paramount) Ronald Colman
One Sheet: $1,300 - $2,000

BEAU GESTE
(1939 - Paramount) Gary Cooper, Ray Milland,
Robert Preston
One Sheet: $1,600 - $2,500   *One*
Sheet(Style with all three stars):$2000-$3000.

One Sheet

BEAU GESTE
(1950R - Paramount) Gary Cooper, Ray
Milland, Robert Preston
One Sheet: $100 - $200   *Re-release.*

BEAU GESTE
(1966 - Universal) Guy Stockwell, Doug
McClure
One Sheet: $7 - $15

BEAU HUNKS
(1931 - MGM) Laurel & Hardy
One Sheet: $4,000 - $6,000

BEAU IDEAL

(1930 - RKO) Loretta Young, Irene Rich
One Sheet: $250 - $500

BEAU JAMES
(1956 - Paramount) Bob Hope, Vera Miles
One Sheet: $50 - $100

BEAU REVEL
(1921 - Paramount) Florence Vidor, Lloyd
Hughes, Lewis S. Stone
One Sheet: $800 - $1,500

BEAU SABREUR
(1928 - Paramount) Gary Cooper, Evelyn Brent
One Sheet: $800 - $1,500

BEAUTICIAN AND THE BEAST
(1997 - Paramount) Fran Drescher, Timothy
Dalton
One Sheet: $7 - $15

BEAUTIES OF THE NIGHT
(1953 - United Artists) Gerard Philipe, Martine
Carol
One Sheet: $30 - $50

BEAUTIFUL AND THE DAMNED, THE
(1922 - Warner Bros.) Marie Prevost
One Sheet: $350 - $750

BEAUTIFUL BLONDE FROM BASHFUL BEND,
THE
(1949 - 20th Century Fox) Betty Grable, Cesar
Romero
One Sheet: $75 - $150

BEAUTIFUL BUT BROKE
(1944 - Columbia) Joan Davis, Jane Frazee
One Sheet: $75 - $125

BEAUTIFUL BUT DANGEROUS
(1954 - RKO) Robert Mitchum, Jean Simmons
One Sheet: $75 - $150   *AKA: SHE*
COULDN'T SAY NO.

BEAUTIFUL BUT DANGEROUS
(1958 - 20th Century Fox) Gina Lollobrigida,
Vittorio Gassman
One Sheet: $15 - $30

BEAUTIFUL BUT DUMB
(1928 - Tiffany-Stahl) Patsy Ruth Miller,
Charles Byer
One Sheet: $150 - $300

BEAUTIFUL CHEAT, THE
(1926 - Universal) Laura La Plante, Harry
Myers
One Sheet: $250 - $500

BEAUTIFUL CHEAT, THE
(1945 - Universal) Noah Beery Jr, Bonita
Granville
One Sheet: $50 - $100

BEAUTIFUL CITY, THE
(1925 - First National) Richard Barthelmess,
Dorothy Gish, William Powell
One Sheet: $800 - $1,500

BEAUTIFUL GIRLS
(1996 - Miramax) Timothy Hutton, Matt Dillon,
Uma Thurman
One Sheet: $5 - $10

BEAUTIFUL STRANGER
(1954 - British Lion) Ginger Rogers, Stanley
Baker
One Sheet: $150 - $300

BEAUTY AND THE BANDIT
(1946 - Monogram) Gilbert Roland, Ramsey
Ames
One Sheet: $40 - $75

BEAUTY AND THE BARGE
(1937 - Twickenham) Gordon Harker, Judy
Gunn
One Sheet: $50 - $100

BEAUTY AND THE BEAST
(1947 - Lopert) Jean Marais, Josette Day
One Sheet: $50 - $100   *Price is for*
American release poster by Lopert. See listing for
LA BELLE ET LA BETE for original French
release poster prices.

BEAUTY AND THE BEAST
(1963 - United Artists) Joyce Taylor, Mark
Damon
One Sheet: $30 - $50

BEAUTY AND THE BEAST
(1991 - Disney) Belle, Gaston, The Beast

One Sheet: $40 - $75   *Cartoon.*
Advance: $65-$100. *The Disney Poster, pg. 92-93.*

BEAUTY AND THE BOSS
(1932 - Warner Bros.) Warren William, Marian Marsh
One Sheet: $100 - $200

BEAUTY AND THE BUS
(1933 - MGM) Thelma Todd, Patsy Kelly
One Sheet: $250 - $500

BEAUTY FOR SALE
(1933 - MGM) Madge Evans, Otto Kruger
One Sheet: $100 - $200

BEAUTY FOR THE ASKING
(1939 - RKO) Lucille Ball, Donald Woods
One Sheet: $125 - $250

BEAUTY ON PARADE
(1950 - Columbia) Robert Hutton, Lola Albright
One Sheet: $30 - $50

BEAUTY PARLOR
(1932 - Chesterfield) Barbara Kent, Joyce Compton
One Sheet: $100 - $200

BEAUTY'S WORTH
(1922 - -) Marion Davies, Forrest Stanley
One Sheet: $500 - $900

BEAUX AND ERRORS
(1938 - RKO) Edgar Kennedy
One Sheet: $150 - $300

BEAVIS AND BUTTHEAD DO AMERICA
(1996 - Paramount) -
One Sheet: $7 - $15   *Cartoon.*

30 x 40 (Advance)

BEBE'S KIDS
(1992 - Paramount) -
One Sheet: $5 - $10   *Cartoon.*

BEBO'S GIRL
(1964 - Reade-Sterling) Claudia Cardinale, George Chakiris
One Sheet: $5 - $10

BECAUSE OF EVE
(1948 - International) Joseph Crehan, Wanda McKay
One Sheet: $10 - $20

BECAUSE OF HIM
(1946 - Universal) Deanna Durbin, Franchot Tone
One Sheet: $75 - $150

BECAUSE OF YOU
(1952 - Universal) Loretta Young, Jeff Chandler
One Sheet: $40 - $75

BECAUSE THEY'RE YOUNG
(1960 - Columbia) Dick Clark, Michael Callan
One Sheet: $30 - $50

BECAUSE YOU'RE MINE
(1952 - MGM) Mario Lanza, Doretta Morrow
One Sheet: $15 - $25

BECKET
(1964 - Paramount) Richard Burton, Peter O'Toole
One Sheet: $40 - $75

BECKY SHARP
(1935 - Pioneer) Miriam Hopkins, Frances Dee
One Sheet: $1,300 - $2,000   *First feature utilizing three-color Technicolor.*

BED AND BREAKFAST
(1930 - Gaumont) Jane Baxter, Richard Cooper
One Sheet: $125 - $250

BED AND BREAKFAST
(1936 - Coronel) Barry Lupino, Mabel Poulton
One Sheet: $75 - $150

BED OF ROSES
(1933 - RKO) Constance Bennett, Joel McCrea
One Sheet: $350 - $750

BED OF ROSES
(1996 - New Line) Christian Slater, Mary Stuart Masterson
One Sheet: $5 - $12

BEDAZZLED
(1967 - 20th Century Fox) Peter Cook, Raquel Welch
One Sheet: $40 - $75

BEDELIA
(1947 - Eagle-Lion) Margaret Lockwood, Ian Hunter
One Sheet: $40 - $75

BEDEVILLED
(1955 - MGM) Anne Baxter, Steve Forrest
One Sheet: $20 - $40

BEDFORD INCIDENT, THE
(1965 - Columbia) Richard Widmark, Sidney Poitier
One Sheet: $10 - $20

BEDKNOBS AND BROOMSTICKS
(1971 - Buena Vista/Disney) Angela Lansbury, David Tomlinson
One Sheet: $15 - $30

BEDLAM
(1946 - RKO) Boris Karloff, Anna Lee
One Sheet: $150 - $300   *Graven Images, pg. 124.*

BEDLAM IN PARADISE
(1955 - Columbia) The Three Stooges (Shemp)
One Sheet: $150 - $300   *Comedy short. Duotone. Remake of HEAVENLY DAZE.*

BEDROOM BLUNDER, A
(1919 - -) Charles Murray, Mary Thurman
One Sheet: $250 - $500

BEDROOM EYES
(1984 - Pan) Kenneth Gilman
One Sheet: $5 - $10

BEDROOM WINDOW, THE
(1924 - Paramount) Ricardo Cortez, May McAvoy
One Sheet: $300 - $700

BEDROOM WINDOW, THE
(1986 - -) Steve Guttenberg, Elizabeth McGovern
One Sheet: $5 - $10

BEDSIDE
(1934 - First National) Warren William, Jean Muir
One Sheet: $100 - $200

BEDSIDE MANNER
(1945 - United Artists) Ruth Hussey, John Carroll
One Sheet: $40 - $75

BED-SITTING ROOM, THE
(1969 - United Artists) Rita Tushingham, Ralph Richardson, Peter Cook
One Sheet: $3 - $5

BEDTIME FOR BONZO
(1951 - Universal) Ronald Reagan, Diana Lynn
One Sheet: $150 - $300

BEDTIME STORY, A
(1933 - Paramount) Maurice Chevalier, Helen Twelvetrees
One Sheet: $800 - $1,500

BEDTIME STORY
(1938 - Grand National) Jac Livesey, Lesley Wareing
One Sheet: $100 - $200

BEDTIME STORY
(1941 - Columbia) Fredric March, Loretta Young
One Sheet: $75 - $150

BEDTIME STORY
(1964 - Universal) Marlon Brando, David Niven
One Sheet: $20 - $40

BEE AT THE BEACH
(1950 - RKO/Disney) Donald Duck
One Sheet: $500 - $900   *Cartoon.*

BEEN DOWN SO LONG IT LOOKS LIKE UP TO ME
(1971 - Paramount) Barry Primus, Linda DeCoff
One Sheet: $5 - $10

BEER AND PRETZELS
(1933 - MGM) Ted Healy and His Stooges (Moe, Larry & Curly)
One Sheet: $10,000 - $15,000   *Comedy musical short.*

BEER BARREL POLECATS
(1946 - Columbia) The Three Stooges (Curly)
One Sheet: $2,500 - $4,000   *Comedy short. Duotone.*

BEES, THE
(1978 - New World) John Saxon, Angel Tompkins
One Sheet: $5 - $10

BEES IN PARADISE
(1944 - Gainsborough) Peter Graves, Anne Shelton
One Sheet: $50 - $100

BEETHOVEN: STORY OF A DOG
(1992 - Universal) Charles Grodin
One Sheet: $3 - $5

BEETHOVEN'S 2ND
(1993 - Universal) Charles Grodin, Bonnie Hunt
One Sheet: $3 - $5

BEETLEJUICE
(1988 - Warner Bros.) Michael Keaton, Alec Baldwin, Gina Davis
One Sheet: $15 - $30

BEEZY BEAR
(1955 - RKO/Disney) Donald Duck and Humphrey Bear
One Sheet: $250 - $600   *Cartoon. Full color.*

BEFORE AND AFTER
(1996 - Hollywood/Buena Vista) Meryl Streep, Liam Neeson
One Sheet: $3 - $5

BEFORE DAWN
(1933 - RKO) Stuart Erwin, Dorothy Wilson
One Sheet: $150 - $300

BEFORE I HANG
(1940 - Columbia) Boris Karloff, Evelyn Keyes
One Sheet: $150 - $300   *Graven Images, pg. 130.*

BEFORE MIDNIGHT
(1933 - Columbia) Ralph Bellamy, June Collyer
One Sheet: $150 - $300

BEFORE MORNING
(1933 - Stage and Screen/Greenblatt) Leo Carillo, Lora Baxter
One Sheet: $100 - $200

BEFORE SUNRISE
(1995 - Columbia) Ethan Hawke, Julie Delpy
One Sheet: $10 - $20

BEFORE THE RAIN
(1995 - Gramercy) Katrin Cartlidge, Rade Serbedzija
One Sheet: $5 - $10

BEFORE WINTER COMES
(1969 - Columbia) David Niven, Topol, Anna Karina, John Hurt
One Sheet: $3 - $5

BEG, BORROW, OR STEAL
(1937 - MGM) Frank Morgan, Florence Rice, John Beal
One Sheet: $75 - $150

BEGGAR, THE
(1927 - Paramount) -
One Sheet: $250 - $500

BEGGAR OF CAWNPORE
(192? - Triangle) Bessie Love
One Sheet: $250 - $500

BEGGAR ON HORSEBACK
(1925 - Famous Players) Edward Everett Horton, Esther Ralston
One Sheet: $300 - $700

BEGGAR PRINCE, THE
(1920 - Haworth) Sessue Hayakawa
One Sheet: $800 - $1,500

BEGGAR STUDENT, THE
(1931 - Amalgamated) Shirley Dale
One Sheet: $75 - $150

BEGGAR'S HOLIDAY
(1932 - Tower Productions) Hardie Albright, J. Farrell MacDonald
One Sheet: $200 - $400

BEGGAR'S OPERA, THE
(1954 - Warner Bros.) Laurence Olivier, Stanley Holloway
One Sheet: $50 - $100

BEGGARS IN ERMINE
(1934 - Monogram) Lionel Atwill, Betty Furness
One Sheet: $75 - $150

BEGGARS OF LIFE
(1928 - Paramount) Louise Brooks, Wallace Beery
One Sheet: $1,600 - $2,500

BEGINNING OF THE END
(1957 - Republic) Peter Graves, Peggie Castle
One Sheet: $150 - $350   *Graven Images, pg. 169.*

BEGINNING OR THE END, THE
(1947 - MGM) Brian Donlevy, Robert Walker, Tom Drake
One Sheet: $50 - $100

BEGUILED, THE
(1971 - Universal) Clint Eastwood, Geraldine Page
One Sheet: $15 - $25

BEHAVE YOURSELF!
(1951 - RKO) Farley Granger, Shelley Winters
One Sheet: $75 - $150   *Vargas art.*

BEHEMOTH, THE SEA MONSTER
(1959 - Eros) Gene Evans, Andre Morell
One Sheet: $50 - $100   *AKA: THE GIANT BEHEMOTH.*

BEHIND CITY LIGHTS
(1945 - Republic) Lynne Roberts, William Terry
One Sheet: $75 - $125

BEHIND GREEN LIGHTS
(1946 - 20th Century Fox) Carole Landis, William Gargan
One Sheet: $75 - $125

BEHIND JURY DOORS
(1933 - Mayfair) Helen Chandler, William Collier, Jr.
One Sheet: $100 - $200

BEHIND LOCKED DOORS
(1948 - Eagle-Lion) Lucille Bremer, Richard Carlson
One Sheet: $30 - $50

BEHIND OFFICE DOORS
(1931 - RKO) Mary Astor, Ricardo Cortez
One Sheet: $250 - $500

BEHIND PRISON GATES
(1939 - Columbia) Brian Donlevy, Jacqueline Wells
One Sheet: $125 - $250

BEHIND PRISON WALLS
(1943 - PRC) Alan Baxter, Gertrude Michael
One Sheet: $40 - $75

BEHIND SOUTHERN LINES
(1951 - Monogram) Guy Madison, Andy Devine
One Sheet: $30 - $50

BEHIND STONE WALLS
(1932 - Action) Priscilla Dean, Robert Elliott
One Sheet: $100 - $200

BEHIND THAT CURTAIN
(1929 - Fox) Warner Baxter, Lois Moran, E. L. Parks (Chan)
One Sheet: $2,200 - $3,500   *Boris Karloff's first sound film (bit part); First Charlie Chan sound film (Chan cameo).*

BEHIND THE EIGHT BALL
(1942 - Universal) Ritz Brothers, Carol Bruce
One Sheet: $100 - $200

BEHIND THE EIGHT BALL
(1949R - Realart) Ritz Brothers, Carol Bruce

One Sheet: $40 - $75   *Re-release.*

BEHIND THE EVIDENCE
(1935 - Columbia) Norman Foster, Donald Cook
One Sheet: $125 - $250

BEHIND THE FRONT
(1926 - Famous Players) Wallace Beery, Raymond Hatten
One Sheet: $200 - $400

BEHIND THE GREEN LIGHTS
(1935 - Mascot) -
One Sheet: $100 - $200

BEHIND THE HEADLINES
(1937 - RKO) Lee Tracy, Diana Gibson
One Sheet: $125 - $250

BEHIND THE HIGH WALL
(1956 - Universal) Tom Tully, Sylvia Sidney
One Sheet: $30 - $50

BEHIND THE IRON MASK
(1977 - Columbia) Beau Bridges, Ursula Andress
One Sheet: $5 - $10   *AKA: THE FIFTH MUSKETEER.*

BEHIND THE MAKE-UP
(1930 - Paramount-Famous Lasky) Fay Wray, Kay Francis, William Powell
One Sheet: $250 - $500

BEHIND THE MASK
(1932 - Columbia) Jack Holt, Boris Karloff
One Sheet: $300 - $700   *Graven Images, pg. 55.*

BEHIND THE MASK
(1946 - Monogram) Kane Richmond, Barbara Reed
One Sheet: $75 - $125

BEHIND THE MASK
(1958 - GW) Michael Redgrave, Vanessa Redgrave
One Sheet: $15 - $25

BEHIND THE MIKE
(1937 - Universal) William Gargan, Judith Barrett
One Sheet: $100 - $200

BEHIND THE NEWS
(1940 - Republic) Lloyd Nolan, Doris Davenport
One Sheet: $75 - $125

BEHIND THE RISING SUN
(1943 - RKO) Margo, Tom Neal, Robert Ryan
One Sheet: $50 - $100

BEHIND THE SCREEN
(1916 - Mutual) Charlie Chaplin, Edna Purviance
One Sheet: $7,500 - $12,000

BEHIND THE SCREEN
(192?R - RKO) Charlie Chaplin, Edna Purviance
One Sheet: $500 - $800   *Re-release.*

BEHIND YOUR BACK
(1937 - Paramount) Jack Livesey, Dinah Sheridan
One Sheet: $100 - $200

BEHOLD A PALE HORSE
(1964 - Columbia) Gregory Peck, Anthony Quinn
One Sheet: $10 - $20

BEHOLD MY WIFE
(1920 - Paramount) Mabel Julienne Scott, Milton Sills
One Sheet: $200 - $400

BEHOLD MY WIFE
(1934 - Paramount) Sylvia Sidney, Gene Raymond
One Sheet: $600 - $1,000

BEING, THE
(1984 - Lorimar) Martin Landau, Jose Ferrer
One Sheet: $3 - $5

BEING HUMAN
(1993 - Warner Bros.) Robin Williams, John Turturro
One Sheet: $3 - $5

BEING THERE
(1979 - United Artists) Peter Sellers, Shirley

MacLaine
One Sheet: $15 - $35   *Academy Award:: Best Supporting Actor (Douglas). Review style:$5-$10. Academy Award Movie Posters #309.*

BEL AMI
(1947 - Levinson-Finney Enterprises) Olga Tschechova, Ilse Werner
One Sheet: $20 - $40

BELA LUGOSI MEETS A BROOKLYN GORILLA
(1952 - Realart) Bela Lugosi
One Sheet: $200 - $400

One Sheet

BELIEVE IN ME
(1971 - MGM) Michael Sarrazin, Jacqueline Bisset
One Sheet: $3 - $5

BELIEVE IT OR NOT
(1931 - Vitaphone) Robert L. Ripley
One Sheet: $700 - $1,200

BELIEVE ME, XANTIPPE
(1918 - Paramount) Wallace Reid, Ann Little
One Sheet: $250 - $500

BELIEVE THE HYPE
(1996 - Fox) -
One Sheet: $3 - $5

BELIEVERS, THE
(1987 - Orion) Martin Sheen, Helen Shaver
One Sheet: $3 - $5

BELIZAIRE THE CAJUN
(1986 - -) Armand Assante, Gail Youngs
One Sheet: $3 - $5

BELL, BOOK AND CANDLE
(1958 - Columbia) James Stewart, Kim Novak
One Sheet: $40 - $75

BELL BOTTOM GEORGE
(1944 - Columbia) George Formby
One Sheet: $30 - $50   *Comedy short. Duotone.*

BELL BOY, THE
(1917 - Famous Players-Lasky) Roscoe "Fatty" Arbuckle
One Sheet: $1,300 - $2,000

BELL FOR ADANO, A
(1945 - 20th Century Fox) Gene Tierney, John Hodiak
One Sheet: $75 - $150

BELL FROM HEAVEN
(1973 - -) -
One Sheet: $3 - $5

BELL JAR, THE
(1979 - Avco/Embassy) Julie Harris, Marilyn Hassett
One Sheet: $3 - $5

BELLA DONNA
(1934 - Gaumont) Conrad Veidt, Mary Ellis
One Sheet: $200 - $400

BELLAMY TRAIL, THE
(1929 - MGM) Leatrice Joy, Betty Bronson
One Sheet: $150 - $350

BELLBOY, THE
(1960 - Paramount) Jerry Lewis, Alex Gerry
One Sheet: $20 - $40

BELLE DE JOUR
(1968 - Allied Artists) Catherine Deneuve
One Sheet: $40 - $75

BELLE DE JOUR

(1995R - Miramax) Catherine Deneuve
One Sheet: $15 - $25   *Re-release.*

BELLE EPOQUE
(1993 - -) Jorge Sanz, Fernando Fernan Gomez
One Sheet: $5 - $10   *Spanish.*

BELLE LE GRAND
(1951 - Republic) John Carroll, Vera (Hruba) Ralston
One Sheet: $15 - $30

BELLE OF NEW YORK, THE
(1951 - MGM) Fred Astaire, Vera Ellen
One Sheet: $125 - $250

BELLE OF OLD MEXICO
(1950 - Republic) Estrelita, Robert Rockwell
One Sheet: $20 - $40

BELLE OF THE NINETIES
(1934 - Paramount) Mae West, Roger Pryor
One Sheet: $1,600 - $2,500

BELLE OF THE YUKON
(1944 - RKO) Dinah Shore, Gypsy Rose Lee
One Sheet: $50 - $100

BELLE SOMMERS
(1962 - Columbia) Polly Bergen, David Janssen
One Sheet: $5 - $10

BELLE STARR
(1941 - 20th Century Fox) Gene Tierney, Randolph Scott
One Sheet: $700 - $1,200   *Cowboy Movie Posters #265.*

BELLE STARR
(1948R - 20th Century Fox) Gene Tierney, Randolph Scott
One Sheet: $100 - $200   *Re-release.*

BELLE STARR'S DAUGHTER
(1948 - 20th Century Fox) Rod Cameron, Ruth Roman
One Sheet: $40 - $75

BELLE STARR'S DAUGHTER
(1955R - 20th Century Fox) Rod Cameron, Ruth Roman
One Sheet: $15 - $25   *Re-release.*

BELLES OF ST. CLEMENTS, THE
(1936 - Paramount) Evelyn Foster
One Sheet: $100 - $200

BELLES ON THEIR TOES
(1952 - 20th Century Fox) Myrna Loy, Jeanne Crain
One Sheet: $30 - $50

BELLHOP, THE
(1921 - Vitagraph) Larry Semon
One Sheet: $250 - $600

BELLS, THE
(1918 - Pathe) Frank Keenan
One Sheet: $500 - $800   *Based on the poem by Edgar Allan Poe.*

BELLS
(1981 - New World) Richard Chamberlain, John Houseman
One Sheet: $5 - $10   *AKA: MURDER BY PHONE.*

BELLS ARE RINGING
(1960 - MGM) Dean Martin, Judy Holliday
One Sheet: $15 - $30

BELLS GO DOWN, THE
(1943 - United Artists) James Mason, Tommy Trinder
One Sheet: $50 - $100

BELLS OF CAPISTRANO
(1942 - Republic) Gene Autry
One Sheet: $150 - $300

BELLS OF CORONADO
(1949 - Republic) Roy Rogers, Dale Evans
One Sheet: $100 - $200

BELLS OF CORONADO
(1956R - Republic) Roy Rogers, Dale Evans
One Sheet: $40 - $75   *Re-release.*

BELLS OF ROSARITA
(1945 - Republic) Roy Rogers, Gabby Hayes
One Sheet: $150 - $350

BELLS OF SAN ANGELO

(1947 - Republic) Roy Rogers, Dale Evans
One Sheet: $125 - $250

BELLS OF SAN FERNANDO
(1947 - Screen Guild) Donald Woods, Gloria Warren
One Sheet: $30 - $50

BELLS OF ST. MARY'S, THE
(1945 - RKO) Bing Crosby, Ingrid Bergman
One Sheet: $125 - $250

ThreeSheet

BELLS OF ST. MARY'S, THE
(1957R - RKO) Bing Crosby, Ingrid Bergman
One Sheet: $75 - $150   *Re-release.*

BELLS OF ST. TRINIANS
(1958 - British Lion) Alistair Sim
One Sheet: $30 - $50

BELOVED
(1934 - Universal) John Boles, Gloria Stuart
One Sheet: $150 - $300

BELOVED BACHELOR, THE
(1931 - Paramount) Paul Lukas, Dorothy Jordan
One Sheet: $125 - $250

BELOVED BRAT, THE
(1938 - Warner Bros.) Bonita Granville, Dolores Costello
One Sheet: $75 - $150

BELOVED ENEMY
(1937 - United Artists) Merle Oberon, Brian Aherne
One Sheet: $100 - $200

BELOVED IMPOSTER
(1936 - RKO) Rene Ray, Fred Conyngham
One Sheet: $125 - $250

BELOVED INFIDEL
(1959 - 20th Century Fox) Gregory Peck, Deborah Kerr
One Sheet: $15 - $30

BELOVED ROGUE, THE
(1927 - United Artists) John Barrymore, Conrad Veidt
One Sheet: $1,300 - $2,000   *One Sheet (Art Cinema re-release):$400-$800.*

BELOVED VAGABOND, THE
(1936 - Columbia) Maurice Chevalier
One Sheet: $150 - $300

BELOW THE BELT
(1980 - Atlantic) Regina Baff
One Sheet: $10 - $20   *Sports (Wrestling). Female wrestling film.*

BELOW THE BORDER
(1942 - Monogram) Rough Riders (Buck Jones, Tim McCoy)
One Sheet: $100 - $200

BELOW THE DEADLINE
(1936 - Chesterfield) Cecilia Parker, Russell Hopton
One Sheet: $75 - $125

BELOW THE DEADLINE
(1946 - Monogram) Warren Douglas, Ramsey Ames
One Sheet: $30 - $50

BELOW THE SAHARA
(1953 - RKO/Pathe) Documentary
One Sheet: $15 - $30

BELOW THE SEA

(1933 - Columbia) Ralph Bellamy, Fay Wray
One Sheet: $500 - $800

BELOW THE SURFACE
(1920 - -) Hobart Bosworth, Grace Darmond
One Sheet: $150 - $300

BELOW ZERO
(1930 - MGM) Laurel & Hardy
One Sheet: $3,500 - $5,000

BELSTONE FOX, THE
(1976 - 20th Century Fox) Eric Porter, Rachel
Roberts
One Sheet: $5 - $10

BEN
(1972 - Cinerama) Joseph Campanella, Arthur
O'Connell
One Sheet: $10 - $20

BEN HUR
(1926 - MGM) Ramon Novarro, Francis X.
Bushman
One Sheet: $3,500 - $5,000 *Sports Movie
Posters #1.*

BEN HUR
(1930R - MGM) Ramon Navarro, Francis X.
Bushman
One Sheet: $200 - $400 *Re-release.*

BEN HUR
(1959 - MGM) Charlton Heston, Jack Hawkins
One Sheet: $150 - $300 *Academy
Award: Best Picture, Best Actor(Heston), Best
Direction(William Wyler). Academy Award Movie
Posters #186-#190 & #192. SportsMovie Posters
#2.*

BEN HUR
(1969R - MGM) Charlton Heston, Jack Hawkins
One Sheet: $15 - $25 *Re-release.*

BEND OF THE RIVER
(1952 - Universal) James Stewart, Arthur
Kennedy
One Sheet: $100 - $200

BENEATH THE 12 MILE REEF
(1953 - 20th Century Fox) Robert Wagner,
Terry Moore
One Sheet: $75 - $150

BENEATH THE PLANET OF THE APES
(1970 - 20th Century Fox) Charlton Heston
One Sheet: $30 - $60

BENEATH WESTERN SKIES
(1944 - Republic) Bob Livingston, Smiley
Burnette
One Sheet: $30 - $50

BENGAL BRIGADE
(1954 - Universal) Rock Hudson, Arlene Dahl
One Sheet: $30 - $50

BENGAL TIGER
(1936 - Warner Bros.) Barton MacLane, June
Travis
One Sheet: $100 - $200

BENGAZI
(1955 - RKO) Richard Carlson, Victor McLaglen
One Sheet: $15 - $30

BENJAMIN
(1968 - Paramount) Pierre Clementi, Catherine
Deneuve
One Sheet: $5 - $10

BENJAMIN FRANKLIN, JR.
(1942 - MGM) Our Gang
One Sheet: $250 - $500

BENJI
(1974 - Mulberry) Peter Breck, Christopher
Connelly
One Sheet: $5 - $10

BENJI
(1975R - Mulberry) Peter Breck, Christopher
Connelly
One Sheet: $2 - $3 *Re-release.*

BENJI, THE HUNTED
(1987 - Buena Vista) Benji
One Sheet: $3 - $5

BENNY AND JOON
(1993 - MGM) Aidan Quinn, Johnny Depp,
Mary-Stuart Masterson
One Sheet: $7 - $15

BENNY GOODMAN STORY, THE
(1956 - Universal) Steve Allen, Donna Reed
One Sheet: $40 - $75

BENNY HILL SHOW, THE
(1969- - -) Benny Hill
One Sheet: $15 - $30

BENSON MURDER CASE, THE
(1930 - Paramount-Famous Lasky) William
Powell
One Sheet: $1,300 - $2,000

BERKELEY SQUARE
(1933 - Fox) Leslie Howard, Heather Angel
One Sheet: $300 - $700

BERLIN CORRESPONDENT
(1942 - 20th Century Fox) Dana Andrews,
Virginia Gilmore
One Sheet: $100 - $200

BERLIN EXPRESS
(1948 - RKO) Merle Oberon, Robert Ryan
One Sheet: $100 - $200

BERMONDSEY KID, THE
(1933 - Warner Bros.) Esmond Knight
One Sheet: $75 - $150

BERMUDA AFFAIR
(1956 - Columbia) Kim Hunter
One Sheet: $30 - $50

BERMUDA MYSTERY
(1944 - 20th Century Fox) Preston Foster, Ann
Rutherford
One Sheet: $50 - $100

BERMUDA TRIANGLE, THE
(1978 - Sunn) Brad Crandall
One Sheet: $5 - $10

BERNADETTE OF LOURDES
(1962 - Janus) Daniele Ajoret
One Sheet: $15 - $30

BERNARDINE
(1957 - 20th Century Fox) Pat Boone, Terry
Moore
One Sheet: $15 - $30

BERSERK
(1968 - Columbia) Joan Crawford, Ty Hardin
One Sheet: $15 - $35

BERTH MARKS
(1929 - MGM) Laurel & Hardy
One Sheet: $3,500 - $5,000

BERYL CORONET, THE
(1922 - Alexander) -
One Sheet: $600 - $1,000

BESS OF HANGTOWN MESA
(1942 - -) Johnny Mack Brown
One Sheet: $50 - $100

BEST BAD MAN, THE
(1925 - Fox) Tom Mix
One Sheet: $500 - $800

BEST DEFENSE
(1984 - Paramount) Dudley Moore, Eddie
Murphy, Kate Capshaw
One Sheet: $3 - $5

BEST FOOT FORWARD
(1943 - MGM) Lucille Ball, June Allyson
One Sheet: $250 - $600

BEST FRIENDS
(1975 - Crown) Richard Hatch, Suzanne
Benton
One Sheet: $7 - $15

BEST FRIENDS
(1982 - Warner Bros.) Burt Reynolds, Goldie
Hawn, Jessica Tandy
One Sheet: $10 - $20

BEST HOUSE IN LONDON, THE
(1969 - MGM) David Hemmings, Joanna Pettet,
George Sanders
One Sheet: $10 - $20

BEST LITTLE WHOREHOUSE IN TEXAS
(1982 - Universal) Dolly Parton, Burt Reynolds,
Dom DeLuise
One Sheet: $7 - $15 *Advance:$15-
25.*

BEST MAN, THE
(1964 - United Artists) Henry Fonda, Cliff
Robertson
One Sheet: $10 - $20

BEST MAN WINS, THE
(1935 - Columbia) Edmund Lowe, Jack Holt,
Bela Lugosi
One Sheet: $200 - $400

BEST MAN WINS, THE
(1948 - Columbia) Edgar Buchanan, Anna Lee,
Gary Gray
One Sheet: $40 - $75

BEST OF ENEMIES
(1933 - Fox) Buddy Rogers, Marian Nixon
One Sheet: $200 - $400

BEST OF ENEMIES
(1962 - Columbia) David Niven, Alberto Sordi
One Sheet: $5 - $10

BEST OF EVERYTHING, THE
(1959 - 20th Century Fox) Hope Lange,
Stephen Boyd
One Sheet: $20 - $40

BEST OF THE BADMEN
(1951 - RKO) Robert Ryan, Claire Trevor
One Sheet: $30 - $50

BEST OF THE BEST
(1989 - -) Eric Roberts, Phillip Rhee,
Christopher Penn
One Sheet: $3 - $5

BEST OF THE BEST II
(1993 - 20th Century Fox) Eric Roberts, Phillip
Rhee, Christopher Penn
One Sheet: $3 - $5

BEST OF TIMES, THE
(1986 - Universal) Robin Williams, Kurt Russell
One Sheet: $3 - $5

**BEST OF WALT DISNEY'S TRUE LIFE
ADVENTURES, THE**
(1975 - Walt Disney) -
One Sheet: $5 - $10 *Documentary.*

BEST SELLER
(1986 - Orion) James Woods, Brian Dennehy
One Sheet: $3 - $5

BEST THINGS IN LIFE ARE FREE, THE
(1956 - 20th Century Fox) Gordon MacRae,
Ernest Borgnine
One Sheet: $40 - $75

BEST YEARS OF OUR LIVES, THE
(1946 - RKO) Myrna Loy, Fredric March, Harold
Russell
One Sheet: $250 - $600 *Academy
Award: Best Picture, Best Actor(March), Best
Supporting Actor(Russell), Best
Direction(WilliamWyler). Academy Award Movie
Posters #104, #105, #107.*

One Sheet

BEST YEARS OF OUR LIVES, THE
(1954R - MGM) Fredric March, Myrna
One Sheet: $50 - $100 *Re-release.*

BETRAYAL
(1929 - Paramount) Emil Jannings, Gary
Cooper
One Sheet: $500 - $800

BETRAYAL
(1932 - Fogwell) Stewart Rome, Marjorie Hume
One Sheet: $150 - $300

BETRAYAL, THE
(1948 - Astor) Myra Stanton, Dir: Oscar
Micheaux
One Sheet: $150 - $300 *Black cast.
Separate Cinema, pg. 25.*

BETRAYAL, THE
(1958 - United Artists) Philip Friend, Diana
Decker
One Sheet: $15 - $30

BETRAYAL
(1983 - 20th Century Fox) Jeremy Irons,
Patricia Hodge
One Sheet: $3 - $5

BETRAYAL FROM THE EAST
(1945 - RKO) Lee Tracy, Nancy Kelly
One Sheet: $75 - $125

BETRAYED
(1917 - Fox) Miriam Cooper, Monte Blue
One Sheet: $200 - $400

BETRAYED
(1948R - King Bros.) Robert Mitchum, Kim
Hunter
One Sheet: $75 - $150 *Re-titled re-
release of "When Strangers Marry".*

BETRAYED
(1954 - MGM) Clark Gable, Lana Turner
One Sheet: $75 - $125

BETRAYED
(1988 - MGM/United Artists) Debra Winger,
Tom Berenger
One Sheet: $3 - $5

BETRAYED WOMEN
(1955 - MGM) Tom Drake, Carole Matthews
One Sheet: $30 - $50

BETSY, THE
(1978 - Allied Artists) Laurence Olivier, Robert
Duvall
One Sheet: $7 - $15

BETSY ROSS
(1917 - World Film) Alice Brady
One Sheet: $250 - $600

BETSY'S BURGLAR
(1917 - Hamilton) Constance Talmadge
One Sheet: $150 - $300

BETSY'S WEDDING
(1990 - Touchstone) Molly Ringwald, Alan Alda
One Sheet: $3 - $5

BETTER A WIDOW
(1969 - Universal) Virna Lisi, Peter McErnery,
Gabrielle Ferzetti
One Sheet: $3 - $5

BETTER LATE THAN NEVER
(1983 - Warner Bros.) David Niven, Art Carney
One Sheet: $3 - $5

BETTER OFF DEAD
(1985 - Warner Bros.) John Cusack, Steve
Holland, Kim Darby
One Sheet: $7 - $15

BETTER TOMORROW, A
(198? - -) Dir: John Woo
One Sheet: $20 - $40

BETTY
(1993 - MK2 Productions) Marie Trintignant,
Stephane Audran
One Sheet: $5 - $10

BETTY BLUE
(1986 - Alive) Jean-Hughes Anglade, Beatrice
Dolle
One Sheet: $15 - $30

BETTY BOOP AND BIMBO STANDEE
(1933 - Paramount) Betty Boop & Bimbo,
Fleischer Studio
One Sheet: $5,000 - $7,500 *Cartoon.
56x38 black & white lobby standee. Huge image
of Betty Boop. 30x26 banner, black on
whitebackground, full images of Betty & Bimbo.*

**BETTY BOOP WITH HENRY THE FUNNIEST
LIVING AMERICAN**
(1935 - Paramount) Betty Boop
One Sheet: $2,500 - $4,000 *Cartoon.
Cartoon Movie Posters #204.*

BETTY BOOP'S LITTLE PAL
(1934 - Paramount) Betty Boop
One Sheet: $2,500 - $4,000 *Cartoon.
Cartoon Movie Posters #203.*

BETTY CO-ED
(1946 - Columbia) Jean Porter, Shirley Mills
One Sheet: $50 - $100

BETWEEN FIGHTING MEN
(1932 - World Wide) Ken Maynard
One Sheet: $250 - $500

BETWEEN HEAVEN AND HELL
(1956 - 20th Century Fox) Robert Wagner,
Terry Moore
One Sheet: $20 - $40

BETWEEN MEN
(1916 - Triangle) William S. Hart
One Sheet: $1,900 - $3,000

BETWEEN MEN
(1920R - -) William S. Hart
One Sheet: $200 - $400   *Re-release.*

BETWEEN MEN
(1935 - Supreme) Johnny Mack Brown
One Sheet: $125 - $250

BETWEEN MIDNIGHT AND DAWN
(1953 - Columbia) Mark Stevens, Edmond
O'Brien
One Sheet: $10 - $20

BETWEEN SHOWERS
(1914 - Keystone) Charlie Chaplin
One Sheet: $7,500 - $12,000

BETWEEN THE LINES
(1977 - Midwest Films) John Heard, Jeff
Goldblum
One Sheet: $15 - $25   *Amsel Art.*

BETWEEN TIME AND ETERNITY
(1960 - Universal) Lilli Palmer, Willy Birgel
One Sheet: $15 - $25

BETWEEN TWO WOMEN
(1937 - MGM) Franchot Tone, Maureen
O'Sullivan
One Sheet: $150 - $300

BETWEEN TWO WOMEN
(1944 - MGM) Marilyn Maxwell, Gloria
DeHaven, Lionel Barrymore
One Sheet: $100 - $200

BETWEEN TWO WORLDS
(1944 - Warner Bros.) John Garfield, Paul
Henreid
One Sheet: $50 - $100

Mini Window Card

BETWEEN US GIRLS
(1942 - Universal) Kay Francis, Diana
Barrymore
One Sheet: $75 - $125

BEVERLY HILLBILLIES, THE
(1993 - 20th Century Fox) Dabney Coleman,
Cloris Leachman, Lily Tomlin
One Sheet: $5 - $10   *T.V. tie-in.*

BEVERLY HILLS COP
(1984 - Paramount) Eddie Murphy
One Sheet: $7 - $15

BEVERLY HILLS COP II
(1987 - Paramount) Eddie Murphy, Judge
Reinhold
One Sheet: $3 - $5

BEVERLY HILLS COP III
(1994 - Paramount) Eddie Murphy, Judge
Reinhold
One Sheet: $3 - $5

BEWARE!

(1946 - Astor) Louis Jourdan, Frank Wilson
One Sheet: $75 - $150   *Black cast.*
Separate Cinema, pg. 95.

BEWARE, MY LOVELY
(1952 - RKO) Ida Lupino, Robert Ryan
One Sheet: $40 - $75

BEWARE OF BACHELORS
(1928 - Warner Bros.) Audrey Ferris
One Sheet: $500 - $800

BEWARE OF BLONDIE
(1950 - Columbia) Penny Singleton, Arthur
Lake
One Sheet: $40 - $75

BEWARE OF CHILDREN
(1961 - AIP) Leslie Phillips, Geraldine McEwan
One Sheet: $7 - $15

BEWARE OF LADIES
(1936 - Republic) Donald Cook, Judith Allen
One Sheet: $75 - $150

BEWARE OF PITY
(1946 - Two Cities) Lilli Palmer, Albert Lieven
One Sheet: $30 - $50

BEWARE SPOOKS!
(1939 - Columbia) Joe E. Brown, Mary Carlisle
One Sheet: $100 - $200

BEWARE! THE BLOB
(1972 - Jack H. Harris) Robert Walker, Carol
Lynley
One Sheet: $15 - $25   *AKA: SON OF*
BLOB.

BEWITCHED
(1945 - MGM) Phyllis Thaxter, Edmund Gwenn
One Sheet: $40 - $75

BEYOND A REASONABLE DOUBT
(1956 - RKO) Dana Andrews, Joan Fontaine
One Sheet: $40 - $75

BEYOND ALL LIMITS
(1961 - State Rights) Jack Palance, Maria Felix
One Sheet: $15 - $25

BEYOND AND BACK
(1977 - Sunn) Narrated by Brad Crandall
One Sheet: $3 - $5

BEYOND ATLANTIS
(1973 - Dimension) John Ashley, Patrick
Wayne
One Sheet: $10 - $20

BEYOND BENGAL
(1933 - Showmens) -
One Sheet: $150 - $300

BEYOND CONTROL
(1971 - Mishkin) Anthony Baker
One Sheet: $7 - $15

BEYOND EVIL
(1980 - Scope III) John Saxon, Lynda Day
George
One Sheet: $3 - $5

BEYOND GLORY
(1948 - Paramount) Alan Ladd, Donna Reed,
Audie Murphy
One Sheet: $75 - $150   *Murphy's film*
debut.

BEYOND MOMBASA
(1956 - Columbia) Donna Reed, Cornel Wilde
One Sheet: $15 - $30

BEYOND PRICE
(1921 - Fox) Pearl White, Vernon Steel, Nora
Reed
One Sheet: $250 - $600

BEYOND RANGOON
(1995 - Columbia) Patricia Arquette, Frances
McDormand
One Sheet: $3 - $5

BEYOND REASONABLE DOUBT
(1980 - Endeavour) David Hemmings, John
Hargreaves
One Sheet: $3 - $5

BEYOND SHAME
(1980 - Cybercraft) Seka, Lori Blue
One Sheet: $5 - $10   *XXX.*

BEYOND THE BLUE HORIZON
(1942 - Paramount) Dorothy Lamour, Richard

Denning
One Sheet: $75 - $150

BEYOND THE CITIES
(1930 - Paramount) Carlyle Blackwell, Edna
Best
One Sheet: $125 - $250

BEYOND THE CURTAIN
(1960 - Rank) Richard Greene, Eva Bartok
One Sheet: $7 - $15

BEYOND THE DARKNESS
(196? - Abco Enterprises) Dagmar Hedrich
One Sheet: $5 - $10

BEYOND THE DOOR
(1974 - Film Ventures) Juliet Mills, Richard
Johnson
One Sheet: $3 - $5

BEYOND THE DOOR
(1979 - Film Ventures) Daria Nicoldi, John
Steiner
One Sheet: $7 - $15

BEYOND THE DOOR II
(1979 - Film Ventures) Daria Nicolodi, John
Steiner
One Sheet: $5 - $10

BEYOND THE FOG
(1981 - Independent-International) Bryant
Haliday, Jill Haworth
One Sheet: $10 - $20   *AKA: TOWER*
OF EVIL; HORROR OF SNAPE ISLAND.

BEYOND THE FOREST
(1949 - Warner Bros.) Bette Davis, Joseph
Cotten
One Sheet: $125 - $250

BEYOND THE LAST FRONTIER
(1943 - Republic) Eddie Dew, Smiley Burnette
One Sheet: $50 - $100

BEYOND THE LAW
(1934 - Columbia) Tim McCoy
One Sheet: $500 - $800

BEYOND THE LAW
(1967 - Roxy) Lee Van Cleef, Lionel Stander
One Sheet: $10 - $20   *Spaghetti*
western.

BEYOND THE LAW
(1968 - Evergreen) Rip Torn, Norman Mailer,
Dir: Norman Mailer
One Sheet: $15 - $25   *TV series*
"Barney Miller" may have been inspired by this
movie.

BEYOND THE LIMIT
(1983 - Paramount) Michael Caine, Richard
Gere
One Sheet: $5 - $10

BEYOND THE PECOS
(1944 - Universal) Rod Cameron, Eddie Dew
One Sheet: $30 - $50

BEYOND THE POSEIDON ADVENTURE
(1979 - Warner Bros.) Michael Caine, Sally
Field
One Sheet: $7 - $15

BEYOND THE PURPLE HILLS
(1950 - Columbia) Gene Autry, Jo Denison
One Sheet: $50 - $100

BEYOND THE REEF
(1981 - Universal) Dayton Kane, Maren Jensen
One Sheet: $3 - $5

BEYOND THE RIO GRANDE
(1930 - Biltmore) Jack Perrin, Franklyn Farnum
One Sheet: $150 - $300

BEYOND THE ROCKIES
(1932 - RKO Pathe) Tom Keene
One Sheet: $125 - $250

BEYOND THE ROCKS
(1922 - Paramount) Gloria Swanson, Rudolph
Valentino
One Sheet: $2,500 - $4,000

BEYOND THE SACRAMENTO
(1940 - Columbia) "Wild Bill" Elliott, Dub Taylor
One Sheet: $75 - $125

BEYOND THE STARS
(1989 - Moviestore) Christian Slater, Martin
Sheen

One Sheet: $5 - $10

BEYOND THE TIME BARRIER
(1959 - AIP) Robert Clarke, Darlene Tompkins
One Sheet: $40 - $75

One Sheet

BEYOND THE VALLEY OF THE DOLLS
(1970 - 20th Century Fox) Dolly Read, Cynthia
Myers, Dir: Russ Meyer
One Sheet: $50 - $100

BEYOND THERAPY
(1987 - New World) Julie Hagerty, Jeff
Goldblum
One Sheet: $3 - $5

BEYOND TOMORROW
(1940 - Academy) Richard Carlson, Jean
Parker
One Sheet: $50 - $100

BEYOND VICTORY
(1931 - RKO Pathe) William Boyd, James
Gleason
One Sheet: $250 - $500

B.F.'S DAUGHTER
(1948 - MGM) Barbara Stanwyck, Van Heflin,
Charles Coburn
One Sheet: $30 - $50

BHOWANI JUNCTION
(1955 - MGM) Ava Gardner, Stewart Granger
One Sheet: $125 - $250

BIBLE, THE
(1967 - 20th Century Fox) Peter O'Toole, John
Huston
One Sheet: $30 - $50

BICYCLE THIEF, THE
(1949 - Mayer-Burstyn) Lamberto Maggiorani
One Sheet: $75 - $150

BIDDY
(1983 - Sands) Cecilia Bannerman
One Sheet: $3 - $5

BIFF BANG BUDDY
(1924 - Weiss Bros.) Buddy Roosevelt, Jean
Arthur, Buck Conners
One Sheet: $200 - $400

BIG
(1988 - 20th Century Fox) Tom Hanks,
Elizabeth Perkins
One Sheet: $7 - $15

BIG AND THE BAD, THE
(1971 - Atlantida) Jack Palance, Bud Spencer
One Sheet: $7 - $15

BIG BAD MAMA
(1974 - New World) Angie Dickinson, William
Shatner
One Sheet: $15 - $30

BIG BAD MAMA II
(1987 - -) Angie Dickenson, Robert Culp
One Sheet: $5 - $10

BIG BANKROLL, THE
(1961 - Allied Artists) Stephen Boyd, Juliette
Green
One Sheet: $7 - $15

BIG BEAT, THE
(1957 - Universal) William Reynolds, Fats
Domino
One Sheet: $50 - $100   *Rock 'n' Roll.*

BIG BIRD CAGE, THE
(1972 - New World) Pam Grier, Anitra Ford

BIG BLOCKADE, THE
(1942 - Ealing) Leslie Banks, Michael Redgrave
One Sheet: $75 - $150

BIG BLUE, THE
(1988 - Weintraub) Rosanna Arquette, Jean-Marc Barr
One Sheet: $10 - $20

BIG BLUFF, THE
(1933 - Tower) Reginald Denny, Claudia Dell
One Sheet: $200 - $400   *AKA: GB: WORTHY DECEIVERS.*

BIG BLUFF, THE
(1955 - United Artists) John Bromfield, Martha Vickers
One Sheet: $30 - $50

BIG BONANZA, THE
(1945 - Republic) Richard Arlen, Jane Frazee
One Sheet: $50 - $100

BIG BOODLE, THE
(1956 - United Artists) Errol Flynn, Rossanna Rory
One Sheet: $50 - $100

BIG BOSS, THE
(1941 - Columbia) Otto Kruger, Gloria Dickson
One Sheet: $75 - $150

BIG BOSS, THE
(1972 - Golden Harvest) Bruce Lee
One Sheet: $75 - $150

BIG BOUNCE, THE
(1969 - Warner Bros.) Ryan O'Neal, Leigh Taylor-Young, James Daly
One Sheet: $5 - $10

BIG BOY
(1930 - Warner Bros.) Al Jolson, Noah Beery
One Sheet: $1,300 - $2,000

BIG BRAIN, THE
(1933 - RKO) George E. Stone, Fay Wray
One Sheet: $150 - $300

One Sheet

BIG BRAWL, THE
(1980 - Warner Bros.) Jackie Chan, Jose Ferrer
One Sheet: $20 - $40

BIG BROADCAST, THE
(1932 - Paramount-Publix) Bing Crosby, Kate Smith
One Sheet: $600 - $1,000

BIG BROADCAST OF 1936, THE
(1935 - Paramount) Jack Oakie, George Burns, Gracie Allen
One Sheet: $250 - $600

BIG BROADCAST OF 1937, THE
(1936 - Paramount) Jack Benny, George Burns, Gracie Allen
One Sheet: $200 - $400

BIG BROADCAST OF 1938, THE
(1938 - Paramount) W. C. Fields, Bob Hope
One Sheet: $1,900 - $3,000   *Hope's first feature film.*

BIG BROWN EYES
(1936 - Paramount) Cary Grant, Joan Bennett
One Sheet: $250 - $600

BIG BULLY
(1996 - Warner Bros.) Tom Arnold, Rick Moranis
One Sheet: $3 - $5

BIG BUS, THE
(1976 - Paramount) Joseph Bologna, John Beck
One Sheet: $3 - $5

BIG BUSINESS
(1929 - MGM) Laurel & Hardy
One Sheet: $3,500 - $5,000

BIG BUSINESS
(1930 - Fox) Frances Day, Barrie Oliver
One Sheet: $200 - $400

BIG BUSINESS
(1934 - Warner Bros.) Eve Gray, Ernest Sefton
One Sheet: $150 - $300

BIG BUSINESS
(1937 - 20th Century Fox) Jed Prouty, Shirley Deane
One Sheet: $150 - $300

BIG BUSINESS
(1988 - Touchstone) Bette Midler, Lily Tomlin
One Sheet: $5 - $10

BIG BUSINESS GIRL
(1931 - First National) Loretta Young, Joan Blondell
One Sheet: $300 - $700

BIG BUST OUT, THE
(1973 - New World) Vonetta McGee, Gordon Mitchell
One Sheet: $10 - $20   *Blaxploitation.*

BIG CAGE, THE
(1933 - Universal) Clyde Beatty, Mickey Rooney
One Sheet: $250 - $500

BIG CALIBRE
(1935 - Supreme) Bob Steele
One Sheet: $500 - $800

BIG CAPER, THE
(1956 - United Artists) Rory Calhoun, Mary Costa
One Sheet: $20 - $40

BIG CARNIVAL, THE
(1951 - Paramount) Kirk Douglas, Jan Sterling, Dir: Billy Wilder
One Sheet: $40 - $75   *AKA: Ace in the Hole*

BIG CAT, THE
(1949 - Eagle-Lion) Lon McCallister, Peggy Ann Garner
One Sheet: $40 - $75

BIG CATCH, THE
(1968 - Independent) David Gallacher, Ronald Sinclair
One Sheet: $5 - $10

BIG CHANCE, THE
(1933 - Eagle) Mickey Rooney
One Sheet: $150 - $300

BIG CHANCE, THE
(1957 - RFD) Adrienne Corri, William Russell
One Sheet: $15 - $25

BIG CHASE, THE
(1954 - Lippert) Lon Chaney, Jr.
One Sheet: $15 - $35

BIG CHILL, THE
(1983 - Columbia) Glenn Close, Jeff Goldblum
One Sheet: $15 - $30

BIG CIRCUS, THE
(1959 - Allied Artists) Victor Mature, Red Buttons, Peter Lorre
One Sheet: $30 - $50

BIG CITY, THE
(1925 - Century Comedy) Edna Marian
One Sheet: $100 - $200

BIG CITY, THE
(1937 - MGM) Luise Rainer, Spencer Tracy
One Sheet: $250 - $500

BIG CITY, THE
(1948 - MGM) Margaret O'Brien, Robert Preston
One Sheet: $50 - $100

BIG CITY BLUES

BIG CITY BLUES
(1932 - Warner Bros.) Joan Blondell, Eric Linden, Humphrey Bogart
One Sheet: $600 - $1,000

BIG CITY BLUES
(1946 - Sack Enterprises) Louis Jordan, The Jubalaires
One Sheet: $250 - $500   *Black cast.*

BIG CLOCK, THE
(1948 - Paramount) Ray Milland, Charles Laughton
One Sheet: $50 - $100

BIG COMBO, THE
(1954 - Allied Artists) Cornel Wilde, Richard Conte
One Sheet: $75 - $125

BIG COUNTRY, THE
(1958 - United Artists) Gregory Peck, Jean Simmons, Burl Ives
One Sheet: $20 - $40   *Academy Award Movie Posters #184.*

BIG CUBE, THE
(1969 - Warner Bros. -7 Arts) Lana Turner, George Chakiris, Richard Egan
One Sheet: $5 - $10

BIG DADDY
(1969 - United) Victor Buono, Joan Blondell
One Sheet: $5 - $10   *AKA: PARADISE ROAD*

BIG DAN
(1923 - Wm. Fox) Buck Jones, Marion Nixon
One Sheet: $500 - $800

BIG DAY, THE
(1960 - Independent Artists) Donald Pleasence
One Sheet: $5 - $10

BIG DEAL ON MADONNA STREET, THE
(1960 - Lux) Vittorio Gassman
One Sheet: $15 - $25   *Remade as CRACKERS.*

BIG DIAMOND ROBBERY, THE
(1929 - FBO) Tom Mix, Kathryn McGuire
One Sheet: $500 - $800

BIG DOLL HOUSE, THE
(1971 - New World) Judy Brown, Pam Grier
One Sheet: $10 - $20   *Sexploitation.*

BIG EASY, THE
(1987 - Kings Road) Dennis Quaid, Ellen Barkin
One Sheet: $7 - $15

BIG EXECUTIVE
(1933 - Paramount) Ricardo Cortez, Elizabeth Young
One Sheet: $125 - $250

BIG FELLA
(1937 - Retlaw) Paul Robeson, Elisabeth Welch
One Sheet: $1,900 - $3,000   *Black cast. Separate Cinema, pg. 45.*

BIG FIGHT, THE
(1930 - World Wide) Guinn Williams, Stepin Fetchit
One Sheet: $800 - $1,500   *Black cast. Sports (Boxing). Sports Movie Posters #125.*

BIG FISHERMAN, THE
(1959 - Buena Vista/Disney) Howard Keel, Susan Kohner
One Sheet: $15 - $30

BIG FIX, THE
(1947 - PRC) James Brown, Sheila Ryan
One Sheet: $50 - $100

BIG FIX, THE
(1978 - Universal) Richard Dreyfuss, Bonnie Bedelia, John Lithgow
One Sheet: $5 - $10

BIG FOOT
(1973 - Gemini-American) John Carradine, Chris Mitchum
One Sheet: $5 - $10

BIG FRAME, THE
(1952 - RKO) Mark Stevens, Jean Kent
One Sheet: $15 - $30

BIG GAMBLE, THE
(1931 - RKO-Pathe) William Boyd, James Gleason
One Sheet: $250 - $600

BIG GAMBLE, THE
(1961 - 20th Century Fox) Stephen Boyd, Juliette Greco
One Sheet: $15 - $25

BIG GAME, THE
(1936 - RKO) Philip Huston, James Gleason
One Sheet: $600 - $1,000   *Sports (Football). Sports Movie Posters #189.*

BIG GAME, THE
(1971 - Comet) Stephen Boyd, Ray Milland
One Sheet: $5 - $10

BIG GUNDOWN, THE
(1968 - Columbia) Lee Van Cleef, Thomas Milan, Luisa Rivelli
One Sheet: $20 - $40

BIG GUSHER, THE
(1951 - Columbia) Preston Foster, Wayne Morris
One Sheet: $30 - $60

BIG GUY, THE
(1939 - Universal) Victor McLaglen, Jackie Cooper
One Sheet: $75 - $150

BIG HAND FOR THE LITTLE LADY, A
(1966 - Warner Bros.) Henry Fonda, Joanne Woodward
One Sheet: $7 - $15

BIG HANGOVER, THE
(1949 - MGM) Van Johnson, Elizabeth Taylor
One Sheet: $50 - $100

BIG HEARTED HERBERT
(1934 - Warner Bros.) Guy Kibbee, Aline MacMahon
One Sheet: $100 - $200

Mini Window Card

BIG HEAT, THE
(1953 - Columbia) Glenn Ford, Gloria Grahame, Jocelyn Brando
One Sheet: $150 - $300

BIG HEAT, THE
(1959R - Columbia) Glenn Ford, Gloria Grahame, Joclyn Brando
One Sheet: $40 - $75   *Re-release.*

BIG HEEL-WATHA
(1944 - MGM) Screwy Squirrel, Tex Avery
One Sheet: $600 - $1,000   *Cartoon. Full color stone litho. Cartoon Movie Posters #292.*

BIG HOP, THE
(1928 - Buck Jones Prod.) Buck Jones, Jobyna Ralston
One Sheet: $600 - $1,000

BIG HOUSE, THE
(1930 - MGM) Chester Morris, Wallace Beery
One Sheet: $150 - $300

BIG HOUSE BLUES
(1941 - Columbia) Color Rhapsodies
One Sheet: $150 - $350   *Cartoon. Full color semi-stock poster with inset of title.*

BIG HOUSE FOR GIRLS, THE
(1931 - Atlantic) Maureen O'Sullivan, John Warburton
One Sheet: $250 - $500

BIG HOUSE, U.S.A.
(1955 - Camden) Broderick Crawford, Ralph Meeker, Charles Bronson
One Sheet: $40 - $75

BIG IDEA, THE
(1918 - Pathe) Harold Lloyd, Bebe Daniels,
Snub Pollard
One Sheet: $500 - $800

BIG IDEA, THE
(1934 - MGM) Ted Healy and His Stooges
(Moe, Larry & Curly)
One Sheet: $250 - $600   *Comedy
musical short.*

BIG JACK
(1949 - MGM) Wallace Beery, Richard Conte
One Sheet: $50 - $100

BIG JAKE
(1971 - National General) John Wayne, Richard
Boone
One Sheet: $40 - $75

Insert

BIG JEETER
(1959 - Citation Films) -
One Sheet: $15 - $30

BIG JIM MCLAIN
(1952 - Warner Bros.) John Wayne, Nancy
Olson, James Arness
One Sheet: $100 - $200

BIG JOB, THE
(1965 - Warner/Pathe) Sidney James, Sylvia
Syms
One Sheet: $10 - $20

BIG KILLING, THE
(1928 - Paramount) Wallace Beery, Mary Brian
One Sheet: $200 - $400

BIG KNIFE, THE
(1955 - United Artists) Jack Palance, Wendell
Cory, Ida Lupino, Shelley Winters
One Sheet: $75 - $150

BIG LAND, THE
(1957 - Warner Bros.) Alan Ladd, Virginia
Mayo, Edmond O'Brien
One Sheet: $20 - $40

BIG LEAGUER, THE
(1953 - MGM) Edward G. Robinson, Vera-Ellen
One Sheet: $50 - $100   *Sports
(Baseball).*

BIG LIFT, THE
(1950 - 20th Century Fox) Montgomery Clift,
Paul Douglas
One Sheet: $75 - $150

BIG LITTLE PERSON, THE
(1919 - Universal) Rudolph Valentino, May
Murray
One Sheet: $500 - $800

BIG MAN ON CAMPUS
(1989 - Vestron) Corey Parker
One Sheet: $3 - $5

BIG MONEY
(1930 - Pathe) Eddie Quillan, Robert Armstrong
One Sheet: $150 - $300

BIG MONEY
(1962 - Rank) Ian Carmichael, Belinda Lee
One Sheet: $15 - $25

BIG MOUTH, THE
(1967 - Columbia) Jerry Lewis, Harold J. Stone
One Sheet: $30 - $50

BIG NEWS
(1929 - Pathe) Robert Armstrong, Carol
Lombard
One Sheet: $500 - $800

BIG NIGHT, THE
(1951 - United Artists) John Barrymore Jr.,
Joan Loring
One Sheet: $40 - $75

BIG NIGHT, THE
(1960 - Paramount) Randy Sparks, Venetia
Stevenson
One Sheet: $10 - $20

BIG NIGHT
(1996 - Samuel Goldwyn) Minnie Driver, Ian
Holm
One Sheet: $5 - $10

BIG NOISE, THE
(1928 - First National) Chester Conklin, Alice
White, Sam Hardy, Bodil Rosing
One Sheet: $250 - $500

BIG NOISE, THE
(1936 - Warner Bros.) Guy Kibbee, Warren Hull
One Sheet: $100 - $200

BIG NOISE, THE
(1936B - 20th Century Fox) Alastair Sim
One Sheet: $125 - $250

BIG NOISE, THE
(1944 - 20th Century Fox) Laurel & Hardy
One Sheet: $250 - $500

BIG NOISE, THE
(1954R - 20th Century Fox) Laurel & Hardy
One Sheet: $40 - $75   *Re-release.*

BIG OPERATOR, THE
(1959 - MGM) Mickey Rooney, Mamie Van
Doren
One Sheet: $40 - $75

BIG PARADE, THE
(1925 - MGM) John Gilbert, Renee Adoree
One Sheet: $1,900 - $3,000

BIG PARADE, THE
(1930R - MGM) John Gilbert, Renee Adoree
One Sheet: $250 - $500   *Re-release.*

BIG PARADE OF COMEDY, THE
(1964 - MGM) Marx Brothers, Three Stooges,
Jean Harlow, All Star Cast
One Sheet: $30 - $50

BIG PARTY, THE
(1930 - Fox) Sue Carol, Dixie Lee
One Sheet: $250 - $500

BIG PAYOFF, THE
(1933 - MAS) Lucien Littlefield, Ralph Ince
One Sheet: $100 - $200

BIG POND, THE
(1930 - Paramount-Publix) Maurice Chevalier,
Claudette Colbert
One Sheet: $250 - $600

BIG PUNCH, THE
(1921 - Fox) Buck Jones, Barbara Bedford
One Sheet: $300 - $700

BIG PUNCH, THE
(1948 - Warner Bros.) Wayne Morris, Lois
Maxwell
One Sheet: $40 - $75

BIG RACE, THE
(1933 - Showmen's) Boots Mallory, John
Darrow
One Sheet: $100 - $200   *Sports (Horse
racing).*

BIG RED
(1962 - Buena Vista/Disney) Walter Pidgeon,
Gilles Payant
One Sheet: $15 - $25

BIG RED ONE, THE
(1980 - United Artists) Lee Marvin, Mark Hamill
One Sheet: $7 - $15

BIG SCORE, THE
(1983 - Almi) John Saxon, Fred Williamson
One Sheet: $7 - $15   *Blaxploitation.*

BIG SHAKEDOWN, THE
(1933 - First National) Bette Davis, Charles
Farrell
One Sheet: $800 - $1,500

BIG SHOT, THE
(1931 - RKO-Pathe) Maureen O'Sullivan, Eddie
Quillan

One Sheet: $100 - $200

BIG SHOT, THE
(1937 - RKO) Guy Kibbee, Cora Witherspoon
One Sheet: $75 - $150

BIG SHOT, THE
(1942 - Warner Bros.) Humphrey Bogart, Irene
Manning
One Sheet: $150 - $300

BIG SHOTS
(1987 - -) Ricky Buster, Darius McCrary
One Sheet: $3 - $5

BIG SHOW, THE
(1926 - Associated Exhibitors) John Lowell,
Evangeline Russell
One Sheet: $250 - $500

BIG SHOW, THE
(1936 - Republic) Gene Autry, Roy Rogers
(Leonard Slye)
One Sheet: $500 - $800

BIG SHOW, THE
(1942R - Republic) Gene Autry, Roy Rogers
(Leonard Slye)
One Sheet: $75 - $150   *Re-release.*

BIG SHOW, THE
(1961 - 20th Century Fox) Esther Williams, Cliff
Robertson
One Sheet: $15 - $35

BIG SHOW-OFF, THE
(1945 - Republic) Arthur Lake, Dale Evans
One Sheet: $75 - $125

BIG SKY, THE
(1952 - RKO) Kirk Douglas, Elizabeth Threatt
One Sheet: $50 - $100

BIG SKY, THE
(1957R - RKO) Kirk Douglas, Elizabeth Thrett
One Sheet: $15 - $30   *Re-release.*

BIG SLEEP, THE
(1946 - Warner Bros.) Humphrey Bogart,
Lauren Bacall
One Sheet: $600 - $1,000

BIG SLEEP, THE
(1956R - Warner Bros.) Humphrey Bogart,
Lauren Bacall
One Sheet: $125 - $250   *Re-release.*

BIG SLEEP, THE
(1978 - United Artists) Robert Mitchum, Sarah
Miles
One Sheet: $15 - $30

One Sheet

BIG SOMBRERO, THE
(1948 - Columbia) Gene Autry, Elena Verdugo
One Sheet: $75 - $125

BIG SPLASH, THE
(1935 - MGM) Frank Pettingell
One Sheet: $100 - $200

BIG STAMPEDE, THE
(1932 - Vitagraph) John Wayne
One Sheet: $1,900 - $3,000

BIG STEAL, THE
(1949 - RKO) Robert Mitchum, Jane Greer
One Sheet: $100 - $200

BIG STORE, THE
(1941 - MGM) The Marx Brothers
One Sheet: $500 - $900

BIG STORE, THE

(1962R - MGM) The Marx Brothers
One Sheet: $10 - $20   *Re-release.*

BIG STREET, THE
(1942 - RKO) Henry Fonda, Lucille Ball
One Sheet: $200 - $400

BIG SWITCH, THE
(1970 - ScreenCom) Sebastian Breaks
One Sheet: $3 - $5

BIG TIMBER
(1924 - Universal) William Desmond, Olive
Hasbrouck
One Sheet: $150 - $300

BIG TIMBER
(1950 - Monogram) Roddy McDowall, Lyle
Talbot
One Sheet: $15 - $30

BIG TIME
(1929 - Fox) Lee Tracy, Mae Clarke
One Sheet: $250 - $500

BIG TIME
(1988 - -) Tom Waits (concert footage)
One Sheet: $10 - $20

BIG TIME OR BUST
(1934 - Tower) Regis Toomey
One Sheet: $100 - $200

BIG TIMERS
(1945 - -) Stepin Fetchit, Tarzana
One Sheet: $100 - $200   *Black cast.
Separate Cinema, pg. 72,73.*

BIG TIP OFF, THE
(1955 - Allied Artists) Richard Conte,
Constance Smith
One Sheet: $10 - $20

BIG T.N.T SHOW, THE
(1966 - AIP) Joan Baez, Bo Diddley, The
Beatles
One Sheet: $75 - $125   *Rock 'n' Roll.*

BIG TOP, THE
(1937 - Educational) Paul Terry Studio
One Sheet: $250 - $500   *Cartoon.
Duotone. Stock poster with inset of title.*

BIG TOP PEE-WEE
(1988 - -) Pee-Wee Herman (Paul Reubens),
Penelope Ann Miller
One Sheet: $10 - $20

BIG TOWN
(1932 - Trojan) Lester Vail, Eric Linden
One Sheet: $125 - $250

BIG TOWN
(1947 - Paramount) Philip Reed, Hillary
Brooke, Robert Lowery
One Sheet: $75 - $150

BIG TOWN, THE
(1987 - Paramount) Matt Dillon, Diane Lane,
Tommy Lee Jones
One Sheet: $5 - $10

BIG TOWN AFTER DARK
(1947 - Paramount) Philip Reed, Hillary
Brooke, Richard Travis
One Sheet: $75 - $150   *AKA:
UNDERWORLD AFTER DARK.*

BIG TOWN CZAR
(1939 - Universal) Barton MacLane, Tom
Brown
One Sheet: $100 - $200

BIG TOWN GIRL
(1937 - 20th Century Fox) Claire Trevor,
Donald Woods
One Sheet: $75 - $150

BIG TOWN IDEAS
(1921 - Fox) Eileen Percy, Kenneth Gibson
One Sheet: $150 - $300

BIG TOWN SCANDAL
(1948 - Paramount) Philip Reed, Hillary Brooke
One Sheet: $40 - $75

BIG TOWN VILLAGE
(1962 - -) Narrated by Tony Randall
One Sheet: $15 - $35   *Documentary.*

BIG TRAIL, THE
(1930 - Fox) John Wayne
One Sheet: $6,500 - $10,000   *Wayne's first
sound film and starring role. Cowboy Movie*

Posters #'s 79, 80.

BIG TREES, THE
(1952 - Warner Bros.) Kirk Douglas, Eve Miller
One Sheet: $30 - $50

BIG TROUBLE
(1985 - -) Peter Falk, Alan Arkin
One Sheet: $5 - $10

BIG TROUBLE IN LITTLE CHINA
(1986 - 20th Century Fox) Kurt Russell, Kim
Cattrall
One Sheet: $10 - $20

BIG WASH, THE
(1948 - RKO/Disney) Goofy
One Sheet: $800 - $1,500   *Cartoon. The
Disney Poster, pg. 70.*

BIG WAVE
(1962 - Allied Artists) Sessue Hayakawa, Ichizo
Itami
One Sheet: $30 - $60

BIG WEDNESDAY
(1978 - Warner Bros.) Jan-Michael Vincent,
William Katt
One Sheet: $40 - $75   *Sports
(Surfing).*

BIG WHEEL, THE
(1949 - United Artists) Mickey Rooney, Thomas
Mitchell
One Sheet: $50 - $100

BIGAMIST, THE
(1953 - Filmmakers) Edmund O'Brien, Joan
Fontaine
One Sheet: $30 - $50

BIGGER THAN LIFE
(1956 - 20th Century Fox) James Mason,
Barbara Rush
One Sheet: $30 - $50

BIGGEST BUNDLE OF THEM ALL, THE
(1968 - MGM) Edward G. Robinson, Robert
Wagner, Raquel Welch
One Sheet: $15 - $25

BIGGEST SHOW ON EARTH, THE
(1918 - Paramount) Enid Bennett, Earl Rodney
One Sheet: $350 - $750

BIGTIME
(1977 - Big Time) Jayne Kennedy, Christopher
Joy
One Sheet: $7 - $15

BIKINI BEACH
(1964 - AIP) Frankie Avalon, Annette Funicello
One Sheet: $40 - $75   *Rock 'n' Roll.
Surfing.*

BILL AND COO
(1948 - Republic) George Burton's lovebirds,
Curley Twifford's Jimmy the Crow
One Sheet: $40 - $75

BILL AND TED'S BOGUS JOURNEY
(1991 - Orion) Keanu Reeves, Alex Winter, Bill
Sadler
One Sheet: $5 - $10

BILL AND TED'S EXCELLENT ADVENTURE
(1989 - Orion) Keanu Reeves, Alex Winter
One Sheet: $7 - $15

BILL CRACKS DOWN
(1937 - Republic) Grant Withers, Beatrice
Roberts
One Sheet: $75 - $150

BILL OF DIVORCEMENT, A
(1932 - RKO) John Barrymore, Katharine
Hepburn
One Sheet: $4,000 - $6,000

BILL OF DIVORCEMENT, A
(1940 - RKO) Maureen O'Hara, Adolphe
Menjou, Fay Bainter
One Sheet: $75 - $150

BILL'S LEGACY
(1931 - Twickenham) Leslie Fuller, Mary Clare
One Sheet: $100 - $200

BILLBOARD GIRL
(1934 - Educational) -
One Sheet: $75 - $150

BILLIE
(1965 - United Artists) Patty Duke, Jim Backus

One Sheet: $5 - $10

BILLION DOLLAR BRAIN
(1967 - United Artists) Michael Caine,
Francoise Dorleac
One Sheet: $20 - $40

BILLION DOLLAR HOBO
(1977 - International Picture Show) Tim
Conway, Will Geer
One Sheet: $5 - $10

BILLION DOLLAR SCANDAL, THE
(1933 - Paramount) Robert Armstrong,
Constance Cummings
One Sheet: $100 - $200

BILLIONS
(1920 - -) Alla Nazimova, Charles Bryant
One Sheet: $350 - $750

BILLPOSTERS
(1940 - RKO/Disney) Donald Duck
One Sheet: $3,500 - $5,000   *Cartoon.
Cartoon Movie Posters #160.*

BILLY BATHGATE
(1991 - Touchstone) Dustin Hoffman, Nicole
Kidman
One Sheet: $5 - $10

BILLY BUDD
(1962 - Allied Artists) Peter Ustinov, Robert
Ryan, Terence Stamp
One Sheet: $7 - $15

BILLY JACK
(1971 - Warner Bros.) Tom Laughlin, Delores
Taylor
One Sheet: $20 - $40

BILLY JACK
(1973R - Warner Bros.) Tom Laughlin, Delores
Taylor
One Sheet: $7 - $15   *Re-release.*

The most
unusual boxoffice
success of all time.

**BILLY
JACK**

TOM LAUGHLIN
DELORES TAYLOR

One Sheet

BILLY JACK GOES TO WASHINGTON
(1977 - Taylor-Laughlin) Tom Laughlin, Delores
Taylor
One Sheet: $10 - $20

BILLY LIAR
(1963 - Continental) Tom Courtenay, Julie
Christie
One Sheet: $30 - $50

BILLY MADISON
(1995 - Universal) Adam Sandler
One Sheet: $3 - $5

BILLY ROSE'S JUMBO
(1962 - MGM) Doris Day, Stephen Boyd
One Sheet: $30 - $50

BILLY THE KID
(1930 - MGM) Johnny Mack Brown, Wallace
Beery
One Sheet: $250 - $600

BILLY THE KID
(1941 - MGM) Robert Taylor, Brian Donlevy
One Sheet: $100 - $200

BILLY THE KID
(1951R - MGM) Robert Taylor, Brian Donlevy
One Sheet: $30 - $50   *Re-release.*

BILLY THE KID
(1955R - MGM) Robert Taylor, Brian Donlevy
One Sheet. $15 - $25   *Re-release.*

BILLY THE KID IN CATTLE STAMPEDE
(1943 - PRC) Buster Crabbe, Al St. John

One Sheet: $40 - $75

BILLY THE KID IN FUGITIVE OF THE PLAINS
(1943 - PRC) Buster Crabbe, Al St. John
One Sheet: $40 - $75

BILLY THE KID IN LAW AND ORDER
(1942 - PRC) Buster Crabbe, Al St. John
One Sheet: $40 - $75

BILLY THE KID IN SANTA FE
(1941 - PRC) Bob Steele
One Sheet: $75 - $125

BILLY THE KID IN TEXAS
(1940 - PRC) Bob Steele
One Sheet: $75 - $125

BILLY THE KID IN THE RENEGADE
(1943 - PRC) Buster Crabbe, Al St. John
One Sheet: $30 - $50

BILLY THE KID OUTLAWED
(1940 - PRC) Bob Steele
One Sheet: $75 - $125

BILLY THE KID RETURNS
(1938 - Republic) Roy Rogers, Mary Hart
One Sheet: $600 - $1,000   *Cowboy
Movie Posters #229.*

BILLY THE KID TRAPPED
(1942 - PRC) Buster Crabbe, Al St. John
One Sheet: $30 - $50

BILLY THE KID VS. DRACULA
(1965 - Embassy) John Carradine
One Sheet: $50 - $100

BILLY THE KID WANTED
(1941 - PRC) Buster Crabbe, Al St. John
One Sheet: $40 - $75

BILLY THE KID'S FIGHTING PALS
(1941 - PRC) Bob Steele
One Sheet: $75 - $125

BILLY THE KID'S GUN JUSTICE
(1940 - PRC) Bob Steele
One Sheet: $75 - $125

BILLY THE KID'S RANGE WAR
(1941 - PRC) Bob Steele
One Sheet: $75 - $125

BILLY THE KID'S ROUND-UP
(1941 - PRC) Buster Crabbe, Al St. John
One Sheet: $30 - $50

BILLY THE KID'S SMOKING GUNS
(1942 - PRC) Buster Crabbe, Al St. John
One Sheet: $30 - $50

BILLY TWO HATS
(1973 - United Artists) Gregory Peck, Desi
Arnaz, Jr.
One Sheet: $7 - $15   *AKA: THE
LADY AND THE OUTLAW*

BILOXI BLUES
(1988 - Universal) Matthew Broderick,
Christopher Walken
One Sheet: $5 - $10

BIMBO THE GREAT
(1961 - Warner Bros.) Claus Holm, Elma
Karlowa
One Sheet: $10 - $20

BING CROSBY STOCK
(1934 - Educational) Bing Crosby
One Sheet: $150 - $300   *Comedy short.*

BINGO
(1991 - TriStar) Cindy Williams, David Rasche
One Sheet: $3 - $5

BINGO BONGO
(1983 - Columbia) Adriano Celentano
One Sheet: $15 - $25   *Italian. Italy's
version of TARZAN.*

**BINGO LONG TRAVELING ALL-STARS AND
MOTOR KINGS, THE**
(1976 - Universal) Billy Dee Williams, James
Earl Jones
One Sheet: $15 - $30   *Sports Movie
Posters #72.*

BIO-DOME
(1996 - MGM/UA) Pauly Shore, Stephen
Baldwin
One Sheet: $3 - $5

BIOGRAPHY OF A BACHELOR GIRL
(1934 - MGM) Ann Harding, Robert
Montgomery
One Sheet: $100 - $200

BIONIC BOY, THE
(1977 - RJR) Johnson Yap, Ron Rogers
One Sheet: $5 - $10

BIRCH INTERVAL
(1976 - GAMMA III) Eddie Albert, Rip Torn
One Sheet: $3 - $5

BIRD
(1988 - Warner Bros.) Forest Whitaker, Diane
Venora, Dir: Clint Eastwood
One Sheet: $15 - $25

BIRD IN THE HEAD, A
(1946 - Columbia) The Three Stooges (Curly)
One Sheet: $2,500 - $4,000   *Comedy short.
Duotone.*

BIRD MAN OF ALCATRAZ
(1962 - United Artists) Burt Lancaster, Karl
Malden
One Sheet: $40 - $75

BIRD OF PARADISE
(1932 - RKO) Dolores Del Rio, Joel McCrea
One Sheet: $800 - $1,500

BIRD OF PARADISE
(1951 - 20th Century Fox) Jeff Chandler, Louis
Jourdan
One Sheet: $75 - $150

BIRD ON A WIRE
(1990 - Universal) Mel Gibson, Goldie Hawn
One Sheet: $10 - $20

BIRD WITH THE CRYSTAL PLUMAGE, THE
(1970 - UMC) Tony Musante, Suzy Kendall
One Sheet: $15 - $30

BIRDCAGE, THE
(1996 - United Artists) Robin Williams, Nathan
Lane
One Sheet: $7 - $15

BIRDS, THE
(1963 - Universal) Rod Taylor, Tippi Hedren,
Dir: Alfred Hitchcock
One Sheet: $200 - $400   *Graven
Images, pg. 204.*

ALFRED
HITCHCOCK'S
"The Birds"
TECHNICOLOR

ROD TAYLOR · JESSICA TANDY · SUZANNE PLESHETTE
and introducing TIPPI HEDREN

Six Sheet

BIRDS AND THE BEES, THE
(1956 - Paramount) George Gobel, Mitzi
Gaynor, David Niven
One Sheet: $30 - $50

BIRDS DO IT
(1966 - Columbia) Soupy Sales, Tab Hunter
One Sheet: $15 - $25

BIRDS DO IT, BEES DO IT
(1975 - Columbia) -
One Sheet: $7 - $15

BIRDS IN PERIL
(1968 - Regional) Jean Seberg, Maurice
Ronet, Piette Brasseur, D. Darrieux
One Sheet: $5 - $10

BIRDS IN THE SPRING
(1933 - United Artists) Silly Symphony
One Sheet: $10,000 - $15,000   *Cartoon. Full
color. The Disney Poster, pg. 11.*

BIRDS OF A FEATHER
(1935 - Universal) George Robey, Horace
Hodges
One Sheet: $125 - $250

BIRDS, THE BEES AND THE ITALIANS, THE
(1967 - Seven Arts) Virna Lisi
One Sheet: $5 - $10

BIRDY
(1984 - TriStar) Matthew Modine, Nicolas Cage
One Sheet: $15 - $25

BIRTH OF A BABY
(1938 - Special) Eleanor King, Richard Gordon
One Sheet: $100 - $200

BIRTH OF A BOY
(1959 - British Lion) Barry Fitzgerald
One Sheet: $15 - $25

BIRTH OF A LEGEND
(1973 - American National) -
One Sheet: $5 - $10

BIRTH OF A NATION, THE
(1915 - Epoch) Dir: D. W. Griffith
One Sheet: $40,000 - $50,000   *Price is for One Sheet (Klansman style). One Sheet (Lincoln shot):$20,000-25,000. No lobby cards were issued for this release.*

One Sheet

BIRTH OF A NATION, THE
(1921R - Epoch) Dir: D.W. Griffith
One Sheet: $4,500 - $7,000   *Re-release. One Sheet is dated and is similar to Klansman style 1915 original.*

BIRTH OF A NATION, THE
(1930R - Epoch) Dir: D.W. Griffith
One Sheet: $100 - $200   *First sound version re-release.*

BIRTH OF A NEW AMERICA, THE
(1934 - Super Film Attractions) -
One Sheet: $100 - $200

BIRTH OF THE BLUES
(1941 - Paramount) Bing Crosby, Mary Martin
One Sheet: $150 - $300

BIRTHDAY PARTY, THE
(1968 - Continental) Robert Shaw, Patrick Magee
One Sheet: $5 - $10

BIRTHDAY PRESENT, THE
(1957 - British Lion) Tony Britton, Sylvia Simms
One Sheet: $10 - $20

BIRTHRIGHT
(1924 - -) Homer Tutt, Evelyn Preer
One Sheet: $100 - $200

BIRTHRIGHT
(1939 - Micheaux) Carman Newsome, Ethel Moses
One Sheet: $250 - $500   *Black cast. Separate Cinema, pg. 18.*

BISCUIT EATER, THE
(1940 - Paramount) Billy Lee, Cordell Hickman, Promise
One Sheet: $100 - $200   *Separate Cinema, pg. 117.*

BISCUIT EATER, THE
(1972 - Buena Vista/Disney) Earl Holliman, Lew Ayres
One Sheet: $10 - $20   *Re-make of the 1940 classic.*

BISHOP MISBEHAVES, THE
(1935 - MGM) Edmund Gwenn, Maureen O'Sullivan
One Sheet: $250 - $500

BISHOP MURDER CASE, THE
(1930 - MGM) Basil Rathbone, Roland Young
One Sheet: $800 - $1,500

BISHOP'S WIFE, THE
(1948 - RKO) Cary Grant, Loretta Young
One Sheet: $75 - $150

BITCH
(1965 - Warhol) Edie Sedgewick
One Sheet: $50 - $100

BITE THE BULLET
(1975 - Columbia) Gene Hackman, Candice Bergen, James Coburn
One Sheet: $15 - $25   *Cowboy Movie Posters #341.*

BITER BIT, THE
(1937 - 20th Century Fox) Billy Caryll, Hilda Murday
One Sheet: $75 - $150

BITTER CREEK
(1954 - Monogram) Bill Elliott, Beverly Garland
One Sheet: $15 - $35

BITTER HARVEST
(1963 - Rank) Janet Munro, John Stride
One Sheet: $20 - $40

BITTER MOON
(1994 - Fine Line) Peter Coyote, Hugh Grant
One Sheet: $10 - $20

BITTER RICE
(1950 - Lux) Silvana Mangano, Doris Dowling
One Sheet: $150 - $300

BITTER SPRINGS
(1950 - British Empire) Tommy Trinder
One Sheet: $10 - $20

BITTER SWEET
(1933 - United Artists) Anna Neagle
One Sheet: $150 - $300

BITTER SWEET
(1940 - MGM) Jeanette MacDonald, Nelson Eddy
One Sheet: $200 - $400

BITTER SWEET
(1962R - MGM) Jeanette MacDonald, Nelson Eddy
One Sheet: $15 - $25   *Re-release.*

BITTER SWEET LOVE
(1967 - Film 2 Associates) Dick Gregory, Don Murray
One Sheet: $5 - $10

BITTER TEA OF GENERAL YEN
(1933 - Columbia) Barbara Stanwyck, Dir: Frank Capra
One Sheet: $4,000 - $6,000

BITTER VICTORY
(1957 - Columbia) Richard Burton, Curt Jurgens
One Sheet: $30 - $50

BITTERSWEET LOVE
(1976 - Avco/Embassy) Lana Turner, Robert Lansing
One Sheet: $7 - $15

BLACK 13
(1954 - 20th Century Fox) Peter Reynolds, Rona Anderson
One Sheet: $15 - $30

BLACK ABBOT, THE
(1934 - RKO) John Stuart, Judy Kelly
One Sheet: $125 - $250

BLACK ACES
(1937 - Universal) Buck Jones
One Sheet: $500 - $800   *Cowboy Movie Posters #211.*

BLACK AND TAN
(1929 - RKO) Duke Ellington, Fredi Washington
One Sheet: $600 - $1,000   *Black cast. Separate Cinema, pg. 90.*

BLACK ANGEL
(1946 - Universal) Dan Duryea, June Vincent, Peter Lorre
One Sheet: $75 - $150

BLACK ANGELS, THE
(1970 - Merrick) Des Roberts, Linda Jackson, John King III

One Sheet: $15 - $25   *Blaxploitation biker film. Real motorcycle gangs were used in filming fight scenes.*

BLACK ARROW
(1944 - Columbia) Robert Scott, Adele Jergens
One Sheet: $75 - $150   *Serial. Western. 15 Chapters. Cowboy Movie Posters #276.*

BLACK ARROW
(1948 - Columbia) Louis Hayward, Janet Blair
One Sheet: $30 - $50

BLACK ARROW
(1955R - Columbia) Robert Scott, Adele Jergens
One Sheet: $30 - $50   *Re-release. Serial. Western.*

BLACK BANDIT, THE
(1938 - Universal) Bob Baker
One Sheet: $50 - $100

BLACK BANDIT, THE
(1950R - Realart) Bob Baker
One Sheet: $30 - $50   *Re-release.*

BLACK BART
(1948 - Universal) Yvonne De Carlo, Dan Duryea
One Sheet: $40 - $75

BLACK BEAUTY
(1921 - Vitagraph) Jean Paige
One Sheet: $600 - $1,000

BLACK BEAUTY
(1933 - Monogram) Esther Ralston, Alexander Kirkland
One Sheet: $200 - $400

BLACK BEAUTY
(1946 - 20th Century Fox) Mona Freeman, Richard Denning
One Sheet: $50 - $100   *One Sheet(text only):$5-10.*

BLACK BEAUTY
(1971 - Paramount) Mark Lester, Walter Slezak
One Sheet: $7 - $15

BLACK BEAUTY
(1974R - Paramount) Mark Lester, Walter Slezak
One Sheet: $5 - $10   *Re-release.*

BLACK BEAUTY
(1994 - Warner Bros.) Sean Bean, David Thewlis
One Sheet: $5 - $10

BLACK BELLY OF THE TARANTULA, THE
(1972 - MGM) Giancarlo Giannini
One Sheet: $30 - $50

BLACK BELT JONES
(1974 - Warner Bros.) Jim Kelly, Gloria Hendry
One Sheet: $15 - $30   *Blaxploitation.*

BLACK BIRD, THE
(1926 - MGM) Owen Moore, Renee Adoree, Lon Chaney
One Sheet: $2,200 - $3,500

BLACK BIRD, THE
(1975 - Columbia) George Segal, Stephane Audran
One Sheet: $5 - $10

BLACK BOOK, THE
(1949 - Eagle-Lion) Robert Cummings, Arlene Dahl
One Sheet: $40 - $75

BLACK BUTTERFLIES
(1953 - -) -
One Sheet: $125 - $250   *Mexican. Vargas art.*

BLACK CAESAR
(1973 - AIP) Fred Williamson, D'Urville Martin
One Sheet: $15 - $25   *Blaxploitation.*

BLACK CAMEL, THE
(1931 - Fox) Warner Oland, Bela Lugosi
One Sheet: $1,600 - $2,500

BLACK CASTLE, THE
(1952 - Universal) Stephen McNally, Richard Greene, Boris Karloff
One Sheet: $75 - $150

BLACK CAT, THE

(1934 - Universal) Boris Karloff, Bela Lugosi
One Sheet: $25,000 - $40,000   *Graven Images, pg. 80, 82.*

Title Card

BLACK CAT, THE
(1941 - Universal) Basil Rathbone, Alan Ladd, Bela Lugosi
One Sheet: $600 - $1,000   *Graven Images, pg. 114.*

BLACK CAT, THE
(1948R - Realart) Basil Rathbone, Alan Ladd, Bela Lugosi
One Sheet: $150 - $300   *Re-release.*

BLACK CAT, THE
(1950R - Realart) Basil Rathbone, Alan Ladd, Bela Lugosi
One Sheet: $100 - $200   *Re-release.*

BLACK CAT, THE
(1966 - Hemisphere) Robert Frost, Robyn Baker
One Sheet: $7 - $15

BLACK CAT, THE
(1984 - World Northal) Patrick Magee
One Sheet: $3 - $5

BLACK CAULDRON, THE
(1985 - Buena Vista/Disney) Richard Rich, voice of Grant Bardsley
One Sheet: $15 - $30   *Cartoon.*

BLACK CHRISTMAS
(1975 - Ambassador) Olivia Hussey, Keir Dullea
One Sheet: $10 - $20   *AKA: SILENT NIGHT, EVIL NIGHT.*

BLACK COFFEE
(1931 - Twickenham) Austin Trevor
One Sheet: $150 - $350

BLACK COIN, THE
(1936 - Weiss-Mintz) Ralph Graves, Ruth Mix
One Sheet: $125 - $250   *Serial.15 Chapters.*

BLACK CURSE
(1953R - -) -
One Sheet: $15 - $25   *Re-release.*

BLACK DAKOTAS, THE
(1954 - Columbia) Gary Merrill, Wanda Hendrix
One Sheet: $20 - $40

BLACK DIAMOND EXPRESS, THE
(1927 - Warner Bros.) Monte Blue
One Sheet: $200 - $400

BLACK DIAMONDS
(1932 - Hammer) John Martin
One Sheet: $100 - $200

BLACK DIAMONDS
(1940 - Universal) Richard Arlen, Andy Devine
One Sheet: $100 - $200

BLACK DOLL, THE
(1938 - Universal) Nan Grey, Donald Woods
One Sheet: $250 - $600   *Horror.*

BLACK DRAGON
(1977 - -) Ron Van Cliff
One Sheet: $10 - $20   *Blaxploitation martial arts.*

BLACK DRAGONS
(1942 - Monogram) Bela Lugosi, Joan Barclay
One Sheet: $250 - $600   *Graven Images, pg. 133.*

BLACK DRAGONS
(1947R - Monogram) Bela Lugosi, Joan Barclay
One Sheet: $50 - $100   *Re-release.*

BLACK DUKE, THE
(1964 - PRC) Cameron Mitchell, Gloria Milland
One Sheet: $10 - $20

BLACK EAGLE
(1948 - Columbia) William Bishop, Virginia Patton
One Sheet: $20 - $40

BLACK EAGLE
(1988 - -) Jean Claude Van Damme, Sho Kosugi
One Sheet: $7 - $15

BLACK EYES
(1940 - Film Alliance) Otto Kruger, Mary McGuire
One Sheet: $50 - $100

BLACK EYES
(1974 - Warner Bros.) Fred Williamson, Rosemary Forsyth
One Sheet: $7 - $15   *Blaxploitation.*

BLACK FOX, THE
(1962 - Astor) Marlene Dietrich
One Sheet: $20 - $40   *Documentary about Adolf Hitler. Academy Award: Best Documentary.*

BLACK FRIDAY
(1940 - Universal) Boris Karloff, Bela Lugosi
One Sheet: $2,500 - $4,000   *Graven Images, pg. 114.*

BLACK FURY
(1935 - First National) Paul Muni, Karen Morley
One Sheet: $250 - $500   *One Sheet(Leader Press):$300-$600.*

One Sheet

BLACK GESTAPO, THE
(1975 - Bryanston) Rod Perry, Charles P. Robinson
One Sheet: $15 - $30   *Blaxploitation.*

BLACK GIRL
(1973 - Cinerama) Brock Peters, Leslie Uggams, Claudie McNei
One Sheet: $15 - $25   *Blaxploitation.*
Dir: Ossie Davis.

BLACK GLOVE, THE
(1953 - Lippert) Alex Nichol, Eleanor Summerfield
One Sheet: $30 - $50

BLACK GODFATHER
(1974 - -) Jimmy Witherspoon, Rod Perry
One Sheet: $10 - $20   *Blaxploitation.*

BLACK GOLD
(1928 - Norman) Lawrence Criner, Kathryn Boyd
One Sheet: $600 - $1,000   *Black cast.*
Separate Cinema, pg. 4.

BLACK GOLD
(193? - -) Frankie Darro
One Sheet: $40 - $75

BLACK GOLD
(1947 - Allied Artists) Anthony Quinn, Katherine DeMille
One Sheet: $30 - $50

BLACK GOLD
(1962 - Warner Bros.) Philip Carey, Diane McBain
One Sheet: $5 - $10

BLACK GUNN
(1972 - Columbia) Jim Brown, Martin Landau
One Sheet: $15 - $25   *Blaxploitation.*
Sports Movie Posters #362.

BLACK HAND
(1949 - MGM) Gene Kelly, J. Carroll Naish, Teresa Celli
One Sheet: $50 - $100

BLACK HAND GANG, THE
(1930 - British International) Wee Georgie Wood
One Sheet: $250 - $500

BLACK HANDS & SOAP SUDS
(1920 - Christie) Billie Rhodes, Harry Ham, Eddie Barry
One Sheet: $125 - $250

BLACK HILLS
(1947 - PRC) Eddie Dean, Roscoe Ates
One Sheet: $30 - $50

BLACK HILLS AMBUSH
(1952 - Republic) Allan "Rocky" Lane
One Sheet: $20 - $40

BLACK HILLS EXPRESS, THE
(1943 - Republic) Don "Red" Barry
One Sheet: $30 - $50

BLACK HOLE, THE
(1979 - Walt Disney) Maximillian Schell, Robert Foster, Anthony Perkins
One Sheet: $10 - $20

BLACK HORSE CANYON
(1954 - Universal) Joel McCrea, Mari Blanchard
One Sheet: $15 - $30

BLACK ICE, THE
(1957 - Archway) Paul Carpenter, Gordon Jackson
One Sheet: $15 - $30

BLACK JACK
(1973 - AIP) George Stanford Brown, Brandon De Wilde
One Sheet: $7 - $15   *Blaxploitation.*
Aka: Wild In The Sky.

BLACK JACK
(1979 - National) Jean Franval
One Sheet: $5 - $10

BLACK JESUS
(1971 - -) Woody Strode, Jean Servais
One Sheet: $30 - $50   *Black cast.*

BLACK JOY
(1977 - Milchan) Norman Beaton, Trevor Thomas
One Sheet: $5 - $10

BLACK KING, THE
(1932 - Sack Amusement) A.B. Comethiere, Vivianne Baber
One Sheet: $200 - $400   *Black cast.*
Duotone. Separate Cinema, pg. 128.

BLACK KLANSMAN, THE
(1966 - U.S. Films) Richard Glidden, Rima Kutner
One Sheet: $30 - $50

One Sheet

BLACK KNIGHT, THE
(1954 - Warwick) Alan Ladd, Patricia Medina
One Sheet: $30 - $50

BLACK LASH, THE

(1951 - Western Adventure) Lash LaRue
One Sheet: $30 - $60

BLACK LEGION
(1936 - Warner Bros.) Humphrey Bogart, Dick Foran
One Sheet: $250 - $600

BLACK LIGHTNING
(1924 - -) Clara Bow
One Sheet: $600 - $1,000

BLACK LIKE ME
(1964 - Reade-Sterling) James Whitmore, Dan Priest
One Sheet: $30 - $50

BLACK LIMELIGHT
(1938 - Alliance) Raymond Massey, Joan Marion
One Sheet: $75 - $150

BLACK MAGIC
(1945 - Monogram) Sidney Toler, Mantan Moreland
One Sheet: $100 - $200

BLACK MAGIC
(1949 - United Artists) Orson Welles, Nancy Guild
One Sheet: $40 - $75

BLACK MAGIC WOMAN
(1991 - Trimark) Mark Hamill, Amanda Wyss, Apollonia
One Sheet: $5 - $10

BLACK MAMA, WHITE MAMA
(1972 - AIP) Margaret Markow, Pam Grier
One Sheet: $15 - $35   *Black sexploitation. "Chicks in chains!..."*

BLACK MARBLE, THE
(1980 - Avco/Embassy) Robert Foxworth, Paula Prentiss
One Sheet: $2 - $3

BLACK MARKET BABIES
(1945 - Monogram) Ralph Morgan, Jane Edwards
One Sheet: $75 - $150

BLACK MARKET RUSTLERS
(1943 - Monogram) Range Busters
One Sheet: $30 - $60

BLACK MASK
(1935 - Warner Bros.) Wylie Watson
One Sheet: $150 - $300

BLACK MEMORY
(1947 - Ambassador) Michael Atkinson, Myra O'Connell
One Sheet: $50 - $100

BLACK MIDNIGHT
(1949 - Monogram) Roddy McDowall, Damian O'Flynn
One Sheet: $30 - $50

BLACK MOON
(1934 - Columbia) Jack Holt, Fay Wray
One Sheet: $1,300 - $2,000   *Graven Images, pg. 64.*

BLACK MOON RISING
(1986 - New World) Tommy Lee Jones, Linda Hamilton
One Sheet: $7 - $15

BLACK MOSES OF SOUL - ISAAC HAYES
(197? - -) Isaac Hayes
One Sheet: $15 - $25   *Black cast.*
Soul music concert.

BLACK NARCISSUS
(1946 - Universal-International) Deborah Kerr, Sabu, David Farrar
One Sheet: $200 - $400

BLACK OAK CONSPIRACY
(1977 - New World) Jesse Vint, Karen Carlson
One Sheet: $5 - $10

BLACK ON WHITE
(1969 - Audobon) Anita Sanders, Nine Segurino, Terry Carter
One Sheet: $5 - $10

BLACK ORCHID, THE
(1958 - Paramount) Sophia Loren, Anthony Quinn
One Sheet: $20 - $40

BLACK ORPHEUS
(1959 - Lopert) Breno Mello, Marpessa Dawn
One Sheet: $200 - $400   *French.*
Academy Award: Best Foreign Film. Separate Cinema, pg. 36.

BLACK OXEN
(1924 - Associated First National) Corinne Griffith, Conway Tearle
One Sheet: $150 - $300

BLACK OXFORDS
(1924 - Pathecomedy) Mack Sennett
One Sheet: $150 - $300   *Sports (Horse racing). Sports Movie Posters #241.*

BLACK PANTHER, THE
(1956 - Howes) Sabu, Carol Varga
One Sheet: $30 - $50

BLACK PANTHER, THE
(1977 - Impics) Donald Sumpter
One Sheet: $15 - $25

BLACK PARACHUTE, THE
(1944 - Columbia) John Carradine, Bela Lugosi
One Sheet: $75 - $150

BLACK PATCH
(1957 - Montgomery) George Montgomery, Diane Brewster
One Sheet: $15 - $30

BLACK PIRATE, THE
(1926 - United Artists) Douglas Fairbanks
One Sheet: $6,500 - $10,000

BLACK PIRATES, THE
(1954 - Lippert) Anthony Dexter, Lon Chaney
One Sheet: $40 - $75

BLACK PIT OF DR. M
(1958 - United Releasing) Raphael Bertrand, Mary Cortez
One Sheet: $20 - $40

BLACK RAIN
(1989 - Paramount) Michael Douglas, Andy Garcia, Kate Capshaw
One Sheet: $10 - $20

BLACK RAVEN, THE
(1943 - PRC) George Zucco, Wanda McKay
One Sheet: $125 - $250

BLACK RIDER, THE
(1954 - Butcher) Jim Hanley, Rona Anderson
One Sheet: $20 - $40

BLACK ROBE
(1991 - -) Lothaire Bluteau
One Sheet: $5 - $10

BLACK RODEO
(1972 - Cinerama) Woody Strode, Archie Wycoff, Muhammad Ali
One Sheet: $15 - $35   *Black cast western. Sports (rodeo). Sports Movie Posters #303.*

BLACK ROOM, THE
(1935 - Columbia) Boris Karloff, Marian Marsh
One Sheet: $1,300 - $2,000   *Graven Images, pg. 86.*

BLACK ROOM, THE
(1944R - Columbia) Boris Karloff, Marian Marsh
One Sheet: $150 - $350   *Re-release.*

BLACK ROOM, THE
(1955R - Columbia) Boris Karloff, Marian Marsh
One Sheet: $75 - $125   *Re-release.*

BLACK ROOM, THE
(1985 - -) Stephen Knight, Cassandra Gavioca
One Sheet: $5 - $10

BLACK ROSE, THE
(1950 - 20th Century Fox) Tyrone Power, Orson Welles
One Sheet: $75 - $150

BLACK ROSES
(1921 - -) -
One Sheet: $100 - $200

BLACK ROSES
(1936 - UFA) Lillian Harvey, Esmond Knight
One Sheet: $100 - $200   *AKA: DID I BETRAY?*

BLACK SABBATH

(1964 - AIP) Boris Karloff, Mark Damon
One Sheet: $40 - $75   *Graven Images, pg. 210.*

BLACK SAMSON
(1974 - Warner Bros.) Rockne Tarkington
One Sheet: $15 - $25   *Blaxploitation.*

BLACK SCORPION, THE
(1957 - Warner Bros.) Richard Denning, Mara Corday
One Sheet: $50 - $100   *Animation by Willis (King Kong) O'Brien.*

BLACK SHAMPOO
(1976 - Dimension) John Daniel, Tanya Boyd
One Sheet: $15 - $25   *Blaxploitation.*

BLACK SHEEP
(1935 - Fox) Edmund Lowe, Claire Trevor
One Sheet: $150 - $300

BLACK SHEEP
(1941 - United Artists) Will Hay, John Mills
One Sheet: $75 - $125

BLACK SHEEP
(1996 - Paramount) Chris Farley, David Spade, Tim Matheson
One Sheet: $3 - $5   *Comedy.*

BLACK SHIELD OF FALWORTH, THE
(1954 - Universal) Tony Curtis, Janet Leigh
One Sheet: $40 - $75

BLACK SIX, THE
(1974 - Cinemation) Gene Washington, Carl Eller
One Sheet: $20 - $40

BLACK SLEEP, THE
(1956 - United Artists) Basil Rathbone, Akim Tamiroff, Bela Lugosi, Lon Chaney Jr.
One Sheet: $50 - $100

BLACK SNAKE
(197? - -) -
One Sheet: $3 - $5

BLACK SPIDER, THE
(1983 - Europa) Beatrice Kessler, Walo Lueoend
One Sheet: $10 - $20

BLACK SPURS
(1965 - Paramount) Rory Calhoun, Terry Moore
One Sheet: $15 - $25

BLACK STALLION
(1979 - United Artists) Terri Garr, Mickey Rooney
One Sheet: $10 - $20

BLACK STALLION RETURNS, THE
(1983 - MGM/United Artists) Kelly Reno, Vincent Spano
One Sheet: $5 - $10

BLACK STARLET
(1974 - -) Juanita Brown, Rockne Tarkington
One Sheet: $15 - $30   *Blaxploitation.*

BLACK SUNDAY
(1961 - AIP) Barbara Steele, John Richardson, Dir: Bava
One Sheet: $125 - $250   *Graven Images, pg. 210.*

BLACK SUNDAY
(1977 - Paramount) Robert Shaw, Bruce Dern
One Sheet: $15 - $30   *Sports Movie Posters #205. One Sheet(Mylar advance):$15-$25.*

BLACK SWAN, THE
(1942 - 20th Century Fox) Tyrone Power, Maureen O'Hara
One Sheet: $800 - $1,500

BLACK SWAN, THE
(1952R - 20th Century Fox) Tyrone Power, Maureen O'Hara
One Sheet: $50 - $100   *Re-release.*

BLACK TENT, THE
(1957 - Rank) Anthony Steel, Donald Sinden
One Sheet: $15 - $25

BLACK TIDE
(1958 - Astor) John Ireland
One Sheet: $20 - $40

BLACK TIGHTS
(1962 - Magna) Moira Shearer

One Sheet: $20 - $40   *Dancing (Ballet).*

One Sheet

BLACK TORMENT, THE
(1965 - Compton-Tekli) John Turner, Heather Sears
One Sheet: $10 - $20

BLACK TUESDAY
(1954 - United Artists) Edward G. Robinson, Peter Graves
One Sheet: $30 - $50

BLACK TULIP, THE
(1937 - 20th Century Fox) Patrick Waddington, Ann Soreen
One Sheet: $100 - $200

BLACK VEIL FOR LISA
(1969 - Commonwealth United) John Mills, Luciana Paluzzi
One Sheet: $5 - $10

BLACK WATCH, THE
(1929 - Fox) Victor McLaglen, Myrna Loy
One Sheet: $250 - $600

BLACK WATERS
(1930 - Sono Art-World Wide) James Kirkwood, Mary Brian
One Sheet: $150 - $300

BLACK WHIP, THE
(1956 - 20th Century Fox) Hugh Marlowe, Coleen Gray, Angie Dickinson
One Sheet: $30 - $50

BLACK WIDOW, THE
(1947 - Republic) Bruce Edwards, Virginia Lindley
One Sheet: $150 - $350   *Serial. 13 Chapters.*

BLACK WIDOW
(1951 - Hammer) Christine Norden, Robert Ayres
One Sheet: $30 - $50

BLACK WIDOW
(1954 - 20th Century Fox) Gene Tierney, Van Heflin, Ginger Rogers
One Sheet: $40 - $75

BLACK WIDOW
(1987 - 20th Century Fox) Debra Winger, Theresa Russell, Dennis Hopper
One Sheet: $3 - $5

BLACK WINDMILL, THE
(1974 - Universal) Michael Caine, Janet Suzman
One Sheet: $5 - $10

BLACK WITCH, THE
(1929 - Fox) Myrna Loy
One Sheet: $250 - $600

BLACK ZOO, THE
(1963 - Allied Artists) Michael Gough, Jeanne Cooper
One Sheet: $20 - $40

BLACKBEARD THE PIRATE
(1952 - RKO) Linda Darnell, Robert Newton
One Sheet: $30 - $50

BLACKBEARD THE PIRATE
(1957R - RKO) Linda Darnell, Robert Newton
One Sheet: $10 - $20   *Re-release.*

BLACKBEARD'S GHOST
(1968 - Buena Vista/Disney) Peter Ustinov, Suzanne Pleshette

One Sheet: $15 - $25

BLACKBEARD'S GHOST
(1976R - Buena Vista/Disney) Peter Ustinov, Suzanne Pleshette
One Sheet: $7 - $15   *Re-release.*

BLACKBOARD JUNGLE, THE
(1955 - MGM) Glenn Ford, Anne Francis, Sidney Poitier
One Sheet: $75 - $150

BLACKENSTEIN
(1973 - Exclusive International) John Hart, Ivory Stone
One Sheet: $30 - $50   *Blaxploitation.*

BLACKHAWK
(1952 - Columbia) Kirk Alyn
One Sheet: $100 - $200   *Serial. 15 Chapters.*

BLACKJACK KETCHUM, DESPERADO
(1956 - Columbia) Howard Duff, Maggie Mahoney
One Sheet: $15 - $25

BLACKMAIL
(1930 - Sono Art/World Wide) Anny Ondra, John Lundgren, Dir: Alfred Hitchcock
One Sheet: $3,500 - $5,000   *Hitchcock's first talkie.*

BLACKMAIL
(1939 - MGM) Edward G. Robinson, Ruth Hussey
One Sheet: $100 - $200

BLACKMAIL
(1947 - Republic) William Marshall, Adele Mara
One Sheet: $40 - $75

BLACKMAILED
(1951 - General) Mai Zetterling, Dirk Bogarde
One Sheet: $15 - $30

BLACKMAILER, THE
(1936 - Columbia) William Gargan, Florence Rice
One Sheet: $150 - $300

BLACKOUT
(1940 - United Artists) Conrad Veidt, Valerie Hobson
One Sheet: $75 - $150   *AKA: CONTRABAND.*

BLACKOUT
(1950 - Eros) Maxwell Reed
One Sheet: $30 - $50

BLACKOUT
(1954 - Hammer/Lippert) Dane Clark, Belinda Lee
One Sheet: $20 - $40

BLACKOUT
(1978 - New World) Robert Carradine, June Allyson
One Sheet: $5 - $10

BLACKOUT
(1989 - Magnum) Carol Lynley, Michael Keyshall
One Sheet: $3 - $5

BLACKSMITH, THE
(1922 - Comique) Buster Keaton
One Sheet: $10,000 - $15,000

BLACKSMITH'S LOVE, THE
(1911 - Selig) -
One Sheet: $350 - $750

BLACKWELL'S ISLAND
(1939 - Warner Bros.) John Garfield, Rosemary Lane
One Sheet: $100 - $200

BLACULA
(1972 - AIP) William Marshall, Denise Nicholas
One Sheet: $30 - $60   *Blaxploitation.*

BLADE
(1973 - Pintoff) John Marley, Jon Cypher
One Sheet: $5 - $10

BLADE RUNNER
(1982 - Warner Bros.) Harrison Ford, Rutger Hauer
One Sheet: $75 - $125

BLADE RUNNER
(1992R - Warner Bros.) Harrison Ford, Rutger

Hauer
One Sheet: $15 - $25   *Re-release. "Director's cut".*

BLADE-PSYCHO KARATE KILLER
(1973 - -) -
One Sheet: $5 - $10

BLADES
(1989 - Troma) Robert North, Jeremy Whelan
One Sheet: $3 - $5

BLADES OF THE MUSKETEERS
(1953 - Howco) Robert Clarke, John Hubbard
One Sheet: $15 - $25

BLAKE OF SCOTLAND YARD
(1937 - Victory) Ralph Byrd, Joan Barclay
One Sheet: $125 - $250   *Serial. 15 Episodes.*

BLAME IT ON RIO
(1983 - 20th Century Fox) Michael Caine, Joseph Bologna
One Sheet: $5 - $10

BLAME IT ON THE NIGHT
(1984 - TriStar) Nick Mancuso
One Sheet: $3 - $5

BLAME THE WOMAN
(1932 - Principal) Adolphe Menjou, Benita Hume
One Sheet: $100 - $200   *AKA: DIAMOND CUT DIAMOND.*

BLANC ET NOIR
(1890 - -) -
One Sheet: $350 - $750   *French. Early projected slide show.*

BLANCHE FURY
(1947 - Eagle Lion) Stewart Granger, Valerie Hobson
One Sheet: $15 - $35

BLANK CHECK
(1994 - Disney) Brian Bonsall, Karen Duffy
One Sheet: $3 - $5

BLARNEY KISS
(1933 - British & Dominion) Tom Walls, Anne Grey
One Sheet: $150 - $300   *AKA: THE BLARNEY STONE.*

BLAST
(1976 - -) Billy Dee Williams, D'urville
One Sheet: $10 - $20   *Blaxploitation.*

BLAST OF SILENCE
(1961 - Universal) Allen Baron, Molly McCarthy
One Sheet: $7 - $15

BLAST OFF GIRLS
(1967 - -) Dir: Hershell Gordon Lewis, Dan Conway, Tom Tyrell
One Sheet: $30 - $50

BLAST-OFF
(1967 - -) See "Those Fantastic Flying Fools"

BLAZE
(1989 - Touchstone) Paul Newman, Lolita Davidovich
One Sheet: $3 - $5

BLAZE O'GLORY
(1930 - Sono-Art) Eddie Dowling, Betty Compson
One Sheet: $125 - $250

BLAZE O'GLORY
(1963 - Argo) Gary Cockrell
One Sheet: $5 - $10

BLAZE OF NOON
(1947 - Paramount) Anne Baxter, William Holden
One Sheet: $40 - $75

BLAZING ACROSS THE PECOS
(1948 - Columbia) Charles Starrett, Smiley Burnette
One Sheet: $30 - $50

BLAZING BARRIERS
(1937 - Monogram) Edward Arnold, Florine McKinney
One Sheet: $75 - $125

BLAZING BULLETS
(1951 - -) Johnny Mack Brown, Lois Hall
One Sheet: $15 - $35

BLAZING FOREST, THE
(1952 - Paramount) John Payne, Agnes Moorehead
One Sheet: $15 - $25

BLAZING FRONTIER
(1943 - PRC) Buster Crabbe
One Sheet: $40 - $75

BLAZING GUNS
(1943 - Monogram) Ken Maynard, Hoot Gibson
One Sheet: $100 - $200

One Sheet

BLAZING SADDLES
(1974 - Warner Bros.) Cleavon Little, Gene Wilder, Slim Pickens, Dir: Mel Brooks
One Sheet: $30 - $50   *Western spoof (classic). Among highest-grossing westerns ever.*

BLAZING SIX SHOOTERS
(1940 - Columbia) Charles Starrett
One Sheet: $50 - $100

BLAZING SIXES
(1937 - Warner Bros.) Dick Foran
One Sheet: $50 - $100

BLAZING SUN, THE
(1950 - Columbia) Gene Autry, Pat Buttram, Lynne Roberts
One Sheet: $50 - $100

BLAZING THE OVERLAND TRAIL
(1956 - Columbia) Lee Roberts, Dennis Moore
One Sheet: $40 - $75   *Serial. Western. 15 Chapters.*

BLAZING THE WAY
(1920 - Universal) James B. Warner
One Sheet: $200 - $400

BLAZING THE WESTERN TRAIL
(1945 - Columbia) Charles Starrett, Tex Harding
One Sheet: $40 - $75

BLAZING TRAIL, THE
(1949 - Columbia) Charles Starrett
One Sheet: $40 - $75

BLEAK MOMENTS
(1972 - Contemporary) Anne Raitt
One Sheet: $3 - $5

BLESS 'EM ALL
(1949 - Adolphi) Hal Monty
One Sheet: $40 - $75

BLESS THE BEASTS AND CHILDREN
(1971 - Columbia) Bill Mumy, Barry Robins
One Sheet: $7 - $15

BLESS THEIR LITTLE HEARTS
(1984 - Black Independent Features) Nate Hardman, Kaycee Moore
One Sheet: $7 - $15   *Black cast.*

BLESSED EVENT
(1932 - Warner Bros.) Lee Tracy, Dick Powell
One Sheet: $250 - $500

BLESSING
(1995 - Starr Valley Films) Melora Griffis, Guy Griffis
One Sheet: $4 - $8

BLIND ADVENTURE
(1933 - RKO) Ralph Bellamy, Robert Armstrong
One Sheet: $75 - $150

BLIND ALIBI
(1938 - RKO) Richard Dix, Whitney Bourne
One Sheet: $75 - $150

BLIND ALLEY
(1939 - Columbia) Chester Morris, Ralph Bellamy
One Sheet: $75 - $150

BLIND ALLEYS
(1927 - Paramount) Thomas Meighan, Evelyn Brent
One Sheet: $150 - $300

BLIND BARGAIN, A
(1922 - Goldwyn) Lon Chaney
One Sheet: $1,900 - $3,000   *Graven Images, pg. 33.*

BLIND DATE
(1934 - Columbia) Ann Sothern, Paul Kelly, Mickey Rooney
One Sheet: $100 - $200

BLIND DATE
(1984 - New Line) Joseph Bottoms, Kirstie Alley
One Sheet: $5 - $10

BLIND DATE
(1987 - TriStar) Kim Basinger, Bruce Willis
One Sheet: $5 - $10

BLIND DEAD, THE
(1972 - Hallmark) Lone Fleming, Cesar Burner
One Sheet: $15 - $25   *AKA: TOMBS OF THE BLIND DEAD.*

BLIND FOLLY
(1939 - RKO) Lilli Palmer, Clifford Mollison
One Sheet: $75 - $150

BLIND FURY
(1990 - -) Rutger Hauer
One Sheet: $3 - $5

BLIND GODDESS, THE
(1948 - GFD) Eric Portman, Anne Crawford
One Sheet: $30 - $50

BLIND HEARTS
(1921 - Associated) Hobarth Bosworth, Wade Boteler
One Sheet: $600 - $1,000

BLIND HUSBANDS
(1919 - Universal) Erich von Stroheim, Gibson Gowland
One Sheet: $4,000 - $6,000

BLIND JUSTICE
(1934 - Real Art) Eva Moore, John Mills
One Sheet: $100 - $200

BLIND MAN'S BLUFF
(1952 - Apex) Zena Marshall
One Sheet: $20 - $40

BLIND SPOT
(1932 - Warner Bros.) Percy Marmont
One Sheet: $100 - $200

BLIND SPOT
(1947 - Columbia) Chester Morris, Constance Dowling
One Sheet: $50 - $100

BLIND SPOT
(1958 - Butchers) Robert Mackenzie, Delphi Lawrence
One Sheet: $10 - $20

BLINDFOLD
(1966 - Universal) Rock Hudson, Claudia Cardinale
One Sheet: $15 - $25

BLINDMAN
(1972 - 20th Century Fox) Tony Anthony, Ringo Starr
One Sheet: $15 - $25

BLINDNESS OF DIVORCE, THE
(1918 - William Fox) -
One Sheet: $300 - $700

BLINK
(1994 - New Line) Madeleine Stowe, Aidan Quinn
One Sheet: $3 - $5

BLISS
(1997 - Triumph) Craig Sheffer, Sheryl Lee
One Sheet: $4 - $8

BLISS OF MRS. BLOSSOM, THE
(1968 - Paramount) Shirley MacLaine, Richard Attenborough
One Sheet: $7 - $15

BLITHE SPIRIT
(1945 - United Artists) Rex Harrison, Constance Cummings
One Sheet: $50 - $100

BLITZ WOLF
(1942 - MGM) Dir: Tex Avery
One Sheet: $3,500 - $5,000   *Cartoon.*
Cartoon Movie Posters #285.

One Sheet

BLOB, THE
(1958 - Paramount) Steve McQueen, Aneta Corseaut
One Sheet: $200 - $400   *McQueen's first starring role. Graven Images, pg. 179.*

BLOB, THE
(1988 - TriStar) Shawnee Smith, Donovan Leitch
One Sheet: $5 - $10

BLOB, THE/DINOSAURUS
(1964R - Paramount) Steve McQueen, Aneta Corseaut, Ward Ramsey
One Sheet: $20 - $40   *Re-release. Double feature poster.*

BLOCK BUSTERS
(1944 - Monogram) East Side Kids, Harry Langdon
One Sheet: $75 - $125

BLOCKADE
(1928 - New Era) J.P. Kennedy
One Sheet: $200 - $400

BLOCKADE
(1929 - RKO) Anna Q. Nilsson
One Sheet: $150 - $300

BLOCKADE
(1938 - United Artists) Madeleine Carroll, Henry Fonda
One Sheet: $250 - $500

BLOCKED TRAIL, THE
(1943 - Republic) Three Mesquiteers (Tom Tyler, Bob Steele, Jimmie Dodd)
One Sheet: $50 - $100

BLOCK-HEADS
(1938 - MGM) Laurel and Hardy
One Sheet: $1,600 - $2,500

BLOCK-HEADS
(1947R - MGM) Laurel & Hardy
One Sheet: $40 - $75   *Re-release.*

BLOCKHOUSE, THE
(1974 - Hemdale) Peter Sellers, Charles Aznavour
One Sheet: $7 - $15

BLOND CHEAT
(1938 - RKO) Joan Fontaine, Derrick de Marnay
One Sheet: $100 - $200

BLONDE ALIBI
(1946 - Universal) Tom Neal, Martha O'Driscoll
One Sheet: $75 - $125

BLONDE AND GROOM
(1943 - Columbia) Harry Langdon
One Sheet: $100 - $200   *Comedy short. Duotone.*

BLONDE BAIT
(1956 - Associated) Beverly Michaels, Jim Davis
One Sheet: $75 - $125   *Sexploitation.*

BLONDE BANDIT, THE
(1949 - Republic) Gerald Mohr, Dorothy Patrick
One Sheet: $50 - $100

BLONDE BLACKMAILER
(1958 - Allied Artists) Richard Arlen, Susan Shaw
One Sheet: $20 - $40

BLONDE BOMBER, THE
(1936 - Vitaphone) -
One Sheet: $500 - $800   *Sports (Boxing). Joe Palooka series.*

BLONDE BOMBSHELL
(1933 - MGM) Jean Harlow, Lee Tracy
One Sheet: $1,300 - $2,000

BLONDE CAPTIVE, THE
(1931 - Imperial) Narrated by Lowell Thomas
One Sheet: $250 - $500

BLONDE CAPTIVE, THE
(194?R - Imperial) Narrated by Lowell Thomas
One Sheet: $30 - $50   *Re-release.*

BLONDE COMET
(1941 - PRC) Virginia Vale, Robert Kent
One Sheet: $50 - $100

BLONDE CRAZY
(1931 - Warner Bros.) James Cagney, Joan Blondell
One Sheet: $2,500 - $4,000

One Sheet

BLONDE DYNAMITE
(1950 - Monogram) Leo Gorcey, Huntz Hall
One Sheet: $40 - $75

BLONDE FEVER
(1944 - MGM) Mary Astor, Phillip Dorn
One Sheet: $75 - $125

BLONDE FOR A DAY
(1946 - PRC) Hugh Beaumont, Kathryn Adams
One Sheet: $40 - $75

BLONDE FOR A NIGHT
(1928 - Pathe) Marie Prevost
One Sheet: $250 - $600

BLONDE FROM BROOKLYN
(1945 - Columbia) Robert Stanton, Lynn Merrick
One Sheet: $50 - $100

BLONDE FROM SINGAPORE, THE
(1941 - Columbia) Florence Rice, Leif Erickson
One Sheet: $75 - $125

BLONDE ICE
(1948 - Film Classics) Robert Paige, Leslie Brooks
One Sheet: $50 - $100

BLONDE INSPIRATION
(1941 - MGM) John Shelton, Virginia Grey
One Sheet: $100 - $200

BLONDE OR BRUNETTE
(1927 - Paramount) Adolphe Menjou, Greta Nissen
One Sheet: $200 - $400

BLONDE PICKUP
(1955 - Globe) Peaches Page, Timothy Farrell
One Sheet: $50 - $100

BLONDE RANSOM
(1945 - Universal) Donald Cook, Virginia Grey

One Sheet: $50 - $100

BLONDE SAVAGE
(1947 - Ensign) Leif Erickson, Gale Sherwood
One Sheet: $30 - $50

BLONDE SINNER
(1956 - Allied Artists) Diana Dors, Michael Ripper
One Sheet: $50 - $100

BLONDE TROUBLE
(1937 - Paramount) Johnny Downs, Eleanor Whitney
One Sheet: $100 - $200

BLONDE VAMPIRE, THE
(1922 - Allen Rock) De Sacia Moores, Joseph Smiley
One Sheet: $700 - $1,200

BLONDE VENUS
(1932 - Paramount-Publix) Marlene Dietrich, Cary Grant
One Sheet: $5,000 - $8,000

BLONDES AT WORK
(1937 - Warner Bros.) Glenda Farrell, Barton MacLane
One Sheet: $75 - $125

BLONDES BEWARE
(1928 - Educational) Johnny Arthur
One Sheet: $250 - $500

BLONDES FOR DANGER
(1938 - British Lion) Gordon Harker
One Sheet: $125 - $250

BLONDIE
(1938 - Columbia) Penny Singleton, Arthur Lake
One Sheet: $1,300 - $2,000

BLONDIE
(1950R - Columbia) Penny Singleton, Arthur Lake
One Sheet: $100 - $200   Re-release.

BLONDIE BRINGS UP BABY
(1939 - Columbia) Penny Singleton, Arthur Lake, Larry Simms
One Sheet: $200 - $400

BLONDIE BRINGS UP BABY
(1950R - Columbia) Penny Singleton, Arthur Lake, Larry Simms
One Sheet: $30 - $50   Re-release.

BLONDIE FOR VICTORY
(1942 - Columbia) Penny Singleton, Arthur Lake
One Sheet: $75 - $150

BLONDIE GOES LATIN
(1941 - Columbia) Penny Singleton, Arthur Lake
One Sheet: $75 - $150

BLONDIE GOES TO COLLEGE
(1942 - Columbia) Penny Singleton, Arthur Lake, Larry Parks
One Sheet: $75 - $150

BLONDIE GOES TO COLLEGE
(1950R - Columbia) Penny Singleton, Arthur Lake, Larry Parks
One Sheet: $15 - $30   Re-release.

BLONDIE HAS SERVANT TROUBLE
(1940 - Columbia) Penny Singleton, Arthur Lake, Larry Parks
One Sheet: $75 - $150

BLONDIE HITS THE JACKPOT
(1949 - Columbia) Penny Singleton, Arthur Lake
One Sheet: $50 - $100

BLONDIE IN SOCIETY
(1941 - Columbia) Penny Singleton, Arthur Lake
One Sheet: $75 - $150

BLONDIE IN THE DOUGH
(1947 - Columbia) Penny Singleton, Arthur Lake, Larry Simms
One Sheet: $50 - $100

BLONDIE JOHNSON
(1933 - First National) Joan Blondell, Chester Morris
One Sheet: $500 - $800

BLONDIE KNOWS BEST
(1946 - Columbia) Penny Singleton, Arthur Lake, Shemp Howard
One Sheet: $100 - $200

BLONDIE MEETS THE BOSS
(1939 - Columbia) Penny Singleton, Arthur Lake
One Sheet: $150 - $300

BLONDIE OF THE FOLLIES
(1932 - MGM) Marion Davies, Robert Montgomery
One Sheet: $600 - $1,000

BLONDIE ON A BUDGET
(1940 - Columbia) Penny Singleton, Arthur Lake, Rita Hayworth
One Sheet: $150 - $300

BLONDIE PLAYS CUPID
(1940 - Columbia) Penny Singleton, Arthur Lake, Glenn Ford
One Sheet: $100 - $200

BLONDIE TAKES A VACATION
(1939 - Columbia) Penny Singleton, Arthur Lake
One Sheet: $125 - $250

BLONDIE'S ANNIVERSARY
(1947 - Columbia) Penny Singleton, Arthur Lake, Adele Jergens
One Sheet: $50 - $100

BLONDIE'S BIG DEAL
(1949 - Columbia) Penny Singleton, Arthur Lake, Larry Simms
One Sheet: $50 - $100

BLONDIE'S BIG MOMENT
(1947 - Columbia) Penny Singleton, Arthur Lake, Anita Louise
One Sheet: $50 - $100

BLONDIE'S BLESSED EVENT
(1942 - Columbia) Penny Singleton, Arthur Lake
One Sheet: $100 - $200

BLONDIE'S HERO
(1950 - Columbia) Arthur Lake, Penny Singleton
One Sheet: $40 - $75

BLONDIE'S HOLIDAY
(1947 - Columbia) Penny Singleton, Arthur Lake, Larry Simms
One Sheet: $50 - $100

BLONDIE'S LUCKY DAY
(1946 - Columbia) Penny Singleton, Arthur Lake
One Sheet: $50 - $100

BLONDIE'S REWARD
(1948 - Columbia) Penny Singleton, Arthur Lake, Larry Simms
One Sheet: $50 - $100

BLONDIE'S SECRET
(1948 - Columbia) Penny Singleton, Arthur Lake, Jerome Cowan
One Sheet: $50 - $100

BLOOD
(1974 - Bryanston) Allan Berendt, Hope Stansbury
One Sheet: $10 - $20

BLOOD ALLEY
(1955 - Warner Bros.) John Wayne, Lauren Bacall
One Sheet: $75 - $125

BLOOD AND BLACK LACE
(1965 - Allied Artists) Cameron Mitchell, Eva Bartok
One Sheet: $30 - $60

BLOOD AND GUTS
(1978 - Ambassador) William Smith, Micheline Lanctot
One Sheet: $15 - $30

BLOOD AND LACE
(1971 - AIP) Gloria Grahame, Milton Selzer
One Sheet: $15 - $35

BLOOD AND ROSES
(1961 - Paramount) Mel Ferrer, Elsa Martinelli
One Sheet: $20 - $45

BLOOD AND SAND

(1922 - Paramount) Rudolph Valentino
One Sheet: $3,500 - $5,000

BLOOD AND SAND
(1941 - 20th Century Fox) Tyrone Power, Linda Darnell
One Sheet: $250 - $500

BLOOD AND SAND
(1948R - 20th Century Fox) Tyrone Power, Linda Darnell
One Sheet: $125 - $250   Re-release.

BLOOD AND STEEL
(1959 - 20th Century Fox) John Lupton, James Edwards
One Sheet: $15 - $25

BLOOD ARROW
(1958 - Regal) Scott Brady, Paul Richards
One Sheet: $7 - $15

BLOOD BATH
(1966 - AIP) William Campbell, Marissa Mathes
One Sheet: $50 - $100

BLOOD BATH
(1976 - Ambassador) P.J. Soles, Harve Presnell
One Sheet: $10 - $20

BLOOD BEACH
(1981 - Gross) John Saxon, David Huffman
One Sheet: $5 - $10

BLOOD BEAST FROM OUTER SPACE
(1965 - New Art) John Saxon, Maurice Denham
One Sheet: $30 - $50

BLOOD BEAST TERROR, THE
(1967 - Eastman) Peter Cushing, Robert Flemying
One Sheet: $40 - $75   AKA: THE VAMPIRE-BEAST CRAVES BLOOD.

BLOOD CREATURE
(1959 - Valiant) Francis Lederer, Greta Thyssen
One Sheet: $40 - $75   AKA: TERROR IS A MAN.

BLOOD DEMON
(1969 - Hemisphere) Christopher Lee, Karin Dor, Lex Barker
One Sheet: $15 - $35

BLOOD DINER
(1987 - -) Rick Burks, Carl Crew
One Sheet: $7 - $15

BLOOD DRINKERS
(1966 - Hemisphere) Ronald Remy, Amalia Fuentes
One Sheet: $20 - $40   AKA: THE VAMPIRE PEOPLE.

BLOOD FEAST
(1963 - Box Office Spectacular) Mal Arnold, Connie Mason, Dir: H.G. Lewis
One Sheet: $100 - $200   Graven Images, pg. 211.

BLOOD FEAST
(1976 - Cannon) Barbara Bouchet
One Sheet: $15 - $25   AKA: FEAST OF FLESH.

BLOOD FIEND
(1969 - Hemisphere) Christopher Lee, Julian Glover
One Sheet: $30 - $50

BLOOD FROM THE MUMMY'S TOMB
(1972 - AIP) Andrew Keir, Valerie Leon
One Sheet: $15 - $30

BLOOD IN, BLOOD OUT
(1993 - Buena Vista) Jesse Borrego, Benjamine Bratt
One Sheet: $3 - $5

BLOOD IN THE STREETS
(1975 - Independent-International) Oliver Reed
One Sheet: $7 - $15   AKA: THE REVOLVER.

BLOOD LUST/BLOOD MANIA
(1971 - -) -
One Sheet: $15 - $25   Double feature poster.

BLOOD MANIA
(1971 - Crown) Peter Carpenter, Maria DeAragon

One Sheet: $15 - $35

BLOOD MONEY
(1933 - 20th Century) George Bancroft, Judith Anderson
One Sheet: $600 - $1,000

BLOOD MONEY
(1974 - Harbor) Lee Van Cleef
One Sheet: $10 - $20

BLOOD OF DRACULA
(1957 - AIP) Sandra Harrison, Louise Lewis
One Sheet: $125 - $250   Graven Images, pg. 191.

One Sheet

BLOOD OF DRACULA'S CASTLE
(1969 - Crown) John Carradine, Paula Raymond
One Sheet: $15 - $35

BLOOD OF FRANKENSTEIN
(1970 - Independent-International) Lon Chaney, Jr., J. Carroll Naish
One Sheet: $15 - $30   AKA: DRACULA VS. FRANKENSTEIN; THEY'RE COMING TO GET YOU.

BLOOD OF FU MANCHU, THE
(1968 - Udastex) Christopher Lee, George Gotz
One Sheet: $15 - $35   AKA: KISS AND KILL.

BLOOD OF HEROES, THE
(1990 - -) Rutger Hauer, Joan Chen
One Sheet: $3 - $5

BLOOD OF JESUS
(1941 - Sack) Dir: Spencer Williams
One Sheet: $300 - $700   Black cast.
Separate Cinema, pg. 20.

One Sheet

BLOOD OF THE VAMPIRE
(1958 - Universal) Donald Wolfit, Barbara Shelly
One Sheet: $40 - $75

BLOOD OF THE VIRGINS
(1969 - -) -
One Sheet: $15 - $30

BLOOD ON SATAN'S CLAW
(1971 - Cannon) Patrick Wymark, Michele Dotrice
One Sheet: $15 - $25

BLOOD ON THE ARROW
(1964 - Allied Artists) Dale Robertson, Martha Hyer
One Sheet: $10 - $20

BLOOD ON THE MOON

(1948 - RKO) Robert Mitchum, Barbara Bel Geddes
One Sheet: $125 - $250

BLOOD ON THE SUN
(1945 - United Artists) James Cagney, Sylvia Sidney
One Sheet: $125 - $250

BLOOD ORANGE
(1953 - Hammer) Tom Conway, Mila Parely
One Sheet: $40 - $75

BLOOD ORGY OF THE SHE-DEVILS
(1973 - Gemini) Lila Zaborin
One Sheet: $30 - $50

BLOOD RELATIVES
(1978 - Filmcorp.) Donald Sutherland, Donald Pleasence
One Sheet: $5 - $10

BLOOD ROSE, THE
(1970 - Allied Artists) Philippe Lemaire, Anny Duperey
One Sheet: $15 - $25

BLOOD SIMPLE
(1984 - River Road) John Getz, Frances McDormand, Dir: Coen Brothers
One Sheet: $40 - $75   *Directorial debut of the Coen Brothers. Art House one sheet (smaller size):$20-$25.*

BLOOD SISTERS
(1987 - -) Amy Brentano, Shannon McMahon
One Sheet: $3 - $5

BLOOD SPATTERED BRIDE, THE
(1973 - Europix) Simon Andrew, Maribel Martin
One Sheet: $10 - $20

BLOOD, SWEAT AND FEAR
(1975 - Cinema Shares) Lee J. Cobb
One Sheet: $7 - $15

BLOOD THIRST
(1965 - -) Robert Winston, Yvonne Nielson
One Sheet: $15 - $25

BLOOD TIDE
(1982 - Century) James Earl Jones, Jose Ferrer
One Sheet: $3 - $5   *AKA: THE RED TIDE.*

BLOOD WATERS OF DOCTOR Z
(1982 - Barton Film Capital) Marshall Grauer, Wade Popwell
One Sheet: $5 - $10

BLOOD WILL TELL
(1927 - Pathe) Buck Jones, Kathryn Perry
One Sheet: $350 - $750

BLOODBATH AT THE HOUSE OF DEATH
(1984 - Wildwood) Kenny Everett, Vincent Price
One Sheet: $10 - $20

BLOODBROTHERS
(1978 - Warner Bros.) Paul Sorvino, Richard Gere
One Sheet: $5 - $10

BLOODEATERS
(1980 - Parker National) Charles Austin, Beverly Shapiro
One Sheet: $7 - $15   *AKA: FOREST OF FEAR.*

BLOODHOUNDS OF BROADWAY
(1952 - 20th Century Fox) Mitzi Gaynor, Scott Brady
One Sheet: $20 - $40

BLOODLINE
(1979 - Paramount) Audrey Hepburn, Ben Gazzara
One Sheet: $10 - $20

BLOODLUST
(1959 - Crown) Wilton Graff, June Kenney, Robert Reed
One Sheet: $30 - $50

BLOODSPORT
(1985 - -) William Shatner, Heather Locklear
One Sheet: $10 - $20   *T.J. Hooker TV tie-in.*

BLOODSPORT
(1988 - Cannon) Jean-Claude Van Damme, Forest Whitaker

One Sheet: $10 - $20

BLOODSUCKERS, THE
(1967 - Paramount) John Carradine, Lon Chaney Jr.
One Sheet: $15 - $35   *AKA: DR. TERROR'S GALLERY OF HORRORS.*

BLOODSUCKERS, THE
(1970 - Titan) Patrick Macnee, Peter Cushing
One Sheet: $15 - $25

BLOODSUCKERS/BLOOD THIRST
(1971 - -) -
One Sheet: $15 - $25   *Double feature poster.*

BLOODSUCKING FREAKS
(1982 - Troma) Seamus O'Brien
One Sheet: $15 - $25   *AKA: THE INCREDIBLE TORTURE SHOW.*

BLOODTHIRSTY BUTCHERS
(1970 - Mishkin) John Miranda, Anabella Wood
One Sheet: $15 - $25

BLOODY BROOD
(1960 - Allied Artists) Barbara Lord, Jack Bett
One Sheet: $7 - $15

BLOODY KIDS
(1983 - Black Lion) Derrick O'Connor, Gary Holton
One Sheet: $3 - $5

BLOODY MAMA
(1970 - AIP) Shelly Winters, Robert DeNiro, Dir: Roger Corman
One Sheet: $15 - $30

BLOODY PIT OF HORROR
(1969 - Pacemaker) Mickey Hargitay
One Sheet: $20 - $40

BLOOMFIELD
(1971 - World Film Sales) Richard Harris, Kim Burfield
One Sheet: $5 - $10   *AKA: THE HERO.*

BLOSSOM TIME
(1937 - British) Richard Tauber
One Sheet: $150 - $350   *U.S. title "APRIL BLOSSOMS".*

BLOSSOMS IN THE DUST
(1941 - MGM) Greer Garson, Walter Pidgeon
One Sheet: $75 - $150

BLOSSOMS ON BROADWAY
(1937 - Paramount) Edward Arnold, Shirley Ross
One Sheet: $100 - $200

BLOT, THE
(1921 - Lois Weber) Philip Hubbard, Margaret McWade
One Sheet: $600 - $1,000

BLOTTO
(1930 - MGM) Laurel & Hardy
One Sheet: $3,500 - $5,000

BLOW OUT
(1981 - Filmways) John Travolta, Nancy Allen
One Sheet: $15 - $25

BLOW YOUR OWN TRUMPET
(1958 - CFF) Michael Crawford
One Sheet: $15 - $25

BLOWING WILD
(1953 - Warner Bros.) Gary Cooper, Barbara Stanwyck
One Sheet: $40 - $75

BLOWN AWAY
(1994 - MGM) Jeff Bridges, Tommy Lee Jones
One Sheet: $7 - $15

BLOW-UP
(1967 - MGM) Vanessa Redgrave, David Hemmings, The Yardbirds
One Sheet: $50 - $100   *Price is for One Sheet showing Jeff Beck and Jimmy Page playing guitar. Itlian one sheet or two sheet:$400-$800.*

BLUE
(1968 - Paramount) Terence Stamp, Joanna Pettit
One Sheet: $5 - $10

BLUE

(1993 - Artificial Eye) Juliette Binoche, Benoit Regent
One Sheet: $5 - $10

BLUE ANGEL, THE
(1930 - UFA) Marlene Dietrich, Emil Jannings
One Sheet: $16,000 - $25,000   *German. Aka: Der Blaue Engel. Original German release prior to U.S. release. Two known to exist. One sold in Germany 5/92,$22,000.*

BLUE ANGEL, THE
(1931 - Paramount-Publix) Emil Jannings, Marlene Dietrich
One Sheet: $13,000 - $20,000

BLUE ANGEL, THE
(1959 - 20th Century Fox) Curt Jurgens, May Britt
One Sheet: $15 - $35

BLUE BIRD, THE
(1940 - 20th Century Fox) Shirley Temple, Nigel Bruce
One Sheet: $250 - $600   *Price is for either style. Temple not pictured.*

One Sheet

BLUE BIRD
(1976 - 20th Century Fox) Elizabeth Taylor, Jane Fonda, Ava Gardner
One Sheet: $15 - $30

BLUE BLAZES RAWDEN
(1918 - -) William S. Hart, Maude George
One Sheet: $800 - $1,500   *Cowboy Movie Posters #12.*

BLUE BLOOD
(1925 - Chadwick) George Walsh, Cecille Evans
One Sheet: $250 - $500

BLUE BLOOD
(1951 - Monogram) Bill Williams, Jane Nigh
One Sheet: $15 - $25

BLUE BLOOD
(1973 - Mallard-Impact Quadrant) Oliver Reed, Derek Jacobi
One Sheet: $5 - $10

BLUE CANADIAN ROCKIES
(1952 - Columbia) Gene Autry, Pat Buttram
One Sheet: $50 - $100

BLUE CHIPS
(1994 - Paramount) Nick Nolte, Mary McDonnell, Shaquille O'Neal
One Sheet: $7 - $15   *Sports (Basketball). Sports Movie Posters #102.*

BLUE CITY
(1986 - Paramount) Judd Nelson, Ally Sheedy
One Sheet: $3 - $5

BLUE COLLAR
(1978 - Universal) Richard Pryor, Yaphet Kotto
One Sheet: $7 - $15   *Black cast.*

BLUE DAHLIA, THE
(1946 - Paramount) Alan Ladd, Veronica Lake
One Sheet: $1,600 - $2,500

BLUE DANUBE
(1931 - Paramount-Publix) Brigitte Helm
One Sheet: $100 - $200

BLUE DEMON VERSUS THE INFERNAL BRAINS
(1967 - Cinematographica) Alejandro Cruz
One Sheet: $20 - $40

BLUE DENIM
(1959 - 20th Century Fox) Carol Lynley,

Brandon de Wilde
One Sheet: $15 - $25   *AKA: BLUE JEANS.*

BLUE FIN
(1978 - Roadshow) Hardy Kruger
One Sheet: $5 - $10

BLUE GARDENIA, THE
(1953 - Warner Bros.) Anne Baxter, Richard Conte
One Sheet: $40 - $80

BLUE GRASS OF KENTUCKY, THE
(1950 - Monogram) Bill Williams, Jane Nigh
One Sheet: $50 - $100

BLUE HAWAII
(1961 - Paramount) Elvis Presley, Joan Blackman
One Sheet: $75 - $175

One Sheet

BLUE IGUANA, THE
(1988 - -) Dylan McDermott, Jessica Harper
One Sheet: $15 - $30

BLUE KITE, THE
(1994 - Kino International) Lu Liping, Li Xuejian
One Sheet: $4 - $8

BLUE LAGOON, THE
(1949 - Universal) Jean Simmons, Donald Houston
One Sheet: $40 - $75

BLUE LAGOON, THE
(1980 - Columbia) Brooke Shields, Christopher Atkins
One Sheet: $5 - $10

BLUE LAMP, THE
(1950 - GFD) Jack Warner, Jimmy Hanley, Dirk Bogarde
One Sheet: $100 - $200

BLUE MAX, THE
(1966 - 20th Century Fox) George Peppard, James Mason
One Sheet: $30 - $50

BLUE MONEY
(1975 - -) Alain-Patrick Chappuis, Barbara Caron
One Sheet: $3 - $5

BLUE MONKEY, THE
(1987 - -) Steve Railsback, Susan Anspach
One Sheet: $10 - $20

BLUE MONTANA SKIES
(1939 - Republic) Gene Autry, Smiley Burnette
One Sheet: $200 - $400

BLUE MONTANA SKIES
(194?R - Republic) Gene Autry, Smiley Burnette
One Sheet: $75 - $150   *Re-release.*

BLUE MOON, THE
(192? - American) Paul Trenton, Elinor Field
One Sheet: $100 - $200

BLUE MURDER AT ST. TRINIAN'S
(1958 - British Lion) Joyce Grenfell, Terry-Thomas
One Sheet: $15 - $25

BLUE PARROT, THE
(1953 - Monarch) Dermot Walsh, Jacqueline Hill
One Sheet: $30 - $50

BLUE PETER, THE

(1957 - DCA) Greta Gynt, Kieron Moore
One Sheet:　$15 - $30

BLUE SCAR
(1949 - British Lion) Emrys Jones, Gwyneth Vaughan
One Sheet:　$50 - $100

BLUE SIERRA
(1946 - MGM) Elizabeth Taylor, Frank Morgan
One Sheet:　$50 - $100

BLUE SKIES
(1946 - Paramount) Bing Crosby, Fred Astaire
One Sheet:　$125 - $250

BLUE SKIES AGAIN
(1983 - Samuel Bronston) Harry Hamlin, Mimi Rogers
One Sheet:　$3 - $5

BLUE SKY
(1994 - Orion) Tommy Lee Jones, Jessica Lange
One Sheet:　$7 - $15　　*Academy Award: Best Actress (Lange). Academy Award Movie Posters #392.*

BLUE SMOKE
(1935 - 20th Century Fox) Tamara Desni, Ralph Ince
One Sheet:　$100 - $200

BLUE SQUADRON, THE
(1934 - Warner Bros.) Esmond Knight, John Stuart
One Sheet:　$125 - $250

BLUE STEEL
(1934 - Monogram) John Wayne
One Sheet:　$800 - $1,500

BLUE STEEL
(1990 - MGM) Jamie Lee Curtis, Ron Silver
One Sheet:　$3 - $5

BLUE SUMMER
(1973 - Monarch) Darcey Hollingsworth, Bo White
One Sheet:　$3 - $5

BLUE SUNSHINE
(1978 - Cinema Shares) Zalman King, Deborah Winters
One Sheet:　$3 - $5

BLUE THUNDER
(1983 - Columbia) Roy Scheider, Malcolm McDowell, Candy Clark
One Sheet:　$3 - $5

BLUE VEIL, THE
(1947 - Cinematographique) Gaby Morlay, Elvire Popesco
One Sheet:　$30 - $50　　*French.*

BLUE VEIL, THE
(1951 - RKO) Jane Wyman, Charles Laughton
One Sheet:　$40 - $75

BLUE VELVET
(1986 - DeLaurentis) Kyle MacLachlan, Isabella Rosellini, Dir: David Lynch
One Sheet:　$100 - $200

BLUE WATER, WHITE DEATH
(1971 - Cinema Center) -
One Sheet:　$10 - $20

BLUE, WHITE, AND PERFECT
(1941 - 20th Century Fox) Lloyd Nolan, Mary Beth Hughes
One Sheet:　$100 - $200

BLUEBEARD
(1909 - Edison) -
One Sheet:　$500 - $800

BLUEBEARD
(1944 - PRC) John Carradine, Jean Parker
One Sheet:　$75 - $150　　*Graven Images, pg. 135.*

BLUEBEARD
(1972 - Cinerama) Richard Burton, Raquel Welch, Joey Heatherton
One Sheet:　$7 - $15

BLUEBEARD'S EIGHTH WIFE
(1923 - Paramount) Gloria Swanson
One Sheet:　$1,900 - $3,000

BLUEBEARD'S EIGHTH WIFE
(1938 - Paramount) Gary Cooper, Claudette

Colbert
One Sheet:　$800 - $1,500

BLUEBEARD'S SEVEN WIVES
(1926 - First National) Ben Lyon, Lois Wilson
One Sheet:　$1,600 - $2,500

BLUEBEARD'S TEN HONEYMOONS
(1960 - Allied Artists) George Sanders, Corinne Calvert
One Sheet:　$15 - $30

BLUEPRINT FOR MURDER, A
(1953 - 20th Century Fox) Jean Peters, Joseph Cotten
One Sheet:　$40 - $75

BLUEPRINT FOR ROBBERY
(1961 - Paramount) Robert Wilkie, J. Pat O'Malley
One Sheet:　$7 - $15

BLUES
(1955 - Cine Vog) Sidney Bechet, Vivianne Romance
One Sheet:　$200 - $400　　*Black cast. Separate Cinema, pg. 104.*

BLUES BROTHERS, THE
(1980 - Universal) John Belushi, Dan Aykroyd
One Sheet:　$75 - $125

BLUES BUSTERS
(1950 - Monogram) Leo Gorcey, Huntz Hall
One Sheet:　$40 - $75

BLUES FOR LOVERS
(1966 - 20th Century Fox) Ray Charles, Tom Bell
One Sheet:　$40 - $75　　*Rock 'n' Roll. Duotone.*

BLUES IN THE NIGHT
(1941 - Warner Bros.) Richard Whorf, Priscilla Lane
One Sheet:　$50 - $100

BLUME IN LOVE
(1973 - Warner Bros.) George Segal, Susan Anspach
One Sheet:　$3 - $5

BLUNDER BOYS
(1955 - Columbia) The Three Stooges (Shemp)
One Sheet:　$150 - $300　　*Comedy short. Duotone.*

BMX BANDITS
(1983 - Nilsen Premiere) David Argue, Nicole Kidman
One Sheet:　$3 - $5

BOARDING HOUSE BLUES
(1948 - -) Dusty Fletcher
One Sheet:　$150 - $300　　*Black cast. Separate Cinema, pg. 74.*

BOARDWALK
(1979 - Atlantic) Ruth Gordon, Lee Strasberg
One Sheet:　$5 - $10

BOAT, THE
(1922 - Comique) Buster Keaton
One Sheet:　$5,000 - $7,500

Lobby Card

BOAT FROM SHANGHAI
(1931 - MGM) Leon M. Lion, Elizabeth Allan
One Sheet:　$150 - $300

BOATNIKS, THE
(1970 - Walt Disney) Robert Morse, Stefanie Powers
One Sheet:　$7 - $15

BOB & CAROL & TED & ALICE
(1969 - Columbia) Robert Culp, Natalie Wood, Elliott Gould, Dyan Cannon
One Sheet:　$15 - $35　　*Review Style:$100 - $15.*

BOB ARMSTRONG'S REWARD
(1916 - Unicorn Film Service) -
One Sheet:　$200 - $400

BOB LE FLAMBEUR
(1955 - -) Isabel Corey, Roger Duchesne
One Sheet:　$40 - $75　　*French.*

BOB LE FLAMBEUR
(1982R - Columbia) -
One Sheet:　$5 - $10　　*Re-release. French.*

BOB MATHIAS STORY, THE
(1954 - Allied Artists) Bob Mathias, Melba Mathias
One Sheet:　$75 - $150　　*Sports (Baseball). Sports Movie Posters #287.*

BOB ROBERTS
(1992 - Miramax/Paramount) Tim Robbins, Alan Rickman, Gore Vidal
One Sheet:　$7 - $15

BOB STEELE - AN ALL-TALKING PRODUCTION
(1930 - Tiffany) Bob Steele
One Sheet:　$500 - $800　　*Cowboy Movie Posters #78.*

BOB WILLS AND HIS TEXAS PLAYBOYS
(1944 - Warner Bros.) Bob Wills and band
One Sheet:　$75 - $150　　*Country musical. Texas swing.*

BOB'S YOUR UNCLE
(1941 - Butchers) Albert Modley, Jean Collin
One Sheet:　$40 - $75

BOBBED HAIR
(1925 - Warner Bros.) Marie Prevost
One Sheet:　$300 - $700

BOBBIE JO AND THE OUTLAW
(1976 - AIP) Linda Carter, Marjoe Gortner
One Sheet:　$7 - $15

BOBBIKINS
(1960 - 20th Century Fox) Max Bygraves, Shirley Jones
One Sheet:　$7 - $15

BOBBY BUMPS GETS PA'S GOAT
(1915 - Universal) -
One Sheet:　$800 - $1,400　　*Cartoon.*

BOBBY DEERFIELD
(1977 - Columbia) Al Pacino, Martha Keller
One Sheet:　$7 - $15

BOBBY WARE IS MISSING
(1955 - Allied Artists) Neville Brand, Arthur Franz
One Sheet:　$20 - $40

BOBO, THE
(1967 - Warner Bros.-Seven Arts) Peter Sellers, Britt Ekland
One Sheet:　$7 - $15

BOCCACCIO '70
(1962 - Avco/Embassy) Sophia Loren, Anita Ekberg
One Sheet:　$30 - $50

BODIES, REST, & MOTION
(1993 - Fineline) Phoebes Cates, Bridget Fonda, Tim Roth, Eric Stoltz
One Sheet:　$5 - $10

BODY AND SOUL
(1920 - -) Alice Lake, William Lawrence
One Sheet:　$100 - $200

BODY AND SOUL
(1924 - Micheaux) Paul Robeson, Mercedes Gilbert
One Sheet:　$1,600 - $2,500　　*Black cast?*

BODY AND SOUL
(1927 - -) Aileen Pringle, Norman Kerry, Lionel Barrymore
One Sheet:　$350 - $750

BODY AND SOUL
(1931 - Fox) Humphrey Bogart, Charles Farrell, Elissa Landi
One Sheet:　$350 - $750　　*Bogart not*

pictured.

BODY AND SOUL
(1947 - Roberts) John Garfield, Lilli Palmer
One Sheet:　$200 - $400　　*Sports Movie Posters #146.*

BODY AND SOUL
(1953R - -) John Garfield, Lilli Palmer
One Sheet:　$30 - $50　　*Re-release.*

BODY AND SOUL
(1981 - Cannon) Leon Issac Kennedy, Jayne Kennedy, Muhammad Ali
One Sheet:　$5 - $10

BODY DISAPPEARS, THE
(1941 - Warner Bros.) Jeffrey Lynn, Jane Wyman
One Sheet:　$30 - $50

BODY DOUBLE
(1984 - Columbia) Craig Wasson, Gregg Henry, Melanie Griffith
One Sheet:　$7 - $15　　*One Sheet(Skin):$10-$20.*

BODY HEAT
(1981 - Warner Bros.) William Hurt, Kathleen Turner
One Sheet:　$15 - $25

BODY OF EVIDENCE
(1993 - MGM/UA) Madonna, Willem Dafoe
One Sheet:$5 - $10

BODY PARTS
(1991 - Paramount) -
One Sheet:　$3 - $5

BODY ROCK
(1984 - New World) Lorenzo Lamas, Vicki Frederick
One Sheet:　$3 - $5

BODY SAID NO! THE
(1950 - New World Angel) Michael Rennie
One Sheet:　$15 - $30

BODY SNATCHER, THE
(1945 - RKO) Boris Karloff, Bela Lugosi, Dir: Val Lewton
One Sheet:　$600 - $1,000　　*Graven Images, pg. 125. Best of the Lewton thrillers.*

One Sheet

BODY SNATCHER FROM HELL/BLOODY PIT OF HORROR
(1971 - TFC-2 Pacemaker) -
One Sheet:　$15 - $35　　*Double feature poster. Tritone.*

BODY SNATCHERS
(1994 - Warner Bros.) Meg Tilly, Gabrielle Anwar, Forest Whitaker
One Sheet:　$7 - $15

BODY STEALERS, THE
(1970 - Allied Artists) George Sanders, Lorna Wilde
One Sheet:　$15 - $25

BODYGUARD, THE
(1944 - MGM) Tom & Jerry
One Sheet:　$500 - $800　　*Cartoon. Full color stone litho.*

BODYGUARD
(1948 - RKO) Lawrence Tierney, Priscilla Lane
One Sheet:　$75 - $125

BODYGUARD, THE
(1992 - Warner Bros.) Kevin Costner, Whitney Houston

One Sheet: $5 - $10

BODYHOLD
(1950 - Columbia) Willard Parker, Lola Albright
One Sheet: $20 - $40

BOEING, BOEING
(1965 - Paramount) Jerry Lewis, Tony Curtis
One Sheet: $15 - $30

BOFORS GUN, THE
(1968 - Universal) Nicol Williamson, Ian Holm
One Sheet: $7 - $15

BOGARD
(1974 - -) Richard Lawson
One Sheet: $15 - $25 *Blaxploitation.*

BOGUS
(1996 - Warner Bros.) Gerard Depardieu, Whoopi Goldberg
One Sheet: $3 - $6

BOGUS BANDITS
(1947?R - Astor) Stan Laurel, Oliver Hardy
One Sheet: $40 - $75 *Re-release of THE DEVIL'S BROTHER.*

BOHEMIAN GIRL, THE
(1936 - MGM) Laurel and Hardy
One Sheet: $1,900 - $3,000

Title Card

BOHEMIAN GIRL, THE
(1946R - MGM) Laurel and Hardy
One Sheet: $150 - $300 *Re-release.*

BOILING POINT, THE
(1932 - Allied) Hoot Gibson, George "Gabby" Hayes
One Sheet: $200 - $400

BOILING POINT
(1993 - Warner Bros.) Wesley Snipes, Dennis Hopper
One Sheet: $3 - $5

BOL LE FLAMBEUR
(1982 - Columbia) Isabel Corey, Roger Duchesne
One Sheet: $5 - $10 *French.*

BOLD AND THE BRAVE, THE
(1956 - RKO) Wendell Corey, Mickey Rooney, Don Taylor
One Sheet: $10 - $20

BOLD CABALLERO, THE
(1937 - Republic) Robert Livingston, Heather Angel
One Sheet: $125 - $250 *First color Republic release.*

BOLD FRONTIERSMAN, THE
(1948 - Republic) Allan Lane, Eddie Waller
One Sheet: $40 - $80

BOLERO
(1934 - Paramount) George Raft, Carole Lombard
One Sheet: $4,000 - $6,000

BOLERO
(1982 - Double) James Caan
One Sheet: $3 - $5

BOLERO
(1984 - Cannon) Bo Derek, George Kennedy
One Sheet: $5 - $10

BOLSHOI BALLET, THE
(1958 - Rank) Galina Ulanova
One Sheet: $40 - $75 *Dancing (Ballet).*

BOLTED DOOR, THE
(1937 - Vitaphone) Floyd Gibbons
One Sheet: $125 - $250

BOMB FOR A DICTATOR, A
(1960 - Medallion) Pierre Fresnay, Michel Auclair
One Sheet: $5 - $10

BOMB IN THE HIGH STREET
(1961 - Hemisphere) Ronald Howard, Suzanne Leigh
One Sheet: $7 - $15

BOMBA AND THE HIDDEN CITY
(1950 - -) See HIDDEN CITY for prices

BOMBA AND THE JUNGLE GIRL
(1952 - Monogram) Johnny Sheffield, Karen Sharpe
One Sheet: $30 - $50

BOMBA ON PANTHER ISLAND
(1949 - Monogram) Johnny Sheffield, Allene Roberts
One Sheet: $40 - $75

BOMBA, THE JUNGLE BOY
(1949 - Monogram) Johnny Sheffield, Peggy Ann Garner
One Sheet: $40 - $75

BOMBARDIER
(1943 - RKO) Pat O'Brien, Randolph Scott
One Sheet: $50 - $100

BOMBAY CLIPPER
(1941 - Universal) William Gargan, Irene Hervey
One Sheet: $75 - $150

BOMBAY MAIL
(1934 - Universal) Edmund Lowe, Shirley Grey
One Sheet: $250 - $500

BOMBER'S MOON
(1943 - 20th Century Fox) George Montgomery, Annabella
One Sheet: $50 - $100

BOMBERS B-52
(1957 - Warner Bros.) Karl Malden, Natalie Wood
One Sheet: $15 - $25

BOMBS OVER BURMA
(1942 - PRC) Anna May Wong, Noel Madison
One Sheet: $50 - $100

BOMBS OVER LONDON
(1942 - Film Alliance) Charles Farrell
One Sheet: $50 - $100

BOMBSHELL
(1933 - MGM) Jean Harlow, Lee Tracy
One Sheet: $1,300 - $2,000 *AKA: BLONDE BOMBSHELL. Title was released both ways.*

BOMBSIGHT STOLEN
(1941 - General) Leslie Banks, Alastair Sim
One Sheet: $40 - $75 *AKA: (GB:) COTTAGE TO LET.*

BON VOYAGE
(1962 - Buena Vista/Disney) Fred MacMurray, Jane Wyman
One Sheet: $10 - $20

BON VOYAGE, CHARLIE BROWN
(1980 - -) Charlie Brown, Peanuts characters
One Sheet: $15 - $25 *Cartoon.*

BONANZA
(1960S - General) Lorne Greene, Michael Landon, Dan Blocker
One Sheet: $50 - $100 *Foreign film release of an American TV program.*

BONANZA TOWN
(1951 - Columbia) Charles Starrett, Smiley Burnette
One Sheet: $20 - $40

BOND, THE
(1918 - Liberty Loan) Charlie Chaplin, Edna Purviance
One Sheet: $6,500 - $10,000

BOND OF FEAR
(1956 - Eros) Dermot Walsh, Jane Barrett
One Sheet: $15 - $25

BOND STREET
(1948 - Pathe) Jean Kent, Roland Young
One Sheet: $30 - $50

BONDAGE
(1933 - Fox) Jane Darwell
One Sheet: $200 - $400

BONDBOY, THE
(1922 - First National) Richard Barthelmess
One Sheet: $250 - $600

BONDED WOMAN, THE
(1922 - Paramount) Betty Compson, Richard Dix
One Sheet: $150 - $300

BONDS OF HONOR
(1919 - Haworth) Sessue Hayakawa, Tsuru Aoki, Marin Sais
One Sheet: $350 - $750

BONDS OF LOVE
(1919 - Goldwyn) Pauline Frederick
One Sheet: $250 - $500

BONE
(1972 - -) Yaphet Kotto
One Sheet: $15 - $25 *Blaxploitation.*

BONE TROUBLE
(1940 - RKO/Disney) Pluto
One Sheet: $1,900 - $3,000 *Cartoon. The Disney Poster, pg. 30. Cartoon Movie Posters #186.*

BONFIRE OF THE VANITIES, THE
(1990 - -) Bruce Willis, Tom Hanks, Melanie Griffith
One Sheet: $7 - $15

BONITA OF EL CAJON
(1912 - American) -
One Sheet: $500 - $800

BONJOUR TRISTESSE
(1958 - Columbia) Deborah Kerr, David Niven
One Sheet: $125 - $250 *Saul Bass art.*

BONNIE AND CLYDE
(1967 - Warner Bros.) Warren Beatty, Faye Dunaway
One Sheet: $75 - $175 *Academy Award Movie Posters #245.*

BONNIE PARKER STORY, THE
(1958 - AIP) Dorothy Provine, Jack Hogan
One Sheet: $50 - $100

BONNIE PRINCE CHARLIE
(1949 - London) David Niven, Margaret Leighton
One Sheet: $40 - $75

BONNIE SCOTLAND
(1935 - MGM) Laurel and Hardy
One Sheet: $2,200 - $3,500

BONZO GOES TO COLLEGE
(1952 - Universal) Edmund Gwenn, Maureen O'Sullivan
One Sheet: $40 - $75

BOO MOON
(1954 - -) Casper the Ghost
One Sheet: $600 - $1,000 *Cartoon. 3-D. Cartoon Movie Posters #230.*

BOOB, THE
(1925 - MGM) Joan Crawford, George K. Arthur
One Sheet: $1,300 - $2,000

BOOB TUBE, THE
(197? - -) John Alderman
One Sheet: $5 - $10

BOOBS IN ARMS
(1941 - Columbia) The Three Stooges (Curly)
One Sheet: $5,000 - $7,500 *Comedy short. Duotone.*

BOOBY DUPES
(1945 - Columbia) The Three Stooges (Curly)
One Sheet: $2,500 - $4,000 *Comedy short. Duotone.*

BOOBY TRAP
(1957 - Jaywell) Sydney Tafler
One Sheet: $15 - $30

BOOGENS
(1981 - Taft) Rebecca Balding, Fred McCarren
One Sheet: $5 - $10

BOOGEY MAN, THE
(1980 - Gross) Suzanna Love, John Carradine
One Sheet: $5 - $10

BOOGEYMAN II
(1983 - New West Films) Suzanna Love, John Carradine
One Sheet: $3 - $5

BOOGIE MAN WILL GET YOU, THE
(1942 - Columbia) Boris Karloff, Peter Lorre
One Sheet: $200 - $400

BOOGIE WOOGIE DREAM
(1944 - -) -
One Sheet: $100 - $200

BOOK OF LOVE
(1990 - -) Chris Young, Keith Coogan
One Sheet: $3 - $5

BOOK OF NUMBERS
(1973 - Avco/Embassy) Raymond St. Jacques, Freda Payne
One Sheet: $10 - $20 *Blaxploitation.*

One Sheet

BOOLOO
(1938 - Paramount) Colin Tapley, Suratna Asmaka
One Sheet: $100 - $200

BOOM!
(1968 - Universal) Elizabeth Taylor, Richard Burton, Noel Coward
One Sheet: $10 - $20

BOOM TOWN
(1940 - MGM) Clark Gable, Spencer Tracy, Claudette Colbert, Hedy Lamarr
One Sheet: $250 - $600

One Sheet

BOOM TOWN
(1946R - MGM) Clark Gable, Spencer Tracy, Claudette Colbert, Hedy Lamarr
One Sheet: $75 - $150 *Re-release.*

BOOM TOWN
(1955R - MGM) Clark Gable, Spencer Tracy, Claudette Colbert, Hedy Lamarr
One Sheet: $50 - $100 *Re-release.*

BOOMERANG
(1919 - Pioneer) Henry B. Walthall, Melbourne McDowell
One Sheet: $250 - $500

BOOMERANG
(1934 - Columbia) Nora Swinburne
One Sheet: $125 - $250

BOOMERANG!
(1947 - 20th Century Fox) Dana Andrews, Jane

Wyatt
One Sheet: $75 - $150

BOOMERANG
(1960 - Deutsche) Hardy Kruger
One Sheet: $15 - $35   *German. AKA: CRY DOUBLECROSS.*

BOOMERANG
(1992 - Paramount) Eddie Murphy
One Sheet: $7 - $15

BOOST, THE
(1988 - -) James Woods, Sean Young
One Sheet: $3 - $5

BOOSTER, THE
(1928 - MGM) Charley Chase, Ed Kennedy
One Sheet: $250 - $600

BOOT HILL
(1969 - Film Ventures) Terence Hill, Bud Spencer
One Sheet: $10 - $20

BOOT HILL BANDITS
(1942 - Monogram) The Range Busters
One Sheet: $30 - $50

BOOTHILL BRIGADE
(1937 - Republic) Johnny Mack Brown
One Sheet: $75 - $125

BOOTLEG BABIES
(1940' - -) -
One Sheet: $75 - $150   *Exploitation.*

BOOTLEGGERS
(1974 - Howco) Slim Pickens, Paul Koslo, Jaclyn Smith
One Sheet: $7 - $15   *Price is for both styles.*

BOOTS AND SADDLES
(1937 - Republic) Gene Autry, Judith Allen, Bill Elliott (Gordon)
One Sheet: $250 - $500

BOOTS AND SADDLES
(194?R - Republic) Gene Autry, Judith Allen, Bill Elliott (Gordon)
One Sheet: $75 - $150   *Re-release.*

BOOTS! BOOTS!
(1934 - Butchers) George Formby
One Sheet: $125 - $250

BOOTS MALONE
(1951 - Columbia) William Holden, Johnny Stewart
One Sheet: $30 - $50

BOOTS OF DESTINY
(1937 - Grand National) Ken Maynard, Claire Dodd
One Sheet: $250 - $600

BOOTY AND THE BEAST
(1953 - Columbia) The Three Stooges (Shemp)
One Sheet: $150 - $350   *Comedy short. Duotone.*

BOOTY CALL
(1997 - Columbia) Jamie Foxx, Vivica A. Fox
One Sheet: $3 - $5

BOP GIRL
(1957 - United Artists) Mary Kaye Trio, The Goofers, Lord Flea
One Sheet: $50 - $100   *Rock 'n' Roll. "It's a Rock 'n' Roll Riot!"*

BOPHA!
(1993 - Paramount) Danny Glover, Alfre Woodard, Dir: Morgan Freeman
One Sheet: $3 - $5

BORA BORA
(1970 - AIP) Haydee Politoff, Corrado Pani
One Sheet: $5 - $10

BORDER, THE
(1981 - Universal) Jack Nicholson
One Sheet: $7 - $15

BORDER BADMEN
(1945 - PRC) Buster Crabbe, Al St. John
One Sheet: $30 - $50

BORDER BANDITS
(1945 - Monogram) Johnny Mack Brown
One Sheet: $30 - $50

BORDER BRIGANDS

(1935 - Universal) Buck Jones
One Sheet: $250 - $500

BORDER BUCKAROOS
(1943 - PRC) Dave O'Brien
One Sheet: $30 - $50

BORDER CABALLERO
(1936 - Puritan) Tim McCoy, Lois January
One Sheet: $150 - $300

BORDER CAFE
(1937 - RKO) Harry Carey, John Beal, Armida
One Sheet: $100 - $200

BORDER CITY RUSTLERS
(1953 - Allied Artists) Guy Madison, Andy Devine
One Sheet: $30 - $50   *Wild Bill Hickok series.*

BORDER DEVILS
(1932 - Supreme) Harry Carey, Kathleen Collins
One Sheet: $150 - $300

BORDER FEUD
(1947 - PRC) Lash LaRue, Fuzzy St. John
One Sheet: $30 - $60

BORDER FLIGHT
(1936 - Paramount) Frances Farmer, John Howard, Robert Cummings
One Sheet: $200 - $400

BORDER G-MAN
(1938 - RKO) George O'Brien, Ray Whitley
One Sheet: $100 - $200

BORDER INCIDENT
(1949 - MGM) Ricardo Montalban, George Murphy
One Sheet: $40 - $75

BORDER LAW
(1931 - Columbia) Buck Jones, Lupita Tovar
One Sheet: $700 - $1,200   *Cowboy Movie Posters # 96.00.*

BORDER LEGION, THE
(1924 - Famous Players-Lasky) Antonio Moreno, Helene Chadwick
One Sheet: $150 - $300   *Cowboy Movie Posters #48.*

BORDER LEGION, THE
(1930 - Paramount Publix) Jack Holt
One Sheet: $150 - $300

BORDER LEGION, THE
(1940 - Republic) Roy Rogers, Gabby Hayes, Carol Hughes
One Sheet: $150 - $300

BORDER OUTLAWS
(1950 - Eagle-Lion) Spade Cooley, Maria Hart
One Sheet: $20 - $40

BORDER PATROL
(1942 - United Artists) William Boyd (Hopalong Cassidy), Andy Clyde
One Sheet: $200 - $400

BORDER PATROLMAN, THE
(1936 - 20th Century Fox) George O'Brien
One Sheet: $100 - $200

BORDER PHANTOM
(1936 - Republic) Bob Steele
One Sheet: $150 - $300

BORDER RANGERS
(1950 - Lippert) Don Barry, Robert Lowery
One Sheet: $15 - $25

BORDER RIVER
(1953 - Universal) Joel McCrea, Yvonne De Carlo
One Sheet: $15 - $30

BORDER ROMANCE
(1930 - Tiffany) Armida, Don Terry
One Sheet: $75 - $150

BORDER ROUNDUP
(1943 - PRC) George Houston
One Sheet: $30 - $50

BORDER SADDLEMATES
(1952 - Republic) Rex Allen
One Sheet: $30 - $50

BORDER SHERIFF, THE
(1926 - Universal) Jack Hoxie

One Sheet: $250 - $500   *A Blue Streak Western.*

BORDER TREASURE
(1950 - Republic) Tim Holt, Jane Nigh
One Sheet: $15 - $30

BORDER VIGILANTES
(1941 - Paramount) William Boyd, Russell Hayden, Andy Clyde
One Sheet: $200 - $400

BORDER WHIRLWIND
(1925 - -) Bob Custer, Sally Long
One Sheet: $250 - $600

BORDER WIRELESS, THE
(1918 - Artcraft) William S. Hart
One Sheet: $2,200 - $3,500   *Cowboy Movie Posters #13.*

BORDER WOLVES
(1938 - Universal) Bob Baker, Constance Moore
One Sheet: $75 - $150

BORDERLAND
(1937 - Paramount) William Boyd, George "Gabby" Hayes
One Sheet: $250 - $600

BORDERLINE
(1930 - -) -
One Sheet: $100 - $200

BORDERLINE
(1949 - Universal) Fred MacMurray, Claire Trevor
One Sheet: $50 - $100

BORDERLINE
(1980 - ITC) Charles Bronson, Bruno Kirby
One Sheet: $5 - $10

BORDERTOWN
(1934 - Warner Bros.) Bette Davis, Paul Muni
One Sheet: $5,000 - $8,000

BORDERTOWN
(1938R - Warner Bros.) Bette Davis, Paul Muni
One Sheet: $125 - $250   *Re-release.*

BORDERTOWN GUN FIGHTERS
(1943 - Republic) Bill Elliott, Gabby Hayes
One Sheet: $125 - $250

BORDERTOWN TRAIL
(1944 - Republic) Smiley Burnette, Sunset Carson
One Sheet: $40 - $75

BORED OF EDUCATION
(1950R - Monogram) Little Rascals
One Sheet: $40 - $75   *Re-release.*

BORIS AND NATASHA
(1990 - M.C.E.G.) Sally Kellerman, Dave Thomas
One Sheet: $3 - $5

BORIS GODUNOV
(1959 - Artkino) Al Pirogov
One Sheet: $5 - $10   *Russian.*

BORN AGAIN
(1978 - Avco/Embassy) Dean Jones, Anne Francis
One Sheet: $5 - $10

BORN AMERICAN
(1986 - -) Mike Norris, Steve Durham
One Sheet: $3 - $5

BORN FOR GLORY
(1935 - Gaumont-British) Betty Balfour, John Mills
One Sheet: $50 - $100

BORN FREE
(1966 - Columbia) Virginia McKenna, Bill Travers
One Sheet: $15 - $30

BORN IN EAST L.A.
(1987 - -) Cheech Marin, Daniel Stern, Paul Rodriguez
One Sheet: $3 - $5

BORN IN FLAMES
(1983 - First Run) Honey, Adele Bertei
One Sheet: $7 - $15

BORN LOSERS, THE
(1967 - AIP) Tom Laughlin, Jane Russell

One Sheet: $15 - $35   *First Billy Jack film.*

BORN LOSERS, THE
(1974R - AIP) Tom Laughlin, Jane Russell
One Sheet: $15 - $25   *Re-release.*

BORN LUCKY
(1932 - MGM) Talbot O'Farrell, Rene Ray
One Sheet: $150 - $300

BORN ON THE FOURTH OF JULY
(1989 - United Artists) Tom Cruise, Willem Dafoe
One Sheet: $15 - $25   *Academy Award: Best Director (Oliver Stone). Academy Award Movie Posters #364.*

BORN RECKLESS
(1930 - Fox) Edmund Lowe, Lee Tracy
One Sheet: $150 - $300

BORN RECKLESS
(1937 - 20th Century Fox) Rochelle Hudson, Brian Donlevy
One Sheet: $75 - $150

BORN RECKLESS
(1959 - Warner Bros.) Mamie Van Doren, Jeff Richards
One Sheet: $40 - $75

BORN THAT WAY
(1937 - Randall) Elliott Mason, Kathleen Gibson
One Sheet: $75 - $150

BORN TO BE BAD
(1934 - United Artists) Loretta Young, Cary Grant
One Sheet: $1,300 - $2,000

BORN TO BE BAD
(1950 - RKO) Joan Fontaine, Robert Ryan
One Sheet: $100 - $200

BORN TO BE KISSED
(1934 - MGM) Jean Harlow, Lionel Barrymore
One Sheet: $250 - $500   *Price is for Window Card which is the only poster that exists for this title. See THE GIRL FROM MISSOURI for one sheet value.*

BORN TO BE LOVED
(1958 - Universal-International) Carol Morris, Hugo Haas
One Sheet: $30 - $50

BORN TO BE WILD
(1938 - Republic) Ralph Byrd, Doris Weston
One Sheet: $75 - $150

BORN TO BE WILD
(1995 - Warner Bros.) Wil Horneff, Helen Shaver
One Sheet: $3 - $5

BORN TO BUCK
(196? - Casey Tibbs) Wild Horse Roundup documentary narrated by Henry Fonda
One Sheet: $7 - $15   *Duotone.*

BORN TO DANCE
(1936 - MGM) Eleanor Powell, James Stewart
One Sheet: $250 - $500

One Sheet

BORN TO FIGHT
(1938 - Conn) Frankie Darro, Kane Richmond
One Sheet: $50 - $100

BORN TO GAMBLE
(1935 - Liberty) Onslow Stevens, H. B. Warner
One Sheet: $125 - $250

BORN TO KILL
(1947 - RKO) Lawrence Tierney, Claire Trevor
One Sheet: $200 - $400

BORN TO KILL
(1975 - New World) Warren Oates, Harry Dean
Stanton
One Sheet: $5 - $10   *AKA:*
COCKFIGHTER.

BORN TO LOVE
(1931 - RKO-Pathe) Constance Bennett, Joel
McCrea
One Sheet: $800 - $1,500

BORN TO RACE
(1988 - 20th Century Fox) Joseph Bottoms,
George Kennedy
One Sheet: $15 - $25   *Sports (Auto*
racing).

BORN TO RUN
(1977 - DVT) -
One Sheet: $15 - $35

BORN TO SING
(1942 - MGM) Virginia Weidler, Ray McDonald
One Sheet: $50 - $100

BORN TO SPEED
(1947 - PRC) Johnny Sands, Terry Austin
One Sheet: $50 - $100   *Sports (Midget*
car racing).

BORN TO THE SADDLE
(1953 - Astor) Chuck Courtney, Leif Erickson
One Sheet: $15 - $25

BORN TO THE WEST
(1926 - Paramount) Jack Holt, Margret Morris
One Sheet: $150 - $300

BORN TO THE WEST
(1937 - Paramount) John Wayne, Marsha Hunt
One Sheet: $600 - $1,000

BORN TO WIN
(1971 - United Artists) George Segal, Paula
Prentiss, Karen Black
One Sheet: $5 - $10

BORN WILD
(1968 - AIP) Tom Nardini, Patty McCormack
One Sheet: $15 - $25

BORN YESTERDAY
(1950 - Columbia) Judy Holliday, Broderick
Crawford
One Sheet: $75 - $125   *Academy*
Award: Best Actress. Academy Award Movie
Posters #131.

BORN YESTERDAY
(1993 - Buena Vista) Melanie Griffith, Don
Johnson, John Goodman
One Sheet: $3 - $5

BORNEO
(1937 - 20th Century Fox) Mr. and Mrs. Martin
Johnson
One Sheet: $250 - $500

BORROW A MILLION
(1934 - Fox) Reginald Gardiner, Vera Bogetti
One Sheet: $150 - $300

BORROWED CLOTHES
(1934 - Columbia) Anne Grey, Lester Matthews
One Sheet: $125 - $250

BORROWED HERO
(1942 - Monogram) Alan Baxter, Florence Rice
One Sheet: $40 - $75

BORROWED TROUBLE
(1948 - United Artists) William Boyd, Andy
Clyde
One Sheet: $75 - $125

BORROWED WIVES
(1930 - Tiffany) Rex Lease, Vera Reynolds
One Sheet: $100 - $200

BORROWING TROUBLE
(1937 - 20th Century Fox) Jed Prouty, Spring
Byington
One Sheet: $50 - $100

BORSALINO
(1970 - Paramount) Alain Delon, Catherine
Rouvel
One Sheet: $5 - $10

BOSAMBO
(1935 - -) Paul Robeson, Leslie Banks
One Sheet: $250 - $500   *Separate*
Cinema, pg. 42. Also see "SANDERS OF THE
RIVER." Price is for Belgian poster by Regina
Dist. One Sheet(Argentina by
GuaranteedPictures):$300-500.

BOSCO
(1933 - Vitaphone short subject) Bosco
One Sheet: $2,500 - $4,000   *Cartoon.*
Cartoon Movie Posters #96.

One Sheet

BOSKO AND THE PIRATES
(1937 - MGM) Happy Harmonies
One Sheet: $500 - $800   *Cartoon.*
Cartoon Movie Posters #240.

BOSS, THE
(1956 - United Artists) John Payne, Doe
Avedan
One Sheet: $10 - $20

BOSS COWBOY
(1934 - -) -
One Sheet: $100 - $200

BOSS NIGGER
(1974 - Dimension) Fred Williamson, D'Urville
Martin
One Sheet: $20 - $40   *Blaxploitation*
western.

BOSS OF BIG TOWN, THE
(1942 - PRC) John Litel, Florence Rice
One Sheet: $30 - $50

BOSS OF BOOMTOWN
(1944 - Universal) Rod Cameron
One Sheet: $50 - $100

BOSS OF BULLION CITY
(1940 - Universal) Johnny Mack Brown
One Sheet: $50 - $100

BOSS OF HANGTOWN MESA
(1942 - Universal) Johnny Mack Brown
One Sheet: $50 - $100

BOSS OF LONELY VALLEY
(1937 - Universal) Buck Jones
One Sheet: $250 - $600

BOSS OF RAWHIDE
(1943 - PRC) Dave O'Brien
One Sheet: $40 - $75

BOSS RIDER OF GUN CREEK, THE
(1936 - Universal) Buck Jones
One Sheet: $300 - $700   *Cowboy*
Movie Posters #196.

BOSS'S SON, THE
(1978 - New American) Asher Brauner, Rita
Moreno
One Sheet: $5 - $10

BOSTON BEANIE
(1947 - Columbia) -
One Sheet: $75 - $150   *Cartoon.*

BOSTON BLACKIE AND THE LAW
(1946 - Columbia) Chester Morris, Trudy
Marshall
One Sheet: $75 - $125

BOSTON BLACKIE BOOKED ON SUSPICION
(1945 - Columbia) Chester Morris, Lynn
Merrick
One Sheet: $50 - $100

BOSTON BLACKIE GOES HOLLYWOOD
(1942 - Columbia) Chester Morris, George E.

Stone
One Sheet: $75 - $150

BOSTON BLACKIE'S CHINESE VENTURE
(1949 - Columbia) Chester Morris, Bendon
Fong
One Sheet: $40 - $75

BOSTON BLACKIE'S RENDEZVOUS
(1945 - Columbia) Chester Morris, Nina Foch
One Sheet: $50 - $100

BOSTON STRANGLER, THE
(1968 - 20th Century Fox) Tony Curtis, Henry
Fonda, George Kennedy
One Sheet: $15 - $25   *Film based on*
the atrocities of mass-murderer Albert DeSalvo.

BOSTONIANS, THE
(1984 - Merchant Ivory) Christopher Reeve,
Vanessa Redgrave
One Sheet: $7 - $15

BOTANY BAY
(1952 - Paramount) Alan Ladd, James Mason,
Patricia Medina
One Sheet: $30 - $60

BOTH BARRELS BLAZING
(1945 - Columbia) Charles Starrett
One Sheet: $40 - $75

BOTH SIDES OF THE LAW
(1953 - Universal-International) Peggy
Cummins, Anne Crawford.
One Sheet: $30 - $60

BOTTLE ROCKET
(1995 - Columbia) Andrew, Luke & Owen
Wilson
One Sheet: $5 - $10

BOTTOM OF THE BOTTLE, THE
(1956 - 20th Century Fox) Van Johnson,
Joseph Cotten, Jack Carson
One Sheet: $20 - $40

BOTTOMS UP
(1934 - Fox) Pat Paterson, Spencer Tracy
One Sheet: $150 - $300

One Sheet

BOTTOMS UP
(1960 - Associated-British) Jimmy Edwards
One Sheet: $5 - $10

BOUDOIR DIPLOMAT
(1930 - Universal) Betty Compson, Ian Keith
One Sheet: $150 - $300

BOUGHT
(1931 - Warner Bros.) Constance Bennett, Ray
Milland
One Sheet: $150 - $300

BOULDER DAM
(1936 - Warner Bros.) Ross Alexander, Lyle
Talbot
One Sheet: $50 - $100

BOULEVARD DU RHUM
(1971 - Gaumont) Brigitte Bardot, Lino Ventura
One Sheet: $75 - $125   *French.*

BOULEVARD NIGHTS
(1979 - Warner Bros.) Richard Yniguez
One Sheet: $3 - $5

BOUND AND GAGGED: A LOVE STORY
(1993 - -) -
One Sheet: $10 - $20

BOUND BY HONOR
(1993 - Buena Vista) Damian Chapa, Benjamin

Bratt
One Sheet: $3 - $5

BOUND FOR GLORY
(1976 - United Artists) David Carradine, Ronny
Cox
One Sheet: $5 - $10

BOUNTY, THE
(1983 - Orion) Mel Gibson, Anthony Hopkins
One Sheet: $7 - $15

BOUNTY HUNTER, THE
(1954 - Warner Bros.) Randolph Scott, Dolores
Dorn
One Sheet: $20 - $40

BOUNTY HUNTERS, THE
(1970 - Cinematografica) Yul Brynner, Dean
Reed
One Sheet: $10 - $20

BOUNTY KILLER, THE
(1965 - Embassy) Dan Duryea, Rod Cameron
One Sheet: $7 - $15

BOWERY, THE
(1933 - 20th Century) Wallace Beery, George
Raft, Jackie Cooper
One Sheet: $600 - $1,000   *First*
production by 20th Century. Gable was sought for
the Raft role but was unavailable.

BOWERY, THE
(1946R - 20th Century Fox) Wallace Beery,
George Raft, Jackie Cooper
One Sheet: $50 - $100   *Re-release.*

BOWERY AT MIDNIGHT
(1942 - Monogram) Bela Lugosi, John Archer
One Sheet: $250 - $500   *Graven*
Images, pg. 132.

BOWERY BATTALION
(1951 - Monogram) Leo Gorcey, Huntz Hall
One Sheet: $40 - $75

BOWERY BLITZKRIEG
(1941 - Monogram) The East Side Kids, Warren
Hull
One Sheet: $75 - $125

BOWERY BOMBSHELL
(1946 - Monogram) Leo Gorcey, Huntz Hall
One Sheet: $50 - $100

BOWERY BOY
(1940 - Republic) Dennis O'Keefe, Jimmy
Lydon
One Sheet: $50 - $100

BOWERY BOYS MEET THE MONSTERS, THE
(1954 - Allied Artists) Leo Gorcey, Huntz Hall
One Sheet: $75 - $125

BOWERY BUCKAROOS
(1947 - Monogram) Leo Gorcey, Huntz Hall
One Sheet: $40 - $75

BOWERY CHAMPS
(1944 - Monogram) East Side Kids, Anne
Sterling
One Sheet: $75 - $125

BOWERY TO BAGHDAD
(1954 - Monogram) Leo Gorcey, Huntz Hall
One Sheet: $50 - $100

BOWERY TO BROADWAY
(1944 - Universal) Maria Montez, Jack Oakie,
Universal Stars and Players
One Sheet: $75 - $150

BOWLING ALLEY CAT, THE
(1947R - MGM) Tom & Jerry
One Sheet: $150 - $300   *Re-release.*
Cartoon. Sports (Bowling). Full color stone litho.

BOWLING TRICKS
(1947 - MGM) Pete Smith
One Sheet: $150 - $300   *Sports*
(Bowling). Sports Movie Posters #109.

BOXCAR BERTHA
(1972 - AIP) David Carradine, Barbara Hershey
One Sheet: $10 - $20

BOXING HELENA
(1993 - Orion) Sherilyn Fenn, Julian Sands
One Sheet: $7 - $15

BOXOFFICE
(1982 - Josef Bogdanovich) Robin Clarke,
Monica Lewis

One Sheet: $3 - $5

BOY! WHAT A GIRL
(1947 - Herald) Tim Moore, Elswood Smith
One Sheet: $75 - $150 *Black cast.*

BOY, A GIRL AND A BIKE, A
(1949 - General) Honor Blackman, John McCallum
One Sheet: $40 - $75

BOY, A GIRL, AND A DOG, A
(1946 - Film Classics) Jerry Hunter, Sharon Moffett
One Sheet: $30 - $50

BOY AND HIS DOG, A
(1936 - Columbia) Scrappy
One Sheet: $1,300 - $2,000 *Cartoon. A Color Rhapsody.*

BOY AND HIS DOG, A
(1975 - LQJaf) Don Johnson, Jason Robards
One Sheet: $15 - $30

BOY AND THE BRIDGE, THE
(1959 - Columbia) Ian Maclaine
One Sheet: $10 - $20

BOY AND THE LAUGHING DOG, THE
(1959 - Warner Bros.) Walter Brennan, Phil Harris
One Sheet: $15 - $30

BOY AND THE PIRATES, THE
(1960 - United Artists) Charles Herbert, Susan Gordon
One Sheet: $5 - $10

BOY AND THE WOLF, THE
(1943 - MGM) -
One Sheet: $250 - $600 *Cartoon. Full color stone litho. Cartoon Movie Posters #249.*

BOY CRIED MURDER, THE
(1966 - Universal) Veronica Hurst, Phil Brown
One Sheet: $5 - $10

BOY, DID I GET A WRONG NUMBER
(1966 - United Artists) Bob Hope, Elke Sommer, Phillis Dyller
One Sheet: $15 - $35

BOY FRIEND
(1939 - 20th Century Fox) Jane Withers, Richard Bond
One Sheet: $100 - $200

BOY FRIEND, THE
(1971 - MGM) Twiggy, Christopher Gable
One Sheet: $20 - $40

BOY FROM INDIANA
(1950 - Eagle-Lion) Lon McCallister, Lois Butler
One Sheet: $20 - $40

BOY FROM OKLAHOMA, THE
(1953 - Warner Bros.) Will Rogers Jr., Nancy Olson, Lon Chaney, Jr
One Sheet: $15 - $30

BOY FROM STALINGRAD, THE
(1943 - Columbia) Bobby Samarzich, Conrad Vinyon
One Sheet: $50 - $100

BOY IN BLUE, THE
(1986 - -) Nicolas Cage, Cynthia Dale
One Sheet: $5 - $10

BOY MEETS GIRL
(1938 - Warner Bros.) James Cagney, Pat O'Brien, Ronald Reagan
One Sheet: $250 - $500

BOY NAMED CHARLIE BROWN, A
(1970 - National General) Charlie Brown
One Sheet: $15 - $35 *Cartoon.*

BOY OF FLANDERS, A
(1924 - Metro) Jackie Coogan, Lionel Barrymore
One Sheet: $600 - $1,000

BOY OF MINE
(1923 - Associated First National) Ben Alexander, Rockliffe Fellows
One Sheet: $200 - $400

BOY OF THE STREETS
(1937 - Monogram) Jackie Cooper, Maureen O'Connor
One Sheet: $75 - $150

BOY ON A DOLPHIN
(1957 - 20th Century Fox) Alan Ladd, Sophia Loren
One Sheet: $30 - $50

BOY SLAVES
(1939 - RKO) Anne Shirley, Roger Daniel
One Sheet: $75 - $125

BOY TEN FEET TALL, A
(1965 - Paramount) Edward G. Robinson, Fergus McClelland
One Sheet: $10 - $20

BOY TROUBLE
(1939 - Paramount) Charles Ruggles, Mary Boland, Donald O'Connor
One Sheet: $75 - $125

BOY WHO CAUGHT A CROOK
(1961 - United Artists) Wanda Hendrix, Don Beddoe
One Sheet: $5 - $10

BOY WHO COULD FLY, THE
(1986 - Lorimar) Lucy Deakins, Jay Underwood, Bonnie Bedelia
One Sheet: $5 - $10

BOY WHO CRIED WEREWOLF, THE
(1973 - Universal) Kerwin Matthews, Elaine Devry
One Sheet: $10 - $20

BOY WHO STOLE A MILLION, THE
(1960 - Paramount) Virgillio Texera, Maurice Reyna
One Sheet: $5 - $10

BOY WHO TURNED YELLOW, THE
(1972 - Children's) Mark Dightam, Helen Weir
One Sheet: $5 - $10

BOY WITH GREEN HAIR, THE
(1948 - RKO) Pat O'Brien, Robert Ryan, Dean Stockwell
One Sheet: $75 - $150

BOY'S PRISON
(195?R - Astor) William Bendix, Allen Martin Jr.
One Sheet: $10 - $20 *Re-release, reissue of: JOHNNY HOLIDAY.*

BOY...A GIRL, A
(1969 - Cinema) Dina Martin Jr., Karen Steele
One Sheet: $5 - $10

BOYCOTTED BABY, THE
(1915 - VIM) Babe Hardy, Kate Price
One Sheet: $800 - $1,500

BOYD'S SHOP
(1960 - RFD) Eileen Crowe, Geoffrey Golden
One Sheet: $7 - $15

BOYS, THE
(1962 - Gala) Richard Todd, Robert Morley
One Sheet: $7 - $15

BOYS FROM BRAZIL, THE
(1978 - 20th Century Fox) Gregory Peck, Laurence Olivier
One Sheet: $15 - $30

BOYS FROM SYRACUSE, THE
(1940 - Universal) Martha Raye, Allan Jones
One Sheet: $75 - $125

BOYS IN BROWN
(1949 - General) Jack Warner, Richard Attenborough
One Sheet: $30 - $50

BOYS IN COMPANY "C", THE
(1978 - Columbia) Stan Shaw, Andrew Stevens
One Sheet: $7 - $15

BOYS IN THE BAND, THE
(1970 - National General) Kenneth Nelson, Leonard Frey, Cliff Gorman
One Sheet: $50 - $100

BOYS NEXT DOOR, THE
(1985 - -) Maxwell Caulfield, Charlie Sheen
One Sheet: $3 - $5

BOYS OF PAUL STREET, THE
(1969 - 20th Century Fox) Anthony Kemp
One Sheet: $3 - $5

BOYS OF THE CITY
(1940 - Monogram) The East Side Kids, Dave O'Brien
One Sheet: $75 - $125

BOYS ON THE SIDE
(1995 - Warner Bros.) Whoopi Goldberg, Mary Louise Parker, Drew Barrymore
One Sheet: $5 - $12

BOYS TOWN
(1938 - MGM) Spencer Tracy, Mickey Rooney
One Sheet: $250 - $600 *Academy Award: Best Actor(Tracy, his 2nd year in a row). Academy Award Movie Posters #60.*

BOYS TOWN
(1957R - MGM) Spencer Tracy, Mickey Rooney
One Sheet: $40 - $75 *Re-release.*

BOYS WILL BE BOYS
(1921 - Goldwyn) Will Rogers
One Sheet: $200 - $400

BOYS WILL BE BOYS
(1935 - Gaumont-British) Will Hay
One Sheet: $150 - $300 *First Will Hay film.*

BOYS WILL BE GIRLS
(1937 - Fuller) Leslie Fuller, Nellie Wallace
One Sheet: $100 - $200

BOYS' NIGHT OUT
(1962 - MGM) KIM NOVAK, JAMES GARNER
One Sheet: $10 - $20

BOYS' RANCH
(1946 - MGM) James Craig, Butch Jenkins
One Sheet: $40 - $75

BOYS' REFORMATORY
(1939 - Monogram) Frankie Darro, Grant Withers
One Sheet: $75 - $150

BOYS' SCHOOL
(1939 - Columbia) Erich Von Stroheim
One Sheet: $100 - $200

BOYZ N THE HOOD
(1991 - -) Cuba Gooding Jr., Larry Fishburne
One Sheet: $15 - $25

BRACELETS
(1931 - Gaumont) Bert Coote, Joyce Kennedy
One Sheet: $125 - $250

BRADDOCK: MISSING IN ACTION III
(1988 - -) Chuck Norris, Aki Aleong
One Sheet: $3 - $5

BRADY BUNCH MOVIE, THE
(1995 - Paramount) Shelly Long, Gary Cole
One Sheet: $5 - $10

One Sheet

BRADY'S ESCAPE
(1984 - Satori) John Savage, Kelly Reno
One Sheet: $3 - $5

BRAIN, THE
(1965 - Governor) Anne Heywood, Peter Van Eyck
One Sheet: $7 - $15

BRAIN, THE
(1969 - Paramount) David Niven, Jean-Paul Belmondo
One Sheet: $10 - $20

BRAIN DAMAGE
(1988 - -) Rick Herbst, Jennifer Lowry
One Sheet: $5 - $10

BRAIN DEAD
(1990 - -) Bill Pullman, George Kennedy
One Sheet: $3 - $5

BRAIN EATERS, THE
(1958 - AIP) Edwin Nelson, Alan Frost
One Sheet: $100 - $200

BRAIN FROM PLANET AROUS, THE
(1957 - Howco) John Agar, Joyce Meadows
One Sheet: $200 - $400

BRAIN MACHINE, THE
(1954 - RKO) Patrick Barr, Elizabeth Allen
One Sheet: $50 - $100

BRAIN OF BLOOD
(1971 - Hemisphere) Kent Taylor, John Bloom
One Sheet: $15 - $30 *AKA: THE CREATURE'S REVENGE.*

One Sheet

BRAIN THAT WOULDN'T DIE, THE
(1959 - Sterling) Herb Evers, Virginia Leath
One Sheet: $50 - $100

BRAIN THAT WOULDN'T DIE/INVASION OF THE STAR CREATURES COMBO
(1963 - AIP) -
One Sheet: $20 - $40 *Double feature poster.*

BRAINIAC, THE
(1961 - -) Abel Salazar, Ariadne Welter
One Sheet: $40 - $75 *Mexican.*

BRAINSCAN
(1994 - Triumph) Edward Furlong, T. Ryder Smith
One Sheet: $3 - $5

BRAINSTORM
(1965 - Warner Bros.) Jeff Hunter, Ann Francis
One Sheet: $10 - $20

BRAINSTORM
(1983 - MGM) Christopher Walken, Natalie Wood
One Sheet: $5 - $10

BRAINWASHED
(1961 - Allied Artists) Curt Jurgens, Claire Bloom
One Sheet: $5 - $10

BRAINWAVES
(1983 - Motion Picture Marketing) Keir Dullea, Suzanna Love
One Sheet: $3 - $5

BRAM STOKER'S DRACULA
(1992 - Columbia) Gary Oldman, Anthony Hopkins, Winona Ryder
One Sheet: $15 - $30 *Advance(A or B):$10-20.*

BRAMBLE BUSH, THE
(1960 - Warner Bros.) Richard Burton, Barbara Rush
One Sheet: $7 - $15

BRAND OF FEAR
(1949 - Monogram) Jimmy Wakely
One Sheet: $30 - $60

BRAND OF HATE
(1934 - -) Bob Steele, George "Gabby" Hayes
One Sheet: $200 - $400

BRAND OF THE DEVIL
(1944 - PRC) Dave O'Brien, Jim Newill
One Sheet: $30 - $50

BRAND OF THE OUTLAWS
(1936 - -) Bob Steele, Margaret Marquis
One Sheet: $150 - $300

BRAND X
(1970 - C.M.B.) Taylor Mead, Sally Kirkland
One Sheet: $5 - $10

BRANDED
(1931 - Columbia) Buck Jones
One Sheet: $350 - $750

BRANDED
(1951 - Paramount) Alan Ladd, Mona Freeman
One Sheet: $30 - $50

BRANDED A COWARD
(1935 - Superior) Johnny Mack Brown
One Sheet: $150 - $300

BRANDED MEN
(1931 - Tiffany) Ken Maynard
One Sheet: $200 - $400

BRANDED WOMAN, THE
(1921 - First National) Norma Talmadge
One Sheet: $350 - $750

BRANDING BROADWAY
(1918 - Paramount-Artcraft) William S. Hart,
Seena Owen
One Sheet: $1,900 - $3,000

BRANDS OF FEAR
(1949 - Monogram) Jimmy Wakely, Gail Davis
One Sheet: $15 - $30

BRANDY FOR THE PARSON
(1952 - Associated British) Jean Lodge, James
Donald
One Sheet: $15 - $25

BRANNIGAN
(1975 - United Artists) John Wayne, Richard
Attenborough
One Sheet: $30 - $50

BRASHER DOUBLOON, THE
(1947 - 20th Century Fox) George Montgomery,
Nancy Guild
One Sheet: $200 - $400

BRASS BOTTLE, THE
(1923 - -) Harry Myers, Ernest Torrence
One Sheet: $150 - $300

BRASS BOTTLE, THE
(1964 - Universal) Tony Randall, Barbara
Eden, Burl Ives
One Sheet: $20 - $40 *Inspired "I
Dream of Jeannie" TV series.*

One Sheet

BRASS BULLET, THE
(1918 - Universal) Juanita Hansen, Jack
Mulhall
One Sheet: $250 - $500 *Serial. 18
Chapters.*

BRASS CHECK, THE
(1918 - Metro) Francis X. Bushman, Beverly
Bayne
One Sheet: $250 - $600

BRASS KNUCKLES
(1927 - Warner Bros.) Monte Blue, Betty
Bronson
One Sheet: $250 - $600

BRASS LEGEND, THE
(1956 - United Artists) Hugh O'Brian, Nancy
Gates
One Sheet: $10 - $20

BRASS RING, THE
(1975 - E.O.) Earl Owensby, Doug Hale,
Elizabeth Upton
One Sheet: $5 - $10 *AKA:*

● *Manhunter (1983).*

BRASS TARGET
(1978 - MGM/United Artists) Sophia Loren,
John Cassevetes
One Sheet: $7 - $15

BRASSED OFF
(1997 - Miramax) Pete Postlethwaite, Ewan
McGregor
One Sheet: $4 - $8

BRAT, THE
(1919 - Metro) Alla Nazimova, Charles Bryant
One Sheet: $600 - $1,000

BRAT, THE
(1930 - United Artists) Betty Balfour, John
Stuart
One Sheet: $150 - $300

BRAT, THE
(1931 - Fox) Sally O'Neill, Alan Dinehart
One Sheet: $800 - $1,500

BRATS
(1930 - MGM) Laurel & Hardy
One Sheet: $3,500 - $5,000

BRAVADOS, THE
(1958 - 20th Century Fox) Gregory Peck, Joan
Collins
One Sheet: $20 - $40

BRAVE BULLS, THE
(1951 - Rossen Enterprises) Mel Ferrer,
Miroslava
One Sheet: $20 - $40

BRAVE DON'T CRY, THE
(1952 - Associated British) John Gregson
One Sheet: $10 - $20

BRAVE LITTLE TAILOR, THE
(1938 - RKO/Disney) Mickey Mouse
One Sheet: $13,000 - $20,000 *Cartoon.
Cartoon Movie Posters #144.*

BRAVE LITTLE TAILOR, THE
(1950R - RKO/Disney) Mickey Mouse
One Sheet: $700 - $1,200 *Re-release.
Cartoon. Full color.*

BRAVE LITTLE TAILOR, THE
(1969 - Childhood Productions) -
One Sheet: $3 - $5

BRAVE ONE, THE
(1956 - RKO) Michel Ray, Rodolfo Hoyos
One Sheet: $20 - $40

BRAVE TIN SOLDIER, THE
(1934 - Celebrity) -
One Sheet: $500 - $800 *Cartoon.
Cartoon Movie Posters #124.*

BRAVE WARRIOR
(1952 - Columbia) Jon Hall, Christine Larson
One Sheet: $15 - $35

BRAVEHEART
(1995 - Paramount) Mel Gibson, Sophie
Marceau
One Sheet: $10 - $20 *Academy
Award: Best Picture, Best Director (Mel Gibson).*

BRAWN OF THE NORTH
(1922 - First National) Irene Rich, Lee
Shumway
One Sheet: $125 - $250

BRAZIL
(1944 - Republic) Tito Guizar, Roy Rogers,
Virginia Bruce
One Sheet: $75 - $150

BRAZIL
(1985 - Universal) Jonathan Pryce, Kim Greist,
Robert De Niro
One Sheet: $40 - $75

BREACH OF PROMISE
(1932 - Berschleiser) Chester Morris, Mae
Clark
One Sheet: $100 - $200

BREAD, LOVE AND DREAMS
(1953 - Titanis) Gina Lollabrigida, Vittorio De
Sica
One Sheet: $15 - $35

BREAK, THE
(1963 - Mancunian) Tony Britton, William Lucas
One Sheet: $3 - $5

BREAK, THE
(1995 - Trimark) Vincent Van Patton, Ben
Jorgensen
One Sheet: $3 - $5 *Sports
(Tennis).*

BREAK IN THE CIRCLE
(1967 - 20th Century Fox) Forrest Tucker, Eva
Bartok
One Sheet: $5 - $10

BREAK OF HEARTS
(1935 - RKO) Katharine Hepburn, Charles
Boyer
One Sheet: $600 - $1,000

BREAK THE NEWS
(1941 - Monogram) Jack Buchanan, Maurice
Chevalier
One Sheet: $150 - $300

BREAKAWAY
(1956 - RKO) Tom Conway, Honor Blackman
One Sheet: $15 - $30

BREAKDOWN
(1952 - Realart) Ann Richards, William Todd
One Sheet: $15 - $30

BREAKDOWN
(1997 - Paramount) Kurt Russell, J.T. Walsh,
Kathleen Quinlan
One Sheet: $3 - $5

BREAKER! BREAKER!
(1977 - AIP) Chuck Norris, George Mudock
One Sheet: $7 - $15

BREAKER MORANT
(1979 - New World) Edward Woodward, Bryan
Brown
One Sheet: $15 - $30

BREAKERS AHEAD
(1935 - Reunion) Barrie Livesey
One Sheet: $100 - $200

BREAKERS AHEAD
(1938 - General) Belle Chrystal
One Sheet: $75 - $150 *AKA: AS WE
FORGIVE.*

BREAKFAST AT SUNRISE
(1927 - First National) Contance Talmadge,
Don Alvarado
One Sheet: $600 - $1,000

BREAKFAST AT TIFFANY'S
(1961 - Paramount) Audrey Hepburn, George
Peppard
One Sheet: $800 - $1,500

One Sheet

BREAKFAST AT TIFFANY'S
(1965R - Paramount) Audrey Hepburn, George
Peppard
One Sheet: $150 - $300 *Re-release.*

BREAKFAST AT TIFFANY'S/SABRINA COMBO
(1963R - Paramount) Audrey Hepburn, George
Peppard, Humphrey Bogart
One Sheet: $100 - $200 *Re-release.*

BREAKFAST CLUB, THE
(1985 - Universal) Emilio Estevez, Molly
Ringwald, Ally Sheedy
One Sheet: $30 - $50

BREAKFAST FOR TWO
(1937 - RKO) Barbara Stanwyck, Herbert
Marshall
One Sheet: $200 - $400

BREAKFAST IN BED
(1978 - Hausge) Jenny Sullivan, John Ritter
One Sheet: $5 - $10

BREAKFAST IN HOLLYWOOD
(1946 - Golden) Tom Breneman, Bonita
Granville, Spike Jones
One Sheet: $75 - $150

BREAKHEART PASS
(1976 - United Artists) Charles Bronson, Ben
Johnson
One Sheet: $7 - $15 *Price is for
both styles.*

BREAKIN'
(1984 - MGM) Lucinda Dickey, Shabba-Doo
One Sheet: $7 - $15

BREAKIN' 2 ELECTRIC BOOGALOO
(1984 - TriStar) Lucinda Dickey, Adolfo
Quinones
One Sheet: $5 - $10

BREAKIN' IT DOWN
(1946 - Universal) -
One Sheet: $50 - $100

BREAKING ALL THE RULES
(1985 - -) Carl Marlotte, Carolyn Dunn
One Sheet: $3 - $5

BREAKING AWAY
(1979 - 20th Century Fox) Dennis Quaid,
Dennis Christopher
One Sheet: $10 - $20 *Sports
(Bicycle racing). Sports Movie Posters #107.*

BREAKING GLASS
(1980 - Paramount) Phil Daniels, Hazel
O'Connor
One Sheet: $3 - $5

BREAKING IN
(1989 - -) Burt Reynolds, Casey Siemaszko
One Sheet: $5 - $10

BREAKING INTO THE BIG LEAGUE
(1913 - Kalem) Manager McGraw, Christy
Mathewson
One Sheet: $800 - $1,500 *Sports
(Baseball). Sports Movie Posters #29.*

BREAKING POINT
(1950 - Warner Bros.) John Garfield, Patricia
Neal
One Sheet: $50 - $100

BREAKING POINT, THE
(1961 - Butchers) Peter Reynolds
One Sheet: $10 - $20

BREAKING POINT
(1976 - 20th Century Fox) Bo Svenson, Robert
Culp
One Sheet: $3 - $5

BREAKING THE ICE
(1925 - Pathe) Ralph Graves
One Sheet: $250 - $500

BREAKING THE ICE
(1938 - RKO) Bobby Breen, Irene Dare
One Sheet: $75 - $150

BREAKING THE RULES
(199? - Miramax) Jason Bateman, C. Thomas
Howell, Annie Potts
One Sheet: $5 - $10

BREAKING THE SOUND BARRIER
(1952 - United Artists) Ann Todd, Ralph
Richardson
One Sheet: $75 - $125

BREAKOUT
(1960 - Continental) Richard Todd, Richard
Attenborough
One Sheet: $30 - $50

BREAKOUT
(1975 - Columbia) Charles Bronson, Robert
Duvall
One Sheet: $10 - $20

BREAKOUT
(1984 - Eyeline) David Jackson, Simon Nash
One Sheet: $3 - $5

BREAKTHROUGH
(1950 - Warner Bros.) David Brian, John Agar
One Sheet: $20 - $40

BREAKTHROUGH

(1978 - Maverick) Richard Burton, Rod Steiger
One Sheet: $7 - $15

BREATH OF LIFE
(1962 - British Lion) George Moon
One Sheet: $10 - $20

BREATH OF SCANDAL, A
(1960 - Paramount) Sophia Loren, John Gavin
One Sheet: $15 - $30

BREATH OF THE GODS, THE
(1920 - Universal) Tsuru Aoki, Stanhope
Wheatcroft
One Sheet: $250 - $500

BREATHLESS
(1959 - Imperia) Jean-Paul Belmondo, Jean
Seberg
One Sheet: $250 - $500   *French Title:
A BOUT DE SOUFFLE. Price is for original
French one-panel(47x63).*

BREATHLESS
(1983 - Orion) Richard Gere, Valerie Kaprisky
One Sheet: $5 - $10

BREED APART, A
(1986 - -) Rutger Hauer, Kathleen Turner,
Powers Boothe
One Sheet: $3 - $5

BREED OF MEN
(1919 - Artcraft) William S. Hart
One Sheet: $800 - $1,500

One Sheet

BREED OF THE BORDER
(1933 - Monogram) Bob Steele
One Sheet: $250 - $500   *Cowboy
Movie Posters # 152.*

BREEZING HOME
(1937 - Universal) Binnie Barnes, William
Gargan
One Sheet: $75 - $150

BREEZY
(1973 - Universal) William Holden, Kay Lenz,
Dir: Clint Eastwood
One Sheet: $7 - $15

BREEZY BILL
(1930 - -) Bob Steele, Alfred Hewston, Edna
Astin
One Sheet: $150 - $300

BREMENTOWN MUSICIANS, THE
(1935 - Celebrity) Animated by Ub Iwerks
One Sheet: $800 - $1,500   *Cartoon.
Cartoon Movie Posters #113.*

BRENDA STARR, REPORTER
(1945 - Columbia) Joan Woodbury, Kane
Richmond
One Sheet: $125 - $250   *Serial. 13
Chapters.*

BREWSTER McCLOUD
(1970 - MGM) Bud Cort, Sally Kellerman
One Sheet: $5 - $10

BREWSTER'S MILLIONS
(1921 - Paramount) Roscoe "Fatty" Arbuckle,
Betty Ross Clark
One Sheet: $1,900 - $3,000

BREWSTER'S MILLIONS
(1935 - British & Dominion Films) Jack
Buchanan, Lili Damita
One Sheet: $150 - $300

BREWSTER'S MILLIONS
(1945 - United Artists) Dennis O'Keefe, Helen
Walker
One Sheet: $75 - $125

BREWSTER'S MILLIONS
(1985 - Universal) Richard Pryor, John Candy
One Sheet: $5 - $10

BRIBE, THE
(1949 - MGM) Robert Taylor, Ava Gardner,
Vincent Price
One Sheet: $75 - $125

One Sheet

BRICK BRADFORD
(1947 - Columbia) Kane Richmond, Rick Vallin
One Sheet: $125 - $250   *Serial. 15
Chapters.*

BRIDAL PATH, THE
(1959 - British Lion) Bill Travers, Alex
Mackenzie
One Sheet: $10 - $20

BRIDAL SUITE
(1939 - MGM) Robert Young, Annabella
One Sheet: $100 - $200

BRIDE, THE
(1985 - Columbia) Sting, Jennifer Beals
One Sheet: $7 - $15   *One Sheet
(Style B):$15-25.*

BRIDE 13
(1920 - Fox) -
One Sheet: $200 - $400   *Serial. 15
Chapters.*

BRIDE AND GLOOM
(1922R - Pathe) Harold Lloyd
One Sheet: $500 - $800   *Re-release.*

BRIDE AND THE BEAST, THE
(1958 - Allied Artists) Lance Fuller, Charlotte
Austin
One Sheet: $125 - $250

BRIDE BY MISTAKE
(1944 - RKO) Laraine Day, Alan Marshall
One Sheet: $50 - $100

BRIDE CAME C.O.D., THE
(1941 - Warner Bros.) James Cagney, Bette
Davis
One Sheet: $300 - $700

BRIDE COMES HOME, THE
(1936 - Paramount) Claudette Colbert, Robert
Young, Fred MacMurray
One Sheet: $250 - $600

BRIDE FOR HENRY, A
(1937 - Monogram) Anne Nagel, Warren Hull
One Sheet: $75 - $150

BRIDE FOR SALE
(1949 - RKO) Claudette Colbert, Robert Young
One Sheet: $50 - $100

BRIDE GOES WILD, THE
(1948 - MGM) Van Johnson, June Allyson
One Sheet: $50 - $100

BRIDE IS MUCH TOO BEAUTIFUL, THE
(1958 - Ellis-Lax) Brigitte Bardot, Louis Jordan
One Sheet: $75 - $150

BRIDE OF FRANKENSTEIN
(1935 - Universal) Boris Karloff, Colin Clive,
Elsa Lanchester
One Sheet: $145,000 - $200,000   *Graven
Images, pg. 43, 84-85. Advance: $150,000 -
$250,000.*

BRIDE OF FRANKENSTEIN

(1953R - Realart) Boris Karloff, Colin Clive,
Elsa Lanchester
One Sheet: $350 - $750   *Re-release.*

BRIDE OF RE-ANIMATOR, THE
(1990 - -) Jeffery Combs
One Sheet: $15 - $30

BRIDE OF THE DESERT
(1929 - Rayart) Alice Calhoun, LeRoy Mason
One Sheet: $150 - $300

BRIDE OF THE GORILLA, THE
(1951 - Realart) Lon Chaney Jr., Barbara
Payton
One Sheet: $50 - $100

BRIDE OF THE LAKE
(1934 - Ameranglo) Gina Malo, John Garrick
One Sheet: $75 - $150   *AKA: LILY OF
KILLARNEY.*

BRIDE OF THE MONSTER
(1956 - Banner) Bela Lugosi, Dir: Ed Wood
One Sheet: $250 - $500   *Graven
Images, pg. 189.*

BRIDE OF THE REGIMENT
(1930 - First National) Vivienne Segal, Allan
Prior
One Sheet: $100 - $200

BRIDE OF VENGEANCE
(1949 - Paramount) Paulette Goddard, John
Lund
One Sheet: $50 - $100

BRIDE WALKS OUT, THE
(1936 - RKO) Barbara Stanwyck, Robert Young
One Sheet: $250 - $600

BRIDE WORE BLACK, THE
(1968 - Lopert) Jeanne Moreau, Jean-Claude
Brialy, Michel Bouquet
One Sheet: $15 - $25

BRIDE WORE BOOTS, THE
(1946 - Paramount) Barbara Stanwyck, Robert
Cummings
One Sheet: $75 - $125

BRIDE WORE CRUTCHES, THE
(1941 - 20th Century Fox) Lynne Roberts, Ted
North
One Sheet: $50 - $100

BRIDE WORE RED, THE
(1937 - MGM) Joan Crawford, Franchot Tone,
Robert Young
One Sheet: $500 - $800

BRIDEGROOM FOR TWO
(1932 - British-International) Gene Gerrard,
Muriel Angelus
One Sheet: $75 - $150

BRIDELESS GROOM
(1947 - Columbia) The Three Stooges (Shemp)
One Sheet: $350 - $750   *Comedy short.
Duotone.*

BRIDES ARE LIKE THAT
(1936 - Warner Bros.) Anita Louise, Gene
Lockhart
One Sheet: $75 - $180

BRIDES OF BLOOD
(1969 - -) John Ashley, Kent Taylor
One Sheet: $15 - $35

BRIDES OF DRACULA
(1960 - Universal) Peter Cushing, Freda
Jackson
One Sheet: $150 - $350   *Graven
Images, pg. 212-213.*

BRIDES OF FU MANCHU, THE
(1966 - Seven Arts) Christopher Lee, Douglas
Wilmer
One Sheet: $15 - $30

BRIDES TO BE
(1934 - Paramount) Betty Stockfield,
Constance Shotter
One Sheet: $150 - $300

BRIDGE, THE
(1961 - Allied Artists) Fritz Wepper, Volker
Bohnet
One Sheet: $5 - $10

BRIDGE AT REMAGEN, THE
(1969 - United Artists) George Segal, Robert
Vaughn, Ben Gazzara

One Sheet: $5 - $10

BRIDGE OF SAN LUIS REY, THE
(1929 - MGM) Lily Damita, Ernest Torrence
One Sheet: $150 - $350

BRIDGE OF SAN LUIS REY, THE
(1944 - United Artists) Lynn Bari, Akim
Tamiroff, Frances Lederer
One Sheet: $50 - $100

BRIDGE OF SIGHS
(1936 - Invincible) Jack LaRue, Dorothy Tree
One Sheet: $75 - $150

BRIDGE ON THE RIVER KWAI, THE
(1957 - Columbia) William Holden, Alec
Guinness
One Sheet: $75 - $150   *Academy
Award: Best Picture, Best Actor(Guiness), Best
Direction(David Lean). One Sheet(Style B):$100-
200.Academy Award Movie Posters #174-#176.*

BRIDGE ON THE RIVER KWAI, THE
(1963R - Columbia) William Holden, Alec
Guiness
One Sheet: $30 - $50   *Re-release.*

BRIDGE ON THE RIVER KWAI, THE
(1981R - Columbia) William Holden, Alec
Guiness
One Sheet: $10 - $20   *Re-release.*

BRIDGE TO GLORY
(1964 - Jillo) Reunato Salvatori, Nino
Castelnuovo
One Sheet: $7 - $15

BRIDGE TO THE SUN
(1961 - MGM) Carroll Baker, James Shigeta
One Sheet: $15 - $30

BRIDGE TOO FAR, A
(1977 - United Artists) Sean Connery, Gene
Hackman, Anthony Hopkins
One Sheet: $15 - $35   *Advance:$20-
$40.*

BRIDGES AT TOKO-RI, THE
(1954 - Paramount) Fredric March, William
Holden, Grace Kelly
One Sheet: $75 - $125

BRIDGES AT TOKO-RI, THE
(1959R - Paramount) Fredric March, William
Holden, Grace Kelly
One Sheet: $10 - $20   *Re-release.*

BRIDGES OF MADISON COUNTY, THE
(1995 - Warner Bros.) Clint Eastwood, Meryl
Streep
One Sheet: $7 - $15

BRIEF ECSTACY
(1937 - Phoenix) Paul Lukas, Linden Travers
One Sheet: $75 - $150

BRIEF ENCOUNTER
(1946 - Universal) Celia Johnson, Trevor
Howard
One Sheet: $50 - $100

BRIEF HISTORY OF TIME, A
(1992 - Triton) -
One Sheet: $3 - $5

BRIEF MOMENT
(1933 - Columbia) Carole Lombard, Gene
Raymond
One Sheet: $1,300 - $2,000

BRIEF VACATION, A
(1975 - Allied Artists) Florinda Boldan, Renato
Salvatori, Dir: Vittorio De Sica
One Sheet: $10 - $20   *Italian.*

BRIGADOON
(1954 - MGM) Gene Kelly, Van Johnson
One Sheet: $50 - $100

BRIGAND, THE
(1952 - Columbia) Anthony Dexter, Anthony
Quinn
One Sheet: $20 - $40

BRIGAND OF KANDAHAR, THE
(1966 - Columbia) Ronald Lewis, Oliver Reed
One Sheet: $5 - $10

BRIGGS FAMILY, THE
(1940 - Warner Bros.) Edward Chapman
One Sheet: $40 - $75

BRIGHAM YOUNG-FRONTIERSMAN

(1940 - 20th Century Fox) Dean Jagger, Tyrone Power, Linda Darnell
One Sheet: $250 - $600 *Cowboy Movie Posters #256.*

BRIGHT EYES
(1934 - Fox) Shirley Temple, James Dunn
One Sheet: $1,600 - $2,500 *Temple sings "On The Good Ship Lollipop."*

One Sheet

BRIGHT LEAF
(1950 - Warner Bros.) Gary Cooper, Lauren Bacall
One Sheet: $75 - $150

BRIGHT LIGHTS
(1916 - Triangle) Roscoe "Fatty" Arbuckle
One Sheet: $1,300 - $2,000

BRIGHT LIGHTS
(1930 - First National) Dorothy MacKail, Noah Beery
One Sheet: $150 - $300

BRIGHT LIGHTS
(1935 - Warner Bros.) Joe E. Brown, Ann Dvorak
One Sheet: $100 - $200

BRIGHT LIGHTS, BIG CITY
(1988 - MGM/UA) Michael J. Fox, Kiefer Sutherland, Phoebe Cates
One Sheet: $3 - $5

BRIGHT ROAD
(1953 - MGM) Dorothy Dandridge, Philip Hepburn, Harry Belafonte
One Sheet: $40 - $75 *Black cast. Separate Cinema, pg. 84.*

BRIGHT SHAWL, THE
(1923 - First National) Richard Barthelmess, Mary Astor, Edward G. Robinson
One Sheet: $250 - $600

BRIGHT VICTORY
(1950 - Universal) Arthur Kennedy, Peggy Dow
One Sheet: $30 - $50

BRIGHTON BEACH MEMOIRS
(1986 - Universal) Blythe Danner, Bob Dishy, Judith Ivey
One Sheet: $3 - $5

BRIGHTON ROCK
(1947 - Associated British) Richard Attenborough, Harcourt Williams
One Sheet: $30 - $50

BRIGHTON STRANGLER, THE
(1945 - RKO) John Loder, Rose Hobart
One Sheet: $50 - $100

BRIGHTY OF THE GRAND CANYON
(1967 - Feature Films) Pat Conway, Joseph Cotten
One Sheet: $5 - $10

BRILLIANT MARRIAGE
(1936 - Invincible) Joan Marsh, Ray Walker
One Sheet: $100 - $200

BRIMSTONE
(1949 - Republic) Rod Cameron, Walter Brennan
One Sheet: $40 - $75

BRIMSTONE AND TREACLE
(1982 - Namara/United Artists) Denholm Elliot, Sting, Joan Plowright
One Sheet: $15 - $25

BRING 'EM BACK ALIVE

(1932 - RKO) Documentary: Frank Buck
One Sheet: $500 - $800

BRING 'EM BACK ALIVE
(1948R - RKO) (Documentary) Frank Buck
One Sheet: $40 - $75 *Re-release.*

BRING ME THE HEAD OF ALFREDO GARCIA
(1974 - United Artists) Warren Oates, Isela Vega
One Sheet: $20 - $40 *Price is for both styles.*

BRING ON THE GIRLS
(1945 - Paramount) Veronica Lake, Sonny Tufts
One Sheet: $100 - $200

BRING ON THE NIGHT
(1985 - -) Sting
One Sheet: $20 - $40 *Rock'N'Roll documentary.*

BRING YOUR SMILE ALONG
(1955 - Columbia) Frankie Laine, Keefe Brasselle
One Sheet: $15 - $35

BRINGING UP BABY
(1938 - RKO Radio) Cary Grant, Katharine Hepburn
One Sheet: $1,900 - $3,000

BRINGING UP FATHER
(1920 - McManus) -
One Sheet: $800 - $1,500 *Cartoon.*

BRINGING UP FATHER
(1946 - Monogram) Joe Yule, Renie Riano
One Sheet: $50 - $100

BRINK'S JOB, THE
(1978 - Universal) Peter Falk, Peter Boyle
One Sheet: $3 - $5

BRITISH AGENT
(1934 - First National) Leslie Howard, Kay Francis
One Sheet: $150 - $300

BRITISH INTELLIGENCE
(1940 - Warner Bros.) Boris Karloff, Margaret Lindsay
One Sheet: $200 - $400

BRITTANIA HOSPITAL
(1982 - Universal) Leonard Rossiter, Malcolm McDowell
One Sheet: $3 - $5

BRITTANIA OF BILLINGSGATE
(1933 - Gaumont) Violet Loraine, Gordon Harker
One Sheet: $150 - $300

BROADCAST NEWS
(1987 - 20th Century Fox) William Hurt, Holly Hunter, Albert Brooks
One Sheet: $7 - $15

BROADCASTING
(1920 - Educational) The Chimps
One Sheet: $150 - $300

BROADMINDED
(1931 - First National) Bela Lugosi, Joe E. Brown
One Sheet: $600 - $1,000

BROADWAY
(1929 - Universal) Glenn Tyron, Evelyn Brent
One Sheet: $1,600 - $2,500

BROADWAY
(1942 - Universal) George Raft, Pat O'Brien
One Sheet: $100 - $200

BROADWAY
(1948R - Universal) George Raft, Pat O'Brien
One Sheet: $40 - $75 *Re-release.*

BROADWAY BABIES
(1929 - First National) Alice White, Charles Delaney
One Sheet: $250 - $500

BROADWAY BAD
(1933 - Fox) Joan Blondell, Ricardo Cortez, Ginger Rogers
One Sheet: $500 - $800

BROADWAY BIG SHOT
(1942 - PRC) Ralph Byrd, Virginia Vale
One Sheet: $75 - $150

BROADWAY BILL
(1934 - Columbia) Warner Baxter, Myrna Loy, Dir: Frank Capra
One Sheet: $600 - $1,000

BROADWAY COWBOY, A
(1920 - -) William Demond
One Sheet: $200 - $400

BROADWAY DANNY ROSE
(1984 - Orion) Woody Allen, Mia Farrow
One Sheet: $7 - $15

BROADWAY GONDOLIER
(1935 - Warner Bros.) Dick Powell, Joan Blondell
One Sheet: $150 - $300

BROADWAY HOOFER, THE
(1929 - Columbia) Marie Saxon, Jack Egan
One Sheet: $200 - $400

BROADWAY HOSTESS
(1935 - Warner Bros.) Wini Shaw, Lyle Talbot
One Sheet: $125 - $250

BROADWAY JONES
(1917 - Artcraft) George M. Cohan
One Sheet: $600 - $1,000 *Cohan's first appearance in films.*

BROADWAY LIMITED
(1941 - United Artists) Dennis O'Keefe, Victor McLaglen
One Sheet: $75 - $150

BROADWAY MELODY
(1929 - MGM) Charles King, Bessie Love, Anita Page
One Sheet: $1,900 - $3,000 *Academy Award: Best Picture. First musical in U.S. film. Academy Award Movie Posters #11.*

BROADWAY MELODY OF 1936
(1935 - MGM) Jack Benny, Robert Taylor, Eleanor Powell
One Sheet: $600 - $1,000

BROADWAY MELODY OF 1938
(1937 - MGM) Eleanor Powell, Robert Taylor, Judy Garland
One Sheet: $500 - $800

BROADWAY MELODY OF 1940
(1940 - MGM) Fred Astaire, Eleanor Powell
One Sheet: $250 - $500

BROADWAY MUSKETEERS
(1938 - Warner Bros.) Ann Sheridan, Marie Wilson, Margaret Lindsay
One Sheet: $75 - $150

BROADWAY NIGHTS
(1928 - First National) Lois Silson, Sam Hardy
One Sheet: $250 - $500

BROADWAY RHYTHM
(1944 - MGM) George Murphy, Ginny Simms
One Sheet: $75 - $150

BROADWAY ROSE
(1922 - Metro) Mae Murray
One Sheet: $500 - $800

BROADWAY SCANDAL, A
(1918 - Bluebird) Carmel Myers, Lon Chaney, W.H. Bainbridge
One Sheet: $500 - $800

BROADWAY SCANDALS
(1929 - Columbia) Sally O'Neill, Jack Egan
One Sheet: $350 - $750

BROADWAY SERENADE
(1939 - MGM) Jeanette MacDonald, Lew Ayres
One Sheet: $150 - $300

BROADWAY THROUGH A KEYHOLE
(1933 - United Artists) Constance Cummings, Russ Columbo
One Sheet: $250 - $600

BROADWAY TO CHEYENNE
(1932 - Monogram) Rex Bell
One Sheet: $150 - $350

BROADWAY TO HOLLYWOOD
(1933 - MGM) Alice Brady, Frank Morgan
One Sheet: $600 - $1,000 *Style C(one sheet)-stone litho.*

BROKEN ARROW
(1950 - 20th Century Fox) James Stewart, Jeff

Chandler
One Sheet: $150 - $300

BROKEN ARROW
(1996 - Fox) Christian Slater, John Travolta, Dir: John Woo
One Sheet: $7 - $15

BROKEN BLOSSOMS
(1919 - United Artists) Lillian Gish, Dir: D. W. Griffith
One Sheet: $2,500 - $4,000

Lobby Card

BROKEN BLOSSOMS
(1936 - Twickenham) Dolly Haas, Emlyn Williams
One Sheet: $100 - $200

BROKEN CHAINS
(1923 - -) Wilfred Kimball
One Sheet: $200 - $400

BROKEN DREAMS
(1934 - Monogram) Randolph Scott, Martha Sleeper
One Sheet: $150 - $300

BROKEN EARTH
(1939 - Sack) Clarence Muse
One Sheet: $150 - $300 *Black cast. Duotone. Separate Cinema, pg. 131.*

BROKEN ENGLISH
(1981 - Lorimar) Beverly Ross, Jacques Martial
One Sheet: $3 - $5

BROKEN GATE, THE
(1927 - Tiffany) Dorothy Phillips, William Collier Jr.
One Sheet: $250 - $500

BROKEN HARVEST
(1995 - Destiny) Colin Lane, Marian Quinn
One Sheet: $3 - $5

BROKEN HEARTS OF HOLLYWOOD
(1926 - Warner Bros) Patsy Ruth Miller, Louise Dressler, Douglas Fairbanks, Jr.
One Sheet: $700 - $1,200

BROKEN HORSESHOE, THE
(1953 - Butcher) Robert Beatty, Elizabeth Sellars
One Sheet: $15 - $25

BROKEN JOURNEY
(1947 - Eagle-Lion) Phyllis Calvert, Margot Grahame
One Sheet: $40 - $75

BROKEN LANCE
(1954 - 20th Century Fox) Spencer Tracy, Robert Wagner, Richard Widmark
One Sheet: $30 - $50

BROKEN LAND
(1962 - 20th Century Fox) Kent Taylor, Dianna Darrin, Jack Nicholson
One Sheet: $15 - $25

BROKEN LULLABY
(1932 - Paramount-Publix) Lionel Barrymore, Nancy Carroll
One Sheet: $200 - $400

BROKEN MELODY, THE
(1934 - Associated) John Garrick, Margot Grahame
One Sheet: $100 - $200

BROKEN MELODY
(1938 - British Empire) Lloyd Hughes, Diane DuCane

One Sheet: $75 - $150

BROKEN RAINBOW
(1985 - -) Narrated by Martin Sheen
One Sheet: $15 - $30   *Documentary
about Navajo relocation. Academy Award: Best
Documentary.*

BROKEN STAR
(1956 - United Artists) Howard Duff, Lita Baron,
Bill Williams
One Sheet: $20 - $40

BROKEN STRINGS
(1940 - International Roadshows) Clarence
Muse, Cyril Lewis
One Sheet: $150 - $300   *Black cast.
Separate Cinema, pg. 131.*

BROKEN WING, THE
(1932 - Paramount) Lupe Velez, Melvyn
Douglas
One Sheet: $200 - $400

BROMO AND JULIET
(1926 - Pathe) Charley Chase
One Sheet: $350 - $750

BRONCHO BILLY'S CONSCIENCE
(1915 - Essanay) G.M. Anderson
One Sheet: $800 - $1,500   *Cowboy
Movie Posters #7.*

BRONCO BILLY
(1980 - Warner Bros.) Clint Eastwood, Sondra
Locke
One Sheet: $15 - $25   *Cowboy
Movie Posters #353. Advance:$20-40.*

BRONCO BULLFROG
(1972 - British Lion) Del Walker, Sam
Shepherd
One Sheet: $5 - $10

BRONCO BUSTER
(1952 - Universal) John Lund, Scott Brady
One Sheet: $15 - $30

BRONX TALE, A
(1993 - Savoy Pictures) Robert DeNiro (Dir.),
Chazz Palminteri, Francis Capra
One Sheet: $5 - $15

BRONZE BUCKAROO, THE
(1939 - Sack) Herbert Jeffrey, Artie Young
One Sheet: $500 - $800   *Black cast.
Full color. Separate Cinema, pg. 55. Cowboy
Movie Posters #231.*

BRONZE VENUS, THE
(1943R - Toddy) Lena Horne
One Sheet: $200 - $400   *Black cast.
Re-titled, Re-release of "THE DUKE IS TOPS".
Separate Cinema, pg. 80,81.*

BROOD, THE
(1979 - New World) Oliver Reed, Samantha
Eggar, Dir: David Cronenberg
One Sheet: $10 - $20

BROOKLYN ORCHID
(1942 - United Artists) Marjorie Woodworth,
William Bendix
One Sheet: $75 - $125

BROTHER ALFRED
(1932 - British International) Gene Gerrard,
Molly Lamont
One Sheet: $150 - $300

BROTHER FRANCIS
(1930 - -) -
One Sheet: $150 - $300

BROTHER FROM ANOTHER PLANET, THE
(1984 - A-Train) Joe Morton, Darryl Edwards
One Sheet: $10 - $20   *Black cast.*

BROTHER FUTURE
(1991 - PME) Phil Lewis, Frank Converse
One Sheet: $10 - $20   *Black cast.*

BROTHER JOHN
(1971 - Columbia) Sidney Poitier, Will Geer
One Sheet: $15 - $25

BROTHER MARTIN, SERVANT OF JESUS
(1943 - Jenkins & Bourgeois) Spencer Williams
One Sheet: $250 - $500   *Black cast.*

BROTHER OF THE WIND
(1972 - Sun International) Dick Robinson
One Sheet: $5 - $10

BROTHER ORCHID
(1940 - Warner Bros.) Edward G. Robinson,
Ann Sothern, Humphrey Bogart
One Sheet: $150 - $300

BROTHER RAT
(1938 - Warner Bros.) Wayne Morris, Priscilla
Lane, Ronald Reagan
One Sheet: $200 - $400

BROTHER RAT AND A BABY
(1940 - Warner Bros.) Wayne Morris, Priscilla
Lane, Ronald Reagan
One Sheet: $125 - $250

BROTHER SUN, SISTER MOON
(1973 - Paramount) Graham Faulkner, Judi
Bowker
One Sheet: $15 - $25   *Life of St.
Francis of Assisi.*

BROTHERHOOD, THE
(1968 - Paramount) Alex Cord, Irene Papas,
Kirk Douglas
One Sheet: $7 - $15

One Sheet

BROTHERHOOD OF SATAN, THE
(1971 - Columbia) Strother Martin, L. Q. Jones
One Sheet: $15 - $30

BROTHERLY LOVE
(1936 - Paramount) Popeye, Fleischer Studio
One Sheet: $2,500 - $4,000   *Cartoon.
Duotone. Cartoon Movie Posters #212.*

BROTHERLY LOVE
(1970 - MGM) Peter O'Toole, Susannah York,
Michael Craig
One Sheet: $7 - $15

BROTHERS
(1929 - Rayart) Cornelius Keefe, Barbara
Bedford, Arthur Rankin
One Sheet: $250 - $500

BROTHERS
(1930 - Columbia) Bert Lytell, Dorothy
Sebastian
One Sheet: $250 - $500

BROTHERS, THE
(1947 - Universal International) Will Fyffe,
Patricia Roc, Finlay Currie
One Sheet: $30 - $50

BROTHERS
(1977 - Warner Bros.) Bernie Casey, Vonetta
McGee
One Sheet: $15 - $25   *Blaxploitation.*

BROTHERS AND SISTERS
(1980 - British Film Institute) Carolyn Pickles,
Sam Dale
One Sheet: $3 - $5

BROTHERS IN LAW
(1957 - BC) Richard Attenborough, Ian
Carmichael
One Sheet: $7 - $15

BROTHERS IN THE SADDLE
(1949 - RKO) Tim Holt, Richard Martin
One Sheet: $30 - $50

BROTHERS KARAMAZOV, THE
(1957 - MGM) Yul Brynner, Maria Schell,
William Shatner(film debut)
One Sheet: $30 - $60

BROTHERS O'TOOLE, THE
(1973 - CVD) John Astin, Lee Meriwether
One Sheet: $3 - $5

BROTHERS OF THE WEST
(1938 - Victory) Tom Tyler, Lois Wilde
One Sheet: $150 - $300

BROTHERS RICO, THE
(1957 - Columbia) Richard Conte, Dianne
Foster
One Sheet: $15 - $25

BROWN OF HARVARD
(1925 - MGM) Willaim Haines, Francis X.
Bushman
One Sheet: $300 - $700   *Sports
(Football). Sports Movie Posters #s 175, 176.*

BROWN SUGAR
(1931 - Warner Bros.) Constance Carpenter,
Francis Lister
One Sheet: $250 - $500

BROWN WALLET, THE
(1936 - Warner Bros.) Patric Knowles, Nancy
O'Neil
One Sheet: $75 - $150

BROWNING VERSION, THE
(1951 - Universal) Michael Redgrave, Jean
Kent
One Sheet: $100 - $200

BROWNING VERSION, THE
(1994 - Paramount) Albert Finney, Greta
Scacchi, Matthew Modine
One Sheet: $5 - $10

BRUBAKER
(1980 - 20th Century Fox) Robert Redford,
Yopher Kotto
One Sheet: $5 - $10

BRUCE GENTRY-DAREDEVEL OF THE SKIES
(1949 - Columbia) Tom Neal, Judy Clark
One Sheet: $75 - $125   *Serial.
Aviation. 15 Chapters.*

BRUCE LEE AND I
(1976 - Shaw Bros.) Betty Ting Pei, Li Hsiu
Hsien
One Sheet: $50 - $100

BRUCE LEE FIGHTS BACK FROM THE GRAVE
(1978 - -) -
One Sheet: $10 - $20

BRUCE LEE: THE MAN/THE MYTH
(1977 - Cinema Shares) Bruce Li, Linda Herst
One Sheet: $30 - $50

BRUCE LEE-TRUE STORY
(1976 - Eternal) Ho Chung Tao
One Sheet: $30 - $50

BRUSHFIRE
(1961 - Obelisk) John Ireland, Everett Sloane
One Sheet: $10 - $20

BRUTE, THE
(1927 - Warner Bros.) Monte Blue, Lelia Hyams
One Sheet: $150 - $300

BRUTE AND THE BEAST, THE
(1968 - AIP) Franco Nero, George Hilton
One Sheet: $7 - $15

BRUTE FORCE
(1947 - Universal) Burt Lancaster, Hume
Cronyn
One Sheet: $150 - $300

BRUTE FORCE
(1956R - Universal) Burt Lancaster, Hume
Cronyn
One Sheet: $20 - $40   *Re-release.*

BRUTE MAN, THE
(1946 - PRC) Rondo Hatton, Jane Adams
One Sheet: $250 - $500   *Graven
Images, pg. 141.*

B.S., I LOVE YOU
(1971 - 20th Century Fox) Peter Kastner,
Joanna Barnes
One Sheet: $10 - $20

BUBBLE, THE
(1967 - Arch) Michael Cole, Deborah Walley
One Sheet: $15 - $25   *AKA:
FANTASTIC INVASION OF PLANET EARTH*

BUBBLE BEE
(1949 - RKO/Disney) Pluto
One Sheet: $600 - $1,000   *Cartoon. The
Disney Poster, pg. 40.*

BUBBLE TROUBLE
(1953 - Columbia) The Three Stooges (Shemp)
One Sheet: $150 - $350   *Comedy short.
Duotone.*

BUBBLING OVER
(1934 - RKO) Ethel Waters
One Sheet: $200 - $400   *Black cast.
Separate Cinema, pg. 83.*

BUCCANEER, THE
(1938 - Paramount) Fredric March, Franciska
Gaal
One Sheet: $600 - $1,000

BUCCANEER, THE
(1958 - Paramount) Yul Brynner, Charlton
Heston
One Sheet: $20 - $40

BUCCANEER'S GIRL
(1950 - Universal) Yvonne De Carlo, Philip
Friend
One Sheet: $30 - $50

BUCHANAN RIDES ALONE
(1958 - Columbia) Randolph Scott, Craig
Stevens
One Sheet: $30 - $50

BUCK AND BUBBLES LAFF JAMBOREE
(1940 - Toddy) Buck & Bubbles compilation
One Sheet: $200 - $400   *Black cast.*

BUCK AND THE PREACHER
(1972 - Columbia) Sidney Poitier, Harry
Belafonte
One Sheet: $15 - $25

BUCK BENNY RIDES AGAIN
(1940 - Paramount) Jack Benny, Eddie
"Rochester" Anderson, Phil Harris
One Sheet: $150 - $300

One Sheet

BUCK PRIVATES
(1941 - Universal) Bud Abbott, Lou Costello
One Sheet: $250 - $600

BUCK PRIVATES
(1953R - Realart) Bud Abbott, Lou Costello
One Sheet: $50 - $100   *Re-release.*

BUCK PRIVATES COME HOME
(1947 - Universal) Bud Abbott, Lou Costello
One Sheet: $75 - $150

BUCK ROGERS
(1939 - Universal) Larry "Buster" Crabbe,
Constance Moore
One Sheet: $1,000 - $1,800   *Serial. Sci-Fi.
12 Chapters. Price is for duotone Chapters 2-15.
Stock one-sheet (full color):$2500-$4000.
GravenImages, pg. 98.*

BUCK ROGERS
(197?R - Crystal) Buster Crabbe
One Sheet: $15 - $25   *Re-release.
Feature film comprised of compiled footage of
1939 serial chapters.*

BUCK ROGERS IN THE 25TH CENTURY
(1979 - Universal) Gil Gerard, Pamela Hensley,
Erin Gray
One Sheet: $15 - $30   *Advance:$20-
$40.*

BUCKAROO BANZAI
(1984 - -) See ADVENTURES OF BUCKAROO
BANZAI

BUCKAROO BROADCAST, A
(1938 - RKO) Ray Whitley, Dick Elliott
One Sheet: $75 - $150

BUCKAROO FROM POWDER RIVER
(1947 - Columbia) Charles Starrett, Smiley Burnette
One Sheet: $30 - $60

BUCKAROO SHERIFF OF TEXAS
(1951 - Republic) Michael Chapin, Eilene Janssen
One Sheet: $20 - $40

BUCKET OF BLOOD
(1934 - Fox) Norman Dryden, John Kelt
One Sheet: $600 - $1,000   *AKA: (GB) THE TELL-TALE HEART.*

BUCKET OF BLOOD, A
(1959 - AIP) Dick Miller, Barboura Morris, Dir: Roger Corman
One Sheet: $75 - $150

BUCKSKIN
(1968 - Paramount) Barry Sullivan, Joan Caulfield, Wendell Corey
One Sheet: $5 - $10

BUCKSKIN FRONTIER
(1943 - United Artists) George Reeves, Richard Dix
One Sheet: $75 - $125

BUCKSKIN LADY, THE
(1957 - United Artists) Patricia Medina, Richard Denning
One Sheet: $15 - $30

BUCKTOWN
(1975 - AIP) Pam Grier, Fred Williamson
One Sheet: $15 - $25   *Blaxploitation.*

BUDDHA
(1963 - United Artists) Kojiro Hongo, Charito Solis
One Sheet: $30 - $50   *Japanese.*

BUDDY & COOKIE
(1933 - Vitaphone Short Subject) Buddy & Cookie
One Sheet: $1,300 - $2,000   *Cartoon. Cartoon Movie Posters #98.*

BUDDY AT THE BAT
(1923 - Universal) Buddy Messinger
One Sheet: $125 - $250

BUDDY BUDDY
(1981 - MGM) Jack Lemmon, Walter Matthau
One Sheet: $5 - $10

BUDDY HOLLY STORY, THE
(1978 - Columbia) Gary Busey, Don Stroud
One Sheet: $15 - $30   *Style B:$20-$40.*

BUDDY SYSTEM, THE
(1984 - -) Richard Dreyfuss, Susan Sarandon
One Sheet: $3 - $5

BUFFALO BILL
(1944 - 20th Century Fox) Maureen O'Hara, Joel McCrea
One Sheet: $100 - $200

BUFFALO BILL
(1956R - 20th Century Fox) Maureen O'Hara, Joel McCrea
One Sheet: $20 - $40   *Re-release.*

BUFFALO BILL AND THE INDIANS, OR SITTING BULL'S HISTORY LESSON
(1976 - United Artists) Paul Newman, Harvey Keitel
One Sheet: $15 - $25   *Cowboy Movie Posters #343.*

BUFFALO BILL, HERO OF THE FAR WEST
(1962 - Gloria) Gordon Scott
One Sheet: $15 - $30

BUFFALO BILL IN TOMAHAWK TERRITORY
(1952 - United Artists) Clayton Moore, Slim Andrews
One Sheet: $30 - $60

BUFFALO BILL, JR.
(1921 - Artclass) -
One Sheet: $300 - $700

BUFFALO BILL RIDES AGAIN
(1946 - Screen Guild) Richard Arlen, Jennifer Holt
One Sheet: $40 - $75

BUFFALO GUN

● (1961 - Globe) Marty Robbins, Webb Pierce
● One Sheet: $20 - $40   *Country musical.*

● **BUFFALO RIDER**
● (1977 - Star Fire) Rick Quinn, John Freeman
● One Sheet: $5 - $10

● **BUFFY, THE VAMPIRE SLAYER**
● (1992 - 20th Century Fox) Kristy Swanson, Luke Perry
● One Sheet: $7 - $15

● **BUG**
● (1975 - Paramount) Bradford Dillman
● One Sheet: $7 - $15   *Sci-fi.*

● **BUGLE SOUNDS, THE**
● (1941 - MGM) Wallace Beery, Marjorie Main
● One Sheet: $100 - $200

● **BUGLES IN THE AFTERNOON**
● (1951 - Warner Bros.) Ray Milland, George Reeves
● One Sheet: $30 - $50

● **BUGS BUNNY CARTOON STOCK**
● (1941 - Warner Bros.) Bugs Bunny
● One Sheet: $700 - $1,200   *Cartoon.*

● **BUGS BUNNY CARTOON STOCK**
● (1948 - Warner Bros.) Bugs Bunny
● One Sheet: $350 - $750   *Cartoon.*

● **BUGS BUNNY CARTOON STOCK**
● (1952R - Warner Bros.) Bugs Bunny
● One Sheet: $125 - $250   *Re-release. Cartoon.*

● **BUGS BUNNY IN CONCERT**
● (1990 - Warner Bros.) Bugs Bunny
● One Sheet: $7 - $15   *Cartoon.*

● **BUGS BUNNY SUPERSTAR**
● (1975 - Warner Bros.) Bugs Bunny
● One Sheet: $15 - $25   *Cartoon.*

● **BUGS BUNNY'S CARTOON REVIEW**
● (1953 - Warner Bros.) -
● One Sheet: $250 - $500   *Cartoon. Full color. Stock poster with large image of Bugs.*

● **BUGS BUNNY'S THIRD MOVIE-1001 RABBIT TALES**
● (1982 - Warner Bros.) -
● One Sheet: $15 - $25   *Cartoon.*

● **BUGS BUNNY/ROAD RUNNER MOVIE, THE**
● (1979 - Warner Bros.) -
● One Sheet: $15 - $35   *Cartoon.*

● **BUGS IN LOVE**
● (1932 - United Artists) Silly Symphony
● One Sheet: $10,000 - $15,000   *Cartoon. Full color. The Disney Poster, pg. 10.*

● **BUGSY**
● (1991 - TriStar) Warren Beatty, Annette Bening
● One Sheet: $7 - $15

● **BUGSY MALONE**
● (1976 - Paramount) Scott Baio, Jodie Foster
● One Sheet: $15 - $25

● **BUILDING A BUILDING**
● (1933 - United Artists) Mickey Mouse
● One Sheet: $40,000 - $50,000   *Cartoon. The Disney Poster, pg. 25.*

● **BUILDING A BUILDING**
● (1974R - United Artists) -
● One Sheet: $15 - $30   *Re-release. Cartoon.*

● **BULL DURHAM**
● (1988 - Orion) Kevin Costner, Susan Sarandon
● One Sheet: $30 - $50   *Sports (Baseball). Advance:$40-$75. Sports Movie Posters #s 77, 78.*

● **BULLDOG BREED, THE**
● (1960 - Rank) Norman Wisdom, Ian Hunter
● One Sheet: $10 - $20

● **BULLDOG COURAGE**
● (1936 - Puritan) Tim McCoy
● One Sheet: $200 - $400

● **BULLDOG DRUMMOND**
● (1929 - Samuel Goldwyn) Ronald Colman, Claud Allister
● One Sheet: $3,500 - $5,000

● **BULLDOG DRUMMOND AT BAY**

● (1937 - Republic) John Lodge, Dorothy Mackaill
One Sheet: $200 - $400

BULLDOG DRUMMOND AT BAY
(1947 - Columbia) Ron Randell, Anita Louise
● One Sheet: $75 - $125

BULLDOG DRUMMOND COMES BACK
(1937 - Paramount) John Howard, John Barrymore
● One Sheet: $150 - $300

BULLDOG DRUMMOND ESCAPES
(1937 - Paramount) Ray Milland, Heather Angel
● One Sheet: $100 - $200

BULLDOG DRUMMOND IN AFRICA
(1938 - Paramount) John Howard, Heather Angel
● One Sheet: $100 - $200

BULLDOG DRUMMOND STRIKES BACK
(1934 - 20th Century) Ronald Colman, Loretta Young, Warner Oland
● One Sheet: $1,300 - $2,000

BULLDOG DRUMMOND STRIKES BACK
(1947 - Columbia) Ron Randell, Gloria Henry
● One Sheet: $50 - $100

BULLDOG DRUMMOND'S BRIDE
(1939 - Paramount) John Howard, Heather Angel
● One Sheet: $100 - $200

BULLDOG DRUMMOND'S PERIL
(1938 - Paramount) John Howard, Louise Campbell
● One Sheet: $100 - $200

BULLDOG DRUMMOND'S REVENGE
(1937 - Paramount) John Howard, John Barrymore
● One Sheet: $125 - $250

BULLDOG DRUMMOND'S REVENGE
(1948R - Paramount) John Howard, John Barrymore
● One Sheet: $40 - $75   *Re-release.*

BULLDOG DRUMMOND'S SECRET POLICE
(1939 - Paramount) John Howard, Heather Angel
● One Sheet: $100 - $200

BULLDOG EDITION
(1936 - Republic) Ray Walker, Evelyn Knapp
One Sheet: $100 - $200

● **BULLDOG JACK**
(1935 - Gaumont) Fay Wray, Jack Hulbert
One Sheet: $600 - $1,000   *AKA: ALIAS BULLDOG DRUMMOND.*

● **BULLDOG SEES IT THROUGH**
(1940 - ABPC) Jack Buchanan, Greta Gynt
One Sheet: $75 - $150

● **BULL-DOGGER, THE**
(1923 - Norman) Bill Pickett
● One Sheet: $1,300 - $2,000   *Black cast. First Black cowboy. Cowboy Movie Posters #'s 40, 42. Sports Movie Posters #300.*

● **BULLET CODE**
(1940 - RKO) George O'Brien, Virginia Vale
One Sheet: $75 - $150

● **BULLET FOR A BADMAN**
(1964 - Universal) Audie Murphy, Darren McGavin
One Sheet: $15 - $30

● **BULLET FOR BILLY THE KID, A**
(1963 - -) Gaston Sands, Steve Brodie
One Sheet: $7 - $15

● **BULLET FOR JOEY, A**
(1955 - United Artists) George Raft, Edward G. Robinson
One Sheet: $40 - $75

● **BULLET FOR PRETTY BOY, A**
(1970 - AIP) Fabian Forte, Jocelyn Lane
One Sheet: $15 - $30

● **BULLET FOR SANDOVAL, A**
(1970 - UMC) Ernest Borgnine, George Hilton
● One Sheet: $15 - $25

● **BULLET FOR THE GENERAL, A**
(1969 - Avco/Embassy) Gian Maria Volonte, Klaus Kinski, Martine Beswick

---

● One Sheet: $5 - $10

● **BULLET IN THE HEAD**
(198? - -) Dir: John Woo
One Sheet: $30 - $50

● **BULLET IS WAITING, A**
(1954 - Columbia) Rory Calhoun, Jean Simmons
One Sheet: $15 - $30

● **BULLET SCARS**
(1942 - Warner Bros.) Regis Toomey, Adele Longmire
One Sheet: $40 - $75

● **BULLETPROOF**
(1996 - Universal) Damon Wayans, Adam Sandler
One Sheet: $3 - $5

● **BULLETPROOF HEART**
(1995 - Keystone) Anthony LaPaglia, Mimi Rogers
One Sheet: $5 - $10

● **BULLETS AND BALLADS**
(1940 - Universal) Armida, Ken Stevens
One Sheet: $75 - $125

● **BULLETS AND SADDLES**
(1943 - Monogram) The Range Busters
One Sheet: $20 - $40

● **BULLETS FOR BANDITS**
(1942 - Columbia) Bill Elliott, Tex Ritter
One Sheet: $50 - $100

● **BULLETS FOR BANDITS**
(1953R - Columbia) Bill Elliott, Tex Ritter
One Sheet: $15 - $30   *Re-release.*

● **BULLETS FOR O'HARA**
(1941 - Warner Bros.) Joan Perry, Roger Pryor
One Sheet: $50 - $100

● **BULLETS FOR RUSTLERS**
(1940 - Columbia) Charles Starrett, Lorna Gray
One Sheet: $75 - $125

● **BULLETS OR BALLOTS**
(1936 - Warner Bros.) Edward G. Robinson, Joan Blondell, Humphrey Bogart
One Sheet: $600 - $1,000

● **BULLETS OVER BROADWAY**
(1994 - Miramax) John Cusack, Diane Wiest, Dir: Woody Allen
One Sheet: $15 - $25   *Academy Award: Best Supporting Actress (Wiest). Academy Award Movie Posters #393.*

● **BULLFIGHTER AND THE LADY**
(1951 - Republic) Robert Stack, Joy Page
One Sheet: $30 - $50

● **BULLFIGHTERS, THE**
(1945 - 20th Century Fox) Laurel and Hardy
One Sheet: $200 - $400

● **BULLIES**
(1986 - Universal) Jonathan Crombie, Janet Laine Green
One Sheet: $5 - $10

● **BULLITT**
(1968 - Warner Bros.) Steve McQueen, Robert Vaughn, Jacqueline Bisset, Don Gordon
One Sheet: $100 - $200   *One Sheet (Style B):$200-$300.*

● **BULLS AND BEARS**
(1930 - Educational) Daphne Pollard, Andy Clyde
One Sheet: $250 - $600

● **BULLSHOT**
(1983 - Handmade) Alan Shearman, Diz White
One Sheet: $3 - $5

● **BULLWHIP**
(1958 - Allied Artists) Guy Madison, Rhonda Fleming
One Sheet: $20 - $40

● **BULLY FROG, A**
(1936 - Educational) Paul Terry Studio
One Sheet: $500 - $800   *Cartoon. Duotone. Stock poster with inset of title.*

● **BULLY ROMANCE, A**
(1938 - 20th Century Fox) Terry-toons
One Sheet: $100 - $200   *Cartoon. Full color stone litho. Stock poster with inset title.*

BUM'S RUSH, THE
(1920 - Artclass) Snub Pollard
One Sheet: $200 - $400

BUMMER
(1973 - -) Kipp Whitman
One Sheet: $10 - $20

BUNCO SQUAD
(1950 - RKO) Robert Sterling, Joan Dixon
One Sheet: $75 - $125

BUNDLE OF BLUES
(1933 - Paramount) -
One Sheet: $150 - $300

BUNDLE OF JOY
(1956 - RKO) Eddie Fisher, Debbie Reynolds
One Sheet: $30 - $50

BUNGALOW 13
(1948 - 20th Century Fox) Tom Conway,
Margaret Hamilton
One Sheet: $40 - $75

BUNGALOW TROUBLES
(1920 - Paramount) Louise Fazenda, Billy
Beyan
One Sheet: $250 - $500

BUNKER BEAN
(1936 - RKO) Owen Davis Jr., Louise Latimer
One Sheet: $100 - $200

BUNNY LAKE IS MISSING
(1965 - Columbia) Laurence Olivier, Carol
Lynley
One Sheet: $40 - $75   *Saul Bass art.*

BUNNY O'HARE
(1971 - AIP) Bette Davis, Ernest Borgnine
One Sheet: $15 - $25

BUNTY PULLS THE STRINGS
(1920 - Goldwyn) Leatrice Joy, Russell
Simpson
One Sheet: $125 - $250

BUONA SERA, MRS. CAMPBELL
(1968 - United Artists) Gina Lollobrigida,
Shelley Winters
One Sheet: $15 - $25

BURBS, THE
(1989 - -) Tom Hanks, Bruce Dern, Carrie
Fisher
One Sheet: $5 - $10

BURDEN OF TRUTH
(1957 - Allend) -
One Sheet: $10 - $20

BURDENS OF RACE, THE
(1933 - -) -
One Sheet: $600 - $1,000

BUREAU OF MISSING PERSONS
(1933 - First National) Bette Davis, Pat O'Brien
One Sheet: $800 - $1,500

BURGLAR, THE
(1907 - Vitagraph) -
One Sheet: $200 - $400   *"...or, A
MIDNIGHT SURPRISE."*

BURGLAR, THE
(1957 - Columbia) Dan Duryea, Jayne
Mansfield
One Sheet: $75 - $150

BURGLAR
(1987 - -) Whoopi Goldberg, Bob Goldthwait
One Sheet: $5 - $10

BURGLARS, THE
(1972 - Columbia) Omar Sharif, Jean-Paul
Belmondo
One Sheet: $5 - $10

BURIAL GROUND
(1985 - -) Karen Well, Peter Bark
One Sheet: $5 - $10

BURKE AND HARE
(1972 - Armitage) Harry Andrews, Derren
Nesbitt
One Sheet: $5 - $10

BURLESQUE IN HARLEM
(1950 - -) -
One Sheet: $150 - $300   *Black cast.
Sexploitation.*

BURMA CONVOY
(1941 - Universal) Charles Bickford, Evelyn
Ankers
One Sheet: $75 - $125

BURN
(1970 - United Artists) Marlon Brando, Evaristo
Marquez
One Sheet: $15 - $25

BURN 'EM UP BARNES
(1921 - Affiliated) Johnny Hines, Betty
Carpenter
One Sheet: $500 - $800

BURN 'EM UP BARNES
(1934 - Mascot) Frankie Darro, Jack Mulhall
One Sheet: $500 - $800   *Serial. 12
Chapters. Price is for stock one sheet.*

BURN 'EM UP O'CONNOR
(1939 - MGM) Dennis O'Keefe, Cecelia Parker
One Sheet: $100 - $200

BURN, WITCH, BURN
(1962 - AIP) Janet Blair, Peter Wyngarde
One Sheet: $40 - $75   *Graven
Images, pg. 217.*

BURNING, THE
(1981 - Filmways) Brian Matthews, Leah Ayres
One Sheet: $5 - $10

BURNING AN ILLUSION
(1982 - British Film Institute) Cassie
MacFarlane
One Sheet: $5 - $10

BURNING CROSS, THE
(1947 - Somerset) Hank Daniels, Virginia
Patton
One Sheet: $100 - $200

BURNING DAYLIGHT
(1914 - Paramount) Hobart Bosworth
One Sheet: $1,300 - $2,000

BURNING GOLD
(1936 - Republic) William Boyd
One Sheet: $125 - $250

BURNING HILLS, THE
(1956 - Warner Bros.) Natalie Wood, Tab
Hunter
One Sheet: $30 - $50

BURNING SANDS
(1922 - Paramount) Wanda Hawley, Milton Sills
One Sheet: $300 - $700

BURNING SECRET
(1988 - Vestron) Faye Dunaway, Klaus Maria
Brandauer
One Sheet: $5 - $10

BURNING THE WIND
(1928 - Universal) Hoot Gibson
One Sheet: $200 - $400

BURNING TRAIL, THE
(1925 - Universal) William Desmond, Albert J.
Smith
One Sheet: $150 - $300

BURNING UP
(1930 - Paramount) Richard Arlen, Mary Brian
One Sheet: $150 - $350

BURNT BY THE SUN
(1995 - Sony) Nikita Mikhalkov, Oleg
Menchikov
One Sheet: $5 - $10

BURNT EVIDENCE
(1954 - Monarch) Jane Hylton, Duncan Lamont
One Sheet: $15 - $30

BURNT OFFERINGS
(1976 - United Artists) Bette Davis, Karen
Black
One Sheet: $10 - $20

BURY ME AN ANGEL
(1972 - New World) Dixie Peabody
One Sheet: $15 - $30   *Biker film.*

BURY ME DEAD
(1947 - Pathe) Cathy O'Donnell, June Lockhart,
Hugh Beaumont
One Sheet: $40 - $75

BURY ME NOT ON THE LONE PRAIRIE
(1940 - Universal) Johnny Mack Brown
One Sheet: $75 - $150

BUS IS COMING, THE
(1971 - Thompson International) Mike Simms
One Sheet: $3 - $5

BUS PESTS
(1945 - MGM) Narrated by Pete Smith
One Sheet: $100 - $200

BUS RILEY'S BACK IN TOWN
(1965 - Universal) Ann-Margret, Michael Parks
One Sheet: $30 - $60

BUS STOP
(1956 - 20th Century Fox) Marilyn Monroe, Don
Murray, Hope Lange
One Sheet: $250 - $600

One Sheet

BUSH CHRISTMAS
(1947 - Universal International) Chips Rafferty,
John Fernside
One Sheet: $50 - $100

BUSH CHRISTMAS
(1983 - Hoyts) John Ewart, Nicole Kidman
One Sheet: $5 - $10

BUSH PILOT
(1947 - Dominion) Rochelle Hudson, Jack La
Rue
One Sheet: $30 - $50

BUSHBABY, THE
(1970 - MGM) Margaret Brooks, Louis Gossett
One Sheet: $5 - $10

BUSHER, THE
(1919 - Ince) Grover Cleveland Alexander
One Sheet: $800 - $1,500

BUSHIDO BLADE, THE
(1982 - Trident) Richard Boone, Toshiro Mifune
One Sheet: $5 - $10   *AKA: THE
BLOODY BUSHIDO BLADE.*

BUSHWHACKERS, THE
(1951 - Realart) John Ireland, Wayne Morris
One Sheet: $30 - $50

BUSINESS AFFAIR, A
(1995 - Skouras) Carole Bouquet, Christopher
Walken
One Sheet: $3 - $5

BUSINESS AND PLEASURE
(1932 - Fox) Will Rogers, Jetta Goudal
One Sheet: $500 - $800

BUSMAN'S HOLIDAY
(1936 - GS) Wally Patch, Muriel George
One Sheet: $100 - $200

BUSMAN'S HONEYMOON
(1940 - MGM) Robert Montgomery, Constance
Cummings
One Sheet: $75 - $150   *AKA:
HAUNTED HONEYMOON.*

BUSSES ROAR
(1942 - Warner Bros.) Richard Travis, Julie
Bishop
One Sheet: $50 - $100

BUSTER
(1988 - Hemdale) Phil Collins, Julie Waters
One Sheet: $5 - $10

BUSTER AND BILLIE
(1974 - Columbia) Jan-Michael Vincent,
Pamela Sue Martin
One Sheet: $7 - $15

BUSTER KEATON STORY, THE

BUSTER KEATON STORY, THE
(1956 - Paramount) Donald O'Connor, Ann
Blyth
One Sheet: $30 - $50

BUSTER'S NOSE DIVE
(1925 - Stern Bros.) Arthur Trimble, Doreen
Turner
One Sheet: $350 - $750

BUSTIN' LOOSE
(1981 - Universal) Richard Pryor, Cicely Tyson
One Sheet: $7 - $15   *Poster shows
Pryor in front of KKK.*

BUSTING
(1974 - United Artists) Elliott Gould, Robert
Blake
One Sheet: $5 - $10

BUSTING OUT
(1950 - -) Blaze Starr
One Sheet: $20 - $40   *Sexploitation.*

BUSY BODIES
(1933 - MGM) Laurel & Hardy
One Sheet: $2,500 - $4,000

BUSY BODY, THE
(1967 - Paramount) Sid Caesar, Robert Ryan,
Richard Pryor
One Sheet: $20 - $40   *Pryor's 1st
film. Art by Frank Frazetta.*

BUSY BUDDIES
(1944 - Columbia) The Three Stooges (Curly)
One Sheet: $2,500 - $4,000   *Comedy short.
Duotone.*

BUSY DAY, A
(1914 - Keystone) Charlie Chaplin
One Sheet: $6,500 - $10,000

BUSYBODY BEAR
(1952 - MGM) Bucky Beaver and Barney Bear
One Sheet: $200 - $400   *Cartoon.*

BUSYBODY BEAR
(1967R - MGM) Bucky Beaver and Barney Bear
One Sheet: $20 - $40   *Re-release.
Cartoon.*

BUT NOT FOR ME
(1959 - Paramount) Clark Gable, Carroll Baker,
Mamie Van Doren
One Sheet: $40 - $75

BUT NOT IN VAIN
(1948 - Butcher) Raymond Lovell
One Sheet: $30 - $50

BUT THE FLESH IS WEAK
(1932 - MGM) Robert Montgomery, Aubrey
Smith
One Sheet: $200 - $400

BUTCH AND SUNDANCE: THE EARLY DAYS
(1979 - 20th Century Fox) William Katt, Tom
Berenger
One Sheet: $7 - $15

BUTCH CASSIDY AND THE SUNDANCE KID
(1969 - 20th Century Fox) Paul Newman,
Robert Redford, Katherine Ross
One Sheet: $125 - $250   *Cowboy
Movie Posters #322. One Sheet(Advance):$150-
300. One Sheet(StyleB):$150-300.*

BUTCH CASSIDY AND THE SUNDANCE KID
(1973R - 20th Century Fox) Paul Newman,
Robert Redford, Katherine Ross
One Sheet: $30 - $50   *Re-release.*

BUTCH MINDS THE BABY
(1942 - Universal) Broderick Crawford, Virginia
Bruce
One Sheet: $75 - $125

BUTCHER BAKER (NIGHTMARE MAKER)
(1982 - International) Jimmy McNichol, Susan
Tyrrell
One Sheet: $7 - $15   *AKA: NIGHT
WARNING; NIGHTMARE MAKER.*

BUTCHER OF SEVILLE, THE
(1942 - 20th Century Fox) Terry-toons
One Sheet: $200 - $400   *Cartoon. Full
color stock poster with inset title. Large image of
Supermouse and Gandy Goose.*

BUTCHER'S WIFE, THE
(1991 - Paramount) Demi Moore, Jeff Daniels
One Sheet: $7 - $15

BUTLER'S DILEMMA, THE

(1943 - Shaftesbury) Francis L. Sullivan, Judy Kelly
One Sheet: $30 - $50

BUTLEY
(1974 - American Film Theatre) Alan Bates, Jessica Tandy
One Sheet: $5 - $10

BUTTERCUP CHAIN, THE
(1971 - Columbia) Hywell Bennett, Leigh Taylor-Young
One Sheet: $7 - $15

BUTTERFIELD 8
(1960 - MGM) Elizabeth Taylor, Eddie Fisher
One Sheet: $75 - $150   *Academy Award: Best Actress. Academy Award Movie Posters #195.*

One Sheet

BUTTERFIELD 8
(1966R - MGM) Elizabeth Taylor, Eddie Fisher
One Sheet: $20 - $40   *Re-release.*

BUTTERFLIES ARE FREE
(1972 - Columbia) Goldie Hawn, Edward Albert, Eileen Heckart
One Sheet: $15 - $30   *Academy Award: Best Supporting Actress (Heckart).*

BUTTERFLY
(1924 - Universal) Laura La Plante, Norman Kerry
One Sheet: $300 - $700

BUTTERFLY, THE
(1981 - Par Par) Stacy Keach, Pia Zadora, Orson Welles
One Sheet: $7 - $15

BUTTERFLY AFFAIR, THE
(1970 - -) Claudia Cardinale, Henri Charriere
One Sheet: $5 - $10

BUY ME THAT TOWN
(1941 - Paramount) Lloyd Nolan, Constance Moore
One Sheet: $50 - $100

BUY UNITED STATES SAVINGS BONDS AND STAMPS
(1942 - Republic) Gene Autry
One Sheet: $800 - $1,500   *National Defense promotion poster.*

BUZZIN' AROUND
(1933 - Vitaphone) Fatty Arbuckle
One Sheet: $350 - $750

BUZZY RIDES THE RANGE
(1940 - Elkay) Dave O'Brien
One Sheet: $50 - $100

BWANA DEVIL
(1952 - United Artists) Robert Stack, Barbara Britton
One Sheet: $100 - $200   *First film in 3-D (Natural Vision).*

BY APPOINTMENT ONLY
(1933 - Invincible) Lew Cody, Aileen Pringle
One Sheet: $100 - $200

BY CANDLELIGHT
(1933 - Universal) Paul Lukas, Elissa Landi
One Sheet: $100 - $200

BY LOVE POSSESSED
(1961 - United Artists) Lana Turner, Efrem Zimbalist Jr.
One Sheet: $15 - $30

BY THE LIGHT OF THE SILVERY MOON

(1952 - Warner Bros.) Doris Day, Gordon MacRae
One Sheet: $75 - $125

BY THE SEA
(1915 - Essanay) Charlie Chaplin, Edna Purviance
One Sheet: $6,500 - $10,000

BY THE SEA
(1931 - Educational) Animated by Paul Terry
One Sheet: $600 - $1,000   *Cartoon. Cartoon Movie Posters #79.*

BY WHOSE HAND?
(1932 - Columbia) Ben Lyon, Barbara Weeks
One Sheet: $250 - $500

BY YOUR LEAVE
(1934 - RKO) Betty Grable, Frank Morgan
One Sheet: $200 - $400

BYE BYE BIRDIE
(1963 - Columbia) Janet Leigh, Ann-Margret
One Sheet: $30 - $50

One Sheet

BYE BYE BRAVERMAN
(1968 - Warner Bros.-Seven Arts) George Segal, Jessica Walter
One Sheet: $5 - $10

BYE BYE, LOVE
(1995 - 20th Century Fox) Paul Reiser, Randy Quaid
One Sheet: $3 - $5

BYPASS TO HAPPINESS
(1934 - Fox) Tamara Desni, Maurice Evans
One Sheet: $150 - $300

C. C. AND COMPANY
(1970 - Avco/Embassy) Joe Namath, Ann-Margret
One Sheet: $15 - $25

C'MON, LET'S LIVE A LITTLE!
(1967 - Paramount) Bobby Vee, Jackie De Shannon
One Sheet: $20 - $40

CABALLERO DROOPY
(1952 - MGM) Droopy
One Sheet: $100 - $200   *Cartoon.*

CABARET
(1972 - Allied Artists) Liza Minnelli, Michael York, Joel Grey
One Sheet: $40 - $75   *Academy Award: Best Director(Bob Fosse), Best Actress(Minnelli), Best Supporting Actor (Grey). OneSheet(Polish):$200-300. Academy Award Movie Posters #272 & #273.*

One Sheet

CABARET
(1974R - Allied Artists) Liza Minnelli, Michael York, Joel Grey
One Sheet: $15 - $35   *Re-release.*

CABIN BOY
(1994 - Touchstone) Chris Elliot
One Sheet: $3 - $5

CABIN IN THE COTTON, THE
(1943 - Warner Bros.) Bette Davis, Richard Barthelmess
One Sheet: $50 - $120

CABIN IN THE SKY
(1943 - MGM) Ethel Waters, Lena Horne
One Sheet: $1,600 - $2,500   *Black cast. Price is for Hirschfeld art style. One Sheet (Style D, see Separate Cinema, pg. 31):$300-$600.*

One Sheet

CABINET OF CALIGARI, THE
(1962 - 20th Century Fox) Glynis Johns, Dan O'Herlihy
One Sheet: $15 - $25

CABINET OF DR. CALIGARI, THE
(1919 - Decla-Bioscop) Conrad Veidt, Werner Krauss
One Sheet: $50,000 - $70,000   *First horror classic. Graven Images, pg. 6, 12-13, 14. Price is for original German release. At least four different one sheet styles are known to exist in archives. None known to be in private collections.*

CABINET OF DR. CALIGARI, THE
(1921 - Goldwyn) Conrad Veidt, Werner Krauss
One Sheet: $19,000 - $30,000   *Price is for U.S. release one sheet.*

CABLE GUY
(1996 - Columbia) Jim Carrey, Matthew Broderick
One Sheet: $5 - $10

CABOBLANCO
(1981 - Avco/Embassy) Charles Bronson, Jason Robards, Jr.
One Sheet: $5 - $10

CACTUS CAPERS
(1942 - RKO) Ray Whitley, Virginia Vale
One Sheet: $40 - $75

CACTUS CUT-UP, THE
(1949 - RKO) Leon Errol, Dorothy Granger
One Sheet: $40 - $75

CACTUS FLOWER
(1969 - Columbia) Walter Matthau, Ingrid Bergman, Goldie Hawn
One Sheet: $15 - $30   *Academy Award Movie Posters #257. AA Goldie Hawn, Best Supporting Actress.*

CACTUS KID, THE
(1930 - Columbia) Mickey Mouse
One Sheet: $19,000 - $30,000   *Cartoon.*

CACTUS MAKES PERFECT
(1942 - Columbia) The Three Stooges (Curly)
One Sheet: $3,500 - $5,000   *Comedy short. Duotone.*

CADDIE
(1976 - Atlantic) Helen Morse, Takis Emmanuel
One Sheet: $7 - $15

CADDY, THE
(1953 - Paramount) Dean Martin, Jerry Lewis, Donna Reed
One Sheet: $75 - $150   *Sports Movie Posters #226.*

CADDY, THE
(1964R - Paramount) Dean Martin, Jerry Lewis, Donna Reed
One Sheet: $20 - $40   *Re-release. Sports (Golf).*

CADDYSHACK
(1980 - Orion) Chevy Chase, Rodney Dangerfield
One Sheet: $30 - $60   *Sports (Golf).*

CADDYSHACK II
(1988 - Orion) Jackie Mason, Dyan Cannon, Robert Stack
One Sheet: $7 - $15   *Sports (Golf).*

CADET GIRL
(1941 - 20th Century Fox) Carole Landis, George Montgomery
One Sheet: $75 - $150

CADET-ROUSSELLE
(1954 - Pathe) Francois Perier, Dany Robin
One Sheet: $15 - $25

CADETS ON PARADE
(1942 - Columbia) Freddie Bartholomew, Jimmy Lydon
One Sheet: $50 - $100

CADILLAC MAN
(1990 - Orion) Robin Williams, Tim Robbins, Pamela Reed
One Sheet: $5 - $10

CAESAR AND CLEOPATRA
(1946 - United Artists) Claude Rains, Vivien Leigh
One Sheet: $250 - $500

One Sheet

CAESAR THE CONQUEROR
(1963 - Medallion) Cameron Mitchell, Rick Battaglia
One Sheet: $15 - $30

CAFE AU LAIT
(1994 - New Yorker) Julie Maudeuch, Hubert Kounde
One Sheet: $5 - $10   *French.*

CAFE COLETTE
(1937 - Associated British) Paul Cavanagh, Greta Nissen
One Sheet: $75 - $150   *AKA: DANGER IN PARIS.*

CAFE DE PARIS
(1938 - Regina Production) Jules Berry, Vera Korene
One Sheet: $100 - $200

CAFE EXPRESS
(1980 - Vides Cinematografica) Nino Manfredi, Adolfo Celi
One Sheet: $5 - $10

CAFE HOSTESS
(1939 - Columbia) Preston Foster, Ann Dvorak
One Sheet: $75 - $150

CAFE MASCOT
(1936 - Pascal/Paramount) Geraldine Fitzgerald, Derrick de Mamey
One Sheet: $125 - $250

CAFE METROPOLE
(1937 - 20th Century Fox) Adolphe Menjou, Loretta Young, Tyrone Power
One Sheet: $500 - $800

CAFE SOCIETY
(1939 - Paramount) Madeleine Carroll, Fred MacMurray, Shirley Ross
One Sheet: $200 - $400

CAGE OF EVIL
(1960 - United Artists) Ronald Foster, Pat Blair
One Sheet: $20 - $40

CAGE OF GOLD
(1950 - General/Ealing) Jean Simmons, David Farrar
One Sheet: $15 - $30

CAGE OF NIGHTINGALES, A
(1947 - Gaumont) Noel-Noel, Micheline Francey
One Sheet: $50 - $100

CAGED
(1950 - Warner Bros.) Eleanor Parker, Agnes Moorehead
One Sheet: $50 - $100

CAGED FURY
(1948 - Paramount) Richard Denning, Sheila Ryan, Buster Crabbe
One Sheet: $40 - $75

CAGED HEAT
(1974 - New World) Erica Gavin, Juanita Brown
One Sheet: $10 - $20   *AKA: RENEGADE GIRLS.*

CAGLIOSTRO
(1975 - Fox) Bekim Fehmiu, Curt Jurgens
One Sheet: $5 - $10

CAHILL: UNITED STATES MARSHAL
(1973 - Warner Bros.) John Wayne, Gary Grimes
One Sheet: $50 - $100

CAIN AND MABEL
(1936 - Warner Bros.) Clark Gable, Marion Davies
One Sheet: $600 - $1,000   *Sports Movie Posters #s 134, 135.*

CAIN'S WAY
(1969 - Associates/Fanfare) John Carradine, Scott Brady
One Sheet: $5 - $10   *AKA: CAIN'S CUTTHROATS; THE BLOOD SEEKERS.*

CAINE MUTINY, THE
(1954 - Columbia) Humphrey Bogart, Jose Ferrer, Fred MacMurray
One Sheet: $100 - $200

CAINE MUTINY, THE
(1959R - Columbia) Humphrey Bogart, Jose Ferrer, Fred MacMurray
One Sheet: $40 - $75   *Re-release.*

CAIRO
(1942 - MGM) Jeanette MacDonald, Robert Young
One Sheet: $100 - $200

CAIRO
(1963 - MGM) George Sanders, Richard Johnson
One Sheet: $7 - $15

CAIRO ROAD
(1950 - Associated British-Pathe) Eric Portman, Laurence Harvey
One Sheet: $15 - $25

CALABOOSE
(1942 - United Artists) Jimmy Rogers, Noah Beery Jr.
One Sheet: $40 - $75

CALABOOSE
(1948R - United Artists) Jimmy Rogers, Noah Beery Jr.
One Sheet: $15 - $25   *Re-release.*

CALABUCH
(1956 - Ciftesa) Edmund Gwenn, Valentina Cortese
One Sheet: $15 - $30

CALAMITY JANE
(1954 - Warner Bros.) Doris Day, Howard Keel
One Sheet: $75 - $125

CALAMITY JANE AND SAM BASS
(1949 - Universal) Yvonne De Carlo, Howard Duff
One Sheet: $40 - $75

CALAMITY THE COW
(1967 - Island-Shepperton) John Moulder-Brown, Elizabeth Dear
One Sheet: $5 - $10

CALCULATED RISK
(1963 - McLeod/Brantston) William Lucas, John Rutland
One Sheet: $5 - $10

CALCUTTA
(1947 - Paramount) Alan Ladd, Gail Russell, William Bendix
One Sheet: $250 - $500

CALDONIA
(1945 - Astor) Louis Jordan
One Sheet: $1,600 - $2,500   *Black cast. Musical short. Separate Cinema, pg. 94.*

CALENDAR, THE
(1931 - Gainsborough/British Lion) Herbert Marshall, Edna Best
One Sheet: $150 - $300

CALENDAR, THE
(1948 - General) Greta Gynt, John McCallum
One Sheet: $30 - $50

CALENDAR GIRL
(1947 - Republic) Jane Frazee, William Marshall
One Sheet: $40 - $75

CALENDAR GIRL
(1993 - Columbia) Jason Priestley, Joe Pantoliano
One Sheet: $3 - $5

CALGARY STAMPEDE, THE
(1925 - Universal) Hoot Gibson
One Sheet: $300 - $700   *Sports (Rodeo). Sports Movie Posters #301.*

CALIFORNIA
(1927 - MGM) Tim McCoy
One Sheet: $350 - $750

CALIFORNIA
(1947 - Paramount) Ray Milland, Barbara Stanwyck
One Sheet: $75 - $150

CALIFORNIA
(1963 - AIP) Jock Mahoney, Faith Domergue
One Sheet: $7 - $15

CALIFORNIA CONQUEST
(1952 - Columbia) Cornel Wilde, Teresa Wright
One Sheet: $20 - $40

CALIFORNIA DOLLS
(1981 - MGM/UA) Peter Falk, Vicki Frederick
One Sheet: $5 - $10   *AKA: ...All The Marbles.*

CALIFORNIA DREAMING
(1979 - AIP) Glynnis O'Connor, Seymour Cassel
One Sheet: $3 - $5

CALIFORNIA ER BUST
(1945 - RKO/Disney) Goofy
One Sheet: $1,300 - $2,000   *Cartoon. The Disney Poster, pg. 74.*

CALIFORNIA FIREBRAND
(1948 - Republic) Monte Hale, Adrian Booth
One Sheet: $50 - $100

CALIFORNIA FRONTIER
(1938 - Columbia) Buck Jones, Carmen Bailey
One Sheet: $250 - $500

CALIFORNIA GOLD RUSH
(1946 - Republic) "Wild Bill" Elliott, Alice Fleming
One Sheet: $50 - $100

CALIFORNIA GOLD RUSH
(1950R - Republic) Wild Bill Elliot, Alica Fleming
One Sheet: $15 - $25   *Re-release. Duotone.*

CALIFORNIA HOLIDAY
(1966 - MGM) Elvis Presley, Shelley Fabares
One Sheet: $20 - $40   *U.S. title: "SPINOUT".*

CALIFORNIA JOE
(1943 - Republic) Don "Red" Barry, Helen Talbot
One Sheet: $40 - $75

CALIFORNIA KID, THE
(197? - -) Martin Sheen, Vic Morrow
One Sheet: $5 - $10

CALIFORNIA MAIL
(1936 - Warner Bros.) Dick Foran
One Sheet: $100 - $200

CALIFORNIA OR BUST
(1927 - Paramount) Richard Dix
One Sheet: $500 - $800   *Sports (Auto racing). Sports Movie Posters #7.*

CALIFORNIA OR BUST
(1941 - RKO) Ron Whitley
One Sheet: $75 - $125

CALIFORNIA OUTPOST
(1953R - Republic) Bill Elliott, Catherine McLeod, Andy Devine
One Sheet: $15 - $25   *Re-titled re-release of OLD LOS ANGELES.*

CALIFORNIA PASSAGE
(1950 - Republic) Forrest Tucker, Adele Mara
One Sheet: $20 - $40

CALIFORNIA SPLIT
(1974 - Columbia) George Segal, Elliot Gould
One Sheet: $5 - $10

CALIFORNIA STRAIGHT AHEAD
(1937 - Universal) John Wayne, Louise Latimer
One Sheet: $250 - $600

CALIFORNIA STRAIGHT AHEAD
(1948R - Universal) John Wayne, Louise Latimer
One Sheet: $75 - $175   *Re-release.*

CALIFORNIA SUITE
(1978 - Columbia) Jane Fonda, Alan Alda, Maggie Smith
One Sheet: $7 - $15   *Academy Award: Best Supporting Actress(Smith). Academy Award Movie Posters #305.*

One Sheet

CALIFORNIA TRAIL, THE
(1933 - Columbia) Buck Jones
One Sheet: $300 - $700

CALIFORNIAN, THE
(1937 - Principal) Richardo Cortez, Marjorie Weaver
One Sheet: $75 - $150

CALIGULA
(1983 - Penthouse) Malcolm McDowell, Peter O'toole
One Sheet: $15 - $25

CALL, THE
(1938 - Best) Jean Yonnel, Pierre de Guigand
One Sheet: $75 - $150

CALL A MESSENGER
(1939 - Universal) The Little Tough Guys, Robert Armstrong
One Sheet: $75 - $150

CALL FOR MR. CAVEMAN
(1919 - Pathe) Snub Pollard
One Sheet: $250 - $500

CALL HER SAVAGE
(1932 - Fox) Clara Bow, Thelma Todd, Gilbert Roland
One Sheet: $600 - $1,000

CALL HIM MR. SHATTER
(1976 - Avco/Embassy) Stuart Whitman, Ti Lung

One Sheet: $3 - $5   *AKA: SHATTER.*

CALL IT A DAY
(1937 - Warner Bros.) Olivia de Havilland, Ian Hunter
One Sheet: $100 - $200

CALL IT LUCK
(1934 - Fox) Pat Peterson, Herbert Mundin
One Sheet: $150 - $350

CALL IT MURDER
(1946R - Guaranteed) Humphrey Bogart
One Sheet: $40 - $75   *Re-titled, re-release of "MIDNIGHT".*

One Sheet

CALL ME
(1988 - -) Patricia Charbonneau, Patti D'Arbanville
One Sheet: $3 - $5

CALL ME BWANA
(1963 - United Artists) Bob Hope, Anita Ekberg
One Sheet: $20 - $40

CALL ME DADDY
(1922 - Pioneer) -
One Sheet: $200 - $400   *From the Facts And Follies series.*

CALL ME GENIUS
(1961 - Associated British) Tony Hancock, George Sanders
One Sheet: $7 - $15   *(GB): THE REBEL.*

CALL ME MADAM
(1953 - 20th Century Fox) Ethel Merman, Donald O'Connor
One Sheet: $20 - $40

CALL ME MAME
(1933 - Warner Bros./First National) Ethel Irving, John Batten
One Sheet: $150 - $300

CALL ME MISTER
(1951 - 20th Century Fox) Dan Dailey, Betty Grable
One Sheet: $30 - $60

CALL NORTHSIDE 777
(1948 - 20th Century Fox) James Stewart, Richard Conte
One Sheet: $100 - $200

CALL NORTHSIDE 777
(1955R - 20th Century Fox) James Stewart, Richard Conte
One Sheet: $30 - $60   *Re-release.*

Title Card

CALL OF COURAGE, THE
(1925 - Universal) Art Acord, Olive Hasbrouck
One Sheet: $250 - $500

CALL OF THE BLOOD
(1948 - British Lion) Kay Hammond, John Clements
One Sheet: $30 - $50

CALL OF THE CANYON
(1923 - Paramount) Richard Dix, Lois Wilson
One Sheet: $150 - $300

CALL OF THE CANYON
(1942 - Republic) Gene Autry
One Sheet: $150 - $300

CALL OF THE CIRCUS
(1930 - Burr Enterprises) Francis X. Bushman, Ethel Clayton
One Sheet: $250 - $600

CALL OF THE FLESH
(1930 - MGM) Ramon Novarro, Dorothy Jordon
One Sheet: $150 - $300

CALL OF THE FOREST
(1949 - Lippert) Robert Lowery, Ken Curtis
One Sheet: $15 - $35

CALL OF THE JUNGLE
(1944 - Monogram) Ann Corio, James Bush
One Sheet: $50 - $100

CALL OF THE KLONDIKE
(1950 - Monogram) Kirby Grant, Chinook
One Sheet: $15 - $25

CALL OF THE PRAIRIE
(1936 - Paramount) William Boyd
One Sheet: $250 - $600

CALL OF THE ROCKIES
(1931 - Road-Show) Ben Lyons
One Sheet: $75 - $150

CALL OF THE ROCKIES
(1938 - Columbia) Charles Starrett
One Sheet: $75 - $150

CALL OF THE ROCKIES
(1944 - Republic) Sunset Carson, Smiley Burnette
One Sheet: $40 - $75

CALL OF THE SAVAGE, THE
(1935 - Universal) Noah Beery, Jr., Dorothy Short
One Sheet: $125 - $250

CALL OF THE SEA, THE
(1930 - Twickenham/Warner Bros.) Henry Edwards, Chrissie White
One Sheet: $150 - $300

CALL OF THE SOUTH SEAS
(1944 - Republic) Janet Martin, Allan Lane
One Sheet: $50 - $100

CALL OF THE WEST
(1930 - Columbia) Nat Moore
One Sheet: $125 - $250

CALL OF THE WILD, THE
(1923 - Pathe) -
One Sheet: $1,300 - $2,000

CALL OF THE WILD, THE
(1935 - United Artists) Clark Gable, Loretta Young
One Sheet: $800 - $1,500

CALL OF THE WILD, THE
(1943R - Fox) Clark Gable, Loretta Young
One Sheet: $100 - $200   *Re-release.*

CALL OF THE WILD, THE
(1953R - United Artists) Clark Gable, Loretta Young
One Sheet: $75 - $150   *Re-release.*

CALL OF THE WILD, THE
(1972 - MGM) Charlton Heston, Michele Mercier
One Sheet: $7 - $15

CALL OF THE WILDERNESS
(1972 - American National) -
One Sheet: $3 - $5

CALL OF THE YUKON
(1938 - Republic) Richard Arlen, Beverly Roberts
One Sheet: $75 - $150

CALL OUT THE MARINES
(1942 - RKO) Victor McLaglen
One Sheet: $50 - $100

CALL THE MESQUITEERS
(1938 - Republic) Ray Corrigan, Robert Livingston, Max Terhune
One Sheet: $75 - $150

CALL TO DUTY
(1940' - -) -
One Sheet: $150 - $300   *Black cast. Documentary narrated by Walter Huston.*

CALLAN
(1975 - Cinema National) Edward Woodward, Eric Porter
One Sheet: $3 - $5

CALLAWAY WENT THATAWAY
(1951 - MGM) Fred MacMurray, Dorothy McGuire
One Sheet: $30 - $50

CALLBOX MYSTERY, THE
(1932 - Samuelson) Warwick Ward, Harold French
One Sheet: $200 - $400

CALLED BACK
(1933 - Real Art) Franklin Dyall, Lester Matthews
One Sheet: $125 - $250

CALLING ALL CARS
(1934 - Empire) Jack LaRue, Lillian Miles
One Sheet: $100 - $200

CALLING ALL CROOKS
(1938 - Mancunian) Duggie Wakefield, Billy Nelson
One Sheet: $75 - $150

CALLING ALL CURS
(1939 - Columbia) The Three Stooges (Curly)
One Sheet: $7,500 - $12,000   *Comedy short. Duotone.*

CALLING ALL HUSBANDS
(1940 - Warner Bros.) Ernest Truex, Florence Bates
One Sheet: $50 - $100

CALLING ALL KIDS
(1943 - MGM) Our Gang
One Sheet: $250 - $500

CALLING ALL MARINES
(1939 - Republic) Don Barry, Helen Mack
One Sheet: $75 - $125

CALLING BULLDOG DRUMMOND
(1951 - MGM) Walter Pidgeon, Margaret Leighton
One Sheet: $30 - $50

CALLING DOCTOR MAGOO
(1956 - Columbia) Mr. Magoo
One Sheet: $100 - $200   *Cartoon.*

CALLING DR. DEATH
(1943 - Universal) Lon Chaney Jr., Patricia Morison
One Sheet: $250 - $500   *First Inner Sanctum film.*

CALLING DR. DEATH
(1953R - Universal) Lon Chaney Jr., Patricia Morrison
One Sheet: $75 - $125   *Re-release.*

CALLING DR. GILLESPIE
(1942 - MGM) Lionel Barrymore, Donna Reed
One Sheet: $75 - $150

CALLING DR. KILDARE
(1939 - MGM) Lionel Barrymore, Lew Ayres, Lana Turner
One Sheet: $75 - $150

CALLING HOMICIDE
(1956 - Allied Artists) Bill Elliott, Don Haggerty
One Sheet: $20 - $40

CALLING HUBBY'S BLUFF
(1929 - Pathe) Billy Bevan, Carmelita Geraghty
One Sheet: $300 - $700

CALLING OF DAN MATTHEWS, THE
(1935 - Columbia) Richard Arlen, Charlotte Wynters
One Sheet: $100 - $200

CALLING PAUL TEMPLE
(1948 - Nettlefold) John Bentley, Dinah Sheridan
One Sheet: $40 - $75

CALLING PHILO VANCE
(1940 - Warner Bros.) James Stephenson, Margot Stevenson
One Sheet: $50 - $100

CALLING THE TUNE
(1936 - Phoenix-Intercontinental) Adele Dixon, Clifford Evans
One Sheet: $100 - $200

CALLING WILD BILL ELLIOTT
(1943 - Republic) Bill Elliott, Gabby Hayes
One Sheet: $75 - $150

CALLING WILD BILL ELLIOTT
(1952R - Republic) Bill Elliott, Gabby Hayes
One Sheet: $30 - $50   *Re-release.*

CALM YOURSELF
(1935 - MGM) Robert Young, Madge Evans
One Sheet: $100 - $200

CALTIKI, THE IMMORTAL MONSTER
(1960 - Allied Artists) John Merivale, Didi Sullivan
One Sheet: $75 - $125

CALYPSO
(1959 - Enalpa/Fimsonor) Cy Grant, Sally Neal
One Sheet: $30 - $50

CALYPSO HEAT WAVE
(1957 - Columbia) Johnny Desmond, Merry Anders
One Sheet: $30 - $50

CALYPSO JOE
(1957 - Allied Artists) Herb Jeffries, Angie Dickinson
One Sheet: $15 - $35

CAMBODIAN IDYLL, A
(1913 - G. Melies) -
One Sheet: $800 - $1,500

CAME A HOT FRIDAY
(1985 - Orion Classics) Peter Bland, Philip Gordon
One Sheet: $3 - $5

CAME THE BRAWN
(1938 - MGM) Our Gang
One Sheet: $600 - $1,000

CAME THE BRAWN
(1952R - Monogram) Little Rascals
One Sheet: $40 - $75   *Re-release.*

CAMELOT
(1967 - Warner Bros./Seven Arts) Richard Harris, Vanessa Redgrave
One Sheet: $30 - $50   *Bob Peak art.*

CAMELOT
(1973R - Warner Bros.) Richard Harris, Vanessa Redgrave
One Sheet: $15 - $30   *Re-release. Bob Peak Art.*

CAMELS ARE COMING, THE
(1934 - Gaumont-British) Jack Hulbert, Anna Lee
One Sheet: $250 - $600

CAMEO KIRBY
(1923 - -) Gertrude Olmstead, Alan Hale
One Sheet: $200 - $400

CAMEO KIRBY
(1930 - Fox) J. Harold Murray, Norma Terris
One Sheet: $125 - $250

Insert

CAMERA BUFF
(1983 - Cinegate/New Yorker) Jerzy Stuhr, Malgorzata Zabkowska
One Sheet: $5 - $10

CAMERA SHY
(1930 - Educational) Lloyd Hamilton
One Sheet: $250 - $500

CAMERA THRILLS
(1936 - Universal) -
One Sheet: $75 - $175   *Film devoted to one reel film makers.*

CAMERAMAN, THE
(1928 - MGM) Buster Keaton, Marceline Day
One Sheet: $6,500 - $10,000

CAMERON OF THE ROYAL MOUNTED
(1922 - Winnipeg) -
One Sheet: $150 - $300

CAMERON'S CLOSET
(1989 - -) Cotter Smith, Mel Haris
One Sheet: $3 - $5

CAMILLA
(1994 - -) Jessica Tandy, Bridget Fonda
One Sheet: $5 - $10

CAMILLE
(1912 - -) Sarah Bernhardt
One Sheet: $1,600 - $2,500

CAMILLE
(1916 - -) Clara Kimbell Young, Robert Cummings
One Sheet: $250 - $500

CAMILLE
(1917 - -) Theda Bara, Albert Roscoe, Alice Gale
One Sheet: $1,300 - $2,000

CAMILLE
(1921 - Metro) Rudolph Valentino, Alla Nazimova
One Sheet: $2,500 - $4,000

CAMILLE
(1927 - Warner Bros.) Norma Talmadge, Gilbert Roland
One Sheet: $300 - $650

CAMILLE
(1936 - MGM) Greta Garbo, Robert Taylor
One Sheet: $1,900 - $3,000

One Sheet

CAMILLE 2000
(1969 - Audobon) Danielle Gaubert, Nino Castelnuovo
One Sheet: $10 - $20

CAMILLE CLAUDEL
(1989 - Orion) Isabelle Adjani, Gerard Depardieu
One Sheet: $15 - $25

CAMILLE OF THE BARBARY COAST
(1925 - -) Mae Busch, Owen Moore
One Sheet: $250 - $600

CAMILLE OF THE YUKON
(1920 - Fox) -
One Sheet: $500 - $800

CAMMINACAMMINA
(1983 - Gaumont) Alberto Fumagalli, Antonio Cuccarre
One Sheet: $3 - $5

CAMP DOG
(1950 - RKO/Disney) Pluto
One Sheet: $125 - $250   *Cartoon.*

CAMP NOWHERE
(1996 - Hollywood) Christopher Lloyd,
Jonathan Jackson
One Sheet: $4 - $8

CAMP ON BLOOD ISLAND, THE
(1957 - Hammer) Carl Mohner, Andre Morell
One Sheet: $30 - $50

CAMPBELL'S KINGDOM
(1957 - J. Arthur Rank) Dirk Bogarde, Stanley
Baker
One Sheet: $15 - $25

CAMPUS CONFESSIONS
(1938 - Paramount) Betty Grable
One Sheet: $600 - $1,000   *Sports Movie
Posters #377.*

CAMPUS FLIRT, THE
(1926 - Paramount) Bebe Daniels
One Sheet: $500 - $800

CAMPUS HONEYMOON
(1948 - Republic) Lynn Wilde, Lee Wilde, Adele
Mara
One Sheet: $30 - $60

CAMPUS MAN
(1987 - -) John Dye, Steve Lyon, Morgan
Fairchild
One Sheet: $3 - $5

CAMPUS RHYTHM
(1943 - Monogram) Gale Storm, Robert Lowery
One Sheet: $50 - $100

CAMPUS SLEUTH
(1948 - Monogram) Freddie Stewart, June
Preisser
One Sheet: $30 - $50

**CAN HIERONYMUS MERKIN EVER FORGET
MERCY HUMPPE AND FIND TRUE
HAPPINESS?**
(1969 - Regional) Anthony Newley, Joan
Collins, Milton Berle, George Jessel
One Sheet: $15 - $25

CAN SHE BAKE A CHERRY PIE?
(1983 - International Rainbow/Jagfilm) Karen
Black, Michael Emil
One Sheet: $3 - $5

CAN THIS BE DIXIE?
(1936 - 20th Century Fox) Jane Withers, Slim
Summerville
One Sheet: $125 - $250

CAN YOU HEAR ME MOTHER?
(1935 - New Ideal) Sandy Powell, Mary Lawson
One Sheet: $100 - $200

CAN'T BUY ME LOVE
(1987 - Buena Vista) Patrick Dempsey,
Amanda Peterson
One Sheet: $5 - $10

CAN'T HELP SINGING
(1944 - Universal) Deanna Durbin, Robert
Paige
One Sheet: $50 - $100

CAN'T STOP THE MUSIC
(1980 - Associated) The Village People, Valerie
Perrine
One Sheet: $7 - $15   *Rock 'n' Roll
musical.*

**CANADIAN MOUNTIES VS. ATOMIC
INVADERS**
(1953 - Republic) Bill Henry, Susan Morrow
One Sheet: $50 - $100   *Serial. 12
Chapters.*

CANADIAN PACIFIC
(1949 - 20th Century Fox) Randolph Scott,
Jane Wyatt
One Sheet: $50 - $100

CANADIANS, THE
(1961 - 20th Century Fox) Robert Ryan, Torin
Thatcher
One Sheet: $5 - $10

CANAL ZONE
(1942 - Columbia) Chester Morris, Harriet
Hilliard (Nelson)
One Sheet: $50 - $100

CANARIES SOMETIMES SING
(1930 - Woodfall/Gaumont) Tom Walls, Yvonne
Arnaud
One Sheet: $200 - $400

CANARIS
(1955 - Europa/Fama) O.E. Hasse, Adrian
Hovan
One Sheet: $30 - $50   *AKA:
CANARIS, MASTER SPY.*

CANARY COMES ACROSS, THE
(1938 - MGM) Erik Rhodes, Virginia Grey
One Sheet: $100 - $200

CANARY MURDER CASE, THE
(1929 - Paramount) William Powell, James
Hall, Louise Brooks
One Sheet: $10,000 - $15,000

CAN-CAN
(1960 - 20th Century Fox) Frank Sinatra,
Shirley MacLaine
One Sheet: $75 - $125

CANCEL MY RESERVATION
(1972 - Warner Bros.) Bob Hope, Eva Marie
Saint
One Sheet: $10 - $20

CANDIDATE, THE
(1964 - Atlantic) Mamie Van Doren, June
Wilkinson
One Sheet: $30 - $50

CANDIDATE, THE
(1972 - Warner Bros.) Robert Redford, Peter
Boyle
One Sheet: $7 - $15

CANDIDATE FOR MURDER
(1966 - Schoenfield) Michael Gough, Erika
Remberg
One Sheet: $5 - $10

CANDIDE
(1962 - Pathe) Jean-Pierre Cassel, Dahlia Lavi
One Sheet: $15 - $25

CANDLELIGHT IN ALGERIA
(1944 - Eagle-Lion) James Mason, Carl
Lehmann
One Sheet: $30 - $50

CANDLES AT NINE
(1944 - Anglo-American/British National) Jessie
Matthews, John Stuart
One Sheet: $30 - $50

CANDLESHOE
(1977 - Walt Disney) David Niven, Helen Hayes
One Sheet: $7 - $15

CANDY
(1968 - Cinerama) Ewa Aulin, Charles
Aznavour, Marlon Brando, Richard Burton
One Sheet: $30 - $50

CANDY MAN, THE
(1969 - Sagittarius) George Sanders, Leslie
Parrish
One Sheet: $5 - $10

CANDY MAN
(1992 - TriStar) Virginia Madsen, Tony Todd
One Sheet: $3 - $5

CANDYMAN: FAREWELL TO THE FLESH
(1995 - Gramercy) Tony Todd, Kelly Rowan
One Sheet: $3 - $5

CANGACEIRO
(1953 - Columbia) Alberto Ruschel, Marisa
Prado
One Sheet: $15 - $25

CANINE CADDY
(1941 - RKO/Disney) Mickey Mouse, Pluto
One Sheet: $3,500 - $5,000   *Cartoon.
Sports (Golf). The Disney Poster, pg. 29. Sports
Movie Posters #222.*

CANINE CASANOVA
(1945 - RKO/Disney) Pluto
One Sheet: $700 - $1,200   *Cartoon. Full
color. Cartoon Movie Posters #190.*

CANINE PATROL
(1945 - RKO/Disney) Pluto
One Sheet: $700 - $1,200   *Cartoon. Full
color. The Disney Poster, pg. 39.*

CANNABIS
(1970 - Oceanic) Serge Gainsbourg, Jane
Birkin
One Sheet: $15 - $35

CANNERY ROW
(1981 - MGM) Nick Nolte, Debra Winger
One Sheet: $5 - $10

CANNIBAL ATTACK
(1954 - Columbia) Johnny Weissmuller, Judy
Walsh, David Bruce
One Sheet: $50 - $100   *Jungle Jim
Series.*

CANNIBAL GIRLS
(1973 - AIP) Eugene Levy, Andrea Martin
One Sheet: $15 - $35   *Horror
comedy.*

CANNIBAL HOLOCAUST
(1978 - -) Francesca Ciardi, Luca Barbareschi,
Dir: Ruggero Deodato
One Sheet: $15 - $25

CANNIBALS, THE
(1970 - Doria-San Marco) Britt Ekland, Pierre
Clementi
One Sheet: $7 - $15

CANNIBALS IN THE STREETS
(1982 - Almi Cinema) John Saxon, Elizabeth
Turner
One Sheet: $7 - $15   *AKA:
SAVAGE APOCALYPSE; INVASION OF THE
FLESH HUNTERS.*

CANNON AND THE NIGHTINGALE, THE
(1969 - Sisyphus) Niki Triandafylidou, George
Georgis
One Sheet: $5 - $10

CANNON FOR CORDOBA
(1970 - United Artists) George Peppard,
Giovanna Ralli
One Sheet: $3 - $5

CANNONBALL, THE
(1931 - Educational) Andy Clyde
One Sheet: $125 - $250

CANNONBALL
(1976 - New World) David Carradine, Bill
McKinney
One Sheet: $5 - $10   *(GB:)
CARQUAKE.*

CANNONBALL EXPRESS
(1932 - Sono Art/World Wide) Tom Moore, Rex
Lease
One Sheet: $200 - $400

CANNONBALL RUN, THE
(1981 - 20th Century Fox) Burt Reynolds,
Farrah Fawcett
One Sheet: $7 - $15   *Sports (Auto
racing).*

CANNONBALL RUN II
(1984 - Warner Bros.) Burt Reynolds, Dom
DeLuise
One Sheet: $5 - $10   *Sports (Auto
racing).*

CANON CITY
(1948 - Eagle-Lion) Scott Brady, Jeff Corey,
DeForest Kelly
One Sheet: $15 - $30

CANTERBURY TALE, A
(1944 - Eagle-Lion) Eric Portman, Sheila Sim
One Sheet: $40 - $75

CANTERVILLE GHOST, THE
(1944 - MGM) Charles Laughton, Margaret
O'Brien
One Sheet: $150 - $350

CANTINFLAS
(1960 - -) -
One Sheet: $7 - $15

CANTOR'S SON, THE
(1937 - Eron) Moishe Oysher, Florence Weiss
One Sheet: $30 - $60

CANYON AMBUSH
(1952 - Monogram) Johnny Mack Brown
One Sheet: $30 - $50

CANYON CITY
(1943 - Republic) Don Barry, Helen Talbot
One Sheet: $30 - $50

CANYON CROSSROADS
(1955 - United Artists) Richard Basehart,
Phyllis Kirk
One Sheet: $15 - $25

CANYON HAWKS
(1930 - National Players/Big 4) Wally Wales,
Buzz Barton
One Sheet: $125 - $250

CANYON OF ADVENTURE
(1928 - First National) Ken Maynard, Eric
Mayne
One Sheet: $500 - $800

CANYON OF MISSING MEN, THE
(1930 - Syndicate) Tom Tyler, Sheila LeGay
One Sheet: $200 - $400

CANYON PASSAGE
(1946 - Universal) Dana Andrews, Susan
Hayward
One Sheet: $100 - $200

CANYON RAIDERS
(1951 - Monogram) Whip Wilson, Phyllis
Coates
One Sheet: $40 - $75

CANYON RIVER
(1956 - Allied Artists) George Montgomery,
Marcia Henderson
One Sheet: $7 - $15

CAPE CANAVERAL MONSTERS
(1960 - CCM) Scott Peters, Linda Connell
One Sheet: $15 - $35

CAPE FEAR
(1962 - Universal) Gregory Peck, Robert
Mitchum
One Sheet: $75 - $150

CAPE FEAR
(1991 - Universal) Robert De Niro, Nick Nolte,
Jessica Lange
One Sheet: $7 - $15

CAPER OF THE GOLDEN BULLS, THE
(1967 - Embassy) Stephen Boyd, Yvette
Mimieux
One Sheet: $5 - $10

CAPETOWN AFFAIR
(1967 - 20th Century Fox) James Brolin,
Jacqueline Bisset
One Sheet: $5 - $10

CAPONE
(1975 - Fox) Ben Gazzara, Susan Blakely
One Sheet: $7 - $15

CAPPY RICK RETURNS
(1935 - Republic) Robert McWade, Ray Walker
One Sheet: $100 - $200

CAPPY RICKS
(1921 - Paramount) Thomas Meighan
One Sheet: $250 - $500

CAPRICE
(1967 - 20th Century Fox) Doris Day, Richard
Harris
One Sheet: $15 - $25

CAPRICIOUS SUMMER
(1968 - Barrandov Studios) Rudolf Hrusinsky,
Vlastimil Brodsky
One Sheet: $7 - $15

CAPRICORN ONE
(1978 - Warner Bros.) Elliott Gould, James
Brolin, O. J. Simpson
One Sheet: $5 - $10

CAPTAIN AMERICA
(1944 - Republic) Dick Purcell, Lorna Gray
One Sheet: $350 - $750   *Serial. 15
Chapters. One Sheet:(Chapter 1, all art):$600-
2000. Chapter 2-15 One Sheets are color with
duotone photo inset.*

CAPTAIN AMERICA
(1979 - -) Reb Brown, Steve Forrest
One Sheet: $7 - $15

CAPTAIN AMERICA
(1990 - -) -
One Sheet: $10 - $20   *Film was
never released theatrically. Poster exists only as
an advance.*

CAPTAIN APACHE
(1971 - Scotia International) Lee Van Cleef,

Carroll Baker
One Sheet: $5 - $10

CAPTAIN APPLEJACK
(1931 - Warner Bros.) John Halliday, Mary Brian
One Sheet: $125 - $250

CAPTAIN BILL
(1935 - Fuller) Leslie Fuller, Judy Kelly
One Sheet: $100 - $200

CAPTAIN BLACKJACK
(1951 - United Artists) George Sanders
One Sheet: $15 - $30

CAPTAIN BLOOD
(1935 - Warner Bros.) Errol Flynn, Olivia de Havilland
One Sheet: $3,500 - $5,000   *Flynn's first U.S. film.*

CAPTAIN BLOOD
(1951R - Warner Bros.) Errol Flynn, Olivia DeHavilland
One Sheet: $50 - $100   *Re-release.*

CAPTAIN BLOOD
(1955R - Warner Bros.) Errol Flynn, Olivia DeHavilland
One Sheet: $40 - $75   *Re-release.*

CAPTAIN BOYCOTT
(1947 - Universal) Stewart Granger, Kathleen Ryan
One Sheet: $40 - $75

CAPTAIN CALAMITY
(1936 - Grand National) George Houston, Movita
One Sheet: $75 - $125

CAPTAIN CARELESS
(1928 - F.B.O.) Bob Steele, Jack Donovan, Mary Mabery
One Sheet: $250 - $500

CAPTAIN CAREY, U.S.A.
(1949 - Paramount) Alan Ladd, Wanda Hendrix
One Sheet: $50 - $100

CAPTAIN CAUTION
(1940 - United Artists) Victor Mature, Louise Platt
One Sheet: $50 - $100

CAPTAIN CHINA
(1949 - Paramount) John Payne, Gail Russell
One Sheet: $20 - $40

CAPTAIN EDDIE
(1945 - 20th Century Fox) Fred MacMurray, Lynn Bari
One Sheet: $50 - $100

CAPTAIN FROM CASTILE
(1947 - 20th Century Fox) Tyrone Power, Jean Peters
One Sheet: $200 - $400

CAPTAIN FROM KOEPENICK, THE
(1933 - American-Rumanian) Max Adalbert, Willi Schur
One Sheet: $250 - $500   *AKA: HAUPTMANN VON KOEPENICK.*

CAPTAIN FROM KOEPENICK, THE
(1956 - DCA) Heinz Ruhmann
One Sheet: $10 - $20

CAPTAIN FURY
(1939 - United Artists) Brian Aherne, Victor McLaglen
One Sheet: $75 - $150

CAPTAIN FURY
(194?R - Favorite Films) Brian Aherne, Victor McLaglen
One Sheet: $20 - $40   *Re-release.*

CAPTAIN GRANT'S CHILDREN
(1939 - Amkino/Mosfilm) Y. Yurief, I. Chuvelef
One Sheet: $50 - $100   *Russian.*

CAPTAIN HATES THE SEA, THE
(1934 - Columbia) John Gilbert, Victor McLaglen, Three Stooges (Curly)
One Sheet: $5,500 - $9,000   *Price is valid only if Stooges are pictured, otherwise $600-$1200. Gilbert's last film.*

CAPTAIN HORATIO HORNBLOWER
(1950 - Warner Bros.) Gregory Peck, Virginia Mayo

One Sheet: $30 - $50

CAPTAIN HURRICANE
(1935 - RKO) James Barton, Lon Chaney
One Sheet: $100 - $200

CAPTAIN IS A LADY, THE
(1940 - MGM) Charles Coburn, Beulah Bondi
One Sheet: $75 - $150

CAPTAIN JANUARY
(1936 - 20th Century Fox) Shirley Temple, Guy Kibbee
One Sheet: $800 - $1,500

Mini Window Card

CAPTAIN JOHN SMITH AND POCAHONTAS
(1953 - United Artists) Anthony Dexter, Jody Lawrence
One Sheet: $15 - $35

CAPTAIN KIDD
(1945 - United Artists) Charles Laughton, Randolph Scott
One Sheet: $75 - $150

CAPTAIN KIDD
(1952R - United Artists) Charles Laughton, Randolph Scott
One Sheet: $15 - $30   *Re-release.*

CAPTAIN KIDD AND THE SLAVE GIRL
(1954 - United Artists) Anthony Dexter, Eva Gabor
One Sheet: $30 - $50

CAPTAIN KIDD, JR.
(1919 - Artcraft) Mary Pickford, Douglas MacLean
One Sheet: $600 - $1,000

CAPTAIN KIDD'S KIDS
(1920 - Pathe) Harold Lloyd
One Sheet: $1,300 - $2,000

CAPTAIN KIDD'S KIDS
(192?R - Pathe) Harold Lloyd
One Sheet: $150 - $300   *Re-release.*

CAPTAIN KRONOS: VAMPIRE HUNTER
(1974 - Paramount/Hammer) Horst Janson, Caroline Munro
One Sheet: $15 - $25

CAPTAIN LASH
(1929 - Fox) Victor McLaglen, Claire Windsor
One Sheet: $250 - $500

CAPTAIN LIGHTFOOT
(1955 - Universal) Rock Hudson, Barbara Rush
One Sheet: $20 - $40

CAPTAIN MIDNIGHT
(1942 - Columbia) Dave O'Brien, Dorothy Short
One Sheet: $250 - $500   *Serial. 15 Chapters.*

CAPTAIN MILKSHAKE
(1970 - Richmark) Geoff Gage, Andrea Cagan
One Sheet: $5 - $10

CAPTAIN MOONLIGHT
(1940 - Atlas) John Garrick
One Sheet: $50 - $100

CAPTAIN NEMO AND THE UNDERWATER CITY
(1970 - MGM) Robert Ryan, Chuck Connors, Nanette Newman
One Sheet: $15 - $25

CAPTAIN NEWMAN, M.D.
(1964 - Universal) Gregory Peck, Tony Curtis
One Sheet: $15 - $25

CAPTAIN OF THE GUARD
(1930 - Universal) John Boles, Laura La Plante
One Sheet: $300 - $700

CAPTAIN PIRATE
(1952 - Columbia) Louis Hayward, Patricia Medina
One Sheet: $15 - $35

Half Sheet

CAPTAIN RON
(1992 - Touchstone) Kurt Russell, Martin Short
One Sheet: $3 - $5

CAPTAIN SALVATION
(1927 - MGM) Lars Hanson, Marceline Day
One Sheet: $600 - $1,000

CAPTAIN SCARLETT
(1952 - United Artists) Richard Greene, Leonora Amar
One Sheet: $15 - $30

CAPTAIN SINBAD
(1963 - MGM) Guy Williams, Heidi Bruhl
One Sheet: $15 - $25

CAPTAIN SPANKY'S SHOW BOAT
(1939 - MGM) Our Gang
One Sheet: $600 - $1,000

CAPTAIN THUNDER
(1930 - Warner Bros.) Victor Varconi, Fay Wray
One Sheet: $200 - $400

CAPTAIN TUGBOAT ANNIE
(1945 - Republic) Jane Darwell, Edgar Kennedy
One Sheet: $30 - $50

CAPTAIN VIDEO
(1951 - Columbia) Judd Holdren, Larry Stewart
One Sheet: $100 - $200   *Serial. 15 Chapters. Graven Images, pg. 181.*

CAPTAIN'S KID, THE
(1936 - Warner Bros.) Guy Kibbee, May Robson
One Sheet: $50 - $100

CAPTAIN'S ORDERS
(1937 - Liberty) Henry Edwards, Jane Carr
One Sheet: $75 - $125

CAPTAIN'S PARADISE, THE
(1953 - United Artists) Alec Guinness, Yvonne De Carlo
One Sheet: $15 - $35

CAPTAIN'S TABLE, THE
(1936 - MGM) Percy Marmont, Marian Spencer
One Sheet: $75 - $150

CAPTAIN'S TABLE, THE
(1960 - 20th Century Fox) John Gregson, Peggy Cummins
One Sheet: $5 - $10

CAPTAINS COURAGEOUS
(1937 - MGM) Spencer Tracy, Freddie Bartholomew, Lionel Barrymore
One Sheet: $300 - $700   *Academy Award: Best Actor(Tracy). Academy Award Movie Posters #53.*

CAPTAINS COURAGEOUS
(1946R - MGM) Spencer Tracy, Freddie Bartholomew, Lionel Barrymore
One Sheet: $75 - $150   *Re-release.*

CAPTAINS COURAGEOUS
(1962R - MGM) Spencer Tracy, Freddie Bartholomew, Lionel Barrymore
One Sheet: $10 - $20   *Re-release.*

CAPTAINS OF THE CLOUDS
(1942 - Warner Bros.) James Cagney, Dennis Morgan, Alan Hale
One Sheet: $125 - $250

CAPTAINS OF THE CLOUDS
(1962R - Warner Bros.) James Cagney, Dennis Morgan, Alan Hale
One Sheet: $15 - $25   *Re-release.*

CAPTIVATION
(1931 - Capital) Conway Tearle, Betty Stockfeld
One Sheet: $150 - $300

CAPTIVE CITY
(1952 - United Artists) John Forsythe, Joan Camden
One Sheet: $15 - $30

CAPTIVE CITY, THE
(1963 - Paramount) David Niven, Lea Massari
One Sheet: $5 - $10   *Italian title: LA CITTA' PRIGIONIERA.*

CAPTIVE GIRL
(1950 - Columbia) Johnny Weissmuller, Buster Crabbe
One Sheet: $30 - $50

CAPTIVE GOD, THE
(1916 - Triangle) William S. Hart, Enid Markey
One Sheet: $1,300 - $2,000

CAPTIVE HEART, THE
(1947 - Universal International) Michael Redgrave, Mervyn Johns
One Sheet: $20 - $40

CAPTIVE OF BILLY THE KID
(1951 - Republic) Allan "Rocky" Lane
One Sheet: $20 - $40

CAPTIVE WILD WOMAN
(1943 - Universal) John Carradine, Evelyn Ankers, Acquanetta
One Sheet: $75 - $150

Mini Window Card

CAPTIVE WOMEN
(1952 - RKO) Robert Clarke, Margaret Field
One Sheet: $50 - $100

CAPTURE, THE
(1950 - RKO) Lew Ayres, Teresa Wright
One Sheet: $15 - $35

CAPTURE THAT CAPSULE
(1961 - Will Zens) Richard Miller, Dick O'Neil
One Sheet: $5 - $10

CAPTURED!
(1933 - Warner Bros.) Leslie Howard, Douglas Fairbanks Jr.
One Sheet: $250 - $500

CAR, THE
(1977 - Universal) James Brolin, Kathleen Lloyd, John Marley
One Sheet: $10 - $20

CAR 99
(1935 - Paramount) Fred MacMurray, Ann Sheridan
One Sheet: $75 - $150

CAR OF DREAMS
(1935 - Gaumont) John Mills, Mark Lester
One Sheet: $150 - $300

CAR OF TOMORROW
(1951 - MGM) Tex Avery
One Sheet: $200 - $400   *Cartoon.*

Cartoon Movie Posters #312.

CAR WASH
(1976 - Universal) Richard Pryor, The Pointer Sisters
One Sheet: $10 - $20   *Black cast.*

CARAVAN
(1934 - Fox) Charles Boyer, Loretta Young
One Sheet: $250 - $600

CARAVAN
(1947 - Eagle-Lion) Stewart Granger, Jean Kent, Anne Crawford
One Sheet: $15 - $30

CARAVAN TO VACCARES
(1974 - Fox) Charlotte Rampling, David Birney
One Sheet: $3 - $5

CARAVAN TRAIL, THE
(1946 - PRC) Eddie Dean, Al LaRue
One Sheet: $20 - $40

CARAVANS
(1978 - Universal) Anthony Quinn, Jennifer O'Neill
One Sheet: $3 - $5

CARBINE WILLIAMS
(1952 - MGM) James Stewart, Wendell Corey, Jean Hagen
One Sheet: $125 - $250

CARBINE WILLIAMS
(1965R - MGM) James Stewart, Wendell Corey, Jean Hagen
One Sheet: $40 - $75   *Re-release.*

CARBON COPY
(1981 - Helmdale) George Segal, Susan Saint James
One Sheet: $5 - $10

CARDBOARD CAVALIER, THE
(1949 - General) Sid Field, Margaret Lockwood
One Sheet: $15 - $30

CARDIAC ARREST
(1980 - Film Ventures) Garry Goodron, Mike Chan
One Sheet: $3 - $5

CARDINAL, THE
(1936 - Pathe) Matheson Lang, Eric Portman
One Sheet: $75 - $150

CARDINAL, THE
(1963 - Columbia) Tom Tryon, Carol Lynley
One Sheet: $30 - $50   *Saul Bass art.*

CARDINAL RICHELIEU
(1935 - 20th Century) George Arliss, Edward Arnold
One Sheet: $500 - $800

CARE BEARS 2
(1989 - Columbia) -
One Sheet: $3 - $5   *Cartoon.*

CARE BEARS MOVIE, THE
(1985 - Nelvana) -
One Sheet: $5 - $10   *Cartoon.*

CAREER
(1939 - RKO) Anne Shirley, Edward Ellis
One Sheet: $75 - $150

CAREER
(1959 - Paramount) Dean Martin, Anthony Franciosa, Shirley MacLaine
One Sheet: $15 - $30

CAREER GIRL
(1943 - PRC) Frances Langford, Craig Wood
One Sheet: $30 - $50

CAREER GIRL
(1960 - Astor Woodburn Films) June Wilkinson, Charles Robert Keane
One Sheet: $30 - $60

CAREER OPPORTUNITIES
(1991 - Universal) Frank Whaley
One Sheet: $5 - $10

CAREER WOMAN
(1936 - 20th Century Fox) Claire Trevor, Michael Whalen
One Sheet: $150 - $300

CAREERS
(1929 - First National) Billie Dove, Antonio Moreno

One Sheet: $150 - $300

CAREFREE
(1938 - RKO) Fred Astaire, Ginger Rogers
One Sheet: $2,500 - $4,000   *Dance musical.*

CAREFUL, SOFT SHOULDER
(1942 - 20th Century Fox) James Ellison, Virginia Bruce
One Sheet: $50 - $100

CARELESS AGE
(1929 - First National) Douglas Fairbanks, Jr., Loretta Young
One Sheet: $200 - $400

CARELESS LADY
(1932 - Fox) Joan Bennett, John Boles
One Sheet: $1,300 - $2,000

CARELESS YEARS, THE
(1957 - Michael) Dean Stockwell, Natalie Trundy
One Sheet: $15 - $25

CARESSED
(1965 - Joseph Brenner Associates) Robert Howay, Angela Gann
One Sheet: $5 - $10

CARETAKER, THE
(1964 - United Artists) Alan Bates, Donald Pleasance, Robert Shaw
One Sheet: $5 - $10

CARETAKER'S DAUGHTER, THE
(1952 - Manchester/Macunian) Hugh Wakefield, Derek Bond
One Sheet: $15 - $30   *British title: LOVE'S A LUXURY.*

CARETAKERS, THE
(1963 - United Artists) Robert Stack, Polly Bergen, Joan Crawford
One Sheet: $20 - $40

CAREY TREATMENT, THE
(1972 - MGM) James Coburn, Jennifer O'Neill
One Sheet: $3 - $5

CARGO TO CAPETOWN
(1950 - Columbia) John Ireland, Ellen Drew
One Sheet: $15 - $30

CARIBBEAN
(1952 - Paramount) John Payne, Arlene Dahl
One Sheet: $30 - $50

CARIBBEAN MYSTERY
(1945 - 20th Century Fox) James Dunn, Sheila Ryan
One Sheet: $50 - $100

CARIBE
(1987 - -) John Savage, Kara Glover
One Sheet: $3 - $5

CARIBOO TRAIL
(1950 - 20th Century Fox) Randolph Scott, Bill Williams
One Sheet: $20 - $40

CARLITO'S WAY
(1993 - Universal) Al Pacino, Sean Penn
One Sheet: $7 - $15   *Advance:$10-$15.*

CARMELA
(1949 - Lopert) Doris Durante, Paul Javor
One Sheet: $15 - $30

CARMEN
(1913 - Monopol) Marion Leonard
One Sheet: $250 - $500

CARMEN
(1914 - Fox) Theda Bara
One Sheet: $1,600 - $2,500

CARMEN
(1915 - Paramount) Geraldine Farrar, Wallace Reid
One Sheet: $2,500 - $4,000

CARMEN
(1916 - Essanay) Charlie Chaplin, Edna Purviance
One Sheet: $10,000 - $15,000

CARMEN
(1932 - Powers) Marguerite Namara, Thomas Burke
One Sheet: $100 - $200

CARMEN
(1946 - Superfilm) Viviane Romance, Ellie Parvo
One Sheet: $15 - $30

CARMEN
(1949 - Clasa-Mohme/Ariston) Imperio Argentina, Rafael Rivelles
One Sheet: $15 - $30

CARMEN
(1983 - Orion) Antonio Gades, Laura del Sol
One Sheet: $3 - $5

CARMEN
(1984 - Orion) Julia Migenes-Johnson, Placido Domingo
One Sheet: $15 - $25

CARMEN, BABY
(1967 - Audubon) Uta Levka, Claude Ringer
One Sheet: $10 - $20

CARMEN JONES
(1954 - 20th Century Fox) Dorothy Dandridge, Harry Belafonte
One Sheet: $250 - $500   *Black cast. Separate Cinema, pg. 34.*

CARMEN OF THE BORDER
(1923 - Goldstone) Grace Cunard
One Sheet: $250 - $600

CARNABY, M.D.
(1967 - J. Arthur Rank) Leslie Phillips, James Robertson Justice
One Sheet: $5 - $10

CARNAL KNOWLEDGE
(1971 - Avco/Embassy) Jack Nicholson, Art Garfunkle, Ann-Margret
One Sheet: $20 - $40   *Text only Style:$10-15.*

CARNATION KID, THE
(1929 - Paramount) Douglas MacLean
One Sheet: $200 - $400

CARNEGIE HALL
(1947 - Federal) Marsha Hunt, William Prince
One Sheet: $30 - $60

CARNIVAL
(1931 - Gaumont) Matheson Lang, Joseph Schildkraut
One Sheet: $250 - $500   *AKA: VENETIAN NIGHTS.*

CARNIVAL
(1935 - Columbia) Lee Tracy, Jimmy Durante, Sally Eilers
One Sheet: $200 - $400

CARNIVAL
(1946 - Rank) Sally Gray, Michael Wilding
One Sheet: $30 - $50

CARNIVAL
(1953 - Gaumont) Fernandel, Jacqueline Pagnol
One Sheet: $15 - $30

CARNIVAL BOAT
(1932 - RKO-Pathe) Ginger Rogers, William Boyd
One Sheet: $700 - $1,200

CARNIVAL IN COSTA RICA
(1947 - 20th Century Fox) Dick Haymes, Celeste Holm
One Sheet: $40 - $75

CARNIVAL IN FLANDERS
(1936 - American Tobis) Francoise Rosay, Jean Murat
One Sheet: $150 - $300

CARNIVAL IN RHYTHM
(1944 - -) -
One Sheet: $50 - $120

CARNIVAL LADY
(1933 - Goldsmith/Hollywood) Boots Mallory, Allen Vincent
One Sheet: $125 - $250

CARNIVAL OF BLOOD
(1976 - Kirk/Monarch) Earle Edgerton, Judith Resnick
One Sheet: $15 - $25

CARNIVAL OF CRIME
(1964 - Crown) Jean-Pierre Aumont

One Sheet: $15 - $25

CARNIVAL OF SINNERS
(1947 - Distinguished) Pierre Fresnay, Josseline Gael
One Sheet: $50 - $100

CARNIVAL OF SOULS
(1962 - Herts-Lion) Candace Hilligoss, Herk Harvey
One Sheet: $125 - $250   *Graven Images, pg. 211.*

CARNIVAL QUEEN
(1937 - Universal) Dorothea Kent, Robert Wilcox
One Sheet: $100 - $200

CARNIVAL ROCK
(1957 - Howco) Susan Cabot, Dick Miller, Dir: Roger Corman
One Sheet: $40 - $75   *Rock 'n' Roll. Features The Platters.*

CARNIVAL STORY
(1954 - RKO) Anne Baxter, Steve Cochran
One Sheet: $15 - $35

CARNY
(1980 - Lorimar) Gary Bussey, Jodie Foster
One Sheet: $7 - $15

One Sheet

CAROLINA
(1934 - Fox) Janet Gaynor, Lionel Barrymore, Robert Young
One Sheet: $200 - $400

CAROLINA BLUES
(1944 - Columbia) Victor Moore, Kay Kyser, Ann Miller
One Sheet: $75 - $150

CAROLINA CANNONBALL
(1955 - Republic) Judy Canova, Andy Clyde
One Sheet: $15 - $35

CAROLINA MOON
(1940 - Republic) Gene Autry, Smiley Burnette
One Sheet: $200 - $400

CAROLINA MOON
(1947R - Republic) Gene Autry, Smiley Burnette
One Sheet: $50 - $100   *Re-release.*

CAROLINE CHERIE
(1951 - Cinephonic/Gaumont) Martine Carol, Jacques Dacqmine
One Sheet: $10 - $20

CAROLINE CHERIE
(1968 - Cineurop/Nordeutsche) France Anglade, Vittorio De Sica
One Sheet: $5 - $10

CAROUSEL
(1956 - 20th Century Fox) Gordon MacRae, Shirley Jones
One Sheet: $75 - $150

CARPETBAGGERS, THE
(1964 - Paramount) Carroll Baker, George Peppard
One Sheet: $15 - $35

CARPETBAGGERS, THE/NEVADA SMITH
(1968R - Paramount) Steve McQueen, George Peppard, Alan Ladd, Caroll Baker
One Sheet: $15 - $25   *Re-release double feature poster.*

CARRIE
(1951 - Paramount) Laurence Olivier, Jennifer

Jones
One Sheet: $40 - $75

CARRIE
(1976 - United Artists) Sissy Spacek, Piper Laurie
One Sheet: $20 - $40   *Horror.*

One Sheet

CARRIED AWAY
(1996 - Fine Line) Dennis Hopper, Amy Locane
One Sheet: $4 - $8

CARRINGTON
(1995 - Gramercy) Emma Thompson, Jonathan Pryce
One Sheet: $5 - $10

CARRY HARRY
(1942 - Columbia) Harry Langdon
One Sheet: $100 - $200   *Comedy short. Duotone.*

CARRY IT ON
(1970 - Maron) Joan Baez
One Sheet: $15 - $30

CARRY ON ADMIRAL
(1957 - Renown) David Tomlinson, Peggy Cummins
One Sheet: $10 - $20   *AKA: THE SHIP WAS LOADED.*

CARRY ON AGAIN, DOCTOR
(1969 - Rank) Kenneth Williams, Sidney James
One Sheet: $5 - $10

CARRY ON CABBIE
(1963 - Warner Bros./Pathe) Sidney James, Hattie Jacques
One Sheet: $15 - $25

CARRY ON CAMPING
(1972 - Rank) Sidney James, Kenneth Williams
One Sheet: $7 - $15

CARRY ON CLEO
(1965 - Governor) Sidney James, Amanda Barrie
One Sheet: $15 - $25

CARRY ON CONSTABLE
(1961 - Governor) Sidney James, Eric Ranker
One Sheet: $15 - $25

CARRY ON COWBOY
(1966 - Warner Bros./Pathe) Sidney James, Kenneth Williams
One Sheet: $5 - $10

CARRY ON CRUISING
(1962 - Anglo-Amalgamated) Sidney James, Kenneth Williams
One Sheet: $5 - $10

CARRY ON DOCTOR
(1972 - AIP) Frankie Howerd, Kenneth Williams
One Sheet: $7 - $15

CARRY ON EMMANNUELLE
(1978 - Hemdale International) Suzanne Danielle, Kenneth Williams
One Sheet: $5 - $10

CARRY ON ENGLAND
(1976 - 20th Century Fox) Kenneth Connor, Windsor Davies
One Sheet: $5 - $10

CARRY ON HENRY VIII
(1970 - AIP) Sidney James, Kenneth Williams
One Sheet: $7 - $15

CARRY ON JACK

(1963 - Warner Bros.) Bernard Cribbins, Juliet Mills
One Sheet: $5 - $10   *AKA: CARRY ON VENUS.*

CARRY ON LOVING
(1970 - Rank) Sidney James, Kenneth Williams
One Sheet: $5 - $10

CARRY ON NURSE
(1960 - Governor) Terence Longdon, Kenneth Connor
One Sheet: $15 - $25

CARRY ON, REGARDLESS
(1961 - Anglo) Sidney James
One Sheet: $5 - $10

CARRY ON SCREAMING
(1966 - Warner Bros.) Harry H. Corbett, Kenneth Williams
One Sheet: $5 - $10

CARRY ON SERGEANT
(1959 - Anglo) Bob Monkhouse, William Hartnell
One Sheet: $15 - $30

CARRY ON SPYING
(1965 - Governor) Barbara Windsor, Kenneth Williams
One Sheet: $5 - $10

CARRY ON TEACHER
(1962 - Governor) Kenneth Connor, Charles Hawtry
One Sheet: $15 - $25

CARRY ON UP THE JUNGLE
(1970 - Rank) Joan Sims, Sidney James
One Sheet: $5 - $10

CARRY ON, UP THE KHYBER
(1968 - Rank) Sidney James, Kenneth Williams
One Sheet: $5 - $10

CARRYING THE MAIL
(1934 - Imperial) Wally Wales, Peggy Darling
One Sheet: $200 - $400

One Sheet

CARS THAT ATE PARIS, THE
(1974 - Salt-Pan) Terry Camilleri, John Meillon
One Sheet: $15 - $25   *Australian. AKA:The Cars That Eat People.*

CARS THAT EAT PEOPLE, THE
(1977 - Salt-Pan) Terry Camilleri, John Meillon
One Sheet: $15 - $25   *AKA:The Cars That Ate Paris.*

CARSON CITY
(1952 - Warner Bros.) Randolph Scott, Raymond Massey
One Sheet: $30 - $50

CARSON CITY CYCLONE
(1943 - Republic) Don Barry, Lynn Merrick
One Sheet: $30 - $50

CARSON CITY KID, THE
(1940 - Republic) Roy Rogers, Gabby Hayes, Bob Steele
One Sheet: $200 - $400

CARSON CITY RAIDERS, THE
(1948 - Republic) Rocky Lane, Eddie Waller
One Sheet: $30 - $50

CARTER CASE, THE
(1947 - Republic) James Ellison, Virginia Gilmore
One Sheet: $30 - $50

CARTHAGE IN FLAMES
(1961 - Columbia) June Suarez, Anne Heywood
One Sheet: $5 - $10

CARTOON SHORT SUBJECTS
(1971 - Disney) -
One Sheet: $20 - $40   *Cartoon.*

CARTOUCHE
(1930S - ALB) Paul Lalloz, Lucien Blondeau
One Sheet: $100 - $200   *French.*

CARTOUCHE
(1955 - RKO) Richard Basehart, Patricia Roe, Akim Tamiroff
One Sheet: $10 - $20

CARTOUCHE
(1962 - Embassy) Jean-Paul Belmondo, Claudia Cardinale
One Sheet: $50 - $100

CARVE HER NAME WITH PRIDE
(1958 - Rank) Virginia McKenna, Paul Scofield
One Sheet: $7 - $15

CARYL OF THE MOUNTAINS
(1936 - Reliable) Rin Tin Tin, Jr., Francis X. Bushman, Jr.
One Sheet: $150 - $300

CASA MANANA
(1951 - Monogram) Robert Clarke, Virginia Welles
One Sheet: $15 - $30

CASABLANCA
(1943 - Warner Bros.) Humphrey Bogart, Ingrid Bergman
One Sheet: $4,500 - $7,000   *Academy Award: Best Picture, Best Direction(Michael Curtiz). One sheet and three sheet are brownish duotone. Academy AwardMovie Posters #87 & #88.*

One Sheet

CASABLANCA
(1949R - Warner Bros.) Humphrey Bogart, Ingrid Bergman
One Sheet: $250 - $500   *Re-release.*

CASABLANCA
(1956R - Warner Bros.) Humphrey Bogart, Ingrid Bergman
One Sheet: $150 - $300   *Re-release.*

CASANOVA
(1976 - Universal) Donald Sutherland, Tina Aumont
One Sheet: $5 - $10   *AKA: FELLINI'S CASANOVA.*

CASANOVA '70
(1965 - Embassy) Marcello Mastroianni, Virna Lisi
One Sheet: $10 - $20

CASANOVA BROWN
(1944 - International) Gary Cooper, Teresa Wright
One Sheet: $75 - $150

CASANOVA CAT
(1951 - MGM) Tom & Jerry
One Sheet: $300 - $650   *Cartoon. Full color stone litho.*

CASANOVA IN BURLESQUE
(1943 - Republic) Joe E. Brown, June Havoc, Dale Evans
One Sheet: $50 - $100

CASANOVA'S BIG NIGHT
(1953 - Columbia) Bob Hope, Joan Fontaine

One Sheet: $30 - $50

CASBAH
(1948 - Universal) Yvonne De Carlo, Tony Martin, Peter Lorre
One Sheet: $50 - $100

CASE AGAINST BROOKLYN, THE
(1958 - Columbia) Darren McGavin, Maggie Hayes
One Sheet: $20 - $40

CASE AGAINST FERRO, THE
(1980 - Specialty) Yves Montand, Simone Signoret
One Sheet: $3 - $5

CASE AGAINST MRS. AMES, THE
(1936 - Paramount) George Brent, Madeleine Carroll
One Sheet: $100 - $200

CASE FOR PC 49, A
(1951 - Hammer) Brian Reece, Joy Shelton
One Sheet: $30 - $50

CASE FOR THE CROWN, THE
(1934 - Paramount) Miles Mander, Meriel Forbes
One Sheet: $150 - $300

CASE OF CHARLES PEACE, THE
(1949 - Argyle/Monarch) Michael Martin Harvey, Chili Bouchier
One Sheet: $15 - $35

CASE OF CLARA DEANE, THE
(1932 - Paramount) See STRANGE CASE OF CLARA DEANE

CASE OF DR. LAURENT, THE
(1958 - Trans-Lux) Jean Gabin, Nicole Courcel
One Sheet: $10 - $20

CASE OF GABRIEL PERRY, THE
(1935 - British Lion) Henry Oscar, Olga Lindo
One Sheet: $125 - $250

CASE OF PATTY SMITH, THE
(1962 - Leo A. Handel) Merry Anders, J. Edward McKinley
One Sheet: $10 - $20

CASE OF SERGEANT GRISCHA, THE
(1930 - RKO) Jean Hersholt, Chester Morris, Betty Compson
One Sheet: $150 - $300

CASE OF THE 44'S, THE
(1964 - D & A) Ian Carmichael, Lotte Tarp
One Sheet: $5 - $10

CASE OF THE BABY SITTER, THE
(1947 - Screen Art) Tom Neal, Pamela Blake
One Sheet: $40 - $75

CASE OF THE BLACK CAT, THE
(1936 - Warner Bros.) Ricardo Cortez, June Travis
One Sheet: $150 - $350

CASE OF THE BLACK PARROT, THE
(1941 - Warner Bros.) William Lundigan, Maris Wrixon
One Sheet: $75 - $150

CASE OF THE CURIOUS BRIDE, THE
(1935 - First National) Warren William, Margaret Lindsay, Errol Flynn
One Sheet: $600 - $1,000

CASE OF THE FRIGHTENED LADY, THE
(1940 - British Lion) Marius Goring, Helen Hayes
One Sheet: $75 - $125   *AKA: THE FRIGHTENED LADY.*

CASE OF THE HOWLING DOG, THE
(1934 - First National) Warren William, Mary Astor
One Sheet: $250 - $600

CASE OF THE LUCKY LEGS, THE
(1935 - First National) Warren William, Genevieve Tobin
One Sheet: $250 - $600

CASE OF THE MISSING MAN, THE
(1935 - Columbia) Roger Pryor, Joan Perry
One Sheet: $150 - $350

CASE OF THE NAVES BROTHERS, THE
(1972 - Europix International) Raoul Cortez,

Joea De Olivere
One Sheet: $7 - $15

CASE OF THE RED MONKEY
(1955 - Todon) Richard Conte, Rona Anderson
One Sheet: $10 - $20

CASE OF THE STUTTERING BISHOP, THE
(1937 - Warner Bros.) Donald Woods, Ann Dvorak
One Sheet: $150 - $300

CASE OF THE VELVET CLAWS, THE
(1936 - First National) Warren William, Claire Dodd
One Sheet: $250 - $500

CASE VAN GELDERN
(1932 - Richter/Tonfilm/Suedfilm) Paul Richter, Ellen Richter
One Sheet: $100 - $200

CASEY AT THE BAT
(1927 - Paramount) Wallace Beery, Ford Sterling
One Sheet: $800 - $1,500   *Sports (Baseball). Sports Movie Posters #s 38, 40.*

CASEY AT THE BAT
(1954 - Disney) -
One Sheet: $250 - $500   *Cartoon. Sports (Baseball).*

CASEY BATS AGAIN
(1954 - RKO/Disney) -
One Sheet: $200 - $400   *Cartoon. Sports (Baseball). Full color. Sports Movie Posters #64.*

CASEY JONES
(1927 - Rayart) Ralph Lewis, Kate Price, Jason Robards
One Sheet: $250 - $600

CASEY'S SHADOW
(1978 - Columbia) Walter Matthau, Alexis Smith
One Sheet: $5 - $10

CASH
(1934 - London) Robert Donat, Edmund Gwenn
One Sheet: $250 - $600

CASH AND CARRY
(1937 - Columbia) The Three Stooges (Curly)
One Sheet: $8,500 - $14,000   *Comedy short. Duotone.*

CASH McCALL
(1960 - Warner Bros.) James Garner, Natalie Wood
One Sheet: $15 - $35

CASH ON DELIVERY
(1954 - RKO) Shelley Winters, John Gregson
One Sheet: $15 - $30

CASH ON DEMAND
(1962 - Columbia) Peter Cushing, Andre Morrell
One Sheet: $7 - $15

CASINO
(1995 - Universal) Robert De Niro, Sharon Stone, Joe Pesci
One Sheet: $7 - $15

CASINO DE PARIS
(1957 - Pathe) Caterina Valente, Gilbert Becaud
One Sheet: $15 - $25

CASINO MURDER CASE, THE
(1935 - MGM) Paul Lukas, Rosalind Russell, Alison Skipworth
One Sheet: $200 - $400

CASINO ROYALE
(1967 - Columbia) Peter Sellers, Ursula Andress
One Sheet: $30 - $60   *Price is for either style.*

CASPER
(1995 - Universal) Christina Ricci, Bill Pullman, Eric Idle
One Sheet: $5 - $10

CASPER STOCK
(1950 - Paramount) -
One Sheet: $500 - $800   *Cartoon. Full color stock poster with large image of Casper. Cartoon Movie Posters #231.*

CASPER THE FRIENDLY GHOST IN 3-D
(1954 - -) See "BOO MOON"

CASQUE D'OR
(1956 - Speva/Paris) Simone Signoret, Serge Reggiani
One Sheet: $30 - $50   *AKA: GOLDEN MARIE.*

CASS TIMBERLANE
(1947 - MGM) Spencer Tracy, Lana Turner, Zachary Scott
One Sheet: $40 - $75

CASSANDRA CROSSING, THE
(1977 - Avco/Embassy) Sophia Loren, Richard Harris
One Sheet: $10 - $20

CASSIDY OF BAR 20
(1938 - Paramount) William Boyd, Frank Darlen
One Sheet: $250 - $600

CASSIUS CLAY VS. FLOYD PATTERSON
(1965 - Turn of the Century Fights) -
One Sheet: $200 - $400   *Sports (Boxing).*

CAST A DARK SHADOW
(1957 - Eros) Dirk Bogarde, Margaret Lockwood
One Sheet: $10 - $20

CAST A GIANT SHADOW
(1966 - United Artists) John Wayne, Frank Sinatra, Kirk Douglas
One Sheet: $30 - $50

CAST A LONG SHADOW
(1959 - United Artists) Audie Murphy, Terry Moore
One Sheet: $15 - $35

CAST AMID BOOMERANG THROWERS
(1913 - G. Melies) -
One Sheet: $600 - $1,000

CAST UP BY THE SEA
(1907 - Vitagraph) -
One Sheet: $100 - $200

CASTAWAY COWBOY
(1974 - Buena Vista/Disney) James Garner
One Sheet: $10 - $20

CASTAWAY COWBOY
(1987 - Cannon) Oliver Reed, Amanda Donohoe
One Sheet: $2 - $3

CASTAWAYS
(1981 - -) See IN SEARCH OF...

CASTE
(1913 - Edison) -
One Sheet: $250 - $500

CASTE
(1930 - United Artists) Hermione Baddeley, Nora Swinburne
One Sheet: $150 - $300

CASTILIAN, THE
(1963 - Warner Bros.) Cesar Romero, Broderick Crawford
One Sheet: $10 - $20

CASTLE, THE
(1969 - Continental) Maximilian Schell, Cordula Trantow, Trudik Daniel
One Sheet: $7 - $15

CASTLE IN THE AIR
(1952 - Associated British-Pathe) David Tomlinson, Helen Cherry
One Sheet: $15 - $25

CASTLE IN THE DESERT
(1942 - 20th Century Fox) Sidney Toler, Arleen Whelan
One Sheet: $100 - $200

CASTLE KEEP
(1969 - Columbia) Burt Lancaster, Patrick O'Neal, Jean Pierre Aumont
One Sheet: $7 - $15

CASTLE OF BLOOD
(1964 - Woolner) Barbara Steele
One Sheet: $30 - $50

CASTLE OF CRIMES

(1944 - PRC) Kenneth Kent, Diana Churchill
One Sheet: $50 - $100

CASTLE OF EVIL
(1969 - United) Scott Brady, Virginia Mayo
One Sheet: $15 - $30

CASTLE OF FU MANCHU
(1968 - Balcazar) Christopher Lee, Richard Greene
One Sheet: $15 - $25

CASTLE OF PURITY
(1974 - Ripstein) Claudio Brook, Rita Macedo
One Sheet: $3 - $5

CASTLE OF THE LIVING DEAD
(1964 - Malasky) Christopher Lee, Donald Sutherland
One Sheet: $15 - $35

CASTLE OF THE MONSTERS
(1958 - Sotomayor) Antonio Espino Clavillazo, Evangelina Elizondo
One Sheet: $30 - $50   *Mexican.*

CASTLE ON THE HUDSON
(1940 - Warner Bros.) John Garfield, Ann Sheridan
One Sheet: $125 - $250   *Duotone.*

One Sheet

CASTLE ON THE HUDSON
(1949R - Warner Bros.) John Garfield, Ann Sheridan
One Sheet: $40 - $75   *Re-release. Duotone.*

CASTLE SINISTER
(1932 - Delta) Haddon Mason, Eric Adeney
One Sheet: $600 - $1,000

CASUAL SEX?
(1988 - -) Lea Thompson, Victoria Jackson, Stephen Shellen
One Sheet: $5 - $10

CASUALTIES OF WAR
(1988 - Columbia) Michael J. Fox, Sean Penn
One Sheet: $5 - $10

CAT, THE
(1959 - Essex) Francoise Arnoul, Bernard Wicki
One Sheet: $5 - $10

CAT, THE
(1966 - Embassy) Roger Perry, Peggy Ann Garner
One Sheet: $7 - $15

CAT, THE
(1975 - Joseph Green) Jean Gabin, Simone Signoret
One Sheet: $5 - $10

CAT AND MOUSE
(1958 - Anvil/Eros) Lee Patterson, Ann Sears
One Sheet: $10 - $20   *AKA: THE DESPERATE MEN.*

CAT AND MOUSE
(1978 - Quartet) Michele Morgan, Serge Reggiani
One Sheet: $3 - $5

CAT AND THE CANARY, THE
(1927 - Universal) Laura La Plante, Tully Marshall
One Sheet: $2,200 - $3,500   *Graven Images, pg. 11, 29.*

CAT AND THE CANARY, THE
(1939 - Paramount) Bob Hope, Paulette

Goddard
One Sheet: $1,300 - $2,000   *Graven Images, pg. 102.*

One Sheet

CAT AND THE CANARY, THE
(1979 - Cinema Shares) Honor Blackman, Michael Callen
One Sheet: $5 - $10

CAT AND THE FIDDLE, THE
(1934 - MGM) Ramon Novarro, Jeanette MacDonald
One Sheet: $200 - $400

CAT AND THE MERMOUSE, THE
(1949 - MGM) Tom & Jerry
One Sheet: $300 - $700   *Cartoon. Full color stone litho.*

CAT ATE THE PARAKEET, THE
(1972 - KEP) Phillip Pine, Robert Mantell
One Sheet: $5 - $10

CAT BALLOU
(1965 - Columbia) Jane Fonda, Lee Marvin, Nat King Cole
One Sheet: $30 - $65   *Academy Award Movie Posters #230.*

CAT BURGLAR, THE
(1961 - United Artists) Jack Hogan, June Kenney
One Sheet: $10 - $20

CAT CONCERTO, THE
(1947 - MGM) Tom & Jerry
One Sheet: $800 - $1,500   *Cartoon. Academy Award: Best Cartoon Short. Full color stone litho. Cartoon Movie Posters #276.*

CAT CREEPS, THE
(1930 - Universal) Jean Hersholt
One Sheet: $1,300 - $2,000   *Graven Images, pg. 50.*

CAT CREEPS, THE
(1946 - Universal) Lois Collier, Noah Beery, Jr., Paul Kelly
One Sheet: $125 - $250

CAT CREEPS, THE
(1951R - Realart) Lois Collier, Noah Beery, Jr., Paul Kelly
One Sheet: $40 - $75   *Re-release.*

CAT FROM OUTER SPACE
(1978 - Disney) Ken Berry, Sandy Duncan
One Sheet: $10 - $20   *Price is for both styles.*

CAT GANG, THE
(1959 - Realist) Francesca Annis, John Pike
One Sheet: $10 - $20

CAT GIRL, THE
(1957 - AIP) Barbara Shelley, Robert Ayers
One Sheet: $50 - $100

CAT IN THE SACK, THE
(1967 - Pathe Contemporary) Claude Godbout, Barbara Ulrich
One Sheet: $5 - $10

CAT MEETS MOUSE
(1940 - 20th Century Fox) Terry-toons
One Sheet: $100 - $200   *Cartoon. Full color stone litho. Stock poster with inset title.*

CAT MURKIL AND THE SILKS
(1976 - Gamma III) David Kyle, Steve Bond
One Sheet: $3 - $5

CAT O'NINE TAILS, THE

(1971 - National General) Karl Malden, James Franciscus
One Sheet: $5 - $10

CAT ON A HOT TIN ROOF
(1958 - MGM) Elizabeth Taylor, Paul Newman
One Sheet: $200 - $400

CAT ON A HOT TIN ROOF
(1964R - MGM) Elizabeth Taylor, Paul Newman
One Sheet: $30 - $60   *Re-release.*

CAT ON A HOT TIN ROOF
(1966R - MGM) Elizabeth Taylor, Paul Newman
One Sheet: $20 - $40   *Re-release.*

CAT ON A HOT TIN ROOF/BUTTERFIELD 8
(1966R - MGM) Elizabeth Taylor, Paul Newman, Eddie Fisher
One Sheet: $20 - $40   *Re-release double feature poster.*

CAT PEOPLE
(1942 - RKO) Simone Simon, Tom Conway
One Sheet: $1,600 - $2,500   *Graven Images, pg. xiii, 122.*

One Sheet

CAT PEOPLE
(1952R - RKO) Simone Simon, Tom Conway
One Sheet: $250 - $600   *Re-release.*

CAT PEOPLE
(1982 - Universal) Natassha Kinski, Malcolm McDowell
One Sheet: $10 - $20   *Advance style:$25-40.*

CAT THAT HATED PEOPLE, THE
(1948 - MGM) Prod. by Fred Quimby
One Sheet: $250 - $500   *Cartoon. Cartoon Movie Posters #305.*

CAT WOMEN OF THE MOON
(1954 - Astor) Sonny Tufts, Victor Jory, Marie Windsor
One Sheet: $250 - $500   *Graven Images, pg. 187.*

CAT'S EYE
(1985 - MGM/UA) Drew Barrymore, James Woods
One Sheet: $5 - $10

CAT'S MEOW, THE
(1924 - Pathecomedy) Harry Langdon
One Sheet: $300 - $700

CAT'S PAW, THE
(1934 - Fox) Harold Lloyd
One Sheet: $500 - $900

CATALINA CAPER
(1967 - Crown) Tommy Kirk
One Sheet: $4 - $8

CATAMOUNT KILLING, THE
(1975 - Hallmark) Horst Bucholz, Ann Wedgeworth
One Sheet: $5 - $10

CATCH AS CATCH CAN
(1937 - Atlantic Episode) James Mason, Viki Dibson
One Sheet: $75 - $150   *AKA: ATLANTIC EPISODE.*

CATCH AS CATCH CAN
(1968 - Embassy) Vittorio Gassman, Martha Hyer
One Sheet: $4 - $8

CATCH ME A SPY
(1971 - J. Arthur Rank) Kirk Douglas, Marlene

Jobert
One Sheet: $7 - $15

CATCH MY SOUL
(1974 - Cinerama/Metromedia) Richie Havens, Lance Le Gault
One Sheet: $10 - $20   *Rock musical. AKA: TO CATCH A SPY, SANTA FE SATAN.*

CATCH-22
(1970 - Paramount) Alan Arkin, Richard Benjamin, Jon Voight, Orson Welles
One Sheet: $15 - $30

CATERED AFFAIR, THE
(1956 - MGM) Bette Davis, Ernest Borgnine
One Sheet: $30 - $50

CATHERINE & CO.
(1976 - Warner Bros.) Jane Birkin, Patrick Dewaere
One Sheet: $3 - $5

CATHERINE THE GREAT
(1934 - United Artists) Doublas Fairbanks Jr., Elisabeth Bergner
One Sheet: $350 - $750

CATHY'S CHILD
(1979 - Roadshow) Michelle Fawdon, Alan Cassell
One Sheet: $3 - $5

CATHY'S CURSE
(1977 - 21st Century) Alan Scarfe, Beverley Murray
One Sheet: $3 - $5

CATLOW
(1971 - MGM) Yul Brynner, Richard Crenna, Leonard Nimoy
One Sheet: $5 - $10

CATMAN OF PARIS, THE
(1946 - Republic) Carl Esmond, Lenore Aubert
One Sheet: $250 - $500

Half Sheet

CATMAN OF PARIS, THE/VALLEY OF THE ZOMBIES
(1956R - Twin Features) -
One Sheet: $30 - $50   *Re-release double feature poster.*

CATNIP CAPERS
(1939 - 20th Century Fox) Terry-toons
One Sheet: $75 - $150   *Cartoon. Full color stone litho. Stock poster with inset title.*

CATSKILL HONEYMOON
(1949 - Yiddish-American) Michael Michalesko, Jan Bart
One Sheet: $10 - $20

CATTLE ANNIE AND LITTLE BRITCHES
(1981 - Universal) Burt Lancaster, Rod Steiger, Diane Lane
One Sheet: $3 - $5

CATTLE DRIVE
(1951 - Universal) Joel McCrea, Dean Stockwell
One Sheet: $20 - $40

CATTLE EMPIRE
(1958 - 20th Century Fox) Joel McCrea, Gloria Talbott
One Sheet: $20 - $40

CATTLE KING
(1963 - MGM) Robert Taylor, Joan Caulfield
One Sheet: $5 - $10

CATTLE QUEEN

(1951 - Pathe/United) Maria Hart, William Fawcett
One Sheet: $15 - $25

CATTLE QUEEN OF MONTANA
(1954 - RKO) Barbara Stanwyck, Ronald Reagan
One Sheet: $75 - $125

CATTLE RAIDERS
(1938 - Columbia) Charles Starrett, Iris Meredith
One Sheet: $75 - $125

CATTLE STAMPEDE
(1943 - PRC) Buster Crabbe
One Sheet: $30 - $50

CATTLE THIEF, THE
(1936 - Columbia) Ken Maynard
One Sheet: $250 - $500

CATTLE THIEF'S ESCAPE, THE
(1913 - Selig) -
One Sheet: $250 - $600   *Cowboy Movie Posters #3.*

CATTLE TOWN
(1952 - Warner Bros.) Dennis Morgan, Philip Carey
One Sheet: $15 - $30

CAUGHT
(1931 - Paramount) Richard Arlen, Frances Dee
One Sheet: $250 - $500

CAUGHT
(1949 - Enterprise) James Mason, Barbara Bel Geddes
One Sheet: $40 - $75

CAUGHT BLUFFING
(1922 - Universal) Frank Mayo
One Sheet: $350 - $750

CAUGHT CHEATING
(1931 - Tiffany) Charles Murray, George Sidney
One Sheet: $150 - $300

CAUGHT IN A CABARET
(1914 - Keystone) Charlie Chaplin
One Sheet: $6,500 - $10,000

CAUGHT IN THE ACT
(1941 - PRC) Henry Armetta, Iris Meredith
One Sheet: $50 - $100

CAUGHT IN THE BOURBON ST. SHADOWS
(1962 - MPA) Richard Derr, Mark Daniels, Helen Westcott
One Sheet: $30 - $50

CAUGHT IN THE DRAFT
(1941 - Paramount) Bob Hope, Dorothy Lamour
One Sheet: $125 - $250

CAUGHT IN THE FOG
(1928 - Warner Bros.) May McAvoy, Conrad Nagel
One Sheet: $200 - $400

CAUGHT IN THE NET
(1960 - Wallace) Jeremy Bulloch, Joanna Horlock
One Sheet: $5 - $10

CAUGHT IN THE RAIN
(1914 - Keystone) Charlie Chaplin
One Sheet: $6,500 - $10,000

CAUGHT PLASTERED
(1931 - RKO) Wheeler and Woolsey
One Sheet: $250 - $500

CAUGHT SHORT
(1930 - MGM) Marie Dressler, Polly Moran
One Sheet: $100 - $200

CAULDRON OF BLOOD
(1971 - Cannon) Boris Karloff, Viveca Lindfors
One Sheet: $15 - $30

CAULDRON OF BLOOD/CRUCIBLE OF HORROR
(1977?R - Cannon) -
One Sheet: $10 - $20   *Re-release double feature poster.*

CAUSE FOR ALARM
(1950 - MGM) Loretta Young, Barry Sullivan
One Sheet: $30 - $50

CAVALCADE
(1933 - Fox) Clive Brook, Diana Wynyard
One Sheet: $1,900 - $3,000   *Academy Award: Best Picture, Best Direction(Frank Lloyd). Academy Award Movie Posters #28 & #29.*

CAVALCADE OF THE WEST
(1936 - Diversion) Hoot Gibson, Rex Lease
One Sheet: $250 - $600

CAVALIER, THE
(1928 - Tiffany-Stahl) Richard Talmadge, Barbara Bedford
One Sheet: $200 - $400

CAVALIER OF THE WEST
(1931 - Weiss Bros.) Harry Carey, Kane Richmond
One Sheet: $150 - $300   *Cowboy Movie Posters # 137.*

CAVALRY
(1936 - Republic) Bob Steele
One Sheet: $150 - $300

CAVALRY CHARGE
(1961 - Citation) Ronald Reagan, Rhonda Fleming
One Sheet: $15 - $25   *Re-issue of THE LAST OUTPOST.*

CAVALRY SCOUT
(1951 - Monogram) Rod Cameron, Audrey Long
One Sheet: $15 - $35

CAVE OF OUTLAWS
(1951 - Universal) Macdonald Carey, Alexis Smith
One Sheet: $20 - $40

CAVEMAN
(1981 - United Artists) Ringo Starr, Barbara Bach, Dennis Quaid
One Sheet: $7 - $15

CAVERN, THE
(1965 - 20th Century Fox) Rosanna Schiaffino, John Saxon
One Sheet: $10 - $20

CB4
(1993 - Universal) Chris Rock, Phil Hartman
One Sheet: $3 - $5

CEASE FIRE!
(1953 - Paramount) American G.I.s In Korea
One Sheet: $30 - $50   *3-D.*

CEASE FIRE
(1985 - Cineworld) Don Johnson, Lisa Blount
One Sheet: $3 - $5

CEILING ZERO
(1936 - Warner Bros.) James Cagney, Pat O'Brien
One Sheet: $700 - $1,200

CEILING ZERO
(1956R - Warner Bros.) James Cagney, Pat O'Brien
One Sheet: $40 - $75   *Re-release.*

CELEBRATION AT BIG SUR
(1971 - 20th Century Fox) Joan Baez, John Sebastian
One Sheet: $15 - $25

CELEBRITY
(1928 - Pathe) Lina Basquette, Robert Armstrong, Clyde Cook
One Sheet: $200 - $400

CELL 2455, DEATH ROW
(1955 - Columbia) William Campbell, Robert Campbell
One Sheet: $30 - $60

CELLULOID CLOSET, THE
(1996 - Sony Classics) Dirs: Robert Epstein, Jeffrey Friedman
One Sheet: $5 - $10

CELTIC PRIDE
(1996 - Hollywood Pictures) Dan Ackroyd, Daniel Stern, Damon Wayans
One Sheet: $5 - $10   *Sports (Basketball).*

CEMENT GARDEN, THE
(1994 - October) Andrew Robertson, Sinead Cusach
One Sheet: $3 - $6

CEMETARY CLUB, THE
(1993 - Buena Vista) Ellen Burstyn, Diane Ladd, Olympia Dukakis
One Sheet: $3 - $5

CEMETERYMAN
(1996 - October) Dir: Michele Soavi
One Sheet: $4 - $8

CENTENNIAL SUMMER
(1946 - 20th Century Fox) Linda Darnell, Cornel Wilde
One Sheet: $100 - $200

CENTRAL AIRPORT
(1933 - First National) Tom Brown, Sally Eilers, Richard Barthelmess, John Wayne
One Sheet: $500 - $800

CENTRAL PARK
(1932 - First National) Joan Blondell, Guy Kibbee
One Sheet: $200 - $400

CENTURY
(1994 - I.R.S.) Charles Dance, Miranda Richardson, Clive Owen
One Sheet: $3 - $5

CEREMONY, THE
(1963 - United Artists) Laurence Harvey, Sarah Miles
One Sheet: $7 - $15

CERTAIN FURY
(1985 - New World) Tatum O'Neal, Irene Cara
One Sheet: $3 - $5

CERTAIN SMILE, A
(1958 - 20th Century Fox) Joan Fontaine, Rossano Brazzi
One Sheet: $15 - $25

CESAR AND ROSALIE
(1972 - Cinema 5) Yves Montand, Romy Schneider
One Sheet: $5 - $10

CHA-CHA-CHA-BOOM!
(1956 - Columbia) Stephen Dunne, Alix Talton
One Sheet: $20 - $40

CHAD HANNA
(1940 - 20th Century Fox) Henry Fonda, Dorothy Lamour
One Sheet: $100 - $200   *Price is for style A (photo). One Sheet(Style B, artwork):$200-$400.*

CHAIN GANG
(1950 - Columbia) Douglas Kennedy, Marjorie Lord
One Sheet: $30 - $50

CHAIN LIGHTNING
(1927 - Fox) Buck Jones
One Sheet: $250 - $600   *Cowboy Movie Posters #61.*

CHAIN LIGHTNING
(1950 - Warner Bros.) Humphrey Bogart, Eleanor Parker
One Sheet: $50 - $100

CHAIN OF CIRCUMSTANCE
(1951 - Columbia) Richard Grayson, Margaret Field
One Sheet: $15 - $30

CHAIN OF EVIDENCE
(1957 - Allied Artists) Bill Elliott, James Lydon
One Sheet: $15 - $35

CHAIN REACTION
(1996 - Fox) Keanu Reeves, Morgan Freeman
One Sheet: $5 - $10

CHAINED
(1934 - MGM) Joan Crawford, Clark Gable
One Sheet: $2,500 - $4,000   *Price is for black style 'B'. One Sheet(Style A, white):$600-$1,000.*

CHAINED FOR LIFE
(1951 - Classic) Hilton Sisters
One Sheet: $125 - $250

CHAINED GIRLS
(1965 - AFD) -
One Sheet: $15 - $30

CHAINED HEAT
(1983 - -) Linda Blair, John Vernon
One Sheet: $7 - $15

CHAINGANG WOMEN
(1971 - -) Micheal Sterns, Linda York
One Sheet: $15 - $30

CHAINS OF GOLD
(1990 - M.C.E.G.) John Travolta
One Sheet: $5 - $10

CHAIRMAN, THE
(1969 - 20th Century Fox) Gregory Peck, Anne Heywood, Arthur Hill
One Sheet: $7 - $15

CHALK GARDEN, THE
(1964 - Universal) Deborah Kerr, Hayley Mills
One Sheet: $20 - $40

CHALLENGE, THE
(1948 - 20th Century Fox) Tom Conway, June Vincent, Richard Stapley
One Sheet: $40 - $75

CHALLENGE
(1974 - Cinemation) Earl Owensby
One Sheet: $5 - $10

CHALLENGE, THE
(1982 - CBS) Scott Glenn, Toshiro Mifune
One Sheet: $3 - $5

CHALLENGE FOR ROBINHOOD, A
(1969 - 20th Century Fox) Barrie Ingham, James Hayter, Leon Greene, Peter Blythe
One Sheet: $7 - $15

CHALLENGE OF CHANCE, THE
(1919 - Continental) Jess Willard, Arline Pretty
One Sheet: $200 - $400   *Sports Movie Posters #354.*

CHALLENGE OF THE RANGE
(1949 - Columbia) Charles Starrett, Smiley Burnette
One Sheet: $30 - $50

CHALLENGE THE WILD
(1954 - United Artists) Sheilah & George Graham
One Sheet: $15 - $25

CHALLENGE TO BE FREE
(1974 - Pacific International) Mike Mazurki, Jimmy Kane
One Sheet: $5 - $10

CHALLENGE TO LASSIE
(1949 - MGM) Edmund Gwenn, Donald Crisp, Lassie
One Sheet: $75 - $150

CHAMBER, THE
(1996 - Universal) Chris O'Donnell, Gene Hackman
One Sheet: $5 - $10

CHAMBER OF HORRORS
(1966 - Warner Bros.) Cesare Danova, Laura Devon
One Sheet: $30 - $50

CHAMP, THE
(1931 - MGM) Wallace Beery, Jackie Cooper
One Sheet: $700 - $1,200   *Sports (Boxing). Academy Award Movie Posters #25. Sports Movie Posters #s 127, 129.*

CHAMP, THE
(1954R - MGM) Wallace Beery, Jackie Cooper
One Sheet: $40 - $75   *Re-release. Sports (Boxing).*

CHAMP, THE
(1979 - MGM) Ricky Schroder, Jon Voight, Faye Dunaway
One Sheet: $5 - $10   *Sports (Boxing).*

CHAMP FOR A DAY
(1953 - Republic) Alex Nicol, Audrey Totter, Charles Winninger
One Sheet: $30 - $50

CHAMPAGNE
(1928 - British International) Betty Balfour, Jean Bradin, Dir: Alfred Hitchcock
One Sheet: $3,500 - $5,000

CHAMPAGNE CHARLIE
(1936 - 20th Century Fox) Paul Cavanaugh, Minna Gombell
One Sheet: $125 - $250

CHAMPAGNE CHARLIE

(1944 - Universal) Tommy Trinder, Stanley Holloway
One Sheet: $50 - $100

CHAMPAGNE FOR BREAKFAST
(1935 - Columbia) Mary Carlisle, Hardie Albright
One Sheet: $75 - $150

CHAMPAGNE FOR CAESAR
(1950 - United Artists) Ronald Colman, Celeste Holm
One Sheet: $50 - $100

CHAMPAGNE MURDERS, THE
(1968 - Universal) Anthony Perkins, Maurice Ronet
One Sheet: $7 - $15

CHAMPAGNE MUSIC OF LAWRENCE WELK, THE
(1939 - Paramount) Lawrence Welk, Lois Best
One Sheet: $200 - $400   *Big band musical.*

CHAMPAGNE SAFARI
(1953 - Jackson Leighter Associates) -
One Sheet: $15 - $25

CHAMPAGNE WALTZ
(1937 - Paramount) Gladys Swarthout, Fred MacMurray
One Sheet: $75 - $150

CHAMPEEN, THE
(1923 - Pathe) Our Gang
One Sheet: $1,300 - $2,000   *Separate Cinema, pg. 114.*

CHAMPION, THE
(1915 - Essanay) Charlie Chaplin, Edna Purviance
One Sheet: $7,500 - $12,000

CHAMPION, THE
(1921R - Kremer) Charlie Chaplin, Edna Purviance
One Sheet: $350 - $750   *Re-release.*

CHAMPION
(1949 - United Artists) Kirk Douglas, Marilyn Maxwell
One Sheet: $50 - $100

CHAMPION OF LOST CAUSES
(1925 - Fox) Edmund Lowe, Barbara Bedford
One Sheet: $250 - $500

CHAN IS MISSING
(1982 - New Yorker) Wood Moy, Marc Hayashi
One Sheet: $7 - $15

CHANCE AT HEAVEN
(1933 - RKO) Ginger Rogers, Joel McCrea, Andy Devine
One Sheet: $250 - $600

CHANCE MEETING
(1954 - Pacemaker) David Knight, Odile Versois
One Sheet: $15 - $25

CHANCE MEETING
(1960 - Paramount) Hardy Kruger, Micheline Presle
One Sheet: $7 - $15

CHANCE OF A LIFETIME, THE
(1943 - Columbia) Chester Morris, Jeanne Bates
One Sheet: $50 - $100

CHANCE OF A LIFETIME, THE
(1950 - Pilgrim) Bernard Miles, Basil Rathbone
One Sheet: $20 - $40

CHANCES
(1931 - First National) Douglas Fairbanks Jr., Rose Hobart
One Sheet: $200 - $400

CHANCES ARE
(1989 - -) Cybill Shepherd, Robert Downey, Jr.
One Sheet: $5 - $10

CHANDLER
(1971 - MGM) Warren Oates, Leslie Caron
One Sheet: $7 - $15

CHANDU THE MAGICIAN
(1932 - Fox) Edmund Lowe, Bela Lugosi
One Sheet: $1,600 - $2,500   *Graven Images, pg. 59.*

CHANEL SOLITAIRE
(1981 - United Film) Marie-France Pisier, Timothy Dalton, Rutger Hauer
One Sheet: $5 - $10

CHANG
(1927 - Paramount) -
One Sheet: $500 - $900

CHANGE IN THE WIND, A
(1972 - Cinerama) William Devane, Anne Meara
One Sheet: $3 - $5

CHANGE OF HABIT
(1969 - Universal) Elvis Presley, Mary Tyler Moore
One Sheet: $30 - $50

One Sheet

CHANGE OF HEART
(1934 - Fox) Janet Gaynor, Charles Farrell
One Sheet: $250 - $500

CHANGE OF HEART
(1938 - 20th Century Fox) Gloria Stuart, Michael Whalen
One Sheet: $100 - $200

CHANGE OF HEART
(1943 - Republic) Susan Hayward, John Carroll, Count Basie & Orchestra
One Sheet: $75 - $150

CHANGE OF MIND
(1969 - Cinerama) Raymond St. Jacques, Susan Oliver, Leslie Nielson
One Sheet: $5 - $10   *Blaxploitation. "Black Body, White Brain—World's First Brain Transplant!"*

CHANGE OF SEASONS, A
(1980 - 20th Century Fox) Shirley MacLaine, Anthony Hopkins
One Sheet: $5 - $10

CHANGELING, THE
(1980 - Associated) George C. Scott, Trish van Devere
One Sheet: $5 - $10

CHANGES
(1969 - Cinerama) Kent Lane, Michele Carey, Manuela Hiess
One Sheet: $5 - $10

CHAPLIN
(1992 - TriStar) Robert Downey, Jr., Dan Aykroyd
One Sheet: $7 - $15

CHAPLIN REVUE
(1958 - -) Charlie Chaplin compilation
One Sheet: $30 - $50   *Narrated by Chaplin.*

CHAPLIN'S ART OF COMEDY
(1966 - -) Charlie Chaplin
One Sheet: $20 - $40

CHAPMAN REPORT, THE
(1962 - Warner Bros.) Jane Fonda, Efrem Zimbalist Jr.
One Sheet: $15 - $35

CHAPPAQUA
(1967 - Regional) Jean-Louis Barrault, Conrad Rook
One Sheet: $5 - $10

CHAPTER TWO
(1979 - Columbia) James Caan, Marsha Mason
One Sheet: $3 - $5

CHARADE
(1963 - Universal) Cary Grant, Audrey Hepburn
One Sheet: $100 - $200 *One Sheet*
(duotone Parent's Magazine style):$20-$30.

CHARADE/FATHER GOOSE
(1968R - Universal) Cary Grant, Audrey Hepburn, Leslie Caron
One Sheet: $30 - $50 *Re-release double feature poster.*

CHARGE AT FEATHER RIVER, THE
(1953 - Warner Bros.) Guy Madison, Frank Lovejoy
One Sheet: $50 - $100 *3-D.*

CHARGE OF THE LANCERS, THE
(1953 - Columbia) Jean Pierre Aumont, Paulette Goddard
One Sheet: $20 - $40

CHARGE OF THE LIGHT BRIGADE, THE
(1912 - Edison) -
One Sheet: $1,600 - $2,500

CHARGE OF THE LIGHT BRIGADE, THE
(1936 - Warner Bros.) Errol Flynn, Olivia de Havilland
One Sheet: $1,300 - $2,000

One Sheet

CHARGE OF THE LIGHT BRIGADE, THE
(1968 - United Artists) Trevor Howard, Vanessa Redgrave, John Gielgud
One Sheet: $10 - $20

CHARIOTS OF FIRE
(1981 - 20th Century Fox) Ben Cross, Ian Charleson
One Sheet: $10 - $20 *Academy Award: Best Picture. Sports (Marathon running). Academy Award Movie Posters #316. Sports Movie Posters #288.*

CHARIOTS OF THE GODS
(1972 - Sun International) Documentary based on Von Daniken's book
One Sheet: $5 - $10

CHARLEY AND THE ANGEL
(1972 - Buena Vista) Fred MacMurray, Cloris Leachman
One Sheet: $7 - $15

CHARLEY ONE-EYE
(1973 - Paramount) Richard Roundtree, Roy Thinnes
One Sheet: $5 - $10

CHARLEY VARRICK
(1973 - Universal) Walter Matthau, Joe Don Baker
One Sheet: $5 - $10

CHARLEY'S AUNT
(1925 - Producers Distributing) Syd Chaplin, Ethel Shannon
One Sheet: $200 - $400

CHARLEY'S AUNT
(1930 - Columbia) Charlie Ruggles, June Collyer
One Sheet: $125 - $250

CHARLEY'S AUNT
(1941 - 20th Century Fox) Jack Benny, Kay Francis
One Sheet: $100 - $200

CHARLIE BUBBLES
(1968 - Regional) Albert Finney, Liza Minnelli
One Sheet: $5 - $10

CHARLIE CHAN AND THE CURSE OF THE

DRAGON QUEEN
(1981 - American Cinema) Peter Ustinov, Lee Grant, Angie Dickinson
One Sheet: $7 - $15

CHARLIE CHAN AT MONTE CARLO
(1938 - 20th Century Fox) Warner Oland, Keye Luke, Virginia Field
One Sheet: $600 - $1,000

CHARLIE CHAN AT THE CIRCUS
(1936 - 20th Century Fox) Warner Oland, Keye Luke, Francis Ford
One Sheet: $1,700 - $2,800

CHARLIE CHAN AT THE OLYMPICS
(1937 - 20th Century Fox) Warner Oland, Keye Luke, Katherine DeMille
One Sheet: $500 - $900

CHARLIE CHAN AT THE OPERA
(1937 - 20th Century Fox) Warner Oland, Boris Karloff
One Sheet: $1,300 - $2,000 *Graven Images, pg. 86.*

CHARLIE CHAN AT THE RACE TRACK
(1936 - 20th Century Fox) Warner Oland, Keye Luke, Helen Wood
One Sheet: $800 - $1,500

CHARLIE CHAN AT THE WAX MUSEUM
(1940 - 20th Century Fox) Sidney Toler, Sen Young, C. Henry Gordon
One Sheet: $250 - $500

CHARLIE CHAN AT TREASURE ISLAND
(1939 - 20th Century Fox) Sidney Toler, Cesar Romero
One Sheet: $200 - $400

One Sheet

CHARLIE CHAN CARRIES ON
(1931 - Fox) Warner Oland (his 1st as Chan), Joan Garrick
One Sheet: $1,900 - $3,000

CHARLIE CHAN IN CITY OF DARKNESS
(1939 - 20th Century Fox) Sidney Toler, Lynn Bari
One Sheet: $200 - $400

CHARLIE CHAN IN EGYPT
(1935 - Fox) Warner Oland, Pat Paterson, Rita Cansino (Hayworth)
One Sheet: $600 - $1,000

CHARLIE CHAN IN HONOLULU
(1938 - 20th Century Fox) Sidney Toler, Phyllis Brooks
One Sheet: $200 - $400

CHARLIE CHAN IN LONDON
(1934 - Fox) Warner Oland, Ray Milland
One Sheet: $600 - $1,000

CHARLIE CHAN IN PANAMA
(1940 - 20th Century Fox) Sidney Toler, Jean Rogers
One Sheet: $200 - $400

CHARLIE CHAN IN PARIS
(1935 - Fox) Warner Oland, Mary Brian
One Sheet: $600 - $1,000

CHARLIE CHAN IN RENO
(1939 - 20th Century Fox) Sidney Toler, Ricardo Cortez
One Sheet: $200 - $400

CHARLIE CHAN IN RIO
(1941 - 20th Century Fox) Sidney Toler, Mary Beth Hughes
One Sheet: $150 - $300

CHARLIE CHAN IN SHANGHAI
(1935 - 20th Century Fox) Warner Oland, Irene Hervey
One Sheet: $600 - $1,000

CHARLIE CHAN IN THE SECRET SERVICE
(1944 - Monogram) Sidney Toler, Gwen Kenyon, Mantan Moreland
One Sheet: $100 - $200

CHARLIE CHAN ON BROADWAY
(1937 - 20th Century Fox) Warner Oland, Keye Luke, Joan Marsh
One Sheet: $600 - $1,100

CHARLIE CHAN'S CHANCE
(1931 - Fox) Warner Oland, Linda Watkins
One Sheet: $1,300 - $2,000

CHARLIE CHAN'S COURAGE
(1934 - Fox) Warner Oland, Donald Woods
One Sheet: $600 - $1,000

CHARLIE CHAN'S GREATEST CASE
(1933 - Fox) Warner Oland, Heather Angel
One Sheet: $1,300 - $2,000

CHARLIE CHAN'S MURDER CRUISE
(1940 - 20th Century Fox) Sidney Toler, Sen Yung, Marjorie Weaver
One Sheet: $150 - $300

CHARLIE CHAN'S SECRET
(1936 - 20th Century Fox) Warner Oland, Rosina Lawrence
One Sheet: $600 - $1,000

CHARLIE CHAPLIN CARNIVAL
(1960S - Guaranteed) Chaplin compilation
One Sheet: $10 - $20

CHARLIE CHAPLIN CAVALCADE, THE
(1960S - Guaranteed) Chaplin compilation
One Sheet: $10 - $20 *Feature film comprised of six early Chaplin shorts.*

One Sheet

CHARLIE CHAPLIN FESTIVAL
(1960S - Guaranteed) Chaplin compilation
One Sheet: $10 - $20 *Feature film comprised of six early Chaplin shorts.*

One Sheet

CHARLIE MCCARTHY, DETECTIVE
(1939 - Universal) Edgar Bergen, Charlie McCarthy, Mortimer Snerd
One Sheet: $600 - $1,000

CHARLIE ONE-EYE
(1973 - Paramount) Richard Roundtree, Roy Thimes
One Sheet: $7 - $15

CHARLIE THE LONESOME COUGAR
(1967 - Buena Vista/Disney) Ron Brown, Brian Russell
One Sheet: $15 - $25

CHARLIE'S ABENTEUER
(1928 - Humboldt) Charlie Chaplin
One Sheet: $600 - $1,100 *German.*

CHARLOTTE
(1975 - -) -
One Sheet: $5 - $10

CHARLOTTE'S WEB
(1973 - Paramount) -
One Sheet: $15 - $25 *Cartoon.*

CHARLY
(1968 - Cinema Releasing) Cliff Robertson, Claire Bloom
One Sheet: $15 - $30 *Academy Award: Best Actor (Robertson). Academy Award Movie Posters #247.*

CHARM SCHOOL, THE
(1920 - Paramount) Wallace Reed
One Sheet: $500 - $800

CHARMING SINNERS
(1929 - Paramount) Clive Brook, Ruth Chatterton, William Powell
One Sheet: $800 - $1,500

CHARRO
(1969 - National General) Elvis Presley, Ina Balin
One Sheet: $30 - $50

CHARTER PILOT
(1940 - 20th Century Fox) Lloyd Nolan, Lynn Bari
One Sheet: $50 - $100

CHARTROOSE CABOOSE
(1960 - Universal) Molly Bee, Ben Cooper
One Sheet: $15 - $25

CHASE, THE
(1946 - Nero) Robert Cummings, Michele Morgan, Peter Lorre
One Sheet: $50 - $100

CHASE, THE
(1966 - Columbia) Marlon Brando, Jane Fonda, Robert Redford
One Sheet: $30 - $60

CHASE A CROOKED SHADOW
(1957 - Warner Bros.) Richard Todd, Anne Baxter
One Sheet: $15 - $30

CHASE ME, CHARLIE
(1948 - Capital) Charlie Chaplin, Edna Purviance, Leo White
One Sheet: $75 - $150

CHASER, THE
(1938 - MGM) Dennis O'Keefe, Ann Morris
One Sheet: $75 - $150

CHASING AMY
(1997 - Miramax) Ben Affleck, Joey Adams, Jason Lee
One Sheet: $4 - $8

CHASING DANGER
(1939 - 20th Century Fox) Preston Foster, Lynn Bari
One Sheet: $50 - $100

CHASING RAINBOWS
(1930 - MGM) Bessie Love, Charles King
One Sheet: $200 - $400

CHASING TROUBLE
(1926 - Universal) Pete Morrison, Ione Reed
One Sheet: $100 - $200

CHASING TROUBLE
(1940 - Monogram) Frankie Darro, Marjorie Reynolds
One Sheet: $40 - $75

CHASING YESTERDAY
(1935 - RKO) Anne Shirley, Helen Westley
One Sheet: $125 - $250

CHASTITY
(1969 - AIP) Cher, Barbara London
One Sheet: $30 - $50 *Cher's film debut.*

CHATO'S LAND
(1972 - United Artists) Charles Bronson, Jack Palance
One Sheet: $15 - $25

CHATTAHOOCHEE
(1990 - Hemdale) Dennis Hopper, Frances McDormand
One Sheet: $5 - $10

CHATTANOOGA CHOO CHOO
(1984 - April Fools Release) Barbara Eden, George Kennedy
One Sheet: $5 - $10

One Sheet

CHATTERBOX
(1936 - RKO) Lucille Ball, Anne Shirley
One Sheet: $250 - $500

CHATTERBOX
(1943 - Republic) Joe E. Brown, Judy Canova, The Mills Bros.
One Sheet: $50 - $100   *Mills Bros. featured on most posters.*

CHATTERBOX
(1976 - Lips) Candice Rialson, Larry Gelman
One Sheet: $5 - $10

CHE!
(1969 - 20th Century Fox) Omar Sharif, Jack Palance
One Sheet: $7 - $15

CHE COMANDATE AMIGO
(1978 - Hernandez) Dir: Bernabe Hernandez
One Sheet: $250 - $600   *Price is for Cuban 20"x30" poster.*

CHEAP DETECTIVE, THE
(1978 - Columbia) Peter Falk, Ann-Margret
One Sheet: $7 - $15

CHEAPER BY THE DOZEN
(1950 - 20th Century Fox) Jeanne Crain, Clifton Webb, Myrna Loy
One Sheet: $30 - $50

CHEAPER TO KEEP HER
(1980 - American Cinema) Mac Davis, Priscilla Lopez
One Sheet: $3 - $5

CHEAT, THE
(1923 - Paramount) Pola Negri, Jack Holt
One Sheet: $700 - $1,200

CHEAT, THE
(1931 - Paramount) Tallulah Bankhead, Irving Pichel
One Sheet: $500 - $800

CHEATER, THE
(1920 - Metro) May Allison, Rudolph Valentino (unbilled)
One Sheet: $250 - $500   *Valentino appears on the half sheet.*

CHEATERS
(1934 - Liberty) Bill Boyd, Dorothy Mackaill
One Sheet: $100 - $200

CHEATERS, THE
(1945 - Republic) Joseph Schildkraut, Billie Burke
One Sheet: $50 - $100

CHEATERS AT PLAY
(1932 - Fox) Thomas Meighan, Charlotte Greenwood
One Sheet: $150 - $300

CHEATING BLONDES

(1933 - Equitable) Thelma Todd
One Sheet: $200 - $400

CHEATING CHEATER
(1934 - Universal) Cesar Romero
One Sheet: $250 - $500

CHEATING CHEATERS
(1927 - Universal) Kenneth Harlan, Betty Compson, Fay Wray
One Sheet: $200 - $400

CHEATING CHEATERS
(1934 - Universal) Fay Wray, Cesar Romero
One Sheet: $150 - $350

CHECK AND DOUBLE CHECK
(1930 - RKO) Amos and Andy
One Sheet: $3,500 - $5,000   *Team's only film.*

CHECK YOUR GUNS
(1948 - Pathe Industries) Eddie Dean, Roscoe Ates
One Sheet: $30 - $50

CHECKERED COAT, THE
(1948 - 20th Century Fox) Tom Conway, Noreen Nash
One Sheet: $30 - $50

CHECKERED FLAG OR CRASH
(1977 - Universal) Joe Don Baker, Susan Sarandon
One Sheet: $10 - $20   *Sports (Auto racing).*

CHECKERS
(1938 - 20th Century Fox) Jane Withers, Stuart Erwin
One Sheet: $75 - $150

CHECK-MATE
(1953 - Princess) -
One Sheet: $30 - $50

CHECKPOINT
(1957 - Rank) Anthony Steel, Odile Versois
One Sheet: $30 - $60   *Sports (Auto racing).*

CHEECH & CHONG'S NEXT MOVIE
(1980 - Universal) Cheech & Chong
One Sheet: $7 - $15

CHEECH & CHONG'S THE CORSICAN BROTHERS
(1984 - Orion) Cheech & Chong
One Sheet: $5 - $10

CHEECH AND CHONG'S NICE DREAMS
(1981 - -) Cheech Marin, Tommy Chong, Pee-Wee Herman
One Sheet: $5 - $10

CHEECH AND CHONG'S UP IN SMOKE
(1978 - Paramount) Cheech Marin, Tommy Chong
One Sheet: $10 - $20

CHEER UP AND SMILE
(1930 - Fox) Dixie Lee, Arthur Lake
One Sheet: $150 - $300

CHEERLEADERS, THE
(1972 - Glickler) Stephanie Fondue, Denise Dillaway
One Sheet: $5 - $10

CHEERS FOR MISS BISHOP
(1941 - United Artists) Martha Scott, William Gargan
One Sheet: $50 - $100

CHEERS OF THE CROWD
(1935 - Monogram) Russell Hopton
One Sheet: $125 - $250

CHEETAH
(1993 - Disney) -
One Sheet: $5 - $10

CHEROKEE FLASH
(1945 - Republic) Sunset Carson, Linda Stirling
One Sheet: $40 - $75

CHEROKEE STRIP
(1937 - Warner Bros.) Dick Foran
One Sheet: $75 - $150

CHEROKEE STRIP
(1940 - Paramount) Richard Dix, Florence Rice
One Sheet: $75 - $150

CHEROKEE UPRISING
(1950 - Monogram) Whip Wilson, Andy Clyde
One Sheet: $30 - $50

CHERRY 2000
(1988 - Orion) Melanie Griffith, Ben Johnson, Harry Carey, Jr.
One Sheet: $10 - $20

CHERRY, HARRY & RAQUEL
(1969 - Eve) Linda Ashton, Charles Napier, Dir: Russ Meyer
One Sheet: $20 - $40   *Sexploitation.*

CHETNIKS
(1942 - 20th Century Fox) Philip Dorn, Anna Sten
One Sheet: $50 - $100

CHEYENNE
(1929 - First National) Ken Maynard
One Sheet: $250 - $600

CHEYENNE
(1947 - Warner Bros.) Dennis Morgan, Jane Wyman
One Sheet: $40 - $75

CHEYENNE AUTUMN
(1964 - Warner Bros.) Richard Widmark, Caroll Baker
One Sheet: $30 - $50

CHEYENNE COWBOY
(1948 - Universal) Tex Williams
One Sheet: $30 - $50

CHEYENNE CYCLONE, THE
(1932 - Kent) Lane Chandler
One Sheet: $100 - $200

CHEYENNE KID
(1933 - RKO) Tom Keene
One Sheet: $125 - $250

CHEYENNE KID
(1940 - Monogram) Jack Randall, Louise Stanley
One Sheet: $50 - $100

CHEYENNE RIDES AGAIN
(1937 - Victory) Tom Tyler
One Sheet: $150 - $300

CHEYENNE ROUNDUP
(1942 - Universal) Johnny Mack Brown, Tex Ritter
One Sheet: $75 - $150

CHEYENNE SOCIAL CLUB
(1970 - National General) James Stewart, Henry Fonda, Shirley Jones
One Sheet: $10 - $20

CHEYENNE TAKES OVER
(1947 - PRC) "Lash" LaRue, "Fuzzy" St. John
One Sheet: $40 - $75

CHEYENNE WILDCAT
(1944 - Republic) Bill Elliott, Bobby Blake
One Sheet: $40 - $75

CHICAGO AFTER DARK
(1946 - All American) Lollypop Jones
One Sheet: $150 - $300   *Black cast. Separate Cinema, pg. 135.*

CHICAGO CALLING
(1951 - United Artists) Dan Duryea, Mary Anderson
One Sheet: $20 - $40

CHICAGO CONFIDENTIAL
(1957 - United Artists) Brian Keith, Beverly Garland
One Sheet: $30 - $50

CHICAGO DEADLINE
(1949 - Paramount) Alan Ladd, Donna Reed
One Sheet: $50 - $100

CHICAGO JOE AND THE SHOWGIRL
(1990 - -) Kieffer Sutherland
One Sheet: $5 - $10

CHICAGO KID, THE
(1945 - Republic) Don "Red" Barry, Otto Kruger, Lynne Roberts
One Sheet: $50 - $100

CHICAGO SYNDICATE
(1955 - Columbia) Dennis O'Keefe, Abbe Lane
One Sheet: $30 - $50

CHICK CARTER, DETECTIVE
(1946 - Columbia) Lyle Talbot, Douglas Fowley
One Sheet: $75 - $150   *Serial. 15 Chapters.*

CHICKASHA BONE CRUSHER, THE
(1923 - -) See THE LEATHER PUSHERS (SERIAL) Chapter 9.

CHICKEN CHRONICLES, THE
(1977 - Avco) Phil Silvers, Steven Guttenberg
One Sheet: $3 - $5

CHICKEN EVERY SUNDAY
(1949 - 20th Century Fox) Dan Dailey, Celeste Holm, Natalie Wood
One Sheet: $75 - $150

CHICKEN FEED
(1927 - Pathe) Our Gang
One Sheet: $800 - $1,500

Title Card

CHICKEN LITTLE
(1943 - RKO/Disney) Chicken Little
One Sheet: $1,300 - $2,000   *Cartoon. Cartoon Movie Posters #197.*

CHICKEN WAGON FAMILY
(1939 - 20th Century Fox) Jane Withers, Leo Carrillo
One Sheet: $100 - $200

CHICKENS
(1921 - Paramount) Douglas MacLean, Gladys George
One Sheet: $100 - $200

CHICKENS COME HOME
(1930 - MGM) Laurel & Hardy, Mae Busch, Thelma Todd
One Sheet: $3,500 - $5,000

CHIEF, THE
(1933 - MGM) Ed Wynn, Bill (Stage) Boyd
One Sheet: $250 - $500

CHIEF CRAZY HORSE
(1955 - Universal) Victor Mature, Susan Ball
One Sheet: $15 - $30

CHILD BRIDE
(1933 - Mack Enterprises) -
One Sheet: $125 - $250   *Exploitation.*

CHILD FOR SALE, A
(1920 - Graphic) Gladys Leslie, Creighton Hale
One Sheet: $100 - $200

CHILD IS BORN, A
(1939 - Warner Bros.) Geraldine Fitzgerald, Jeffrey Lynn
One Sheet: $75 - $150

CHILD IS WAITING, A
(1963 - United Artists) Burt Lancaster, Judy Garland
One Sheet: $30 - $50

CHILD OF DIVORCE
(1946 - RKO) Sharyn Moffett, Regis Toomey
One Sheet: $50 - $100

CHILD OF MANHATTAN
(1933 - Columbia) Nancy Carroll, John Boles
One Sheet: $250 - $500

CHILD'S PLAY
(1954 - British Lion) Mona Washbourne
One Sheet: $15 - $25

CHILD'S PLAY
(1972 - Paramount) Robert Preston, Beau

Bridges, James Mason
One Sheet: $5 - $10

CHILD'S PLAY
(1988 - -) Alex Vincent, Catherine Hicks, Chris Sarandon
One Sheet: $5 - $10

CHILD'S PLAY 2
(1990 - Universal) Alex Vincent, Jenny Agutter
One Sheet: $3 - $5

CHILD'S PLAY 3
(1991 - Universal) Justin Whalin, Brad Dourif
One Sheet: $3 - $5

CHILDISH THINGS
(1969 - Filmworld) Don Murray, Linda Evans
One Sheet: $5 - $10

CHILDREN, THE
(1980 - World) Martin Shaker, Gil Rogers
One Sheet: $3 - $5

CHILDREN NOT WANTED
(1920 - Republic) Edith Day, Ruth Sullivan
One Sheet: $250 - $500

CHILDREN OF A LESSER GOD
(1986 - Paramount) Marlee Matlin, William Hurt, Piper Laurie
One Sheet: $10 - $20   *Academy Award: Best Actress(Matlin). Academy Award Movie Posters #350.*

CHILDREN OF DIVORCE
(1927 - -) Clara Bow
One Sheet: $800 - $1,500

CHILDREN OF DREAMS
(1931 - Warner Bros.) Margaret Schilling, Paul Gregory
One Sheet: $150 - $300

CHILDREN OF JAZZ
(1923 - Famous Players-Lasky) Eileen Percy, Theodore Kosloff
One Sheet: $200 - $400

CHILDREN OF LONELINESS
(1934 - Jewel) -
One Sheet: $75 - $150

CHILDREN OF PARADISE
(1945 - Pathe) Arletty, Jean-Louis Barrault
One Sheet: $1,300 - $2,000   *French. Considered by many as the greatest French film ever made. Price is for the original French(47x63"). French(63x94):$2500-4000. One Sheet(U.S.A., exist?)*

CHILDREN OF PLEASURE
(1930 - MGM) Lawrence Gray, Helen Johnson
One Sheet: $200 - $400

CHILDREN OF SANCHEZ, THE
(1978 - Lone Star) Anthony Quinn, Delores Del Rio
One Sheet: $3 - $5

One Sheet

CHILDREN OF THE CORN
(1983 - New World) Peter Horton, Linda Hamilton
One Sheet: $10 - $20   *Advance Style:$10-15.*

CHILDREN OF THE CORN II
(1992 - Paramount) Terence Knox
One Sheet: $3 - $5

CHILDREN OF THE DAMNED
(1964 - MGM) Ian Hendry, Alan Badel
One Sheet: $30 - $60

CHILDREN OF THE FEUD
(1916 - Vitagraph) Dorothy Gish, Charles Gorman
One Sheet: $200 - $400

CHILDREN OF THE NIGHT
(1921 - Fox) William Russell, Ruth Renick
One Sheet: $250 - $600

CHILDREN OF THE REVOLUTION
(1996 - Miramax) Judy Davis, Sam Neill, F. Murray Abraham
One Sheet: $5 - $10

CHILDREN OF THE RITZ
(1929 - First National) Dorothy Mackaill, Jack Mulhall, James Ford
One Sheet: $200 - $400

CHILDREN OF THE SUN
(1934 - Jewel) -
One Sheet: $75 - $150

CHILDREN SHOULDN'T PLAY WITH DEAD THINGS
(1972 - Genini) Alan Ormsby, Jane Daly
One Sheet: $30 - $60

CHILDREN'S HOUR, THE
(1962 - United Artists) Audrey Hepburn, Shirley MacLaine
One Sheet: $40 - $75

CHIMES AT MIDNIGHT
(1967 - Internacional) Orson Welles, Jeanne Moreau
One Sheet: $40 - $75

CHIMP, THE
(1932 - MGM) Laurel & Hardy
One Sheet: $1,300 - $2,000

CHINA
(1943 - Paramount) Alan Ladd, Loretta Young
One Sheet: $150 - $300

CHINA & SILK
(1983 - -) -
One Sheet: $10 - $20   *XXX.*

CHINA CLIPPER
(1936 - Warner Bros.) Pat O'Brien, Beverly Roberts, Humphrey Bogart
One Sheet: $350 - $750

CHINA CORSAIR
(1951 - Columbia) Jon Hall, Lisa Ferraday
One Sheet: $15 - $35

CHINA DOLL
(1958 - United Artists) Victor Mature, Li Li Hua
One Sheet: $30 - $50

CHINA GATE
(1957 - 20th Century Fox) Nat King Cole, Gene Barry
One Sheet: $75 - $125

CHINA GIRL
(1943 - 20th Century Fox) Gene Tierney, Lynn Bari
One Sheet: $300 - $700

One Sheet

CHINA PASSAGE
(1937 - RKO) Constance Worth, Vinton Hayworth
One Sheet: $75 - $150

CHINA SEAS
(1935 - MGM) Clark Gable, Jean Harlow, Wallace Beery
One Sheet: $1,300 - $2,000

CHINA SKY
(1945 - RKO) Randolph Scott, Ruth Warrick
One Sheet: $40 - $75

CHINA SYNDROME
(1979 - Columbia) Jane Fonda, Michael Douglas
One Sheet: $10 - $20

CHINA VENTURE
(1953 - Columbia) Edmond O'Brien, Barry Sullivan, Jocelyn Brando
One Sheet: $20 - $40

CHINA'S LITTLE DEVILS
(1945 - Monogram) Harry Carey, Paul Kelly
One Sheet: $30 - $50

CHINATOWN
(1974 - Paramount) Jack Nicholson, Faye Dunaway, Dir: Roman Polanski
One Sheet: $100 - $200   *40x60: $250-$500.*

One Sheet

CHINATOWN AT MIDNIGHT
(1949 - Columbia) Hurd Hatfield, Jean Willes
One Sheet: $50 - $100

CHINATOWN CHARLIE
(1928 - First National) Johnny Hines, Louise Lorraine
One Sheet: $200 - $400

CHINATOWN NIGHTS
(1929 - Paramount) Wallace Beery, Florence Vidor, Warner Oland
One Sheet: $800 - $1,500

CHINATOWN SQUAD
(1935 - Universal) Lyle Talbot, Andy Devine
One Sheet: $200 - $400

CHINESE CAT, THE
(1944 - Monogram) Sidney Toler, Joan Woodbury
One Sheet: $150 - $300   *Charlie Chan series.*

CHINESE CONNECTION, THE
(1973 - National General) Bruce Lee, James Tien
One Sheet: $75 - $150   *Sports Movie Posters #261.*

CHINESE GODFATHER
(1974 - -) Chan Wei-Min, Wu Chin, Cheng Lei
One Sheet: $15 - $35   *Martial arts.*

CHINESE RING, THE
(1947 - Monogram) Roland Winters, Mantan Moreland, Warren Douglas
One Sheet: $100 - $200   *Charlie Chan series.*

CHINO
(1976 - Intercontinental) Charles Bronson, Jill Ireland
One Sheet: $10 - $20   *Cowboy Movie Posters #337.*

CHIP OF THE FLYING U
(1939 - Universal) Johnny Mack Brown, Bob Baker
One Sheet: $75 - $150

CHIP OFF THE OLD BLOCK
(1944 - Universal) Donald O'Connor, Peggy Ryan
One Sheet: $50 - $100

CHIPMUNK'S ADVENTURE, THE
(1987 - Goldwyn) Alvin, Theodore & Simon

One Sheet: $5 - $10   *Cartoon.*

CHIPS AHOY
(1956 - RKO/Disney) Donald Duck, Chip & Dale
One Sheet: $250 - $600   *Cartoon. Full color.*

CHIPS OFF THE OLD BLOCK
(1942 - MGM) -
One Sheet: $150 - $300   *Cartoon. Cartoon Movie Posters #248.*

CHISELERS OF HOLLYWOOD
(1930 - Willis Kent) -
One Sheet: $75 - $150

CHISUM
(1970 - Warner Bros.) John Wayne
One Sheet: $50 - $100

CHITTY CHITTY BANG BANG
(1968 - United Artists) Dick Van Dyke, Sally Ann Howes, Lionel Jeffries
One Sheet: $20 - $40

CHLOE IN THE AFTERNOON
(1972 - Columbia) Bernard Verley, Zouzou
One Sheet: $5 - $10

CHOCOLATE COWBOY, A
(1925 - Cyclone) Fred Parker, Teddy Reavis
One Sheet: $600 - $1,000   *Black cast. Separate Cinema, pg. 6.*

CHOCOLATE SOLDIER
(1941 - MGM) Nelson Eddy, Rise Stevens
One Sheet: $150 - $300

CHOCOLATE SOLDIER
(1962R - MGM) Nelson Eddy, Rise Stevens
One Sheet: $10 - $20   *Re-release.*

CHOIRBOYS, THE
(1977 - Universal) James Woods, Charles Durning, Lou Gossett Jr.
One Sheet: $7 - $15

CHOKE CANYON
(1986 - -) Stephen Collins, Janet Julian
One Sheet: $3 - $5

C.H.O.M.P.S.
(1979 - AID) Wesley Eure, Valerie Bertinelli
One Sheet: $3 - $5

CHOOSE ME
(1984 - Island Alive) Genevieve Bujold, Keith Carradine
One Sheet: $3 - $5

CHOPPERS, THE
(1962 - Fairway-International) Arch Hall, Jr., Marianne Gaba
One Sheet: $10 - $20   *Sports (Drag-racing).*

CHOPPING MALL
(1986 - -) Kelli Maroney, Tony O'Dell
One Sheet: $3 - $5

CHORUS LINE, A
(1985 - Embassy) Michael Douglas, Terrance Mann, Alyson Reed
One Sheet: $7 - $15

CHOSEN, THE
(1978 - AIP) Kirk Douglas, Simon Ward
One Sheet: $5 - $10   *AKA: HOLOCAUST 2000.*

CHOSEN, THE
(1982 - Contemporary) Rod Steiger, Robby Benson
One Sheet: $5 - $10

CHOSEN SURVIVORS
(1974 - Columbia) Jackie Cooper, Alex Cord
One Sheet: $3 - $5

CHRIS AND THE WONDERFUL LAMP
(1917 - Conquest) -
One Sheet: $250 - $500

CHRIS COLUMBO
(1938 - 20th Century Fox) Terry-toons
One Sheet: $100 - $200   *Cartoon. Full color stone Litho. Stock poster with inset of title.*

CHRISTIAN LICORICE STORE, THE
(1971 - National General) Beau Bridges, Maud Adams
One Sheet: $5 - $10

CHRISTIANE F.

(1981 - 20th Century Fox) Natja Brunckhorst
One Sheet: $7 - $15   *German.*

CHRISTINE
(1983 - Columbia) Keith Gordon, John
Stockwell
One Sheet: $5 - $10   *Advance:$8-
15.*

CHRISTINE JORGENSON STORY, THE
(1970 - United Artists) John Hansen, Joan
Tompkins
One Sheet: $7 - $15

CHRISTMAS CAROL, A
(1938 - MGM) Reginald Owen, Gene Lockhart
One Sheet: $250 - $500

CHRISTMAS CAROL, A
(1951 - United Artists) Alistair Sim, Jack
Warner
One Sheet: $100 - $200

CHRISTMAS EVE
(1947 - Miracle) George Raft, George Brent,
Randolph Scott, Ann Harding
One Sheet: $75 - $125

CHRISTMAS HANDICAP, THE
(1924 - Universal-Jewel) Billy Sullivan
One Sheet: $150 - $300   *#4 in the Fast
Steppers series.*

CHRISTMAS HOLIDAY
(1944 - Universal) Deanna Durbin, Gene Kelly
One Sheet: $125 - $250

Mini Window Card

CHRISTMAS IN CONNECTICUT
(1945 - Warner Bros.) Barbara Stanwyck,
Dennis Morgan
One Sheet: $125 - $250

CHRISTMAS IN JULY
(1940 - Paramount) Dick Powell, Ellen Drew
One Sheet: $300 - $700

CHRISTMAS JOLLITIES
(1953 - RKO/Disney) -
One Sheet: $150 - $300   *Cartoon. Two-
color poster with new artwork. A collection of
cartoon shorts re-released as a feature.*

CHRISTMAS STORY, A
(1983 - MGM/United Artists) Peter Billingsly,
Darren McGavin, Melinda Dillon
One Sheet: $15 - $30   *Robert
Tannenbaum art.*

CHRISTMAS THAT ALMOST WASN'T, THE
(1966 - Childhood) Rossano Brazzi, Paul Tripp
One Sheet: $10 - $20

CHRISTMAS TREE, THE
(1969 - Continental) William Holden, Virna Lisi
One Sheet: $7 - $15

CHRISTOPHER BEAN
(1933 - MGM) Marie Dressler, Lionel
Barrymore
One Sheet: $200 - $400

CHRISTOPHER COLUMBUS
(1949 - Universal-International) Fredric March,
Florence Eldridge
One Sheet: $50 - $100

CHRISTOPHER COLUMBUS: THE DISCOVERY
(1992 - Warner Bros.) Marlon Brando, Tom
Selleck
One Sheet: $5 - $10

CHRISTOPHER CRUMPET
(1953 - Columbia) Jolly Frolics

One Sheet: $200 - $400   *Cartoon. First
appearance of Christopher Crumpet. Duotone.*

CHRISTOPHER STRONG
(1933 - RKO) Katharine Hepburn, Colin Clive
One Sheet: $1,900 - $3,000

CHROME AND HOT LEATHER
(1971 - AIP) William Smith, Tony Young
One Sheet: $15 - $30   *Biker film.*

CHRONOPOLIS
(1982 - -) -
One Sheet: $30 - $50   *French. Sci-fi.
3-D animation.*

CHUBASCO
(1968 - Warner Bros./Seven Arts) Richard
Egan, Susan Strasberg
One Sheet: $4 - $8

CHU-CHIN-CHOW
(1934 - Gaumont British) George Robey, Fritz
Kortner, Anna May Wong
One Sheet: $150 - $350

C.H.U.D.
(1984 - New World) John Heard, Daniel Stern,
Kim Greist
One Sheet: $5 - $10

CHUKA
(1967 - Paramount) Rod Taylor, Ernest
Borgnine
One Sheet: $5 - $10

CHUMP AT OXFORD, A
(1940 - United Artists) Stan Laurel, Oliver
Hardy
One Sheet: $500 - $800

CHUMP AT OXFORD, A
(1946R - United Artists) Stan Laurel, Oliver
Hardy
One Sheet: $100 - $200   *Re-release.*

CHUMP CHAMP, THE
(1950 - MGM) Droopy, Tex Avery
One Sheet: $500 - $900   *Cartoon. Full
color stone litho.*

CHUMP TAKES A BUMP
(1939 - Columbia) Charlie Chase
One Sheet: $50 - $100   *Comedy short.
Duotone.*

CHURCH, THE
(1991 - -) Hugh Quarshie, Tomas Arana
One Sheet: $3 - $5

CHURCHMOUSE, THE
(1934 - First National) Ian Hunter, Laura La
Plante
One Sheet: $100 - $200

CIAO! MANHATTAN
(1973 - -) John Phillips, Richie Hovens
One Sheet: $100 - $200   *Dutch.*

CIGARETTE GIRL
(1947 - Columbia) Leslie Brooks, Jimmy Lloyd
One Sheet: $75 - $125

CIMARRON
(1930 - RKO) Richard Dix, Irene Dunne
One Sheet: $6,500 - $10,000   *Academy
Award: Best Picture. Academy Award Movie
Posters #19. Cowboy Movie Posters #'s 81,82.*

CIMARRON
(1960 - MGM) Glenn Ford, Anne Baxter
One Sheet: $30 - $50

CIMARRON KID, THE
(1951 - Universal) Audie Murphy, Beverly Tyler
One Sheet: $40 - $75

CINCINNATI KID, THE
(1965 - MGM) Steve McQueen, Edward G.
Robinson
One Sheet: $40 - $75

CINDERELLA
(1950 - RKO/Disney) -
One Sheet: $250 - $600   *Cartoon.
Cartoon Movie Posters #380.*

CINDERELLA
(1957R - RKO/Disney) -
One Sheet: $40 - $75   *Re-release.
Cartoon.*

CINDERELLA
(1966 - Childhood) Paul Tripp (not a cartoon)

One Sheet: $5 - $10

CINDERELLA
(1966R - Disney) -
One Sheet: $30 - $50   *Re-release.
Cartoon.*

CINDERELLA
(1971R - Disney) -
One Sheet: $20 - $45   *Re-release.
Cartoon.*

CINDERELLA
(1973R - Buena Vista/Disney) -
One Sheet: $20 - $40   *Re-release.
Cartoon. Full color.*

CINDERELLA
(1981R - Disney) -
One Sheet: $15 - $30   *Re-release.
Cartoon.*

CINDERELLA
(1987R - Disney) -
One Sheet: $10 - $20   *Re-release.
Cartoon.*

CINDERELLA JONES
(1946 - Warner Bros.) Joan Leslie, Robert Alda
One Sheet: $50 - $100

CINDERELLA LIBERTY
(1974 - 20th Century Fox) James Caan,
Marsha Mason
One Sheet: $5 - $10

CINDERELLA SWINGS IT
(1943 - Pyramid) Guy Kibbee, Gloria Warren
One Sheet: $50 - $100

CINDERELLA SWINGS IT
(1956R - -) Guy Kibbe, Gloria Warren
One Sheet: $15 - $25   *Re-release.*

CINDERFELLA
(1960 - Paramount) Jerry Lewis, Ed Wynn
One Sheet: $50 - $100   *Norman
Rockwell art.*

CINDERFELLA
(1967R - Paramount) Jerry Lewis, Ed Wynn
One Sheet: $15 - $30   *Re-release.*

CINDY AND DONNA
(1970 - -) Debbie Osborne, Nancy Ison
One Sheet: $7 - $15

CINEMA OF UNEASE, A
(1996 - Miramax) New Zealand Documentary
(Sam Neill)
One Sheet: $5 - $10

CINEMA PARADISO
(1989 - Sovereign) Philippe Noiret, Jacques
Perrin
One Sheet: $30 - $50

CINEMATOGRAPHE LUMIERE
(1896 - Lumiere) -
One Sheet: $1,900 - $3,000   *French.*

CINERAMA SOUTH SEAS ADVENTURE
(1958 - Stanley Warner Cinerama) -
One Sheet: $50 - $100

CIPHER BUREAU
(1938 - Grand National) Leon Ames, Joan
Woodbury
One Sheet: $75 - $125

CIRCLE, THE
(1925 - MGM) Eleanor Boardman, Malcolm
McGregor
One Sheet: $250 - $500

CIRCLE, THE
(1959 - Kassler) John Mills, Derek Farr
One Sheet: $15 - $30

CIRCLE OF DANGER
(1950 - Eagle Lion Classics) Ray Milland,
Patricia Roc
One Sheet: $15 - $30

CIRCLE OF DEATH
(1935 - Willis Kent) Montie Montana, Tove
Lindan
One Sheet: $150 - $350

CIRCLE OF DECEIT
(1982 - United Artists Classics) Bruno Ganz,
Hanna Schygulla
One Sheet: $5 - $10

CIRCLE OF DECEPTION, A
(1961 - 20th Century Fox) Bradford Dillman,
Suzzy Parker
One Sheet: $7 - $15

CIRCLE OF FRIENDS
(1994 - Savoy) Chris O'Donnell, Minnie Driver
One Sheet: $3 - $5

CIRCLE OF IRON
(1978 - Avco/Embassy) David Carradine,
Roddy McDowall
One Sheet: $7 - $15

CIRCLE OF LOVE
(1965 - Reade Sterling) Jane Fonda, Maurice
Ronet
One Sheet: $30 - $50

CIRCUMSTANTIAL EVIDENCE
(1935 - Chesterfield) Chick Chandler, Shirley
Grey
One Sheet: $75 - $150

CIRCUMSTANTIAL EVIDENCE
(1945 - 20th Century Fox) Michael O'Shea,
Lloyd Nolan
One Sheet: $50 - $100

CIRCUS, THE
(1928 - United Artists) Charlie Chaplin
One Sheet: $6,500 - $10,000   *Special
Acadamy Award for Chaplin.*

CIRCUS, THE
(1970R - United Artists) Charlie Chaplin
One Sheet: $15 - $30   *Re-release.*

CIRCUS CLOWN
(1934 - First National) Joe E. Brown, Patricia
Ellis
One Sheet: $250 - $600

CIRCUS DAYS
(1921 - First National) Jackie Coogan
One Sheet: $600 - $1,000

CIRCUS GIRL
(1937 - Republic) June Travis, Bob Livingston
One Sheet: $100 - $200

CIRCUS GIRL
(1956 - Republic) Kristina Soederbaum
One Sheet: $30 - $50

Lobby Card

CIRCUS OF HORRORS
(1960 - AIP) Anton Diffring, Erika Remberg
One Sheet: $40 - $75

CIRCUS QUEEN MURDER, THE
(1933 - Columbia) Adolphe Menjou, Greta
Nissen
One Sheet: $500 - $800

CIRCUS SHADOWS
(1935 - Peerless) Dorothy Wilson, Kane
Richmond, Dorothy Revier
One Sheet: $75 - $150

CIRCUS STARS
(1960 - -) -
One Sheet: $15 - $25

CIRCUS WORLD
(1964 - Paramount) John Wayne, Claudia
Cardinale
One Sheet: $40 - $80   *One Sheet
"Cinerama": $100-$200.*

CISCO KID, THE
(1931 - Fox) Warner Baxter
One Sheet: $1,300 - $2,000

CISCO KID AND THE LADY, THE
(1939 - 20th Century Fox) Cesar Romero, Virginia Field
One Sheet: $100 - $200

CISCO KID IN OLD MEXICO, THE
(1945 - Monogram) Duncan Renaldo
One Sheet: $75 - $125

CISCO KID RETURNS, THE
(1945 - Monogram) Duncan Renaldo, Martin Garralaga
One Sheet: $50 - $100

CISCO PIKE
(1971 - Columbia) Karen Black, Gene Hackman
One Sheet: $7 - $15

CITADEL, THE
(1938 - MGM) Robert Donat, Rosalind Russell
One Sheet: $100 - $200

CITADEL OF CRIME
(1941 - Republic) Robert Armstrong, Linda Hayes
One Sheet: $50 - $100

CITIZEN KANE
(1941 - RKO) Orson Welles, Joseph Cotten
One Sheet: $13,000 - $20,000   *Price is for close-up style (Kane with two women). One Sheet(Welles standing):$3,000-$4,000.*

One Sheet

CITIZEN KANE
(1956R - RKO) Orson Welles, Joseph Cotton
One Sheet: $125 - $250   *Re-release.*

CITIZEN KANE
(1991R - Paramount) Orson Welles, Joseph Cotten
One Sheet: $15 - $35   *Re-release, 50th Anniversary.*

CITIZEN RUTH
(1996 - Miramax) Laura Dern, Swoosie Kurtz
One Sheet: $5 - $10

CITIZEN SAINT
(1947 - Clyde Elliott) Jed Prouty, Carla Dare, Julie Hadon
One Sheet: $30 - $50

CITIZENS BAND
(1977 - Paramount) Paul LeMat, Candy Clark
One Sheet: $5 - $10

CITY, THE
(1926 - Fox) May Allison, Richard Walling
One Sheet: $250 - $500

CITY ACROSS THE RIVER
(1949 - Universal) Stephen McNally, Thelma Ritter
One Sheet: $30 - $50

CITY AFTER MIDNIGHT
(1959 - Monarch) Phyllis Kirk, Dan O'Herlihy
One Sheet: $15 - $30

CITY BENEATH THE SEA
(1953 - Universal) Robert Ryan, Mala Powers
One Sheet: $30 - $50

CITY FOR CONQUEST
(1940 - Warner Bros.) James Cagney, Ann Sheridan
One Sheet: $600 - $1,000   *Sports Movie Posters #142.*

CITY FOR CONQUEST
(1946R - Warner Bros.) James Cagney, Ann Sheridan
One Sheet: $100 - $200   *Re-release.*

CITY GIRL
(1930 - Fox) Phyllis Brooks, Ricardo Cortez
One Sheet: $150 - $300

CITY GIRL
(1938 - 20th Century Fox) Sidney Toler, Lynn Bari
One Sheet: $100 - $200

CITY GONE WILD, THE
(1927 - Paramount) Thomas Meighan, Marietta Millner
One Sheet: $600 - $1,000

CITY HALL
(1996 - Castle Rock/Columbia) Al Pacino, John Cusack
One Sheet: $5 - $10

CITY HEAT
(1984 - Warner Bros.) Clint Eastwood, Burt Reynolds, Madeline Kahn
One Sheet: $7 - $15

CITY IN DARKNESS
(1939 - -) See CHARLIE CHAN IN THE CITY OF DARKNESS

CITY LIGHTS
(1931 - United Artists) Charlie Chaplin, Virginia Cherrill
One Sheet: $25,000 - $40,000   *Prices vary widely. Price is for cityscape style one sheet. One Sheet (other style):$8000-$15,000. Sports MoviePosters #128.*

CITY LIGHTS
(1951R - United Artists) Charlie Chaplin, Virginia Cherrill
One Sheet: $75 - $150   *Re-release.*

CITY LIGHTS
(1972R - United Artists) Charlie Chaplin, Virginia Cherrill
One Sheet: $15 - $30   *Re-release.*

CITY LIMITS
(1934 - Monogram) Frank Craven, Sally Blane
One Sheet: $100 - $200

CITY LIMITS
(1985 - -) Darrell Larson, Kim Cattrall, John Stockwell
One Sheet: $3 - $5

CITY OF BAD MEN
(1953 - 20th Century Fox) Jeanne Crain, Dale Robertson
One Sheet: $15 - $30

CITY OF CHANCE
(1940 - 20th Century Fox) Lynn Bari, Donald Woods
One Sheet: $75 - $125

CITY OF CHILDREN
(1949 - -) Nesbitt
One Sheet: $40 - $80

CITY OF DIM FACES, THE
(1918 - Paramount) Sussue Hiyakawa, Doris Pawn
One Sheet: $800 - $1,500

CITY OF FEAR
(1958 - Columbia) Vince Edwards, Lyle Talbot
One Sheet: $15 - $25

CITY OF FEAR
(1965 - Allied Artists) Terry Moore
One Sheet: $10 - $20

CITY OF JOY
(1992 - TriStar) Patrick Swayze, Pauline Collins
One Sheet: $5 - $10

CITY OF LOST CHILDREN, THE
(1995 - Sony Classics) Ron Perlman, Judith Vittet
One Sheet: $4 - $8

CITY OF MISSING GIRLS
(1941 - Select Attractions) John Arden, Gale Storm
One Sheet: $50 - $100

CITY OF SHADOWS
(1955 - Republic) Victor McLaglen, John Baer
One Sheet: $15 - $25

CITY OF SILENT MEN

(1921 - Paramount) Thomas Meighan, Lois Wilson, Kate Bruce
One Sheet: $200 - $400

CITY OF SILENT MEN
(1942 - PRC) Frank Albertson, June Lang
One Sheet: $40 - $75

CITY OF THE WALKING DEAD
(1983 - 20th Century Fox) Mel Ferrer, Hugo Stiglitz
One Sheet: $7 - $15   *AKA: NIGHTMARE CITY.*

CITY OF WOMEN
(1981 - Gaumont) Marcello Mastroianni, Dir: Frederico Fellini
One Sheet: $7 - $15

CITY PARK
(1934 - Chesterfield) Sally Blane, Henry B. Walthall
One Sheet: $100 - $200

CITY SLICKERS
(1991 - Columbia) Jack Palance, Billy Crystal
One Sheet: $10 - $20   *Academy Award: Best Supporting Actor(Palance). Academy Award Movie Posters #378. Cowboy Movie Posters #360.*

CITY SLICKERS II
(1994 - Columbia) Billy Crystal, Jack Palance
One Sheet: $5 - $10

CITY STREETS
(1931 - Paramount Publix) Gary Cooper, Sylvia Sidney
One Sheet: $1,300 - $2,000

CITY STREETS
(1938 - Columbia) Edith Fellows, Leo Carrillo
One Sheet: $100 - $200

CITY THAT NEVER SLEEPS
(1953 - Republic) Gig Young, Mala Powers
One Sheet: $40 - $75

CITY THAT STOPPED HITLER - HEROIC STALINGRAD
(1943 - Paramount) Narrated by Brian Donlevy
One Sheet: $100 - $200

CITY WITHOUT MEN
(1943 - Columbia) Linda Darnell, Glenda Farrell
One Sheet: $75 - $150

CIVILIZATION
(1916 - Thomas Ince) -
One Sheet: $1,900 - $3,000

CIVILIZATION
(1921R - Thomas Ince) -
One Sheet: $250 - $600   *Re-release.*

CLAIRE'S KNEE
(1971 - Columbia) Jean-Claude Brialy, Aurora Cornu, Beatrice Romand
One Sheet: $3 - $5

CLAIRVOYANT, THE
(1935 - Gaumont British) Claude Rains, Fay Wray
One Sheet: $800 - $1,500   *Graven Images, pg. 94.*

CLAMBAKE
(1967 - United Artists) Elvis Presley, Shelley Fabares
One Sheet: $40 - $75

One Sheet

CLAN OF THE CAVE BEAR

(1986 - Warner Bros.) Daryl Hannah, Pamela Reed, James Remar
One Sheet: $15 - $35

CLANCY OF THE MOUNTED
(1933 - Universal) Tom Tyler, Jacqueline Wells
One Sheet: $250 - $500

CLANCY STREET BOYS
(1943 - Monogram) The East Side Kids, Noah Beery, Jr.
One Sheet: $50 - $100

CLARA'S HEART
(1988 - -) Whoopi Goldberg, Michael Ontkean, Neil Patrick Harris
One Sheet: $3 - $5

CLARENCE
(1937 - Paramount) Roscoe Karns, Charlotte Wynters
One Sheet: $75 - $150

CLARENCE THE CROSS-EYED LION
(1965 - MGM) Marshall Thompson, Betsy Drake
One Sheet: $7 - $15

CLARENCE THE CROSS-EYED LION
(1972R - MGM) Marshall Thompson, Betsy Drake
One Sheet: $5 - $10   *Re-release.*

CLASH BY NIGHT
(1952 - RKO) Barbara Stanwyck, Marilyn Monroe, Paul Douglas
One Sheet: $125 - $250

CLASH OF THE TITANS
(1981 - MGM) Laurence Olivier, Harry Hamlin, Maggie Smith
One Sheet: $30 - $50   *Advance Style:$20-30. Harryhausen effects. Hildebrandt art.*

CLASS
(1983 - Orion) Jacqueline Bisset, Rob Lowe
One Sheet: $5 - $10

CLASS ACT
(1992 - Warner Bros.) Christopher "Kid" Reid, Christopher "Play" Martin
One Sheet: $3 - $5   *Black cast.*

CLASS ACTION
(1991 - 20th Century Fox) Gene Hackman, Mary Elizabeth Mastrantonio
One Sheet: $7 - $15

CLASS OF '44
(1973 - Warner Bros.) Gary Grimes, Jerry Houser
One Sheet: $5 - $10

CLASS OF '74, THE
(1972 - General) Pat Woodell, Mark Bey
One Sheet: $3 - $5

CLASS OF 1984
(1982 - United Film) Perry King, Merrie Lynn Ross, Roddy McDowall
One Sheet: $5 - $10

CLASS OF 1999
(1990 - -) Bradley Gregg, Traci Lind, Staci Keach
One Sheet: $7 - $15

CLASS OF MISS MACMICHAEL, THE
(1978 - -) Glenda Jackson, Oliver Reed
One Sheet: $3 - $5

CLASS OF NUKE 'EM HIGH
(1986 - Troma) Samuel Weil, Janelle Brady
One Sheet: $7 - $15

CLASS REUNION
(- - -) See National Lampoon's Class Reunion

CLASSIFIED
(1925 - First National) Corinne Griffith
One Sheet: $600 - $1,000

CLAUDELLE INGLISH
(1961 - Warner Bros.) Diane McBain, Arthur Kennedy
One Sheet: $10 - $20

CLAUDIA
(1943 - 20th Century Fox) Dorothy McGuire (film debut), Robert Young
One Sheet: $75 - $125

CLAUDIA AND DAVID
(1946 - 20th Century Fox) Dorothy McGuire, Robert Young
One Sheet: $40 - $75

CLAUDINE
(1974 - Fox) James Earl Jones, Diahann Carroll
One Sheet: $10 - $20   *Black cast.*

CLAWS
(1923 - Sun) -
One Sheet: $200 - $400

CLAWS OF THE HUN, THE
(1918 - -) Charles Ray, Jane Novak
One Sheet: $150 - $350

CLAY PIGEON
(1949 - RKO) Bill Williams, Barbara Hale
One Sheet: $30 - $50

CLAY PIGEON
(1971 - MGM) Telly Savalas, Robert Vaughn
One Sheet: $3 - $5

CLAY VS. LISTON
(1964 - -) Cassius Clay, Sonny Liston
One Sheet: $125 - $250

CLEAN AND SOBER
(1988 - -) Michael Keaton, Kathy Baker, Morgan Freeman
One Sheet: $3 - $5

CLEAN SHAVEN MAN, A
(1936 - Paramount) Popeye
One Sheet: $2,500 - $4,000   *Cartoon. Duotone. Cartoon Movie Posters #211.*

CLEAN SLATE
(1994 - MGM) Dana Carvey, Valeria Golino
One Sheet: $2 - $3

CLEANING HOUSE
(1938 - MGM) Captain & The Kids
One Sheet: $500 - $800   *Cartoon.*

CLEAR ALL WIRES
(1933 - MGM) James Gleason, Lee Tracy
One Sheet: $100 - $200

CLEAR AND PRESENT DANGER
(1994 - Paramount) Harrison Ford, Willem Dafoe, Anne Archer
One Sheet: $7 - $15

CLEARING THE RANGE
(1931 - Allied) Hoot Gibson, Sally Bilers
One Sheet: $150 - $300

CLEOPATRA
(1917 - Fox) Theda Bara
One Sheet: $10,000 - $15,000

CLEOPATRA
(1934 - Paramount) Claudette Colbert, Warren William
One Sheet: $4,500 - $7,000   *Price is for Style A. One Sheet(Style B):$800-1500.*

CLEOPATRA
(1952R - Paramount) Claudette Colbert, Warren William
One Sheet: $75 - $150   *Re-release.*

CLEOPATRA
(1963 - 20th Century Fox) Elizabeth Taylor, Richard Burton
One Sheet: $100 - $200   *Price is for style A or B. One Sheet (Todd-AO roadshow style): $300-$600.*

One Sheet

CLEOPATRA JONES
(1973 - Warner Bros.) Tamara Dobson, Bernie Casey
One Sheet: $15 - $35   *Blaxploitation.*

CLEOPATRA JONES AND THE CASINO OF GOLD
(1975 - Warner Bros.) Tamara Dobson, Stella Stevens
One Sheet: $10 - $20   *Blaxploitation.*

CLEOPATRA'S DAUGHTER
(1960 - McDallion) Debra Paget, Robert Alda
One Sheet: $7 - $15

CLERKS
(1994 - Miramax) Brian O'Halloran, Jeff Anderson
One Sheet: $10 - $20

CLEVER MRS. CARFAX, THE
(1917 - Paramount) Julian Eltinge
One Sheet: $250 - $600

CLIENT, THE
(1994 - Warner Bros.) Tommy Lee Jones, Susan Sarandon
One Sheet: $7 - $15

CLIFF EDWARDS AND HIS BUCKAROOS
(1940 - Warner Bros.) Cliff Edwards & band
One Sheet: $50 - $100   *Country musical.*

CLIFFHANGER
(1993 - TriStar) Sly Stallone, Michael Rooker, Janine Turner
One Sheet: $7 - $15   *Sports Movie Posters #280.*

CLIFFORD
(1994 - Orion) Martin Short, Charles Grodin
One Sheet: $5 - $10

CLIMAX, THE
(1930 - Universal) Jean Hersholt, Kathryn Crawford, LeRoy Mason
One Sheet: $200 - $400

CLIMAX, THE
(1944 - Universal) Boris Karloff, Susanna Foster, Turhan Bey
One Sheet: $125 - $250   *Graven Images, pg. 140.*

CLIMBING MT. WASHINGTON/GATHERING BANANAS AND COCOANUTS
(1917 - Edison) -
One Sheet: $500 - $900

CLIMBING THE MATTERHORN
(1948 - Monogram) -
One Sheet: $50 - $100

CLINGING VINE, THE
(1926 - Cecil B. DeMille) Leatrice Joy, Tom Moore
One Sheet: $250 - $500

CLIPPED WINGS
(1953 - Monogram) Bowery Boys
One Sheet: $40 - $75

CLIVE OF INDIA
(1935 - United Artists) Ronald Colman, Loretta Young
One Sheet: $1,300 - $2,000   *Undated posters with 20th Century-Fox emblem are re-issue. One Sheet(20th Century Fox):$400-600.*

CLOAK AND DAGGER
(1946 - Warner Bros.) Gary Cooper, Lilli Palmer
One Sheet: $100 - $200

CLOAK AND DAGGER
(1984 - Universal) Henry Thomas, Dabney Coleman
One Sheet: $3 - $5

CLOCK, THE
(1945 - MGM) Judy Garland, Robert Walker
One Sheet: $200 - $400

CLOCK WATCHER, THE
(1945 - RKO/Disney) Donald Duck
One Sheet: $3,500 - $5,000   *Cartoon. Cartoon Movie Posters #175.*

CLOCKERS
(1995 - Universal) Harvey Keitel, John Turturro, Dir: Spike Lee
One Sheet: $15 - $25   *Price is for One Sheet style with Saul Bass "Anatomy Of A Murder" design rip-off.*

CLOCKWISE
(1939 - RKO) Edgar Kennedy
One Sheet: $100 - $200

CLOCKWISE
(1986 - EMI) John Cleese, Penelope Wilton
One Sheet: $5 - $10

CLOCKWORK ORANGE, A
(1971 - Warner Bros.) Malcolm McDowell, Patrick Magee, Dir: Stanley Kubrick
One Sheet: $75 - $150   *Price is for X-rated style; One Sheet(R-rated):$75-100.*

CLOCKWORK ORANGE, A
(1982R - Warner Bros.) Malcolm McDowell, Patrick Magee Dir: Stanley Kubrick
One Sheet: $15 - $25   *Re-release. New artwork.*

CLODHOPPER, THE
(1917 - Triangle) Charles Ray, Margery Wilson
One Sheet: $500 - $800

CLOISTERED
(1936 - Best) -
One Sheet: $200 - $400

CLOSE CALL FOR BOSTON BLACKIE, A
(1946 - Columbia) Chester Morris, Richard Lane
One Sheet: $75 - $125

CLOSE CALL FOR ELLERY QUEEN, A
(1942 - Columbia) William Gargan, Margaret Lindsay
One Sheet: $100 - $200

CLOSE ENCOUNTERS OF THE THIRD KIND
(1977 - Columbia) Richard Dreyfuss, Teri Garr
One Sheet: $20 - $40

CLOSE ENCOUNTERS OF THE THIRD KIND
(1980R - Columbia) Richard Dreyfuss, Teri Garr
One Sheet: $7 - $15   *Re-release with added footage.*

CLOSE TO MY HEART
(1951 - Warner Bros.) Ray Milland, Gene Tierney
One Sheet: $40 - $75

CLOSED VISION
(1954 - Film Archives) -
One Sheet: $15 - $25

CLOSE-UP
(1948 - Eagle-Lion) Alan Baxter, Virginia Gilmore
One Sheet: $30 - $50

CLOUD DANCER
(1980 - Blossom) David Carradine, Jennifer O'Neill
One Sheet: $5 - $10

CLOUDBURST
(1952 - United Artists) Robert Preston, Elizabeth Sellars
One Sheet: $15 - $25

CLOUDED YELLOW, THE
(1950 - Columbia) Jean Simmons, Trevor Howard
One Sheet: $15 - $30

CLOUDS OVER EUROPE
(1939 - Columbia) Laurence Olivier, Trevor Howard, Valerie Hobson
One Sheet: $200 - $400

CLOUDS OVER ISRAEL
(1966 - Harold Cornsweet-Israel) Yiftach Spector, Ehud Banal
One Sheet: $10 - $20

CLOWN, THE
(1952 - MGM) Red Skelton, Tim Considine
One Sheet: $75 - $150

CLOWN AND THE KID, THE
(1961 - United Artists) John Lupton, Mike McGreeney
One Sheet: $7 - $15

CLOWN AND THE KIDS, THE
(1968 - Childhood) Emmett Kelly, Burt Stratford
One Sheet: $7 - $15

CLOWN PRINCES
(1939 - MGM) Our Gang
One Sheet: $350 - $750

CLOWNING
(1931 - Educational) Animated by Paul Terry
One Sheet: $250 - $600   *Cartoon. Cartoon Movie Posters #78.*

CLUB HAVANA
(1945 - Eagle Lion) Tom Neal, Margaret Lindsay
One Sheet: $50 - $100

CLUB PARADISE
(1985 - Warner Bros.) Robin Williams, Peter O'Toole
One Sheet: $3 - $5

CLUE
(1985 - Paramount) Eileen Brennan, Tim Curry, Madeline Kahn
One Sheet: $3 - $5

CLUELESS
(1995 - Paramount) Alicia Silverstone
One Sheet: $5 - $10

CLUNKED ON THE CORNER
(1928 - Pathe) Johnny Burke, Carmelita Geraghty
One Sheet: $250 - $500   *Handy Andy Series.*

CLUNY BROWN
(1946 - 20th Century Fox) Charles Boyer, Jennifer Jones
One Sheet: $50 - $100

CLUTCHING HAND, THE
(1936 - Stage and Screen) Jack Mulhall, Marion Shilling
One Sheet: $600 - $1,000   *Serial. 15 Chapters.*

C-MAN
(1949 - Film Classics) Dean Jagger, John Carradine
One Sheet: $15 - $30

COACH
(1978 - Crown) Cathy Lee Crosby, Michael Biehn
One Sheet: $5 - $10

COAL MINER'S DAUGHTER
(1979 - Universal) Sissy Spacek, Tommy Lee Jones
One Sheet: $10 - $20   *Based on the life of Loretta Lynn. Academy Award: Best Actress(Spacek). Advance: $15-$30. Academy Award Movie Posters#312.*

COAST GUARD
(1939 - Columbia) Randolph Scott, Ralph Bellamy, Frances Dee
One Sheet: $75 - $150

COAST OF FOLLY, THE
(1925 - Paramount) Gloria Swanson
One Sheet: $800 - $1,500

One Sheet

COAST OF SKELETONS
(1965 - Seven Arts) Richard Todd, Derek Nimmo
One Sheet: $7 - $15

COBB
(1994 - Warner Bros.) Tommy Lee Jones, Robert Wuhl
One Sheet: $7 - $15   *Sports*

(Baseball). Film about the life of Ty Cobb. Sports
Movie Posters #85.

COBRA, THE
(1925 - Paramount) Rudolph Valentino
One Sheet: $2,500 - $4,000

COBRA, THE
(1968 - AIP) Anita Ekberg, Dana Andrews
One Sheet: $15 - $25

COBRA
(1986 - Warner Bros.) Sylvester Stallone,
Brigette Nielson
One Sheet: $5 - $10

COBRA STRIKES, THE
(1948 - Eagle Lion) Sheila Ryan, Richard
Fraser, Leslie Brooks
One Sheet: $40 - $75

COBRA WOMAN
(1943 - Universal) Jon Hall, Maria Montez
One Sheet: $200 - $400

COBS AND ROBBERS
(1951 - MGM) Barney Bear
One Sheet: $200 - $400   *Cartoon.*

COBWEB, THE
(1955 - MGM) Richard Widmark, Lauren Bacall,
Charles Boyer
One Sheet: $40 - $75

COCA COLA KID, THE
(1985 - Cinecom) Eric Roberts, Greta Scacchi
One Sheet: $7 - $15

COCAINE FIENDS, THE
(1937 - New-Line Cinemas) Lois January,
Sheila Manners
One Sheet: $100 - $200   *Reefer*
Madness style exploitation.

COCK FIGHTER, THE
(1974 - New World) Warren Oates, Harry Dean
Stanton
One Sheet: $15 - $25   *AKA: Born To*
Kill; Wild Drifter; Gamblin' Man. Filmed in
Georgia.

COCK O' THE WALK
(1930 - Sono Art/World Wide) Joseph
Schildkraut, Myrna Loy
One Sheet: $200 - $400

COCK OF THE AIR
(1932 - United Artists) Chester Morris, Billie
Dove
One Sheet: $150 - $300

COCK-A-DOODLE DOG
(1951 - MGM) Tex Avery
One Sheet: $250 - $600   *Cartoon. Full*
color stone litho.

COCKEYED CAVALIERS
(1934 - RKO) Wheeler and Woolsey, Thelma
Todd
One Sheet: $250 - $500

**COCKEYED COWBOYS OF CALICO COUNTY,
THE**
(1970 - Universal) Dan Blocker, Nanette
Fabray, Jim Backus
One Sheet: $5 - $10

COCKEYED MIRACLE, THE
(1946 - MGM) Frank Morgan, Keenan Wynn
One Sheet: $50 - $100

Window Card

COCKEYED WORLD, THE
(1929 - Fox) Victor McLaglen, Edmund Lowe

One Sheet: $250 - $500

COCKLESHELL HEROES
(1955 - Columbia) Jose Ferrer, Trevor Howard
One Sheet: $15 - $30

COCKTAIL
(1988 - Touchstone) Tom Cruise, Bryan Brown
One Sheet: $10 - $20

COCKTAIL HOUR
(1933 - Columbia) Randolph Scott
One Sheet: $150 - $300

COCOANUT GROVE
(1938 - Paramount) Fred MacMurray, Harriet
Hillard (Nelson)
One Sheet: $75 - $150

COCOANUTS, THE
(1929 - Paramount) The Four Marx Brothers
(film debut), Margaret Dumont
One Sheet: $6,500 - $10,000

COCOON
(1985 - 20th Century Fox) Don Ameche, Wilson
Brimley, Jessica Tandy
One Sheet: $10 - $20   *Academy*
Award: Best Supporting Actor (Ameche).
Academy Award Movie Posters #345.

COCOON: THE RETURN
(1988 - 20th Century Fox) Don Ameche, Jack
Gilford
One Sheet: $5 - $10

C.O.D.
(1932 - West) Garry Marsh, Hope Davy
One Sheet: $150 - $300

C.O.D.
(1983 - -) Chris Lemmon, Olivia Pascal
One Sheet: $3 - $5

CODE 7 VICTIM 5
(1965 - Columbia) Lex Barker, Ann Smyrner
One Sheet: $7 - $15

CODE NAME: EMERALD
(1985 - MGM/United Artists) Ed Harris, Max
von Sydow, Eric Stolz
One Sheet: $3 - $5

CODE NAME: WILDGEESE
(1986 - -) Lewis Collins, Lee Van Cleef, Ernest
Borgnine
One Sheet: $3 - $5

CODE OF SCOTLAND YARD
(1948 - Republic) Oscar Homolka, Derek Farr
One Sheet: $50 - $100

CODE OF SILENCE
(1985 - Orion) Chuck Norris, Henry Silva
One Sheet: $7 - $15

CODE OF THE AIR
(1928 - Bischoff) Kenneth Harlan, June
Marlowe, Arthur Rankin
One Sheet: $150 - $350

CODE OF THE CACTUS
(1939 - Victory) Tim McCoy, Dorothy Short
One Sheet: $50 - $100

CODE OF THE FEARLESS
(1939 - Spectrum) Fred Scott
One Sheet: $50 - $100

CODE OF THE LAWLESS
(1945 - Universal) Kirby Grant, Poni Adams
One Sheet: $40 - $75

CODE OF THE MOUNTED
(1935 - Ambassador) Kermit Maynard
One Sheet: $100 - $200

CODE OF THE NORTHWEST
(1926 - Associated) Richard Lange, Tom
London, Sandow (a dog)
One Sheet: $100 - $200

CODE OF THE OUTLAWS
(1942 - Republic) Three Mesquiteers, Tom
Tyler, Bob Steele
One Sheet: $50 - $100

CODE OF THE PRAIRIE
(1944 - Republic) Smiley Burnette, Sunset
Carson
One Sheet: $40 - $75

CODE OF THE RANGE
(1936 - Columbia) Charles Starrett, Mary Blake

One Sheet: $75 - $150

CODE OF THE RANGERS
(1938 - Monogram) Tim McCoy
One Sheet: $125 - $250

CODE OF THE SADDLE
(1947 - Monogram) Johnny Mack Brown
One Sheet: $40 - $75

CODE OF THE SEA, THE
(1924 - Paramount) Rod La Rocque,
Jacqueline Logan
One Sheet: $250 - $500

CODE OF THE SECRET SERVICE
(1939 - Warner Bros.) Ronald Reagan, Rosella
Towne
One Sheet: $125 - $250

CODE OF THE SILVER SAGE
(1950 - Republic) Rocky Lane, Eddie Waller
One Sheet: $20 - $40

CODE OF THE STREETS
(1939 - Universal) Frankie Thomas, Harry
Carey
One Sheet: $75 - $150

CODE OF THE WEST
(1947 - RKO) James Warren, Debra Alden
One Sheet: $30 - $50

CODE OF THE WEST (ZANE GREY'S)
(1925 - Paramount) Owen Moore, Constance
Bennett, Mabel Ballin
One Sheet: $150 - $300

One Sheet

CODE TWO
(1953 - MGM) Sally Forrest, Ralph Meeker
One Sheet: $10 - $20

CODY OF THE PONY EXPRESS
(1950 - Columbia) Jock O'Mahoney, Dickie
Moore
One Sheet: $40 - $75   *Serial.*
Western. 15 Chapters.

COFFY
(1973 - AIP) Pam Grier, Booker Bradshaw
One Sheet: $15 - $25

COHEN AND TATE
(1989 - -) Roy Scheider, Adam Baldwin
One Sheet: $3 - $5

COHENS & KELLEYS, THE
(1926 - Universal) George Sidney
One Sheet: $150 - $300

COHENS AND THE KELLYS IN SCOTLAND, THE
(1930 - Universal) Maureen O'Sullivan
One Sheet: $125 - $250

COHENS AND THE KELLYS IN TROUBLE, THE
(1933 - Universal) Maureen O'Sullivan
One Sheet: $125 - $250

COL. HEEZA LIAR'S ANCESTOR
(1924 - Bray Productions) Col. Heeza
One Sheet: $500 - $800   *Cartoon.*
Duotone. Cartoon Movie Posters #10.

COLD COMFORT FARM
(1996 - Gramercy) Kate Beckinsale, Sheila
Burrell
One Sheet: $3 - $6

COLD DECK, THE
(1917 - S.A. Lynch) William S. Hart
One Sheet: $5,000 - $8,000

COLD DECK, THE
(192?R - Superlative) William S. Hart
One Sheet: $125 - $250   *Re-release.*

COLD HEAT/COP-OUT
(1989 - AIP) Britt Ekland/ David Buff
One Sheet: $3 - $5   *Double*
feature poster.

COLD RIVER
(1979 - Adirondack Alliance) Suzanna Weber,
Richard Jaeckel
One Sheet: $3 - $5

COLD SWEAT
(1974 - Emerson) Charles Bronson, Liv Ullman
One Sheet: $7 - $15

COLD TURKEY
(1925 - Pathe) Alice Day
One Sheet: $200 - $400

COLD TURKEY
(1951 - RKO/Disney) Pluto
One Sheet: $300 - $700   *Cartoon. Full*
color. The Disney Poster, pg. 41.

COLD TURKEY
(1971 - United Artists) Dick Van Dyke, Bob
Newhart
One Sheet: $5 - $10

COLD WAR
(1951 - RKO/Disney) Goofy
One Sheet: $500 - $800   *Cartoon. The*
Disney Poster, pg. 62.

COLD WIND IN AUGUST, A
(1961 - United Artists) Lola Albright, Scott
Marlowe
One Sheet: $15 - $25

COLDITZ STORY, THE
(1957 - British Lion) John Mills, Eric Portman
One Sheet: $7 - $15

COLE YOUNGER, GUNFIGHTER
(1958 - Allied Artists) Frank Lovejoy, Abby
Dalton
One Sheet: $10 - $20

COLLECTOR, THE
(1965 - Columbia) Terence Stamp, Samantha
Eggar
One Sheet: $10 - $20

COLLEEN
(1936 - Warner Bros.) Ruby Keeler, Dick
Powell
One Sheet: $200 - $400

COLLEGE
(1927 - United Artists) Buster Keaton, Grant
Withers
One Sheet: $5,000 - $7,500   *Sports Movie*
Posters #349.

COLLEGE BOOB, THE
(1926 - FBO) Lefty Flynn, Jean Arthur
One Sheet: $200 - $400

COLLEGE CAPERS
(1954 - Universal) Eileen Barton, Lex Baxter
One Sheet: $30 - $50

COLLEGE COACH
(1933 - Warner Bros.) Pat O'Brien, Dick Powell,
Ann Dvorak
One Sheet: $200 - $400   *Sports*
(Football).

COLLEGE CONFIDENTIAL
(1960 - Universal) Steve Allen, Jayne
Meadows, Mamie Van Doren
One Sheet: $40 - $75

COLLEGE COQUETTE
(1929 - Columbia) Ruth Taylor, William Collier,
Jr.
One Sheet: $250 - $500

COLLEGE HOLIDAY
(1936 - Paramount) Jack Benny, George Burns
One Sheet: $200 - $400

COLLEGE HUMOR
(1933 - Paramount) Bing Crosby, George
Burns, Gracie Allen
One Sheet: $300 - $700

COLLEGE RHYTHM
(1934 - Paramount) Joe Penner, Jack Oakie
One Sheet: $125 - $250

COLLEGE SCANDAL
(1935 - Paramount) Kent Taylor, Wendy Barrie
One Sheet: $125 - $250

COLLEGE SWING
(1938 - Paramount) Martha Raye, Bob Hope,
George Burns, Gracie Allen
One Sheet: $250 - $500   _Sports Movie
Posters #352._

COLLEGIANS, THE
(1926 - Universal) George Lewis, Dorothy
Gulliver
One Sheet: $125 - $250   _Serial. 44
episodes (from 3 series; 1926/27, 1928, 1929)._

COLLEGIATE
(1936 - Paramount) Joe Penner, Betty Grable
One Sheet: $600 - $1,000

COLONEL BLIMP
(1945 - United Artists) Deborah Kerr, Roger
Livesey
One Sheet: $40 - $75

COLONEL CHABERT
(1995 - October Films) Gerard Depardieu,
Fanny Ardant
One Sheet: $3 - $5

COLONEL EFFINGHAM'S RAID
(1945 - 20th Century Fox) Charles Coburn,
Joan Bennett
One Sheet: $50 - $100

COLOR FAVORITES
(1950R - Columbia) -
One Sheet: $75 - $150   _Cartoon._

COLOR ME DEAD
(1969 - Commonwealth United) Tom Tryon,
Carolyn Jones
One Sheet: $7 - $15

COLOR ME RED
(1965 - Box Office Spectacular) Dan Joseph,
Candi Conder, Dir: Herschell Gordon Lewis
One Sheet: $75 - $150

COLOR OF MONEY, THE
(1986 - Touchstone) Paul Newman, Tom Cruise
One Sheet: $30 - $60   _Academy
Award: Best Actor(Newman). Billiards. Sequel to
"The Hustler". Academy Award Movie Posters
#349. Sports MoviePosters #294._

COLOR PURPLE, THE
(1985 - Warner Bros.) Danny Glover, Whoopi
Goldberg, Margret Avery
One Sheet: $15 - $25   _Black cast.
Advance Style:$20-30._

COLOR RHAPSODY CARTOON, A
(1941 - Columbia) -
One Sheet: $100 - $200   _Cartoon. Full
color stock poster with blank space in center._

COLORADO
(1940 - Republic) Roy Rogers, George "Gabby"
Hayes, Pauline Moore
One Sheet: $150 - $300

COLORADO AMBUSH
(1951 - Monogram) Johnny Mack Brown
One Sheet: $15 - $35

COLORADO KID, THE
(1937 - Republic) Bob Steele, Marion Weldon
One Sheet: $125 - $250

COLORADO PIONEERS
(1945 - Republic) Wild Bill Elliott, Bobby Blake
One Sheet: $40 - $75

COLORADO PLUCK
(1921 - Fox) William Russell
One Sheet: $200 - $400

COLORADO RANGER
(1950 - Lippert) Jimmy Ellison, Russ Hayden
One Sheet: $20 - $40

COLORADO SERENADE
(1946 - Pathe) Eddie Dean, Roscoe Ates
One Sheet: $40 - $75

COLORADO SUNDOWN
(1951 - Republic) Rex Allen, Mary Ellen Kay
One Sheet: $15 - $30

COLORADO SUNDOWN
(1952 - Republic) Rex Allen, Mary Ellen Kay
One Sheet: $15 - $30

COLORADO SUNSET
(1939 - Republic) Gene Autry, Smiley Burnette
One Sheet: $200 - $400

COLORADO TERRITORY
(1949 - Warner Bros.) Joel McCrea, Virginia
Mayo
One Sheet: $30 - $50   _Cowboy
Movie Posters #282._

COLORADO TRAIL, THE
(1938 - Columbia) Charles Starrett, Iris
Meredith
One Sheet: $75 - $150

COLORS
(1988 - Orion) Sean Penn, Robert Duvall
One Sheet: $5 - $10

COLOSSAL GAME, THE
(1922 - Universal) Eilleen Sedgwick
One Sheet: $150 - $300   _Serial. 18
Chapters._

COLOSSUS OF NEW YORK, THE
(1958 - Paramount) Robert Hutton, Mala
Powers
One Sheet: $125 - $250   _Graven
Images, pg. 184._

COLOSSUS OF RHODES, THE
(1961 - MGM) Rory Calhoun, Leo Massari
One Sheet: $15 - $30

COLOSSUS: THE FORBIN PROJECT
(1970 - Universal) Eric Braeden, Susan Clark
One Sheet: $5 - $10

COLT .45
(1950 - Warner Bros.) Randolph Scott, Ruth
Roman
One Sheet: $50 - $100

COLT COMRADES
(1943 - United Artists) William Boyd, Victor
Jory, George Reeves
One Sheet: $100 - $200   _Hopalong
Cassidy series._

COLUMBIA PHANTASY CARTOON
(1930S - Columbia) Animated
One Sheet: $75 - $150   _Cartoon._

COLUMBIA PICTURES
(1933 - Columbia) Promotional
One Sheet: $1,600 - $2,500

COLUMN SOUTH
(1953 - Universal) Audie Murphy, Joan Evans,
Robert Sterling
One Sheet: $30 - $60

COMA
(1978 - MGM) Michael Douglas, Genevieve
Bujold
One Sheet: $5 - $10

COMANCHE
(1956 - United Artists) Dana Andrews, Linda
Cristal
One Sheet: $15 - $25

COMANCHE STATION
(1960 - Columbia) Randolph Scott, Claude
Akins
One Sheet: $20 - $40

COMANCHE TERRITORY
(1950 - Universal) Maureen O'Hara, Macdonald
Carey
One Sheet: $15 - $35

COMANCHEROS, THE
(1961 - 20th Century Fox) John Wayne, Stuart
Whitman
One Sheet: $75 - $150

COMBAT SQUAD
(1953 - Columbia) John Ireland, Lon
McCallister
One Sheet: $15 - $25

COME AND GET IT!
(1929 - F.B.O.) Bob Steele, Jimmy Quinn, Betty
Welsh
One Sheet: $250 - $500

COME AND GET IT!
(1936 - United Artists) Edward Arnold, Joel
McCrea, Walter Brennan, Frances Farmer
One Sheet: $150 - $300   _Academy
Award: Best Supporting Actor(Brennan). Academy
Award Movie Posters #49._

COME BACK CHARLESTON BLUE
(1972 - Warner Bros.) Godfrey Cambridge,
Raymond St. Jacques
One Sheet: $15 - $30   _Blaxploitation._

COME BACK, LITTLE SHEBA
(1952 - Paramount) Shirley Booth, Burt
Lancaster
One Sheet: $40 - $75   _Academy
Award: Best Actress. Academy Award Movie
Posters #145._

COME BACK MISS PIPPS
(1942 - MGM) Our Gang
One Sheet: $250 - $500

**COME BACK TO THE FIVE AND DIME, JIMMY
DEAN, JIMMY DEAN**
(1982 - Sandcastle) Sandy Dennis, Cher,
Karen Black
One Sheet: $15 - $25

COME BLOW YOUR HORN
(1963 - Paramount) Frank Sinatra, Lee J. Cobb
One Sheet: $30 - $50

COME CLEAN
(1931 - MGM) Laurel & Hardy
One Sheet: $2,500 - $4,000

COME CLOSER, FOLKS
(1936 - Columbia) James Dunn, Gene Lockhart
One Sheet: $100 - $200

COME DANCE WITH ME
(1960 - Kingsley International) Brigette Bardot
One Sheet: $50 - $100

COME FILL THE CUP
(1951 - Warner Bros.) James Cagney, Phyllis
Thaxter
One Sheet: $30 - $60

COME FLY WITH ME
(1963 - MGM) Dolores Hart, Hugh O'Brian
One Sheet: $7 - $15

COME LIVE WITH ME
(1941 - MGM) Hedy Lamarr, James Stewart
One Sheet: $200 - $400

COME NEXT SPRING
(1955 - Republic) Ann Sheridan, Steve
Cochran
One Sheet: $15 - $35

COME ON, COWBOY!
(1948 - Toddy) Mantan Moreland, Johnny Lee
One Sheet: $100 - $200   _Black cast.
Separate Cinema, pg. 56._

COME ON COWBOYS
(1937 - Republic) Three Mesquiteers (Bob
Livingston, Ray Corrigan)
One Sheet: $50 - $100

COME ON DANGER
(1932 - RKO) Tom Keene
One Sheet: $150 - $300

COME ON DANGER
(1942 - RKO) Tim Holt
One Sheet: $50 - $100

COME ON GEORGE
(1939 - Associated British) George Formby, Pat
Kirkwood
One Sheet: $40 - $75   _Duotone._

COME ON LEATHERNECKS
(1938 - Republic) Richard Cromwell, Marsha
Hunt
One Sheet: $75 - $125

COME ON MARINES!
(1934 - Paramount) Richard Arlen, Ida Lupino
One Sheet: $100 - $200

COME ON OVER
(1922 - Goldwyn) Colleen Moore, Ralph Graves
One Sheet: $500 - $800

COME ON RANGERS
(1938 - Republic) Roy Rogers, Mary Holt
One Sheet: $300 - $700

COME ON TARZAN
(1932 - World Wide) Ken Maynard
One Sheet: $200 - $400

COME OUT FIGHTING
(1945 - Monogram) Leo Gorcey, Huntz Hall
One Sheet: $50 - $100

COME SEE THE PARADISE
(1990 - -) -
One Sheet: $4 - $8

COME SEPTEMBER
(1961 - Universal) Rock Hudson, Gina
Lollabrigida
One Sheet: $20 - $40

COME SPY WITH ME
(1967 - 20th Century Fox) Troy Donahue,
Andrea Dromm
One Sheet: $7 - $15

COME TO THE STABLE
(1949 - 20th Century Fox) Loretta Young,
Celeste Holm, Hugh Marlowe
One Sheet: $50 - $100

COMEDIANS, THE
(1967 - MGM) Richard Burton, Elizabeth Taylor
One Sheet: $15 - $30

COMEDY OF TERRORS, THE
(1963 - AIP) Vincent Price, Peter Lorre, Boris
Karloff
One Sheet: $50 - $100

COME-ON, THE
(1956 - Allied Artists) Anne Baxter, Sterling
Hayden
One Sheet: $20 - $40

COMES A HORSEMAN
(1978 - United Artists) James Caan, Jane
Fonda
One Sheet: $10 - $20   _Cowboy
Movie Posters #351._

COMES MIDNIGHT
(1940 - Sepia) James Baskette
One Sheet: $150 - $300   _Black cast.
Separate Cinema, pg. 72._

COMET OVER BROADWAY
(1938 - First National) Kay Francis, Ian Hunter
One Sheet: $125 - $250

COMFORT AND JOY
(1984 - -) Bill Paterson, Eleanor David
One Sheet: $3 - $5

COMIC, THE
(1969 - Columbia) Dick Van Dyke, Michele Lee,
Mickey Rooney
One Sheet: $10 - $20

COMIC BOOK CONFIDENTIAL
(1988 - -) Stan Lee, Robert Crumb, Jack Kirby
One Sheet: $15 - $25   _Documentary._

COMIN' AT YA!
(1981 - Filmways) Tony Anthony, Victoria Abril
One Sheet: $5 - $10   _3-D_

COMIN' ROUND THE MOUNTAIN
(1936 - Republic) Gene Autry
One Sheet: $500 - $800

COMIN' ROUND THE MOUNTAIN
(1940 - Paramount) Bob Burns, Una Merkel
One Sheet: $50 - $100

COMIN' ROUND THE MOUNTAIN
(1943R - Republic) Gene Autry
One Sheet: $75 - $150   _Re-release._

COMIN' ROUND THE MOUNTAIN
(1948R - Republic) Gene Autry
One Sheet: $40 - $75   _Re-release._

COMIN' ROUND THE MOUNTAIN
(1951 - Universal) Bud Abbott, Lou Costello
One Sheet: $75 - $125

One Sheet

COMING APART
(1969 - -) Rip Torn, Viveca Linfors, Sally Kirkland
One Sheet: $5 - $10

COMING HOME
(1978 - United Artists) Jane Fonda, Jon Voight, Bruce Dern
One Sheet: $7 - $15   *Academy Award: Best Actor(Voight), Best Actress(Fonda). Review style:$6-$10. Academy Award MoviePosters #303.*

COMING OF AMOS, THE
(1925 - Producers) Rod La Rocque, Jetta Goudal
One Sheet: $500 - $800

COMING OUT PARTY
(1934 - Fox) Frances Dee, Gene Raymond
One Sheet: $250 - $600

COMING TO AMERICA
(1987 - Paramount) Eddie Murphy, Arsenio Hall
One Sheet: $5 - $10

COMMAND, THE
(1955 - Warner Bros.) Guy Madison, Joan Weldon
One Sheet: $15 - $25

COMMAND DECISION
(1949 - MGM) Clark Gable, Walter Pidgeon, Van Johnson
One Sheet: $50 - $100

COMMAND PERFORMANCE
(1937 - General) Arthur Tracy, Lilli Palmer
One Sheet: $150 - $300

COMMANDMENTS
(1997 - Gramercy) Aidan Quinn, Courteney Cox, Anthony LaPaglia
One Sheet: $5 - $10

COMMANDO
(1985 - 20th Century Fox) Arnold Schwarzenegger, Rae Dawn Chong
One Sheet: $7 - $15

COMMANDO CODY
(1953 - Republic) Judd Holdren
One Sheet: $75 - $150   *12 Episodes. TV tie-in. Not a serial, released theatrically as one-chapter short subjects. Episode #3 on "...Sky Marshall of the Universe"*

COMMANDOS STRIKE AT DAWN, THE
(1943 - Columbia) Paul Muni, Anna Lee
One Sheet: $75 - $150

COMMITTEE, THE
(1969 - Commonwealth United Entertainment) Don Sturdy, Carl Gottlieb, Christopher Ross
One Sheet: $5 - $10

COMMON CLAY
(1930 - Fox) Constance Bennett, Lew Ayres
One Sheet: $150 - $300

COMMON LAW
(1931 - RKO Pathe) Constance Bennett, Joel McCrea
One Sheet: $200 - $400

COMMOTION ON THE OCEAN
(1956 - Columbia) The Three Stooges (Shemp)
One Sheet: $150 - $300   *Comedy short. Duotone.*

COMMUNION
(1989 - -) Christopher Walken, Lindsay Crouse
One Sheet: $3 - $5

COMPANEROS
(1972 - Cinerama) Franco Nero, Jack Palance
One Sheet: $5 - $10

COMPANIONATE MARRIAGE, THE
(1928 - First National) Betty Bronson, Alec B. Francis
One Sheet: $150 - $300

COMPANY OF KILLERS
(1970 - Universal) Van Johnson, Ray Milland
One Sheet: $5 - $10

COMPANY OF WOLVES,THE
(1985 - Cannon) Angela Lansbury, David Warner
One Sheet: $15 - $25

COMPANY SHE KEEPS, THE

(1950 - RKO) Lizabeth Scott, Dennis O'Keefe
One Sheet: $30 - $50

COMPETITION, THE
(1980 - Columbia) Richard Dreyfuss, Amy Irving
One Sheet: $3 - $5

COMPLEAT BEATLES, THE
(1984 - -) The Beatles
One Sheet: $15 - $35

COMPROMISED
(1931 - First National) Ben Lyon, Rose Hobart
One Sheet: $150 - $300

COMPROMISING POSITIONS
(1985 - Paramount) Susan Sarandon, Raul Julia
One Sheet: $3 - $5

COMPULSION
(1959 - 20th Century Fox) Orson Welles, Diane Varsi
One Sheet: $30 - $50

COMPUTER WORE TENNIS SHOES, THE
(1970 - Buena Vista/Disney) Kurt Russell, Cesar Romero
One Sheet: $15 - $25

COMRADE X
(1940 - MGM) Clark Gable, Hedy Lamarr
One Sheet: $600 - $1,000

CON AIR
(1997 - Buena Vista) Nicolas Cage, John Cusack, John Malkovich
One Sheet: $5 - $10

CON ARTISTS, THE
(1981 - S.J. International) Anthony Quinn, Corinne Clery
One Sheet: $5 - $10   *AKA: The Con Man.*

CONAN THE BARBARIAN
(1982 - Universal) Arnold Schwarzenegger, James Earl Jones
One Sheet: $15 - $30

CONAN THE DESTROYER
(1984 - Universal) Arnold Schwarzenegger, Grace Jones
One Sheet: $10 - $20

CONCENTRATIN' KID, THE
(1930 - Universal) Hoot Gibson, Duke Lee
One Sheet: $250 - $500

CONCERT FOR BANGLADESH
(1972 - -) George Harrison, Eric Clapton, etc.
One Sheet: $40 - $75

CONCERT FOR KAMPUCHEA
(1982 - -) Paul McCartney & Wings
One Sheet: $40 - $75

CONCORDE-AIRPORT '79, THE
(1979 - Universal) Alain Delon, Robert Wagner
One Sheet: $5 - $10

CONCRETE JUNGLE,THE
(1982 - Pentagon) Jill St. John, Tracy Bregman
One Sheet: $2 - $3

CONDEMNED
(1929 - United Artists) Ronald Colman, Ann Harding
One Sheet: $600 - $1,000

CONDEMNED MEN
(1946R - -) Mantan Moreland, Dorothy Dandridge
One Sheet: $150 - $300   *Black cast. Re-titled re-release of "FOUR SHALL DIE."*

CONDEMNED OF ALTONA, THE
(1963 - 20th Century Fox) Sophia Loren, Maximilian Schell
One Sheet: $15 - $30

CONDEMNED TO LIVE
(1935 - Invincible) Ralph Morgan, Mischa Auer
One Sheet: $100 - $200   *Graven Images, pg. 95.*

CONDEMNED WOMEN
(1938 - RKO) Louis Hayward, Sally Eilers
One Sheet: $75 - $150

CONDORMAN
(1981 - Disney) Michael Crawford, Oliver Reed
One Sheet: $5 - $10

CONEHEADS, THE
(1993 - Paramount) Dan Aykroyd, Jane Curtin
One Sheet: $5 - $10

CONEY ISLAND
(1943 - 20th Century Fox) Betty Grable, George Montgomery
One Sheet: $600 - $1,000

CONFESSION
(1937 - Warner Bros.) Kay Francis, Basil Rathbone
One Sheet: $150 - $350

CONFESSION, THE
(1970 - Paramount) Yves Montand, Simone Signoret
One Sheet: $5 - $10

CONFESSIONS OF A CO-ED
(1931 - Paramount Publix) Sylvia Sidney, Phillips Holmes
One Sheet: $250 - $600

CONFESSIONS OF A NAZI SPY
(1939 - Warner Bros.) Edward G. Robinson, Francis Lederer
One Sheet: $75 - $150

CONFESSIONS OF A SORORITY GIRL
(1957 - -) -
One Sheet: $15 - $30   *Sexploitation.*

CONFESSIONS OF A VICE BARON
(1943 - Real Life Dramas) Willy Castello
One Sheet: $50 - $100

CONFESSIONS OF A WINDOW CLEANER
(1974 - Columbia) Anthony Booth, Linda Hayden
One Sheet: $5 - $10

CONFESSIONS OF AN OPIUM EATER
(1962 - Allied Artists) Vincent Price, Linda Ho
One Sheet: $75 - $125

CONFESSIONS OF BOSTON BLACKIE
(1942 - Columbia) Chester Morris, Harriet Hilliard
One Sheet: $75 - $125

CONFESSIONS OF FELIX KRULL, THE
(1958 - United Artists) Harst Buchholz, Lilo Pulver
One Sheet: $7 - $15

CONFIDENCE
(1922 - Universal) Herbert Rawlinson, Harriet Hammond
One Sheet: $150 - $300

CONFIDENCE GIRL
(1952 - United Artists) Tom Conway, Hillary Brooke
One Sheet: $15 - $30

CONFIDENTIAL
(1935 - Mascot) Donald Cook, Evalyn Knapp
One Sheet: $100 - $200

CONFIDENTIAL AGENT
(1945 - Warner Bros.) Charles Boyer, Lauren Bacall
One Sheet: $75 - $150

One Sheet

CONFIDENTIAL REPORT
(1955 - Talbot) Orson Welles, Robert Arden
One Sheet: $125 - $250   *AKA: MR. ARKADIN*

CONFIDENTIALLY CONNIE
(1953 - MGM) Van Johnson, Janet Leigh

One Sheet: $15 - $25

CONFIRM OR DENY
(1941 - 20th Century Fox) Don Ameche, Joan Bennett
One Sheet: $100 - $200

CONFLICT
(1936 - Universal) John Wayne, Ward Bond, Jean Rogers
One Sheet: $350 - $750

CONFLICT
(1945 - Warner Bros.) Humphrey Bogart, Alexis Smith
One Sheet: $150 - $300

CONFLICT
(1949R - Warner Bros.) Humphrey Bogart, Alexis Smith
One Sheet: $40 - $80   *Re-release.*

CONFLICT
(1956R - Warner Bros.) Humphrey Bogart, Alexis Smith
One Sheet: $20 - $40   *Re-release.*

CONGO
(1995 - Paramount) Laura Linney, Dylan Walsh
One Sheet: $4 - $8   *Price is for either style.*

CONGO BILL
(1948 - Columbia) Don McGuire, Cleo Moore
One Sheet: $50 - $100   *Serial. 15 Chapters.*

CONGO BILL
(1957R - Columbia) Don McGuire, Cleo Moore
One Sheet: $15 - $25   *Re-release. Serial.*

CONGO CROSSING
(1956 - Universal) Virginia Mayo, Peter Lorre, George Nader
One Sheet: $30 - $50

CONGO MAISIE
(1940 - MGM) Ann Sothern, John Carroll
One Sheet: $50 - $100

CONGOLAISE
(1950 - Film Classics) -
One Sheet: $15 - $30

CONGORILLA
(1932 - Fox) Mr. & Mrs. Martin Johnson, Simba
One Sheet: $250 - $500

CONGRESS DANCES
(1932 - United Artists) Lillian Harvey, Conrad Veidt
One Sheet: $250 - $500

CONGRESS DANCES
(1956 - Republic) Johanna Matz, Rudolf Prack
One Sheet: $30 - $50

CONJUGAL BED, THE
(1963 - Avco/Embassy) Ugo Tognazzi, Marina Vlady
One Sheet: $5 - $10

CONNECTICUT YANKEE
(1931 - Fox) Will Rogers, William Farnum
One Sheet: $350 - $600

CONNECTICUT YANKEE IN KING ARTHUR'S COURT, A
(1920 - Fox) Emmett J. Flynn
One Sheet: $500 - $800

One Sheet

CONNECTICUT YANKEE IN KING ARTHUR'S

COURT, A
(1949 - Paramount) Bing Crosby, Rhonda Fleming, William Bendix
One Sheet: $100 - $200

CONNECTION, THE
(1961 - Allan/Clarke) William Redfield
One Sheet: $40 - $75   *Drug Documentary.*

CONQUERED CITY
(1962 - AIP) David Niven, Ben Gazzara
One Sheet: $5 - $10

CONQUERING HORDE, THE
(1931 - Paramount Publix) Richard Arlen, Fay Wray
One Sheet: $250 - $500

CONQUERING POWER, THE
(1921 - Metro) Rudolph Valentino
One Sheet: $600 - $1,000

Lobby Card

CONQUEROR, THE
(1917 - Fox) William Farnum, Jewel Carmen
One Sheet: $500 - $800

CONQUEROR, THE
(1956 - RKO) John Wayne, Susan Hayward
One Sheet: $100 - $200

CONQUEROR WORM, THE
(1968 - AIP) Vincent Price, Ian Ogilvy
One Sheet: $30 - $50

CONQUERORS, THE
(1932 - RKO) Richard Dix, Ann Harding
One Sheet: $700 - $1,200   *Cowboy Movie Posters #133.*

CONQUEST
(1937 - MGM) Greta Garbo, Charles Boyer
One Sheet: $1,600 - $2,500

CONQUEST OF CHEYENNE
(1946 - Republic) Wild Bill Elliott, Alice Fleming
One Sheet: $40 - $75   *From the Red Ryder series.*

CONQUEST OF COCHISE
(1953 - Columbia) John Hodiak, Robert Stack
One Sheet: $15 - $25

CONQUEST OF SPACE
(1955 - Paramount) Walter Brooke, Eric Fleming
One Sheet: $75 - $175   *Graven Images, pg. 146.*

CONQUEST OF THE PLANET OF THE APES
(1972 - 20th Century Fox) Roddy McDowall, Don Murray
One Sheet: $30 - $50

CONRACK
(1974 - 20th Century Fox) Jon Voight, Paul Winfield
One Sheet: $5 - $10

CONRAD IN QUEST OF HIS YOUTH
(1920 - Paramount) Thomas Meighan, Kathlyn Williams, Mabel Van Buren
One Sheet: $250 - $500

CONSENTING ADULTS
(1992 - Buena Vista) Kevin Kline, Mary Elizabeth Mastrantonio
One Sheet: $3 - $5

CONSOLATION MARRIAGE
(1931 - RKO) Irene Dunne, Pat O'Brien, Myrna Loy
One Sheet: $150 - $350

CONSPIRACY
(1930 - RKO) Ned Sparks, Bessie Love
One Sheet: $200 - $400

CONSPIRACY
(1939 - RKO) Allan Lane, Linda Hayes
One Sheet: $75 - $150

CONSPIRATOR
(1949 - MGM) Robert Taylor, Elizabeth Taylor
One Sheet: $75 - $125

CONSPIRATORS, THE
(1944 - Warner Bros.) Hedy Lamarr, Paul Henreid
One Sheet: $50 - $100

CONSTANT HUSBAND, THE
(1954 - Stratford) Rex Harrison, Kay Kendall
One Sheet: $15 - $30

CONSTANT NYMPH, THE
(1934 - Fox) Victoria Hopper, Brian Aherne
One Sheet: $150 - $300

CONSTANT NYMPH, THE
(1943 - Warner Bros.) Charles Boyer, Joan Fontaine
One Sheet: $40 - $75

CONSTANT WOMAN, THE
(1933 - World Wide) Conrad Nagel, Leila Hyams
One Sheet: $75 - $150

CONSTANTINE AND THE CROSS
(1962 - Avco/Embassy) Cornel Wilde, Belinda Lee
One Sheet: $7 - $15

CONSTANTINOPLE
(1917 - Educational Films) -
One Sheet: $600 - $1,000

CONTEMPT
(1964 - Concinor) Brigitte Bardot, Jack Palance
One Sheet: $200 - $400   *Price is for original French(47x63). One Sheet(U.S.):$50-$100.*

CONTENDER, THE
(1944 - PRC) Buster Crabbe, Arline Judge
One Sheet: $40 - $75

CONTEST GIRL
(1966 - Continental) Ian Hendry, Janette Scott
One Sheet: $10 - $20

CONTINENTAL DIVIDE
(1981 - Universal) John Belushi, Blair Brown
One Sheet: $15 - $30

CONTRABAND
(1940 - British National) See BLACKOUT

CONTRABAND SPAIN
(1955 - Associated British-Pathe) Richard Greene, Anouk Aimes
One Sheet: $10 - $20

CONTRARY CONDOR
(1944 - RKO/Disney) Donald Duck
One Sheet: $1,300 - $2,000   *Cartoon. Cartoon Movie Posters #174.*

CONTROL YOURSELF
(1925 - William Fox) -
One Sheet: $150 - $350

CONVENTION CITY
(1933 - Fox) Adolphe Menjou, Mary Astor, Joan Blondell
One Sheet: $150 - $300

CONVERSATION, THE
(1974 - Paramount) Gene Hackman, John Cazale, Dir: Francis Ford Coppola
One Sheet: $15 - $35

CONVERSION OF FROSTY BLAKE, THE
(1915 - Broncho) William S. Hart
One Sheet: $1,300 - $2,000   *Cowboy Movie Posters #8.*

CONVICT
(1938 - GFD) Will Hay
One Sheet: $50 - $100

CONVICT 13
(1920 - Metro) Buster Keaton
One Sheet: $5,000 - $8,000

CONVICT STAGE
(1965 - 20th Century Fox) Harry Lauter, Donald Berry
One Sheet: $5 - $10

CONVICT'S CODE
(1939 - Monogram) Robert Kent, Anna Nagel
One Sheet: $50 - $100

CONVICTED
(1938 - Columbia) Charles Quigley, Rita Hayworth
One Sheet: $150 - $300

CONVICTED
(1950 - Columbia) Glenn Ford, Broderick Crawford
One Sheet: $15 - $35

CONVICTED WOMAN
(1940 - Columbia) Rochelle Hudson, June Lang
One Sheet: $75 - $150

CONVICTS 4
(1962 - Allied Artists) Ben Gazzara, Stuart Whitman
One Sheet: $5 - $10

CONVOY
(1941 - RKO) Clive Brook, John Clements
One Sheet: $75 - $125

CONVOY
(1978 - United Artists) Kris Kristofferson, Ali MacGraw, Dir: Peckinpah
One Sheet: $3 - $5

COO-COO BIRD DOG
(1948 - Columbia) Phantasy
One Sheet: $150 - $300   *Cartoon. Full color stock poster.*

COOGAN'S BLUFF
(1968 - Universal) Clint Eastwood, Lee J. Cobb, Susan Clark
One Sheet: $50 - $100

COOKIE
(1989 - -) Peter Falk, Diane Wiest
One Sheet: $3 - $5

COOK, THE THIEF, HIS WIFE AND HER LOVER
(1989 - -) Helen Mirren, Michael Gambon
One Sheet: $10 - $20

COOL AND THE CRAZY, THE
(1958 - AIP) Gigi Perreau, Scott Marlowe
One Sheet: $50 - $100

COOL BREEZE
(1972 - MGM) Thalmus Rasulala, Judy Pace
One Sheet: $10 - $20   *Black cast.*

COOL HAND LUKE
(1967 - Warner Bros.) Paul Newman, George Kennedy
One Sheet: $100 - $200   *Academy Award Movie Posters #244.*

COOL ONES, THE
(1967 - Warner Bros.) Roddy McDowall, Debbie Watson
One Sheet: $15 - $35

COOL RUNNINGS
(1993 - Buena Vista) John Candy, Doug E. Doug
One Sheet: $3 - $5

COOL WORLD, THE
(1964 - Cinema) Hampton Clanton, Carl Lee
One Sheet: $15 - $25

COOL WORLD
(1992 - Paramount) Kim Basinger, Gabriel Byrne, Partial animation
One Sheet: $7 - $15

COOLEY HIGH
(1975 - AIP) Glynn Turman, Lawrence-Hilton Jacobs
One Sheet: $10 - $20   *Black cast.*

COONSKIN
(1975 - Bryanston) Dir: Ralph Bakshi, Voices: Barry White, Scatman Crothers
One Sheet: $15 - $30   *Cartoon.*

COP, THE
(1928 - Pathe) William Boyd, Alan Hale
One Sheet: $150 - $300

COP, THE
(1971 - Audobon) Michel Bouquet, John Garko

One Sheet: $5 - $10

COP
(1987 - -) James Woods, Lesley Ann Warren
One Sheet: $3 - $5

COP AND A HALF
(1993 - Universal) Burt Reynolds, Devon Butler
One Sheet: $3 - $5

COP HATER
(1957 - United Artists) Robert Loggia, Gerald O'Laughlin
One Sheet: $30 - $50

COP OUT
(1968 - Cinema) James Mason, Geraldine Chaplin, Bobby Darin
One Sheet: $5 - $10

COPACABANA
(1947 - United Artists) Groucho Marx, Carmen Miranda
One Sheet: $125 - $250

COPPER CANYON
(1950 - Paramount) Ray Milland, Hedy Lamarr
One Sheet: $40 - $75

COPPER SKY
(1957 - 20th Century Fox) Jeff Morrow, Coleen Gray
One Sheet: $10 - $20

COPS
(1922 - Comique) Buster Keaton
One Sheet: $5,000 - $8,000

Lobby Card

COPS AND ROBBERS
(1973 - United Artists) Cliff Gorman, Joseph Bologna
One Sheet: $5 - $10

COPS AND ROBBERSONS
(1994 - TriStar) Chevy Chase, Jack Palance, Dianne Wiest
One Sheet: $3 - $5

COPS IS ALWAYS RIGHT
(1938 - Paramount) Popeye
One Sheet: $800 - $1,500   *Cartoon. Duotone.*

COPYCAT
(1995 - Warner Bros.) Holly Hunter, Sigourney Weaver, Harry Connick Jr.
One Sheet: $5 - $10

COQUETTE
(1929 - United Artists) Mary Pickford, Johnny Mack Brown
One Sheet: $1,300 - $2,000   *Academy Award: Best Actress. Academy Award Movie Posters #14.*

CORKY OF GASOLINE ALLEY
(1951 - Columbia) Jimmy Lydon, Scotty Beckett
One Sheet: $30 - $50

CORN CHIPS
(1951 - RKO/Disney) Donald Duck, Chip & Dale
One Sheet: $700 - $1,200   *Cartoon. Full color. Cartoon Movie Posters #180.*

CORN IS GREEN, THE
(1945 - Warner Bros.) Bette Davis, John Dall
One Sheet: $200 - $400

CORNBREAD EARL AND ME
(1975 - AIP) Moses Gunn, Rosalind Cash, Bernie Casey
One Sheet: $15 - $25   *Black cast. Sports Movie Posters #93.*

CORNERED
(1932 - Columbia) Tim McCoy
One Sheet: $800 - $1,500   *Cowboy Movie Posters #'s 122, 125.*

Three Sheet

CORNERED
(1945 - RKO) Dick Powell, Micheline Cheirel
One Sheet: $75 - $150

CORNY CASANOVAS
(1952 - Columbia) The Three Stooges (Shemp)
One Sheet: $150 - $350   *Comedy short. Duotone.*

CORONADO
(1935 - Paramount) Johnny Downs, Jack Haley
One Sheet: $75 - $150

CORONER CREEK
(1948 - Columbia) Randolph Scott, Marguerite Chapman
One Sheet: $50 - $100

CORPSE CAME C.O.D., THE
(1947 - Columbia) George Brent, Joan Blondell
One Sheet: $40 - $75

CORPSE EATERS
(1970S - -) -
One Sheet: $15 - $25

CORPSE GRINDERS, THE
(1972 - Geneni) Sean Kennedy, Monika Kelly
One Sheet: $10 - $20

CORPSE VANISHES, THE
(1942 - Monogram) Bela Lugosi, Luana Walters
One Sheet: $500 - $800   *Graven Images, pg. 133.*

CORPUS CHRISTI BANDITS
(1945 - Republic) Allan Lane, Helen Talbot
One Sheet: $50 - $100

CORRALING A SCHOOL MARM
(1940 - RKO) -
One Sheet: $50 - $100

CORREGIDOR
(1943 - PRC) Otto Kruger, Elissa Landi
One Sheet: $40 - $75

CORRIDOR OF MIRRORS
(1949 - Universal) Eric Portman, Barbara Muller
One Sheet: $40 - $75

CORRIDORS OF BLOOD
(1958 - MGM) Boris Karloff, Betta St. John
One Sheet: $40 - $75

CORRIDORS OF BLOOD
(1963R - MGM) Boris Karloff, Betta St. John
One Sheet: $15 - $25   *Re-release.*

CORRINA, CORRINA
(1994 - New Line) Whoopi Goldberg, Ray Liotta, Tina Majorino
One Sheet: $5 - $10

CORRUPT ONES, THE
(1967 - Warner Bros.) Robert Stack, Elke Sommer
One Sheet: $5 - $10

CORRUPTION
(1968 - Columbia) Peter Cushing, Sue Lloyd
One Sheet: $7 - $15

CORRUPTION OF CHRIS MILLER, THE
(19?? - -) Jean Seberg
One Sheet: $3 - $5

CORSAIR
(1931 - United Artists) Chester Morris, Alison Loyd
One Sheet: $150 - $350   *Beware of undated re-release posters.*

CORSICAN BROTHERS, THE
(1920 - United) Dustin Farnum
One Sheet: $250 - $600

CORSICAN BROTHERS, THE
(1941 - United Artists) Douglas Fairbanks, Jr., Ruth Warrick
One Sheet: $125 - $250

One Sheet

CORSICAN BROTHERS, THE
(1947R - United Artists) Douglas Fairbanks Jr., Ruth Warrick
One Sheet: $30 - $50   *Re-release.*

CORVETTE K-225
(1943 - Universal) Randolph Scott, James Brown
One Sheet: $100 - $200

CORVETTE K-225
(1948R - Universal) Randolph Scott, James Brown
One Sheet: $30 - $50   *Re-release.*

CORVETTE SUMMER
(1978 - MGM) Mark Hamill, Annie Potts
One Sheet: $20 - $40   *Sports (Auto Racing). Sports Movie Posters #24. Advance:$12-20.*

COSI
(1996 - Miramax) Ben Mendelson, Toni Collette
One Sheet: $3 - $5   *Comedy.*

COSMIC MAN, THE
(1959 - Allied Artists) Bruce Bennett, John Carradine, Angela Greene
One Sheet: $50 - $100

COSMIC MONSTERS
(1958 - DCA) Forrest Tucker, Gaby Andre
One Sheet: $40 - $75

COSMO JONES, CRIME SMASHER
(1943 - Monogram) Edgar Kennedy, Frank Graham
One Sheet: $50 - $100

COSMOPOLITAN LIFE IN CAIRO
(1912 - Pathe) -
One Sheet: $600 - $1,000

COSSACKS, THE
(1928 - MGM) John Gilbert, Renee Adoree
One Sheet: $200 - $400

COSSACKS, THE
(1960 - Universal) Edmund Purdom, John Drew Barrymore
One Sheet: $7 - $15

COSTELLO CASE, THE
(1930 - Sono Art-World Wide) Tom Moore, Lola Lane
One Sheet: $75 - $150

COTTAGE GARDEN, A
(1924 - Kelley) -
One Sheet: $250 - $500

COTTON CLUB, THE
(1984 - Orion) Richard Gere, Gregory Hines, Dir: Francis Coppola
One Sheet: $7 - $15   *Advance:$40-75.*

COTTON COMES TO HARLEM
(1970 - United Artists) Godfrey Cambridge, Raymond St. Jacques
One Sheet: $15 - $25   *Blaxploitation.*

COUCH, THE
(1962 - Warner Bros.) Grant Williams, Shirley Knight
One Sheet: $15 - $25

COUCH TRIP, THE
(1988 - Orion) Dan Aykroyd, Walter Matthau, Donna Dixon
One Sheet: $3 - $5

COUGAR COUNTRY
(1972 - American National) -
One Sheet: $5 - $10

COUNSEL FOR CRIME
(1937 - Columbia) Otto Kruger, Jacqueline Wells
One Sheet: $100 - $200

COUNSELLOR-AT-LAW
(1933 - Universal) John Barrymore, Bebe Daniels
One Sheet: $800 - $1,500

COUNT, THE
(1916 - Mutual) Charlie Chaplin
One Sheet: $7,500 - $12,000

COUNT DRACULA AND HIS VAMPIRE BRIDE
(1978 - Astral/Hammer) Christopher Lee, Peter Cushing
One Sheet: $15 - $25

COUNT FIVE AND DIE
(1957 - 20th Century Fox) Jeffrey Hunter, Nigel Patrick
One Sheet: $15 - $25

COUNT OF MONTE CRISTO, THE
(1934 - United Artists) Robert Donat, Elissa Landi
One Sheet: $1,600 - $2,500

COUNT OF MONTE CRISTO, THE
(1948R - United Artists) Robert Donat, Elissa Landi
One Sheet: $75 - $150   *Re-release.*

COUNT THE HOURS
(1953 - RKO) Teresa Wright, Macdonald Carey
One Sheet: $15 - $25

COUNT THREE AND PRAY
(1955 - Columbia) Van Heflin, Joanne Woodward
One Sheet: $15 - $25

COUNT YORGA, VAMPIRE
(1970 - AIP) Robert Quarry, Roger Perry
One Sheet: $30 - $50

COUNT YOUR BLESSINGS
(1959 - MGM) Deborah Kerr, Rossano Brazzi
One Sheet: $15 - $25

COUNTDOWN
(1968 - Warner Bros.) James Caan, Joanna Moore
One Sheet: $7 - $15

COUNTED OUT
(1920S - Maco Comedies) Charlie Chaplin, Fatty Arbuckle
One Sheet: $1,600 - $2,500   *Retitled rerelease of "The Knockout."*

COUNTER-ATTACK
(1945 - Columbia) Paul Muni, Margueritte Chapman
One Sheet: $50 - $100

COUNTER-ESPIONAGE
(1942 - Columbia) Warren William, Eric Blore
One Sheet: $50 - $100

COUNTERFEIT
(1936 - Columbia) Chester Morris, Lloyd Nolan
One Sheet: $100 - $200

COUNTERFEIT CAT, THE
(1949 - MGM) -
One Sheet: $600 - $1,000   *Cartoon.*

COUNTERFEIT CONSTABLE, THE
(1966 - Seven Arts) Robert Dhery
One Sheet: $5 - $10

COUNTERFEIT KILLER, THE
(1970 - Universal) Jack Lord, Shirley Knight
One Sheet: $5 - $10

COUNTERFEIT PLAN, THE
(1957 - Warner Bros.) Zachary Scott, Peggie Castle
One Sheet: $7 - $15

COUNTERFEIT TRAITOR, THE
(1962 - Paramount) William Holden, Lilli Palmer
One Sheet: $30 - $50

COUNTERFEITERS
(1948 - 20th Century Fox) John Sutton, Doris Merrick
One Sheet: $40 - $75

COUNTERFEITERS OF PARIS, THE
(1962 - MGM) Jean Gabin, Bernard Blier
One Sheet: $5 - $10

COUNTERFEITERS' CONFEDERATE, THE
(1915 - Kalem) -
One Sheet: $200 - $400

COUNTERPLOT
(1959 - United Artists) Forrest Tucker, Allison Hayes
One Sheet: $7 - $15

COUNTERPOINT
(1968 - Universal) Charlton Heston, Leslie Nielsen
One Sheet: $5 - $10

COUNTERSPY MEETS SCOTLAND YARD
(1950 - Columbia) Howard St. John, Amanda Blake
One Sheet: $20 - $40

COUNTESS DRACULA
(1972 - 20th Century Fox) Ingrid Pitt, Nigel Green
One Sheet: $15 - $25

COUNTESS FROM HONG KONG, A
(1967 - Universal) Marlon Brando, Sophia Loren, Charlie Chaplin
One Sheet: $20 - $40   *Chaplin's last film.*

COUNTESS OF MONTE CRISTO, THE
(1934 - Universal) Fay Wray, Paul Lukas
One Sheet: $250 - $500

COUNTESS OF MONTE CRISTO, THE
(1948 - Universal) Sonja Henie, Olga San Juan, Michael Kirby
One Sheet: $75 - $150

COUNTRY
(1984 - Touchstone) Jessica Lange, Sam Shepard
One Sheet: $3 - $5

COUNTRY BEYOND, THE
(1926 - Fox) Olive Borden, Ralph Graves
One Sheet: $250 - $500

COUNTRY BEYOND, THE
(1936 - 20th Century Fox) Paul Kelly, Rochelle Hudson
One Sheet: $125 - $250

COUNTRY COYOTE GOES HOLLYWOOD, A
(1965 - Disney) Narrated by Rex Allen
One Sheet: $15 - $25

COUNTRY DOCTOR, THE
(1936 - 20th Century Fox) Dionne Quints, Jean Hersholt, June Lang
One Sheet: $100 - $200

COUNTRY FAIR
(1941 - Republic) Eddie Foy Jr., June Clyde
One Sheet: $75 - $125   *Country musical.*

COUNTRY FLAPPER, THE
(1922 - -) Dorothy Gish
One Sheet: $250 - $600

COUNTRY GENTLEMAN
(1936 - Republic) Olsen and Johnson, Leila Lee
One Sheet: $125 - $250

COUNTRY GENTLEMAN
(1945R - Republic) Olsen & Johnson, Leila Lee
One Sheet: $50 - $100   *Re-release.*

COUNTRY GIRL, THE
(1954 - Paramount) Bing Crosby, Grace Kelly, William Holden
One Sheet: $75 - $125   *Academy*

Award Movie Posters #157.

COUNTRY GIRL, THE
(1959R - Paramount) Bing Crosby, Grace Kelly, William Holden
One Sheet: $15 - $30   *Re-release.*

COUNTRY MUSIC
(1972 - Universal) Marty Robbins, Sammy Jackson
One Sheet: $30 - $50   *Country musical.*

COUNTRY MUSIC HOLIDAY
(1958 - Paramount) Ferlin Husky, Zsa Zsa Gabor
One Sheet: $40 - $75   *Country musical.*

COUNTRY MUSIC ON BROADWAY
(1964 - -) -
One Sheet: $40 - $75   *Country musical.*

COUNTRYMAN
(1982 - Islan) Countryman, Bob Marley & The Wailers, The Gladiators
One Sheet: $15 - $30   *Rock n Roll (Reggae).*

COUNTY CHAIRMAN, THE
(1935 - Fox) Will Rogers, Evelyn Venable
One Sheet: $250 - $600

COUNTY FAIR
(1920 - -) Edythe Chapman, David Butler
One Sheet: $250 - $600

COUNTY FAIR
(1932 - Monogram) Hobert Bosworth, Marion Shilling
One Sheet: $100 - $200

COUNTY FAIR
(1933 - MGM) Stewart Rome, Rosalinde Fuller, Dir:John Baxter
One Sheet: $100 - $200   *AKA: "Song Of The Plough".*

COUNTY FAIR
(1937 - Monogram) John Arledge, Mary Lou Lender
One Sheet: $75 - $150   *Sports (Horse racing).*

COUNTY FAIR
(1950 - Monogram) Rory Calhoun, Jane Nigh
One Sheet: $30 - $50   *Sports (Horse racing).*

COUNTY HOSPITAL
(1932 - MGM) Laurel & Hardy
One Sheet: $2,500 - $4,000

COUPE DE VILLE
(1990 - -) Patrick Dempsey, Ayre Gross, Daniel Stern
One Sheet: $5 - $10

COUPLE OF SKATES, A
(1926 - Bluebird) Neely Edwards
One Sheet: $125 - $250

COURAGE
(1930 - Warner Bros.) Belle Bennett, Marian Nixon, Rex Bell
One Sheet: $100 - $200

COURAGE OF BLACK BEAUTY
(1957 - Alco) John Crawford, Diane Brewster
One Sheet: $15 - $30

COURAGE OF COLLINS
(1925 - Mustang) Edmund Cobb
One Sheet: $125 - $250

COURAGE OF LASSIE
(1946 - MGM) Lassie, Frank Morgan, Elizabeth Taylor
One Sheet: $150 - $300

COURAGE OF LASSIE
(1972R - MGM) Lassie, Frank Morgan, Elizabeth Taylor
One Sheet: $15 - $30   *Re-release.*

COURAGE OF THE NORTH
(1935 - -) John Preston, June Love, William Desmond
One Sheet: $150 - $300

COURAGE OF THE WEST
(1937 - Universal) Bob Baker, Lois January
One Sheet: $30 - $50

COURAGE UNDER FIRE
(1996 - Fox) Denzel Washington, Meg Ryan
One Sheet: $5 - $10

COURAGEOUS AVENGER, THE
(1935 - Supreme) Johnny Mack Brown
One Sheet: $75 - $150

One Sheet

COURAGEOUS DR. CHRISTIAN, THE
(1940 - RKO) Jean Hersholt, Dorothy Lovett
One Sheet: $75 - $125

COURAGEOUS MR. PENN, THE
(1943 - Hoffberg Films) Clifford Evans, Deborah Kerr
One Sheet: $40 - $75

COURT JESTER, THE
(1955 - Paramount) Danny Kaye, Glynis Johns
One Sheet: $75 - $125

COURT MARTIAL
(1928 - Columbia) Betty Compson, Jack Holt
One Sheet: $250 - $600

COURT MARTIAL
(1955 - British-Lion) David Niven, Margaret Leighton
One Sheet: $15 - $30

COURTIN' TROUBLE
(1948 - Monogram) Jimmy Wakely, Cannonball Taylor
One Sheet: $30 - $50

COURTING TROUBLE
(1932 - Paramount) Murray, Herring, Stone
One Sheet: $125 - $250

COURT-MARTIAL OF BILLY MITCHELL, THE
(1955 - Warner Bros.) Gary Cooper, Charles Bickford, Ralph Bellamy, Rod Steiger
One Sheet: $40 - $75

COURTNEY AFFAIR, THE
(1947 - British-Lion) Anna Neagle, Michael Wilding
One Sheet: $30 - $60

COURTSHIP OF ANDY HARDY, THE
(1942 - MGM) Mickey Rooney, Lewis Stone
One Sheet: $100 - $200

COURTSHIP OF EDDIE'S FATHER, THE
(1963 - MGM) Glenn Ford, Shirley Jones
One Sheet: $7 - $15

COURTSHIP OF MYLES STANDISH, THE
(1923 - Associated) Charles Ray, Enid Bennett
One Sheet: $200 - $400

COUSIN WILBUR
(1939 - MGM) Our Gang
One Sheet: $600 - $1,000

COUSINS
(1989 - Paramount) Ted Danson, Isabella Rossellini
One Sheet: $3 - $5

COVENANT WITH DEATH, A
(1967 - Warner Bros.) George Maharis, Laura Devon
One Sheet: $15 - $25

COVER GIRL
(1944 - Columbia) Rita Hayworth, Gene Kelly
One Sheet: $250 - $500

COVER GIRL KILLER!
(1960 - Fanfare) Harry H. Corbett, Felicity Young

One Sheet: $15 - $25

COVER ME BABE
(1970 - 20th Century Fox) Robert Forster, Sandra Locke
One Sheet: $3 - $5

COVERED TRAILER, THE
(1939 - Republic) James, Lucille and Russell Gleason
One Sheet: $50 - $100

COVERED WAGON, THE
(1923 - Paramount) Alan Hale, Lois Wilson
One Sheet: $1,300 - $2,000   *Cowboy Movie Posters #'s 34, 35, 36, 37, 38. Price is for Style A. One Sheet(Style B or C):$500-1000.*

COVERED WAGON DAYS
(1940 - Republic) Three Mesquiteers (Livingston, Renaldo, Hatton)
One Sheet: $50 - $100

COVERED WAGON RAID
(1950 - Republic) Allan "Rocky" Lane, Eddie Waller
One Sheet: $15 - $35

COVERED WAGON TRAILS
(1940 - Monogram) Jack Randall
One Sheet: $75 - $150   *Full color stone litho.*

COVER-UP
(1949 - United Artists) William Bendix, Dennis O'Keefe
One Sheet: $50 - $100

COW AND THE SPRITE, THE
(1949 - David A. Smart) -
One Sheet: $20 - $40

COW CAMP BALLADS
(1929 - Paramount) -
One Sheet: $250 - $500

COW COUNTRY
(1953 - Monogram) Edmond O'Brien, Helen Westcott
One Sheet: $10 - $20

COW TOWN
(1950 - Columbia) Gene Autry, Gail Davis
One Sheet: $50 - $100

COWARD, THE
(1927 - FBO) Warner Baxter, Sharon Lynn
One Sheet: $200 - $400

COWBOY, THE
(1954 - Lippert) Documentary narrated by Tex Ritter (et al)
One Sheet: $15 - $25

COWBOY
(1958 - Columbia) Glenn Ford, Jack Lemmon
One Sheet: $20 - $40

COWBOY AND THE BANDIT, THE
(1935 - Superior) Rex Lease, Bobby Nelson
One Sheet: $125 - $250

COWBOY AND THE BLONDE, THE
(1941 - 20th Century Fox) George Montgomery, Mary Beth Hughes
One Sheet: $100 - $200

COWBOY AND THE GIRL
(1954R - -) John Wayne
One Sheet: $125 - $250   *Re-titled Re-release of LADY TAKES A CHANCE.*

COWBOY AND THE INDIANS, THE
(1949 - Columbia) Gene Autry, Clayton Moore
One Sheet: $75 - $125

COWBOY AND THE INDIANS, THE
(1954R - Columbia) Gene Autry, Clayton Moore
One Sheet: $40 - $75   *Re-release.*

COWBOY AND THE KID, THE
(1936 - Universal) Buck Jones
One Sheet: $250 - $500

COWBOY AND THE LADY, THE
(1938 - United Artists) Gary Cooper, Merle Oberon
One Sheet: $250 - $500

COWBOY AND THE LADY, THE
(1944R - Film Classics) Gary Cooper, Merle Oberon
One Sheet: $75 - $150   *Re-release.*

COWBOY AND THE OUTLAW, THE
(1929 - -) Bob Steele, Edna Astin
One Sheet: $200 - $400

COWBOY AND THE PRIZE FIGHTER, THE
(1950 - Eagle-Lion) Jim Bannon, Don Kay Reynolds
One Sheet: $40 - $75   *Sports (Boxing).*

COWBOY AND THE SENORITA
(1944 - Republic) Roy Rogers, Mary Lee
One Sheet: $150 - $350

Window Card

COWBOY BLUES
(1946 - Columbia) Ken Curtis, Jeff Donnell
One Sheet: $50 - $100

COWBOY CANTEEN
(1944 - Columbia) Charles Starrett, Jane Frazee
One Sheet: $40 - $75

COWBOY CAVALIER
(1948 - Monogram) Jimmy Wakely, Cannonball Taylor
One Sheet: $40 - $75

COWBOY COMMANDOS
(1943 - Monogram) Range Busters
One Sheet: $20 - $40

One Sheet

COWBOY COUNSELLOR, THE
(1932 - Allied) Hoot Gibson
One Sheet: $200 - $400

COWBOY FROM BROOKLYN, THE
(1938 - Warner Bros.) Pat O'Brien, Dick Powell, Ronald Reagan
One Sheet: $150 - $300

COWBOY FROM LONESOME RIVER
(1944 - Columbia) Charles Starrett, Vi Athens
One Sheet: $40 - $75

COWBOY FROM SUNDOWN
(1940 - Monogram) Tex Ritter
One Sheet: $100 - $200

COWBOY FROM TEXAS
(1939 - Republic) Three Mesquiteers
One Sheet: $50 - $100

COWBOY IN MANHATTAN
(1943 - Universal) Frances Langford, Robert Paige
One Sheet: $50 - $100

COWBOY IN THE CLOUDS
(1944 - Columbia) Charles Starrett, Julie Duncan
One Sheet: $40 - $75

COWBOY KID
(1929 - Fox) Rex Bell
One Sheet: $150 - $300   *Cowboy Movie Posters #68.*

COWBOY MILLIONAIRE
(1935 - Atherton) Alden Chase, George O'Brien
One Sheet: $150 - $300

COWBOY QUARTERBACK
(1939 - First National) Bert Wheeler, Marie Wilson
One Sheet: $100 - $200   *Sports (Football). Sports Movie Posters #194.*

COWBOY SERENADE
(1942 - Republic) Gene Autry, Smiley Burnette
One Sheet: $125 - $250

COWBOY STAR, THE
(1936 - Columbia) Charles Starrett
One Sheet: $125 - $250

COWBOY WAY, THE
(1994 - Universal) Kiefer Sutherland, Woody Harrelson
One Sheet: $5 - $10

COWBOYS, THE
(1972 - Warner Bros.) John Wayne
One Sheet: $30 - $50   *Duotone. Cowboy Movie Posters #334. One Sheet(Style B):$30-$60.*

COWBOYS FROM TEXAS
(1939 - Republic) Duncan Renaldo, Robert Livingston, Raymond Hatton
One Sheet: $125 - $250   *Three Mesquiteers series.*

COYOTE CANYON
(1949 - Universal) Tex Williams
One Sheet: $20 - $40

COYOTE TRAILS
(1935 - Reliable) Tom Tyler
One Sheet: $150 - $300

CRAB, THE
(1917 - Triangle) Thelma Salter, Frank Keenan
One Sheet: $150 - $300

CRACK IN THE MIRROR
(1960 - 20th Century Fox) Orson Welles, Juliette Greco
One Sheet: $30 - $50

CRACK IN THE WORLD
(1965 - Paramount) Dana Andrews, Janette Scott
One Sheet: $15 - $35

CRACKED NUTS
(1931 - RKO) Wheeler and Woolsey, Edna May Oliver
One Sheet: $150 - $350

CRACKED NUTS
(1941 - Universal) Stu Erwin, Una Merkel
One Sheet: $50 - $100

CRACKERJACK, THE
(1925 - East Coast) Johnny Hines
One Sheet: $125 - $250

CRACKERS
(1984 - Universal) Donald Sutherland, Jack Warden, Sean Penn
One Sheet: $3 - $5

CRACKING UP
(1977 - AIP) Phil Proctor, Peter Bergman
One Sheet: $5 - $10

CRACK-UP
(1936 - 20th Century Fox) Peter Lorre, Brian Donlevy
One Sheet: $600 - $1,000

CRACK-UP
(1946 - RKO) Pat O'Brien, Claire Trevor
One Sheet: $125 - $250

CRADLE, THE
(1922 - Paramount) Ethel Clayton, Charles Meredith
One Sheet: $150 - $300

CRADLE SONG
(1933 - Paramount) Dorothea Wieck, Evelyn Venable
One Sheet: $75 - $150

CRAFT, THE
(1996 - Columbia) Robin Tunney, Fairuza Balk, Neve Campbell
One Sheet: $5 - $10   *Supernatural coming-of-ager.*

CRAIG'S WIFE
(1928 - Pathe) Warner Baxter, Irene Rich
One Sheet: $250 - $500

CRAIG'S WIFE
(1936 - Columbia) Rosalind Russell, John Boles
One Sheet: $150 - $300

CRASH, THE
(1932 - First National) George Brent, Ruth Chatterton
One Sheet: $150 - $300

CRASH
(1977 - Universal) Jose Ferrer, Sue Lyon, John Carradine
One Sheet: $5 - $10

CRASH
(1996 - Fine Line) James Spader, Holly Hunter, Rosanna Arquette
One Sheet: $7 - $15

One Sheet

CRASH DIVE
(1943 - 20th Century Fox) Tyrone Power, Anne Baxter, Dana Andrews
One Sheet: $150 - $300

One Sheet

CRASH DIVE
(1956R - 20th Century Fox) Tyrone Power, Anne Baxter, Dana Andrews
One Sheet: $30 - $50   *Re-release.*

CRASH DONOVAN
(1936 - Universal) Jack Holt, John King
One Sheet: $100 - $200

CRASH GOES THE HASH
(1944 - Columbia) The Three Stooges (Curly)
One Sheet: $2,500 - $4,000   *Comedy short. Duotone.*

CRASH LANDING
(1958 - Columbia) Gary Merrill, Nancy Davis
One Sheet: $15 - $30

CRASH OF SILENCE
(1953 - Universal) Phyllis Calvert, Jack Hawkins
One Sheet: $15 - $30

CRASHING BROADWAY
(1933 - Monogram) Rex Bell
One Sheet: $200 - $400

CRASHING HOLLYWOOD
(1938 - RKO) Lee Tracy, Joan Woodward
One Sheet: $100 - $200

CRASHING LAS VEGAS
(1956 - Allied Artists) Leo Gorcey, Huntz Hall
One Sheet: $50 - $100

Lobby Card

CRASHING THROUGH
(1939 - Grand National) James Newill, Milburn Stone
One Sheet: $50 - $100

CRASHING THROUGH DANGER
(1938 - Excelsior) Ray Walker, Guinn "Big Boy" Williams
One Sheet: $75 - $150

CRASHING THRU
(1949 - Monogram) Whip Wilson(1st starring role)
One Sheet: $20 - $45

CRASHOUT
(1955 - Filmakers) William Bendix, Arthur Kennedy
One Sheet: $15 - $25

CRATER LAKE MONSTER, THE
(1977 - Crown) Richard Cardella, Glenn Roberts
One Sheet: $10 - $20   *Animation by David Allen.*

CRAVING, THE
(1986 - -) Paul Naschy, Julie Saly
One Sheet: $5 - $10

CRAWLING EYE, THE
(1958 - DCA) Forrest Tucker
One Sheet: $100 - $200

CRAWLING HAND, THE
(1963 - AIP) Peter Breck, Arline Judge
One Sheet: $20 - $40

CRAZE
(1974 - Warner Bros.) Jack Palance, Diana Dors
One Sheet: $15 - $35

CRAZIES, THE
(1973 - Cambist) Lane Carroll, Dir: George Romero
One Sheet: $40 - $75

CRAZY FOR LOVE
(1960 - Cite-Films) Brigitte Bardot
One Sheet: $50 - $100   *French.*

CRAZY HOUSE
(1943 - Universal) Ole Olsen & Chic Johnson, Allan Jones
One Sheet: $75 - $150

CRAZY KNIGHTS
(1944 - Monogram) Billy Gilbert, Shemp Howard, Maxie Rosenbloom
One Sheet: $125 - $250

CRAZY LIKE A FOX
(1926 - Pathe) Charlie Chase
One Sheet: $150 - $300

CRAZY MAMA
(1975 - New World) Cloris Leachman, Stuart Whitman
One Sheet: $10 - $20

CRAZY MOON
(1986 - -) Kiefer Sutherland, Peter Spence, Vanessa Vaughan

One Sheet: $5 - $10

CRAZY OVER DAISY
(1950 - RKO/Disney) Donald Duck, Chip N' Dale
One Sheet: $600 - $1,000   *Cartoon. The Disney Poster, pg. 49.*

CRAZY OVER HORSES
(1951 - Monogram) Bowery Boys
One Sheet: $30 - $50

CRAZY PEOPLE
(1990 - Paramount) Dudley Moore, Darryl Hannah
One Sheet: $5 - $10

CRAZY QUILT
(1966 - Continental) Tom Rosqui, Ina Mela
One Sheet: $3 - $5

CRAZY RAY, THE
(1923 - -) Henri Rollan, Madeline Rodriguez, Dir: Rene Clair
One Sheet: $5,000 - $8,000   *Rare, early science fiction.*

CRAZY THAT WAY
(1930 - Fox) Kenneth MacKenna, Joan Bennett
One Sheet: $250 - $500

CRAZY WITH HEAT
(1947 - RKO/Disney) Donald Duck and Goofy
One Sheet: $1,600 - $2,500   *Cartoon. Full color. Cartoon Movie Posters #176.*

CRAZY WORLD OF LAUREL AND HARDY
(1967 - Hal Roach) Narrated by Garry Moore
One Sheet: $20 - $40

CRAZYLEGS
(1953 - Monogram) Lloyd Nolan, Elroy "Crazylegs" Hirsch
One Sheet: $100 - $200   *Sports (Football). Sports Movie Posters #201.*

CREATION OF THE HUMANOIDS
(1962 - Emerson) Don Megowan, Frances McLann
One Sheet: $30 - $50

CREATOR
(1985 - -) Peter O'Toole, Mariel Hemingway, Vincent Spano
One Sheet: $3 - $5

CREATURE
(1985 - Cardinal) Stan Ivar, Wendy Schaal, Klaus Kinski
One Sheet: $5 - $10

CREATURE FROM BLACK LAKE, THE
(1976 - Howco) Jack Elam, Dub Taylor
One Sheet: $15 - $25

CREATURE FROM THE BLACK LAGOON
(1954 - Universal) Richard Carlson, Julia Adams
One Sheet: $2,500 - $4,000   *Graven Images, pg. xiv, 160-161. Posters for 3-D version are worth 50% more. One Sheet (military style,duotone):$150-$300.*

CREATURE FROM THE BLACK LAGOON
(1974R - Universal) Richard Carlson, Julia Adams
One Sheet: $20 - $40   *3-D Re-release.*

CREATURE FROM THE BLACK LAGOON
(1976R - Howco) Richard Carlson, Julia Adams
One Sheet: $20 - $40   *Re-release.*

CREATURE FROM THE HAUNTED SEA
(1961 - Filmgroup) Antony Carbone, Betsy Jones, Dir: Roger Corman
One Sheet: $40 - $75

CREATURE OF DESTRUCTION
(1968 - -) Les Tremayne, Pat Delaney
One Sheet: $15 - $25

CREATURE WALKS AMONG US, THE
(1956 - Universal) Jeff Morrow, Rex Reason, Leigh Snowden
One Sheet: $300 - $700   *Graven Images, pg. 161.*

CREATURE WITH THE ATOM BRAIN
(1955 - Columbia) Richard Denning, Angela Stevens
One Sheet: $100 - $200

CREATURES, THE

(1974 - -) See FROM BEYOND THE GRAVE

CREATURES THE WORLD FORGOT
(1971 - Columbia) Julie Ege, Tony Bonner
One Sheet: $15 - $25

CREEPER, THE
(1948 - 20th Century Fox) Eduardo Ciannelli,
Onslow Stevens
One Sheet: $100 - $200

CREEPERS
(1985 - -) Jennifer Connelly, Donald Pleasence
One Sheet: $7 - $15

CREEPING FLESH, THE
(1972 - Columbia) Christopher Lee, Peter
Cushing
One Sheet: $15 - $35

CREEPING TERROR, THE
(1964 - Metropolitan) Vic Savage, Shannon
O'Neill
One Sheet: $30 - $50

CREEPING UNKNOWN, THE
(1955 - United Artists) Brian Donlevy, Margia
Dean
One Sheet: $40 - $75   *AKA: THE
QUATERMASS EXPERIMENT.*

CREEPS
(1956 - Columbia) The Three Stooges (Shemp)
One Sheet: $150 - $300   *Comedy short.
Duotone.*

CREEPSHOW
(1982 - Warner Bros.) Hal Holbrook, Adrienne
Barbeau
One Sheet: $15 - $25   *Wrightson art.
1st Advance:$40-$80. 2nd Advance:$20-$40.*

One Sheet

CREEPSHOW 2
(1987 - New World) Lois Chiles, George
Kennedy, Dorthy Lamour
One Sheet: $7 - $15

CREMATORS, THE
(1972 - New World) Maria Di Aragon
One Sheet: $10 - $20

CRESCENDO
(1972 - Warner Bros.) Stefanie Powers, James
Olson
One Sheet: $5 - $10

CREST OF THE WAVE
(1954 - MGM) Gene Kelly, Jeff Richards
One Sheet: $30 - $50

CRIES AND WHISPERS
(1973 - New World) Liv Ullmann, Harriet
Andersson
One Sheet: $15 - $35

CRIME AGAINST JOE
(1956 - United Artists) John Bromfield, Julie
London
One Sheet: $15 - $25

CRIME AND PUNISHMENT
(1935 - Columbia) Peter Lorre, Edward Arnold
One Sheet: $3,500 - $5,000

CRIME AND PUNISHMENT
(1945R - Columbia) Peter Lorre, Edward Arnold
One Sheet: $150 - $300   *Re-release.*

CRIME AND PUNISHMENT, USA
(1959 - Allied Artists) George Hamilton, Frank
Silvera
One Sheet: $15 - $25

CRIME BENEATH THE SEA
(1957 - Allied Artists) Mara Corday, Pat
Conway
One Sheet: $20 - $40

CRIME BY NIGHT
(1944 - Warner Bros.) Jane Wyman, Jerome
Cowan
One Sheet: $50 - $100

CRIME DOCTOR
(1934 - RKO) Otto Kruger, Karen Morley
One Sheet: $250 - $500

CRIME DOCTOR
(1943 - Columbia) Warner Baxter, Margaret
Lindsay
One Sheet: $75 - $150   *First of 10
Crime Doctor films.*

CRIME DOCTOR'S COURAGE, THE
(1945 - Columbia) Warner Baxter, Hillary
Brooke
One Sheet: $50 - $100

CRIME DOCTOR'S DIARY
(1949 - Columbia) Warner Baxter, Lois Maxwell
One Sheet: $40 - $75

CRIME DOCTOR'S GAMBLE, THE
(1947 - Columbia) Warner Baxter, Micheline
Cheirel
One Sheet: $40 - $75

CRIME DOCTOR'S MANHUNT, THE
(1946 - Columbia) Warner Baxter, Ellen Drew
One Sheet: $40 - $75

CRIME DOCTOR'S STRANGEST CASE
(1943 - Columbia) Warner Baxter, Lynn Merrick
One Sheet: $50 - $100

CRIME DOCTOR'S WARNING, THE
(1945 - Columbia) Warner Baxter, Dusty
Anderson
One Sheet: $50 - $100

CRIME IN THE STREETS
(1956 - Allied Artists) James Whitmore, John
Cassavetes, Sal Mineo
One Sheet: $20 - $40

CRIME, INC.
(1945 - PRC) Leo Carrillo, Tom Neal
One Sheet: $40 - $75

CRIME NOBODY SAW, THE
(1937 - Paramount) Lew Ayres, Ruth Coleman
One Sheet: $125 - $250

CRIME OF DR. CRESPI, THE
(1935 - Liberty) Erich Von Stroheim, Dwight
Frye
One Sheet: $200 - $400   *Graven
Images, pg. 95.*

CRIME OF DR. FORBES, THE
(1936 - 20th Century Fox) Gloria Stuart, Robert
Kent
One Sheet: $125 - $250

CRIME OF DR. HALLET, THE
(1938 - Universal) Ralph Bellamy, Josephine
Hutchinson
One Sheet: $125 - $250

CRIME OF HELEN STANLEY
(1934 - Columbia) Gail Patrick, Ralph Bellamy
One Sheet: $100 - $200

CRIME OF PASSION
(1956 - United Artists) Barbara Stanwyck,
Sterling Hayden
One Sheet: $30 - $50

CRIME OF THE CENTURY, THE
(1933 - Paramount) Jean Hersholt, Frances
Dee
One Sheet: $200 - $400

CRIME OF THE CENTURY, THE
(1946 - Republic) Stephanie Bachelor, Michael
Browne
One Sheet: $75 - $125

CRIME ON THEIR HANDS
(1948 - Columbia) The Three Stooges (Shemp)
One Sheet: $350 - $750   *Comedy short.
Duotone.*

CRIME PATROL, THE
(1936 - Empire) Ray Walker, Geneva Mitchell
One Sheet: $100 - $200

CRIME RAVE
(1939 - RKO) Leon Errol
One Sheet: $125 - $250

CRIME RING
(1938 - RKO) Allan Lane, Frances Merger
One Sheet: $125 - $250

CRIME SCHOOL
(1938 - Warner Bros.) Humphrey Bogart, "Dead
End Kids"
One Sheet: $2,500 - $4,000

One Sheet

CRIME SMASHER
(1943 - -) See COSMO JONES, CRIME
SMASHER

CRIME TAKES A HOLIDAY
(1938 - Columbia) Jack Holt, Maria Ralston
One Sheet: $100 - $200

CRIME WAVE
(1954 - Warner Bros.) Gene Nelson, Sterling
Hayden
One Sheet: $15 - $30

CRIME WITHOUT PASSION
(1934 - Paramount) Claude Rains, Margo
One Sheet: $200 - $400

CRIME ZONE
(1988 - -) David Carradine, Sherilyn Fenn,
Peter Nelson
One Sheet: $5 - $10

CRIMEBUSTERS
(1979 - United Artists) Terence Hill, Bud
Spencer
One Sheet: $7 - $15   *Jack Davis
art.*

CRIMES AND MISDEMEANORS
(1989 - Orion) Caroline Aaron, Alan Alda
One Sheet: $3 - $5

CRIMES AT THE DARK HOUSE
(1940 - Pennant) Tod Slaughter, Hilary Eaves
One Sheet: $50 - $100

CRIMES OF DR. MABUSE, THE
(1953R - -)
One Sheet: $30 - $50   *Re-release.*

CRIMES OF PASSION
(1984 - New World) Kathleen Turner, Anthony
Perkins
One Sheet: $15 - $25

CRIMES OF THE HEART
(1986 - DeLaurentis) Diane Keaton, Jessica
Lange, Sissy Spacek
One Sheet: $7 - $15

CRIMINAL AFFAIR
(19?? - -)
One Sheet: $3 - $5

CRIMINAL CODE, THE
(1931 - Columbia) Walter Huston, Phillip
Holmes, Boris Karloff
One Sheet: $800 - $1,500

CRIMINAL COURT
(1946 - RKO) Tom Conway, Martha O'Driscoll
One Sheet: $50 - $100

CRIMINAL INVESTIGATOR
(1942 - Monogram) Robert Lowery, Jan Wiley
One Sheet: $50 - $100

CRIMINAL LAW
(1989 - -) Gary Oldman, Kevin Bacon, Karen
Young

CRIMINAL LAWYER
(1937 - RKO) Lee Tracy, Margot Grahame
One Sheet: $100 - $200

CRIMINAL LAWYER
(1951 - Columbia) Pat O'Brien, Jane Wyatt
One Sheet: $30 - $60

CRIMINALS OF THE AIR
(1937 - Columbia) Rosalind Keith, Charles
Quigley
One Sheet: $100 - $200

CRIMINALS WITHIN
(1941 - PRC) Eric Linden, Ann Doran
One Sheet: $40 - $75

CRIMSON ALTAR, THE
(1970 - AIP) Boris Karloff, Christopher Lee
One Sheet: $15 - $30   *AKA: THE
CRIMSON CULT; CURSE OF THE CRIMSON
ALTER.*

CRIMSON BLADE, THE
(1964 - Columbia) Lionel Jeffries, Oliver Reed
One Sheet: $5 - $10

CRIMSON CANARY, THE
(1945 - Universal) Noah Beery Jr., Lois Collier
One Sheet: $50 - $100

CRIMSON CHALLENGE, THE
(1922 - Paramount) Dorothy Dalton, Jack
Mower
One Sheet: $1,300 - $2,000

CRIMSON CIRCLE, THE
(1936 - Universal) Hugh Wakefield, Alfred
Drayton, Noah Beery
One Sheet: $150 - $300

CRIMSON CULT, THE
(1970 - AIP) Boris Karloff, Christopher Lee
One Sheet: $15 - $30   *AKA: Curse
Of The Crimson Altar; The Crimson Altar.*

CRIMSON GHOST, THE
(1946 - Republic) Charles Quigley, Linda
Stirling
One Sheet: $250 - $500   *Serial. 12
Chapters.*

CRIMSON KEY, THE
(1947 - 20th Century Fox) Kent Taylor, Doris
Dowling
One Sheet: $40 - $75

CRIMSON KIMONO, THE
(1959 - Columbia) Victoria Shaw, Glenn
Corbett
One Sheet: $30 - $60

CRIMSON PIRATE, THE
(1952 - Warner Bros.) Burt Lancaster, Eva
Bartok
One Sheet: $40 - $75

CRIMSON ROMANCE
(1934 - Mascot) Ben Lyon, Sari Maritza, Erich
Von Stroheim
One Sheet: $100 - $200

CRIMSON SKULL
(1921 - Norman) Anita Bush, Bill Pickett
One Sheet: $800 - $1,500   *Black cast.
Cowboy Movie Posters #'s 39, 41.*

CRIMSON TIDE
(1995 - Hollywood Pictures) Denzel
Washington, Gene Hackman
One Sheet: $7 - $15   *Price is for
either style.*

CRIMSON TRAIL, THE
(1935 - Universal) Buck Jones
One Sheet: $250 - $600

CRIMSON TRAIL, THE
(1948R - Realart) Buck Jones
One Sheet: $40 - $75   *Re-release.*

CRIPPLE CREEK
(1952 - Columbia) George Montgomery, Karin
Booth
One Sheet: $15 - $35

CRISIS, THE
(1916 - Sherman-Elliott) -
One Sheet: $250 - $500

CRISIS
(1950 - MGM) Cary Grant, Jose Ferrer

One Sheet: $50 - $100

CRISS CROSS
(1948 - Universal) Burt Lancaster, Yvonne De Carlo, Dan Duryea
One Sheet: $150 - $300

CRISS CROSS
(1958R - Realart) Burt Lancaster, Yvonne DeCarlo, Dan Duryea
One Sheet: $40 - $75   *Re-release.*

CRISSCROSS
(1992 - MGM) Goldie Hawn, Keith Carradine
One Sheet: $7 - $15

CRITIC'S CHOICE
(1963 - Warner Bros.) Bob Hope, Lucille Ball
One Sheet: $20 - $40

CRITICAL CONDITION
(1987 - Paramount) Richard Pryor, Ruben Blades, Rachel Ticotin
One Sheet: $3 - $5

CRITTERS
(1986 - New Line) Dee Wallace Stone, M. Emmet Walsh
One Sheet: $5 - $10

CRITTERS 2
(1988 - New Line) Scott Grimes, Liane Curtis
One Sheet: $3 - $5

CROCODILE DUNDEE
(1986 - Paramount) Paul Hogan, Linda Zozlowski
One Sheet: $7 - $15

CROCODILE DUNDEE II
(1988 - Paramount) Paul Hogan, Linda Kozlowski
One Sheet: $3 - $5

CROMWELL
(1970 - Columbia) Richard Harris, Alec Guiness
One Sheet: $7 - $15

CROOKED CIRCLE, THE
(1932 - World Wide) Ben Lyon, ZaSu Pitts, James Gleason
One Sheet: $100 - $200

CROOKED CIRCLE, THE
(194?R - Astor) Ben Lyons, ZaSu Pitts, James Gleason
One Sheet: $15 - $30   *Re-release.*

CROOKED CIRCLE, THE
(1957 - Republic) John Smith, Fay Spain
One Sheet: $10 - $20

CROOKED LADY, THE
(1932 - MGM) George Graves, Austin Trevor
One Sheet: $125 - $250

CROOKED MONEY
(1940 - Toddy) Kenny Washington, Mantan Moreland
One Sheet: $150 - $300   *Black cast.*
Sports (Football). Separate Cinema, pg. 62.

CROOKED RIVER
(1950 - Lippert) James Ellison, Russell Hayden
One Sheet: $15 - $35

CROOKED ROAD, THE
(1940 - Republic) Edmund Lowe, Irene Hervey, Henry Wilcoxon
One Sheet: $75 - $125

CROOKED ROAD, THE
(1965 - Seven Arts) Robert Ryan, Stewart Granger
One Sheet: $5 - $10

CROOKED SKY, THE
(1957 - RFD) Wayne Morris
One Sheet: $10 - $20

CROOKED TRAIL, THE
(1936 - Supreme) Johnny Mack Brown, John Merton
One Sheet: $150 - $300

CROOKED WAY, THE
(1949 - United Artists) John Payne, Sonny Tufts
One Sheet: $30 - $60

CROOKED WEB, THE
(1955 - Columbia) Frank Lovejoy, Mari Blanchard

One Sheet: $15 - $35

CROOKLYN
(1994 - Universal) Zelda Harris, Dir: Spike Lee
One Sheet: $7 - $15

CROOKS ANONYMOUS
(1963 - Janus) Leslie Phillips, Julie Christie
One Sheet: $5 - $10

CROOKS IN CLOISTERS
(1964 - Warner Bros.) Ronald Fraser, Barbara Windor
One Sheet: $5 - $10

CROOKS TOUR
(1940 - Anglo) Basil Radford
One Sheet: $50 - $100

CROONER
(1932 - First National) Ken Murray, Ann Dvorak
One Sheet: $200 - $400

CROP CHASERS
(1939 - Columbia) Ub Iwerks
One Sheet: $250 - $500   *Cartoon.*

CROSBY CASE, THE
(1934 - Universal) Wynne Gibson, Alan Dinehart
One Sheet: $200 - $400

CROSS AND THE SWITCHBLADE, THE
(1970 - Ross) Pat Boone, Erik Estrada
One Sheet: $5 - $10

CROSS CHANNEL
(1955 - Republic) Wayne Morris, Yvonne Furneaux
One Sheet: $15 - $25

CROSS COUNTRY BUNION RACE
(1928 - Stern Bros.) -
One Sheet: $250 - $500

CROSS COUNTRY CRUISE
(1934 - Universal) Lew Ayres
One Sheet: $150 - $300

CROSS COUNTRY ROMANCE
(1940 - RKO) Gene Raymond, Wendy Barrie
One Sheet: $75 - $150

CROSS CREEK
(1983 - Universal) Mary Steenburgen, Rip Torn
One Sheet: $3 - $5

CROSS MY HEART
(1947 - Paramount) Betty Hutton, Sonny Tufts
One Sheet: $40 - $75

CROSS MY HEART
(1987 - -) Martin Short, Annette O'Toole
One Sheet: $3 - $5

CROSS OF IRON
(1977 - Avco/Embassy) James Coburn, Maximilian Schell, Dir: Peckinpah
One Sheet: $10 - $20

CROSS OF LORRAINE, THE
(1943 - MGM) Jean-Pierre Aumont, Gene Kelly
One Sheet: $15 - $30

CROSS STREETS
(1934 - Invincible) Claire Windson, Johnny Mack Brown
One Sheet: $100 - $200

CROSS UP
(1955 - United Artists) Larry Parks, Constance Smith
One Sheet: $15 - $30

CROSSED SWORDS
(1953 - United Artists) Errol Flynn, Gina Lollobrigida
One Sheet: $40 - $75

CROSSED TRAILS
(1948 - Monogram) Johnny Mack Brown, Lynne Carver
One Sheet: $30 - $50

CROSSED WIRES
(1923 - Universal) Gladys Walton, George Stewart
One Sheet: $150 - $350

CROSSFIRE
(1933 - RKO) Tom Keene
One Sheet: $125 - $250

CROSSFIRE

(1947 - RKO) Robert Young, Robert Mitchum, Robert Ryan
One Sheet: $250 - $500

CROSSING DELANCEY
(1988 - Warner Bros.) Amy Irving, Reizl Bozyk
One Sheet: $7 - $15

CROSSING GUARD, THE
(1995 - Miramax) Jack Nicholson, Angelica Huston
One Sheet: $4 - $8

CROSSING THE BRIDGE
(1993 - Buena Vista) Josh Charles, Stephen Baldwin
One Sheet: $3 - $5

CROSSROADS
(1942 - MGM) William Powell, Hedy Lamarr, Basil Rathbone
One Sheet: $250 - $600

CROSSROADS
(1986 - Columbia) Ralph Macchio, Joe Seneca, Jami Gertz
One Sheet: $3 - $5

CROSSROADS OF NEW YORK
(1922 - -) George O'Hara, Noah Beery
One Sheet: $250 - $500

CROSSWINDS
(1951 - Paramount) John Payne, Rhonda Fleming
One Sheet: $20 - $40

CROUCHING BEAST
(1936 - RKO) Ahmed Bey, Ian Fleming
One Sheet: $150 - $300

CROW, THE
(1994 - Miramax) Brandon Lee, Ernie Hudson
One Sheet: $20 - $40

CROW: CITY OF ANGELS, THE
(1996 - Miramax) Vincent Perez, Mia Kirshner
One Sheet: $7 - $15

One Sheet

CROWD, THE
(1928 - MGM) Eleanor Boardman, James Murray
One Sheet: $250 - $600

CROWD ROARS, THE
(1932 - Warner Bros.) James Cagney, Joan Blondell, Ann Dvorak
One Sheet: $1,900 - $3,000   *Sports Movie Posters #8.*

CROWD ROARS, THE
(1938 - MGM) Robert Taylor, Frank Morgan, Jane Wyman
One Sheet: $250 - $500   *Sports (Boxing).*

CROWDED HOUR, THE
(1925 - Paramount) Bebe Daniels, Kenneth Harlan
One Sheet: $250 - $500

CROWDED PARADISE, THE
(1956 - Tudor) Hume Cronyn, Nancy Kelly
One Sheet: $15 - $25

CROWDED SKY, THE
(1960 - Warner Bros.) Dana Andrews, Rhonda Fleming
One Sheet: $7 - $15

CROWN OF THORNS
(1934 - -) Gregori Chimara, Henny Porten
One Sheet: $150 - $300

CROWNING EXPERIENCE, THE
(1960 - -) Muriel Smith, Ann Buckles
One Sheet: $75 - $150   *Black cast.*

CRUCIBLE, THE
(1996 - 20th Century Fox) Winona Ryder, Daniel Day-Lewis
One Sheet: $5 - $10

CRUCIBLE OF HORROR
(1971 - Cannon) Michael Gough, Yvonne Mitchell
One Sheet: $10 - $20

CRUCIFIX, THE
(1934 - Universal) Nancy Price, Sydney Fairbrother
One Sheet: $500 - $800

CRUEL, CRUEL LOVE
(1914 - Keystone) Charlie Chaplin
One Sheet: $5,000 - $8,000

CRUEL SEA, THE
(1952 - Universal International) Jack Hawkins, Donald Sinden
One Sheet: $30 - $60

CRUEL TOWER, THE
(1956 - Allied Artists) John Ericson, Marl Blanchard
One Sheet: $10 - $20

CRUISE CAT
(1952 - MGM) Tom & Jerry
One Sheet: $250 - $500   *Cartoon. Full color stone litho.*

One Sheet

CRUISE OF THE AKI MARU, THE
(1921 - Paramount) -
One Sheet: $150 - $350   *A Paramount-Burton Holmes Travel Picture.*

CRUISIN' DOWN THE RIVER
(1953 - Columbia) Dick Haymes, Audrey Totter
One Sheet: $20 - $40

CRUISING
(1980 - United Artists) Al Pacino
One Sheet: $7 - $15

CRUMB
(1995 - Sony Classics) -
One Sheet: $15 - $25   *Robert Crumb Documentary.*

CRUNCH
(1970 - AIP) Harold Leipnitz, Sybille Maar
One Sheet: $3 - $5

CRUSADE AGAINST RACKETS
(1937 - Principal) Lona Andre, Donald Reed
One Sheet: $50 - $100

CRUSADER, THE
(1932 - Majestic) Evelyn Brent, H. B. Warner
One Sheet: $75 - $150

CRUSADES, THE
(1935 - Paramount) Loretta Young, Henry Wilcoxon
One Sheet: $300 - $700

CRUSADES, THE
(1948R - Paramount) Loretta Young, Henry Wilcoxson
One Sheet: $75 - $150   *Re-release.*

CRUSH, THE
(1993 - Warner Bros.) Gary Elwes, Jennifer Rubin
One Sheet: $3 - $5

CRUSOE
(1988 - Island) Aidan Quinn, Ade Sapara
One Sheet: $3 - $5

CRY BABY
(1989 - Universal) Johnny Depp, Traci Lords
One Sheet: $15 - $25

CRY BABY KILLER, THE
(1958 - Allied Artists) Carolyn Mitchell, Jack
Nicholson(film debut)
One Sheet: $100 - $200

CRY DANGER
(1950 - RKO) Dick Powell, Rhonda Fleming
One Sheet: $75 - $150

CRY DANGER
(1956R - RKO) Dick Powell, Rhonda Fleming
One Sheet: $40 - $75   *Re-release.*

CRY FOR HAPPY
(1961 - Columbia) Glenn Ford, Donald
O'Connor
One Sheet: $10 - $20

CRY FREEDOM
(1987 - Universal) Kevin Kline, Penelope
Wilton
One Sheet: $3 - $5

CRY FROM THE STREETS, A
(1959 - Film Traders) Barbara Murray, Dana
Wilson
One Sheet: $7 - $15

CRY HAVOC
(1944 - MGM) Margaret Sullavan, Ann Sothern,
Joan Blondell
One Sheet: $75 - $125

CRY IN THE DARK, A
(1988 - -) Meryl Streep, Sam Neill
One Sheet: $5 - $10

CRY IN THE NIGHT, A
(1956 - Warner Bros.) Edmond O'Brien, Natalie
Wood, Brian Donlevy
One Sheet: $15 - $25

CRY MURDER
(1950 - Film Classics) Carole Matthews, Jack
Lord
One Sheet: $30 - $50

CRY OF BATTLE
(1963 - Allied Artists) Van Heflin, Rita Moreno,
James MacArthur
One Sheet: $5 - $10

CRY OF THE BANSHEE
(1970 - AIP) Vincent Price, Essy Persson
One Sheet: $15 - $25

CRY OF THE CITY
(1948 - 20th Century Fox) Victor Mature,
Richard Conte, Shelley Winters
One Sheet: $75 - $150

CRY OF THE HUNTED
(1953 - MGM) Polly Bergen, Barry Sullivan
One Sheet: $15 - $25

CRY OF THE WEREWOLF
(1944 - Columbia) Nina Foch, Stephen Crane
One Sheet: $100 - $200

CRY OF THE WILD
(1973 - American National) Documentary of the
Timber Wolf
One Sheet: $5 - $10

CRY TERROR!
(1958 - MGM) James Mason, Rod Steiger
One Sheet: $20 - $40

CRY, THE BELOVED COUNTRY
(1951 - Lopert/United Artists) Canada Lee,
Sidney Poitier
One Sheet: $50 - $100   *Separate
Cinema, pg. 157.*

CRY, THE BELOVED COUNTRY
(1996 - Miramax) James Earl Jones, Richard
Harris
One Sheet: $4 - $8   *Price is for
both styles.*

CRY TOUGH
(1959 - United Artists) John Saxon, Linda
Crystal
One Sheet: $20 - $40

CRY UNCLE
(1971 - -) Allen Garfield, Paul Sorvino
One Sheet: $15 - $35

CRY VENGEANCE
(1954 - Allied Artists) Mark Stevens, Joan Vohs
One Sheet: $15 - $30

CRY WOLF
(1947 - Warner Bros.) Errol Flynn, Barbara
Stanwyck
One Sheet: $75 - $150

CRY-BABY
(1990 - Universal) Johnny Depp, Amy Locane
One Sheet: $5 - $10

CRYING GAME, THE
(1992 - -) Stephen Rea, Miranda Richardson
One Sheet: $15 - $25

One Sheet

CRYPT OF THE LIVING DEAD
(1972 - Atlas) Andrew Prine, Mark Damon
One Sheet: $15 - $30   *Duotone.
AKA: HANNAH, QUEEN OF VAMPIRES.*

CRYSTAL BALL, THE
(1942 - United Artists) Ray Milland, Paulette
Goddard
One Sheet: $75 - $150

CUBA
(1979 - United Artists) Sean Connery, Brooke
Adams
One Sheet: $7 - $15

CUBAN FIREBALL
(1951 - Republic) Estelita Rodriguez, Warren
Douglas
One Sheet: $30 - $50

CUBAN LOVE SONG, THE
(1931 - MGM) Lupe Valez, Jimmy Durante
One Sheet: $500 - $800

CUBAN PETE
(1946 - Universal) Desi Arnaz, Ethel Smith
One Sheet: $50 - $100

CUBAN REBEL GIRLS
(1959 - United Artists) Errol Flynn(last film)
One Sheet: $75 - $125

CUCKOO CAVALIERS
(1940 - Columbia) The Three Stooges (Curly)
One Sheet: $5,000 - $7,500   *Comedy short.
Duotone.*

CUCKOO ON A CHOO CHOO
(1952 - Columbia) The Three Stooges (Shemp)
One Sheet: $150 - $350   *Comedy short.
Duotone.*

CUEBALL CAT
(1950 - MGM) Tom & Jerry
One Sheet: $250 - $600   *Cartoon. Full
color stone litho. Cartoon Movie Posters #283.*

CUJO
(1983 - Warner Bros.) Daniel Hugh-Kelly,
Danny Pintauro
One Sheet: $7 - $15

CUL-DE-SAC
(1966 - Sigma III) Donald Pleasence, Francoise
Dorleac
One Sheet: $30 - $60

CULPEPPER CATTLE CO., THE
(1972 - 20th Century Fox) Gary Grimes, Billy
"Green" Bush
One Sheet: $3 - $5

CULT OF THE COBRA
(1955 - Universal) Faith Domergue, Richard
Long
One Sheet: $50 - $100

CULT OF THE DAMNED, THE
(1969 - AIP) Jennifer Jones, Jordan
Christopher
One Sheet: $15 - $30

CUP OF FURY, THE
(1919 - Goldwyn) Helene Chadwick, Rockcliffe
Fellowes
One Sheet: $500 - $800

CUPID AND THE CLOCK
(1927 - Fox) Dir: Gene Forde
One Sheet: $300 - $700

CUPID RIDES THE RANGE
(1939 - RKO) Ray Whitley, Elvira Rios
One Sheet: $75 - $125

CUPID TAKES A HOLIDAY
(1938 - Fox) Danny Kaye
One Sheet: $100 - $200

CUPID'S ROUND UP
(1918 - Fox) Tom Mix
One Sheet: $800 - $1,500

CURDLED
(1996 - Miramax) William Baldwin, Angela
Jones
One Sheet: $5 - $10

CURE, THE
(1917 - Mutual) Charlie Chaplin, Edna
Purviance
One Sheet: $6,500 - $10,000

CURE, THE
(1923R - Export & Import) Charlie Chaplin,
Edna Purviance
One Sheet: $600 - $1,000   *Re-release.*

CURE, THE
(1995 - Universal) Joseph Mazzello, Brad
Renfro
One Sheet: $5 - $10

CURE, THE
(1995 - Universal) Brad Renfro, Joseph
Mazzello
One Sheet: $3 - $5

CURE FOR LOVE, THE
(1949 - Associated Artists) Robert Donat,
Renee Asherson
One Sheet: $30 - $50

CURED DUCK
(1945 - RKO/Disney) Donald Duck
One Sheet: $1,600 - $2,500   *Cartoon. The
Disney Poster, pg. 55.*

CURIOUS CONTESTS
(1950 - MGM) Narrated by Pete Smith
One Sheet: $50 - $100

CURIOUS FEMALE, THE
(1969 - Fanfare) Angelique Pettyjohn, Charlene
Jones
One Sheet: $10 - $20   *Sexploitation.
Rated X. Duotone.*

CURLEY AND THE GANG
(1947 - Hal Roach Studios) Larry Olsen,
Frances Rafferty, Our Gang
One Sheet: $75 - $150   *Roach's
attempt to revive Our Gang comedies*

CURLY SUE
(1991 - Warner Bros.) James Belushi, Alisan
Porter (Debut)
One Sheet: $5 - $10

CURLY TOP
(1924 - Fox) Shirley Mason, Warner Oland
One Sheet: $1,300 - $2,000

CURLY TOP
(1935 - Fox) Shirley Temple, John Boles
One Sheet: $800 - $1,500

CURSE, THE
(1987 - -) Wil Wheaton, Claude Akins
One Sheet: $3 - $5

CURSE OF DRINK, THE
(1922 - Weber & North) Harry T. Morey,
Edmund Breese
One Sheet: $200 - $400

CURSE OF FRANKENSTEIN, THE
(1957 - Warner Bros.) Peter Cushing,
Christopher Lee
One Sheet: $100 - $200   *Graven
Images, pg. 192-193.*

CURSE OF FRANKENSTEIN, THE
(1964R - Warner Bros.) Peter Cushing,
Christopher Lee
One Sheet: $20 - $40   *Re-release.*

CURSE OF FRANKENSTEIN, THE
(1970R - Hammer) Peter Cushing, Christopher
Lee
One Sheet: $15 - $30   *Re-release.*

**CURSE OF FRANKENSTEIN/HORROR OF
DRACULA COMBO**
(1964R - Warner Bros.) Peter Cushing,
Christopher Lee
One Sheet: $15 - $30   *Re-release.
Combo.*

CURSE OF THE BLACK WIDOW
(1977 - -) Patty Duke, Donna Mills, Tony
Franciosa
One Sheet: $7 - $15   *Made for TV
movie.*

CURSE OF THE CAT PEOPLE, THE
(1944 - RKO) Simone Simon, Kent Smith
One Sheet: $350 - $750   *Graven
Images, pg. 123.*

One Sheet

CURSE OF THE CRIMSON ALTAR
(1970 - AIP) Boris Karloff, Christopher Lee
One Sheet: $15 - $30   *AKA: The
Crimson Cult; The Crimson Altar.*

CURSE OF THE DEMON
(1957 - Columbia) Dana Andrews, Peggy
Cummins
One Sheet: $150 - $300   *Graven
Images, pg. 5. AKA:Night Of The Demon.*

CURSE OF THE FACELESS MAN
(1958 - United Artists) Richard Anderson,
Elaine Edwards
One Sheet: $40 - $75

CURSE OF THE FLY, THE
(1965 - Avco/Embassy) Brian Donlevy, Carole
Gray
One Sheet: $15 - $30

CURSE OF THE FLY/DEVILS OF DARKNESS
(1965 - 20th Century Fox) Brian Donlevy,
William Sylvester
One Sheet: $15 - $30   *Double
feature poster. Duotone.*

CURSE OF THE LIVING CORPSE
(1964 - Lippert) Helen Warren, Roy R. Shielder
One Sheet: $15 - $25

CURSE OF THE LIVING DEAD
(1966 - -) Giacomo Rossi-Stuart
One Sheet: $15 - $35   *AKA: Kill,
Baby, Kill.*

CURSE OF THE MUMMY'S TOMB, THE
(1965 - Columbia) Terence Morgan, Ronald
Howard
One Sheet: $30 - $50

CURSE OF THE PINK PANTHER
(1983 - MGM/United Artists) Ted Wass, David
Niven(last film), Robert Wagner
One Sheet: $5 - $10

CURSE OF THE STARVING CLASS
(1994 - Trimark) James Woods, Kathy Bates,
Randy Quaid

One Sheet: $5 - $10

CURSE OF THE UBANDI, THE
(1947 - Excelsior) -
One Sheet: $50 - $100

CURSE OF THE UNDEAD
(1959 - Universal) Eric Fleming, Michael Pate
One Sheet: $30 - $60

CURSE OF THE VAMPIRES
(1970 - Hemisphere) Amalia Fuentes, Eddie
Garcia
One Sheet: $30 - $50

CURSE OF THE WEREWOLF, THE
(1961 - Universal) Clifford Evans, Oliver Reed
One Sheet: $100 - $200   *Graven*
Images, pg. 214.

CURTAIN AT EIGHT
(1934 - Majestic) Dorothy Mackaill
One Sheet: $200 - $400

One Sheet

CURTAIN CALL
(1940 - RKO) Barbara Read, Alan Mowbray
One Sheet: $75 - $150

CURTAIN CALL AT CACTUS CREEK
(1950 - Universal) Donald O'Connor, Gale
Storm
One Sheet: $30 - $50

CURTAINS
(1983 - Simcon) Samantha Eggar, John Vernon
One Sheet: $3 - $5

CURUCU, BEAST OF THE AMAZON
(1956 - Universal) John Bromfield, Beverly
Garland
One Sheet: $50 - $100

CUSTER OF THE WEST
(1968 - Cinerama) Robert Shaw, Mary Ure
One Sheet: $10 - $20

CUSTER'S LAST FIGHT
(1925 - Quality Amusement) -
One Sheet: $250 - $500

One Sheet

CUSTER'S LAST STAND
(1936 - Weiss) Rex Lease, William Farnum
One Sheet: $250 - $500   *Serial.*
Western. 15 Chapters.

CUSTOMS AGENT
(1950 - Columbia) William Eythe, Marjorie
Reynolds
One Sheet: $15 - $35

CUT AND RUN
(1986 - -) Willie Aames

One Sheet: $3 - $5

CUTTER AND BONE
(1981 - United Artists) Jeff Bridges, John Heard
One Sheet: $10 - $20   *Originally*
pulled from theatres due to censoring. Edited, re-
released and re-titled as CUTTER'S WAY.

CUTTER'S WAY
(1981 - United Artists) Jeff Bridges
One Sheet: $3 - $5

CUTTHROAT ISLAND
(1995 - MGM) Geena Davis, Matthew Modine
One Sheet: $4 - $8   *Advance*
Style: $10-$15.

CUT-THROATS NINE
(19?? - -) -
One Sheet: $40 - $80

CUTTING EDGE, THE
(1992 - MGM-Pathe) D.B. Sweeney, Moira
Kelly
One Sheet: $7 - $15   *Sports Movie*
Posters #259.

CYBORG
(1989 - -) Jean-Claude Van Damme, Deborah
Richter
One Sheet: $10 - $20

CYBORG 2087
(1966 - Feature Films) Michael Rennie,
Wendell Corey, Karen Steele
One Sheet: $30 - $50

CYCLE SAVAGES, THE
(1970 - AIP) Bruce Dern, Melody Patterson
One Sheet: $30 - $50   *Biker film.*

CYCLONE, THE
(1920 - Fox) Tom Mix
One Sheet: $1,300 - $2,000   *Cowboy*
Movie Posters #20.

CYCLONE
(1986 - -) Heather Thomas, Jeffrey Combs
One Sheet: $3 - $5

CYCLONE BLISS
(1921 - -) Jack Hoxie, Frederick Moore
One Sheet: $250 - $600

CYCLONE FURY
(1951 - Columbia) Charles Starrett, Smiley
Burnette
One Sheet: $30 - $50

CYCLONE KID, THE
(1931 - Big Four) Buzz Barton
One Sheet: $100 - $200

CYCLONE KID, THE
(1942 - Republic) Don Red Barry, Rex Lease
One Sheet: $40 - $75

CYCLONE OF THE SADDLE
(1935 - Argosy) Rex Lease
One Sheet: $150 - $300

CYCLONE ON HORSEBACK
(1941 - RKO) Tim Holt
One Sheet: $40 - $75

CYCLONE PRAIRIE RANGERS
(1944 - Columbia) Charles Starrett, Dub Taylor
One Sheet: $30 - $50

CYCLONE RANGER
(1935 - Spectrum) Bill Cody, Nena Quartaro
One Sheet: $250 - $500

CYCLOPS, THE
(1956 - United Artists) James Craig, Gloria
Talbott, Dir: Bert Gordon
One Sheet: $75 - $125

CYCLOTRODE X
(1966 - Republic) -
One Sheet: $10 - $20   *Re-issue:*
Feature version of THE CRIMSON GHOST.

CYNARA
(1932 - United Artists) Ronald Colman, Kay
Francis
One Sheet: $250 - $500   *AKA: I WAS*
FAITHLESS.

CYNTHIA
(1947 - MGM) Elizabeth Taylor, Mary Astor,
George Murphy
One Sheet: $100 - $200

CYPHER MESSAGE, THE
(1913 - Selig) -
One Sheet: $350 - $750

CYRANO DE BERGERAC
(1924 - Atlas) Edmond Rostands, Ododliga
Komed
One Sheet: $200 - $450   *Swedish.*

CYRANO DE BERGERAC
(1950 - United Artists) Jose Ferrer, Mala
Powers
One Sheet: $75 - $175   *Academy*
Award: Best Actor(Ferrer). Academy Award Movie
Posters #129 & #130.

CYRANO DE BERGERAC
(1990 - -) Gerard Despardieu
One Sheet: $20 - $40

CZAR OF BROADWAY
(1930 - Universal) Betty Compson, John Wray
One Sheet: $250 - $600

DA
(1988 - Filmdallas) Martin Sheen, Barnard
Hughes
One Sheet: $3 - $5

DAD
(1989 - Universal) Jack Lemmon, Ted Danson
One Sheet: $5 - $10

DAD, CAN I BORROW THE CAR?
(1970 - Disney) -
One Sheet: $10 - $20

DAD FOR A DAY
(1939 - MGM) Our Gang
One Sheet: $500 - $800

DAD'S ARMY
(1971 - Columbia) Arthur Lowe
One Sheet: $3 - $5

DADDY
(1923 - First National) Jackie Coogan
One Sheet: $500 - $800

DADDY GOES A GRUNTING
(1925 - Pathe) Glenn Tryon
One Sheet: $200 - $400

DADDY LONGLEGS
(1919 - First National) Mary Pickford
One Sheet: $1,600 - $2,500

DADDY LONGLEGS
(1931 - Fox) Janet Gaynor, Warner Baxter
One Sheet: $250 - $600

DADDY LONGLEGS
(1955 - 20th Century Fox) Leslie Caron, Fred
Astaire
One Sheet: $75 - $125

DADDY'S GONE A-HUNTING
(1969 - National General) Carol White, Paul
Burke
One Sheet: $5 - $10

DADDYO
(1959 - AIP) Dick Contino, Sandra Giles
One Sheet: $40 - $75

DAFFY DUCK'S MOVIE: FANTASTIC ISLAND
(1983 - Warner Bros.) Voice of Mel Banc
One Sheet: $10 - $20   *Cartoon.*

DAFFY DUCK'S QUACKBUSTERS
(1989 - -) Cartoon Compilation
One Sheet: $15 - $25   *Cartoon.*

DAGMAR'S HOT PANTS, INC.
(1971 - Trans-American) Diana Kjaer, Anne
Grete, Robert Strauss
One Sheet: $5 - $10

DAGORA THE SPACE MONSTER
(1964 - Toho) Yosuke Natsuki
One Sheet: $40 - $75

DAILY DOZEN, THE
(1928 - Rayart) Ethelyn Gibson, Jerry Mandy
One Sheet: $150 - $300

DAISY KENYON
(1947 - 20th Century Fox) Joan Crawford,
Dana Andrews, Henry Fonda
One Sheet: $75 - $175

DAISY MILLER
(1974 - Paramount) Cybill Shepherd, Barry
Brown

One Sheet: $7 - $15

DAKOTA
(1945 - Republic) John Wayne, Vera Hruba
Ralston
One Sheet: $100 - $200

One Sheet

DAKOTA
(1988 - -) Lou Diamond Phillips, Eli Cummins
One Sheet: $3 - $5

DAKOTA INCIDENT
(1956 - Republic) Linda Darnell, Dale
Robertson
One Sheet: $10 - $20

DAKOTA KID, THE
(1951 - Republic) Michael Chapin, Eilene
Janssen
One Sheet: $15 - $25

DAKOTA LIL
(1950 - 20th Century Fox) George Montgomery,
Rod Cameron, Marie Windsor
One Sheet: $15 - $30   *One*
Sheet(text only style):$3-6.

DAKOTA LIL
(1955R - 20th Century Fox) George
Montgomery, Rod Cameron, Marie Windsor
One Sheet: $7 - $15   *Re-release.*

DALEK- INVASION EARTH 2150 A.D.
(1966 - British Lion) Peter Cushing
One Sheet: $50 - $100   *AKA:*
INVASION EARTH 2150 A.D.

DALLAS
(1950 - Warner Bros.) Gary Cooper, Ruth
Roman
One Sheet: $50 - $100

DALLAS
(1956R - Warner Bros.) Gary Cooper, Ruth
Roman
One Sheet: $10 - $20

DALTON GANG, THE
(1949 - United Artists) Don Barry
One Sheet: $30 - $50

DALTON GIRLS, THE
(1957 - United Artists) Merry Anders, Lisa
Davis
One Sheet: $15 - $25

DALTON THAT GOT AWAY, THE
(1960 - Dalton) Michael Connors
One Sheet: $7 - $15

DALTONS RIDE AGAIN, THE
(1945 - Universal) Alan Curtis, Kent Taylor
One Sheet: $30 - $50

DALTONS RIDE AGAIN, THE
(1951R - Universal) Alan Curtis, Kent Taylor
One Sheet: $10 - $20   *Re-release.*

DALTONS' WOMEN, THE
(1950 - United Artists) Lash LaRue, Jack Holt
One Sheet: $20 - $40

DAM BUSTERS, THE
(1954 - Warner Bros.) Richard Todd, Michael
Redgrave
One Sheet: $15 - $25

DAMAGE
(1993 - New Line) Jeremy Irons, Juliette
Binoche
One Sheet: $3 - $5

DAMAGED GOODS

(1937 - Grand National) Pedro de Cordoba
One Sheet: $125 - $250   *Horrors of syphillis exploitation film.*

DAMAGED LIVES
(1933 - Weldon) Diane Sinclair, Ceclia Parker
One Sheet: $75 - $150

DAMAGED LOVE
(1931 - Sono Art/World Wide) Charles Starrett, Eloise Taylor
One Sheet: $150 - $300

DAMES
(1934 - Warner Bros.) Joan Blondell, Dick Powell
One Sheet: $1,600 - $2,500

DAMES AHOY
(1930 - Universal) Glenn Tryon, Eddie Gribbon
One Sheet: $150 - $300

DAMIEN-OMEN II
(1978 - Fox) William Holden, Lee Grant, Jonathan Scott-Taylor
One Sheet: $7 - $15   *Advance:$5-10.*

DAMN CITIZEN
(1957 - Universal) Keith Andes, Lynn Bari
One Sheet: $15 - $25

DAMN THE DEFIANT
(1962 - Columbia) Alec Guinness, Dirk Bogarde
One Sheet: $7 - $15

DAMN YANKEES
(1958 - Warner Bros.) Tab Hunter, Gwen Verdon
One Sheet: $50 - $100   *Sports (Baseball). Players are not shown on posters. Sports Movie Posters #66/*

DAMNATION ALLEY
(1977 - 20th Century Fox) Jan-Michael Vincent, George Peppard
One Sheet: $10 - $20

DAMNED, THE
(1970 - Warner Bros.) Dirk Bogarde, Ingrid Thulin, Helmut Berger
One Sheet: $15 - $30

DAMNED DON'T CRY, THE
(1950 - Warner Bros.) Joan Crawford, David Brian, Kent Smith
One Sheet: $50 - $100

DAMON AND PYTHIAS
(1962 - MGM) Guy Williams, Don Burnett
One Sheet: $7 - $15

DAMSEL IN DISTRESS, A
(1937 - RKO) Fred Astaire, Ginger Rogers, George Burns, Gracie Allen
One Sheet: $700 - $1,200   *One Sheet(Australian):$150-300.*

DAN DAREDEVIL
(1925 - -) Jack Hoxie
One Sheet: $250 - $600

DAN MATTHEWS
(1936 - Columbia) Richard Arlen
One Sheet: $150 - $300   *AKA: THE CALLING OF DAN MATTHEWS.*

DAN'S MOTEL
(1982 - Barrish) George Berg
One Sheet: $3 - $5

DANCE BAND
(1935 - First Division) Charles Buddy Rogers, June Clyde
One Sheet: $200 - $400

DANCE CHARLIE DANCE
(1937 - First National) Stuart Erwin, Jean Muir
One Sheet: $150 - $300

DANCE, FOOLS, DANCE
(1931 - MGM) Joan Crawford, Lester Vail, Clark Gable
One Sheet: $1,600 - $2,500

DANCE, GIRL, DANCE
(1933 - Invincible) Alan Dinehart, Evalyn Knapp
One Sheet: $150 - $300

DANCE, GIRL, DANCE
(1940 - RKO) Maureen O'Hara, Louis Hayward, Lucille Ball
One Sheet: $200 - $400

DANCE HALL
(1929 - RKO) Olive Borden, Arthur Lake
One Sheet: $150 - $300

DANCE HALL
(1941 - 20th Century Fox) Cesar Romero, Carole Landis
One Sheet: $75 - $150

DANCE HALL
(1950 - GFD) Diana Dors, Petula Clark
One Sheet: $40 - $75

DANCE HALL HOSTESS
(1933 - Mayfair) Helen Chandler, Jason Robards, Sr.
One Sheet: $100 - $200

DANCE LITTLE LADY
(1955 - Renown) Mai Zetterling, Terence Morgan
One Sheet: $15 - $25

DANCE MADNESS
(1926 - MGM) Claire Windsor, Conrad Nagel
One Sheet: $250 - $600

DANCE MY LOVE
(194? - -) Alphonse Bseni, Jenny Arasse
One Sheet: $30 - $50   *Indian.*

DANCE OF DEATH
(1971 - Paramount) Laurence Olivier, Geraldine McEwan
One Sheet: $10 - $20

DANCE OF LIFE
(1929 - Paramount) Hal Skelly, Nancy Carroll
One Sheet: $300 - $700

DANCE OF THE DAMNED
(1988 - -) Cyril O'Rielly, Starr Andreeff
One Sheet: $10 - $20

DANCE OF THE DWARFS
(1983 - Dove) Peter Fonda, John Amos
One Sheet: $5 - $10

DANCE PRETTY LADY
(1932 - Wardour) Ann Casson, Carl Harbord
One Sheet: $150 - $300

DANCE TEAM
(1931 - Fox) James Dunn, Sally Eilers
One Sheet: $200 - $400

One Sheet

DANCE WITH A STRANGER
(1985 - -) Miranda Richardson, Rupert Everett
One Sheet: $3 - $5

DANCE WITH ME HENRY
(1956 - United Artists) Bud Abbott, Lou Costello
One Sheet: $40 - $75   *Last film together.*

DANCERS, THE
(1930 - Fox) Lois Moran, Walter Byron
One Sheet: $200 - $400

DANCERS
(1987 - Cannon) Mikhail Baryshnikov, Alessandra Ferri
One Sheet: $7 - $15

DANCERS IN THE DARK
(1932 - Paramount Publix) Miriam Hopkins, Jack Oakie
One Sheet: $200 - $400

DANCES WITH WOLVES
(1990 - Orion) Kevin Costner, Mary McDonnell
One Sheet: $15 - $30   *Academy*

Award: Best Picture, Best Director (Costner). *Academy Award Movie Posters #369 & #370. Cowboy Movie Posters #359.*

DANCIN' FOOL, THE
(1920 - Paramount Artcraft) Wallace Reid, Bebe Daniels
One Sheet: $500 - $800

DANCING CO-ED
(1939 - MGM) Lana Turner, Richard Carlson
One Sheet: $100 - $200

DANCING DAISIES
(1924 - Universal) Al Art
One Sheet: $200 - $400

DANCING DYNAMITE
(1931 - Talmadge) Richard Talmadge, Robert Ellis
One Sheet: $250 - $500

DANCING FEET
(1936 - Republic) Ben Lyon, Joan Marsh
One Sheet: $125 - $250

DANCING IN MANHATTAN
(1944 - Columbia) Jeff Donnell, Fred Brady
One Sheet: $75 - $150

DANCING IN THE DARK
(1949 - 20th Century Fox) Wiliam Powell, Mark Stevens, Betsy Drake
One Sheet: $75 - $125

DANCING LADY
(1933 - MGM) Joan Crawford, Clark Gable, Fred Astaire, Three Stooges
One Sheet: $1,300 - $2,000   *Astaire's film debut. Lobby Card (Stooges shown): $2000-$4000. Stooges not shown on one sheet.*

One Sheet

DANCING MAN
(1938 - Pyramid) Reginald Denny, Judith Allen
One Sheet: $100 - $200

DANCING MASTERS, THE
(1943 - 20th Century Fox) Stan Laurel, Oliver Hardy, Trudy Marshall
One Sheet: $200 - $400

DANCING MOTHERS
(1926 - Paramount) Conway Tearle, Alice Joyce, Clara Bow
One Sheet: $700 - $1,200

DANCING ON A DIME
(1940 - Paramount) Robert Paige, Grace McDonald
One Sheet: $100 - $200

DANCING PIRATE
(1936 - Pioneer) Frank Morgan, Rita Hayworth
One Sheet: $250 - $500

DANCING PIRATE
(1946R - Pioneer) Frank Morgan, Rita Hayworth
One Sheet: $40 - $75   *Re-release.*

DANCING ROMEO
(1944 - MGM) Our Gang
One Sheet: $250 - $500

DANCING SWEETIES
(1930 - Warner Bros.) Grant Withers, Sue Carol
One Sheet: $200 - $400

DANCING WITH CRIME
(1947 - Paramount) Richard Attenborough
One Sheet: $50 - $100

DANCING YEARS, THE
(1950 - Monogram) Dennis Price, Giselle Preville
One Sheet: $40 - $75

DANDY DICK
(1935 - BIP) Will Hay
One Sheet: $150 - $300

DANDY IN ASPIC, A
(1968 - Columbia) Laurence Harvey, Tom Courtenay
One Sheet: $10 - $20

DANDY, THE ALL AMERICAN GIRL
(1976 - MGM) Stockard Channing, Sam Waterson
One Sheet: $5 - $10

DANGER - LOVE AT WORK
(1937 - 20th Century Fox) Ann Sothern, Jack Haley
One Sheet: $75 - $150

DANGER! WOMEN AT WORK
(1943 - PRC) Patsy Kelly, Mary Brian
One Sheet: $75 - $125

DANGER AHEAD
(1918 - -) Helen Gibson
One Sheet: $150 - $300

DANGER AHEAD
(1935 - Victory) Lawrence Gray, Sheila Mannors
One Sheet: $75 - $150

DANGER AHEAD
(1940 - Monarch) James Newill
One Sheet: $125 - $250   *From the "Renfrew Of The Mounted" series.*

DANGER: DIABOLIK
(1968 - Paramount) John Phillip Law, Marisa Mell
One Sheet: $20 - $40   *Italian:$75-$150.*

DANGER FLIGHT
(1939 - Monogram) John Trent, Marjorie Reynolds
One Sheet: $75 - $125

DANGER IN THE PACIFIC
(1942 - Universal) Dick Foran, Leo Carrillo
One Sheet: $40 - $75

DANGER ISLAND
(1931 - Universal) Kenneth Harlan, Lucile Browne
One Sheet: $150 - $300

DANGER ISLAND
(1939 - 20th Century Fox) Peter Lorre (Mr. Moto), Jean Hersholt
One Sheet: $250 - $500

DANGER LIGHTS
(1930 - RKO) Jean Arthur, Robert Armstrong
One Sheet: $150 - $350

DANGER ON THE AIR
(1938 - Universal) Donald Woods, Nan Grey
One Sheet: $100 - $200

DANGER PATROL
(1937 - RKO) John Beal, Sally Eilers
One Sheet: $75 - $150

DANGER QUEST, THE
(1926 - Rayart) Reed Howes, Ethel Shannon
One Sheet: $150 - $350

DANGER RIDER, THE
(1928 - Universal Jewel) Hoot Gibson, Eugenia Gilbert
One Sheet: $200 - $400

DANGER ROUTE
(1968 - United Artists) Richard Johnson, Diana Dors
One Sheet: $10 - $20

DANGER SICNAL
(1945 - Warner Bros.) Faye Emerson, Zachary Scott
One Sheet: $40 - $75

DANGER STREET
(1947 - Paramount) Jane Withers, Robert Lowery, Bill Edwards
One Sheet: $100 - $200

DANGER TRAILS

(1935 - Beacon) Big Boy Williams
One Sheet: $100 - $200

DANGER VALLEY
(1937 - Monogram) Jack Randall, Lois Wilde
One Sheet: $75 - $125

DANGER WOMAN
(1946 - Universal) Brenda Joyce, Don Porter
One Sheet: $50 - $100

DANGER ZONE
(1951 - Lippert) Richard Travis, Hugh
Beaumont
One Sheet: $20 - $40

DANGEROUS
(1930 - Paramount) Nancy Carroll
One Sheet: $500 - $800

DANGEROUS
(1935 - Warner Bros.) Bette Davis, Franchot
Tone
One Sheet: $2,500 - $4,000 *Academy
Award: Best Actress(Davis). Academy Award
Movie Posters #43.*

DANGEROUS ADVENTURE, A
(1922 - Warner Bros.) Grace Darmond, Philo
McCullough
One Sheet: $200 - $400 *Serial. 15
Chapters.*

DANGEROUS ADVENTURE, A
(1937 - Columbia) Don Terry, Rosalind Keith
One Sheet: $75 - $150

DANGEROUS AFFAIR, A
(1931 - Columbia) Jack Holt, Ralph Graves
One Sheet: $100 - $200

DANGEROUS BLONDES
(1943 - Columbia) Allyn Joslyn, Evelyn Keyes
One Sheet: $75 - $150

DANGEROUS BUSINESS
(1920 - First National) Constance Talmadge,
Kenneth Harlan
One Sheet: $500 - $800

DANGEROUS CORNER
(1934 - RKO) Melvyn Douglas, Virginia Bruce
One Sheet: $125 - $250

DANGEROUS COWARD, THE
(1924 - F.B.O.) Fred Thomson
One Sheet: $250 - $500 *Sports
(Boxing). Sports Movie Posters #120.*

DANGEROUS CROSSING
(1953 - 20th Century Fox) Jeanne Crain,
Michael Rennie
One Sheet: $20 - $40

DANGEROUS CROSSROADS
(1933 - Columbia) -
One Sheet: $150 - $300

DANGEROUS CURVE AHEAD
(1921 - Goldwyn) Helene Chadwick, Richard
Dix
One Sheet: $300 - $600

One Sheet

DANGEROUS CURVES
(1929 - Paramount) Clara Bow, Richard Arlen
One Sheet: $1,300 - $2,000

DANGEROUS DUB, THE
(1926 - Action) Buddy Roosevelt, Peggy
Montgomery
One Sheet: $200 - $400

DANGEROUS EXILE

(1958 - Rank) Louis Jourdan, Belinda Lee
One Sheet: $15 - $25

DANGEROUS FISTS
(1925 - Rayart) Jack Perrin
One Sheet: $250 - $500

DANGEROUS GAME, A
(1941 - Universal) Richard Arlen, Andy Devine
One Sheet: $100 - $200

DANGEROUS HOLIDAY
(1937 - Republic) Hedda Hopper, Guinn
Williams
One Sheet: $75 - $150

DANGEROUS INTRIGUE
(1935 - Columbia) Ralph Bellamy, Gloria Shea
One Sheet: $100 - $200

DANGEROUS INTRUDER
(1945 - PRC) Charles Arnt, Veda Ann Borg
One Sheet: $30 - $60

DANGEROUS JOURNEY
(1944 - 20th Century Fox) Documentary
One Sheet: $20 - $40

DANGEROUS KISS
(1994 - -) Alicia Silverstone
One Sheet: $10 - $20 *Scarce.
Distributed to only a few test markets, then
cancelled.*

DANGEROUS LADY
(1941 - PRC) Nell Hamilton, June Storey
One Sheet: $40 - $75

DANGEROUS LIASONS
(1989 - Warner Bros.) Glenn Close, John
Malkovich
One Sheet: $7 - $15

DANGEROUS MILLIONS
(1946 - 20th Century Fox) Kent Taylor, Donna
Drake
One Sheet: $40 - $75

DANGEROUS MINDS
(1995 - Hollywood) Michelle Pfeiffer
One Sheet: $5 - $12

DANGEROUS MISSION
(1954 - RKO) Victor Mature, Piper Laurie,
Vincent Price
One Sheet: $30 - $50

DANGEROUS MONEY
(1946 - Monogram) Sidney Toler, Gloria
Warren
One Sheet: $50 - $100

DANGEROUS MOONLIGHT
(1941 - RKO) Anton Welbrook, Sally Gray
One Sheet: $50 - $100

DANGEROUS NAN MCGREW
(1930 - Paramount Publix) Helen Kane, Stuart
Erwin
One Sheet: $150 - $300

DANGEROUS NUMBER
(1937 - MGM) Robert Young, Ann Sothern
One Sheet: $100 - $200

DANGEROUS PARADISE
(1930 - Paramount Famous Lasky) Nancy
Carroll, Richard Arlen
One Sheet: $150 - $300

DANGEROUS PARTNERS
(1945 - MGM) James Craig, Signe Hasso
One Sheet: $50 - $100

DANGEROUS PASSAGE
(1944 - Paramount) Robert Lowery, Phyllis
Brooks
One Sheet: $50 - $100

DANGEROUS PROFESSION, A
(1949 - RKO) George Raft, Ella Raines, Pat
O'Brien
One Sheet: $75 - $125

DANGEROUS SECRET
(1938 - Grand National) Paul Lukas, Linden
Tarvers
One Sheet: $75 - $150

DANGEROUS TO KNOW
(1938 - Paramount) Anna May Wong, Akim
Tamiroff
One Sheet: $125 - $250

DANGEROUS VENTURE
(1947 - United Artists) William Boyd, Andy
Clyde
One Sheet: $50 - $100

DANGEROUS VISITOR
(1956R - -) -
One Sheet: $15 - $25 *Re-release.*

DANGEROUS WATERS
(1936 - Universal) Jack Holt, Robert Armstrong
One Sheet: $125 - $250

DANGEROUS WHEN WET
(1953 - MGM) Esther Williams, Fernando
Lamas
One Sheet: $75 - $125

DANGEROUS WOMAN
(1929 - Paramount) Clive Brook
One Sheet: $500 - $800

DANGEROUS WOMAN, A
(1993 - Gramercy) Debra Winger
One Sheet: $3 - $5

DANGEROUS YEARS
(1947 - 20th Century Fox) William (Billy) Halop,
Ann Todd, Marilyn Monroe
One Sheet: $150 - $300 *Monroe's film
debut Monroe is not pictured on most posters.*

DANGEROUS YEARS/INVISIBLE WALL, THE
(1947 - Fox) -
One Sheet: $100 - $200 *Double
feature poster.*

Jumbo Window Card

DANGEROUS YOUTH
(1958 - Warner Bros.) George Baker, Frankie
Vaughn
One Sheet: $40 - $75

DANGEROUSLY CLOSE
(1986 - -) John Stockwell, Carey Lowell, J.
Eddie Peck
One Sheet: $3 - $5

DANGEROUSLY THEY LIVE
(1942 - Warner Bros.) John Garfield, Nancy
Coleman
One Sheet: $100 - $200

DANGEROUSLY YOURS
(1933 - Fox) Warner Baxter, Miriam Jordan
One Sheet: $150 - $300

DANGEROUSLY YOURS
(1937 - 20th Century Fox) Cesar Romero,
Phyllis Brooks
One Sheet: $75 - $150

DANGERS OF THE CANADIAN MOUNTED
(1948 - Republic) Jim Bannon, Virginia Belmont
One Sheet: $75 - $125 *Serial.
Western. 12 Chapters.*

DANGERS OF THE CANADIAN MOUNTED
(1957R - Republic) Jim Bannon, Virginia
Belmont
One Sheet: $15 - $30 *Re-release.
Serial. Western.*

DANIEL
(1913 - Vitagraph) -
One Sheet: $250 - $600

DANIEL
(1983 - Paramount) Timothy Hutton, Edward
Asner
One Sheet: $3 - $5

DANIEL BOONE
(1936 - RKO) George O'Brien, Heather Angel

One Sheet: $150 - $350

DANIEL BOONE THRU THE WILDERNESS
(1926 - -) Roy Stewart, Kathleen Collins
One Sheet: $250 - $500

DANIEL BOONE, TRAIL BLAZER
(1956 - Republic) Bruce Bennett, Lon Chaney
One Sheet: $40 - $75

DANIELLA BY NIGHT
(1962 - Cambist) Elke Sommer, Ivan Desny
One Sheet: $15 - $25

DANNY BOY
(1934 - Butcher) Dorothy Dickson
One Sheet: $250 - $500

DANNY BOY
(1941 - Butcher) Ann Todd, David Farrar
One Sheet: $150 - $300

DANNY BOY
(1945 - PRC) Buz Henry, Eva March
One Sheet: $30 - $50

DANTE'S INFERNO
(1924 - Fox) Lawson Butt, Howard Gaye,
Pauline Starke
One Sheet: $1,600 - $2,500 *Graven
Images, pg. 26.*

One Sheet

DANTE'S INFERNO
(1935 - 20th Century Fox) Spencer Tracy,
Claire Trevor, Rita Hayworth
One Sheet: $1,300 - $2,000 *Graven
Images, pg. 90. Inferno sequence is a classic in
film. Hayworth's first film appearance as a dancer.*

DANTE'S PEAK
(1997 - Universal) Pierce Brosnan, Linda
Hamilton
One Sheet: $3 - $5

DARBY O'GILL AND THE LITTLE PEOPLE
(1959 - Buena Vista/Disney) Albert Sharpe,
Janet Munro, Sean Connery
One Sheet: $30 - $50

DARBY O'GILL AND THE LITTLE PEOPLE
(1969R - Buena Vista/Disney) Albert Sharpe,
Janet Munro, Sean Connery
One Sheet: $15 - $25 *Re-release.*

DARBY O'GILL AND THE LITTLE PEOPLE
(1977R - Buena Vista/Disney) Albert Sharpe,
Janet Munro, Sean Connery
One Sheet: $7 - $15 *Re-release.*

DARBY'S RANGERS
(1958 - Warner Bros.) James Garner, Etchika
Choureau
One Sheet: $7 - $15

DARE THE DEVIL
(1970 - -) Wise
One Sheet: $15 - $25

DAREDEVIL, THE
(1919 - Fox) Tom Mix
One Sheet: $350 - $750 *Cowboy
Movie Posters #28.*

DAREDEVIL, THE
(1971 - Stringer) George Montgomery, Terry
Moore
One Sheet: $7 - $15 *Sports (Auto
racing).*

DAREDEVIL DRIVERS, THE
(1938 - Warner Bros.) Dick Purcell, Beverly
Roberts
One Sheet: $75 - $125 *Sports (Auto*

racing).

DAREDEVIL DROOPY
(1951 - MGM) Droopy, Tex Avery
One Sheet: $500 - $900   *Cartoon. Full color stone litho.*

DAREDEVIL IN THE CASTLE
(1969 - Frank Lee Int.) Toshiro Mifune, Akihiko Hirata
One Sheet: $50 - $100   *Japanese. AKA: DEVIL IN THE CASTLE.*

DAREDEVIL JACK
(1920 - Pathe) Jack Dempsey
One Sheet: $800 - $1,500   *Serial. 15 Chapters.*

DAREDEVILS OF EARTH
(1936 - Hallmark) Ida Lupino, John Loder
One Sheet: ` $150 - $300

DAREDEVILS OF THE CLOUDS
(1948 - Republic) Robert Livingston, Mae Clarke, James Cardwell
One Sheet: $50 - $100

DAREDEVILS OF THE RED CIRCLE
(1939 - Republic) Charles Quigley, Herman Brix
One Sheet: $150 - $350   *Serial. 12 Chapters. One Sheet(Chapter One):$250-$500.*

DAREDEVILS OF THE WEST
(1943 - Republic) Allan Lane, Kay Aldridge
One Sheet: $50 - $100   *Serial. Western. 12 Chapters.*

DARING CABALLERO, THE
(1949 - United Artists) Duncan Renaldo, Leo Carrillo
One Sheet: $30 - $50

DARING DANGER
(1932 - Columbia) Tim McCoy
One Sheet: $500 - $800   *Cowboy Movie Posters # 130.*

DARING DAUGHTERS
(1933 - Tower) Marian Marsh, Joan Marsh
One Sheet: $150 - $300

DARING DAYS
(1925 - Blue Streak) Josie Sedgwick, Edward Hearne
One Sheet: $125 - $250

DARING DOBERMANS, THE
(1973 - Dimension) Charles Knox Robinson, Tim Considine
One Sheet: $3 - $5

DARING GAME
(1968 - Paramount) Lloyd Bridges, Nico Minardos
One Sheet: $5 - $10

DARING YOUNG MAN
(1935 - Fox) James Dunn, Mae Clarke
One Sheet: $150 - $300

DARING YOUNG MAN
(1942 - Columbia) Joe E. Brown, Marguerite Chapman
One Sheet: $75 - $150

DARK, THE
(1979 - Film Ventures) William Devane, Cathy Lee Crosby
One Sheet: $5 - $10

DARK ALIBI
(1946 - Monogram) Sidney Toler, Benson Fong
One Sheet: $75 - $125   *Charlie Chan series.*

DARK ANGEL, THE
(1925 - First National) Ronald Coleman, Vilma Banky
One Sheet: $1,300 - $2,000

DARK ANGEL, THE
(1935 - United Artists) Fredric March, Merle Oberon, Herbert Marshall
One Sheet: $125 - $250

DARK AT THE TOP OF THE STAIRS, THE
(1960 - Warner Bros.) Robert Preston, Dorothy McGuire
One Sheet: $10 - $20

DARK CITY
(1950 - Paramount) Dean Jagger, Lizabeth Scott, Charlton Heston

One Sheet: $75 - $125   *Heston's first major film role.*

DARK COMMAND
(1940 - Republic) Walter Pidgeon, John Wayne
One Sheet: $250 - $600

DARK CORNER, THE
(1946 - 20th Century Fox) Lucille Ball, Clifton Webb
One Sheet: $200 - $400

DARK CRYSTAL, THE
(1983 - Universal) Dir: Jim Henson and Frank Oz
One Sheet: $15 - $25   *Advance (Amsel art):$10-20.*

DARK DELUSION
(1947 - MGM) Lionel Barrymore, James Craig, Lucille Bremer
One Sheet: $50 - $100

DARK END OF THE STREET, THE
(1981 - First Run) Laura Harrington, Lance Henriksen
One Sheet: $3 - $5

DARK EYES
(1980 - -) John Carradine, Britt Ekland
One Sheet: $3 - $5

DARK EYES
(1987 - -) Marcello Mastroianni, Silvana Mangano
One Sheet: $5 - $10

DARK FORCES
(1984 - -) Robert Powell, Broderick Crawford
One Sheet: $3 - $5

DARK HALF, THE
(1993 - Orion) Timothy Hutton, Amy Madigan
One Sheet: $3 - $5

DARK HAZARD
(1934 - First National) Edward G. Robinson, Glenda Farrell
One Sheet: $600 - $1,000

DARK HORSE, THE
(1932 - First National) Warren William, Bette Davis
One Sheet: $800 - $1,500

DARK HORSE, THE
(1946 - Universal) Mark Richman, Leslie Nielsen
One Sheet: $75 - $125

DARK HOUR, THE
(1936 - Chesterfield) Hedda Hopper, E. E. Clive
One Sheet: $100 - $200

DARK INTRUDER
(1965 - Universal) Leslie Nielson, Gilbert Green
One Sheet: $15 - $30

DARK JOURNEY
(1937 - United Artists) Conrad Veidt, Vivien Leigh
One Sheet: $800 - $1,500   *Beware undated re-releases.*

DARK MANHATTAN
(1937 - Renaldo) Ralph Cooper
One Sheet: $150 - $300   *Black cast.*

DARK MIRROR, THE
(1946 - Universal) Olivia de Havilland, Lew Ayres
One Sheet: $75 - $150

DARK MOUNTAIN, THE
(1944 - Paramount) Ellen Drew, Robert Lowery
One Sheet: $50 - $100

DARK ODYSSEY
(1961 - Era) Athan Karras
One Sheet: $7 - $15

DARK OF THE SUN
(1968 - MGM) Rod Taylor, Yvette Mimieux, Jim Brown
One Sheet: $7 - $15

DARK PASSAGE
(1947 - Warner Bros.) Humphrey Bogart, Lauren Bacall
One Sheet: $200 - $400

DARK PASSAGE
(1956R - Dominant) Humphrey Bogart, Lauren

Bacall
One Sheet: $75 - $150   *Re-release.*

DARK PAST, THE
(1949 - Columbia) William Holden, Nina Foch
One Sheet: $40 - $80

DARK PLACES
(1974 - Cinerama) Christopher Lee, Joan Collins
One Sheet: $10 - $20

DARK PURPOSE
(1964 - Universal) Shirley Jones, Rossano Brazzi
One Sheet: $7 - $15

DARK ROAD, THE
(1917 - Triangle) Dorothy Dalton, Robert McKim
One Sheet: $250 - $600

DARK SANDS
(1937 - Record) Paul Robeson, Henry Wilcoxon
One Sheet: $1,300 - $2,000   *Separate Cinema, pg. 44.*

DARK SECRETS
(1923 - Paramount) Dorothy Dalton, Robert Ellis
One Sheet: $250 - $600

DARK STAR
(1975 - Harris) Brian Narelle, Andreijah Pahich
One Sheet: $20 - $40   *John Carpenter's directorial debut. Advance:$30-$60.*

DARK STREETS
(1929 - First National) Jack Mulhall, Lila Lee
One Sheet: $200 - $400

DARK STREETS OF CAIRO
(1940 - Universal) Sigrid Gurie, Ralph Byrd
One Sheet: $75 - $150

DARK TOWER
(1943 - Warner Bros.) Ben Lyon, Herbert Lom
One Sheet: $40 - $75

DARK TOWN FOLLIES
(1929 - Pathe) Buck and Bubbles
One Sheet: $600 - $1,000   *Black cast. Separate Cinema, pg. 67.*

DARK TOWN JUBILEE
(1914 - -) -
One Sheet: $1,300 - $2,000   *Black cast.*

DARK TOWN REVUE
(1931 - -) -
One Sheet: $250 - $500   *Black cast.*

DARK VENTURE
(1956 - First National) John Trevlac, John Carradine
One Sheet: $10 - $20

DARK VICTORY
(1939 - Warner Bros.) Bette Davis, George Brent, Humphrey Bogart
One Sheet: $3,500 - $5,000

Three Sheet

DARK WATERS
(1944 - United Artists) Merle Oberon, Franchot Tone
One Sheet: $100 - $200

DARK WATERS
(195?R - United Artists) Merle Oberon, Franchot Tone
One Sheet: $5 - $10   *Re-release.*

DARKENED ROOMS

(1929 - Paramount) Evelyn Brent, Neil Hamilton
One Sheet: $250 - $500

DARKENED SKIES
(1930 - Capital) Evelyn Brent, Wallace MacDonald
One Sheet: $250 - $600

DARKER THAN AMBER
(1970 - National General) Rod Taylor, Suzy Kendall
One Sheet: $5 - $10

DARKEST AFRICA
(1936 - Republic) Clyde Beatty, Manuel King
One Sheet: $350 - $750   *Serial. 15 Chapters. (The first Republic Serial).*

DARKEST HOUR, THE
(1923 - Pathe) The Spat Family
One Sheet: $250 - $500

DARKMAN
(1990 - Universal) Liam Neeson
One Sheet: $5 - $10   *Advance:$10-$20.*

DARLING
(1965 - Anglo-Amalgamated (British)) Julie Christy, Dirk Bogarde
One Sheet: $40 - $75   *Academy Award: Best Actress. Academy Award Movie Posters #231.*

DARLING HOW COULD YOU!
(1951 - Paramount) Joan Fontaine, John Lund
One Sheet: $20 - $40

DARLING LILI
(1970 - Paramount) Julie Andrews, Rock Hudson
One Sheet: $10 - $20

DARWIN ADVENTURE, THE
(1972 - 20th Century Fox) Nicholas Clay, Ian Richardson
One Sheet: $5 - $10

D.A.R.Y.L.
(1985 - Columbia) Mary Beth Hurt, Michael Mckean
One Sheet: $3 - $5

DAS BOOT
(1982 - Columbia) Jurgen Prochnow, Herbort Gronemeyer
One Sheet: $15 - $30   *German. Dubbed American version titled THE BOAT.*

DATE BAIT
(1960 - Filmgroup) Gary Clark, Marlo Ryan
One Sheet: $30 - $50

DATE WITH AN ANGEL
(1987 - -) Michael E. Knight, Phoebe Cates
One Sheet: $3 - $5

DATE WITH DEATH, A
(1959 - Pacific International) Gerald Mohr, Liz Renay
One Sheet: $40 - $75   *"Psycho-Rama" subliminal film which was ultimately banned by the FCC.*

DATE WITH JUDY, A
(1948 - MGM) Wallace Beery, Jane Powell, Elizabeth Taylor
One Sheet: $75 - $125

DATE WITH THE FALCON, A
(1941 - RKO) George Sanders, Wendy Barrie
One Sheet: $125 - $250

DATES AND NUTS
(1937 - Fox) Herman Timberg, Pat Rooney
One Sheet: $75 - $150

DAUGHTER OF DARKNESS
(1948 - Paramount) Anne Crawford, Maxwell Reed
One Sheet: $50 - $100

DAUGHTER OF DON Q
(1946 - Republic) Adrian Booth, Kirk Alyn
One Sheet: $125 - $250   *Serial. 12 Chapters.*

DAUGHTER OF DR. JEKYLL
(1957 - Allied Artists) John Agar, Gloria Talbott
One Sheet: $40 - $75

DAUGHTER OF PAN, A
(1914 - Warner) Helen Gardner

One Sheet: $200 - $400

DAUGHTER OF ROMANY, A
(1913 - Edison) -
One Sheet: $200 - $400

DAUGHTER OF ROSIE O'GRADY, THE
(1950 - Warner Bros.) June Haver, Gordon MacRae
One Sheet: $15 - $30

DAUGHTER OF SHANGHAI
(1937 - Paramount) Anna May Wong, Larry "Buster" Crabbe
One Sheet: $150 - $300

DAUGHTER OF THE CONGO
(1930 - Micheaux) Kathleen Noisette, Lorenzo Tucker
One Sheet: $150 - $300

DAUGHTER OF THE DRAGON
(1931 - Paramount Publix) Warner Oland, Anna May Wong
One Sheet: $1,300 - $2,000

DAUGHTER OF THE GODS, A
(1916 - Fox) Annette Kellerman
One Sheet: $250 - $500

DAUGHTER OF THE JUNGLE
(1949 - Republic) Lois Hall, James Cardwell
One Sheet: $30 - $50

DAUGHTER OF THE MINES, A
(1910 - Edison) -
One Sheet: $500 - $800

DAUGHTER OF THE SUN GOD
(1962 - Condor) William Holmes, Lisa Montell
One Sheet: $20 - $40

DAUGHTER OF THE TONG
(1939 - Metropolitan) Evelyn Brent, Grant Withers
One Sheet: $150 - $300

DAUGHTER OF THE WEST
(1949 - Film Classics) Martha Vickers, Phillip Reed
One Sheet: $15 - $25

DAUGHTERS COURAGEOUS
(1939 - First National) John Garfield, Priscilla Lane
One Sheet: $75 - $150

DAUGHTERS OF DARKNESS
(1971 - Maron) Delphine Seyrig, John Karlen
One Sheet: $5 - $10

DAUGHTERS OF DESTINY
(1954 - Cinedis) Claudette Colbert
One Sheet: $15 - $35

DAUGHTERS OF DRACULA
(19?? - Lurco) Marianne Morris
One Sheet: $7 - $15

DAUGHTERS OF SATAN
(1972 - United Artists) Tom Selleck, Barra Grant
One Sheet: $15 - $30

DAUGHTERS OF SATAN/SUPERBEAST
(1972 - United Artists) -
One Sheet: $15 - $25   *Double feature poster.*

DAVE
(1993 - Warner Bros.) Kevin Kline, Sigourney Weaver
One Sheet: $3 - $5

DAVID AND BATHSHEBA
(1951 - 20th Century Fox) Gregory Peck, Susan Hayward
One Sheet: $75 - $150

DAVID AND BATHSHEBA
(1960R - 20th Century Fox) Gregory Peck, Susan Hayward
One Sheet: $15 - $25   *Re-release.*

DAVID AND GOLIATH
(1961 - Allied Artists) Orson Welles, Eleonora Rossi Drago
One Sheet: $30 - $50

DAVID AND LISA
(1963 - Continental) Keir Dullea, Janet Margolin
One Sheet: $15 - $25

● **DAVID COPPERFIELD**
(1935 - MGM) W. C. Fields, Freddie Bartholomew
One Sheet: $700 - $1,200   *Price is for either style one sheet.*

Title Card

● **DAVID COPPERFIELD**
(1962R - MGM) W.C. Fields, Freddie Bartholomew
One Sheet: $15 - $25

● **DAVID COPPERFIELD**
(1970 - 20th Century Fox) Richard Attenborough, Cyril Cusack
One Sheet: $3 - $5

● **DAVID HARDING, COUNTERSPY**
(1950 - Columbia) Willard Parker, Audrey Long
One Sheet: $15 - $25

● **DAVID HARUM**
(1934 - Fox) Will Rogers, Evelyn Venable
One Sheet: $250 - $500   *Sports Movie Posters #245.*

● **DAVID HARUM**
(1937R - Fox) Will Rogers, Evelyn Venable
One Sheet: $75 - $150   *Re-release.*

● **DAVY CROCKETT AND THE RIVER PIRATES**
(1956 - Buena Vista/Disney) Fess Parker, Buddy Ebsen
One Sheet: $75 - $150

● **DAVY CROCKETT AT THE FALL OF THE ALAMO**
(1926 - -) Cullen Landis, Kathryn McGuire
One Sheet: $500 - $800

● **DAVY CROCKETT, INDIAN SCOUT**
(1950 - United Artists) George Montgomery, Ellen Drew
One Sheet: $50 - $100

● **DAVY CROCKETT, KING OF THE WILD FRONTIER**
(1955 - Buena Vista/Disney) Fess Parker, Buddy Ebsen
One Sheet: $150 - $350   *Cowboy Movie Posters #302.*

● **DAWN AT SOCORRO**
(1954 - Universal) Rory Calhoun, Piper Laurie
One Sheet: $15 - $30

● **DAWN EXPRESS, THE**
(1942 - PRC) Michael Whalen, Anne Nagel
One Sheet: $50 - $100

● **DAWN MAKER**
(1916 - Triangle) William S. Hart
One Sheet: $1,900 - $3,000

● **DAWN MAKER**
(192?R - -) William S. Hart
One Sheet: $150 - $300   *Re-release.*

● **DAWN OF REVENGE**
(1922 - Aynon) Richard C. Travers
One Sheet: $100 - $200

● **DAWN OF THE DEAD**
(1979 - United) David Emge, Ken Foree, Dir: George Romero
One Sheet: $15 - $35   *Price applies to either style.*

● **DAWN ON THE GREAT DIVIDE**
(1943 - Monogram) Buck Jones, Rex Bell
One Sheet: $100 - $200

● **DAWN PATROL, THE**
(1930 - First National) Richard Barthelmess,

● Douglas Fairbanks, Jr
One Sheet: $1,900 - $3,000

● **DAWN PATROL, THE**
(1938 - Warner Bros.) Errol Flynn, David Niven, Basil Rathbone
One Sheet: $1,600 - $2,500

● **DAWN RIDER, THE**
(1935 - Monogram) John Wayne, Yakima Canutt
One Sheet: $1,900 - $3,000

● **DAWN RIDER, THE**
(194?R - Lone Star) John Wayne, Yakima Canutt
One Sheet: $100 - $200   *Re-release.*

● **DAWN TRAIL, THE**
(1930 - Columbia) Buck Jones
One Sheet: $700 - $1,200

● **DAY AND THE HOUR, THE**
(1964 - MGM) Simone Signoret, Stuart Whitman
One Sheet: $5 - $10

● **DAY AT SINGAPORE, A**
(1913 - G. Melies) -
One Sheet: $900 - $1,600

● **DAY AT THE RACES, A**
(1937 - MGM) The Marx Brothers, Maureen O'Sullivan
One Sheet: $2,200 - $3,500   *Sports Movie Posters #247. One Sheet(Leader Press):$300-$600.*

One Sheet

● **DAY AT THE RACES, A**
(1952R - MGM) The Marx Bros., Maureen O'Sullivan
One Sheet: $75 - $150   *Re-release.*

● **DAY AT THE RACES, A**
(1962R - MGM) The Marx Bros., Maureen O'Sullivan
One Sheet: $15 - $25   *Re-release. Duotone.*

● **DAY FOR NIGHT**
(1973 - Warner Bros/Columbia) Francois Truffaut, Jacqueline Bisset
One Sheet: $30 - $50

● **DAY IN THE DEATH OF JOE EGG, A**
(1972 - Columbia) Alan Bates, Janet Suzman
One Sheet: $3 - $5

● **DAY MARS INVADED EARTH, THE**
(1963 - 20th Century Fox) Kent Taylor, Marie Windsor
One Sheet: $20 - $40

● **DAY OF ANGER**
(1969 - National General) Lee Van Cleef
One Sheet: $10 - $20   *Cowboy Movie Posters #327.*

● **DAY OF FURY, A**
(1956 - Universal) Dale Robertson, Mara Corday
One Sheet: $15 - $25

● **DAY OF RECKONING**
(1933 - MGM) Madge Evans, Una Merkel, Richard Dix
One Sheet: $125 - $250

● **DAY OF THE ASSASSIN**
(1979 - -) Chuck Connors, Glenn Ford
One Sheet: $7 - $15

● **DAY OF THE BADMAN**

● (1958 - Universal) Fred McMurray, Joan Weldon
One Sheet: $15 - $30

● **DAY OF THE DEAD**
(1985 - United) Lori Cardille, Terry Alexander
One Sheet: $15 - $30

● **DAY OF THE DOLPHIN, THE**
(1973 - Avco/Embassy) George C. Scott, Trish Van Devere
One Sheet: $7 - $15   *Advance:$10-$20.*

● **DAY OF THE EVIL GUN**
(1968 - MGM) Glenn Ford, Arthur Kennedy
One Sheet: $7 - $15

● **DAY OF THE JACKAL, THE**
(1973 - Universal) Edward Fox, Delphine Seyrig
One Sheet: $7 - $15

● **DAY OF THE LOCUST**
(1975 - Paramount) Donald Sutherland, Karen Black
One Sheet: $15 - $35

● **DAY OF THE OUTLAW**
(1959 - United Artists) Robert Ryan, Burl Ives
One Sheet: $15 - $30

● **DAY OF THE TRIFFIDS, THE**
(1962 - Allied Artists) Howard Keel, Nicole Maurey
One Sheet: $100 - $200   *Graven Images, pg. 224.*

● **DAY OF THE TRUMPET, THE**
(1957 - People's) -
One Sheet: $30 - $50

● **DAY OF TRIUMPH**
(1954 - Century) Robert Wilson, Lee J. Cobb
One Sheet: $20 - $40

● **DAY THAT SHOOK THE WORLD, THE**
(1977 - AIP) Christopher Plummer, Florinda Bolkan
One Sheet: $5 - $10

● **DAY THE BOOKIES WEPT, THE**
(1939 - RKO) Joe Penner, Betty Grable
One Sheet: $125 - $250   *Sports (Horse racing). Sports Movie Posters #250.*

● **DAY THE EARTH CAUGHT FIRE, THE**
(1962 - Universal) Janet Munro, Leo McKern
One Sheet: $30 - $50

● **DAY THE EARTH FROZE, THE**
(1959 - AIP) Nina Anderson, Jon Powers
One Sheet: $40 - $75

● **DAY THE EARTH FROZE, THE**
(1963R - Renaissance) Nina Anderson, Jon Powers
One Sheet: $15 - $35   *Re-release.*

● **DAY THE EARTH STOOD STILL, THE**
(1951 - 20th Century Fox) Michael Rennie, Patricia Neal
One Sheet: $2,800 - $4,500   *Graven Images, pg. 154-155.*

One Sheet

● **DAY THE EARTH STOOD STILL, THE**
(1994R - Fox) Michael Rennie, Patricia Neal
One Sheet: $10 - $20   *Re-release.*

● **DAY THE FISH CAME OUT, THE**
(1967 - International Classics) Tom Courtenay, Candice Bergen
One Sheet: $7 - $15

DAY THE HOT LINE GOT HOT, THE
(1969 - Commonwealth United) George
Chakiris, Robert Taylor
One Sheet: $7 - $15

DAY THE SKY EXPLODED, THE
(1958 - Excelsior) Paul Hubschmid
One Sheet: $40 - $75

DAY THE SUN ROSE
(1969 - Shochiku) Toshiro Mifune
One Sheet: $15 - $30   *Japanese.*

DAY THE WORLD ENDED, THE
(1955 - AIP) Richard Denning, Dir:Roger
Corman
One Sheet: $150 - $300

One Sheet

DAY THEY ROBBED THE BANK OF ENGLAND, THE
(1960 - MGM) Aldo Ray, Elizabeth Sellars
One Sheet: $15 - $25

DAY TIME ENDED, THE
(1980 - Manson International) Chris Mitchum,
Jim Davis
One Sheet: $7 - $15

DAY TO REMEMBER, A
(1953 - Republic) Stanley Holloway, Joan Rice
One Sheet: $15 - $30

DAY WILL DAWN, THE
(1942 - Paramount-British) Ralph Richardson,
Deborah Kerr
One Sheet: $50 - $100

DAY WITH JACK DEMPSEY, THE
(1921 - -) Jack Dempsey
One Sheet: $1,300 - $2,000

DAY'S PLEASURE, A
(1919 - First National) Charlie Chaplin, Edna
Purviance
One Sheet: $6,500 - $10,000

DAYBREAK
(1931 - MGM) Ramon Novarro, Helen Chandler
One Sheet: $100 - $200

DAYBREAK
(1947 - Universal) Eric Portman, Ann Todd
One Sheet: $30 - $50

DAYDREAMER, THE
(1966 - Embassy) Ray Bolger, Margaret
Hamilton
One Sheet: $15 - $25   *Partial animation.*

DAYDREAMS
(1922 - First National) Buster Keaton
One Sheet: $5,000 - $7,500

DAYLIGHT
(1996 - Universal) Sylvester Stallone, Amy
Brenneman
One Sheet: $5 - $10

DAYS OF BUFFALO BILL
(1946 - Republic) Sunset Carson, Peggy
Stewart
One Sheet: $30 - $50

DAYS OF GLORY
(1944 - RKO) Tamara Tounanova, Gregory
Peck(film debut)
One Sheet: $50 - $100

DAYS OF HEAVEN
(1978 - Paramount) Richard Gere, Brooke
Adams

One Sheet: $7 - $15

DAYS OF JESSE JAMES
(1939 - Republic) Roy Rogers, Gabby Hayes
One Sheet: $250 - $500

DAYS OF OLD CHEYENNE
(1943 - Republic) Don Barry, Lynn Merrick
One Sheet: $40 - $75

DAYS OF THRILLS AND LAUGHTER
(1961 - 20th Century Fox) Douglas Fairbanks,
Charlie Chaplin
One Sheet: $20 - $40

DAYS OF THUNDER
(1990 - Paramount) Tom Cruise, Robert Duvall,
Nicole Kidman
One Sheet: $10 - $20   *Sports (Auto racing). Sports Movie Posters #28.*

DAYS OF WINE AND ROSES
(1963 - Warner Bros.) Jack Lemmon, Lee
Remick
One Sheet: $15 - $30

DAY-TIME WIFE
(1939 - 20th Century Fox) Tyrone Power, Linda
Darnell
One Sheet: $125 - $250

DAYTON'S DEVILS
(1969 - Commonwealth United) Rory Calhoun,
Leslie Nielsen
One Sheet: $7 - $15

DAYTONA BEACH WEEKEND
(1965 - Dominant) Del Shannon, Sue Skeen
One Sheet: $30 - $50

DAYTRIPPERS
(1997 - Cinepix) Hope Davis, Stanley Tucci,
Parker Posey
One Sheet: $5 - $10

DAZED AND CONFUSED
(1993 - Gramercy) Jason London, Rory
Cochrane
One Sheet: $5 - $10

D.C. CAB
(1983 - RKO-Universal) Adam Baldwin, Mr. T.,
Irene Cara
One Sheet: $7 - $15

D-DAY, THE SIXTH OF JUNE
(1956 - 20th Century Fox) Robert Taylor,
Richard Todd, Dana Wynter, Edmond O'Brien
One Sheet: $15 - $25

DE SADE
(1969 - AIP) Keir Dullea, Senta Berger, Lilli
Palmer
One Sheet: $15 - $25

DEAD, THE
(1987 - Vestron) Anjelica Houston, Donal
McCann
One Sheet: $3 - $5

DEAD AGAIN
(1991 - Paramount) Kenneth Branagh, Emma
Thompson
One Sheet: $5 - $10

DEAD AND BURIED
(1981 - Avco/Embassy) James Farentino,
Melody Anderson
One Sheet: $3 - $5

DEAD ARE ALIVE, THE
(1972 - National General) Samantha Eggar,
Alex Cord
One Sheet: $15 - $30

DEAD CALM
(1989 - Warner Bros.) Sam Neill, Nicole
Kidman
One Sheet: $5 - $10

DEAD DON'T DREAM, THE
(1948 - United Artists) William Boyd, Andy
Clyde
One Sheet: $50 - $100

DEAD END
(1937 - United Artists) Sylvia Sidney, Joel
McCrea, Humphrey Bogart
One Sheet: $800 - $1,500

DEAD END
(194?R - Film Classics) Sylvia Sidney, Joel
McCrea, Humphrey Bogart
One Sheet: $75 - $150   *Re-release.*

DEAD END
(1954R - Film Classics) Sylvia Sydney, Joel
McCrea, Humphrey Bogart
One Sheet: $40 - $75   *Re-release.*

DEAD END KIDS ON DRESS PARADE
(1939 - Warner Bros.) Dead End Kids, John
Litel
One Sheet: $75 - $150

DEAD FALL
(1968 - 20th Century Fox) Michael Caine,
Giovanna Ralli, Eric Portman
One Sheet: $5 - $10

DEAD FALL
(1993 - Trimark) Nicolas Cage, Charlie Sheen
One Sheet: $3 - $5

DEAD GAME
(1923 - Universal) Hoot Gibson
One Sheet: $350 - $750   *Cowboy Movie Posters #44.*

DEAD HEAT
(1988 - -) Treat Williams, Joe Piscopo
One Sheet: $5 - $10

DEAD HEAT ON A MERRY-GO-ROUND
(1966 - Columbia) James Coburn, Aldo Ray
One Sheet: $10 - $20

DEAD MAN
(1996 - Miramax) Johnny Depp, Gabriel Byrne,
Robert Mitchum
One Sheet: $5 - $12

DEAD MAN WALKING
(1996 - Gramercy) Susan Sarandon, Sean
Penn
One Sheet: $7 - $15   *Academy Award: Best Actress (Sarandon).*

DEAD MAN'S EYES
(1944 - Universal) Lon Chaney Jr., Jean Parker
One Sheet: $75 - $150

DEAD MAN'S EYES
(1950R - Realart) Lon Chaney, Jr., Jean Parker
One Sheet: $15 - $25   *Re-release.*

DEAD MAN'S GOLD
(1948 - Screen Guild) Lash LaRue, Fuzzy St.
John
One Sheet: $40 - $75

DEAD MAN'S GULCH
(1943 - Republic) Don Barry, Lynn Merrick
One Sheet: $40 - $75

DEAD MAN'S TRAIL
(1952 - Monogram) Johnny Mack Brown
One Sheet: $15 - $25

DEAD MARCH, THE
(1937 - Imperial) Boake Carter
One Sheet: $75 - $125

DEAD MEN DON'T WEAR PLAID
(1981 - Universal) Steve Martin, Rachel Ward
One Sheet: $7 - $15

DEAD MEN TELL
(1941 - 20th Century Fox) Sidney Toler, Jean
Rogers
One Sheet: $75 - $150

DEAD MEN TELL NO TALES
(1939 - Alliance Films) Emlyn Williams
One Sheet: $75 - $150

DEAD MEN WALK
(1943 - PRC) George Zucco, Mary Carlisle
One Sheet: $75 - $150

DEAD OF LAUGHTER
(1957 - -) -
One Sheet: $20 - $40   *Mexican.*

DEAD OF NIGHT
(1945 - United Artists) Mervyn Johns, Roland
Culver
One Sheet: $250 - $600   *Graven Images, pg. 112, 142, 234.*

DEAD OF NIGHT
(1972 - Europix) John Marley, Richard Backus
One Sheet: $10 - $20   *AKA: DEATHDREAM.*

DEAD OF WINTER
(1987 - MGM/United Artists) Mary
Steenburgen, Roddy McDowall

One Sheet: $3 - $5

DEAD ONE, THE
(1961 - Favorite) Monica Davis, John McKay
One Sheet: $20 - $40

DEAD OR ALIVE
(1944 - PRC) Dave O'Brien, Tex Ritter
One Sheet: $30 - $60

Mini Window Card

DEAD POET'S SOCIETY
(1989 - Touchstone) Robin Williams, Robert
Sean Leonard
One Sheet: $30 - $50

DEAD POOL, THE
(1988 - -) Clint Eastwood, Patricia Clarkson
One Sheet: $10 - $20

DEAD PRESIDENTS
(1995 - Caravan) Larenz Tate, Keith David, Dir:
Hughes Brothers
One Sheet: $5 - $10

DEAD RECKONING
(1947 - Columbia) Humphrey Bogart, Lizabeth
Scott
One Sheet: $200 - $400

DEAD RINGER
(1964 - Warner Bros.) Bette Davis, Karl Malden
One Sheet: $30 - $50

DEAD RINGERS
(1988 - -) Jeremy Irons, Genevieve Bujold
One Sheet: $30 - $60

DEAD SHOT, THE
(1918 - -) Helen Gibson
One Sheet: $500 - $800   *Cowboy Movie Posters #18.*

DEAD TO THE WORLD
(1961 - United Artists) Reedy Talton, Jana
Pearce
One Sheet: $7 - $15

DEAD ZONE, THE
(1983 - Paramount) Christopher Walken,
Brooke Adams
One Sheet: $5 - $10

DEAD-BANG
(1989 - Warner Bros.) Don Johnson, Penelope
Ann Miller
One Sheet: $5 - $10

DEAD-END DRIVE-IN
(1986 - -) Ned Manning, Natalie McCurry
One Sheet: $5 - $10

DEADLIER THAN THE MALE
(1967 - Universal) Richard Johnson, Elke
Sommer
One Sheet: $10 - $20

DEADLIEST SIN, THE
(1956 - Allied Artists) Sydney Chaplin, Audrey
Dalton
One Sheet: $15 - $30

DEADLINE
(1931 - Columbia) Buck Jones
One Sheet: $250 - $600   *Cowboy Movie Posters # 118.*

DEADLINE
(1948 - Astor) Sunset Carson, Pat Sterling
One Sheet: $30 - $50

DEADLINE
(1987 - -) Christopher Walken, Hywel Bennett
One Sheet: $5 - $10

DEADLINE AT DAWN
(1946 - RKO) Susan Hayward, Paul Lukas
One Sheet: $100 - $200

DEADLINE FOR MURDER
(1946 - 20th Century Fox) Paul Kelly, Kent Taylor
One Sheet: $75 - $125

DEADLINE U.S.A.
(1952 - 20th Century Fox) Humphrey Bogart, Ethel Barrymore
One Sheet: $75 - $175

DEADLY AFFAIR, THE
(1967 - Columbia) James Mason, Simone Signoret
One Sheet: $5 - $10

DEADLY BEES, THE
(1967 - Paramount) Suzanna Leigh, Guy Doleman
One Sheet: $10 - $20

DEADLY BLESSING
(1981 - Polygram) Maren Jensen, Susan Buckner, Sharon Stone
One Sheet: $5 - $10

DEADLY COMPANIONS, THE
(1961 - Pathe-American) Maureen O'Hara, Brian Keith, Dir: Sam Peckinpah
One Sheet: $40 - $75   *Peckinpah's directorial debut.*

DEADLY DUO
(1962 - United Artists) Craig Hill, Marcia Henderson
One Sheet: $7 - $15

DEADLY EYES
(1982 - Northshore) Sam Groom, Sara Botsford
One Sheet: $3 - $5

DEADLY FEMALES, THE
(1976 - Donwin) Tracy Reed, Heather Chasen
One Sheet: $7 - $15

DEADLY FORCE
(1983 - Embassy) Wings Hauser, Joyce Ingalls
One Sheet: $3 - $5

DEADLY FRIEND
(1986 - Warner Bros.) Matthew Laborteaux, Kristy Swanson
One Sheet: $5 - $10

DEADLY GAME, THE
(1941 - Monogram) Charles Farrell, June Lang
One Sheet: $75 - $125

DEADLY GAME, THE
(1954 - Lippert) Lloyd Bridges, Simone Silva
One Sheet: $10 - $20

DEADLY HERO
(1976 - Avco/Embassy) Don Murray, Diahn Williams, James Earl Jones
One Sheet: $5 - $10

DEADLY IS THE FEMALE
(1950 - United Artists) Peggy Cummins, John Dall
One Sheet: $350 - $750   *Title before change to "GUN CRAZY".*

DEADLY MANTIS, THE
(1957 - Universal) Craig Stevens, Alix Talton
One Sheet: $150 - $300   *Graven Images, pg. 168.*

DEADLY ORGAN
(1970 - -) -
One Sheet: $7 - $15

DEADLY SPAWN, THE
(1983 - 21st Century) Tom DeFranco, Jean Tafler
One Sheet: $5 - $10

DEADLY STRANGERS
(1974 - Rank) Hayley Mills, Simon Ward
One Sheet: $5 - $10

DEADLY TRACKERS, THE
(1973 - Warner Bros.) Richard Harris, Rod Taylor
One Sheet: $3 - $5

DEADLY TRAP, THE
(1972 - National General) Faye Dunaway, Frank Langella
One Sheet: $5 - $10

DEADLY WEAPONS
(1972 - -) Chesty Morgan, Harry Reems
One Sheet: $15 - $25

DEADSHOT CASEY
(1928 - -) Al Hoxie, Al Richmond
One Sheet: $250 - $550

DEADTIME STORIES
(1986 - Cinema Group) Scott Valentine, Melissa Leo
One Sheet: $5 - $10

DEADWOOD '76
(1965 - Fairway) Arch Hall, Jr., Jack Lester
One Sheet: $10 - $20

DEADWOOD DICK
(1940 - Columbia) Don Douglas, Lorna Gray
One Sheet: $250 - $500   *Serial. 15 Chapters.*

DEADWOOD PASS
(1933 - Monarch) Tom Tyler, Alice Dahl
One Sheet: $200 - $400   *Cowboy Movie Posters # 140.*

DEAF SMITH AND JOHNNY EARS
(1973 - MGM) Anthony Quinn, Franco Nero
One Sheet: $5 - $10

DEAL OF THE CENTURY
(1983 - Warner Bros.) Chevy Chase, Sigourney Weaver, Gregory Hines
One Sheet: $3 - $5

DEALING
(1972 - Warner Bros.) Barbara Hershey, Robert F. Lyons
One Sheet: $3 - $5

DEAR BRAT
(1951 - Paramount) Mona Freeman, Edward Arnold
One Sheet: $15 - $30

DEAR BRIGITTE
(1965 - 20th Century Fox) James Stewart, Billy Mumy, Brigitte Bardot
One Sheet: $15 - $30

DEAR, DEAD DELILAH
(1972 - Avco/Embassy) Agnes Moorehead, Will Geer
One Sheet: $5 - $10

DEAR GOD
(1996 - Paramount) Greg Kinnear, Maria Pitillo
One Sheet: $3 - $5

DEAR HEART
(1965 - Warner Bros.) Glenn Ford, Geraldine Page
One Sheet: $10 - $20

DEAR JOHN
(1966 - Sigma III) Jack Kulle, Christina Schollin
One Sheet: $5 - $10

DEAR MR. PROHACK
(1949 - GFD) Cecil Parker, Glynis Johns
One Sheet: $10 - $20

DEAR MR. WONDERFUL
(1983 - Lilienthal) Joe Pesci, Karen Ludwig
One Sheet: $3 - $5

DEAR MURDERER
(1948 - Universal) Eric Portman, Greta Gynt
One Sheet: $50 - $100

DEAR OCTOPUS
(1943 - Gainsborough) Margaret Lockwood, Michael Wilding
One Sheet: $40 - $75

DEAR RUTH
(1947 - Paramount) William Holden, Joan Caulfield
One Sheet: $40 - $75

DEAR WIFE
(1950 - Paramount) William Holden, Joan Caulfield
One Sheet: $30 - $50

DEATH AND THE MAIDEN
(1995 - Fine Line) Sigourney Weaver, Ben Kingsley
One Sheet: $4 - $8

DEATH AT A BROADCAST
(1934 - Phoenix) Ian Hunter, Mary Newland

DEATH BECOMES HER
(1992 - Universal) Meryl Streep, Bruce Willis, Goldie Hawn
One Sheet: $5 - $10

DEATH BEFORE DISHONOR
(1987 - New World) Fred Dryer, Brian Keith, Paul Winfield
One Sheet: $5 - $10

DEATH COLLECTOR
(1976 - Goldstone) Joseph Cortese, Joe Pesci
One Sheet: $5 - $10

DEATH CROONS THE BLUES
(1937 - MGM) Hugh Wakefield, John Turnbull
One Sheet: $150 - $300

DEATH CURSE OF TARTU
(1967 - Falcon) Fred Pinero, Babette Sherrill
One Sheet: $15 - $25

DEATH FANGS
(193? - -) Flash
One Sheet: $50 - $100

DEATH FLIES EAST
(1935 - Columbia) Conrad Nagel, Florence Rice
One Sheet: $100 - $200

DEATH FROM A DISTANCE
(1935 - Invincible) Lola Lane, Russell Hopton
One Sheet: $125 - $250

DEATH GAME
(1977 - Levitt/Pickman) Sondra Locke, Colleen Camp
One Sheet: $5 - $10

DEATH GOES NORTH
(1939 - Warwick) Edgar Edwards, Sheila Bromley
One Sheet: $50 - $100

DEATH GOES TO SCHOOL
(1953 - Eros) Barbara Murray
One Sheet: $10 - $20

DEATH HUNT
(1981 - 20th Century Fox) Charles Bronson, Lee Marvin
One Sheet: $5 - $10

DEATH IN SMALL DOSES
(1957 - Allied Artists) Peter Graves, Mala Powers
One Sheet: $15 - $25

DEATH IN THE SKY
(1937 - Puritan) Lona Andre
One Sheet: $250 - $500   *AKA: PILOT-X.*

DEATH IN VENICE
(1971 - Warner Bros.) Dirk Bogarde, Silvana Mangano
One Sheet: $3 - $5

DEATH KISS, THE
(1933 - K.B.S.) Bela Lugosi, David Manners
One Sheet: $700 - $1,200

DEATH MACHINES
(1976 - -) Ron Marchini, Michael Chong
One Sheet: $5 - $10

DEATH OF A CHAMPION
(1939 - Paramount) Lynne Overman, Virginia Dale
One Sheet: $75 - $150

DEATH OF A GUNFIGHTER
(1969 - Universal) Richard Widmark, Lena Horne
One Sheet: $5 - $10

DEATH OF A SALESMAN
(1951 - Columbia) Fredric March, Mildred Dunnock
One Sheet: $40 - $75

DEATH OF A SCOUNDREL
(1956 - RKO) George Sanders, Yvonne De Carlo, Zsa Zsa Gabor
One Sheet: $15 - $30

DEATH OF A SOLDIER
(1986 - Scotti) James Coburn, Bill Hunter
One Sheet: $3 - $5

DEATH ON THE DIAMOND

(1934 - MGM) Robert Young, Madge Evans, Ted Healy
One Sheet: $150 - $300   *Sports (Baseball).*

One Sheet

DEATH ON THE NILE
(1978 - Paramount) Bette Davis, Peter Ustinov
One Sheet: $10 - $20   *Amsel Art. Advance:$15-$25.*

DEATH PLAY
(1976 - New Line) Karen Leslie, James Keach
One Sheet: $3 - $5

DEATH RACE
(1978 - S.J. International) Yul Brynner, Martin Balsam
One Sheet: $5 - $10

DEATH RIDES A HORSE
(1968 - United Artists) Lee Van Cleef, John Phillip Law
One Sheet: $30 - $50   *Cowboy Movie Posters #325.*

DEATH RIDES THE PLAINS
(1943 - PRC) Robert Livingston
One Sheet: $40 - $75

DEATH RIDES THE RANGE
(1940 - Colony) Ken Maynard
One Sheet: $75 - $150

DEATH SHIP
(1980 - Avco/Embassy) George Kennedy, Richard Crenna
One Sheet: $3 - $5

DEATH SONG, THE
(1912 - Pathe) -
One Sheet: $1,900 - $3,000

DEATH TAKES A HOLIDAY
(1934 - Paramount) Fredric March, Evelyn Venable
One Sheet: $1,300 - $2,000   *Graven Images, pg. 90.*

DEATH VALLEY
(1946 - Lida) Robert Lowery, Helen Gilbert
One Sheet: $30 - $50

DEATH VALLEY
(1982 - Universal) Paul Le Mat, Catherine Hicks, Peter Billingsley
One Sheet: $3 - $5

DEATH VALLEY GUNFIGHTERS
(1949 - Republic) Allan "Rocky" Lane, Eddie Waller
One Sheet: $30 - $50

DEATH VALLEY MANHUNT
(1943 - Republic) Bill Elliott, Gabby Hayes
One Sheet: $40 - $75

DEATH VALLEY OUTLAWS
(1941 - Republic) Don Barry, Lynn Merrick
One Sheet: $40 - $75

DEATH VALLEY RANGERS
(1943 - Monogram) Hoot Gibson, Ken Maynard, Bob Steele
One Sheet: $75 - $150

DEATH VENGEANCE
(1982 - EMI) Tom Skerritt, Michael Sarrazin
One Sheet: $3 - $5

DEATH WARRANT
(1990 - MGM) Jean-Claude Van Damme, Robert Guillaume
One Sheet: $10 - $20

DEATH WHEELERS, THE
(1973 - -) -
One Sheet: $10 - $20

DEATH WISH
(1974 - Paramount) Charles Bronson, Hope Lange
One Sheet: $15 - $35

One Sheet

DEATH WISH II
(1982 - Golan/Globus) Charles Bronson, Jill Ireland
One Sheet: $5 - $10

DEATH WISH III
(1985 - Cannon) Charles Bronson, Deborah Raffin
One Sheet: $3 - $5

DEATH WISH IV: THE CRACKDOWN
(1987 - -) Charles Bronson, Kay Lenz
One Sheet: $3 - $5

DEATH WISH V: THE FACE OF DEATH
(1994 - Trimark) Charles Bronson
One Sheet: $3 - $5

DEATHDREAM
(1972 - Europix) John Marley, Richard Backus
One Sheet: $10 - $20   *AKA: DEAD OF NIGHT.*

DEATHMAKERS
(1972 - -) -
One Sheet: $7 - $15

DEATHMASTER, THE
(1972 - AIP) Robert Quarry
One Sheet: $5 - $10

DEATHRACE 2000
(1975 - New World) David Carradine, Sylvester Stallone
One Sheet: $20 - $40   *Sports (Auto racing).*

DEATHSPORT
(1978 - New World) David Carradine, Claudia Jennings
One Sheet: $10 - $20

DEATHSTALKER
(1983 - Palo Alto) Richard Hill, Barbi Benton
One Sheet: $10 - $20

DEATHSTALKER II
(1987 - -) John Terlesky, Monique Gabrielle
One Sheet: $10 - $20

DEATHTRAP
(1982 - Warner Bros.) Michael Caine, Dyan Cannon, Christopher Reeve
One Sheet: $3 - $5

DEATHWATCH
(1966 - Beverly) Leonard Nimoy, Michael Forest
One Sheet: $7 - $15

DEATHWATCH
(1980 - -) Romy Schneider, Harvey Keitel
One Sheet: $3 - $5

DEBBIE DOES DALLAS
(197? - -) -
One Sheet: $40 - $75   *XXX.*

DEBTOR TO THE LAW, A
(1924 - Pan American) Henry Starr
One Sheet: $800 - $1,500   *Cowboy Movie Posters #45.*

DECAMERON, THE
(1971 - United Artists) Franco Citti, Ninetto Davoli
One Sheet: $5 - $10

DECAMERON NIGHTS
(1952 - RKO) Joan Fontaine, Louis Jourdan
One Sheet: $15 - $30

DECEIVED
(1991 - Disney) Goldie Hawn
One Sheet: $5 - $10

DECEIVER, THE
(1931 - Columbia) Lloyd Hughes, Dorothy Sebastian
One Sheet: $200 - $400

DECEIVERS, THE
(1966 - Goldstone) Jack Ging, Joan Blackman
One Sheet: $3 - $5

DECEIVERS, THE
(1988 - -) Pierce Brosnan, Saeed Jaffrey
One Sheet: $3 - $5

DECEPTION
(1932 - Columbia) Leo Carrillo, Thelma Todd
One Sheet: $250 - $600

DECEPTION
(1946 - Warner Bros.) Bette Davis, Paul Henreid
One Sheet: $75 - $125

DECEPTION
(1993 - -) Andie MacDowell, Liam Neeson
One Sheet: $5 - $10

DECISION AGAINST TIME
(1956 - MGM) Jack Hawkins, Elizabeth Sellars
One Sheet: $7 - $15

DECISION AT SUNDOWN
(1957 - Columbia) Randolph Scott, John Carroll
One Sheet: $15 - $35

DECISION BEFORE DAWN
(1951 - 20th Century Fox) Richard Basehart, Gary Merill
One Sheet: $15 - $30

DECISION OF CHRISTOPHER BLAKE, THE
(1948 - Warner Bros.) Alexis Smith, Robert Douglas
One Sheet: $30 - $50

DECK SPORTS IN THE CELEBES SEA
(1920 - Paramount) -
One Sheet: $150 - $300   *From the Paramount Travel Pictures series.*

DECKS RAN RED, THE
(1958 - MGM) James Mason, Dorothy Dandridge
One Sheet: $15 - $30

DECLINE AND FALL OF A BIRD WATCHER
(1969 - 20th Century Fox) Robin Phillips, Donald Wolfit
One Sheet: $5 - $10

DECLINE OF THE AMERICAN EMPIRE, THE
(1986 - Malo) Dominique Michel, Dorothee Berryman
One Sheet: $3 - $5

DECLINE OF WESTERN CIVILIZATION, THE
(1981 - -) Alice Bag Band, Black Flag, X.
One Sheet: $20 - $40   *Documentary of the punk rock scene in L.A.*

DECLINE OF WESTERN CIVILIZATION PART II: METAL YEARS, THE
(1988 - -) Joe Perry, Steven Tyler, Gene Simmons
One Sheet: $7 - $15   *Documentary of the rock scene in Los Angeles.*

DECORATOR, THE
(1916 - Vitagraph) Jimmy Aubrey
One Sheet: $200 - $400

DECOY
(1946 - Monogram) Jean Gillie, Edward Norris
One Sheet: $75 - $125

DEEP, THE
(1977 - Columbia) Robert Shaw, Jacqueline Bisset, Nick Nolte
One Sheet: $10 - $20

DEEP BLUE SEA, THE
(1955 - 20th Century Fox) Vivien Leigh, Kenneth More
One Sheet: $40 - $75

DEEP COVER
(1992 - New Line) Larry Fishburne, Jeff Goldblum
One Sheet: $5 - $10

DEEP END
(1971 - Paramount) Jane Asher, John Moulder Brown
One Sheet: $3 - $5

DEEP IN MY HEART
(1954 - MGM) Jose Ferrer, Merle Oberon
One Sheet: $30 - $50

DEEP IN THE HEART
(1983 - Warner Bros.) Karen Young, Clayton Day
One Sheet: $3 - $5

DEEP IN THE HEART OF TEXAS
(1942 - Universal) Tex Ritter, Johnny Mack Brown
One Sheet: $75 - $150

DEEP RED
(1976 - Mahler) David Hemmings, Dir: Dario Argento
One Sheet: $5 - $10   *AKA: THE HATCHET MURDERS; DRIPPING DEEP RED; DEEP RED HATCHET MURDERS*

DEEP SIX, THE
(1958 - Warner Bros.) Alan Ladd, William Bendix
One Sheet: $15 - $25

DEEP SOUTH
(1940' - Sack) Willie Best, Daisy Buford
One Sheet: $150 - $300   *Black cast. Separate Cinema, pg. 133.*

DEEP THROAT
(197? - -) Linda Lovelace, Harry Reems
One Sheet: $75 - $150   *XXX.*

DEEP THROAT PART II
(1974 - Damiana) Linda Lovelace
One Sheet: $15 - $30   *R.*

DEEP THRUST-THE HAND OF DEATH
(1973 - AIP) Angela Mao, Chang Yi
One Sheet: $15 - $30   *Kung Fu Women. Sports Movie Posters #266.*

DEEP VALLEY
(1947 - Warner Bros.) Ida Lupino, Dane Clark
One Sheet: $30 - $50

DEEP WATERS
(1920 - Paramount) Jack Gilbert, Barbara Bedford
One Sheet: $150 - $300

DEEP WATERS
(1948 - 20th Century Fox) Dana Andrews, Jean Peters, Cesar Romero
One Sheet: $30 - $50

DEEPSTAR SIX
(1989 - -) Greg Evigan, Nancy Everhard, Miguel Ferrer
One Sheet: $3 - $5

DEER HUNTER, THE
(1978 - Universal) Robert De Niro, John Cazale, Christopher Walken
One Sheet: $30 - $50   *Academy Award: Best Picture, Best Supporting Actor (Walken), Best Director (Cimino). One Sheet(AcademyAwards):$20-$40. One Sheet (De Niro w/ gun to head): $50-$100. Academy Award Movie Posters #301, #302 & #304.*

One Sheet (Awards)

DEERSLAYER, THE
(1943 - Republic) Bruce Kellogg, Jean Parker
One Sheet: $40 - $75

DEERSLAYER, THE
(1957 - 20th Century Fox) Lex Barker, Rita Moreno
One Sheet: $30 - $50

DEF-CON 4
(1985 - New World) Lenore Zann, Maury Chaykin
One Sheet: $7 - $15

DEFECTIVE DETECTIVES
(1944 - Columbia) El Brendel, Harry Langdon
One Sheet: $100 - $200   *Comedy short. Duotone.*

DEFECTOR, THE
(1966 - Seven Arts) Montgomery Clift, Hardy Kruger
One Sheet: $15 - $35

DEFENCE OF THE REALM
(1987 - Rank) Gabriel Byrne, Greta Scacchi, Denholm Elliott
One Sheet: $3 - $5

DEFENDERS OF THE LAW
(1931 - Continental) John Holland, Edmund Breese
One Sheet: $250 - $500

DEFENSE RESTS, THE
(1934 - Columbia) Jack Holt, Jean Arthur
One Sheet: $150 - $300

DEFIANCE
(1980 - Necta) Jan Michael Vincent, Danny Aiello
One Sheet: $3 - $5

DEFIANT ONES, THE
(1958 - United Artists) Tony Curtis, Sidney Poitier
One Sheet: $40 - $75   *Separate Cinema, pg. 159.*

DEFYING THE LAW
(1924 - Wm.B.Brush) Lew Cody, Renee Adoree
One Sheet: $100 - $200

DELICATE BALANCE, A
(1973 - American Film Theatre) Katharine Hepburn, Joseph Cotton
One Sheet: $15 - $25

DELICATE DELINQUENT, THE
(1957 - Paramount) Jerry Lewis, Darren McGavin
One Sheet: $20 - $40

DELICATE DELINQUENT, THE
(1962R - Paramount) Jerry Lewis, Darren McGavin
One Sheet: $10 - $20   *Re-release.*

DELICATESSEN
(1992 - Miramax) Jean Claude Dreyfus, Dominique Pinon
One Sheet: $5 - $10

DELICIOUS
(1931 - Fox) Janet Gaynor, Charles Farrell
One Sheet: $200 - $400

DELICIOUS LITTLE DEVIL, THE
(1919 - Universal) Rudolph Valentino, May Murray
One Sheet: $1,300 - $2,000

DELIGHTFUL ROGUE
(1929 - RKO) Rod LaRocque, Rita LaRoy
One Sheet: $500 - $800

DELIGHTFULLY DANGEROUS
(1945 - United Artists) Ralph Bellamy, Jane Powell, Constance Moore
One Sheet: $50 - $100

DELINQUENT DAUGHTERS
(1944 - PRC) June Carlson, Fifi D'Orsay
One Sheet: $40 - $75

DELINQUENT PARENTS
(1938 - Progressive) Maurice Weston, Doris Weston
One Sheet: $75 - $125

DELINQUENTS, THE
(1957 - United Artists) Tommy Laughlin, Peter Miller, Dir:Robert Altman (his 1st)

One Sheet: $40 - $75

DELIRIOUS
(1991 - MGM-Pathe) John Candy, Mariel Hemmingway
One Sheet: $5 - $10

DELIRIUM
(1979 - World Wide) Debi Chaney
One Sheet: $7 - $15

DELIVER US FROM EVIL
(1975 - -) Marie O'Henry, Renny Roker, Juanita Moore
One Sheet: $15 - $25 *Blaxploitation.*

DELIVERANCE
(1919 - -) Helen Keller
One Sheet: $600 - $1,000

DELIVERANCE
(1928 - Stanley Advertising) Earle Larimore, Mary Gardner
One Sheet: $250 - $500

DELIVERANCE
(1972 - Warner Bros.) Jon Voight, Burt Reynolds, Ned Beatty
One Sheet: $30 - $50

One Sheet

DELTA FACTOR, THE
(1970 - Continental) Yvette Mimieux, Christopher George
One Sheet: $3 - $5

DELTA FORCE, THE
(1986 - Cannon) Chuck Norris, Lee Marvin
One Sheet: $3 - $5

DELTA FORCE 2
(1990 - -) Chuck Norris, Billy Drago
One Sheet: $5 - $10

DELTA FOX
(1979 - Sebastian) Richard Lynch, Stuart Whitman, John Ireland
One Sheet: $5 - $10

DELTA P.
(1985 - Pegasus) Ruth Gordon
One Sheet: $3 - $5

DELUGE
(1933 - RKO) Edward Van Sloan, Peggy Shannon
One Sheet: $250 - $600 *Graven Images, pg. 44.*

DEMENTED
(1980 - Four Features) Salle Elyse, Bryan Charles
One Sheet: $3 - $5

DEMENTIA
(1953 - J.J. Parker) Adrienne Barrett
One Sheet: $75 - $150

DEMENTIA 13
(1963 - AIP) William Campbell, Luana Anders, Dir: Corman/Coppola
One Sheet: $75 - $150 *Graven Images, pg. 3. Coppola's "official" first film (see TONIGHT FOR SURE for his true first film.)*

DEMETRIUS AND THE GLADIATORS
(1954 - 20th Century Fox) Victor Mature, Susan Hayward
One Sheet: $50 - $100

DEMOLITION MAN
(1993 - Warner Bros.) Sly Stallone, Wesley Snipes
One Sheet: $5 - $10

DEMON, THE
(1981 - Gold Key) Jennifer Holmes, Cameron Mitchell
One Sheet: $5 - $10

DEMON (GOD TOLD ME TO)
(1976 - New World) Tony Lo Bianco, Sandy Duncan
One Sheet: $5 - $10

DEMON BARBER OF FLEET STREET, THE
(1939 - -) See: SWEENEY TODD, THE DEMON BARBER OF FLEET STREET

DEMON FOR TROUBLE, A
(1934 - Supreme) Bob Steele, Don Alvarado
One Sheet: $250 - $500

DEMON FROM DEVIL'S LAKE, THE
(1964 - Phillip) Dave Heath
One Sheet: $15 - $25

DEMON IS LOOSE, THE
(1988 - Scena) Ray Lovelock, Olga Karlatos
One Sheet: $3 - $5

DEMON KNIGHT
(1995 - Universal) Billy Zane, William Sadler, Jada Pinkett
One Sheet: $5 - $10 *AKA: TALES FROM THE CRYPT.*

One Sheet

DEMON LOVER
(1977 - 21st Century) Christmas Robbins, Gunnar Hansen
One Sheet: $7 - $15

DEMON POND
(1980 - Kino) Tamasaburo Bando
One Sheet: $5 - $10 *Japanese.*

DEMON RIDER, THE
(1928 - -) Ken Maynard
One Sheet: $200 - $400

DEMON SEED
(1977 - MGM) Julie Christie, Fritz Weaver
One Sheet: $7 - $15 *Dean Koontz Novel.*

DEMONOID
(1981 - American Panorama) Samantha Eggar, Stuart Whitman
One Sheet: $3 - $5

DEMONS
(1986 - -) Urbano Barberini, Natasha Hovey
One Sheet: $5 - $10

DEMONS 2
(1987 - -) David Knight, Nancy Brilli
One Sheet: $5 - $10

DEMONS OF LUDLOW, THE
(1983 - Titan) Paul Von Hausen, James Robinson
One Sheet: $3 - $5

DEMONS OF THE SWAMP
(1959 - -) See ATTACK OF THE GIANT LEECHES

DEMONS OF THE WIND
(1972 - Hammer) Paul Jones, Patrick Magee
One Sheet: $5 - $10

DEMPSEY AND CARPENTIER
(1921 - Tex Rickard) Jack Dempsey, Georges Carpentier
One Sheet: $1,900 - $3,000

DEMPSEY/FIRPO

(1923 - Svenska) Jack Dempsey, Luis Firpo
One Sheet: $500 - $800 *Swedish. Sports (Boxing). Heavyweight championship fight footage.*

DENISE CALLS UP
(1996 - Sony Pictures Classics) Tim Daly, Dana Wheeler Nicholson
One Sheet: $3 - $6 *Comedy.*

DENNIS THE MENACE
(1993 - Warner Bros.) Mason Gamble, Walter Matthau
One Sheet: $3 - $5

DENTAL FOLLIES
(1937 - Educational) Pinky Lee
One Sheet: $100 - $200

DENTON'S MOVING PICTURES
(1910? - Denton) -
One Sheet: $150 - $300

DENVER AND RIO GRANDE, THE
(1952 - Paramount) Edmond O'Brien, Sterling Hayden
One Sheet: $15 - $25

DENVER KID, THE
(1948 - Republic) Allan "Rocky" Lane, Eddie Waller
One Sheet: $20 - $40

DEPORTED
(1950 - Universal) Marta Toren, Jeff Chandler
One Sheet: $20 - $40

DEPUTY MARSHALL
(1949 - United Artists) Jon Hall, Frances Langford
One Sheet: $20 - $40

DER FUEHRER'S FACE
(1943 - RKO/Disney) Donald Duck
One Sheet: $1,600 - $2,500 *Cartoon. Cartoon Movie Posters #169.*

DER HERR DER WELT
(1934 - Tobis/Klangfilm) Harry Piel
One Sheet: $3,500 - $5,000 *German.*

One Sheet

DERANGED
(1974 - AIP) Robert Blossum, Cosette Lee, Dir: Alan Ormsby
One Sheet: $30 - $50 *Based on mass-murderer Ed Gein who also inspired "Psycho", "Texas Chainsaw Massacre", and others.*

DERBY
(1971 - Cinerama) Mike Snell, Charlie O'Connell
One Sheet: $5 - $10 *Sports (Roller Derby).*

DERBY DAY
(1923 - Pathe) Little Rascals
One Sheet: $1,300 - $2,000 *Sports Movie Posters #239.*

DERBY DECADE
(1934 - RKO) -
One Sheet: $150 - $300

DERELICT
(1930 - Paramount) George Bancroft, William Boyd
One Sheet: $150 - $300

DES KINDES EINFLUSS
(1915 - Essanay) G. M. Anderson
One Sheet: $200 - $400 *German.*

DESERT ATTACK
(1960 - 20th Century Fox) John Mills, Sylvia Syms
One Sheet: $5 - $10

DESERT BANDIT
(1941 - Republic) Don Barry, Lynn Merrick
One Sheet: $50 - $100

DESERT BLOOM
(1986 - Columbia) Jon Voight, JoBeth Williams
One Sheet: $5 - $10

DESERT DESPERADOS
(1959 - RKO) Ruth Roman, Akim Tamiroff
One Sheet: $7 - $15

DESERT FLOWER, THE
(1925 - First National) Colleen Moore, Lloyd Hughes
One Sheet: $200 - $400

DESERT FOX, THE
(1951 - 20th Century Fox) James Mason, Jessica Tandy
One Sheet: $50 - $100

DESERT FURY
(1947 - Paramount) John Hodiak, Lizabeth Scott, Burt Lancaster
One Sheet: $100 - $200

DESERT FURY
(1958R - Paramount) John Hodiak, Lizabeth Scott, Burt Lancaster
One Sheet: $20 - $40 *Re-release.*

DESERT GOLD
(1926 - Paramount) Neil Hamilton, Shirley Mason, William Powell
One Sheet: $350 - $750

DESERT GOLD
(1936 - Paramount) Buster Crabbe
One Sheet: $125 - $250

DESERT GOLD
(1951R - Paramount) Buster Crabbe
One Sheet: $20 - $40 *Re-release.*

DESERT GUNS
(1936 - Beaumont) Conway Tearle
One Sheet: $150 - $350

DESERT HAWK, THE
(1944 - Columbia) Gilbert Roland, Mona Maris
One Sheet: $100 - $200 *Serial. 15 Chapters.*

DESERT HAWK, THE
(1950 - Universal) Yvonne De Carlo, Richard Greene
One Sheet: $15 - $30

DESERT HEARTS
(1986 - -) Helen Shaver, Patricia Charbonneau
One Sheet: $30 - $50

DESERT HELL
(1958 - 20th Century Fox) Brian Keith, Barbara Hale
One Sheet: $15 - $25

DESERT HORSEMAN, THE
(1946 - Columbia) Charles Starrett, Smiley Burnette
One Sheet: $40 - $75

DESERT JUSTICE
(1936 - Atlantic) Jack Perrin, David Sharpe
One Sheet: $75 - $150

DESERT LEGION
(1953 - Universal) Alan Ladd, Arlene Dahl
One Sheet: $20 - $40

DESERT MAN, THE
(1917 - -) William S. Hart
One Sheet: $1,300 - $2,000

DESERT MESA
(1935 - Security) Tom Wynn, Tex Miller
One Sheet: $200 - $400

DESERT OF LOST MEN
(1951 - Republic) Allan "Rocky" Lane, Mary Ellen Kay
One Sheet: $30 - $50

DESERT OF THE LOST, THE
(1927 - -) Wally Wales, Peggy Montgomery, William J. Dyer
One Sheet: $100 - $200

DESERT PASSAGE
(1952 - RKO) Tim Holt, Joan Dixon
One Sheet: $15 - $30

DESERT PATROL
(1938 - Republic) Bob Steele, Rex Lease
One Sheet: $100 - $200

DESERT PATROL
(1947R - Republic) Bob Steele
One Sheet: $40 - $75   *Re-release.*

DESERT PATROL
(1962 - Universal) Richard Attenborough
One Sheet: $7 - $15

DESERT PHANTOM, THE
(1937 - Supreme) Johnny Mack Brown
One Sheet: $100 - $200

DESERT PURSUIT
(1952 - Monogram) Wayne Morris, Virginia Grey
One Sheet: $10 - $20

DESERT RATS, THE
(1953 - 20th Century Fox) James Mason, Richard Burton
One Sheet: $30 - $50

DESERT RAVEN
(1965 - Allied Artists) Rachel Romen, Robert Terry
One Sheet: $5 - $10

DESERT SANDS
(1955 - United Artists) Ralph Meeker, Mara English
One Sheet: $15 - $35

DESERT SONG, THE
(1929 - Warner Bros.) John Boles, Myrna Loy
One Sheet: $250 - $500

DESERT SONG, THE
(1943 - Warner Bros.) Dennis Morgan, Irene Manning
One Sheet: $50 - $100

DESERT SONG, THE
(1953 - Warner Bros.) Kathryn Grayson, Gordon MacRae
One Sheet: $30 - $50

DESERT TRAIL
(1935 - Monogram) John Wayne
One Sheet: $1,600 - $2,500

DESERT VALLEY
(1926 - Fox) Buck Jones
One Sheet: $350 - $750   *Cowboy Movie Posters #60.*

DESERT VENGEANCE
(1931 - Columbia) Buck Jones
One Sheet: $1,300 - $2,000   *Cowboy Movie Posters # 99. One Sheet (Buck on horse style): $1500-$3000.*

DESERT VIGILANTE
(1949 - Columbia) Charles Starrett
One Sheet: $30 - $50

DESERT WARRIOR
(1960 - Medallion) Ricardo Montalban, Anna Maria Ferrero
One Sheet: $5 - $10

DESERTER, THE
(1971 - Paramount) Bekim Fehmiu, Ricardo Montalban, Chuck Connors
One Sheet: $3 - $5

DESERTERS, THE
(1983 - Exile) Alan Scarfe, Barbara March
One Sheet: $2 - $3

DESIGN FOR DEATH
(1948 - RKO) -
One Sheet: $40 - $75

DESIGN FOR LIVING
(1933 - Paramount) Fredric March, Gary Cooper, Miriam Hopkins
One Sheet: $800 - $1,500

DESIGN FOR SCANDAL
(1941 - MGM) Walter Pidgeon, Rosalind Russell
One Sheet: $75 - $125

DESIGNING WOMAN
(1957 - MGM) Gregory Peck, Lauren Bacall
One Sheet: $50 - $100

DESIRABLE
(1934 - Warner Bros.) George Brent, Jean Muir
One Sheet: $150 - $300

DESIRE
(1936 - Paramount) Marlene Dietrich, Gary Cooper
One Sheet: $3,500 - $5,000

DESIRE IN THE DUST
(1960 - 20th Century Fox) Raymond Burr, Martha Hyer
One Sheet: $10 - $20

DESIRE ME
(1947 - MGM) Greer Garson, Robert Mitchum
One Sheet: $100 - $200

DESIRE UNDER THE ELMS
(1958 - Paramount) Sophia Loren, Anthony Perkins
One Sheet: $20 - $40

DESIREE
(1954 - 20th Century Fox) Marlon Brando, Jean Simmons
One Sheet: $50 - $100

DESK SET
(1957 - 20th Century Fox) Spencer Tracy, Katharine Hepburn
One Sheet: $75 - $125

DESPAIR
(1978 - Swan) Dirk Bogarde
One Sheet: $3 - $5

DESPERADO, THE
(1954 - Allied Artists) Wayne Morris, Beverly Garland
One Sheet: $15 - $25

DESPERADO
(1995 - Columbia) Antonio Banderas, Cheech Marin, Salma Hayek
One Sheet: $7 - $15

One Sheet

DESPERADO TRAIL, THE
(1966 - Columbia) Lex Barker, Pierre Brice
One Sheet: $10 - $20

DESPERADOES, THE
(1943 - Columbia) Randolph Scott, Glenn Ford
One Sheet: $75 - $150

DESPERADOES, THE
(1969 - Columbia) Vince Edwards, Jack Palance, George Maharis
One Sheet: $5 - $10

DESPERADOES ARE IN TOWN, THE
(1956 - 20th Century Fox) Robert Arthur
One Sheet: $7 - $15

DESPERADOES OF DODGE CITY
(1948 - Republic) Allan "Rocky" Lane, Eddie Waller
One Sheet: $40 - $75

DESPERADOES OF THE WEST
(1950 - Republic) Richard Powers, Judy Clark
One Sheet: $30 - $50   *Serial. Western. 12 Chapters.*

DESPERADOES' OUTPOST
(1952 - Republic) Allan "Rocky" Lane
One Sheet: $15 - $25

DESPERATE
(1947 - RKO) Steve Brodie, Audrey Long
One Sheet: $50 - $100

DESPERATE ADVENTURE, A
(1938 - Republic) Ramon Novarro, Margaret Tallichet
One Sheet: $75 - $125

DESPERATE CARGO
(1941 - PRC) Ralph Byrd, Carl Hughes
One Sheet: $30 - $50

DESPERATE CHANCE FOR ELLERY QUEEN, A
(1942 - Columbia) William Gargan, Jack LaRue
One Sheet: $75 - $150

DESPERATE CHARACTERS
(1942 - Columbia) William Gargan, Margaret Lindsay
One Sheet: $50 - $100

DESPERATE CHARACTERS
(1971 - Paramount) Shirley Maclaine, Kenneth Mars, Sada Thompson
One Sheet: $5 - $10

DESPERATE HOURS, THE
(1955 - Paramount) Humphrey Bogart, Fredric March
One Sheet: $50 - $100

DESPERATE HOURS
(1990 - MGM/United Artists) Mickey Rourke, Kelly Lynch
One Sheet: $5 - $10

DESPERATE JOURNEY
(1942 - Warner Bros.) Errol Flynn, Ronald Reagan
One Sheet: $200 - $400

DESPERATE LIVING
(1977 - J.Waters) Jean Hill, Mink Stole
One Sheet: $50 - $100

DESPERATE MAN, THE
(1959 - Allied Artists) Jill Ireland, Conrad Phillips
One Sheet: $15 - $25

DESPERATE MOMENT
(1953 - Universal International) Dirk Bogarde, Mal Zetterling
One Sheet: $10 - $20

DESPERATE ONES, THE
(1969 - Commonwealth United) Maximillian Schell, Raf Vallone, Irene Papas
One Sheet: $5 - $10

DESPERATE SEARCH
(1952 - MGM) Howard Keel, Jane Greer
One Sheet: $15 - $25

DESPERATE TRAILS
(1939 - Universal) Johnny Mack Brown, Bob Baker
One Sheet: $75 - $150

DESPERATE WOMAN, THE
(1967 - Newman) Anne Appleton
One Sheet: $10 - $20

DESPERATELY SEEKING SUSAN
(1984 - Orion) Rosanna Arquette, Madonna (film debut), Adain Quinn
One Sheet: $15 - $30

DESPOILER, THE
(1915 - Triangle) Charles K. French, Enid Markey
One Sheet: $600 - $1,000

DESTINATION 60,000
(1957 - Allied Artists) Preston Foster, Coleen Gray
One Sheet: $15 - $30

DESTINATION BIG HOUSE
(1950 - Republic) Dorothy Patrick, Robert Rockwell
One Sheet: $10 - $20

DESTINATION GOBI
(1953 - 20th Century Fox) Richard Widmark, Don Taylor
One Sheet: $20 - $40

DESTINATION INNER SPACE
(1966 - Magna) Scott Brady, Sheree North
One Sheet: $10 - $20

DESTINATION MAGOO
(1954 - Columbia) Mr. Magoo
One Sheet: $150 - $300   *Cartoon. Duotone.*

DESTINATION MILAN
(1954 - British Lion) Douglas Fairbanks, Jr.
One Sheet: $7 - $15

DESTINATION MOON
(1950 - Eagle-Lion) John Archer, Warner Anderson
One Sheet: $250 - $500   *Graven Images, pg. 146, 150, 152.*

DESTINATION MURDER
(1950 - RKO) Joyce MacKenzie, Stanley Clements
One Sheet: $15 - $30

DESTINATION TOKYO
(1944 - Warner Bros.) Cary Grant, John Garfield
One Sheet: $50 - $100

One Sheet

DESTINATION UNKNOWN
(1933 - Universal) Pat O'Brien, Ralph Bellamy, Alan Hale
One Sheet: $100 - $200

DESTINATION UNKNOWN
(1942 - Universal) Irene Hervey, William Gargan
One Sheet: $50 - $100

DESTINY
(1944 - Universal) Gloria Jean, Alan Curtis
One Sheet: $40 - $75

DESTINY TURNS ON THE RADIO
(1995 - Savoy) James Le Gros, Dylan McDermott, Quentin Tarantino
One Sheet: $5 - $10

One Sheet

DESTROY ALL MONSTERS
(1969 - AIP) Mothra, Rodan, Godzilla, Manda
One Sheet: $75 - $150

DESTROYER
(1943 - Columbia) Edward G. Robinson, Marguerite Chapman, Glenn Ford
One Sheet: $50 - $100

DESTROYER
(1988 - -) Lyle Alzado, Anthony Perkins
One Sheet: $3 - $5

DESTRUCTORS, THE
(1968 - Feature) Richard Egan, Patricia Owens
One Sheet: $5 - $10

DESTRUCTORS, THE
(1974 - AIP) Michael Caine, Anthony Quinn
One Sheet: $5 - $10

DESTRY
(1954 - Universal) Audie Murphy, Mari

Blanchard
One Sheet: $30 - $60

DESTRY RIDES AGAIN
(1932 - Universal) Tom Mix, ZaSu Pitts
One Sheet: $1,300 - $2,000   *Cowboy Movie Posters # 136.*

DESTRY RIDES AGAIN
(1939 - Universal) James Stewart, Marlene Dietrich
One Sheet: $1,000 - $1,800   *Cowboy Movie Posters #255.*

DESTRY RIDES AGAIN
(1947R - Universal) James Stewart, Marlene Dietrich
One Sheet: $100 - $200   *Re-release.*

DETECTIVE, THE
(1954 - Columbia) Alec Guinness, Joan Greenwood
One Sheet: $15 - $30

DETECTIVE, THE
(1968 - 20th Century Fox) Frank Sinatra, Lee Remick, Jacqueline Bisset
One Sheet: $15 - $30

DETECTIVE, THE
(1985 - -) Jean-Luc Goddard
One Sheet: $5 - $10

DETECTIVE BELLI
(1970 - Plaza) Franco Nero, Florinda Bolkan
One Sheet: $3 - $5

DETECTIVE KITTY O'DAY
(1944 - Monogram) Jean Parker, Tim Ryan
One Sheet: $40 - $75

DETECTIVE LLOYD
(1932 - Universal) Jack Lloyd, Wallace Geoffrey
One Sheet: $150 - $350

DETECTIVE SCHOOL DROPOUTS
(1985 - -) David Landsberg, Lorin Dreyfuss
One Sheet: $3 - $5

DETECTIVE STORY
(1951 - Paramount) Kirk Douglas, William Bendix
One Sheet: $30 - $50

DETECTIVE STORY
(1960R - Paramount) Kirk Douglas, William Bendix
One Sheet: $15 - $25   *Re-release.*

DETOUR
(1945 - PRC) Tom Neal, Ann Savage
One Sheet: $1,300 - $2,000

DETOUR
(1969 - Brandon) Nevena Kipokanova, Ivan Andonov
One Sheet: $5 - $10

DETROIT 9000
(1973 - General) Alex Rocco, Hari Rhodes, Vonetta McGee
One Sheet: $10 - $20   *Blaxploitation.*

DEUCE OF SPADES, THE
(1922 - First National) Charles Ray, Marjorie Maurice
One Sheet: $250 - $500

DEVIL AND DANIEL WEBSTER, THE
(1941 - RKO) Edward Arnold, Walter Huston
One Sheet: $100 - $200

DEVIL AND LEROY BASSETT, THE
(1974 - Marshall Borden) Cory BearPaw, John Goff
One Sheet: $3 - $5

DEVIL AND MAX DEVLIN, THE
(1981 - Buena Vista/Disney) Bill Cosby, Elliot Gould
One Sheet: $7 - $15

DEVIL AND MISS JONES, THE
(1941 - RKO) Jean Arthur, Charles Coburn
One Sheet: $75 - $125

DEVIL AND THE DEEP
(1932 - Paramount) Tallulah Bankhead, Gary Cooper, Charles Laughton
One Sheet: $1,300 - $2,000

DEVIL AT 4 O'CLOCK, THE
(1961 - Columbia) Spencer Tracy, Frank

Sinatra
One Sheet: $15 - $30

DEVIL BAT, THE
(1940 - PRC) Bela Lugosi, Suzanne Kaaren
One Sheet: $150 - $300   *Graven Images, pg. 134.*

DEVIL BAT'S DAUGHTER
(1946 - PRC) Rosemary La Planche, John James
One Sheet: $75 - $150

One Sheet

DEVIL COMMANDS, THE
(1941 - Columbia) Boris Karloff, Amanda Duff
One Sheet: $250 - $600   *Graven Images, pg. 130.*

DEVIL COMMANDS, THE
(1957R - Columbia) Boris Karloff, Amanda Duff
One Sheet: $50 - $100   *Re-release.*

DEVIL DIAMOND
(1937 - Ambassadors) Kane Richmond, June Gale
One Sheet: $50 - $100

DEVIL DOGS OF THE AIR
(1935 - Warner Bros.) James Cagney, Pat O'Brien
One Sheet: $1,600 - $2,500

DEVIL DOLL, THE
(1936 - MGM) Lionel Barrymore, Maureen O'Sullivan, Dir: Tod Browning
One Sheet: $3,500 - $5,000   *Graven Images, pg. 94.*

DEVIL DOLL
(1964 - Associated) Bryant Halliday, William Sylvester
One Sheet: $10 - $20

DEVIL GIRL FROM MARS
(1954 - Spartan) Hugh McDermott, Hazel Court
One Sheet: $600 - $1,000   *Graven Images, pg. 187.*

One Sheet

DEVIL GODDESS
(1955 - Columbia) Johnny Weissmuller, Angela Stevens
One Sheet: $40 - $75

DEVIL HORSE
(1932 - Mascot) Harry Carey, Noah Beery
One Sheet: $150 - $350   *Serial. 12 Chapters.*

DEVIL IN A BLUE DRESS
(1995 - TriStar) Denzel Washington
One Sheet: $10 - $20   *Black cast.*

DEVIL IN LOVE, THE
(1968 - Warner Bros./Seven Arts) Vittorio Gassman, Mickey Rooney
One Sheet: $7 - $15

DEVIL IN THE FLESH
(1949 - Universal) Gerard Philipe, Micheline Presle
One Sheet: $40 - $75

DEVIL INSIDE HER, THE
(1976 - AIP) Joan Collins, Eileen Atkins
One Sheet: $5 - $10

DEVIL IS A SISSY, THE
(1936 - MGM) Freddie Bartholomew, Jackie Cooper, Mickey Rooney
One Sheet: $125 - $250

DEVIL IS A WOMAN, THE
(1935 - Paramount) Marlene Dietrich, Lionel Atwill, Cesar Romero
One Sheet: $7,500 - $12,000   *Price is for style B one sheet. One Sheet(Style A, Dietrich portait):$20,000-$30,000.*

DEVIL IS A WOMAN, THE
(1975 - 20th Century Fox) Glenda Jackson
One Sheet: $7 - $15

DEVIL IS DRIVING, THE
(1932 - Paramount) Edmund Lowe, Dickie Moore
One Sheet: $500 - $800

DEVIL IS DRIVING, THE
(1937 - Columbia) Richard Dix, Joan Perry
One Sheet: $250 - $600

Mini Window Card

DEVIL MADE A WOMAN, THE
(1961 - Medallion) Sarita Montiel, George Mistral
One Sheet: $10 - $20   *Spanish. AKA: A GIRL AGAINST NAPOLEON.*

DEVIL MAKES THREE, THE
(1952 - MGM) Gene Kelly, Pier Angeli
One Sheet: $20 - $40

DEVIL MAY CARE
(1930 - MGM) Ramon Novarro, Marion Harris
One Sheet: $150 - $350

DEVIL MONSTER
(1946 - Weiss and Landres) Barry Norton, Blanche Mahaffey
One Sheet: $100 - $200

DEVIL OF THE DEEP
(1937 - Educational) Paul Terry Studio
One Sheet: $200 - $400   *Cartoon. Duotone. Stock poster with inset of title.*

DEVIL ON DECK, THE
(1932 - Sono Art/World Wide) -
One Sheet: $100 - $200

DEVIL ON HORSEBACK, THE
(1936 - Grand National) Lila Damita, Fred Keating
One Sheet: $125 - $250

DEVIL ON HORSEBACK, THE
(1954 - Grand National) Googie Withers, John McCallum
One Sheet: $15 - $25

DEVIL ON WHEELS, THE
(1947 - PRC) Noreen Nash, Darryl Hickman
One Sheet: $75 - $125

DEVIL PAYS OFF, THE
(1932 - Chesterfield) Jameson Thomas,

Florence Britton
One Sheet: $250 - $600

DEVIL PAYS OFF, THE
(1941 - Republic) Margaret Tallichet, William Wright
One Sheet: $75 - $125

DEVIL RIDER
(1971 - -) Ross Kananza, Sharon Mahon
One Sheet: $15 - $25   *Biker Film.*

DEVIL RIDERS, THE
(1943 - PRC) Buster Crabbe, Al St. John
One Sheet: $30 - $60

DEVIL RIDES OUT, THE
(1968 - Warner/Pathe) Christopher Lee, Charles Gray
One Sheet: $40 - $75   *Graven Images, pg. 216. AKA: THE DEVIL'S BRIDE. Price is for British Quad.*

DEVIL SHIP
(1947 - Columbia) Richard Lane, Louise Campbell
One Sheet: $50 - $100

DEVIL TAKES US, THE
(1950' - RKO) -
One Sheet: $75 - $175

DEVIL THUMBS A RIDE, THE
(1947 - RKO) Lawrence Tierney, Ted North, Nan Leslie
One Sheet: $125 - $250

DEVIL TIGER
(1934 - Fox) Mary Brewster, Marion Burns
One Sheet: $150 - $300

DEVIL TIMES FIVE, THE
(1974 - NCI) Gene Evans, Leif Garrett
One Sheet: $10 - $20

DEVIL TO PAY
(1931 - Samuel Goldwyn) Ronald Colman, Loretta Young
One Sheet: $350 - $750

DEVIL WITH HITLER, THE
(1942 - Hal Roach Studios) Alan Mowbray, Bobby Watson, Joe Devlin
One Sheet: $50 - $100

DEVIL WITH WOMEN, A
(1930 - Fox) Victor McLaglen, Mona Maris, Humphrey Bogart
One Sheet: $600 - $1,500   *Bogart's film debut. Bogart not pictured on posters.*

DEVIL WITHIN HER, THE
(1976 - AIP) Caroline Munro, Hilary Mason
One Sheet: $5 - $10

DEVIL WOMAN
(1976 - Hallmark) Rosemarie Gil
One Sheet: $5 - $10

DEVIL'S AGENT
(1962 - British Lion) Christopher Lee, Macdonald Carey
One Sheet: $7 - $15

DEVIL'S ANGELS
(1967 - AIP) John Cassavetes, Beverly Adams, Dir: Roger Corman
One Sheet: $40 - $90

DEVIL'S APPLE TREE, THE
(1929 - Tiffany-Stahl) Dorothy Sebastian, Larry Kent
One Sheet: $600 - $1,000

DEVIL'S BAIT
(1959 - RFD) Geoffrey Keen
One Sheet: $15 - $25

DEVIL'S BEDROOM, THE
(1964 - Rebel) John Lupton, Valerie Allen
One Sheet: $10 - $20

DEVIL'S BRIDE, THE
(1968 - 20th Century Fox) Christopher Lee, Charles Gray, Nike Arrighi
One Sheet: $75 - $150

DEVIL'S BRIGADE, THE
(1968 - United Artists) William Holden, Vince Edwards, Cliff Robertson
One Sheet: $5 - $10

DEVIL'S BROTHER, THE
(1933 - MGM) Stan Laurel, Oliver Hardy

One Sheet: $3,500 - $5,000

DEVIL'S BROTHER, THE
(194?R - Film Classic) Stan Laurel, Oliver Hardy
One Sheet: $75 - $150 *Re-release.*

DEVIL'S CANYON
(1953 - RKO) Virginia Mayo, Dale Robertson
One Sheet: $30 - $60 *Filmed in 3-D.*

DEVIL'S CARGO, THE
(1925 - Paramount) Wallace Beery, William Collier, Jr.
One Sheet: $250 - $600

DEVIL'S CARGO, THE
(1948 - Falcon) John Calvert, Rochelle Hudson
One Sheet: $30 - $50

DEVIL'S CHAPLAIN, THE
(1929 - Rayart) Cornelius Keefe, Virginia Brown Faire, Boris Karloff
One Sheet: $500 - $800

DEVIL'S CIRCUS, THE
(1926 - MGM) Norma Shearer
One Sheet: $350 - $750

DEVIL'S DAUGHTER, THE
(1939 - Sack) Nina Mae McKinney, Hamtree Harrington
One Sheet: $500 - $800 *Black cast.*
Duotone. Separate Cinema, pg. 125.

DEVIL'S DISCIPLE, THE
(1926 - -) Evelyn Preer, Lawrence Chenault
One Sheet: $150 - $300

DEVIL'S DISCIPLE, THE
(1959 - United Artists) Burt Lancaster, Kirk Douglas, Laurence Olivier
One Sheet: $30 - $50

DEVIL'S DOORWAY
(1950 - MGM) Robert Taylor, Louis Calhern
One Sheet: $20 - $40

DEVIL'S DOUBLE
(1916 - Triangle) William S. Hart, Enid Markey
One Sheet: $1,300 - $2,000 *Cowboy Movie Posters #10.*

DEVIL'S DOUBLE
(192?R - -) William S. Hart, Enid Markey
One Sheet: $150 - $300 *Re-release.*

DEVIL'S EIGHT, THE
(1969 - AIP) Christopher George, Fabian, Leslie Parrish
One Sheet: $15 - $30

DEVIL'S GENERAL, THE
(1956 - DCA) Kurt Jurgens, Marianne Koch
One Sheet: $10 - $20

DEVIL'S HAIRPIN, THE
(1957 - Paramount) Cornel Wilde, Jean Wallace
One Sheet: $40 - $75 *Sports (Auto racing).*

DEVIL'S HAND, THE
(1961 - Crown) Robert Alda, Linda Christian
One Sheet: $15 - $30

DEVIL'S HARBOR
(1954 - 20th Century Fox) Richard Arlen, Greta Gynt
One Sheet: $7 - $15

DEVIL'S HARVEST
(1948 - -) -
One Sheet: $125 - $250 *Marijuana exploitation.*

DEVIL'S HENCHMEN, THE
(1949 - Columbia) Warner Baxter, Mary Beth Hughes
One Sheet: $40 - $75

DEVIL'S HOLIDAY, THE
(1930 - Paramount) Nancy Carroll, Phillip Holmes
One Sheet: $200 - $400

DEVIL'S IMPOSTER, THE
(1973 - Columbia) Olivia de Havilland, Lesley-Anne Down
One Sheet: $5 - $10 *AKA: POPE JOAN.*

DEVIL'S IN LOVE, THE
(1933 - Fox) Loretta Young, Victor Jory

One Sheet: $250 - $500

DEVIL'S ISLAND
(1939 - Warner Bros.) Boris Karloff, James Stephenson
One Sheet: $200 - $400

DEVIL'S LOTTERY
(1932 - Fox) Elissa Landi, Victor McLaglen
One Sheet: $150 - $300

DEVIL'S MASK, THE
(1946 - Columbia) Anita Louise, Jim Bannon
One Sheet: $100 - $200

DEVIL'S MATE
(1933 - Monogram) Peggy Shannon, Preston Foster
One Sheet: $125 - $250

DEVIL'S NEEDLE, THE
(1916 - Triangle) Norma Talmadge, Tully Marshall
One Sheet: $350 - $750

DEVIL'S OWN, THE
(1967 - 20th Century Fox) Joan Fontaine, Kay Walsh
One Sheet: $15 - $35

DEVIL'S OWN, THE
(1997 - Columbia) Harrison Ford, Brad Pitt
One Sheet: $5 - $10 *Cop thriller.*

DEVIL'S PARTNER, THE
(1961 - Filmgroup) Edwin Nelson, Jean Allison
One Sheet: $30 - $50

DEVIL'S PARTY, THE
(1938 - Universal) Victor McLaglen, Beatrice Roberts
One Sheet: $75 - $150

DEVIL'S PASS KEY
(1920 - Universal) Dir: Erich Von Stroheim
One Sheet: $1,900 - $3,000

DEVIL'S PAWN, THE
(1922 - Paramount) Pola Negri
One Sheet: $800 - $1,500

DEVIL'S PIPELINE
(1940 - Universal) Richard Arlen, Andy Devine
One Sheet: $75 - $150

DEVIL'S PLAYGROUND
(1937 - Columbia) Dolores Del Rio, Richard Dix
One Sheet: $150 - $300

DEVIL'S PLAYGROUND, THE
(1946 - United Artists) Bill Boyd, Andy Clyde
One Sheet: $40 - $75

DEVIL'S RAIN, THE
(1975 - Bryanston) Ernest Borgnine, Ida Lupino, Eddie Albert
One Sheet: $7 - $15

DEVIL'S SADDLE LEGION, THE
(1937 - Warner Bros.) Dick Foran, Anne Nagel
One Sheet: $50 - $100

DEVIL'S SQUADRON
(1936 - Columbia) Richard Dix, Lloyd Nolan
One Sheet: $150 - $300

DEVIL'S TRADEMARK
(1928 - FBO) Belle Bennett
One Sheet: $200 - $400

DEVIL'S TRAIL, THE
(1942 - Columbia) Bill Elliott, Tex Ritter
One Sheet: $75 - $125

DEVIL'S TRAIL, THE
(1955R - Columbia) Bill Elliott, Tex Ritter
One Sheet: $30 - $50 *Re-release.*

DEVIL'S TRAP, THE
(1964 - Salisbury) Vietzslan Vejrazka, Vit Olmer
One Sheet: $10 - $20

DEVIL'S TRIANGLE, THE
(1970 - UFO) Vincent Price
One Sheet: $7 - $15

DEVIL'S WEDDING NIGHT, THE
(1973 - Dimension) Mark Damon, Sarah Bay
One Sheet: $10 - $20

DEVIL'S WEED
(1940' - -) Lila Leeds
One Sheet: $125 - $250 *Marijuana*

expose'.

DEVIL'S WIDOW, THE
(1972 - AIP) Ava Gardner, Ian McShane
One Sheet: $10 - $20

DEVILS, THE
(1971 - Warner Bros.) Vanessa Redgrave, Oliver Reed
One Sheet: $10 - $20

DEVILS OF DARKNESS
(1965 - 20th Century Fox) William Sylvester, Hubert Noel
One Sheet: $15 - $30

DEVIL-SHIP PIRATES
(1964 - Columbia) Christopher Lee, Andrew Keir
One Sheet: $30 - $60

DEVONSVILLE TERROR, THE
(1983 - New West) Suzanna Love, Donald Pleasence
One Sheet: $3 - $5

DEVOTION
(1931 - RKO Pathe) Ann Harding, Leslie Howard
One Sheet: $200 - $400

DEVOTION
(1946 - Warner Bros.) Olivia de Havilland, Ida Lupino
One Sheet: $50 - $100

D.I., THE
(1957 - Mark VII Ltd.) Jack Webb, Don Dubbins
One Sheet: $40 - $75

DIABOLIQUE
(1955 - Vera Films) Simone Signoret, Charles Vanel
One Sheet: $100 - $200 *French.*
Graven Images, pg. 199.

DIABOLIQUE
(1996 - Warner Bros.) Sharon Stone, Chazz Palminteri
One Sheet: $5 - $12

DIAGNOSIS: MURDER
(1974 - Silhouette) Jon Finch, Christopher Lee
One Sheet: $7 - $15

DIAL 1119
(1950 - MGM) Marshall Thompson, Virginia Field
One Sheet: $30 - $50

DIAL M FOR MURDER
(1954 - Warner Bros.) Ray Milland, Grace Kelly, Dir: Alfred Hitchcock
One Sheet: $500 - $800

One Sheet

DIAL M FOR MURDER
(1982R - Warner Bros.) Ray Milland, Grace Kelly Dir:Alfred Hitchcock
One Sheet: $7 - $15 *Re-release.*

DIAL P FOR PINK
(1965 - United Artists) Pink Panther
One Sheet: $50 - $100 *Cartoon.*
Duotone stock poster with title inset. Huge image of the Pink Panther.

DIAL RED 0
(1955 - Allied Artists) Bill Elliott, Keith Larson
One Sheet: $15 - $30

DIAMOND CITY
(1949 - GFD) David Farrar, Honor Blackman
One Sheet: $15 - $30

DIAMOND DEMON
(1947 - MGM) -
One Sheet: $250 - $500 *Sports (Baseball) Pete Smith Specialty series. Sports Movie Posters #52.*

DIAMOND FRONTIER
(1940 - Universal) Victor McLaglen, John Loder, Anne Neagle
One Sheet: $75 - $125

DIAMOND HEAD
(1963 - Columbia) Charlton Heston, Yvette Mimieux
One Sheet: $20 - $40

DIAMOND HORSESHOE
(1945 - 20th Century Fox) Betty Grable, Dick Haymes
One Sheet: $150 - $300

DIAMOND JIM
(1935 - Universal) Edward Arnold, Jean Arthur, Binnie Barnes
One Sheet: $250 - $500

DIAMOND QUEEN, THE
(1921 - Universal) Eileen Sedgwick
One Sheet: $200 - $400 *Serial. 18 Chapters.*

DIAMOND QUEEN, THE
(1953 - Warner Bros.) Fernando Lamas, Arlene Dahl
One Sheet: $15 - $30

DIAMOND SAFARI
(1958 - 20th Century Fox) Kevin McCarthy, Audre Morrell
One Sheet: $5 - $12

DIAMOND STUD
(1970 - Walnut) Robert Hall, John Alderman
One Sheet: $5 - $10

DIAMOND TRAIL
(1933 - Monogram) Rex Bell
One Sheet: $250 - $600 *Cowboy Movie Posters #'s 154, 157.*

DIAMOND WIZARD, THE
(1954 - United Artists) Dennis O'Keefe, Margaret Sheridan
One Sheet: $15 - $30

DIAMONDS
(1975 - Avco/Embassy) Robert Shaw, Richard Roundtree, Shelley Winters
One Sheet: $7 - $15 *Blaxploitation.*

DIAMONDS ARE FOREVER
(1971 - United Artists) Sean Connery, Jill St. John
One Sheet: $125 - $250

DIAMONDS FOR BREAKFAST
(1968 - Paramount) Marcello Mastroianni
One Sheet: $15 - $30

DIANE
(1955 - MGM) Lana Turner, Pedro Amendariz
One Sheet: $30 - $50

DIARY OF A BACHELOR
(1964 - AIP) William Traylor, Dagne Crane
One Sheet: $7 - $15

DIARY OF A CHAMBERMAID
(1946 - Camden) Paulette Goddard, Burgess Meredith
One Sheet: $50 - $100

DIARY OF A CHAMBERMAID
(1965 - International Classics) Jeanne Moreau, Michel Piccoli
One Sheet: $7 - $15

DIARY OF A COUNTRY PRIEST
(1950 - UGC) Claude Laydu, Nicole Maurey
One Sheet: $10 - $20

DIARY OF A HIGH SCHOOL BRIDE
(1959 - AIP) Anita Sands, Ronald Foster
One Sheet: $10 - $20

DIARY OF A LOST GIRL
(1929 - Pabst Film) Louise Brooks
One Sheet: $10,000 - $15,000 *German.*

DIARY OF A MAD HOUSEWIFE
(1970 - Universal) Carrie Snodgress, Richard Benjamin
One Sheet: $5 - $10

DIARY OF A MADMAN
(1963 - United Artists) Vincent Price, Nancy Kovack
One Sheet: $50 - $100

DIARY OF A SCHIZOPHRENIC GIRL
(1960 - Allied Artists) Margarita Lozano, Ghislaine D'Orsay
One Sheet: $15 - $25

DIARY OF ANNE FRANK, THE
(1959 - 20th Century Fox) Millie Perkins, Joseph Schildkraut
One Sheet: $30 - $50   *Academy Award Movie Posters #193.*

DICK TRACY
(1937 - Republic) Ralph Byrd, Kay Hughes, Smiley Burnette
One Sheet: $500 - $800   *Serial. 15 Chapters. Price is for Chapters 2-15. One Sheet(Chapter 1):$1,500-$2,500.*

DICK TRACY
(1945 - RKO) Morgan Conway, Anne Jeffreys
One Sheet: $250 - $500

One Sheet

DICK TRACY
(1990 - Disney) Warren Beatty, Madonna, Al Pacino
One Sheet: $10 - $20   *Advance(Style B):$15-$25. One Sheet(Breathless Mahoney):$25-$50. One Sheet(Big Boy Caprice):$15-$30. One Sheet(Flattop):$15-$25.One Sheet(Pruneface):$15-$25.*

DICK TRACY MEETS GRUESOME
(1947 - RKO) Ralph Byrd, Boris Karloff
One Sheet: $100 - $200

DICK TRACY RETURNS
(1938 - Republic) Ralph Byrd, Lynn Roberts
One Sheet: $800 - $1,500   *Serial. 15 Chapters. Price is for Chapters 2-15. One Sheet(Chapter 1):$1,500-$2,500.*

DICK TRACY RETURNS
(1948R - Republic) Ralph Byrd, Lynn Roberts
One Sheet: $75 - $150   *Re-release. Serial.*

DICK TRACY VS. CRIME, INC.
(1941 - Republic) Ralph Byrd, Michael Owen
One Sheet: $150 - $300   *Serial. 15 Chapters.*

DICK TRACY VS. CUEBALL
(1946 - RKO) Morgan Conway, Anne Jeffreys
One Sheet: $150 - $300

DICK TRACY VS. PHANTOM EMPIRE
(1952R - Republic) Ralph Byrd
One Sheet: $30 - $50   *Re-release.*

DICK TRACY'S DILEMMA
(1947 - RKO) Ralph Byrd, Lyle Latelle, Kay Christopher
One Sheet: $75 - $150

DICK TRACY'S DILEMMA
(1955R - Republic) Ralph Byrd, Lyle Lesalle, Kay Christopher
One Sheet: $30 - $50   *Re-release.*

DICK TRACY'S G-MEN
(1939 - Republic) Ralph Byrd
One Sheet: $500 - $600   *Serial. 15 Chapters. Price is for Chapters 2-15. One Sheet(Chapter 1):$500-$1,000.*

DICK TRACY'S G-MEN
(1955R - Republic) Ralph Byrd

One Sheet: $40 - $75   *Re-release. Serial.*

DICK TURPIN
(1925 - Fox) Tom Mix
One Sheet: $300 - $700

DICK TURPIN'S RIDE
(1954 - Columbia) -
One Sheet: $10 - $20

DICK WHITTINGTON'S CAT
(1936 - Celebrity) Animated by Ub Iwerks
One Sheet: $500 - $800   *Cartoon. A ComiColor cartoon. Cartoon Movie Posters #121.*

DICTATOR, THE
(1922 - Paramount) Wallace Reed
One Sheet: $300 - $700

DID YOU HEAR THE ONE ABOUT THE TRAVELING SALESLADY?
(1968 - Universal) Phyllis Diller, Bob Denver, Joe Flynn
One Sheet: $5 - $10

DIE DIE MY DARLING!
(1965 - Columbia) Tallulah Bankhead, Stefanie Powers
One Sheet: $15 - $25

DIE HARD
(1988 - 20th Century Fox) Bruce Willis, Alan Rickman
One Sheet: $15 - $25   *Advance:$20-$40.*

DIE HARD 2
(1990 - 20th Century Fox) Bruce Willis, Bonnie Bedelia
One Sheet: $7 - $15

DIE HARD WITH A VENGEANCE
(1995 - 20th Century Fox) Bruce Willis, Samuel L. Jackson, Jeremy Irons
One Sheet: $5 - $10

DIE LAUGHING
(1980 - Orion) Robby Benson, Charles Durning
One Sheet: $2 - $3

DIE MONSTER DIE!
(1965 - AIP) Boris Karloff, Nick Adams
One Sheet: $50 - $100

One Sheet

DIE REX
(1961 - Universal) Billy Hughes, Rex the Dog
One Sheet: $5 - $10

DIG THAT URANIUM
(1955 - Allied) Leo Gorcey, Huntz Hall
One Sheet: $30 - $60

DIG UP
(1922 - Pathe) "Snub" Pollard
One Sheet: $250 - $500

DIGBY, BIGGEST DOG IN THE WORLD
(1974 - Cinerama) Jim Dale
One Sheet: $3 - $5

DIGGSTOWN
(1992 - MGM) James Woods, Louis Gossett, Jr., Bruce Dern
One Sheet: $4 - $8   *Sports (Boxing). Sports Movie Posters #170.*

DILLINGER
(1945 - Monogram) Lawrence Tierney, Anne Jeffreys
One Sheet: $75 - $150

DILLINGER

(1973 - AIP) Warren Oates, Ben Jonson
One Sheet: $10 - $20

DILLINGER, PUBLIC ENEMY NO. 1
(1934 - Midland) -
One Sheet: $1,300 - $2,000

DIME WITH A HALO
(1963 - MGM) Barbara Luna, Paul Langton
One Sheet: $5 - $10

DIMENSION 5
(1966 - United) Jeffrey Hunter, France Nuyen
One Sheet: $10 - $20

DIMPLES
(1936 - 20th Century Fox) Shirley Temple, Frank Morgan
One Sheet: $1,300 - $2,000

One Sheet

DINER
(1982 - MGM) Steve Guttenberg, Daniel Stern, Mickey Rourke
One Sheet: $30 - $50

DING DONG
(1951 - Roadshow Attractions) -
One Sheet: $20 - $40

DING DONG WILLIAMS
(1945 - RKO) Glenn Vernon, Marcia Maguire
One Sheet: $75 - $125

DINGAKA
(1965 - Embassy) Stanley Baker, Juliet Prowse
One Sheet: $5 - $10

DINGBAT AND SYLVESTER THE FOX
(194? - -) Terrytoon
One Sheet: $150 - $300   *Cartoon.*

DINKY
(1935 - Warner Bros.) Jackie Cooper, Mary Astor
One Sheet: $125 - $250

DINNER AT EIGHT
(1933 - MGM) John Barrymore, Lionel Barrymore, Jean Harlow
One Sheet: $2,200 - $3,500

Title Card

DINNER AT EIGHT
(1962R - MGM) John Barrymore, Lionel Barrymore, Jean Harlow
One Sheet: $15 - $25   *Re-release.*

DINNER AT THE RITZ
(1937 - 20th Century Fox) Annabella, David Niven
One Sheet: $150 - $300

DINO

(1957 - Allied Artists) Sal Mineo, Susah Kohner
One Sheet: $15 - $35

DINOSAURUS!
(1960 - Universal) Ward Ramsey, Kristina Hanson
One Sheet: $75 - $150

DINTY
(1920 - First National) Wesley Barry, Colleen Moore
One Sheet: $800 - $1,500

DIONYSUSIN '69
(1970 - Sigma III) William Finley, William Shephard
One Sheet: $3 - $5

DIPLOMANIACS
(1933 - RKO) Wheeler & Woolsey
One Sheet: $150 - $300

DIPLOMATIC COURIER
(1952 - 20th Century Fox) Tyrone Power, Patricia Neal
One Sheet: $15 - $35

DIRIGIBLE
(1931 - Columbia) Jack Holt, Ralph Graves, Fay Wray
One Sheet: $1,300 - $2,000

DIRT
(1976 - American Cinema) -
One Sheet: $3 - $5

DIRT BIKE KID, THE
(1985 - Trinity) Peter Billingsley, Anne Bloom
One Sheet: $3 - $5

DIRT GANG, THE
(1972 - AIP) Paul Carr, Jon Shank
One Sheet: $10 - $20

DIRTIE GIRTIE FROM HARLEM
(1946 - NCI) Spencer Williams, Francine Everette
One Sheet: $200 - $400   *Black cast.*

DIRTIEST GIRL I EVER MET
(1972 - United) Robin Askwith, Janet Lynn
One Sheet: $5 - $10

DIRTY DANCING
(1987 - Vestron) Jennifer Grey, Patrick Swayze
One Sheet: $15 - $25

DIRTY DINGUS MAGEE
(1970 - MGM) Frank Sinatra, George Kennedy
One Sheet: $15 - $30   *Cowboy Movie Posters #332.*

DIRTY DOZEN, THE
(1967 - MGM) Lee Marvin, Charles Bronson
One Sheet: $50 - $100

DIRTY DOZEN, THE
(1973R - MGM) Lee Marvin, Charles Bronson
One Sheet: $15 - $25   *Re-release.*

DIRTY DUCK
(1977 - -) -
One Sheet: $20 - $40   *Cartoon.*

DIRTY GAME, THE
(1966 - AIP) Henry Fonda, Robert Ryan
One Sheet: $7 - $15

DIRTY HARRY
(1971 - Warner Bros.) Clint Eastwood
One Sheet: $100 - $200

DIRTY HARRY/MAGNUM FORCE COMBO
(1975R - Warner Bros.) Clint Eastwood
One Sheet: $30 - $60   *Double feature poster.*

DIRTY KNIGHT'S WORK
(1976 - Gamma 3) John Mills, Donald Pleasence
One Sheet: $5 - $10   *AKA: TRIAL BY COMBAT; CHOICE OF ARMS.*

DIRTY LITTLE BILLY
(1973 - Columbia) Michael J. Pollard, Lee Purcell
One Sheet: $5 - $10   *Cowboy Movie Posters #335.*

DIRTY MARY CRAZY LARRY
(1974 - 20th Century Fox) Peter Fonda, Susan George
One Sheet: $15 - $25

DIRTY MONEY
(1977 - Allied Artists) Alain Delon, Catherine Deneuve
One Sheet: $7 - $15

DIRTY O'NEIL
(1974 - AIP) Morgan Paul, Pat Anderson
One Sheet: $7 - $15

DIRTY OUTLAWS
(1971 - Transvue) Chip Corman, Rosemarie Dexter
One Sheet: $5 - $10

DIRTY ROTTEN SCOUNDRELS
(1988 - Orion) Steve Martin, Michael Caine
One Sheet: $3 - $5

DIRTY TRICKS
(1981 - Avco/Embassy) Elliott Gould, Kate Jackson
One Sheet: $3 - $5

DIRTY WORK
(1933 - MGM) Laurel & Hardy
One Sheet: $1,900 - $3,000

DIRTY WORK
(1933B - Gaumont) Ralph Lynn, Gordon Harker
One Sheet: $100 - $200

DIRTYMOUTH
(1970 - Superior) Bernie Tarvis
One Sheet: $5 - $10

DISAPPEARANCE, THE
(1977 - World Northal) Donald Sutherland, Christopher Plummer
One Sheet: $5 - $10

DISAPPEARANCE OF THE OKLAHOMA OUTLAWS, THE
(1915 -) William Tillman
One Sheet: $300 - $700

DISASTER
(1948 - Paramount) Richard Denning, Trudy Marshall
One Sheet: $40 - $75

DISBARRED
(1939 - Paramount) Gail Patrick, Otto Kruger
One Sheet: $75 - $150

DISC JOCKEY
(1951 - Allied Artists) Jane Nigh, Michael O'Shea
One Sheet: $40 - $75

DISCARDED LOVERS
(1932 - Tower) Natalie Moorhead, Jason Robards
One Sheet: $200 - $400

DISCIPLE, THE
(1915 - Triangle) William S. Hart, Dorothy Dalton
One Sheet: $1,300 - $2,000

DISCIPLE OF DEATH
(1972 - Avco/Embassy) Mike Raven, Stephen Bradley
One Sheet: $10 - $20

DISCLOSURE
(1994 - Warner Bros.) Michael Douglas, Demi Moore
One Sheet: $5 - $10

DISCO GODFATHER
(1979 -) Silly Dram, Rudy Ray Moore
One Sheet: $10 - $20   *Blaxploitation.*

DISCREET CHARM OF THE BOURGEOISIE, THE
(1972 - 20th Century Fox) Fernando Rey, Delphine Seyrig
One Sheet: $3 - $5

DISEMBODIED, THE
(1957 - Allied Artists) Paul Burke, Allison Hayes
One Sheet: $30 - $60

DISGRACED
(1933 - Paramount) Helen Twelvetrees, Bruce Cabot
One Sheet: $800 - $1,500

DISHONOR BRIGHT
(1936 - Capital) Tom Walls, Betty Stockfeld
One Sheet: $150 - $300

DISHONORED
(1931 - Paramount Publix) Marlene Dietrich,

Victor McLaglen
One Sheet: $5,000 - $7,500

DISHONORED LADY
(1947 - Mars Film) Hedy Lamarr, Dennis O'Keefe
One Sheet: $150 - $300

DISNEYLAND AFTER DARK
(1963 - Buena Vista/Disney) with Louis Armstrong
One Sheet: $40 - $75

DISNEYLAND U.S.A.
(1957 - Disney) -
One Sheet: $40 - $75

DISORDER IN THE COURT
(1936 - Columbia) The Three Stooges (Curly)
One Sheet: $10,000 - $16,000   *Comedy short. Duotone.*

DISORDERLIES
(1987 -) Ralph Bellamy, The Fat Boys
One Sheet: $3 - $5

DISORDERLY CONDUCT
(1932 - Fox) Spencer Tracy, Sally Eilers
One Sheet: $200 - $400

DISORDERLY ORDERLY, THE
(1964 - Paramount) Jerry Lewis, Glenda Farrell
One Sheet: $30 - $60

DISORGANIZED CRIME
(1989 - Touchstone) Hoyt Axton, Corbin Bernsen, Ruben Blades
One Sheet: $5 - $10

DISPATCH FROM REUTERS, A
(1940 - Warner Bros.) Edward G. Robinson, Edna Best
One Sheet: $75 - $125

DISPUTED PASSAGE
(1939 - Paramount) Dorothy Lamour, John Howard
One Sheet: $100 - $200

DISRAELI
(1921 - United Artists) George Arliss, Margaret Dale
One Sheet: $250 - $600

DISRAELI
(1929 - Warner Bros.) George Arliss, Joan Bennett
One Sheet: $500 - $800   *Academy Award: Best Actor. Academy Award Movie Posters #18.*

DISRAELI
(1930R - Warner Bros.) George Arliss, Joan Bennett
One Sheet: $150 - $300   *Re-titled re-release of RETURN ENGAGEMENT.*

DISSATISFIED COBBLER
(1922 - Pathe) Animated by Paul Terry
One Sheet: $1,600 - $2,500   *Cartoon. An Aesop's Fables film. Cartoon Movie Posters #15.*

DISTANCE
(1975 - Coe) James Woods, Paul Benjamin
One Sheet: $5 - $10

DISTANT DRUMS
(1951 - Warner Bros.) Gary Cooper, Mari Aldon
One Sheet: $50 - $100

DISTANT THUNDER
(1988 - Paramount) John Lithgow, Ralph Macchio, Kerrie Keane
One Sheet: $3 - $5

DISTANT TRUMPET, A
(1964 - Warner Bros.) Troy Donahue, Suzanne Pleshette
One Sheet: $15 - $35

DISTINGUISHED GENTLEMAN, THE
(1992 - Buena Vista) Eddie Murphy, Joe Don Baker
One Sheet: $5 - $10

DIVA
(1982 - Palace) Wilhelmenia Wiggins Fernandez
One Sheet: $10 - $20   *French.*

DIVE BOMBER
(1941 - Warner Bros.) Errol Flynn, Fred MacMurray
One Sheet: $125 - $250

DIVIDED HEART, THE
(1954 - Republic) Cornell Borchers, Yvonne Mitchell, Alexander Knox
One Sheet: $7 - $15

DIVIDEND, THE
(1916 - Triangle) Charles Ray, William Thompson
One Sheet: $200 - $400

DIVINE LADY
(1929 - Warner Bros.) Corrine Griffith, Victor Varconi
One Sheet: $250 - $600   *Academy Award: Best Direction(Frank Lloyd). Academy Award Movie Posters #12.*

DIVINE MADNESS
(1980 -) Bette Midler
One Sheet: $10 - $20   *Concert film.*

DIVINE MR. J., THE
(1974 -) John Bassberger, Bette Midler
One Sheet: $7 - $15

DIVINE NYMPH, THE
(1979 - Analysis) Laura Antonelli, Marcello Mastroianni
One Sheet: $15 - $25

DIVINE WOMAN, THE
(1928 - MGM) Greta Garbo, Lars Hanson
One Sheet: $3,500 - $5,000

DIVORCE
(1945 - Monogram) Kay Francis, Bruce Cabot
One Sheet: $40 - $75

DIVORCE AMERICAN STYLE
(1967 - Columbia) Dick Van Dyke, Debbie Reynolds
One Sheet: $5 - $10

DIVORCE AMONG FRIENDS
(1930 - Warner Bros.) James Hall, Lew Cody
One Sheet: $150 - $300

DIVORCE IN THE FAMILY
(1932 - MGM) Jackie Cooper, Conrad Nagel
One Sheet: $300 - $700

DIVORCE ITALIAN STYLE
(1962 - Avco/Embassy) Marcello Mastroianni, Daniela Rocca
One Sheet: $15 - $25

DIVORCE OF LADY X, THE
(1938 - United Artists) Merle Oberon, Laurence Olivier
One Sheet: $500 - $900

DIVORCED SWEETHEARTS
(1930 - Educational) Daphne Pollard, Charles Irwin
One Sheet: $150 - $300

DIVORCEE, THE
(1930 - MGM) Norma Shearer, Conrad Nagel
One Sheet: $600 - $1,000   *Academy Award Movie Posters #16.*

DIXIANA
(1930 - RKO) Wheeler and Woolsey, Bebe Daniels
One Sheet: $300 - $700

DIXIE
(1943 - Paramount) Bing Crosby, Dorothy Lamour
One Sheet: $100 - $200

DIXIE DUGAN
(1942 - 20th Century Fox) James Ellison, Lois Andrews
One Sheet: $50 - $100

DIXIE DYNAMITE
(1976 - Dimension) Warren Oates, Christopher George
One Sheet: $5 - $10

DIXIE JAMBOREE
(1945 - PRC) Frances Langford, Guy Kibbee, Ben Carter Choir
One Sheet: $75 - $125

DIXIE LOVE
(1933 -) -
One Sheet: $100 - $200

DIZZY DAMES
(1935 - Liberty) Marjorie Rambeau, Florine McKinney

One Sheet: $100 - $200

DIZZY DETECTIVES
(1943 - Columbia) The Three Stooges (Curly)
One Sheet: $2,500 - $4,000   *Comedy short. Duotone.*

DIZZY DOCTORS
(1937 - Columbia) The Three Stooges (Curly)
One Sheet: $8,500 - $14,000   *Comedy short. Duotone.*

DIZZY PILOTS
(1943 - Columbia) The Three Stooges (Curly)
One Sheet: $2,500 - $4,000   *Comedy short. Duotone.*

DO DETECTIVES THINK?
(1927 - Pathe) Laurel & Hardy
One Sheet: $4,000 - $6,000

Lobby Card

DO NOT DISTURB
(1965 - 20th Century Fox) Doris Day, Rod Taylor
One Sheet: $15 - $25

DO NOT THROW CUSHIONS INTO THE RING
(1970 -) Ed Asner, Steve Ihnat
One Sheet: $7 - $15

DO OR DIET
(1947 - RKO) Edgar Kennedy, Jason Robards Sr.
One Sheet: $50 - $100

DO THE RIGHT THING
(1989 - Universal) Danny Aiello, Ossie Davis, Spike Lee (Dir.)
One Sheet: $50 - $100   *Price is for double-sided One Sheet.*

DO YOU LOVE ME?
(1946 - 20th Century Fox) Maureen O'Hara, Dick Haymes
One Sheet: $75 - $125

DO YOUR DUTY
(1928 - First National) Charlie Murray, Lucien Littlefield
One Sheet: $150 - $300

D.O.A.
(1950 - United Artists) Edmond O'Brien, Pamela Britton
One Sheet: $250 - $500

D.O.A.
(1988 - United Artists) Dennis Quaid, Meg Ryan, Daniel Stern
One Sheet: $5 - $10

DOBERMAN GANG, THE
(1972 - Dimension) Byron Mabe, Julie Parrish
One Sheet: $5 - $10

DOC
(1971 - United Artists) Stacy Keach, Faye Dunaway, Harris Yulin
One Sheet: $5 - $10

DOC HOLLYWOOD
(1991 - Warner Bros.) Michael J. Fox, Julie Warner
One Sheet: $5 - $10

DOC SAVAGE...THE MAN OF BRONZE
(1975 - Warner Bros.) Ron Ely, Paul Gleason
One Sheet: $7 - $15

DOCKS OF NEW ORLEANS
(1948 - Monogram) Roland Winters, Victor Sen Young, Mantan Moreland
One Sheet: $75 - $125

DOCKS OF NEW YORK
(1928 - Paramount) George Bancroft, Betty Compson
One Sheet: $200 - $400

DOCKS OF NEW YORK
(1945 - Monogram) The East Side Kids, Gloria Pope
One Sheet: $75 - $125

DOCKS OF SAN FRANCISCO
(1932 - Action) Mary Nolan, Jason Robards, Marjorie Beebe, John Davidson
One Sheet: $75 - $150

One Sheet

DOCTOR, THE
(1991 - Touchstone) William Hurt
One Sheet: $5 - $10

DOCTOR AND THE DEVILS, THE
(1985 - Brooksfilm) Timothy Dalton, Jonathan Pryce, Twiggy
One Sheet: $3 - $5

DOCTOR AND THE GIRL, THE
(1949 - MGM) Glenn Ford, Charles Coburn, Gloria de Haven
One Sheet: $40 - $75

DOCTOR AT LARGE
(1957 - Universal-International) Dirk Bogarde, Muriel Pavlow, Shirley Eaton
One Sheet: $7 - $15

DOCTOR AT SEA
(1955 - Republic) Dirk Bogarde, Brenda de Banzie, Brigitte Bardot
One Sheet: $40 - $80

DR. BLACK AND MR. HYDE
(1976 - Dimension) Bernie Casey, Rosalind Cash
One Sheet: $15 - $30

DR. BLOOD'S COFFIN
(1961 - United Artists) Kieron Moore, Hazel Court
One Sheet: $30 - $50

DOCTOR BLUEBIRD
(1936 - Columbia) Charles Mintz Studio
One Sheet: $500 - $900 *Cartoon. Cartoon Movie Posters #38.*

DR. BROADWAY
(1942 - Paramount) Macdonald Carey, Jean Phillips
One Sheet: $75 - $150

DR. BULL
(1933 - Fox) Will Rogers, Louise Dresser, Marion Nixon
One Sheet: $250 - $500

DR. BUTCHER, M.D.
(1982 - Flora) Ian McCulloch
One Sheet: $5 - $10

DR. CHRISTIAN MEETS THE WOMEN
(1940 - RKO) Jean Hersholt, Dorothy Lovett
One Sheet: $75 - $150

DR. COPPELIUS
(1968 - Childhood) Walter Slezak, Claudia Corday, Eileen Elliott
One Sheet: $4 - $8

DR. CRIPPEN
(1964 - Warner Bros.) Donald Pleasence, Coral Browne
One Sheet: $15 - $30

DR. CYCLOPS
(1940 - Paramount) Albert Dekker, Janice Logan
One Sheet: $600 - $1,000 *Graven Images, pg. 120.*

DR. CYCLOPS
(1950R - Paramount) Albert Dekker, Janice Logan
One Sheet: $50 - $100 *Re-release.*

DOCTOR DEATH: SEEKER OF SOULS
(1973 - Cinerama) John Considine, Barry Coe, Moe Howard
One Sheet: $15 - $25

DOCTOR DETROIT
(1983 - -) Dan Aykroyd, Howard Hesseman, Donna Dixon
One Sheet: $3 - $5

DOCTOR DOLITTLE
(1967 - 20th Century Fox) Rex Harrison, Samantha Eggar, Anthony Newley
One Sheet: $50 - $100 *Price is for "Rex on Giraffe" style one sheet dated 1967 in Roman numerals and numbered 8862 on bottom left border. Be sure to check date on posters from this title.*

One Sheet

DOCTOR DOLITTLE
(1969 - 20th Century Fox) Rex Harrison, Samantha Eggar
One Sheet: $20 - $40 *Duotone one sheet with NSS (National Screen Service) date of 1969. No mention of re-release info so this may possibly be an International release.*

DR. EHRLICH'S MAGIC BULLET
(1940 - Warner Bros.) Edward G. Robinson, Ruth Gordon
One Sheet: $125 - $250

DR. FAUSTUS
(1968 - Columbia) Richard Burton, Elizabeth Taylor
One Sheet: $15 - $30

DR. FRANKENSTEIN ON CAMPUS
(1970 - MedFord) Robin Ward, Kathleen Sawyer
One Sheet: $15 - $25

DR. GIGGLES
(1992 - Universal) Larry Drake, Molly Marie Combs
One Sheet: $3 - $5

DR. GILLESPIE'S CRIMINAL CASE
(1943 - MGM) Lionel Barrymore, Van Johnson
One Sheet: $50 - $100

DR. GILLESPIE'S NEW ASSISTANT
(1942 - MGM) Lionel Barrymore, Van Johnson
One Sheet: $75 - $125

DR. GOLDFOOT AND THE BIKINI MACHINE
(1965 - AIP) Vincent Price, Frankie Avalon
One Sheet: $20 - $40

DR. GOLDFOOT AND THE GIRL BOMBS
(1966 - AIP) Vincent Price, Fabian
One Sheet: $20 - $40

DR. HECKYL AND MR. HYPE
(1980 - Cannon) Oliver Reed, Sunny Johnson
One Sheet: $5 - $10

DOCTOR IN DISTRESS
(1964 - Governor) Dirk Bogarde, James Robertson Justice
One Sheet: $10 - $20

DOCTOR IN LOVE
(1962 - Governor) Michael Craig, Virginia Maskell
One Sheet: $10 - $20

DOCTOR IN THE HOUSE
(1954 - Republic) Dirk Bogarde, Muriel Pavlow
One Sheet: $15 - $30

DR. JACK
(1922 - Associated Exhibitors) Harold Lloyd, Mildred Davis
One Sheet: $1,300 - $2,000

DR. JEKYLL AND MR. HYDE
(1921 - Paramount) John Barrymore, Nita Naldi
One Sheet: $13,000 - $20,000 *Graven Images, pg. 23.*

DR. JEKYLL AND MR. HYDE
(1932 - Paramount) Fredric March, Miriam Hopkins
One Sheet: $19,000 - $30,000 *Academy Award: Best Actor. Academy Award Movie Posters #26. Graven Images, pg. 54.*

One Sheet

DR. JEKYLL AND MR. HYDE
(1941 - MGM) Spencer Tracy, Ingrid Bergman, Lana Turner
One Sheet: $500 - $900 *Graven Images, pg. 128.*

DR. JEKYLL AND MR. HYDE
(1954R - MGM) Spencer Tracy, Ingrid Bergman, Lana Turner
One Sheet: $75 - $150 *Re-release.*

DR. JEKYLL AND MR. MOUSE
(1947 - MGM) Tom & Jerry
One Sheet: $800 - $1,500 *Cartoon. Full color stone litho. Cartoon Movie Posters #278.*

DR. JEKYLL AND MS. HYDE
(1995 - Savoy) Tim Daly, Sean Young
One Sheet: $3 - $5

DR. JEKYLL AND SISTER HYDE
(1972 - AIP) Ralph Bates, Martine Beswick
One Sheet: $15 - $25

DR. JEKYLL AND THE WOLFMAN
(1971 - International Cinema) Paul Naschy
One Sheet: $15 - $25

DR. JEKYLL'S DUNGEON OF DEATH
(1982 - Rochelle) James Mathers
One Sheet: $5 - $10

DR. KILDARE GOES HOME
(1940 - MGM) Lew Ayres, Lionel Barrymore, Laraine Day
One Sheet: $75 - $125

DR. KILDARE'S CRISIS
(1940 - MGM) Lew Ayres, Lionel Barrymore, Robert Young
One Sheet: $75 - $125

DR. KILDARE'S STRANGE CASE
(1940 - MGM) Lew Ayres, Lionel Barrymore, Shepperd Strudwick
One Sheet: $75 - $125

DR. KILDARE'S VICTORY
(1941 - MGM) Lew Ayres, Lionel Barrymore, Laraine Day, Red Skelton
One Sheet: $75 - $125

DR. KILDARE'S WEDDING DAY
(1941 - MGM) Lew Ayres, Lionel Barrymore, Red Skelton
One Sheet: $75 - $125

DOCTOR MABUSE THE GAMBLER
(1922 - UFA) Rudolph Klein-Rogge, Dir: Fritz Lang
One Sheet: $25,000 - $40,000 *German. Price is for original German-release poster. Beware re-releases.*

DR. MANIAC
(1936 - Gaumont) Boris Karloff, Anna Lee
One Sheet: $1,300 - $2,000 *AKA: THE MAN WHO LIVED AGAIN; THE BRAINSNATCHERS; THE MAN WHO CHANGED HIS MIND.*

DR. MONICA
(1934 - Warner Bros.) Kay Francis, Warren William
One Sheet: $250 - $600

DR. MYNX
(1975 - Dimension) Edie Williams
One Sheet: $15 - $30

DR. NO
(1963 - United Artists) Sean Connery, Ursula Andress
One Sheet: $250 - $600 *First James Bond film. Graven Images, pg. 225.*

DR. NO
(1980R - United Artists) Sean Connery, Ursula Andress
One Sheet: $30 - $50 *Re-release.*

DR. NO/FROM RUSSIA WITH LOVE
(1966R - United Artists) Sean Connery, Ursual Andress, Daniela Bianchi
One Sheet: $50 - $100 *Re-release double feature poster.*

DR. NO/GOLDFINGER
(1966R - United Artists) Sean Connery, Ursula Andress, Gert Frobe
One Sheet: $50 - $100 *Re-release double feature poster.*

DR. OTTO AND THE RIDDLE OF THE GLOOM BEAM
(1986 - Sweat Equities) Jim Varney
One Sheet: $2 - $3

DR. PHIBES RISES AGAIN
(1972 - AIP) Vincent Price, Peter Cushing
One Sheet: $15 - $30

DOCTOR POLLY
(1914 - Vitagraph) Lillian Walker
One Sheet: $200 - $400

DR. RENAULT'S SECRET
(1942 - 20th Century Fox) George Zucco, J. Carrol Naish
One Sheet: $50 - $100

DR. RHYTHM
(1938 - Paramount) Bing Crosby, Beatrice Little
One Sheet: $75 - $150

DR. SATAN'S ROBOT
(1940 - Republic) Edwardo Channelli, Robert Wilcox
One Sheet: $250 - $600 *Feature length version of MYSTERIOUS DR. SATAN serial.*

DR. SOCRATES
(1935 - Warner Bros.) Paul Muni, Ann Dvorak
One Sheet: $500 - $800

DR. STRANGELOVE
(1963 - Columbia) Peter Sellers, George C. Scott, Dir: Stanley Kubrick
One Sheet: $125 - $250 *Graven Images, pg. 225.*

One Sheet

DR. STRANGELOVE
(1972R - Columbia) Peter Sellers, George C.
Scott Dir: Stanley Kubrick
One Sheet: $20 - $40   *Re-release.*

DR. SYN
(1937 - Gaumont) George Arliss, John Loder
One Sheet: $250 - $500

DR. SYN ALIAS THE SCARECROW
(1972 - Buena Vista/Disney) Patrick
McGoohan, George Cole
One Sheet: $15 - $30

DOCTOR TAKES A WIFE, THE
(1940 - Columbia) Ray Milland, Loretta Young
One Sheet: $75 - $150

DR. TERROR'S HOUSE OF HORRORS
(1965 - Paramount) Peter Cushing, Christopher
Lee
One Sheet: $30 - $50   *Graven
Images, pg. 217. AKA: BLOOD SUCKERS.*

DR. WHO AND THE DALEKS
(1966 - Continental) Peter Cushing, Roy
Castle, Jennie Linden
One Sheet: $100 - $200   *Price is for
U.S. or British one sheet.*

DR. X
(1932 - First National) Lionel Atwill, Fay Wray
One Sheet: $1,900 - $3,000   *Graven
Images, pg. 66.*

DOCTOR YOU'VE GOT TO BE KIDDING
(1967 - MGM) Sandra Dee, George Hamilton
One Sheet: $10 - $20

DOCTOR ZHIVAGO
(1965 - MGM) Omar Sharif, Rod Steiger, Julie
Christie
One Sheet: $150 - $350   *Portrait Style:
$300-$600. Academy Awards Style: $30-$50.
Beware misdated Style B one sheet with copyright
1971.*

DOCTOR ZHIVAGO
(1971R - MGM) Omar Sharif, Rod Steiger, Julie
Christie
One Sheet: $30 - $50   *Re-release.
One Sheet is NSS stamped 1965, but copyright
date is 1971.*

DOCTOR ZHIVAGO
(1974R - MGM) Omar Sharif, Rod Stieger, Julie
Christie
One Sheet: $15 - $25   *Re-release.*

DOCTOR'S DIARY, A
(1937 - Paramount) John Trent, Helen Burgess
One Sheet: $75 - $150

DOCTOR'S DILEMMA, THE
(1958 - MGM) Leslie Caron, Dirk Bogarde
One Sheet: $10 - $20

DOCTORS DON'T TELL
(1941 - Republic) John Beal, Florence Rice
One Sheet: $50 - $100

DOCTORS' WIVES
(1931 - Fox) Warner Baxter, Joan Bennett
One Sheet: $200 - $400

DOCTORS' WIVES
(1971 - Columbia) Dyan Cannon, Richard
Crenna
One Sheet: $5 - $10

DODES KA-DEN
(1970 - -) Yoshitaka Zushi, Dir: Akira Kurosawa
One Sheet: $40 - $75   *Japanese.
Japanese One Sheet:$300-$500.*

DODGE CITY
(1939 - Warner Bros.) Errol Flynn, Olivia de
Havilland
One Sheet: $2,500 - $4,000   *Cowboy
Movie Posters #252.*

DODGE CITY
(1951R - Warner Bros.) Errol Flynn, Olivia
DeHavilland
One Sheet: $75 - $150   *Re-release.*

DODGE CITY TRAIL
(1936 - Columbia) Charles Starrett
One Sheet: $100 - $200

DODSWORTH
(1936 - United Artists) Walter Huston, Ruth
Chatterton, Mary Astor

One Sheet: $700 - $1,200

DODSWORTH
(1946R - United Artists) Walter Huston, Ruth
Chatterton, Mary Astor
One Sheet: $75 - $150   *Re-release.*

DOES IT PAY?
(1923 - Fox) Hope Hampton
One Sheet: $500 - $800

DOG, CAT AND CANARY
(1945 - Columbia) Color Rhapsodies
One Sheet: $150 - $350   *Cartoon. Full
color semi-stock poster with inset of title.*

DOG DAY AFTERNOON
(1975 - Warner Bros.) Al Pacino, Charles
Durning
One Sheet: $15 - $35   *Price applies
to all styles.*

DOG EAT DOG
(1963 - Ajay) Cameron Mitchell, Jayne
Mansfield
One Sheet: $30 - $50

DOG OF FLANDERS, A
(1935 - RKO) Frankie Thomas, Helen Parrish
One Sheet: $100 - $200

DOG OF FLANDERS, A
(1960 - 20th Century Fox) David Ladd, Donald
Crisp
One Sheet: $5 - $10

DOG SNATCHER, THE
(1952 - Columbia) Mr. Magoo
One Sheet: $150 - $300   *Cartoon.
Duotone.*

DOG TROUBLE
(1942 - MGM) Tom & Jerry
One Sheet: $500 - $800   *Cartoon. Full
color stone litho. Cartoon Movie Posters #263.*

DOG'S DREAM, THE
(1940 - 20th Century Fox) Terry-toons
One Sheet: $100 - $200   *Cartoon. Full
color stone litho. Stock poster with inset title.*

DOG'S LIFE, A
(1918 - First National) Charlie Chaplin, Edna
Purviance
One Sheet: $16,000 - $25,000

One Sheet

DOG'S LIFE, A
(1923R - Pathe) Charlie Chaplin, Edna
Purviance
One Sheet: $600 - $1,000   *Re-release.
Three Sheet:$2,000-$3,000. Chaplin not pictured
on One Sheet.*

DOGGONE TIRED
(1949 - MGM) Tex Avery
One Sheet: $300 - $700   *Cartoon. Full
color stone litho. Cartoon Movie Posters #307.*

DOGS
(1977 - MarVista) David McCallum, Sandra
McCabe
One Sheet: $7 - $15

DOGS 'N DUCKS
(1952 - MGM) Pete Smith Specialty
One Sheet: $125 - $250

DOGS IN SPACE
(1988 - -) Michael Hutchence, Saskia Post
One Sheet: $7 - $15

DOGS IS DOGS
(1931 - MGM) Our Gang

One Sheet: $500 - $800

DOIN' THEIR BIT
(1942 - MGM) Our Gang
One Sheet: $300 - $700

DOIN' TIME ON PLANET EARTH
(1988 - -) Adam West, Candice Azzara, Hugh
O'Brian
One Sheet: $7 - $15

DOLEMITE
(1975 - Dimension) Rudy Ray Moore, Jerry
Jones
One Sheet: $15 - $30   *Blaxploitation.*

DOLL FACE
(1946 - 20th Century Fox) Vivian Blaine,
Dennis O'Keefe
One Sheet: $50 - $100

DOLL'S HOUSE, A
(1918 - Paramount) Elsie Ferguson, H.E.
Herbert
One Sheet: $600 - $1,000

DOLL'S HOUSE, A
(1973 - Paramount) Claire Bloom, Anthony
Hopkins
One Sheet: $7 - $15

DOLLARS
(1971 - Columbia) Warren Beatty, Goldie Frobe
One Sheet: $5 - $10   *Price is for
both styles.*

DOLLS
(1987 - -) Ian Patrik Williams, Carolyn Purdy-
Gordon
One Sheet: $7 - $15

DOLLY SISTERS, THE
(1945 - 20th Century Fox) Betty Grable, John
Payne
One Sheet: $100 - $200

DOLORES CLAIBORNE
(1995 - Columbia) Kathy Bates, Jennifer Jason
Leigh
One Sheet: $5 - $10

DOLWYN
(1949 - London) Edith Evans, Emlyn Williams
One Sheet: $30 - $50

DOMINICK AND EUGENE
(1988 - -) Tom Hulce, Ray Liotta, Jamie Lee
Curtis
One Sheet: $5 - $10

DOMINO KID, THE
(1957 - Columbia) Rory Calhoun, Kristine Miller
One Sheet: $15 - $30

DOMINO PRINCIPLE
(1977 - Avco) Gene Hackman, Candice
Bergman
One Sheet: $5 - $10

**DON CAMILLO MONSIGNORE MA NON
TRAPPO**
(1956 - -) Fernandel
One Sheet: $30 - $50   *Italian.*

DON DARE DEVIL
(1925 - Universal) Jack Hoxie, Cathleen
Calhoun
One Sheet: $150 - $300

DON DAREDEVIL RIDES AGAIN
(1951 - Republic) Ken Curtis, Aline Towne
One Sheet: $40 - $75   *Serial.
Western. 12 Chapters.*

DON GIOVANNI
(198? - -) -
One Sheet: $15 - $30   *French.*

DON IS DEAD, THE
(1973 - Universal) Anthony Quinn, Fredric
Forrest
One Sheet: $5 - $10

DON JUAN
(1926 - Warner Bros.) John Barrymore, Mary
Astor
One Sheet: $4,500 - $7,000

DON JUAN DeMARCO
(1995 - New Line) Johnny Depp, Marlon
Brando, Faye Dunaway
One Sheet: $7 - $15

DON JUAN QUILLIGAN

(1945 - 20th Century Fox) William Bendix, Joan
Blondell
One Sheet: $50 - $100

DON Q SON OF ZORRO
(1925 - United Artists) Douglas Fairbanks
One Sheet: $1,300 - $2,000   *Cowboy
Movie Posters #53.*

Title Card

DON QUIXOTE
(1934 - Celebrity) -
One Sheet: $700 - $1,300   *Cartoon.
Cartoon Movie Poster #109.*

DON QUIXOTE
(1935 - DuWorld) George Robey, Sydney Fox
One Sheet: $700 - $1,200

DON QUIXOTE
(1961 - MGM) Nikolai Cherkassov, Arnold
Diamond
One Sheet: $15 - $25

DON RICARDO RETURNS
(1946 - PRC) Fred Colby, Isabelita Pastro
One Sheet: $30 - $50

DON WINSLOW OF THE COAST GUARD
(1942 - Universal) Don Terry
One Sheet: $75 - $150   *Serial. 13
Chapters.*

DON WINSLOW OF THE NAVY
(1942 - Universal) Don Terry, Walter Sande
One Sheet: $75 - $150   *Serial. 12
Chapters.*

DON'S FOUNTAIN OF YOUTH
(1953 - RKO/Disney) Donald Duck
One Sheet: $600 - $1,000   *Cartoon.*

DON'T ANSWER THE PHONE
(1980 - Crown) James Westmoreland, Flo
Gerrish
One Sheet: $5 - $10

**DON'T BE A MENACE TO SOUTH CENTRAL
WHILE DRINKING YOUR JUICE IN THE HOOD**
(1996 - Miramax) Marlon Wayans, Shawn
Wayans
One Sheet: $5 - $10   *Black cast.*

DON'T BE AFRAID OF THE DARK
(1973 - -) Kim Darby, Jim Hutton
One Sheet: $5 - $10   *Made for TV
movie.*

DON'T BET ON BLONDES
(1935 - Warner Bros.) Warren William, Claire
Dodd, Errol Flynn
One Sheet: $300 - $700

DON'T BET ON LOVE
(1933 - Universal) Lew Ayers, Ginger Rogers
One Sheet: $200 - $400

DON'T BET ON WOMEN
(1931 - Fox) Jeanette MacDonald, Roland
Young, Edmund Lowe
One Sheet: $250 - $500

DON'T BITE YOUR DENTIST
(1930 - Educational) Andy Clyde, Daphne
Pollard
One Sheet: $150 - $300

DON'T BOTHER TO KNOCK
(1952 - 20th Century Fox) Richard Widmark,
Marilyn Monroe
One Sheet: $700 - $1,200

DON'T CHANGE YOUR HUSBAND
(1918 - Artcraft) -

One Sheet: $250 - $600

DON'T CRY, IT'S ONLY THUNDER
(1981 - Sanrio) Dennis Christopher, Susan
Saint James, Robert Englund
One Sheet: $5 - $10

DON'T DOUBT YOUR HUSBAND
(1924 - Metro) Viola Dana, Allan Forrest
One Sheet: $200 - $400

DON'T DRINK THE WATER
(1969 - Avco/Embassy) Jackie Gleason, Estelle
Parsons
One Sheet: $5 - $10

DON'T EVER MARRY
(1921 - First National) Matt Moore, Marjorie
Daw, Tom Guise
One Sheet: $250 - $500

DON'T FALL IN LOVE
(1937 - Ambassador-Conn.) Pinky Tomlin
One Sheet: $75 - $150

DON'T FENCE ME IN
(1945 - Republic) Roy Rogers, Dale Evans
One Sheet: $150 - $350

DON'T FENCE ME IN
(1954R - Republic) Roy Rogers, Dale Evans
One Sheet: $40 - $75   *Re-release.*

DON'T GAMBLE WITH LOVE
(1936 - Columbia) Bruce Cabot, Ann Sothern
One Sheet: $125 - $250

DON'T GAMBLE WITH STRANGERS
(1946 - Monogram) Kane Richmond,
Bernardine Hayes
One Sheet: $50 - $100

One Sheet

DON'T GET AROUND MUCH ANYMORE
(1943 - -) -
One Sheet: $125 - $250   *Black cast.*

DON'T GET PERSONAL
(1936 - Universal) James Dunn, Sally Eilers
One Sheet: $100 - $200

DON'T GET PERSONAL
(1942 - Universal) Hugh Herbert, Mischa Auer
One Sheet: $75 - $125

DON'T GIVE UP THE SHIP
(1959 - Paramount) Jerry Lewis, Dina Merrill
One Sheet: $30 - $60

DON'T GIVE UP THE SHIP
(1963R - Paramount) Jerry Lewis, Dina Merrill
One Sheet: $10 - $20   *Re-release.*

DON'T GIVE UP THE SHIP/ROCK-A-BYE BABY
(1963R - Paramount) Jerry Lewis
One Sheet: $10 - $20   *Re-release
double feature poster.*

DON'T GO IN THE HOUSE
(1980 - Film Ventures) Dan Grimaldi, Robert
Osth
One Sheet: $5 - $10

DON'T GO NEAR THE WATER
(1957 - MGM) Glenn Ford, Gia Scala
One Sheet: $15 - $35

DON'T JUST STAND THERE
(1968 - Universal) Robert Wagner, Mary Tyler
Moore
One Sheet: $5 - $10

DON'T KNOCK THE ROCK
(1957 - Columbia) Bill Haley & The Comets,

Alan Freed
One Sheet: $125 - $250   *Rock 'n' Roll.*

DON'T KNOCK THE TWIST
(1962 - Columbia) Chubby Checker, Gene
Chandler
One Sheet: $75 - $125   *Rock 'n' Roll.*

DON'T LIE
(1942 - MGM) Our Gang
One Sheet: $250 - $500

DON'T LOOK BACK
(1967 - Leacock-Pennebaker) Bob Dylan, Joan
Baez
One Sheet: $250 - $500   *24x34:$300-
$600.*

DON'T LOOK IN THE BASEMENT
(1973 - Hallmark) Rosie Holotik, Ann McAdams
One Sheet: $7 - $15

DON'T LOOK NOW
(1969 - Buena Vista) Terry Thomas, Bourvil,
Louis de Funes
One Sheet: $15 - $30

DON'T LOOK NOW
(1974 - Paramount) Julie Christie, Donald
Sutherland
One Sheet: $3 - $5

DON'T MAKE WAVES
(1967 - MGM) Tony Curtis, Sharon Tate
One Sheet: $20 - $40

DON'T MARRY FOR MONEY
(1923 - Weber & North) House Peters, Rubye
De Remer
One Sheet: $125 - $250

DON'T PARK THERE!
(1924 - Pathe) Will Rogers
One Sheet: $500 - $800

DON'T RAISE THE BRIDGE, LOWER THE RIVER
(1968 - Columbia) Jerry Lewis, Jacqueline
Pearce
One Sheet: $10 - $20

DON'T SHOVE
(1919 - Pathe) Harold Lloyd
One Sheet: $600 - $1,100

DON'T TAKE IT TO HEART
(1949 - Eagle-Lion) Richard Greene, Patricia
Medina
One Sheet: $20 - $40

DON'T TELL HER IT'S ME
(1991 - Hemisphere) Steve Guttenberg, Shelley
Long
One Sheet: $5 - $10

DON'T TELL MOM THE BABY SITTER'S DEAD
(1991 - Warner Bros.) Christina Applegate,
Joanna Cassidy
One Sheet: $5 - $10

DON'T TELL THE WIFE
(1937 - RKO) Guy Kibbee, Una Merkel, Lucille
Ball
One Sheet: $150 - $300

DON'T THROW THAT KNIFE
(1951 - Columbia) The Three Stooges (Shemp)
One Sheet: $200 - $400   *Comedy short.
Duotone.*

DON'T TRUST YOUR HUSBAND
(1948 - United Artists) Fred MacMurray,
Madeleine Carroll
One Sheet: $50 - $100

DON'T TURN 'EM LOOSE
(1936 - RKO) Lewis Stone, Bruce Cabot, Betty
Grable
One Sheet: $150 - $350

DON'T WORRY WE'LL THINK OF A TITLE
(1966 - United Artists) Morey Amsterdam, Rose
Marie
One Sheet: $3 - $5

DON'T YOU BELIEVE IT
(1943 - MGM) -
One Sheet: $100 - $200   *John Nesbitt's
Passing Parade.*

DONA HERLINDA AND HER SON
(1986 - -) Guadalupe Del Toro, Arturo Meza
One Sheet: $7 - $15   *Spanish.*

DONALD AND THE WHEEL

(1961 - Disney) Donald Duck
One Sheet: $100 - $200   *Cartoon.*

DONALD APPLECORE
(1952 - RKO/Disney) Donald Duck, Chip N'
Dale
One Sheet: $600 - $1,000   *Cartoon. The
Disney Poster, pg. 46.*

DONALD DUCK AND THE GORILLA
(1944 - RKO/Disney) Donald Duck
One Sheet: $1,600 - $2,500   *Cartoon. The
Disney Poster, pg. 50.*

DONALD DUCK'S BIRTHDAY
(1965 - Disney) Donald Duck
One Sheet: $75 - $125   *Cartoon.*

DONALD'S BETTER SELF
(1938 - RKO/Disney) Donald Duck
One Sheet: $3,500 - $5,000   *Cartoon. Price
is for 14x28 full color silkscreen card used with
lobby standee. Cartoon Movie Posters #150.*

DONALD'S CAMERA
(1941 - RKO/Disney) Donald Duck
One Sheet: $3,500 - $5,000   *Cartoon.
Cartoon Movie Posters #166.*

DONALD'S COUSIN GUS
(1939 - RKO/Disney) Donald Duck
One Sheet: $4,000 - $6,000   *Cartoon.
Cartoon Movie Posters #153.*

DONALD'S CRIME
(1945 - RKO/Disney) Donald Duck
One Sheet: $3,500 - $5,000   *Cartoon.
Cartoon Movie Posters #171.*

DONALD'S DOG LAUNDRY
(1940 - RKO/Disney) Donald Duck and Pluto
One Sheet: $4,000 - $6,000   *Cartoon. Full
color. Cartoon Movie Posters #158.*

DONALD'S DREAM VOICE
(1948 - RKO/Disney) Donald Duck
One Sheet: $1,300 - $2,000   *Cartoon. Full
color.*

DONALD'S GOLF GAME
(1938 - RKO/Disney) Donald Duck
One Sheet: $5,000 - $8,000   *Cartoon.
Sports (Golf).*

DONALD'S GOLF GAME
(1950R - RKO/Disney) Donald Duck
One Sheet: $125 - $250   *Re-release.
Cartoon. Sports (Golf). Sports Movie Posters
#223.*

DONALD'S LUCKY DAY
(1939 - RKO/Disney) Donald Duck
One Sheet: $4,500 - $7,000   *Cartoon.
Cartoon Movie Posters #151.*

DONALD'S OFF DAY
(1944 - RKO/Disney) Donald Duck
One Sheet: $2,500 - $4,000   *Cartoon.
Sports Movie Posters #224.*

DONALD'S TIRE TROUBLE
(1943 - RKO/Disney) Donald Duck
One Sheet: $1,900 - $3,000   *Cartoon. The
Disney Poster, pg. 54.*

DONALD'S VACATION
(1940 - RKO/Disney) Donald Duck
One Sheet: $2,500 - $4,000   *Cartoon. The
Disney Poster, pg. 44.*

DONDI
(1961 - Allied Artists) David Janssen, Patti
Page
One Sheet: $5 - $10

DONKEY SKIN
(1975 - Janus) Catherine Deneuve, Jean
Marais
One Sheet: $30 - $50

DONNIE BRASCO
(1997 - Tri Star) Johnny Depp, Al Pacino,
Bruno Kirby
One Sheet: $5 - $10

DONOVAN AFFAIR, THE
(1929 - Columbia) Jack Holt, Dorothy Revier
One Sheet: $250 - $500

DONOVAN'S BRAIN
(1953 - United Artists) Lew Ayres, Gene Evans,
Nancy Davis
One Sheet: $100 - $200   *Graven
Images, pg. 184.*

DONOVAN'S REEF
(1963 - Paramount) John Wayne, Lee Marvin
One Sheet: $50 - $100

DOOLINS OF OKLAHOMA, THE
(1949 - Columbia) Randolph Scott, George
Macready
One Sheet: $40 - $75

DOOLINS OF OKLAHOMA, THE
(1955R - Columbia) Randolph Scott, George
Macready
One Sheet: $7 - $15   *Re-release.*

DOOMED AT SUNDOWN
(1937 - Republic) Bob Steele, Lorraine Hayes
One Sheet: $100 - $200

DOOMED BATTALION, THE
(1932 - Universal) Tala Birell, Luis Trenker
One Sheet: $100 - $200

DOOMED CARAVAN
(1941 - Paramount) William Boyd, Russell
Hayden
One Sheet: $150 - $300   *Cowboy
Movie Posters #268.*

DOOMED CARGO
(1936 - Gaumont) Edmund Lowe
One Sheet: $250 - $500

DOOMED TO DIE
(1940 - Monogram) Boris Karloff, Grant Withers
One Sheet: $150 - $300

DOOMED TO DIE
(1980 - -) Linzi
One Sheet: $5 - $10

DOOMSDAY
(1938 - 20th Century Fox) Terry-toons
One Sheet: $100 - $200   *Cartoon. Full
color stone litho. Stock poster with inset of title.*

DOOMSDAY MACHINE
(1967 - Rope) Grant Williams, Mala Powers
One Sheet: $7 - $15

DOOMSDAY VOYAGE
(1972 - Futurama) Joseph Cotten, John Gabriel
One Sheet: $5 - $10

DOORS, THE
(1991 - TriStar) Val Kilmer, Meg Ryan
One Sheet: $15 - $25

DOORWAY TO HELL
(1930 - Warner Bros.) Lew Ayres, James
Cagney(2nd film)
One Sheet: $700 - $1,200

DOPEY DICKS
(1950 - Columbia) Three Stooges (Shemp)
One Sheet: $200 - $400   *Comedy short.
Duotone.*

DORIAN GRAY
(1970 - AIP) Helmut Berger, Richard Todd
One Sheet: $30 - $60

DORM THAT DRIPPED BLOOD, THE
(1983 - New Image) David Snow, Pamela
Holland
One Sheet: $5 - $10

DOROTHY GISH STOCK POSTER
(1916? - -) Dorothy Gish
One Sheet: $250 - $600

DOROTHY LAMOUR PERSONALITY POSTER
(1946? - Paramount) Dorothy Lamour
One Sheet: $200 - $400

DOROTHY VERNON OF HADDON HALL
(1924 - United Artists) Mary Pickford
One Sheet: $2,200 - $3,500

DOT AND THE BUNNY
(1983 - Gross) Dir: Yoram Gross
One Sheet: $3 - $5   *Partial
Animation.*

DOUBLE ADVENTURE
(1920 - Pathe) -
One Sheet: $150 - $300   *Serial. 15
Chapters.*

DOUBLE ALIBI
(1940 - Universal) Wayne Morris, William
Lindsay
One Sheet: $75 - $150

130

DOUBLE CONFESSION
(1951 - Stratford) Derek Farr, Joan Hopkins
One Sheet: $20 - $40

DOUBLE CROSS
(1941 - Eagle-Lion) Kane Richmond, Pauline Moore
One Sheet: $75 - $125

DOUBLE CROSS
(1956 - British-Lion) Donald Houston, Anton Diffring
One Sheet: $10 - $20

DOUBLE CROSSBONES
(1950 - Universal) Donald O'Connor, Helena Carter
One Sheet: $15 - $35

DOUBLE CROSSROADS
(1930 - Fox) Robert Ames, Montagu Love
One Sheet: $150 - $350

DOUBLE DANGER
(1938 - RKO) Preston Foster, Whitney Bourne
One Sheet: $50 - $100

DOUBLE DATE
(1941 - Universal) Edmund Lowe, Una Merkel
One Sheet: $75 - $125

DOUBLE DEAL
(1939 - Sack) Monte Hawley
One Sheet: $150 - $300   Black cast.
Separate Cinema, pg. 140.

DOUBLE DEAL
(1950 - RKO) Marie Windsor, Richard Denning
One Sheet: $15 - $25

DOUBLE DEALING
(1923 - Universal) Hoot Gibson, Helen Ferguson
One Sheet: $250 - $500

DOUBLE DOOR, THE
(1934 - Paramount) Mary Morris, Evelyn Venable
One Sheet: $200 - $400   Graven
Images, pg. 64.

DOUBLE DRIBBLE
(1946 - RKO/Disney) Goofy
One Sheet: $1,900 - $3,000   Cartoon.

DOUBLE DYNAMITE
(1951 - RKO) Jane Russell, Groucho Marx, Frank Sinatra
One Sheet: $75 - $150

DOUBLE EVENT, THE
(1934 - Triumph) Jane Baxter, Ruth Taylor
One Sheet: $125 - $250

DOUBLE EXPOSURE
(1944 - Paramount) Chester Morris, Nancy Kelly
One Sheet: $40 - $75

Window Card

DOUBLE EXPOSURE
(1954 - GFD) John Bentley
One Sheet: $7 - $15

DOUBLE EXPOSURE
(1982 - Crown) Michael Callan, James Stacy
One Sheet: $3 - $5

DOUBLE EXPOSURES
(1937 - Paramount) Julien Mitchell, Ruby Miller
One Sheet: $150 - $300

DOUBLE FISTED
(1934 - Rayart) Jack Perrin

One Sheet: $250 - $500   A Whirlwind Western.

DOUBLE HARNESS
(1933 - RKO) William Powell, Ann Harding
One Sheet: $600 - $1,000

DOUBLE IMPACT
(1991 - -) Jean Claude Van Damme, Cory Everson
One Sheet: $7 - $15

DOUBLE INDEMNITY
(1944 - Paramount) Fred MacMurray, Barbara Stanwyck, Edward G. Robinson
One Sheet: $1,300 - $2,000

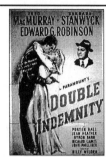
One Sheet

DOUBLE JEOPARDY
(1955 - Republic) Rod Cameron, Gale Robbins
One Sheet: $40 - $75

DOUBLE LIFE, A
(1947 - Universal) Ronald Colman, Signe Hasso, Edmond O'Brien
One Sheet: $75 - $125   Academy
Award: Best Actor(Colman). Academy Award Movie Posters #111.

DOUBLE LIFE OF VERONIQUE, THE
(1991 - -) Irene Jacob, Halina Gryglaszewska
One Sheet: $7 - $15

DOUBLE MAN, THE
(1968 - Warner Bros./Seven Arts) Yul Brynner, Britt Ekland
One Sheet: $5 - $10

DOUBLE NEGATIVE
(1979 - Quadrant) Jerome Simon, George Bloomfield
One Sheet: $4 - $8

DOUBLE OR NOTHING
(1937 - Paramount) Bing Crosby, Martha Raye
One Sheet: $150 - $300

DOUBLE TROUBLE
(1941 - Monogram) Harry Langdon, Buddy Rogers
One Sheet: $50 - $100

DOUBLE TROUBLE
(1960 - 20th Century Fox) Barbara Eden, Tommy Noonan, Pete Marshall
One Sheet: $15 - $25

DOUBLE TROUBLE
(1967 - MGM) Elvis Presley, Annette Day
One Sheet: $40 - $75

One Sheet

DOUBLE WEDDING
(1937 - MGM) William Powell, Myrna Loy

One Sheet: $150 - $350

DOUBLE WHOOPEE
(1929 - MGM) Laurel & Hardy, Jean Harlow
One Sheet: $3,500 - $5,000

DOUBLE-BARRELLED DETECTIVE STORY, THE
(1965 - Saloon) Jeff Siggins, Greta Thyssen
One Sheet: $7 - $15

DOUBLING FOR ROMEO
(1922 - Goldwyn) Will Rogers
One Sheet: $800 - $1,500

DOUBTING THOMAS
(1935 - Fox) Will Rogers, Billie Burke
One Sheet: $250 - $500

DOUGH AND DYNAMITE
(1914 - Keystone) Charlie Chaplin
One Sheet: $6,500 - $10,000

DOUGHBOYS
(1930 - MGM) Buster Keaton, Sally Eilers
One Sheet: $1,900 - $3,000

DOUGHBOYS IN IRELAND
(1943 - Columbia) Kenny Baker, Jeff Donnell
One Sheet: $75 - $125

DOUGHGIRLS, THE
(1944 - Warner Bros.) Ann Sheridan, Alexis Smith, Jane Wyman
One Sheet: $40 - $75

DOUGHNUTS AND SOCIETY
(1936 - Mascot) Ann Rutherford, Louise Fazenda
One Sheet: $100 - $200

DOULO-THE FINGER MAN
(1969 - Pathe Contemp) Jean-Paul Belmondo, Michael Piccoli
One Sheet: $50 - $100

DOVE, THE
(1928 - United Artists) Norma Talmadge, Noah Beery
One Sheet: $500 - $800

DOVE, THE
(1939 - RKO Radio) Leo Carrillo, Steffi Duna
One Sheet: $100 - $200

DOVE, THE
(1974 - Paramount) Joseph Bottoms, Dabney Coleman
One Sheet: $5 - $10

DOWN AMONG THE SHELTERING PALMS
(1952 - 20th Century Fox) Mitzi Gaynor, William Lundigan
One Sheet: $10 - $20

DOWN AND OUT IN BEVERLY HILLS
(1986 - Touchstone) Nick Nolte, Richard Dreyfuss, Bette Midler
One Sheet: $7 - $15

DOWN ARGENTINE WAY
(1940 - 20th Century Fox) Betty Grable, Don Ameche
One Sheet: $800 - $1,500   Price is for style A. One Sheet(Style B):$400-$800.

One Sheet

DOWN BY LAW
(1986 - -) Tom Waits, John Lurie
One Sheet: $20 - $40

DOWN DAKOTA WAY
(1949 - Republic) Roy Rogers, Dale Evans
One Sheet: $100 - $200

DOWN DAKOTA WAY
(1956R - Republic) Roy Rogers, Dale Evans
One Sheet: $40 - $75   Re-release.

DOWN IN ARKANSAS
(1938 - Republic) Ralph Byrd, Weaver Brothers
One Sheet: $75 - $150

DOWN IN SAN DIEGO
(1941 - MGM) Bonita Granville, Ray McDonald
One Sheet: $75 - $150

DOWN LAREDO WAY
(1953 - Republic) Rex Allen
One Sheet: $20 - $40

DOWN MEMORY LANE
(1949 - Eagle-Lion) Bing Crosby, Gloria Swanson, W. C. Fields
One Sheet: $75 - $150

DOWN MEXICO WAY
(1941 - Republic) Gene Autry
One Sheet: $150 - $300

DOWN MISSOURI WAY
(1946 - PRC) Martha O'Driscoll, William Wright
One Sheet: $30 - $50

DOWN ON THE FARM
(1920 - -) Mack Sennett
One Sheet: $250 - $600

DOWN ON THE FARM
(1938 - 20th Century Fox) Jean Prouty, Spring Byington
One Sheet: $75 - $150

DOWN PERISCOPE
(1996 - Twentieth Century Fox) Kelsey Grammer, Lauren Holly
One Sheet: $3 - $5

DOWN RIO GRANDE WAY
(1942 - Columbia) Charles Starrett, Russell Hayden
One Sheet: $75 - $125

DOWN SOUTH IN NEW ZEALAND
(1921 - Paramount) -
One Sheet: $150 - $350   A Paramount-Burton Holmes Travel Picture.

DOWN TEXAS WAY
(1942 - Monogram) Buck Jones, Tim McCoy
One Sheet: $100 - $200

DOWN THE STRETCH
(1936 - Warner Bros.) Mickey Rooney, Dennis Moore
One Sheet: $100 - $200

DOWN THE WYOMING TRAIL
(1939 - Monogram) Tex Ritter, Mary Brodell
One Sheet: $125 - $250

DOWN THREE DARK STREETS
(1954 - United Artists) Broderick Crawford, Ruth Roman
One Sheet: $30 - $50

DOWN TO EARTH
(1917 - Aircraft) Douglas Fairbanks
One Sheet: $250 - $600

DOWN TO EARTH
(1932 - Fox) Will Rogers, Irene Rich
One Sheet: $350 - $750

DOWN TO EARTH
(1947 - Columbia) Rita Hayworth, Larry Parks
One Sheet: $150 - $300

DOWN TO THE SEA
(1932 - Fox) -
One Sheet: $150 - $300

DOWN TO THE SEA
(1936 - Republic) Russell Hardie, Ben Lyon
One Sheet: $75 - $150   AKA: DOWN UNDER THE SEA.

DOWN TO THE SEA IN SHIPS
(1922 - Whaling) Clara Bow, William Walcott
One Sheet: $2,500 - $4,000   Bow's film debut.

DOWN TO THE SEA IN SHIPS
(1949 - 20th Century Fox) Richard Widmark, Lionel Barrymore
One Sheet: $75 - $125

DOWN TO THE SEA IN SHOES
(1923 - Pathe) Mack Sennett

One Sheet: $250 - $500

DOWN TO THEIR LAST YACHT
(1934 - RKO) Mary Boland, Sidney Blackmer
One Sheet: $600 - $1,000   *AKA: HAWAIIAN NIGHTS (Australian).*

DOWN TWISTED
(1987 - -) Carey Lowell, Charles Rocket
One Sheet: $3 - $5

DOWNHILL
(1927 - Gainsborough) Ben Webster, Isabel Jeans, Dir: Alfred Hitchcock
One Sheet: $3,500 - $5,000   *Price is for U.S. one sheet.*

DOWNHILL RACER
(1969 - Paramount) Robert Redford, Gene Hackman, Camilla Sparv
One Sheet: $30 - $50   *Sports (racing). Sports Movie Posters #311.*

DOWNSTAIRS
(1932 - MGM) John Gilbert, Virginia Bruce, Paul Lukas
One Sheet: $150 - $350

DOWNTOWN
(1990 - 20th Century Fox) Anthony Edwards, Forest Whitaker
One Sheet: $3 - $5

DRACULA
(1931 - Universal) Bela Lugosi, Helen Chandler, Dir:Tod Browning
One Sheet: $90,000 - $125,000   *Price is for Style B(duotone) one sheet. One Sheet(Style A, fullcolor):$150,000-$200,000; One Sheet (Style C, Dracula not shown):$50,000-$100,000; One Sheet (Style F, best image): $150,000-$200,000. Graven Images, pg. 40, 46.*

One Sheet (Style A)

DRACULA
(1939R - Universal) Bela Lugosi, Helen Chandler Dir: Tod Browing
One Sheet: $5,000 - $8,000   *Re-release. Posters and lobby cards are duotone.*

DRACULA
(1947R - Universal) Bela Lugosi, Helen Chandler Dir: Tod Browning
One Sheet: $6,500 - $10,000   *Re-release. Graven Images, pg. viii. One Sheet is full color.*

DRACULA
(1951R - Realart) Bela Lugosi, Helen Chandler Dir: Tod Browning
One Sheet: $1,300 - $2,000   *Re-release.*

DRACULA
(1963R - Universal) Bela Lugosi, Helen Chandler Dir: Tod Browning
One Sheet: $100 - $200   *Re-release.*

DRACULA
(1979 - Universal) Frank Langella, Laurence Olivier
One Sheet: $10 - $20   *Review:$8-$10; Non-Airbrush Style:$25-$40.*

DRACULA A.D. 1972
(1972 - Warner Bros.) Christopher Lee, Peter Cushing
One Sheet: $30 - $50

DRACULA AND SON (1976 - Gaumont) Christoph r Lee,
mard Mendez One Sheet:
$20 - $40

DRACULA AND THE SEVEN GOLDEN VAMPIRES

(1978 - Shaw-Hammer) David Chang, Peter Cushing
One Sheet: $10 - $20   *AKA: THE LEGEND OF THE SEVEN GOLDEN VAMPIRES.*

DRACULA: DEAD AND LOVING IT
(1995 - Columbia) Leslie Nielson, Harvey Korman, Peter MacNicol
One Sheet: $7 - $15

One Sheet

DRACULA HAS RISEN FROM THE GRAVE
(1969 - Warner Bros.) Christopher Lee, Rupert Davies
One Sheet: $30 - $60   *Hammer Film. Graven Images, pg. 215.*

DRACULA VS. FRANKENSTEIN
(1971 - Universal) Lon Chaney, Jr., J. Carroll Naish
One Sheet: $30 - $50   *Last film for both stars.*

DRACULA'S DAUGHTER
(1936 - Universal) Gloria Holden, Otto Kruger
One Sheet: $3,500 - $5,000   *Graven Images, pg. 91.*

DRACULA'S DAUGHTER
(1949R - Realart) Otto Kruger, Gloria Holden
One Sheet: $250 - $500   *Re-release.*

DRACULA'S DOG
(1978 - Crown) Jose Ferrer, Michael Pataki
One Sheet: $5 - $10

DRACULA'S GREAT LOVE
(1972 - Cinema Shares) Paul Naschy, Rosanna Yanni
One Sheet: $10 - $20

DRACULA/FRANKENSTEIN COMBO
(1938R - Universal) Bela Lugosi, Boris Karloff
One Sheet: $5,000 - $8,000   *Re-release double feature poster.*

DRACULA-PRINCE OF DARKNESS
(1966 - 20th Century Fox) Christopher Lee, Barbara Shelley
One Sheet: $75 - $125   *Graven Images, pg. 213.*

DRACULA-PRINCE OF DARKNESS/PLAGUE OF THE ZOMBIES
(1966 - 20th Century Fox) Christopher Lee, Barbara Shelley, Andre Morrell, Diane Clare
One Sheet: $30 - $60   *Double feature poster.*

DRAEGERMAN COURAGE
(1936 - Warner Bros.) Barton MacLane, Jean Muir
One Sheet: $50 - $100

DRAG
(1929 - Warner Bros.) Alice Day, Lila Lee
One Sheet: $250 - $600

DRAG RACER
(1973 - Artists International) Jeremy Slate, Deborah Walley
One Sheet: $15 - $30   *Sports (Auto racing).*

DRAGNET, THE
(1928 - Paramount) George Bancroft, William Powell, Evelyn Brent
One Sheet: $1,900 - $3,000

DRAGNET
(1947 - Fortune) Henry Wilcoxon, Mary Brian
One Sheet: $30 - $60

DRAGNET
(1954 - Mark VII) Jack Webb, Ben Alexander

One Sheet: $75 - $125

DRAGNET
(1987 - Universal) Dan Aykroyd, Tom Hanks
One Sheet: $3 - $5

DRAGNET PATROL
(1932 - Action) Vera Reynolds, Glenn Tryon
One Sheet: $150 - $300

DRAGON DIES HARD, THE
(1975 - Allied Artists) -
One Sheet: $20 - $40   *The Bruce Lee story.*

DRAGON FLIES, THE
(1975 - 20th Century Fox) Jimmy Wang Yu, George Lazenby
One Sheet: $30 - $50   *AKA: THE MAN FROM HONG KONG.*

DRAGON LEE VS...THE FIVE BROTHERS
(1981 - Fury) Dragon Lee, Kan-Chia Fong
One Sheet: $5 - $10

DRAGON LIVES, THE
(1970 - -) Documentary: Bruce Lee
One Sheet: $30 - $60

DRAGON MURDER CASE, THE
(1934 - First National) Warren William, Margaret Lindsay
One Sheet: $500 - $800

DRAGON SEED
(1944 - MGM) Katharine Hepburn, Walter Huston
One Sheet: $100 - $200

DRAGON SKY
(1964 - Lopert) Naria Hem, Sam El
One Sheet: $7 - $15

DRAGON: THE BRUCE LEE STORY
(1993 - Universal) Jason Scott Lee, Lauren Holly
One Sheet: $5 - $10   *Sports Movie Posters #270. Advance:$10-$15.*

DRAGON'S GOLD
(1953 - United Artists) John Archer, Hillary Brooke
One Sheet: $15 - $30

DRAGONFLY SQUADRON
(1953 - Monogram) Barbara Britton, John Hodiak
One Sheet: $15 - $25

DRAGONHEART
(1996 - Universal) Dennis Quaid, Julie Christie
One Sheet: $5 - $12

DRAGONSLAYER (1981 - Paramount/Disney) P
er MacNicol, Caitlin Clarke
One Sheet: $10 - $20   *One Sheet(Advance styles):$20-$40.*

DRAGONWYCK
(1946 - 20th Century Fox) Gene Tierney, Walter Huston, Vincent Price
One Sheet: $200 - $400

DRAGOON WELLS MASSACRE
(1957 - Allied Artists) Barry Sullivan, Mona Freeman
One Sheet: $10 - $20

DRAGSTRIP GIRL
(1957 - AIP) Fay Spain, John Ashley
One Sheet: $50 - $100   *Sports (Auto racing). Sports Movie Posters #14.*

DRAGSTRIP RIOT
(1958 - AIP) Yvonne Lime, Gary Clark
One Sheet: $50 - $100   *Sports (Auto racing).*

DRAKE CASE, THE
(1929 - Universal) Gladys Brockwell, Forrest Stanley
One Sheet: $150 - $350   **DRAKE THE PIRATE** (1935 - First Divis
) Matheson Lang, Athene Sey   One
heet: $100

5   **DRAMATIC CHOOL** (1938 - MGM) Luise Rainer, Paulette oddard One Sheet: $
- $250   **DRANGO** (1957   nited Artis

eff   Cha
ler, Ronald Howard One Sheet: $30

50

DRAUGHTSMAN'S CONTRACT, THE
(1983 - United Artists) Anthony Higgins, Janet Suzman
One Sheet: $15 - $25

DREAM GIRL
(1948 - Paramount) Betty Hutton, Macdonald Carey
One Sheet: $40 - $75

DREAM KIDS, THE
(1943 - Columbia) Fox & Crow
One Sheet: $500 - $800   *Cartoon. Full color poster with scene inset.*

DREAM LOVER
(1986 - MGM/UA) Kristy McNichol, Ben Masters
One Sheet: $5 - $10

DREAM LOVER
(1994 - Gramercy) James Spader, Madchen Amick
One Sheet: $4 - $8

DREAM MAKER, THE
(1964 - Universal) Tommy Steele, Michael Medwin
One Sheet: $5 - $10

DREAM OF KINGS, A
(1969 - National General) Anthony Quinn, Irene Papas, Inger Stevens
One Sheet: $5 - $10

DREAM OF LOVE
(1928 - MGM) Joan Crawford
One Sheet: $1,300 - $2,000

DREAM ON
(1981 - Magic Cinema) Ed Harris, Erin Nico
One Sheet: $3 - $5

DREAM STREET
(1921 - United Artists) Carol Dempster, Ralph Graves, Dir: D.W. Griffith
One Sheet: $1,300 - $2,000

DREAM TEAM, THE
(1989 - Universal) Michael Keaton, Christopher Lloyd
One Sheet: $5 - $10

DREAM WIFE
(1953 - MGM) Cary Grant, Deborah Kerr
One Sheet: $40 - $75

DREAMBOAT
(1952 - 20th Century Fox) Clifton Webb, Ginger Rogers
One Sheet: $30 - $50

DREAMER, THE
(1948 - Astor) Mantan Moreland
One Sheet: $100 - $200   *Black cast. Separate Cinema, pg. 68.*

DREAMER
(1979 - 20th Century Fox) Tim Matheson, Susan Blakely
One Sheet: $7 - $15   *Sports (Bowling). Sports Movie Posters #110.*

DREAMING LIPS
(1937 - United Artists) Elisabeth Bergner, Raymond Massey
One Sheet: $75 - $150

DREAMING OUT LOUD
(1940 - RKO) Lum & Abner, Frances Langford
One Sheet: $100 - $200

DREAMING OUT LOUD
(1950R - RKO) Lum & Abner, Frances Langford
One Sheet: $40 - $75   *Re-release.*

DREAMLAND CAPERS
(1958 - Harry Wald) -
One Sheet: $15 - $30

DREAMS
(1955 - Janus) Harriet Anderson, Gunnar Bjornstrand, Dir: Ingmar Bergman
One Sheet: $150 - $300

DREAMS
(1990 - -) Akira Terao, Martin Scorcese, Dir: Akira Kurosawa
One Sheet: $10 - $20

DREAMS OF GLASS
(1970 - Universal) John Denos, Caroline

Barrett
One Sheet: $3 - $5

DREAMS THAT MONEY CAN BUY
(1948 - Film Rights) Jack Bittners, Max Ernest
One Sheet: $10 - $20

DREAMSCAPE
(1984 - 20th Century Fox) Dennis Quaid, Max
von Sydow
One Sheet: $5 - $10

DRESS PARADE
(1927 - Pathe) William Boyd, Bessie Love
One Sheet: $200 - $400

DRESS REHEARSAL
(1939 - Sepia-Art) Eddie Green
One Sheet: $150 - $300   *Black cast.
Separate Cinema, pg. 72.*

DRESSED TO KILL
(1941 - 20th Century Fox) Lloyd Nolan, Mary
Beth Hughes
One Sheet: $75 - $125

DRESSED TO KILL
(1946 - Universal) Basil Rathbone, Nigel Bruce
One Sheet: $250 - $600   *Sherlock
Holmes series.*

DRESSED TO KILL
(1980 - Filmways) Micheal Caine, Angie
Dickinson, Dir: DePalma
One Sheet: $15 - $25

DRESSED TO THRILL
(1935 - Fox) Tutta Rolf, Clive Brook
One Sheet: $125 - $250

DRESSER, THE
(1983 - Columbia) Albert Finney, Tom
Courtenay
One Sheet: $3 - $5

DREYFUS CASE, THE (1931 - Columbia) Cedri
Hardwicke, Beatrix Thomson One Sheet:
$200 - $400   **DRIFT FEN**   (1936
Paramount) Bus
Crabbe
One Sheet: $75 - $150

DRIFT FENCE
(1951R - Paramount) Buster Crabbe
One Sheet: $15 - $30   *Re-release.*

DRIFTER, THE
(1932 - State Rights) William Farnum, Noah
Beery
One Sheet: $250 - $600

DRIFTER, THE
(1943 - PRC) Buster Crabbe, Al St. John
One Sheet: $40 - $75

DRIFTER, THE
(1966 - Surfilms) John Tracy, Sadja Marr
One Sheet: $5 - $10

DRIFTER
(1975 - Bizarre) Joe Adair, Joe Caruso
One Sheet: $5 - $10   *AKA: TWO-
WAY DRIFTER.*

DRIFTER, THE
(1988 - Concorde) Kim Delaney, Miles O'Keefe
One Sheet: $3 - $5

DRIFTIN' KID, THE
(1941 - Monogram) Tom Keene
One Sheet: $40 - $75

DRIFTIN' RIVER
(1946 - PRC) Eddie Dean, Shirley Patterson
One Sheet: $30 - $60

DRIFTING
(1932 - Tower) Shirley Grey
One Sheet: $150 - $300

DRIFTING ALONG
(1946 - Monogram) Johnny Mack Brown,
Raymond Hatton
One Sheet: $40 - $75

DRIFTING WESTWARD
(1939 - Monogram) Jack Randall, Edna Duran
One Sheet: $30 - $60

DRIFTWOOD
(1928 - Columbia) Don Alvarado
One Sheet: $200 - $400

DRIFTWOOD

(1947 - Republic) Natalie Wood, Ruth Warrick,
Walter Brennan
One Sheet: $75 - $125

DRILLER KILLER
(1979 - Rochelle) Carolyn Marz, Jimmy Lane
One Sheet: $10 - $20

DRIP DIPPY DONALD
(1948 - RKO/Disney) Donald Duck
One Sheet: $1,600 - $2,500   *Cartoon.
Cartoon Movie Posters #178.*

DRIVE A CROOKED ROAD
(1954 - Columbia) Mickey Rooney, Dianne
Foster
One Sheet: $15 - $35

DRIVE HARD, DRIVE FAST
(1969 - -) Joan Collins
One Sheet: $7 - $15   *Posters may
not exist for this made-for-TV movie.*

DRIVE, HE SAID
(1971 - Columbia) William Tepper, Karen Black
One Sheet: $7 - $15

DRIVE-IN
(1976 - Columbia) Lisa Lemole, Glen
Morshower
One Sheet: $3 - $5

DRIVE-IN MASSACRE
(1976 - New American) Jake Barnes, Adam
Lawrence
One Sheet: $7 - $15

DRIVER, THE
(1978 - Fox) Ryan O'Neal, Bruce Dern, Isabella
Adjani
One Sheet: $15 - $30

DRIVER'S SEAT, THE
(1975 - Avco/Embassy) Elizabeth Taylor, Andy
Warhol
One Sheet: $15 - $25

DRIVING MISS DAISY
(1989 - Warner Bros.) Morgan Freeman,
Jessica Tandy
One Sheet: $15 - $25   *Academy
Award: Best Picture, Best Actress(Tandy).
Academy Award Movie Posters #363 & #366.*

DROOPY'S DOUBLE TROUBLE
(1951 - MGM) Droopy, Tex Avery
One Sheet: $500 - $900   *Cartoon. Full
color stone litho.*

DROOPY'S GOOD DEED
(1951 - MGM) Droopy, Tex Avery
One Sheet: $500 - $900   *Cartoon. Full
color stone litho.*

DROP DEAD FRED
(1991 - New Line) Phoebe Cates, Rik Mayall
One Sheet: $3 - $5

DROP ZONE
(1994 - Paramount) Wesley Snipes, Gary
Busey
One Sheet: $3 - $6

DROWNING POOL, THE
(1975 - Warner Bros.) Paul Newman, Joanne
Woodward
One Sheet: $10 - $20

DRUG STORE COWBOY
(1925 - -) Franklyn Farnum, Jean Arthur
One Sheet: $200 - $400

DRUGSTORE COWBOY
(1989 - Avenue) Matt Dillon, Kelly Lynch
One Sheet: $30 - $50

DRUM
(1976 - United Artists) Warren Oates, Ken
Norton, Pam Grier
One Sheet: $7 - $15   *Black cast.
Sequel to MANDINGO.*

DRUM BEAT
(1954 - Warner Bros.) Alan Ladd, Audrey
Dalton, Charles Bronson
One Sheet: $30 - $50

DRUMMING IT IN
(1930 - Educational) Raymond McKee
One Sheet: $100 - $200

DRUMS
(1938 - United Artists) Raymond Massey, Sabu
One Sheet: $125 - $250

DRUMS ACROSS THE RIVER
(1954 - Universal) Audie Murphy, Walter
Brennan
One Sheet: $15 - $35

DRUMS ALONG THE MOHAWK
(1939 - 20th Century Fox) Henry Fonda,
Claudette Colbert, Edna May Oliver
One Sheet: $500 - $900   *Cowboy
Movie Posters #254.*

DRUMS IN THE DEEP SOUTH
(1951 -
O) James Craig, Guy Madison One Sheet:
$30 - $50   **DRUMS O'**

O (1934 - S
geplay) Laura Bowman, Edna Barr One Sheet:
$100 - $200   *AKA: SH
EVIL.* **DRUMS OF AFRICA (1**

MGM) Frankie Av
on, Lloyd Bochner, Torin Thatcher One Sheet:
$15 - $25

DRUMS OF DESTINY
(1935 - Crescent) Tom Keene
One Sheet: $75 - $150

DRUMS OF FATE
(1923 - -) Mary Miles Minter, Maurice B. Flynn
One Sheet: $250 - $600

DRUMS OF FU MANCHU
(1940 - Republic) Henry Brandon, William
Royle
One Sheet: $300 - $700   *Serial. 15
Chapters. One Sheet(Chapter 1):$400-$750.
Graven Images, pg. 139.*

One Sheet (Chapter 14)

DRUMS OF FU MANCHU
(1943 - Republic) Henry Brandon, William
Royle
One Sheet: $250 - $500

DRUMS OF JEOPARDY
(1931 - Tiffany) Warner Oland, June Collye
One Sheet:
$200 - $400   *Graven Ima*

g. 58.   **DRUMS**
LOVE (1928 - United Artists) Mary Philbi
Lionel Barrymore, Dir: D.W.

ith   One Sheet:
$800 - $1,500   **DRUMS OF TAHITI** (195
Columbia) Dennis O'Keefe, Patricia Medina
One Sheet: $10 - $20

DRUMS OF THE CONGO
(1942 - Universal) Stuart Erwin, Ona Munson
One Sheet: $40 - $75

DRUMS OF THE DESERT
(1940 - Monogram) Ralph Byrd, Lorna Gray
One Sheet: $50 - $100

DRUMTAPS
(1933 - Tiffany) Ken Maynard, Dorothy Dix
One Sheet: $250 - $500

DRUNKEN ANGEL
(1948 - Toho) Toshiro Mifune
One Sheet: $50 - $100   *Japanese.*

DRY WHITE SEASON, A
(1989 - MGM/United Artists) Donald
Sutherland, Janet Suzman,Marlon Brando
One Sheet: $5 - $10

DU BARRY
(1914 - Kleine) Leslie Carter, Richard Thornton

One Sheet: $250 - $500

DU BARRY WAS A LADY
(1943 - MGM) Red Skelton, Lucille Ball,
Tommy Dorsey Orch.
One Sheet: $500 - $800   *Price is for
Petty Art One Sheet. Non-Petty art:$100-$200.*

DU BARRY, WOMAN OF PASSION
(1930 - United Artists) Norma Talmadge,
William Farnum
One Sheet: $250 - $500

DUAL ALIBI
(1947 - Pathe) Herbert Lom, Sebastian Cabot
One Sheet: $15 - $30

DUCHESS AND THE DIRTWATER FOX, THE
(1976 - 20th Century Fox) George Segal,
Goldie Hawn
One Sheet: $7 - $15

DUCHESS OF IDAHO
(1950 - MGM) Esther Williams, Van Johnson
One Sheet: $15 - $35

DUCK DOCTOR, THE
(1952 - MGM) Tom & Jerry
One Sheet: $250 - $600   *Cartoon. Full
color stone litho.*

DUCK SOUP
(1927 - Pathe) Laurel & Hardy
One Sheet: $4,000 - $6,000

DUCK SOUP
(1933 - Paramount) The Four Marx Brothers
One Sheet: $5,000 - $8,000

**DUCK TALES THE MOVIE TREASURE OF THE
LOST LAMP**
(1990 - Buena Vista/Disney) Uncle Scrooge
One Sheet: $7 - $15   *Cartoon. The
Disney Poster, pg. 90.*

One Sheet

DUCKI YOU SUCKER
(1972 - United Artists) Rod Steiger, James
Coburn, Dir: Sergio Leone
One Sheet: $10 - $20   *Spaghetti
Western. AKA: A FISTUL OF DYNAMITE.*

DUDE BANDIT, THE
(1933 - Allied Artists) Hoot Gibson
One Sheet: $150 - $350

DUDE COWBOY
(1941 - RKO) Tim Holt
One Sheet: $50 - $100

DUDE DUCK
(1951 - RKO/Disney) Donald Duck
One Sheet: $600 - $1,000   *Cartoon. Full
color.*

DUDE GOES WEST, THE
(1948 - Allied Artists) Eddie Albert, Gale Storm
One Sheet: $15 - $25

DUDE RANCH
(1931 - Paramount) Jack Oakie, Stuart Erwin
One Sheet: $250 - $600

DUDE RANGER, THE
(1934 - Atherton) George O'Brien, James
Mason
One Sheet: $125 - $250   **DUD
WRANGLER, THE**
1930 - Sono Art/World Wide) George Duryea,
Francis X. Bushman
One Sheet: $100 - $200

DUDES
(1987 - -) John Cryer, Daniel Roebuck

One Sheet: $3 - $5

DUDES ARE PRETTY PEOPLE
(1942 - United Artists) Marjorie Woodworth,
Jimmy Rogers
One Sheet: $50 - $100

DUEL, THE
(1964 - Artkino) Oleg Stristhenov, Vladimir
Druzhnikov
One Sheet: $3 - $5

DUEL
(1972 - -) Dennis Weaver, Eddie Firestone, Dir:
Steven Spielberg
One Sheet: $50 - $100   *Made for TV-Movie: released theatrically overseas.*

DUEL AT APACHE WELLS
(1957 - Republic) Ben Cooper, Anna Maria
Alberghetti
One Sheet: $15 - $25

DUEL AT DIABLO
(1966 - United Artists) James Garner, Sidney
Poitier, Dennis Weaver
One Sheet: $20 - $40

DUEL AT SILVER CREEK, THE
(1952 - Universal) Audie Murphy, Faith
Domergue
One Sheet: $40 - $75

DUEL IN THE JUNGLE
(1954 - Warner Bros.) Dana Andrews, Jeanne
Crain
One Sheet: $15 - $30

DUEL IN THE SUN
(1946 - Selznick) Jennifer Jones, Joseph
Cotten, Gregory Peck
One Sheet: $100 - $200   *Cowboy Movie Posters #277.*

DUEL IN THE SUN
(1960R - -) Jennifer Jones, Joseph Cotten,
Gregory Peck
One Sheet: $15 - $30   *Re-release.*

DUEL OF CHAMPIONS
(1964 - Medallion) Alan Ladd, Franca Bettoja
One Sheet: $10 - $20

DUEL OF THE TITANS
(1963 - Paramount) Steve Reeves, Gordon
Scott
One Sheet: $40 - $75

DUEL ON THE MISSISSIPPI
(1955 - Columbia) Lex Barker, Patricia Medina
One Sheet: $15 - $35

DUELLISTS, THE
(1977 - Paramount) Keith Carradine, Harvey
Keitel
One Sheet: $15 - $25

DUET FOR ONE
(1986 - Cannon) Julie Andrews, Alan Bates,
Max von Sydow
One Sheet: $3 - $5

DUFFY
(1968 - Columbia) James Coburn, James
Mason, James Fox, Susannah York
One Sheet: $5 - $10

DUFFY OF SAN QUENTIN
(1954 - Allied Artists) Paul Kelly, Maureen
O'Sullivan
One Sheet: $7 - $15

DUFFY'S TAVERN
(1945 - Paramount) Alan Ladd, Veronica Lake,
All Star Cast
One Sheet: $100 - $200

DUKE COMES BACK, THE
(1937 - Republic) Allan Lane, Heather Angel
One Sheet: $75 - $150

DUKE IS TOPS, THE
(1938 - Million Dollar) Ralph Cooper, Lena
Horne
One Sheet: $600 - $1,000   *Black cast.*
Separate Cinema, pg. 80.

DUKE OF CHICAGO
(1949 - Republic) Tom Brown, Audrey Long,
Paul Harvey
One Sheet: $40 - $75

DUKE OF THE NAVY
(1942 - PRC) Ralph Byrd, Veda Ann Borg

One Sheet: $30 - $60

DUKE OF WEST POINT, THE
(1939 - United Artists) Louis Hayward, Joan
Fontaine
One Sheet: $100 - $200   *Sports Movie Posters #229.*

DUKE STEPS OUT, THE
(1929 - MGM) Joan Crawford, William Haines
One Sheet: $1,300 - $2,000

DULCIMA
(1972 - Cinevision) Carol White, John Mills
One Sheet: $5 - $10

DULCIMER STREET
(1948 - Universal) Richard Attenborough,
Alastair Sim
One Sheet: $30 - $60

DULCY
(1940 - MGM) Ann Sothern, Ian Hunter
One Sheet: $50 - $100

DUMB AND DUMBER
(1994 - New Line) Jim Carrey, Jeff Daniels,
Lauren Holly
One Sheet: $5 - $12   *Advance Style: $5-$7.*

DUMB DICKS
(1932 - RKO/Pathe) Benny Rubin, Harry
Gribbon
One Sheet: $125 - $250

DUMB LUCK
(1926 - Universal) Joe Murphy, Fay Tincher
One Sheet: $150 - $300   *From The Gumps series (1925/26, No. 11).*

DUMB LUCK
(1935 - Educational) Goodman Ace, Jane Ace
("Easy Aces")
One Sheet: $100 - $200

DUMB'S THE WORD
(1937 - RKO) Edgar Kennedy
One Sheet: $100 - $200

DUMB-BELLS IN ERMINE
(1930 - Warner Bros.) Robert Armstrong,
Barbara Kent
One Sheet: $200 - $400

One Sheet

DUMBELL OF THE YUKON
(1946 - RKO/Disney) Donald Duck
One Sheet: $1,300 - $2,000   *Cartoon. The Disney Poster, pg. 58.*

DUMB-HOUNDED
(1943 - MGM) Dir: Tex Avery
One Sheet: $500 - $800   *Cartoon. Cartoon Movie Posters #289.*

DUMBO
(1941 - RKO/Disney) Dumbo
One Sheet: $2,500 - $4,000   *Cartoon. Cartoon Movie Posters #350-#361. The Disney Poster, pg. 82.*

DUMBO
(1959R - Buena Vista) -
One Sheet: $50 - $100   *Re-release. Cartoon.*

DUMBO
(1972R - Buena Vista/Disney) Dumbo
One Sheet: $30 - $50   *Re-release. Cartoon. Full color.*

DUMBO
(1976R - Disney) -

One Sheet: $15 - $35   *Re-release. Cartoon.*

DUMBO/LEGEND OF LOBO, THE
(1972R - Disney) -
One Sheet: $15 - $25   *Re-release double feature poster.*

DUMBO/SALUDOS AMIGOS
(1949R - Disney) Animation
One Sheet: $50 - $100   *Re-release double feature poster.*

DUMMIES
(1928 - Educational) Larry Semon
One Sheet: $150 - $350

DUNE
(1984 - Universal) Kyle MacLachlan, Max von
Sydow, Sting
One Sheet: $20 - $40   *Advance (Two moon style):$50-$100; Advance (Romance style):$30-$50; One Sheet(Style B):$15-$30.*

DUNGEON, THE
(1922 - -) William E. Fountaine, Shingzie
Howard
One Sheet: $200 - $400

DUNGEONMASTER, THE
(1985 - Empire) Jeffery Byron, Richard Moll,
Leslie Wing
One Sheet: $5 - $10

DUNGEONS OF HARROW
(1964 - Herts-Lion) Russ Harvey, Helen Hogan
One Sheet: $5 - $10

DUNKED IN THE DEEP
(1949 - Columbia) The Three Stooges (Shemp)
One Sheet: $350 - $750   *Comedy short. Duotone.*

DUNKIRK
(1958 - MGM) John Mills, Robert Urquhart
One Sheet: $15 - $25

DUNWICH HORROR, THE
(1971 - AIP) Sandra Dee, Dean Stockwell
One Sheet: $7 - $15

DUPE, THE
(1916 - Paramount) Blanche Sweet
One Sheet: $250 - $500

DURAND OF THE BADLANDS
(1925 - Wm. Fox) Buck Jones, Marion Nixon
One Sheet: $500 - $800

DURANGO KID, THE
(1940 - Columbia) Charles Starrett, Luana
Walters
One Sheet: $100 - $200

DURANGO VALLEY RAIDERS
(1938 - Republic) Bob Steele, Louise Stanley
One Sheet: $100 - $200

DURANGO VALLEY RAIDERS
(1942R - Republic) Bob Steele, Louise Stanley
One Sheet: $50 - $100   *Re-release. Full color.*

DUSKY VIRGIN
(1933 - -) -
One Sheet: $250 - $500

DUST BE MY DESTINY
(1939 - Warner Bros.) John Garfield, Priscilla
Lane
One Sheet: $75 - $175

One Sheet

DUSTY AND SWEETS McGEE
(1971 - Warner Bros.) Documentary

One Sheet: $5 - $10

DUTCHMAN
(1967 - Continental) Shirley Knight, Al
Freeman, Jr.
One Sheet: $3 - $5

DUTIFUL BUT DUMB
(1941 - Columbia) The Three Stooges (Curly)
One Sheet: $4,000 - $6,000   *Comedy short. Duotone.*

DYING YOUNG
(1991 - 20th Century Fox) Julia Roberts,
Campbell Scott
One Sheet: $7 - $15

DYNAMITE
(1929 - MGM) Conrad Nagle, Joel McCrea
One Sheet: $250 - $600

DYNAMITE
(1949 - Paramount) William Gargan, Virginia
Welles
One Sheet: $20 - $40

DYNAMITE CANYON
(1941 - Monogram) Tom Keene, Evelyn Finley
One Sheet: $40 - $75

DYNAMITE CHICKEN
(1982 - -) Richard Pryor
One Sheet: $15 - $25

DYNAMITE DELANEY
(1938 - Imperial) Weldon Heyburn, Eve Farrell
One Sheet: $100 - $200

DYNAMITE DENNY
(1932 - Mayfair) Jay Wilsey, Blanche Mehaffey
One Sheet: $100 - $200

DYNAMITE PASS
(1950 - RKO) Tim Holt, Lynne Robert
One Sheet: $15 - $35

DYNAMITE RANCH
(1932 - Tiffany) Ken Maynard
One Sheet: $250 - $500

DYNAMITERS, THE
(1956 - Astor) Wayne Morris, Patrick Holt
One Sheet: $5 - $12

EACH DAWN I DIE
(1939 - Warner Bros.) James Cagney, George
Raft
One Sheet: $600 - $1,000

EACH DAWN I DIE
(1947R - Warner Bros.) James Cagney, George
Raft
One Sheet: $50 - $100   *Re-release.*

EACH DAWN I DIE
(1956R - Warner Bros.) James Cagney, George
Raft
One Sheet: $30 - $50   *Re-release.*

EADIE WAS A LADY
(1945 - Columbia) Ann Miller, Joe Besser, Hal
McIntyre
One Sheet: $75 - $125

EAGLE, THE
(1925 - United Artists) Rudolph Valentino
One Sheet: $4,500 - $7,000   *Beware unmarked re-release one sheets.*

OneSheet

EAGLE, THE
(1935R - United Artists) Rudolph Valentino
One Sheet: $150 - $350   *First sound re-release.*

EAGLE AND THE HAWK, THE
(1933 - Paramount) Fredric March, Cary Grant
One Sheet: $800 - $1,500

EAGLE AND THE HAWK, THE
(1950 - Paramount) John Payne, Rhonda
Fleming
One Sheet: $15 - $30

EAGLE HAS LANDED, THE
(1976 - Columbia) Michael Caine, Donald
Sutherland, Robert Duvall
One Sheet: $7 - $15

EAGLE IN A CAGE
(1972 - National General) Kenneth Haigh, Billie
Whitelaw
One Sheet: $3 - $5

EAGLE ROCK
(1964 - World Safari) Pip Rolls, Christine
Thomas
One Sheet: $5 - $10

EAGLE SQUADRON
(1942 - Universal) Robert Stack, Diana
Barrymore
One Sheet: $40 - $75

EAGLE WITH TWO HEADS
(1948 - VOG) Jean Marais
One Sheet: $40 - $75   French.

EAGLE'S BROOD, THE
(1935 - Paramount) William "Hopalong" Boyd,
Gabby Hayes
One Sheet: $250 - $500   Cowboy
Movie Posters # 175.

EAGLE'S EYE, THE
(1918 - Whartons) -
One Sheet: $300 - $650

EAGLE'S WING
(1979 - Rank) Martin Sheen, Harvey Keitel
One Sheet: $10 - $20

EARL CARROLL SKETCHBOOK
(1946 - Republic) Constance Moore, William
Marshall
One Sheet: $75 - $150

EARL CARROLL VANITIES
(1945 - Republic) Dennis O'Keefe, Eve Arden
One Sheet: $100 - $200

EARL OF CHICAGO, THE
(1940 - MGM) Robert Montgomery, Edward
Arnold
One Sheet: $100 - $200

EARL OF PUDDLESTONE
(1940 - Republic) James, Lucille & Russell
Gleason
One Sheet: $50 - $100

EARLY ARIZONA
(1938R - -) -
One Sheet: $50 - $100   Re-release.

EARLY BIRD, THE
(1928 - Pathe) Animated by Paul Terry
One Sheet: $600 - $1,000   Cartoon.
Duotone. An Aesop's Fables film. Cartoon Movie
Posters #17.

EARLY BIRD, THE
(1936 - Paramount) Richard Hayward
One Sheet: $100 - $200

EARLY BIRD, THE
(1965 - Rank) Norman Wisdom, Edward
Chapman
One Sheet: $5 - $10

EARLY BIRD DOOD IT
(1942 - MGM) Dir: Tex Avery
One Sheet: $800 - $1,500   Cartoon.
Cartoon Movie Posters #286.

EARLY BIRD DOOD IT
(1950R - MGM) Dir: Tex Avery
One Sheet: $150 - $350   Re-release.
Cartoon. Full color stone litho.

EARLY TO BED
(1928 - MGM) Laurel & Hardy
One Sheet: $3,500 - $5,000

EARLY TO BED
(1933 - Gaumont) Edmund Gwenn, Heather
Angel
One Sheet: $150 - $300

EARLY TO BED
(1936 - Paramount) Charlie Ruggles, Mary
Boland
One Sheet: $75 - $150

EARLY TO BED
(1941 - RKO/Disney) Donald Duck
One Sheet: $4,500 - $7,000   Cartoon.

EARRINGS OF MADAME DE..., THE
(1954 - Arlan) Charles Boyer, Danielle Darrieux
One Sheet: $15 - $30

EARTH
(1930 - Amkino) Stepan Shkurat
One Sheet: $5,000 - $7,500   Russian.

EARTH DIES SCREAMING, THE
(1964 - 20th Century Fox) Willard Parker,
Virginia Field
One Sheet: $20 - $40

EARTH GIRLS ARE EASY
(1989 - Vestron) Geena Davis, Jeff Goldblum
One Sheet: $5 - $10

EARTH VS. THE FLYING SAUCERS
(1956 - Columbia) Hugh Marlowe, Joan Taylor
One Sheet: $350 - $750   Harryhausen
effects. No title cards were produced. Graven
Images, pg. 177.

EARTH VS. THE SPIDER
(1958 - Santa Rosa) Ed Kremmer, June
Kennedy
One Sheet: $75 - $125

EARTH2
(1971 - MGM) Gary Lockwood, Scott Hylands
One Sheet: $5 - $10

EARTHBOUND
(1940 - 20th Century Fox) Warner Baxter,
Andrea Leeds
One Sheet: $75 - $125

EARTHBOUND
(1980 - Taft International) Burl Ives, Joseph
Campanella
One Sheet: $3 - $5

EARTHLING, THE
(1980 - Filmways) William Holden, Ricky
Schroder
One Sheet: $3 - $5

EARTHQUAKE
(1974 - Universal) Charlton Heston, Ava
Gardner
One Sheet: $5 - $10

EARTHWORM TRACTORS
(1936 - Warner Bros.) Joe E. Brown, June
Travis
One Sheet: $150 - $300

One Sheet

EASIEST WAY, THE
(1931 - MGM) Constance Bennett, Robert
Montgomery, Clark Gable
One Sheet: $800 - $1,500   Gable's
second film.

EAST IS WEST
(1922 - First National) Constance Talmadge
One Sheet: $800 - $1,500

EAST IS WEST
(1930 - Universal) Edward G. Robinson, Lupe
Velez
One Sheet: $350 - $750

EAST LYNNE
(1921 - Pathe) Edward Earle, Mabel Ballin

One Sheet: $250 - $500

EAST LYNNE
(1931 - Fox) Ann Harding, Clive Brook
One Sheet: $350 - $750

EAST LYNNE ON THE WESTERN FRONT
(1931 - Gaumont) Herbert Mundin, Wilfred
Lawson
One Sheet: $100 - $200

EAST MEETS WEST
(1936 - Gaumont-British) George Arliss,
Godfrey Tearle
One Sheet: $75 - $150

EAST OF BORNEO
(1931 - Universal) Charles Bickford, Rose
Hobart
One Sheet: $700 - $1,200

EAST OF EDEN
(1955 - Warner Bros.) James Dean, Julie
Harris
One Sheet: $250 - $500   Dean's first
starring role. Academy Award Movie Posters
#166.

EAST OF ELEPHANT ROCK
(1976 - Kendon) Jeremy Kemp, John Hurt
One Sheet: $7 - $15

EAST OF FIFTH AVENUE
(1933 - Columbia) Wallace Ford, Dorothy Tree
One Sheet: $125 - $250

EAST OF JAVA
(1935 - Universal) Frank Albertson, Charles
Bickford
One Sheet: $100 - $200

EAST OF JAVA REGULAR
(1969 - -) Maximilian Schell, Diane Baker
One Sheet: $5 - $10

EAST OF KILIMANJARO
(1962 - Dudley) Marshall Thompson, Gaby
Andre
One Sheet: $5 - $10

EAST OF SUDAN
(1964 - Columbia) Anthony Quayle, Sylvia
Syms
One Sheet: $7 - $15

EAST OF SUEZ
(1926 - Paramount) Pola Negri
One Sheet: $250 - $500

EAST OF SUMATRA
(1953 - Universal) Jeff Chandler, Anthony
Quinn
One Sheet: $30 - $50

EAST OF THE RIVER
(1940 - Warner Bros.) John Garfield, Brenda
Marshall
One Sheet: $75 - $150

One Sheet

EAST OF THE WATER PLUG
(1924 - Pathe) Ralph Graves
One Sheet: $150 - $350

EAST SIDE KIDS
(1940 - Monogram) Dennis Moore, Vince
Barnett
One Sheet: $75 - $175

EAST SIDE OF HEAVEN
(1939 - Universal) Bing Crosby, Joan Blondell
One Sheet: $100 - $200

EAST SIDE OF HEAVEN
(1945R - Universal) Bing Crosby, Joan Blondell

One Sheet: $30 - $50   Re-release.

EAST SIDE SADIE
(1929 - World Art) Bertine Golden, Jack Ellis
One Sheet: $200 - $400   Part Talkie.

EAST SIDE, WEST SIDE
(1949 - MGM) Barbara Stanwyck, James
Mason
One Sheet: $30 - $50

EASTER PARADE
(1948 - MGM) Judy Garland, Fred Astaire,
Peter Lawford
One Sheet: $250 - $600   Price is for
style D. One Sheet(Style C):$200-400.

EASTER PARADE
(1962R - MGM) Judy Garland, Fred Astaire,
Peter Lawford
One Sheet: $30 - $50   Re-release.

EASTERN WESTERNER, AN
(1920 - Pathe) Harold Lloyd
One Sheet: $1,300 - $2,000

EASY ACES
(1935 - RKO) -
One Sheet: $100 - $200

EASY COME, EASY GO
(1928 - Paramount) Richard Dix, Nancy Carroll
One Sheet: $250 - $600

EASY COME, EASY GO
(1947 - Paramount) Barry Fitzgerald, Sonny
Tufts
One Sheet: $40 - $75

EASY COME, EASY GO
(1967 - Paramount) Elvis Presley, Dodie
Marshall
One Sheet: $40 - $75

One Sheet

EASY LIVING
(1937 - Paramount) Jean Arthur, Ray Milland
One Sheet: $250 - $500

EASY LIVING
(1949 - RKO) Victor Mature, Lucille Ball
One Sheet: $50 - $100

EASY MILLIONS
(1933 - Freuler) Skeets Gallagher, Noah Beery
One Sheet: $125 - $250

EASY MONEY
(1934 - Paramount) Mary Newland, Gerald
Rawlinson
One Sheet: $125 - $250

EASY MONEY
(1936 - Invincible) Onslow Stevens, Kay
Linaker
One Sheet: $75 - $150

EASY MONEY
(1948 - Eagle-Lion) Greta Gynt, Dennis Price
One Sheet: $50 - $100

EASY MONEY
(1983 - Orion) Rodney Dangerfield, Joe Pesci,
Geraldine Fitzgerald
One Sheet: $3 - $5

EASY ON THE EYES
(1933 - Paramount) Franklyn Pangborn
One Sheet: $125 - $250

EASY RICHES
(1938 - RKO) George Carney, Marjorie Taylor
One Sheet: $75 - $150

EASY RIDER

(1969 - Columbia) Peter Fonda, Dennis Hopper, Jack Nicholson
One Sheet: $125 - $250   *Above price is for Style C one sheet. One Sheet (Style B Quotes style):$20-$40. One Sheet(Cannes):$150-$300.*

One Sheet

EASY RIDER
(1972R - Columbia) Peter Fonda, Dennis Hopper, Jack Nicholson
One Sheet: $75 - $150   *Re-release.*

EASY ROAD
(1920 - Paramount) Thomas Meighan
One Sheet: $200 - $400

EASY STREET
(1917 - Mutual) Charlie Chaplin, Edna Purviance
One Sheet: $7,500 - $12,000

EASY STREET
(1930 - Micheaux) Richard B. Harison
One Sheet: $75 - $150

EASY TO LOOK AT
(1945 - Universal) Gloria Jean, Kirby Grant
One Sheet: $50 - $100

EASY TO LOVE
(1933 - Warner Bros.) Adolphe Menjou, Mary Astor
One Sheet: $150 - $300

EASY TO LOVE
(1953 - MGM) Esther Williams, Van Johnson
One Sheet: $20 - $40

EASY TO TAKE
(1933 - Warner Bros.) -
One Sheet: $75 - $150

EASY TO TAKE
(1936 - Paramount) Marsha Hunt, Eugene Pallette
One Sheet: $100 - $200

EASY TO WED
(1946 - MGM) Van Johnson, Esther Williams, Lucille Ball
One Sheet: $75 - $150

EASY VIRTUE
(1927 - Gainsborough) Isabel Jeans, Ian Hunter, Dir: Alfred Hitchcock
One Sheet: $2,500 - $4,000

EAT AND RUN
(1924 - Universal) Al Alt, Harry McCoy
One Sheet: $200 - $400

EAT MY DUST
(1976 - New World) Ron Howard, Christopher Norris, Dir: Roger Corman
One Sheet: $15 - $35

One Sheet

EAT THE PEACH
(1986 - Strongbow) Stephen Brennan, Eamon Morrissey
One Sheet: $5 - $10

EAT THE RICH
(1987 - -) Nosher Powell, Lanah Pellay
One Sheet: $5 - $10

EATEN ALIVE
(1977 - Virgo) Neville Brand, Mel Ferrer, Stuart Whitman
One Sheet: $15 - $30   *AKA: HORROR HOTEL MASSACRE; LEGEND OF THE BAYOU.*

EATING
(1991 - Paramount) Nelly Alard, Lisa Richards
One Sheet: $3 - $5

EATING RAOUL
(1982 - Bartel) Paul Bartel, Mary Woronov
One Sheet: $15 - $35

EBB TIDE
(1932 - Paramount) Joan Barry, Merle Oberon (her 2nd feature film).
One Sheet: $125 - $250

EBB TIDE
(1937 - Paramount) Oscar Homolka, Frances Farmer
One Sheet: $250 - $600

EBONY PARADE
(1947 - Astor) Cab Calloway, Count Basie
One Sheet: $200 - $400   *Black cast. Separate Cinema, pg. 101.*

ECHO MURDERS, THE
(1945 - Anglo American) David Farrar, Dennis Price
One Sheet: $40 - $75

ECHO OF BARBARA
(1961 - Independent Artists) Mervyn Johns, Maureen Connel
One Sheet: $5 - $10

ECHO OF DIANA
(1963 - Butchers) Vincent Ball, Clare Owen
One Sheet: $5 - $10

ECHO PARK
(1986 - -) Susan Dey, Thomas Hulce, Michael Bowen
One Sheet: $3 - $5

ECHO RANCH
(1948 - Universal) Red River Dave
One Sheet: $50 - $100

ECHOES
(1983 - Continental) Richard Alfieri, Gale Sondergaard
One Sheet: $3 - $5

ECHOES OF A SUMMER
(1976 - Cine Artists) Richard Harris, Jodie Foster
One Sheet: $7 - $15   *AKA: THE LAST CASTLE.*

ECHOES OF SILENCE
(1966 - Goldman) Miguel Chacour
One Sheet: $5 - $10

ECLIPSE
(1962 - Interopa) Monica Vitti, Alain Delon
One Sheet: $7 - $15   *French/Italian.*

ECSTASY
(1933 - Eureka) Hedy Lamarr, Jaromir Rogoz
One Sheet: $2,200 - $3,500   *(German) Hedy Lamarr's first starring role (3 minor roles precede this), imported to the U.S. in 1934 and banned, shown in only 400theatres in the U.S. during the next 20 years. Posters are rare. Beware re-releases.*

ECSTASY
(195?R - Euraka) Hedy Lamarr, Jaromir Rogoz
One Sheet: $100 - $200   *Re-release.*

ED
(1996 - Universal) Matt LeBlanc, Jayne Brook
One Sheet: $7 - $15   *Sports (Baseball). Sports Movie Posters #88.*

ED THORGERSEN'S SPORTS REVIEWS
(1936 - 20th Century Fox) Ed Thorgersen
One Sheet: $150 - $300   *Sports Movie Posters #345.*

ED WOOD
(1994 - Buena Vista) Johnny Depp, Martin Landau, Jeffrey Jones
One Sheet: $10 - $20   *Academy Award: Best Supporting Actor (Landau). Academy Award Movie Posters #394.*

EDDIE AND THE CRUISERS
(1983 - Embassy) Tom Berenger, Michael Pare
One Sheet: $7 - $15

EDDIE AND THE CRUISERS II: EDDIE LIVES
(1989 - -) Michael Pare, Marina Orsini
One Sheet: $3 - $5

EDDIE CANTOR STORY, THE
(1955 - Warner Bros.) Keefe Brasselle, Marilyn Erskine
One Sheet: $40 - $75

EDDIE MACON'S RUN
(1983 - Universal) Kirk Douglas, John Schneider, Leah Ayres
One Sheet: $3 - $5

EDDIE MURPHY RAW
(1987 - -) Eddie Murphy
One Sheet: $5 - $10

EDDIE'S LAUGH JAMBOREE
(1940' - -) -
One Sheet: $125 - $250

EDDY DUCHIN STORY, THE
(1956 - Columbia) Tyrone Power, Kim Novak
One Sheet: $30 - $50

EDEN CRIED
(1967 - Continental) Tom Pace, Carol Holland
One Sheet: $5 - $10

EDGAR RUNS AGAIN
(1939 - 20th Century Fox) Terry-toons
One Sheet: $100 - $200   *Cartoon. Full color stone litho. Stock poster with inset title.*

EDGE, THE
(1969 - Filmaker's) Jack Rader, Tom Griffin
One Sheet: $5 - $10

EDGE OF DARKNESS
(1943 - Warner Bros.) Errol Flynn, Ann Sheridan
One Sheet: $75 - $150

One Sheet

EDGE OF DOOM
(1950 - RKO) Dana Andrews, Farley Granger
One Sheet: $20 - $40

EDGE OF ETERNITY
(1959 - Columbia) Cornel Wilde, Victoria Shaw
One Sheet: $10 - $20

EDGE OF FURY
(1958 - United Artists) Michael Higgins, Louis Holmes
One Sheet: $7 - $15

EDGE OF HELL
(1954 - Universal) Hugo Haas, Francesca de Scaffa
One Sheet: $15 - $25

EDGE OF SANITY
(1989 - -) Anthony Perkins, Glynis Barber
One Sheet: $5 - $10

EDGE OF THE CITY
(1956 - MGM) John Cassavetes, Sidney Poitier
One Sheet: $30 - $50

EDGE OF THE WORLD, THE
(1937 - Pax) Niall McGinnis, Finlay Carrie

One Sheet: $100 - $200

EDISON, THE MAN
(1940 - MGM) Spencer Tracy, Rita Johnson
One Sheet: $75 - $150

EDUCATED EVANS
(1936 - Warner Bros.) Max Miller, Nancy O'Neil
One Sheet: $75 - $150

EDUCATING FATHER
(1936 - 20th Century Fox) Jed Prouty, Spring Byington
One Sheet: $100 - $200

One Sheet

EDUCATING RITA
(1983 - Columbia) Michael Caine, Julie Walters
One Sheet: $3 - $5

EDUCATION OF ELIZABETH, THE
(1920 - Paramount) Billie Burke
One Sheet: $250 - $600

EDUCATION OF SONNY CARSON, THE
(1974 - Paramount) Rony Clanton, Don Gordon
One Sheet: $7 - $15

EDWARD AND CAROLINE
(1952 - Commercial) Anne Vernon, Daniel Gelin
One Sheet: $15 - $25   *French.*

EDWARD II
(1992 - -) Steven Waddington, Andrew Tiernan
One Sheet: $5 - $10

EDWARD, MY SON
(1949 - MGM) Spencer Tracy, Deborah Kerr
One Sheet: $30 - $50

EDWARD SCISSORHANDS
(1990 - 20th Century Fox) Johnny Dep, Winona Ryder
One Sheet: $10 - $20

EDWIN'S BADGE OF HONOR
(1913 - Biograph) -
One Sheet: $250 - $500

EEGAH
(1962 - Fairway International) Marilyn Manning, Richard Kiel
One Sheet: $30 - $50

EFFECT OF GAMMA RAYS ON MAN-IN-THE-MOON MARIGOLDS, THE
(1973 - 20th Century Fox) Joanne Woodward, Nell Potts, Roberta Wallach
One Sheet: $10 - $20

EFFECTS
(1980 - Image) John Harrison, Tom Savini
One Sheet: $3 - $5

EFFICIENCY EXPERT, THE
(1992 - -) Anthony Hopkins, Ben Mendelsohn
One Sheet: $5 - $10

EGG AND I, THE
(1947 - Universal-International) Claudette Colbert, Fred MacMurray
One Sheet: $75 - $150

EGG AND I, THE
(1954R - Universal) Claudette Colbert, Fred MacMurray
One Sheet: $15 - $25   *Re-release.*

EGG CRACKER SUITE
(1943 - Universal) Oswald the Rabbit, Walter Lantz
One Sheet: $350 - $750   *Cartoon. Duotone. Cartoon Movie Posters #50.*

EGG-CRATE WALLOP, THE
(1919 - NCI) Charles Ray, Colleen Moore
One Sheet: $150 - $300

EGYPT BY THREE
(1953 - Filmakers) Ann Stanfield, Jackie Craven
One Sheet: $10 - $20

EGYPTIAN, THE
(1954 - 20th Century Fox) Jean Simmons, Gene Tierney
One Sheet: $75 - $150

EIGER SANCTION, THE
(1975 - Universal) Clint Eastwood, George Kennedy
One Sheet: $15 - $30

8-1/2
(1963 - Embassy) Marcello Mastroianni, Claudia Cordivale
One Sheet: $150 - $300   *Italian. AKA: FEDERICO FELLINI'S 8-1/2. Price is for U.S. one sheet. Original Italian (55x78, Cinertz):$900-1600.*

EIGHT BELLS
(1935 - Columbia) Ann Sothern, Ralph Bellamy
One Sheet: $100 - $200

EIGHT GIRLS IN A BOAT
(1932 - Fanal) Theodor Loos, Karin Hardt
One Sheet: $200 - $400   *German.*

EIGHT GIRLS IN A BOAT
(1934 - Paramount) Dorothy Wilson, Douglas Montgomery
One Sheet: $100 - $200

EIGHT IRON MEN
(1952 - Columbia) Lee Marvin, Bonar Colleano
One Sheet: $30 - $50

EIGHT MEN OUT
(1988 - Orion) John Cusack, Clifton Jones, Christopher Lloyd
One Sheet: $15 - $30   *Sports (Baseball). Sports Movie Posters #76.*

EIGHT MILLION WAYS TO DIE
(1985 - TriStar) Jeff Bridges, Rosanna Arquette
One Sheet: $3 - $5

EIGHT O'CLOCK WALK
(1954 - Lion) Richard Attenborough, Ian Hunter
One Sheet: $15 - $25

EIGHT ON THE LAM
(1967 - United Artists) Bob Hope, Phyllis Diller
One Sheet: $15 - $25   *Jack Davis art.*

8 SECONDS
(1994 - New Line) Luke Perry, Stephen Baldwin
One Sheet: $7 - $15   *Sports (Rodeo). Sports Movie Posters #304.*

18 AGAIN
(1988 - -) George Burns, Charlie Schlatter
One Sheet: $3 - $5

EIGHTEEN AND ANXIOUS
(1957 - Republic) Martha Scott, Jim Backus
One Sheet: $15 - $30

18 MINUTES
(1935 - Pathe) Gregory Ratoff, Benita Hume
One Sheet: $150 - $300

84 CHARING CROSS ROAD
(1987 - Columbia) Anne Bancroft, Anthony Hopkins
One Sheet: $3 - $5

84 CHARLIE MOPIC
(1989 - New Century/Vista) Jonathan Emerson, Nicholas Cascone
One Sheet: $3 - $5

EIGHTY STEPS TO JONAH
(1969 - Warner Bros.) Wayne Newton, Jo Van Fleet
One Sheet: $7 - $15

80,000 SUSPECTS
(1963 - Rank) Claire Bloom, Cyril Cusack
One Sheet: $5 - $10

EL
(1955 - Nacional Film) Arturo De Cordova, Delia Graces
One Sheet: $50 - $100   *Mexican. AKA: THIS STRANGE PASSION; TORMENTS.*

EL ALAMEIN
(1953 - Columbia) Scott Brady, Edward Ashley
One Sheet: $10 - $20

EL CID
(1961 - Allied Artists) Charlton Heston, Sophia Loren
One Sheet: $40 - $75

EL CONDOR
(1970 - National General) Jim Brown, Lee Van Cleef, Patrick O'Neal
One Sheet: $7 - $15

EL DESPERTAR DE LA MOMIA
(1983 - NCI) Brenda King
One Sheet: $3 - $5   *Spanish.*

EL DIABLO RIDES
(1939 - Metropolitan) Bob Steele
One Sheet: $100 - $200

EL DORADO
(1967 - Paramount) John Wayne, Robert Mitchum
One Sheet: $50 - $100

One Sheet

EL DORADO PASS
(1948 - Columbia) Charles Starrett, Smiley Burnette
One Sheet: $20 - $40

EL GAUCHO GOOFY
(1955 - RKO/Disney) Goofy
One Sheet: $250 - $600   *Cartoon.*

EL GRECO
(1966 - 20th Century Fox) Mel Ferrer, Rosanna Schiaffino
One Sheet: $7 - $15

EL MARIACHI
(1993 - Columbia) Carlos Gallardo, Consuelo Gomez
One Sheet: $15 - $35   *Dubbed English.*

EL NORTE
(1984 - Independent Productions) Zaide Silvia Gutierrez, David Villalpando
One Sheet: $5 - $10

EL PASO
(1949 - Paramount) John Payne, Gail Russell, Gabby Hayes
One Sheet: $40 - $75

EL PASO KID, THE
(1946 - Republic) Sunset Carson, Marie Harmon
One Sheet: $40 - $75

EL PASO STAMPEDE
(1953 - Republic) Allan "Rocky" Lane
One Sheet: $30 - $50

EL TOPO
(1967 - -) Alexandro Jodorowski
One Sheet: $50 - $100

ELDER BROTHER, THE
(1937 - Paramount) John Stuart, Marjorie Taylor
One Sheet: $75 - $150

ELECTION DAY GAIETIES
(1953 - RKO/Disney) Mickey Mouse, Donald Duck, Pluto
One Sheet: $100 - $200   *Cartoon.*

ELECTION DAZE
(1943 - MGM) Our Gang
One Sheet: $250 - $600

ELECTRA
(1963 - Finos) Irene Papas, Aleka Katselli
One Sheet: $10 - $20

ELECTRA GUIDE IN BLUE
(1973 - United Artists) Robert Blake, Billy "Green" Bush
One Sheet: $7 - $15   *Advance:$20-35.*

ELECTRIC DREAMS
(1984 - MGM/United Artists) Lenny Von Dohlen, Virginia Madsen
One Sheet: $3 - $5

ELECTRIC HORSEMAN, THE
(1979 - Columbia) Jane Fonda, Robert Redford
One Sheet: $7 - $15

ELECTRIC HOUSE, THE
(1922 - Associated First National) Buster Keaton
One Sheet: $7,500 - $12,000

ELECTRONIC MONSTER, THE
(1960 - Columbia) Rod Cameron, Mary Murphy
One Sheet: $50 - $100

ELENI
(1985 - CBS) Kate Nelligan, John Malkovich
One Sheet: $3 - $5

ELEPHANT BOY
(1937 - London) Sabu(film debut), Walter Hudd
One Sheet: $150 - $300

ELEPHANT CALLED SLOWLY, AN
(1970 - -) Virginia McKenna, Bill Travers
One Sheet: $3 - $5

ELEPHANT GUN
(1959 - Rank) Belinda Lee, Patrick McGoohan
One Sheet: $7 - $15

ELEPHANT MAN, THE
(1980 - Paramount) Anthony Hopkins, John Hurt
One Sheet: $15 - $25

ELEPHANT STAMPEDE
(1951 - Monogram) Johnny Sheffield, Donna Martell
One Sheet: $15 - $30

ELEPHANT WALK
(1954 - Paramount) Elizabeth Taylor, Dana Andrews
One Sheet: $75 - $125

ELEPHANT WALK
(1960R - Paramount) Elizabeth Taylor, Dana Andrews
One Sheet: $15 - $25   *Re-release.*

ELEVATING FATHER
(1916 - Universal) Louise Orth, Dan Russell, Ray Griffith
One Sheet: $250 - $600

11 HARROWHOUSE
(1974 - 20th Century Fox) Charles Grodin, Candice Bergen
One Sheet: $5 - $10

ELEVENTH COMMANDMENT
(1933 - Allied) Marian Marsh, Alan Hale
One Sheet: $150 - $300

ELEVENTH HOUR, THE
(1923 - Fox) Chuck Jones, Shirley Mason
One Sheet: $250 - $600

ELI ELI
(1940 - Cinema Service) Esther Field, Lazar Freed
One Sheet: $75 - $125

ELIMINATOR, THE
(1982 - -) JoAnn Harris, Steve Railsback
One Sheet: $3 - $5

ELIMINATORS
(1986 - Empire) Andrew Prine, Denise Crosby
One Sheet: $2 - $3

ELINOR NORTON
(1934 - Fox) Claire Trevor, Gilbert Roland
One Sheet: $250 - $600

ELIZA COMES TO STAY
(1936 - Twickenham) Betty Balfour, Seymour Hicks
One Sheet: $100 - $200

ELIZA ON ICE
(1943 - 20th Century Fox) Mighty Mouse
One Sheet: $250 - $600   *Cartoon. Full color stock poster with printed title. Huge image of Mighty Mouse on yellow background.*

ELIZA'S HOROSCOPE
(1975 - O-Zali) Tommy Lee Jones, Elizabeth Moorman
One Sheet: $7 - $15

ELIZABETH OF LADYMEAD
(1949 - Imperadio) Anne Neagle, Bernard Lee
One Sheet: $30 - $50

ELLA CINDERS
(1926 - First National) Colleen Moore, Lloyd Hughes
One Sheet: $500 - $800

ELLERY QUEEN AND THE MURDER RING
(1941 - Columbia) Ralph Bellamy, Margaret Lindsay, Mona Barrie
One Sheet: $150 - $300

ELLERY QUEEN AND THE PERFECT CRIME
(1941 - Columbia) Ralph Bellamy, Margaret Lindsay, Spring Byington
One Sheet: $150 - $300

One Sheet

ELLERY QUEEN, MASTER DETECTIVE
(1940 - Columbia) Ralph Bellamy, Margaret Lindsay, Michael Whalen
One Sheet: $150 - $300

ELLERY QUEEN'S PENTHOUSE MYSTERY
(1941 - Columbia) Ralph Bellamy, Margaret Lindsay, Anna May Wong
One Sheet: $150 - $300

ELLIS ISLAND
(1936 - Invincible) Donald Cook, Jack LaRue
One Sheet: $75 - $150

ELMER AND ELSIE
(1934 - Paramount) George Bancroft, Francis Fuller
One Sheet: $100 - $200

ELMER GANTRY
(1960 - United Artists) Burt Lancaster, Jean Simmons
One Sheet: $30 - $50   *Academy Award: Best Actor(Lancaster). Academy Award Movie Posters #198 & #200.*

ELMER THE GREAT
(1933 - First National) Joe E. Brown, Patricia Ellis
One Sheet: $150 - $350   *Sport Movie Posters #41.*

ELMO THE MIGHTY
(1919 - Universal) Elmo Lincoln, Grace Cunard
One Sheet: $350 - $750   *Serial. 18 Chapters.*

ELOPEMENT
(1951 - 20th Century Fox) Clifton Webb, Anne Francis
One Sheet: $15 - $30

ELSA MAXWELL'S HOTEL FOR WOMEN
(1939 - 20th Century Fox) Linda Darnell, James Ellison, Ann Sothern
One Sheet: $800 - $1,500   *Petty art on posters.*

ELSA MAXWELL'S PUBLIC DEBATE NO. 1
(1940 - 20th Century Fox) Brenda Joyce, Elsa Maxwell, Mischa Auer
One Sheet: $75 - $150

ELVIRA, MISTRESS OF THE DARK
(1988 - -) Elvira (Cassandra Peterson), W. Morgan Sheppard
One Sheet: $15 - $25

ELVIS - THE MOVIE
(1979 - -) Kurt Russell, Shelley Winters
One Sheet: $15 - $30   *Made for TV Movie.*

ELVIS! ELVIS!
(1977 - Moviemakers) Lele Dorazio
One Sheet: $15 - $30   *Swedish.*

ELVIS ON TOUR
(1972 - MGM) Elvis Presley
One Sheet: $40 - $75

One Sheet

ELVIS-THAT'S THE WAY IT IS
(1970 - MGM) Elvis Presley
One Sheet: $50 - $100   *Documentary.*

EMBALMER, THE
(1966 - Europix) Maureen Brown, Gin Mart
One Sheet: $15 - $30

EMBARRASSING MOMENTS
(1930 - Universal) Reginald Denny, Merna Kennedy
One Sheet: $200 - $400

EMBARRASSING MOMENTS
(1934 - Universal) Chester Morris, Marion Nixon
One Sheet: $150 - $300

EMBASSY
(1972 - Hemdale) Richard Roundtree, Chuck Connors
One Sheet: $7 - $15

EMBEZZLER, THE
(1954 - Kenilworth) Charles Victor, Zena Marshall
One Sheet: $15 - $25

EMBRACEABLE YOU
(1948 - Warner Bros.) Dane Clark, Geraldine Brooks
One Sheet: $20 - $40

EMBRACERS, THE
(1966 - Yucca) Lois Adams, Gary Garver
One Sheet: $5 - $10

EMBRYO
(1976 - CineArtist) Rock Hudson, Barbara Carrera
One Sheet: $10 - $20

EMERALD FOREST, THE
(1985 - Embassy) Powers Boothe, Meg Foster, Charley Boorman
One Sheet: $5 - $10

EMERGENCY CALL
(1933 - RKO) Betty Furness, William Boyd
One Sheet: $75 - $150

EMERGENCY HOSPITAL
(1956 - United Artists) Margaret Lindsay, Byron Palmer
One Sheet: $10 - $20

EMERGENCY LANDING
(1941 - PRC) Carol Hughes, Forrest Tucker
One Sheet: $40 - $75

EMERGENCY SQUAD
(1939 - Paramount) William Henry, Louise Campbell
One Sheet: $75 - $150

EMERGENCY WEDDING

(1950 - Columbia) Larry Parks, Barbara Hale
One Sheet: $20 - $40

EMIGRANTS, THE
(1972 - Warner Bros.) Max von Sydow, Liv Ullmann
One Sheet: $5 - $10

EMIL
(1938 - Gaumont) George Hayes, Mary Glynne
One Sheet: $75 - $150

EMIL AND THE DETECTIVES
(1964 - Buena Vista/Disney) Walter Slezak, Heinz Schubert
One Sheet: $15 - $25

EMILY
(1976 - -) Koo Stark, Sarah Brackett
One Sheet: $5 - $10

EMMA
(1932 - MGM) Marie Dressler, Richard Cromwell
One Sheet: $100 - $200

EMMA
(1996 - Miramax) Gwyneth Paltrow, Toni Collette, Greta Scacchi
One Sheet: $4 - $8

EMMA MAE
(1976 - Pro-International) Jerri Hayes, Eddie Allen
One Sheet: $10 - $20   *Black cast.*

EMMANUELLE
(1975 - Columbia) Alain Cuny, Sylvia Kristel
One Sheet: $10 - $20   *Advance:$20-30.*

EMMANUELLE, THE JOYS OF A WOMAN
(1976 - Paramount) Silvia Kristel, Umberto Orsini
One Sheet: $5 - $10

EMPEROR AND A GENERAL, THE
(1968 - Toho) Toshiro Mifune
One Sheet: $20 - $40   *Japanese.*

EMPEROR JONES, THE
(1933 - United Artists) Paul Robeson, Dudley Digges
One Sheet: $7,500 - $12,000   *Black cast. Separate Cinema, pg. 40.*

One Sheet

EMPEROR JONES, THE
(1940R - United Artists) Paul Robeson, Dudley Digges
One Sheet: $700 - $1,200   *Black cast. Re-release. Duotone. Separate Cinema, pg. 40.*

EMPEROR OF THE NORTH
(1973 - 20th Century Fox) Lee Marvin, Ernest Borgnine
One Sheet: $5 - $10

EMPEROR WALTZ, THE
(1948 - Paramount) Bing Crosby, Joan Fontaine
One Sheet: $30 - $50

EMPEROR'S CANDLESTICKS, THE
(1937 - MGM) William Powell, Luise Rainer
One Sheet: $600 - $1,000

EMPEROR'S NEW CLOTHES, THE
(1953 - Columbia) Jolly Frolics
One Sheet: $150 - $300   *Cartoon. Duotone.*

EMPIRE OF THE ANTS
(1977 - AIP) Joan Collins, Dir: Bert I. Gordon
One Sheet: $15 - $30

EMPIRE OF THE SUN
(1987 - Warner Bros.) Christian Bale, John Malkovich
One Sheet: $10 - $20

EMPIRE RECORDS
(1995 - Warner Bros.) Anthony LaPaglia, Liv Tyler
One Sheet: $5 - $10

EMPIRE STRIKES BACK, THE
(1980 - 20th Century Fox) Mark Hamill, Harrison Ford
One Sheet: $40 - $80   *Price is for Style B one sheet. Advance:$50-$100. One Sheet(Style A):$100-$200.*

One Sheet (Advance)

EMPIRE STRIKES BACK, THE
(1982R - 20th Century Fox) Mark Hamill, Harrison Ford
One Sheet: $15 - $30   *Re-release.*

EMPIRE STRIKES BACK, THE
(1990R - 20th Century Fox) Mark Hamill, Harrison Ford
One Sheet: $15 - $25   *Re-release. 10th Anniversary poster. Gold Mylar:$75-125. Silver Mylar:$40-50.*

EMPLOYEE'S ENTRANCE
(1933 - First National) Loretta Young, Warren William
One Sheet: $500 - $800

EMPTY CANVAS, THE
(1964 - Embassy) Bette Davis, Horst Buchholz
One Sheet: $15 - $30

EMPTY HOLSTERS
(1937 - Warner Bros.) Dick Foran, Patricia Walthall
One Sheet: $50 - $100

EMPTY HOLSTERS
(194?R - Warner Bros.) Dick Foran, Patricia Walthall
One Sheet: $10 - $20   *Re-release. Duotone.*

EMPTY SADDLES
(1936 - Universal) Buck Jones, Louise Brooks
One Sheet: $250 - $600

EMPTY STALL, THE
(1924 - Universal-Jewel) Billy Sullivan
One Sheet: $150 - $300   *#2 in the Fast Steppers series.*

ENCHANTED APRIL
(1935 - RKO) Ann Harding, Frank Morgan
One Sheet: $125 - $250

ENCHANTED APRIL
(1992 - Miramax) Miranda Richardson, Joan Plowright
One Sheet: $3 - $5

ENCHANTED COTTAGE, THE
(1924 - First National) Richard Barthelmess, May McAvoy
One Sheet: $250 - $500

ENCHANTED COTTAGE, THE
(1945 - RKO) Dorothy McGuire, Robert Young
One Sheet: $75 - $150

ENCHANTED FOREST, THE
(1945 - PRC) Harry Davenport, Edmund Lowe
One Sheet: $75 - $150   *Best example of Cinecolor process.*

ENCHANTED HILL, THE
(1926 - Paramount) Jack Holt, Florence Vidor

One Sheet: $150 - $350

ENCHANTED ISLAND
(1958 - Warner Bros.) Dana Andrews, Jane Powell
One Sheet: $15 - $25

ENCHANTED JOURNEY, THE
(1984 - -) Voices: Jim Backus, Orson Welles
One Sheet: $15 - $25   *Cartoon.*

ENCHANTED VALLEY, THE
(1947 - Pathe) Alan Curtis, Anne Gwynne
One Sheet: $15 - $25

ENCHANTMENT
(1948 - Goldwyn) David Niven, Teresa Wright
One Sheet: $40 - $75

ENCINO MAN
(1992 - Buena Vista) Sean Astin, Pauly Shore, Brendan Frasner
One Sheet: $5 - $10

ENCORE
(1951 - Paramount) Roland Culver, Glynis Johns
One Sheet: $40 - $75

ENCOUNTER WITH THE UNKNOWN
(1973 - Libert) Rosie Holotick, Gene Ross
One Sheet: $5 - $10

END, THE
(1978 - United Artists) Burt Reynolds, Dom De Luise, Sally Fields
One Sheet: $7 - $15   *Price is for both styles.*

END OF AUGUST, THE
(1982 - Quartet) Sally Sharp, David Marshall
One Sheet: $3 - $5

END OF THE AFFAIR, THE
(1954 - Columbia) Deborah Kerr, Van Johnson
One Sheet: $30 - $50

END OF THE DAY, THE
(1939 - Juno) Victor Fangen
One Sheet: $40 - $75

END OF THE GAME
(1976 - 20th Century Fox) Jon Voight, Jacqueline Bisset
One Sheet: $7 - $15   *AKA: GETTING AWAY WITH MURDER.*

END OF THE LINE
(1959 - United Artists) Alan Baxter, Barbara Shelley
One Sheet: $7 - $15

END OF THE LINE
(1988 - Orion Classics) Wilford Brimley, Mary Steenburgen
One Sheet: $3 - $5

END OF THE RIVER, THE
(1947 - Universal International) Sabu, Bibi Ferreira
One Sheet: $40 - $75

END OF THE ROAD
(1936 - Fox) Harry Lauder, Ruth Haven
One Sheet: $150 - $300

END OF THE ROAD
(1944 - Republic) Edward Norris, June Storey
One Sheet: $40 - $75

END OF THE ROAD
(1954 - British Lion) Edward Chapman, George Merritt
One Sheet: $15 - $25

END OF THE ROAD
(1970 - Allied Artists) Stacy Keach, Harris Yulin, Dorothy Tristan, James Earl Jones
One Sheet: $3 - $5

END OF THE TRAIL
(1932 - Columbia) Tim McCoy
One Sheet: $250 - $600

END OF THE TRAIL
(1936 - Columbia) Jack Holt, Louise Henry
One Sheet: $100 - $200

END OF THE WORLD, THE
(1930 - L'Ecran d'Art) Abel Gance, Victor Francen
One Sheet: $800 - $1,500   *French. Science fiction. French title: LA FIN DU MONDE. Price is for original French (47x63) poster.*

END OF THE WORLD
(1977 - Charles Band) Christopher Lee, Sue
Lyon
One Sheet: $15 - $25

**END OF THE WORLD (IN OUR USUAL BED IN A
NIGHT FULL OF RAIN), THE**
(1978 - Warner Bros.) Giancarlo Giannini,
Candice Bergen
One Sheet: $5 - $10

END PLAY
(1975 - Hexagon) George Mallaby
One Sheet: $5 - $10

ENDANGERED SPECIES
(1982 - MGM) Robert Urich, Jo Beth Williams
One Sheet: $3 - $5

ENDLESS LOVE
(1981 - Polygram) Brooke Shields, Martin
Hewitt
One Sheet: $5 - $10

ENDLESS NIGHT
(1971 - British Lion) Hayley Mills, George
Sanders
One Sheet: $7 - $15

ENDLESS SUMMER, THE
(1966 - Columbia) -
One Sheet: $150 - $300   *Sports
documentary (Surfing). Sports Movie Posters
#319. Cinemax release:$250-$300.*

ENDLESS SUMMER II, THE
(1994 - New Line) Robert Weaver, Patrick
O'Connell
One Sheet: $15 - $25   *Sports
documentary (Surfing). Sports Movie Posters
#323.*

ENEMIES: A LOVE STORY
(1989 - 20th Century Fox) Anjelica Huston, Ron
Silver, Lena Olin
One Sheet: $3 - $5

ENEMIES OF THE LAW
(1931 - Independent) Mary Nolan, Johnny
Walker
One Sheet: $150 - $300

ENEMIES OF WOMEN, THE
(1923 - Goldwyn) Lionel Barrymore, Alma
Rubens
One Sheet: $1,300 - $2,000

ENEMY, THE
(1927 - MGM) Lillian Gish, Ralph Forbes
One Sheet: $800 - $1,500

ENEMY AGENT
(1940 - Universal) Richard Cromwell, Helen
Vinson
One Sheet: $75 - $125

ENEMY AGENTS MEET ELLERY QUEEN
(1942 - Columbia) William Gargan, Margaret
Lindsay, Gale Sondergaard
One Sheet: $125 - $250

ENEMY BELOW, THE
(1957 - 20th Century Fox) Robert Mitchum,
Curt Jurgens
One Sheet: $30 - $50

ENEMY FROM SPACE
(1957 - United Artists) Brian Donlevy, Sydney
James
One Sheet: $30 - $50   *AKA:
QUATERMASS II.*

ENEMY GENERAL, THE
(1960 - Columbia) Van Johnson, Jean-Pierre
Aumont
One Sheet: $5 - $10

ENEMY MINE
(1985 - 20th Century Fox) Dennis Quaid, Louis
Gossett, Jr.
One Sheet: $5 - $10

ENEMY OF THE LAW
(1945 - PRC) Dave O'Brien, Tex Ritter
One Sheet: $30 - $50

ENEMY OF THE PEOPLE, AN
(1978 - Warner Bros.) Steve McQueen, Charles
Durning
One Sheet: $10 - $20

ENEMY OF THE POLICE
(1933 - Warner Bros.) John Stuart, Viola Keats

One Sheet: $125 - $250

ENEMY OF WOMEN
(1944 - United Artists) Paul Andor, Claudia
Drake, Donald Woods
One Sheet: $50 - $100

ENEMY SEX
(1924 - Paramount) Betty Compson, Percy
Marmont
One Sheet: $250 - $600

ENFORCER, THE
(1951 - Warner Bros.) Humphrey Bogart, Zero
Mostel
One Sheet: $75 - $125

ENFORCER, THE
(1976 - Warner Bros.) Clint Eastwood, Tyne
Daly
One Sheet: $40 - $75   *Insert
(rare):$75-150.*

ENGLAND MADE ME
(1973 - Hemdale) Peter Finch, Michael York
One Sheet: $5 - $10

ENGLISH PATIENT, THE
(1996 - Miramax) Ralph Fiennes, Kristin Scott
Thomas
One Sheet: $15 - $25

**ENGLISHMAN WHO WENT UP A HILL BUT
CAME DOWN A MOUNTAIN, THE**
(1995 - Miramax) Hugh Grant, Tara Fitzgerald,
Colm Meaney
One Sheet: $5 - $10

ENIGMA
(1983 - Embassy) Martin Sheen, Sam Neill
One Sheet: $3 - $5

ENLIGHTEN THY DAUGHTER
(1933 - Exploitation) Herbert Rawlinson, Beth
Barton
One Sheet: $125 - $250   *Sexploitation.*

ENSIGN PULVER
(1964 - Warner Bros.) Robert Walker, Burl Ives
One Sheet: $5 - $10

ENTER ARSENE LUPIN
(1944 - Universal) Charles Korvin, Ella Raines
One Sheet: $40 - $80

ENTER INSPECTOR DUVAL
(1961 - Columbia) Anton Diffring, Diane Hart
One Sheet: $5 - $10

ENTER LAUGHING
(1967 - Columbia) Jose Ferrer, Shelley Winters
One Sheet: $5 - $10

ENTER MADAME!
(1935 - Paramount) Elissa Landi, Cary Grant
One Sheet: $200 - $400

ENTER THE DRAGON
(1973 - Warner Bros.) Bruce Lee, John Saxon
One Sheet: $75 - $150   *Lee's last
complete film. Sports Movie Posters #'s 264, 265.*

One Sheet

ENTER THE DRAGON
(1977R - Warner Bros.) Bruce Lee, John Saxon
One Sheet: $30 - $50   *Re-release.*

ENTER THE DRAGON
(1979R - Warner Bros.) Bruce Lee, John Saxon
One Sheet: $15 - $35   *Re-release.*

ENTER THE DRAGON/HOT POTATO
(1976R - Warner Bros.) Bruce Lee, John Saxon
One Sheet: $15 - $30   *Re-release
double feature.*

ENTER THE NINJA
(1981 - Cannon) Frank Nero, Susan George,
Sho Kosugi
One Sheet: $3 - $5

ENTERTAINER, THE
(1960 - Continental) Laurence Olivier, Brenda
deBanzie
One Sheet: $30 - $50

ENTERTAINER, THE
(1975 - Stigwood) Jack Lemmon, Ray Bolger
One Sheet: $7 - $15

ENTERTAINING MR. SLOANE
(1970 - Continental) Beryl Reid, Harry
Andrews, Peter McEnery
One Sheet: $3 - $5

ENTITY, THE
(1983 - 20th Century Fox) Barbara Hershey,
Ron Silver
One Sheet: $3 - $5

EQUINOX
(1970 - Tonylyn) Edward Connell, Barbara
Hewitt
One Sheet: $15 - $35   *Minor Horror
Classic.*

EQUINOX
(1992 - S.C. Entertainment) Matthew Modine,
Lara Flynn Boyle
One Sheet: $3 - $5

EQUUS
(1977 - United Artists) Richard Burton, Peter
Firth
One Sheet: $10 - $20   *Price is for
both styles.*

ERASER
(1996 - Warner Bros.) Arnold Schwarzenegger,
Vanessa Williams
One Sheet: $5 - $12

ERASERHEAD
(1978 - Libra) John Nance, Charlotte Stewart,
Dir: David Lynch
One Sheet: $40 - $80   *Small size art
house poster:$35-55.*

ERIC THE CONQUEROR
(1963 - AIP) Cameron Mitchell, Alice Kessler
One Sheet: $15 - $25

ERIK THE VIKING
(1989 - Orion) Tim Robbins, Mickey Rooney,
Eartha Kitt
One Sheet: $5 - $10

ERNEST GOES TO CAMP
(1987 - Buena Vista/Disney) Jim Varney, Victor
Racimo
One Sheet: $3 - $5

ERNEST GOES TO JAIL
(1990 - Buena Vista/Disney) Jim Varney,
Gailard Sartain
One Sheet: $3 - $5

ERNEST SAVES CHRISTMAS
(1988 - Buena Vista/Disney) Jim Varney,
Douglas Seale
One Sheet: $3 - $5

ERNEST SCARED STUPID
(1992 - Buena Vista/Disney) Jim Varney
One Sheet: $2 - $3

ERRAND BOY, THE
(1961 - Paramount) Jerry Lewis, Brian Donlevy
One Sheet: $20 - $40

ERSTWHILE SUSAN
(1919 - Realart) Constance Binney
One Sheet: $150 - $350

ESCAPADE
(1932 - Chesterfield) Anthony Bushell, Sally
Blane
One Sheet: $125 - $250

ESCAPADE
(1935 - MGM) William Powell, Luise Rainer
One Sheet: $100 - $200

ESCAPADE
(1955 - Eros) John Mills, Alastair Sim
One Sheet: $20 - $40

ESCAPADE IN FLORENCE
(1962 - Buena Vista/Disney) Ivan Desny,

Tommy Kirk, Annette Funicello
One Sheet: $20 - $40   *Walt Disney's
Wonderful World Of Color TV movie.*

ESCAPADE IN JAPAN
(1957 - RKO) Teresa Wright, Cameron Mitchell
One Sheet: $15 - $30

ESCAPE
(1930 - RKO) Gerald du Maurier, Edna Best
One Sheet: $250 - $500

ESCAPE, THE
(1939 - 20th Century Fox) Kane Richmond,
June Gale
One Sheet: $75 - $150

ESCAPE
(1940 - MGM) Norma Shearer, Robert Taylor
One Sheet: $100 - $200

ESCAPE
(1948 - 20th Century Fox) Rex Harrison, Peggy
Cummins
One Sheet: $40 - $75

One Sheet

ESCAPE 2000
(1983 - Filmco) Steve Railsback, Oliva Hussey
One Sheet: $3 - $5   *AKA:
TURKEY SHOOT.*

ESCAPE ARTIST, THE
(1982 - Zoetrope) Griffin O'Neal, Raul Julia,
Terri Garr
One Sheet: $3 - $5

ESCAPE BY NIGHT
(1937 - Republic) William Hall, Anne Nagle
One Sheet: $75 - $125

ESCAPE BY NIGHT
(1954 - Eros) Bonar Colleano, Sidney James
One Sheet: $15 - $25

ESCAPE BY NIGHT
(1964 - Allied Artists) Terence Longdon,
Jennifer Jayne
One Sheet: $5 - $10

ESCAPE DANGEROUS
(1947 - DS Films) Beresford Egan, Mary Stone
One Sheet: $40 - $75

ESCAPE FROM ALCATRAZ
(1979 - Paramount) Clint Eastwood, Patrick
McGoohan
One Sheet: $20 - $40

Half Sheet

ESCAPE FROM CRIME
(1942 - Warner Bros.) Richard Travis, Julis
Bishop
One Sheet: $75 - $125

ESCAPE FROM DEATH ROW

(1981 - -) Lee Van Cleef
One Sheet: $5 - $10

ESCAPE FROM DEVIL'S ISLAND
(1935 - Columbia) Victor Jory, Florence Rice
One Sheet: $250 - $500

ESCAPE FROM EAST BERLIN
(1962 - MGM) Don Murray, Christine Kaufmann
One Sheet: $10 - $20

ESCAPE FROM FORT BRAVO
(1953 - MGM) William Holden, Eleanor Parker
One Sheet: $30 - $60

ESCAPE FROM FORT BRAVO
(1962R - MGM) Willaim Holden, Eleanor Parker
One Sheet: $7 - $15   *Re-release.*

ESCAPE FROM HELL
(1964 - Crown) Mark Stevens
One Sheet: $7 - $15

ESCAPE FROM HONG KONG
(1942 - Universal) Leo Carrillo, Andy Devine, Marjorie Lord
One Sheet: $75 - $125

ESCAPE FROM L.A.
(1996 - Paramount) Kurt Russell, Valeria Golino, Peter Fonda
One Sheet: $10 - $20   *Sci-fi.*
Advance Style: $20-$30.

ESCAPE FROM NEW YORK
(1981 - Avco/Embassy) Kurt Russell, Lee Van Cleef, Ernest Borgnine
One Sheet: $20 - $40   *Advance:$30-50.*

ESCAPE FROM RED ROCK
(1957 - 20th Century Fox) Brian Donlevy, Eilene Janssen
One Sheet: $7 - $15

ESCAPE FROM SAN QUENTIN
(1957 - Columbia) Johnny Desmond, Merry Anders
One Sheet: $15 - $25

ESCAPE FROM TERROR
(1960 - Googan-Rogers) Jackie Coogan, Mona Knox
One Sheet: $15 - $30

ESCAPE FROM THE PLANET OF THE APES
(1971 - 20th Century Fox) Roddy McDowall, Kim Hunter
One Sheet: $30 - $50

ESCAPE FROM ZAHRAIN
(1962 - Paramount) Yul Brynner, Sal Mineo
One Sheet: $15 - $25

ESCAPE IN THE DESERT
(1945 - Warner Bros.) Philip Dorn, Helmut Dantine
One Sheet: $50 - $100

ESCAPE IN THE FOG
(1945 - Columbia) Otto Kruger, Nina Foch
One Sheet: $75 - $125

ESCAPE IN THE SUN
(1956 - Paramount) John Bentley, Martin Boddey
One Sheet: $15 - $25

ESCAPE ME NEVER
(1935 - United Artists) Elisabeth Bergner
One Sheet: $100 - $200

ESCAPE ME NEVER
(1947 - Warner Bros.) Errol Flynn, Ida Lupino
One Sheet: $75 - $150

ESCAPE OF JIM DOLAN, THE
(1913 - Selig) -
One Sheet: $500 - $900   *Cowboy Movie Posters #4.*

ESCAPE TO ATHENA
(1979 - Grade) Roger Moore, Telly Savalas, David Nivens
One Sheet: $5 - $10

ESCAPE TO BURMA
(1955 - RKO) Barbara Stanwyck, Robert Ryan
One Sheet: $20 - $40

ESCAPE TO DANGER
(1944 - RKO) Eric Portman, Ann Dvorak
One Sheet: $50 - $100

ESCAPE TO GLORY
(1940 - Columbia) Pat O'Brien, Constance Bennett
One Sheet: $75 - $150

ESCAPE TO PARADISE
(1939 - RKO) Bobby Breen, Kent Taylor
One Sheet: $75 - $150

ESCAPE TO THE SUN
(1972 - Cinevision) Laurence Harvey, Josephine Chaplin
One Sheet: $3 - $5

ESCAPE TO WITCH MOUNTAIN
(1975 - Buena Vista/Disney) Eddie Albert, Ray Milland
One Sheet: $7 - $15

ESCORT GIRL
(1941 - Continental) -
One Sheet: $75 - $125

ESCORT WEST
(1959 - United Artists) Victor Mature, Elaine Stewart
One Sheet: $5 - $10

ESKIMO
(1934 - MGM) Mala, Lotus, W. S. Van Dyke
One Sheet: $150 - $300

One Sheet

ESPECIALLY ON SUNDAY
(1993 - Miramax) Bruno Ganz, Ornella Muti
One Sheet: $3 - $5   *Italian.*

ESPIONAGE
(1937 - MGM) Edmund Lowe, Madge Evans
One Sheet: $75 - $150

ESPIONAGE AGENT
(1939 - Warner Bros.) Joel McCrea, Brenda Marshall
One Sheet: $75 - $125

ESTHER AND THE KING
(1960 - 20th Century Fox) Joan Collins, Richard Egan
One Sheet: $10 - $20

ESTHER WATERS
(1948 - GFD) Dirk Bogarde, Kathleen Ryan
One Sheet: $30 - $50

ET SATAN CONDUITE LE BAL
(19?? - Vadim) Catherine Deneuve
One Sheet: $30 - $50   *French.*

E.T., THE EXTRA-TERRESTRIAL
(1982 - Universal) Dee Wallace, Henry Thomas
One Sheet: $20 - $40   *Price is for Stle A one sheet. One Sheet(Style B, bicycle):$200-400. One Sheet(spaceship landing):$75-$125.*

One Sheet (Style A)

E.T., THE EXTRA-TERRESTRIAL
(1985R - Universal) Dee Wallace, Henry Thomas
One Sheet: $7 - $15   *Re-release.*

ETERNAL FEMININE, THE
(1931 - Paramount) Guy Newall, Doria March
One Sheet: $150 - $300

ETERNAL FLAME, THE
(1922 - First National) Norma Talmadge
One Sheet: $700 - $1,200

ETERNAL LOVE
(1929 - United Artists) John Barrymore, Dir: Ernst Lubitsch
One Sheet: $600 - $1,000

ETERNAL SEA, THE
(1955 - Republic) Sterling Hayden, Alexis Smith
One Sheet: $10 - $20

ETERNAL SIN, THE
(1917 - Selznick) Florence Reed
One Sheet: $250 - $600

ETERNAL SUMMER
(1961 - Viscaya) Gwen DeCastro, Jeff Brown
One Sheet: $10 - $20

ETERNAL TWO, THE
(1923 - -) Corliss Palmer
One Sheet: $250 - $600

ETERNALLY YOURS
(1939 - United Artists) Loretta Young, David Niven
One Sheet: $100 - $200

ETHAN FROME
(1993 - Miramax) Liam Neeson, Patricia Arquette
One Sheet: $3 - $5

ETHEL SMITH AND THE HENRY KING ORCHESTRA
(1950 - Universal) Ethel Smith
One Sheet: $75 - $125

EUREKA
(1985 - MGM) Gene Hackman, Theresa Russell, Rutger Hauer
One Sheet: $5 - $10

EUROPEANS, THE
(1979 - Levitt-Pickman) Lee Remick
One Sheet: $5 - $10

EVA
(1965 - Times) Jeanne Moreau, Stanley Baker
One Sheet: $15 - $25
French(47x63):$125-250.

EVANGELINE
(1919 - Fox) Miriam Cooper, Albert Roscoe
One Sheet: $350 - $750

EVANGELINE
(1929 - United Artists) Dolores Del Rio, Rolan Drew
One Sheet: $200 - $400

EVE
(1969 - Commonwealth United) Celeste Tarnall, Robert Walker, Herbert Lom
One Sheet: $5 - $10

EVE AND THE DRAGON
(1960 - AIP) -
One Sheet: $7 - $15

EVE KNEW HER APPLES

(1945 - Columbia) Ann Miller, William Wright
One Sheet: $75 - $125

EVE OF ST. MARK, THE
(1944 - 20th Century Fox) Anne Baxter, William Eythe
One Sheet: $50 - $100

EVE'S LEAVES
(1926 - Producer's Dist.) Leatrice Joy, Dir: Cecil B. DeMille
One Sheet: $250 - $500

EVE'S LOVE LETTERS
(1927 - Pathe) Laurel & Hardy
One Sheet: $4,000 - $6,000

EVEL KNIEVEL
(1971 - Fanfare) George Hamilton, Sue Lyon
One Sheet: $15 - $30   *Sports Movie Posters #273. Price is for both styles.*

EVELYN PRENTICE
(1934 - MGM) Myrna Loy, William Powell, Rosalind Russell (film debut)
One Sheet: $800 - $1,500

EVEN AS I.O.U.
(1942 - Columbia) The Three Stooges (Curly)
One Sheet: $3,500 - $5,000   *Comedy short. Duotone.*

EVEN COWGIRLS GET THE BLUES
(1994 - Fine Line) Uma Thurman, John Hurt
One Sheet: $7 - $15

EVENING STAR, THE
(1996 - Paramount) Shirley McLaine, Jack Nicholson, Juliette Lewis
One Sheet: $5 - $10

EVENING WITH BATMAN AND ROBIN, AN
(1965R - Columbia) Robert Lowery, John Duncan
One Sheet: $50 - $100   *Re-release of BATMAN AND ROBIN serial.*

EVENINGS FOR SALE
(1932 - Paramount Publix) Herbert Marshall, Mary Boland
One Sheet: $150 - $300

EVENSONG
(1934 - Gaumont) Emlyn Williams, Evelyn Laye
One Sheet: $75 - $150

EVER IN MY HEART
(1933 - Warner Bros.) Barbara Stanwyck, Ralph Bellamy
One Sheet: $250 - $600

EVER SINCE EVE
(1934 - Fox) George O'Brien, Mary Brian
One Sheet: $200 - $400

EVER SINCE EVE
(1937 - Warner Bros.) Robert Montgomery, Marion Davies
One Sheet: $150 - $300

EVER SINCE VENUS
(1944 - Columbia) Ina Ray Hutton, Ann Savage
One Sheet: $50 - $100

EVERGREEN
(1934 - Gaumont) Jessie Matthews, Sonnie Hale
One Sheet: $100 - $200

EVERY BASTARD A KING
(1970 - Continental) Pier Angeli, William Berger
One Sheet: $5 - $10

EVERY DAY IS A HOLIDAY
(1966 - Columbia) Marisol, Angel Peralta
One Sheet: $5 - $10

EVERY DAY'S A HOLIDAY
(1937 - Paramount) Mae West, Edmund Lowe
One Sheet: $800 - $1,500

EVERY GIRL SHOULD BE MARRIED
(1948 - RKO) Cary Grant, Franchot Tone
One Sheet: $50 - $100

EVERY LITTLE CROOK AND NANNY
(1972 - MGM) Victor Mature, Lynn Redgrave
One Sheet: $3 - $5

EVERY NIGHT AT EIGHT
(1935 - Paramount) George Raft, Alice Faye
One Sheet: $250 - $500

EVERY SATURDAY NIGHT

(1936 - 20th Century Fox) June Lang, Thomas Beck
One Sheet: $75 - $150

One Sheet

EVERY SPARROW MUST FALL
(1964 - Jay Gee) Robert Shea
One Sheet: $10 - $20

EVERY TIME WE SAY GOODBYE
(1987 - -) Tom Hanks, Christina Marsillach
One Sheet: $7 - $15

EVERY WEEK A BIG STAR
(1934 - Warner Bros.) Stock promo poster
One Sheet: $2,200 - $3,500

EVERY WHICH WAY BUT LOOSE
(1978 - Warner Bros.) Clint Eastwood, Sondra Locke, Beverly D'Angelo
One Sheet: $15 - $25   *Price is for both styles.*

EVERY WOMAN'S MAN
(1933 - MGM) Myrna Loy, Max Baer, Otto Krueger
One Sheet: $200 - $400   *British. Sports (Boxing). AKA:The Prizefighter And The Lady.*

EVERYBODY DANCE
(1936 - Gaumont-British) Ernest Truex, C. Courtneidge
One Sheet: $75 - $150

EVERYBODY DOES IT
(1949 - 20th Century Fox) Paul Douglas, Linda Darnell
One Sheet: $30 - $50

EVERYBODY SING
(1938 - MGM) Judy Garland, Fanny Brice
One Sheet: $350 - $750

EVERYBODY WINS
(1990 - -) Debra Winger, Nick Nolte
One Sheet: $5 - $10

EVERYBODY'S ALL-AMERICAN
(1988 - Warner Bros.) Jessica Lange, Dennis Quaid
One Sheet: $3 - $5   *Sports Movie Posters #213.*

EVERYBODY'S BABY
(1939 - 20th Century Fox) Jed Prouty, Spring Byington
One Sheet: $75 - $125

EVERYBODY'S DANCIN'
(1950 - Lippert) Spade Cooley, Richard Lane
One Sheet: $40 - $75

EVERYBODY'S DOING IT
(1938 - RKO) Sally Eilers, Preston Foster
One Sheet: $75 - $150

EVERYBODY'S HOBBY
(1939 - Warner Bros.) Irene Rich, Jackie Maran
One Sheet: $30 - $50

EVERYBODY'S OLD MAN
(1936 - 20th Century Fox) Rochelle Hudson, Johnny Downs
One Sheet: $75 - $150

EVERYMAN'S LAW
(1936 - Republic) Johnny Mack Brown, Beth Marion
One Sheet: $75 - $150

EVERYONE SAYS I LOVE YOU
(1996 - Miramax) Woody Allen, Goldie Hawn, Julia Roberts, Drew Barrymore
One Sheet: $5 - $10

EVERYTHING BUT THE TRUTH
(1956 - Universal) Maureen O'Hara, John Forsythe
One Sheet: $15 - $35

EVERYTHING HAPPENS AT NIGHT
(1939 - 20th Century Fox) Sonja Henie, Ray Milland, Robert Cummings
One Sheet: $75 - $150

One Sheet

EVERYTHING HAPPENS TO ME
(1938 - Warner Bros.) Max Miller, Dorthy Bouchier
One Sheet: $75 - $150

EVERYTHING I HAVE IS YOURS
(1952 - MGM) Dennis O'Keefe, Marge & Gower Champion
One Sheet: $30 - $50

EVERYTHING IN LIFE
(1936 - Columbia) Gitta Alpar, Neil Hamilton
One Sheet: $125 - $250

EVERYTHING IS RHYTHM
(1940 - Astor) Harry Roy, Princess Pearl
One Sheet: $150 - $300

EVERYTHING IS THUNDER
(1936 - Gaumont-British) Constance Bennett, Oscar Homolka
One Sheet: $75 - $125

EVERYTHING OKAY
(1936 - City) Betty Fields, Leslie Bradley
One Sheet: $50 - $100

EVERYTHING YOU ALWAYS WANTED TO KNOW ABOUT SEX BUT WERE AFRAID TO ASK
(1972 - United Artists) Woody Allen, Gene Wilder, Burt Reynolds
One Sheet: $15 - $30   *Advance:$15-25. One Sheet (Style B):$30-$50.*

EVERYTHING'S BEEN DONE BEFORE
(1935 - MGM) Jean Harlow, William Powell
One Sheet: $1,900 - $3,000

EVERYTHING'S DUCKY
(1961 - Columbia) Mickey Rooney, Buddy Hackett
One Sheet: $10 - $20

EVERYTHING'S ON ICE
(1939 - RKO) Irene Dare, Edgar Kennedy
One Sheet: $75 - $125

EVERYTHING'S ROSIE
(1931 - RKO) Anita Louise, Robert Woolsey
One Sheet: $150 - $300

EVICTORS, THE
(1979 - AIP) Vic Morrow, Jessica Harper
One Sheet: $5 - $10

EVIDENCE
(1929 - Warner Bros.) Pauline Frederick, Conway Tearle
One Sheet: $250 - $600

EVIL, THE
(1978 - New World) Richard Crenna, Victor Buono
One Sheet: $7 - $15

EVIL CLUTCH
(1988 - -) Caralina Tassoni, Diego Ribon
One Sheet: $5 - $10

EVIL DEAD, THE
(1983 - Renaissance) Bruce Campbell, Ellen Sandweiss
One Sheet: $30 - $60

EVIL DEAD 2, THE
(1987 - -) Bruce Campbell, Sarah Berry
One Sheet: $15 - $25

EVIL EYE
(1964 - AIP) John Saxon, Leticia Roman, Dir: Bava
One Sheet: $30 - $50

EVIL IN THE DEEP
(1976 - D&R) Stephen Boyd, Rosey Grier, Cheryl Ladd, Chuck Woolery
One Sheet: $5 - $10   *AKA: THE TREASURE OF JAMAICA REEF.*

EVIL LAUGH
(1987 - -) Steven Baio, Dominick Brascia
One Sheet: $5 - $10

EVIL OF FRANKENSTEIN, THE
(1964 - Universal) Peter Cushing, James Maxwell
One Sheet: $75 - $150   *Graven Images, pg. 215.*

EVIL OF FRANKENSTEIN/HYSTERIA
(1965R - Universal) -
One Sheet: $30 - $50   *Re-release double feature poster.*

EVIL THAT MEN DO, THE
(1984 - ITC) Charles Bronson, Theresa Saldana, Joseph Maher
One Sheet: $5 - $10

EVIL UNDER THE SUN
(1982 - Universal) Peter Ustinov, Jane Birkin
One Sheet: $3 - $5

EVILSPEAK
(1982 - Moreno) Clint Howard, R. G. Armstrong
One Sheet: $5 - $10

EVITA
(1996 - Hollywood) Madonna, Antonio Banderas
One Sheet: $7 - $15

EX-BAD BOY
(1931 - Universal) Robert Armstrong, Jean Arthur
One Sheet: $200 - $400

EXCALIBUR
(1981 - Warner Bros.) Nicol Williamson, Nigel Terry, Helen Mirren
One Sheet: $40 - $75   *Bob Peak art. Advance(not Peak):$30-60.*

EXCESS BAGGAGE
(1926 - Educational) Big Boy
One Sheet: $200 - $400

EXCESS BAGGAGE
(1933 - Real Art) Frank Pettingell, Claud Allister
One Sheet: $100 - $200

EXCESSIVE FORCE
(1993 - New Line) Thomas Ian Griffith, James Earl Jones, Lance Henriksen
One Sheet: $3 - $5

EX-CHAMP
(1939 - Universal) Victor McLaglen, Tom Brown
One Sheet: $75 - $150   *Sports (Boxing).*

EXCHANGE, THE
(1996 - Columbia) Jean-Claude Van Damme, Natasha Henstridge
One Sheet: $4 - $8

EXCITEMENT
(1924 - Universal) Laura La Plante, Edward Hearne
One Sheet: $250 - $500

EXCLUSIVE
(1937 - Paramount) Fred MacMurray, Frances Farmer
One Sheet: $150 - $300

EXCLUSIVE STORY
(1936 - MGM) Franchot Tone, Madge Evans
One Sheet: $100 - $200

EXCUSE MY DUST
(1951 - MGM) Red Skelton, Sally Forrest
One Sheet: $50 - $100

EXCUSE MY DUST
(1962R - MGM) Red Skelton, Sally Forrest

One Sheet: $7 - $15   *Re-release.*

EXCUSE MY GLOVE
(1936 - Alexander) Len Harvey, Betty Ann Davies
One Sheet: $100 - $200

EXECUTIONER, THE
(1970 - Columbia) George Peppard, Joan Collins
One Sheet: $7 - $15

EXECUTIONER, THE
(1985 - -) Valerie Harper, Michael Lerner
One Sheet: $3 - $5

EXECUTIVE ACTION
(1973 - National General) Burt Lancaster, Robert Ryan
One Sheet: $5 - $10

EXECUTIVE DECISION
(1996 - Warner Bros.) Kurt Russell
One Sheet: $4 - $8

EXECUTIVE SUITE
(1954 - MGM) William Holden, June Allyson
One Sheet: $30 - $50

EX-FLAME
(1931 - Tiffany) Neil Hamilton, Marian Nixon
One Sheet: $150 - $300

EXILE, THE
(1931 - Empire) Eunice Brooks, Dir: Oscar Micheaux
One Sheet: $1,300 - $2,000   *Black cast. Separate Cinema, pg. 12.*

EXILE, THE
(1948 - Universal) Douglas Fairbanks, Jr., Maria Montez, Nigel Bruce
One Sheet: $30 - $50

EXILE EXPRESS
(1939 - United Players) Anna Sten, Alan Marshall
One Sheet: $50 - $100

EXILED TO SHANGHAI
(1937 - Republic) June Travis, Wallace Ford
One Sheet: $75 - $125

EXILES, THE
(1923 - -) John Gilbert
One Sheet: $200 - $400

EXIT THE DRAGON, ENTER THE TIGER
(1977 - Dimension) David Lee
One Sheet: $20 - $40

EXIT TO EDEN
(1994 - Savoy) Dana Delany, Iman, Dan Aykroid, Rosie O'Donnell
One Sheet: $4 - $8

EX-LADY
(1933 - Warner Bros.) Bette Davis, Gene Raymond
One Sheet: $5,000 - $8,000

EX-MRS. BRADFORD, THE
(1936 - RKO) William Powell, Jean Arthur
One Sheet: $500 - $800

EXODUS
(1960 - United Artists) Paul Newman, Eva Marie Saint
One Sheet: $75 - $125   *Saul Bass art.*

EXORCIST, THE
(1973 - Warner Bros.) Ellen Burstyn, Max von Sydow, Linda Blair
One Sheet: $30 - $60

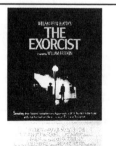
One Sheet

EXORCIST II: THE HERETIC
(1977 - Warner Bros.) Richard Burton, Linda Blair
One Sheet: $10 - $20

EXORCIST III, THE
(1990 - -) George C. Scott
One Sheet: $5 - $10

EXOTIC ONES, THE
(1968 - Ormond) Ron Ormond, June Ormond
One Sheet: $15 - $25

EXOTICA
(1995 - Miramax) Bruce Greenwood, Mia Kirshner
One Sheet: $5 - $10

EXPENSIVE HUSBANDS
(1937 - Warner Bros.) Beverly Roberts, Patric Knowles
One Sheet: $75 - $125

EXPENSIVE WOMEN
(1931 - Warner Bros.) Dolores Costello, Warren William
One Sheet: $600 - $1,000

EXPERIENCE PREFERRED...BUT NOT ESSENTIAL
(1983 - Goldwyn) Elizabeth Edmonds
One Sheet: $3 - $5

EXPERIMENT ALCATRAZ
(1950 - RKO) John Howard, Joan Dixon
One Sheet: $30 - $50

EXPERIMENT IN TERROR
(1963 - Columbia) Glenn Ford, Lee Remick
One Sheet: $10 - $20

EXPERIMENT PERILOUS
(1944 - RKO) Hedy Lamarr, George Brent
One Sheet: $50 - $100

EXPERT, THE
(1932 - Vitaphone) Lois Wilson, Dickie Moore
One Sheet: $75 - $150

EXPERT'S OPINION
(1935 - Paramount) Lucille Lisle, Leslie Perrins
One Sheet: $125 - $250

EXPERTS, THE
(1989 - Paramount) John Travolta, Ayre Gross
One Sheet: $5 - $10

EXPLORER, THE
(1931 - Educational) Paul Terry Toons
One Sheet: $500 - $800   *Cartoon. Cartoon Movie Posters #75.*

EXPLORERS
(1985 - Paramount) Ethan Hawke, River Phoenix
One Sheet: $7 - $15

EXPLOSION
(1970 - AIP) Don Stroud, Gordon Thomson
One Sheet: $3 - $5

EXPLOSIVE GENERATION, THE
(1961 - United Artists) William Shatner, Patty McCormack
One Sheet: $15 - $25

EXPOSED
(1932 - Eagle) Barbara Kent, Raymond Hatton
One Sheet: $100 - $200

EXPOSED
(1938 - Universal) Glenda Farrell, Otto Kruger
One Sheet: $50 - $100

EXPOSED
(1947 - Republic) Adele Mara, Robert Scott
One Sheet: $30 - $60

EXPOSED
(1983 - MGM/United Artists) Nastassia Kinski, Rudolph Nureyev
One Sheet: $10 - $20

EXPRESS MESSENGER
(1919 - A1) Helen Holmes
One Sheet: $150 - $300

EXPRESSO BONGO
(1960 - Continental) Laurence Harvey, Sylvia Syms
One Sheet: $30 - $50

EXQUISITE LAKE LOUISE

(1915 - Paramount) -
One Sheet: $500 - $800   *Paramount Travel Pictures series.*

EXTERMINATOR, THE
(1980 - Avco) Robert Ginty, Christopher George
One Sheet: $5 - $10

EXTERMINATOR 2
(1984 - Cannon) Robert Ginty, Mario Van Peebles
One Sheet: $3 - $5

EXTORTION
(1938 - Columbia) Scott Colton, Mary Russell
One Sheet: $75 - $150

EXTRA DAY, THE
(1956 - British Lion) Richard Basehart, Simone Simon
One Sheet: $15 - $25

EXTRA GIRL, THE
(1923 - Associated Exhibitors) Mabel Normand, Ralph Graves
One Sheet: $250 - $500

EXTRAORDINARY SEAMAN, THE
(1969 - MGM) David Niven, Faye Dunaway, Alan Alda, Mickey Rooney
One Sheet: $7 - $15

EXTRAVAGANCE
(1930 - Tiffany) Owen Moore, June Collyer
One Sheet: $150 - $300

EXTREME CLOSE-UP
(1973 - National General) James McMullan, Kate Woodville
One Sheet: $3 - $5

EXTREME MEASURES
(1996 - Columbia) Hugh Grant, Gene Hackman
One Sheet: $5 - $10

EXTREME PREJUDICE
(1987 - TriStar) Nick Nolte, Powers Boothe, Maria Conchita Alonso
One Sheet: $3 - $5

EXTREMITIES
(1986 - Atlantic) Farrah Fawcett, James Russo
One Sheet: $3 - $5

EYE CREATURES, THE
(1965 - AIP) John Ashley, Cynthia Hull
One Sheet: $15 - $30

EYE FOR AN EYE, AN
(1966 - Embassy) Robert Lansing, Pat Wayne, Slim Pickens
One Sheet: $5 - $10

EYE FOR AN EYE, AN
(1975 - Embassy) Tom Basham, Gene Carlson
One Sheet: $3 - $5

EYE FOR AN EYE, AN
(1981 - Avco/Embassy) Chuck Norris, Christopher Lee
One Sheet: $5 - $10

EYE FOR AN EYE
(1995 - Paramount) Kiefer Sutherland, Sally Field
One Sheet: $3 - $5

EYE FOR EYE
(1918 - Metro) Nazimova
One Sheet: $300 - $700

EYE OF DEATH, THE
(192? - Capital) James J. Corbett
One Sheet: $200 - $400

EYE OF THE CAT
(1969 - Universal) Michael Sarrazin, Gayle Hunnicutt, Eleanor Parker
One Sheet: $5 - $10

EYE OF THE DEVIL
(1967 - MGM) David Niven, Deborah Kerr, Sharon Tate
One Sheet: $7 - $15

EYE OF THE NEEDLE
(1981 - United Artists) Donald Sutherland, Kate Nelligan
One Sheet: $5 - $10

EYE OF THE TIGER
(1986 - Scotti Bros.) Gary Busey, Yaphet Kotto
One Sheet: $3 - $5

EYE WITNESS
(1949 - Eagle-Lion) Robert Montgomery, Leslie Banks
One Sheet: $30 - $50

EYE WITNESS
(1956 - Rank) Donald Sinden, Belinda Lee
One Sheet: $15 - $25

EYES IN THE NIGHT
(1942 - MGM) Edward Arnold, Ann Harding
One Sheet: $75 - $125

EYES OF A STRANGER
(1981 - Warner Bros.) Lauren Tewes, Jennifer Jason Leigh, John DiSanti
One Sheet: $5 - $10

EYES OF AMARYLLIS, THE
(1982 - -) Jonathan Boyd, Ruth Ford
One Sheet: $3 - $5

EYES OF ANNIE JONES, THE
(1964 - 20th Century Fox) Richard Conte, Francesca Annis
One Sheet: $5 - $10

EYES OF FATE
(1933 - Universal) Allan Jeayes, Valerie Hobson
One Sheet: $125 - $250

EYES OF HELL
(1961 - Warner Bros.) Paul Stevens, Claudette Nevins
One Sheet: $20 - $40   *3-D. AKA: THE MASK.*

EYES OF LAURA MARS
(1978 - Columbia) Faye Dunaway, Tommy Lee Jones
One Sheet: $10 - $20

EYES OF TEXAS
(1948 - Republic) Roy Rogers, Lynne Roberts
One Sheet: $100 - $200

EYES OF TEXAS
(1952R - Republic) Roy Rogers, Lynne Roberts
One Sheet: $40 - $75   *Re-release.*

EYES OF THE FOREST
(1923 - Fox) Tom Mix, Pauline Starke, Sid Jordan
One Sheet: $250 - $600

EYES OF THE JUNGLE
(1953 - Arrow) Jon Hall
One Sheet: $15 - $30

EYES OF THE UNDERWORLD
(1942 - Universal) Wendy Barrie, Richard Dix, Lon Chaney, Jr.
One Sheet: $100 - $200

EYES OF THE WORLD, THE
(1917 - Classics Cinema) Jane Novak, Jack Livingston
One Sheet: $200 - $400

One Sheet

EYES OF THE WORLD, THE
(1930 - United Artists) Hugh Huntley, Una Merkel
One Sheet: $150 - $300

EYES OF YOUTH
(1919 - -) Rudolph Valentino
One Sheet: $600 - $1,000

EYES THAT KILL
(1947 - Condor) Robert Berkeley, Sandra Dorne
One Sheet: $30 - $50

EYEWITNESS
(1981 - 20th Century Fox) William Hurt, Sigourney Weaver, Christopher Plummer
One Sheet: $5 - $10

F FOR FAKE
(1973 - -) Orson Welles
One Sheet: $30 - $50

F MAN
(1936 - Paramount) Jack Haley, William Frawley
One Sheet: $100 - $200

FABIAN OF THE YARD
(1954 - Eros) Bruce Seton, Richard Pearson
One Sheet: $15 - $25

FABIOLA
(1951 - United Artists) Michele Morgan, Henri Vidal
One Sheet: $15 - $25

FABLE, A
(1971 - MFR) Al Freeman, Jr., Hildy Brooks
One Sheet: $3 - $5   *AKA: THE SLAVE.*

FABULOUS BAKER BOYS, THE
(1989 - 20th Century Fox) Michelle Pfeiffer, Beau Bridges, Jeff Bridges
One Sheet: $7 - $15

FABULOUS DORSEYS, THE
(1947 - United Artists) Tommy Dorsey, Jimmy Dorsey, Janet Blair
One Sheet: $125 - $250   *Big Band Musical.*

FABULOUS JOE, THE
(1947 - Hal Roach Studios) Walter Abel, Marie Wilson
One Sheet: $40 - $75

FABULOUS SENORITA, THE
(1952 - Republic) Estelita Rodriguez, Robert Clarke
One Sheet: $15 - $25

FABULOUS SUZANNE, THE
(1946 - Republic) Barbara Britton, Rudy Vallee
One Sheet: $40 - $75

FABULOUS TEXAN, THE
(1947 - Republic) William Elliott, John Carroll
One Sheet: $30 - $60

FABULOUS WORLD OF JULES VERNE, THE
(1961 - Warner Bros.) Lubor Tolos, Arnest Navratil
One Sheet: $30 - $50   *Graven Images, pg. 176.*

FACE AT THE WINDOW, THE
(1932 - RKO) Raymond Massey, Isla Bevan
One Sheet: $125 - $250

FACE AT THE WINDOW, THE
(1939 - British Lion) Tod Slaughter, Marjorie Taylor
One Sheet: $75 - $150

FACE BEHIND THE MASK, THE
(1941 - Columbia) Peter Lorre, Evelyn Keyes
One Sheet: $150 - $300   *Graven Images, pg. 131.*

FACE BEHIND THE SCAR
(1940 - Premier/Stafford) Griffith Jones, Rosalyn Boulter
One Sheet: $75 - $150

FACE IN THE CROWD, A
(1957 - Warner Bros.) Andy Griffith(film debut), Patricia Neal
One Sheet: $40 - $75

FACE IN THE FOG, A
(1936 - Victory) June Collyer, Lloyd Hughes
One Sheet: $100 - $200

FACE IN THE RAIN, A
(1963 - Embassy) Rory Calhoun
One Sheet: $15 - $25

FACE IN THE SKY, THE
(1933 - Fox) Spencer Tracy, Marian Nixon
One Sheet: $250 - $500

FACE OF A FUGITIVE
(1959 - Columbia) Fred MacMurray, James Coburn
One Sheet: $10 - $20

FACE OF A STRANGER
(1964 - Allied Artists) Jeremy Kemp, Jean Marsh
One Sheet: $7 - $15

FACE OF FIRE
(1958 - Allied Artists) Cameron Mitchell, James Whitmore
One Sheet: $15 - $25

FACE OF FU MANCHU, THE
(1965 - Seven Arts) Christopher Lee, Nigel Green
One Sheet: $30 - $60

FACE OF MARBLE, THE
(1946 - Monogram) John Carradine, Claudia Drake
One Sheet: $50 - $100

FACE OF THE CAT, THE
(1959 - MGM) Francoise Arnoul, Bernard Wicki
One Sheet: $30 - $50   AKA: The Cat.

FACE OF THE SCREAMING WEREWOLF
(1965 - Diana) Lon Chaney Jr., Landa Varle
One Sheet: $30 - $50   AKA: HOUSE OF TERROR.

FACE ON THE BARROOM FLOOR, THE
(1914 - Keystone) Charlie Chaplin
One Sheet: $10,000 - $15,000

FACE ON THE BARROOM FLOOR, THE
(1932 - Invincible) Dulcie Cooper, Alice Ward
One Sheet: $150 - $300

FACE TO FACE
(1952 - RKO) James Mason, Robert Preston
One Sheet: $15 - $30

FACE TO FACE
(1975 - Paramount) Liv Ullmann, Erland Josephson, Dir: Ingmar Bergman
One Sheet: $15 - $35

FACE VALUE
(1927 - Sterling) Fritzie Ridgeway, Gene Gowing, Joe Bonner
One Sheet: $200 - $400

FACES
(1934 - Paramount) Anna Lee, Harold French
One Sheet: $150 - $350

FACES
(1968 - Continental) John Marley, Gena Rowlands, Lynn Carlin
One Sheet: $50 - $100

FACES IN THE DARK
(1960 - Rank) John Gregson, Mai Zetterling
One Sheet: $15 - $30

FACES IN THE FOG
(1944 - Republic) Jane Withers, Paul Kelly
One Sheet: $50 - $100

FACING THE MUSIC
(1933 - Wardour) Stanley Lupino, Nancy Brown
One Sheet: $100 - $200

FACING THE MUSIC
(1941 - Butcher) Bunny Doyle, Betty Driver
One Sheet: $50 - $100

FACTS OF LIFE, THE
(1960 - United Artists) Bob Hope, Lucille Ball
One Sheet: $30 - $50

FACTS OF LOVE
(1949 - Oxford) Gordon Harker, Betty Balfour
One Sheet: $30 - $50

FADE TO BLACK
(1980 - American Cinema) Dennis Christopher, Mickey Rourke
One Sheet: $5 - $10

FAHRENHEIT 451
(1967 - Universal) Oskar Werner, Julie Christie
One Sheet: $50 - $100   British One Sheet (Style B):$250. Graven Images, pg. 222.

FAILSAFE
(1964 - Columbia) Dan O'Herlihy, Walter Matthau
One Sheet: $15 - $30

FAINT PERFUME
(1925 - Schulberg) Seena Owen, William Powell
One Sheet: $600 - $1,000

FAIR BUT FOOLISH
(1926 - Educational) Jimmie Adams
One Sheet: $125 - $250

FAIR CO-ED, THE
(1927 - MGM) Marion Davies, Johnny Mack Brown
One Sheet: $250 - $500

FAIR EXCHANGE
(1936 - Warner Bros.) Patric Knowles, Roscoe Ates
One Sheet: $100 - $200

FAIR GAME
(1995 - Warner Bros.) William Baldwin, Cindy Crawford
One Sheet: $7 - $15

One Sheet

FAIR WARNING
(1930 - Fox) George O'Brien, George Brent
One Sheet: $250 - $500   Cowboy Movie Posters #85.

FAIR WARNING
(1937 - 20th Century Fox) Betty Furness, J. Edward Bromberg
One Sheet: $75 - $150

FAIR WIND TO JAVA
(1953 - Republic) Fred MacMurray, Vera Ralston
One Sheet: $15 - $30

FAITHFUL
(1936 - Warner Bros.) Jean Muir, Gene Gerrard
One Sheet: $100 - $200

FAITHFUL CITY
(1952 - RKO) Jamie Smith, John Slater
One Sheet: $15 - $25

FAITHFUL HEART
(1933 - Gaumont) Herbert Marshall, Edna Best
One Sheet: $100 - $200

FAITHFUL IN MY FASHION
(1946 - MGM) Donna Reed, Tom Drake
One Sheet: $50 - $100

FAITHFUL SERVITOR, THE
(1913 - Gaumont) -
One Sheet: $250 - $600

FAITHLESS
(1932 - MGM) Tallulah Bankhead, Robert Montgomery
One Sheet: $1,600 - $2,500

FAKE, THE
(1953 - United Artists) Dennis O'Keefe, Coleen Gray
One Sheet: $15 - $25

FAKE'S PROGRESS
(1950 - Falcon) Lou Cass, Harry Nova
One Sheet: $15 - $25

FALCON AND THE CO-EDS, THE
(1943 - RKO) Tom Conway, Jean Brooks, Isabel Jewell
One Sheet: $75 - $150

FALCON AND THE SNOWMAN, THE
(1985 - Orion) Timothy Hutton, Sean Penn
One Sheet: $5 - $10

FALCON IN DANGER, THE
(1943 - RKO) Tom Conway, Jean Brooks, Elaine Shepard
One Sheet: $75 - $150

FALCON IN HOLLYWOOD, THE
(1944 - RKO) Tom Conway, Barbara Hale,

Veda Ann Borg
One Sheet: $75 - $150

FALCON IN MEXICO, THE
(1944 - RKO) Tom Conway, Mona Maris
One Sheet: $50 - $100

FALCON IN SAN FRANCISCO, THE
(1945 - RKO) Tom Conway, Rita Corday
One Sheet: $50 - $100

FALCON OUT WEST, THE
(1944 - RKO) Tom Conway, Barbara Hale, Lyle Talbot
One Sheet: $50 - $100

FALCON STRIKES BACK, THE
(1943 - RKO) Tom Conway, Harriet Hilliard (Nelson)
One Sheet: $75 - $150

FALCON TAKES OVER, THE
(1942 - RKO) George Sanders, Lynn Bari
One Sheet: $100 - $200

FALCON'S ADVENTURE, THE
(1947 - RKO) Tom Conway, Madge Meredith
One Sheet: $40 - $75

FALCON'S ALIBI, THE
(1946 - RKO) Tom Conway, Rita Corday
One Sheet: $40 - $75

FALCON'S BROTHER, THE
(1942 - RKO) George Sanders, Tom Conway, Jane Randolph
One Sheet: $100 - $200

FALL GIRL
(1961 - Medallion) John Agar, Greta Chi
One Sheet: $7 - $15

FALL GUY, THE
(1920 - -) Larry Semon
One Sheet: $200 - $400

FALL GUY, THE
(1930 - RKO) Jack Mulhall, Mae Clarke
One Sheet: $125 - $250

FALL IN
(1942 - Hal Roach Studios) William Tracy, Jean Porter
One Sheet: $50 - $100

FALL OF BABYLON, THE
(1919 - -) Dir: D.W. Griffith
One Sheet: $1,300 - $2,000

FALL OF EVE, THE
(1929 - Columbia) Patsy Ruth Miller
One Sheet: $250 - $500

FALL OF THE HOUSE OF USHER, THE
(1952 - Vigilant) Kay Tendeter, Gwen Watford
One Sheet: $15 - $30

FALL OF THE HOUSE OF USHER, THE
(1960 - AIP) Vincent Price, Mark Damon
One Sheet: $75 - $125   AKA: HOUSE OF USHER.

FALL OF THE ROMAN EMPIRE, THE
(1964 - Paramount) Sophia Loren, Stephen Boyd
One Sheet: $15 - $35

FALL OF THE ROMANOFFS, THE
(1917 - Iliodor) Iliodor (former confidant of Rasputin)
One Sheet: $500 - $900

One Sheet

FALL OUT FALL IN
(1943 - RKO/Disney) Donald Duck

One Sheet: $350 - $750   Cartoon. The Disney Poster, pg. 45.

FALLEN ANGEL
(1945 - 20th Century Fox) Alice Faye, Dana Andrews
One Sheet: $125 - $250

FALLEN ANGEL
(1953R - 20th Century Fox) Alice Faye, Dana Andrews
One Sheet: $40 - $75   Re-release.

FALLEN IDOL, THE
(1949 - British Lion) Bobby Henrey, Ralph Richardson
One Sheet: $125 - $250

FALLEN SPARROW
(1943 - RKO) John Garfield, Maureen O'Hara
One Sheet: $150 - $350

FALLGUY
(1947 - Monogram) Cliff Penn, Teala Loring, Robert Armstrong
One Sheet: $50 - $100

FALLGUY
(1962 - International) Ed Dugan
One Sheet: $5 - $10

FALLING DOWN
(1993 - Warner Bros.) Michael Douglas, Robert Duvall
One Sheet: $3 - $5

FALLING FOR YOU
(1933 - Gainsborough) Jack Hulbert, Tamara Desni
One Sheet: $100 - $200

FALLING FROM GRACE
(1991 - Columbia) John Mellencamp (Debut), Mariel Hemingway
One Sheet: $5 - $10

FALLING IN LOVE
(1984 - Paramount) Robert Di Niro, Meryl Streep
One Sheet: $7 - $15

FALLING IN LOVE AGAIN
(1980 - International Picture Show) Elliot Gould, Susannah York
One Sheet: $3 - $5

FALSE ALARM
(1933 - Columbia) Scrappy
One Sheet: $600 - $1,000   Cartoon. Cartoon Movie Posters #36.

FALSE ALARMS
(1936 - Columbia) Three Stooges (Curly)
One Sheet: $10,000 - $16,000   Comedy short. Duotone.

FALSE COLORS
(1943 - United Artists) William Boyd, Robert Mitchum
One Sheet: $125 - $250

FALSE EVIDENCE
(1919 - Metro) Viola Dana
One Sheet: $250 - $500

FALSE EVIDENCE
(1937 - Paramount) Gwen Gill, Michael Hogarth
One Sheet: $75 - $150

FALSE FACES
(1932 - World Wide) Lowell Sherman
One Sheet: $100 - $200

FALSE FACES

(1943 - Republic) Rex Williams, Bill Henry
One Sheet: $40 - $75

FALSE KISSES
(1921 - Universal) Miss Du Pont, Pat O'Malley
One Sheet: $150 - $300

FALSE MADONNA, THE
(1931 - Paramount Publix) Kay Francis, William "Stage" Boyd
One Sheet: $150 - $300

FALSE PARADISE
(1948 - United Artists) William Boyd, Andy Clyde
One Sheet: $50 - $100   *Hopalong Cassidy series.*

FALSE PRETENSES
(1935 - Chesterfield) Irene Ware, Sidney Blackmer
One Sheet: $50 - $100

FALSE RAPTURE
(1940 - Film Alliance) Otto Kruger, Mary Maguire
One Sheet: $50 - $100

FALSTAFF
(1967 - Peppercorn/Wormser/Saltzman) Orson Welles, Jeanne Moreau, John Gielgud
One Sheet: $20 - $40

FAME
(1936 - General Films) Sydney Howard
One Sheet: $75 - $150

FAME
(1980 - MGM) Irene Cara, Debbie Allen, Dir: Alan Parker
One Sheet: $5 - $10

FAME AND FORTUNE
(1918 - Fox) Tom Mix, Kathleen O'Connor
One Sheet: $600 - $1,000

FAME IS THE SPUR
(1946 - GFD) Michael Redgrave, Rosamund John
One Sheet: $40 - $75

FAME STREET
(1932 - Monogram) Henry B. Walthall, Aileen Pringle
One Sheet: $150 - $300

FAMILY, THE
(1974 - International) Charles Bronson, Telly Savalas
One Sheet: $7 - $15

FAMILY AFFAIR, A
(1937 - MGM) Lionel Barrymore, Spring Byington, Mickey Rooney
One Sheet: $200 - $400

FAMILY AFFAIR
(1954 - Hammer) Bebe Daniels, Ben Lyon
One Sheet: $30 - $50

FAMILY BUSINESS
(1989 - TriStar) Sean Connery, Dustin Hoffman, Matthew Broderick
One Sheet: $5 - $10

FAMILY DIARY
(1963 - Titanus) Marcello Mastroianni
One Sheet: $5 - $10

FAMILY HONEYMOON
(1948 - Universal) Claudette Colbert, Fred MacMurray
One Sheet: $50 - $100

FAMILY HONOR
(1973 - Cinerama) Anthony Page, Vera Visconti
One Sheet: $5 - $10

FAMILY JEWELS, THE
(1965 - Paramount) Jerry Lewis, Donna Butterworth
One Sheet: $20 - $40

FAMILY LIFE
(1971 - Kestrel) Sandy Ratcliff
One Sheet: $3 - $5

FAMILY NEXT DOOR, THE
(1939 - Universal) Hugh Herbert, Joy Hodges
One Sheet: $75 - $125

FAMILY PLOT
(1976 - Universal) Karen Black, Bruce Dern, Dir: Alfred Hitchcock

---

One Sheet: $20 - $40

FAMILY SECRET, THE
(1951 - Columbia) John Derek, Lee J. Cobb
One Sheet: $20 - $40

FAMILY THING, A
(1996 - United Artists) Robert Duvall, James Earl Jones
One Sheet: $3 - $5

FAMILY WAY, THE
(1967 - Warner Bros./Seven Arts) Hayley Mills, John Mills
One Sheet: $15 - $30

FAMOUS FERGUSON CASE, THE
(1932 - First National) Joan Blondell, Leslie Fenton
One Sheet: $200 - $400

FAN, THE
(1949 - 20th Century Fox) Jeanne Crain, Madeleine Carroll, George Sanders
One Sheet: $50 - $100

FAN, THE
(1981 - Paramount) Lauren Bacall, Michael Biehn, James Garner
One Sheet: $5 - $10

FAN, THE
(1996 - TriStar) Robert DeNiro, Wesley Snipes
One Sheet: $5 - $10   *Psycho-thriller.*

FAN FAN THE TULIP
(1952 - Lopert) Gina Lollobrigida
One Sheet: $30 - $50   *AKA: SOLDIER IN LOVE.*

FAN'S NOTES, A
(1972 - Warner Bros.) Jerry Orbach, Burgess Meredith
One Sheet: $3 - $5

FANCY BAGGAGE
(1929 - Warner Bros.) Myrna Loy, George Fawcett
One Sheet: $250 - $600

FANCY PANTS
(1950 - Paramount) Bob Hope, Lucille Ball
One Sheet: $40 - $75

FANCY PANTS
(1962R - Paramount) Bob Hope, Lucille Ball
One Sheet: $15 - $35   *Re-release.*

FANDANGO
(1970 - Tivoli) James Whitworth
One Sheet: $3 - $5

FANDANGO
(1985 - -) Kevin Costner, Judd Nelson
One Sheet: $10 - $20

FANG AND CLAW
(1935 - Van Beuren) Frank Buck
One Sheet: $250 - $500

FANGS
(1926 - Sun) Eileen Sedgwick, Lightnin'
One Sheet: $200 - $400

FANGS OF DESTINY
(1927 - -) Edmund Cobb, Dynamite(the dog)
One Sheet: $250 - $600

FANGS OF THE ARCTIC
(1953 - Monogram) Kirby Grant, Lorna Hansen
One Sheet: $20 - $40

FANGS OF THE WILD
(1954 - Lippert) Charles Chaplin Jr., Onslow Stevens
One Sheet: $15 - $30

FANNY
(1948 - Pagnol) Raimu, Pierre Fresnay
One Sheet: $50 - $100

FANNY
(1961 - Warner Bros.) Maurice Chevalier, Leslie Caron, Charles Boyer
One Sheet: $15 - $30

FANNY AND ALEXANDER
(1983 - Embassy) Pernilla Allwin, Bertil Guve
One Sheet: $20 - $40

FANNY BY GASLIGHT
(1944 - Gainsborough) Phyllis Calvert, James Mason

One Sheet: $30 - $50

FANNY FOLEY HERSELF
(1931 - RKO) Edna May Oliver, Rochelle Hudson
One Sheet: $125 - $250

FANNY HILL
(1965 - Favorite) Miriam Hopkins, Letitia Roman
One Sheet: $15 - $25

FANNY HILL
(1971 - Cinemation) Diana Kjaer, Hans Ernback
One Sheet: $5 - $10

FANNY HILL/INGA
(1971 - Cinemation) -
One Sheet: $5 - $10   *Double feature poster.*

FANNY'S WEDDING DAY
(1933 - Educational) Paul Terry Toons
Cartoon. See "Terrytoons Stock" for prices. Cartoon Movie Posters #80.

FANTASIA
(1940 - RKO/Disney) Mickey Mouse
One Sheet: $4,000 - $6,500   *Cartoon. Cartoon Movie Posters #337-#349. The Disney Poster, pg. 81.*

FANTASIA
(1946R - RKO/Disney) Mickey Mouse
One Sheet: $250 - $600   *Re-release. Cartoon.*

FANTASIA
(1950R - Disney) Mickey Mouse
One Sheet: $50 - $100   *Re-release. Cartoon.*

FANTASIA
(1956R - Disney) Mickey Mouse
One Sheet: $40 - $75   *Re-release. Cartoon.*

FANTASIA
(1963R - Disney) Mickey Mouse
One Sheet: $40 - $75   *Re-release. Cartoon.*

FANTASIA
(1969R - Disney) Mickey Mouse
One Sheet: $30 - $50   *Re-release. Cartoon.*

FANTASIA
(1970R - Disney) Mickey Mouse
One Sheet: $50 - $100   *Re-release. Cartoon. Psychedelic day-glo One Sheet.*

FANTASIA
(1980R - Disney) Mickey Mouse
One Sheet: $15 - $30   *Re-release. Cartoon.*

FANTASIA
(1982R - Disney) Mickey Mouse
One Sheet: $10 - $20   *Re-release. Cartoon.*

FANTASIA
(1990R - Disney) Mickey Mouse
One Sheet: $30 - $50   *Re-release. Cartoon. 50th Anniversary.*

FANTASIES
(1981 - Brenner) Bo Derek
One Sheet: $5 - $10

FANTASM
(1976 - Filmways) John Bluthal
One Sheet: $3 - $5

FANTASTIC 4
(1994 - New Horizon) -
One Sheet: $40 - $75   *Poster to never-released film. Posters were available through National Screen Service for a few weeks, then were destroyed. Scarce.*

FANTASTIC ANIMATION FESTIVAL
(1977 - -) Animated Compilation
One Sheet: $10 - $20   *Cartoon. 14 award-winning shorts including "Closed Mondays," "The Last Cartoon Man," "French Windows," "Moonshadow," and"Cosmic Cartoon."*

FANTASTIC INVASION OF PLANET EARTH
(1967 - Monarch) Michael Cole, Deborah Walley
One Sheet: $15 - $30   *3-D. AKA:*

THE BUBBLE

FANTASTIC PLANET
(1974 - New World) Roger Corman presents
One Sheet: $20 - $40   *Cartoon.*

FANTASTIC PLASTIC MACHINE, THE
(1969 - Crown) Nat Young, Bob McTavish, George Greenough
One Sheet: $5 - $10

FANTASTIC VOYAGE
(1966 - 20th Century Fox) Stephen Boyd, Raquel Welch
One Sheet: $40 - $75   *Graven Images, pg. 226.*

FANTOMAS
(1966 - Lopert) Jean Marais, Louis De Funes
One Sheet: $15 - $25

FANTOMAS STRIKES BACK
(1965 - Victory) Jean Marais
One Sheet: $15 - $25

FAR AND AWAY
(1992 - Universal) Tom Cruise, Nicole Kidman, Dir: Ron Howard
One Sheet: $7 - $15

FAR AWAY SO CLOSE!
(1993 - Sony Classics) Peter Falk, Bruno Ganz
One Sheet: $5 - $10   *Sequel to Cult Film "WAGES OF DESIRE".*

FAR COUNTRY, THE
(1954 - Universal) James Stewart, Ruth Roman
One Sheet: $75 - $150

One Sheet

FAR FROM HOME: THE ADVENTURES OF YELLOW DOG
(1995 - 20th Century Fox) Jesse Bradford, Bruce Davison, Mimi Rogers
One Sheet: $3 - $5

FAR FROM THE CROWD
(1937 - -) Mary Tsagonis
One Sheet: $50 - $100

FAR FROM THE MADDING CROWD
(1967 - MGM) Julie Christie, Terence Stamp
One Sheet: $7 - $15   *One Sheet (Roadshow 70mm):$100-$200.*

FAR FRONTIER, THE
(1949 - Republic) Roy Rogers, Andy Devine
One Sheet: $75 - $175

FAR HORIZONS, THE
(1955 - Paramount) Charlton Heston, Fred MacMurray
One Sheet: $50 - $100

FAR OFF PLACE, A
(1993 - Buena Vista) Reese Witherspoon, Ethan Randall
One Sheet: $3 - $5

FAR OUT MAN
(1990 - -) Tommy Chong, Shelby Chong, Paris Chong
One Sheet: $3 - $5

FAREWELL AGAIN
(1937 - London) Leslie Banks, Flora Robson
One Sheet: $50 - $100

FAREWELL, FRIEND
(1968 - Greenwich) Alain Delon, Charles Bronson
One Sheet: $5 - $10

FAREWELL MY LOVELY
(1975 - Avco/Embassy) Robert Mitchum,

Charlotte Rampling
One Sheet: $15 - $30

FAREWELL PERFORMANCE
(1963 - Sevenay) David Kernan
One Sheet: $5 - $10

FAREWELL TO ARMS, A
(1933 - Paramount) Helen Hayes, Gary Cooper
One Sheet: $1,900 - $3,000

FAREWELL TO ARMS, A
(1957 - 20th Century Fox) Rock Hudson,
Jennifer Jones
One Sheet: $40 - $75

FAREWELL TO CINDERELLA
(1937 - RKO) Anne Pichon, John Robinson
One Sheet: $100 - $200

FAREWELL TO LOVE
(1931 - Madison) Betty Stockfield, Heather
Angel
One Sheet: $50 - $100

FAREWELL TO THE KING
(1983 - -) Nick Nolte
One Sheet: $5 - $10

FAREWELL TO YESTERDAY
(1950 - 20th Century Fox) -
One Sheet: $10 - $20

FARGO
(1952 - Monogram) Bill Elliott, Phyllis Coates
One Sheet: $15 - $25

FARGO
(1996 - Gramercy) Frances McDormand, Steve
Buscemi, Dir: Coen Bros.
One Sheet: $15 - $30   *Academy
Award: Best Actress (McDormand).*

One Sheet

FARGO EXPRESS
(1932 - World Wide) Ken Maynard, Helen Mack
One Sheet: $200 - $400

FARGO KID, THE
(1940 - RKO) Tim Holt, Ray Whitley
One Sheet: $50 - $100

FARGO PHANTOM, THE
(1949 - Universal) Tex Williams
One Sheet: $20 - $40

FARINELLI
(1995 - Sony Classics) Enrico Loverso, Stefano
Dionisi
One Sheet: $4 - $8

FARMER, THE
(1977 - Columbia) Gary Conway
One Sheet: $3 - $5

FARMER IN THE DELL, THE
(1936 - RKO) Fred Stone, Jean Parker
One Sheet: $100 - $200

FARMER TAKES A WIFE, THE
(1935 - Fox) Janet Gaynor, Henry Fonda (film
debut)
One Sheet: $200 - $400

FARMER TAKES A WIFE, THE
(1953 - 20th Century Fox) Betty Grable, Dale
Robertson
One Sheet: $40 - $75

FARMER'S DAUGHTER, THE
(1940 - Paramount) Martha Raye, Charlie
Ruggles
One Sheet: $50 - $100

FARMER'S DAUGHTER, THE

(1947 - RKO) Loretta Young, Joseph Cotten
One Sheet: $75 - $150   *Academy
Award: Best Actress (Young). Academy Award
Movie Posters #112.*

FARMER'S DAUGHTER, THE
(1954R - RKO) Loretta Young, Joseph Cotten
One Sheet: $15 - $30   *Re-release.*

FARMER'S OTHER DAUGHTER
(1965 - United Producers) Judy Pennebaker
One Sheet: $5 - $10

FARMER'S WIFE, THE
(1928 - British International) Jameson Thomas,
Lillian Hall-Davies, Dir: Alfred Hitchcock
One Sheet: $2,500 - $4,000

FARMER'S WIFE, THE
(1941 - Pathe) Basil Sydney, Nora Swinburne
One Sheet: $50 - $100

FARMYARD SYMPHONY
(1949R - RKO/Disney) -
One Sheet: $250 - $500   *Re-release.
Cartoon. Duotone.*

FARO NELL
(1929 - Paramount) -
One Sheet: $150 - $300   *or "IN OLD
CALIFORNY"*

FASCINATION
(1931 - British International) Madeleine Carroll,
Freddie Bartholomew
One Sheet: $125 - $250

FASHION MODEL
(1945 - Monogram) Robert Lowery, Marjorie
Weaver
One Sheet: $75 - $125

FASHIONS IN LOVE
(1929 - Paramount) Adolpe Menjou, Fay
Compton
One Sheet: $250 - $500

FASHIONS OF 1934
(1934 - Warner Bros.) William Powell, Bette
Davis
One Sheet: $1,600 - $2,500

FAST AND FURIOUS
(1927 - Universal) Reginald Denny, Barbara
Worth
One Sheet: $200 - $450

FAST AND FURIOUS
(1939 - MGM) Ann Sothern, Franchot Tone
One Sheet: $100 - $200   *Art Deco
style.*

FAST AND LOOSE
(1930 - Paramount Publix) Carole Lombard,
Miriam Hopkins(1st film)
One Sheet: $800 - $1,500

FAST AND LOOSE
(1939 - MGM) Robert Montgomery, Rosalind
Russell
One Sheet: $75 - $150

FAST AND LOOSE
(1954 - General) Stanley Holloway, Kay
Kendall
One Sheet: $15 - $25

FAST AND SEXY
(1960 - Columbia) Gina Lollobrigida, Dale
Robertson
One Sheet: $15 - $30

FAST AND THE FURIOUS, THE
(1954 - AIP) John Ireland, Dorothy Malone
One Sheet: $15 - $25

FAST BREAK
(1979 - Columbia) Gabe Kaplan, Larry
Fishburne
One Sheet: $3 - $5

FAST BULLETS
(1936 - Reliable) Tom Tyler, Rex Lease
One Sheet: $150 - $300

FAST CHARLIE...THE MOONBEAM RIDER
(1979 - Universal) David Carradine, Brenda
Vaccaro
One Sheet: $7 - $15   *Sports Movie
Posters #275.*

FAST COMPANIONS
(1932 - Universal) Tom Brown, Maureen
O'Sullivan

One Sheet: $150 - $300

FAST COMPANY
(1929 - Paramount) Evelyn Brent, Jack Oakie
One Sheet: $150 - $300

FAST COMPANY
(1938 - MGM) Melvyn Douglas, Florence Rice
One Sheet: $125 - $250

FAST COMPANY
(1953 - MGM) Howard Keel, Nina Foch
One Sheet: $15 - $30

FAST EXPRESS, THE
(1924 - Universal) -
One Sheet: $150 - $300   *Serial. 15
Chapters.*

FAST FOOD
(1989 - Fries Entertainment) Clark Brandon,
Jim Varney, Traci Lords
One Sheet: $3 - $5   *Style showing
Tracy Lords:$10-20.*

FAST FORWARD
(1985 - Columbia) John Scott Clough, Dir:
Sidney Poitier, Quincy Jones
One Sheet: $10 - $20

FAST LADY
(1963 - Rank) Julie Christie, Leslie Phillip
One Sheet: $15 - $25   *Sports (Auto
Racing). Sports Movie Posters #17.*

FAST LIFE
(1929 - Warner Bros.) Douglas Fairbanks, Jr.,
Loretta Young
One Sheet: $250 - $500

FAST LIFE
(1932 - MGM) William Haines, Madge Evans
One Sheet: $100 - $200

FAST MAIL
(1924 - Fox) Carles Jones
One Sheet: $250 - $600

FAST ON THE DRAW
(1950 - Lippert) James Ellison, Russell Hayden
One Sheet: $15 - $35

FAST STEPPERS
(1924 - Universal-Jewel) Billy Sullivan
One Sheet: $150 - $300   *Serial. 6
Chapters.*

FAST TIMES AT RIDGEMONT HIGH
(1982 - Universal) Sean Penn, Jennifer Jason
Leigh
One Sheet: $15 - $25

FAST WORK
(1930 - MGM) Charley Chase
One Sheet: $125 - $250   *Stone litho.*

FAST WORKERS
(1933 - MGM) John Gilbert, Mae Clarke
One Sheet: $500 - $800

FASTER PUSSYCAT, KILL! KILL!
(1964 - Eve Productions) Tura Santana, Haji,
Dir: Russ Meyers
One Sheet: $300 - $700   *Price is for
style A one sheet. One Sheet (Style B):$500-
$900.*

FASTEST GUITAR ALIVE, THE
(1967 - MGM) Roy Orbison, Maggie Pierce
One Sheet: $30 - $50

FASTEST GUN ALIVE, THE
(1956 - MGM) Glenn Ford, Jeanne Crain
One Sheet: $30 - $50

FAST-WALKING
(1982 - Lorimar) James Woods, Kay Lenz
One Sheet: $5 - $10

FAT ANGELS
(1980 - Impala) Farnham Scott, January
Stevens
One Sheet: $5 - $10

FAT CITY
(1972 - Columbia) Stacy Keach, Jeff Bridges,
Susan Tyrrell
One Sheet: $10 - $20

FAT MAN, THE
(1950 - Universal) J. Scott Smart, Julie London,
Rock Hudson
One Sheet: $40 - $75

FAT MAN AND LITTLE BOY
(1989 - Paramount) Paul Newman, Dwight
Schultz, John Cusack
One Sheet: $5 - $10

FAT SPY
(1966 - Magna) Phyllis Diller, Jayne Mansfield
One Sheet: $15 - $25

FATAL ATTRACTION
(1987 - Paramount) Michael Douglas, Glenn
Close
One Sheet: $7 - $15

FATAL BEAUTY
(1987 - -) Whoopi Goldberg, Sam Elliot, Ruben
Blades
One Sheet: $3 - $5

FATAL DESIRE
(1953 - Excelsa) Anthony Quinn
One Sheet: $15 - $25

FATAL HOUR, THE
(1937 - Paramount) Edward Rigby, Moira Reed
One Sheet: $100 - $200

FATAL HOUR, THE
(1940 - Monogram) Boris Karloff, Marjorie
Reynolds
One Sheet: $100 - $200

FATAL INSTINCT
(1993 - MGM) Armand Assante, Sean Young
One Sheet: $3 - $5

FATAL LADY
(1936 - Paramount) Mary Ellis, Walter Pidgeon
One Sheet: $100 - $200

FATAL MALLET, THE
(1914 - Keystone) Charlie Chaplin
One Sheet: $8,500 - $14,000

FATAL MARRIAGE, THE
(1924 - -) Lillian Gish
One Sheet: $500 - $900

FATAL NIGHT, THE
(1948 - Columbia) Patrick Macnee, Jean Short
One Sheet: $50 - $100

FATAL WARNING, THE
(1930 - Mascot) Helene Costello, Ralph Graves
One Sheet: $75 - $150

FATAL WITNESS, THE
(1945 - Republic) Evelyn Ankers, Richard
Fraser
One Sheet: $100 - $200

FATE IS THE HUNTER
(1964 - 20th Century Fox) Glenn Ford, Nancy
Kwan
One Sheet: $10 - $20

FATE TAKES A HAND
(1962 - MGM) Ronald Howard, Christina Gregg
One Sheet: $5 - $10

FATHER AND SON
(1929 - Columbia) Jack Holt, Dorothy Revier
One Sheet: $150 - $350

FATHER AND SON
(1934 - Warner Bros.) Edmund Gwenn,
Esmond Knight
One Sheet: $125 - $250

FATHER BROWN
(1954 - Columbia) Alec Guiness, Joan
Greenwood
One Sheet: $10 - $20

FATHER BROWN, DETECTIVE
(1934 - Paramount) Paul Lukas, Gertrude
Michael
One Sheet: $150 - $300

FATHER CAME TOO
(1964 - Rank) Leslie Phillips, James Robertson
Justice
One Sheet: $5 - $10

FATHER GOOSE
(1965 - Universal) Cary Grant, Leslie Caron
One Sheet: $40 - $75

FATHER HOOD
(1993 - Buena Vista) Patrick Swayze, Halle
Berry
One Sheet: $3 - $5

FATHER IS A BACHELOR

(1950 - Columbia) William Holden, Coleen Gray
One Sheet: $15 - $30

FATHER IS A PRINCE
(1940 - Warner Bros.) Grant Mitchell, Nana Bryant
One Sheet: $50 - $100

FATHER MAKES GOOD
(1950 - Monogram) Raymond Walburn, Walter Catlett
One Sheet $10 - $20

FATHER NOAH'S ARK
(1933 - United Artists) Silly Symphony
One Sheet: $10,000 - $15,000   *Cartoon. The Disney Poster, pg. 6.*

FATHER OF THE BRIDE
(1950 - MGM) Spencer Tracy, Elizabeth Taylor, Joan Bennett
One Sheet: $100 - $200

FATHER OF THE BRIDE
(1962R - MGM) Spencer Tracy, Elizabeth Taylor, Joan Bennett
One Sheet: $20 - $40   *Re-release.*

FATHER OF THE BRIDE
(1991 - Buena Vista) Steve Martin
One Sheet: $5 - $10

FATHER OF THE BRIDE PART II
(1995 - Touchstone) Steve Martin, Diane Keaton, Martin Short
One Sheet: $3 - $7

FATHER STEPS OUT
(1937 - RKO) George Carney, Dinah Sheridan
One Sheet: $75 - $150

FATHER STEPS OUT
(1941 - Monogram) Frank Albertson, Lorna Gray
One Sheet: $40 - $75

FATHER TAKES A WIFE
(1941 - RKO) Adolphe Menjou, Gloria Swanson
One Sheet: $75 - $125

FATHER TAKES THE AIR
(1951 - Monogram) Raymond Walburn, Walter Catlett
One Sheet: $20 - $40

FATHER WAS A FULLBACK
(1949 - 20th Century Fox) Fred MacMurray, Maureen O'Hara
One Sheet: $50 - $100

FATHER'S DAY OFF
(1953 - RKO/Disney) Goofy
One Sheet: $250 - $500   *Cartoon. Full color. The Disney Poster, pg. 68.*

FATHER'S DOING FINE
(1953 - Stratford) Richard Attenborough, Heather Thatcher
One Sheet: $15 - $25

FATHER'S LITTLE DIVIDEND
(1950 - MGM) Spencer Tracy, Elizabeth Taylor, Joan Bennett
One Sheet: $50 - $100

FATHER'S SON
(1931 - First National) Leon Janney, Lewis Stone
One Sheet: $75 - $150

FATHER'S SON
(1941 - Warner Bros.) John Litel, Frieda Inescort
One Sheet: $50 - $100

FATHER'S WEEK-END
(1953 - RKO/Disney) Goofy
One Sheet: $250 - $600   *Cartoon. The Disney Poster, pg. 69.*

FATHER'S WILD GAME
(1950 - Monogram) Jane Darwell, Raymond Walburn
One Sheet: $15 - $25

FATHERS ARE PEOPLE
(1951 - RKO/Disney) Goofy
One Sheet: $250 - $550   *Cartoon. Full color.*

FATHOM
(1967 - 20th Century Fox) Raquel Welch, Tony Franciosa
One Sheet: $15 - $25

FATSO
(1980 - 20th Century Fox) Dom DeLuise, Anne Bancroft
One Sheet: $3 - $5

FATTY AND MABEL'S SIMPLE LIFE
(1915 - Keystone) Roscoe "Fatty" Arbuckle
One Sheet: $1,900 - $3,000

FATTY'S DAY OFF
(1913 - Keystone) Roscoe "Fatty" Arbuckle
One Sheet: $2,500 - $4,000

FATTY'S FLIRTATION
(1916 - -) Roscoe "Fatty" Arbuckle
One Sheet: $1,900 - $3,000

FAUST
(1915 - -) Porter J. White
One Sheet: $250 - $600

FAUST
(1926 - MGM) Emil Jannings
One Sheet: $2,800 - $4,500   *U. S. release.*

Insert

FAUST
(1926 - UFA) Emil Jannings, Gosta Ekman
One Sheet: $5,500 - $9,000   *German. Graven Images, pg. 15.*

FAVOR, THE
(1994 - Orion) Harley Jane Kozak, Elizabeth McGovern
One Sheet: $3 - $5

FAZIL
(1928 - -) Charles Farrell, Greta Nissen
One Sheet: $150 - $350

FBI CODE 98
(1964 - Warner Bros.) Jack Kelly, Ray Danton
One Sheet: $10 - $20

FBI GIRL
(1951 - Lippert) Cesar Romero, Audrey Totter
One Sheet: $15 - $30

FBI STORY, THE
(1959 - Warner Bros.) James Stewart, Vera Miles
One Sheet: $75 - $125

FEAR
(1946 - Monogram) Peter Cookson, Warren William
One Sheet: $40 - $75

FEAR
(1956 - Minerva) Ingrid Bergman
One Sheet: $50 - $100   *German.*

FEAR
(1996 - Universal) Mark Wahlberg, Reese Witherspoon
One Sheet: $3 - $6   *Drama.*

FEAR AND DESIRE
(1953 - Kubrick/Burstyn) Frank Silvera, Kenneth Harp, Dir: Stanley Kubrick
Kubrick's first film. Probably never released theatrically. No known posters exist.

FEAR CHAMBER, THE
(1968 - Azteca) Boris Karloff, Yerye Beirut
One Sheet: $75 - $125   *One of the rarely-seen last efforts of Karloff.*

FEAR CITY
(1984 - Zupnick) Tom Berenger, Billy Dee Williams, Melanie Griffith
One Sheet: $3 - $5

FEAR IN THE NIGHT

(1947 - Paramount) Paul Kelly, De Forest Kelly
One Sheet: $50 - $100

FEAR IN THE NIGHT
(1972 - Hammer) Peter Cushing, Joan Collins
One Sheet: $10 - $20

FEAR IS THE KEY
(1973 - Paramount) Suzy Kendall, Barry Newman
One Sheet: $5 - $10

FEAR NO EVIL
(1981 - Avco/Embassy) Stefan Arngrim, Elizabeth Hoffman
One Sheet: $5 - $10

FEAR NO MORE
(1961 - Sutton) Jacques Bergerac, Mala Powers
One Sheet: $7 - $15

FEAR O' GOD
(1926 - Gainsborough) Bernard Goetzke, Dir: Alfred Hitchcock
One Sheet: $3,500 - $5,000   *British.*

FEAR SHIP, THE
(1933 - Paramount) Cyril McLaglen, Dorothy Bartlam
One Sheet: $125 - $250

FEAR STRIKES OUT
(1956 - Paramount) Anthony Perkins (as Jim Piersall), Karl Malden
One Sheet: $75 - $175   *Sports (Baseball). Story of baseball's Jim Piersall. Sports Movie Posters #65.*

FEARLESS
(1993 - Warner Bros.) Jeff Bridges, Isabella Rossellini, Rosie Perez
One Sheet: $3 - $5

FEARLESS FAGAN
(1952 - MGM) Janet Leigh, Carleton Carpenter
One Sheet: $10 - $20

FEARLESS FRANK
(1969 - AIP) Jon Voight, Monique Van Vooren
One Sheet: $5 - $10

FEARLESS VAMPIRE KILLERS or PARDON ME, BUT YOUR TEETH ARE IN MY NECK
(1967 - MGM) Sharon Tate, Jack McGowran
One Sheet: $75 - $150   *Price is for Style A one sheet with Frazetta art. Graven Images, pg. 207. StyleB (black and white): $40-$75.*

FEARMAKERS, THE
(1958 - United Artists) Dana Andrews, Dick Foran
One Sheet: $10 - $20

FEATHER, THE
(1929 - United Artists) Jameson Thomas, Mary Clare
One Sheet: $200 - $400

FEATHER IN HER HAT, A
(1935 - Columbia) Basil Rathbone, Louis Hayward
One Sheet: $125 - $250

FEATHER YOUR NEST
(1937 - Associated British) George Formby, Polly Ward
One Sheet: $100 - $200

FEATHERED SERPENT, THE
(1934 - Columbia) Enid Stamp Taylor, Tom Helmore
One Sheet: $150 - $300

FEATHERED SERPENT, THE
(1949 - Monogram) Roland Winters, Keye Luke
One Sheet: $100 - $200   *Charlie Chan series.*

FEDERAL AGENT
(1936 - Republic) William Boyd, Irene Ware
One Sheet: $150 - $300

FEDERAL AGENT AT LARGE
(1950 - Republic) Dorothy Patrick, Robert Rockwell
One Sheet: $15 - $35

FEDERAL AGENTS VS. UNDERWORLD, INC.
(1949 - Republic) Kirk Alyn, Rosemary La Planche
One Sheet: $75 - $150   *Serial. 12 Chapters.*

FEDERAL BULLETS
(1937 - Monogram) Terry Walker, Milburn Stone
One Sheet: $50 - $100

FEDERAL FUGITIVES
(1941 - Monogram) Neil Hamilton, Doris Day
One Sheet: $50 - $100

FEDERAL HILL
(1994 - Trimark) Nicholas Turturro, Anthony De Sando
One Sheet: $3 - $5

FEDERAL MAN
(1950 - Eagle-Lion) William Henry, Pamela Blake
One Sheet: $15 - $30

FEDERAL MAN-HUNT
(1938 - Republic) Robert Livingston, June Travis
One Sheet: $50 - $100

FEDERAL OPERATOR 99
(1:45 - Republic) Marten Lamont, Helen Talbot
One Sheet: $250 - $500   *Serial. 12 Chapters.*

FEDORA
(1978 - United Artists) William Holden, Jose Ferrer, Martha Keller
One Sheet: $5 - $10

FEDS
(1988 - Warner Bros.) Rebecca DeMornay, Mary Gross
One Sheet: $2 - $3

FEEL MY PULSE
(1928 - Paramount) Bebe Daniels, Melbourne MacDowell
One Sheet: $250 - $500

FEELING MINNESOTA
(1996 - Fine Line) Keanu Reeves, Cameron Diaz
One Sheet: $5 - $10

FEET FIRST
(1930 - United Artists) Harold Lloyd, Barbara Kent
One Sheet: $1,900 - $3,000

FEET OF CLAY
(1924 - -) Vera Reynolds, Rod La Rocque, Dir: Cecil B. DeMille
One Sheet: $600 - $1,000

FEET OF MUD
(1924 - Pathecomedy) Harry Langdon
One Sheet: $700 - $1,300   *Sports (Football). Sports Movie Posters #172.*

FELIX THE CAT SHATTERS THE SHEIK
(1926 - Educational) Felix The Cat
One Sheet: $1,900 - $3,000   *Cartoon. Cartoon Movie Posters #14.*

FELIX THE CAT: THE MOVIE
(1989 - New World) Felix The Cat
One Sheet: $10 - $20   *Cartoon.*

FELIX THE CAT TRIPS THRU TOYLAND
(1925 - Educational) Felix The Cat
One Sheet: $1,900 - $3,000   *Cartoon. Cartoon Movie Posters #13.*

FELLER NEEDS A FRIEND
(1932 - Cosmopolitan) Jackie Cooper, Chic Sale
One Sheet: $150 - $300

FELLINI SATYRICON
(1970 - United Artists) Martin Potter, Hiram Keller
One Sheet: $15 - $30

FEMALE, THE
(1924 - Paramount) Betty Compson
One Sheet: $200 - $400

FEMALE
(1933 - First National) Ruth Chatterton, George Brent, Johnny Mack Brown
One Sheet: $150 - $350

FEMALE, THE
(1960 - Pathe) Brigitte Bardot
One Sheet: $50 - $100   *French title:LA FEMME ET LE PAUTIN. For original French price, see LA FEMME... Above price is for U.S. release one sheet.*

FEMALE ANIMAL, THE
(1957 - Universal) Hedy Lamarr, Jane Powell
One Sheet: $30 - $50

FEMALE BUNCH, THE
(1971 - Dalia) Russ Tamblyn, Lon Chaney, Jr.
One Sheet: $7 - $15

FEMALE BUTCHER, THE
(1972 - Film Ventures) Lucia Bose, Ewa Aulin
One Sheet: $7 - $15

FEMALE FIENDS
(1960 - Cinema Associates) Lex Barker, Carole Mathews
One Sheet: $20 - $40

FEMALE FUGITIVE
(1938 - Monogram) Evelyn Venable, Craig Reynolds
One Sheet: $50 - $100

FEMALE JUNGLE
(1956 - AIP) Jayne Mansfield, Lawrence Tierney
One Sheet: $30 - $50

FEMALE ON THE BEACH
(1955 - Universal) Joan Crawford, Jeff Chandler
One Sheet: $30 - $50

FEMALE RESPONSE, THE
(1972 - Trans-American) Raina Barrett
One Sheet: $7 - $15

FEMALE TROUBLE
(1975 - New Line) Divine, David Lochary, Mary Vivian
One Sheet: $75 - $150

FEMININE TOUCH, THE
(1941 - MGM) Rosalind Russell, Don Ameche
One Sheet: $50 - $100

FENCE RIDERS
(1950 - Monogram) Whip Wilson, Reno Browne
One Sheet: $30 - $50

FERDINAND THE BULL
(1938 - RKO/Disney) Ferdinand
One Sheet: $10,000 - $15,000   *Cartoon. Academy Award:Best Short (Cartoon). Cartoon Movie Posters #195.*

FERNGULLY...THE LAST RAINFOREST
(1992 - 20th Century Fox) -
One Sheet: $7 - $15   *Cartoon.*

FEROCIOUS PAL
(1934 - Principal) Kazan the dog, Harry Dunkinson
One Sheet: $75 - $150

FERRIS BUELLER'S DAY OFF
(1986 - Paramount) Matthew Broderick, Alan Ruck
One Sheet: $10 - $20

FERRY ACROSS THE MERSEY
(1965 - United Artists) Gerry and the Pacemakers
One Sheet: $30 - $50   *Rock 'n' Roll.*

FERRY TO HONG KONG
(1961 - 20th Century Fox) Curt Jurgens, Orson Welles
One Sheet: $30 - $50

FESTIVAL OF FUN
(1962 - MGM) Tom & Jerry
One Sheet: $75 - $150   *Cartoon.*

FEUD MAKER
(1938 - Republic) Bob Steele, Marion Weldon
One Sheet: $100 - $200

FEUD OF THE RANGE
(1939 - Metropolitan) Bob Steele, Richard Cramer
One Sheet: $100 - $200

FEUD OF THE TRAIL
(1938 - Monogram) Tom Tyler, Marlene Wood
One Sheet: $125 - $250

FEUD OF THE WEST
(1936 - Diversion) Hoot Gibson, Buzz Barton
One Sheet: $125 - $250

FEUDIN' FOOLS
(1952 - Monogram) Leo Gorcey, Huntz Hall
One Sheet: $30 - $50

FEUDIN', FUSSIN', AND A-FIGHTIN'
(1948 - Universal) Donald O'Connor, Marjorie Main
One Sheet: $40 - $75

FEUDIN' RHYTHM
(1949 - Columbia) Eddy Arnold, Gloria Henry
One Sheet: $30 - $50

FEVER HEAT
(1968 - Paramount) Nick Adams, Jeannine Riley
One Sheet: $15 - $25

FEVER IN THE BLOOD, A
(1961 - Warner Bros.) Efrem Zimbalist, Jr., Angie Dickinson
One Sheet: $10 - $20

FEVER PITCH
(1985 - MGM/UA) Ryan O'Neal, Catherine Hicks
One Sheet: $2 - $3

FEW GOOD MEN, A
(1992 - Columbia) Tom Cruise, Jack Nicholson, Demi Moore
One Sheet: $15 - $25

FFOLKES
(1979 - Universal) Roger Moore, James Mason
One Sheet: $3 - $5

FICKLE FATTY'S FALL
(1917 - Triangle) Roscoe "Fatty" Arbuckle
One Sheet: $1,900 - $3,000

FICKLE FINGER OF FATE, THE
(1967 - PRC) Tab Hunter
One Sheet: $15 - $30

FICTION-MAKERS
(196? - -) Roger Moore
One Sheet: $40 - $75   *"The Saint" TV tie-in.*

FIDDLER ON THE ROOF
(1971 - United Artists) Topol, Norma Crane, Leonard Frey, Molly Picon
One Sheet: $15 - $30

FIDDLER ON THE ROOF
(1979R - United Artists) Topol, Norma Crane, Leonard Frey, Molly Picon
One Sheet: $10 - $20   *Re-release. Full color.*

FIDDLERS THREE
(1944 - Ealing) Tommy Trinder, Frances Day
One Sheet: $30 - $50

FIDDLERS THREE
(1948 - Columbia) The Three Stooges (Shemp)
One Sheet: $350 - $750   *Comedy short. Duotone.*

FIDDLIN' BUCKAROO, THE
(1933 - Universal) Ken Maynard, Gloria Shea
One Sheet: $250 - $500

FIDDLIN' DOLL, THE
(1924 - Universal-Jewel) Billy Sullivan
One Sheet: $150 - $300   *#1 in the Fast Steppers series.*

FIELD, THE
(1990 - -) Richard Harris
One Sheet: $3 - $5

FIELD MOUSE, THE
(1941 - MGM) -
One Sheet: $500 - $800   *Cartoon. Cartoon Movie Posters #244.*

FIELD OF DREAMS
(1989 - Universal) Kevin Costner, Amy Madigan
One Sheet: $50 - $100   *Sports (Baseball). Sports Movie Posters #79.*

FIEND
(1980 - Cinema Enterprises) Don Leifert
One Sheet: $3 - $5

FIEND WHO WALKED THE WEST, THE
(1958 - 20th Century Fox) Hugh O'Brian, Robert Evans
One Sheet: $30 - $50

FIEND WITHOUT A FACE
(1957 - MGM) Marshall Thompson, Terence Kiburn
One Sheet: $125 - $250   *Graven*

Images, pg. 178.

FIENDISH PLOT OF DR. FU MANCHU, THE
(1980 - Orion) Peter Sellers, Helen Mirren
One Sheet: $5 - $10

FIERCEST HEART, THE
(1961 - 20th Century Fox) Stuart Whitman, Juliet Prowse
One Sheet: $15 - $25

FIESTA
(1941 - United Artists) Anne Ayars, George Negrette
One Sheet: $75 - $125

FIESTA
(1947 - MGM) Esther Williams, Akim Tamiroff
One Sheet: $50 - $100   *Sports Movie Posters #376.*

FIFI BLOWS HER TOP
(1958 - Columbia) The Three Stooges (Joe Besser)
One Sheet: $75 - $125   *Comedy short. Duotone.*

FIFTEEN MAIDEN LANE
(1936 - Fox) Claire Trevor, Cesar Romero
One Sheet: $150 - $300

FIFTEEN WIVES
(1934 - Invincible) Conway Tearle, Raymond Hutton
One Sheet: $125 - $250

FIFTH AVENUE GIRL
(1939 - RKO) Ginger Rogers, James Ellison
One Sheet: $500 - $800

FIFTH ELEMENT, THE
(1997 - Columbia) Bruce Willis, Milla Jovovich, Gary Oldman
One Sheet: $7 - $15

FIFTH FLOOR, THE
(1980 - Film Ventures) Bo Hopkins, Robert Englund
One Sheet: $3 - $5

FIFTH MUSKETEER, THE
(1979 - Columbia) Beau Bridges, Ursula Andress
One Sheet: $5 - $10   *AKA: BEHIND THE IRON MASK.*

FIFTY FATHOMS DEEP
(1931 - Columbia) Jack Holt, Richard Cromwell
One Sheet: $100 - $200

FIFTY-FIFTY
(1916 - Hallmark) Norma Talmadge, J.W. Johnston
One Sheet: $250 - $600

55 DAYS AT PEKING
(1963 - Allied Artists) Charlton Heston, Ava Gardner
One Sheet: $75 - $125

FIFTY MILLION FRENCHMEN
(1931 - Warner Bros.) Ole Olsen, Chic Johnson, William Gaxton
One Sheet: $125 - $250

FIFTY ROADS TO TOWN
(1937 - 20th Century Fox) Ann Sothern, Don Ameche
One Sheet: $125 - $250

52ND STREET
(1937 - United Artists) Kenny Baker, ZaSu Pitts
One Sheet: $150 - $300

FIFTY-SHILLING BOXER
(1937 - RKO) Bruce Seton, Eve Gray
One Sheet: $100 - $200   *Sports (Boxing).*

52 PICK-UP
(1986 - Cannon) Roy Scheider, Ann-Margret
One Sheet: $5 - $10

50 YEARS BEFORE YOUR EYES
(1950' - -) -
One Sheet: $15 - $25

FIG LEAF FOR EVE, A
(1930S - -) Jan Wiley
One Sheet: $40 - $75

FIG LEAVES
(1926 - Fox) George O'Brien, Olive Borden, Dir: Howard Hawks

FIGARO AND CLEO
(1943 - RKO/Disney) Figaro and Cleo
One Sheet: $1,600 - $2,500   *Cartoon. Cartoon Movie Posters #184.*

FIGHT, THE
(1924 - William Fox) by Richard Harding Davis
One Sheet: $250 - $500

FIGHT FOR LIFE
(1940 - Columbia) Myron McCormick
One Sheet: $50 - $100

FIGHT FOR YOUR LADY
(1937 - RKO) John Boles, Ida Lupino
One Sheet: $100 - $200

One Sheet

FIGHT FOR YOUR LIFE
(1977 - Mishkin) William Sanderson
One Sheet: $3 - $5

FIGHT NEVER ENDS
(1947 - Alexander Releasing) Joe Louis, Ruby Dee
One Sheet: $250 - $500   *Black cast. Sports (Boxing). Duotone. Separate Cinema, pg. 60. Sports Movie Posters #147.*

FIGHT NEVER ENDS
(1948R - Toddy) Joe Louis
One Sheet: $150 - $300   *Re-release. Black cast. Sports (Boxing). Undated black and red duotone.*

FIGHT OF THE WILD STALLIONS
(1948 - Universal) -
One Sheet: $30 - $50

FIGHT THAT GHOST
(1946 - Toddy) Pigmeat "Alamo" Markham, Rastus Murray
One Sheet: $150 - $300   *Black cast. Separate Cinema, pg. 70.*

FIGHT TO THE FINISH, A
(1937 - Columbia) Don Terry, Rosalind Keith
One Sheet: $75 - $125

FIGHT TO THE FINISH, A
(1943 - 20th Century Fox) Mighty Mouse
One Sheet: $250 - $600   *Cartoon. Full color stock poster with printed title. Huge image of Mighty Mouse on yellow background.*

FIGHTER, THE
(1952 - United Artists) Richard Conte, Vanessa Brown
One Sheet: $15 - $25

FIGHTER ATTACK
(1953 - Allied Artists) Sterling Hayden, J. Carroll Naish
One Sheet: $15 - $25

FIGHTER SQUADRON
(1948 - Warner Bros.) Edmond O'Brien, Robert Stack
One Sheet: $30 - $50

FIGHTIN' MAD
(1917 - Metro) William Desmond, Virginia Brown
One Sheet: $250 - $500

FIGHTIN' PALS
(1940 - Paramount) Popeye
One Sheet: $2,200 - $3,500   *Cartoon. Duotone. Cartoon Movie Posters #218.*

FIGHTING 69TH, THE
(1940 - Warner Bros.) James Cagney, Pat O'Brien

One Sheet: $200 - $400   *Duotone.*

One Sheet

FIGHTING 69TH, THE
(1948R - Warner Bros.) James Cagney, Pat
O'Brien
One Sheet: $50 - $100   *Re-release.*
Duotone.

FIGHTING 69TH, THE
(1956R - Warner Bros.) James Cagney, Pat
O'Brien
One Sheet: $15 - $30   *Re-release.*
Duotone.

FIGHTING AMERICAN, THE
(1924 - Universal) Pat O'Malley, Mary Astor,
Raymond Hatton
One Sheet: $250 - $600

FIGHTING BACK
(1948 - 20th Century Fox) Paul Langton, Jean
Rogers
One Sheet: $40 - $75

FIGHTING BACK
(1982 - -) Tom Skerrit, Patti LuPone
One Sheet: $2 - $3

FIGHTING BACK
(1983 - Enterprise) Lewis Fitzgerald, Paul
Smith
One Sheet: $2 - $3

FIGHTING BILL CARSON
(1945 - PRC) Buster Crabbe, Al St. John
One Sheet: $75 - $150

FIGHTING BILL FARGO
(1941 - Universal) Johnny Mack Brown, Fuzzy
Knight
One Sheet: $50 - $100

FIGHTING BUCKAROO, THE
(1943 - Columbia) Charles Starrett, Ernest
Tubb
One Sheet: $75 - $125

FIGHTING CABALLERO
(1935 - Superior) Rex Lease
One Sheet: $100 - $200

FIGHTING CARAVANS
(1931 - Paramount Publix) Gary Cooper, Lily
Damita
One Sheet: $700 - $1,200   *Cowboy
Movie Posters # 112.*

FIGHTING CARAVANS
(1950R - Favorite) Gary Cooper, Lily Damita
One Sheet: $40 - $80   *Re-release.*

FIGHTING CHAMP, THE
(1933 - Monogram) Bob Steele, Gabby Hayes
One Sheet: $200 - $400

FIGHTING CHANCE, THE
(1955 - Republic) Rod Cameron, Julie London
One Sheet: $15 - $25

FIGHTING COAST GUARD
(1951 - Republic) Brian Donlevy, Ella Raines
One Sheet: $15 - $25

FIGHTING CODE, THE
(1933 - Columbia) Buck Jones, Ward Bond,
Diane Sinclair
One Sheet: $350 - $750   *Cowboy
Movie Posters #170.*

FIGHTING COWARD
(1936 - Victory) -
One Sheet: $75 - $150

FIGHTING COWBOY, THE

(1933 - Superior) Buffalo Bill, Jr., Genee
Boutell
One Sheet: $250 - $500

FIGHTING CRUSADER
(194?R - -) Tim McCoy
One Sheet: $75 - $125   *Re-release.*

FIGHTING DEPUTY, THE
(1937 - Spectrum) Fred Scott, Al St. John
One Sheet: $75 - $150

FIGHTING DEVIL DOGS
(1938 - Republic) Lee Powell, Herman Brix
One Sheet: $200 - $400   *Serial. 12
Chapters. One Sheet(Chapter 1):$400-800.*

FIGHTING EAGLE, THE
(1927 - -) Rod LaRocque, Phyllis Haver
One Sheet: $250 - $600

FIGHTING FATE
(1921 - Vitagraph) William Duncan, Edith
Johnson
One Sheet: $250 - $500   *Serial. 15
Chapters.*

FIGHTING FATHER DUNNE
(1948 - RKO) Pat O'Brien, Darryl Hickman
One Sheet: $30 - $60

FIGHTING FOOL, THE
(1932 - Columbia) Tim McCoy, Marceline Day
One Sheet: $600 - $1,000   *Cowboy
Movie Posters # 120.*

FIGHTING FOOLS
(1949 - Monogram) Leo Gorcey, Huntz Hall
One Sheet: $50 - $100

FIGHTING FOR JUSTICE
(1932 - Columbia) Tim McCoy
One Sheet: $350 - $750   *Cowboy
Movie Posters # 129.*

FIGHTING FRONTIER
(1942 - RKO) Tim Holt, Eddie Dew
One Sheet: $50 - $100

FIGHTING FRONTIERSMAN, THE
(1946 - Columbia) Charles Starrett (Durango
Kid), Smiley Burnette
One Sheet: $30 - $50

FIGHTING FURY
(1934 - -) John King, Tom London
One Sheet: $100 - $200   *AKA:
OUTLAW'S HIGHWAY.*

FIGHTING GENTLEMAN, THE
(1932 - Freuler) William Collier Jr., Josephine
Dunn
One Sheet: $15 - $25   *Sports
(Boxing). Brown duotone.*

One Sheet

FIGHTING GRINGO, THE
(1939 - RKO) George O'Brien, Slim Whitaker
One Sheet: $100 - $200

FIGHTING GUARDSMAN, THE
(1945 - Columbia) Willard Parker, George
Macready
One Sheet: $50 - $100

FIGHTING HERO
(1934 - Reliable) Tom Tyler, Renee Borden
One Sheet: $100 - $200

FIGHTING KENTUCKIAN, THE
(1949 - Republic) John Wayne, Vera Ralston,
Oliver Hardy
One Sheet: $200 - $400

FIGHTING LADY, THE

(1934 - Fanchon Royer) Peggy Shannon, Jack
Mulhall
One Sheet: $125 - $250

FIGHTING LADY
(1944 - 20th Century Fox) -
One Sheet: $50 - $100   *Documentary.*

FIGHTING LAWMAN, THE
(1953 - Allied Artists) Wayne Morris, Virginia
Grey
One Sheet: $10 - $20

FIGHTING LEGION, THE
(1930 - Universal) Ken Maynard, Dorothy Dwan
One Sheet: $700 - $1,200   *Cowboy
Movie Posters # 83.00*

FIGHTING MAD
(1939 - Criterion) James Newill, Sally Blane
One Sheet: $50 - $100

FIGHTING MAD
(1948 - Monogram) Leon Errol, Elyse Knox
One Sheet: $30 - $50

FIGHTING MAD
(1957 - New Realm) Joe Robinson, Adrienne
Scott
One Sheet: $10 - $20

FIGHTING MAD
(1976 - 20th Century Fox) Peter Fonda, Scott
Glenn
One Sheet: $5 - $10

FIGHTING MAD
(197? - -) Jayne Kennedy, Leon Isaac
One Sheet: $10 - $20   *Blaxploitation.*

FIGHTING MAN OF THE PLAINS
(1949 - 20th Century Fox) Randolph Scott,
Jane Nigh
One Sheet: $30 - $50

FIGHTING MARINE, THE
(1926 - Pathe) Gene Tunney
One Sheet: $250 - $600   *Serial. 10
Episodes. Sports Movie Posters #356.*

FIGHTING MARINES
(1935 - Mascot) Grant Withers, Adrian Morris,
Ann Rutherford
One Sheet: $150 - $300   *Serial. 12
Chapters.*

FIGHTING MARSHAL, THE
(1931 - Columbia) Tim McCoy
One Sheet: $250 - $500   *Cowboy
Movie Posters # 119.*

FIGHTING MEN, THE
(1953 - Lippert) -
One Sheet: $7 - $15

FIGHTING MUSTANG
(1948 - -) Sunset Carson, Lee Roberts
One Sheet: $30 - $50

FIGHTING O'FLYNN, THE
(1949 - United Artists) Douglas Fairbanks Jr.,
Helena Carter
One Sheet: $50 - $100

FIGHTING PARSON, THE
(1930 - MGM) Harry Langdon, Thelma Todd
One Sheet: $250 - $600

FIGHTING PARSON, THE
(1933 - Allied) Hoot Gibson, Marceline Day
One Sheet: $200 - $400

FIGHTING PEACEMAKER, THE
(1926 - Blue Streak) Jack Hoxie
One Sheet: $150 - $300

FIGHTING PILOT
(1935 - Ajax) Dick Talmadge
One Sheet: $200 - $400

FIGHTING PIMPERNEL
(1950 - British Lion) David Niven, Jack
Hawkins
One Sheet: $15 - $25

FIGHTING PIONEERS
(1935 - Resolute) Rex Bell, Ruth Mix
One Sheet: $125 - $250

FIGHTING PLAYBOY
(1937 - Northern) Nick Stuart, Lucille Browne
One Sheet: $75 - $125

FIGHTING PRESIDENT, THE

(1933 - Universal) -
One Sheet: $150 - $300   *Documentary
about Franklin D. Roosevelt.*

FIGHTING PRINCE OF DONEGAL, THE
(1966 - Disney) Peter McEnery, Susan
Hampshire
One Sheet: $10 - $20

FIGHTING RANGER, THE
(1925 - Adventure) Jack Daugherty
One Sheet: $200 - $400   *Serial.
Western. 18 Chapters.*

FIGHTING RANGER, THE
(1934 - Columbia) Buck Jones
One Sheet: $250 - $600

FIGHTING RANGER, THE
(1948 - Monogram) Johnny Mack Brown,
Christine Larson
One Sheet: $30 - $60

FIGHTING REDHEAD, THE
(1949 - Eagle-Lion) Jim Bannon, Peggy
Stewart
One Sheet: $20 - $40

FIGHTING RENEGADE
(1939 - Victory) Tim McCoy, Joyce Bryant
One Sheet: $75 - $150

FIGHTING ROOKIE, THE
(1934 - Mayfair) Jack LaRue, Mathew Betz
One Sheet: $75 - $150

FIGHTING SAP, THE
(1924 - F.B.O.) Fred Thomson
One Sheet: $500 - $800

FIGHTING SEABEES, THE
(1944 - Republic) John Wayne, Dennis O'Keefe
One Sheet: $200 - $400

FIGHTING SEABEES, THE
(1954R - Republic) John Wayne, Dennis
O'Keefe
One Sheet: $30 - $50   *Re-release.*

FIGHTING SHADOWS
(1935 - Columbia) Tim McCoy, Bob Allen
One Sheet: $250 - $500

FIGHTING SHEPHERDESS
(1920 - Associated First National) Anita
Stewart, Noah Beery
One Sheet: $200 - $400

FIGHTING SHERIFF, THE
(1931 - Columbia) Buck Jones, Paul Fix,
Loretta Sayers
One Sheet: $250 - $600

FIGHTING STALLION, THE
(1950 - Eagle-Lion) Bill Edwards, Doris Merrick
One Sheet: $15 - $30

FIGHTING STOCK
(1935 - Gainsborough) Tom Walls, Ralph Lynn
One Sheet: $125 - $250

FIGHTING STREAK, THE
(1922 - Fox) Tom Mix
One Sheet: $350 - $750

FIGHTING SULLIVANS
(1951R - 20th Century Fox) Anne Baxter,
Thomas Mitchell
One Sheet: $15 - $25   *Re-titled, re-
release of THE SULLIVANS.*

FIGHTING TEXAN
(1937 - Ambassador) Kermit Maynard, Frank
LaRue
One Sheet: $75 - $175

FIGHTING TEXANS
(1933 - Monogram) Rex Bell, Luana Walters
One Sheet: $100 - $200   *Cowboy
Movie Posters # 155.*

FIGHTING THOROUGHBREDS
(1939 - Republic) Ralph Byrd, Mary Carlisle
One Sheet: $75 - $150

FIGHTING THROUGH
(1934 - Kent) Reb Russell
One Sheet: $75 - $150

FIGHTING THRU
(1931 - Tiffany) Ken Maynard, Jeanette Loff
One Sheet: $200 - $400

FIGHTING TRAIL, THE

(1917 - Vitagraph) William Duncan, Carol Holloway
One Sheet: $200 - $400   *Serial. Western. 15 Chapters.*

FIGHTING TROOPER, THE
(1934 - Ambassador) Kermit Maynard
One Sheet: $125 - $250

FIGHTING TROUBLE
(1956 - Allied Artists) Huntz Hall, Stanley Clements
One Sheet: $30 - $50

FIGHTING VAGABONDS
(1937 - -) Bobby Nelson, Donald Reed
One Sheet: $40 - $75

FIGHTING VALLEY
(1943 - PRC) Dave O'Brien, Jim Newill
One Sheet: $30 - $60

FIGHTING VIGILANTES, THE
(1947 - Pathe) Lash LaRue, Fuzzy St. John
One Sheet: $30 - $60

FIGHTING WILDCATS, THE
(1957 - Republic) Keefe Brasselle, Kay Callard
One Sheet: $7 - $15

FIGHTING WITH KIT CARSON
(1933 - Mascot) Johnny Mack Brown, Betsy King Ross
One Sheet: $350 - $750   *Serial. Western. 12 Chapters.*

FIGHTING YOUTH
(1935 - Universal) Charles Farrell, Ann Sheridan
One Sheet: $75 - $150

FIGI DOES ITS BIT
(1920 - Paramount) -
One Sheet: $200 - $400   *A Paramount-Burton Holmes Travel Picture.*

FIGURES IN A LANDSCAPE
(1971 - National General) Robert Shaw, Malcolm McDowell
One Sheet: $3 - $5

FILE 113
(1932 - Associated Producers) Lew Cody, Clara Kimball Young
One Sheet: $125 - $250

FILE OF THE GOLDEN GOOSE, THE
(1969 - United Artists) Yul Brynner, Charles Gray
One Sheet: $5 - $10

FILE ON THELMA JORDAN, THE
(1949 - Paramount) Barbara Stanwyck, Wendell Corey
One Sheet: $125 - $250   *AKA: THELMA JORDAN*

FILES FROM SCOTLAND YARD
(1951 - Parthian) John Harvey, Moira Lister
One Sheet: $15 - $25

FILLMORE
(1972 - 20th Century Fox) Santana, The Grateful Dead
One Sheet: $40 - $75   *Rock and roll.*

FILM JOHNNIE, A
(1914 - Keystone) Charlie Chaplin
One Sheet: $7,500 - $12,000   *AKA: His Million Dollar Job.*

FILM PARADE
(1933 - Ross & Woods) All star cast
One Sheet: $200 - $400

FINAL ANALYSIS
(1992 - Warner Bros) Richard Gere, Uma Thurman, Kim Basinger
One Sheet: $3 - $5

FINAL APPOINTMENT
(1954 - Monarch) John Bentley, Jean Lodge
One Sheet: $15 - $25

FINAL ASSIGNMENT
(1980 - Persephone) Genevieve Bujold, Michael York
One Sheet: $3 - $5

FINAL CHAPTER-WALKING TALL
(1977 - AIP) Bo Svenson, Forrest Tucker
One Sheet: $5 - $10

FINAL CLOSE-UP, THE

(1919 - Paramount) Shirley Mason, Francis McDonald
One Sheet: $200 - $400

FINAL COLUMN, THE
(1955 - Paramount) Ron Randell, Christopher Lee
One Sheet: $15 - $25

FINAL COMEDOWN, THE
(1972 - New World) Billy Dee Williams
One Sheet: $5 - $10

FINAL CONFLICT, THE
(1981 - 20th Century Fox) Sam Neill, Rossano Brazzi
One Sheet: $3 - $5

FINAL COUNTDOWN, THE
(1980 - United Artists) Kirk Douglas, Martin Sheen
One Sheet: $3 - $5

FINAL EDITION, THE
(1932 - Columbia) Pat O'Brien, Mae Clarke
One Sheet: $150 - $300

FINAL EXAM
(1981 - MPM) Cecile Bagdadi, Joel Rice
One Sheet: $5 - $10

FINAL HOUR, THE
(1936 - Columbia) Ralph Bellamy, Marguerite Churchill
One Sheet: $100 - $200

FINAL OPTION, THE
(1982 - MGM) Lewis Collins, Judy Davis, Richard Widmark
One Sheet: $3 - $5

FINAL RECKONING, THE
(1932 - Equity) James Benton, Margaret Delane
One Sheet: $150 - $300

FINAL TERROR, THE
(1983 - Cromworld) Rachel Ward, Darryl Hannah
One Sheet: $5 - $10

FINAL TEST, THE
(1953 - GFD) Jack Warner, Adrianne Allen
One Sheet: $10 - $20

FIND THE BLACKMAILER
(1943 - Warner Bros.) Faye Emerson, Jerome Cowan
One Sheet: $30 - $60

FIND THE LADY
(1936 - Fox) George Sanders, Althea Henley
One Sheet: $125 - $250

FIND THE LADY
(1956 - Major) Mervyn Johns, Beverley Brooks
One Sheet: $15 - $25

FIND THE LADY
(1975 - -) John Candy, Peter Cook
One Sheet: $5 - $10

FIND THE WITNESS
(1937 - Columbia) Rosalind Keith, Charles Quigley
One Sheet: $100 - $200

FIND YOUR MAN
(1924 - Warner Bros.) Rin-Tin-Tin
One Sheet: $250 - $600

FINDERS KEEPERS
(1951 - Universal) Tom Ewell, Julia Adams
One Sheet: $15 - $25

FINDERS KEEPERS
(1967 - United Artists) Cliff Richard, Robert Morley
One Sheet: $5 - $10

FINDERS KEEPERS
(1984 - CBS) Michael O'Keeke, Beverly D'Angelo
One Sheet: $2 - $3

FINDERS KEEPERS, LOVERS WEEPERS
(1968 - Eve Productions) Anne Chapman, Paul Lockwood, Dir: Russ Meyers
One Sheet: $50 - $100   *Sexploitation.*

FINE FEATHERED FRIEND
(1948 - MGM) Tom and Jerry
One Sheet: $250 - $500   *Cartoon. Beware of re-release posters. Cartoon Movie*

Posters #264.

FINE FEATHERS
(1937 - British Lion) Renee Houston, Donald Stewart
One Sheet: $75 - $150

FINE MADNESS, A
(1966 - Warner Bros.) Joanne Woodward, Sean Connery
One Sheet: $10 - $20

FINE MESS, A
(1986 - Columbia) Ted Danson, Howie Mandel
One Sheet: $3 - $5

FINE PAIR, A
(1969 - National General) Rock Hudson, Claudia Cardinale
One Sheet: $7 - $15

FINE ROMANCE, A
(1992 - Castle Hill) -
One Sheet: $3 - $5

FINE SPECIMEN, A
(1995 - Tara Releasing/IN Pictures) Lisa Eichhorn, Stanley Tucci
One Sheet: $3 - $7

FINEST HOURS, THE
(1964 - Columbia) Winston Churchill documentary narrated by Orson Welles
One Sheet: $15 - $25

FINGER MAN
(1955 - Allied Artists) Frank Lovejoy, Peggie Castle, Forest Tucker
One Sheet: $30 - $55

FINGER OF GUILT
(1956 - RKO) Richard Basehart, Mary Murphy
One Sheet: $7 - $15

FINGER ON THE TRIGGER
(1965 - Allied Artists) Rory Calhoun, James Philbrook
One Sheet: $7 - $15

FINGER POINTS, THE
(1931 - First National) Richard Barthelmess, Fay Wray, Clark Gable
One Sheet: $1,000 - $1,800

FINGER PRINTS
(1931 - Universal) Kenneth Harlan, Edna Murphy
One Sheet: $250 - $600   *Serial. 10 Chapters.*

FINGERPRINTS DON'T LIE
(1951 - Spartan) Tom Neal, Sheila Ryan, Richard Travis
One Sheet: $30 - $60

FINGERS
(1940 - Warner Bros.) Cliff Evans, Roland Culver
One Sheet: $50 - $100

FINGERS
(1978 - Brut) Harvey Keitel, Jim Brown
One Sheet: $7 - $15

FINGERS AT THE WINDOW
(1942 - MGM) Lew Ayres, Basil Rathbone
One Sheet: $100 - $200

FINIAN'S RAINBOW
(1968 - Warner Bros.) Fred Astaire, Petula Clark
One Sheet: $15 - $25   *One Sheet (Todd-AO roadshow style):$100-$200.*

FINISHING SCHOOL
(1934 - RKO) Ginger Rogers, Bruce Cabot
One Sheet: $200 - $400

FINISHING TOUCH, THE
(1928 - MGM) Laurel & Hardy
One Sheet: $4,000 - $6,000

FINN AND HATTIE
(1931 - Paramount Publix) Leon Errol, Mitzi Green
One Sheet: $150 - $300

FINNEGANS WAKE
(1965 - Expanding Cinema) Martin J. Kelly, Jane Reilly
One Sheet: $10 - $20   *Mixture of Animation, Stock Footage & Live Action.*

FIORILE

(1994 - -) -
One Sheet: $15 - $25

FIRE AND ICE
(1983 - 20th Century Fox) Animation by Frank Frazetta
One Sheet: $30 - $60   *Cartoon. Frazetta art.*

One Sheet

FIRE BRIDE, THE
(1922 - Robertson-Cole) Ruth Renick, Edward Hearn
One Sheet: $250 - $500

FIRE CHIEF
(1940 - RKO/Disney) Donald Duck
One Sheet: $5,000 - $8,000   *Cartoon. Cartoon Movie Posters #165.*

FIRE DETECTIVE, THE
(1929 - Pathe)
One Sheet: $300 - $600   *Serial. 10 Chapters.*

One Sheet

FIRE DOWN BELOW
(1957 - Columbia) Rita Hayworth, Robert Mitchum, Jack Lemmon
One Sheet: $75 - $125

FIRE EATER, THE
(1921 - Universal) Hoot Gibson, Louise Lorraine
One Sheet: $600 - $1,000

FIRE HAS BEEN ARRANGED, A
(1935 - Twickenham) Bud Flanagan, Mary Lawson
One Sheet: $100 - $200

FIRE IN THE SKY
(1993 - Paramount) D.B. Sweeney, James Garner, Robert Patrick
One Sheet: $3 - $5

FIRE MAIDENS FROM OUTER SPACE
(1956 - Topaz) Anthony Dexter, Susan Shaw
One Sheet: $150 - $300   *Graven Images, pg. 187. AKA: FIRE MAIDENS OF OUTER SPACE.*

FIRE OVER AFRICA
(1954 - Columbia) Maureen O'Hara, Macdonald Carey
One Sheet: $20 - $40

FIRE OVER ENGLAND
(1937 - London) Flora Robson, Laurence Olivier, Vivien Leigh
One Sheet: $1,600 - $2,500

FIRE PATROL
(1922 - Chadwick) Anna Q. Nilsson
One Sheet: $200 - $400

FIRE RAISERS, THE
(1933 - Gaumont) Leslie Banks, Anne Grey
One Sheet: $125 - $250

FIRE SALE
(1977 - 20th Century Fox) Alan Arkin, Rob
Reiner
One Sheet: $5 - $10

FIRE WITH FIRE
(1986 - Paramount) Craig Sheffer, Virginia
Madsen
One Sheet: $3 - $5

FIREBALL, THE
(1950 - 20th Century Fox) Mickey Rooney, Pat
O'Brien, Marilyn Monroe
One Sheet: $50 - $100   *Sports (Roller
Derby). Sports Movie Posters #305.*

FIREBALL 500
(1966 - AIP) Frankie Avalon, Chill Wills,
Annette Funicello
One Sheet: $30 - $50   *Sports (Auto
Racing).*

One Sheet

FIREBALL JUNGLE
(1968 - Americana) Lon Chaney Jr., Alan Mixon
One Sheet: $10 - $20

FIREBIRD, THE
(1934 - Warner Bros.) Ricardo Cortez, Lionell
Atwill
One Sheet: $150 - $300

FIREBIRD 2015 A.D.
(1981 - Mara) Darren McGavin, Doug McClure
One Sheet: $7 - $15

FIREBIRDS
(1990 - Buena Vista) Nicolas Cage, Tommy
Lee Jones, Sean Young
One Sheet: $3 - $5

FIREBRAND, THE
(1962 - 20th Century Fox) Kent Taylor, Sid
Haig, Tom Daly
One Sheet: $5 - $10

FIREBRAND JORDAN
(1930 - Big Four) Lane Chandler, Yakima
Canutt
One Sheet: $150 - $300

FIREBRAND TREVISON
(1920 - Fox) Buck Jones
One Sheet: $150 - $300

Three Sheet

FIREBRANDS OF ARIZONA
(1944 - Republic) Smiley Burnette, Sunset
Carson
One Sheet: $30 - $50

FIRECHASERS, THE

(1970 - RFD) Chad Everett, John Loder
One Sheet: $5 - $10

FIRECRACKER
(1981 - New World) Jillian Kesner, Ken
Metcalfe
One Sheet: $3 - $5

FIRECREEK
(1968 - Warner Bros./Seven Arts) James
Stewart, Henry Fonda
One Sheet: $40 - $75

FIRED WIFE
(1943 - Universal) Louise Albritton, Robert
Paige
One Sheet: $50 - $100

FIREFLY, THE
(1937 - MGM) Jeanette MacDonald, Allan
Jones
One Sheet: $250 - $500

Insert

FIREFLY, THE
(1962R - MGM) Jeanette MacDonald, Allan
Jones
One Sheet: $15 - $25   *Re-release.*

FIREFOX
(1982 - Warner Bros.) Clint Eastwood
One Sheet: $7 - $15

FIREMAN, THE
(1916 - Mutual) Charlie Chaplin, Edna
Purviance
One Sheet: $8,000 - $13,000

FIREMAN, THE
(192?R - Lone Star) Charlie Chaplan, Edna
Purviance
One Sheet: $500 - $800   *Re-release.*

FIREMAN, SAVE MY CHILD
(1932 - First National) Joe E. Brown, Guy
Kibbee
One Sheet: $150 - $300

FIREMAN SAVE MY CHILD
(1954 - Universal) Spike Jones, The City
Slickers
One Sheet: $40 - $75

FIREMEN, SAVE MY CHILD
(1927 - Paramount) Wallace Beery, Raymond
Hatton
One Sheet: $250 - $500

FIREPOWER
(1979 - Associated) Sophia Loren, James
Coburn
One Sheet: $5 - $10

FIRES OF FATE
(1932 - Power) Lester Matthews
One Sheet: $150 - $300

FIRES OF HATE
(1932 - British International) Lester Matthews,
Dorothy Bartlam
One Sheet: $150 - $300

FIRESTARTER
(1984 - Universal) Drew Barrymore, Martin
Sheen
One Sheet: $7 - $15

FIRETRAP, THE
(1936 - Empire) Norman Foster, Evalyn Knapp
One Sheet: $75 - $150

FIREWALKER
(1986 - Cannon) Chuck Norris, Lou Gossett,
Melody Anderson
One Sheet: $5 - $10

FIRM, THE
(1993 - Paramount) Tom Cruise, Ed Harris
One Sheet: $7 - $15

FIRM MAN, THE
(1975 - Australian Film) Peter Cummins, Eileen
Chapman
One Sheet: $3 - $5

FIRST 100 YEARS, THE
(1924 - Pathe) Harry Langdon
One Sheet: $250 - $600

FIRST 100 YEARS, THE
(1938 - MGM) Robert Montgomery, Virginia
Bruce
One Sheet: $75 - $150

FIRST A GIRL
(1935 - Gaumont British) Jessie Matthews,
Sonnie Hale, Anna Lee
One Sheet: $50 - $100

FIRST AID
(1931 - Sono Art/World Wide) Grant Withers,
Marjorie Beebe
One Sheet: $100 - $200

FIRST AIDERS
(1944 - RKO/Disney) Mini Mouse and Pluto
One Sheet: $800 - $1,500   *Cartoon. Full
color. Cartoon Movie Posters #189.*

FIRST AUTO, THE
(1927 - Warner Bros.) Barney Oldfield, Patsy
Ruth Miller
One Sheet: $350-$700

One Sheet

FIRST BABY, THE
(1936 - 20th Century Fox) Johnny Downs, Jane
Darwell
One Sheet: $150 - $300

FIRST BLOOD
(1982 - Orion) Sylvester Stallone, Richard
Crenna
One Sheet: $10 - $20

FIRST COMES COURAGE
(1943 - Columbia) Brian Aherne, Merle Oberon
One Sheet: $50 - $100

FIRST DEADLY SIN, THE
(1980 - Filmways) Frank Sinatra, Faye
Dunaway
One Sheet: $7 - $15

**FIRST ESSANAY-CHAPLIN REVUE OF 1916,
THE**
(1916 - General Film Service) —
One Sheet: $5,000 - $8,000

FIRST FAMILY
(1980 - Warner Bros.) Bob Newhart, Gilda
Radner
One Sheet: $5 - $10

FIRST HUNDRED YEARS, THE
(1938 - MGM) Robert Montgomery, Virginia
Bruce
One Sheet: $75 - $150

FIRST KISS
(1928 - Paramount) Gary Cooper, Fay Wray
One Sheet: $1,300 - $2,000

FIRST KNIGHT
(1995 - Columbia) Richard Gere, Sean Connery
One Sheet: $5 - $10

FIRST LADY
(1937 - Warner Bros.) Kay Francis, Preston
Foster

One Sheet: $50 - $100

FIRST LEGION, THE
(1951 - United Artists) Charles Boyer, Barbara
Rush
One Sheet: $7 - $15

FIRST LOVE
(1939 - Universal) Deanna Durbin, Robert
Stack
One Sheet: $125 - $250

FIRST LOVE
(1977 - Paramount) William Katt, Susan Dey
One Sheet: $5 - $10

FIRST MAN INTO SPACE
(1958 - MGM) Marshall Thompson, Marla Landi
One Sheet: $30 - $50

FIRST MEN IN THE MOON
(1964 - Columbia) Edward Judd, Martha Hyer
One Sheet: $100 - $200   *Ray
Harryhausen effects. Graven Images, pg. 224.*

FIRST MONDAY IN OCTOBER, THE
(1981 - Paramount) Walter Matthau, Jill
Clayburgh
One Sheet: $3 - $5

FIRST NATIONAL ANNIVERSARY WEEK
(1920 - First National) Stock Poster
One Sheet: $150 - $300

FIRST NATIONAL MONTH
(1924 - First National) Various Stars
One Sheet: $500 - $800   *January
theatre promotion.*

FIRST NIGHT
(1937 - Paramount) Jack Livesey, Rani Waller
One Sheet: $75 - $150

FIRST NUDIE MUSICAL, THE
(1976 - Paramount) Cindy Williams, Stephen
Nathan
One Sheet: $10 - $20

FIRST OF THE FEW, THE
(1942 - Howard/General) Leslie Howard, David
Niven
One Sheet: $40 - $75

FIRST OFFENCE
(1936 - Gaumont) John Mills, Lilli Palmer
One Sheet: $125 - $250   *AKA: BAD
BLOOD.*

FIRST OFFENDERS
(1939 - Columbia) Walter Abel, Beverly
Roberts
One Sheet: $75 - $125

FIRST POWER, THE
(1990 - -) Lou Diamond Phillips, Tracy Griffith
One Sheet: $3 - $5

FIRST SNOW, THE
(1943 - 20th Century Fox) Mighty Mouse
One Sheet: $250 - $600   *Cartoon. Full
color stock poster with printed title. Huge image of
Mighty Mouse on yellow background.*

FIRST SPACESHIP ON VENUS
(1960 - Crown) Yoki Tani, Oldrich Lukes
One Sheet: $100 - $200

FIRST SWALLOW, THE
(1942 - MGM) -
One Sheet: $250 - $600   *Cartoon.
Cartoon Movie Posters #245.*

FIRST TEXAN, THE
(1956 - Allied Artists) Joel McCrea, Felicia Farr
One Sheet: $20 - $40

FIRST TIME, THE
(1952 - Columbia) Robert Cummings, Barbara
Hale
One Sheet: $15 - $25

FIRST TIME, THE
(1969 - United Artists) Jacqueline Bisset, Wes
Stern, Rick Kelman,
One Sheet: $10 - $20

FIRST TIME, THE
(1983 - New Line) Tim Choate, Krista Erickson
One Sheet: $3 - $5

FIRST TO FIGHT
(1967 - Warner Bros.) Chad Everett, Gene
Hackman
One Sheet: $5 - $10

FIRST TRAVELING SALESLADY, THE
(1956 - RKO) Ginger Rogers, Barry Nelson
One Sheet: $15 - $25

FIRST WORLD WAR, THE
(1934 - Fox) -
One Sheet: $250 - $500

FIRST YANK INTO TOKYO
(1945 - RKO) Tom Neal, Barbara Hale
One Sheet: $40 - $75

FIRST YEAR, THE
(1932 - Fox) Janet Gaynor, Charles Farrell
One Sheet: $150 - $300

FIRSTBORN
(1984 - Paramount) Teri Garr, Peter Weller
One Sheet: $3 - $5

FISH CALLED WANDA, A
(1988 - MGM/UA) John Cleese, Jamie Lee
Curtis
One Sheet: $7 - $15   *Academy Award Movie Posters #361.*

FISH THAT SAVED PITTSBURGH, THE
(1979 - United Artists) Julius Erving, Jonathan
Winters, Meadowlark Lemon
One Sheet: $15 - $25   *Sports (Basketball). Sports Movie Posters #95.*

FISHER KING, THE
(1991 - TriStar) Robin Williams, Jeff Bridges,
Mercedes Ruell
One Sheet: $15 - $25   *Academy Award: Best Supporting Actress (Ruell). Academy Award Movie Posters #379.*

FISHERMAN'S WHARF
(1939 - RKO) Bobby Breen, Henry Armetta
One Sheet: $50 - $100

One Sheet

FISHY TALES
(1937 - MGM) Our Gang
One Sheet: $250 - $600

FISHY TALES
(1951R - MGM) Our Gang
One Sheet: $100 - $200   *Re-release.*

F.I.S.T.
(1978 - United Artists) Sylvester Stallone, Rod
Steiger
One Sheet: $7 - $15   *Price is for both styles.*

FIST OF FEAR, TOUCH OF DEATH
(1980 - Aquarius) Fred Williamson, Ron Van
Clief
One Sheet: $10 - $20   *Blaxploitation.*

FISTFUL OF DOLLARS, A
(1967 - United Artists) Clint Eastwood,
Marianna Koch
One Sheet: $250 - $600   *Eastwood's first Spaghetti Western. One Sheet(Advance):$400-$700.*

FISTFUL OF DOLLARS/FOR A FEW DOLLARS MORE
(1969R - United Artists) Clint Eastwood,
Marianna Koch/Clint Eastwood, Lee Van Cleef
One Sheet: $40 - $75   *Re-release double feature poster.*

FISTFUL OF DYNAMITE, A
(1972 - United Artists) Rod Steiger, James
Coburn, Dir: Sergio Leone
One Sheet: $15 - $25   *AKA: DUCK, YOU SUCKER.*

FISTS OF FURY

(1973 - National General) Bruce Lee
One Sheet: $75 - $125   *Sports Movie Posters #262.*

FISTS OF FURY/CHINESE CONNECTION
(1980R - National General) Bruce Lee/Bruce
Lee, James Tien
One Sheet: $20 - $40   *Re-release double feature poster.*

FIT FOR A KING
(1937 - RKO) Joe E. Brown, Helen Mack
One Sheet: $125 - $250

FIT FOR A KING
(1947R - Trinity Pictures) Joe E. Brown, Helen
Mack, Paul Kelly
One Sheet: $30 - $50   *Re-release.*

FITZCARRALDO
(1982 - New World) Klans Kinski, Claudia
Cardinale
One Sheet: $15 - $25

FITZWILLY
(1967 - United Artists) Dick Van Dyke, Barbara
Feldon, Sam Waterston
One Sheet: $7 - $15

FIVE
(1951 - Columbia) William Phipps, Susan
Douglas
One Sheet: $40 - $75   *Graven Images, pg. 170.*

FIVE AGAINST THE HOUSE
(1955 - Columbia) Guy Madison, Kim Novak
One Sheet: $50 - $100

One Sheet

FIVE AND TEN
(1931 - MGM) Leslie Howard, Marion Davies
One Sheet: $1,000 - $1,800

FIVE AND TEN CENT ANNIE
(1928 - Warner Bros.) Louise Fazenda, Clyde
Cook, William Demarest
One Sheet: $200 - $400

FIVE ANGLES ON MURDER
(1950 - Gaumont) Jean Kent, Dirk Bogarde
One Sheet: $15 - $25

FIVE BAD MEN
(1935 - -) Noah Beery Jr., Buffalo Bill Jr., Art
Mix
One Sheet: $150 - $350

FIVE BOLD WOMEN
(1960 - Citation) Jeff Morrow, Merry Anders
One Sheet: $5 - $10

FIVE BRANDED WOMEN
(1960 - Paramount) Silvana Mangano, Vera
Miles, Van Heflin
One Sheet: $10 - $20

FIVE CAME BACK
(1939 - RKO) Chester Morris, Wendy Barrie,
Lucille Ball
One Sheet: $100 - $200

FIVE CARD STUD
(1968 - Paramount) Dean Martin, Robert
Mitchum
One Sheet: $20 - $40

FIVE CORNERS
(1988 - Cineplex Odeon) Jodie Foster, Tim
Robbins
One Sheet: $5 - $10

FIVE DAYS FROM HOME
(1978 - Universal) George Peppard, Neville
Brand

One Sheet: $5 - $10

FIVE DAYS ONE SUMMER
(1982 - Warner Bros.) Sean Connery, Betsy
Brantley
One Sheet: $7 - $15   *Sports Movie Posters #278.*

FIVE EASY PIECES
(1970 - Columbia) Jack Nicholson, Karen Black
One Sheet: $15 - $30   *Review:$15-25.*

FIVE FINGER EXERCISE
(1962 - Columbia) Rosalind Russell, Jack
Hawkins
One Sheet: $15 - $25

FIVE FINGERS
(1952 - 20th Century Fox) James Mason,
Danielle Darrieux
One Sheet: $15 - $35

FIVE FINGERS OF DEATH
(1973 - Warner Bros.) Lo Lieh, Wang Ping
One Sheet: $15 - $30   *Martial arts.*

One Sheet

FIVE GATES TO HELL
(1959 - 20th Century Fox) Neville Brand, Ken
Scott
One Sheet: $10 - $20

FIVE GOLDEN DRAGONS
(1967 - Warner Bros.) Robert Cummings, Klaus
Kinski
One Sheet: $15 - $30

FIVE GOLDEN HOURS
(1961 - Columbia) Cyd Charisse, Ernie Kovacs
One Sheet: $10 - $20

FIVE GRAVES TO CAIRO
(1943 - Paramount) Franchot Tone, Erich Von
Stroheim, Dir: Billy Wilder
One Sheet: $100 - $200

FIVE GUNS TO TOMBSTONE
(1961 - United Artists) James Brown, John
Wilder
One Sheet: $15 - $25

FIVE GUNS WEST
(1954 - AIP) John Lund, Dorothy Malone
One Sheet: $10 - $20

FIVE HEARTBEATS, THE
(1991 - Universal) Robert Townsend, Micheal
Wright, Diahann Carroll
One Sheet: $10 - $20   *Black cast rock musical.*

FIVE LITTLE PEPPERS AND HOW THEY GREW
(1939 - Columbia) Edith Fellows, Dorothy
Peterson
One Sheet: $50 - $100

FIVE LITTLE PEPPERS AT HOME
(1940 - Columbia) Edith Fellows, Dorothy
Peterson
One Sheet: $50 - $100

FIVE LITTLE PEPPERS IN TROUBLE
(1940 - Columbia) Edith Fellows, Dorothy Ann
Seese
One Sheet: $50 - $100

FIVE MAN ARMY, THE
(1970 - MGM) Peter Graves, James Daly
One Sheet: $3 - $5

FIVE MILES TO MIDNIGHT
(1963 - United Artists) Sophia Loren, Anthony
Perkins
One Sheet: $15 - $30

FIVE MILLION YEARS TO EARTH
(1968 - 20th Century Fox) James Donald,
Barbara Shelley
One Sheet: $20 - $40

FIVE MINUTES TO LIVE
(1961 - Sutton) Johnny Cash (film debut), Vic
Tayback
One Sheet: $20 - $40

FIVE OF A KIND
(1938 - 20th Century Fox) Dionne Quintuplets
One Sheet: $150 - $300

FIVE ON THE BLACK HAND SIDE
(1973 - United Artists) Clarice Tayler, Leonard
Jackson, Virginia Capers
One Sheet: $15 - $25   *Black cast.*

FIVE PENNIES, THE
(1959 - Paramount) Barbara Bel Geddes,
Danny Kaye
One Sheet: $30 - $60

FIVE POUND MAN, THE
(1937 - Fox British) Judy Gunn, Frank Allenby
One Sheet: $100 - $200

FIVE STAR FINAL
(1931 - First National) Edward G. Robinson,
Boris Karloff
One Sheet: $800 - $1,500

FIVE STEPS TO DANGER
(1956 - United Artists) Sterling Hayden, Ruth
Roman
One Sheet: $15 - $30

FIVE SUMMER STORIES
(197? - MacGillivray-Freeman Films) Surfing
Documentary
One Sheet: $15 - $30

FIVE SUMMER STORIES PLUS FOUR
(197? - MacGillivray-Freeman Films) Surfing
Documentary
One Sheet: $15 - $30

$5,000 REWARD
(1918 - Bluebird) Franklyn Farnum, Gloria
Hope
One Sheet: $200 - $400

5,000 FINGERS OF DR. T, THE
(1952 - Columbia) Peter Lind Hayes, Mary
Healy
One Sheet: $150 - $300   *Graven Images, pg. 183.*

FIVE TO ONE
(1963 - Allied Artists) Lee Montague, Brian
McDermott
One Sheet: $7 - $15

FIVE WEEKS IN A BALLOON
(1962 - 20th Century Fox) Red Buttons, Fabian
One Sheet: $7 - $15

FIXED BAYONETS
(1951 - 20th Century Fox) Michael O'Shea,
Richard Basehart
One Sheet: $15 - $30

FIXER, THE
(1968 - MGM) Alan Bates, Dirk Bogarde,
Georgia Brown
One Sheet: $3 - $5

FIXER DUGAN
(1939 - RKO) Lee Tracy, Virginia Weidler
One Sheet: $75 - $150

FIXER UPPERS, THE
(1935 - MGM) Laurel & Hardy
One Sheet: $2,500 - $4,000

FLAG LIEUTENANT, THE
(1932 - Gaumont) Henry Edwards, Anna
Neagle
One Sheet: $150 - $300

FLAGPOLE JITTERS
(1956 - Columbia) Three Stooges (Shemp)
One Sheet: $150 - $300   *Comedy short. Duotone. Remake of HOCUS POCUS.*

FLAME, THE
(1947 - Republic) John Carroll, Vera Ralston,
Robert Paige
One Sheet: $30 - $60

FLAME AND THE ARROW, THE
(1950 - Warner Bros.) Burt Lancaster, Virginia

Mayo
One Sheet: $30 - $50

FLAME AND THE FLESH, THE
(1954 - MGM) Lana Turner, Carlos Thompson
One Sheet: $20 - $40

FLAME BARRIER, THE
(1958 - United Artists) Arthur Franz, Kathleen Crowley
One Sheet: $7 - $15

FLAME IN THE HEATHER
(1935 - Paramount) Barry Clifton, Bruce Seton
One Sheet: $125 - $250

FLAME IN THE STREETS
(1961 - Rank) John Mills, Sylvia Syms
One Sheet: $10 - $20

FLAME OF ARABY
(1951 - Universal) Maureen O'Hara, Jeff Chandler
One Sheet: $30 - $50

FLAME OF CALCUTTA
(1953 - Columbia) Denise Darcel, Patric Knowles
One Sheet: $20 - $40

FLAME OF LOVE, THE
(1930 - British International) Anna May Wong, John Longden
One Sheet: $100 - $200

FLAME OF MEXICO
(1952 - Juliet Barrett Rublee) -
One Sheet: $15 - $30

FLAME OF NEW ORLEANS, THE
(1941 - Universal) Marlene Dietrich, Bruce Cabot
One Sheet: $800 - $1,400   *Vargas art on Lobby Card borders.*

FLAME OF NEW ORLEANS, THE
(1949R - Realart) Marlene Dietrich, Bruce Cabot
One Sheet: $50 - $100   *Re-release.*

FLAME OF PARIS
(1951 - -) Josephine Baker
One Sheet: $200 - $400

FLAME OF STAMBOUL
(1957 - Columbia) Richard Denning, Lisa Ferraday
One Sheet: $15 - $25

FLAME OF THE BARBARY COAST
(1945 - Republic) John Wayne, Ann Dvorak
One Sheet: $100 - $200

FLAME OF THE ISLANDS
(1955 - Republic) Yvonne De Carlo, Zachary Scott
One Sheet: $10 - $20

FLAME OF THE WEST
(1945 - Monogram) Johnny Mack Brown, Raymond Hatton
One Sheet: $30 - $50

FLAME OF THE YUKON, THE
(1917 - Keystone) Dorothy Dalton, Melbourne McDowell
One Sheet: $300 - $700

FLAME OF THE YUKON, THE
(1926 - Metropolitan) Seena Owen, Arnold Gray
One Sheet: $75 - $150

FLAME OF YOUTH
(1922 - Fox) Shirley Mason
One Sheet: $250 - $500

FLAME OF YOUTH
(1949 - Republic) Barbara Fuller, Ray McDonald
One Sheet: $30 - $50

FLAME OVER INDIA
(1960 - 20th Century Fox) Lauren Bacall, Kenneth More
One Sheet: $15 - $30

FLAME WITHIN, THE
(1935 - MGM) Ann Harding, Herbert Marshall
One Sheet: $150 - $300

FLAMES
(1932 - Monogram) Johnny Mack Brown, Noel Francis

One Sheet: $125 - $250

FLAMES OF DESIRE
(192? - William Fox) -
One Sheet: $150 - $300   *Adapted from Ouida's "Strathmore."*

FLAMES OF THE FLESH
(1920 - Fox) Gladys Brockwell, William Scott
One Sheet: $125 - $250

FLAMING BULLETS
(1945 - PRC) Tex Ritter, Dave O'Brien
One Sheet: $30 - $60

FLAMING CRISIS, THE
(1924 - Monarch) Calvin Nicholson
One Sheet: $800 - $1,500   *Black cast. Cowboy Movie Posters #43. Separate Cinema, pg. 7. Sports Movie Posters #240.*

FLAMING FATHERS
(192? - Pathecomedy) Max Davidson
One Sheet: $200 - $400

FLAMING FEATHER
(1951 - Paramount) Sterling Hayden, Arleen Whelan
One Sheet: $15 - $30

FLAMING FLAPPERS
(1925 - Pathecomedy) Glenn Tryon
One Sheet: $150 - $300

One Sheet

FLAMING FOREST, THE
(1926 - MGM) Antonio Moreno, Renee Adoree
One Sheet: $200 - $400

FLAMING FRONTIER, THE
(1926 - Universal) Hoot Gibson, Dustin Farnum
One Sheet: $500 - $800

FLAMING FRONTIER
(1958 - 20th Century Fox) Bruce Bennett, Jim Davis
One Sheet: $7 - $15

FLAMING FRONTIER
(1968 - Warner Bros.) Stewart Granger, Letitia Roman
One Sheet: $3 - $5

FLAMING FRONTIERS
(1938 - Universal) John Mack Brown
One Sheet: $125 - $250   *Serial. Western. 15 Chapters. One Sheet(Stock full color):$125-450.*

FLAMING FURY
(1949 - Republic) Roy Roberts, George Cooper
One Sheet: $40 - $75

FLAMING GOLD
(1933 - RKO) William Boyd, Pat O'Brien
One Sheet: $125 - $250

FLAMING GUNS
(1932 - Universal) Tom Mix, Ruth Hall
One Sheet: $800 - $1,500

FLAMING LEAD
(1939 - Colony) Ken Maynard, Eleanor Stewart
One Sheet: $75 - $150

FLAMING SIGNAL
(1933 - Invincible) Marceline Day, Noah Beery
One Sheet: $150 - $300

FLAMING STAR
(1960 - 20th Century Fox) Elvis Presley, Barbara Eden
One Sheet: $75 - $150

FLAMING TEEN-AGE, THE

(1956 - Truman) Noel Reyburn, Ethel Barrett
One Sheet: $30 - $60   *Drug Exploitation.*

FLAMING YOUTH
(1923 - Associated First National) Colleen Moore, Milton Sills
One Sheet: $150 - $300

FLAMINGO AFFAIR, THE
(1948 - Grand National) Denis Webb, Colette Melville
One Sheet: $30 - $50   *AKA: BLONDE FOR DANGER.*

FLAMINGO KID, THE
(1983 - 20th Century Fox) Matt Dillon, Richard Crenna, Frances Peach
One Sheet: $5 - $10

FLAMINGO ROAD
(1949 - Warner Bros.) Joan Crawford, Zachary Scott
One Sheet: $50 - $100

FLAP
(1970 - Warner Bros.) Anthony Quinn, Shelley Winters
One Sheet: $5 - $10

FLAREUP
(1969 - MGM) Raquel Welch, James Stacy, Luke Askew
One Sheet: $15 - $25

FLASH, THE
(1990 - Warner) John Wesley Shipp, Amanda Pays
One Sheet: $5 - $10   *Pilot for TV series.*

FLASH AND THE FIRECAT
(1976 - Sebastian) Roger Davis
One Sheet: $3 - $5

FLASH GORDON
(1936 - Universal) Larry "Buster" Crabbe, Jean Rogers
One Sheet: $10,000 - $15,000   *Serial. 13 Chapters. Price is for chapters 2-13. One Sheet(Stock full color):$10000-25000. Graven Images, pg. 45, 98.*

FLASH GORDON
(1980 - Universal) Sam J. Jones, Melody Anderson, Timothy Dalton
One Sheet: $7 - $15

FLASH GORDON CONQUERS THE UNIVERSE
(1940 - Universal) Larry "Buster" Crabbe, Carol Hughes
One Sheet: $800 - $1,500   *Serial. 15 chapters. Price is for duotone chapters. One Sheet(Full color):$4000-8000. GravenImages, pg. 139.*

One Sheet

FLASH GORDON CONQUERS THE UNIVERSE
(1945R - Universal) Larry "Buster" Crabbe, Carol Hughes
One Sheet: $250 - $500   *Re-release. Serial.*

FLASH GORDON'S TRIP TO MARS
(1938 - Universal) Larry "Buster" Crabbe
One Sheet: $1,600 - $2,500   *Serial. 15 Chapters. Above price is for duotone Chapters. One Sheet(full color Chapter 1):$6,000-12,000. Graven Images,pg. 98.*

FLASH OF GREEN, A
(1984 - Spectra) Ed Harris, Blair Brown
One Sheet: $2 - $3

FLASH OF THE FOREST, THE

(1928 - William Pizor) Braveheart (a dog)
One Sheet: $150 - $300

FLASH, THE TEENAGE OTTER
(1961 - Disney) Flash
One Sheet: $15 - $35

FLASHBACK
(1990 - Paramount) Dennis Hopper, Kiefer Sutherland, Carol Kane
One Sheet: $5 - $10

FLASHDANCE
(1983 - Paramount) Jennifer Beals, Michael Nouri
One Sheet: $15 - $30

FLASHING GUNS
(1947 - Monogram) Johnny Mack Brown
One Sheet: $40 - $75

FLASHPOINT
(1984 - HBO) Kris Kristofferson, Treat Williams
One Sheet: $3 - $5

FLAT FOOT STOOGES
(1938 - Columbia) The Three Stooges (Curly)
One Sheet: $7,500 - $12,000   *Comedy short. Duotone.*

FLAT TOP
(1952 - Monogram) Sterling Hayden, Richard Carlson
One Sheet: $40 - $75

FLATBUSH, FLORIDA
(1950 - Paramount) The Brooklyn Dodgers
One Sheet: $600 - $1,000   *Sports (Baseball).*

FLATLINERS
(1990 - Columbia) Kiefer Sutherland, Julia Roberts, Kevin Bacon
One Sheet: $10 - $20

FLAW, THE
(1933 - Paramount) Henry Kendall, Phyllis Clare
One Sheet: $100 - $200

FLAW, THE
(1955 - Renown) John Bentley, Donald Houston
One Sheet: $15 - $30

FLAXY MARTIN
(1949 - Warner Bros.) Virginia Mayo, Zachary Scott, Dorothy Malone
One Sheet: $15 - $30

FLEA IN HER EAR, A
(1968 - 20th Century Fox) Rex Harrison, Rosemary Harris, Louis Jourdan
One Sheet: $7 - $15

FLED
(1996 - MGM/UA) Laurence Fishburne, Stephen Baldwin
One Sheet: $3 - $5

FLEET'S IN, THE
(1928 - Paramount) Clara Bow
One Sheet: $1,300 - $2,000   *William J. Hanneman artwork.*

FLEET'S IN, THE
(1942 - Paramount) Dorothy Lamour, William Holden, Jimmy Dorsey Orch.
One Sheet: $100 - $200

FLESH
(1932 - MGM) Wallace Beery, Karen Morley, Dir:John Ford(1st at MGM)
One Sheet: $600 - $1,000   *Sports (Wrestling).*

FLESH
(1968 - Factory) Joe Dallesandro, Geraldine Smith
One Sheet: $75 - $125

FLESH AND BLOOD
(1922 - Western) Lon Chaney
One Sheet: $800 - $1,500

FLESH AND BLOOD
(1985 - Orion) Rutger Hauer, Jennifer Jason Leigh
One Sheet: $7 - $15

FLESH AND BLOOD SHOW, THE
(1974 - Entertainment Ventures) Ray Brooks
One Sheet: $7 - $15   *3-D. AKA: ASYLUM OF THE INSANE.*

FLESH AND BONE
(1993 - Paramount) Dennis Quaid, Meg Ryan
One Sheet: $3 - $5

FLESH AND FANTASY
(1943 - Universal) Charles Boyer, Edward G.
Robinson, Barbara Stanwyck
One Sheet: $75 - $150

FLESH AND FURY
(1952 - Universal) Tony Curtis, Mona Freeman
One Sheet: $20 - $40

FLESH AND THE DEVIL
(1926 - MGM) John Gilbert, Greta Garbo
One Sheet: $2,500 - $4,000

FLESH AND THE DEVIL
(1929R - MGM) John Gilbert, Greta Garbo
One Sheet: $600 - $1,000   *Re-release.*

FLESH AND THE SPUR
(1956 - AIP) John Agar, Marla English
One Sheet: $20 - $40

FLESH AND THE WOMAN
(1954 - Dominant) Gina Lollobrigida
One Sheet: $15 - $30   *AKA: THE
BIG GAME.*

FLESH EATERS, THE
(1964 - Vulcan) Rita Morley, Byron Sanders
One Sheet: $50 - $100

FLESH FEAST
(1970 - Cine World) Veronica Lake, Phil Philbin
One Sheet: $20 - $40   *Lake's last
film.*

FLESH GORDON
(1974 - Mammoth) Jason Williams, Suzanne
Fields
One Sheet: $15 - $30

One Sheet

FLESH IS WEAK, THE
(1957 - Eros) John Derek, Milly Vitale
One Sheet: $15 - $25

FLESH MERCHANT, THE
(1955 - Sonny Amusement Enterprises) Joy
Reynolds, Mariko Perri
One Sheet: $15 - $30

FLETCH
(1985 - Universal) Chevy Chase, Dana
Wheeler-Nicholson
One Sheet: $20 - $40

FLETCH LIVES
(1989 - Universal) Chevy Chase, Hal Holbrook,
Julianne Phillips
One Sheet: $5 - $10

FLICKERING YOUTH
(1924 - Pathe) Harry Langdon
One Sheet: $250 - $600

FLIGHT
(1929 - Columbia) Jack Holt, Ralph Graves,
Dir: Frank Capra
One Sheet: $800 - $1,500

FLIGHT
(1960 - Columbia) Efrain Ramirez, Edward
O'Brien
One Sheet: $7 - $15

FLIGHT ANGELS
(1940 - Warner Bros.) Jane Wyman, Dennis
Morgan
One Sheet: $40 - $75

FLIGHT AT MIDNIGHT

(1939 - Republic) Col. Roscoe Turner, Phil
Regan
One Sheet: $75 - $125

FLIGHT COMMAND
(1940 - MGM) Robert Taylor, Ruth Hussey
One Sheet: $75 - $150

FLIGHT FOR FREEDOM
(1943 - RKO) Rosalind Russell, Fred
MacMurray
One Sheet: $40 - $75

FLIGHT FROM ASHIYA
(1964 - United Artists) Yul Brynner, Richard
Widmark
One Sheet: $5 - $10

FLIGHT FROM DESTINY
(1941 - Warner Bros.) Thomas Mitchell,
Geraldine Fitzgerald
One Sheet: $40 - $75

FLIGHT FROM FOLLY
(1945 - Warner Bros.) Pat Kirkwood, Hugh
Sinclair
One Sheet: $40 - $75

FLIGHT FROM GLORY
(1937 - RKO) Chester Morris, Whitney Bourne
One Sheet: $75 - $150

FLIGHT INTO NOWHERE
(1938 - Columbia) Jack Holt, Jacqueline Wells
One Sheet: $75 - $125

FLIGHT LIEUTENANT
(1942 - Columbia) Pat O'Brien, Glenn Ford
One Sheet: $50 - $100

FLIGHT NURSE
(1953 - Republic) Joan Leslie, Forrest Tucker
One Sheet: $10 - $20

FLIGHT OF THE DOVES
(1971 - Columbia) Ron Moody, Jack Wild
One Sheet: $3 - $5

FLIGHT OF THE INNOCENT
(1993 - MGM) -
One Sheet: $3 - $5   *Italian.*

FLIGHT OF THE INTRUDER
(1991 - Paramount) Danny Glover, Willem
Dafoe
One Sheet: $75 - $150

FLIGHT OF THE LOST BALLOON
(1961 - AIP) Mala Powers, Marshall Thompson
One Sheet: $15 - $30

FLIGHT OF THE LOST BALLOON
(1961 - Woolner Bros.) Marshall Thompson,
Mala Power
One Sheet: $15 - $30

FLIGHT OF THE NAVIGATOR
(1986 - Buena Vista/Disney) Joey Cramer,
Veronica Cartwright
One Sheet: $3 - $5

FLIGHT OF THE PHOENIX
(1966 - 20th Century Fox) James Stewart,
Richard Attenborough
One Sheet: $20 - $40

FLIGHT THAT DISAPPEARED, THE
(1961 - United Artists) Craig Hill, Paula
Raymond
One Sheet: $15 - $30

FLIGHT TO FAME
(1938 - Columbia) Charles Farrell, Jacqueline
Wells
One Sheet: $50 - $100

FLIGHT TO FURY
(1966 - 20th Century Fox) Dewey Martin, Fay
Spain, Jack Nicholson
One Sheet: $10 - $20

FLIGHT TO HONG KONG
(1956 - United Artists) Rory Calhoun, Dolores
Donlon
One Sheet: $10 - $20

FLIGHT TO MARS
(1951 - Monogram) Marguerite Chapman,
Cameron Mitchell
One Sheet: $150 - $300   *Graven
Images, pg. 152.*

FLIGHT TO NOWHERE
(1946 - Screen Guild) Alan Curtis, Jack Holt

One Sheet: $20 - $40

FLIGHT TO TANGIER
(1953 - Paramount) Joan Fontaine, Jack
Palance
One Sheet: $15 - $35   *3-D.*

FLIM-FLAM MAN, THE
(1967 - 20th Century Fox) George C. Scott,
Sue Lyon
One Sheet: $7 - $15

FLING IN THE RING
(1955 - Columbia) The Three Stooges (Shemp)
One Sheet: $150 - $300   *Comedy short.
Sports (Boxing). Duotone. Remake of FRIGHT
NIGHT.*

One Sheet

FLINTSTONES, THE
(1994 - Universal) John Goodman, Rick
Moranis
One Sheet: $5 - $10

FLIP FLOPS
(1923 - Pathe) -
One Sheet: $100 - $200

FLIP THE FROG
(1931 - MGM) Dir: UB Iwerks
One Sheet: $4,000 - $6,000   *Cartoon.
Cartoon Movie Posters #238.*

FLIPPER
(1963 - MGM) Chuck Connors, Luke Halpin
One Sheet: $40 - $75   *TV Tie-In.*

FLIPPER
(1970R - MGM) Chuck Conners, Luke Halpin
One Sheet: $7 - $15   *Re-release.*

FLIPPER
(1996 - Universal) Paul Hogan, Elijah Wood
One Sheet: $4 - $8   *Family
adventure.*

FLIPPER'S NEW ADVENTURE
(1964 - MGM) Luke Halpin, Pamela Franklin
One Sheet: $40 - $75   *TV Tie-In.*

FLIRT, THE
(1922 - Universal) Eileen Percy, George
Nichols
One Sheet: $250 - $600

FLIRTATION WALK
(1934 - Warner Bros.) Ruby Keeler, Dick
Powell, Tyrone Power(film debut)
One Sheet: $250 - $600

FLIRTING
(1992 - Samuel Goldwyn) Noah Taylor, Nicole
Kidman
One Sheet: $3 - $5

FLIRTING IN THE PARK
(1933 - RKO) -
One Sheet: $75 - $150

FLIRTING WIDOW, THE
(1930 - First National) Basil Rathbone, Leila
Hyams
One Sheet: $150 - $350

FLIRTING WITH DANGER
(1934 - Monogram) Robert Armstrong, William
Cagney
One Sheet: $75 - $125

FLIRTING WITH DISASTER
(1996 - Miramax) Ben Stiller, Patricia Arquette,
Tea Leoni
One Sheet: $4 - $8

FLIRTING WITH FATE

(1938 - MGM) Joe E. Brown, Leo Carrillo
One Sheet: $150 - $300   *Hirschfeld art.*

FLIRTING WITH LOVE
(1924 - First National) Colleen Moore
One Sheet: $800 - $1,500

FLIRTING WITH THE MOVIES
(1919 - Clarion) -
One Sheet: $200 - $400   *A Lucky Strike
Comedy.*

FLOATING DUTCHMAN, THE
(1953 - Allied Artists) Dermot Walsh
One Sheet: $15 - $30

FLOOD, THE
(1931 - Columbia) Eleanor Boardman, Monte
Blue
One Sheet: $700 - $1,200

FLOOD, THE
(1963 - Pathe) Waveney Lee
One Sheet: $5 - $10

FLOOD, THE
(1997 - Paramount) Christian Slater, Morgan
Freeman, Minnie Driver
One Sheet: $4 - $8

FLOOD TIDE
(1957 - Universal) George Nader, Cornell
Borchers
One Sheet: $7 - $15

FLOODS OF FEAR
(1959 - Universal) Howard Keel, Anne
Heywood
One Sheet: $20 - $40

FLOODTIDE
(1949 - General Films) Gordon Jackson
One Sheet: $30 - $50

FLOORWALKER, THE
(1916 - Mutual) Charlie Chaplin, Edna
Purviance
One Sheet: $10,000 - $15,000   *First Mutual
release.*

FLOORWALKER, THE
(1920R - C. C. Pictures) Charlie Chaplin, Edna
Purviance
One Sheet: $2,200 - $3,500   *Re-release.*

FLORADORA GIRL, THE
(1930 - MGM) Marion Davies, Lawrence Gray
One Sheet: $200 - $400

FLORENTINE DAGGER, THE
(1935 - Warner Bros.) Margaret Lindsay, C.
Aubrey Smith
One Sheet: $100 - $200

FLORIAN
(1940 - MGM) Robert Young, Helen Gilbert
One Sheet: $75 - $125

FLORIDA SPECIAL
(1936 - Paramount) Jack Oakie, Sally Eilers
One Sheet: $125 - $250

FLORIDA STRAITS
(1987 - -) Raul Julia, Fred Ward
One Sheet: $3 - $5

FLOUNDERING
(1994 - Strand) James Le Gros
One Sheet: $5 - $10

FLOWER DRUM SONG
(1962 - Universal) Nancy Kwan, James Shigeta
One Sheet: $40 - $75

FLOWER OF MY SECRET, THE
(1996 - Sony Classics) Marisa Paredes, Juan
Echanove
One Sheet: $5 - $10

FLOWER OF THE NORTH
(1922 - Vitagraph) Henry B. Walthall, Pauline
Starke
One Sheet: $500 - $800   *Cowboy
Movie Posters #30.*

FLOWERS AND TREES
(1932 - United Artists) Silly Symphony
One Sheet: $16,000 - $25,000   *Cartoon.
Academy Award: Best Short Subject. First cartoon
to win an Oscar. Full color. The Disney Poster,
pg. 9.*

FLOWERS IN THE ATTIC
(1987 - -) Louise Fletcher, Victoria Tennant

One Sheet: $5 - $10

FLOWING GOLD
(1924 - Associated First National) Anna Q. Nilsson, Milton Sills
One Sheet: $200 - $400

FLOWING GOLD
(1940 - Warner Bros.) John Garfield, Pat O'Brien, Frances Farmer
One Sheet: $125 - $250

FLUFFY
(1965 - Universal) Tony Randall, Shirley Jones
One Sheet: $7 - $15

FLUKE
(1995 - MGM) Matthew Modine, Nancy Travis, Eric Stoltz
One Sheet: $3 - $5

FLY, THE
(1958 - 20th Century Fox) Al Hedison, Patricia Owens, Vincent Price
One Sheet: $75 - $150   *Graven Images, pg. 185.*

FLY, THE
(1986 - 20th Century Fox) Jeff Goldblum, Geena Davis
One Sheet: $10 - $20   *One Sheet (Style B): $40-$60.*

FLY BY NIGHT
(1942 - Paramount) Nancy Kelly, Richard Carlson
One Sheet: $50 - $100

FLY II, THE
(1989 - -) Eric Stolz, Daphne Zuniga
One Sheet: $3 - $5

FLY ME
(1973 - New World) Pat Anderson, Lenore Kasdorf
One Sheet: $7 - $15

FLY MY KITE
(1951R - Monogram) -
One Sheet: $50 - $100   *Re-release.*

FLY, THE/RETURN OF THE FLY
(1959 - 20th Century Fox) Vincent Price
One Sheet: $50 - $100   *Double feature poster. Graven Images, pg. 185.*

FLY-AWAY BABY
(1937 - Warner Bros.) Glenda Farrell, Barton MacLane
One Sheet: $75 - $125

FLY-COP, THE
(1920 - Vitagraph) Larry Semon
One Sheet: $250 - $500

FLYING ACE, THE
(1926 - Norman) Lawrence Criner, Kathryn Boyd
One Sheet: $800 - $1,500   *Black cast. Separate Cinema, pg. 5.*

FLYING AGE, THE
(1928 - Pathe) Cartoonist: Paul Terry
One Sheet: $600 - $1,000   *Cartoon. An Aesop's Film Fable.*

FLYING BEAR, THE
(1941 - MGM) -
One Sheet: $150 - $300   *Cartoon.*

FLYING BLIND
(1941 - Paramount) Richard Arlen, Jean Parker
One Sheet: $30 - $60

FLYING CADETS
(1941 - Universal) William Gargan, Peggy Moran
One Sheet: $50 - $100

FLYING CAT, THE
(1952 - MGM) Tom & Jerry
One Sheet: $250 - $600   *Cartoon. Full color stone litho.*

FLYING DEUCES, THE
(1939 - MGM) Stan Laurel, Oliver Hardy
One Sheet: $250 - $500

FLYING DEUCES, THE
(1947R - Astor) Stan Laurel, Oliver Hardy
One Sheet: $50 - $100   *Re-release.*

FLYING DEVILS
(1933 - RKO) Ralph Bellamy, Arline Judge

One Sheet: $150 - $350

FLYING DISC MAN FROM MARS
(1951 - Republic) Walter Reed, Lois Collier, Gregory Gay
One Sheet: $250 - $500   *Serial. 12 Chapters. Graven Images, pg. 181.*

FLYING DOWN TO RIO
(1933 - RKO) Dolores Del Rio, Gene Raymond, Fred Astaire, Ginger Rogers
One Sheet: $19,000 - $30,000   *First pairing of Astaire & Rogers. Price is for uncensored one sheet. OneSheet(censored):$10,000-$15,000.*

FLYING ELEPHANTS
(1927 - Pathecomedy) Stan Laurel, Oliver Hardy
One Sheet: $1,300 - $2,000

FLYING FEVER
(1924 - Fables) Paul Terry Animation
One Sheet: $800 - $1,500   *Cartoon.*

FLYING FISTS
(1937 - Victory) Herman Brix, Jean Martel
One Sheet: $40 - $90

FLYING FLEET, THE
(1929 - MGM) Ramon Novarro, Ralph Graves, Anita Page
One Sheet: $350 - $750

FLYING FONTAINES, THE
(1959 - Columbia) Michael Callan, Evy Norlund
One Sheet: $5 - $10

FLYING FOOL, THE
(1929 - Pathe) William Boyd, Marie Prevost
One Sheet: $250 - $500

Insert

FLYING FOOL, THE
(1931 - Wardour) Henry Kendall, Charles Farrell
One Sheet: $200 - $400

FLYING FORTRESS
(1942 - Warner Bros.) Richard Greene, Donald Stewart
One Sheet: $40 - $85

FLYING G-MEN
(1939 - Columbia) Robert Paige, Robert Fiske
One Sheet: $700 - $1,200   *Serial. 15 Chapters.*

FLYING GUILLOTINE, THE
(1975 - Shaw Bros.) Ma Teng, Hsuing Kang
One Sheet: $10 - $20

FLYING HIGH
(1931 - MGM) Bert Lahr, Charlotte Greenwood, Pat O'Brien
One Sheet: $100 - $200

FLYING HOOFS
(1925 - -) Jack Hoxie
One Sheet: $125 - $250

FLYING HORSEMAN, THE
(1926 - Wm. Fox) Buck Jones, Gladys McConnell
One Sheet: $250 - $600   *Cowboy Movie Posters #59.*

FLYING HOSTESS
(1936 - Universal) William Gargan, Judith Barrett
One Sheet: $500 - $800

FLYING IRISHMAN, THE
(1939 - RKO) Douglas Corrigan, Paul Kelly
One Sheet: $75 - $150

FLYING JALOPY
(1943 - RKO/Disney) Donald Duck
One Sheet: $3,500 - $5,000   *Cartoon. Cartoon Movie Posters #170.*

FLYING LEATHERNECKS
(1951 - RKO) John Wayne, Robert Ryan
One Sheet: $100 - $200

FLYING LEATHERNECKS
(1960R - RKO) John Wayne, Robert Ryan
One Sheet: $30 - $50   *Re-release.*

FLYING LUCK
(1927 - Pathe) Monty Banks, Jean Arthur
One Sheet: $200 - $400

FLYING MARINE, THE
(1929 - Columbia) Ben Lyon, Jason Robards Sr.
One Sheet: $150 - $300

FLYING MISSILE, THE
(1951 - Columbia) Glenn Ford, Viveca Lindfors
One Sheet: $20 - $40

FLYING PAT
(1920 - Paramount) Dorothy Gish
One Sheet: $800 - $1,500

FLYING SAUCER, THE
(1949 - Colonial) Mikel Conrad, Pat Garrison
One Sheet: $100 - $200   *Graven Images, pg. 170. First Flying Saucer film.*

FLYING SAUCER DAFFY
(1958 - Columbia) The Three Stooges (Joe Besser)
One Sheet: $75 - $125   *Comedy short. Duotone.*

FLYING SCOTSMAN, THE
(1929 - Warner Bros.) Ray Milland, Pauline Johnson
One Sheet: $200 - $400

FLYING SERPENT, THE
(1946 - PRC) George Zucco, Ralph Lewis
One Sheet: $40 - $75

FLYING SORCERER, THE
(1974 - Anvil) Kim Burfield
One Sheet: $10 - $20

FLYING SQUAD, THE
(1932 - British Lion) Edward Chapman
One Sheet: $150 - $300

FLYING SQUAD, THE
(1940 - Associated Artists) Phyllis Brooks, Basil Radford
One Sheet: $30 - $50

FLYING SQUIRREL
(1954 - RKO/Disney) Donald Duck
One Sheet: $250 - $500   *Cartoon. Full color.*

FLYING TIGERS
(1942 - Republic) John Wayne, John Carroll
One Sheet: $1,300 - $2,000

FLYING TIGERS
(1948R - Republic) John Wayne, John Carroll
One Sheet: $150 - $300   *Re-release.*

FLYING TIGERS
(1954R - Republic) John Wayne, John Carroll
One Sheet: $30 - $60   *Re-release.*

FLYING WHEELS
(1925 - Universal) Wanda Wiley
One Sheet: $250 - $500   *A Century Comedy.*

FLYING WILD
(1941 - Monogram) The East Side Kids, David O'Brien
One Sheet: $75 - $125

FLYING WILD
(1949R - Monogram) The East Side Kids, David O'Brien
One Sheet: $10 - $20   *Re-release.*

FLYING WITH MUSIC
(1942 - United Artists) Marjorie Woodworth, George Givot
One Sheet: $30 - $60

FM
(1978 - Universal) Michael Brandon, Eileen Brennan
One Sheet: $5 - $10   *Advance:$10-*

12.

FOES
(1977 - Coats) MacDonald Carey
One Sheet: $5 - $10

FOG, THE
(1923 - Metro) Mildred Harris
One Sheet: $200 - $400

FOG
(1933 - Columbia) Donald Cook, Mary Brian
One Sheet: $200 - $400

FOG, THE
(1979 - Avco/Embassy) Adrienne Barbeau, Jamie Lee Curtis, Dir: John Carpenter
One Sheet: $10 - $20   *Advance (Style B):$25-$50.*

One Sheet

FOG BOUND
(1923 - Paramount) Dorothy Dalton, David Powell
One Sheet: $500 - $800

FOG ISLAND
(1945 - PRC) Lionel Atwill, George Zucco
One Sheet: $40 - $75

FOG OVER FRISCO
(1934 - First National) Bette Davis, Lyle Talbot
One Sheet: $1,300 - $2,000

FOLIES BERGERE
(1935 - 20th Century Fox) Maurice Chevalier, Ann Sothern
One Sheet: $250 - $500

FOLKS
(1992 - 20th Century Fox) Tom Selleck, Don Ameche
One Sheet: $3 - $5

FOLKS AT RED WOLF INN, THE
(1972 - Scope III) Linda Gillian, Arthur Space
One Sheet: $3 - $5

FOLLIES
(1929 - Fox) -
One Sheet: $600 - $1,000

FOLLIES GIRL
(1943 - PRC) Wendy Barrie, Gordon Oliver
One Sheet: $20 - $40

FOLLIES REVUE
(195? - Globe) -
One Sheet: $40 - $75   *Sexploitation.*

FOLLOW A STAR
(1959 - Rank) Norman Wisdom
One Sheet: $10 - $20

FOLLOW ME
(1969 - Cinerama) Bob Purrey, Claude Cogdon, Mary Lou McGinnis
One Sheet: $3 - $5   *Sports (Surfing). Sports Movie Posters #320.*

FOLLOW ME, BOYS!
(1966 - Disney) Fred McMurray, Vera Miles, Lillian Gish
One Sheet: $15 - $25

FOLLOW ME, BOYS!
(1976R - Buena Vista/Disney) Fred MacMurray, Vera Miles, Lillian Gish
One Sheet: $5 - $10   *Re-release.*

FOLLOW ME QUIETLY
(1949 - RKO) William Lundigan, Dorothy Patrick, Jeff Corey
One Sheet: $15 - $25

FOLLOW THAT BIRD
(1985 - Warner Bros.) John Candy, Chevy Chase
One Sheet: $5 - $10

FOLLOW THAT CAMEL
(1967 - Rank) Phil Silvers, Jim Dale
One Sheet: $7 - $15

FOLLOW THAT DREAM
(1962 - United Artists) Elvis Presley, Arthur O'Connell
One Sheet: $50 - $100

One Sheet

FOLLOW THAT WOMAN
(1945 - Paramount) William Gargan, Nancy Kelly
One Sheet: $20 - $40

FOLLOW THE BAND
(1943 - Universal) Leon Errol, Mary Beth Hughes
One Sheet: $30 - $65

FOLLOW THE BOYS
(1944 - Universal) W.C. Fields, Marlene Dietrich, All-Star Cast
One Sheet: $40 - $75   *One Sheet is all text, no graphics.*

FOLLOW THE BOYS
(1963 - MGM) Connie Francis, Paula Prentiss
One Sheet: $15 - $35

FOLLOW THE FLEET
(1936 - RKO) Fred Astaire, Ginger Rogers, Lucille Ball
One Sheet: $4,000 - $6,000

One Sheet

FOLLOW THE FLEET
(1953R - RKO) Fred Astaire, Ginger Rogers, Lucille Ball
One Sheet: $75 - $150   *Re-release.*

FOLLOW THE LEADER
(1930 - Paramount Publix) Ed Wynn, Ginger Rogers
One Sheet: $250 - $600

FOLLOW THE LEADER
(1944 - Monogram) The East Side Kids, Joan Marsh,
One Sheet: $30 - $50

FOLLOW THE SUN
(1951 - 20th Century Fox) Anne Baxter, Glenn Ford
One Sheet: $100 - $200   *Sports (Golf). Cult film about golfer Ben Hogan.*

FOLLOW THRU
(1930 - Paramount) Charles Rogers, Nancy Carroll

One Sheet: $75 - $180

FOLLOW YOUR HEART
(1936 - Republic) Marion Talley, Nigel Bruce
One Sheet: $40 - $90

FOLLOW YOUR STAR
(1938 - General) Arthur Tracy
One Sheet: $75 - $150

FOLLY TO BE WISE
(1953 - Fine Arts) Alastair Sim, Roland Culver
One Sheet: $15 - $25

FOOD FOR FEUDIN'
(1950 - Disney) Pluto
One Sheet: $250 - $600   *Cartoon. The Disney Poster, pg. 30.*

FOOD OF THE GODS
(1976 - AIP) Marjoe Gortner, Ida Lupino, Pamela Franklin
One Sheet: $10 - $20

FOOL COVERAGE
(1939 - RKO) Edgar Kennedy
One Sheet: $100 - $200

FOOL KILLER, THE
(1965 - Allied Artists) Anthony Perkins, Edward Albert
One Sheet: $15 - $25

FOOL THERE WAS, A
(1922 - William Fox) Estelle Taylor, Lewis Stone, Irene Rich
One Sheet: $150 - $300

FOOL'S FIRST
(1922 - First National) Richard Dix
One Sheet: $200 - $400

FOOL'S GOLD
(1947 - United Artists) William Boyd, Andy Clyde
One Sheet: $50 - $100   *Hopalong Cassidy series.*

FOOLIN' AROUND
(1979 - Columbia) Gary Busey, Annette O'toole
One Sheet: $5 - $10

FOOLISH AGE, THE
(1919 - -) Chester Conklin
One Sheet: $250 - $600

FOOLISH WIVES
(1922 - Universal) Erich von Stroheim, Mae Busch
One Sheet: $700 - $1,200

FOOLS
(1970 - Cinerama) Katharine Ross, Jason Robards Jr.
One Sheet: $3 - $5

FOOLS FOR LOVE
(1985 - Cannon) Sam Shephard, Kim Basinger
One Sheet: $5 - $10

FOOLS FOR LUCK
(1928 - Paramount) W.C. Fields, Chester Conklin
One Sheet: $800 - $1,500

FOOLS FOR SCANDAL
(1938 - Warner Bros.) Fernand Gravet, Carole Lombard, Ralph Bellamy
One Sheet: $250 - $500

FOOLS OF DESIRE
(1941 - Continental) Byron Foulger, Constance Bergen
One Sheet: $40 - $75

FOOLS RUSH IN
(1949 - Rank) Sally Ann Howes, Guy Rolfe
One Sheet: $30 - $50

FOOLS RUSH IN
(1997 - Columbia) Matthew Perry, Salma Hayek
One Sheet: $4 - $8

FOOLS' PARADE
(1971 - Columbia) James Stewart, George Kennedy
One Sheet: $10 - $20

FOOTBALL, NOW AND THEN
(1953 - RKO/Disney) -
One Sheet: $150 - $350   *Cartoon. Sports (Football). Full color.*

FOOTBALL THRILLS
(1931 - Columbia) Sports Short
One Sheet: $600 - $1,000   *Sports Movie Posters #179.*

FOOTBALL THRILLS
(1938 - MGM) Number 1
One Sheet: $250 - $500   *Serial. Sports (Football). Pete Smith Specialty series.*

FOOTBALL THRILLS
(1946 - MGM) Number 9
One Sheet: $200 - $375   *Serial. Sports (Football). Pete Smith Specialty series.*

FOOTLIGHT FEVER
(1941 - RKO) Alan Mowbray, Donald McBride
One Sheet: $20 - $40

FOOTLIGHT GLAMOUR
(1943 - Columbia) Penny Singleton, Arthur Lake
One Sheet: $40 - $80

FOOTLIGHT PARADE
(1933 - Warner Bros.) James Cagney, Joan Blondell
One Sheet: $19,000 - $30,000

FOOTLIGHT RANGER, THE
(1923 - Fox) Charles Jones, Fritzi Brunette
One Sheet: $200 - $400

FOOTLIGHT SERENADE
(1942 - 20th Century Fox) John Payne, Betty Grable
One Sheet: $300 - $700

Window Card

FOOTLIGHT VARIETIES
(1951 - RKO) -
One Sheet: $15 - $35

FOOTLIGHTS
(1921 - PDC) Vera Reynolds, Zasu Pitts, Edmund Burns
One Sheet: $600 - $1,000

FOOTLIGHTS AND FOOLS
(1929 - Warner Bros.) Fredric March, Colleen Moore
One Sheet: $150 - $300

FOOTLIGHTS AND SHADOWS
(1920 - Selznick) Olive Thomas, Alex Onslow
One Sheet: $150 - $300

FOOTLOOSE
(1984 - Paramount) Kevin Bacon, Lori Singer
One Sheet: $7 - $15   *Dance musical.*

FOOTLOOSE HEIRESS, THE
(1937 - Warner Bros.) Craig Reynolds, Ann Sheridan
One Sheet: $75 - $150

FOOTPRINTS ON THE MOON
(1973 - 20th Century Fox) Florinda Bolkan
One Sheet: $10 - $20

FOOTSTEPS IN THE DARK
(1941 - Warner Bros.) Errol Flynn, Brenda Marshall
One Sheet: $100 - $200

FOOTSTEPS IN THE FOG
(1955 - Columbia) Jean Simmons, Stewart Granger
One Sheet: $15 - $35

FOOTSTEPS IN THE NIGHT
(1932 - RKO) Benita Hume, Harold Huth
One Sheet: $125 - $250

FOOTSTEPS IN THE NIGHT
(1957 - Allied Artists) Bill Elliott, Don Haggerty
One Sheet: $15 - $30

FOOTSTEPS IN THE SNOW
(1966 - Evergreen) Veronica Lake
One Sheet: $15 - $25

FOR A FEW DOLLARS MORE
(1967 - United Artists) Clint Eastwood, Lee Van Cleef
One Sheet: $200 - $450   *Spaghetti Western. Cowboy Movie Posters #317.*

FOR A FEW DOLLARS MORE
(1980R - United Artists) Clint Eastwood, Lee Van Cleef
One Sheet: $30 - $50   *Re-release. Spaghetti Western.*

FOR ALL MANKIND
(1989 - -) -
One Sheet: $5 - $10   *Documentary.*

FOR BEAUTY'S SAKE
(1940 - 20th Century Fox) Ted North, Marjorie Weaver
One Sheet: $40 - $80

FOR BETTER, FOR WORSE
(1955 - Stratford) Dirk Bogarde, Cecil Parker
One Sheet: $15 - $20

FOR CRIME'S SAKE
(1923 - Paramount) Krazy Kat
One Sheet: $2,500 - $4,000   *Cartoon. Duotone.*

FOR CRIMIN' OUT LOUD
(1956 - Columbia) The Three Stooges (Shemp)
One Sheet: $150 - $300   *Comedy short. Duotone.*

FOR HEAVEN'S SAKE
(1926 - Paramount) Harold Lloyd, James Mason
One Sheet: $1,300 - $2,000

FOR HEAVEN'S SAKE
(1950 - 20th Century Fox) Clifton Webb, Joan Bennett
One Sheet: $20 - $40

FOR HIS MASTER
(1914 - Mutual) -
One Sheet: $250 - $550

FOR KEEPS?
(1988 - -) Molly Ringwald, Randall Batnikoff
One Sheet: $5 - $10

FOR LOVE OF BENJI
(1977 - Mulberry Square) Benji, Patsy Garrett
One Sheet: $3 - $5

FOR LOVE OF IVY
(1968 - Palomar) Sidney Poitier, Beau Bridges
One Sheet: $15 - $25

FOR LOVE OR MONEY
(1933 - London) Robert Donat, Wendy Barrie, Edmund Gwenn
One Sheet: $100 - $225

FOR LOVE OR MONEY
(1939 - Universal) June Lang, Robert Kent
One Sheet: $75 - $175

FOR LOVE OR MONEY
(1963 - Universal) Kirk Douglas, Mitzi Gaynor
One Sheet: $15 - $30

FOR LOVE OR MONEY
(1993 - Universal) Michael J. Fox, Gabriella Anwar
One Sheet: $3 - $5

FOR MAMA'S SAKE
(1911 - -) -
One Sheet: $500 - $900

FOR ME AND MY GAL
(1942 - MGM) Judy Garland, Gene Kelly(film debut)
One Sheet: $250 - $600

FOR MEN ONLY
(1951 - Lippert) Paul Henreid, Margaret Field
One Sheet: $20 - $40

FOR PETE'S SAKE
(1951R - Monogram) Little Rascals
One Sheet: $50 - $100   *Re-release.*

FOR PETE'S SAKE!
(1966 - World-Wide) Billy Graham, Terry Garr
One Sheet: $30 - $50 *Preacher Graham's only film appearance.*

FOR PETE'S SAKE
(1977 - Columbia) Barbra Streisand, Michael Sarrazin
One Sheet: $5 - $10

FOR SADIE'S SAKE
(1926 - Educational) Jimmie Adams
One Sheet: $125 - $250

FOR SINGLES ONLY
(1968 - Universal) John Saxon, Mary Ann Mobley
One Sheet: $7 - $15

FOR THE BOYS
(1991 - 20th Century Fox) Bette Midler, James Caan
One Sheet: $7 - $15

FOR THE DEFENSE
(1930 - Paramount Publix) William Powell, Kay Francis
One Sheet: $600 - $1,000

FOR THE FIRST TIME
(1959 - MGM) Mario Lanza, Zsa Zsa Gabor
One Sheet: $5 - $10

FOR THE LOVE O' LIL
(1930 - Columbia) Jack Mulhall, Elliott Nugent
One Sheet: $100 - $200

FOR THE LOVE OF FANNY
(1931 - Educational) Glenn Tryon, Helen Mann
One Sheet: $125 - $250

FOR THE LOVE OF MARY
(1948 - Universal) Deanna Durbin, Edmond O'Brien
One Sheet: $50 - $120

FOR THE LOVE OF MIKE
(1933 - Wardour) Bobby Howes
One Sheet: $100 - $200

FOR THE LOVE OF MIKE
(1960 - 20th Century Fox) Richard Basehart, Stu Erwin
One Sheet: $5 - $10

FOR THE LOVE OF PETE
(1936 - Vitaphone) Robert Norton (Joe Palooka), Shemp Howard
One Sheet: $500 - $800 *Sports (Boxing). Sports Movie Posters #137.*

FOR THE LOVE OF RUSTY
(1947 - Columbia) Ted Donaldson, Tom Powers
One Sheet: $20 - $40

FOR THE SERVICE
(1936 - Universal) Buck Jones
One Sheet: $300 - $700

FOR THE SOUL OF RAFAEL
(1920 - Equity) Clara Kimball Young
One Sheet: $150 - $300

FOR THEM THAT TRESPASS
(1950 - Stratford) Richard Todd, Patricia Plunkett
One Sheet: $15 - $25

FOR THOSE IN PERIL
(1944 - Ealing) David Farrar
One Sheet: $30 - $50

FOR THOSE WHO THINK YOUNG
(1964 - United Artists) James Darren, Pamela Tiffin
One Sheet: $15 - $25

FOR VALOR
(1937 - Capital) Tom Wall, Ralph Lynn
One Sheet: $75 - $125

FOR WHOM THE BELL TOLLS
(1943 - Paramount) Gary Cooper, Ingrid Bergman
One Sheet: $350 - $750 *Academy Award Movie Posters #92.*

FOR WHOM THE BELL TOLLS
(1957R - Paramount) Gary Cooper, Ingrid Bergman
One Sheet: $30 - $60 *Re-release.*

FOR WHOM THE BULLS TOIL
(1953 - RKO/Disney) Goofy

One Sheet: $250 - $600 *Cartoon. The Disney Poster, pg. 62.*

FOR YOU I DIE
(1947 - Film Classics) Cathy Downs, Paul Langton
One Sheet: $15 - $25

FOR YOUR EYES ONLY
(1981 - United Artists) Roger Moore, Carole Bouquet
One Sheet: $30 - $50 *Advance:$40-75.*

FOR YOUR EYES ONLY

One Sheet

FORBIDDEN
(1932 - Columbia) Barbara Stanwyck, Adolphe Menjou, Ralph Bellamy
One Sheet: $1,300 - $2,000

FORBIDDEN
(1953 - Universal) Tony Curtis, Joanne Dru
One Sheet: $30 - $50

FORBIDDEN ADVENTURE
(1931 - Paramount Publix) Mitzi Green, Edna May Oliver
One Sheet: $150 - $300

FORBIDDEN ADVENTURE
(1934 - Road Show Attractions) -
One Sheet: $75 - $150

FORBIDDEN CARGO
(1954 - GFD) Nigel Patrick, Elizabeth Sellars
One Sheet: $10 - $20

FORBIDDEN CITY, THE
(1918 - -) Norma Talmadge, Thomas Meighan
One Sheet: $500 - $800

FORBIDDEN COMPANY
(1932 - Invincible) Sally Blane, John Darrow
One Sheet: $75 - $185

FORBIDDEN DANCE, THE
(1990 - -) Laura Herring, Jeff James
One Sheet: $4 - $8

FORBIDDEN FRUIT
(1920 - Famous Players-Lasky) Dir: Cecil B. DeMille
One Sheet: $250 - $600

FORBIDDEN HEAVEN
(1935 - Republic) Charles Farrell, Charlotte Henry
One Sheet: $75 - $125

FORBIDDEN ISLAND
(1958 - Columbia) Jon Hall, Nan Adams
One Sheet: $10 - $20

FORBIDDEN JUNGLE
(1949 - Eagle-Lion) Don Harvey, Forrest Taylor
One Sheet: $20 - $40

FORBIDDEN LOVE
(1927 - -) Lily Damita, Paul Richter
One Sheet: $250 - $600

FORBIDDEN PARADISE
(1924 - Paramount) Pola Negri, Rod LaRocque
One Sheet: $800 - $1,500

FORBIDDEN PARADISE
(1950' - -) -
One Sheet: $15 - $30

FORBIDDEN PATH, THE
(1918 - Fox) Theda Bara
One Sheet: $1,900 - $3,000

FORBIDDEN PLANET
(1956 - MGM) Walter Pidgeon, Anne Francis,

Leslie Nielsen
One Sheet: $1,900 - $3,000 *Graven Images, pg. 172-173.*

One Sheet

FORBIDDEN PLANET
(1972R - MGM) Walter Pigeon, Anne Francis, Leslie Nielsen
One Sheet: $20 - $40 *Re-release.*

FORBIDDEN STREET, THE
(1949 - 20th Century Fox) Dana Andrews, Maureen O'Hara
One Sheet: $50 - $100

FORBIDDEN TRAIL
(1936 - Columbia) Buck Jones
One Sheet: $250 - $600

FORBIDDEN TRAILS
(1942 - Monogram) Rough Riders (Buck Jones, Tim McCoy)
One Sheet: $100 - $200

FORBIDDEN VALLEY
(1938 - Universal) Noah Beery Jr., Francis Robinson
One Sheet: $125 - $250

FORBIDDEN WOMAN, THE
(1920 - Equity) Clara Kimball Young, Conway Tearle
One Sheet: $150 - $300

FORBIDDEN WOMEN
(1940S - -) -
One Sheet: $75 - $125 *Sexploitation.*

FORBIDDEN WORLD
(1982 - New World) Jesse Vint, Dawn Dunlap
One Sheet: $5 - $10

One Sheet

FORBIDDEN ZONE
(1980 - Borack) Herve Villechaize, Oingo Boingo (Rock Group)
One Sheet: $5 - $10

FORCE 10 FROM NAVARONE
(1978 - AIP) Robert Shaw, Harrison Ford
One Sheet: $10 - $20 *Style B:$12-$25.*

FORCE BEYOND, THE
(1978 - Film Ventures) Don Elkins
One Sheet: $3 - $5

FORCE: FIVE
(1981 - American Cinema) Joe Lewis, Pam Huntington
One Sheet: $3 - $5

FORCE OF ARMS
(1951 - Warner Bros.) William Holden, Nancy Olson

One Sheet: $30 - $50

FORCE OF EVIL
(1949 - MGM) John Garfield, Beatrice Pearson
One Sheet: $75 - $150

FORCE OF IMPULSE
(1961 - Sutton) Robert Alda, Jeff Donnell
One Sheet: $7 - $15

FORCE OF ONE, A
(1979 - American Cinema) Chuck Norris, Jennifer O'Neill
One Sheet: $7 - $15

FORCED ENTRY
(1975 - Century International) Tanya Roberts, Nancy Allen
One Sheet: $3 - $5

FORCED LANDING
(1935 - Republic) Onslow Stevens, Sidney Blackmer
One Sheet: $50 - $100

FORCED LANDING
(1941 - Paramount) Richard Arlen, Eva Gabor
One Sheet: $30 - $60

FORCED VENGEANCE
(1982 - MGM) Chuck Norris, Mary Louise Weller
One Sheet: $5 - $10

FORD EDUCATIONAL WEEKLY
(1919 - Goldwyn) -
One Sheet: $350 - $750 *"The Truth About The Liberty Motor."*

FOREIGN AFFAIR, A
(1948 - Paramount) Jean Arthur, Marlene Dietrich, John Lund
One Sheet: $50 - $120

FOREIGN AGENT
(1942 - Monogram) John Shelton, Gale Storm
One Sheet: $40 - $75

FOREIGN CORRESPONDENT
(1940 - United Artists) Joel McCrea, Laraine Day, Dir: Alfred Hitchcock
One Sheet: $1,900 - $3,000

One Sheet

FOREIGN CORRESPONDENT
(1947R - United Artists) Joel McCrea, Laraine Day, Dir: Alfred Hitchcock
One Sheet: $150 - $300 *Re-release.*

FOREIGN INTRIGUE
(1956 - United Artists) Robert Mitchum, Genevieve Page
One Sheet: $30 - $60

FOREIGN LEGION, THE
(1928 - Universal) Norman Kerry, Lewis Stone, Mary Nolan
One Sheet: $200 - $400

FOREIGNER, THE
(1978 - Visions) Eric Mitchell, Deborah Harry
One Sheet: $3 - $5

FOREPLAY
(1975 - Cinema National) Zero Mostel, Estelle Parsons
One Sheet: $7 - $15

FOREST, THE
(1983 - Fury) Dean Russell, Michael Brody
One Sheet: $2 - $3

FOREST RANGERS, THE
(1942 - Paramount) Fred MacMurray, Paulette Goddard

One Sheet: $50 - $100

FOREST RANGERS, THE
(1958R - Paramount) Fred MacMurray,
Paulette Goddard
One Sheet: $15 - $25   *Re-release.*

FOREVER AMBER
(1947 - 20th Century Fox) Linda Darnell,
Cornel Wilde
One Sheet: $30 - $60

FOREVER AND A DAY
(1943 - RKO) Brian Aherne, Robert Cummings,
All Star Cast
One Sheet: $75 - $125

FOREVER DARLING
(1955 - MGM) Lucille Ball, Desi Arnaz, James
Mason
One Sheet: $75 - $150

FOREVER FEMALE
(1953 - Paramount) William Holden, Ginger
Rogers, Paul Douglas
One Sheet: $20 - $40

FOREVER LULU
(1987 - -) Hanna Schygulla, Alec Baldwin
One Sheet: $2 - $3

FOREVER MY HEART
(1954 - British Lion) Douglas Fairbanks Jr,
Anouk Aimee
One Sheet: $15 - $25

FOREVER MY LOVE
(1962 - Paramount) Romy Schneider, Karl
Boehm
One Sheet: $15 - $25

FOREVER YOUNG
(1992 - Warner Bros.) Mel Gibson, Jamie Lee
Curtis
One Sheet: $5 - $10

FOREVER YOUNG, FOREVER FREE
(1976 - Universal) Jose Ferrer, Karen Valentine
One Sheet: $3 - $5

FOREVER YOURS
(1937 - United Artists) Beniamino Gigil, Joan
Gardner, Ivan Brandt
One Sheet: $40 - $80

FOREVER YOURS
(1944 - Monogram) Gale Storm, Johnny Mack
Brown
One Sheet: $30 - $60

FORGED PASSPORT
(1939 - Republic) Paul Kelly, Lyle Talbot
One Sheet: $30 - $50

FORGET PARIS
(1995 - Columbia) Billy Crystal, Debra Winger
One Sheet: $3 - $5

FORGOTTEN
(1933 - Chesterfield) Jane Clyde, William
Collier, Jr.
One Sheet: $100 - $200

FORGOTTEN COMMANDMENTS
(1932 - Paramount Publix) Gene Raymond,
Marguerite Churchill
One Sheet: $100 - $200

FORGOTTEN FACES
(1936 - Paramount) Herbert Marshall, Robert
Cummings
One Sheet: $50 - $100

FORGOTTEN GIRLS
(1940 - Republic) Louise Platt, Donald Woods
One Sheet: $50 - $100

FORGOTTEN WOMAN
(1939 - Universal) Sigrid Gurie, William
Lundigan
One Sheet: $75 - $125

FORGOTTEN WOMEN
(1932 - Monogram) Marion Shilling, Rex Bell
One Sheet: $150 - $300

FORGOTTEN WOMEN
(1949 - Monogram) Elyse Knox, Edward Norris
One Sheet: $15 - $35

FORLORN RIVER
(1937 - Paramount) June Martel, Buster
Crabbe
One Sheet: $40 - $80

FORMULA, THE
(1980 - MGM) George C. Scott, Marlon Brando
One Sheet: $5 - $10

FORREST GUMP
(1994 - Paramount) Tom Hanks, Sally Field
One Sheet: $10 - $20   *Academy
Award: Best Picture, Best Actor (Hanks), Best
Director (Zemecki). Academy Award Movie
Posters #390 & #391.*

One Sheet

FORSAKING ALL OTHERS
(1934 - MGM) Joan Crawford, Clark Gable
One Sheet: $1,300 - $2,000

FORSYTHE SAGA, THE
(1949R - MGM) -
One Sheet: $15 - $35   *Re-release.
MGM Silver Anniversary Picture.*

FORT ALGIERS
(1953 - United Artists) Yvonne De Carlo,
Carlos Thompson
One Sheet: $20 - $40

FORT APACHE
(1948 - RKO) Henry Fonda, John Wayne,
Shirley Temple, Dir: John Ford
One Sheet: $250 - $600

FORT APACHE
(1957R - RKO) Henry Fonda, John Wayne,
Shirley Temple, Dir: John Ford
One Sheet: $30 - $50   *Re-release.*

FORT APACHE, THE BRONX
(1981 - 20th Century Fox) Paul Newman, Ken
Wahl
One Sheet: $7 - $15

FORT BOWIE
(1958 - United Artists) Ben Johnson, Jan
Harrison
One Sheet: $10 - $20

FORT COURAGEOUS
(1965 - 20th Century Fox) Fred Beir, Harry
Lauter
One Sheet: $5 - $10

FORT DEFIANCE
(1951 - United Artists) Dane Clark, Ben
Johnson
One Sheet: $20 - $40

FORT DOBBS
(1958 - Warner Bros.) Clint Walker, Virginia
Mayo
One Sheet: $15 - $35

FORT DODGE STAMPEDE
(1951 - Republic) Allan "Rocky" Lane
One Sheet: $20 - $40

FORT MASSACRE
(1958 - United Artists) Joel McCrea, Forrest
Tucker
One Sheet: $15 - $30

FORT OSAGE
(1951 - Monogram) Rod Cameron, Jane Nigh
One Sheet: $15 - $30

FORT SAVAGE RAIDERS
(1951 - Columbia) Charles Starrett, Smiley
Burnette
One Sheet: $15 - $30

FORT TI
(1953 - Columbia) George Montgomery, Joan
Vohs
One Sheet: $15 - $35

FORT UTAH
(1967 - Paramount) John Ireland, Virginia Mayo
One Sheet: $10 - $20

FORT VENGEANCE
(1953 - Monogram) James Craig, Rita Moreno
One Sheet: $15 - $30

FORT WORTH
(1951 - Warner Bros.) Randolph Scott, David
Brian
One Sheet: $50 - $100

FORT YUMA
(1955 - United Artists) Peter Graves, Joan
Vohs
One Sheet: $15 - $35

FORTRESS
(1993 - Miramax) Christopher Lambert, Jeffrey
Combs
One Sheet: $3 - $5

FORTRESS OF AMERIKKA
(1989 - -) Gene LeBrok, Kellee Bradley
One Sheet: $5 - $10

FORTUNE, THE
(1975 - Columbia) Warren Beatty, Jack
Nicholson
One Sheet: $7 - $15

One Sheet

FORTUNE AND MEN'S EYES
(1971 - MGM) Wendell Burton, Michael Greer
One Sheet: $5 - $10

FORTUNE COOKIE, THE
(1966 - United Artists) Jack Lemmon, Walter
Matthau
One Sheet: $15 - $25   *Academy
Award Movie Posters #237.*

FORTUNE HUNTER, THE
(1915 - Unicorn) -
One Sheet: $250 - $600

FORTUNE HUNTERS
(1940 - 20th Century Fox) Gandy Goose
One Sheet: $75 - $150   *Cartoon.*

FORTUNES OF CAPTAIN BLOOD
(1950 - Columbia) Louis Hayward, Patricia
Medina
One Sheet: $15 - $30

FORTY ACRE FEUD
(1965 - Craddock) Minnie Pearl, Loretta Lynn
One Sheet: $30 - $50   *Country music
comedy.*

40 CARATS
(1973 - Columbia) Liv Ullmann, Edward Albert,
Gene Kelly
One Sheet: $5 - $10

FORTY DEUCE
(1982 - Island) Orson Bean, Kevin Bacon
One Sheet: $3 - $5

48 HOURS
(1944 - United Artists) Leslie Banks, Basil
Sydney
One Sheet: $30 - $60

48 HOURS
(1982 - Paramount) Eddie Murphy, Nick Nolte
One Sheet: $7 - $15

48 HOURS TO LIVE
(1960 - Cinema Assoc.) Anthony Steel, Marlies
Behrens
One Sheet: $5 - $10

45 FATHERS
(1937 - 20th Century Fox) Jane Withers,
Thomas Beck
One Sheet: $75 - $150

FORTY GUNS
(1957 - 20th Century Fox) Barbara Stanwyck,
Barry Sullivan
One Sheet: $30 - $50

FORTY GUNS TO APACHE PASS
(1967 - Columbia) Audie Murphy, Micheal
Burns
One Sheet: $15 - $30

FORTY LITTLE MOTHERS
(1940 - MGM) Eddie Cantor, Judith Anderson
One Sheet: $40 - $75

FORTY NAUGHTY GIRLS
(1937 - RKO) James Gleason, ZaSu Pitts
One Sheet: $50 - $100

49TH MAN, THE
(1953 - Columbia) John Ireland, Richard
Denning
One Sheet: $15 - $25

FORTY POUNDS OF TROUBLE
(1963 - Universal) Tony Curtis, Suzanne
Pleshette
One Sheet: $10 - $20

42ND STREET
(1933 - Warner Bros.) Warner Baxter, Bebe
Daniels, Ruby Keeler, Dick Powell
One Sheet: $10,000 - $15,000   *One
Sheet(Advertisement):$1000-2000.*

FORTY THIEVES
(1944 - United Artists) William Boyd, Andy
Clyde
One Sheet: $150 - $300

40,000 MILES WITH LINDBERGH
(1928 - MGM) Charles Lindbergh
One Sheet: $1,900 - $3,000

FORTY WINKS
(1925 - Paramount) Raymond Griffith, Anna
May Wong
One Sheet: $100 - $200

FORTYNINERS, THE
(1932 - Monarch) Tom Tyler, Betty Mack
One Sheet: $250 - $600   *Cowboy
Movie Posters #114.*

FORTYNINERS, THE
(1954 - Allied Artists) Bill Elliott, Virginia Grey
One Sheet: $15 - $35

FORWARD PASS, THE
(1929 - Warner Bros.) Douglas Fairbanks Jr.,
Loretta Young
One Sheet: $250 - $500

FOUL HUNTING
(1947 - RKO/Disney) Goofy
One Sheet: $500 - $800   *Cartoon.*

FOUL PLAY
(1978 - Paramount) Goldie Hawn, Chevy
Chase, Burgess Meredith
One Sheet: $7 - $15   *Advance:$10-
20.*

FOUND ALIVE
(1934 - Ideal) Barbara Bedford, Maurice
Murphy
One Sheet: $100 - $220

FOUNTAIN, THE
(1934 - RKO) Ann Harding, Paul Lukas
One Sheet: $75 - $175

FOUNTAINHEAD, THE
(1949 - Warner Bros.) Gary Cooper, Patricia
Neal
One Sheet: $250 - $500

FOUR BAGS FULL
(1957 - TransLux) Jean Gabin, Bourvil
One Sheet: $10 - $20

FOUR BOYS AND A GUN
(1956 - United Artists) Frank Sutton, James
Franciscus
One Sheet: $20 - $40

FOUR CLOWNS
(1970 - 20th Century Fox) Laurel and Hardy,
Buster Keaton, Charley Chase
One Sheet: $15 - $30

4-D MAN
(1959 - Universal) Robert Lansing, Lee
Meriwether
One Sheet: $30 - $60

FOUR DAUGHTERS
(1938 - Warner Bros.) Lane Sisters, Claude
Rains, John Garfield (film debut)
One Sheet: $250 - $600

Title Card

FOUR DAYS
(1951 - Grand National) Hugh McDermott,
Kathleen Byron
One Sheet: $15 - $30

FOUR DAYS IN NOVEMBER
(1964 - United Artists) -
One Sheet: $20 - $40   *Documentary
on the assassination of John F. Kennedy.*

FOUR DAYS LEAVE
(1950 - Film Classics) Cornel Wilde, Josette
Day
One Sheet: $15 - $30

FOUR DAYS OF NAPLES
(1963 - MGM) Regina Bianchi, Aldo Giuffre
One Sheet: $40 - $75   *Academy
Award: Best Foreign Film.*

FOUR DAYS WONDER
(1936 - Universal) Jeanne Dante, Kenneth
Howell
One Sheet: $75 - $140

FOUR DESPERATE MEN
(1960 - Continental) Aldo Ray, Heather Sears
One Sheet: $10 - $20

FOUR DEUCES, THE
(1976 - Avco/Embassy) Jack Palance, Carol
Lynley
One Sheet: $5 - $10

FOUR DEVILS
(1929 - Fox) Farrell MacDonald, Anders
Randolf
One Sheet: $150 - $350

FOUR FACES WEST
(1948 - United Artists) Joel McCrea, Frances
Dee
One Sheet: $50 - $100

FOUR FAST GUNS
(1960 - Universal) James Craig, Martha Vickers
One Sheet: $15 - $25

FOUR FEATHERS, THE
(1929 - Paramount) William Powell, Fay Wray,
Richard Arlen
One Sheet: $800 - $1,500

FOUR FEATHERS, THE
(1939 - United Artists) John Clements, Ralph
Richardson, June Duprez
One Sheet: $600 - $1,000

FOUR FLAMING DAYS
(1925 - MGM) Eleanor Boardman, Conrad
Nagel
One Sheet: $300 - $700

FOUR FLIES ON GREY VELVET
(1972 - Paramount) Michael Brandon, Mimsy
Farmer, Dir: Dario Argento
One Sheet: $15 - $30

FOUR FOR TEXAS
(1964 - Warner Bros.) Frank Sinatra, Dean
Martin, Three Stooges (Curly Joe)
One Sheet: $30 - $60

FOUR FOR THE MORGUE

(1962 - MPA) Stacy Harris, Louis Sirgo
One Sheet: $5 - $10

FOUR FRIENDS
(1981 - Filmways) Craig Wasson, Jodi Thelen
One Sheet: $2 - $3

FOUR FRIGHTENED PEOPLE
(1934 - Paramount) Herbert Marshall,
Claudette Colbert
One Sheet: $600 - $1,000

FOUR GIRLS IN TOWN
(1956 - Universal) Julie Adams, Marianne Cook
One Sheet: $15 - $30

FOUR GIRLS IN WHITE
(1939 - MGM) Florence Rice, Kent Taylor
One Sheet: $75 - $125

FOUR GUNS TO THE BORDER
(1954 - Universal) Rory Calhoun, Colleen Miller
One Sheet: $10 - $20

FOUR HORSEMEN OF THE APOCALYPSE
(1921 - Metro) Rudolph Valentino, Alice Terry
One Sheet: $250 - $600   *The part that
made him a superstar. Price is for one sheet
without Valentino pictured. One
Sheet(Valentinostyle):$2000-3000.*

FOUR HORSEMEN OF THE APOCALYPSE
(1962 - MGM) Glenn Ford, Ingrid Thulin
One Sheet: $15 - $25

FOUR HOURS TO KILL
(1935 - Paramount) Richard Barthelmess, Ray
Milland
One Sheet: $75 - $150

400 BLOWS, THE
(1959 - Janus) Patrick Auffay, Albert Remy
One Sheet: $200 - $400   *Price is for
French 23x32. French(Cocinor,47x65):$300-600.
Italian(Cinerz,13x28):$100-200.*

FOUR JACKS AND A JILL
(1941 - RKO) Ray Bolger, Desi Arnaz
One Sheet: $75 - $150

FOUR JILLS IN A JEEP
(1944 - 20th Century Fox) Carole Landis, Kay
Francis
One Sheet: $50 - $100

FOUR MASKED MEN
(1934 - Universal) John Stuart, Judy Kelly
One Sheet: $150 - $300

FOUR MEN AND A PRAYER
(1938 - 20th Century Fox) Loretta Young,
Richard Greene
One Sheet: $100 - $200

One Sheet

FOUR MOTHERS
(1941 - Warner Bros.) Priscilla Lane, Rosemary
Lane, Claude Rains
One Sheet: $50 - $100

FOUR MUSKETEERS, THE
(1975 - 20th Century Fox) Oliver Reed, Raquel
Welch, Richard Chamberlain
One Sheet: $10 - $20

FOUR POSTER, THE
(1952 - Columbia) Rex Harrison, Lilli Palmer
One Sheet: $15 - $25

FOUR RODE OUT
(1969 - Sagittarius) Leslie Nielsen, Sue Lyon
One Sheet: $5 - $10

FOUR ROOMS
(1995 - Miramax) Antonio Banderas, Madonna,

Tim Roth, Dir:Quentin Tarantino
One Sheet: $7 - $15

FOUR SEASONS, THE
(1981 - Universal) Alan Alda, Carol Burnett
One Sheet: $3 - $5

FOUR SHALL DIE
(1946 - Million Dollar) Dorothy Dandridge,
Mantan Moreland
One Sheet: $500 - $800   *Black cast.
Separate Cinema, pg. 140.*

FOUR SIDED TRIANGLE
(1952 - Hammer) Stephen Murray, Barbara
Payton
One Sheet: $50 - $100

FOUR SKULLS OF JONATHAN DRAKE, THE
(1959 - United Artists) Eduard Franz, Grant
Richards
One Sheet: $20 - $40

FOUR SONS
(1928 - Fox) James Hall, Margaret Mann
One Sheet: $600 - $1,000

FOUR SONS
(1940 - 20th Century Fox) Don Ameche, Alan
Curtis
One Sheet: $75 - $150

FOUR SQUARE STEVE
(1929 - Mustang) Edmund Cobb
One Sheet: $125 - $250

FOUR TIMES THAT NIGHT
(1970 - -) -
One Sheet: $3 - $5

FOUR WALLS
(1928 - MGM) Joan Crawford, John Gilbert
One Sheet: $1,300 - $2,000

FOUR WAYS OUT
(1954 - Carroll Pictures) Gina Lollobrigida
One Sheet: $30 - $50

FOUR WEDDINGS AND A FUNERAL
(1994 - Gramercy) Hugh Grant, Andy
MacDowell
One Sheet: $10 - $20

FOUR WIVES
(1940 - Warner Bros.) Claude Rains, Gale
Page, Lane Sisters
One Sheet: $50 - $100

FOUR'S A CROWD
(1938 - Warner Bros.) Errol Flynn, Rosalind
Russell
One Sheet: $200 - $400

FOURTEEN HOURS
(1951 - 20th Century Fox) Paul Douglas,
Richard Basehart, Grace Kelly
One Sheet: $30 - $60

1492: THE CONQUEST OF PARADISE
(1992 - Paramount) Gerard Depardieu, Armand
Assante, Sigourney Weaver
One Sheet: $5 - $12

FOURTEENTH LOVER, THE
(1921 - Metro) Viola Dana, Jack Mulhall
One Sheet: $250 - $600

FOURTH ALARM, THE
(1930 - Continental) Nick Stewart, Ralph Lewis
One Sheet: $700 - $1,200

FOURTH HORSEMAN, THE
(1932 - Universal) Tom Mix, Margaret Lindsay
One Sheet: $700 - $1,200

4TH MAN, THE
(1984 - -) Jeroen Krabbe, Renee Soutendijk
One Sheet: $30 - $50   *Dutch.*

FOURTH OF JULY FIRECRACKERS
(1953 - RKO/Disney) -
One Sheet: $150 - $300   *Cartoon. Two-
color poster with new artwork. A collection of
cartoon shorts re-released as a feature.*

FOURTH PROTOCOL, THE
(1987 - Rank) Michael Caine, Pierce Brosnan,
Joanna Cassidy
One Sheet: $2 - $3

FOURTH WAR, THE
(1990 - -) Roy Scheider, Jurgen Prochnow
One Sheet: $3 - $5

FOWL PLAY
(1933? - Supreme) Buck & Bubbles
One Sheet: $250 - $600   *Black cast.
Duotone.*

FOX, THE
(1921 - Universal) Harry Carey, George Nichols
One Sheet: $800 - $1,500

FOX, THE
(1968 - Warner Bros.) Anne Heywood, Sandy
Dennis, Keir Dullea
One Sheet: $10 - $20

FOX AND CROW
(1943 - Columbia) Stock Poster
One Sheet: $100 - $200   *Cartoon.*

FOX AND THE HOUND, THE
(1981 - Disney) -
One Sheet: $15 - $30   *Cartoon.*

FOX MOVIETONE FOLLIES
(1929 - Fox) John Breeden, Lola Lane
One Sheet: $1,300 - $2,000   *AKA:
MOVIETONE FOLLIES OF 1929.*

FOX MOVIETONE FOLLIES OF 1930
(1930 - 20th Century Fox) El Brendel, Marjorie
White
One Sheet: $600 - $1,000

FOX MOVIETONE NEWS
(1930S - Fox) -
One Sheet: $250 - $600

FOX STYLE
(1973 - -) Chuck Daniel, Juanita Moore
One Sheet: $10 - $20   *Black cast.*

FOXES
(1980 - United Artists) Jodie Foster, Scott Baio
One Sheet: $5 - $10

FOXES OF HARROW, THE
(1947 - 20th Century Fox) Rex Harrison,
Maureen O'Hara
One Sheet: $30 - $60

FOXEY FLATFOOTS
(1943 - Columbia) Fox & Crow
One Sheet: $350 - $750   *Cartoon. Full
color poster with scene inset.*

FOXFIRE
(1955 - Universal) Jeff Chandler, Jane Russell
One Sheet: $15 - $25

FOXHOLE IN CAIRO
(1961 - British Lion) James Robertson Justice,
Adrian Hoven
One Sheet: $5 - $10

FOXTRAP
(1986 - Snizzlefritz) Fred Williamson, Chris
Connely
One Sheet: $10 - $20   *Blaxploitation.*

FOXTROT
(1977 - New World) Peter O'Toole, Max von
Sydow
One Sheet: $3 - $5

FOXY BROWN
(1974 - AIP) Pam Grier, Antonio Fargas
One Sheet: $15 - $35   *Blaxploitation.*

FOXY LADY
(1971 - Cinepix) Alan Gordon, Sylvia Feigel
One Sheet: $7 - $15

F.P. 1
(1933 - Fox) Conrad Veidt, Leslie Fenton
One Sheet: $600 - $1,000   *Peter
Lorre(German version), Charles Boyer(French
Version). Graven Images, pg. 75.*

FRA DIAVOLO
(1933 - MGM) Laurel & Hardy, Dennis King
One Sheet: $2,500 - $4,000   *AKA: THE
DEVIL'S BROTHER.*

FRAGMENT OF FEAR
(1971 - Columbia) David Hemmings, Gayle
Hunnicutt
One Sheet: $3 - $5

FRAIDY CAT, THE
(1924 - Pathe) Our Gang, Charley Chase
One Sheet: $600 - $1,000

FRAIDY CAT
(1942 - MGM) Tom and Jerry
One Sheet: $600 - $1,000   *Cartoon.*

Cartoon Movie Posters #262.

FRAIL WOMEN
(1932 - Radio Pictures) Edmund Gwenn, Mary Newcomb
One Sheet: $150 - $300

FRAMED
(1930 - RKO) Evelyn Brent, Regis Toomey
One Sheet: $300 - $700

FRAMED
(1940 - Universal) Frank Albertson, Constance Moore
One Sheet: $50 - $100

FRAMED
(1947 - Universal) Glenn Ford, Janis Carter
One Sheet: $40 - $75

FRAMED
(1975 - Paramount) Joe Don Baker, Conny Van Dyke
One Sheet: $3 - $5

FRAMED CAT, THE
(1950 - MGM) Tom & Jerry
One Sheet: $300 - $700   *Cartoon. Full color.*

FRAMEUP, THE
(1937 - Columbia) Paul Kelly, Jacqueline Wells
One Sheet: $100 - $200

FRAME-UP, THE
(1938 - 20th Century Fox) Terry-toons
One Sheet: $100 - $200   *Cartoon. Full color stone litho. Stock poster with inset of title.*

FRAMING OF THE SHREW
(1947 - -) -
One Sheet: $100 - $200   *Black cast.*

FRANCES
(1982 - Universal) Jessica Lange, Kim Stanley
One Sheet: $5 - $10

FRANCHISE AFFAIR, THE
(1952 - Associated British-Pathe) Michael Denison, Dulcie Gray
One Sheet: $15 - $25

FRANCIS
(1949 - Universal) Donald O'Connor, Patricia Medina
One Sheet: $100 - $200

FRANCIS COVERS THE BIG TOWN
(1952 - Universal) Donald O'Connor, Nancy Guild
One Sheet: $40 - $75

FRANCIS GOES TO THE RACES
(1951 - Universal) Donald O'Connor, Piper Laurie
One Sheet: $50 - $100

FRANCIS GOES TO WEST POINT
(1952 - Universal) Donald O'Connor, Lori Nelson
One Sheet: $40 - $75

FRANCIS IN THE HAUNTED HOUSE
(1955 - Universal) Mickey Rooney, Virginia Welles
One Sheet: $40 - $75

FRANCIS IN THE NAVY
(1955 - Universal) Donald O'Connor, Martha Hyer, Clint Eastwood
One Sheet: $30 - $50

FRANCIS JOINS THE WACS
(1954 - Universal) Donald O'Connor, Julie Adams, Mamie Van Doren
One Sheet: $30 - $50

FRANCIS OF ASSISI
(1961 - 20th Century Fox) Bradford Dillman, Dolores Hart
One Sheet: $15 - $25

FRANK BUCK'S JUNGLE CAVALCADE
(1951 - RKO Radio) -
One Sheet: $20 - $40

FRANK DUCK BRINGS 'EM BACK ALIVE
(1946 - RKO/Disney) Donald Duck
One Sheet: $900 - $1,600   *Cartoon. Cartoon Movie Posters #172.*

FRANKENHOOKER
(1990 - -) Patty Mullen, James Lorinz, Louise Lasser

One Sheet: $15 - $30

FRANKENSTEIN
(- - -) Also see Mary Shelley's Frankenstein

FRANKENSTEIN
(1910 - Edison) Charles Ogle
No posters known to exist. Value unknown.

FRANKENSTEIN
(1931 - Universal) Boris Karloff, Colin Clive, Mae Clarke
One Sheet: $130,000 - $180,000   *Graven Images, pg. 47-49. One Sheet(Advance):$150,000-$200,000.*

One Sheet

FRANKENSTEIN
(1938R - Universal) Boris Karloff, Colin Clive, Mae Clarke
One Sheet: $4,000 - $6,000   *First re-release. One sheet and Lobby Card Set are green duotone.*

FRANKENSTEIN
(1947R - Universal) Boris Karloff, Colin Clive, Mae Clarke
One Sheet: $5,000 - $8,000   *Re-release. Graven Images, pg. viii.*

FRANKENSTEIN
(1951R - Realart) Boris Karloff, Colin Clive, Mae Clarke
One Sheet: $1,600 - $2,500   *Re-release.*

FRANKENSTEIN
(1961R - Universal) Boris Karloff, Colin Clive, Mae Clarke
One Sheet: $125 - $250   *Re-release.*

FRANKENSTEIN
(1973 - -) Robert Foxworth, Bo Svenson, Susan Strasberg
One Sheet: $7 - $15   *Made for TV movie.*

FRANKENSTEIN
(1974R - Film Classics Library) Boris Karloff, Colin Clive, Mae Clarke
One Sheet: $30 - $50   *Re-release.*

FRANKENSTEIN 1970
(1958 - Allied Artists) Boris Karloff, Jana Lund
One Sheet: $75 - $150

FRANKENSTEIN AND THE MONSTER FROM HELL
(1974 - Paramount) Peter Cushing, Shane Bryant
One Sheet: $30 - $50   *Last Hammer film.*

FRANKENSTEIN CONQUERS THE WORLD
(1966 - AIP) Nick Adams, Tadao Takashima, Baragon
One Sheet: $40 - $80

FRANKENSTEIN CREATED WOMAN
(1967 - 20th Century Fox) Peter Cushing, Susan Denberg
One Sheet: $30 - $50

FRANKENSTEIN CREATED WOMAN/ MUMMY'S SHROUD
(1967 - 20th Century Fox) Hammer Films
One Sheet: $15 - $30   *Double feature poster.*

FRANKENSTEIN MEETS THE SPACE MONSTER
(1965 - Allied Artists) James Karen, Nancy Marshall
One Sheet: $50 - $100

FRANKENSTEIN MEETS THE SPACE MONSTER/CURSE OF THE VOODOO

(1965 - Allied Artists) -
One Sheet: $40 - $75   *Double feature poster.*

FRANKENSTEIN MEETS THE WOLF MAN
(1943 - Universal) Lon Chaney, Jr., Bela Lugosi
One Sheet: $2,500 - $4,000   *Graven Images, pg. 110, 117.*

FRANKENSTEIN MEETS THE WOLF MAN
(1950R - Realart) Lon Chaney, Jr., Bela Lugosi
One Sheet: $300 - $700   *Re-release.*

FRANKENSTEIN MUST BE DESTROYED
(1970 - Warner Bros.) Peter Cushing, Simon Ward
One Sheet: $20 - $40

FRANKENSTEIN ON CAMPUS
(1971 - -) -
One Sheet: $15 - $25

FRANKENSTEIN UNBOUND
(1990 - -) John Hurt, Raul Julia, Dir: Roger Corman
One Sheet: $40 - $75

FRANKENSTEIN'S BLOODY TERROR
(1968 - Independent-International) Paul Naschy, Diana Zura
One Sheet: $15 - $25   *Duotone.*

FRANKENSTEIN'S CASTLE OF FREAK
(1973 - Cinerama) -
One Sheet: $15 - $25

FRANKENSTEIN'S CAT
(1942 - 20th Century) Terry-toons
One Sheet: $150 - $300   *Cartoon.*

FRANKENSTEIN'S DAUGHTER
(1958 - Astor) John Ashley, Sandra Knight
One Sheet: $75 - $125

FRANKIE AND JOHNNY
(1936 - Republic) Helen Morgan, Chester Morris
One Sheet: $75 - $150

FRANKIE AND JOHNNY
(1966 - United Artists) Elvis Presley, Donna Douglas
One Sheet: $40 - $75

One Sheet

FRANKIE AND JOHNNY
(1991 - Paramount) Michelle Pfeiffer, Al Pacino
One Sheet: $5 - $10

FRANKIE STARLIGHT
(1995 - Fine Line) Matt Dillon, Anne Parillaud
One Sheet: $4 - $8

FRANTIC
(1988 - Warner Bros.) Harrison Ford, Emmanuelle Seigner
One Sheet: $7 - $15

FRATERNITY ROW
(1977 - Paramount) Peter Fox, Gregory Harrison
One Sheet: $3 - $5

FRATERNITY VACATION
(1985 - New World) Stephen Geoffreys, Sheree J. Wilson
One Sheet: $3 - $5

FRAULEIN
(1958 - 20th Century Fox) Mel Ferrer, Dana Wynter
One Sheet: $15 - $25

FRAULEIN DOKTOR

(1969 - Paramount) Suzy Kendall, Kenneth More
One Sheet: $15 - $25

FREAKED
(1993 - 20th Century Fox) Keanu Reeves, Alex Winter, Randy Quaid, Mr. T.
One Sheet: $3 - $5

FREAKS
(1932 - MGM) Olga Baclanova, Henry Victor, Dir: Tod Browning
One Sheet: $60,000 - $80,000   *Graven Images, pg. 62. Original release banned, posters very rare. Beware Dwain Esper re-releases, see below.*

FREAKS
(1950R - Excelsior) Olga Baclanova, Henry Victor, Dir: Tod Browning
One Sheet: $150 - $350   *Graven Images, pg. 62. Dwain Esper re-release of banned 30's cult film.*

FREAKY FRIDAY
(1976 - Buena Vista) Barbara Harris, Jodie Foster
One Sheet: $10 - $20

FREAKY FRIDAY
(1977R - Buena Vista) Barbara Harris, Jodie Foster
One Sheet: $5 - $10   *Re-release.*

FRECKLES
(1935 - RKO) Tom Brown, Virginia Weidler
One Sheet: $125 - $250

FRECKLES
(1960 - 20th Century Fox) Martin West, Carol Christensen
One Sheet: $5 - $10

FRECKLES COMES HOME
(1942 - Monogram) Johnny Downs, Gale Storm
One Sheet: $50 - $100

FREDDIE STEPS OUT
(1946 - Monogram) Freddie Stewart, June Preisser
One Sheet: $20 - $40

FREDDY'S DEAD: THE FINAL NIGHTMARE
(1991 - New Line) -
One Sheet: $5 - $10

FREDDY'S NARROW ESCAPE
(1916 - Vitagraph) William Dangman, Helen Gurney
One Sheet: $250 - $500

FREE AND EASY
(1930 - MGM) Buster Keaton, Anita Page
One Sheet: $2,200 - $3,500

FREE AND EASY
(1941 - MGM) Robert Cummings, Ruth Hussey
One Sheet: $75 - $125

FREE, BLONDE AND 21
(1940 - 20th Century Fox) Lynn Bari, Joan Davis
One Sheet: $100 - $200

FREE FOR ALL
(1949 - Universal) Robert Cummings, Ann Blyth
One Sheet: $30 - $50

FREE GRASS
(1969 - Hollywood Star) Russ Tamblyn, Lana Wood
One Sheet: $15 - $30

FREE LOVE
(1930 - Universal) Conrad Nagel, Genevieve Tobin
One Sheet: $250 - $500

FREE SOUL, A
(1931 - MGM) Norma Shearer, Lionel Barrymore, Clark Gable
One Sheet: $1,300 - $2,000   *Academy Award: Best Actor(Lionel Barrymore). Academy Award Movie Posters #20.*

FREE TO LOVE
(1925 - B.P. Schulberg) Clara Bow, Donald Keith
One Sheet: $125 - $250

FREE, WHITE AND 21
(1963 - AIP) Frederick O'Neal, Annalena Lund
One Sheet: $20 - $40

FREE WILLY
(1993 - Warner Bros.) Jason James Richter, Lori Petty
One Sheet: $5 - $10

FREE WILLY 2: THE ADVENTURE HOME
(1995 - Warner Bros.) Jason James Richter, Michael Madsen
One Sheet: $4 - $8

FREEBIE AND THE BEAN
(1974 - Warner Bros.) Alan Arkin, James Caan
One Sheet: $5 - $10

FREEDOM OF THE PRESS
(1928 - Universal) Lewis Stone, Marceline Day
One Sheet: $250 - $600

FREEJACK
(1992 - Warner Bros.) Emilio Estevez, Mick Jagger, Anthony Hopkins, Robin Hite
One Sheet: $7 - $15

FREEWAYPHOBIA
(1965 - Buena Vista/Disney) Goofy
One Sheet: $100 - $200   *Cartoon.*

FREEZE OUT, THE
(1921 - Universal) Harry Carey, Helen Ferguson
One Sheet: $800 - $1,500

FREIGHTERS OF DESTINY
(1931 - RKO/Pathe) Tom Keene, Barbara Kent
One Sheet: $125 - $250

FRENCH CANCAN
(1954 - Gaumont) Jean Gabin, Francoise Arnoul
One Sheet: $1,600 - $2,500   *French.*

FRENCH CONNECTION, THE
(1971 - 20th Century Fox) Gene Hackman, Fernando Rey, Roy Scheider
One Sheet: $30 - $60   *Academy Award: Best Actor(Hackman), Best Director(Friedkin). Academy Award Movie Posters #264 &#265.*

One Sheet

FRENCH CONNECTION II
(1975 - 20th Century Fox) Gene Hackman, Fernando Rey
One Sheet: $7 - $15

FRENCH DOLL, THE
(1923 - Tiffany) Mae Murray, Orville Caldwell
One Sheet: $350 - $750

FRENCH FOLLIES
(1951 - Broadway Roadshow) -
One Sheet: $30 - $50

FRENCH FRIED
(1930 - Educational) Paul Terry Studio
One Sheet: $1,900 - $3,000   *Cartoon. Duotone. Cartoon Movie Posters #73.*

FRENCH KEY, THE
(1946 - Republic) Albert Dekker, Mike Mazurki
One Sheet: $30 - $50

FRENCH KISS
(1995 - 20th Century Fox) Meg Ryan, Kevin Kline
One Sheet: $5 - $10

FRENCH LEAVE
(1931 - Talking Picture) Madeleine Carroll, Sydney Howard
One Sheet: $150 - $300

FRENCH LEAVE
(1948 - Monogram) Jackie Cooper, Jackie Coogan, Ralph Sanford
One Sheet: $40 - $75

FRENCH LIEUTENANT'S WOMAN, THE
(1981 - United Artists) Meryl Streep, Jeremy Irons, Leo McKern
One Sheet: $7 - $15

FRENCH LINE, THE
(1953 - RKO) Jane Russell, Gilbert Roland
One Sheet: $50 - $100   *3-D.*

FRENCH PEEK A BOO
(1957 - -) -
One Sheet: $50 - $100   *Sexploitation.*

FRENCH PEEP SHOW, A
(1950 - T.N.T.) -
One Sheet: $30 - $50   *Sexploitation.*

FRENCH POSTCARDS
(1970 - Paramount) Debra Winger, Mandy Patinkin
One Sheet: $5 - $10

FRENCH TWIST
(1996 - Miramax) Victoria Abril, Alain Chabat
One Sheet: $5 - $10

FRENCH WAY, THE
(1952 - -) Josephine Baker (4th film)
One Sheet: $250 - $500   *First release in the U. S.*

FRENCH WITHOUT TEARS
(1940 - Paramount British) Ray Milland, Ellen Drew
One Sheet: $75 - $125

FRENCHIE
(1950 - Universal) Joel McCrea, Shelley Winters
One Sheet: $20 - $40

FRENCHMAN'S CREEK
(1944 - Paramount) Joan Fontaine, Basil Rathbone
One Sheet: $40 - $75

FRENZIED FLAMES
(1926 - Ellbee) Cullen Landis, Mary Carr
One Sheet: $500 - $800

FRENZY
(1972 - Universal) Jon Finch, Barry Foster, Alec McCowen, Dir: Alfred Hitchcock
One Sheet: $15 - $30

One Sheet

FRESH FROM PARIS
(1955 - Allied Artists) Forrest Tucker, Margaret Whiting
One Sheet: $10 - $20

FRESH HORSES
(1988 - Columbia) Molly Ringwald, Andrew McCarthy
One Sheet: $3 - $5

FRESH LAID PLANS
(1950 - MGM) -
One Sheet: $200 - $400   *Cartoon. Full color stone litho.*

FRESHMAN, THE
(1925 - Pathe) Harold Lloyd, Jobyna Ralston
One Sheet: $3,500 - $5,000

FRESHMAN, THE
(1990 - -) Marlon Brando, Matthew Broderick
One Sheet: $7 - $15

FRESHMAN LOVE
(1936 - Warner Bros.) Frank McHugh, Patricia Ellis
One Sheet: $75 - $150

FRESHMAN YEAR
(1938 - Universal) Dixie Dunbar, Ernest Truex
One Sheet: $75 - $150

FREUD
(1962 - Universal) Montgomery Clift, Susannah York
One Sheet: $15 - $30   *AKA: THE SECRET PASSION.*

FRIDAY
(1995 - New Line) Ice Cube, Chris Tucker
One Sheet: $5 - $10   *Black cast.*

FRIDAY FOSTER
(1976 - AIP) Pam Grier, Yaphet Kotto
One Sheet: $40 - $75   *Blaxploitation. "Wham! Bam! Here Comes Pam!"*

FRIDAY THE 13TH
(1922 - Pathe) Paul Parrott
One Sheet: $600 - $1,000

FRIDAY THE 13TH
(1980 - Paramount) Betsy Palmer, Adrienne King
One Sheet: $20 - $40

One Sheet

FRIDAY THE 13TH: JASON GOES TO HELL
(1993 - New Line) Kane Hodder
One Sheet: $5 - $10

FRIDAY THE 13TH PART 2
(1981 - Paramount) Betsy Palmer, Amy Steel
One Sheet: $10 - $20

FRIDAY THE 13TH PART 3-D
(1982 - Paramount) Dana Kimmell, Paul Kratka
One Sheet: $7 - $15

FRIDAY THE 13TH PART 4: THE FINAL CHAPTER
(1984 - Paramount) Crispin Glover, Kimberly Beck
One Sheet: $7 - $15

FRIDAY THE 13TH PART 5: A NEW BEGINNING
(1985 - Paramount) Frank Mancuso Jr., John Shepard
One Sheet: $7 - $15

FRIDAY THE 13TH PART 6: JASON LIVES
(1986 - Paramount) Thom Matthews, Jennifer Cooke
One Sheet: $7 - $15

FRIDAY THE 13TH PART 7: THE NEW BLOOD
(1987 - Paramount) Lar Park Lincoln, Terry Kiser
One Sheet: $7 - $15

FRIDAY THE 13TH PART 8: JASON TAKES MANHATTAN
(1989 - Paramount) Jensen Daggett, Kane Hodder
One Sheet: $7 - $15

FRIDAY THE 13TH...THE ORPHAN
(1979 - World Northal) Mark Owens, Peggy Feury
One Sheet: $10 - $20

FRIED GREEN TOMATOES
(1991 - Universal) Kathy Bates, Jessica Tandy
One Sheet: $10 - $20

FRIEDA
(1947 - Universal International) David Farrar, Mai Zetterling
One Sheet: $30 - $50

FRIENDLY ENEMIES

FRIENDLY ENEMIES
(1942 - United Artists) Charles Winninger, Charlie Ruggles
One Sheet: $50 - $100

FRIENDLY HUSBAND, A
(1922 - Fox) Lupino Lane
One Sheet: $150 - $300

FRIENDLY NEIGHBORS
(1940 - Republic) Weaver Brothers & Elviry
One Sheet: $50 - $100

FRIENDLY PERSUASION
(1956 - Allied Artists) Gary Cooper, Dorothy McGuire
One Sheet: $75 - $150

FRIENDLY PERSUASION
(1961R - Allied Artists) Gary Cooper, Dorothy McGuire
One Sheet: $15 - $30   *Re-release.*

FRIENDS
(1971 - Paramount) Sean Bury, Anicee Alvina
One Sheet: $5 - $10

FRIENDS AND LOVERS
(1931 - RKO) Laurence Olivier, Adolphe Menjou, Lily Damita
One Sheet: $1,300 - $2,000

FRIENDS OF EDDIE COYLE, THE
(1973 - Paramount) Robert Mitchum, Peter Boyle
One Sheet: $5 - $10

FRIENDS OF MR. SWEENEY
(1934 - Warner Bros.) Charlie Ruggles, Ann Dvorak
One Sheet: $75 - $150

FRIGHT
(1972 - Allied Artists) Susan George, Honor Blackman
One Sheet: $5 - $10   *AKA: NIGHT LEGS*

FRIGHT HOUSE
(1989 - -) Al Lewis, Duane Jones
One Sheet: $5 - $10

FRIGHT NIGHT
(1947 - Columbia) The Three Stooges (Shemp's 1st)
One Sheet: $600 - $1,000   *Comedy short. Duotone.*

FRIGHT NIGHT
(1985 - Columbia) Chris Sarandon, William Ragsdale
One Sheet: $15 - $25

FRIGHT NIGHT PART 2
(1989 - -) Roddy McDowall, Traci Lin, William Ragsdale
One Sheet: $10 - $20

FRIGHTENED BRIDE
(1953 - Grand National) Andre Morrell, Flora Robson
One Sheet: $15 - $25

FRIGHTENED CITY, THE
(1962 - Allied Artists) Herbert Lom, John Gregson
One Sheet: $3 - $5

FRIGHTENERS, THE
(1996 - Universal) Michael J. Fox, Trini Alvarado
One Sheet: $5 - $10
Advance(lenticular 3-D effect): $60-$120.

FRIGHTMARE
(1974 - Ellman) Rupert Davis, Sheila Keith
One Sheet: $10 - $20

FRIGHTMARE
(1983 - Saturn) Ferdinand Mayne
One Sheet: $5 - $10

FRINGE DWELLERS, THE
(1987 - -) Kristina Nehm, Justine Saunders
One Sheet: $3 - $5

FRISCO JENNY
(1933 - First National) Ruth Chatterton, Louis Colhern
One Sheet: $250 - $500

FRISCO KID
(1935 - Warner Bros.) James Cagney, Margaret Lindsay
One Sheet: $1,900 - $3,000   *Duotone.*

FRISCO KID
(1942R - Warner Bros.) James Cagney
One Sheet: $30 - $50   *Re-release.*
Duotone.

One Sheet (1942R)

FRISCO KID
(1979 - Warner Bros.) Gene Wilder, Harrison Ford
One Sheet: $7 - $15

FRISCO LIL
(1942 - Universal) Irene Hervey, Kent Taylor
One Sheet: $75 - $125

FRISCO SAL
(1945 - Universal) Susanna Foster, Alan Curtis
One Sheet: $50 - $100

FRISCO SALLY LEVY
(1927 - MGM) Sally O'Neill
One Sheet: $150 - $300

FRISCO TORNADO
(1950 - Republic) Allan "Rocky" Lane, Eddie Waller
One Sheet: $20 - $40

FRISCO WATERFRONT
(1935 - Republic) Helen Twelvetrees, Ben Lyon
One Sheet: $75 - $150

FRISKY
(1956 - DCA) Gina Lollobrigida, Vittorio De Sica
One Sheet: $30 - $50

FRISKY MRS. JOHNSON, THE
(1920 - Paramount) Billie Burke
One Sheet: $300 - $700

FRITZ THE CAT
(1971 - Aurica) Ralph Bakshi(animator), Robert Crumb(cartoonist)
One Sheet: $30 - $50   *Cartoon.*
Cartoon Movie Posters #391.

One Sheet

FRITZ THE CAT/9 LIVES OF FRITZ THE CAT
(1975R - --) Fritz the Cat
One Sheet: $10 - $20   *Re-release*
double feature poster. Cartoon.

FRITZ THE CAT/HEAVY TRAFFIC
(1988R - Aurica/AIP) Ralph Bakshi(animator), Robert Crumb(cartoonist)/
One Sheet: $10 - $20   *Cartoon. Re-*
release double feature poster.

FRIVOLOUS SAL
(1925 - First National) Mae Busch, Eugene O'Brien
One Sheet: $200 - $400

FROG, THE

(1937 - 20th Century Fox) Gordon Harker, Noah Beery
One Sheet: $100 - $200

FROGMEN, THE
(1951 - 20th Century Fox) Richard Widmark, Dana Andrews
One Sheet: $7 - $15

FROGS
(1972 - AIP) Ray Milland, Adam Roarke
One Sheet: $7 - $15

FROGWOMAN
(1959 - --) -
One Sheet: $30 - $50

FROM A WHISPER TO A SCREAM
(1986 - --) Vincent Price, Ted Whittenbarger
One Sheet: $7 - $15   *AKA: THE*
OFFSPRING.

FROM BEYOND
(1986 - --) Jeffrey Combs, Barbara Crampton
One Sheet: $7 - $15

FROM BEYOND THE GRAVE
(1974 - Amicus) Peter Cushing, Leslie-Anne Down
One Sheet: $10 - $20

FROM DUSK TILL DAWN
(1996 - Miramax) George Clooney, Harvey Keitel, Quentin Tarantino
One Sheet: $7 - $15

FROM FARM TO FAME
(1922 - --) Corliss Palmer, Mary Pickford, Lillian Gish
One Sheet: $800 - $1,500

FROM HAND TO MOUTH
(1920 - Pathe) Harold Lloyd
One Sheet: $800 - $1,500

FROM HAND TO MOUTH
(1924R - Pathe) Harold Lloyd
One Sheet: $150 - $300   *Re-release.*

FROM HEADQUARTERS
(1929 - Warner Bros.) Monte Blue, Guinn Williams
One Sheet: $250 - $500

FROM HEADQUARTERS
(1933 - Warner Bros.) George Brent, Margaret Lindsay
One Sheet: $100 - $200

FROM HELL IT CAME
(1957 - Allied Artists) Tod Andrews, Tina Carver
One Sheet: $75 - $150

FROM HELL TO HEAVEN
(1933 - Paramount) Carole Lombard, Jack Oakie
One Sheet: $500 - $800

FROM HELL TO TEXAS
(1958 - 20th Century Fox) Don Murray, Diane Varsi
One Sheet: $30 - $60

FROM HELL TO VICTORY
(1979 - New Film) George Peppard, Geroge Hamilton
One Sheet: $5 - $10

FROM HERE TO ETERNITY
(1953 - Columbia) Burt Lancaster, Donna Reed, Frank Sinatra
One Sheet: $125 - $250   *Academy*
Award: Best Picture, Best Direction(Fred Zinneman), Best Supporting Actor(Sinatra), Best Supporting Actress(Reed). Academy Award Movie Posters #148, #149, #153. Sports Movie Posters #152.

FROM NASHVILLE WITH MUSIC
(1969 - Craddock) Marilyn Maxwell
One Sheet: $30 - $60   *Country*
musical.

FROM NOON TO THREE
(1976 - United Artists) Charles Bronson, Jill Ireland
One Sheet: $7 - $15

FROM NURSE TO WORSE
(1940 - Columbia) The Three Stooges (Curly)
One Sheet: $5,000 - $7,500   *Comedy short.*
Duotone.

FROM RUSSIA WITH LOVE
(1964 - United Artists) Sean Connery, Daniela Bianchi
One Sheet: $150 - $350   *Price is for*
Style A or B.

FROM RUSSIA WITH LOVE
(1972R - United Artists) Sean Connery, Daniela Bianchi
One Sheet: $15 - $35   *Re-release.*

FROM SOUP TO NUTS
(1928 - MGM) Laurel & Hardy
One Sheet: $4,000 - $6,000

FROM THE EARTH TO THE MOON
(1958 - Warner Bros.) Joseph Cotten, George Sanders
One Sheet: $40 - $75

One Sheet

FROM THE HIP
(1987 - DeLaurentius) Judd Nelson, Elizabeth Perkins, John Jurt
One Sheet: $3 - $5

FROM THE MANGER TO THE CROSS
(1913 - Kalem) Gene Gaunthier, Jack Clark
One Sheet: $600 - $1,000   *An enormous*
artistic and commercial success and was still being shown in 1938 when it was reissued with sound.

FROM THE MANGER TO THE CROSS
(1938R - Kalem) Gene Gaunthier, Jack Clark
One Sheet: $150 - $300   *Re-release.*

FROM THE MIXED-UP FILES OF MRS. BASIL E. FRANKWEILER
(1973 - Cinema 5) Ingrid Bergman, Madeline Kahn
One Sheet: $5 - $10   *AKA: THE*
HIDEAWAYS.

FROM THE TERRACE
(1960 - 20th Century Fox) Paul Newman, Joanne Woodward
One Sheet: $20 - $40

FROM THIS DAY FORWARD
(1946 - RKO) Joan Fontaine, Mark Stevens
One Sheet: $30 - $50

FRONT, THE
(1976 - Columbia) Woody Allen, Zero Mostel
One Sheet: $15 - $25   *Advance:$20-*
30.

FRONT PAGE, THE
(1931 - United Artists) Adolphe Menjou, Pat O'Brien (Debut)
One Sheet: $75 - $175

FRONT PAGE, THE
(1975 - Universal) Walter Matthau, Jack Lemmon
One Sheet: $7 - $15

FRONT PAGE STORY
(1954 - British-Lion) Jack Hawkins, Eva Bartok
One Sheet: $15 - $25

FRONT PAGE WOMAN
(1935 - Warner Bros.) Bette Davis, George Brent
One Sheet: $1,300 - $2,000

FRONTIER AGENT
(1948 - Monogram) Johnny Mack Brown, Raymond Hatton
One Sheet: $40 - $75

FRONTIER BADMEN
(1943 - Universal) Robert Paige, Anne Gwynne
One Sheet: $75 - $125

FRONTIER CRUSADER
(1940 - PRC) Tim McCoy
One Sheet: $50 - $100

FRONTIER DAYS
(1934 - Spectrum) Bill Cody, William Desmond
One Sheet: $125 - $250

FRONTIER DAYS
(1945 - The Vitaphone Co.) Robert Shayne
One Sheet: $30 - $50

FRONTIER FEUD
(1945 - Monogram) Johnny Mack Brown
One Sheet: $40 - $75

FRONTIER FIGHTERS
(1947 - PRC) Buster Crabbe, Al "Fuzzy" St. John
One Sheet: $15 - $35

FRONTIER FROLIC
(1946 - Universal) -
One Sheet: $30 - $50

FRONTIER FUGITIVES
(1945 - PRC) Dave O'Brien, Tex Ritter
One Sheet: $40 - $75

FRONTIER FURY
(1943 - Columbia) Charles Starrett, Arthur Hunnicutt
One Sheet: $30 - $60

FRONTIER GAL
(1945 - Universal) Yvonne De Carlo, Rod Cameron
One Sheet: $30 - $50

FRONTIER GAMBLER
(1956 - Associated Film) John Bromfield, Jim Davis
One Sheet: $15 - $30

FRONTIER GUN
(1958 - 20th Century Fox) John Agar, Robert Strauss
One Sheet: $15 - $25

FRONTIER GUN LAW
(1946 - Columbia) Charles Starrett, Jean Stevens
One Sheet: $15 - $35

FRONTIER HELLCAT
(1966 - Columbia) Steward Granger, Elke Sommer
One Sheet: $5 - $10

FRONTIER INVESTIGATOR
(1949 - Republic) Allan "Rocky" Lane
One Sheet: $30 - $50

FRONTIER JUSTICE
(1936 - Diversion) Hoot Gibson
One Sheet: $100 - $200

One Sheet

FRONTIER LAW
(1943 - Universal) Russell Hayden, Jennifer Holt
One Sheet: $50 - $100

FRONTIER MARSHAL
(1934 - Fox) George O'Brien, Irene Bentley
One Sheet: $125 - $250   *Cowboy*
Movie Posters # 165.

FRONTIER MARSHAL
(1939 - 20th Century Fox) Randolph Scott, Nancy Kelly
One Sheet: $100 - $200

FRONTIER MARSHAL

(1948R - 20th Century Fox) Randolph Scott, Nancy Kelly
One Sheet: $20 - $40   *Re-release.*

FRONTIER OF THE STARS, THE
(1920 - Famous Players-Lasky) Thomas Meighan, Faire Binney
One Sheet: $250 - $500

FRONTIER OUTLAWS
(1944 - PRC) Buster Crabbe, Al St. John
One Sheet: $40 - $75

FRONTIER OUTPOST
(1949 - Columbia) Charles Starrett, Smiley Burnette
One Sheet: $30 - $50

FRONTIER PHANTOM, THE
(1951 - Western Adventure) Lash LaRue
One Sheet: $30 - $50

FRONTIER PONY EXPRESS
(1939 - Republic) Roy Rogers, Mary Hart
One Sheet: $250 - $500

One Sheet

FRONTIER REVENGE
(1948 - Screen Guild) Lash LaRue, Fuzzy St. John
One Sheet: $30 - $50

FRONTIER SCOUT
(1938 - Fine Arts) George Houston, Al St. John
One Sheet: $75 - $125

FRONTIER SCOUT
(1956 - United Artists) Tony Martin, Peggy Castle
One Sheet: $15 - $35

FRONTIER TOWN
(1937 - Grand National) Tex Ritter
One Sheet: $100 - $200

FRONTIER UPRISING
(1961 - United Artists) Jim Davis, Nancy Hadley
One Sheet: $10 - $20

FRONTIER VENGEANCE
(1940 - Republic) Don Barry, Betty Moran
One Sheet: $40 - $75

FRONTIER WOMAN
(1956 - Top) Cindy Carson, Lance Fuller
One Sheet: $7 - $15

FRONTIERS OF '49
(1938 - Columbia) Bill Elliott
One Sheet: $75 - $150

FRONTIERS OF '49
(194?R - Columbia) Bill Elliott
One Sheet: $30 - $60   *Re-release.*

FRONTIERSMAN, THE
(1938 - Paramount) William Boyd, Russell Hayden
One Sheet: $150 - $350

FROZEN ALIVE
(1966 - Magna) Mark Stevens, Marianne Koch
One Sheet: $5 - $10

FROZEN DEAD, THE
(1967 - Warner Bros./Seven Arts) Dana Andrews, Anna Palk
One Sheet: $15 - $35

FROZEN FEET
(1938 - 20th Century Fox) Terry-toons
Cartoon. See "Terrytoons Stock" for prices. Cartoon Movie Posters #85.

FROZEN GHOST, THE
(1944 - Universal) Lon Chaney Jr., Evelyn Ankers
One Sheet: $100 - $200

FROZEN GHOST, THE
(1954R - Realart) Lon Chaney Jr., Evelyn Ankers
One Sheet: $40 - $75   *Re-release.*

FROZEN JUSTICE
(1929 - Fox) Lenore Ulric, Robert Frazer
One Sheet: $150 - $300

FROZEN NORTH, THE
(1922 - -) Buster Keaton
One Sheet: $7,500 - $12,000

FROZEN RIVER
(1929 - Warner Bros.) Davey Lee, Rin-Tin-Tin
One Sheet: $250 - $500

F.T.A.
(1972 - AIP) Jane Fonda, Donald Sutherland
One Sheet: $10 - $20

FUELIN' AROUND
(1949 - Columbia) The Three Stooges (Shemp)
One Sheet: $350 - $750   *Comedy short. Duotone.*

FUGITIVE, THE
(1933 - Monogram) Rex Bell, Gabby Hayes
One Sheet: $150 - $300   *Cowboy Movie Posters # 156.*

FUGITIVE, THE
(1940 - Universal) Ralph Richardson, Diana Wynyard
One Sheet: $75 - $150

FUGITIVE, THE
(1947 - RKO) Henry Fonda, Dolores Del Rio
One Sheet: $125 - $250

FUGITIVE, THE
(1993 - Warner Bros.) Harrison Ford, Tommy Lee Jones
One Sheet: $7 - $15   *Academy Award: Best Supporting Actor (Jones). Style B:$20-$40. Advance:$15-$25. Academy Award Movie Posters #388.*

FUGITIVE AT LARGE
(1939 - Columbia) Jack Holt, Patricia Ellis
One Sheet: $75 - $125

FUGITIVE FROM A PRISON CAMP
(1940 - Columbia) Jack Holt, Marian Marsh
One Sheet: $75 - $125

FUGITIVE FROM JUSTICE, A
(1940 - Warner Bros.) Roger Pryor, Don Douglas
One Sheet: $50 - $100

FUGITIVE FROM SONORA
(1943 - Republic) Don Barry, Lynn Merrick
One Sheet: $30 - $50

FUGITIVE IN THE SKY
(1936 - Warner Bros.) Warren Hull, Jean Muir
One Sheet: $100 - $200

FUGITIVE KIND, THE
(1960 - United Artists) Marlon Brando, Anna Magnani, Joanne Woodward
One Sheet: $40 - $75

FUGITIVE LADY
(1934 - Columbia) Neil Hamilton, Florence Rice
One Sheet: $100 - $200

FUGITIVE LADY
(1951 - Republic) Janis Paige, Binnie Barnes
One Sheet: $30 - $50

FUGITIVE LOVERS
(1934 - MGM) Robert Montgomery, Madge Evans, Ted Healy & Stooges (Curly)
One Sheet: $250 - $600   *Price assumes Three Stooges not pictured on the one sheet.*

FUGITIVE OF THE PLAINS
(1943 - PRC) Buster Crabbe, Al St. John
One Sheet: $40 - $75   *Billy The Kid series.*

FUGITIVE ROAD
(1934 - Invincible) Erich von Stroheim, Wera Engels
One Sheet: $100 - $200

FUGITIVE SHERIFF
(1936 - Columbia) Ken Maynard
One Sheet: $150 - $350

FUGITIVE VALLEY
(1941 - Monogram) Range Busters
One Sheet: $30 - $50

FUGITIVES
(1929 - Fox) Madge Bellamy, Don Terry
One Sheet: $50 - $100

FUGITIVES FOR A NIGHT
(1938 - RKO) Frank Albertson, Eleanor Lynn
One Sheet: $75 - $150

FULL CIRCLE
(1935 - Warner Bros.) Rene Ray, Garry Marsh
One Sheet: $150 - $300

FULL CONFESSION
(1939 - RKO) Victor McLaglen, Sally Eilers
One Sheet: $50 - $100

FULL FATHOM FIVE
(1990 - -) Michael Moriarty, Maria Rangel
One Sheet: $5 - $10

FULL METAL JACKET
(1987 - Warner Bros.) Matthew Modine, Adam Baldwin, Dir: Stanley Kubrick
One Sheet: $20 - $40   *Price is for Style A one sheet. One Sheet (Style B):$10-$20; One Sheet (Style C):$50-$100.Advance (any of four styles):$30-$50.*

FULL MOON HIGH
(1982 - Filmways) Adam & Alan Arkin, Pat Morita
One Sheet: $3 - $5

FULL MOON IN BLUE WATER
(1988 - -) Gene Hackman, Teir Garr, Burgess Meredith
One Sheet: $3 - $5

FULL OF LIFE
(1956 - Columbia) Judy Holliday, Richard Conte
One Sheet: $15 - $35

FULLER BRUSH GIRL, THE
(1950 - Columbia) Lucille Ball, Eddie Albert
One Sheet: $75 - $150

FULLER BRUSH MAN, THE
(1948 - Columbia) Red Skelton, Janet Blair
One Sheet: $100 - $200

FUN AND FANCY FREE
(1947 - RKO/Disney) Edgar Bergen, Dinah Shore
One Sheet: $150 - $350

One Sheet

FUN IN ACAPULCO
(1963 - Paramount) Elvis Presley, Ursula Andress
One Sheet: $50 - $100

FUN ON A WEEKEND
(1947 - Andrew Stone Enterprises) Eddie Bracken, Priscilla Lane
One Sheet: $15 - $30

FUN WITH DICK AND JANE
(1977 - Columbia) Jane Fonda, George Segal
One Sheet: $15 - $30

FUNERAL FOR AN ASSASSIN
(1977 - Four Star) Vic Morrow
One Sheet: $3 - $5

FUNERAL IN BERLIN
(1967 - Paramount) Michael Caine, Paul

Hubschmid
One Sheet: $15 - $25

FUNHOUSE, THE
(1981 - Universal) Elizabeth Berridge, Miles Chapin
One Sheet: $5 - $10   *One Sheet(Style B):$20-40.*

FUNLAND
(1987 - -) David Lander, William Windom
One Sheet: $2 - $3

FUNNY ABOUT LOVE
(1990 - Paramount) Gene Wilder, Christine Lahti
One Sheet: $5 - $10

FUNNY BONES
(1995 - Buena Vista) Oliver Platt, Lee Evans, Jerry Lewis
One Sheet: $5 - $10

FUNNY CAR SUMMER
(1973 - Ambassador) Jim Dunn
One Sheet: $5 - $10

FUNNY FACE
(1956 - Paramount) Audrey Hepburn, Fred Astaire
One Sheet: $150 - $300

FUNNY FARM
(1988 - -) Chevy Chase, Madolyn Smith
One Sheet: $3 - $5

FUNNY GIRL
(1968 - Columbia) Barbra Streisand, Omar Sharif, Kay Medford
One Sheet: $75 - $150   *Academy Award: Best Actress(Streisand). Price is for pre-Academy Award style. Academy Award Movie Posters #249.*

FUNNY GIRL
(1972R - Columbia) Barbra Streisand, Omar Sharif, Kay Medford
One Sheet: $10 - $20   *Re-release.*

FUNNY LADY
(1975 - Columbia) Barbra Streisand, James Caan
One Sheet: $15 - $30

FUNNY LITTLE BUNNIES
(1950R - RKO/Disney)
One Sheet: $300 - $700   *Re-release. Cartoon. Full color.*

FUNNY THING HAPPENED ON THE WAY TO THE FORUM, A
(1966 - United Artists) Zero Mostel, Phil Silvers
One Sheet: $50 - $100

FUNNYMAN
(1967 - New Yorker) Peter Bonerz, Sandra Archer
One Sheet: $5 - $10

FUN-O-RAMA
(1959 - Columbia) Three Stooges (Curly Joe)
One Sheet: $75 - $150

FURIES, THE
(1930 - First National) Lois Wilson, H. B. Warner
One Sheet: $150 - $350

FURIES, THE
(1950 - Paramount) Barbara Stanwyck, Wendell Corey
One Sheet: $30 - $50

FURTHER ADVENTURES OF TENNESSEE BUCK, THE
(1988 - -) David Keith, Kathy Shower
One Sheet: $5 - $10

FURTHER PERILS OF LAUREL AND HARDY, THE
(1967 - 20th Century Fox) Stan Laurel, Oliver Hardy
One Sheet: $30 - $50

FURY
(1922 - First National) Richard Barthelmess, Dorothy Gish
One Sheet: $300 - $650

FURY
(1936 - MGM) Spencer Tracy, Sylvia Sidney, Dir:Fritz Lang
One Sheet: $2,500 - $4,000   *Lang's first American film.*

FURY, THE
(1978 - 20th Century Fox) Kirk Douglas, Amy Irving, Andrew Stevens, Dir:De Palma
One Sheet: $5 - $10

FURY AND THE WOMAN
(1937 - Rialto) William Gargan, Molly Lamont
One Sheet: $75 - $150

FURY AT FURNACE CREEK
(1948 - 20th Century Fox) Victor Mature, Coleen Gray
One Sheet: $15 - $30

FURY AT GUNSIGHT PASS
(1956 - Columbia) David Brian, Neville Brand
One Sheet: $10 - $20

FURY AT SHOWDOWN
(1957 - United Artists) Nick Adams, John Derek
One Sheet: $10 - $20

FURY AT SMUGGLER'S BAY
(1963 - Embassy) Peter Cushing, John Fraser
One Sheet: $15 - $25

FURY BELOW
(1938 - J. E. Baum) Russell Gleason, Maxine Doyle
One Sheet: $50 - $100

FURY IN PARADISE
(1955 - Gibraltar Motion Picture) Peter Thompson, Rea Iturbi
One Sheet: $15 - $35

FURY OF HERCULES, THE
(1961 - Medallion) Brad Harris, Brigitte Corey
One Sheet: $15 - $25

FURY OF THE CONGO
(1951 - Columbia) Johnny Weissmuller, Sherry Moreland
One Sheet: $30 - $50

FURY OF THE JUNGLE
(1933 - Columbia) Donald Cook, Peggy Shannon
One Sheet: $100 - $200

FURY OF THE PAGANS
(1962 - Columbia) Edmund Purdon
One Sheet: $15 - $30

FURY OF THE SUCCUBUS
(1982 - MPM) Britt Ekland, Lana Wood, John Carradine
One Sheet: $7 - $15

One Sheet

FURY RIVER
(1961 - MGM) Keith Larson, Buddy Ebsen
One Sheet: $5 - $10

FUTURE KILL
(1985 - International Film Marketing) Edwin Neal, Marilyn Burns
One Sheet: $15 - $30

FUTUREWORLD
(1976 - AIP) Peter Fonda, Blythe Danner
One Sheet: $7 - $15

FUTZ
(1969 - Commonwealth United) Seth Allen, John Bakos
One Sheet: $5 - $10

FUZZ
(1972 - United Artists) Yul Brynner, Burt Reynolds
One Sheet: $15 - $25   *Price is for both styles.*

FUZZY PINK NIGHTGOWN, THE
(1957 - United Artists) Jane Russell, Keenan Wynn
One Sheet: $15 - $35

FUZZY SETTLES DOWN
(1944 - PRC) Buster Crabbe, Fuzzy St. John
One Sheet: $40 - $75

FX
(1986 - Orion) Bryan Brown, Brian Dennehy
One Sheet: $5 - $10

FX2: THE DEADLY ART OF ILLUSION
(1991 - -) Bryan Brown, Brian Dennehy
One Sheet: $5 - $10

G. I. BLUES
(1960 - Paramount) Elvis Presley, Juliet Prowse
One Sheet: $150 - $300

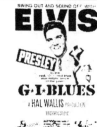
One Sheet

G. I. HONEYMOON
(1945 - Monogram) Gale Storm, Peter Cookson
One Sheet: $50 - $100

G. I. JANE
(1951 - Lippert) Jean Porter, Tom Neal
One Sheet: $30 - $60

G. I. WAR BRIDES
(1946 - Republic) James Ellison, Anna Lee
One Sheet: $40 - $75

GABLE AND LOMBARD
(1976 - Universal) James Brolin, Jill Clayburgh
One Sheet: $7 - $15

GABLES MYSTERY, THE
(1932 - Powers) Anne Grey, Lester Matthews
One Sheet: $100 - $200

GABLES MYSTERY, THE
(1938 - MGM) Francis L. Sullivan
One Sheet: $75 - $150

GABRIEL OVER THE WHITE HOUSE
(1933 - MGM) Walter Huston, Karen Morley
One Sheet: $150 - $350

GABY
(1956 - MGM) Leslie Caron, John Kerr
One Sheet: $15 - $25

GABY: A TRUE STORY
(1987 - -) Liv Ullmann, Norma Aleandro, Robert Loggia
One Sheet: $4 - $8

GAILY, GAILY
(1969 - United Artists) Beau Bridges, Melina Mercouri, Brian Keith
One Sheet: $5 - $10

GAITY GIRLS
(1938 - United Artists) Jack Hulbert, Patricia Ellis
One Sheet: $75 - $125

GAL WHO TOOK THE WEST, THE
(1949 - Universal) Yvonne De Carlo, Scott Brady
One Sheet: $30 - $50

GAL YOUNG UN
(1979 - Nunez) Dana Preu, David Peck
One Sheet: $3 - $5

GALAXINA
(1980 - Crown) Avery Schreiber, Dorothy Stratten
One Sheet: $10 - $20

GALAXY EXPRESS

(1982 - New World) -
One Sheet: $7 - $15   *Cartoon.*

GALAXY OF TERROR
(1982 - New World) Edward Albert, Erin Moran, Dir: Roger Corman
One Sheet: $15 - $30

GALILEO
(1975 - American) Topol, John Gielgud
One Sheet: $3 - $5

GALLANT BESS
(1946 - MGM) Marshall Thompson, George Tobias
One Sheet: $30 - $60

GALLANT BLADE, THE
(1948 - Columbia) Larry Parks, Marguerite Chapman
One Sheet: $15 - $30

GALLANT DEFENDER
(1935 - Columbia) Charles Starrett
One Sheet: $125 - $250   *Starrett's first western starring role.*

GALLANT FOOL, THE
(1933 - Monogram) Bob Steele, George Hayes
One Sheet: $150 - $300

GALLANT HOURS, THE
(1960 - United Artists) James Cagney, Dennis Weaver
One Sheet: $15 - $25

GALLANT JOURNEY
(1946 - Columbia) Glenn Ford, Janet Blair
One Sheet: $30 - $50

GALLANT LADY
(1934 - United Artists) Ann Harding, Clive Brook, Dickie Moore
One Sheet: $125 - $250

GALLANT LADY
(1942 - PRC) Rose Hobart, Sidney Blackmer
One Sheet: $30 - $60

GALLANT LEGION, THE
(1948 - Republic) William Elliott, Joseph Schildkraut
One Sheet: $75 - $125

GALLANT LEGION, THE
(1955R - Republic) Bill Elliott
One Sheet: $20 - $40   *Re-release.*

GALLANT ONE, THE
(1964 - Gillman) Henry Heller
One Sheet: $5 - $10

GALLANT SONS
(1940 - MGM) Jackie Cooper, Bonita Granville, Gene Reynolds
One Sheet: $75 - $150

GALLIPOLI
(1981 - Paramount) Mel Gibson, Mark Lee
One Sheet: $15 - $30

GALLOPIN' GALS
(1951 - MGM) -
One Sheet: $250 - $600   *Cartoon. Full color stone litho.*

GALLOPING ACE, THE
(1924 - Universal) Jack Hoxie
One Sheet: $200 - $400

GALLOPING BUNGALOWS
(1924 - Pathe) -
One Sheet: $150 - $300

GALLOPING DYNAMITE
(1937 - Ambassador) Kermit Maynard
One Sheet: $75 - $150

GALLOPING GHOST, THE
(1931 - Mascot) Harold (Red) Grange, Dorothy Gulliver
One Sheet: $350 - $750   *Serial. Western. 12 Chapters.*

GALLOPING JINX
(1925 - -) Buddy Roosevelt, Gloria Heller
One Sheet: $125 - $250

GALLOPING KID, THE
(1922 - Universal) Hoot Gibson
One Sheet: $250 - $600

GALLOPING MAJOR, THE
(1951 - IFD) Basil Radford

(1982 - New World) -
One Sheet: $10 - $20

GALLOPING RIDER
(1950 - -) Jim Bannon
One Sheet: $20 - $40

GALLOPING ROMEO
(1933 - Monogram) Bob Steele, George Hayes
One Sheet: $200 - $400

GALLOPING THRU
(1932 - Monogram) Tom Tyler, Betty Mack
One Sheet: $125 - $250

GALLOPING THRU
(194?R - Astor) Tom Tyler, Betty Mack
One Sheet: $30 - $60   *Re-release.*

GALLOPING THUNDER
(1946 - Columbia) Charles Starrett, Smiley Burnette
One Sheet: $15 - $35

GALS, INCORPORATED
(1943 - Universal) Leon Errol, Grace McDonald
One Sheet: $75 - $125

GAMBIT
(1966 - Universal) Shirley Maclaine, Michael Caine
One Sheet: $7 - $15

GAMBLER, THE
(1958 - Gaumont) Gerard Philipe
One Sheet: $30 - $50   *French.*

GAMBLER, THE
(1974 - Paramount) James Caan, Lauren Hutton
One Sheet: $15 - $25

GAMBLER AND THE LADY, THE
(1952 - Hammer) Dane Clark, Naomi Chance
One Sheet: $30 - $50

GAMBLER FROM NATCHEZ, THE
(1954 - 20th Century Fox) Dale Robertson, Debra Paget
One Sheet: $20 - $40

GAMBLER WORE A GUN, THE
(1961 - United Artists) Jim Davis, Merry Anders
One Sheet: $15 - $25

GAMBLER'S CHOICE
(1944 - Paramount) Chester Morris, Nancy Kelly
One Sheet: $75 - $150

GAMBLERS, THE
(1929 - Warner Bros.) H. B. Warner, Dir: Michael Curtiz
One Sheet: $600 - $1,000   *First sound film.*

GAMBLERS, THE
(1970 - U.M.) Don Gordon, Suzy Kendall
One Sheet: $5 - $10

GAMBLING
(1934 - Fox) George M. Cohan, Wynne Gibson
One Sheet: $250 - $600

GAMBLING DAUGHTERS
(1941 - PRC) Cecelia Parker, Roger Pryor
One Sheet: $40 - $75

GAMBLING HOUSE
(1951 - RKO) Victor Mature, Terry Moore
One Sheet: $40 - $75

GAMBLING LADY
(1934 - Warner Bros.) Barbara Stanwyck, Pat O'Brien
One Sheet: $200 - $400

GAMBLING ON THE HIGH SEAS
(1940 - Warner Bros.) Wayne Morris, Jane Wyman
One Sheet: $75 - $150

GAMBLING SEX
(1932 - Monarch) Ruth Hall, Grant Withers
One Sheet: $100 - $200

GAMBLING SHIP
(1933 - Paramount) Cary Grant, Benita Hume
One Sheet: $500 - $900

Mini Window Card

GAMBLING SHIP
(1938 - Universal) Robert Wilcox, Helen Mack
One Sheet: $75 - $150

GAMBLING TERROR, THE
(1937 - Republic) Johnny Mack Brown, Iris Meredith
One Sheet: $50 - $100

GAMBLING WITH SOULS
(1936 - Jay Dee Kay) Martha Chapin, Robert Frazer
One Sheet: $75 - $150

GAME FOR VULTURES, A
(1980 - New Line Cinema) Richard Harris, Richard Roundtree
One Sheet: $3 - $5

GAME IS OVER, THE
(1967 - Royal) Jane Fonda
One Sheet: $15 - $25

GAME OF CHANCE, A
(1932 - Equity) Margaret Delane
One Sheet: $150 - $300

GAME OF DEATH, A
(1945 - RKO) John Loder, Audrey Long
One Sheet: $75 - $150

GAME OF DEATH, THE
(1979 - Columbia) Bruce Lee, Gig Young, Kareem Abdul-Jabbar
One Sheet: $50 - $100 *Lee Died during production. AKA: GOODBYE, BRUCE LEE: HIS LAST GAME OF DEATH.*

GAME OF LOVE
(1955 - Times) Nicole Berger
One Sheet: $40 - $75

GAME THAT KILLS, THE
(1937 - Columbia) Charles Quigley, Rita Hayworth
One Sheet: $150 - $300 *Sports (Hockey). Sports Movie Posters #230.*

GAMEKEEPER, THE
(1980 - Network) Phil Askham
One Sheet: $3 - $5

GAMERA, THE INVINCIBLE
(1966 - World Entertainment) Brian Donlevy, Albert Dekker
One Sheet: $75 - $150 *First Gamera film. Japanese poster:$500-$700.*

GAMERA VS BARUGON
(1966 - King Features) Kojiro Hongo
One Sheet: $75 - $150 *One Sheet is Day-Glo.*

GAMERA VS GAOS
(1967 - Daiei) Kojiro Hongo
One Sheet: $50 - $100

GAMERA VS GUIRON
(1969 - Daiei) Nobuhiro Kashima
One Sheet: $50 - $100

GAMERA VS MONSTER X
(1970 - AIP) Tsutomo Takakuwa
One Sheet: $40 - $75

GAMERA VS VIRAS
(1968 - Daiei) Kojiro Hongo
One Sheet: $50 - $100

GAMERA VS ZIGRA
(1971 - Daiei) Reiko Kasahara
One Sheet: $40 - $75

GAMES
(1967 - Universal) Simone Signoret, James Caan, Katharine Ross
One Sheet: $5 - $10

GAMES, THE
(1970 - 20th Century Fox) Michael Crawford, Stanley Baker, Ryan O'Neal
One Sheet: $5 - $10

GAMMA PEOPLE, THE
(1956 - Columbia) Paul Douglas, Eva Bartok
One Sheet: $40 - $75

GAMMERA THE INVINCIBLE
(1966 - -) See GAMERA THE INVINCIBLE

GANDHI
(1982 - Columbia) Ben Kingsley, Candice Bergen
One Sheet: $10 - $20 *Academy Award: Best Picture, Best Actor (Kingsley), Best Director (Attenborough). AcademyAward Movie Posters #323-#325.*

GANG BULLETS
(1938 - Monogram) Anne Nagel, Robert Kent
One Sheet: $75 - $150

GANG BUSTERS
(1931 - Paramount) Jack Oakie, Jean Arthur
One Sheet: $200 - $400

GANG BUSTERS
(1942 - Universal) Kent Taylor, Irene Hervey
One Sheet: $250 - $600 *Serial. 13 Chapters.*

GANG BUSTERS
(1954 - Visual Drama) Myron Healey, Don C. Harvey
One Sheet: $20 - $40

GANG SHOW, THE
(1937 - GFD) Ralph Reader, Gina Malo
One Sheet: $100 - $200 *AKA: THE GANG.*

GANG SMASHERS
(1930 - Million Dollar) Nina Mae McKinney
One Sheet: $1,300 - $2,000 *Black cast. Duotone. Separate Cinema, pg. 137.*

GANG THAT COULDN'T SHOOT STRAIGHT, THE
(1971 - MGM) Jerry Orbach, Leigh Taylor-Young
One Sheet: $3 - $5

GANG WAR
(1929 - FBO) Jack Pickford, Olive Borden
One Sheet: $600 - $1,000

GANG WAR
(1940 - Sack) Ralph Cooper, Gladys Snyder
One Sheet: $200 - $400 *Black cast.*

GANG WAR
(1958 - 20th Century Fox) Charles Bronson, Kent Taylor
One Sheet: $30 - $50

GANG WAR
(1962 - United Artists) Sean Kelly
One Sheet: $10 - $20

GANG'S ALL HERE, THE
(1941 - Monogram) Frankie Darro, Marcia Mae Jones
One Sheet: $50 - $100

GANG'S ALL HERE, THE
(1943 - 20th Century Fox) Alice Faye, Carmen Miranda
One Sheet: $150 - $300

GANGS OF CHICAGO
(1940 - Republic) Lloyd Nolan, Barton MacLane, Lola Lane
One Sheet: $75 - $150

GANGS OF NEW YORK

(1938 - Republic) Charles Bickford, Ann Dvorak
One Sheet: $100 - $200

GANGS OF SONORA
(1941 - Republic) Three Mesquiteers (Livingston, Steele, Davis)
One Sheet: $50 - $100

GANGS OF THE WATERFRONT
(1945 - Republic) Robert Armstrong, Stephanie Bachelor
One Sheet: $40 - $75

GANGSTER, THE
(1947 - Allied Artists) Barry Sullivan, Belita
One Sheet: $40 - $75

GANGSTER STORY
(1960 - RCI) Walter Matthau, Carol Grace
One Sheet: $10 - $20

GANGSTER'S BOY
(1938 - Monogram) Jackie Cooper, Lucy Gilman
One Sheet: $75 - $150

GANGSTER'S DEN
(1945 - PRC) Buster Crabbe, Al St. John
One Sheet: $30 - $50

GANGSTERS OF THE FRONTIER
(1944 - PRC) Dave O'Brien, Tex Ritter
One Sheet: $30 - $60

GANGSTERS ON THE LOOSE
(1937 - Toddy) Ralph Cooper
One Sheet: $250 - $500 *Black cast. Duotone. Separate Cinema, pg. 138.*

GANGWAY
(1937 - Gaumont) Jessie Matthews, Nat Pendleton
One Sheet: $150 - $300

GANGWAY FOR TOMORROW
(1943 - RKO) Margo, Robert Ryan, John Carradine
One Sheet: $50 - $100

GANJA AND HESS
(1973 - Kelly-Jordon) Duane Jones, Marlene Clark
One Sheet: $5 - $10 *Blaxploitation Vampire film. AKA: BLOOD COUPLE.*

GAPPA THE TRIFIBIAN MONSTER
(1967 - Nikkatsu) Tamio Kawaji, Yoko Yamamoto
One Sheet: $50 - $100

GARAGE, THE
(1919 - Famous Players-Lasky) Roscoe "Fatty" Arbuckle
One Sheet: $2,500 - $4,000

GARBAGE PAIL KIDS MOVIE, THE
(1987 - -) Anthony Newly, Mackenzie Astin
One Sheet: $3 - $5

GARBO TALKS
(1984 - MGM/United Artists) Anne Bancroft, Ron Silver, Carrie Fisher
One Sheet: $7 - $15

GARDEN MURDER CASE, THE
(1936 - MGM) Virginia Bruce, Benita Hume
One Sheet: $150 - $300

GARDEN OF ALLAH, THE
(1936 - United Artists) Marlene Dietrich, Charles Boyer
One Sheet: $1,300 - $2,000

GARDEN OF ALLAH, THE
(1949R - Eagle-Lion) Marlene Dietrich, Charles Boyer
One Sheet: $75 - $150 *Re-release.*

GARDEN OF EDEN, THE
(1928 - United Artists) Corinne Griffith
One Sheet: $500 - $900

GARDEN OF EDEN
(1954 - Excelsior) Mickey Knox, Jamie O'Hara
One Sheet: $30 - $60

GARDEN OF EVIL
(1954 - 20th Century Fox) Gary Cooper, Susan Hayward
One Sheet: $100 - $200

GARDEN OF THE DEAD
(1972 - Clover/Pyramid) John Dennis, Duncan McCloud

One Sheet: $7 - $15

GARDEN OF THE FINZI-CONTINIS, THE
(1976 - Titanus) Dominique Sanda, Lino Capolicchio, Dir: Vittorio De Sica
One Sheet: $30 - $50 *Italian.*

GARDEN OF THE MOON
(1938 - Warner Bros.) Pat O'Brien, John Payne
One Sheet: $150 - $300

GARDENS OF STONE
(1987 - TriStar) James Caan, Angelica Huston
One Sheet: $5 - $10

GARMENT JUNGLE, THE
(1957 - Columbia) Lee J. Cobb, Richard Boone
One Sheet: $15 - $35

GARMENTS OF TRUTH
(1921 - Metro) Gareth Hughes, Ethel Grandin
One Sheet: $150 - $300

GAS
(1981 - Paramount) Donald Sutherland, Howie Mandel
One Sheet: $3 - $5

GAS HOUSE KIDS
(1946 - PRC) Robert Lowery, Teala Loring
One Sheet: $40 - $75

GAS HOUSE KIDS GO WEST
(1947 - PRC) Emory Parnell, Chili Williams
One Sheet: $30 - $50

GAS HOUSE KIDS IN HOLLYWOOD
(1947 - Eagle-Lion) Carl "Alfalfa" Switzer, Benny Bartlett
One Sheet: $40 - $75

GASLIGHT
(1940 - Anglo) Anton Walbrook, Diana Wynyard
One Sheet: $40 - $75 *AKA: ANGEL STREET.*

GASLIGHT
(1944 - MGM) Ingrid Bergman, Charles Boyer, Angela Lansbury
One Sheet: $250 - $600 *Academy Award: Best Actress (Bergman). Academy Award Movie Posters #96.*

One Sheet

GASLIGHT FOLLIES
(1955 - -) Charlie Chaplin, Douglas Fairbanks, et al
One Sheet: $40 - $75

GASOLINE ALLEY
(1951 - Columbia) Scotty Beckett, Jimmy Lydon
One Sheet: $50 - $100

GASOLINE GUS
(1921 - Paramount) Roscoe "Fatty" Arbuckle, Lila Lee
One Sheet: $1,900 - $3,000

GAS-S-S-S
(1970 - AIP) Cindy Williams, Talia Shire, Dir: Roger Corman
One Sheet: $7 - $15

GATE, THE
(1987 - -) Stephen Dorff, Christa Denton
One Sheet: $3 - $5

GATE OF HELL
(1954 - Daiei) Machiko Kyo, Isao Yamagata
One Sheet: $75 - $125 *Academy Award: Best Foreign film.*

GATES OF HEAVEN
(1987 - -) Documentary
One Sheet: $5 - $10 *Documentary*

about pet cemeteries.

GATES OF HELL, THE
(1983 - Motion Picture) Venantino Venantini, Daniela Doria
One Sheet: $5 - $10

GATEWAY
(1938 - 20th Century Fox) Don Ameche, Arleen Whelan
One Sheet: $100 - $200

GATEWAYS TO THE MIND
(1958 - N. W. Ayer & Son) -
One Sheet: $30 - $50

GATHERING OF EAGLES, A
(1963 - Universal) Rock Hudson, Rod Taylor
One Sheet: $15 - $25

GATLING GUN, THE
(1972 - Ellman) Guy Stockwell, John Carradine
One Sheet: $3 - $5

GATOR
(1976 - United Artists) Burt Reynolds, Lauren Hutton
One Sheet: $10 - $20

GATOR BAIT
(1973 - Sebastian) Claudia Jennings
One Sheet: $7 - $15

GAUCHO, THE
(1927 - United Artists) Douglas Fairbanks, Sr.
One Sheet: $2,200 - $3,500

GAUCHO SERENADE
(1940 - Republic) Gene Autry, Smiley Burnette
One Sheet: $125 - $250

GAUCHO SERENADE
(194?R - Republic) Gene Autry, Smiley Burnette
One Sheet: $50 - $100   *Re-release.*

GAUCHOS OF ELDORADO
(1941 - Republic) The Three Mesquiteers
One Sheet: $40 - $75

GAUNTLET, THE
(1977 - Warner Bros.) Clint Eastwood, Sondra Locke
One Sheet: $30 - $50   *Frazetta art.*
Price is for both styles.

One Sheet

GAVILAN
(1968 - Craddock) Christopher George
One Sheet: $7 - $15

GAY ADVENTURE, THE
(1953 - United Artists) Burgess Meredith, Jean-Pierre Aumont
One Sheet: $30 - $50

GAY AMIGO, THE
(1949 - United Artists) Duncan Renaldo, Leo Carrillo
One Sheet: $50 - $100

GAY BLADES
(1946 - Republic) Allan Lane, Jean Rogers
One Sheet: $50 - $100

GAY BRIDE, THE
(1934 - MGM) Carole Lombard, Chester Morris
One Sheet: $350 - $750

GAY BUCKAROO, THE
(1932 - Allied) Hoot Gibson
One Sheet: $125 - $250

GAY CABALLERO, THE
(1932 - Fox) George O'Brien, Victor McLaglen

One Sheet: $125 - $250

GAY CABALLERO, THE
(1938 - 20th Century Fox) Cesar Romero, Sheila Ryan
One Sheet: $100 - $200

GAY CAVALIER, THE
(1946 - Monogram) Gilbert Roland, Martin Garralaga
One Sheet: $40 - $75

GAY DECEIVERS, THE
(1969 - Fanfare) Kevin Coughlin, Brook Bundy, JoAnn Harris
One Sheet: $30 - $60

GAY DECEPTION, THE
(1935 - 20th Century Fox) Francis Lederer, Frances Dee
One Sheet: $250 - $600

GAY DESPERADO, THE
(1936 - United Artists) Nino Martini, Ida Lupino
One Sheet: $150 - $300

GAY DIPLOMAT, THE
(1931 - RKO) Ilka Chase, Ivan Lebedeff
One Sheet: $500 - $800

GAY DIVORCEE, THE
(1934 - RKO) Fred Astaire, Ginger Rogers
One Sheet: $4,000 - $6,500

GAY DOG, THE
(1954 - Eros) Wilfred Pickles, Petula Clark
One Sheet: $20 - $40

GAY FALCON, THE
(1941 - RKO) George Sanders, Wendy Barrie
One Sheet: $200 - $400

GAY INTRUDERS, THE
(1948 - 20th Century Fox) John Emery, Tamara Geva
One Sheet: $40 - $75

GAY LADY, THE
(1949 - Eagle-Lion) Jean Kent, James Donald
One Sheet: $125 - $250

GAY LOVE
(1934 - Pam) Sophie Tucker, Florence Desmond
One Sheet: $600 - $1,000

GAY OLD DOG
(1936 - RKO) Edward Rigby, Moore Marriott
One Sheet: $150 - $300

GAY PURR-EE
(1963 - UPA) Voice of Judy Garland
One Sheet: $30 - $50   *Cartoon.*

GAY RANCHERO, THE
(1948 - Republic) Roy Rogers, Jane Frazee
One Sheet: $100 - $200

GAY SENORITA, THE
(1945 - Columbia) Jinx Falkenberg, Jim Bannon
One Sheet: $40 - $75

GAY SISTERS, THE
(1942 - Warner Bros.) Barbara Stanwyck, George Brent
One Sheet: $100 - $200

GAY VAGABOND, THE
(1941 - Republic) Roscoe Karns, Ruth Donnelly
One Sheet: $75 - $125

GAZEBO, THE
(1960 - MGM) Glenn Ford, Debbie Reynolds
One Sheet: $10 - $20

GEISHA BOY, THE
(1958 - Paramount) Jerry Lewis, Marie McDonald
One Sheet: $30 - $60

GEISHA GIRL
(1952 - Realart) Martha Hyer, Williams Andrews
One Sheet: $15 - $25

GEISHA PLAYMATES
(1960 - United Producers) -
One Sheet: $30 - $50

GEM OF A JAM, A
(1943 - Columbia) Three Stooges (Curly)
One Sheet: $2,500 - $4,000   *Comedy short. Duotone.*

GEMINI AFFAIR
(1975 - MCI) Marta Kristin, Kathy Kersh, Anne Seymour
One Sheet: $5 - $10

GENE AUTRY AND THE MOUNTIES
(1950 - Columbia) Gene Autry, Elena Verdugo
One Sheet: $50 - $100

GENE AUTRY STOCK POSTER
(1930S - Republic) Gene Autry
One Sheet: $200 - $400

GENE KRUPA STORY, THE
(1959 - Columbia) Sal Mineo, Susan Kohner
One Sheet: $15 - $30

GENERAL, THE
(1927 - United Artists) Buster Keaton
One Sheet: $16,000 - $25,000

Three Sheet

GENERAL CRACK
(1929 - Warner Bros.) John Barrymore, Armida
One Sheet: $800 - $1,500   *Barrymore's 1st talkie.*

GENERAL CUSTER AT THE LITTLE BIG HORN
(1926 - Sunset) Roy Stewart
One Sheet: $250 - $600   *Cowboy Movie Posters #56.*

GENERAL DIED AT DAWN, THE
(1936 - Paramount) Gary Cooper, Madeleine Carroll, Akim Tamiroff
One Sheet: $3,500 - $5,000

GENERAL DIED AT DAWN, THE
(1942R - Paramount) Gary Cooper, Madeleine Carroll, Akim Tamiroff
One Sheet: $200 - $400   *Re-release.*

GENERAL NUISANCE
(1941 - Columbia) Buster Keaton
One Sheet: $250 - $500

GENERAL SPANKY
(1936 - MGM) Spanky, Buckwheat, Alfalfa
One Sheet: $700 - $1,200

GENERAL/POOL SHARKS
(1970 - -) Buster Keaton, W.C. Fields
One Sheet: $15 - $25   *Double feature poster.*

GENERATION
(1969 - Avco/Embassy) David Janssen, Kim Darby, Carl Reiner
One Sheet: $5 - $10

GENEVIEVE
(1953 - Universal International) Dinah Sheridan, John Gregson
One Sheet: $30 - $50

GENGHIS KHAN
(1965 - Columbia) Omar Sharif, Stephen Boyd
One Sheet: $15 - $25

GENIUS AT WORK
(1946 - RKO) Wally Brown, Alan Carney, Bela Lugosi, Lionel Atwill
One Sheet: $200 - $400

GENTLE ANNIE
(1944 - MGM) James Craig, Donna Reed
One Sheet: $50 - $100

GENTLE GANGSTER, A
(1943 - Republic) Barton MacLane, Molly Lamont
One Sheet: $40 - $75

GENTLE GIANT

(1967 - Paramount) Dennis Weaver, Vera Miles
One Sheet: $5 - $10

GENTLE GUNMAN, THE
(1952 - GFD) John Mills, Dirk Bogarde
One Sheet: $15 - $25

GENTLE JULIA
(1936 - 20th Century Fox) Jane Withers, Tom Brown
One Sheet: $100 - $200

One Sheet

GENTLE RAIN, THE
(1966 - Comet) Christopher George, Lynda Day, Fay Spain
One Sheet: $5 - $10

GENTLE SEX, THE
(1943 - Two Cities) Rosamund John, Joyce Howard
One Sheet: $75 - $125

GENTLE TOUCH, THE
(1957 - Rank) George Baker, Belinda Lee
One Sheet: $7 - $15

GENTLEMAN AFTER DARK, A
(1942 - United Artists) Miriam Hopkins, Brian Donlevy
One Sheet: $50 - $100

GENTLEMAN AT HEART, A
(1942 - 20th Century Fox) Cesar Romero, Carole Landis, Milton Berle
One Sheet: $75 - $150

GENTLEMAN FROM ARIZONA
(1939 - Monogram) Craig Reynolds, John King
One Sheet: $50 - $100

GENTLEMAN FROM DIXIE
(1941 - Monogram) Jack LaRue, Marian Marsh
One Sheet: $75 - $150

GENTLEMAN FROM LOUISIANA, THE
(1936 - Republic) Eddie Quillan, Charlotte Henry
One Sheet: $100 - $200

GENTLEMAN FROM MISSISSIPPI, A
(1914 - World) Thomas A. Wise
One Sheet: $200 - $400

GENTLEMAN FROM NOWHERE, THE
(1948 - Columbia) Warner Baxter, Fay Baker
One Sheet: $40 - $75

GENTLEMAN FROM TEXAS, THE
(1946 - Monogram) Johnny Mack Brown, Claudia Drake
One Sheet: $40 - $75

GENTLEMAN JIM
(1942 - Warner Bros.) Errol Flynn, Alexis Smith
One Sheet: $150 - $300

GENTLEMAN JOE PALOOKA
(1946 - Monogram) Leon Errol, Joe Kirkwood
One Sheet: $75 - $150

GENTLEMAN MISBEHAVES, THE
(1946 - Columbia) Osa Massen, Robert Stanton
One Sheet: $40 - $75

GENTLEMAN OF PARIS, A
(1927 - Paramount) Adolphe Menjou, Shirley O'Hara
One Sheet: $250 - $500

GENTLEMAN'S AGREEMENT
(1947 - 20th Century Fox) Gregory Peck, Dorothy McGuire, Celeste Holm
One Sheet: $100 - $200   *Academy Award: Best Picture, Best Supporting*

Actress(Holm), Best Direction(Elia Kazan). AcademyAward Movie Posters #109, #110 & #113.

GENTLEMAN'S AGREEMENT
(1953R - 20th Century Fox) Gregory Peck, Dorothy McGuire, Celeste Holm
One Sheet: $30 - $50   *1st Re-release.*

GENTLEMAN'S FATE
(1931 - MGM) John Gilbert, Anita Page
One Sheet: $150 - $300

GENTLEMAN'S GENTLEMAN, A
(1941 - RKO/Disney) Mickey Mouse, Pluto
One Sheet: $1,600 - $2,500   *Cartoon.*
Cartoon Movie Posters #146.

GENTLEMEN ARE BORN
(1934 - First National) Franchot Tone, Ann Dvorak
One Sheet: $75 - $150

GENTLEMEN DON'T EAT POETS
(1997 - Live Entertainment) Alan Bates, Sting, Theresa Russell
One Sheet: $5 - $10

GENTLEMEN MARRY BRUNETTES
(1955 - United Artists) Jane Russell, Jeanne Crain
One Sheet: $30 - $50

GENTLEMEN OF NERVE
(1914 - Keystone) Charlie Chaplin
One Sheet: $10,000 - $15,000

GENTLEMEN OF THE PRESS
(1929 - Paramount) Walter Huston, Kay Francis
One Sheet: $250 - $500

GENTLEMEN PREFER BLONDES
(1953 - 20th Century Fox) Marilyn Monroe, Jane Russell
One Sheet: $500 - $800

GENTLEMEN PREFER BLONDES
(1958R - 20th Century Fox) Marilyn Monroe, Jane Russell
One Sheet: $350 - $750   *Re-release.*

GENTLEMEN WITH GUNS
(1946 - PRC) Buster Crabbe, Al St. John
One Sheet: $20 - $40

GENTS IN A JAM
(1952 - Columbia) The Three Stooges (Shemp)
One Sheet: $150 - $350   *Comedy short.*
Duotone.

GENTS WITHOUT CENTS
(1944 - Columbia) The Three Stooges (Curly)
One Sheet: $2,500 - $4,000   *Comedy short.*
Duotone.

GEORGE
(1972 - Capital) Marshall Thompson, Jack Mullaney
One Sheet: $3 - $5

GEORGE AND MARGARET
(1940 - Warner Bros.) Marie Lohr, Judy Kelly
One Sheet: $75 - $125

GEORGE BALANCHINE'S THE NUTCRACKER
(1993 - Warner Bros.) Macauley Culkin, Jessica Lynn Cohen
One Sheet: $3 - $5

GEORGE IN CIVVY STREET
(1946 - Columbia) George Formby, Ian Fleming
One Sheet: $30 - $50

GEORGE MEETS GEORGE
(1927 - Stern Bros.) -
One Sheet: $250 - $500

GEORGE OF THE JUNGLE
(1997 - Disney) -
One Sheet: $5 - $10

GEORGE RAFT STORY, THE
(1961 - Allied Artists) Ray Danton, Jayne Mansfield
One Sheet: $15 - $30

GEORGE WASHINGTON CARVER
(1940 - Bryant) G. W. Carver, Booker T. Washington III
One Sheet: $250 - $500   *Black cast.*
Biography.

GEORGE WASHINGTON SLEPT HERE

(1942 - Warner Bros.) Jack Benny, Ann Sheridan
One Sheet: $75 - $150

GEORGE WHITE'S 1935 SCANDALS
(1935 - Fox) James Dunn, Alice Faye, Eleanor Powell
One Sheet: $250 - $600

GEORGE WHITE'S SCANDALS
(1934 - Fox) Rudy Vallee, Jimmy Durante, Alice Faye
One Sheet: $1,300 - $2,000

GEORGE WHITE'S SCANDALS
(1945 - RKO) Joan Davis, Jack Haley
One Sheet: $125 - $250

GEORGIA
(1996 - Miramax) Jennifer Jason Leigh, Mare Winningham
One Sheet: $5 - $10

GEORGIA, GEORGIA
(1972 - Cinerama) Diana Sands, Dirk Benedict
One Sheet: $7 - $15   *Black cast.*
Written by Maya Angelou.

GEORGY GIRL
(1966 - Columbia) James Mason, Lynn Redgrave
One Sheet: $15 - $25

GERALDINE
(1929 - Pathe) Marion Nixon, Eddie Quillan
One Sheet: $600 - $1,000

GERALDINE
(1953 - Republic) John Carroll, Mala Powers
One Sheet: $15 - $25

GERONIMO
(1940 - Paramount) Preston Foster, Andy Devine
One Sheet: $75 - $125

GERONIMO
(1962 - United Artists) Chuck Connors, Kamala Devi
One Sheet: $15 - $30   *Sports Movie Posters #371.*

GERONIMO: AN AMERICAN LEGEND
(1993 - Columbia) Wes Studi, Robert Duvall, Gene Hackman, Jason Patric
One Sheet: $3 - $5

GERTIE THE DINOSAUR
(1914 - L-KO Motion Picture Kompany) Winsor McKay - animator
One Sheet: $16,000 - $25,000   *Cartoon. First cartoon. Five Gertie cartoons were produced from 1914-1916, the poster may possibly be astock poster used for all five.*

GET AWAY DAY
(1924 - Universal-Jewel) Billy Sullivan
One Sheet: $150 - $300   *#6 in the Fast Steppers series.*

GET BACK
(1973 - Clearwater) Michael Peck, Bonnie Bedelia
One Sheet: $3 - $5

GET CARTER
(1971 - MGM) Michael Caine, John Osborne
One Sheet: $10 - $20   *Advance(pop-art style):$50-$100.*

GET CRAZY
(1983 - Embassy) Daniel Stern, Malcolm McDowell
One Sheet: $5 - $10

GET GOING
(1943 - Universal) Grace McDonald, Robert Paige
One Sheet: $75 - $125

GET HEP TO LOVE
(1942 - Universal) Gloria Jean, Robert Paige
One Sheet: $75 - $150

GET ON THE BUS
(1996 - Columbia) Charles S. Dutton, Ossie Davis, Dir: Spike Lee
One Sheet: $5 - $10

GET RICH QUICK
(1951 - Disney) Goofy
One Sheet: $250 - $600   *Cartoon.*

GET SHORTY

(1995 - MGM) John Travolta, Gene Hackman, Danny DeVito
One Sheet: $10 - $20

GET THAT GIRL
(1932 - Talmadge) Richard Talmadge, Shirley Grey
One Sheet: $100 - $200

GET THAT MAN
(1935 - Empire Film) Wallace Ford, Leon Ames
One Sheet: $50 - $100

GET THEE BEHIND ME...
(1918 - Nordisk) -
One Sheet: $500 - $800

GET TO KNOW YOUR RABBIT
(1972 - Warner Bros.) Tom Smothers, Orson Welles
One Sheet: $15 - $25

GET YOUR MAN
(1921 - Fox) Buck Jones, William Lawrence
One Sheet: $350 - $750

GET YOUR MAN
(1927 - Paramount) Clara Bow
One Sheet: $800 - $1,500

GET YOUR MAN
(1934 - Paramount) Dorothy Boyd, Sebastian Shaw
One Sheet: $150 - $300

GET YOURSELF A COLLEGE GIRL
(1964 - MGM) Mary Ann Mobley, Nancy Sinatra, The Animals, Dave Clark Five
One Sheet: $40 - $75   *Rock-n-Roll film.*

GET-AWAY, THE
(1941 - MGM) Robert Sterling, Donna Reed
One Sheet: $50 - $100

GETAWAY, THE
(1972 - National General) Steve McQueen, Ali McGraw
One Sheet: $30 - $60

GETAWAY, THE
(1994 - Universal) Alec Baldwin, Kim Basinger, James Woods
One Sheet: $5 - $10

GETTING ACQUAINTED
(1914 - Keystone) Charlie Chaplin
One Sheet: $7,500 - $12,000

GETTING EVEN
(1981 - Quantum) Matthew Faison
One Sheet: $3 - $5

GETTING EVEN WITH DAD
(1994 - MGM) Macauley Culkin, Ted Dansen
One Sheet: $5 - $10

GETTING GERTIE'S GARTER
(1945 - United Artists) Dennis O'Keefe, Marie McDonald
One Sheet: $50 - $100

GETTING IT RIGHT
(1989 - -) Jesse Birdsall, Helena Bonham Carter
One Sheet: $3 - $5

GETTING OVER
(1981 - Continental) John R. Daniels
One Sheet: $3 - $5

GETTING STRAIGHT
(1970 - Columbia) Elliott Gould, Candice Bergen
One Sheet: $5 - $10

GETTING TOGETHER
(1976 - Total Impact) Malcolm Groome
One Sheet: $5 - $10

GETTING TRIMMED
(1925 - Universal) Wanda Wiley
One Sheet: $200 - $400   *A Century Comedy.*

GETTING WASTED
(1980 - Diversified) Brian Kerwin, Stephen Furst
One Sheet: $5 - $10

GETTYSBERG
(1993 - New Line) Tom Berenger, Sam Elliot, Jeff Daniels
One Sheet: $10 - $20

GHASTLY ONES, THE
(1968 - JER) Veronica Radbrook, Don Williams
One Sheet: $7 - $15

GHETTO, THE
(1928 - Tiffany-Stahl) George Jessel
One Sheet: $600 - $1,000

GHETTO FREAKS
(1960S - World International) Allen Wakefield, Cathy Holen
One Sheet: $125 - $250

GHIDRAH, THE THREE-HEADED MONSTER
(1965 - Continental) Yosuke Natsuki, Yuriko Hoshi
One Sheet: $75 - $150   *First Ghidrah film.*

GHOST, THE
(1963 - Magna) Barbara Steele, Peter Baldwin
One Sheet: $20 - $40

GHOST
(1990 - Paramount) Patrick Swayze, Demi Moore
One Sheet: $7 - $15   *Academy Award Movie Posters #373.*

GHOST AND MR. CHICKEN, THE
(1966 - Universal) Don Knotts, Joan Staley
One Sheet: $50 - $100

GHOST AND MRS. MUIR, THE
(1947 - 20th Century Fox) Gene Tierney, Rex Harrison
One Sheet: $125 - $250   *Graven Images, pg. 121.*

GHOST AND THE GUEST, THE
(1943 - PRC) Florence Rice, Jimmy Dunn
One Sheet: $40 - $75

GHOST BREAKER, THE
(1922 - Paramount) Lila Lee, Walter Hiers
One Sheet: $250 - $600

GHOST BREAKERS, THE
(1940 - Paramount) Bob Hope, Paulette Goddard
One Sheet: $800 - $1,500   *Graven Images, pg. 143.*

GHOST CAMERA, THE
(1933 - Realart) Ida Lupino, Henry Kendall
One Sheet: $150 - $300

GHOST CATCHERS
(1944 - Universal) Olsen & Johnson, Gloria Jean
One Sheet: $125 - $250

GHOST CATCHERS
(1949R - Realart) Olsen & Johnson, Gloria Jean
One Sheet: $40 - $75   *Re-release.*

GHOST CHASERS
(1951 - Monogram) Leo Gorcey, Huntz Hall
One Sheet: $50 - $100

GHOST CITY, THE
(1922 - Universal) Pete Morrison
One Sheet: $200 - $400   *Serial. 15 Chapters.*

GHOST CITY
(1932 - Monogram) Bill Boyd, Kate Campbell
One Sheet: $200 - $400

GHOST COMES HOME, THE
(1940 - MGM) Frank Morgan, Billie Burke, Ann Rutherford
One Sheet: $100 - $200

GHOST DAD
(1990 - Universal) Bill Cosby, Kimberly Russell
One Sheet: $3 - $5

GHOST DIVER
(1957 - 20th Century Fox) James Craig, Audrey Totter
One Sheet: $7 - $15

GHOST FEVER
(1987 - -) Sherman Helmsley, Jennifer Rhodes
One Sheet: $3 - $5

GHOST GOES WEST, THE
(1936 - United Artists) Robert Donat, Jean Parker
One Sheet: $125 - $250

GHOST GOES WILD, THE
(1947 - Republic) James Ellison, Anne Gwynne
One Sheet: $40 - $75

GHOST GUNS
(1944 - Monogram) Johnny Mack Brown
One Sheet: $30 - $50

GHOST IN THE INVISIBLE BIKINI, THE
(1966 - AIP) Boris Karloff, Tommy Kirk
One Sheet: $40 - $75

GHOST IN THE MACHINE
(1993 - 20th Century Fox) Karen Allen, Wil
Horneff
One Sheet: $3 - $5

GHOST OF CROSSBONE CANYON
(1952 - Allied Artists) Guy Madison
One Sheet: $30 - $50

GHOST OF DRAGSTRIP HOLLOW, THE
(1959 - AIP) Jody Fair, Martin Braddock
One Sheet: $75 - $150   *Sports (Auto racing).*

GHOST OF FRANKENSTEIN, THE
(1942 - Universal) Lon Chaney Jr., Evelyn
Ankers
One Sheet: $4,000 - $6,000   *Graven Images, pg. 116.*

Title Card

GHOST OF HIDDEN VALLEY
(1946 - PRC) Buster Crabbe, Al "Fuzzy" St.
John
One Sheet: $15 - $30

GHOST OF SLUMBER MOUNTAIN, THE
(1919 - World Pictures) Early Willis O'Brien
(King Kong) animation
One Sheet: $1,300 - $2,000   *Graven Images, pg. 24.*

GHOST OF THE CHINA SEA
(1958 - Columbia) David Brian, Lynn Bernay
One Sheet: $10 - $20

GHOST OF ZORRO
(1949 - Republic) Clayton Moore, Pamela
Blake
One Sheet: $75 - $150   *Serial.
Western. 12 Chapters.*

GHOST OF ZORRO
(1958R - Republic) Clayton Moore, Pamela
Blake
One Sheet: $30 - $60   *Re-release.
Serial.*

GHOST PATROL
(1936 - Puritan) Tim McCoy, Claudia Dell
One Sheet: $250 - $600   *Western
Science Fiction.*

GHOST RIDER, THE
(1935 - Superior) Rex Lease, Ann Carol
One Sheet: $150 - $300

GHOST RIDER, THE
(1943 - Monogram) Johnny Mack Brown
One Sheet: $75 - $125

GHOST RIDERS OF THE WEST
(1954R - Republic) Robert Kent, Peggy Stewart
One Sheet: $30 - $50   *Re-titled, re-release of 1946 Serial "THE PHANTOM RIDER",
12 chapters.*

GHOST SHIP, THE
(1943 - RKO) Richard Dix, Russell Wade, Dir:
Val Lewton
One Sheet: $150 - $300   *Graven
Images, pg. 123.*

GHOST SHIP, THE
(1949R - RKO) Dir: Val Lewton, Richard Dix,
Russell Wade
One Sheet: $75 - $175   *Re-release.
Full color, same art as original.*

GHOST SHIP
(1953 - Lippert) Dermot Walsh, Hazel Court
One Sheet: $30 - $50

GHOST STORY
(1974 - Weeks) Murray Melvin, Larry Dann,
Marianne Faithfull
One Sheet: $5 - $10

GHOST STORY
(1981 - Universal) Fred Astaire, Melvyn
Douglas, Douglas Fairbanks, Jr.
One Sheet: $5 - $10

GHOST TALKS, THE
(1931 - Fox) Helen Twelvetrees, Charles Eaton
One Sheet: $800 - $1,500

GHOST TALKS, THE
(1949 - Columbia) The Three Stooges (Shemp)
One Sheet: $350 - $750   *Comedy short.
Duotone.*

GHOST THAT WALKS ALONE, THE
(1944 - Columbia) Arthur Lake, Lynne Roberts
One Sheet: $75 - $150

GHOST TOWN
(1937 - Commodore) Harry Carey, Ruth Findlay
One Sheet: $100 - $200

GHOST TOWN
(1956 - United Artists) Kent Taylor, Marian Carr
One Sheet: $10 - $20

GHOST TOWN GOLD
(1936 - Republic) Three Mesquiteers (Bob
Livingston, Ray Corrigan,Max Terhune)
One Sheet: $75 - $150

GHOST TOWN LAW
(1942 - Monogram) Rough Riders (Buck Jones,
Tim McCoy)
One Sheet: $100 - $200

GHOST TOWN RENEGADES
(1947 - PRC) Al "Lash" LaRue, Al "Fuzzy" St.
John
One Sheet: $40 - $75

GHOST TOWN RIDERS
(1938 - Universal) Bob Baker, Fay Shannon
One Sheet: $75 - $150

GHOST TRAIN, THE
(1933 - Gaumont) Jack Hulbert
One Sheet: $150 - $300

GHOST TRAIN, THE
(1941 - GFD) Arthur Askey, Richard Murdock
One Sheet: $50 - $100

GHOST VALLEY
(1932 - RKO) Tom Keene
One Sheet: $100 - $200

GHOST VALLEY RAIDERS
(1940 - Republic) Donald Barry, Lona Andre
One Sheet: $40 - $75

GHOST WALKS, THE
(1934 - Chesterfield) John Miljan, June Collyer
One Sheet: $150 - $350

GHOSTBUSTERS
(1984 - Columbia) Bill Murray, Dan Aykroyd
One Sheet: $7 - $15   *Advance:$15-30.*

One Sheet

GHOSTBUSTERS 2
(1989 - Columbia) Bill Murray, Dan Aykroyd
One Sheet: $4 - $8

GHOSTS - ITALIAN STYLE
(1969 - MGM) Sophia Loren, Vittorio Gassman,
Marlo Adorf
One Sheet: $15 - $25   *Style B:$30-50.*

GHOSTS CAN'T DO IT
(1990 - -) -
One Sheet: $3 - $5

GHOSTS OF MISSISSIPPI
(1996 - Columbia) Alec Baldwin, Whoopi
Goldberg, James Woods
One Sheet: $5 - $10

GHOSTS OF YESTERDAY
(1918 - Selznick) Norma Talmadge, Eugene
O'Brien
One Sheet: $350 - $750

GHOSTS ON THE LOOSE
(1943 - Monogram) The Dead End Kids, Bela
Lugosi
One Sheet: $200 - $400

GHOUL, THE
(1933 - Gaumont) Boris Karloff, Cedric
Hardwicke
One Sheet: $1,300 - $2,000   *Graven
Images, pg. 68.*

GHOUL, THE
(1975 - Rank) Peter Cushing, John Hurt
One Sheet: $10 - $20

GHOUL SHOW
(1971 - -) -
One Sheet: $10 - $20

GHOULIES
(1985 - Empire) Peter Liapis, Lisa Pelikan
One Sheet: $7 - $15

GHOULIES II
(1987 - Empire) Damon Martin, Royal Dano
One Sheet: $5 - $10

G.I. WANNA GO HOME
(1946 - Columbia) The Three Stooges (Curly)
One Sheet: $2,500 - $4,000   *Comedy short.
Duotone.*

GIANT
(1956 - Warner Bros.) Elizabeth Taylor, Rock
Hudson, James Dean
One Sheet: $250 - $500   *Academy
Award: Best Direction(George Stevens). Academy
Award Movie Posters #169.*

GIANT
(1963R - Warner Bros.) Elizabeth Taylor, Rock
Hudson, James Dean
One Sheet: $50 - $100   *Re-release.*

GIANT
(1970R - Warner Bros.) Elizabeth Taylor, Rock
Hudson, James Dean
One Sheet: $30 - $50   *Re-release.*

GIANT
(1982R - Warner Bros.) Elizabeth Taylor, Rock
Hudson, James Dean
One Sheet: $15 - $25   *Re-release.*

GIANT
(1996R - Warner Bros.) James Dean, Elizabeth
Taylor, Rock Hudson
One Sheet: $15 - $25   *Re-release.*

GIANT BEHEMOTH, THE
(1959 - Allied Artists) Gene Evans, Andre
Morell
One Sheet: $125 - $250   *Graven
Images, pg. 165.*

GIANT CLAW, THE
(1957 - Columbia) Jeff Morrow, Mara Corday
One Sheet: $150 - $300   *Graven
Images, pg. 178.*

GIANT FROM THE UNKNOWN
(1958 - Astor) Buddy Baer, Bob Steele
One Sheet: $40 - $75

GIANT GILA MONSTER, THE
(1959 - McLendon) Don Sullivan, Lisa Simone
One Sheet: $75 - $125

GIANT LEECHES, THE

(1959 - -) See "ATTACK OF..." for prices

GIANT OF MARATHON, THE
(1960 - MGM) Steve Reeves, Mylene
Demongeot
One Sheet: $30 - $50

GIANT SPIDER INVASION, THE
(1975 - Transcentury) Barbara Hale, Steve
Brodie, Leslie Parrish
One Sheet: $15 - $25

GIDEON OF SCOTLAND YARD
(1958 - Columbia) Jack Hawkins, Anna Massey
One Sheet: $10 - $20

GIDGET
(1959 - Columbia) James Darren, Sandra Dee
One Sheet: $30 - $50

GIDGET GOES HAWAIIAN
(1961 - Columbia) James Darren, Deborah
Walley
One Sheet: $30 - $50

GIDGET GOES TO ROME
(1963 - Columbia) James Darren, Cindy Carol
One Sheet: $15 - $30

GIFT OF GAB
(1934 - Universal) Boris Karloff, Bela Lugosi,
All-Star Cast
One Sheet: $700 - $1,200

GIFT OF LOVE, THE
(1958 - 20th Century Fox) Lauren Bacall,
Robert Stack
One Sheet: $20 - $40

GIG, THE
(1985 - Gig Company) Wayne Rogers, Cleavon
Little
One Sheet: $2 - $3

GIG AND SADDLE
(1940S - Goldberg) Lucky Millinder
One Sheet: $150 - $300   *Black cast.
Separate Cinema, pg. 92.*

GIGANTIS, THE FIRE MONSTER
(1959 - Warner Bros.) Hiroshi Koizumi
One Sheet: $75 - $125   *Duotone.
Advance:$100-150. Japanese poster:$1000-$1500. Graven Images, pg. 167.*

GIGI
(1958 - MGM) Maurice Chevalier, Leslie Caron
One Sheet: $75 - $150   *Academy:
Best Picture, Best Direction(Vincente Minnelli).
Academy Award Movie Posters #179-#181.*

GIGI
(1966R - MGM) Maurice Chevalier, Leslie
Caron
One Sheet: $30 - $50   *Re-release.*

GIGOLETTE
(1935 - RKO) Adrienne Ames, Ralph Bellamy
One Sheet: $100 - $200

GIGOLETTES OF PARIS
(1933 - Equitable) Madge Bellamy, Gilbert
Roland
One Sheet: $500 - $900

GIGOT
(1962 - 20th Century Fox) Jackie Gleason,
Katherine Kath
One Sheet: $15 - $25

GILDA
(1946 - Columbia) Rita Hayworth, Glenn Ford
One Sheet: $700 - $1,200   *Above price is
for Style A. One Sheet(Style B):$4000-7000.*

One Sheet (Style B)

GILDA
(1950R - Columbia) Rita Hayworth, Glenn Ford
One Sheet: $125 - $250   *One sheet is same image as original but tri-tone.*

GILDA
(1959R - Columbia) Rita Hayworth, Glenn Ford
One Sheet: $100 - $200   *Re-release.*

GILDED CAGE, THE
(1954 - Eros) Alex Nichol, Veronica Hurst
One Sheet: $15 - $25

GILDED LILY, THE
(1921 - Paramount) Mae Murray
One Sheet: $700 - $1,200

GILDED LILY, THE
(1935 - Paramount) Claudette Colbert, Fred MacMurray
One Sheet: $700 - $1,200

GILDERSLEEVE ON BROADWAY
(1943 - RKO) Harold Peary, Billie Burke
One Sheet: $75 - $125

GILDERSLEEVE'S BAD DAY
(1943 - RKO) Harold Peary, Jane Darwell
One Sheet: $75 - $125

GILDERSLEEVE'S GHOST
(1944 - RKO) Harold Peary, Marion Martin
One Sheet: $75 - $125

GIMME SHELTER
(1971 - -) Rolling Stones
One Sheet: $200 - $400   *Rock 'n' Roll documentary.*

GINGER
(1935 - Fox) Jane Withers, Jackie Searle
One Sheet: $125 - $250

GINGER
(1946 - Monogram) Frank Albertson, Barbara Reed
One Sheet: $30 - $50

GINGER AND FRED
(1986 - -) Giulietta Masina, Marcello Mastorianni, Dir: Fellini
One Sheet: $15 - $25

GINGER IN THE MORNING
(1973 - National) Monte Markham, Sissy Spacek
One Sheet: $3 - $5

GIRL 6
(1996 - Fox Searchlight) Theresa Randle, Dir: Spike Lee
One Sheet: $5 - $10

GIRL, A GUY AND A GOB, A
(1941 - RKO) George Murphy, Lucille Ball, Edmond O'Brien
One Sheet: $125 - $250

GIRL AND THE GAMBLER, THE
(1939 - RKO) Leo Carrillo, Steffi Duna, Tim Holt
One Sheet: $100 - $200

GIRL AND THE GENERAL, THE
(1967 - MGM) Rod Steiger, Virna Lisi
One Sheet: $10 - $20

GIRL CAN'T HELP IT, THE
(1956 - 20th Century Fox) Tom Ewell, Jayne Mansfield
One Sheet: $125 - $250

One Sheet

GIRL CRAZY

(1932 - RKO) Bert Wheeler, Robert Woolsey
One Sheet: $150 - $300

GIRL CRAZY
(1943 - MGM) Mickey Rooney, Judy Garland
One Sheet: $200 - $400

GIRL DOWNSTAIRS, THE
(1938 - MGM) Franchot Tone, Franciska Gaal
One Sheet: $100 - $200

GIRL FEVER
(1961 - General Screen) Count Gregory
One Sheet: $7 - $15

GIRL FRIEND, THE
(1935 - Columbia) Ann Sothern, Jack Haley
One Sheet: $100 - $200

GIRL FROM ALASKA
(1942 - Republic) Ray Middleton, Jean Parker
One Sheet: $30 - $60

GIRL FROM AVENUE "A"
(1940 - 20th Century Fox) Jane Withers, Kent Taylor
One Sheet: $75 - $150

GIRL FROM CALGARY
(1937 - Monogram) Paul Kelly, Fifi D'Orsay
One Sheet: $50 - $100

GIRL FROM CHICAGO
(1927 - Warner Bros.) Myrna Loy, Conrad Nagel
One Sheet: $350 - $750

GIRL FROM CHICAGO
(1932 - Micheaux) Grace Smith, Carl Mahon
One Sheet: $2,500 - $4,000   *Black cast. Separate Cinema, pg. 13.*

GIRL FROM GOD'S COUNTRY
(1940 - Republic) Chester Morris, Charles Bickford, Jane Wyatt
One Sheet: $50 - $100

GIRL FROM HAVANA
(1929 - Fox) Lola Lane, Paul Page
One Sheet: $250 - $500

GIRL FROM HAVANA
(1940 - Republic) Dennis O'Keefe, Claire Carleton
One Sheet: $50 - $100

GIRL FROM JONES BEACH, THE
(1949 - Warner Bros.) Ronald Reagan, Virginia Mayo
One Sheet: $40 - $75

GIRL FROM MANDALAY
(1936 - Republic) Conrad Nagel, Kay Linaker
One Sheet: $75 - $125

GIRL FROM MANHATTAN
(1948 - United Artists) Dorothy Lamour, George Montgomery
One Sheet: $40 - $75

GIRL FROM MEXICO, THE
(1939 - RKO) Lupe Velez, Leon Errol
One Sheet: $50 - $100

GIRL FROM MISSOURI, THE
(1934 - MGM) Jean Harlow, Franchot Tone
One Sheet: $4,000 - $6,000   *AKA: BORN TO BE KISSED.*

GIRL FROM MONTEREY, THE
(1943 - PRC) Armida, Edgar Kennedy
One Sheet: $40 - $75

GIRL FROM PETROVKA, THE
(1974 - Universal) Goldie Hawn, Anthony Hopkins
One Sheet: $5 - $10

GIRL FROM RIO, THE
(1939 - Monogram) Movita, Warren Hull
One Sheet: $50 - $100

GIRL FROM SAN LORENZO, THE
(1950 - United Artists) Duncan Renaldo, Leo Carrillo
One Sheet: $30 - $50

GIRL FROM SCOTLAND YARD, THE
(1937 - Paramount) Karen Morley, Robert Baldwin
One Sheet: $100 - $200

GIRL FROM STARSHIP VENUS, THE
(1975 - Intercontinental) Monika Ringwald

One Sheet: $15 - $35

GIRL FROM TENTH AVENUE, THE
(1935 - First National) Bette Davis, Ian Hunter
One Sheet: $4,500 - $7,000

GIRL FROM THE MARSHES, THE
(1950 - Josephy Burstyn) -
One Sheet: $10 - $20

GIRL FROM WOOLWORTH'S, THE
(1929 - Warner Bros.) Alice White, Wheeler Oakman
One Sheet: $200 - $400

GIRL GANG
(1954 - -) -
One Sheet: $30 - $50

GIRL GETTERS, THE
(1966 - AIP) Oliver Reed, Jane Merrow
One Sheet: $10 - $20

GIRL GRABBERS, THE
(1968 - August) Paul Cox, Jackie Richards
One Sheet: $7 - $15

GIRL HABIT
(1931 - Paramount Publix) Charlie Ruggles, Helen Mack, Margaret Dumont
One Sheet: $200 - $400

GIRL HAPPY
(1965 - MGM) Elvis Presley, Shelley Fabares
One Sheet: $50 - $100

One Sheet

GIRL HE LEFT BEHIND, THE
(1957 - Warner Bros.) Tab Hunter, Natalie Wood
One Sheet: $15 - $35

GIRL HUNTERS, THE
(1963 - Colorama) Mickey Spillane, Shirley Eaton
One Sheet: $30 - $50

GIRL IN 313
(1940 - 20th Century Fox) Kent Taylor, Florence Rice
One Sheet: $50 - $100

GIRL IN 419
(1933 - Paramount) James Dunn, Gloria Stuart
One Sheet: $100 - $200

GIRL IN A MILLION, A
(1946 - London) Joan Greenwood, Hugh Williams
One Sheet: $50 - $100

GIRL IN A SWING, THE
(1989 - -) Meg Tilly, Rupert Frazer
One Sheet: $3 - $5

GIRL IN BLACK STOCKINGS
(1956 - United Artists) Mamie Van Doren, Lex Barker
One Sheet: $50 - $100

GIRL IN DANGER
(1934 - Columbia) Ralph Bellamy, Shirley Grey
One Sheet: $100 - $200

GIRL IN DISTRESS
(1941 - GFD) Barbara Mullen, Michael Redgrave
One Sheet: $40 - $75

GIRL IN EVERY PORT, A
(1928 - Fox) Victor McLaglen, Robert Armstrong, Louise Brooks
One Sheet: $250 - $600

GIRL IN EVERY PORT, A

(1952 - RKO) Groucho Marx, Marie Wilson, William Bendix
One Sheet: $75 - $150

GIRL IN GOLD BOOTS
(1968 - Geneni) Jody Daniels, Tom Pace
One Sheet: $15 - $25

GIRL IN LOVER'S LANE, THE
(1960 - Filmgroup) Breyt Halsey, Joyce Meadows
One Sheet: $10 - $20

GIRL IN POSSESSION
(1934 - Warner Bros.) Laura La Plante, Henry Kendall
One Sheet: $150 - $300

GIRL IN ROOM 13
(1961 - Astor) Brian Donlevy, Elizabeth Howard
One Sheet: $50 - $100

GIRL IN ROOM 20, THE
(1946 - United Films) Geraldine Brock, Spencer Williams
One Sheet: $200 - $400   *Black cast. Separate Cinema, pg. 24.*

GIRL IN THE BIKINI, THE
(1958 - Atlantis) Brigitte Bardot
One Sheet: $50 - $100   *Price is for U.S. release. French title:MANINA, LA FILLE SANS VOILE. Original French(47x63):$300-500.*

GIRL IN THE CASE
(1944 - Columbia) Edmund Lowe, Janis Carter
One Sheet: $50 - $100

GIRL IN THE GLASS CAGE, THE
(1929 - Warner Bros.) Loretta Young, Carroll Nye
One Sheet: $200 - $400

GIRL IN THE KREMLIN, THE
(1957 - Universal) Lex Barker, Zsa Zsa Gabor
One Sheet: $30 - $60

GIRL IN THE NEWS, THE
(1941 - 20th Century Fox) Margaret Lockwood, Barry Barnes
One Sheet: $50 - $100

GIRL IN THE NIGHT, THE
(1931 - Wardour) Henry Edwards, Dorothy Boyd
One Sheet: $100 - $200

GIRL IN THE PAINTING, THE
(1948 - Universal) Mai Zetterling, Robert Beatty
One Sheet: $50 - $100

GIRL IN THE PICTURE, THE
(1956 - Eros) Donald Houston, Junia Crawford
One Sheet: $15 - $25

GIRL IN THE RED VELVET SWING, THE
(1955 - 20th Century Fox) Ray Milland, Joan Collins
One Sheet: $40 - $75

GIRL IN THE SHOW, THE
(1929 - MGM) Bessie Love, Jed Prouty
One Sheet: $150 - $300

GIRL IN THE STREET
(1938 - Gaumont) Anna Neagle, Tullio Carminati
One Sheet: $50 - $100

GIRL IN THE WOODS
(1957 - Republic) Forrest Tucker, Barton MacLane
One Sheet: $10 - $20

GIRL IN TROUBLE
(1963 - Vanguard) Tammy Clark, Larry Johnson
One Sheet: $7 - $15

GIRL IN WHITE, THE
(1952 - MGM) June Allyson, Arthur Kennedy
One Sheet: $15 - $35

GIRL IS MINE, THE
(1950 - British Lion) Patrick Macnee, Pamela Deeming
One Sheet: $15 - $25

GIRL LOVES BOY
(1937 - Grand National) Eric Linden, Cecelia Parker
One Sheet: $50 - $100

GIRL MISSING

(1933 - Warner Bros.) Glenda Farrell, Ben Lyon
One Sheet: $100 - $200

GIRL MOST LIKELY, THE
(1957 - RKO) Jane Powell, Cliff Robertson
One Sheet: $15 - $35

GIRL MUST LIVE, A
(1941 - 20th Century Fox) Renee Houston,
Margaret Lockwood
One Sheet: $50 - $100

GIRL NAMED TAMIKO, A
(1963 - Paramount) Laurence Harvey, France
Nuyen
One Sheet: $15 - $25

GIRL NEXT DOOR, THE
(1953 - 20th Century Fox) June Haver, Dan
Dailey
One Sheet: $15 - $30

GIRL O' MY DREAMS
(1934 - Monogram) Mary Carlisle, Eddie
Nugent
One Sheet: $75 - $150

GIRL OF THE GOLDEN WEST, THE
(1915 - Lasky) Mabel Van Buren, Dir: Cecil B.
DeMille
One Sheet: $1,900 - $3,000

GIRL OF THE GOLDEN WEST, THE
(1923 - Associated First National) Sylvia
Breamer, J. Warren Kerrigan
One Sheet: $700 - $1,200

GIRL OF THE GOLDEN WEST
(1930 - First National) Ann Harding, James
Rennie
One Sheet: $150 - $350

GIRL OF THE GOLDEN WEST, THE
(1938 - MGM) Jeanette MacDonald, Nelson
Eddy
One Sheet: $200 - $400

GIRL OF THE LIMBERLOST
(1934 - Monogram) Louise Dresser, Ralph
Morgan
One Sheet: $75 - $150

GIRL OF THE LIMBERLOST, THE
(1945 - Columbia) Ruth Nelson, Dorinda Clifton
One Sheet: $15 - $30

GIRL OF THE NIGHT
(1960 - Warner Bros.) Anne Francis, Lloyd
Nolan
One Sheet: $15 - $25

GIRL OF THE OZARKS
(1936 - Paramount) Virginia Weidler, Leif
Erikson
One Sheet: $75 - $150

GIRL OF THE PORT
(1930 - RKO) Sally O'Neil, Arthur Clayton
One Sheet: $100 - $200

GIRL OF THE RIO
(1932 - RKO) Dolores Del Rio, Leo Carrillo
One Sheet: $75 - $150

GIRL OF THE YEAR
(1950 - Columbia) Robert Cummings, Joan
Caulfield
One Sheet: $150 - $300   *Petty art.*

GIRL ON A CHAIN GANG
(1966 - Gross) William Watson, Julie Ange
One Sheet: $20 - $40

GIRL ON A MOTORCYCLE, THE
(1968 - Claridge) Alain Delon, Marianne
Faithfull, Roger Mutton
One Sheet: $30 - $50   *AKA: NAKED
UNDER LEATHER.*

GIRL ON THE BARGE, THE
(1929 - Universal) Jean Hersholt, Nancy Kelly
One Sheet: $200 - $400

GIRL ON THE BRIDGE
(1951 - 20th Century Fox) Hugo Haas, Beverly
Michaels
One Sheet: $10 - $20

GIRL ON THE FRONT PAGE, THE
(1936 - Universal) Edmund Lowe, Gloria Stuart
One Sheet: $75 - $150

GIRL ON THE PIER, THE
(1953 - Apex) Veronica Hurst

One Sheet: $15 - $25

GIRL ON THE RUN
(1961 - Astor) Richard Coogan, Rosemary
Pettit
One Sheet: $7 - $15

GIRL ON THE SPOT
(1945 - Universal) Lois Collier, Jess Barker
One Sheet: $50 - $100

GIRL ON THE STAIRS, THE
(1924 - Peninsula) Patsy Ruth Miller, Frances
Raymond, Arline Pretty
One Sheet: $150 - $300

GIRL OVERBOARD
(1929 - Universal) Mary Philbin, Edmund
Breese
One Sheet: $200 - $400

GIRL OVERBOARD
(1937 - Universal) Gloria Stuart, Walter
Pidgeon
One Sheet: $150 - $300

GIRL RUSH
(1944 - RKO) Frances Langford, Wally Brown
One Sheet: $30 - $50

GIRL RUSH, THE
(1955 - Paramount) Rosalind Russell,
Fernando Lamas, Gloria De Haven
One Sheet: $30 - $50

GIRL SAID NO, THE
(1930 - MGM) Polly Moran, Marie Dressler
One Sheet: $250 - $500

GIRL SAID NO, THE
(1937 - Grand National) Robert Armstrong,
Irene Hervey
One Sheet: $75 - $150

GIRL SHY
(1924 - Pathe) Harold Lloyd, Jobyna Ralston
One Sheet: $800 - $1,500

GIRL SMUGGLERS
(1967 - Sack) Lucky Kargo
One Sheet: $30 - $50

GIRL, THE BODY, AND THE PILL, THE
(1967 - Dominant) Pamela Rhea, Dir: H.G.
Lewis
One Sheet: $30 - $50   *AKA: THE
PILL.*

GIRL, THE COP, THE BURGLAR, THE
(1914 - Essanay) -
One Sheet: $350 - $750

GIRL THIEF, THE
(1938 - Associated British) Marian Marsh,
Stanley Holloway
One Sheet: $75 - $150

GIRL TROUBLE
(1934 - Vitaphone) -
One Sheet: $100 - $200

GIRL TROUBLE
(1942 - 20th Century Fox) Don Ameche, Joan
Bennett
One Sheet: $50 - $100

GIRL WAS YOUNG, THE
(1938 - Gaumont British) Nova Pilbeam,
Derrick de Marney, Dir: Alfred Hitchcock
One Sheet: $3,500 - $5,000   *AKA: YOUNG
AND INNOCENT.*

GIRL WHO CAME BACK, THE
(1935 - Chesterfield Motion) Sidney Blackmer,
Shirley Grey
One Sheet: $75 - $150

GIRL WHO COULDN'T SAY NO, THE
(1969 - 20th Century Fox) Virna Lisi, George
Segal, Lila Kedrova
One Sheet: $10 - $20

GIRL WHO DARED, THE
(1944 - Republic) Lorna Gray, Peter Cookson
One Sheet: $40 - $75

GIRL WHO HAD EVERYTHING, THE
(1952 - MGM) Elizabeth Taylor, Fernando
Lamas
One Sheet: $75 - $150

GIRL WHO KNEW TOO MUCH, THE
(1969 - Commonwealth United) Adam West,
Nancy Kwan

One Sheet: $7 - $15

GIRL WITH AN ITCH
(1958 - -) -
One Sheet: $50 - $100

GIRL WITH GREEN EYES
(1964 - Lopert) Rita Tushingham, Peter Finch
One Sheet: $15 - $25

GIRL WITH IDEAS, A
(1937 - Universal) Wendy Barrie, Walter
Pidgeon
One Sheet: $50 - $100

GIRL WITH THE SUITCASE, THE
(1961 - Titanus) Claudia Cardinale, Jacques
Perrin
One Sheet: $30 - $50

GIRL WITHOUT A ROOM
(1933 - Paramount) Charles Farrell, Marguerite
Churchill
One Sheet: $1,300 - $2,000

One Sheet

GIRL'S BEST YEARS, A
(1937 - MGM) Mary Doran, John Warburton
One Sheet: $125 - $250

GIRLFRIENDS
(1978 - Warner Bros.) Melanie Mayron, Eli
Wallach
One Sheet: $5 - $10

GIRLS ABOUT TOWN
(1931 - Paramount Publix) Kay Francis, Joel
McCrea
One Sheet: $125 - $250

GIRLS CAN PLAY
(1937 - Columbia) Charles Quigley, Jacqueline
Wells
One Sheet: $150 - $350   *Sports Movie
Posters #44.*

GIRLS DEMAND EXCITEMENT
(1931 - Fox) Virginia Cherrill, John Wayne
One Sheet: $125 - $250   *Wayne is
probably not pictured on posters. Lobby
Card(Wayne):$300-500.*

GIRLS FROM THUNDER STRIP, THE
(1966 - Borealis) Jody McCrea, Lindsay Crosby
One Sheet: $20 - $40   *Biker film.*

GIRLS! GIRLS! GIRLS!
(1962 - Paramount) Elvis Presley, Stella
Stevens
One Sheet: $75 - $125

One Sheet

GIRLS IN CHAINS
(1943 - PRC) Arline Judge, Roger Clark
One Sheet: $40 - $75

GIRLS IN PRISON
(1956 - AIP) Richard Denning, Joan Taylor
One Sheet: $15 - $35

GIRLS IN THE NIGHT
(1953 - Universal) Joyce Holden, Glenda
Farrell
One Sheet: $20 - $40

GIRLS IN THE STREET
(1937 - General) Anna Neagle
One Sheet: $75 - $125

GIRLS JUST WANT TO HAVE FUN
(1985 - New World) Sarah Jessica Parker, Lee
Montgomery
One Sheet: $3 - $5

GIRLS NEXT DOOR, THE
(1979 - Columbus American) Kristen Baker,
Perry Lang
One Sheet: $5 - $10

GIRLS OF LATIN QUARTER
(1960 - New Realm) Jill Ireland, Bernard
Hunter
One Sheet: $15 - $25

GIRLS OF PLEASURE ISLAND, THE
(1953 - Paramount) Don Taylor, Leo Genn
One Sheet: $15 - $30

GIRLS OF THE BIG HOUSE
(1945 - Republic) Lynne Roberts, Adele Mara
One Sheet: $30 - $50

GIRLS OF THE ROAD
(1940 - Columbia) Ann Dvorak, Helen Mack,
Lola Lane
One Sheet: $50 - $100

GIRLS ON PROBATION
(1938 - Warner Bros.) Ronald Reagan, Jane
Bryan, Susan Hayward
One Sheet: $125 - $250

GIRLS ON THE BEACH
(1965 - Paramount) Martin West, Noreen
Corcoran
One Sheet: $20 - $40

GIRLS ON THE LOOSE
(1958 - Universal International) Mara Corday,
Lita Milan
One Sheet: $30 - $50

GIRLS UNDER 21
(1940 - Columbia) Paul Kelly, Rochelle Hudson
One Sheet: $50 - $100

GIRLS WILL BE BOYS
(1934 - Alliance) Dolly Haas
One Sheet: $125 - $250

GIRLS' DORMITORY
(1936 - 20th Century Fox) Herbert Marshall,
Simone Simon (her first film)
One Sheet: $250 - $600

GIRLS' SCHOOL
(1938 - Columbia) Anne Shirley, Nan Grey
One Sheet: $75 - $150

GIRLS' SCHOOL
(1950 - Columbia) Joyce Reynolds, Ross Ford
One Sheet: $15 - $30

GIRLS' TOWN
(1942 - PRC) June Storey, Edith Fellows,
One Sheet: $30 - $50

GIRLS' TOWN
(1959 - MGM) Mamie Van Doren, Mel Torme,
Paul Anka
One Sheet: $15 - $30

GIRLY
(1970 - Cinerama) Michael Bryant, Ursula
Howells, Vanessa Howard
One Sheet: $7 - $15

GIRO CITY
(1982 - Cinegate) Glenda Jackson
One Sheet: $3 - $5

GITI
(1965 - Avco/Embassy) Jack Chaplain, Heather
North, Leslie Bradley
One Sheet: $5 - $10

GIT ALONG, LITTLE DOGIES
(1937 - Republic) Gene Autry, Judith Allen
One Sheet: $250 - $600   *Cowboy
Movie Posters #218.*

GIT ALONG, LITTLE DOGIES
(1942R - Republic) Gene Autry, Judith Allen
One Sheet: $75 - $150   *Re-release.*

GIT ALONG, LITTLE DOGIES
(1944R - Republic) Gene Autry, Judith Allen
One Sheet: $50 - $100   *Re-release.*

GIT-ROCK THE RENEGADE HOUND
(1965 - Embassy) Jack Chaplain, Seldom-Seen Souix
One Sheet: $4 - $8

GIVE 'EM HELL HARRY
(1975 - Theatre TV) James Whitmore
One Sheet: $3 - $5

GIVE A GIRL A BREAK
(1953 - MGM) Debbie Reynolds, The Champions
One Sheet: $30 - $50

GIVE AND TAKE
(1929 - Universal) Jean Hersholt, George Lewis
One Sheet: $200 - $400

GIVE ME A SAILOR
(1938 - Paramount) Martha Raye, Bob Hope
One Sheet: $100 - $200

GIVE ME YOUR HEART
(1936 - Warner Bros.) Kay Francis, George Brent
One Sheet: $100 - $200

One Sheet

GIVE MY REGARDS TO BROAD STREET
(1984 - 20th Century Fox) Paul McCartney, Bryan Brown
One Sheet: $10 - $20

GIVE MY REGARDS TO BROADWAY
(1948 - 20th Century Fox) Dan Dailey, Charles Winninger
One Sheet: $50 - $100

GIVE OUT, SISTERS
(1942 - Universal) Andrews Sisters, Richard Davies
One Sheet: $75 - $150

GIVE US THE MOON
(1944 - GFD) Margaret Lockwood, Vic Oliver
One Sheet: $15 - $30

GIVE US THIS NIGHT
(1936 - Paramount) Jan Kiepura, Gladys Swarthout
One Sheet: $75 - $125

GIVE US WINGS
(1940 - Universal) Dead End Kids, Wallace Ford
One Sheet: $75 - $125

GLACIER FOX, THE
(1979 - -) Arthur Hill (Narrator)
One Sheet: $2 - $3

GLAD RAG DOLL, THE
(1929 - Warner Bros.) Dolores Costello, Ralph Graves
One Sheet: $200 - $400

GLAD RAGS TO RICHES
(1933 - Educational) Shirley Temple
One Sheet: $200 - $400   *From the Baby Burlesk series.*

GLADIATOR, THE
(1938 - Columbia) Joe E. Brown, June Travis
One Sheet: $100 - $200   *Sports Movie Posters #339.*

GLADIATOR
(1992 - Columbia) Cuba Gooding Jr., James Marshall
One Sheet: $7 - $15   *Sports (Boxing). Sports Movie Posters #169.*

GLADIATORS 7
(1964 - MGM) Richard Harrison, Loredana Nusciak
One Sheet: $7 - $15

GLAMOROUS NIGHT
(1938 - Republic) Mary Ellis, Victor Jory
One Sheet: $75 - $125

GLAMOUR
(1934 - Universal) Paul Lukas, Constance Cummings
One Sheet: $150 - $300

GLAMOUR BOY
(1941 - Paramount) Susanna Foster, Jackie Cooper
One Sheet: $50 - $100

GLAMOUR FOR SALE
(1940 - Columbia) Roger Pryor, Anita Louise
One Sheet: $75 - $150

GLAMOUR GIRL
(1938 - Warner Bros.) Gene Gerrard, Lesley Brook
One Sheet: $75 - $125

GLAMOUR GIRL
(1948 - Columbia) Virginia Grey, Gene Krupa Orchestra
One Sheet: $50 - $100

GLASS ALIBI, THE
(1946 - Republic) Paul Kelly, Anne Gwynne
One Sheet: $40 - $75

GLASS BOTTOM BOAT, THE
(1966 - MGM) Doris Day, Rod Taylor
One Sheet: $20 - $40

GLASS CAGE, THE
(1964 - Futuramic) Arline Sax, John Hoyt
One Sheet: $10 - $20

GLASS HOUSES
(1972 - Columbia) Bernard Barrow, Jennifer O'Neill
One Sheet: $3 - $5

GLASS KEY, THE
(1935 - Paramount) George Raft, Edward Arnold, Ray Milland
One Sheet: $500 - $800

GLASS KEY, THE
(1942 - Paramount) Brian Donlevy, Veronica Lake, Alan Ladd
One Sheet: $1,300 - $2,000

One Sheet

GLASS MENAGERIE, THE
(1950 - Warner Bros.) Kirk Douglas, Jane Wyman, Gertrude Lawrence
One Sheet: $30 - $50

GLASS MOUNTAIN, THE
(1949 - Eagle-Lion) Valentina Cortese, Dulcie Gray
One Sheet: $15 - $25

GLASS SLIPPER, THE
(1955 - MGM) Leslie Caron, Michael Wilding
One Sheet: $15 - $35

GLASS TOMB, THE
(1955 - Lippert) John Ireland, Honor Blackman
One Sheet: $15 - $30

GLASS WALL, THE
(1953 - Columbia) Vittorio Gassman, Gloria Grahame
One Sheet: $15 - $35

GLASS WEB, THE
(1953 - Universal) Edward G. Robinson, John Forsythe
One Sheet: $40 - $75

GLEAMING THE CUBE
(1989 - 20th Century Fox) Christian Slater, Steven Bauer
One Sheet: $7 - $15   *Sports (Skateboarding). Sports Movie Posters #308.*

GLEN AND RANDA
(1971 - UMC) Steven Curry, Shelley Plimpton
One Sheet: $3 - $5

GLEN OR GLENDA
(1953 - Paramount) Bela Lugosi, Dolores Fuller, Daniel Davis (Edward Wood Jr.)
One Sheet: $200 - $400   *Sex change film. Graven Images, pg. 189. AKA: I Led Two Lives.*

One Sheet

GLENGARRY GLEN ROSS
(1992 - New Line) Al Pacino, Jack Lemmon, Alan Arkin, Ed Harris, Alec Baldwin
One Sheet: $7 - $15

GLENN MILLER STORY, THE
(1954 - Universal International) James Stewart, June Allyson
One Sheet: $150 - $300

GLENN MILLER STORY, THE
(1960R - Universal) James Stewart, June Allyson
One Sheet: $20 - $40   *Re-release.*

GLENN MILLER STORY, THE
(1983R - Universal) James Stewart, June Allyson
One Sheet: $10 - $20   *Re-release.*

GLOBAL AFFAIR, A
(1964 - MGM) Bob Hope, Yvonne De Carlo
One Sheet: $15 - $35

GLOOM CHASER, THE
(1928 - Educational) Big Boy
One Sheet: $200 - $400

GLORIA
(1980 - Columbia) Gena Rowlands, Juan Adames
One Sheet: $3 - $5

GLORIFYING THE AMERICAN GIRL
(1929 - Paramount) Mary Eaton, Edward Crandall, all star cast as themselves
One Sheet: $800 - $1,500

GLORIOUS BETSY
(1928 - Warner Bros.) Dolores Costello, Conrad Nagel
One Sheet: $150 - $300

GLORIOUS LADY, THE
(1919 - Selznick) Olive Thomas, Matt Moore
One Sheet: $350 - $750

GLORIOUS TRAIL, THE
(1928 - First National) Ken Maynard, Gladys McConnell
One Sheet: $600 - $1,000

GLORY
(1955 - RKO) Margaret O'Brien, Walter Brennan
One Sheet: $15 - $35

GLORY
(1989 - TriStar) Matthew Broderick, Denzel Washington
One Sheet: $10 - $20   *Academy Award Movie Posters #368.*

GLORY
(1992 - -) Daniel Day Lewis
One Sheet: $5 - $10

GLORY ALLEY
(1952 - MGM) Leslie Caron, Ralph Meeker
One Sheet: $15 - $35

GLORY AT SEA
(1952 - British Lion) Trevor Howard, Richard Attenborough
One Sheet: $15 - $25

GLORY BOY
(1971 - Cinerama) William Devane, Michael Moriarty
One Sheet: $4 - $8

GLORY BRIGADE, THE
(1953   20th Century Fox) Victor Mature, Richard Egan
One Sheet: $15 - $30

GLORY GUYS, THE
(1965 - United Artists) Tom Tryon, Harve Presnell
One Sheet: $10 - $20

GLORY STOMPERS, THE
(1967 - AIP) Dennis Hopper, Jody McCrea
One Sheet: $20 - $40   *Biker film.*

GLORY TRAIL, THE
(1937 - Crescent) Tom Keene, Joan Barclay
One Sheet: $75 - $125

GLOVE, THE
(1980 - Pro International) John Saxon, Joanna Cassidy
One Sheet: $7 - $15   *Sports Movie Posters #365.*

G-MAN JITTERS
(1939 - 20th Century Fox) Terry-toons
One Sheet: $100 - $200   *Cartoon. Full color stone litho. Stock poster with inset title.*

G-MEN
(1935 - First National) James Cagney, Ann Dvorak
One Sheet: $5,000 - $8,000

One Sheet

G-MEN
(1949R - Warner Bros.) James Cagney, Ann Dvorak
One Sheet: $125 - $250   *Re-release.*

G-MEN NEVER FORGET
(1948 - Republic) Clayton Moore, Roy Barcroft
One Sheet: $75 - $125   *Serial. 12 Chapters.*

G-MEN VS. THE BLACK DRAGON
(1943 - Republic) Rod Cameron, Roland Got
One Sheet: $75 - $150   *Serial. 15 Chapters. Serial version of "BLACK DRAGON OF MANZANAR".*

GNAW: FOOD OF THE GODS II
(1989 - -) Paul Coufas, Lisa Schrage
One Sheet: $10 - $20

GNOME-MOBILE, THE
(1967 - Disney) Walter Brennan, Karen Dotrice
One Sheet: $20 - $40

GNOME-MOBILE, THE

(1976R - Disney) Walter Brennan, Karen Dotrice
One Sheet: $5 - $10   *Re-release.*

GO APE!
(1974 - 20th Century Fox) Planet Of The Apes multi-feature
One Sheet: $125 - $250

One Sheet

GO CHASE YOURSELF
(1938 - RKO) Joe Penner, Lucille Ball
One Sheet: $75 - $150

GO DOWN, DEATH
(1944 - Sack) Dir:Spencer Williams
One Sheet: $200 - $400   *Black cast. Separate Cinema, pg. 23.*

GO FISH
(1974 - -) -
One Sheet: $5 - $10

GO FOR BROKE
(1950 - MGM) Van Johnson, Warner Anderson
One Sheet: $40 - $75

GO FOR BROKE
(1962R - MGM) Van Johnson, Warner Anderson
One Sheet: $5 - $10   *Re-release.*

GO FOR IT
(1976 - World Entertainment) -
One Sheet: $5 - $10

GO GET 'EM HAINES
(1936 - Republic) William Boyd
One Sheet: $150 - $300

GO GO MANIA
(1965 - -) All Star Cast
One Sheet: $40 - $75   *Rock 'n' Roll film with the Beatles.*

GO INTO YOUR DANCE
(1935 - First National) Al Jolson, Ruby Keeler
One Sheet: $1,300 - $2,000

GO JOHNNY GO!
(1959 - Hal Roach Studios) Alan Freed, Chuck Berry
One Sheet: $125 - $250   *Rock 'n' Roll.*

GO, MAN, GO!
(1954 - United Artists) Harlem Globetrotters, Dane Clark, Sidney Poitier
One Sheet: $75 - $150   *Separate Cinema, pg. 62. Sports Movie Posters #s 91, 92.*

GO NAKED IN THE WORLD
(1961 - MGM) Gina Lollobrigida, Anthony Franciosa
One Sheet: $15 - $35

GO TELL THE SPARTANS
(1978 - Avco/Embassy) Burt Lancaster
One Sheet: $3 - $5

GO WEST
(1925 - Metro-Goldwyn) Buster Keaton, Kathleen Myers, "Brown Eyes the cow"
One Sheet: $6,500 - $10,000

GO WEST
(1940 - MGM) Marx Brothers, John Carroll
One Sheet: $600 - $1,000

GO WEST, BIG BOY
(1931 - Educational) Animated by Paul Terry
One Sheet: $250 - $600   *Cartoon. Cartoon Movie Posters #76.*

GO WEST, YOUNG LADY
(1941 - Columbia) Penny Singleton, Glenn Ford

One Sheet: $75 - $125

GO WEST, YOUNG MAN
(1936 - Paramount) Mae West, Randolph Scott, Warren William
One Sheet: $800 - $1,500

GOAT, THE
(1921 - Metro) Buster Keaton
One Sheet: $7,500 - $12,000

GO-BETWEEN, THE
(1971 - Columbia) Julie Christie, Alan Bates, Margaret Leighton,
One Sheet: $3 - $5

GOBOTS: BATTLE OF THE ROCK LORDS
(1986 - -) Voices of Margot Kidder, Roddy McDowall, Telly Savalas
One Sheet: $7 - $15   *Cartoon.*

GOBS AND GALS
(1952 - Republic) George Bernard, Cathy Downs
One Sheet: $15 - $30

GOD FORGIVES, I DON'T!
(1969 - AIP) Terence Hill, Bud Spencer
One Sheet: $15 - $25

GOD IS MY CO-PILOT
(1945 - Warner Bros.) Dennis Morgan, Dane Clark
One Sheet: $50 - $100

GOD IS MY PARTNER
(1957 - 20th Century Fox) Walter Brennan, Marion Ross
One Sheet: $15 - $25

GOD IS MY WITNESS
(1931 - Astor) Bob McKenzie, John Aldridge
One Sheet: $150 - $300

GOD TOLD ME TO
(1976 - -) See DEMON for prices

GOD'S COUNTRY
(1946 - Action) Robert Lowery, Helen Gilbert, Buster Keaton
One Sheet: $75 - $150

GOD'S COUNTRY AND THE MAN
(1931 - Syndicate) Tom Tyler, George Hayes
One Sheet: $150 - $300

GOD'S COUNTRY AND THE MAN
(1937 - Monogram) Tom Keene, Betty Compson
One Sheet: $100 - $200

GOD'S COUNTRY AND THE WOMAN
(1936 - Warner Bros.) Beverly Roberts, George Brent
One Sheet: $75 - $125

GOD'S COUNTRY AND THE WOMAN
(1948R - Warner Bros.) Beverly Roberts, George Brent
One Sheet: $15 - $25   *Re-release.*

GOD'S GIFT TO WOMEN
(1931 - Warner Bros.) Frank Fay, Joan Blondell
One Sheet: $100 - $200

GOD'S GUN
(1977 - Yablans) Lee Van Cleef, Jack Palance
One Sheet: $15 - $25

GOD'S LITTLE ACRE
(1958 - United Artists) Aldo Ray, Robert Ryan, Michael Landon
One Sheet: $15 - $30

GOD'S STEPCHILDREN
(1937 - Micheaux) Alice B. Russell, Carman Newsome
One Sheet: $600 - $1,000   *Black cast.*

GODDESS, THE
(1958 - Columbia) Kim Stanley, Lloyd Bridges
One Sheet: $30 - $50

GODDESS OF LOVE, THE
(1960 - 20th Century Fox) Belinda Lee, Jacques Sernas
One Sheet: $7 - $15

GODFATHER, THE
(1972 - Paramount) Marlon Brando, Al Pacino, James Caan
One Sheet: $75 - $125   *Academy Award: Best Picture, Best Actor (Brando). Academy Award Movie Posters #269 & #270.*

GODFATHER OF HARLEM
(1973 - AIP) Fred Williamson, Minnie Gentry
One Sheet: $30 - $50

GODFATHER PART II, THE
(1974 - Paramount) Al Pacino, Robert De Niro, Robert Duvall
One Sheet: $40 - $75   *Academy Award: Best Picture, Best Supporting Actor (De Niro), Best Director (Coppola). Academy AwardMovie Posters #280, #282 & #284.*

GODFATHER PART III, THE
(1990 - Paramount) Al Pacino, Andy Garcia
One Sheet: $15 - $30   *Advance:$25- $50.*

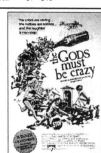

One Sheet

GODLESS GIRL, THE
(1929 - Pathe) Marie Prevost, Noah Beery, Dir: C.B. De Mille
One Sheet: $1,300 - $2,000   *De Mille's first sound film.*

GODS MUST BE CRAZY, THE
(1984 - 20th Century Fox) Marius Weyers, Sandra Prinsloo
One Sheet: $7 - $15

One Sheet

GODS MUST BE CRAZY II, THE
(1989 - -) N!xau, Lena Farugia, Hans Strydom
One Sheet: $3 - $5

GODSEND, THE
(1980 - Cannon) Cyd Hayman, Malcolm Stoddard
One Sheet: $3 - $5

GODSON, THE
(1972 - Artists International) Alain Delon
One Sheet: $3 - $5

GODSPELL
(1973 - Columbia) Victor Garber, David Haskell
One Sheet: $5 - $10

GODZILLA 1985
(1985 - New World) Raymond Burr, Keiju Kobayashi
One Sheet: $15 - $25

GODZILLA, KING OF THE MONSTERS
(1956 - Transworld) Raymond Burr, Akira Takarada
One Sheet: $800 - $1,500   *First Godzilla film. Graven Images, pg. 166. Japanese poster:$3500-$5000.*

GODZILLA ON MONSTER ISLAND
(1972 - Downtown Dist.) Hiroshi Ishikawa
One Sheet: $40 - $75   *AKA: GODZILLA VS. GIGAN.*

GODZILLA VS GIGAN

(1971 - Cinema Shares) -
One Sheet: $40 - $75

GODZILLA VS MECHAGODZILLA
(1975 - -) Masaaki Daimon
One Sheet: $40 - $75

GODZILLA VS MEGALON
(1976 - Cinema Shares) Katsuhiko Sasaki
One Sheet: $40 - $75   *Style B (duotone):$25-$50.*

GODZILLA VS MONSTER ZERO
(1966 - -) Nick Adams, Akira Takarada
One Sheet: $50 - $100

GODZILLA VS THE BIONIC MONSTER
(1974 - -) See GODZILLA VS THE COSMIC MONSTER

GODZILLA VS THE COSMIC MONSTER
(1974 - Cinema Shares) Masaaki Daimon
One Sheet: $40 - $75   *Price is for style A (Gogos art). Style B (four monsters):$30- $50.*

GODZILLA VS THE SEA MONSTER
(1966 - Continental) -
One Sheet: $75 - $150

GODZILLA VS THE SMOG MONSTER
(1972 - AIP) Akira Yamauchi, Hiroyuki Kawase
One Sheet: $75 - $125   *International Title: Godzilla Vs. Hedra ($50-$80).*

GODZILLA VS THE THING
(1964 - AIP) Akira Takarada
One Sheet: $75 - $175   *AKA: GODZILLA VS MOTHRA. Half Sheet (different artwork):$100-$200.*

GODZILLA'S REVENGE
(1969 - Maron Films) Kenji Sahara, Tomonori Yazaki
One Sheet: $30 - $60   *Two versions: double-billed w/ Island of the Burning Damned ($35-$60); double-billed w/ War of the Gargantuas($50-$100).*

GOG
(1953 - United Artists) Richard Egan, Constance Dowling
One Sheet: $30 - $50   *Graven Images, pg. 180.*

GO-GETTER, THE
(1937 - Warner Bros.) George Brent, Anita Louise
One Sheet: $75 - $125

GOGGLE FISHING BEAR
(1947 - MGM) Barney Bear
One Sheet: $300 - $650   *Cartoon. Full color stone litho. Cartoon Movie Posters #258.*

GOIN' ALL THE WAY
(1982 - -) Deborah Van Rhyn, Dan Waldman
One Sheet: $3 - $5

GOIN' COCONUTS
(1978 - Osmond) Donny & Marie Osmond, Kenneth Mars
One Sheet: $15 - $25

GOIN' DOWN THE ROAD
(1970 - Chevron) Doug McGrath, Paul Bradley
One Sheet: $3 - $5

GOIN' HOME
(1976 - Prentiss) Todd Christiansen
One Sheet: $3 - $5

GOIN' SOUTH
(1978 - Paramount) Jack Nicholson, Mary Steenburgen, John Belushi
One Sheet: $15 - $25

GOIN' TO TOWN
(1935 - Paramount) Mae West, Paul Cavanagh
One Sheet: $800 - $1,500   *One Sheet(Celebrate Mae Day):$300-$500.*

GOIN' TO TOWN
(1944 - RKO) Lum (Chester Lauck), Abner (Norris Goff)
One Sheet: $75 - $125

GOING APE
(1981 - Paramount) Tony Danza, Danny Devito
One Sheet: $3 - $5

GOING BANANAS
(1988 - -) Dom DeLuise, Jimmy Walker
One Sheet: $3 - $5

GOING BERSERK
(1983 - Universal) John Candy, Joe Flaherty, Eugene Levy
One Sheet: $3 - $5

GOING BYE-BYE
(1934 - MGM) Stan Laurel, Oliver Hardy
One Sheet: $2,200 - $3,500

GOING CROOKED
(1926 - Fox) Bessie Love, Oscar Shaw
One Sheet: $350 - $750

GOING HIGHBROW
(1935 - Warner Bros.) Guy Kibbee, ZaSu Pitts
One Sheet: $100 - $200

GOING HOLLYWOOD
(1933 - MGM) Bing Crosby, Marion Davies
One Sheet: $600 - $1,000

GOING HOME
(1971 - MGM) Robert Mitchum, Brenda Vaccaro
One Sheet: $10 - $20

GOING IN STYLE
(1979 - Warner Bros.) George Burns, Art Carney
One Sheet: $7 - $15

GOING MY WAY
(1944 - Paramount) Bing Crosby, Rise Stevens
One Sheet: $150 - $300 *Academy Award: Best Picture, Best Actor, Best Direction(Leo McCarey). Academy Award Movie Posters #93-#95 & #97.*

GOING PLACES
(1938 - Warner Bros.) Dick Powell, Anita Louise, Louis Armstrong, Ronald Reagan
One Sheet: $100 - $200

One Sheet

GOING SPANISH
(1934 - Educational) Bob Hope, Leah Ray
One Sheet: $125 - $250

GOING STEADY
(1958 - Columbia) Molly Bee, Alan Reed Jr.
One Sheet: $10 - $20

GOING STRAIGHT
(1916 - -) Norma Talmadge
One Sheet: $250 - $600

GOING TO CONGRESS
(1924 - Pathe) Will Rogers
One Sheet: $600 - $1,000

GOING TO GLORY-COME TO SEE JESUS
(1946 - -) Royal Gospel Choir
One Sheet: $125 - $250 *Black cast.*

GOING TO PRESS
(1942 - MGM) Our Gang
One Sheet: $250 - $600

GOING UNDERCOVER
(1988 - -) Chris Lemmon, Jean Simmons
One Sheet: $2 - $3

GOING UP
(1923 - Encore) Douglas MacLean, Hallam Cooley
One Sheet: $200 - $400

GOING WILD
(1930 - First National) Joe E. Brown, Walter Pidgeon
One Sheet: $150 - $300

GOLD
(1932 - Majestic) Jack Hoxie, Alice Day

One Sheet: $150 - $300

GOLD
(1974 - Allied Artists) Roger Moore, Susannah York
One Sheet: $7 - $15

GOLD AND GRIT
(1925 - Weiss) Buddy Roosevelt
One Sheet: $75 - $150

GOLD AND THE GIRL
(1925 - Fox) Buck Jones, Elinor Fair
One Sheet: $600 - $1,000 *Cowboy Movie Posters #49.*

GOLD DIGGERS IN PARIS
(1938 - Warner Bros.) Rudy Vallee, Rosemary Lane
One Sheet: $100 - $200

GOLD DIGGERS OF 1933
(1933 - Warner Bros.) Ginger Rogers, Joan Blondell, Ruby Keeler, Dick Powell
One Sheet: $4,000 - $6,000

GOLD DIGGERS OF 1935
(1935 - First National) Dick Powell, Adolphe Menjou
One Sheet: $1,600 - $2,500

GOLD DIGGERS OF 1935/FOOTLIGHT PARADE
(1970R - Warner Bros.) Dick Powell, Adolphe Menjou/James Cagney, Joan Blondell
One Sheet: $15 - $35 *Re-release double feature poster.*

GOLD DIGGERS OF 1937
(1937 - First National) Dick Powell, Joan Blondell
One Sheet: $100 - $200

GOLD DIGGERS OF BROADWAY
(1929 - Warner Bros.) Nancy Welford, Conway Tearle
One Sheet: $600 - $1,000

GOLD DIGGERS: THE SECRET OF BEAR MOUNTAIN
(1995 - Universal) Christina Ricci, Anna Chlumsky
One Sheet: $4 - $8

GOLD DUST GERTIE
(1931 - Warner Bros.) Olsen and Johnson
One Sheet: $125 - $250

GOLD FEVER
(1952 - Monogram) John Calvert, Ralph Morgan
One Sheet: $15 - $30

GOLD FOR THE CAESARS
(1964 - MGM) Jeffrey Hunter, Mylene Demongeot
One Sheet: $5 - $10

GOLD GHOST, THE
(1934 - -) -
One Sheet: $75 - $125

GOLD GUITAR, THE
(1966 - Craddock) Del Reeves
One Sheet: $30 - $50 *Country musical.*

GOLD IS WHERE YOU FIND IT
(1938 - Warner Bros.) George Brent, Claude Rains, Olivia De Havilland
One Sheet: $75 - $150

GOLD MINE IN THE SKY
(1938 - Republic) Gene Autry, Carol Hughes
One Sheet: $250 - $500

GOLD MINE IN THE SKY
(1942R - Republic) Gene Autry, Carol Hughes
One Sheet: $75 - $150 *Re-release. Full color.*

GOLD OF NAPLES, THE
(1954 - -) Sophia Loren, Vittorio De Sica
One Sheet: $30 - $50

GOLD OF THE DESERT
(1918 - Diamond Dot) -
One Sheet: $150 - $300

GOLD OF THE SEVEN SAINTS
(1961 - Warner Bros.) Clint Walker, Roger Moore
One Sheet: $15 - $25

GOLD RACKET, THE
(1936 - Grand National) Conrad Nagel, Eleanor Hunt
One Sheet: $75 - $150

GOLD RAIDERS, THE
(1951 - United Artists) George O'Brien, Sheila Ryan, The Three Stooges (Shemp)
One Sheet: $200 - $450 *Price assumes stooges not pictured. Lobby Card(Stooges scene):$100-$200.*

GOLD RUSH, THE
(1925 - United Artists) Charlie Chaplin, Mac Swain
One Sheet: $45,000 - $60,000 *One Sheet shows Chaplin and woman in red standing. Poster is not dated and does not have a releasing company emblem.*

One Sheet

GOLD RUSH, THE
(1942 - United Artists) Charlie Chaplin
One Sheet: $125 - $250 *Edited from earlier (1925) film with narration by Chaplin.*

GOLD RUSH MAISIE
(1947 - MGM) Ann Sothern, Lee Bowman, Virginia Weidler
One Sheet: $30 - $50

GOLD STRIKE
(1950 - Universal) -
One Sheet: $10 - $20

GOLDBERGS, THE
(1950 - Paramount) Gertrude Berg, Barbara Rush
One Sheet: $15 - $35

GOLDEN AGE OF COMEDY, THE
(1958 - Ro-Corp) Laurel and Hardy, Ben Turpin
One Sheet: $10 - $20

GOLDEN ARROW, THE
(1936 - First National) Bette Davis, George Brent
One Sheet: $2,500 - $4,000

GOLDEN ARROW, THE
(1964 - MGM) Tab Hunter, Rosanna Podesta
One Sheet: $15 - $25

GOLDEN BED, THE
(1925 - Paramount) Lillian Rich, Vera Reynolds, Dir: Cecil B. DeMille
One Sheet: $250 - $500

GOLDEN BLADE, THE
(1953 - Universal) Rock Hudson, Piper Laurie
One Sheet: $15 - $25

GOLDEN BOX, THE
(1970 - Hollywood Cinema) Marsha Jordan
One Sheet: $3 - $5

GOLDEN BOY
(1939 - Columbia) Barbara Stanwyck, Adolphe Menjou, William Holden
One Sheet: $600 - $1,000 *Sports Movie Posters #144.*

GOLDEN BOY
(1947R - Columbia) Barbara Stanwyck, Adolphe Menjou, William Holden
One Sheet: $50 - $100 *Re-release.*

GOLDEN CAGE, THE
(1933 - MGM) Anne Grey
One Sheet: $100 - $200

GOLDEN CALF, THE
(1930 - Fox) Jack Mulhall, Sue Carol
One Sheet: $150 - $300

GOLDEN CHILD, THE
(1986 - Paramount) Eddie Murphy, Charlotte Lewis
One Sheet: $5 - $10

GOLDEN DAWN
(1930 - Warner Bros.) Walter Woolf, Vivienne Segal
One Sheet: $100 - $200

GOLDEN DREAMS
(1922 - Goldwyn) Claire Adams, Carl Gantvoort, Rose Dione
One Sheet: $200 - $400

GOLDEN EARRINGS
(1947 - Paramount) Ray Milland, Marlene Dietrich
One Sheet: $125 - $250

GOLDEN EYE, THE
(1948 - Monogram) Roland Winters, Mantan Moreland
One Sheet: $75 - $150 *Charlie Chan series.*

GOLDEN FLEECING, THE
(1940 - MGM) Lew Ayres, Rita Johnson, Lloyd Nolan
One Sheet: $50 - $100

GOLDEN GATE
(1994 - Samuel Goldwyn) Matt Dillon, Joan Chen
One Sheet: $5 - $10

GOLDEN GIRL
(1952 - 20th Century Fox) Mitzi Gaynor, Dale Robertson
One Sheet: $15 - $35

GOLDEN GLOVES
(1940 - Paramount) Jean Cagney, Richard Denning
One Sheet: $75 - $150 *Sports (Boxing).*

GOLDEN GLOVES STORY, THE
(1950 - Eagle-Lion) James Dunn, Dewey Martin
One Sheet: $50 - $100 *Sports (Boxing). Sports Movie Posters #150.*

GOLDEN HARVEST
(1932 - Paramount) Richard Arlen, Chester Morris
One Sheet: $125 - $250

GOLDEN HAWK, THE
(1952 - Columbia) Sterling Hayden, Rhonda Fleming
One Sheet: $40 - $75

GOLDEN HOOFS
(1941 - 20th Century Fox) Jane Withers, Charles "Buddy" Rogers
One Sheet: $75 - $150

GOLDEN HORDE, THE
(1951 - Universal) Ann Blyth, David Farrar
One Sheet: $15 - $25

GOLDEN IDOL, THE
(1954 - Allied Artists) Johnny Sheffield
One Sheet: $15 - $35

GOLDEN MADONNA, THE
(1949 - Monogram) Phyllis Calvert, Michael Rennie
One Sheet: $30 - $50

GOLDEN MASK, THE
(1952 - United Artists) Van Heflin, Wanda Hendrix
One Sheet: $10 - $20

GOLDEN MISTRESS, THE
(1954 - United Artists) John Agar, Rosemarie Bowe
One Sheet: $15 - $25

GOLDEN NEEDLES
(1974 - AIP) Joe Don Baker, Elizabeth Ashley
One Sheet: $5 - $10

GOLDEN RENDEZVOUS
(1977 - Film Trust) Richard Harris, David Janssen
One Sheet: $5 - $10

GOLDEN SALAMANDER
(1950 - General) Trevor Howard, Herbert Lom
One Sheet: $15 - $25

GOLDEN SEAL, THE

(1983 - New Realm) Steve Railsback, Michael Beck
One Sheet: $3 - $5

GOLDEN STALLION, THE
(1927 - Levine) "Lefty" Flynn, Joe Bonomo
One Sheet: $250 - $500   *Serial. Western. 12 Chapters.*

GOLDEN STALLION, THE
(1949 - Republic) Roy Rogers, Dale Evans
One Sheet: $100 - $200

GOLDEN STALLION, THE
(1956R - Republic) Roy Rogers, Dale Evans
One Sheet: $30 - $50   *Re-release.*

GOLDEN THOUGHT, THE
(1916 - Selig) Tom Mix
One Sheet: $1,300 - $2,000

GOLDEN TRAIL, THE
(1940 - Monogram) Tex Ritter, Slim Andrews
One Sheet: $75 - $150

GOLDEN TWENTIES, THE
(1949 - Time Inc.) Al Jolson, Rudolph Valentino
One Sheet: $30 - $50

GOLDEN VOYAGE OF SINBAD, THE
(1973 - Columbia) John Phillip Law, Caroline Munro
One Sheet: $15 - $25

GOLDEN WEST, THE
(1932 - Fox) George O'Brien, Janet Chandler
One Sheet: $500 - $800   *Cowboy Movie Posters # 116.*

GOLDENEYE
(1995 - MGM/UA) Pierce Brosnan, Famke Janssen
One Sheet: $10 - $20   *Advance Style (double-sided laminated version with either November or Christmas date): $30-$60.*

One Sheet (Advance)

GOLDENGIRL
(1979 - Avco/Embassy) Susan Anton, James Coburn
One Sheet: $5 - $10

GOLDENROD
(1977 - -) Tony LoBianco, Gloria Carlin
One Sheet: $3 - $5

GOLDFINGER
(1964 - United Artists) Sean Connery, Gert Frobe
One Sheet: $250 - $500   *Price is for either style one sheet.*

One Sheet

GOLDFINGER
(1980R - United Artists) Sean Connery, Gert Frobe

One Sheet: $30 - $50   *Re-release.*

GOLDFINGER/DR. NO
(1972R - United Artists) Sean Connery, Gert Frobe/Sean Connery, Ursula Andress
One Sheet: $15 - $30   *Re-release double feature poster.*

GOLDIE
(1931 - Fox) Spencer Tracy, Jean Harlow
One Sheet: $1,900 - $3,000

GOLDIE GETS ALONG
(1933 - RKO) Lili Damita, Charles Morton
One Sheet: $250 - $500

GOLDILOCKS AND THE THREE BEARS
(1947R - MGM) -
One Sheet: $200 - $400   *Re-release. Cartoon. Full color stone litho.*

GOLDSTEIN
(1965 - Montrose) Lou Gilbert, Ellen Madison
One Sheet: $5 - $10

GOLDTOWN GHOST RIDERS
(1953 - Columbia) Gene Autry, Smiley Burnette
One Sheet: $40 - $75

GOLDWYN BRAY COMIC
(1919 - Goldwyn) Koko the Clown
One Sheet: $3,500 - $5,000   *Cartoon. Full color stone litho. Stock poster. Max Fleischer worked for Bray Studios at this time. Early Koko the Clown. Cartoon MoviePosters #2.*

GOLDWYN FOLLIES, THE
(1938 - Samuel Goldwyn) Adolphe Menjou, Andrea Leeds
One Sheet: $150 - $350

GOLDWYN FOLLIES, THE
(1944R - Samuel Goldwyn) Adolphe Menjou, Andrea Leeds
One Sheet: $30 - $50   *Re-release.*

GOLEM, THE
(1920 - UFA) Paul Wegener, Albert Steinruck
One Sheet: $19,000 - $30,000   *German. Price is for original German poster. Graven Images, pg. 8, 18.*

GOLF SPECIALIST, THE
(1930 - RKO) W.C. Fields
One Sheet: $3,500 - $5,000   *Sports (Golf). Comedy short of classic vaudeville sketch.*

GOLIATH AGAINST THE GIANTS
(1963 - Medallion) Brad Harris, Fernando Rey
One Sheet: $15 - $35

GOLIATH AND THE BARBARIANS
(1959 - AIP) Steve Reeves, Chelo Alonso
One Sheet: $15 - $35

GOLIATH AND THE DRAGON
(1960 - AIP) Mark Forest, Broderick Crawford
One Sheet: $15 - $35

GOLIATH AND THE SINS OF BABYLON
(1963 - AIP) Mark Forest, Jose Greci
One Sheet: $15 - $35

GOLIATH AND THE VAMPIRES
(1964 - AIP) Gordon Scott, Gianna Maria Canale
One Sheet: $15 - $35

GOLIATH AWAITS
(1981 - -) Mark Harmon, Christopher Lee, Emma Samms
One Sheet: $5 - $10

GONE ARE THE DAYS
(1963 - Hammer) Ruby Dee, Ossie Davis
One Sheet: $40 - $75   *Black cast. AKA: THE MAN FROM C.O.T.T.O.N. Separate Cinema, pg. 75.*

GONE HARLEM
(1939 - -) Ethel Moses
One Sheet: $500 - $800   *Black cast.*

GONE IN 60 SECONDS
(1974 - HBH) H. B. Halicki, Parnelli Jones
One Sheet: $10 - $20   *Auto theft.*

GONE WITH THE WIND
(1939 - MGM) Clark Gable, Vivien Leigh
One Sheet: $5,000 - $8,000   *Academy Award: Best Picture, Actress(Leigh), Direction(Victor Fleming). Art by Richard Seguso. Price is for "frame" style onesheet. One Sheet (Scarlett running through streets of burning*

Atlanta):$8,000-$12,000.

One Sheet

GONE WITH THE WIND
(1940R - MGM) Clark Gable, Vivian Leigh
One Sheet: $1,600 - $2,500   *Re-release. Roadshow poster. "Nothing Cut but the Price."*

GONE WITH THE WIND
(1943R - MGM) Clark Gable, Vivian Leigh
One Sheet: $800 - $1,500   *Re-release.*

GONE WITH THE WIND
(1948R - MGM) Clark Gable, Vivian Leigh
One Sheet: $500 - $900   *Re-release. Poster is only stone litho available on this title.*

GONE WITH THE WIND
(1954R - MGM) Clark Gable, Vivien Leigh
One Sheet: $250 - $500   *Re-release.*

GONE WITH THE WIND
(1961R - MGM) Clark Gable, Vivien Leigh
One Sheet: $100 - $200   *Re-release.*

GONE WITH THE WIND
(1967R - MGM) Clark Gable, Vivien Leigh
One Sheet: $75 - $150   *Re-release. Same image as the 1968R one sheet but on flat stock.*

GONE WITH THE WIND
(1968R - MGM) Clark Gable, Vivien Leigh
One Sheet: $75 - $150   *Re-release.*

GONE WITH THE WIND
(1974R - MGM) Clark Gable, Vivien Leigh
One Sheet: $30 - $50   *Re-release.*

GONE WITH THE WIND
(1980R - MGM) Clark Gable, Vivien Leigh
One Sheet: $15 - $30   *Re-release.*

GONE WITH THE WIND
(1989R - MGM) Clark Gable, Vivien Leigh
One Sheet: $15 - $30   *Re-release. 50th Anniversary.*

GONG SHOW MOVIE, THE
(1980 - Universal) Chuck Barris, Robin Altman
One Sheet: $5 - $10   *TV tie-in.*

GONKS GO BEAT
(1965 - Titan) British Rock & Roll bands
One Sheet: $40 - $80   *Rock 'n' Roll.*

GONZALES MYSTERY
(1921 - -) -
One Sheet: $250 - $600

GOOD BAD BOYS
(193? - MGM) Our Gang
One Sheet: $600 - $1,000

GOOD BAD GIRL, THE
(1931 - Columbia) Mae Clarke, James Hall
One Sheet: $200 - $400

GOOD BAD MAN, THE
(1916 - Triangle) Douglas Fairbanks
One Sheet: $600 - $1,000

GOOD BEGINNING, THE
(1954 - Pathe) John Frazer, Lana Morris
One Sheet: $10 - $20

GOOD COMPANIONS, THE
(1933 - Fox) Jessie Matthews, Edmund Gwenn, John Gielgud
One Sheet: $100 - $200

GOOD COMPANIONS, THE
(1957 - Associated British-Pathe) Eric Portman, Hugh Griffith
One Sheet: $5 - $10

GOOD DAME
(1934 - Paramount) Sylvia Sydney, Fredric March
One Sheet: $500 - $800

GOOD DAY FOR A HANGING
(1958 - Columbia) Fred MacMurray, Maggie Hayes
One Sheet: $15 - $25

GOOD DIE YOUNG, THE
(1954 - United Artists) Richard Basehart, Gloria Grahame
One Sheet: $15 - $30

GOOD EARTH, THE
(1937 - MGM) Paul Muni, Luise Rainer
One Sheet: $600 - $1,000   *Academy Award: Best Actress (Rainer, her 2nd year in a row). Academy Award Movie Posters #54.*

GOOD EARTH, THE
(1962R - MGM) Paul Muni, Luise Rainer
One Sheet: $15 - $25   *Re-release.*

GOOD FAIRY, THE
(1935 - Universal) Margaret Sullavan, Herbert Marshall
One Sheet: $150 - $300

GOOD FATHER, THE
(1987 - -) Anthony Hopkins, Jim Broadbert, Harriet Walter
One Sheet: $5 - $10

GOOD FELLOWS, THE
(1943 - Paramount) Cecil Kellaway, Helen Walker
One Sheet: $50 - $100

GOOD GIRLS BEWARE
(1960 - -) -
One Sheet: $20 - $40

GOOD GIRLS GO TO PARIS
(1939 - Columbia) Melvyn Douglas, Joan Blondell
One Sheet: $75 - $150

GOOD GUYS AND THE BAD GUYS, THE
(1969 - Warner Bros.) Robert Mitchum, George Kennedy, Tina Louise
One Sheet: $15 - $30

GOOD GUYS WEAR BLACK
(1978 - MarVista) Chuck Norris, Anne Archer, Dana Andrews
One Sheet: $7 - $15

GOOD HUMOR MAN, THE
(1950 - Columbia) Jack Carson, Lola Albright
One Sheet: $15 - $35

GOOD INTENTIONS
(1930 - Fox) Edmund Lowe, Marguerite Churchill
One Sheet: $125 - $250

GOOD LUCK, MR. YATES
(1943 - Columbia) Claire Trevor, Jess Barker
One Sheet: $40 - $75

GOOD MAN IN AFRICA, A
(1994 - Gramercy) Colin Friels, Sean Connery, John Lithgow
One Sheet: $5 - $10

GOOD MEN AND TRUE
(1922 - R-C) Harry Carey, Vola Vale, Noah Beery
One Sheet: $200 - $400

GOOD MORNING, JUDGE
(1943 - Universal) Dennis O'Keefe, Louise Albritton
One Sheet: $50 - $100

GOOD MORNING, MISS DOVE
(1955 - 20th Century Fox) Jennifer Jones, Robert Stack
One Sheet: $15 - $30

GOOD MORNING, SHERIFF
(1930 - Educational) -
One Sheet: $50 - $100

GOOD MORNING VIETNAM
(1987 - Touchstone) Robin Williams, Forest Whitaker
One Sheet: $5 - $10

GOOD MORNING...AND GOODBYE
(1967 - Eve) Don Johnson, Alaina Capri, Dir:

Russ Meyer
One Sheet: $15 - $35

GOOD MOTHER, THE
(1988 - Touchstone) Diane Keaton, Liam Neeson
One Sheet: $3 - $5

GOOD NEIGHBOR SAM
(1964 - Columbia) Jack Lemmon, Romy Schneider
One Sheet: $15 - $25

GOOD NEWS
(1930 - MGM) Mary Lawlor, Stanley Smith
One Sheet: $150 - $300

GOOD NEWS
(1947 - MGM) June Allyson, Peter Lawford
One Sheet: $100 - $200

GOOD OLD DAYS, THE
(1923 - Pathe) Animated by Paul Terry
One Sheet: $250 - $600 *Cartoon. An Aesop's Fables film. Cartoon Movie Posters #18.*

GOOD OLD IRISH TUNES
(1940 - 20th Century Fox) Terry-toons
One Sheet: $100 - $200 *Cartoon. Full color stone litho. Stock poster with inset title.*

GOOD OLD SOAK, THE
(1937 - MGM) Wallace Beery, Betty Furness
One Sheet: $50 - $100

GOOD OLD SUMMER TIME, THE
(1913 - Kalem) -
One Sheet: $200 - $400

GOOD REFERENCES
(1920 - -) Constance Talmadge
One Sheet: $250 - $500

One Sheet

GOOD SAM
(1948 - RKO) Gary Cooper, Ann Sheridan
One Sheet: $40 - $75

GOOD SON, THE
(1993 - 20th Century Fox) Macaulay Culkin, Elijah Wood
One Sheet: $3 - $5 *Advance (rare due to recall):$20-$30.*

GOOD SPORT
(1931 - Fox) Linda Watkins, John Boles
One Sheet: $150 - $300

GOOD, THE BAD, AND THE SUB HUMANOID, THE
(199? - -) -
One Sheet: $4 - $8

GOOD, THE BAD AND THE UGLY, THE
(1967 - United Artists) Clint Eastwood, Eli Wallach, Lee Van Cleef
One Sheet: $200 - $400 *Spaghetti Western. Cowboy Movie Posters #316. Italian 34" x 55": $800.*

GOOD, THE BAD AND THE UGLY, THE
(1980R - United Artists) Clint Eastwood, Eli Wallach, Lee Van Cleef
One Sheet: $30 - $50 *Re-release. Spaghetti Western.*

GOOD, THE BAD AND THE UGLY, THE/HANG 'EM HIGH
(1969R - United Artists) Clint Eastwood, Eli Wallach, Lee Van Cleef/Clint Eastwood
One Sheet: $40 - $75 *Re-release double feature poster.*

GOOD TIME FOR A DIME, A
(1941 - RKO/Disney) Donald Duck

One Sheet: $4,000 - $6,000 *Cartoon. Full color. Cartoon Movie Posters #162.*

GOOD TIME GIRL
(1950 - Eagle-Lion) Jean Kent, Dennis Price
One Sheet: $20 - $40

GOOD TIMES
(1967 - Columbia) Sonny and Cher
One Sheet: $30 - $50 *Rock 'n' Roll.*

GOOD WIFE, THE
(1987 - -) Rachel Ward, Bryan Brown
One Sheet: $3 - $5

GOODBYE AGAIN
(1933 - First National) Warren William, Joan Blondell
One Sheet: $100 - $200

GOODBYE AGAIN
(1961 - United Artists) Ingrid Bergman, Yves Montand
One Sheet: $15 - $30

GOODBYE BILL
(1918 - Paramount) Shirley Mason, Ernest Truex
One Sheet: $250 - $500

GOODBYE BROADWAY
(1938 - Universal) Alice Brady, Charles Winninger
One Sheet: $125 - $250

GOODBYE CHARLIE
(1964 - 20th Century Fox) Tony Curtis, Debbie Reynolds
One Sheet: $10 - $20 *Sex change film.*

GOODBYE COLUMBUS
(1969 - Paramount) Richard Benjamin, Ali MacGraw, Jack Klugman
One Sheet: $15 - $25

GOODBYE GEMINI
(1970 - Cinerama) Judy Geeson, Martin Potter
One Sheet: $2 - $3

GOODBYE GIRL, THE
(1977 - MGM/Warner Bros.) Richard Dreyfuss, Marsha Mason
One Sheet: $7 - $15 *Academy Award: Best Actor(Dreyfuss). Academy Award Movie Posters #298.*

GOODBYE KISS, THE
(1928 - First National) Johnny Burke, Sally Eilers
One Sheet: $250 - $500

GOODBYE LOVE
(1933 - RKO) Charles Ruggles, Sidney Blackmer
One Sheet: $100 - $200

GOODBYE MR. CHIPS
(1939 - MGM) Robert Donat, Greer Garson
One Sheet: $200 - $400 *Price is for style D one sheet. Other styles 50% less. Acadamy Award Movie Posters #65.*

GOODBYE MR. CHIPS
(1969 - MGM) Peter O'Toole, Petula Clark, Sian Phillips
One Sheet: $15 - $30

GOODBYE MY FANCY
(1951 - Warner Bros.) Joan Crawford, Frank Lovejoy, Robert Young
One Sheet: $30 - $60

GOODBYE, MY LADY
(1956 - Warner Bros.) Walter Brennan, Phil Harris
One Sheet: $15 - $25

GOODBYE PEOPLE, THE
(1984 - Embassy) Martin Balsam, Judd Hirsch
One Sheet: $5 - $10

GOODFELLAS
(1990 - Warner Bros.) Robert De Niro, Joe Pesci
One Sheet: $20 - $40 *Academy Award Movie Posters #374.*

GOODNIGHT SWEETHEART
(1944 - Republic) Robert Livingston, Ruth Terry
One Sheet: $30 - $50

GOOF ON THE ROOF
(1953 - Columbia) The Three Stooges (Shemp)

One Sheet: $150 - $350 *Comedy short. Duotone.*

GOOFS AND SADDLES
(1937 - Columbia) Three Stooges (Curly)
One Sheet: $8,500 - $14,000 *Comedy short.*

GOOFY AGE, THE
(1924 - Pathe) Glenn Tryon
One Sheet: $200 - $400

GOOFY, ALSO
(1942 - RKO/Disney) Goofy
One Sheet: $200 - $400 *Cartoon. Stock poster, 24"x25".*

GOOFY AND WILBUR
(1939 - RKO) Goofy
One Sheet: $7,500 - $12,000 *Cartoon. First all-Goofy cartoon. Cartoon Movie Posters #181.*

GOOFY AND WILBUR
(1948R - RKO/Disney) Goofy
One Sheet: $200 - $400 *Re-release. Cartoon. Duotone.*

GOOFY GYMNASTICS
(1948 - RKO/Disney) Goofy
One Sheet: $250 - $500 *Cartoon.*

GOOFY MOVIE, A
(1995 - Buena Vista) Goofy, Max
One Sheet: $5 - $10 *Cartoon.*

One Sheet

GOOFY'S GLIDER
(1940 - RKO/Disney) Goofy
One Sheet: $1,900 - $3,000 *Cartoon. The Disney Poster, pg. 76.*

GOONIES, THE
(1985 - Warner Bros.) Sean Astin, Josh Brolin
One Sheet: $5 - $10

GOOSE AND THE GANDER, THE
(1935 - First National) Kay Francis, George Brent
One Sheet: $100 - $200

GOOSE FLIES HIGH, THE
(1937 - 20th Century Fox) Terry-toons
One Sheet: $100 - $200 *Cartoon. Full color stone litho. Stock poster with inset of title.*

GOOSE HANGS HIGH, THE
(1925 - Paramount) Constance Bennett, Myrtle Stedman
One Sheet: $100 - $200

GOOSE STEP, THE
(1939 - PRC) Roland Drew, Steffi Duna, Alan Ladd
One Sheet: $50 - $100

GOOSE WOMAN, THE
(1925 - Universal) Louise Dresser, Jack Pickford
One Sheet: $300 - $700

GORATH
(1964 - Columbia) Ryo Ikebe, Akihiko Hirata
One Sheet: $30 - $50

GORDON OF GHOST CITY
(1933 - Universal) Buck Jones, Madge Bellamy
One Sheet: $500 - $800 *Serial. 12 Episodes.*

GORDON'S WAR
(1973 - 20th Century Fox) Paul Winfield, Carl Lee, Dir: Ossie Davis
One Sheet: $15 - $25 *Blaxploitation.*

GORE GORE GIRLS, THE
(1972 - Lewis) -

One Sheet: $15 - $35

GORGEOUS HUSSY, THE
(1936 - MGM) Joan Crawford, Robert Taylor, James Stewart
One Sheet: $200 - $400

GORGO
(1961 - MGM) Bill Travers, William Sylvester
One Sheet: $75 - $150 *Graven Images, pg. 224.*

One Sheet

GORGON, THE
(1965 - Columbia) Peter Cushing, Christopher Lee
One Sheet: $30 - $50

GORGON CASE, THE
(196? - Film Polski) -
One Sheet: $30 - $50 *Polish.*

GORGON/CURSE OF THE MUMMY'S TOMB
(1965 - Columbia) -
One Sheet: $30 - $50 *Double feature poster.*

GORILLA, THE
(1927 - First National) Charlie Murray, Fred Kelsey
One Sheet: $600 - $1,000 *Graven Images, pg. 31.*

GORILLA, THE
(1930 - First National) Lila Lee, Walter Pidgeon
One Sheet: $500 - $800

GORILLA, THE
(1939 - 20th Century Fox) The Ritz Brothers, Patsy Kelly, Bela Lugosi
One Sheet: $150 - $350

One Sheet

GORILLA AT LARGE
(1954 - 20th Century Fox) Cameron Mitchell, Anne Bancroft
One Sheet: $50 - $100

GORILLA GANG, THE
(1973 - Saxton) -
One Sheet: $3 - $5

GORILLA HUNT, THE
(1939 - Columbia) Scrappy
One Sheet: $700 - $1,200 *Cartoon.*

GORILLA MAN, THE
(1943 - Warner Bros.) John Loder, Ruth Ford
One Sheet: $75 - $125

GORILLA SHIP, THE
(1932 - Mayfair) Ralph Ince, Wheeler Oakman
One Sheet: $75 - $125

GORILLAS IN THE MIST
(1988 - Universal) Sigourney Weaver, Bryan

Brown, Julie Harris
One Sheet:　$5 - $10

GORKY PARK
(1983 - Orion) William Hurt, Lee Marvin
One Sheet:　$5 - $10

GORP
(1980 - AIP) Michael Lembeck, Dennis Quaid
One Sheet:　$3 - $5

GOSPEL ACCORDING TO VIC, THE
(1985 - -) Tom Conti, Helen Mirren
One Sheet:　$3 - $5

GOSPEL ROAD, THE
(1973 - 20th Century Fox) Robert Elfstrom, June Carter Cash
One Sheet:　$15 - $25

GOSSIPY PLUMBER, THE
(1930 - RKO Pathe Comedy) Arthur Wanzer, Vivian Oakland, Al Alt
One Sheet:　$200 - $400

GOT WHAT SHE WANTED
(1930 - Tiffany) Betty Compson, Lee Tracy
One Sheet:　$150 - $300

GOTCHA!
(1985 - -) Anthony Edwards, Linda Fiorentino
One Sheet:　$3 - $5

GOTHIC
(1987 - Virgin Visions) Gabriel Byrne, Natasha Richardson, Julian Sands
One Sheet:　$15 - $25

GOUCHO, THE
(1927 - United Artists) Douglas Fairbanks
One Sheet:　$1,900 - $3,000

GOVERNMENT AGENTS VS. PHANTOM LEGION
(1951 - Republic) Walter Reed, Mary Ellen Kay
One Sheet:　$40 - $75　　*Serial. 12 Chapters.*

GOVERNMENT GIRL
(1943 - RKO) Olivia de Havilland, Sonny Tufts
One Sheet:　$75 - $125

GRACE QUIGLEY
(1985 - Cannon) Katherine Hepburn, Nick Nolte
One Sheet:　$7 - $15

GRACIE ALLEN MURDER CASE, THE
(1939 - Paramount) Gracie Allen, Warren William, Kent Taylor
One Sheet:　$250 - $600

GRADUATE, THE
(1967 - Embassy) Anne Bancroft, Dustin Hoffman
One Sheet:　$150 - $350　　*Academy Award: Best Direction(Mike Nichols). Price is for Style A (leg style). Style B (sketch style):$300-$600. Academy AwardsStyle: $40-$75. Academy Award Movie Posters #239 & #240.*

GRADUATE, THE
(1972R - Embassy) Anne Bancroft, Dustin Hoffman
One Sheet:　$40 - $75　　*Re-release.*

GRADUATION DAY
(1981 - Scope) Christopher George, Patch MacKenzie
One Sheet:　$3 - $5

GRAFFITI BRIDGE
(1990 - Warner Bros.) Prince, Morris Day, Tevin Campbell
One Sheet:　$15 - $25　　*Rock 'n' Roll.*

GRAFT
(1931 - Universal) Regis Toomey, Sue Carol, Boris Karloff
One Sheet:　$250 - $500

GRAND CANARY
(1934 - Fox) Warner Baxter, H. B. Warner
One Sheet:　$150 - $300

GRAND CANYON
(1949 - Screen Guild) Richard Arlen, Mary Beth Hughes
One Sheet:　$20 - $40

GRAND CANYON
(1958 - Disney) -
One Sheet:　$40 - $75　　*Documentary. Academy Award: Best Short Subject.*

GRAND CANYON
(1991 - 20th Century Fox) Steve Martin, Danny Glover, Kevin Kline
One Sheet:　$5 - $10

GRAND CANYON TRAIL
(1948 - Republic) Roy Rogers, Jane Frazee
One Sheet:　$100 - $200

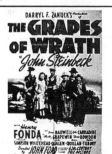
One Sheet

GRAND CENTRAL MURDER
(1942 - MGM) Van Heflin, Patricia Dane
One Sheet:　$100 - $200

GRAND EXIT
(1935 - Columbia) Ann Sothern, Edmund Lowe
One Sheet:　$125 - $250

GRAND HOTEL
(1932 - MGM) Greta Garbo, John Barrymore, Lionel Barrymore, Joan Crawford
One Sheet:　$10,000 - $15,000　*Academy Award: Best Picture. Academy Award Movie Posters #23.*

GRAND HOTEL
(1962R - MGM) Greta Garbo, John Barrymore, Lionel Barrymore, Joan Crawford
One Sheet:　$30 - $50　　*Re-release. Duotone.*

GRAND ILLUSION
(1938 - World) Jean Gabin, Erich von Stroheim
One Sheet:　$75 - $150

GRAND JURY
(1936 - RKO) Fred Stone, Louise Latimer
One Sheet:　$100 - $200

GRAND JURY SECRETS
(1939 - Paramount) John Howard, Gail Patrick
One Sheet:　$75 - $150

GRAND OLD GIRL
(1935 - RKO) Fred MacMurray, May Robson
One Sheet:　$100 - $200

GRAND OLE OPRY
(1940 - Republic) Weaver Bros. and Elviry, Allan Lane, Roy Acuff
One Sheet:　$75 - $150　　*Country musical.*

GRAND PARADE, THE
(1930 - Pathe) Helen Twelvetrees, Fred Scott
One Sheet:　$150 - $300

GRAND PRIX
(1934 - Columbia) John Stuart, Gillian Sande
One Sheet:　$200 - $400　　*Sports (Auto racing).*

GRAND PRIX
(1966 - MGM) James Garner, Eva Marie Saint
One Sheet:　$30 - $50　　*Sports (Auto racing). "Cinerama" One Sheet: $125-$250. Sports Movie Posters #18.*

GRAND SLAM
(1933 - First National) Loretta Young, Paul Lukas
One Sheet:　$250 - $600

GRAND SLAM
(1968 - Paramount) Edward G. Robinson, Janet Leigh
One Sheet:　$7 - $15

GRAND THEFT AUTO
(1977 - New World) Ron Howard, Nancy Morgan, Dir: Ron Howard
One Sheet:　$15 - $25

GRANDMA'S BOY
(1922 - Pathe) Harold Lloyd, Anna Townsend

One Sheet:　$1,900 - $3,000　*Lloyd's First great film. Beware undated re-releases.*

GRANDPA GOES TO TOWN
(1940 - Republic) James, Lucille, and Russell Gleason
One Sheet:　$50 - $100

GRANDPA'S BOY
(1927 - Educational) Big Boy
One Sheet:　$200 - $400

GRANDVIEW U.S.A.
(1984 - Warner Bros.) Jamie Lee Curtis, Patrick Swayze, Thomas Howell
One Sheet:　$5 - $10

GRANNY GET YOUR GUN
(1940 - Warner Bros.) May Robson, Margot Stevenson
One Sheet:　$50 - $100

GRAPES OF WRATH, THE
(1940 - 20th Century Fox) Henry Fonda, Jane Darwell
One Sheet:　$2,200 - $3,500　*Academy Award: Best Direction(John Ford), Best Supporting Actress(Darwell). Price is for photographic style onesheet. One Sheet(all text):$400-$800. Academy Award Movie Posters #69, #72, & #74.*

One Sheet (Style B)

GRAPES OF WRATH, THE
(1947R - 20th Century Fox) Henry Fonda, Jane Darwell
One Sheet:　$125 - $250　　*Re-release.*

GRAPES OF WRATH, THE
(1956R - 20th Century Fox) Henry Fonda, Jane Darwell
One Sheet:　$15 - $30　　*Re-release. One Sheet is text only.*

GRASS
(1925 - Paramount) Dir: Merian C. Cooper
One Sheet:　$600 - $1,000

GRASS EATER, THE
(1961 - Leder) Rue McClanahan, Paul Leder
One Sheet:　$7 - $15

GRASS HARP, THE
(1995 - Fine Line) Sissy Spacek, Piper Laurie, Edward Furlong
One Sheet:　$4 - $8

GRASS IS GREENER, THE
(1961 - Universal) Cary Grant, Deborah Kerr
One Sheet:　$15 - $25

GRASSHOPPER, THE
(1970 - National General) Jacqueline Bisset, Jim Brown, Joseph Cotten
One Sheet:　$5 - $10　　*Price is for both styles.*

GRASSHOPPER AND THE ANTS, THE
(1949R - RKO/Disney) -
One Sheet:　$500 - $900　　*Re-release. Cartoon. No one sheet was issued for the original release.*

GRATEFUL DEAD, THE
(1977 - Rand Reels) The Grateful Dead
One Sheet:　$500 - $800　　*Rock 'n' Roll. Poster is smaller than one sheet.*

GRAUSIGE NACHTS
(1920 - Phonix-Film Vertrieb) Conrad Veidt, Reinhold Shunzel
One Sheet:　$1,300 - $2,000　*German. U.S. title: Horrible Nights.*

GRAUSTARK

(1915 - Essanay) Francis X. Bushman, Beverly Bayne, Edna Mayo
One Sheet:　$250 - $500

GRAUSTARK
(1925 - Schenck) Norma Talmadge, Eugene O'Brien
One Sheet:　$200 - $400

GRAVE OF THE VAMPIRE
(1972 - Pyramid) William Smith, Michael Pataki
One Sheet:　$20 - $40

GRAVEYARD SHIFT
(1990 - Paramount) David Andrews, Kelly Wolf
One Sheet:　$5 - $10

One Sheet

GRAVY TRAIN, THE
(1974 - Columbia) Stacy Keach, Margot Kidder
One Sheet:　$3 - $5

GRAY LADY DOWN
(1978 - Universal) Charlton Heston, David Carradine
One Sheet:　$5 - $10

GRAYEAGLE
(1977 - AIP) Ben Johnson, Alex Cord
One Sheet:　$3 - $5

GREASE
(1978 - Paramount) John Travolta, Olivia Newton-John
One Sheet:　$30 - $50　　*Photo style:$20-30. 40" x 60": $250. Three sheet: $200.*

GREASE
(1980R - Paramount) John Travolta, Olivia Newton-John
One Sheet:　$10 - $20　　*Re-release.*

GREASE 2
(1982 - Paramount) Maxwell Caulfield, Michelle Pfeiffer
One Sheet:　$5 - $10

GREASE/SATURDAY NIGHT FEVER
(1978R - Paramount) John Travolta, Olivia Newton-John/John Travolta, Lynn Gorney
One Sheet:　$15 - $30　　*Re-release double feature poster.*

GREASED LIGHTNING
(1977 - Warner Bros.) Richard Pryor, Pam Grier, Beau Bridges
One Sheet:　$20 - $40　　*Sports (Auto racing). Black cast. Biography of Wendell Scott, First Black NASCAR Driver. Sport Movie Posters#23.*

GREASER'S PALACE
(1972 - G.P. LTD.) Herve Villechaize, All Arbus
One Sheet:　$5 - $10

GREAT ADVENTURE, THE
(1950 - Lippert) Dennis Price, Jack Hawkins
One Sheet:　$15 - $25

GREAT ADVENTURE, THE
(1976 - Pacific International) Jack Palance, Joan Collins
One Sheet:　$7 - $15

GREAT ADVENTURES OF CAPTAIN KIDD, THE
(1953 - Columbia) Richard Crane, David Bruce
One Sheet:　$40 - $75　　*Serial. 15 Chapters.*

GREAT ADVENTURES OF WILD BILL HICKOK, THE
(1938 - Columbia) Gordon Elliott, Monte Blue
One Sheet:　$75 - $150

GREAT ALASKAN MYSTERY, THE

(1944 - Universal) Milburn Stone, Marjorie Weaver
One Sheet: $50 - $100 *Serial. 13 Chapters.*

GREAT ALLIGATOR
(1980 - -) Mel Ferrer, Barbara Bach
One Sheet: $3 - $5

GREAT AMERICAN BROADCAST, THE
(1941 - 20th Century Fox) Alice Faye, Jack Oakie, John Payne, Cesar Romero
One Sheet: $100 - $200

GREAT AMERICAN COWBOY, THE
(1974 - AIP) Joel McCrea, Larry Mahan
One Sheet: $15 - $30 *Academy Award: Best Documentary Feature.*

GREAT AMERICAN PASTIME, THE
(1956 - MGM) Tom Ewell, Ann Miller
One Sheet: $20 - $40 *Sports (Baseball). Film about Little League baseball.*

GREAT ARMORED CAR SWINDLE, THE
(1964 - Falcon) Peter Reynolds, Dermot Walsh
One Sheet: $7 - $15

GREAT BALLS OF FIRE
(1989 - Orion) Dennis Quaid, Winona Ryder
One Sheet: $5 - $10 *Based on the life of Rock and Roll star Jerry Lee Lewis.*

GREAT BANK HOAX, THE
(1977 - Jacoby) Burgess Meredith, Richard Basehart
One Sheet: $3 - $5

GREAT BANK ROBBERY, THE
(1969 - Warner Bros.) Zero Mostel, Kim Novak, Clint Walker
One Sheet: $15 - $25

GREAT BARRIER, THE
(1937 - Gaumont-British) Richard Arlen
One Sheet: $50 - $100

GREAT BRAIN, THE
(1978 - Osmond) Cliff & Jimmy Osmond, Pat Delaney
One Sheet: $7 - $15

GREAT BRITISH TRAIN ROBBERY, THE
(1967 - Peppercorn/Wormser) Horst Tappert
One Sheet: $7 - $15

GREAT CARUSO, THE
(1951 - MGM) Mario Lanza, Ann Blyth
One Sheet: $40 - $75

GREAT CARUSO, THE
(1962R - MGM) Mario Lanza, Ann Blyth
One Sheet: $10 - $20 *Re-release.*

GREAT CATHERINE
(1968 - Warner Bros./Seven Arts) Peter O'Toole, Zero Mostel, Jeanne Moreau
One Sheet: $15 - $25

GREAT CHASE, THE
(1963 - Continental) Buster Keaton, Douglas Fairbanks Sr., Lillian Gish
One Sheet: $15 - $30

GREAT CIRCUS MYSTERY
(1925 - Universal) -
One Sheet: $200 - $400 *Serial. 15 Chapters.*

GREAT COMMANDMENT, THE
(1941 - 20th Century Fox) John Beal, Maurice Moscovich, Albert Dekker
One Sheet: $50 - $100

GREAT DAN PATCH, THE
(1949 - United Artists) Dennis O'Keefe, Gail Russell
One Sheet: $15 - $35

GREAT DAY
(1944 - RKO) Eric Portman, Flora Robson
One Sheet: $50 - $100

GREAT DAY IN HARLEM, A
(1995 - Castle Hill) -
One Sheet: $15 - $25 *Jazz documentary.*

GREAT DAY IN THE MORNING
(1956 - RKO) Virginia Mayo, Robert Stack
One Sheet: $15 - $25

GREAT DIAMOND MYSTERY, THE
(1924 - Fox) Shirley Mason

One Sheet: $150 - $300

GREAT DIAMOND ROBBERY, THE
(1953 - MGM) Red Skelton, Cara Williams
One Sheet: $30 - $60

GREAT DICTATOR, THE
(1940 - United Artists) Charles Chaplin, Paulette Goddard
One Sheet: $600 - $1,000

GREAT DIVIDE, THE
(1930 - Warner Bros.) Dorothy Mackaill, Ian Keith
One Sheet: $500 - $800

GREAT ESCAPE, THE
(1963 - United Artists) Steve McQueen, Charles Bronson, James Garner
One Sheet: $150 - $300

GREAT ESCAPE, THE
(1980R - -) Steve McQueen, Charles Bronson, James Garner
One Sheet: $30 - $50 *Re-release.*

GREAT EXPECTATIONS
(1920 - Hopp Hadley) Buddy Martin
One Sheet: $250 - $500

GREAT EXPECTATIONS
(1934 - Universal) Phillips Holmes, Jane Wyatt
One Sheet: $200 - $400

GREAT EXPECTATIONS
(1947 - Universal) John Mills, Valerie Hobson
One Sheet: $75 - $150

GREAT EXPECTATIONS
(1951R - Realart) John Mills, Valerie Hobson
One Sheet: $30 - $50 *Re-release.*

GREAT EXPECTATIONS
(1975 - Transcontinental) Michael York, Sarah Miles
One Sheet: $3 - $5

GREAT FLAMARION, THE
(1945 - Republic) Erich von Stroheim, Mary Beth Hughes
One Sheet: $40 - $75

GREAT FLIRTATION, THE
(1934 - Paramount) Adolphe Menjou, Elissa Landi
One Sheet: $100 - $200

GREAT GABBO, THE
(1930 - Sono Art) Erich von Stroheim, Betty Compson
One Sheet: $250 - $600

GREAT GAMBINI, THE
(1937 - Paramount) Akim Tamiroff, Marian Marsh
One Sheet: $100 - $200

GREAT GAMBLE, THE
(1919 - Pathe) Ann Luther, Charles Hutchison
One Sheet: $250 - $500

GREAT GARRICK, THE
(1937 - Warner Bros.) Brian Aherne, Olivia de Havilland, Lana Turner
One Sheet: $75 - $150

GREAT GATSBY, THE
(1949 - Paramount) Alan Ladd, Betty Field
One Sheet: $125 - $250

GREAT GATSBY, THE
(1974 - Paramount) Robert Redford, Mia Farrow
One Sheet: $15 - $25

GREAT GILDERSLEEVE, THE
(1943 - RKO) Harold Peary, Freddie Mercer
One Sheet: $50 - $100

GREAT GOD GOLD
(1935 - Monogram) Sidney Blackmer, Regis Toomey
One Sheet: $100 - $200

GREAT GUNDOWN, THE
(1977 - Sun) Robert Padilla
One Sheet: $3 - $5

GREAT GUNS
(1941 - 20th Century Fox) Laurel and Hardy, Sheila Ryan
One Sheet: $150 - $300

GREAT GUY

(1937 - Grand National) James Cagney, Mae Clarke
One Sheet: $150 - $300

GREAT HOSPITAL MYSTERY, THE
(1937 - 20th Century Fox) Sally Blane, Jane Darwell
One Sheet: $100 - $200

GREAT HOTEL MURDER, THE
(1935 - Fox) Edmund Lowe, Victor McLaglen
One Sheet: $150 - $300

GREAT IMPERSONATION, THE
(1935 - Universal) Edmund Lowe, Valerie Hobson
One Sheet: $100 - $200

GREAT IMPERSONATION, THE
(1942 - Universal) Ralph Bellamy, Evelyn Ankers
One Sheet: $75 - $150

GREAT IMPOSTER, THE
(1961 - Universal) Tony Curtis, Edmond O'Brien
One Sheet: $7 - $15

GREAT JASPER, THE
(1933 - RKO) Richard Dix, Bruce Cabot
One Sheet: $150 - $300

GREAT JESSE JAMES RAID, THE
(1953 - Lippert) Willard Parker, Barbara Payton
One Sheet: $10 - $20

GREAT JEWEL ROBBER, THE
(1949 - Warner Bros.) David Brian, Marjorie Reynolds
One Sheet: $30 - $60

GREAT JOHN L., THE
(1945 - United Artists) Greg McClure, Linda Darnell
One Sheet: $30 - $50 *Bing Crosby, Bob Hope & Frank Sinatra on One Sheet.*

GREAT K&A TRAIN ROBBERY, THE
(1926 - Fox) Tom Mix, Dorothy Dwan
One Sheet: $600 - $1,000

GREAT LAND OF SMALL, THE
(1987 - New World) Karen Elkin, Micheal Blouin
One Sheet: $5 - $10

GREAT LIE, THE
(1941 - Warner Bros.) Bette Davis, George Brent, Mary Astor
One Sheet: $200 - $400 *Academy Award: Best Supporting Actress(Astor). Academy Award Movie Posters #81.*

One Sheet

GREAT LOCOMOTIVE CHASE, THE
(1956 - Buena Vista/Disney) Fess Parker, Jeffrey Hunter
One Sheet: $40 - $75

GREAT LOVE, THE
(1918 - Artcraft) Lillian Gish, Henry Walthall
One Sheet: $700 - $1,200

GREAT LOVER, THE
(1931 - MGM) Adolphe Menjou, Irene Dunne
One Sheet: $500 - $800

GREAT LOVER, THE
(1949 - Paramount) Bob Hope, Rhonda Fleming
One Sheet: $75 - $150

GREAT MAN, THE
(1956 - Universal) Jose Ferrer, Dean Jagger, Keenan Wynn

One Sheet: $15 - $25

GREAT MAN VOTES, THE
(1939 - RKO) John Barrymore, Katherine Alexander, Virginia Weidler
One Sheet: $100 - $200

GREAT MAN'S LADY, THE
(1942 - Paramount) Joel McCrea, Barbara Stanwyck
One Sheet: $75 - $150

GREAT MANHUNT, THE
(1951 - Columbia) Douglas Fairbanks Jr., Glynis Johns
One Sheet: $15 - $30

GREAT MCGINTY, THE
(1940 - Paramount) Brian Donlevy, Akim Tamiroff, Muriel Angelus
One Sheet: $200 - $400

GREAT MCGONAGALL, THE
(1975 - Darltan) Peter Sellers, Spike Milligan
One Sheet: $5 - $10

GREAT MEADOW, THE
(1931 - MGM) Johnny Mack Brown, Anita Louise
One Sheet: $100 - $200

GREAT MIKE, THE
(1944 - PRC) Robert Henry, Stuart Erwin
One Sheet: $30 - $50

GREAT MISSOURI RAID, THE
(1951 - Paramount) Wendell Corey, Macdonald Carey
One Sheet: $15 - $30

GREAT MOMENT, THE
(1921 - -) Gloria Swanson, Milton Sills, Alec B. Francis
One Sheet: $1,300 - $2,000

GREAT MOMENT, THE
(1944 - Paramount) Joel McCrea, Betty Field
One Sheet: $125 - $250

GREAT MOUSE DETECTIVE, THE
(1986 - Disney) Voices of Ron Clements, Dave Michener
One Sheet: $15 - $25 *Cartoon.*

GREAT MR. HANDEL, THE
(1943 - Midfilm) Wilfred Lawson, Elizabeth Allen
One Sheet: $40 - $75

GREAT MR. NOBODY, THE
(1941 - Warner Bros.) Eddie Albert, Joan Leslie, Alan Hale
One Sheet: $50 - $100

GREAT MUPPET CAPER, THE
(1981 - Universal) The Muppets, voices of: Jim Henson, Frank Oz
One Sheet: $5 - $10

GREAT NORTHFIELD MINNESOTA RAID, THE
(1972 - Universal) Cliff Robertson, Robert Duvall
One Sheet: $3 - $5

GREAT O'MALLEY, THE
(1936 - Warner Bros.) Pat O'Brien, Ann Sheridan, Humphrey Bogart
One Sheet: $125 - $250 *Window Card(only poster picturing Bogart):$300-$600.*

GREAT OCEAN CATASTROPHE or FIRE AT SEA
(1913 - Great Northern) -
One Sheet: $200 - $450

GREAT OUTDOORS, THE
(1988 - -) Dan Aykroyd, John Candy
One Sheet: $3 - $5

GREAT PLANE ROBBERY, THE
(1940 - Columbia) Jack Holt, Vicki Lester
One Sheet: $75 - $125

GREAT PLANE ROBBERY, THE
(1950 - United Artists) Tom Conway, Margaret Hamilton
One Sheet: $15 - $25

GREAT POWER, THE
(1929 - MGM) Minna Gombell, Hershel Mayall
One Sheet: $200 - $400

GREAT PROFILE, THE
(1940 - 20th Century Fox) John Barrymore, Mary Beth Hughes, Gregory Ratoff

One Sheet: $100 - $200

GREAT RACE, THE
(1966 - Warner Bros.) Jack Lemmon, Tony Curtis
One Sheet: $15 - $30   *Sports (Auto racing).*

GREAT REDEEMER, THE
(1920 - Metro) House Peters, Marjorie Daw
One Sheet: $250 - $500

GREAT RUPERT, THE
(1949 - United Artists) Jimmy Durante, Terry Moore
One Sheet: $50 - $100

GREAT SANTINI, THE
(1980 - Warner Bros.) Robert Duvall
One Sheet: $10 - $20   *Sports Movie Posters #96.*

GREAT SCOUT AND CATHOUSE THURSDAY, THE
(1976 - AIP) Lee Marvin, Oliver Reed
One Sheet: $3 - $5

GREAT SINNER, THE
(1949 - MGM) Gregory Peck, Ava Gardner
One Sheet: $40 - $75

GREAT SIOUX MASSACRE, THE
(1965 - Columbia) Joseph Cotten, Darren McGavin
One Sheet: $10 - $20

GREAT SIOUX UPRISING, THE
(1953 - Universal) Jeff Chandler, Faith Domergue
One Sheet: $15 - $25

GREAT SMOKEY ROADBLOCK, THE
(1978 - Dimension) Henry Fonda, Robert Englund
One Sheet: $7 - $15

GREAT SPY CHASE, THE
(1966 - AIP) Lino Ventura, Bernard Blair
One Sheet: $5 - $10

GREAT ST. LOUIS BANK ROBBERY
(1958 - United Artists) Steve McQueen, David Clarke
One Sheet: $40 - $75

GREAT STAGECOACH ROBBERY
(1945 - Republic) Bill Elliott, Bobby Blake
One Sheet: $50 - $100   *Red Ryder series.*

GREAT SWINDLE, THE
(1941 - Columbia) Jack Holt, Marjorie Reynolds
One Sheet: $40 - $75

GREAT TEXAS DYNAMITE CHASE, THE
(1976 - New World) Claudia Jennings
One Sheet: $5 - $10

GREAT TRAIN ROBBERY, THE
(1941 - Republic) Bob Steele, Claire Carleton
One Sheet: $75 - $150

GREAT TRAIN ROBBERY, THE
(1979 - United Artists) Sean Connery, Donald Sutherland
One Sheet: $15 - $25

GREAT VAN ROBBERY, THE
(1963 - United Artists) Denis Shaw, Kay Callard
One Sheet: $5 - $10

GREAT VICTOR HERBERT, THE
(1939 - Paramount) Allan Jones, Mary Martin
One Sheet: $50 - $100

One Sheet

GREAT WALDO PEPPER, THE
(1975 - Universal) Robert Redford, Susan Sarandon
One Sheet: $15 - $25

GREAT WALTZ, THE
(1938 - MGM) Luise Rainer, Fernand Gravet
One Sheet: $350 - $750

GREAT WALTZ, THE
(1946R - MGM) Luise Rainer, Fernand Gravet
One Sheet: $50 - $100   *Re-release.*

GREAT WALTZ, THE
(1972 - MGM) Mary Costa, Horst Buchholz, Rossano Brazzi
One Sheet: $3 - $5

GREAT WAR, THE
(1961 - Lopert) Vittorio Gassman, Silvana Mangano
One Sheet: $5 - $10

GREAT WHITE, THE
(1982 - Film Ventures) James Fanciscus, Vic Morrow
One Sheet: $3 - $5

GREAT WHITE HOPE, THE
(1970 - 20th Century Fox) James Earl Jones, Jane Alexander
One Sheet: $10 - $20   *Sports (Boxing). Drama about boxing champ Jack Johnson.*

GREAT WHITE HYPE, THE
(1996 - Fox) Samuel L. Jackson, Damon Wayans, Jeff Goldblum
One Sheet: $3 - $7

GREAT WHITE NORTH
(1925 - William Fox)
One Sheet: $250 - $500   *Documentary.*

GREAT ZIEGFELD, THE
(1936 - MGM) William Powell, Luise Rainer, Myrna Loy
One Sheet: $1,600 - $2,500   *Academy Award: Best Picture, Best Actress(Rainer). Academy Award Movie Posters #45 & #48.*

One Sheet

GREATER GLORY, THE
(1926 - First National) Conway Tearle, Anna Q. Nilsson
One Sheet: $250 - $600

GREATEST, THE
(1977 - Columbia) Muhammad Ali, Ernest Borgnine
One Sheet: $40 - $75   *Sports (Boxing). Sports Movie Posters #156.*

GREATEST LOVE, THE
(1951 - Lux) Ingrid Bergman, Alexander Knox
One Sheet: $40 - $75

GREATEST SHOW ON EARTH, THE
(1952 - Paramount) James Stewart, Betty Hutton, Charlton Heston
One Sheet: $100 - $200   *Academy Award: Best Picture. Academy Award Movie Posters #141 & #142.*

GREATEST SHOW ON EARTH, THE
(1960R - Paramount) James Stewart, Betty Hutton, Charlton Heston
One Sheet: $20 - $40   *Re-release.*

GREATEST SHOW ON EARTH, THE
(1964R - Paramount) James Stewart, Betty Hutton, Charlton Heston
One Sheet: $15 - $25   *Re-release.*

GREATEST STORY EVER TOLD, THE
(1965 - United Artists) Max Von Sydow, All-Star Cast
One Sheet: $20 - $40   *"Cinerama" one sheet: $125-$250.*

GREATEST THING IN LIFE, THE
(1918 - Artcraft) Lillian Gish, Dir: D. W. Griffith
One Sheet: $250 - $600

One Sheet

GREED
(1924 - Metro Goldwyn) Jean Hersholt, ZaSu Pitts
One Sheet: $6,500 - $10,000

GREED IN THE SUN
(1965 - MGM) Jean-Paul Belmondo, Lino Ventura
One Sheet: $7 - $15

GREED OF WILLIAM HART, THE
(1948 - Ambassador) Tod Slaughter, Henry Oscar
One Sheet: $40 - $75   *AKA: HORROR MANIACS.*

GREEDY
(1993 - Universal) Michael J. Fox, Kirk Douglas, Olivia d'Abo
One Sheet: $4 - $8

GREEK TYCOON, THE
(1978 - Universal) Anthony Quinn, Jacqueline Bisset
One Sheet: $5 - $10

GREEKS HAD A WORD FOR THEM, THE
(1932 - United Artists) Madge Evans, Joan Blondell, Ina Claire
One Sheet: $100 - $200

GREEN ARCHER, THE
(1940 - Columbia) Victor Jory, Iris Meredith
One Sheet: $600 - $1,000   *Serial. 15 Chapters.*

GREEN BERETS, THE
(1968 - Warner Bros.) John Wayne, David Janssen, Jim Hutton, George Takei
One Sheet: $40 - $75

GREEN BUDDHA, THE
(1954 - Republic) Wayne Morris, Mary Germaine
One Sheet: $15 - $30

GREEN CARD
(1990 - Touchstone) Gerard Depardieu, Andie MacDowell
One Sheet: $3 - $5

GREEN COCKATOO, THE
(1947 - Devonshire) John Mills, Rene Ray
One Sheet: $75 - $150

GREEN DOLPHIN STREET
(1947 - MGM) Lana Turner, Van Heflin, Donna Reed
One Sheet: $50 - $100

GREEN DOLPHIN STREET
(1955R - MGM) Lana Turner, Van Heflin, Donna Reed
One Sheet: $10 - $20   *Re-release.*

GREEN EYED MONSTER, THE
(1925 - Norman Film) -
One Sheet: $1,300 - $2,000   *Black cast.*

GREEN EYES
(1934 - Chesterfield) Shirley Grey, Charles Starrett

One Sheet: $125 - $250

GREEN FIELDS
(1937 - New Star) Helen Beverley, Michael Goldstein
One Sheet: $50 - $100

GREEN FINGERS
(1947 - Anglo-American) Robert Beatty, Carol Raye
One Sheet: $40 - $75

GREEN FIRE
(1955 - MGM) Grace Kelly, Stewart Granger
One Sheet: $40 - $75

GREEN FOR DANGER
(1947 - GFD) Alastair Sim, Sally Gray
One Sheet: $20 - $40

GREEN GLOVE, THE
(1952 - United Artists) Glenn Ford, Geraldine Brooks
One Sheet: $15 - $35

GREEN GODDESS, THE
(1930 - First National) George Arliss, H.B. Warner
One Sheet: $200 - $400

GREEN GRASS OF WYOMING
(1948 - 20th Century Fox) Peggy Cummins, Charles Coburn
One Sheet: $30 - $50

GREEN GRASS WIDOWS
(1928 - Tiffany-Stahl) Walter Hagen, Gertrude Olmstead
One Sheet: $75 - $150

GREEN GROW THE RUSHES
(1951 - ACT Films) Roger Livesey, Richard Burton
One Sheet: $20 - $40

GREEN HELL
(1939 - Universal) Douglas Fairbanks, Jr., Joan Bennett
One Sheet: $200 - $400

GREEN HELMET, THE
(1961 - MGM) Bill Travers, Nancy Walters
One Sheet: $15 - $25

GREEN HORNET, THE
(1940 - Universal) Gordon Jones, Wade Boteler
One Sheet: $700 - $1,200   *Serial. 13 Chapters.*

GREEN HORNET, THE
(1974 - 20th Century Fox) Bruce Lee, Van Williams
One Sheet: $75 - $150   *T.V. tie-in. Sports Movie Posters #260. A and B style same price.*

GREEN HORNET STRIKES AGAIN, THE
(1940 - Universal) Warren Hull, Keye Luke
One Sheet: $350 - $750   *Serial. 13 Chapters.*

GREEN ICE
(1981 - ITC) Ryan O'Neal, Omar Sharif
One Sheet: $3 - $5

GREEN LIGHT, THE
(1937 - Warner Bros.) Errol Flynn, Anita Louise
One Sheet: $250 - $500

GREEN LINE, THE
(1943 - 20th Century Fox) Mighty Mouse
One Sheet: $250 - $600   *Cartoon. Full color stock poster with printed title. Huge image of Mighty Mouse on yellow background.*

GREEN MAN, THE
(1957 - British-Lion) Alastair Sim, Terry-Thomas
One Sheet: $30 - $50

GREEN MANSIONS
(1959 - MGM) Audrey Hepburn, Anthony Perkins
One Sheet: $75 - $150

GREEN PASTURES, THE
(1936 - Warner Bros.) Rex Ingram, Oscar Polk
One Sheet: $250 - $500   *Black cast. Separate Cinema, pg. 30. One Sheet(all text):$150-300. One Sheet(Belgian):$200-400.*

GREEN PROMISE, THE
(1949 - RKO) Marguerite Chapman, Walter Brennan

One Sheet: $30 - $50

GREEN SCARF, THE
(1955 - British Lion) Michael Redgrave, Ann Todd
One Sheet: $10 - $20

GREEN SLIME, THE
(1969 - MGM) Robert Horton, Luciana Paluzzi
One Sheet: $30 - $50

GREEN YEARS, THE
(1946 - MGM) Charles Coburn, Dean Stockwell
One Sheet: $40 - $75

Window Card

GREENE MURDER CASE, THE
(1929 - Paramount) William Powell, Jean Arthur
One Sheet: $1,600 - $2,500

GREEN-EYED BLONDE, THE
(1957 - Warner Bros.) Susan Oliver, Juanita Moore
One Sheet: $30 - $50

GREENGAGE SUMMER
(1961 - Columbia) Kenneth More, Danielle Darrieux
One Sheet: $5 - $10

GREENWICH VILLAGE
(1944 - 20th Century Fox) Don Ameche, Carmen Miranda
One Sheet: $150 - $300

GREENWICH VILLAGE STORY
(1963 - Lion International) Robert Hogan, Melinda Plank
One Sheet: $15 - $30

GREETINGS
(1968 - Sigma III) Robert DeNiro, Jonathan Warden
One Sheet: $15 - $25

GREGORY'S GIRL
(1981 - Goldwyn) John Sinclair, Dee Hepburn
One Sheet: $3 - $5

GREMLINS
(1984 - Warner Bros.) Zach Galligan, Phoebe Cates
One Sheet: $5 - $10

GREMLINS 2 THE NEW BATCH
(1990 - Warner Bros.) Zach Galligan, Phoebe Cates
One Sheet: $5 - $10

GRETA GARBO PORTRAIT POSTER
(1930S - MGM) Greta Garbo
One Sheet: $1,400 - $2,200   *French. Price is for French 22"x30" poster.*

GREY FOX, THE
(1982 - United Artists) Richard Farnsworth, Jackie Burroughs
One Sheet: $3 - $5

GREYFRIARS BOBBY
(1961 - Disney) Donald Crisp, Laurence Naismith
One Sheet: $15 - $30

GREYHOUND AND THE RABBIT, THE
(1939 - Columbia) Color Rhapsodies
One Sheet: $200 - $400   *Cartoon. Full color semi-stock poster with inset of title.*

GREYHOUND LIMITED, THE
(1929 - Warner Bros.) Monte Blue, Grant Withers
One Sheet: $200 - $400

GREYSTOKE: THE LEGEND OF TARZAN, LORD OF THE APES
(1984 - Warner Bros.) Christopher Lambert, Andie MacDowell
One Sheet: $5 - $10

GRIDIRON FLASH
(1934 - RKO) Eddie Quillan, Betty Furness
One Sheet: $150 - $300   *Sports (Football).*

GRIDLOCK'D
(1997 - Gramercy) Tupac Shakur, Tim Roth
One Sheet: $5 - $10

GRIEF STREET
(1931 - Chesterfield) John Holland, Barbara Kent
One Sheet: $125 - $250

GRIFTERS, THE
(1990 - Miramax) Anjelica Huston, John Cusack, Annette Bening
One Sheet: $7 - $15

GRIM GAME, THE
(1919 - Paramount) Harry Houdini
One Sheet: $13,000 - $20,000

One Sheet

GRIM REAPER, THE
(1981 - -) Tisa Farrow, Vanessa Steiger
One Sheet: $3 - $5

GRIN AND BEAR IT
(1933 - RKO) -
One Sheet: $100 - $200

GRINGO
(1963 - Jolly) Richard Harrison
One Sheet: $10 - $20

GRIP OF THE YUKON
(1928 - Universal) Francis X. Bushman, Neil Hamilton
One Sheet: $250 - $600

GRIPS, GRUNTS, AND GROANS
(1937 - Columbia) The Three Stooges (Curly)
One Sheet: $8,500 - $14,000   *Comedy short. Duotone.*

GRISSLY'S MILLIONS
(1944 - Republic) Paul Kelly, Virginia Grey
One Sheet: $50 - $100

GRISSOM GANG, THE
(1971 - Cinerama) Kim Darby, Scott Wilson
One Sheet: $3 - $5

GRIT
(1924 - -) Clara Bow, Glenn Hunter
One Sheet: $600 - $1,000

GRIZZLY
(1976 - Film Ventures International) Christopher George, Andrew Prine
One Sheet: $2 - $3

GROOM WORE SPURS, THE
(1950 - Universal-International) Ginger Rogers, Jack Carson
One Sheet: $30 - $60

GROOVE TUBE, THE
(1974 - Levitt) Chevy Chase (Debut), Ken Shapiro
One Sheet: $7 - $15

GROSS ANATOMY
(1989 - -) Matthew Modine, Daphne Zuniga
One Sheet: $3 - $5

GROSSE POINTE BLANK
(1997 - Hollywood) John Cusak, Joan Cusak

One Sheet: $3 - $5

GROUND ZERO
(1973 - Flocker) Ron Casteel
One Sheet: $3 - $5

GROUND ZERO
(1988 - -) Bruce Myles, Colin Friels
One Sheet: $3 - $5

GROUNDHOG DAY
(1993 - Columbia) Bill Murray, Andie MacDowell
One Sheet: $10 - $20

GROUNDS FOR MARRIAGE
(1950 - MGM) Van Johnson, Kathryn Grayson
One Sheet: $15 - $35

GROUNDSTAR CONSPIRACY, THE
(1972 - Universal) George Peppard, Michael Sarrazin
One Sheet: $2 - $3

GROUP, THE
(1966 - United Artists) Candice Bergen, Joan Hackett
One Sheet: $5 - $10

GROUP MARRIAGE
(1972 - Dimension) Victoria Vetri, Claudia Jennings
One Sheet: $5 - $10

GRUB STAKE, THE
(1923 - -) Neil Shipman, Hugh Thompson
One Sheet: $125 - $250

GRUESOME TWOSOME, THE
(1967 - Mayflower) Elizabeth Davis, Chris Martell, Dir: Herschell G. Lewis
One Sheet: $40 - $75

GRUMPIER OLD MEN
(1995 - Warner Bros.) Jack Lemmon, Walter Matthau, Ann-Margret, Sophia Loren
One Sheet: $5 - $10

GRUMPY
(1930 - Paramount Publix) Phillips Holmes, Paul Lukas
One Sheet: $75 - $150

GRUMPY OLD MEN
(1994 - Warner Bros.) Jack Lemmon, Walter Matthau
One Sheet: $5 - $10

GUADALCANAL DIARY
(1943 - 20th Century Fox) Preston Foster, Lloyd Nolan
One Sheet: $75 - $150

GUARD THAT GIRL
(1935 - Columbia) Robert Allen, Florence Rice
One Sheet: $75 - $150

GUARDIAN, THE
(1990 - Universal) Jenny Seagrove, Dwier Brown
One Sheet: $5 - $10

GUARDIAN OF THE WILDERNESS
(1977 - Sunn Classic) Denver Pyle, Ken Berry
One Sheet: $3 - $5

GUARDING TESS
(1994 - TriStar) Shirley MacLaine, Nicholas Cage
One Sheet: $5 - $10

GUARDSMAN, THE
(1931 - MGM) Alfred Lunt, Lynn Fontanne
One Sheet: $100 - $200

GUERRILLA GIRL
(1953 - United Artists) Helmut Dantine, Marianna
One Sheet: $10 - $20

GUESS WHAT HAPPENED TO COUNT DRACULA
(1970 - Merrick) Des Roberts, Claudia Barron
One Sheet: $5 - $10

GUESS WHAT WE LEARNED IN SCHOOL TODAY
(1971 - Cannon) Richard Carballo, Zachary Haines
One Sheet: $15 - $30

GUESS WHO'S COMING TO DINNER
(1967 - Columbia) Spencer Tracy, Sidney Poitier, Katharine Hepburn

One Sheet: $50 - $100   *Academy Award: Best Actress. Separate Cinema, pg. 159. Academy Award Movie Posters #242 &#243.*

GUESS WHO'S COMING TO DINNER
(1972R - Columbia) Spencer Tracy, Sidney Poitier, Katharine Hepburn
One Sheet: $15 - $25   *Re-release.*

GUESS WHO'S COMING TO DINNER/TO SIR WITH LOVE COMBO
(1969R - Columbia) Sidney Poitier
One Sheet: $40 - $75   *Double feature re-release poster.*

GUEST, THE
(1964 - Janus) Alan Bates, Donald Pleasence
One Sheet: $3 - $5

GUEST IN THE HOUSE
(1944 - United Artists) Anne Baxter, Ralph Bellamy
One Sheet: $40 - $75

GUEST OF HONOR
(1925 - Fox) Van Bibber Series #6
One Sheet: $150 - $300

GUEST OF HONOR
(1934 - First National) Henry Kendall, Edward Chapman
One Sheet: $100 - $200

GUEST WIFE
(1945 - United Artists) Claudette Colbert, Don Ameche
One Sheet: $75 - $175

GUEST WIFE
(1952R - United Artists) Claudette Colbert, Don Ameche
One Sheet: $40 - $75   *Re-release.*

GUIDE FOR THE MARRIED MAN, A
(1967 - 20th Century Fox) Walter Matthau, Robert Morse
One Sheet: $7 - $15

GUILE OF WOMEN
(1921 - Goldwyn) Will Rogers, Mary Warren
One Sheet: $800 - $1,500

GUILT
(1930 - Paramount) James Carew, Anne Grey
One Sheet: $200 - $400

GUILT IS MY SHADOW
(1951 - Stratford) Peter Reynolds, Elizabeth Sellars
One Sheet: $15 - $25

GUILT OF JANET AMES, THE
(1947 - Columbia) Rosalind Russell, Melvyn Douglas, Sid Caesar
One Sheet: $50 - $100

GUILTY
(1930 - Columbia) Virginia Valli, John Holland
One Sheet: $150 - $300

GUILTY, THE
(1947 - Monogram) Bonita Granville, Don Castle
One Sheet: $50 - $100

GUILTY?
(1956 - Grand National) John Justin, Barbara Laage
One Sheet: $15 - $25

GUILTY AS HELL
(1932 - Paramount) Edmund Lowe, Victor McLaglen
One Sheet: $700 - $1,200

GUILTY AS SIN
(1993 - Buena Vista) Rebecca DeMornay, Don Johnson
One Sheet: $3 - $5

GUILTY BY SUSPICION
(1991 - -) Robert De Niro, Annette Bening
One Sheet: $5 - $10

GUILTY BYSTANDER
(1950 - Film Classics) Zachary Scott, Faye Emerson
One Sheet: $10 - $20

GUILTY GENERATION, THE
(1931 - Columbia) Leo Carrillo, Constance Cummings
One Sheet: $100 - $200

GUILTY HANDS
(1931 - MGM) Lionel Barrymore, Madge Evans
One Sheet: $150 - $350

GUILTY OF TREASON
(1950 - Eagle-Lion) Charles Bickford, Paul Kelly, Bonita Granville
One Sheet: $15 - $25

GUILTY OR NOT GUILTY
(1933 - Monogram) -
One Sheet: $100 - $200

GUILTY PARENTS
(1934 - JDK) Jean Lacy, Blen Boles
One Sheet: $100 - $200

GUILTY TRAILS
(1938 - Universal) Bob Baker, Marjorie Reynolds
One Sheet: $50 - $100

GULLIVER'S TRAVELS
(1939 - Paramount) Max Fleischer
One Sheet: $1,300 - $2,000   *Cartoon. Price is for either style one sheet. Cartoon Movie Posters #235, #236. Graven Images, pg. 97.*

One Sheet

GULLIVER'S TRAVELS
(1957R - Paramount) Max Fleischer
One Sheet: $125 - $250   *Re-release. Cartoon.*

GUMBALL RALLY, THE
(1976 - Warner Bros.) Michael Sarrazin, Gary Busey
One Sheet: $10 - $20   *Sports (Auto racing). Sports Movie Posters #22.*

GUMSHOE
(1972 - Columbia) Albert Finney, Billie Whitelaw, Frank Finlay
One Sheet: $7 - $15

GUN BATTLE AT MONTEREY
(1957 - Allied Artists) Sterling Hayden, Lee Van Cleef
One Sheet: $15 - $30

GUN BELT
(1953 - United Artists) George Montgomery, Tab Hunter
One Sheet: $7 - $15

GUN BROTHERS
(1956 - United Artists) Buster Crabbe, Neville Brand
One Sheet: $10 - $20

GUN CODE
(1940 - PRC) Tim McCoy
One Sheet: $40 - $75

GUN CRAZY
(1950 - United Artists) Peggy Cummins, John Dall
One Sheet: $1,300 - $2,000   *AKA:DEADLY IS THE FEMALE.*

GUN DUEL IN DURANGO
(1957 - United Artists) George Montgomery, Ann Robinson
One Sheet: $15 - $30

GUN FEVER
(1958 - United Artists) Mark Stevens, John Lupton
One Sheet: $5 - $10

GUN FOR A COWARD
(1956 - Universal) Fred MacMurray, Jeffrey Hunter
One Sheet: $15 - $25

GUN FURY
(1953 - Columbia) Rock Hudson, Donna Reed
One Sheet: $20 - $40

GUN GAME, THE
(1920 - Universal) Bob Reeves, Josephine Hill
One Sheet: $250 - $500

GUN GIRLS
(1957 - -) -
One Sheet: $30 - $65   *Sexploitation.*

GUN GLORY
(1957 - MGM) Stewart Granger, Rhonda Fleming
One Sheet: $15 - $25

GUN HAWK, THE
(1963 - Allied Artists) Rory Calhoun, Rod Cameron
One Sheet: $5 - $10

GUN IN BETTY LOU'S HANDBAG, THE
(1992 - Touchstone) Penelope Ann Miller, Cathy Moriarty
One Sheet: $5 - $10

GUN JUSTICE
(1933 - Universal) Ken Maynard
One Sheet: $250 - $500

GUN JUSTICE
(1944R - Universal) Ken Maynard
One Sheet: $50 - $100   *Re-release.*

GUN LAW
(1933 - Majestic) Jack Hoxie
One Sheet: $150 - $300   *Cowboy Movie Posters #73.*

GUN LAW
(1938 - RKO) George O'Brien
One Sheet: $100 - $200

GUN LAW
(1947R - RKO) George O'Brien
One Sheet: $20 - $40   *Re-release.*

GUN LAW JUSTICE
(1949 - Monogram) Jimmy Wakely, Cannonball Taylor
One Sheet: $15 - $35

GUN LORDS OF STIRRUP BASIN
(1937 - Republic) Bob Steele, Louise Stanley
One Sheet: $250 - $500

GUN PACKER
(1938 - Monogram) Jack Randall
One Sheet: $50 - $100

GUN PLAY
(1936 - Beacon) Big Boy Williams, Marion Shilling, Wally Wales
One Sheet: $150 - $300

GUN PLAY
(1951 - RKO) Tim Holt, Joan Dixon
One Sheet: $15 - $35

GUN RANGER, THE
(1936 - Republic) Bob Steele, Eleanor Stewart
One Sheet: $100 - $200

GUN RIDERS, THE
(1969 - Independent International) Robert Dix, John Carradine
One Sheet: $5 - $10

GUN RUNNER
(1949 - Monogram) Jimmy Wakely, Cannonball Taylor
One Sheet: $30 - $50

GUN RUNNERS, THE
(1958 - United Artists) Audie Murphy, Eddie Albert
One Sheet: $15 - $35

GUN SMOKE
(1931 - Paramount) William "Stage" Boyd, Richard Arlen
One Sheet: $500 - $800   *Cowboy Movie Posters # 100.*

GUN SMOKE
(1936 - Kent) Buck Coburn, Marion Shilling
One Sheet: $100 - $200

GUN SMOKE
(1945 - Monogram) Johnny Mack Brown
One Sheet: $40 - $75

GUN SMUGGLERS
(1949 - RKO) Tim Holt, Richard Martin
One Sheet: $20 - $40

GUN STREET
(1961 - United Artists) James Brown, John Clarke
One Sheet: $10 - $20

GUN TALK
(1947 - Monogram) Johnny Mack Brown, Raymond Hatton
One Sheet: $40 - $75

GUN THAT WON THE WEST, THE
(1955 - Columbia) Dennis Morgan, Paula Raymond
One Sheet: $15 - $25

GUN THE MAN DOWN
(1956 - United Artists) James Arness, Angie Dickinson
One Sheet: $20 - $40

GUN TO GUN
(1944 - Warner Bros.) Robert Shayne
One Sheet: $30 - $50

GUN TOWN
(1945 - Universal) Kirby Grant, Fuzzy Knight
One Sheet: $40 - $75

GUNFIGHT
(1961 - United Artists) James Brown, Joan Staley
One Sheet: $10 - $20

GUNFIGHT, A
(1971 - Paramount) Kirk Douglas, Johnny Cash
One Sheet: $10 - $20

GUNFIGHT AT COMANCHE CREEK
(1963 - Allied Artists) Audie Murphy, Ben Cooper
One Sheet: $15 - $30

GUNFIGHT AT DODGE CITY, THE
(1959 - United Artists) Joel McCrea, Julie Adams
One Sheet: $15 - $30

GUNFIGHT AT INDIAN GAP
(1957 - -) Vera Ralston
One Sheet: $20 - $40

GUNFIGHT AT THE O.K. CORRAL
(1957 - Paramount) Burt Lancaster, Kirk Douglas, Rhonda Fleming
One Sheet: $100 - $200

GUNFIGHT AT THE O.K. CORRAL
(1964R - Paramount) Burt Lancaster, Kirk Douglas, Rhonda Fleming
One Sheet: $20 - $40   *Re-release.*

GUNFIGHT IN ABILENE
(1967 - Universal) Bobby Darin, Emily Banks
One Sheet: $15 - $25

GUNFIGHTER
(1917 - S.A. Lynch) William S. Hart, Margery Wilson
One Sheet: $1,900 - $3,000   *Beware undated re-release posters. Cowboy Movie Posters #14.*

GUNFIGHTER, THE
(1923 - -) William Farnum, Doris May
One Sheet: $250 - $600

GUNFIGHTER, THE
(1950 - 20th Century Fox) 19egory Peck, Helen Westcott
One Sheet: $150 - $350   *Cowboy Movie Posters #s 286, 287.*

GUNFIGHTERS
(1947 - Columbia) Randolph Scott, Barbara Britton
One Sheet: $50 - $100

GUNFIGHTERS
(1953R - Columbia) Randolph Scott, Barbara Britton
One Sheet: $15 - $25   *Re-release.*

GUNFIGHTERS OF ABILENE
(1960 - United Artists) Buster Crabbe, Barton MacLane
One Sheet: $15 - $25

GUNFIGHTERS OF CASA GRANDE
(1965 - MGM) Alex Nicol, Jorge Mistral
One Sheet: $5 - $10

GUNFIGHTERS OF THE NORTHWEST
(1954 - Columbia) Jack Mahoney, Clayton Moore
One Sheet: $40 - $75   *Serial. Western. 15 Chapters.*

GUNFIRE
(1950 - Lippert) Don Barry, Wally Vernon
One Sheet: $15 - $30

GUNFIRE AT INDIAN GAP
(1957 - Republic) Vera Ralston, Anthony George
One Sheet: $10 - $20

GUNG HO!
(1943 - Universal) Randolph Scott, Grace McDonald
One Sheet: $75 - $150

GUNG HO!
(1986 - Paramount) Michael Keaton, Gedde Watanabe
One Sheet: $3 - $5

GUNGA DIN
(1939 - RKO) Cary Grant, Victor McLaglen
One Sheet: $1,600 - $2,500   *Price is for either style one sheet.*

One Sheet

GUNGA DIN
(1942R - RKO) Cary Grant, Victor McLaglen
One Sheet: $150 - $300   *Re-release.*

GUNMAN, THE
(1952 - Monogram) Whip Wilson, Fuzzy Knight
One Sheet: $40 - $75

GUNMAN FROM BODIE, THE
(1941 - Monogram) Rough Riders (Tim McCoy, Buck Jones)
One Sheet: $75 - $150

GUNMAN'S CODE
(1946 - Universal) Kirby Grant, Fuzzy Knight
One Sheet: $30 - $50

GUNMAN'S WALK
(1958 - Columbia) Van Heflin, Tab Hunter
One Sheet: $15 - $25

GUNMEN FROM LAREDO
(1958 - Columbia) Robert Knapp, Jana Davi
One Sheet: $10 - $20

GUNMEN OF ABILENE
(1950 - Republic) Allan "Rocky" Lane, Eddy Waller
One Sheet: $15 - $35

GUNMEN OF THE RIO GRANDE
(1965 - Allied Artists) Guy Madison, Madeleine Lebeau
One Sheet: $10 - $20

GUNN
(1967 - Paramount) Craig Stevens, Laura Devon
One Sheet: $5 - $10

GUNNERS AND GUNS
(1935 - -) Black King, Edna Aselin
One Sheet: $150 - $300

GUNNING FOR JUSTICE
(1948 - Monogram) Johnny Mack Brown, Raymond Hatton
One Sheet: $15 - $35

GUNNING FOR VENGEANCE
(1946 - Columbia) Charles Starrett, Phyllis Adair
One Sheet: $30 - $50

GUNPOINT
(1955 - Allied Artists) Fred MacMurray, Dorothy Malone, Walter Brennan
One Sheet: $15 - $35

GUNPOINT
(1966 - Universal) Audie Murphy, Joan Staley
One Sheet: $15 - $30

GUNS A'BLAZIN
(194?R - Realart) Walter Huston, Walter Brennan
One Sheet: $20 - $40   *Re-titled re-release of LAW AND ORDER. Western. Full color.*

GUNS AND GUITARS
(1936 - Republic) Gene Autry, Smiley Burnette
One Sheet: $250 - $500

GUNS AND GUITARS
(1941R - Republic) Gene Autry, Smiley Burnette
One Sheet: $75 - $150   *Re-release.*

GUNS AND THE FURY, THE
(1983 - Bordeaux) Peter Graves, Cameron Mitchell
One Sheet: $3 - $5

GUNS A-POPPIN'
(1957 - Columbia) The Three Stooges (Joe Besser)
One Sheet: $75 - $125   *Comedy short. Duotone.*

GUNS AT BATASI
(1964 - 20th Century Fox) Richard Attenborough, Flora Robson
One Sheet: $5 - $10

GUNS DON'T ARGUE
(1957 - Visual Drama) Myron Healey, Jean Harvey
One Sheet: $10 - $20

GUNS FOR SAN SEBASTIAN
(1968 - MGM) Anthony Quinn, Anjanette Comer
One Sheet: $7 - $15

GUNS, GIRLS AND GANGSTERS
(1958 - United Artists) Mamie Van Doren, Gerald Mohr
One Sheet: $40 - $75

GUNS IN THE AFTERNOON
(1962 - -) See RIDE THE HIGH COUNTRY

GUNS IN THE DARK
(1937 - Republic) Johnny Mack Brown
One Sheet: $100 - $200

GUNS OF A STRANGER
(1973 - Universal) Marty Robbins, Chill Wills
One Sheet: $30 - $50   *Western. Country musical.*

GUNS OF DARKNESS
(1962 - Warner Bros.) David Niven, Leslie Caron
One Sheet: $15 - $25

GUNS OF DIABLO
(1964 - MGM) Charles Bronson, Kurt Russell
One Sheet: $15 - $25

GUNS OF FORT PETTICOAT, THE
(1957 - Columbia) Audie Murphy, Kathryn Grant
One Sheet: $30 - $50

GUNS OF HATE
(1948 - RKO) Tim Holt, Nan Leslie
One Sheet: $15 - $35

GUNS OF NAVARONE, THE
(1961 - Columbia) Gregory Peck, David Niven, Anthony Quinn
One Sheet: $75 - $150

GUNS OF NAVARONE, THE
(1966R - Columbia) Gregory Peck, David Niven, Anthony Quinn
One Sheet: $15 - $25   *Re-release.*

GUNS OF NAVARONE, THE
(1979R - Columbia) Gregory Peck, David Niven, Anthony Quinn
One Sheet: $5 - $10   *Re-release.*

GUNS OF THE BLACK WITCH
(1962 - AIP) Don Megowan, Silvana Pampanini
One Sheet: $7 - $15

GUNS OF THE LAW

(1944 - PRC) Dave O'Brien, Jim Newill
One Sheet: $20 - $40

GUNS OF THE MAGNIFICENT SEVEN
(1969 - United Artists) George Kennedy, James Whitmore, Monte Markham
One Sheet: $7 - $15

GUNS OF THE PECOS
(1936 - Warner Bros.) Dick Foran, Eddie Acuff
One Sheet: $75 - $150

GUNS OF THE TIMBERLAND
(1960 - Warner Bros.) Alan Ladd, Jeanne Crain, Frankie Avalon
One Sheet: $15 - $25

GUNSIGHT RIDGE
(1957 - United Artists) Joel McCrea, Mark Stevens
One Sheet: $15 - $25

GUNSLINGER, THE
(1956 - AIP) John Ireland, Beverly Garland
One Sheet: $20 - $40

GUNSLINGERS
(1950 - Monogram) Whip Wilson
One Sheet: $15 - $30

GUNSMOKE
(1953 - Universal) Audie Murphy, Susan Cabot
One Sheet: $40 - $75

GUNSMOKE IN TUCSON
(1958 - Allied Artists) Mark Stevens, Gale Robbins
One Sheet: $5 - $10

GUNSMOKE MESA
(1944 - PRC) Dave O'Brien, Jim Newill
One Sheet: $30 - $50

GUNSMOKE RANCH
(1937 - Republic) Three Mesquiteers (Livingston, Corrigan, Terhune)
One Sheet: $75 - $150

GUNSMOKE TRAIL
(1938 - Monogram) Jack Randall
One Sheet: $75 - $125

GURU, THE
(1969 - 20th Century Fox) Michael York, Saeed Jaffrey, Utpal Dutt
One Sheet: $10 - $20

GURU, THE MAD MONK
(1971 - Nova) Neil Flanagan
One Sheet: $15 - $25

GUS
(1976 - Buena Vista/Disney) Ed Asner, Don Knotts
One Sheet: $7 - $15

GUTTERSNIPE, THE
(1922 - Universal) Gladys Walton, Walter Perry
One Sheet: $150 - $300

GUY, A GAL, AND A PAL, A
(1945 - Columbia) Lynn Merrick, Ross Hunter
One Sheet: $40 - $75

GUY COULD CHANGE, A
(1945 - Republic) Allan Lane, Jane Frazee
One Sheet: $30 - $60

GUY NAMED JOE, A
(1944 - MGM) Spencer Tracy, Irene Dunne
One Sheet: $125 - $250

GUY NAMED JOE, A
(1955R - MGM) Spencer Tracy, Irene Dunn
One Sheet: $30 - $50   *Re-release. Duotone.*

GUY WHO CAME BACK, THE
(1951 - 20th Century Fox) Paul Douglas, Joan Bennett
One Sheet: $15 - $25

GUYANA, CULT OF THE DAMNED
(1980 - -) Stuart Whitman, Joseph Cotten
One Sheet: $15 - $25

GUYS AND DOLLS
(1955 - MGM) Marlon Brando, Jean Simmons, Frank Sinatra
One Sheet: $75 - $150

GYMKATA
(1985 - MGM/UA) Kurt Thomas, Tetchie Agbayani

One Sheet: $10 - $20   *Sports (Gymnastics). Sports Movie Posters #289.*

GYPPED IN THE PENTHOUSE
(1955 - Columbia) The Three Stooges (Shemp)
One Sheet: $150 - $300   *Comedy short. Duotone.*

One Sheet

GYPSY
(1937 - Warner Bros.) Roland Young
One Sheet: $50 - $100

GYPSY
(1962 - Warner Bros.) Natalie Wood, Rosalind Russell
One Sheet: $40 - $75

GYPSY AND THE GENTLEMAN, THE
(1958 - Rank Films) Melina Mercouri, Keith Mitchell
One Sheet: $10 - $20

GYPSY BLOOD
(1921 - -) Pola Negri, Dir: Ernst Lubitsch
One Sheet: $700 - $1,200   *German.*

GYPSY COLT
(1954 - MGM) Donna Corcoran, Frances Dee
One Sheet: $15 - $25

GYPSY FURY
(1951 - Monogram) Viveca Lindfors, Christopher Kent
One Sheet: $15 - $30

GYPSY GIRL
(1966 - Rank) Hayley Mills, Ian McShane
One Sheet: $10 - $20

GYPSY LIFE
(1943 - 20th Century Fox) Mighty Mouse
One Sheet: $250 - $600   *Cartoon. Full color stock poster with printed title. Huge image of Mighty Mouse on yellow background.*

GYPSY MELODY
(1936 - Wardour) Lupe Velez, Alfred Rode
One Sheet: $100 - $200

GYPSY MOTHS, THE
(1969 - MGM) Burt Lancaster, Deborah Kerr, Gene Hackman
One Sheet: $5 - $10

GYPSY PASSION
(1922 - Vitagraph) Ivor Novello, Rejane, Charles Vanel
One Sheet: $250 - $600

GYPSY WILDCAT
(1944 - Universal) Maria Montez, Jon Hall
One Sheet: $50 - $100

GYPSY WILDCAT
(1950R - Realart) Maria Montez, Jon Hall
One Sheet: $15 - $25   *Re-release.*

H. M. PULLMAN, ESQUIRE
(1940 - MGM) Robert Young, Ruth Hussey, Hedy Lamarr
One Sheet: $75 - $150

HABEAS CORPUS
(1928 - MGM) Laurel & Hardy
One Sheet: $4,000 - $6,000

HACKERS
(1995 - United Artists) Jonny Lee Miller, Angelina Jolie
One Sheet: $3 - $5

HAIL
(1973 - Cine-Globe) Dan Resin, Richard B. Shull

One Sheet: $3 - $5

HAIL AND FAREWELL
(1936 - Warner Bros.) Claude Hulbert, Nicholas Hannen
One Sheet: $100 - $200

HAIL! HAIL! ROCK N' ROLL
(1987 - -) Chuck Berry
One Sheet: $15 - $25   *Rock 'n' Roll.*

HAIL HERO!
(1969 - National General) Arthur Kennedy, Michael Douglas (film debut)
One Sheet: $5 - $10

HAIL MAFIA
(1965 - Goldstone) Jack Klugman, Henry Silva
One Sheet: $7 - $15

HAIL THE CONQUERING HERO
(1944 - Paramount) Eddie Bracken, Ella Raines, Dir: Preston Sturgess
One Sheet: $150 - $300

HAIL TO THE RANGERS
(1943 - Columbia) Charles Starrett
One Sheet: $40 - $75

HAIR
(1979 - United Artists) Treat Williams, John Savage
One Sheet: $15 - $25

One Sheet

HAIR OF THE DOG
(1962 - RFD) Dorinda Stevens, Reginald Beckwith
One Sheet: $5 - $10

HAIR TRIGGER BAXTER
(1926 - Triangle) Bob Custer, Lew Meehan
One Sheet: $250 - $600

HAIR TRIGGER CASEY
(1922 - -) Frank Borzage, Chick Morrison
One Sheet: $600 - $1,000

HAIR TRIGGER CASEY
(1936 - -) Jack Perrin
One Sheet: $200 - $400

HAIRDRESSER'S HUSBAND, THE
(1993 - Triton) -
One Sheet: $3 - $5

HAIRSPRAY
(1988 - NewLine) Sonny Bono, Debbie Harry, Divine
One Sheet: $15 - $30

HAIRY APE, THE
(1944 - United Artists) William Bendix, Susan Hayward
One Sheet: $50 - $100

HAL ROACH COMEDY CARNIVAL
(1947 - United Artists) -
One Sheet: $50 - $100

HALF A BRIDE
(1928 - Paramount) Gary Cooper, Esther Ralston
One Sheet: $600 - $1,000

HALF A HERO
(1953 - MGM) Red Skelton, Jean Hagen
One Sheet: $50 - $100

HALF A MAN
(1925 - Standard) Stan Laurel, Blanche Payson
One Sheet: $500 - $900

HALF A SINNER
(1934 - Universal) Sallie Blane, Joel McCrea
One Sheet: $125 - $250

HALF A SINNER
(1940 - 20th Century Fox) Heather Angel, John King
One Sheet: $75 - $125

HALF A SIXPENCE
(1968 - Paramount) Tommy Steele, Julia Foster
One Sheet: $5 - $10

HALF ANGEL
(1936 - 20th Century Fox) Frances Dee, Brian Donlevy
One Sheet: $150 - $300

HALF ANGEL
(1951 - 20th Century Fox) Loretta Young, Joseph Cotten
One Sheet: $20 - $40

HALF HUMAN/MONSTER FROM THE GREEN HELL
(1958 - DCA) John Carradine, Akira Takarada
One Sheet: $50 - $100   *Double feature poster.*

HALF MARRIAGE
(1929 - RKO) Olive Borden, Morgan Farley
One Sheet: $250 - $600

HALF MOON STREET
(1986 - -) Michael Caine, Sigourney Weaver
One Sheet: $5 - $10

HALF PAST MIDNIGHT
(1948 - 20th Century Fox) Kent Taylor, Peggy Knudsen
One Sheet: $20 - $40

HALF PINT, THE
(1960 - Sterling) Tommy Blackman, Pat Goldin
One Sheet: $7 - $15

HALF SHOT AT SUNRISE
(1930 - RKO) Bert Wheeler, Robert Woolsey
One Sheet: $150 - $300

HALF WAY GIRL, THE
(1925 - First National) Doris Kenyon, Lloyd Hughes
One Sheet: $250 - $500

HALF WAY TO SHANGHAI
(1942 - Universal) Irene Hervey, Kent Taylor
One Sheet: $50 - $100

HALF-A-DOLLAR BILL
(1924 - Graf) -
One Sheet: $200 - $400

HALF-BREED, THE
(1916 - -) Douglas Fairbanks, Alma Rubens
One Sheet: $800 - $1,500

HALF-BREED, THE
(1927R - -) Douglas Fairbanks, Alma Rubens
One Sheet: $250 - $500   *Cowboy Movie Posters #33. Re-release.*

HALF-BREED, THE
(1952 - RKO) Robert Young, Janis Carter
One Sheet: $15 - $25

HALF-NAKED TRUTH, THE
(1932 - RKO) Lee Tracy, Lupe Velez
One Sheet: $75 - $150

HALF-SHOT SHOOTERS
(1936 - Columbia) The Three Stooges (Curly)
One Sheet: $10,000 - $16,000   *Comedy short. Duotone.*

HALFWAY HOUSE, THE
(1943 - Ealing) Mervyn Johns, Francoise Rosay
One Sheet: $30 - $50

HALFWAY TO HEAVEN
(1929 - Paramount) Charles "Buddy" Rogers
One Sheet: $100 - $200

HALF-WITS HOLIDAY
(1947 - Columbia) The Three Stooges (Curly)
One Sheet: $2,500 - $4,000   *Comedy short. Duotone. Curly's last full picture. Remake of HOI POLLOI.*

HALLELUJAH!
(1929 - MGM) Daniel Haynes, William Fountaine
One Sheet: $19,000 - $30,000   *Black cast. Second all-black feature (see Hearts In Dixie). Separate Cinema, pg. 28.*

HALLELUJAH HILLS, THE
(1963 - Vermont) Peter H. Beard, Marty Greenbaum
One Sheet: $3 - $5

HALLELUJAH, I'M A BUM
(1933 - United Artists) Al Jolson, Harry Langdon, Madge Evans
One Sheet: $300 - $700   *Beware re-releases.*

HALLELUJAH TRAIL, THE
(1965 - United Artists) Burt Lancaster, Lee Remick
One Sheet: $15 - $25

HALLIDAY BRAND, THE
(1957 - United Artists) Joseph Cotten, Viveca Lindfors
One Sheet: $15 - $25

HALLOWEEN
(1978 - Falcon International) Donald Pleasence, Jamie Lee Curtis
One Sheet: $30 - $50
Advance:$125-$200.

HALLOWEEN HILARITIES
(1953 - Disney) -
One Sheet: $200 - $400   *Cartoon.*

HALLOWEEN II
(1981 - Universal) Jamie Lee Curtis, Donald Pleasence
One Sheet: $7 - $15

HALLOWEEN III: SEASON OF THE WITCH
(1983 - Universal) Tom Atkins, Stacey Nelkin
One Sheet: $5 - $10

HALLOWEEN IV: THE RETURN OF MICHAEL MYERS
(1988 - Universal) Donald Pleasence, Ellie Cornell
One Sheet: $5 - $10

HALLOWEEN: THE CURSE OF MICHAEL MYERS
(1995 - Miramax) Donald Pleasance, Paul Rudd
One Sheet: $7 - $15

HALLOWEEN V
(1989 - Universal) Donald Pleasence, Danielle Harris
One Sheet: $5 - $10

HALLS OF ANGER
(1970 - United Artists) Calvin Lockhart, Janet MacLachlan
One Sheet: $7 - $15   *Black cast.*

HALLS OF MONTEZUMA
(1951 - 20th Century Fox) Richard Widmark, Jack Palance
One Sheet: $50 - $100

HALLS OF MONTEZUMA
(1956R - 20th Century Fox) Richard Widmark, Jack Palance
One Sheet: $10 - $20   *Re-release.*

HALLUCINATION GENERATION
(1966 - Trans-American) George Montegomery
One Sheet: $15 - $25   *Drug film.*

HAM AND EGGS AT THE FRONT
(1927 - Warner Bros.) Myrna Loy
One Sheet: $500 - $800

HAMBURGER HILL
(1987 - RKO) Anthony Barrie, Michael Patrick Boatman
One Sheet: $3 - $5

HAMBURGER: THE MOTION PICTURE
(1986 - -) Leigh McCloskey, Dick Butkus
One Sheet: $3 - $5

HAMLET
(1921 - Art Film) -
One Sheet: $1,600 - $2,500   *German.*

HAMLET
(1948 - Universal International) Laurence Olivier, Jean Simmons
One Sheet: $250 - $600   *Academy Award: Best Picture, Best Actor. Academy Award Movie Posters #115 & #117.*

HAMLET
(1953R - Universal-International) Laurence Olivier, Jean Simmons
One Sheet: $100 - $200   *Re-release.*

HAMLET
(1962 - Weiler) Maximillian Schell
One Sheet: $10 - $20   *German.*

HAMLET
(1964 - Warner Bros.) Richard Burton, Hume Cronyn
One Sheet: $30 - $50

HAMLET
(1970 - Columbia) Nicol Williamson, Gordon Jackson, Judy Parfitt
One Sheet: $5 - $10

HAMLET
(1976 - Royal College) Anthony Meyer, Helen Mirren
One Sheet: $5 - $10

HAMLET
(1990 - Warner Bros.) Mel Gibson, Glenn Close
One Sheet: $7 - $15

HAMLET
(1996 - Columbia) Kenneth Branagh, Kate Winslet
One Sheet: $3 - $5

HAMMER
(1972 - United Artists) Fred Williamson, Bernie Hamilton, Vonneta McGee
One Sheet: $15 - $25   *Black cast. Sports Movie Posters #361.*

HAMMER THE TOFF
(1952 - Butchers) John Bentley, Patricia Danton
One Sheet: $15 - $25

HAMMERHEAD
(1968 - Columbia) Vince Edwards, Judy Geeson, Diana Dors
One Sheet: $5 - $10

HAMMERSMITH IS OUT
(1972 - Cinerama) Elizabeth Taylor, Richard Burton, Peter Ustinov
One Sheet: $7 - $15

HAMMETT
(1983 - Orion) Frederic Forrest, Marilu Henner, Dir: Wim Wenders
One Sheet: $7 - $15

HAND, THE
(1961 - AIP) Derek Bond, Ronald Lee Hunt
One Sheet: $15 - $25

HAND, THE
(1981 - Warner Bros.) Michael Caine, Andrea Marcovicci
One Sheet: $3 - $5

HAND IN HAND
(1961 - Columbia) John Gregson, Dame Sybil Thorndike
One Sheet: $3 - $5

HAND OF DEATH
(1962 - 20th Century Fox) John Agar, Paula Raymond
One Sheet: $30 - $50

Half Sheet

HAND OF NIGHT, THE
(1968 - Pathe) William Sylvester
One Sheet: $10 - $20   *AKA: BEAST OF MOROCCO.*

HAND THAT ROCKS THE CRADLE
(1992 - Buena Vista) Rebecca DeMornay
One Sheet: $5 - $10

HAND WRITING ON THE WALL
(1987 - -) Greg Shelton
One Sheet: $3 - $5

HANDCUFFED
(1929 - Rayart) Wheeler Oakman, Virginia Brown Faire
One Sheet: $200 - $400

HANDCUFFS, LONDON
(1955 - Eros) Bruce Seton
One Sheet: $15 - $25

HANDFUL OF DUST, A
(1988 - -) James Wilby, Kristin Scott, Anjelica Huston
One Sheet: $3 - $5

HANDLE WITH CARE
(1932 - Fox) James Dunn, Boots Mallory
One Sheet: $100 - $200

HANDLE WITH CARE
(1935 - RKO) Molly Lamont, Jack Hobbs
One Sheet: $100 - $200

HANDLE WITH CARE
(1958 - MGM) Dean Jones, Joan O'Brien
One Sheet: $10 - $20

HANDLE WITH CARE
(1964 - Sonac) Georgia Carr, Otis Greene
One Sheet: $40 - $75   *Black cast musical.*

HANDMAID'S TALE, THE
(1990 - -) Natasha Richardson, Robert Duvall, Faye Dunaway
One Sheet: $10 - $20

HANDS ACROSS THE BORDER
(1926 - F.B.O.) Fred Thomson
One Sheet: $600 - $1,000

HANDS ACROSS THE BORDER
(1943 - Republic) Roy Rogers, Ruth Terry
One Sheet: $150 - $300

HANDS ACROSS THE ROCKIES
(1941 - Columbia) Bill Elliott
One Sheet: $50 - $100

HANDS ACROSS THE TABLE
(1935 - Paramount) Carole Lombard, Fred MacMurray
One Sheet: $600 - $1,000

HANDS OF A STRANGER
(1962 - Allied Artists) Joan Harvey, Irish McCalla
One Sheet: $15 - $30

HANDS OF DESTINY
(1954 - Grovenor) Hilda Fenemore
One Sheet: $15 - $25

HANDS OF NARA, THE
(1922 - Metro) Clara Kimball Young
One Sheet: $200 - $400

HANDS OF ORLAC, THE
(1961 - Continental) Mel Ferrer, Dany Carrell
One Sheet: $5 - $10

HANDS OF STEEL
(1986 - -) Daniel Green, John Saxon
One Sheet: $3 - $5

HANDS OF THE RIPPER
(1972 - Universal) Eric Porter, Jane Merrow
One Sheet: $15 - $35

HANDS OFF!
(1920 - Fox) Tom Mix, Pauline Curley
One Sheet: $600 - $1,000

HANDS UP
(1922 - Arrow) Bobby Dunn
One Sheet: $150 - $300

HANDS UP
(1926 - Paramount) Raymond Griffith, Marion Nixon
One Sheet: $250 - $500

HANDY ANDY
(1934 - Fox) Will Rogers, Robert Taylor
One Sheet: $250 - $600   *Sports Movie Posters #220.*

HANG 'EM HIGH
(1968 - United Artists) Clint Eastwood, Inger Stevens, Ed Begley
One Sheet: $75 - $150   *Spaghetti western.*

HANG 'EM HIGH/THE GOOD, THE BAD AND

THE UGLY
(1969R - United Artists) Clint Eastwood, Inger Stevens, Ed Begley/Clint Eastwood
One Sheet: $30 - $60   *Re-release double feature poster.*

HANG YOUR HAT ON THE WIND
(1969 - Disney) Ric Natoli, Judson Pratt
One Sheet: $7 - $15

HANGAR 18
(1980 - Sunn Classics) Darren McGavin, Robert Vaughn
One Sheet: $7 - $15

HANGED MAN, THE
(1974 - -) Steve Forrest, Cameron Mitchell
One Sheet: $5 - $10

HANGING TREE, THE
(1959 - Warner Bros.) Gary Cooper, Maria Schell, George C. Scott(film debut)
One Sheet: $30 - $50

HANGMAN, THE
(1959 - Paramount) Robert Taylor, Tina Louise
One Sheet: $7 - $15

HANGMAN WAITS, THE
(1947 - Butchers) John Turnbull, Beatrice Cambell
One Sheet: $40 - $75

HANGMAN'S HOUSE
(1928 - Fox) June Collyer, Victor McLaglen, John Wayne(extra)
One Sheet: $250 - $500

HANGMAN'S KNOT
(1952 - Columbia) Randolph Scott, Donna Reed
One Sheet: $30 - $60

HANGMAN'S KNOT
(1961R - Columbia) Randolph Scott, Donna Reed
One Sheet: $10 - $20   *Re-release.*

HANGMAN'S WHARF
(1950 - DUK) John Witty
One Sheet: $15 - $25

HANGMEN ALSO DIE!
(1943 - United Artists) Brian Donlevy, Walter Brennan, Dir:Fritz Lang
One Sheet: $150 - $350

HANGOVER SQUARE
(1944 - 20th Century Fox) Laird Cregar, Linda Darnell
One Sheet: $125 - $250   *Graven Images, pg. 129.*

One Sheet

HANGUP
(1974 - Warner Bros.) William Elliott, Micheal Lerner, Marki Bey
One Sheet: $10 - $20   *Blaxploitation. "His job was busting junkies. His mistake was loving one."*

HANKY PANKY
(1982 - Columbia) Gene Wilder, Gilda Radner
One Sheet: $3 - $5

HANNA'S WAR
(1988 - Cannon) Ellen Burstyn, Maruschka Detmers
One Sheet: $2 - $3

HANNAH AND HER SISTERS
(1985 - Orion) Woody Allen, Michael Caine, Dianne Wiest
One Sheet: $10 - $20   *Academy Award: Best Supporting Actor(Caine), Best*

Supporting Actress(Wiest). Academy Award Movie Posters #351& #352.

HANNAH K
(1983 - Universal) Jill Clayburgh, Gabriel Byrne
One Sheet: $3 - $5

HANNIBAL
(1960 - Warner Bros.) Victor Mature, Rita Gam
One Sheet: $15 - $25

HANNIBAL BROOKS
(1969 - United Artists) Oliver Reed, Michael J. Pollard, Karin Baal
One Sheet: $7 - $15

HANNIE CAULDER
(1972 - Paramount) Raquel Welch, Robert Culp, Ernest Borgnine
One Sheet: $7 - $15

HANOI HILTON
(1987 - -) Michael Moriarty, Paul LeMat
One Sheet: $3 - $5

HANOVER STREET
(1979 - Columbia) Harrison Ford, Lesley-Anne Down, Christopher Plummer
One Sheet: $10 - $20   *Price is for both styles.*

HANS CHRISTIAN ANDERSEN
(1952 - RKO) Danny Kaye, Farley Granger
One Sheet: $30 - $50

HANSEL AND GRETEL
(1954 - RKO) Voices of Anna Russell, Mildred Dunnock
One Sheet: $40 - $75   *Cartoon.*

HANSEL AND GRETEL
(1965R - New Trends) Voices of Anna Russell, Mildred Dunnock
One Sheet: $3 - $5   *Re-release. Cartoon.*

HANSEL AND GRETEL
(1972R - -) -
One Sheet: $5 - $10   *Re-release. Cartoon.*

HANSOM CABMAN, THE
(1924 - Pathe) Harry Langdon
One Sheet: $500 - $800

HAPPENING, THE
(1967 - Columbia) Anthony Quinn, Faye Dunaway(film debut)
One Sheet: $15 - $30

HAPPIDROME
(1943 - MGM) Robbie Vincent, Cecil Frederick
One Sheet: $50 - $100

HAPPIEST DAYS OF YOUR LIFE, THE
(1950 - London) Alastair Sim, Margaret Rutherford
One Sheet: $15 - $25

HAPPIEST MILLIONAIRE, THE
(1967 - Disney) Fred McMurray, Greer Garson
One Sheet: $20 - $40

HAPPILY EVER AFTER
(1993 - First National) Snow White adaptation
One Sheet: $7 - $15   *Cartoon.*

One Sheet (Advance)

HAPPINESS
(1924 - Metro) Laurette Taylor, Pat O'Malley
One Sheet: $150 - $300

HAPPINESS AHEAD
(1934 - First National) Dick Powell, Frank McHugh

One Sheet: $100 - $200

HAPPINESS CAGE, THE
(1972 - Cinerama) Christopher Walken
One Sheet: $7 - $15   *AKA: THE MIND SNATCHERS.*

HAPPINESS C.O.D.
(1935 - Chesterfield) Maude Eburne, Donald Meek
One Sheet: $50 - $100

HAPPINESS OF THREE WOMEN, THE
(1954 - Advance) Petula Clark, Brenda Banzie
One Sheet: $15 - $30

HAPPY
(1934 - Wardour) Stanley Lupino
One Sheet: $100 - $200

HAPPY ANNIVERSARY
(1959 - United Artists) David Niven, Mitzi Gaynor
One Sheet: $15 - $25

HAPPY ANNIVERSARY 007
(1987 - -) Sean Connery, Roger Moore, George Lazenby, Timothy Dalton
One Sheet: $30 - $50

HAPPY AS THE GRASS WAS GREEN
(1973 - Martin) Geraldine Page
One Sheet: $3 - $5

HAPPY BIRTHDAY, GEMINI
(1980 - United Artists) Madeline Kahn, Rita Moreno
One Sheet: $3 - $5

HAPPY BIRTHDAY TO ME
(1981 - Columbia) Melissa Sue Anderson, Glenn Ford
One Sheet: $5 - $10

HAPPY BIRTHDAY, WANDA JUNE
(1971 - Columbia) Rod Steiger, Susannah York
One Sheet: $5 - $10

HAPPY DAYS
(1930 - Fox) Charles E. Evans, Janet Gaynor
One Sheet: $600 - $1,000

HAPPY DAYS
(1936 - Celebrity) Animated by Ub Iwerks
One Sheet: $600 - $1,000   *Cartoon. Full color stone litho. Cartoon Movie Posters #123.*

HAPPY ENDING, THE
(1931 - Gaumont) Anne Grey, Benita Hume
One Sheet: $125 - $250

HAPPY ENDING, THE
(1969 - United Artists) Jean Simmons, John Forsythe, Lloyd Bridges, Shirley Jones
One Sheet: $3 - $5

HAPPY GILMORE
(1996 - Universal) Adam Sandler
One Sheet: $4 - $8   *Sports Movie Posters #227.*

HAPPY GO LOVELY
(1951 - Excelsior) Vera-Ellen, David Niven
One Sheet: $10 - $20

HAPPY GO LUCKY
(1936 - Republic) Phil Regan, Evelyn Venable
One Sheet: $40 - $75

HAPPY GO LUCKY
(1943 - Paramount) Mary Martin, Dick Powell, Rudy Vallee
One Sheet: $75 - $150

HAPPY HOOKER, THE
(1975 - Cannon) Lynn Redgrave, Jean Pierre Aumont
One Sheet: $7 - $15

HAPPY HOOKER GOES TO HOLLYWOOD, THE
(1980 - Cannon) Martine Beswicke, Adam West, Phil Silvers
One Sheet: $7 - $15

HAPPY HOOKER GOES TO WASHINGTON, THE
(1977 - Cannon) Joey Heatherton, George Hamilton
One Sheet: $7 - $15

HAPPY IS THE BRIDE
(1957 - Panther) Ian Carmichael, Janette Scott
One Sheet: $10 - $20

HAPPY LAND
(1943 - 20th Century Fox) Don Ameche, Frances Dee, Natalie Wood (Age 5)
One Sheet: $75 - $150

HAPPY LANDING
(1934 - Monogram) Noah Beery, Jr., Julie Bishop
One Sheet: $75 - $150

HAPPY LANDING
(1938 - 20th Century Fox) Sonja Henie, Don Ameche
One Sheet: $100 - $200

HAPPY MARRIED COUPLE, A
(1916 - -) Neal Burns, Betty Compson
One Sheet: $200 - $400

HAPPY MOTHER'S DAY...LOVE, GEORGE
(1973 - Cinema 5) Ron Howard, Patricia Neal
One Sheet: $5 - $10

HAPPY NEW YEAR
(1987 - Columbia) Peter Falk, Wendy Hughes
One Sheet: $2 - $3

HAPPY ROAD, THE
(1956 - MGM) Gene Kelly, Barbara Laage
One Sheet: $15 - $30

HAPPY THIEVES, THE
(1962 - United Artists) Rex Harrison, Rita Hayworth
One Sheet: $10 - $20

HAPPY TIME, THE
(1952 - Columbia) Charles Boyer, Louis Jourdan
One Sheet: $10 - $20

HAPPY YEARS, THE
(1950 - MGM) Dean Stockwell, Darryl Hickman
One Sheet: $15 - $25

HARAKIRI
(1964 - Toho) Tatsuya Nakadai
One Sheet: $15 - $30   *Japanese.*

HARASSED HERO, THE
(1954 - Pathe) Guy Middleton
One Sheet: $15 - $25

HARBOR LIGHTS
(1963 - 20th Century Fox) Kent Taylor, Miriam Colon
One Sheet: $5 - $10

HARBOR OF MISSING MEN
(1950 - Republic) Richard Denning, Barbra Fuller
One Sheet: $15 - $35

HARD BODIES
(1984 - Columbia) Grant Cramer, Gary Wood
One Sheet: $5 - $10

HARD CONTRACT
(1969 - 20th Century Fox) James Coburn, Lee Remick, Lilli Palmer
One Sheet: $3 - $5

HARD COUNTRY
(1981 - Associated Film) Jan-Michael Vincent, Kim Basinger
One Sheet: $2 - $3

HARD DAY'S NIGHT, A
(1964 - United Artists) The Beatles (1st film)
One Sheet: $150 - $350   *Rock 'n' Roll. Duotone.*

One Sheet

HARD DAY'S NIGHT, A
(1982R - United Artists) The Beatles

One Sheet:　$30 - $50　　*Re-release.*

HARD, FAST AND BEAUTIFUL
(1951 - RKO) Claire Trevor, Robert Clarke
One Sheet:　$75 - $150　　*Sports (Tennis). Sports Movie Posters #333.*

HARD FEELINGS
(1981 - -) Carl Marotte, Alan Katz
One Sheet:　$3 - $5

HARD GUY
(1941 - PRC) Jack LaRue, Mary Healy
One Sheet:　$30 - $50

HARD HEADS, THE
(1980 - K-Tel) Alex Karras, Scott MacKenzie, Bob Ridgely
One Sheet:　$7 - $15　　*Sports Movie Posters #366.*

HARD HOMBRE, THE
(1931 - Allied) Hoot Gibson
One Sheet:　$200 - $400

HARD KILLER, THE
(1967 - -) Robert Weber, Franco Nero
One Sheet:　$7 - $15

HARD LUCK
(1921 - Metro) Buster Keaton
One Sheet:　$5,000 - $8,000

HARD MAN, THE
(1957 - Columbia) Guy Madison, Valerie French
One Sheet:　$10 - $20

HARD PROMISES
(1992 - Columbia) Sissy Spacek, William Peterson
One Sheet:　$3 - $5

HARD RIDE, THE
(1971 - AIP) Robert Fuller, Sherry Bain
One Sheet:　$5 - $10

HARD ROAD, THE
(1970 - Excelsior) Connie Nelson, John Alderman
One Sheet:　$5 - $10

HARD ROCK HARRIGAN
(1935 - Atherton) George O'Brien, Irene Hervey
One Sheet:　$100 - $200

HARD STEEL
(1941 - General Films) Wilfrid Lawson, Betty Stockfield
One Sheet:　$100 - $200

HARD TARGET
(1993 - Universal) Jean-Claude Van Damme, Lance Henriksen, Dir: John Woo
One Sheet:　$7 - $15

HARD TICKET TO HAWAII
(1987 - -) Dona Speir, Hope Marie Carlton
One Sheet:　$5 - $10

HARD TIMES
(1975 - Columbia) Charles Bronson, James Coburn
One Sheet:　$15 - $30　　*Sports (Bare-knuckle boxing).*

HARD TO GET
(1929 - Warner Bros.) Dorothy Mackaill, Edmund Burns
One Sheet:　$150 - $300

HARD TO GET
(1938 - Warner Bros.) Olivia de Havilland, Dick Powell
One Sheet:　$100 - $200

One Sheet

HARD TO HANDLE
(1933 - Warner Bros.) James Cagney, Mary Brian
One Sheet:　$1,600 - $2,500

HARD TO HOLD
(1984 - Universal) Rick Springfield, Janet Eilber
One Sheet:　$5 - $10

HARD TO KILL
(1990 - -) Steven Seagal, Kelly LeBrock
One Sheet:　$7 - $15

HARD TRAIL
(1969 - Brentwood) Lash LaRue, Donna Bradley
One Sheet:　$15 - $30

HARD WAY, THE
(1943 - Warner Bros.) Ida Lupino, Dennis Morgan
One Sheet:　$20 - $40

HARD WAY, THE
(1980 - -) Patrick McGoohan, Lee Van Cleef
One Sheet:　$3 - $5

HARD WAY, THE
(1991 - Universal) James Woods, Michael J. Fox
One Sheet:　$3 - $5

HARD WAY TO DIE, A
(1980 - -) Billy Chong, Carl Scott
One Sheet:　$3 - $5

HARDBODIES
(1984 - Columbia) Grant Cramer, Gary Wood
One Sheet:　$3 - $5

HARDBODIES 2
(1986 - -) Brad Zutaut, Fabiano Udinio
One Sheet:　$3 - $5

HARD-BOILED
(1992 - Rim) Chow Yun-Fat, Dir: John Woo
One Sheet:　$15 - $30　　*Chinese.*

HARD-BOILED CANARY, THE
(1941 - Paramount) Allan Jones, Susanna Foster
One Sheet:　$50 - $100

HARD-BOILED MAHONEY
(1947 - Monogram) Bowery Boys (Leo Gorcey, Huntz Hall)
One Sheet:　$30 - $60

HARDBOILED ROSE
(1929 - Warner Bros.) Myrna Loy, William Collier, Jr.
One Sheet:　$600 - $1,000

HARDCORE
(1979 - Columbia) George C. Scott, Season Hubley
One Sheet:　$7 - $15

HARDER THEY COME, THE
(1973 - New World) Jimmy Cliff, Janet Barkley
One Sheet:　$30 - $50

HARDER THEY FALL, THE
(1956 - Columbia) Humphrey Bogart (last film), Rod Steiger
One Sheet:　$50 - $100　　*Sports (Boxing). Sports Movie Posters #154.*

HARDLY WORKING
(1981 - 20th Century Fox) Jerry Lewis, Susan Oliver
One Sheet:　$3 - $5

HARDWARE
(1990 - -) Dylan McDermott, Iggy Pop, Stacey Travis
One Sheet:　$10 - $20

HARDYS RIDE HIGH, THE
(1939 - MGM) Lewis Stone, Mickey Rooney
One Sheet:　$100 - $200

HAREM GIRL
(1952 - Columbia) Joan Davis, Peggy Castle
One Sheet:　$30 - $50

HARLEM AFTER MIDNIGHT
(1935 - Micheaux) -
One Sheet:　$250 - $500　　*Black cast.*

HARLEM FOLLIES
(1955 - Futurity Films) -

One Sheet:　$40 - $75　　*Black cast.*

HARLEM GLOBETROTTERS, THE
(1951 - Columbia) Thomas Gomez, Harlem Globetrotters
One Sheet:　$75 - $150　　*Sports (Basketball). Sports Movie Posters #s 89, 90.*

HARLEM GLOBETROTTERS, THE
(1957R - Columbia) Thomas Gomez, Harlem Globetrotters
One Sheet:　$50 - $100　　*Re-release. Players appear white!*

HARLEM IS HEAVEN
(1932 - Lincoln) Bill "Bojangles" Robinson
One Sheet:　$600 - $1,000　　*Black cast. Separate Cinema, pg. 93.*

HARLEM NIGHTS
(1989 - -) Eddie Murphy, Richard Pryor
One Sheet:　$7 - $15　　*Black cast.*

HARLEM ON PARADE
(1945 - Sack) Lena Horne, Lucky Millinder
One Sheet:　$350 - $750　　*Black cast. Teddy Wilson's Orch.*

HARLEM ON THE PRAIRIE
(1939 - Toddy) Herbert Jeffrey, Mantan Moreland
One Sheet:　$250 - $600　　*Black cast. Cowboy Movie Posters #234. Separate Cinema, pgs. 52-53.*

HARLEM RIDES THE RANGE
(1939 - Sack Amusement) Herbert Jeffrey
One Sheet:　$250 - $600　　*Black cast. Separate Cinema, pg. 51.*

HARLEQUIN
(1980 - Hemdale) Robert Powell
One Sheet:　$3 - $5

HARLEY DAVIDSON AND THE MARLBORO MAN
(1991 - MGM/Pathe) Mickey Rourke, Don Johnson
One Sheet:　$15 - $25

HARLOW
(1965 - Magna) Carol Lynley, Ginger Rogers
One Sheet:　$20 - $40

One Sheet

HARLOW
(1965 - Paramount) Carroll Baker, Peter Lawford, Martin Balsam
One Sheet:　$7 - $15

HARMON OF MICHIGAN
(1941 - Columbia) Tommy Harmon, Anita Louise
One Sheet:　$200 - $400　　*Sports (Football). Film biography of Tom Harmon.*

HARMONY AT HOME
(1930 - Fox) William Collier, Sr., Charlotte Henry
One Sheet:　$200 - $400

HARMONY HEAVEN
(1930 - British International) Polly Ward, Stuart Hall
One Sheet:　$100 - $200

HARMONY LANE
(1935 - Mascot) Douglas Montgomery, Evelyn Venable
One Sheet:　$100 - $200

HAROLD AND MAUDE
(1971 - Paramount) Ruth Gordon, Bud Cort, Vivian Pickles
One Sheet:　$7 - $15

HAROLD LLOYD'S WORLD OF COMEDY
(1962 - Continental) Compilation
One Sheet:　$15 - $25

HAROLD TEEN
(1928 - First National) Arthur Lake, Mary Brian
One Sheet:　$250 - $500

HAROLD TEEN
(1934 - Vitagraph) Hal Leroy, Rochelle Hudson
One Sheet:　$200 - $400　　*From the comic strip by Carl Ed.*

One Sheet

HARP OF TARA
(1914 - Mutual) -
One Sheet:　$500 - $800

HARPER
(1966 - Warner Bros.) Paul Newman, Lauren Bacall
One Sheet:　$15 - $25

HARPER VALLEY P.T.A.
(1978 - April Fools Release) Barbara Eden, Ronny Cox
One Sheet:　$10 - $20　　*Harvey Kurtzman art (Mad Magazine artist).*

HARPOON
(1948 - Danches Bros.) John Bromfield, Alice Lewis
One Sheet:　$15 - $30

HARRAD EXPERIMENT, THE
(1973 - Cinerama) James Whitmore, Tippi Hedren, Don Johnson
One Sheet:　$3 - $5

HARRAD SUMMER
(1974 - Cinerama) Richard Doran, Victoria Thompson
One Sheet:　$3 - $5

HARRIET CRAIG
(1950 - Columbia) Joan Crawford, Wendell Corey
One Sheet:　$50 - $100

HARRIET THE SPY
(1996 - Paramount) Rosie O'Donnell, Michelle Trachtenberg
One Sheet:　$4 - $8

HARRIGAN'S KID
(1943 - MGM) Bobby Readick, William Gargan
One Sheet:　$50 - $100

HARRY AND SON
(1983 - Orion) Paul Newman, Robby Benson
One Sheet:　$3 - $5

HARRY AND THE HENDERSONS
(1987 - Amblin) John Lithgow, Melinda Dillon
One Sheet:　$3 - $5

HARRY AND TONTO
(1974 - Fox) Art Carney, Ellen Burstyn, Chief Dan George
One Sheet:　$15 - $25　　*Academy Award: Best Actor (Carney). Academy Award Movie Posters #283.*

HARRY AND WALTER GO TO NEW YORK
(1976 - Columbia) James Caan, Michael Caine
One Sheet:　$5 - $10　　*Price is for either style.*

HARRY BLACK AND THE TIGER
(1958 - 20th Century Fox) Stewart Granger, Barbara Rush
One Sheet:　$15 - $25

HARRY IN YOUR POCKET

(1973 - United Artists) James Coburn, Michael Sarrazin
One Sheet: $4 - $8   *Price is for either style.*

HARRY TRACY
(1982 - Quartet) Bruce Dern, Helen Shaver
One Sheet: $3 - $5

HARRY'S WAR
(1980 - Taft International) Edward Herrmann, Geraldine Page
One Sheet: $3 - $5

HARUM SCARUM
(1965 - MGM) Elvis Presley, Mary Ann Mobley
One Sheet: $40 - $85

One Sheet

HARVARD, HERE I COME
(1941 - Columbia) Maxie Rosenbloom, Arline Judge
One Sheet: $100 - $200

HARVEST MELODY
(1943 - PRC) Rosemary Lane, Johnny Downs
One Sheet: $30 - $60

HARVESTER, THE
(1927 - F.B.O.) Orville Caldwell, Natalie Kingston
One Sheet: $200 - $400

HARVESTER, THE
(1936 - Republic) Alice Brady, Russell Hardie
One Sheet: $40 - $75

HARVEY
(1950 - Universal) James Stewart, Josephine Hull
One Sheet: $600 - $1,000   *Academy Award Movie Posters #133.*

HARVEY GIRLS, THE
(1945 - MGM) Judy Garland, John Hodiak
One Sheet: $300 - $700

HARVEY MIDDLEMAN, FIREMAN
(1965 - Columbia) Gene Troobnick, Hermione Gingold
One Sheet: $7 - $15

HAS ANYBODY SEEN MY GAL
(1952 - Universal) Piper Laurie, Rock Hudson, Charles Coburn
One Sheet: $30 - $50

HASTY HEART, THE
(1950 - Warner Bros.) Ronald Reagan, Patricia Neal
One Sheet: $75 - $125

HAT CHECK GIRL
(1932 - Fox) Sally Eilers, Ben Lyon, Ginger Rogers
One Sheet: $200 - $400

HAT CHECK HONEY
(1944 - Universal) Grace McDonald, Leon Errol
One Sheet: $50 - $100

HAT, COAT, AND GLOVE
(1934 - RKO) Ricardo Cortez, John Beal
One Sheet: $75 - $150

HATARI!
(1962 - Paramount) John Wayne, Hardy Kruger
One Sheet: $40 - $75

HATARI!
(1967R - Paramount) John Wayne, Hardy Kruger
One Sheet: $15 - $30   *Re-release.*

HAT-BOX MYSTERY, THE

(1947 - Screen Art) Tom Neal, Pamela Blake
One Sheet: $30 - $60

HATCH UP YOUR TROUBLES
(1949 - MGM) Tom & Jerry
One Sheet: $300 - $700   *Cartoon. Full color stone litho. Cartoon Movie Posters #277.*

HATCHET FOR A HONEYMOON
(1969 - GGP) Stephen Forsyth, Dagmar Lassander
One Sheet: $7 - $15

HATCHET MAN, THE
(1932 - First National) Edward G. Robinson, Loretta Young
One Sheet: $250 - $600

HATCHET MURDERS
(1976 - -) Dir: Dario Argento
One Sheet: $7 - $15

HATE
(1996 - Gramercy) Dir: Mathieu Kassovitz
One Sheet: $5 - $10

HATE FOR HATE
(1967 - West Film) John Ireland, Antonio Sabato
One Sheet: $15 - $35   *Spaghetti Western.*

HATE SHIP, THE
(1930 - British International) Jameson Thomas, Jean Colin
One Sheet: $100 - $200

HATFUL OF RAIN, A
(1957 - 20th Century Fox) Eva Marie Saint, Don Murray
One Sheet: $15 - $30

HATS OFF
(1927 - MGM) Laurel & Hardy
One Sheet: $4,000 - $6,000

HATS OFF
(1936 - Grand National) Mae Clarke, John Payne
One Sheet: $75 - $150

HATTER'S CASTLE
(1941 - Paramount) Robert Newton, James Mason, Deborah Kerr
One Sheet: $75 - $150

HAUNTED, THE
(1976 - Northgate) Virginia Mayo, Aldo Ray
One Sheet: $5 - $10

HAUNTED GOLD
(1933 - Vitagraph) John Wayne, Sheila Terry
One Sheet: $3,500 - $5,000   *Cowboy Movie Posters # 139.*

HAUNTED GOLD
(1953R - Warner Bros.) John Wayne, Sheila Terry
One Sheet: $40 - $75   *Re-release. Duotone.*

HAUNTED HARBOR
(1944 - Republic) Kane Richmond, Kay Aldridge
One Sheet: $50 - $100   *Serial. 15 Chapters.*

HAUNTED HONEYMOON
(1925 - Pathe) Glenn Tryon
One Sheet: $200 - $400

HAUNTED HONEYMOON
(1940 - MGM) Robert Montgomery, Constance Cummings
One Sheet: $75 - $150

HAUNTED HONEYMOON
(1985 - Orion) Gene Wilder, Gilda Radner
One Sheet: $5 - $10

HAUNTED HOUSE, THE
(1921 - Metro) Buster Keaton
One Sheet: $7,500 - $12,000

HAUNTED HOUSE, THE
(1925 - Pathe) Harold Lloyd
One Sheet: $600 - $1,000

HAUNTED HOUSE, THE
(1928 - First National) Chester Conklin, Thelma Todd
One Sheet: $250 - $500   *Graven Images, pg. 31.*

HAUNTED HOUSE, THE
(1940 - Monogram) Marcia Mae Jones, Jackie Moran
One Sheet: $75 - $150

HAUNTED MINE, THE
(1945 - Monogram) Johnny Mack Brown, Linda Johnson
One Sheet: $40 - $75

HAUNTED PALACE, THE
(1963 - AIP) Vincent Price, Lon Chaney
One Sheet: $40 - $75

HAUNTED RANCH
(1926 - Davis) Ken Maynard, Alma Rayford
One Sheet: $250 - $500   *AKA: THE HAUNTED RANGE.*

HAUNTED RANCH
(1943 - Monogram) The Range Busters
One Sheet: $30 - $50

HAUNTED RANGE, THE
(1926 - Davis Dist.) Ken Maynard
One Sheet: $200 - $400

HAUNTED SPOOKS
(1920 - Pathe) Harold Lloyd
One Sheet: $1,600 - $2,500

HAUNTED SPOOKS
(192?R - Pathe) Harold Lloyd
One Sheet: $600 - $1,000   *Re-release.*

HAUNTED STRANGLER, THE
(1957 - MGM) Boris Karloff, Anthony Dawson
One Sheet: $150 - $300

One Sheet

HAUNTED STRANGLER, THE
(1962R - MGM) Boris Karloff, Anthony Dawson
One Sheet: $20 - $40   *Re-release.*

HAUNTED SUMMER
(1988 - Cannon) Phillip Anglim, Laura Dern
One Sheet: $2 - $3

HAUNTED TRAILS
(1949 - Monogram) Whip Wilson, Andy Clyde
One Sheet: $40 - $75

HAUNTED VALLEY
(1923 - Pathe) Ruth Roland
One Sheet: $250 - $600   *Serial. 15 Chapters.*

HAUNTING, THE
(1963 - MGM) Julie Harris, Claire Bloom
One Sheet: $50 - $100   *Advance one sheet: $75-$150. Graven Images, pg. 218.*

HAUNTING OF JULIA, THE
(1977 - Fester) Mia Farrow, Keir Dullea
One Sheet: $5 - $10   *AKA: FULL CIRCLE.*

HAUNTING OF M, THE
(1979 - New Image) Sheelagh Gilbey, Alan Hay
One Sheet: $5 - $10

HAUNTING OF MORELLA, THE
(1989 - Concorde) David McCallum, Nicole Eggert
One Sheet: $10 - $20

HAUNTING OF ROSALIND, THE
(1973 - -) Susan Sarandon
One Sheet: $3 - $5

HAUNTS
(1977 - Intercontinental) May Britts, Cameron Mitchell
One Sheet: $3 - $5

HAVANA
(1990 - Universal) Robert Redford, Lena Olin
One Sheet: $7 - $15

HAVANA ROSE
(1951 - Republic) Estelita Rodriguez, Hugh Herbert
One Sheet: $20 - $40

HAVANA WIDOWS
(1933 - First National) Joan Blondell, Glenda Farrell
One Sheet: $150 - $300

HAVE A HEART
(1934 - MGM) Jean Parker, James Dunn
One Sheet: $100 - $200

HAVE A NICE WEEKEND
(1975 - Weekend) M.B. Miller, Valerie Shepherd
One Sheet: $5 - $10

HAVE ROCKET WILL TRAVEL
(1959 - Columbia) The 3 Stooges (Curly Joe)
One Sheet: $75 - $150

HAVING A WILD WEEKEND
(1965 - Warner Bros.) Dave Clark Five
One Sheet: $30 - $60

HAVING WONDERFUL CRIME
(1944 - RKO) Pat O'Brien, George Murphy, Carole Landis
One Sheet: $75 - $150

HAVING WONDERFUL TIME
(1938 - RKO) Ginger Rogers, Douglas Fairbanks, Jr., Lucille Ball
One Sheet: $200 - $400

HAWAII
(1966 - United Artists) Julie Andrews, Max von Sydow
One Sheet: $30 - $50

HAWAII CALLS
(1938 - RKO) Bobby Breen, Ned Sparks
One Sheet: $75 - $150

One Sheet

HAWAIIAN BUCKAROO
(1938 - Principal) Pat O'Brien, Evalyn Knapp, Smith Ballew
One Sheet: $30 - $60

One Sheet

HAWAIIAN HOLIDAY
(1947R - RKO/Disney) Mickey Mouse, Donald Duck
One Sheet: $1,300 - $2,000   *Re-release. Cartoon. One Sheets for the original 1930's release were not produced.*

HAWAIIAN NIGHTS
(1934 - RKO) Sidney Blackmer, Mary Boland

One Sheet: $500 - $800 *Australian.*
AKA: DOWN TO THEIR LAST YACHT.

HAWAIIAN NIGHTS
(1939 - Universal) Johnny Downs, Constance
Moore
One Sheet: $150 - $300

HAWAIIANS, THE
(1970 - United Artists) Charlton Heston,
Geraldine Chaplin
One Sheet: $10 - $20

HAWK OF POWDER RIVER, THE
(1947 - Pathe) Eddie Dean, Jennifer Holt
One Sheet: $15 - $25

HAWK OF THE HILLS
(1929 - Pathe) Allene Ray, Walter Miller
One Sheet: $150 - $300 *Serial. 10
Chapters.*

HAWK OF THE WILDERNESS
(1938 - Republic) Herman Brix, Mala, Monte
Blue
One Sheet: $150 - $300 *Serial.
Western. 12 Chapters.*

HAWK OF WILD RIVER, THE
(1952 - Columbia) Charles Starrett, Smiley
Burnette
One Sheet: $15 - $25

HAWK THE SLAYER
(1980 - ITC) Jack Palance, John Terry
One Sheet: $5 - $10

HAWKS OF THE SEA
(1924 - Pathe) -
One Sheet: $900 - $1,600 *Cartoon.*

HAWLEY'S OF HIGH STREET
(1933 - Wardour) Leslie Fuller, Judy Kelly
One Sheet: $150 - $300

HAWMPS
(1976 - Mulberry) James Hampton, Slim Picken
One Sheet: $3 - $5

HAY FOOT
(1941 - United Artists) William Tracy, James
Gleason
One Sheet: $50 - $100

HAYFOOT, STRAWFOOT
(1919 - Famous Players-Lasky) Charles Ray,
Doris Lee (May)
One Sheet: $250 - $500

HAYSEED, THE
(1922 - William Fox) Buster Keaton, Fatty
Arbuckle
One Sheet: $5,500 - $9,000

HAZARD
(1948 - Paramount) Paulette Goddard,
Macdonald Carey
One Sheet: $40 - $75

HAZARDS OF HELEN
(1914 - Kalem) -
One Sheet: $500 - $800

HAZEL FROM HOLLYWOOD
(1918 - -) Dorothy Devore
One Sheet: $250 - $500

HAZEL'S PEOPLE
(1978 - People Place) Geraldine Page, Pat
Hingle
One Sheet: $3 - $5

HAZING, THE
(1978 - Miraleste) Jeff East, Charlie Martin
Smith
One Sheet: $5 - $10

HE CAN'T MAKE IT STICK
(1941 - Columbia) Color Rhapsodies
One Sheet: $250 - $500 *Cartoon. Full
color semi-stock poster with inset of title. Large
image of Hitler.*

HE COOKED HIS GOOSE
(1952 - Columbia) The Three Stooges (Shemp)
One Sheet: $150 - $350 *Comedy short.
Duotone.*

HE COULDN'T SAY NO
(1937 - Warner Bros.) Frank McHugh, Jane
Wyman
One Sheet: $50 - $100

HE COULDN'T TAKE IT

(1934 - Monogram) Ray Walker, Virginia
Cherrill
One Sheet: $50 - $100

HE DID AND HE DIDN'T
(1916 - Triangle) Roscoe "Fatty" Arbuckle,
Mabel Normand
One Sheet: $1,600 - $2,500

HE FOUND A STAR
(1941 - General) Sarah Churchill, Vic Oliver
One Sheet: $40 - $75

HE HIRED THE BOSS
(1942 - 20th Century Fox) Stuart Erwin, Evelyn
Venable
One Sheet: $75 - $150

HE KNEW WOMEN
(1930 - RKO) Lowell Sherman, Alice Joyce
One Sheet: $200 - $400

HE KNOWS YOU'RE ALONE
(1981 - MGM) Don Scardino, Caitlin O'Heaney
One Sheet: $3 - $5

HE LAUGHED LAST
(1956 - Columbia) Frankie Laine, Lucy Marlow
One Sheet: $10 - $20

HE LEARNED ABOUT WOMEN
(1932 - Paramount Publix) Alison Skipworth,
Stuart Erwin
One Sheet: $125 - $250

HE LOVED AN ACTRESS
(1938 - Biltmore) Ben Lyon, Bebe Daniels
One Sheet: $50 - $100

HE MARRIED HIS WIFE
(1940 - 20th Century Fox) Joel McCrea, Nancy
Kelly
One Sheet: $75 - $150

HE MARRIED HIS WIFE
(1951R - 20th Century Fox) Joel McCrea,
Nancy Kelly
One Sheet: $10 - $20 *Re-release.*

HE RAISED KANE
(1923 - -) See THE LEATHER PUSHERS
(SERIAL)

HE RAN ALL THE WAY
(1951 - United Artists) John Garfield, Shelley
Winters
One Sheet: $40 - $75 *Garfield's last
film.*

HE RIDES TALL
(1964 - Universal) Tony Young, Dan Duryea
One Sheet: $3 - $5

HE SAID, SHE SAID
(1991 - Paramount) Kevin Bacon, Elizabeth
Perkins
One Sheet: $3 - $5

HE SNOOPS TO CONQUER
(1944 - Columbia) George Formby
One Sheet: $50 - $100 *Comedy short.
Duotone.*

HE STAYED FOR BREAKFAST
(1940 - Columbia) Loretta Young, Melvyn
Douglas
One Sheet: $50 - $100

HE WALKED BY NIGHT
(1948 - Pathe) Richard Basehart, Scott Brady
One Sheet: $50 - $100

HE WAS HER MAN
(1934 - Warner Bros.) James Cagney, Joan
Blondell
One Sheet: $1,600 - $2,500

HE WHO GETS SLAPPED
(1924 - MGM) Lon Chaney, Norma Shearer
One Sheet: $3,500 - $5,000 *MGM's first
production.*

HE WHO MUST DIE
(1965 - Lopert) Melina Mercouri
One Sheet: $7 - $15

HE WHO RIDES A TIGER
(1966 - Sigma III) Tom Bell, Judy Dench
One Sheet: $7 - $15

HE'S A COCKEYED WONDER
(1950 - Columbia) Mickey Rooney, Terry Moore
One Sheet: $30 - $50

HE'S MY GUY
(1943 - Universal) Dick Foran, Joan Davis
One Sheet: $50 - $100

HEAD, THE
(1962 - Rapid) Horst Frank
One Sheet: $15 - $30 *AKA: THE
SCREAMING HEAD.*

HEAD
(1968 - Columbia) The Monkees, Jack
Nicholson
One Sheet: $75 - $150 *Rock 'n' Roll.*

HEAD OF A TYRANT
(1960 - Universal) Massimo Girotti, Isabelle
Corey
One Sheet: $7 - $15

HEAD OF THE FAMILY
(1933 - Warner Bros.) Arthur Maude
One Sheet: $150 - $300

HEAD OFFICE
(1936 - Warner Bros.) Owen Nares, Arthur
Margetson
One Sheet: $100 - $200

HEAD OFFICE
(1986 - -) Judge Reinhold, Eddie Albert, Jane
Seymour
One Sheet: $3 - $5

HEAD ON
(1971 - Leon) Michael Witney
One Sheet: $3 - $5

HEAD ON
(1981 - Grant) Sally Kellerman, Stephen Lack
One Sheet: $3 - $5

HEAD OVER HEELS
(1922 - Goldwyn) Mabel Normand, Hugh
Thompson
One Sheet: $300 - $700

HEAD OVER HEELS IN LOVE
(1937 - Gaumont) Jessie Matthews, Louis
Borrell
One Sheet: $100 - $200

HEADIN' EAST
(1943 - Columbia) Buck Jones, Ruth Colman
One Sheet: $150 - $300

HEADIN' FOR BROADWAY
(1980 - 20th Century Fox) Rex Smith, Vivian
Reed
One Sheet: $5 - $10

HEADIN' FOR GOD'S COUNTRY
(1943 - Republic) William Lundigan, Virginia
Dale
One Sheet: $50 - $100

HEADIN' FOR THE RIO GRANDE
(1936 - Grand National) Tex Ritter, Eleanor
Stewart
One Sheet: $100 - $200

HEADIN' FOR TROUBLE
(1931 - Big 4) Bob Custer, Betty Mack
One Sheet: $125 - $250

HEADIN' HOME
(1920 - -) Babe Ruth
One Sheet: $16,000 - $25,000 *Sports
(Baseball). Sports Movie Posters #32.*

HEADIN' NORTH
(1930 - Tiffany) Bob Steele
One Sheet: $200 - $450

HEADING FOR BROADWAY
(1980 - 20th Century Fox) Rex Smith
One Sheet: $5 - $10

HEADING FOR HEAVEN
(1948 - PRC) Stuart Erwin, Glenda Farrell
One Sheet: $20 - $40

HEADING WEST
(1946 - -) Charles Starrett, Smiley Burnette
One Sheet: $30 - $50

HEADLESS GHOST, THE
(1959 - AIP) Richard Lyon, Liliane Scottane
One Sheet: $30 - $50

HEADLESS HORSEMAN, THE
(1934 - Celebrity) UB Iwerks
One Sheet: $1,300 - $2,000 *Cartoon.
Cartoon Movie Poster #108.*

HEADLEYS AT HOME, THE
(1938 - Standard) Evelyn Venable
One Sheet: $40 - $75

HEADLINE
(1943 - Ealing) David Farrar, Anne Crawford
One Sheet: $50 - $100

HEADLINE CRASHER
(1937 - Guaranteed) Frankie Darro, Kane
Richmond
One Sheet: $75 - $150

HEADLINE HUNTERS
(1955 - Republic) Rod Cameron, Julie Bishop
One Sheet: $20 - $40

HEADLINE HUNTERS
(1968 - Ansus) Susan Payne, Jeffrey Chandler
One Sheet: $10 - $20

HEADLINE SHOOTER
(1933 - RKO) William Gargan, Frances Dee,
Ralph Bellamy
One Sheet: $125 - $250

HEADLINE WOMAN, THE
(1935 - Mascot) Heather Angel, Roger Pryor
One Sheet: $75 - $150

HEADS UP
(1930 - Paramount) Charles "Buddy" Rogers,
Helen Kane
One Sheet: $100 - $200

HEADS WE GO
(1933 - United Artists) Constance Cummings,
Frank Lawton
One Sheet: $75 - $150

HEALER, THE
(1935 - Monogram) Ralph Bellamy, Mickey
Rooney
One Sheet: $150 - $300

HEALTH
(1980 - 20th Century Fox) Glenda Jackson,
Carol Burnett
One Sheet: $3 - $5

HEALTH FARM, THE
(1936 - Educational) Paul Terry Studio
*Cartoon. See "Terrytoons Stock" for prices.
Cartoon Movie Posters #82.*

HEALTHY, WEALTHY, AND DUMB
(1938 - Columbia) The Three Stooges (Curly)
One Sheet: $7,500 - $12,000 *Comedy short.
Duotone.*

HEAR ME GOOD
(1957 - Paramount) Hal March, Joe E. Ross
One Sheet: $15 - $35

HEAR NO EVIL
(1993 - 20th Century Fox) Marlee Matlin, D.B.
Sweeney
One Sheet: $3 - $5

HEARSE, THE
(1980 - Crown) Trish Van Devere, Joseph
Cotten
One Sheet: $5 - $10

HEART AND SOUL
(1950 - Crest) Vittorio De Sica, Maria Mercader
One Sheet: $20 - $40

HEART AND SOULS
(1993 - Universal) Robert Downey Jr., Charles
Grodin
One Sheet: $3 - $5

HEART BEAT
(1979 - Warner Bros.) Nick Nolte, Sissy Spacek
One Sheet: $7 - $15

HEART BREAKER, THE
(1925 - Fox) -
One Sheet: $100 - $200

HEART CONDITION
(1990 - New Line) Bob Hoskins, Denzel
Washington
One Sheet: $4 - $8

HEART IS A LONELY HUNTER, THE
(1968 - Warner Bros.) Alan Arkin, Sondra
Locke, Stacy Keach
One Sheet: $5 - $10

HEART LIKE A WHEEL
(1983 - 20th Century Fox) Bonnie Bedalia,
Beau Bridges

One Sheet: $7 - $15   *Sports (Auto Racing). Sports Movie Posters #26.*

HEART LINE, THE
(1921 - Pathe) Anthony F. Beck
One Sheet: $125 - $250

Lobby Card

HEART O' THE HILLS
(1919 - First National) Mary Pickford, Harold Goodwin
One Sheet: $600 - $1,000

HEART OF A BRUTE, THE
(191? - Balboa) -
One Sheet: $300 - $700

HEART OF A CHILD, THE
(1920 - -) Alla Nazimova, Charles Bryant
One Sheet: $250 - $600

HEART OF A LION, THE
(1918 - Fox) William Farnum, Wanda Petit, Mary Martin
One Sheet: $250 - $500

HEART OF A MAN
(1959 - Rank) Frankie Vaughan, Anne Heywood
One Sheet: $5 - $12

HEART OF A NATION, THE
(1943 - A.F.E.) Raimu, Michelle Morgan, Louis Jounet
One Sheet: $40 - $75

HEART OF A PEDDLER
(1918 - Unicorn) -
One Sheet: $125 - $250

HEART OF ARIZONA
(1938 - Paramount) William Boyd, Gabby Hayes
One Sheet: $500 - $800   *Hopalong Cassidy series. Cowboy Movie Posters #230.*

HEART OF ARIZONA
(1948R - Screen Guild) William Boyd, Gabby Hayes
One Sheet: $50 - $100   *Re-release.*

HEART OF DIXIE
(1989 - Orion) Ally Sheedy, Virginia Madsen, Phoebe Cates
One Sheet: $7 - $15

HEART OF HUMANITY, THE
(1919 - Jewel) Dorothy Phillips, Erich Von Stroheim, William Stowell
One Sheet: $250 - $500

HEART OF MARYLAND, THE
(1915 - Tiffany) Leslie Carter, William E. Shay
One Sheet: $500 - $800

HEART OF MIDNIGHT
(1989 - -) Jennifer Jason Leigh, Peter Coyote
One Sheet: $7 - $15

HEART OF NEW YORK
(1929 - Atlantic) Al Jolson, Madge Evans
One Sheet: $600 - $1,000

HEART O' NEW YORK
(1932 - Warner Bros.) Smith & Dale, Ruth Hall
One Sheet: $125 - $250

HEART OF PARIS
(1939 - TriNational) Raimu, Jeanne Provost
One Sheet: $600 - $1,000

HEART OF SHOW BUSINESS
(1957 - Columbia) -
One Sheet: $15 - $30

HEART OF TEXAS RYAN, THE
(1917 - Exclusive) Tom Mix, Bessie Eyton, George Fawcett
One Sheet: $800 - $1,500

HEART OF THE GOLDEN WEST
(1942 - Republic) Roy Rogers
One Sheet: $200 - $400

HEART OF THE GOLDEN WEST
(1955R - Republic) Roy Rogers
One Sheet: $40 - $75   *Re-release. Duotone.*

HEART OF THE MATTER, THE
(1954 - Associated Artists) Trevor Howard, Maria Schell
One Sheet: $7 - $15

HEART OF THE NORTH
(1938 - Warner Bros.) Dick Foran, James Stephenson
One Sheet: $100 - $200

HEART OF THE RIO GRANDE
(1942 - Republic) Gene Autry, Sarah Padden
One Sheet: $125 - $250

HEART OF THE ROCKIES
(1937 - Republic) The Three Mesquiteers
One Sheet: $75 - $125

HEART OF THE ROCKIES
(1951 - Republic) Roy Rogers, Penny Edwards
One Sheet: $75 - $150

HEART OF THE WEST
(1936 - Paramount) William Boyd, Gabby Hayes
One Sheet: $300 - $700   *Hopalong Cassidy series.*

HEART OF VIRGINIA
(1948 - Republic) Janet Martin, Robert Lowery
One Sheet: $30 - $50

HEART PUNCH
(1932 - Mayfair) Lloyd Hughes, Marian Schilling
One Sheet: $75 - $125

HEART SONG
(1934 - Fox) Lillian Harvey, Charles Boyer
One Sheet: $150 - $300

HEART SPECIALIST, THE
(1922 - Realart) Mary Miles Minter
One Sheet: $600 - $1,000

HEART WITHIN, THE
(1957 - Rank) Earl Cameron, David Hemmings
One Sheet: $7 - $15

HEARTACHES
(1947 - Pathe) Sheila Ryan, Edward Norris
One Sheet: $20 - $40

HEARTACHES
(1981 - Rising Star) Margot Kidder, Annie Potts
One Sheet: $3 - $5

HEARTBEAT
(1946 - RKO) Ginger Rogers, Jean-Pierre Aumont
One Sheet: $75 - $150

HEARTBEEPS
(1981 - Universal) Bernadette Peters, Andy Kaufman
One Sheet: $5 - $10

HEARTBREAK
(1931 - Fox) Charles Farrell, Madge Evans
One Sheet: $200 - $400

HEARTBREAK HOTEL
(1988 - -) David Keith, Tuesday Weld, Charlie Schlatter
One Sheet: $5 - $10

HEARTBREAK KID, THE
(1946 - RKO) Ginger Rogers, Basil Rathbone
One Sheet: $75 - $150

HEARTBREAK KID, THE
(1972 - 20th Century Fox) Charles Grodin, Cybill Shepherd
One Sheet: $7 - $15

HEARTBREAK MOTEL
(1978 - -) Leslie Uggams, Shelly Winters
One Sheet: $7 - $15

HEARTBREAK RIDGE
(1986 - Warner Bros.) Clint Eastwood, Marsha Mason
One Sheet: $10 - $20

HEARTBREAKER
(1983 - Emerson) Fernando Allende, Miguel Ferrar
One Sheet: $3 - $5

HEARTBURN
(1986 - Paramount) Meryl Streep, Jack Nicholson
One Sheet: $5 - $10

HEARTLAND
(1980 - Filmhaus) Rip Torn, Conchata Ferrell
One Sheet: $5 - $10

HEARTS AFLAME
(1923 - Louis B. Mayer) Anna Q. Nilsson, Frank Keenan
One Sheet: $150 - $300

HEARTS AND MINDS
(1978 - -) -
One Sheet: $20 - $40   *Academy Award: Best Documentary. Vietnam war film.*

HEARTS AND SOULS
(1993 - Universal) Robert Downey, Jr., Charles Grodin
One Sheet: $3 - $5

HEARTS AND SPURS
(1925 - Fox) Buck Jones, Carole Lombard(film debut)
One Sheet: $1,300 - $2,000   *Lombard on the One Sheet and some Lobbies.*

HEARTS AND TREASURES
(1918 - Renters) Derwent Hall Caine
One Sheet: $150 - $300

HEARTS DESIRE
(1937 - Wardour) Richard Tauber, Kathleen Kelly
One Sheet: $250 - $500

HEARTS DIVIDED
(1936 - Warner Bros.) Dick Powell, Marion Davies
One Sheet: $75 - $150

HEARTS IN BONDAGE
(1936 - Republic) James Dunn, Mae Clarke
One Sheet: $75 - $150

HEARTS IN DIXIE
(1929 - Fox) Clarence Muse, Stepin Fetchit
One Sheet: $19,000 - $30,000   *Black cast. First all-black feature film. Separate Cinema, pg. 29.*

HEARTS IN EXILE
(1929 - Warner Bros.) Dolores Costello, Grant Withers
One Sheet: $250 - $500

HEARTS OF DARKNESS
(1992 - -) Francis Coppola, Robert Duvall, Martin Sheen
One Sheet: $3 - $5   *Documentary film about the making of "Apocalypse Now".*

HEARTS OF FIRE
(1987 - Warner Bros.) Fiona, Bob Dylan
One Sheet: $5 - $10

HEARTS OF HUMANITY
(1932 - Majestic) Jean Hersholt, Jackie Searl
One Sheet: $150 - $300

HEARTS OF HUMANITY
(1936 - UK) Wilfrid Walter, Eric Portman
One Sheet: $100 - $200

HEARTS OF THE WEST
(1975 - MGM) Jeff Bridges, Andy Griffith
One Sheet: $5 - $10   *Price is for both styles.*

HEARTS OF THE WORLD
(1918 - Artcraft) Lillian & Dorothy Gish, Dir: D.W. Griffith
One Sheet: $1,900 - $3,000

HEAT
(1970 - Marvin) Isabel Sarli, Armando Bo
One Sheet: $7 - $15

HEAT
(1972 - Warhol) Joe Dallesandro, Sylvia Miles
One Sheet: $15 - $30   *Drug film.*

Produced by Andy Warhol.

HEAT
(1987 - New Century) Burt Reynolds, Karen Young
One Sheet: $3 - $5

HEAT
(1995 - Warner Bros.) Al Pacino, Robert DeNiro, Val Kilmer
One Sheet: $7 - $15

HEAT AND DUST
(1983 - Merchant Ivory) Julie Christie, Greta Scacchi
One Sheet: $3 - $5

HEAT LIGHTNING
(1934 - Warner Bros.) Ann Dvorak, Preston Foster
One Sheet: $75 - $150

HEAT WAVE
(1953 - Lippert) Alex Nicol, Hillary Brooke
One Sheet: $10 - $20

HEAT'S ON, THE
(194? - Columbia) Mae West, Victor Moore
One Sheet: $125 - $250   *West's last film until 1970.*

HEAT'S ON, THE
(1949R - Columbia) Mae West, Victor Moore
One Sheet: $15 - $30   *Re-release.*

HEATHERS
(1989 - New World) Winona Ryder, Christian Slater
One Sheet: $75 - $150

HEATWAVE
(1935 - Gaumont) Les Allen, Anna Lee
One Sheet: $150 - $300

HEATWAVE
(1983 - New Line) Judy Davis, Richard Moir
One Sheet: $3 - $5

HEAVEN
(1987 - -) Dir: Diane Keaton
One Sheet: $5 - $10

HEAVEN AND EARTH
(1993 - Warner Bros.) Tommy Lee Jones, Hiep Thi Le, Joan Chen
One Sheet: $5 - $10

HEAVEN CAN WAIT
(1943 - 20th Century Fox) Don Ameche, Gene Tierney
One Sheet: $150 - $300

One Sheet

HEAVEN CAN WAIT
(1978 - Paramount) Warren Beatty, Julie Christie
One Sheet: $7 - $15   *Sports Movie Posters #209.*

HEAVEN HELP US
(1985 - TriStar) Donald Sutherland, John Heard
One Sheet: $3 - $5

HEAVEN IS A PLAYGROUND
(1991 - New Line) D.B. Sweeney, Michael Warren
One Sheet: $10 - $20   *Sports (Basketball). Sports Movie Posters #100.*

HEAVEN IS ROUND THE CORNER
(1944 - Anglo) Will Fyffe, Leslie Perrins
One Sheet: $30 - $50

HEAVEN KNOWS, MR. ALLISON
(1957 - 20th Century Fox) Deborah Kerr,

Robert Mitchum
One Sheet: $50 - $100

HEAVEN ON EARTH
(1931 - Universal) Lew Ayres, Anita Louise
One Sheet: $200 - $400

HEAVEN ON EARTH
(1961 - J. B. Films) Barbara Florian, Charles
Fawcett
One Sheet: $3 - $5

HEAVEN ONLY KNOWS
(1947 - United Artists) Robert Cummings, Brian
Donlevy
One Sheet: $15 - $30

HEAVEN WITH A BARBED WIRE FENCE
(1939 - 20th Century Fox) Jean Rogers, Glenn
Ford (film debut)
One Sheet: $100 - $200

HEAVEN WITH A GUN
(1969 - MGM) Glenn Ford, Carolyn Jones
One Sheet: $5 - $10

HEAVEN'S GATE
(1981 - United Artists) Kris Kristofferson,
Christopher Walken
One Sheet: $5 - $10   *Advance:$10-*
15. Style B:$15-25. Cowboy Movie Posters #354.

HEAVENLY BODIES
(1985 - MGM/UA) Cynthia Dale, Richard
Rebiere
One Sheet: $7 - $15   *Sports*
(Aerobics). Sports Movie Posters #338.

HEAVENLY BODY, THE
(1944 - MGM) William Powell, Hedy Lamarr
One Sheet: $125 - $250

HEAVENLY DAYS
(1944 - RKO) Jim Jordan, Marian Jordan
One Sheet: $50 - $100

HEAVENLY DAZE
(1948 - Columbia) The Three Stooges (Shemp)
One Sheet: $350 - $750   *Comedy short.*
Duotone.

HEAVENLY KID, THE
(1985 - Orion) Lewis Smith, Jane Kaczmarek,
Jason Gedrick
One Sheet: $3 - $5

HEAVENLY MUSIC
(1943 - MGM) Mary Elliott, Eric Blore, Fred
Brady
One Sheet: $100 - $200

HEAVENLY PUSS
(1949 - MGM) Tom & Jerry
One Sheet: $300 - $700   *Cartoon. Full*
color stone litho.

HEAVENS ABOVE
(1963 - Janus) Peter Sellers, Cecil Parker
One Sheet: $10 - $20

HEAVY METAL
(1981 - Columbia) Black Sabbath, various
groups
One Sheet: $30 - $50   *Cartoon. Price*
is for Style A. Style B(Corben art):$40-$75.

HEAVY PETTING
(1989 - Skouras)
One Sheet: $5 - $10   *Documentary.*

HEAVY TRAFFIC
(1973 - AIP) Ralph Bakshi animation
One Sheet: $20 - $40   *Cartoon.*

HEAVYWEIGHTS
(1995 - Buena Vista) Ben Stiller, Aaron
Schwartz
One Sheet: $3 - $6

HEDDA
(1975 - Brut) Glenda Jackson, Timothy West
One Sheet: $3 - $5

HEIDI
(1937 - 20th Century Fox) Shirley Temple,
Jean Hersholt
One Sheet: $1,300 - $2,000   *Price is for*
photo litho style. One Sheet(stone litho):$2500-
4000.

HEIDI
(1954 - United Artists) Elsbeth Sigmund,
Heinrich Gretler
One Sheet: $15 - $30

HEIDI
(1968 - Warner Bros.) Eva Maria Singhammer,
Gertraud Mittermayr
One Sheet: $5 - $10

HEIDI
(1975R - Paramount) Eva Maria Singhammer,
Gertraud Mittermayr
One Sheet: $2 - $3   *Re-release.*

HEIDI AND PETER
(1955 - United Artists) Elsbeth Sigmund,
Heinrich Gretler
One Sheet: $15 - $30

HEIDI AND PETER
(1975R - Paramount) -
One Sheet: $3 - $5   *Re-release.*

HEIDI'S SONG
(1982 - Paramount) Voices: Lorne Green,
Sammy Davis, Jr.
One Sheet: $5 - $10   *Cartoon.*

HEIGHTS OF DANGER
(1962 - Continental) Basil Appleby, Sebastian
Cabot
One Sheet: $4 - $8

HEIR BEAR
(1952 - MGM) Barney Bear
One Sheet: $250 - $500   *Cartoon. Full*
color stone litho.

HEIR TO TROUBLE
(1935 - Columbia) Ken Maynard
One Sheet: $200 - $400

HEIRESS, THE
(1949 - Paramount) Olivia de Havilland,
Montgomery Clift
One Sheet: $75 - $150   *Academy*
Award: Best Actress. Academy Award Movie
Posters #123.

HEIRLOOM MYSTERY, THE
(1936 - RKO) Edward Rigby, Mary Glynne
One Sheet: $200 - $400

HEIST, THE
(1979 - First American) Robert Hossein, Virna
Lisi
One Sheet: $3 - $5

HELD FOR RANSOM
(1938 - Grand National) Blanche Mehaffey,
Grant Withers
One Sheet: $50 - $100

HELD IN TRUST
(1949 - DoUKnow) Ian Procter, Dorothy Shaw
One Sheet: $15 - $30

HELEN MORGAN STORY, THE
(1957 - Warner Bros.) Ann Blyth, Paul Newman
One Sheet: $15 - $30

HELEN OF TROY
(1956 - Warner Bros.) Jacques Sernas,
Rosanna Podesta, Brigitte Bardot (minor role)
One Sheet: $40 - $80

HELGA
(1968 - AIP) Ruth Gassman
One Sheet: $3 - $5

HELICOPTER SPIES, THE
(1968 - MGM) Robert Vaughan, David
McCallum
One Sheet: $30 - $60   *T.V. tie-in:*
MAN FROM U.N.C.L.E.

HELIOTROPE
(1920 - Paramount) Wilfred Lytell, Diana Allen
One Sheet: $150 - $300

HELL AND HIGH WATER
(1933 - Paramount) Richard Arlen, Judith Allen
One Sheet: $250 - $600

HELL AND HIGH WATER
(1954 - 20th Century Fox) Richard Widmark,
Bella Darvi
One Sheet: $10 - $20

HELL BELOW
(1933 - MGM) Robert Montgomery, Walter
Huston
One Sheet: $75 - $150

HELL BELOW ZERO
(1954 - Columbia) Alan Ladd, Joan Tetzel
One Sheet: $30 - $50

HELL BENT FOR FRISCO
(1931 - Sono Art/World Wide) Charles Delaney,
Vera Reynolds
One Sheet: $100 - $200

HELL BENT FOR LEATHER
(1960 - Universal) Audie Murphy, Felicia Farr
One Sheet: $15 - $35

HELL BENT FOR LOVE
(1934 - Colmbia) Tim McCoy, Lillian Bond
One Sheet: $700 - $1,200

HELL BOATS
(1970 - United Artists) James Franciscus
One Sheet: $3 - $5

HELL BOUND
(1931 - Tiffany) Leo Carrillo, Lola Lane
One Sheet: $200 - $400

HELL BOUND
(1957 - United Artists) John Russell, June Blair
One Sheet: $7 - $15

HELL CAMP
(1986 - -) -
One Sheet: $3 - $5

HELL CANYON OUTLAWS
(1957 - Republic) Dale Robertson, Brian Keith
One Sheet: $10 - $20

HELL CAT, THE
(1934 - Columbia) Robert Armstrong, Ann
Sothern
One Sheet: $250 - $600

HELL COMES TO FROGTOWN
(1987 - -) Roddy Piper, Sandahl Bergman
One Sheet: $3 - $5

HELL DIVERS
(1932 - MGM) Wallace Beery, Clark Gable,
Dorothy Jordan
One Sheet: $600 - $1,000

HELL DIVERS
(1937R - MGM) Wallace Beery, Clark Gable,
Dorothy Jordan
One Sheet: $50 - $100   *Re-release.*

HELL DRIVERS
(1958 - Rank) Stanley Baker, Patrick
McGoohan
One Sheet: $30 - $50

HELL FIRE AUSTIN
(1932 - Tiffany) Ken Maynard, Ivy Merton, Jack
Perrin
One Sheet: $250 - $500

HELL HARBOR
(1930 - United Artists) Jean Hersholt, Lupe
Velez
One Sheet: $150 - $300

Three Sheet

HELL HARBOR
(1937R - Inspiration) Jean Hersholt, Lupe
Velez
One Sheet: $250 - $500   *Re-release.*

HELL, HEAVEN, OR HOBOKEN
(1959 - National Trade) Clifton Jones, Joan
Mills
One Sheet: $15 - $30

HELL IN A CIRCUS
(1935 - KBS) Conrad Nagel, Leila Hyams
One Sheet: $100 - $200

HELL IN KOREA
(1959 - Hal Roach Studios) Michael Caine,
Robert Shaw
One Sheet: $30 - $50

HELL IN THE HEAVENS
(1934 - Fox) Warner Baxter, Conchita
Montenegro
One Sheet: $150 - $300

HELL IN THE PACIFIC
(1969 - Cinerama) Lee Marvin, Toshiro Mifune
One Sheet: $5 - $10

HELL IS A CITY
(1960 - Columbia) Stanley Baker, Maxine
Audley
One Sheet: $5 - $10

HELL IS EMPTY
(1967 - Rank) Martine Carol, Anthony Steel
One Sheet: $5 - $10

HELL IS FOR HEROES
(1962 - Paramount) Steve McQueen, Bobby
Darin
One Sheet: $20 - $40

HELL IS SOLD OUT
(1952 - Modern Sound) Richard Attenborough,
Mai Zetterling
One Sheet: $15 - $25

HELL NIGHT
(1981 - Compass) Linda Blair, Vincent Van
Patten
One Sheet: $5 - $10

HELL ON DEVIL'S ISLAND
(1957 - 20th Century Fox) Helmet Dantine,
William Talman
One Sheet: $10 - $20

HELL ON EARTH
(1934 - H. William Fitelson) George Peclet,
Hugh Douglas
One Sheet: $100 - $200

HELL ON FRISCO BAY
(1956 - Warner Bros.) Alan Ladd, Edward G.
Robinson, Joanne Dru
One Sheet: $30 - $50

HELL ON WHEELS
(1967 - Crown) Marty Robbins, John Ashley
One Sheet: $15 - $35   *Sports (Auto*
racing).

HELL RAIDERS
(1968 - AIP) John Agar, Richard Webb
One Sheet: $5 - $12

HELL ROARIN' REFORM
(1919 - Fox) Tom Mix, Kathleen Conners
One Sheet: $600 - $1,000

HELL SHIP MUTINY
(1957 - Columbia) Jon Hall, John Carradine
One Sheet: $30 - $50

HELL SQUAD
(1958 - AIP) Wally Campo, Fred Gavlin
One Sheet: $10 - $20

HELL TO ETERNITY
(1960 - Allied Artists) Jeffrey Hunter, David
Janssen
One Sheet: $7 - $15

HELL UP IN HARLEM
(1974 - AMI) Fred Williamson
One Sheet: $15 - $30   *Blaxploitation.*
Outstanding poster design.

HELL WITH HEROES, THE
(1968 - Universal) Rod Taylor, Claudia
Cardinale
One Sheet: $5 - $10

HELL'S ANGELS
(1930 - United Artists) Ben Lyon, James Hall,
Jean Harlow
One Sheet: $6,500 - $10,000   *Beware re-*
releases.

HELL'S ANGELS
(1937R - United Artists) Ben Lyon, James Hall,
Jean Harlow
One Sheet: $700 - $1,200   *Re-release.*
Lobby Cards are identical to original issue except
for date and lack of United Artists logo.

HELL'S ANGELS
(1940R - Astor) Ben Lyon, James Hall, Jean
Harlow
One Sheet: $75 - $150   *Streamlined*

re-release.

HELL'S ANGELS
(1978R - -) Ben Lyon, James Hall, Jean Harlow
One Sheet: $15 - $25   *Re-release.*

HELL'S ANGELS '69
(1969 - AIP) Tom Stern, Jeremy Slate
One Sheet: $15 - $30   *Biker film.*

HELL'S ANGELS ON WHEELS
(1967 - Fanfare) Jack Nicholson, Adam Roarke
One Sheet: $30 - $50   *Biker film.*

HELL'S BELLES
(1969 - AIP) Jeremy Slate, Adam Roarke
One Sheet: $15 - $30   *Biker film.*

HELL'S BLOODY DEVILS
(1970 - East-West-Four) Broderick Crawford, John Carradine
One Sheet: $20 - $40

HELL'S CARGO
(1935 - Wardour) Jack Doyle, Tamara Desni
One Sheet: $200 - $400

HELL'S CARGO
(1940 - Film Alliance) Walter Rilla
One Sheet: $30 - $60

HELL'S CHOSEN FEW
(1968 - Thunderbird International) Jody Daniels, Kelly Ross
One Sheet: $50 - $100   *Biker film.*

HELL'S CROSSROADS
(1957 - Republic) Stephen McNally, Peggie Castle
One Sheet: $7 - $15

HELL'S DEVILS
(1939 - PRC) Alan Ladd, Steffi Duna
One Sheet: $100 - $200

HELL'S FIVE HOURS
(1958 - Allied Artists) Stephen McNally, Vic Morrow
One Sheet: $15 - $30

HELL'S HALF ACRE
(1954 - Republic) Wendell Corey, Evelyn Keyes
One Sheet: $10 - $20

HELL'S HEADQUARTERS
(1932 - Capital) Jack Mulhall, Barbara Weeks
One Sheet: $100 - $200

HELL'S HEROES
(1929 - Universal) Charles Bickford, Raymond Hatton
One Sheet: $200 - $400

HELL'S HIGHWAY
(1932 - RKO) Richard Dix, Tom Brown
One Sheet: $100 - $200

HELL'S HINGES
(1916 - Triangle) William S. Hart, Clara Williams
One Sheet: $1,900 - $3,000   *Beware re-releases. Cowboy Movie Posters #11.*

HELL'S HOLE
(1923 - Fox) Buck Jones
One Sheet: $1,600 - $2,500   *Superb One Sheet design.*

HELL'S HORIZON
(1955 - Columbia) John Ireland, Marla English
One Sheet: $10 - $20

HELL'S HOUSE
(1932 - Capital) Bette Davis, Pat O'Brien
One Sheet: $800 - $1,500   *Beware re-releases (Astor).*

HELL'S HOUSE
(1938R - Astor) Bette Davis, Pat O'Brien
One Sheet: $100 - $200   *Re-release.*

HELL'S ISLAND
(1930 - Columbia) Jack Holt, Ralph Graves
One Sheet: $200 - $400

HELL'S ISLAND
(1954 - Paramount) John Payne, Mary Murphy
One Sheet: $15 - $30

HELL'S KITCHEN
(1939 - Warner Bros.) Billy Halop, Bobby Jordan, Ronald Reagan
One Sheet: $200 - $400

HELL'S OUTPOST
(1954 - Republic) Rod Cameron, Joan Leslie
One Sheet: $15 - $25

HELL'S PLAYGROUND
(1967 - Commercial) Jane Ashley, Skip Everett
One Sheet: $7 - $15

HELL'S VALLEY
(1931 - Big 4) Wally Wales
One Sheet: $100 - $200

HELLBENDERS, THE
(1967 - Embassy) Joseph Cotten
One Sheet: $10 - $20

HELLBOUND
(1993 - Cannon) Chuck Norris
One Sheet: $3 - $5

HELLBOUND: HELLRAISER II
(1988 - New World) Ashley Laurence, Clare Higgins
One Sheet: $10 - $20

HELLCATS, THE
(1968 - Crown) Ross Hagen
One Sheet: $10 - $20

HELLCATS OF THE NAVY
(1957 - Columbia) Ronald Reagan, Nancy Davis
One Sheet: $40 - $75   *Ronald & Nancy's only film appearance together.*

One Sheet

HELLDORADO
(1934 - Fox) Richard Arlen, Madge Evans
One Sheet: $125 - $250

HELLDORADO
(1946 - Republic) Roy Rogers, Gabby Hayes
One Sheet: $200 - $400

HELLER IN PINK TIGHTS
(1960 - Paramount) Sophia Loren, Anthony Quinn
One Sheet: $20 - $40

HELLFIGHTERS
(1969 - Universal) John Wayne, Katharine Ross
One Sheet: $30 - $60

HELLFIRE
(1949 - Republic) Bill Elliott, Marie Windsor
One Sheet: $40 - $75

HELLFIRE
(1954R - Republic) Bill Elliott
One Sheet: $20 - $40   *Re-release.*

HELLFIRE CLUB, THE
(1963 - Embassy) Keith Michell, Peter Cushing
One Sheet: $5 - $12

HELLGATE
(1952 - Lippert) Sterling Hayden, Joan Leslie
One Sheet: $15 - $30

HELLIONS, THE
(1962 - Columbia) Richard Todd, Anne Aubrey
One Sheet: $5 - $12

HELLO AGAIN
(1987 - Paramount) Shelley Long, Judith Ivey
One Sheet: $3 - $5

HELLO ALOHA
(1951 - RKO/Disney) Goofy
One Sheet: $250 - $600   *Full color.*

HELLO ANNAPOLIS
(1942 - Columbia) Jean Parker, Tom Brown
One Sheet: $30 - $50

HELLO, DOLLY!
(1969 - 20th Century Fox) Barbra Streisand, Walter Matthau, Louis Armstrong
One Sheet: $30 - $50

One Sheet

HELLO, DOLLY!
(1970R - 20th Century Fox) Barbara Streisand, Walter Matthau
One Sheet: $10 - $20   *Re-release. Academy awards style. Blue/red duotone.*

HELLO DOWN THERE
(1969 - Paramount) Jim Backus, Tony Randall, Janet Leigh
One Sheet: $15 - $25

HELLO, EVERYBODY
(1933 - Paramount) Kate Smith, Randolph Scott
One Sheet: $125 - $250

HELLO, FRISCO, HELLO
(1943 - 20th Century Fox) Alice Faye, John Payne
One Sheet: $125 - $250

HELLO GOD
(1951 - Flynn) Errol Flynn, Sherry Jackson
One Sheet: $30 - $60

HELLO, HOW AM I?
(1939 - Paramount) Popeye
One Sheet: $1,900 - $3,000   *Cartoon. Duotone. Cartoon Movie Posters #217.*

HELLO LONDON
(1958 - 20th Century Fox) Sonja Henie, Michael Wilding
One Sheet: $15 - $25

HELLO MARY LOU: PROM NIGHT II
(1987 - Samuel Goldwyn) Michael Ironside, Wendy Lyon
One Sheet: $5 - $10

HELLO POP
(1933 - MGM) Ted Healy and His Stooges (Moe, Larry and Curly)
One Sheet: $22,000 - $35,000   *Comedy musical short. One Sheet has Hirschfeld art with Stooges pictured.*

HELLO PROSPERITY
(1934 - Educational) -
One Sheet: $50 - $100

HELLO SISTER
(1930 - Sono Art/World Wide) Olive Borden, Lloyd Hughes
One Sheet: $100 - $200

HELLO SISTER
(1933 - Fox) James Dunn, Boots Mallory, ZaSu Pitts
One Sheet: $125 - $250

HELLO SUCKER
(1941 - Universal) Hugh Herbert, Peggy Moran
One Sheet: $75 - $150

HELLO SWEETHEART
(1935 - Warner Bros.) Claude Hulbert, Jane Carr
One Sheet: $200 - $400

HELLO TEACHER
(1918 - Pathe) Harry Pollard, Bebe Daniels
One Sheet: $300 - $700

HELLO TROUBLE
(1932 - Columbia) Buck Jones, Lina Basquette
One Sheet: $500 - $800   *Cowboy Movie Posters # 132.*

HELLO-GOODBYE
(1970 - 20th Century Fox) Michael Crawford, Curt Jurgens
One Sheet: $3 - $5

HELLRAISER
(1987 - Miramax) Andrew Robinson, Clare Higgins
One Sheet: $20 - $40

HELLRAISER: BLOODLINE
(1995 - Miramax) Doug Bradley
One Sheet: $7 - $15

HELLRAISER III: HELL ON EARTH
(1992 - Miramax) Doug Bradley, Terry Farrell, Paula Marshall
One Sheet: $7 - $15

HELL-SHIP MORGAN
(1936 - Columbia) Ann Sothern, George Bancroft
One Sheet: $150 - $300

HELLSTROM CHRONICLE, THE
(1971 - Cinema 5) Documentary
One Sheet: $3 - $5

HELLZAPOPPIN'
(1941 - Universal) Ole Olsen, Chic Johnson, Martha Raye
One Sheet: $75 - $150

HELP!
(1965 - United Artists) The Beatles
One Sheet: $250 - $500   *Rock 'n' Roll.*

One Sheet

HELP WANTED FEMALE
(1950S - -) -
One Sheet: $30 - $50   *Sexploitation.*

HELP YOURSELF
(1932 - Warner Bros.) Benita Hume, Martin Walker
One Sheet: $250 - $500

HELP/HARD DAY'S NIGHT
(1965 - United Artists) Beatles
One Sheet: $125 - $250   *Rock 'n' Roll. Double feature poster. Duotone. Features same images as HARD DAY'S NIGHT one sheet.*

HELPFUL AL
(1925 - Universal) Al Alt
One Sheet: $200 - $400   *A Century Comedy.*

HELPMATES
(1931 - MGM) Laurel & Hardy
One Sheet: $2,500 - $4,000

(image of Helpmates poster)
One Sheet

HELTER SKELTER
(1949 - General) Carol Marsh, David Tomlinson

One Sheet: $75 - $150

HEMINGWAY'S ADVENTURES OF A YOUNG MAN
(1962 - 20th Century Fox) Richard Beymer, Diane Baker, Paul Newman
One Sheet: $15 - $25   *AKA: Adventures Of A Young Man.*

HENNESSY
(1975 - AIP) Rod Steiger, Lee Remick
One Sheet: $3 - $5

HENPECKED HOBOES
(1946 - MGM) Tex Avery
One Sheet: $350 - $750   *Cartoon. Full color stone litho. Cartoon Movie Posters #301.*

HENRY ALDRICH, BOY SCOUT
(1944 - Paramount) Jimmy Lydon, Charles Smith, Diana Lynn
One Sheet: $50 - $100

HENRY ALDRICH, EDITOR
(1942 - Paramount) Jimmy Lydon, Charles Smith, Rita Quigley
One Sheet: $50 - $100

HENRY ALDRICH FOR PRESIDENT
(1941 - Paramount) Jimmy Lydon, Charles Smith, June Preisser
One Sheet: $50 - $100

HENRY ALDRICH GETS GLAMOUR
(1943 - Paramount) Jimmy Lydon, Charles Smith, Diana Lynn
One Sheet: $50 - $100

HENRY ALDRICH HAUNTS A HOUSE
(1943 - Paramount) Jimmy Lydon, Charles Smith, Joan Mortimer
One Sheet: $50 - $100

HENRY ALDRICH PLAYS CUPID
(1944 - Paramount) Jimmy Lydon, Charles Smith, Diana Lynn
One Sheet: $40 - $75

HENRY ALDRICH SWINGS IT
(1943 - Paramount) Jimmy Lydon, Charles Smith, Mimi Chandler
One Sheet: $40 - $75

HENRY ALDRICH'S LITTLE SECRET
(1944 - Paramount) Jimmy Lydon, Charles Smith, Joan Mortimer
One Sheet: $40 - $75

HENRY AND DIZZY
(1942 - Paramount) Jimmy Lydon, Charles Smith, Mary Anderson
One Sheet: $50 - $100

HENRY AND JUNE
(1990 - Universal) Uma Thurman
One Sheet: $15 - $30

HENRY GOES ARIZONA
(1939 - MGM) Frank Morgan, Guy Kibbee
One Sheet: $75 - $150

HENRY: PORTRAIT OF A SERIAL KILLER
(1990 - -) Michael Rooker, Tracy Arnold
One Sheet: $15 - $35

HENRY STEPS OUT
(1940 - AIP) George Turner, Wally Patch
One Sheet: $50 - $100

HENRY THE RAINMAKER
(1949 - Monogram) Raymond Walburn, Walter Catlett
One Sheet: $15 - $30

HENRY V
(1945 - Paramount) Laurence Olivier, Robert Newton
One Sheet: $125 - $250

HENRY V
(1989 - -) Kenneth Branagh, Derek Jacobi, Brian Blessed
One Sheet: $20 - $40

HENRY VII AND HIS WIVES
(1972 - MGM) Keith Michell, Donald Pleasence
One Sheet: $5 - $10

HEP HEP JUMPIN' JIVE
(1939 - -) Cab Calloway
One Sheet: $1,300 - $2,000   *Black cast.*

HER ADVENTUROUS NIGHT
(1946 - Universal) Dennis O'Keefe, Helen

Walker
One Sheet: $40 - $75

HER ALIBI
(1989 - Warner Bros.) Tom Selleck, Paulina Porizkova
One Sheet: $5 - $10

HER BODYGUARD
(1933 - Paramount) Edmund Lowe, Wynne Gibson
One Sheet: $200 - $400

HER CARDBOARD LOVER
(1942 - MGM) Norma Shearer, Robert Taylor
One Sheet: $75 - $150

HER DAILY DOZEN
(1924 - Universal) Edna Marian
One Sheet: $150 - $350

HER FAVORITE HUSBAND
(1951 - Eagle-Lion) Jean Kent, Robert Beatty
One Sheet: $15 - $35

HER FIRST AFFAIRE
(1932 - Sterling) Ida Lupino(1st starring role), George Curzon
One Sheet: $600 - $1,000

HER FIRST BEAU
(1941 - Columbia) Jane Withers, Jackie Cooper, Edith Fellows
One Sheet: $75 - $125

HER FIRST MATE
(1933 - Universal) ZaSu Pitts, Una Merkel
One Sheet: $125 - $250

HER FIRST ROMANCE
(1940 - Monarch) Edith Fellows, Alan Ladd
One Sheet: $100 - $200

HER FIRST ROMANCE
(1951 - Columbia) Margaret O'Brien, Allen Martin Jr.
One Sheet: $15 - $35

HER FORGOTTEN PAST
(1933 - Golden Arrow) Monte Blue, Barbara Ken
One Sheet: $100 - $200

HER FRIEND THE BANDIT
(1914 - Keystone) Charlie Chaplin
One Sheet: $7,500 - $12,000

HER GILDED CAGE
(1922 - Paramount) Gloria Swanson
One Sheet: $250 - $600

HER HIGHNESS AND THE BELLBOY
(1945 - MGM) Hedy Lamarr, Robert Walker
One Sheet: $50 - $100

HER HUSBAND LIES
(1937 - Paramount) Ricardo Cortez, Gail Patrick
One Sheet: $75 - $150

HER HUSBAND'S AFFAIRS
(1947 - Columbia) Lucille Ball, Franchot Tone
One Sheet: $75 - $150

HER HUSBAND'S AFFAIRS
(1955R - Columbia) Lucille Ball, Franchot Tone
One Sheet: $30 - $50   *Re-release.*

HER HUSBAND'S SECRETARY
(1937 - Warner Bros.) Jean Muir, Warren Hull
One Sheet: $50 - $100

Mini Window Card

HER HUSBAND'S TRADEMARK
(1922 - Paramount) Gloria Swanson

One Sheet: $3,500 - $5,000

HER IMAGINARY LOVER
(1933 - Warner Bros.) Laura la Plante, Roland Culver
One Sheet: $500 - $800

HER JUNGLE LOVE
(1938 - Paramount) Dorothy Lamour, Ray Milland
One Sheet: $100 - $200

HER KIND OF MAN
(1946 - Warner Bros.) Dane Clark, Janis Paige
One Sheet: $30 - $60

HER LAST AFFAIR
(1935 - Producers) Hugh Williams, Sophie Stewart
One Sheet: $150 - $300

HER LOVE STORY
(1924 - Paramount) Gloria Swanson
One Sheet: $2,000 - $3,200

HER LUCKY NIGHT
(1945 - Universal) The Andrews Sisters, Noah Beery, Jr.
One Sheet: $75 - $150

HER MAD NIGHT
(1932 - Mayfair) Irene Rich, Conway Tearle
One Sheet: $100 - $200

HER MAJESTY LOVE
(1931 - First National) W.C. Fields, Marilyn Miller, Ben Lyon
One Sheet: $1,300 - $2,000

HER MAN
(1930 - Pathe) Helen Twelvetrees, Ricardo Cortez
One Sheet: $150 - $300

HER MAN GILBEY
(1948 - Universal) Margaret Rutherford, Peggy Cummins
One Sheet: $30 - $50

HER MASTER'S VOICE
(1936 - Paramount) E. E. Horton, Peggy Conklin
One Sheet: $125 - $250

HER NIGHT OUT
(1932 - First National) Lester Matthews, Dorothy Bartlam
One Sheet: $250 - $500

HER PANELLED DOOR
(1951 - Associated British) Phyllis Calvert, Richard Burton
One Sheet: $15 - $30

HER PRIMITIVE MAN
(1944 - Universal) Robert Paige, Louise Allbritton, Robert Benchley
One Sheet: $50 - $100

HER PRIVATE AFFAIR
(1930 - Pathe) Ann Harding, John Loder
One Sheet: $250 - $600

HER PRIVATE LIFE
(1929 - First National) Walter Pidgeon, Billie Dove
One Sheet: $250 - $600

HER REPUTATION
(1931 - Paramount) Iris Hoey, Malcolm Tearle
One Sheet: $250 - $600

HER RESALE VALUE
(1933 - Mayfair) Noel Francis, Ralf Harolde
One Sheet: $75 - $150

HER SISTER'S SECRET
(1946 - PRC) Nancy Coleman, Regis Toomey
One Sheet: $30 - $50

HER SPLENDID FOLLY
(1933 - Progressive) Lillian Bond, Beryl Mercer
One Sheet: $150 - $300

HER STRANGE DESIRE
(1932 - Powers) Laurence Olivier, Nora Swinburne
One Sheet: $350 - $750

HER SWEETHEART
(1933 - MGM) Marie Dressler, Lionel Barrymore
One Sheet: $150 - $300

HER TEMPORARY HUSBAND
(1923 - First National) Owen Moore, Sylvia Breamer, Sydney Chaplin
One Sheet: $250 - $600

HER THREE BACHELORS
(1954 - Eros) Jerry Desmond, Pauline Stroud
One Sheet: $15 - $30

HER TWELVE MEN
(1955 - MGM) Greer Garson, James Arness
One Sheet: $15 - $35

HER WEDDING NIGHT
(1930 - Paramount Publix) Clara Bow, Charles Ruggles
One Sheet: $1,900 - $3,000

HER WILD OAT
(1927 - -) Colleen Moore
One Sheet: $200 - $400

HERBIE GOES BANANAS
(1980 - Disney) Cloris Leachman, Harvey Korman
One Sheet: $5 - $10

HERBIE GOES TO MONTE CARLO
(1977 - Buena Vista/Disney) Dean Jones, Don Knotts
One Sheet: $5 - $10

HERBIE RIDES AGAIN
(1974 - Buena Vista/Disney) Helen Hayes, Ken Berry
One Sheet: $7 - $15

HERCULES
(1959 - Warner Bros.) Steve Reeves, Sylva Koscina
One Sheet: $125 - $250

HERCULES
(1983 - MGM) Lou Ferrigno, Mirella D'Angelo
One Sheet: $7 - $15   *Sports Movie Posters #378.*

One Sheet

HERCULES
(1997 - Disney) -
One Sheet: $7 - $15   *Cartoon.*

One Sheet (Advance)

HERCULES AGAINST THE MOON MEN
(1965 - Cinematografica) Alan Steel, Jany Clair
One Sheet: $40 - $75

HERCULES AGAINST THE SONS OF THE SUN
(1964 - Screen Gems) Mark Forest, Anna Maria Pace
One Sheet: $15 - $25

HERCULES AND THE CAPTIVE WOMEN
(1963 - SPA) Reg Park, Fay Spain
One Sheet: $40 - $75

HERCULES II
(1985 - Cannon) Lou Ferrigno, Milly Carlucci
One Sheet: $5 - $10

HERCULES IN NEW YORK
(1970 - United) Arnold Strong
(Schwarzenegger)
One Sheet: $100 - $200

40 x 60

HERCULES IN NEW YORK
(1983R - United) Arnold Strong
(Schwarzenegger)
One Sheet: $15 - $30   *Re-release.*

HERCULES IN THE HAUNTED WORLD
(1964 - Woolner) Reg Park, Christopher Lee
One Sheet: $20 - $40

HERCULES, SAMSON AND ULYSSES
(1965 - MGM) Kirk Morris, Richard Lloyd
One Sheet: $15 - $25

HERCULES UNCHAINED
(1960 - Embassy/Warner Bros.) Steve Reeves,
Sylva Koscina
One Sheet: $75 - $175

HERCULES VS. THE GIANT WARRIORS
(1965 - Cinematografica) Dan Vadis, Moria
Orfei
One Sheet: $15 - $35

HERE AND NOW
(197? - Cinepix) Danielle Quimet, Chantal
Renaud
One Sheet: $3 - $5

HERE AND NOW
(1983 - -) Richard Pryor
One Sheet: $5 - $10

HERE COME THE CO-EDS
(1945 - Universal) Bud Abbott, Lou Costello
One Sheet: $150 - $300

HERE COME THE GIRLS
(1918 - Pathe) Harold Lloyd, Bebe Daniels,
Snub Pollard
One Sheet: $600 - $1,000

HERE COME THE GIRLS
(1926R - Pathe) Harold Lloyd
One Sheet: $150 - $300   *Re-release.*

HERE COME THE GIRLS
(1953 - Paramount) Bob Hope, Rosemary
Clooney
One Sheet: $30 - $50

HERE COME THE HUGGETTS
(1948 - Rank) Jack Warner, Petula Clark
One Sheet: $15 - $25

HERE COME THE JETS
(1959 - 20th Century Fox) Steve Brodie, John
Doucette
One Sheet: $15 - $25

HERE COME THE LITTLES: THE MOVIE
(1985 - Atlantic) -
One Sheet: $3 - $5   *Cartoon.*

HERE COME THE MARINES
(1943 - Monogram) Wallace Ford, Toby Wing
One Sheet: $50 - $100   *AKA: The
Marines Come Through.*

HERE COME THE MARINES
(1952 - Monogram) Leo Gorcey, Huntz Hall
One Sheet: $30 - $60

HERE COME THE NELSONS
(1952 - Universal) Ozzie Nelson, Harriet
Nelson

HERE COME THE WAVES
(1944 - Paramount) Bing Crosby, Betty Hutton
One Sheet: $75 - $125

HERE COMES CARTER
(1936 - First National) Ross Alexander, Anne
Nagel
One Sheet: $100 - $200

HERE COMES COOKIE
(1935 - Paramount) George Burns, Gracie
Allen, Betty Furness
One Sheet: $200 - $400

HERE COMES ELMER
(1943 - Republic) Al Pearce, Dale Evans
One Sheet: $50 - $100

HERE COMES HAPPINESS
(1941 - Warner Bros.) Mildred Coles, Edward
Norris
One Sheet: $30 - $50

HERE COMES KELLY
(1943 - Monogram) Eddie Quillan, Joan
Woodbury
One Sheet: $30 - $50

HERE COMES MR. JORDAN
(1941 - Columbia) Robert Montgomery, Rita
Johnson, Claude Rains
One Sheet: $150 - $350

HERE COMES MR. JORDAN
(1953R - Columbia) Robert Montgomery, Rita
Johnson, Claude Rains
One Sheet: $30 - $50   *Re-release.*

HERE COMES THAT NASHVILLE SOUND
(1970 - Embassador Films) Randy Boone,
Sheb Wooley, Country music stars
One Sheet: $15 - $25   *Yellow
duotone.*

HERE COMES THE BAND
(1935 - MGM) Virginia Bruce, Ted Lewis and
his band
One Sheet: $150 - $300

HERE COMES THE CAVALRY
(1941 - Warner Bros.) William Justice
One Sheet: $30 - $50

HERE COMES THE GROOM
(1934 - Paramount) Jack Haley, Mary Boland
One Sheet: $150 - $300

HERE COMES THE GROOM
(1951 - Paramount) Bing Crosby, Jane Wyman
One Sheet: $20 - $40

HERE COMES THE NAVY
(1934 - Warner Bros.) James Cagney, Pat
O'Brien
One Sheet: $800 - $1,500

One Sheet

HERE COMES THE NAVY
(1939R - Warner Bros.) James Cagney, Pat
O'Brien
One Sheet: $50 - $100   *Re-release.
Duotone.*

HERE COMES THE SUN
(1945 - GFD) Bud Flanagan, Chesney Allen
One Sheet: $15 - $30

HERE COMES THE TIGERS
(1978 - AIP) Richard Lincoln, Samantha Grey
One Sheet: $5 - $10

HERE COMES TROUBLE
(1936 - 20th Century Fox) Paul Kelly, Mona

Barrie
One Sheet: $125 - $250

HERE COMES TROUBLE
(1948 - Hal Roach Studios) William Tracy, Joe
Sawyer
One Sheet: $30 - $50

HERE I AM A STRANGER
(1939 - 20th Century Fox) Richard Greene,
Brenda Joyce
One Sheet: $100 - $200

HERE IS MY HEART
(1934 - Paramount) Bing Crosby, Kitty Carlisle
One Sheet: $250 - $600

HERE WE GO AGAIN
(1942 - RKO) Fibber McGee & Molly, Edgar
Bergen & Charlie McCarthy
One Sheet: $200 - $400

HERE WE GO ROUND THE MULBERRY BUSH
(1968 - Lopert) Barry Evans, Judy Geeson
One Sheet: $5 - $10

HERE'S FLASH CASEY
(1937 - Grand National) Eric Linden, Boots
Mallory
One Sheet: $100 - $200

HERE'S GEORGE
(1932 - Producers) George Clarke, Pat
Paterson
One Sheet: $150 - $300

HERE'S TO GOOD OLD JAIL
(1937 - Educational) Terry Toon's
One Sheet: $150 - $300   *Cartoon.
Duotone. Stock poster with inset of title.*

HERE'S TO ROMANCE
(1935 - 20th Century Fox) Nino Martini, Anita
Louise
One Sheet: $100 - $200

HEREDITY
(1912 - Biograph) D.W. Griffith
One Sheet: $2,500 - $4,000

HERITAGE OF THE DESERT
(1924 - -) Bebe Daniels, Noah Beery
One Sheet: $125 - $250

HERITAGE OF THE DESERT
(1932 - Paramount) Randolph Scott
One Sheet: $250 - $500

HERITAGE OF THE DESERT
(1939 - Paramount) Russell Hayden, Evelyn
Venable, Donald Woods
One Sheet: $75 - $150

HERO, THE
(1972 - Avco/Embassy) Richard Harris, Romy
Schneider
One Sheet: $3 - $5

HERO
(1982 - Maya) Derek McGuire, Caroline Kennell
One Sheet: $3 - $5

HERO
(1992 - Columbia) Dustin Hoffman, Geena
Davis, Andy Garcia
One Sheet: $3 - $5

HERO AIN'T NOTHIN' BUT A SANDWICH, A
(1977 - New World) Cicely Tyson, Larry B.
Scott
One Sheet: $7 - $15   *Black cast.*

HERO AND THE TERROR
(1989 - -) Chuck Norris, Brynn Thayer
One Sheet: $3 - $5

HERO AT LARGE
(1980 - MGM) John Ritter, Anne Archer
One Sheet: $3 - $5

HERO FOR A DAY
(1939 - Universal) Charles Grapewin, Anita
Louise
One Sheet: $75 - $150

HERO OF BABYLON
(1963 - Avco/Embassy) Gordon Scott, Michael
Lane
One Sheet: $15 - $25

HERO'S ISLAND
(1962 - United Artists) James Mason, Neville
Brand
One Sheet: $5 - $10

HEROD THE GREAT
(1960 - Allied Artists) Edmund Purdom, Sylvia
Lopez
One Sheet: $7 - $15

HEROES
(1977 - Universal) Henry Winkler, Sally Fields,
Harrison Ford
One Sheet: $7 - $15

HEROES DIE YOUNG
(1960 - Allied Artists) Erika Peters, Scott
Borland
One Sheet: $7 - $15

HEROES FOR SALE
(1933 - First National) Loretta Young, Richard
Barthelmess
One Sheet: $500 - $800

HEROES IN BLUE
(1939 - Monogram) Dick Purcell, Betty Hayes
One Sheet: $40 - $75

HEROES OF TELEMARK, THE
(1966 - Columbia) Kirk Douglas, Richard Harris
One Sheet: $15 - $30

HEROES OF THE ALAMO
(1937 - Columbia) Rex Lease, Bruce Warren,
Ruth Findlay
One Sheet: $100 - $200

HEROES OF THE HILLS
(1938 - Republic) The Three Mesquiteers
One Sheet: $75 - $150

HEROES OF THE RANGE
(1936 - Columbia) Ken Maynard, June Gale
One Sheet: $200 - $400

HEROES OF THE SADDLE
(1940 - Republic) Duncan Renaldo, Bob
Livingston, Ray Hatton
One Sheet: $100 - $200

HEROES OF THE WEST
(1932 - Universal) Noah Beery, Jr., Diane
Duval
One Sheet: $150 - $300

HEROIC FRANCE
(1919 - Mutual) -
One Sheet: $200 - $400

HEROINA
(1965 - Royal) Jaime Sanchez, Nidia Caro
One Sheet: $5 - $10

HERS TO HOLD
(1943 - Universal) Deanna Durbin, Joseph
Cotten
One Sheet: $100 - $200

HESTER STREET
(1975 - Midwest) Steven Keats, Carol Kane
One Sheet: $3 - $5

HEXED
(1993 - Columbia) Arye Gross, Claudia
Christian
One Sheet: $3 - $5

HEY BOY! HEY BOY!
(1950 - Columbia) -
One Sheet: $15 - $35

HEY BOY! HEY GIRL!
(1959 - Columbia) Louis Prima, Keely Smith
One Sheet: $5 - $10

HEY, GOOD LOOKIN'
(1982 - Warner Bros.) Dir:Ralph Bakshi
One Sheet: $10 - $20   *Cartoon.*

HEY! HEY! COWBOY
(1927 - Universal) Hoot Gibson, Slim
Summerville
One Sheet: $250 - $600

HEY! HEY! U.S.A.
(1938 - GFD) Edgar Kennedy, Will Hay
One Sheet: $150 - $300

HEY, LET'S TWIST!
(1961 - Paramount) Joey Dee, Teddy
Randazzo
One Sheet: $40 - $75   *Rock and roll.*

HEY, ROOKIE
(1943 - Columbia) Ann Miller, Larry Parks
One Sheet: $50 - $100

HEY THERE, IT'S YOGI BEAR
(1964 - Columbia) Yogi Bear
One Sheet: $40 - $75   *Cartoon. Full color.*

HEZ
(1973 - 20th Century Fox) Christina Raines, Scott Glenn (debut)
One Sheet: $5 - $10

H.G. WELLS' "THE SHAPE OF THINGS TO COME"
(1979 - Film Ventures) Jack Palance, Carol Lynley
One Sheet: $10 - $20

HI, BEAUTIFUL!
(1944 - Universal) Martha O'Driscoll, Noah Beery, Jr.
One Sheet: $50 - $100

HI, BUDDY!
(1943 - Universal) Dick Foran, Harriet Hilliard
One Sheet: $40 - $75

HI DIDDLE DIDDLE
(1943 - United Artists) Adolphe Menjou, Martha Scott
One Sheet: $40 - $75

HI, GANG!
(1941 - GFD) Bebe Daniels, Ben Lyon
One Sheet: $40 - $75

HI, GAUCHO!
(1935 - RKO) John Carroll, Steffi Duna
One Sheet: $75 - $150

HI, GOOD LOOKIN!
(1944 - Universal) Eddie Quillan, Harriet Hilliard (Nelson)
One Sheet: $30 - $50

HI MOM!
(1970 - Sigma 3) Robert De Niro, Jennifer Salt
One Sheet: $5 - $10

HI, NEIGHBOR!
(1942 - Republic) Jean Parker, John Archer
One Sheet: $30 - $50

HI, NELLIE!
(1934 - Warner Bros.) Paul Muni, Glenda Farrell
One Sheet: $250 - $600

HI, YA, CHUM
(1943 - Universal) The Ritz Brothers, Jane Frazee, Robert Paige
One Sheet: $50 - $100

HI, YA, SAILOR
(1943 - Universal) Donald Woods, Elyse Knox
One Sheet: $40 - $75

HIAWATHA
(1937 - A Walt Disney Silly Symphony) Little Hiawatha
One Sheet: $10,000 - $15,000   *Cartoon. 40x60 known to exist. Cartoon Movie Posters #70.*

HIAWATHA
(1952 - Monogram) Vincent Edwards, Yvette Dugay
One Sheet: $15 - $35

HICK CHICK, THE
(1946 - MGM) Tex Avery
One Sheet: $800 - $1,500   *Cartoon. Cartoon Movie Posters #299.*

HICKEY AND BOGGS
(1972 - United Artists) Bill Cosby, Robert Culp
One Sheet: $7 - $15

HICKVILLE TERRORS, THE
(1922 - Lon Rogers) Jane Lee, Katherine Lee
One Sheet: $150 - $350

HIDDEN, THE
(1987 - --) Michael Nouri, Kyle MacLachlan
One Sheet: $5 - $10

HIDDEN CITY, THE
(1950 - Monogram) Johnny Sheffield, Sue England
One Sheet: $30 - $60   *Bomba series.*

HIDDEN CORPSE, THE
(1932 - Tiffany) ZaSu Pitts, Lucien Littlefield
One Sheet: $100 - $200

HIDDEN DANGER
(1948 - Monogram) Johnny Mack Brown

One Sheet: $30 - $60

HIDDEN DANGERS
(1920 - Vitagraph) Joe Ryan, Jean Paige
One Sheet: $250 - $500   *Serial. 15 Chapters.*

HIDDEN ENEMY
(1940 - Monogram) Warren Hull, Kay Lunaker
One Sheet: $40 - $75

HIDDEN EYE, THE
(1945 - MGM) Edward Arnold, Ray Collins
One Sheet: $50 - $100

HIDDEN FACE, THE
(1954 - Howco) Steve Reeves, Dolores Fuller
One Sheet: $30 - $60

HIDDEN FEAR
(1957 - United Artists) John Payne, Conrad Nagel
One Sheet: $15 - $25

HIDDEN FORTRESS, THE
(1959 - Toho) Toshiro Mifune
One Sheet: $75 - $150

HIDDEN GOLD
(1932 - Universal) Tom Mix
One Sheet: $1,000 - $1,800

HIDDEN GOLD
(1940 - Paramount) William Boyd, Russell Hayden
One Sheet: $200 - $400   *Hopalong Cassidy series.*

HIDDEN GUNS
(1955 - Republic) Bruce Bennett, Richard Arlen
One Sheet: $7 - $15

HIDDEN HAND, THE
(1942 - Warner Bros.) Craig Stevens, Elisabeth Fraser
One Sheet: $40 - $75

HIDDEN HOMICIDE
(1956 - Republic) Griffith Jones, Patricia Laffan
One Sheet: $15 - $30

HIDDEN MENACE, THE
(1925 - William Steiner) Charles Hutchison
One Sheet: $250 - $500

HIDDEN MENACE, THE
(1938 - Alliance) Otto Kruger, Gertrude Michael
One Sheet: $75 - $125

HIDDEN POWER
(1936 - Gaumont-British) Sylvia Sydney, Robert Donat, Dir: Alfred Hitchcock
One Sheet: $2,500 - $4,000

HIDDEN POWER
(1939 - Columbia) Jack Holt, Gertrude Michael
One Sheet: $75 - $150

HIDDEN ROOM, THE
(1949 - GFD) Robert Newton, Sally Gray
One Sheet: $15 - $25

HIDDEN VALLEY
(1932 - Columbia) Bob Steele, Francis McDonald
One Sheet: $200 - $400

HIDDEN VALLEY DAYS
(1948 - Universal) Red River Dave
One Sheet: $30 - $60

HIDDEN VALLEY OUTLAWS
(1944 - Republic) Bill Elliott, Gabby Hayes
One Sheet: $75 - $150

Six Sheet

HIDE AND SEEK
(1964 - Universal) Ian Carmichael, Janet Munro
One Sheet: $7 - $15

HIDE IN PLAIN SIGHT
(1979 - MGM/United Artists) James Caan, Danny Aiello
One Sheet: $5 - $10

HIDEAWAY
(1937 - RKO) Fred Stone, Marjorie Lord
One Sheet: $50 - $100

HIDEAWAY
(1995 - TriStar) Jeff Goldblum
One Sheet: $4 - $8

HIDEAWAY GIRL
(1936 - Paramount) Martha Raye, Shirley Ross
One Sheet: $100 - $200

HI-DE-HO
(1947 - All American) Cab Calloway, Dusty Fletcher
One Sheet: $1,600 - $2,500   *Separate Cinema, pg. 97.*

HIDEOUS SUN DEMON, THE
(1959 - Pacific International) Robert Clarke, Patricia Manning
One Sheet: $75 - $150

HIDE-OUT, THE
(1930 - Universal) James Murray, Kathryn Crawford
One Sheet: $250 - $500

HIDE-OUT
(1934 - MGM) Robert Montgomery, Maureen O'Sullivan
One Sheet: $100 - $200

HIDEOUT
(1948 - Constellation) Valerie Hobson, James Donald
One Sheet: $15 - $30

HIDEOUT
(1949 - Republic) Lloyd Bridges, Adrian Booth
One Sheet: $30 - $60

HIDEOUT, THE
(1956 - Major) Dermot Walsh, Ronald Howard
One Sheet: $15 - $25

HIDEOUT IN THE ALPS
(1937 - Grand National) Jane Baxter, Anthony Bushell
One Sheet: $40 - $75

HIDEOUT IN THE SUN
(1950S - -) -
One Sheet: $30 - $60   *Nudist film.*

HIDING OUT
(1987 - -) John Cryer, Annabeth Gish, Keith Coogan
One Sheet: $3 - $5

HIDING PLACE, THE
(1975 - World Wide) Julie Harris, Arthur O'Connell
One Sheet: $5 - $10

HIGGINS FAMILY, THE
(1938 - Republic) James, Lucile, and Russell Gleason
One Sheet: $50 - $100

HIGH
(1969 - Brenner) Astri Thorvik, Lanny Beckman
One Sheet: $15 - $25   *Drug film.*

HIGH AND DIZZY
(1920 - Pathe) Harold Lloyd
One Sheet: $600 - $1,000

HIGH AND DRY
(1922 - William Fox) Clyde Cook
One Sheet: $250 - $500

HIGH AND DRY
(1954 - Universal International) Paul Douglas, Alex Mackenzie
One Sheet: $15 - $25

HIGH AND LOW
(1963 - Toho) Toshiro Mifune
One Sheet: $30 - $60   *Japanese.*

HIGH AND THE MIGHTY, THE
(1954 - Warner Bros.) John Wayne, Claire Trevor, Laraine Day, Jan Sterling

One Sheet: $100 - $200

One Sheet

HIGH ANXIETY
(1977 - 20th Century Fox) Mel Brooks, Madeline Kahn, Cloris Leachman
One Sheet: $10 - $20

HIGH BALLIN'
(1978 - AIP) Peter Fonda, Jerry Reed
One Sheet: $7 - $15

HIGH BARBAREE
(1947 - MGM) Van Johnson, June Allyson
One Sheet: $20 - $40

HIGH COMMAND, THE
(1938 - Grand National) Lionel Atwill, Lucy Mannheim
One Sheet: $50 - $100

HIGH COMMISSIONER, THE
(1968 - Cinerama) Rod Taylor, Christopher Plummer, Lilli Palmer
One Sheet: $4 - $8

HIGH CONQUEST
(1947 - Monogram) Anna Lee, Warren Douglas
One Sheet: $20 - $40

HIGH COST OF LOVING, THE
(1957 - MGM) Jose Ferrer, Gene Rowlands
One Sheet: $20 - $40

HIGH COUNTRY, THE
(1981 - Crown) Timothy Bottom, Linda Purl
One Sheet: $3 - $5

HIGH EXPLOSIVES
(1943 - Paramount) Chester Morris, Jean Parker
One Sheet: $40 - $75

HIGH FINANCE
(1933 - Warner Bros.) Ida Lupino, Gibb McLaughlin
One Sheet: $500 - $800

HIGH FLIGHT
(1957 - Columbia) Ray Milland, Anthony Newley
One Sheet: $10 - $20

HIGH FLYERS
(1937 - RKO) Wheeler and Woolsey, Lupe Velez
One Sheet: $100 - $200

HIGH FURY
(1948 - United Artists) Madeleine Carroll, Ian Hunter
One Sheet: $15 - $30

HIGH GEAR
(1933 - Goldsmith) Joan Marsh, James Murray
One Sheet: $125 - $250

HIGH HAT
(1937 - Imperial) Dorothy Davie, Frank Luther
One Sheet: $200 - $400

HIGH HEELS
(1992 - Miramax) -
One Sheet: $15 - $30

HIGH HELL
(1958 - Rich & Rich Ltd.) John Derek, Elaine Stewart
One Sheet: $15 - $30

HIGH JINKS IN SOCIETY
(1949 - Advance) Barbara Shaw, Basil Appleby
One Sheet: $30 - $60

HIGH JUMP

(1959 - United Artists) Lisa Daniely, Leigh Madison
One Sheet: $7 - $15

HIGH LONESOME
(1950 - Eagle-Lion) John Barrymore Jr., Chill Wills
One Sheet: $30 - $50

HIGH NOON
(1952 - United Artists) Gary Cooper, Grace Kelly
One Sheet: $600 - $1,000   *Academy Award: Best Actor. Academy Award Movie Posters #144. Cowboy Movie Posters #s 293, 294, 295.*

One Sheet

HIGH NOON
(1956R - United Artists) Gary Cooper, Grace Kelly
One Sheet: $40 - $75   *Re-release.*

HIGH PERIL
(1940 - Warner Bros.) Edna Best, William Powell
One Sheet: $50 - $100

HIGH PLAINS DRIFTER
(1973 - Universal) Clint Eastwood, Verna Bloom
One Sheet: $125 - $250   *Cowboy Movie Posters #339. 40" x 60": $200-$400.*

HIGH POWERED
(1945 - Paramount) Robert Lowery, Phyllis Brooks
One Sheet: $40 - $75

HIGH POWERED RIFLE, THE
(1960 - 20th Century Fox) Willard Parker, Allison Hayes
One Sheet: $5 - $10

HIGH PRESSURE
(1932 - Warner Bros.) William Powell, Evelyn Brent
One Sheet: $600 - $1,000

HIGH RISK
(1981 - Viacom) James Brolin, Anthony Quinn
One Sheet: $5 - $10

HIGH ROAD TO CHINA
(1983 - Warner Bros.) Tom Selleck, Bess Armstrong
One Sheet: $5 - $10

HIGH ROLLING
(1977 - Hexagon) Joseph Bottoms, Judy Davis
One Sheet: $5 - $10

HIGH ROLLING IN A HOT CORVETTE
(1978 - Martin) Judy Davis, Wendy Hughes
One Sheet: $10 - $20   *Sports (Auto racing).*

HIGH SCHOOL
(1940 - 20th Century Fox) Jane Withers, Joe Brown, Jr.
One Sheet: $75 - $125

HIGH SCHOOL BIG SHOT
(1959 - Sparta) Virginia Aldridge, Tom Pittman
One Sheet: $15 - $35

HIGH SCHOOL CAESAR
(1960 - Marathon) John Ashley, Gary Vinson
One Sheet: $15 - $30   *Teen exploitation.*

HIGH SCHOOL CONFIDENTIAL
(1958 - MGM) Mamie Van Doren, Jerry Lee Lewis, Russ Tamblyn
One Sheet: $50 - $100   *Rock and roll.*

HIGH SCHOOL GIRL
(1935 - Foy) Noel Warwick, Cecilia Parker
One Sheet: $250 - $500

HIGH SCHOOL HELLCATS
(1958 - AIP) Yvonne Lime, Brett Halsey
One Sheet: $40 - $75

HIGH SCHOOL HERO
(1946 - Monogram) Freddie Stewart, June Preisser
One Sheet: $50 - $100

HIGH SEAS
(1929 - Pathe) Lillian Rich, John Stuart
One Sheet: $250 - $600

HIGH SIERRA
(1941 - Warner Bros.) Humphrey Bogart, Ida Lupino
One Sheet: $700 - $1,200

One Sheet

HIGH SIERRA
(1952R - Warner Bros.) Humphrey Bogart, Ida Lupino
One Sheet: $50 - $100   *Re-release. One Sheet is duotone.*

HIGH SIERRA
(1956R - Dominant) Humprhrey Bogart, Ida Lupino
One Sheet: $30 - $50   *Re-release.*

HIGH SIGN, THE
(1920 - Metro) Buster Keaton
One Sheet: $6,500 - $10,000

HIGH SOCIETY
(1955 - Allied Artists) Leo Gorcey, Huntz Hall, Amanda Blake
One Sheet: $30 - $50

HIGH SOCIETY
(1956 - MGM) Bing Crosby, Frank Sinatra, Grace Kelly, Louis Armstrong
One Sheet: $100 - $200

HIGH SOCIETY BLUES
(1930 - Fox) Janet Gaynor, Hedda Hopper
One Sheet: $150 - $300

HIGH SPEED
(1932 - Columbia) Buck Jones, Loretta Sayers
One Sheet: $250 - $500

HIGH SPIRITS
(1988 - -) Daryl Hannah, Peter O'Toole, Liam Neeson
One Sheet: $5 - $10

HIGH STAKES
(1931 - RKO) Lowell Sherman, Mae Murray
One Sheet: $125 - $250

HIGH TENSION
(1936 - 20th Century Fox) Brian Donlevy, Glenda Farrell
One Sheet: $100 - $200

HIGH TERRACE, THE
(1956 - Allied Artists) Dale Robertson, Lois Maxwell
One Sheet: $15 - $30

HIGH TEST GIRLS
(197? - SRC) Lisa Robertson, Nancy Patricks
One Sheet: $15 - $25   *Sexploitation.*

HIGH TIDE
(1947 - Monogram) Don Castle, Lee Tracy
One Sheet: $15 - $30

HIGH TIDE AT NOON

(1957 - Rank) Betta St. John, William Sylvester
One Sheet: $10 - $20

HIGH TIME
(1960 - 20th Century Fox) Bing Crosby, Fabian
One Sheet: $15 - $30

HIGH TONES
(1929 - Pathe) Buck and Bubbles
One Sheet: $600 - $1,000   *Black cast. Separate Cinema, pg. 67.*

HIGH TREASON
(1930 - Gaumont) Jameson Thomas, Benita Hume
One Sheet: $250 - $500   *Graven Images, pg. 39.*

HIGH TREASON
(1937 - RKO) Leslie Perrins, John Garrick
One Sheet: $200 - $400

HIGH TREASON
(1951 - GFD) Liam Redmond, Mary Morris
One Sheet: $10 - $20

HIGH VELOCITY
(1977 - First Asian) Ben Gazzara, Britt Ekland
One Sheet: $3 - $5

HIGH VENTURE
(1951 - Paramount) -
One Sheet: $10 - $20

HIGH VOLTAGE
(1929 - Pathe) William Boyd, Carole Lombard
One Sheet: $600 - $1,000

HIGH WALL
(1948 - MGM) Robert Taylor, Audrey Totter
One Sheet: $30 - $50

HIGH, WIDE, AND HANDSOME
(1937 - Paramount) Irene Dunne, Randolph Scott
One Sheet: $100 - $200

HIGH, WILD AND FREE
(1968 - AIP) -
One Sheet: $3 - $5   *Documentary.*

HIGH WIND IN JAMAICA, A
(1965 - 20th Century Fox) Anthony Quinn, James Coburn
One Sheet: $3 - $5

HIGH YELLOW
(1965 - Thunder) Cynthia Hall, Warren Hammack
One Sheet: $15 - $35

HIGHER AND HIGHER
(1943 - RKO) Michele Morgan, Frank Sinatra(star debut)
One Sheet: $125 - $250

HIGHER LEARNING
(1995 - Columbia) Omar Epps, Kristy Swanson, Laurence Fishburne
One Sheet: $7 - $15

HIGHER THAN A KITE
(1943 - Columbia) The Three Stooges (Curly)
One Sheet: $2,500 - $4,000   *Comedy short. Duotone.*

HIGHLAND FLING
(1936 - Fox) Jimmy Gold, Charlie Naughton
One Sheet: $350 - $750

HIGHLANDER
(1986 - 20th Century Fox) Christopher Lambert, Roxanne Hart, Sean Connery
One Sheet: $40 - $75

HIGHLANDER III: THE SORCERER
(1994 - Miramax) Christopher Lambert, Mario Van Peebles
One Sheet: $5 - $12

HIGHLIGHTS AND SHADOWS
(1916 - Centaur) Margaret Gibson, William Clifford
One Sheet: $250 - $500

HIGHLY DANGEROUS
(1951 - Lippert) Dane Clark, Margaret Lockwood
One Sheet: $15 - $30

HIGHWAY 13
(1949 - Screen Guild) Robert Lowery, Pamela Blake
One Sheet: $15 - $25

HIGHWAY 301
(1950 - Warner Bros.) Steve Cochran, Virginia Grey
One Sheet: $15 - $30

HIGHWAY DRAGNET
(1954 - Allied Artists) Richard Conte, Joan Bennett, Dir: Roger Corman
One Sheet: $50 - $100   *Corman's first film.*

HIGHWAY PATROL
(1938 - Columbia) Jacqueline Wells, Robert Paige
One Sheet: $75 - $150

HIGHWAY TO BATTLE
(1961 - Paramount) Gerard Heinz, Vincent Ball
One Sheet: $5 - $10

HIGHWAY WEST
(1941 - Warner Bros.) Brenda Marshall, William Lundigan
One Sheet: $30 - $50

HIGHWAYMAN, THE
(1951 - Allied Artists) Wanda Hendrix, Charles Coburn
One Sheet: $15 - $25

HIGHWAYMAN RIDES, THE
(1930 - MGM) Johnny Mack Brown, Kay Johnson
One Sheet: $125 - $250

HIGHWAYS BY NIGHT
(1942 - RKO) Richard Carlson, Jane Randolph
One Sheet: $50 - $100

HI-HO HOLLYWOOD
(1938 - Fox) Harriet Hutchins
One Sheet: $150 - $300

HI-JACKED
(1950 - Lippert) Jim Davis, Marsha Jones
One Sheet: $10 - $20

HI-JACKERS, THE
(1963 - Butchers) Jacqueline Ellis, Anthony Booth
One Sheet: $7 - $15

HILDA CRANE
(1956 - 20th Century Fox) Jean Simmons, Guy Madison
One Sheet: $30 - $50

HILDUR AND THE MAGICIAN
(1969 - Canyon) John Graham, Hildur Mahl
One Sheet: $5 - $10

HILL, THE
(1965 - MGM) Sean Connery, Harry Andrews
One Sheet: $15 - $25

HILLBILLY BLITZKRIEG
(1942 - Capital) Edgar Kennedy, Bud Duncan
One Sheet: $50 - $100

HILLBILLYS IN A HAUNTED HOUSE
(1967 - Woolner) Ferlin Husky, Lon Chaney, Basil Rathbone
One Sheet: $30 - $50   *Country musical.*

HILLS HAVE EYES, THE
(1977 - Vanguard) Susan Lanier, Robert Houston, Dee Wallace
One Sheet: $15 - $25

HILLS HAVE EYES PART 2, THE
(1985 - -) Michael Berryman, John Laughlin
One Sheet: $7 - $15

HILLS OF DONEGAL, THE
(1947 - Butcher) Dinah Sheridan, John Bentley
One Sheet: $20 - $40

HILLS OF HOME
(1948 - MGM) Lassie, Edmund Gwenn, Tom Drake
One Sheet: $75 - $150

HILLS OF HOME
(1972R - MGM) Lassie, Edmund Gwenn, Tom Drake
One Sheet: $7 - $15   *Re-release.*

HILLS OF KENTUCKY
(1927 - Warner Bros.) Rin-Tin-Tin, Jason Robards
One Sheet: $250 - $600

HILLS OF OKLAHOMA
(1950 - Republic) Rex Allen, Elizabeth Frazer
One Sheet: $30 - $60

HILLS OF OLD WYOMING
(1937 - Paramount) William Boyd, Gabby Hayes
One Sheet: $250 - $500   *Hopalong Cassidy series.*

HILLS OF UTAH
(1951 - Columbia) Gene Autry, Donna Marshall
One Sheet: $50 - $100

HILLS RUN RED, THE
(1967 - United Artists) Thomas Hunter, Henry Silva
One Sheet: $3 - $5

HINDENBERG
(1975 - Universal) George C. Scott, Anne Bancroft
One Sheet: $7 - $15

HINDLE WAKES
(1931 - Gaumont) Sybil Thorndike, John Stuart
One Sheet: $600 - $1,000

HIPPODROME
(1961 - Continental) Gerhard Reidmann, Willy Birgel
One Sheet: $5 - $10

HIPS, HIPS, HOORAY
(1934 - RKO) Wheeler & Woolsey, Ruth Etting
One Sheet: $150 - $300

HIRED GUN, THE
(1957 - MGM) Rory Calhoun, Anne Francis
One Sheet: $15 - $25

HIRED HAND, THE
(1971 - Universal) Peter Fonda, Warren Oates
One Sheet: $7 - $15

HIRED KILLER, THE
(1967 - Paramount) Robert Webber, Franco Nero
One Sheet: $7 - $15

HIRED WIFE
(1934 - Pinnacle) Greta Nissen
One Sheet: $200 - $400

HIRED WIFE
(1940 - Universal) Rosalind Russell, Brian Aherne
One Sheet: $75 - $150

HIRELING, THE
(1973 - Columbia) Sarah Miles, Robert Shaw
One Sheet: $2 - $3

HI-RIDERS
(1978 - Dimension) Mel Ferrer, Neville Brand
One Sheet: $3 - $5

HIROSHIMA
(1953 - East West Films) -
One Sheet: $50 - $100

HIROSHIMA, MON AMOUR
(1959 - Pathe/Zenith) Emmanuelle Riva, Eiji Okada
One Sheet: $40 - $75

HIS ANCESTORS
(1913 - Edison) -
One Sheet: $200 - $400

HIS AND HERS
(1961 - Eros) Terry-Thomas, Janette Scott
One Sheet: $7 - $15

HIS BRIDAL FRIGHT
(1940 - Columbia) Charley Chase
One Sheet: $75 - $150   *Comedy short. Duotone.*

HIS BROTHER'S GHOST
(1945 - PRC) Buster Crabbe, Al St. John
One Sheet: $30 - $50

HIS BROTHER'S KEEPER
(1939 - Warner Bros.) Clifford Evans, Tamara Desni
One Sheet: $150 - $300

HIS BROTHER'S WIFE
(1936 - MGM) Robert Taylor, Barbara Stanwyck
One Sheet: $150 - $300

HIS BUTLER'S SISTER

(1943 - Universal) Deanna Durbin, Franchot Tone
One Sheet: $75 - $150

HIS CAPTIVE WOMAN
(1929 - First National) Milton Sills, Dorothy MacKaill
One Sheet: $250 - $500

HIS CHILDREN'S CHILDREN
(1923 - Famous Players/Lasky) Bebe Daniels, James Rennie
One Sheet: $150 - $300

HIS DOUBLE LIFE
(1933 - Paramount) Lillian Gish, Roland Young
One Sheet: $150 - $300

HIS EXCELLENCY
(1956 - Ealing) Eric Portman, Cecil Parker
One Sheet: $7 - $15

HIS EXCITING NIGHT
(1938 - Universal) Charles Ruggles, Ona Munson
One Sheet: $75 - $150

HIS FAMILY TREE
(1935 - RKO) James Barton, Addison Randall
One Sheet: $75 - $150

HIS FAVORITE PASTIME
(1914 - Keystone) Charlie Chaplin, Roscoe "Fatty" Arbuckle
One Sheet: $10,000 - $15,000

HIS FIGHTING BLOOD
(1935 - Ambassador) Kermit Maynard
One Sheet: $75 - $150

HIS FIRST COMMAND
(1930 - Pathe) William Boyd, Dorothy Sebastian
One Sheet: $125 - $250

HIS GIRL FRIDAY
(1939 - Columbia) Cary Grant, Rosalind Russell
One Sheet: $1,300 - $2,000

HIS GLORIOUS NIGHT
(1929 - MGM) John Gilbert, Catherine Dale Owen
One Sheet: $250 - $600

HIS GRACE GIVES NOTICE
(1933 - RKO) Viola Keats, Arthur Margetson
One Sheet: $200 - $400

HIS GREATEST GAMBLE
(1934 - RKO) Richard Dix, Bruce Cabot
One Sheet: $75 - $150

HIS HARLEM WIFE
(1938 - Toddy) Louise Beavers
One Sheet: $250 - $500   *Black cast.*

HIS JONAH DAY
(1920 - Vitagraph) Jimmy Aubrey
One Sheet: $250 - $500

HIS KIND OF WOMAN
(1951 - RKO) Jane Russell, Robert Mitchum
One Sheet: $125 - $250

HIS LAST CROOKED DEAL
(1913 - Lubin) -
One Sheet: $250 - $600

HIS LAST DOLLAR
(1914 - Paramount) David Higgins, Betty Gray
One Sheet: $250 - $500

HIS LAST FALSE STEP
(1919 - Paramount) Ford Sterling
One Sheet: $200 - $400

HIS LAST HAUL
(1928 - FBO) Tom Moore, Seena Owen
One Sheet: $150 - $300

HIS LAST TWELVE HOURS
(1953 - Pathe) Jean Gabin, Julien Carette
One Sheet: $10 - $20

HIS LORDSHIP
(1932 - United Artists) Jerry Verno, Polly Ward
One Sheet: $250 - $500

HIS LORDSHIP GOES TO PRESS
(1939 - RKO) Hugh Williams, June Clyde
One Sheet: $500 - $800

HIS LORDSHIP REGRETS

(1938 - RKO) Claude Hulbert, Gina Malo
One Sheet: $300 - $700

HIS LUCKY DAY
(1929 - Universal) Reginald Denny, Otis Harlan
One Sheet: $250 - $500

HIS MAJESTY AND CO
(1935 - Fox) Wally Patch, John Garrick
One Sheet: $250 - $600

HIS MAJESTY O'KEEFE
(1955 - Warner Bros.) Burt Lancaster, Joan Rice
One Sheet: $50 - $100

HIS MAJESTY, THE AMERICAN
(1919 - United Artists) Douglas Fairbanks, Marjorie Daw
One Sheet: $600 - $1,000

HIS MILLION DOLLAR JOB
(1914 - Keystone) Charlie Chaplin, Roscoe "Fatty" Arbuckle
One Sheet: $6,500 - $10,000   *AKA: A FILM JOHNNIE.*

HIS MOUSE FRIDAY
(1950 - MGM) Tom & Jerry
One Sheet: $600 - $1,000   *Cartoon. Cartoon Movie Posters #282.*

HIS MUSICAL CAREER
(1914 - Keystone) Charlie Chaplin
One Sheet: $7,500 - $12,000

HIS NEIGHBOR'S WIFE
(1913 - Universal) Lillie Langtry
One Sheet: $250 - $500

HIS NEW JOB
(1915 - Essanay) Charlie Chaplin
One Sheet: $7,500 - $12,000   *First film for Essanay. Cameo appearance by Gloria Swanson.*

HIS NEW MAMMA
(1924 - Pathe) Harry Langdon
One Sheet: $1,300 - $2,000   *Sports (Baseball). Sports Movie Posters #33.*

HIS NEW PROFESSION
(1914 - Keystone) Charlie Chaplin
One Sheet: $7,500 - $12,000

HIS NIGHT OUT
(1935 - Universal) Edward Everett Horton, Irene Hervey
One Sheet: $125 - $250

HIS PEST FRIEND
(1938 - RKO) Leon Errol
One Sheet: $200 - $400

HIS PICTURE IN THE PAPERS
(1916 - -) Douglas Fairbanks, Loretta Blake
One Sheet: $800 - $1,500

HIS PREHISTORIC PAST
(1914 - Keystone) Charlie Chaplin
One Sheet: $7,500 - $12,000

HIS PRIVATE LIFE
(1928 - Paramount) Adolphe Menjou, Kathryn Carver
One Sheet: $150 - $300

HIS PRIVATE SECRETARY
(1933 - Screencraft) John Wayne, Evalyn Knapp
One Sheet: $75 - $150   *All posters are green duotone.*

HIS REGENERATION
(1915 - -) Charlie Chaplin guest appearance
One Sheet: $2,500 - $4,000

HIS ROYAL HIGHNESS
(1932 - Universal) George Wallace, Cyril Scott
One Sheet: $250 - $600

HIS SWEETHEART
(1917 - Paramount) George Beban
One Sheet: $250 - $500

HIS TIGER LADY
(1928 - Paramount) Adolphe Menjou, Evelyn Brent
One Sheet: $150 - $300

HIS TRYSTING PLACE
(1914 - Keystone) Charlie Chaplin
One Sheet: $7,500 - $12,000

HIS WAITING CAREER
(1916 - Unicorn) Billy West
One Sheet: $700 - $1,200

HIS WEDDING NIGHT
(1917 - Triangle) Roscoe "Fatty" Arbuckle
One Sheet: $1,900 - $3,000

HIS WIFE'S MISTAKE
(1916 - Triangle) Roscoe "Fatty" Arbuckle
One Sheet: $1,600 - $2,500

HIS WIFE'S MOTHER
(1932 - Wardour) Jerry Verno, Jack Hobbs
One Sheet: $150 - $350

HIS WOMAN
(1931 - Paramount Publix) Gary Cooper, Claudette Colbert
One Sheet: $800 - $1,500

HISTORY IS MADE AT NIGHT
(1937 - United Artists) Charles Boyer, Jean Arthur
One Sheet: $350 - $750

HISTORY OF MR. POLLY, THE
(1949 - Rank/GFD) John Mills, Sally Ann Howes
One Sheet: $15 - $30

HISTORY OF THE WORLD - PART 1
(1981 - 20th Century Fox) Mel Brooks, Dom DeLuise, Madeline Kahn
One Sheet: $10 - $20

One Sheet

HIT
(1973 - Paramount) Billy Dee Williams, Richard Pryor
One Sheet: $10 - $20   *Black cast.*

HIT AND RUN
(1924 - Universal) Hoot Gibson
One Sheet: $250 - $500

HIT AND RUN
(1957 - United Artists) Cleo Moore, Hugo Haas
One Sheet: $40 - $75

HIT AND RUN
(1982 - Comworld) Paul Perri, Claudia Cron
One Sheet: $3 - $5

HIT HIM AGAIN
(1918 - Pathe) Harold Lloyd
One Sheet: $4,000 - $6,000

HIT HIM AGAIN
(192?R - Pathe) Harold Lloyd
One Sheet: $350 - $750   *Re-release.*

HIT MAN
(1972 - MGM) Bernie Casey, Pam Grier
One Sheet: $15 - $25   *Blaxploitation. Grier not shown on one sheet.*

HIT OF THE SHOW
(1928 - FBO) Gertrude Olmstead, Joe E. Brown
One Sheet: $200 - $400

HIT PARADE OF 1937
(1937 - Republic) Francis Langford, Phil Regan
One Sheet: $100 - $200

HIT PARADE OF 1941
(1941 - Republic) Kenny Baker, Francis Langford
One Sheet: $100 - $200

HIT PARADE OF 1943
(1943 - Republic) John Carroll, Susan Hayward
One Sheet: $50 - $100

HIT PARADE OF 1947

(1947 - Republic) Eddie Albert, Woody Herman and his band
One Sheet: $50 - $100

HIT PARADE OF 1951
(1951 - Republic) John Carroll, Marie McDonald
One Sheet: $15 - $30

HIT THE DECK
(1930 - RKO) Jack Oakie, Polly Walker
One Sheet: $100 - $200

HIT THE DECK
(1955 - MGM) Jane Powell, Tony Martin
One Sheet: $20 - $40

HIT THE HAY
(1945 - Columbia) Judy Canova, Ross Hunter
One Sheet: $30 - $50

HIT THE ICE
(1943 - Universal) Bud Abbott, Lou Costello
One Sheet: $150 - $300

One Sheet

HIT THE ICE
(1949R - Realart) Bud Abbott, Lou Costello
One Sheet: $50 - $100 *Re-release.*

HIT THE ROAD
(1941 - Universal) Gladys George, Barton MacLane, Dead End Kids
One Sheet: $75 - $125

HIT THE SADDLE
(1937 - Republic) The Three Mesquiteers
One Sheet: $100 - $200

One Sheet

HIT TUNE JAMBOREE
(1942 - Universal) Mills Brothers
One Sheet: $200 - $400 *Musical short.*

HITCH HIKE TO HEAVEN
(1935 - Invincible) Herbert Rawlinson, Anita Page
One Sheet: $75 - $150

HITCH IN TIME, A
(1978 - Eyeline) Patrick Troughton, Michael McVey
One Sheet: $5 - $10

HITCHER, THE
(1986 - -) Rutger Hauer, Jennifer Jason Leigh, C. Thomas Howell
One Sheet: $7 - $15

HITCH-HIKE LADY
(1936 - Republic) Mae Clark, Alison Skipworth
One Sheet: $50 - $100

HITCH-HIKE TO HAPPINESS
(1945 - Republic) Al Pearce, Dale Evans, Brad Tayler

HITCH-HIKER, THE
(1953 - RKO Radio) Edmond O'Brien, Frank Lovejoy
One Sheet: $50 - $100

HITCHHIKERS, THE
(1972 - Entertainment Ventures) Misty Rowe, Norman Klar
One Sheet: $3 - $5

HITLER
(1962 - Allied Artists) Richard Basehart
One Sheet: $7 - $15 *AKA: WOMEN OF NAZI GERMANY.*

HITLER - DEAD OR ALIVE
(1942 - C. House) Ward Bond, Dorothy Tree, Warren Hymer
One Sheet: $50 - $100

HITLER GANG, THE
(1944 - Paramount) Robert Watson, Roman Bohner
One Sheet: $75 - $125

HITLER: THE LAST TEN DAYS
(1972 - Paramount) Alec Guinness, Simon Ward
One Sheet: $5 - $10

HITLER'S CHILDREN
(1943 - RKO) Tim Holt, Bonita Granville
One Sheet: $50 - $100

HITLER'S MADMAN
(1943 - MGM) Patricia Morison, John Carradine, Alan Curtis
One Sheet: $50 - $100

Mini Window Card

HITLER-BEAST OF BERLIN
(1940 - -) Alan Ladd
One Sheet: $75 - $150

HIT-THE-TRAIL HOLLIDAY
(1918 - Artcraft) George H. Cohan
One Sheet: $350 - $750

HITTIN' THE TRAIL
(1937 - Grand National) Tex Ritter
One Sheet: $100 - $200

HITTING A NEW HIGH
(1937 - RKO) Lily Pons, Jack Oakie
One Sheet: $100 - $200

HI-YO-SILVER
(1940 - Republic) Lee Powell, Silver, Chief Thunder Cloud
One Sheet: $150 - $300

H-MAN
(1959 - Columbia) Yumi Shirakawa, Kenji Sahara
One Sheet: $40 - $75

HOA BINH
(1971 - Transvue) Phi Lan, Huynh Cazenas
One Sheet: $3 - $5

HOAX, THE
(1972 - All-Scope) Frank Bonner, Bill Ewing
One Sheet: $3 - $5

HOAXTERS, THE
(1952 - MGM) -
One Sheet: $15 - $25

HOBSON'S CHOICE
(1931 - Wardour) James Harcourt, Viola Lyel
One Sheet: $150 - $300

HOBSON'S CHOICE

(1954 - United Artists) Charles Laughton, John Mills
One Sheet: $30 - $50

HOCKEY CHAMP, THE
(1939 - RKO/Disney) Donald Duck & Nephews
One Sheet: $7,500 - $12,000 *Cartoon. Sports (Hockey). Full color. Cartoon Movie Posters #152. Sports Movie Posters #231.*

HOCUS POCUS
(1949 - Columbia) The Three Stooges (Shemp)
One Sheet: $350 - $750 *Comedy short. Duotone.*

HOCUS POCUS
(1993 - Buena Vista) Bette Midler, Sarah Jessica Parker, Kathy Najimy
One Sheet: $3 - $5

HOEDOWN
(1950 - Columbia) Eddy Arnold, Jeff Donnell
One Sheet: $50 - $100 *Country musical.*

HOFFA
(1992 - 20th Century Fox) Jack Nicholson, Danny DeVito
One Sheet: $5 - $10

HOFFMAN
(1970 - British films) Peter Sellers, Sinead Cusack
One Sheet: $7 - $15

HOG WILD
(1930 - MGM) Laurel & Hardy
One Sheet: $2,500 - $4,000

HOG WILD
(1980 - Avco/Embassy) Michael Biehn, Patti D'Arbanville
One Sheet: $3 - $5

HOI POLLOI
(1935 - Columbia) The Three Stooges (Curly)
One Sheet: $13,000 - $20,000 *Comedy short. Duotone.*

HOLD 'EM JAIL
(1932 - RKO) Betty Grable, Wheeler and Woolsey
One Sheet: $250 - $500 *Sports (Football). Sports Movie Posters #184.*

HOLD 'EM NAVY
(1937 - Paramount) Lew Ayres, Mary Carlisle
One Sheet: $150 - $300 *Sports (Football).*

HOLD 'EM YALE
(1928 - Pathe) Rod La Rocque, Jeanette Loff
One Sheet: $250 - $600 *Sports (Football). Aka: At Yale.*

HOLD 'EM YALE
(1935 - Paramount) Buster Crabbe, Cesar Romero
One Sheet: $250 - $500 *Sports (Football). Sports Movie Posters #374.*

HOLD BACK THE DAWN
(1941 - Paramount) Charles Boyer, Olivia de Havilland
One Sheet: $100 - $200

HOLD BACK THE NIGHT
(1956 - Allied Artists) John Payne, Mona Freeman
One Sheet: $30 - $50

HOLD BACK TOMORROW
(1955 - Universal) Cleo Moore, John Agar
One Sheet: $30 - $60

HOLD EVERYTHING
(1930 - Warner Bros.) Winnie Lightner, Joe E. Brown
One Sheet: $200 - $400 *Sports (Boxing). Sports Movie Posters #126.*

HOLD ME TIGHT
(1933 - Fox) James Dunn, Sally Eilers
One Sheet: $100 - $200

HOLD MY HAND
(1938 - Associated) Stanley Lupino, Barbara Blair
One Sheet: $150 - $350

HOLD ON!
(1966 - MGM) Herman's Hermits
One Sheet: $30 - $60 *Rock and roll.*

HOLD THAT BABY!
(1949 - Monogram) Leo Gorcey, Huntz Hall, Gabriel Dell
One Sheet: $40 - $75

HOLD THAT BLONDE
(1945 - Paramount) Eddie Bracken, Veronica Lake
One Sheet: $75 - $150

HOLD THAT CO-ED
(1938 - 20th Century Fox) John Barrymore, George Murphy
One Sheet: $200 - $400 *Sports (Football). Sports Movie Posters #353.*

HOLD THAT GHOST
(1941 - Universal) Bud Abbott, Lou Costello
One Sheet: $200 - $400 *Graven Images, pg. 143.*

HOLD THAT GIRL
(1934 - Fox) James Dunn, Claire Trevor
One Sheet: $100 - $200

HOLD THAT HYPNOTIST
(1957 - Allied Artists) Huntz Hall, Stanley Clements
One Sheet: $15 - $30

HOLD THAT KISS
(1938 - MGM) Maureen O'Sullivan, Mickey Rooney
One Sheet: $100 - $200

HOLD THAT LINE
(1952 - Monogram) Bowery Boys
One Sheet: $40 - $75 *Sports (Football). Sports Movie Posters #202.*

HOLD THAT LION
(1947 - Columbia) The Three Stooges (Shemp), Curly (cameo)
One Sheet: $1,900 - $3,000 *Comedy short. Duotone. Only film in which all three Howard brothers (Moe, Curly & Shemp) appear.*

HOLD THAT POSE
(1950 - RKO/Disney) Goofy
One Sheet: $250 - $600 *Cartoon. Full color.*

HOLD THAT WOMAN
(1940 - PRC) James Dunn, Frances Gifford
One Sheet: $40 - $75

HOLD THE PRESS
(1933 - Columbia) Tim McCoy, Shirley Grey
One Sheet: $150 - $300

HOLD YOUR BREATH
(1924 - Christie) Dorothy Devore, Walter Hiers
One Sheet: $150 - $300

HOLD YOUR MAN
(1933 - MGM) Jean Harlow, Clark Gable
One Sheet: $1,900 - $3,000

HOLD-UP AT DEVIL'S PASS, THE
(1915 - Unicorn) -
One Sheet: $800 - $1,500

HOLE IN THE HEAD, A
(1959 - United Artists) Frank Sinatra, Edward G. Robinson
One Sheet: $40 - $75

HOLE IN THE WALL
(1921 - Metro) Alice Lake, Allan Forrest
One Sheet: $150 - $300

HOLE IN THE WALL
(1929 - Paramount) Edward G. Robinson, Claudette Colbert
One Sheet: $800 - $1,500

HOLIDAY
(1930 - Pathe) Ann Harding, Mary Astor
One Sheet: $350 - $750

HOLIDAY
(1938 - Columbia) Katharine Hepburn, Cary Grant
One Sheet: $1,300 - $2,000

HOLIDAY AFFAIR
(1949 - RKO) Robert Mitchum, Janet Leigh, Wendell Corey
One Sheet: $75 - $125

HOLIDAY CAMP
(1947 - Universal) Jack Warner, Flora Robson
One Sheet: $40 - $75

HOLIDAY FOR HENRIETTA
(1955 - Ardee) Dany Robin, Hildagarde Neff
One Sheet: $10 - $20

HOLIDAY FOR LOVERS
(1959 - 20th Century Fox) Clifton Webb, Jane Wyman
One Sheet: $5 - $10

HOLIDAY FOR SINNERS
(1952 - MGM) Keenan Wynn, Janice Rule, Gig Young
One Sheet: $15 - $35

HOLIDAY IN HAVANA
(1949 - Columbia) Desi Arnaz, Mary Hatcher
One Sheet: $50 - $100

HOLIDAY IN MEXICO
(1946 - MGM) Walter Pidgeon, Jane Powell
One Sheet: $30 - $50

HOLIDAY INN
(1942 - Paramount) Bing Crosby, Fred Astaire
One Sheet: $250 - $500

HOLIDAY INN
(1949R - Paramount) Bing Crosby, Fred Astaire
One Sheet: $50 - $100   *Re-release.*

HOLIDAY RHYTHM
(1950 - Lippert) Mary Beth Hughes, David Street
One Sheet: $30 - $50   *Musical variety.*

HOLIDAY WEEK
(1952 - Monarch) Lisa Daniely, Leslie Dwyer
One Sheet: $7 - $15

HOLIDAY'S END
(1937 - Paramount) Wally Patch, Sally Stewart
One Sheet: $100 - $200

HOLIDAYS WITH PAY
(1948 - Mancunian) Tessie O'Shea, Dan Young
One Sheet: $10 - $20

HOLLOW TRIUMPH
(1948 - PRC   .) Paul Henreid, Joan Bennett
One Sheet: $20 - $40

HOLLY AND THE IVY, THE
(1953 - London) Ralph Richardson, Margaret Leighton
One Sheet: $15 - $35

HOLLYWOOD
(1923 - Paramount) All Star Cast
One Sheet: $5,000 - $8,000

HOLLYWOOD AND VINE
(1945 - PRC) James Ellison, Wanda McKay
One Sheet: $75 - $125

HOLLYWOOD BARN DANCE
(1947 - Screen Guild) Ernest Tubb
One Sheet: $75 - $150   *Country musical.*

HOLLYWOOD BOULEVARD
(1936 - Paramount) John Halliday, Robert Cummings
One Sheet: $150 - $300

HOLLYWOOD BOULEVARD
(1976 - -) Candice Realson, Mary Woronov
One Sheet: $7 - $15

HOLLYWOOD BRONC BUSTERS
(1955 - Columbia) -
One Sheet: $15 - $25

HOLLYWOOD BURLESQUE
(1952 - -) Jenny & Hillary Dawn
One Sheet: $20 - $40   *Sexploitation.*

HOLLYWOOD CANTEEN
(1945 - Warner Bros.) Bette Davis, John Garfield, All-Star cast
One Sheet: $75 - $150

HOLLYWOOD CAVALCADE
(1939 - 20th Century Fox) Alice Faye, Don Ameche
One Sheet: $250 - $500

HOLLYWOOD CHAINSAW HOOKERS
(1988 - -) Gunnar Hansen, Linnea Quigley
One Sheet: $15 - $25

HOLLYWOOD COWBOY
(1937 - RKO) George O'Brien
One Sheet: $150 - $300

HOLLYWOOD DETOUR, A
(1941 - Columbia) Color Rhapsodies
One Sheet: $500 - $800   *Cartoon. Full color semi-stock poster with inset of title. Caricatures of W.C. Fields, Katharine Hepburn, etc.*

HOLLYWOOD EXTRA
(1936 - MGM) -
One Sheet: $200 - $400

HOLLYWOOD GAD-ABOUT, THE
(1934 - Educational) Walter Winchell
One Sheet: $200 - $400

HOLLYWOOD GRADUATION
(1938 - Columbia) -
One Sheet: $250 - $600   *Cartoon. Cartoon Movie Posters #43.*

HOLLYWOOD HARRY
(1985 - -) Robert Forster, Joe Spinell
One Sheet: $3 - $5

HOLLYWOOD HIGH
(1977 - PPP) Sherry Hardin, Nancy Albrecht
One Sheet: $5 - $10

HOLLYWOOD HOTEL
(1937 - Warner Bros.) Dick Powell, Rosemary Lane
One Sheet: $500 - $800

HOLLYWOOD KID, THE
(1924 - Pathe) Mack Sennett Comedy
One Sheet: $350 - $750

HOLLYWOOD KNIGHTS, THE
(1980 - Columbia) Tony Danza(film debut), Michelle Pfeiffer
One Sheet: $3 - $5

HOLLYWOOD MYSTERY
(1934 - Regal) Frank Albertson, June Clyde
One Sheet: $100 - $200

HOLLYWOOD OR BUST
(1956 - Paramount) Dean Martin, Jerry Lewis
One Sheet: $40 - $75   *Their last film as a team.*

HOLLYWOOD PARTY
(1934 - MGM) Laurel & Hardy, Jimmy Durante
One Sheet: $3,500 - $5,500   *Mickey Mouse shown on One Sheet.*

HOLLYWOOD REVELS
(19?? - -) Aleene, Follies Bergere
One Sheet: $15 - $30

HOLLYWOOD REVUE OF 1929, THE
(1929 - MGM) Joan Crawford, Jack Benny, Buster Keaton
One Sheet: $3,500 - $5,000

HOLLYWOOD ROUNDUP
(1937 - Columbia) Buck Jones, Shemp Howard
One Sheet: $250 - $500   *Cowboy Movie Posters #213.*

HOLLYWOOD SHUFFLE
(1987 - -) Robert Townsend, Anne-Marie Johnson
One Sheet: $7 - $15   *Shuffling comedy.*

HOLLYWOOD SPEAKS
(1932 - Columbia) Pat O'Brien, Genevieve Tobin
One Sheet: $500 - $800

One Sheet

HOLLYWOOD STADIUM MYSTERY
(1938 - Republic) Neil Hamilton, Evelyn

Venable
One Sheet: $100 - $200

HOLLYWOOD STORY
(1951 - Universal) Richard Conte, Julie Adams
One Sheet: $15 - $25

HOLLYWOOD THRILLMAKERS
(1954 - B.B. Ray) James Gleason, Bill Henry
One Sheet: $15 - $30

HOLLYWOOD VARIETIES
(1950 - Lippert) Robert Alda, Peggy Stewart
One Sheet: $20 - $40

HOLLYWOOD VICE SQUAD
(1986 - -) Trish VanDevere, Ronny Cox, Leon Isaac Kennedy
One Sheet: $3 - $5

HOLT OF THE SECRET SERVICE
(1941 - Columbia) Jack Holt, Evelyn Brent
One Sheet: $100 - $200   *Serial. 15 Chapters.*

HOLY MATRIMONY
(1943 - 20th Century Fox) Monty Woolley, Gracie Fields
One Sheet: $75 - $125

One Sheet

HOLY MOUNTAIN
(1969 - -) Alexandro Jodorowski
One Sheet: $50 - $100

HOLY TERROR, A
(1931 - Fox) George O'Brien, Humphrey Bogart
One Sheet: $700 - $1,200   *Lobby Card(Bogart):$400-800. Bogart not shown on one sheet.*

HOLY TERROR, THE
(1937 - 20th Century Fox) Jane Withers, Tony Martin
One Sheet: $75 - $150

One Sheet

HOLY YEAR 1950
(1950 - 20th Century Fox) -
One Sheet: $15 - $30

HOLY YEAR AT THE VATICAN
(1952 - -) -
One Sheet: $30 - $50   *Documentary.*

HOLYFIELD VS. TYSON
(1991 - -) Boxing promo
One Sheet: $30 - $50   *Sports (Boxing). This fight never took place.*

HOMBRE
(1966 - 20th Century Fox) Paul Newman, Fredric March, Richard Boone
One Sheet: $30 - $50

HOME

(1915 - -) Fred Groves, A.V. Bramble
One Sheet: $250 - $500

HOME
(1916 - Triangle) Bessie Barriscale, Clara Williams
One Sheet: $250 - $500

HOME
(1919 - Universal/Jewel) Mildred Harris, Frank Elliott
One Sheet: $250 - $500

HOME ALONE
(1990 - 20th Century Fox) Macaulay Culkin, Catherine O'Hara
One Sheet: $7 - $15

HOME ALONE 2: LOST IN NEW YORK
(1992 - 20th Century Fox) Macaulay Culkin, Joe Pesci
One Sheet: $5 - $10

HOME AND AWAY
(1956 - Conquest) Jack Warner, Kathleen Harrison
One Sheet: $5 - $10

HOME AT SEVEN
(1953 - British-Lion) Ralph Richardson, Jack Hawkins
One Sheet: $10 - $20

HOME BEFORE DARK
(1958 - Warner Bros) Jean Simmons, Dan O'Herlihy
One Sheet: $15 - $25

HOME FOR THE HOLIDAYS
(1995 - Paramount) Holly Hunter, Anne Bancroft, Robert Downey Jr.
One Sheet: $5 - $12

HOME FREE ALL
(1983 - P.O.P.) Allan Nicholls, Larry Goldman
One Sheet: $3 - $5

HOME FROM HOME
(1939 - British Lion) Sandy Powell, Wally Patch
One Sheet: $50 - $100

HOME FROM THE HILL
(1960 - MGM) Robert Mitchum, Eleanor Parker
One Sheet: $20 - $40

HOME IN INDIANA
(1944 - 20th Century Fox) Walter Brennan, Lon McCallister
One Sheet: $40 - $75

HOME IN OKLAHOMA
(1946 - Republic) Roy Acuff, Jacqueline Thomas
One Sheet: $50 - $100   *Country musical.*

HOME IN SAN ANTONE
(1949 - Columbia) Roy Acuff, Smoky Mountain Boys
One Sheet: $50 - $100   *Country musical.*

HOME IN WYOMIN'
(1942 - Republic) Gene Autry
One Sheet: $150 - $300

HOME IS THE HERO
(1961 - SCOA) Arthur Kennedy, Walter Macken
One Sheet: $3 - $5

HOME IS WHERE THE HEART IS
(1987 - -) Jason Robards, Jane Alexander, Winona Ryder
One Sheet: $3 - $5   *Originally titled SQUARE DANCE.*

HOME LIFE IN JAPAN
(1913 - G. Melies) -
One Sheet: $500 - $900

HOME MOVIES
(1979 - United Artists) Kirk Douglas, Nancy Allen
One Sheet: $5 - $10

HOME OF OUR OWN
(1993 - -) Kathy Bates, Edward Furlong
One Sheet: $3 - $5

HOME OF THE BRAVE
(1949 - United Artists) Douglas Dick, Lloyd Bridges, James Edwards
One Sheet: $50 - $100   *Separate Cinema, pg. 148.*

HOME OF THE BRAVE
(1986 - -) Laurie Anderson
One Sheet: $3 - $5   *Concert Film.*

HOME ON THE PRAIRIE
(1939 - Republic) Gene Autry
One Sheet: $200 - $400

HOME ON THE RANGE
(1934 - Paramount) Randolph Scott, Jackie
Coogan
One Sheet: $200 - $400

HOME ON THE RANGE
(1940 - MGM) -
One Sheet: $500 - $800   *Cartoon.*
Cartoon Movie Posters #241.

HOME ON THE RANGE
(1946 - Republic) Monte Hale, Adrian Booth
One Sheet: $40 - $75

HOME STRETCH, THE
(1921 - Paramount) Douglas MacLean,
Beatrice Burnham
One Sheet: $250 - $500

HOME, SWEET HOME
(1933 - RKO) John Stuart, Marie Ney
One Sheet: $100 - $200

HOME SWEET HOME
(1945 - Butcher) Tony Pendrell, Nicolette Roeg
One Sheet: $15 - $25

HOME SWEET HOME
(1981 - -) Jake Steinfeld, Sallee Elyse
One Sheet: $3 - $5

HOME SWEET HOMICIDE
(1946 - 20th Century Fox) Peggy Ann Garner,
Randolph Scott
One Sheet: $75 - $125

HOME TALENT
(1921 - Sennett) Ben Turpin
One Sheet: $150 - $350

HOME TO DANGER
(1951 - Eros) Guy Rolfe, Rona Anderson
One Sheet: $15 - $30

HOME TOWNERS, THE
(1928 - Warner Bros.) Richard Bennett, Robert
McWade
One Sheet: $250 - $600

HOMEBODIES
(1974 - Avco/Embassy) Frances Fuller, Linda
Marsh
One Sheet: $5 - $10

HOMEBOY
(1989 - -) Mickey Rourke, Christopher Walken,
Debra Feuer
One Sheet: $3 - $5

HOMEBREAKER, THE
(1919 - -) Rudolph Valentino
One Sheet: $600 - $1,000

HOMECOMING
(1948 - MGM) Clark Gable, Lana Turner
One Sheet: $50 - $100

HOMECOMING, THE
(1973 - American Film) Ian Holm, Cyril Cusack
One Sheet: $3 - $5

HOMEMAKER
(1923 - Universal) Alice Joyce, Clyde Brook
One Sheet: $150 - $300

HOMER
(1970 - National General) Don Scardino, Alex
Nicol, Tisa Farrow
One Sheet: $3 - $5

HOMER'S ODYSSEY
(1909 - Monopol) -
One Sheet: $1,300 - $2,000

HOMESPUN VAMP, A
(1921 - Realart) May McAvoy
One Sheet: $125 - $250

HOMESTEADER, THE
(1922 - -) Evelyn Preer
One Sheet: $250 - $500

HOMESTEADERS, THE
(1953 - Monogram) Bill Elliott
One Sheet: $15 - $35

HOMESTEADERS OF PARADISE VALLEY
(1947 - Republic) Allen Lane, Bobby Blake
One Sheet: $30 - $60   *Red Ryder
series.*

HOMESTRETCH, THE
(1947 - 20th Century Fox) Cornel Wilde,
Maureen O'Hara
One Sheet: $75 - $125

HOMETOWN GIRL
(1950S - -) -
One Sheet: $30 - $50   *Sexploitation.*

HOMETOWN STORY
(1951 - MGM) Marilyn Monroe, Jeffrey Lynn
One Sheet: $125 - $250

HOMETOWN U.S.A.
(1979 - Film Ventures) David Wilson, Gary
Springer
One Sheet: $3 - $5

HOMEWARD BOUND
(1923 - Famous Players/Lasky) Thomas
Meighan, Lila Lee
One Sheet: $200 - $400

**HOMEWARD BOUND II-LOST IN SAN
FRANCISCO**
(1996 - Walt Disney) Voices of Michael J. Fox,
Don Ameche
One Sheet: $3 - $7   *Cartoon.*

**HOMEWARD BOUND: THE INCREDIBLE
JOURNEY**
(1993 - Buena Vista) Kim Greist, Robert Hayes
One Sheet: $3 - $5

HOMEWORK
(1982 - Jensen Farley) Joan Collins, Michael
Morgan
One Sheet: $10 - $20

HOMICIDAL
(1961 - Columbia) Glenn Corbett, Patricia
Breslin
One Sheet: $30 - $50   *Graven
Images, pg. 206.*

HOMICIDE
(1949 - Warner Bros.) Robert Douglas, Helen
Westcott
One Sheet: $40 - $75

HOMICIDE BUREAU
(1938 - Columbia) Bruce Cabot, Rita Hayworth
One Sheet: $125 - $250

HOMICIDE FOR THREE
(1948 - Republic) Audrey Long, Warren
Douglas
One Sheet: $30 - $50

HOMICIDE SQUAD, THE
(1931 - Universal) Leo Carrillo, Noah Berry, Sr.
One Sheet: $150 - $300

HOMUNCULUS
(1916 - Bioscop) Dir: Otto Rippert
One Sheet: $16,000 - $25,000   *Graven
Images, pg. 15.*

HONDO
(1953 - Warner Bros.) John Wayne, Geraldine
Page
One Sheet: $300 - $700   *One Sheet (3-
D):$400-$800. Cowboy Movie Posters #s 298,
301.*

HONEY
(1930 - Paramount Famous Lasky) Nancy
Carroll, Murray Roth
One Sheet: $100 - $200

HONEY, I BLEW UP THE KID
(1992 - Buena Vista/Disney) Rick Moranis
One Sheet: $3 - $5

HONEY, I SHRUNK THE KIDS
(1989 - Buena Vista/Disney) Rick Moranis, Matt
Frewer
One Sheet: $3 - $5

HONEY POT, THE
(1967 - United Artists) Rex Harrison, Susan
Hayward
One Sheet: $5 - $10

HONEYBABY, HONEYBABY
(1974 - Jordon) Calvin Lockhart, Diana Sands
One Sheet: $5 - $10

HONEYCHILE
(1951 - Republic) Judy Canova, Eddie Foy, Jr.
One Sheet: $15 - $25

HONEYMOON
(1947 - RKO Radio) Shirley Temple, Franchot
Tone
One Sheet: $40 - $75

HONEYMOON ADVENTURE
(1940 - British Lion) Peter Hannen, Benita
Hume
One Sheet: $30 - $50

HONEYMOON AHEAD
(1945 - Universal) Allan Jones, Grace
McDonald
One Sheet: $40 - $75

HONEYMOON DEFERRED
(1940 - Universal) Edmund Lowe, Margaret
Lindsay
One Sheet: $75 - $125

HONEYMOON DEFERRED
(1951 - Vic) Griffith Jones, Sally Ann Howes
One Sheet: $10 - $20

HONEYMOON FOR THREE
(1935 - British Pathe) Stanley Lupino, Dennis
Hoey, Aileen Marson
One Sheet: $100 - $200

HONEYMOON FOR THREE
(1941 - Warner Bros.) Ann Sheridan, George
Brent, Charles Ruggles
One Sheet: $40 - $75

HONEYMOON HATE
(1927 - Paramount) Florence Vidor, William
Austin
One Sheet: $200 - $400

HONEYMOON HOTEL
(1946 - Butcher) Norman Evans, Nat Jackley
One Sheet: $15 - $30

HONEYMOON HOTEL
(1964 - MGM) Robert Goulet, Nancy Kwan
One Sheet: $5 - $10

HONEYMOON IN BALI
(1939 - Paramount) Fred MacMurray,
Madeleine Carroll
One Sheet: $100 - $200

One Sheet

HONEYMOON IN VEGAS
(1992 - Columbia) James Caan, Nicolas Cage,
Sarah Jessica Parker
One Sheet: $5 - $10

HONEYMOON KILLERS, THE
(1970 - Cinerama) Shirley Stoler, Tony
LoBianco
One Sheet: $7 - $15

HONEYMOON LANE
(1931 - Paramount Publix) Eddie Dowling, June
Collyer
One Sheet: $100 - $200

HONEYMOON LIMITED
(1935 - Monogram) Neil Hamilton, Irene Hervey
One Sheet: $75 - $150

HONEYMOON LODGE
(1943 - Universal) David Bruce, Harriet Hilliard
One Sheet: $40 - $75

HONEYMOON MACHINE, THE
(1961 - MGM) Steve McQueen, Jim Hutton
One Sheet: $20 - $40

HONEYMOON MERRY-GO-ROUND

(1939 - RKO) Claude Hulbert, Princess Pearl
One Sheet: $75 - $150   *AKA:
OLYMPIC HONEYMOON.*

HONEYMOON OF HORROR
(1964 - Manson) Robert Parsons
One Sheet: $15 - $30

HONEYMOON'S OVER, THE
(1939 - 20th Century Fox) Marjorie Weaver,
Stuart Erwin
One Sheet: $75 - $125

HONEYSUCKLE ROSE
(1980 - Warner Bros.) Dyan Cannon, Willie
Nelson
One Sheet: $5 - $10

HONG KONG
(1951 - Paramount) Ronald Reagan, Rhonda
Fleming
One Sheet: $40 - $75

HONG KONG AFFAIR
(1958 - Allied Artists) Jack Kelly, May Wynn
One Sheet: $15 - $25

HONG KONG CONFIDENTIAL
(1958 - Vogue) Gene Barry, Beverly Tyler
One Sheet: $15 - $25

HONG KONG NIGHTS
(1935 - Futter) Tom Keene, Wera Engels
One Sheet: $75 - $150

HONKERS, THE
(1972 - United Artists) James Coburn, Lois
Nettleton
One Sheet: $5 - $10

HONKY
(1971 - Harris) Brenda Sykes, John Neilson
One Sheet: $7 - $15

HONKY TONK
(1929 - Warner Bros.) Sophie Tucker, Lila Lee
One Sheet: $800 - $1,500

HONKY TONK
(1941 - MGM) Clark Gable, Lana Turner
One Sheet: $125 - $250

HONKY TONK
(1955R - MGM) Clark Gable, Lana Turner
One Sheet: $40 - $75   *Re-release.*

HONKY TONK BURLESQUE
(1953 - Sonney Amusement Enterprises) -
One Sheet: $30 - $60   *Sexploitation.*

HONKY TONK FREEWAY
(1981 - Universal) Beau Bridges, Hume
Cronyn, Beverly D'Angelo
One Sheet: $3 - $5

HONKYTONK MAN
(1982 - Warner Bros.) Clint Eastwood
One Sheet: $15 - $25

HONOLULU
(1939 - MGM) Eleanor Powell, George Burns,
Gracie Allen, Robert Young
One Sheet: $125 - $250

HONOLULU LU
(1941 - Columbia) Lupe Velez, Forrest Tucker
One Sheet: $50 - $100

HONOR AMONG LOVERS
(1931 - Paramont Publix) Claudette Colbert,
Fredric March
One Sheet: $500 - $800

HONOR OF HIS HOUSE, THE
(1918 - Paramount) Sessue Hayakawa
One Sheet: $500 - $900

HONOR OF THE FAMILY
(1931 - First National) Bebe Daniels, Warren
William
One Sheet: $100 - $200

HONOR OF THE FORCE, THE
(1913 - Edison) -
One Sheet: $500 - $800

HONOR OF THE MOUNTED
(1932 - Monarch) Tom Tyler, Tom London
One Sheet: $125 - $250

HONOR OF THE PRESS
(1932 - Mayfair) Edward J. Nugent, Rita LaRoy
One Sheet: $100 - $200

HONOR OF THE RANGE
(1934 - Universal) Ken Maynard
One Sheet: $600 - $1,000   *Cowboy Movie Posters #171.*

HONOR OF THE RANGE
(1943R - Universal) Ken Maynard
One Sheet: $30 - $50   *Re-release. Duotone.*

HONOR OF THE WEST
(1938 - Universal) Bob Baker
One Sheet: $75 - $125

HONOURABLE MURDER, AN
(1959 - Pathe) Norman Wooland, Lisa Daniely
One Sheet: $7 - $15

HONOURS EASY
(1935 - British International) Greta Nissen, Ivan Samson
One Sheet: $75 - $150

HOODLUM, THE
(1919 - First National) Mary Pickford
One Sheet: $1,300 - $2,000

HOODLUM, THE
(1951 - United Artists) Lawrence Tierney, Allene Roberts
One Sheet: $75 - $125

HOODLUM EMPIRE
(1952 - Republic) Brian Donlevy, Claire Trevor
One Sheet: $20 - $40

HOODLUM PRIEST, THE
(1961 - United Artists) Don Murray, Larry Gates
One Sheet: $15 - $25

HOODLUM SAINT, THE
(1946 - MGM) William Powell, Esther Williams
One Sheet: $75 - $125

HOODWINK
(1981 - New South) John Hargreaves, Judy Davis
One Sheet: $3 - $5

HOOFBEATS OF VENGEANCE
(1929 - Universal) Rex the Wonder Horse, Jack Perrin, Helen Foster
One Sheet: $250 - $500

HOOFS AND GOOFS
(1957 - Columbia) The Three Stooges (Joe Besser)
One Sheet: $75 - $125   *Comedy Short. Duotone.*

HOOK, THE
(1963 - MGM) Kirk Douglas, Robert Walker
One Sheet: $15 - $25

HOOK
(1991 - TriStar) Robin Williams, Dustin Hoffman
One Sheet: $7 - $15

HOOK AND LADDER
(1951R - -) -
One Sheet: $40 - $75   *Re-release.*

HOOK, LINE AND SINKER
(1922 - Pathe) Snub Pollard
One Sheet: $250 - $600

HOOK, LINE AND SINKER
(1930 - RKO) Wheeler & Woolsey, Natalie Moorehead
One Sheet: $250 - $500

HOOK, LINE AND SINKER
(1939 - 20th Century Fox) Terry-toons
One Sheet: $150 - $300   *Cartoon. Full color stone litho. Stock poster with inset title.*

HOOK, LINE AND SINKER
(1969 - Columbia) Jerry Lewis, Peter Lawford, Anne Francis
One Sheet: $15 - $25

HOOKED BEAR
(1956 - Disney) -
One Sheet: $150 - $300   *Cartoon.*

HOOKED GENERATION, THE
(1969 - Allied Artists) Jeremy Slate, Steve Alaimo, John Davis Chandler
One Sheet: $20 - $40   *Drug film.*

HOOP DREAMS
(1995 - Fine Line) William Gates, Arthur Agee
One Sheet: $10 - $20   *Sports*

(Basketball). *Sports Movie Posters #105.*

HOOPER
(1978 - Warner Bros.) Burt Reynolds, Jan-Michael Vincent, Sally Field
One Sheet: $15 - $25   *Price is for all styles.*

HOOP-LA
(1933 - Fox) Clara Bow
One Sheet: $600 - $1,000

HOORAY FOR LOVE
(1935 - RKO) Ann Sothern, Gene Raymond
One Sheet: $350 - $750

HOOSEGOW, THE
(1929 - MGM) Laurel & Hardy
One Sheet: $3,500 - $5,000

HOOSIER HOLIDAY
(1943 - Republic) Dale Evans, George Byron
One Sheet: $50 - $100

HOOSIER SCHOOLBOY
(1937 - Monogram) Mickey Rooney, Anne Nagel
One Sheet: $75 - $150

HOOSIER SCHOOLBOY
(1941R - Monogram) Mickey Rooney, Anne Nagel
One Sheet: $20 - $40   *Re-release.*

HOOSIER SCHOOLMASTER, THE
(1924 - -) Henry Hull, Jane Thomas
One Sheet: $150 - $300

HOOSIER SCHOOLMASTER, THE
(1935 - Monogram) Charlotte Henry, Norman Foster
One Sheet: $125 - $250

HOOSIERS
(1986 - Orion) Gene Hackman, Dennis Hopper, Barbara Hershey
One Sheet: $30 - $50   *Sports (Basketball). Sports Movie Posters #99.*

HOOTENANNY HOOT
(1963 - MGM) Johnny Cash, Sheb Wooley, Peter Breck
One Sheet: $30 - $50   *Country musical.*

HOOTS MON!
(1939 - Warner Bros.) Max Miller, Florence Desmond
One Sheet: $50 - $100

HOP HARRIGAN
(1946 - Columbia) William Blakewell, Jennifer Holt
One Sheet: $100 - $200   *Serial. 15 Chapters.*

HOP HARRIGAN
(1957R - Columbia) William Blakewell, Jennifer Holt
One Sheet: $30 - $50   *Re-release. Serial. 15 Chapters.*

HOPALONG CASSIDY
(1935 - Paramount) William Boyd, Gabby Hayes
One Sheet: $1,600 - $2,500   *Beware of unmarked re-issues on all Hoppy titles. Cowboy Movie Posters #s 173,174.*

HOPALONG CASSIDY ENTERS
(1938 - Paramount) William Boyd, Gabby Hayes
One Sheet: $150 - $300

HOPALONG CASSIDY ENTERS
(1948R - Goodwill) William Boyd, Jimmy Ellison
One Sheet: $50 - $100   *Re-release.*

HOPALONG CASSIDY RETURNS
(1936 - Paramount) William Boyd, Gabby Hayes
One Sheet: $1,600 - $2,500   *Cowboy Movie Posters #202.*

HOPALONG RIDES AGAIN
(1937 - Paramount) William Boyd, Gabby Hayes
One Sheet: $500 - $800

HOPALONG RIDES AGAIN
(1956R - Western Classics) William Boyd
One Sheet: $50 - $100   *Re-release.*

HOPE AND GLORY

(1986 - Columbia) Sarah Miles, David Hayman
One Sheet: $3 - $5

HOPE OF HIS SIDE
(1935 - United Artists) Sydney Howard, Wally Patch
One Sheet: $50 - $100

HOPPY SERVES A WRIT
(1942 - United Artists) William Boyd, Victor Jory, Robert Mitchum
One Sheet: $150 - $300

HOPPY'S HOLIDAY
(1947 - United Artists) William Boyd, Andy Clyde
One Sheet: $75 - $150

HOPSCOTCH
(1980 - Avco) Walter Matthau, Glenda Jackson
One Sheet: $3 - $5

HORIZONS WEST
(1952 - Universal) Robert Ryan, Rock Hudson
One Sheet: $15 - $30

HORIZONTAL LIEUTENANT, THE
(1962 - MGM) Jim Hutton, Paula Prentiss
One Sheet: $15 - $30

HORN BLOWS AT MIDNIGHT, THE
(1945 - Warner Bros.) Jack Benny, Alexis Smith
One Sheet: $75 - $125

HORNET'S NEST, THE
(1955 - General) Charles Farrell, June Thorburn
One Sheet: $5 - $10

HORNETS' NEST
(1970 - United Artists) Rock Hudson, Sylva Koscina
One Sheet: $7 - $15

HORRIBLE DR. HICHCOCK, THE
(1964 - Sigma III) Barbara Steele, Robert Fleming
One Sheet: $40 - $75

HORROR, THE
(1934 - F.P. Pictures) Dir: Bud Pollard
One Sheet: $800 - $1,500   *Graven Images, pg. 65.*

HORROR CASTLE
(1963 - Zodiac) Rossana Podesta, Christopher Lee
One Sheet: $15 - $30   *AKA: TERROR CASTLE; CASTLE OF TERROR; CASTLE OF THE LIVING DEAD.*

HORROR CHAMBER OF DR. FAUSTUS, THE
(1959 - Lopert) Alida Valli, Pierre Brasseur
One Sheet: $50 - $100   *French(47x63):$300-500.*

HORROR CHAMBER OF DR. FAUSTUS, THE/ MANSTER, THE
(1962 - United Artists) -
One Sheet: $15 - $25   *Double feature poster.*

HORROR EXPRESS
(1972 - Granada) Christopher Lee, Peter Cushing
One Sheet: $10 - $20

HORROR HIGH
(1974 - Crown) Pat Cardi
One Sheet: $10 - $20

HORROR HOSPITAL
(1973 - Hallmark) Michael Gough
One Sheet: $15 - $25   *AKA: COMPUTER KILLERS.*

HORROR HOTEL
(1960 - Vulcan) Patricia Jessel, Betta St. John, Christopher Lee
One Sheet: $75 - $125

HORROR HOUSE
(1970 - AIP) Frankie Avalon, Jill Haworth, Dennis Price
One Sheet: $15 - $25   *AKA: THE DARK.*

HORROR ISLAND
(1941 - Universal) Dick Foran, Leo Carrillo
One Sheet: $150 - $300

HORROR MANIAC/STRANGLER'S MORGUE
(195?R - Hoffberg) Tod Slaughter

One Sheet: $50 - $100   *Re-release double feature poster.*

HORROR MANIACS
(1948 - -) See THE GREED OF WILLIAM HART

HORROR OF BLACKWOOD CASTLE, THE
(197? - Sunset International) -
One Sheet: $10 - $20

HORROR OF DRACULA
(1958 - Universal) Peter Cushing, Michael Gough, Christopher Lee
One Sheet: $150 - $350   *Graven Images, pg. 194-195.*

HORROR OF FRANKENSTEIN, THE
(1970 - American Continental) Ralph Bates, Kate O'Mara
One Sheet: $30 - $60

HORROR OF IT ALL, THE
(1964 - Lippert) Pat Boone, Erica Rogers
One Sheet: $15 - $25

HORROR OF PARTY BEACH, THE
(1964 - 20th Century) John Scott, Alice Lyon
One Sheet: $30 - $60

HORROR OF PARTY BEACH/CURSE OF THE LIVING CORPSE
(1964 - 20th Century Fox) -
One Sheet: $15 - $30   *Double feature poster.*

HORROR OF THE BLOOD MONSTER
(1970 - Independent-International) John Carradine, Robert Dix
One Sheet: $15 - $25

HORROR OF THE ZOMBIES
(1974 - Independent-International) Maria Perschy, Jack Taylor
One Sheet: $15 - $25

HORROR ON SNAPE ISLAND
(1972 - Fanfare) Bryant Holiday, Jill Haworth
One Sheet: $15 - $25

HORROR PLANET
(1982 - Jupiter) Judy Geeson, Robin Clarke
One Sheet: $7 - $15

HORROR SHOW, THE
(1989 - United Artists) Lance Henriksen, Brion James
One Sheet: $5 - $10

HORRORS OF SPIDER ISLAND
(1959 - Pacemaker) Barbara Valentin, Alex Darcy
One Sheet: $30 - $50   *AKA: IT'S HOT IN PARADISE.*

HORRORS OF THE BLACK MUSEUM
(1959 - AIP) Michael Gough, Graham Curnow
One Sheet: $50 - $100

One Sheet

HORSE FEATHERS
(1932 - Paramount Publix) The Marx Brothers
One Sheet: $3,500 - $5,000   *Sports Movie Posters #351.*

HORSE FLY OPERA
(1940 - 20th Century Fox) Terry-toons
Cartoon. See "Terrytoons Stock" for prices. Cartoon Movie Posters #86.

HORSE IN THE GREY FLANNEL SUIT, THE
(1968 - Buena Vista/Disney) Dean Jones, Diane Baker, Lloyd Bochner
One Sheet: $20 - $40

HORSE SOLDIERS, THE

(1959 - United Artists) John Wayne, William Holden
One Sheet: $100 - $200

One Sheet

HORSE'S MOUTH, THE
(1953 - GFD) Michael Medwin, Robert Beatty
One Sheet: $7 - $15

HORSE'S MOUTH, THE
(1958 - Knightsbridge) Alec Guinness, Kay Walsh
One Sheet: $7 - $15

HORSEMAN OF THE PLAINS, A
(1928 - Fox) Tom Mix, Sally Blane
One Sheet: $250 - $600

HORSEMEN, THE
(1971 - Columbia) Omar Sharif, Leigh Taylor-Young
One Sheet: $3 - $5

HORSEMEN OF THE SIERRAS
(1949 - Columbia) Charles Starrett, Smiley Burnette
One Sheet: $30 - $60

HORSEPLAY
(1933 - Universal) Slim Summerville, Andy Devine
One Sheet: $125 - $250

HORSES COLLARS
(1935 - Columbia) The Three Stooges (Curly)
One Sheet: $13,000 - $20,000   *Comedy short. Duotone.*

HORSIE
(1951 - United Artists) Phyllis Avery, Darren McGavin
One Sheet: $15 - $25

HORSING AROUND
(1957 - Columbia) The Three Stooges (Joe Besser)
One Sheet: $75 - $125   *Comedy short. Duotone.*

HOSPITAL, THE
(1971 - United Artists) George C. Scott, Diana Rigg
One Sheet: $5 - $10

HOSPITAL MASSACRE
(1982 - Cannon) Barbi Benton, Chip Lucia
One Sheet: $5 - $12

HOSTAGE, THE
(1956 - Eros) Mary Parker, Ron Randell
One Sheet: $7 - $15

HOSTAGE, THE
(1966 - Crown) John Carradine, Harry Dean Stanton
One Sheet: $5 - $10

HOSTAGES
(1943 - Paramount) Luise Rainer, William Bendix, Arturo de Cordova
One Sheet: $40 - $75

HOSTILE COUNTRY
(1950 - Lippert) James Ellison, Russell Hayden
One Sheet: $10 - $20

HOSTILE GUNS
(1967 - Paramount) George Montgomery, Yvonne de Carlo
One Sheet: $15 - $30

HOSTILE WITNESS
(1968 - United Artists) Ray Milland, Sylvia Sims
One Sheet: $5 - $10

HOT AND DEADLY
(1983 - -) Thayer
One Sheet: $5 - $10

HOT ANGEL, THE
(1958 - Paramount) Jackie Loughery, Edward Kemmer
One Sheet: $30 - $60

HOT BLOOD
(1953 - Columbia) Marlon Brando, Mary Murphy
One Sheet: $500 - $900   *Pre-title for THE WILD ONE.*

HOT BLOOD
(1956 - Columbia) Jane Russell, Cornel Wilde
One Sheet: $30 - $50

HOT BOX, THE
(1972 - New World) Andrea Cagan, Margaret Mankor
One Sheet: $5 - $10

HOT CAR GIRL
(1958 - Allied Artists) Richard Bakalyan, June Kennedy
One Sheet: $40 - $75

HOT CARGO
(1946 - Paramount) William Gargan, Phillip Reed
One Sheet: $30 - $50

HOT CARS
(1956 - United Artists) John Bromfield, Joi Lansing
One Sheet: $30 - $50

HOT CURVES
(1930 - Tiffany) Marceline (Alice) Day, Benny Rubin
One Sheet: $125 - $250

HOT DOG, THE
(1924 - Universal-Jewel) Billy Sullivan
One Sheet: $150 - $300   *#5 in the Fast Steppers series.*

HOT DOG: THE MOVIE
(1984 - MGM) David Naughton, Tracy N. Smith
One Sheet: $7 - $15   *Sports (Skiing). Sports Movie Posters #313.*

HOT FOOT
(1920 - -) Bobbie Dunn
One Sheet: $150 - $300

HOT FOOT LIGHTS
(1945 - Columbia) Color Rhapsodies
One Sheet: $150 - $300   *Cartoon. Full color semi-stock poster with inset of title.*

HOT FOR PARIS
(1930 - Fox) Victor McLaglen, Fifi Dorsay
One Sheet: $250 - $500

HOT HEIRESS, THE
(1931 - First National) Walter Pidgeon, Ona Munson
One Sheet: $125 - $250

HOT ICE
(1932 - Paramount) -
One Sheet: $100 - $200

HOT ICE
(1952 - Apex) Barbara Murray, John Justin
One Sheet: $10 - $20

HOT ICE
(1955 - Columbia) The Three Stooges (Shemp)
One Sheet: $150 - $300   *Comedy short. Duotone.*

HOT LEAD
(1951 - RKO) Tim Holt, Richard Martin
One Sheet: $30 - $60

HOT LEAD AND COLD FEET
(1978 - Disney/Buena Vista) Jim Dale, Karen Valentine
One Sheet: $4 - $8

HOT MILLIONS
(1968 - MGM) Peter Ustinov, Maggie Smith, Karl Malden
One Sheet: $5 - $10

HOT MONEY
(1936 - Warner Bros.) Ross Alexander, Beverly Roberts
One Sheet: $75 - $150

HOT MONEY GIRL
(1962 - United) Willy Witte, Dawn Addams
One Sheet: $30 - $50

HOT MOVES
(1984 - Cardinal) Michael Zorek, Adam Silbar
One Sheet: $3 - $5

HOT NEWS
(1928 - Paramount) Bebe Daniels, Neil Hamilton
One Sheet: $250 - $500

HOT NEWS
(1936 - Columbia) Phyllis Clare, Lupino Lane
One Sheet: $100 - $200

HOT NEWS
(1953 - Monogram) Stanley Clements, Gloria Henry
One Sheet: $15 - $30

HOT OFF THE PRESS
(1935 - Victory) Jack LaRue, Monte Blue
One Sheet: $100 - $200

HOT PEPPER
(1933 - Fox) Victor McLaglen, Edmund Lowe, Lupe Velez
One Sheet: $200 - $400

HOT POTATO
(1976 - Warner Bros.) Jim Kelly, Geoffrey Binney
One Sheet: $15 - $35

HOT PURSUIT
(1987 - -) John Cusack, Robert Loggia
One Sheet: $3 - $5

HOT RHYTHM
(1944 - Monogram) Dona Drake, Robert Lowery
One Sheet: $50 - $100   *Big Band musical.*

HOT ROCK, THE
(1972 - 20th Century Fox) Robert Redford, George Segal, Zero Mostel
One Sheet: $7 - $15

HOT ROD
(1950 - Monogram) James Lydon, Art Baker
One Sheet: $50 - $100

HOT ROD GANG
(1958 - AIP) John Ashley, Jody Fair
One Sheet: $75 - $125

HOT ROD GIRL
(1956 - AIP) Lori Nelson, John Smith, Chuck Connors
One Sheet: $75 - $125

HOT ROD HULLABALOO
(1966 - Allied Artists) John Arnold, Arlen Dean Snyder, Marsha Mason
One Sheet: $30 - $50

HOT ROD RUMBLE
(1957 - Allied Artists) Leigh Snowden, Brett Halsey
One Sheet: $50 - $100   *Sports Movie Posters #13.*

One Sheet

HOT RODS TO HELL
(1967 - MGM) Dana Andres, Jeanne Crain
One Sheet: $30 - $60

HOT SATURDAY
(1932 - Paramount Publix) Cary Grant, Nancy Carroll
One Sheet: $600 - $1,000

HOT SCOTS

(1948 - Columbia) The Three Stooges (Shemp)
One Sheet: $350 - $750   *Comedy short. Duotone.*

HOT SHOTS
(1956 - Allied) Huntz Hall, Stanley Clements
One Sheet: $30 - $60

HOT SHOTS
(1991 - 20th Century Fox) Charlie Sheen, Lloyd Bridges, Cary Elwes
One Sheet: $5 - $10

HOT SHOTS PART DEUX
(1993 - 20th Century Fox) Charlie Sheen, Valerie Golino
One Sheet: $3 - $5

HOT SPELL
(1958 - Paramount) Shirley Booth, Anthony Quinn, Shirley MacLaine
One Sheet: $15 - $35

HOT SPOT
(1941 - Fox) Betty Grable, Victor Mature
One Sheet: $600 - $1,000   *AKA: I WAKE UP SCREAMING.*

One Sheet

HOT SPOT, THE
(1990 - -) Don Johnson, Virginia Madsen
One Sheet: $10 - $20

HOT SPUR
(1968 - Republic Amusements) Joseph Mascolo, James Arena
One Sheet: $5 - $10

HOT STEEL
(1940 - Universal) Richard Arlen, Andy Devine
One Sheet: $75 - $125

HOT STUFF
(1929 - First National) Louise Fazenda, Alice White
One Sheet: $250 - $600

HOT STUFF
(1956 - Columbia) The Three Stooges (Shemp)
One Sheet: $150 - $300   *Comedy short. Duotone.*

HOT STUFF
(1979 - Columbia) Dom DeLuise, Suzanne Pleshette
One Sheet: $5 - $10

HOT SUMMER NIGHT
(1957 - MGM) Leslie Nielsen, Colleen Miller
One Sheet: $15 - $25

HOT SUMMER WEEK
(1973 - Fanfare) Diane Hall. Kathleen Cody
One Sheet: $3 - $5

HOT TIMES
(1974 - Mishkin) Henry Cory, Amy Farber
One Sheet: $3 - $7

HOT TIP
(1935 - RKO) ZaSu Pitts, James Gleason
One Sheet: $100 - $200

HOT TO TROT
(1988 - Warner Bros.) Bob Goldthwait, Virginia Madsen, Dabney Coleman
One Sheet: $3 - $5

HOT TOMORROWS
(1978 - American Film) Ray Sharkey, Herve Villechaize
One Sheet: $3 - $6

HOT VARIETY
(1933 - Screencraft) Olive Borden, Hal Skelly

One Sheet: $75 - $150

HOT WATER
(1924 - Pathe) Harold Lloyd, Jobyna Ralston
One Sheet: $600 - $1,000

HOT WATER
(1937 - 20th Century Fox) Spring Byington, Jed Prouty
One Sheet: $100 - $200

HOTEL
(1967 - Warner Bros.) Rod Taylor, Catherine Spaak
One Sheet: $15 - $25

HOTEL BERLIN
(1945 - Warner Bros.) Helmut Dantine, Faye Emerson, Peter Lorre
One Sheet: $75 - $150

HOTEL CONTINENTAL
(1945 - Tiffany) Peggy Shannon, Theodore von Eltz
One Sheet: $20 - $40

HOTEL FOR WOMEN
(1939 - 20th Century Fox) Ann Sothern, Linda Darnell
One Sheet: $800 - $1,500   *Art by McClelland Barclay.*

HOTEL HAYWIRE
(1937 - Paramount) Leo Carrillo, Mary Carlisle
One Sheet: $75 - $125

HOTEL IMPERIAL
(1927 - Paramount) Pola Negri, James Hall
One Sheet: $250 - $500

HOTEL IMPERIAL
(1939 - Paramount) Isa Miranda, Ray Milland
One Sheet: $50 - $100

HOTEL NEW HAMPSHIRE, THE
(1984 - Orion) Rob Lowe, Jodie Foster, Beau Bridges
One Sheet: $5 - $10

HOTEL PARADISO
(1966 - MGM) Alec Guiness, Gina Lollobrigida
One Sheet: $15 - $35

HOTEL RESERVE
(1943 - RKO) James Mason, Lucie Mannheim
One Sheet: $20 - $40

HOTEL SAHARA
(1951 - United Artists) Yvonne De Carlo, Roland Culver
One Sheet: $15 - $25

HOTEL SPLENDIDE
(1932 - Ideal) Jerry Verno, Anthony Holles
One Sheet: $75 - $125

HOTHEAD
(1963 - RKO) John Delgar, Robert Glenn
One Sheet: $10 - $20

H.O.T.S.
(1979 - Derio) Susan Kiger, Lisa London
One Sheet: $5 - $10

HOTTENTOT, THE
(1922 - First National) Douglas MacLean, Madge Bellamy
One Sheet: $200 - $400

HOUDINI
(1953 - Paramount) Tony Curtis, Janet Leigh
One Sheet: $75 - $150   *Magic.*

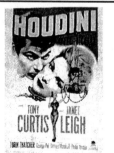

One Sheet

HOUND HUNTERS

(1947 - MGM) Tex Avery
One Sheet: $300 - $700   *Cartoon. Full color stone litho.*

HOUND OF THE BASKERVILLES, THE
(1932 - First Anglo) John Stuart, Heather Angel
One Sheet: $1,600 - $2,500

HOUND OF THE BASKERVILLES, THE
(1939 - 20th Century Fox) Richard Greene, Basil Rathbone
One Sheet: $3,500 - $5,000   *Graven Images, pg. 103.*

One Sheet

HOUND OF THE BASKERVILLES, THE
(1959 - United Artists) Peter Cushing, Christopher Lee
One Sheet: $75 - $150   *Hammer Films. Graven Images, pg. 196.*

HOUND OF THE BASKERVILLES, THE
(1980 - Hemdale) Peter Cook, Dudley Moore
One Sheet: $5 - $10

HOUND OF THE BASKERVILLES, THE
(1983 - Weintraub) Ian Richardson, Donald Churchill
One Sheet: $5 - $10

HOUND THAT THOUGHT HE WAS A RACCOON, THE
(1960 - Disney)
One Sheet: $15 - $25

HOUND-DOG MAN
(1959 - 20th Century Fox) Fabian, Carol Lynley, Stuart Whitman, Dodie Stevens
One Sheet: $30 - $50   *Rock 'n' Roll.*

One Sheet

HOUNDED MEN
(1933 - -) Joseph Krimsky
One Sheet: $75 - $150

HOUNDS OF NOTRE DAME, THE
(1980 - Fraser) Barry Morse, Thomas Peacocke
One Sheet: $3 - $6

HOUR BEFORE THE DAWN, THE
(1944 - Paramount) Veronica Lake, Franchot Tone
One Sheet: $200 - $400

HOUR OF 13, THE
(1952 - MGM) Peter Lawford, Dawn Addams
One Sheet: $15 - $30

HOUR OF DECISION
(1957 - Astor) Jeff Morrow, Hazel Court
One Sheet: $7 - $15

HOUR OF THE ASSASSIN
(1987 - -) Erik Estrada, Robert Vaughn
One Sheet: $3 - $5

HOUR OF THE GUN
(1967 - United Artists) James Garner, Jason Robards, Jon Voight
One Sheet: $30 - $50

HOUR OF THE PIG, THE
(1994 - Miramax) Colin Firth, Ian Holm
One Sheet: $4 - $8

HOUR OF THE WOLF
(1968 - Lopert) Max von Sydow, Liv Ullmann
One Sheet: $15 - $30

HOURS OF LONELINESS
(1930 - Warner Bros.) Carl Harbord, Sunday Wilshin
One Sheet: $100 - $200

HOUSE
(1986 - New World) William Katt, George Wendt, Richard Moll
One Sheet: $5 - $10

HOUSE ACROSS THE BAY, THE
(1940 - United Artists) George Raft, Joan Bennett
One Sheet: $50 - $100

HOUSE ACROSS THE STREET, THE
(1949 - Warner Bros.) Wayne Morris, Janis Paige
One Sheet: $20 - $40

HOUSE BROKEN
(1936 - Dominions) Mary Lawson, Louis Borell
One Sheet: $75 - $125

HOUSE BY THE CEMETERY, THE
(1983 - -) Katherine MacColl, Paolo Malco
One Sheet: $7 - $15

HOUSE BY THE LAKE, THE
(1976 - AIP) Brenda Vaccaro, Don Stroud
One Sheet: $5 - $10

HOUSE BY THE RIVER, THE
(1950 - Republic) Louis Hayward, Jane Wyatt
One Sheet: $15 - $35

HOUSE CALLS
(1978 - Universal) Walter Matthau, Art Carney
One Sheet: $5 - $10

HOUSE DIVIDED, A
(1931 - Universal) Walter Huston, Kent Douglas
One Sheet: $200 - $400

HOUSE I LIVE IN, THE
(1945 - RKO) Frank Sinatra, Mervyn Leroy
One Sheet: $75 - $150

HOUSE II: THE SECOND STORY
(1987 - New World) Arye Gross, Jonathan Stark
One Sheet: $5 - $10

HOUSE IN MARSH ROAD, THE
(1960 - Grand National) Sandra Dorne, Tony Wright
One Sheet: $5 - $10

HOUSE IN THE WOODS, THE
(1957 - Archway) Patricia Roc, Ronald Howard
One Sheet: $5 - $10

HOUSE IS NOT A HOME, A
(1964 - Embassy) Shelley Winters, Robert Taylor
One Sheet: $10 - $20

HOUSE NEXT DOOR, THE
(1914 - Lubin) Gaston Bell, George Trimble
One Sheet: $250 - $500

HOUSE OF 1,000 DOLLS
(1967 - AIP) Vincent Price, Martha Hyer
One Sheet: $15 - $30

HOUSE OF 1000 PLEASURES
(197? - Group 1) -
One Sheet: $5 - $10   *Sexploitation.*

HOUSE OF A THOUSAND CANDLES, THE
(1936 - Republic) Mae Clarke, Phillip Holmes
One Sheet: $75 - $150

HOUSE OF BAMBOO
(1955 - 20th Century Fox) Robert Stack, Robery Ryan
One Sheet: $30 - $50

HOUSE OF BLACKMAIL

(1950 - Modern Sound) William Sylvester, Mary Germaine
One Sheet: $20 - $40

HOUSE OF CARDS
(1969 - Universal) George Peppard, Inger Stevens, Orson Welles
One Sheet: $15 - $25

HOUSE OF CARDS
(1993 - Miramax) Kathleen Turner, Tommy Lee Jones
One Sheet: $3 - $5

HOUSE OF DANGER
(1934 - Peerless) Onslow Stevens, Janet Chandler
One Sheet: $75 - $150

HOUSE OF DARK SHADOWS
(1970 - MGM) Jonathan Frid, Joan Bennett
One Sheet: $50 - $100   *TV tie-in. Color Photo Style:$75-125.*

HOUSE OF DARKNESS
(1948 - British Lion) Lesley Brook, Lawrence Harvey
One Sheet: $75 - $125

HOUSE OF DRACULA
(1945 - Universal) Lon Chaney Jr., Onslow Stevens, John Carradine
One Sheet: $1,400 - $2,200   *Military release One Sheet(duotone):$75-100. Graven Images, pg. 112, 118.*

HOUSE OF DRACULA
(1950R - Realart) Lon Chaney Jr., Onslow Stevens, John Carradine
One Sheet: $250 - $500   *Re-release.*

HOUSE OF ERRORS
(1942 - PRC) Harry Langdon, Charles Rogers
One Sheet: $50 - $100

HOUSE OF EVIL
(1968 - Columbia) Boris Karloff (last film)
One Sheet: $15 - $30

HOUSE OF EXORCISM, THE
(1976 - Peppercorn/Wormser) Elke Sommer, Telly Savalas
One Sheet: $7 - $15

HOUSE OF FEAR
(1939 - Universal) William Gargan, Irene Hervey
One Sheet: $250 - $600

HOUSE OF FEAR, THE
(1945 - Universal) Basil Rathbone, Nigel Bruce
One Sheet: $350 - $750   *Sherlock Holmes series.*

One Sheet

HOUSE OF FRANKENSTEIN
(1944 - Universal) Boris Karloff, Lon Chaney Jr., John Carradine
One Sheet: $2,200 - $3,500   *Graven Images, pg. 112, 118.*

HOUSE OF FRANKENSTEIN
(1950R - Realart) Boris Karloff, Lon Chaney Jr., John Carradine
One Sheet: $250 - $500   *Re-release.*

HOUSE OF FRANKENSTEIN/MUMMY'S CURSE
(1945 - Universal) Karloff/Chaney
One Sheet: $75 - $150   *Combo. Exists only as a window card.*

HOUSE OF FREAKS
(1973 - Cinerama) Michael Dunn, Christiane Royce
One Sheet: $5 - $12

HOUSE OF FRIGHT
(1961 - AIP) Christopher Lee, Paul Massie, Dawn Addams
One Sheet: $20 - $40 *AKA: TWO FACES OF DR. JEKYLL.*

HOUSE OF GAMES
(1987 - -) Lindsay Crouse, Joe Mantegna
One Sheet: $7 - $15

HOUSE OF HORROR
(1929 - First National) Louise Fazenda, Chester Conklin
One Sheet: $600 - $1,000

HOUSE OF HORRORS
(1946 - Universal) Martin Kosleck, Rondo Hatton, Robert Lowery
One Sheet: $250 - $500 *Graven Images, pg. 141.*

HOUSE OF HORRORS
(1952R - Realart) Martin Kosleck, Rondo Hatton, Robert Lowery
One Sheet: $100 - $200 *Re-release.*

HOUSE OF INTRIGUE
(1959 - Allied Artists) Curt Jurgens, Dawn Addams
One Sheet: $20 - $40

HOUSE OF LONG SHADOWS
(1984 - Cannon) Vincent Price, John Carradine
One Sheet: $7 - $15

HOUSE OF MISSING GIRLS
(1970 - Tonylyn/VIP) Anna Gael, Hans Meyer
One Sheet: $5 - $10

HOUSE OF MYSTERY, THE
(1934 - Monogram) Ed Lowry, Verna Hillie
One Sheet: $250 - $500 *Graven Images, pg. 65.*

HOUSE OF MYSTERY, THE
(1938 - NCI) Jack Holt, Beverly Roberts
One Sheet: $125 - $250

HOUSE OF MYSTERY
(1941 - Monogram) Kenneth Kent, Judith Kelly
One Sheet: $75 - $150

HOUSE OF MYSTERY
(1961 - Allied Artists) Peter Dyneley, Jane Hylton
One Sheet: $5 - $10

HOUSE OF NUMBERS
(1957 - MGM) Jack Palance, Barbara Lang
One Sheet: $10 - $20

HOUSE OF ROTHSCHILD, THE
(1934 - United Artists) George Arliss, Robert Young, Boris Karloff
One Sheet: $1,300 - $2,000

HOUSE OF SECRETS, THE
(1929 - Chesterfield) Marcia Manning, Joseph Striker
One Sheet: $200 - $400

HOUSE OF SECRETS, THE
(1936 - Chesterfield) Leslie Fenton, Muriel Evans
One Sheet: $100 - $200

HOUSE OF SECRETS, THE
(1957 - Rank) Michael Craig, Julia Arnall
One Sheet: $15 - $25

HOUSE OF SEVEN CORPSES, THE
(1974 - International Amusements) John Ireland, John Carradine
One Sheet: $5 - $12

HOUSE OF SEVEN GABLES, THE
(1940 - Universal) George Sanders, Margaret Lindsay, Nan Grey, Vincent Price
One Sheet: $150 - $300

HOUSE OF STRANGERS
(1949 - 20th Century Fox) Edward G. Robinson, Susan Hayward, Richard Conte
One Sheet: $40 - $75

HOUSE OF TEMPERLEY, THE
(1913 - Jury) Charles Maude, Ben Webster
One Sheet: $250 - $500

HOUSE OF TERROR
(1972 - Garnalex) Jenifer Bishop
One Sheet: $10 - $20

HOUSE OF THE ARROW, THE
(1930 - Twickenham) Benita Hume, Richard Cooper
One Sheet: $100 - $200

HOUSE OF THE ARROW, THE
(1954 - Stratford) Oscar Homoka, Yvonne Furneaux
One Sheet: $10 - $20

HOUSE OF THE BLACK DEATH
(1965 - Medallion) Lon Chaeny Jr., John Carradine
One Sheet: $10 - $20 *aka: Night of the Beast.*

HOUSE OF THE DAMNED
(1963 - 20th Century Fox) Ronald Foster, Merry Anders
One Sheet: $15 - $30

HOUSE OF THE LIVING DEAD
(1973 - Associated Fillm Producers) Mark Burns, David Oxley
One Sheet: $7 - $15

HOUSE OF THE LOST CORD, THE
(1915 - Edison) Gertrude McCoy, Viola Dana
One Sheet: $250 - $600

HOUSE OF THE SEVEN HAWKS, THE
(1959 - MGM) Robert Taylor, Nicole Maurey
One Sheet: $7 - $15

HOUSE OF THE SPANIARD, THE
(1936 - Phoenix) Peter Haddon, Jean Galland
One Sheet: $75 - $150

HOUSE OF THE SPIRITS, THE
(1994 - Fine Line) Meryl Streep, Glenn Close, Winona Ryder
One Sheet: $4 - $8

HOUSE OF TOMORROW, THE
(1949 - MGM) -
One Sheet: $250 - $500 *Cartoon.*

HOUSE OF TRENT
(1933 - Butcher) John Stuart, Anne Grey
One Sheet: $75 - $150

HOUSE OF UNREST, THE
(1931 - Associated Pictures) Malcolm Keen, Dorothy Boyd
One Sheet: $100 - $200

HOUSE OF USHER
(1960 - AIP) Vincent Price, Mark Damon
One Sheet: $75 - $125 *International title to THE FALL OF THE HOUSE OF USHER. Graven Images, pg. 208.*

HOUSE OF WAX
(1953 - Warner Bros.) Frank Lovejoy, Vincent Price, Charles Bronson
One Sheet: $200 - $400 *Graven Images, pg. 163. 3-D.*

HOUSE OF WAX
(1954R - Warner Bros.) Frank Lovejoy, Vincent Price, Charles Bronson
One Sheet: $75 - $150 *Re-release. 2-D. Duotone.*

HOUSE OF WAX
(1981R - Warner Bros.) Frank Lovejoy, Vincent Price, Charles Bronson
One Sheet: $15 - $25 *Re-release.*

HOUSE OF WHIPCORD
(1974 - AIP) Barbara Markham, Patrick Barr
One Sheet: $7 - $15

HOUSE OF WOMEN
(1962 - Warner Brothers) Shirley Knight, Andrew Duggan
One Sheet: $15 - $25

HOUSE OF YOUTH, THE
(1924 - Regal) Malcolm McGregor, Jacqueline Logan
One Sheet: $150 - $300

HOUSE ON 56TH STREET, THE
(1933 - Warner Bros.) Kay Francis, Gene Raymond
One Sheet: $150 - $300

HOUSE ON 92ND STREET, THE
(1945 - 20th Century Fox) William Eythe, Lloyd Nolan
One Sheet: $75 - $125

HOUSE ON CARROLL STREET, THE

(1988 - -) Kelly McGillis, Jeff Daniels
One Sheet: $3 - $5

HOUSE ON HAUNTED HILL
(1958 - Allied Artists) Vincent Price, Carol Ohmart
One Sheet: $350 - $750 *Graven Images, pg. 190.*

HOUSE ON HAUNTED HILL/DAUGHTER OF DR. JEKYLL
(1965R - Allied Artists) Vincent Price, Carol Ohmart/John Agar, Gloria Talbott
One Sheet: $30 - $50 *Re-release double feature poster.*

HOUSE ON SKULL MOUNTAIN, THE
(1974 - 20th Century Fox) Victor French, Janee Michelle
One Sheet: $15 - $25 *Black sexploitation horror film. Scarce film produced by group of Atlanta business men.*

HOUSE ON SORORITY ROW, THE
(1983 - Film Ventures) Kathryn McNeil, Eileen Davidson
One Sheet: $5 - $12

HOUSE ON TELEGRAPH HILL, THE
(1951 - 20th Century Fox) Valentina Cortesa, William Lundigan
One Sheet: $75 - $150

HOUSE ON THE EDGE OF THE PARK
(1985 - Trio Entertainment) David Hess, Annie Belle
One Sheet: $5 - $10

HOUSE ON THE MARSH, THE
(1920 - Jury) Cecil Humphreys, Peggy Patterson
One Sheet: $150 - $300

HOUSE ON THE SAND
(1967 - Emerson) Sandra Evans, Clayton Foster
One Sheet: $5 - $10

HOUSE OPPOSITE, THE
(1931 - Pathe) Henry Kendall, Molly Lamont
One Sheet: $100 - $200

HOUSE PARTY
(1990 - New Line) Kid 'n Play (Christopher Reid & Christopher Wells)
One Sheet: $7 - $15 *Black cast.*

HOUSE PARTY II
(1991 - New Line) Kid 'n Play
One Sheet: $5 - $10 *Black cast.*

HOUSE PARTY III
(1994 - New Line) Kid 'n Play
One Sheet: $5 - $10 *Black cast.*

HOUSE RENT PARTY
(1946 - Toddy) Pigmeat "Alamo" Markham, Rastus Murray
One Sheet: $200 - $400 *Black cast. Separate Cinema, pg. 71.*

One Sheet

HOUSE THAT DRIPPED BLOOD, THE
(1971 - Cinerama) Christopher Lee, Peter Cushing
One Sheet: $15 - $25

HOUSE THAT SCREAMED, THE
(1971 - AIP) Lilli Palmer, Christina Galbo
One Sheet: $15 - $25

HOUSE THAT VANISHED, THE
(1974 - AIP) Judy Matheson, Andrea Allan
One Sheet: $7 - $15 *AKA: SCREAM AND DIE.*

HOUSE WITH CLOSED SHUTTERS, THE
(1910 - -) -
One Sheet: $600 - $1,000

HOUSEBOAT
(1958 - Paramount) Cary Grant, Sophia Loren
One Sheet: $40 - $75

HOUSEGUEST
(1995 - Caravan) Sinbad, Phil Hartman, Kim Greist
One Sheet: $5 - $10

HOUSEHOLD SAINTS
(1993 - Fine Line) Tracey Ullman, Vincent D'Onofrio, Lili Taylor
One Sheet: $3 - $5

HOUSEKEEPER'S DAUGHTER, THE
(1939 - United Artists) Joan Bennett, Adolphe Menjou, Victor Mature
One Sheet: $75 - $125

HOUSEKEEPING
(1987 - Columbia) Christine Lahti, Sara Walker, Andrea Burchill
One Sheet: $7 - $15

HOUSEMASTER
(1938 - Alliance) Otto Kruger
One Sheet: $75 - $125

HOUSESITTER
(1992 - Universal) Steve Martin, Goldie Hawn
One Sheet: $5 - $10

HOUSEWIFE
(1934 - Warner Bros.) Bette Davis, George Brent
One Sheet: $800 - $1,500

HOUSEWIFE
(1973 - Jack H. Harris) Yaphet Kotto, Jeannie Berlin
One Sheet: $10 - $20

HOUSEWIFE HERMAN
(1938 - 20th Century Fox) Terrytoons
One Sheet: $75 - $150 *Cartoon.*

HOUSTON STORY, THE
(1956 - Columbia) Gene Barry, Barbara Hale, Edward Arnold
One Sheet: $15 - $30

HOVERBUG
(1970 - Fanfare) Jill Riddick, Gary Cann
One Sheet: $3 - $5

HOW BELLA WAS WON
(1911 - Edison) —
One Sheet: $800 - $1,500

HOW CALIFORNIA HARVESTS WHEAT
(1915 - Paramount) -
One Sheet: $250 - $500 *Paramount Travel Pictures series.*

HOW COME NOBODY'S ON OUR SIDE?
(1975 - American Films) Adam Roarke, Rob Reiner
One Sheet: $3 - $7

HOW COULD YOU, JEAN?
(1918 - Artcraft) Mary Pickford
One Sheet: $2,200 - $3,500

HOW DO I LOVE THEE?
(1970 - Cinerama) Jackie Gleason, Maureen O'Hara
One Sheet: $5 - $10

HOW DO YOU DO?
(1946 - PRC) Bert Gordon, Harry Von Zell
One Sheet: $30 - $50

HOW GREEN WAS MY VALLEY
(1941 - 20th Century Fox) Walter Pidgeon, Maureen O'Hara, Donald Crisp
One Sheet: $500 - $800 *Academy Award: Best Picture, Best Direction(John Ford), Best Supporting Actor(Crisp). AcademyAward Movie Posters #76, #79, & #80.*

HOW HIGH IS UP?
(1940 - Columbia) The Three Stooges (Curly)
One Sheet: $5,000 - $7,500 *Comedy short. Duotone.*

HOW I GOT INTO COLLEGE
(1989 - -) Anthony Edwards, Lara Flynn Boyle, Corey Parker
One Sheet: $3 - $5

HOW I WON THE WAR
(1967 - United Artists) John Lennon, Michael Crawford
One Sheet: $40 - $75

HOW MOLLY MADE GOOD
(1915 - Photo Drama) Marguerite Gale
One Sheet: $75 - $150

HOW SWEET IT IS!
(1968 - National General) James Garner, Debbie Reynolds, Maurice Ronet
One Sheet: $7 - $15

HOW THE WEST WAS WON
(1962 - MGM) John Wayne, Gregory Peck, Jimmy Stewart, All star cast
One Sheet: $100 - $200   _Cinerama One Sheet: $200-$400._

HOW THE WEST WAS WON
(1964R - MGM) Jimmy Stewart, Gregory Peck, John Wayne, all-star cast
One Sheet: $50 - $100   _Re-release._

HOW THE WEST WAS WON
(1970R - MGM) John Wayne
One Sheet: $15 - $30   _Re-release._

HOW TO BE A DETECTIVE
(1952 - RKO/Disney) Goofy
One Sheet: $500 - $800   _Cartoon. The Disney Poster, pg. 72._

HOW TO BE VERY VERY POPULAR
(1955 - 20th Century Fox) Betty Grable, Charles Coburn
One Sheet: $30 - $50   _Grable's last film._

One Sheet

HOW TO BEAT THE HIGH COST OF LIVING
(1980 - AIP) Susan St. James, Jessica Lange
One Sheet: $5 - $10

HOW TO COMMIT MARRIAGE
(1969 - Cinerama) Bob Hope, Jack Gleason, Jane Wyman, Tina Louise
One Sheet: $15 - $30

HOW TO DANCE
(1953 - RKO/Disney) Goofy
One Sheet: $300 - $700   _Cartoon._

HOW TO EAT
(1939 - MGM) Robert Benchley
One Sheet: $600 - $1,000

HOW TO FISH
(1942 - RKO/Disney) Goofy
One Sheet: $800 - $1,500   _Cartoon. The Disney Poster, pg. 67._

HOW TO FRAME A FIGG
(1971 - Universal) Don Knotts, Joe Flynn
One Sheet: $7 - $15

HOW TO MAKE A MONSTER
(1958 - AIP) Robert Harris, Paul Brinegar
One Sheet: $75 - $150

HOW TO MAKE A MONSTER/TEENAGE CAVEMAN
(1958 - AIP) Robert Harris, Robert Vaughn
One Sheet: $40 - $75   _Double feature poster._

HOW TO MAKE AN AMERICAN QUILT
(1995 - Universal) Winona Ryder, Ellen Burstyn, Anne Bancroft
One Sheet: $5 - $10

HOW TO MAKE IT
(1969 - Corman/ABC) Vic Morrow, Suzanne

Pleshette, Cesar Romero
One Sheet: $10 - $20   _AKA: TARGET: HARRY._

HOW TO MARRY A MILLIONAIRE
(1954 - 20th Century Fox) Marilyn Monroe, Betty Grable, Lauren Bacall
One Sheet: $350 - $750

HOW TO MURDER A RICH UNCLE
(1957 - Columbia) Charles Coburn, Nigel Patrick
One Sheet: $15 - $25

HOW TO MURDER YOUR WIFE
(1965 - United Artists) Jack Lemmon, Virna Lisi
One Sheet: $15 - $25

HOW TO PLAY BASEBALL
(1942 - RKO/Disney) Goofy
One Sheet: $4,500 - $7,000   _Cartoon. Sports (Baseball). Sports Movie Posters #45._

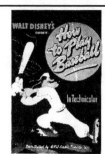

One Sheet

HOW TO RIDE A HORSE
(1950 - RKO/Disney) Goofy
One Sheet: $800 - $1,500   _Cartoon. Cartoon Movie Posters #183._

HOW TO SAVE A MARRIAGE - AND RUIN YOUR LIFE
(1968 - Columbia) Dean Martin, Stella Stevens
One Sheet: $10 - $20

HOW TO SEDUCE A WOMAN
(1973 - Cinerama) Angus Duncan, Alexandra Hay
One Sheet: $7 - $15

HOW TO SLEEP
(1953 - RKO/Disney) Goofy
One Sheet: $250 - $600   _Cartoon. Full color. The Disney Poster, pg. 71._

HOW TO START THE DAY
(1937 - MGM) Robert Benchley
One Sheet: $100 - $200

HOW TO STEAL A MILLION
(1966 - 20th Century Fox) Audrey Hepburn, Peter O'Toole
One Sheet: $40 - $75

HOW TO STEAL THE WORLD
(1967 - MGM) Robert Vaughn, David McCallum
One Sheet: $40 - $75   _From "The Man From U.N.C.L.E." TV show._

HOW TO STUFF A WILD BIKINI
(1965 - AIP) Annette Funicello, Dwayne Hickman, Buster Keaton
One Sheet: $30 - $60

HOW TO SUCCEED IN BUSINESS WITHOUT REALLY TRYING
(1967 - United Artists) Robert Morse, Michele Lee
One Sheet: $10 - $20

HOW TO SWIM
(1942 - RKO/Disney) Goofy
One Sheet: $1,600 - $2,500   _Cartoon. Full color. The Disney Poster, pg. 66._

HOW WILLINGLY YOU SING
(1975 - Melbourne) Garry Patterson, Jerry Powderly
One Sheet: $3 - $5

HOW'S ABOUT IT?
(1943 - Universal) The Andrews Sisters, Robert Paige, Shemp Howard, Buddy Rich
One Sheet: $100 - $200   _Big Band._

HOWARD CASE, THE

(1936 - Universal) Arthur Seaton, Jack Livesey
One Sheet: $125 - $250

HOWARD STERN'S PRIVATE PARTS
(1997 - Paramount) Howard Stern, Mary McCormack, Robin Quivers
One Sheet: $5 - $10

HOWARD THE DUCK
(1986 - Universal) Lea Thompson, Jeffrey Jones
One Sheet: $3 - $5   _Comic book tie-in._

HOWARDS END
(1992 - Sony Classics) Anthony Hopkins, Vanessa Redgrave, Emma Thompson
One Sheet: $7 - $15   _Academy Award: Best Actress (Thompson). Academy Award Movie Posters #383._

HOWARDS OF VIRGINIA, THE
(1940 - Columbia) Cary Grant, Martha Scott
One Sheet: $100 - $200

HOWLING, THE
(1981 - Avco/Embassy) Dee Wallace, Patrick Macnee
One Sheet: $10 - $20

HOWLING II, THE
(1985 - EMI) Christopher Lee, Annie McEnroe
One Sheet: $7 - $15

HOWLING III
(1987 - -) Barry Otto, Imogen Annesley
One Sheet: $5 - $10

HOWLING IV
(1988 - -) Romy Windsor, Michael Weiss
One Sheet: $5 - $10

HOWLING V - THE REBIRTH
(1989 - -) Phillip Davis
One Sheet: $3 - $5

HOWLING VI: THE FREAKS
(1990 - -) Brendan Hughes, Michele Matheson, Carol Lynley
One Sheet: $5 - $10

HOWZER
(1973 - URI) Melissa Stocking, Peter Desiante
One Sheet: $3 - $5

HUCK AND TOM
(1918 - Paramount) Jack Pickford, Robert Gordon
One Sheet: $600 - $1,000

HUCKLEBERRY FINN
(1920 - Paramount) Lewis Sargent, Gordon Griffith
One Sheet: $600 - $1,000

HUCKLEBERRY FINN
(1931 - Paramount Publix) Jackie Coogan, Junior Durkin
One Sheet: $200 - $400

HUCKLEBERRY FINN
(1939 - MGM) Mickey Rooney, William Frawley
One Sheet: $125 - $250

HUCKLEBERRY FINN
(1974 - United Artists) Jeff East, Paul Winfield
One Sheet: $5 - $10

HUCKSTERS, THE
(1947 - MGM) Clark Gable, Deborah Kerr
One Sheet: $100 - $200

HUD
(1963 - Paramount) Paul Newman, Patricia Neal
One Sheet: $50 - $100   _Academy Award: Best Actress. Academy Award Movie Posters #215 & #217._

HUDDLE
(1932 - MGM) Ramon Novarro, Una Merkel
One Sheet: $100 - $200

HUDSON HAWK
(1991 - TriStar) Bruce Willis, Danny Aiello, Andie MacDowell
One Sheet: $3 - $5

HUDSON'S BAY
(1941 - 20th Century Fox) Paul Muni, John Sutton, Gene Tierney
One Sheet: $100 - $200

HUDSUCKER PROXY, THE

(1994 - Warner Bros.) Tim Robbins, Paul Newman, Jennifer Jason Lee
One Sheet: $7 - $15

HUE AND CRY
(1947 - GFD) Alistair Sim, Jack Warner
One Sheet: $150 - $300

HUGGETTS ABROAD, THE
(1949 - GFD) Jack Warner, Kathleen Harrison
One Sheet: $15 - $25

HUGHES AND HARLOW
(1977 - Pro Int'l) Lindsay Bloom, Vic Holchak
One Sheet: $5 - $10

HUGHS AND HARLOW: ANGELS IN HELL
(1977 - Pro International) Victor Holchak, Lindsay Bloom
One Sheet: $7 - $15

HUGO THE HIPPO
(1975 - 20th Century Fox) Voices of: Paul Lynde, Robert Morley, Burl Ives
One Sheet: $10 - $20   _Cartoon._

HUGS AND MUGS
(1950 - Columbia) The Three Stooges (Shemp)
One Sheet: $200 - $400   _Comedy short. Duotone._

HUK!
(1956 - United Artists) George Montgomery, Mona Freeman
One Sheet: $15 - $30

HULA
(1927 - -) Clara Bow
One Sheet: $1,300 - $2,000

HULA-LA-LA
(1951 - Columbia) Three Stooges (Shemp)
One Sheet: $200 - $400   _Comedy short. Duotone._

HULLABALOO
(1940 - MGM) Frank Morgan, Billie Burke
One Sheet: $50 - $100

HULLABALOO OVER GEORGE AND BONNIE'S PICTURES
(1974 - Contemporary) Peggy Ashcroft, Larry Pines
One Sheet: $3 - $7

HU-MAN
(1975 - Romantique) Terence Stamp, Jeanne Moreau
One Sheet: $5 - $10

HUMAN CARGO
(1936 - 20th Century Fox) Claire Trevor, Brian Donlevy
One Sheet: $125 - $250

HUMAN COMEDY
(1943 - MGM) Mickey Rooney, James Craig, Frank Morgan
One Sheet: $75 - $150

HUMAN DESIRE
(1954 - Columbia) Glenn Ford, Gloria Grahame
One Sheet: $50 - $100

HUMAN DESIRES
(1924 - Gaumont) Clive Brook, Marjorie Dew
One Sheet: $150 - $300

HUMAN DUPLICATORS, THE
(1965 - Allied Artists) George Nader, Barbara Nichols
One Sheet: $15 - $30

HUMAN EXPERIMENTS
(1980 - Crown) Linda Haynes, Aldo Rey, Jackie Coogan
One Sheet: $4 - $8

HUMAN FACTOR, THE
(1975 - Bryanston) George Kennedy, John Mills
One Sheet: $3 - $7

HUMAN FACTOR, THE
(1979 - MGM) Richard Attenborough, John Gielgud
One Sheet: $7 - $15

HUMAN HIGHWAY
(1982 - Shakey) Russ Tamblyn, Dean Stockwell
One Sheet: $5 - $10

HUMAN JUNGLE, THE
(1954 - Allied Artists) Gary Merrill, Jan Sterling

One Sheet: $15 - $30

HUMAN MONSTER, THE
(1940 - Monogram) Bela Lugosi, Hugh Williams
One Sheet: $250 - $500   *Graven Images, pg. 102.*

HUMAN SIDE, THE
(1934 - Universal) Adolphe Menjou, Doris Kenyon
One Sheet: $150 - $300

HUMAN STUFF
(1920 - Universal) Harry Carey, Bobby Mack
One Sheet: $600 - $1,000   *Cowboy Movie Posters #22.*

HUMAN TARGETS
(1932 - Big 4) Rin-Tin-Tin, Buzz Barton
One Sheet: $125 - $250

HUMAN TORNADO, THE
(1976 - Dimension) Rudy Ray Moore, Lady Reed
One Sheet: $15 - $25   *AKA: DOLEMITE 2: HUMAN TORNADO.*

HUMAN VAPOR, THE
(1964 - Toho) Yoshio Tsuchiya, Kaoru Yachigusa
One Sheet: $15 - $30

HUMANITY
(1933 - Fox) Ralph Morgan, Boots Mallory
One Sheet: $200 - $400

HUMANOID, THE
(1979 - Columbia) Richard Kiel, Barbara Bach
One Sheet: $5 - $10

HUMANOIDS FROM THE DEEP
(1980 - New World) Doug McClure, Ann Turkel
One Sheet: $7 - $15

HUMMING BIRD, THE
(1924 - Paramount) Gloria Swanson
One Sheet: $1,300 - $2,000

HUMONGOUS
(1981 - Embassy) Janet Julian, David Wallace
One Sheet: $3 - $5

HUMORESQUE
(1920 - Paramount) Alma Rubens, Gaston Glass
One Sheet: $250 - $500

HUMORESQUE
(1947 - Warner Bros.) Joan Crawford, John Garfield
One Sheet: $75 - $150

HUMPHREY TAKES A CHANCE
(1950 - Monarch) Joe Kirkwood, Leon Errol
One Sheet: $15 - $30

HUMPTY DUMPTY
(1935 - Celebrity) By Ub Iwerks
One Sheet: $1,300 - $2,000   *Cartoon. A ComiColor Cartoon. Cartoon Movie Posters #118.*

HUN WITHIN, THE
(1918 - Paramount) George Fawcett, Dorothy Gish
One Sheet: $600 - $1,000

HUNCH, THE
(1921 - Metro) Gareth Hughes, Ethel Grandin
One Sheet: $150 - $300

HUNCH, THE
(1967 - Anvil) Alex Norton, Amanda Jones
One Sheet: $5 - $10

HUNCHBACK OF NOTRE DAME, THE
(1923 - Universal) Lon Chaney, Patsy Ruth Miller
One Sheet: $19,000 - $30,000   *Graven Images, pg. 34. Prices vary widely.*

HUNCHBACK OF NOTRE DAME, THE
(1939 - RKO) Charles Laughton
One Sheet: $1,600 - $2,500   *Graven Images, pg. 104.*

HUNCHBACK OF NOTRE DAME, THE
(1947R - RKO) Charles Laughton
One Sheet: $100 - $200   *Re-release.*

HUNCHBACK OF NOTRE DAME, THE
(1952R - RKO) Charles Laughton
One Sheet: $50 - $100   *Re-release.*

HUNCHBACK OF NOTRE DAME, THE

(1957 - Paris/Panitalia) Gina Lollobrigida, Anthony Quinn
One Sheet: $30 - $60

HUNCHBACK OF NOTRE DAME
(1996 - Disney) Voices of Demi Moore, Tom Hulce
One Sheet: $20 - $40   *Cartoon. Advance Style:$20-30.*

HUNCHBACK OF ROME
(1963 - Royal) Gerard Blain, Anna Maria Ferrero
One Sheet: $10 - $20

HUNCHBACK OF THE MORGUE, THE
(1972 - Cinemation) Paul Naschy, Maria Perschy
One Sheet: $7 - $15

HUNDRED HOUR HUNT
(1953 - Butcher) Jack Warner, Joy Shelton
One Sheet: $10 - $20

HUNDRED POUND WINDOW, THE
(1943 - Warner Bros.) Frederick Leister, Anne Crawford
One Sheet: $30 - $60

HUNG UP
(1969 - 20th Century Fox) -
One Sheet: $30 - $60

HUNGER, THE
(1983 - MGM/United Artists) David Bowie, Catherine Deneuve
One Sheet: $15 - $35

HUNGRY HEARTS
(1922 - Goldwyn) Rosa Rosanova, Bryant Washburn
One Sheet: $250 - $500

HUNGRY HILL
(1948 - Universal) Margaret Lockwood, Cecil Parker
One Sheet: $15 - $30

HUNGRY WIVES
(1973 - Harris) Jan White, Dir: George Romero
One Sheet: $15 - $25

HUNK
(1987 - -) John Allen Nelson, Deborah Shelton, James Coco
One Sheet: $3 - $5

HUNT FOR RED OCTOBER
(1989 - Paramount) Sean Connery, Alec Baldwin
One Sheet: $10 - $20

HUNT THE MAN DOWN
(1951 - RKO) Gig Young, Lynne Roberts
One Sheet: $15 - $25

HUNTED, THE
(1947 - Allied Artists) Belita, Preston Foster
One Sheet: $20 - $40

HUNTED, THE
(1988 - -) Andrew Buckland, Richard Carlson
One Sheet: $3 - $5

HUNTED, THE
(1995 - Universal) Christopher Lambert, John Lone, Joan Chen
One Sheet: $3 - $5

HUNTED IN HOLLYWOOD
(1961 - Wessex) Sean Scully, Sandra Spurr
One Sheet: $7 - $15

HUNTED MEN
(1930 - Syndicate) Bob Steele, Jean Reno
One Sheet: $500 - $800

HUNTED MEN
(1938 - Paramount) Lloyd Nolan, May Carlisle
One Sheet: $75 - $150

HUNTER, THE
(1931 - Universal) Oswald (the Lucky Rabbit)
One Sheet: $1,300 - $2,000   *Cartoon. Cartoon Movie Posters #51.*

HUNTER, THE
(1980 - Paramount) Steve McQueen, Eli Wallach
One Sheet: $5 - $10

HUNTER'S BLOOD
(1987 - -) Sam Bottoms, Clu Gulager
One Sheet: $3 - $5

HUNTERS, THE
(1958 - 20th Century Fox) Robert Mitchum, Robert Wagner
One Sheet: $40 - $75

HUNTERS OF THE DEEP
(1954 - DCA) -
One Sheet: $15 - $25   *Documentary.*

HUNTING PARTY, THE
(1971 - United Artists) Candice Bergen, Oliver Reed
One Sheet: $3 - $5

HUNTINGTOWER
(1927 - Paramount) Sir Harry Lauder, Vera Veronia
One Sheet: $125 - $250

HUNTRESS, THE
(1923 - Associated First National) Lloyd Hughes, Colleen Moore
One Sheet: $100 - $200

HUNTSMAN, THE
(1921 - Fox) Clyde Cook
One Sheet: $250 - $500

HURLY BURLY
(1950 - Cinetech) -
One Sheet: $20 - $40   *Sexploitation.*

HURRICANE, THE
(1926 - Truart) Stuart Holmes, Alice Lake
One Sheet: $150 - $300

HURRICANE
(1929 - Columbia) Johnny Mack Brown, Hobart Bosworth
One Sheet: $250 - $600

HURRICANE, THE
(1937 - United Artists) Dorothy Lamour, Jon Hall
One Sheet: $800 - $1,500

HURRICANE
(1979 - Paramount) Jason Robards, Mia Farrow
One Sheet: $5 - $10

HURRICANE EXPRESS, THE
(1932 - Mascot) John Wayne, Shirley Grey
One Sheet: $1,300 - $2,000   *Serial. Western. 12 Episodes.*

HURRICANE HORSEMAN
(1931 - State Rights) Lane Chandler
One Sheet: $150 - $300

HURRICANE HUTCH
(1921 - Pathe) Warner Oland
One Sheet: $250 - $600   *Serial. 15 Chapters.*

HURRICANE ISLAND
(1951 - Columbia) Jon Hall, Marie Windsor
One Sheet: $20 - $40

HURRICANE KID, THE
(1925 - Universal) Hoot Gibson, William A. Steele
One Sheet: $250 - $500

HURRICANE SMITH
(1941 - Republic) Ray Middleton, Jane Wyatt
One Sheet: $40 - $75

HURRICANE SMITH
(1952 - Paramount) Yvonne De Carlo, John Ireland
One Sheet: $15 - $25

HURRICANE SMITH
(1992 - Warner Bros.) Carl Weathers, Jurgen Prochnow, Cassandra Delaney
One Sheet: $7 - $15   *Black cast.*

HURRICANE'S GAL
(1922 - First National) Dorothy Phillips
One Sheet: $250 - $500

HURRY, CHARLIE, HURRY
(1941 - RKO) Leon Errol, Mildred Coles
One Sheet: $50 - $100

HURRY SUNDOWN
(1967 - Paramount) Michael Caine, Jane Fonda
One Sheet: $15 - $25

HURRY UP OR I'LL BE 30
(1973 - Avco/Embassy) John Lefkowitz, Danny De Vito

One Sheet: $3 - $5

HURRY WEST
(1921 - Pathe) Eddie Boland
One Sheet: $125 - $250

HUSBAND HUNTERS
(1927 - Tiffany) Mae Busch, Jean Arthur
One Sheet: $150 - $300

HUSBAND'S HOLIDAY
(1931 - Paramount) Clive Brook, Vivienne Osborne, Charlie Ruggles
One Sheet: $150 - $350

HUSBANDS
(1970 - Columbia) Ben Gazzara, Peter Falk, John Cassavetes
One Sheet: $3 - $5

HUSBANDS AND LOVERS
(1924 - First National) Florence Vidor, Lewis S. Stone
One Sheet: $200 - $400

HUSBANDS AND WIVES
(1992 - TriStar) Woody Allen, Mia Farrow
One Sheet: $5 - $10

HUSBANDS BEWARE
(1956 - Columbia) The Three Stooges (Shemp)
One Sheet: $150 - $300   *Comedy short. Duotone.*

HUSBANDS FOR RENT
(1927 - Warner Bros.) Helene Costello, Owen Moore
One Sheet: $150 - $300

HUSH MONEY
(1921 - Real Art) Alice Brady, George Fawcett
One Sheet: $150 - $300

HUSH MONEY
(1931 - Fox) Myrna Loy, George Raft, Joan Bennett
One Sheet: $250 - $600

HUSH...HUSH, SWEET CHARLOTTE
(1965 - 20th Century Fox) Bette Davis, Olivia de Havilland
One Sheet: $30 - $50

HUSTLE!
(1975 - Paramount) Burt Reynolds, Catherine Deneuve
One Sheet: $10 - $20

HUSTLER, THE
(1961 - 20th Century Fox) Paul Newman, Jackie Gleason
One Sheet: $150 - $300   *Sports (Billiards). Sports Movie Posters #'s 292, 293.*

One Sheet

HUSTLER, THE
(1964R - 20th Century Fox) Paul Newman, Jackie Gleason
One Sheet: $200 - $400   *Re-release. Sports (Billiards). Collectors prefer this one sheet over the original because its artwork featuresbilliards.*

HUSTLER SQUAD
(1974 - Geneni) Micheal Ansara
One Sheet: $5 - $10   *AKA: THE DOLL SQUAD.*

HUSTLER SQUAD
(1976R - Feature Fare) Micheal Ansara
One Sheet: $5 - $10   *Re-release.*

HUSTLER SQUAD
(1980R - Crown) Micheal Ansara
One Sheet: $5 - $10   *Re-release.*

HUTCH STIRS 'EM UP
(1923 - Ideal) Charles Hutchison, Joan Barry
One Sheet: $150 - $300

HYPNOTIC EYE, THE
(1960 - Allied Artists) Jacques Bergerac, Merry Anders
One Sheet: $40 - $75

HYPNOTISM CONFIDENTIAL
(1957 - PAD) -
One Sheet: $30 - $50

HYPNOTIZED
(1932 - World Wide) Wallace Ford, Moran & Mack
One Sheet: $250 - $600   *Separate Cinema, pg. 111.*

HYPOCRITES
(1914 - Bosworth) Dir: Lois Weber
One Sheet: $500 - $800

HYSTERIA
(1964 - MGM) Robert Webber, Anthony Newlands
One Sheet: $10 - $20

HYSTERICAL
(1983 - Embassy) Hudson Bros., Julie Newmar
One Sheet: $5 - $10

I ACCUSE!
(1957 - MGM) Jose Ferrer, Anton Walbrook
One Sheet: $15 - $25

I ACCUSE MY PARENTS
(1944 - PRC) Robert Lowell, Mary Beth Hughes
One Sheet: $30 - $50

I AIM AT THE STARS
(1960 - Columbia) Curt Jurgens, Victoria Shaw
One Sheet: $20 - $40

I AIN'T GONNA OPEN THAT DOOR
(1947 - Astor) Stepin Fetchit
One Sheet: $200 - $400   *Black cast.*

Mini Window Card

I AM A CAMERA
(1955 - DCA) Julie Harris, Shelley Winters
One Sheet: $15 - $25

I AM A CRIMINAL
(1938 - Monogram) John Carroll, Mary Kornman
One Sheet: $75 - $150

I AM A FUGITIVE FROM A CHAIN GANG
(1932 - Warner Bros.) Paul Muni, Glenda Farrell
One Sheet: $5,000 - $7,500

I AM A THIEF
(1935 - Warner Bros.) Ricardo Cortez, Mary Astor
One Sheet: $75 - $150

I AM CURIOUS (Blue)
(1970 - Grove) Lena Nyman, Borje Ahlstedt, Peter Lindgren
One Sheet: $5 - $10

I AM GUILTY
(1921 - Associated) Louise Glaum, Mahlon Hamilton
One Sheet: $150 - $300

I AM SUZANNE
(1933 - Fox) Lillian Harvey
One Sheet: $150 - $300

I AM THE LAW
(1938 - Columbia) Edward G. Robinson, Wendy Barrie

One Sheet: $250 - $500

I AM THE LAW
(1955R - Columbia) Edward G. Robinson, Wendy Barrie
One Sheet: $15 - $30   *Re-release. Duotone.*

I BECAME A CRIMINAL
(1948 - Warner Bros.) Sally Gray, Trevor Howard
One Sheet: $40 - $75

I BELIEVE IN YOU
(1951 - Universal International) Celia Johnson, Cecil Parker
One Sheet: $15 - $25

I BELIEVED IN YOU
(1934 - Fox) Rosemary Ames, Victor Jory, John Boles
One Sheet: $100 - $200

I BOMBED PEARL HARBOUR
(1961 - Toho) Yosuke Natsuki, Toshiro Mifune
One Sheet: $15 - $35   *Japanese.*

I BURY THE LIVING
(1957 - United Artists) Richard Boone, Theodore Bikel
One Sheet: $75 - $125

One Sheet

I CAN GET IT FOR YOU WHOLESALE
(1951 - 20th Century Fox) Susan Hayward, Dan Dailey
One Sheet: $40 - $75

I CAN HARDLY WAIT
(1943 - Columbia) The Three Stooges (Curly)
One Sheet: $2,500 - $4,000   *Comedy short. Duotone.*

I CAN'T ESCAPE
(1934 - Beacon) Onslow Stevens, Lila Lee
One Sheet: $150 - $300

I CAN'T GIVE YOU ANYTHING BUT LOVE
(1940 - Universal) Broderick Crawford, Peggy Moran
One Sheet: $50 - $100

I CHEATED THE LAW
(1949 - 20th Century Fox) Tom Conway, Steve Brodie
One Sheet: $15 - $30

I COME IN PEACE
(1990 - -) Dolph Lundgren
One Sheet: $7 - $15

I CONFESS
(1953 - Warner Bros.) Montgomery Clift, Anne Baxter, Dir: Alfred Hitchcock
One Sheet: $150 - $300

One Sheet

I CONQUER THE SEA
(1936 - Academy) Dennis Morgan, Steffi Duna
One Sheet: $75 - $125

I COULD GO ON SINGING
(1963 - United Artists) Judy Garland, Dirk Bogarde
One Sheet: $15 - $30

I COULDN'T MARRY
(1955 - Futurity) -
One Sheet: $15 - $25

I COVER THE BIG TOWN
(1947 - Paramount) Phillip Reed, Hillary Brooke, Robert Lowery
One Sheet: $40 - $75

I COVER THE UNDERWORLD
(1955 - Republic) Sean McClory, Joanne Jordan
One Sheet: $15 - $30

I COVER THE WAR
(1937 - Universal) John Wayne, Gwen Gaze
One Sheet: $250 - $500

I COVER THE WAR
(1947R - Realart) John Wayne, Gwen Gaze
One Sheet: $75 - $125   *Re-release.*

I COVER THE WATERFRONT
(1933 - United Artists) Claudette Colbert, Ben Lyon
One Sheet: $500 - $800

I CROSSED THE COLOR LINE
(1966 - U.S. Films) Richard Gilden, Harry Lovejoy
One Sheet: $30 - $50   *Separate Cinema, pg. 152.*

One Sheet

I DEAL IN DANGER
(1966 - 20th Century Fox) Robert Goulet, Christine Carere
One Sheet: $5 - $10

I DEMAND PAYMENT
(1938 - Imperial) Jack LaRue, Betty Burgess
One Sheet: $75 - $125

I DIDN'T DO IT
(1945 - Columbia) George Formby, Billy Caryl
One Sheet: $30 - $50   *Comedy short. Duotone.*

I DIED A THOUSAND TIMES
(1955 - Warner Bros.) Jack Palance, Shelley Winters
One Sheet: $30 - $50

I DISMEMBERED MAMA
(1973 - Europix) Zooey Hall, Geri Reischl
One Sheet: $15 - $30

I DISMEMBERED MAMA/THE BLOOD SPATTERED BRIDE
(1973 - Europix) -
One Sheet: $10 - $20   *Double feature poster.*

I DO
(1921 - Associated) Harold Lloyd
One Sheet: $1,300 - $2,000

I DO
(192?R - Associated) Harold Lloyd
One Sheet: $250 - $600   *Re-release.*

I DON'T BUY KISSES
(199? - -) -
One Sheet: $3 - $5

I DON'T CARE GIRL, THE
(1953 - 20th Century Fox) Mitzi Gaynor, David Wayne
One Sheet: $15 - $25

I DON'T DARE SHOW MY FACE
(- - -) See THE TRUE STORY OF LYNN STUART

I DOOD IT
(1943 - MGM) Red Skelton, Eleanor Powell, Jimmy Dorsey Orch.
One Sheet: $75 - $125   *Big Band musical.*

I DREAM OF JEANIE
(1952 - Republic) Ray Middleton, Muriel Lawrence
One Sheet: $30 - $50

I DREAM TOO MUCH
(1935 - RKO) Lily Pons, Henry Fonda
One Sheet: $150 - $300

I DRINK YOUR BLOOD
(1971 - Cinemation) Bhaskar, Jadine Wong
One Sheet: $20 - $40

I DRINK YOUR BLOOD/I EAT YOUR SKIN
(1971 - Cinemation) Bhaskar/William Joyce
One Sheet: $15 - $30   *Double feature poster.*

I EAT YOUR SKIN
(1971 - Cinemation) William Joyce, Heather Hewitt
One Sheet: $15 - $35

I ESCAPED FROM DEVIL'S ISLAND
(1973 - United Artists) Jim Brown, Christopher George, Prod.: Roger Corman
One Sheet: $15 - $30

I ESCAPED FROM THE GESTAPO
(1943 - Monogram) Dean Jagger, John Carradine
One Sheet: $50 - $100

I FOUND STELLA PARISH
(1935 - Warner Bros.) Kay Francis, Ian Hunter
One Sheet: $250 - $500

I GIVE MY LOVE
(1934 - Universal) Paul Lukas, Eric Linden
One Sheet: $75 - $150

I HATE WOMEN
(1934 - Goldsmith) Wallace ford, June Clyde
One Sheet: $150 - $300

I HAVE LIVED
(1933 - Chesterfield) Alan Dinehart, Anita Page
One Sheet: $100 - $200

I HEARD THE OWL CALL MY NAME
(1973 - -) Tom Courtenay, Dean Jagger
One Sheet: $3 - $5

I JANE DOE
(1948 - Republic) Ruth Hussey, John Carroll, Vera Ralston
One Sheet: $30 - $50

I KILLED GERONIMO
(1950 - Eagle-Lion) James Ellison, Smith Ballew
One Sheet: $15 - $35

I KILLED THAT MAN
(1941 - Monogram) Ricardo Cortez, Joan Woodbury
One Sheet: $30 - $60

I KILLED WILD BILL HICKOK
(1956 - Wheeler) Tom Brown, Frank Carpenter
One Sheet: $7 - $15

I KNOW WHERE I'M GOING
(1947 - Universal) Wendy Hiller, Roger Livesey
One Sheet: $30 - $50

I LED TWO LIVES
(1953 - -) See GLEN OR GLENDA

I LIKE IT LIKE THAT
(1994 - Columbia) Lauren Velez, Rita Moreno, Griffin Dunne
One Sheet: $5 - $10

I LIKE IT THAT WAY
(1934 - Universal) Gloria Stuart, Roger Pryor, Mickey Rooney
One Sheet: $100 - $200

I LIKE MONEY
(1962 - 20th Century Fox) Peter Sellers, Nadia Gray
One Sheet: $15 - $25 *AKA: MR. TOPAZE.*

I LIKE YOUR NERVE
(1931 - First National) Douglas Fairbanks, Jr., Boris Karloff
One Sheet: $350 - $750

I LIVE FOR LOVE
(1935 - Warner Bros.) Dolores Del Rio, Everett Marshall
One Sheet: $100 - $200

I LIVE MY LIFE
(1935 - MGM) Joan Crawford, Brian Aherne
One Sheet: $800 - $1,500

I LIVE ON DANGER
(1942 - Paramount) Chester Morris, Jean Parker
One Sheet: $75 - $125

I LOVE A BANDLEADER
(1945 - Columbia) Phil Harris, Eddie "Rochester" Anderson, Leslie Brooks
One Sheet: $75 - $125

I LOVE A MYSTERY
(1945 - Columbia) Nina Foch, Jim Bannon
One Sheet: $40 - $75

I LOVE A SOLDIER
(1944 - Paramount) Paulette Goddard, Sonny Tufts
One Sheet: $75 - $150

One Sheet

I LOVE MELVIN
(1952 - MGM) Donald O'Connor, Debbie Reynolds
One Sheet: $30 - $60

I LOVE MY WIFE
(1970 - Universal) Elliott Gould, Brenda Vaccaro
One Sheet: $5 - $10

I LOVE THAT MAN
(1933 - Paramount) Nancy Carroll, Edmund Lowe, Robert Armstrong
One Sheet: $100 - $200

I LOVE TROUBLE
(1947 - Columbia) Franchot Tone, Janet Blair
One Sheet: $30 - $50

I LOVE TROUBLE
(1994 - Buena Vista) Julia Roberts, Nick Nolte
One Sheet: $3 - $5

I LOVE YOU
(1918 - Triangle) Alma Rubens, John Lince
One Sheet: $150 - $300

I LOVE YOU AGAIN
(1940 - MGM) William Powell, Myrna Loy
One Sheet: $125 - $250

I LOVE YOU, ALICE B. TOKLAS
(1968 - Warner Bros.) Peter Sellers, Jo Van Fleet
One Sheet: $15 - $30

I LOVE YOU TO DEATH
(1990 - -) Kevin Kline, Tracey Ullman, Joan Plowright
One Sheet: $5 - $10

I LOVED A WOMAN
(1933 - First National) Edward G. Robinson, Kay Francis
One Sheet: $150 - $300

I LOVED YOU WEDNESDAY
(1933 - Fox) Warner Baxter, Elissa Landi
One Sheet: $200 - $400

I, MADMAN
(1990 - -) Jenny Wright, Clayton Rohner
One Sheet: $10 - $20

I MARRIED A COMMUNIST
(1949 - RKO) Laraine Day, Robert Ryan
One Sheet: $40 - $75

I MARRIED A DOCTOR
(1936 - Warner Bros.) Pat O'Brien, Josephine Hutchinson
One Sheet: $75 - $150

I MARRIED A DOCTOR
(1940 - Columbia) Osa Johnson
One Sheet: $40 - $75

I MARRIED A MONSTER FROM OUTER SPACE
(1958 - Paramount) Tom Tryon, Gloria Talbott
One Sheet: $75 - $150 *Graven Images, pg. 179.*

I MARRIED A MURDERER
(1936 - Gaumont) Sylvia Sydney, Oscar Homolka, Dir: Alfred Hitchcock
One Sheet: $2,500 - $4,000 *AKA: THE WOMAN ALONE.*

I MARRIED A SAVAGE
(1949 - Futurity) -
One Sheet: $30 - $50

I MARRIED A SPY
(1938 - Grand National) Neil Hamilton, Brigitte Horney
One Sheet: $75 - $150

I MARRIED A WITCH
(1942 - United Artists) Fredric March, Veronica Lake
One Sheet: $600 - $1,000 *Graven Images, pg. 121.*

I MARRIED A WITCH
(1947R - United Artists) Fredric March, Veronica Lake
One Sheet: $75 - $125 *Re-release.*

I MARRIED A WITCH
(195? - Masterpiece) -
One Sheet: $40 - $75 *Re-release.*

I MARRIED A WOMAN
(1956 - Universal-International) George Gobel, Jessie Royce Landis, Diana Dors
One Sheet: $30 - $50 *John Wayne cameo (as himself).*

One Sheet

I MARRIED ADVENTURE
(1940 - -) -
One Sheet: $40 - $75 *Documentary.*

I MARRIED AN ANGEL
(1942 - MGM) Nelson Eddy & Jeanette MacDonald (last film together)
One Sheet: $150 - $300

I MARRIED AN AXE MURDERER
(1993 - TriStar) Mike Meyers, Amanda Plummer
One Sheet: $5 - $10

I MET HIM IN PARIS
(1937 - Paramount) Claudette Colbert, Melvyn Douglas
One Sheet: $250 - $500

I MET MY LOVE AGAIN
(1938 - United Artists) Joan Bennett, Henry Fonda
One Sheet: $125 - $250

I, MOBSTER
(1958 - 20th Century Fox) Steve Cochran, Lita Milan
One Sheet: $15 - $30

I NEVER SANG FOR MY FATHER
(1970 - Columbia) Melvyn Douglas, Gene Hackman
One Sheet: $3 - $5

I OUGHT TO BE IN PICTURES
(1982 - 20th Century Fox) Walter Matthau, Ann-Margret
One Sheet: $3 - $5

I PASSED FOR WHITE
(1960 - Allied Artists) Sonja Wilde, James Franciscus
One Sheet: $30 - $50 *Separate Cinema, pg. 152.*

I PROMISE TO PAY
(1937 - Columbia) Leo Carrillo, Chester Morris
One Sheet: $75 - $150

Mini Window Card

I REMEMBER MAMA
(1948 - RKO) Irene Dunne, Barbara Bel Geddes, Oscar Homolka
One Sheet: $40 - $75

I REMEMBER MAMA
(1955R - RKO) Irene Dunne, Barbara Bel Geddes, Oscar Homolka
One Sheet: $15 - $25 *Re-release.*

I RING DOORBELLS
(1946 - PRC) Robert Shayne, Ann Gwynne
One Sheet: $15 - $30

I SAW WHAT YOU DID
(1965 - Universal) Joan Crawford, John Ireland
One Sheet: $30 - $50

I SELL ANYTHING
(1934 - First National) Pat O'Brien, Claire Dodd
One Sheet: $125 - $250

I SHOT ANDY WARHOL
(1996 - Samuel Goldwyn/Orion) Lili Taylor, Jared Harris, Martha Plimpton
One Sheet: $7 - $15

I SHOT BILLY THE KID
(1950 - Lippert) Don Barry, Robert Lowery
One Sheet: $15 - $25

I SHOT JESSE JAMES
(1949 - Screen Guild) Preston Foster, Barbara Britton
One Sheet: $20 - $40

I SPIED FOR YOU
(1943 - Columbia) El Brendel
One Sheet: $75 - $150 *Comedy short. Duotone.*

I SPIT ON YOUR GRAVE
(1983 - Cinemagic) Camille Keaton, Richard Pace
One Sheet: $15 - $35

I STAND ACCUSED
(1938 - Republic) Robert Cummings, Helen Mack
One Sheet: $50 - $100

I STAND CONDEMNED
(1936 - United Artists) Laurence Olivier, Harry Baur
One Sheet: $250 - $600

I STOLE A MILLION
(1939 - Universal) George Raft, Claire Trevor
One Sheet: $75 - $150

I SURRENDER DEAR
(1948 - Columbia) Gloria Jean, David Street
One Sheet: $30 - $50

I TAKE THIS OATH
(1940 - PRC) Gordon Jones, Joyce Compton
One Sheet: $40 - $75

I TAKE THIS WOMAN
(1931 - Paramount Publix) Gary Cooper, Carole Lombard
One Sheet: $800 - $1,500

I TAKE THIS WOMAN
(1940 - MGM) Spencer Tracy, Hedy Lamarr
One Sheet: $250 - $500

I THANK A FOOL
(1962 - MGM) Susan Hayward, Peter Finch
One Sheet: $15 - $30

I, THE JURY
(1953 - United Artists) Biff Elliott, Peggie Castle
One Sheet: $100 - $200 *3-D.*

I, THE JURY
(1982 - American Cinema) Armand Assante, Barbara Carrera
One Sheet: $5 - $10

I VAMPIRI
(1960S - Titanus) Gianna Maria Canale, Carlo d'Angelo
One Sheet: $75 - $175 *Italian.*

I WAKE UP SCREAMING
(1941 - 20th Century Fox) Betty Grable, Victor Mature
One Sheet: $350 - $750 *AKA: HOT SPOT.*

I WAKE UP SCREAMING
(1948R - 20th Century Fox) Betty Grable
One Sheet: $50 - $100 *Re-release.*

I WALK ALONE
(1947 - Paramount) Burt Lancaster, Lizabeth Scott, Kirk Douglas
One Sheet: $125 - $250

I WALK THE LINE
(1970 - Columbia) Gregory Peck, Tuesday Weld
One Sheet: $7 - $15

I WALKED WITH A ZOMBIE
(1943 - RKO) James Ellison, Frances Dee, Dir: Val Lewton
One Sheet: $500 - $800 *Graven Images, pg. 123.*

I WALKED WITH A ZOMBIE
(1952R - RKO) James Ellison, Francis Dee, Dir: Val Lewton
One Sheet: $75 - $125 *Re-release.*

I WANNA HOLD YOUR HAND
(1978 - Universal) Nancy Allen, Bobby DiCicco
One Sheet: $15 - $30

I WANT A DIVORCE
(1940 - Paramount) Dick Powell, Joan Blondell
One Sheet: $75 - $150

I WANT TO LIVE!
(1958 - United Artists) Susan Hayward, Simon Oakland
One Sheet: $50 - $100 *Academy Award: Best Actress. One Sheet (Advance):$200-$400.*

I WANT WHAT I WANT
(1972 - Cinerama) Anne Heywood, Harry Andrews
One Sheet: $2 - $3

I WANT YOU
(1951 - RKO) Dana Andrews, Dorothy McGuire
One Sheet: $15 - $30

I WANTED WINGS
(1941 - Paramount) Ray Milland, William Holden, Veronica Lake
One Sheet: $250 - $500

I WAS A CAPTIVE OF NAZI GERMANY
(1936 - Malvina) Isobel Lillian Steele
One Sheet: $200 - $400

I WAS A COMMUNIST FOR THE F.B.I.
(1951 - Warner Bros.) Frank Lovejoy, Dorothy Hart
One Sheet: $30 - $50

I WAS A CONVICT
(1939 - Republic) Barton MacLane, Beverly Roberts
One Sheet: $50 - $100

I WAS A MALE WAR BRIDE
(1949 - 20th Century Fox) Cary Grant, Ann Sheridan
One Sheet: $50 - $100

I WAS A MALE WAR BRIDE
(1953R - 20th Century Fox) Cary Grant, Ann Sheridan
One Sheet: $10 - $20   *Re-release.*

I WAS A PRISONER IN KOREA
(1954 - Columbia) -
One Sheet: $30 - $50

I WAS A PRISONER ON DEVIL'S ISLAND
(1941 - Columbia) Sally Eilers, Donald Woods
One Sheet: $100 - $200

I WAS A SHOPLIFTER
(1950 - Universal) Scott Brady, Mona Freeman
One Sheet: $15 - $30

I WAS A SPY
(1933 - Fox) Conrad Veidt, Madeleine Carroll
One Sheet: $1,300 - $2,000

I WAS A TEENAGE FRANKENSTEIN
(1957 - AIP) Whit Bissell, Phyllis Coates
One Sheet: $150 - $300   *Graven Images, pg. 191.*

I WAS A TEENAGE FRANKENSTEIN/BLOOD OF DRACULA
(1957 - AIP) Whit Bissell, Sandra Harrison
One Sheet: $75 - $175   *Double feature poster.*

I WAS A TEENAGE WEREWOLF
(1957 - AIP) Michael Landon, Yvonne Lime
One Sheet: $150 - $300   *Graven Images, pg. 191.*

I WAS A TEENAGE WEREWOLF/INVASION OF THE SAUCERMEN
(1957 - AIP) -
One Sheet: $125 - $250   *Double feature poster.*

I WAS AN ADVENTURESS
(1940 - 20th Century Fox) Erich Von Stroheim, Vera Zorina, Peter Lorre
One Sheet: $100 - $200

I WAS AN AMERICAN SPY
(1951 - Allied Artists) Ann Dvorak, Gene Evans
One Sheet: $40 - $75

I WAS FAITHLESS
(1932 - United Artists) Ronald Colman, Kay Francis
One Sheet: $250 - $500   *AKA: CYNARA.*

I WAS FRAMED
(1942 - Warner Bros.) Michael Ames, Julie Bishop
One Sheet: $30 - $50

I WILL...I WILL...FOR NOW
(1976 - 20th Century Fox) Elliott Gould, Diane Keaton
One Sheet: $5 - $10

I WONDER WHO'S KISSING HER NOW
(1947 - 20th Century Fox) June Haver, Mark Stevens
One Sheet: $50 - $100

I WOULDN'T BE IN YOUR SHOES
(1948 - Monogram) Don Castle, Elyse Knox
One Sheet: $15 - $30

I'D CLIMB THE HIGHEST MOUNTAIN
(1951 - 20th Century Fox) Susan Hayward, William Lundigan
One Sheet: $30 - $50

I'D GIVE MY LIFE
(1936 - Paramount) Tom Brown, Frances Drake
One Sheet: $100 - $200

I'D RATHER BE RICH
(1964 - Universal) Sandra Dee, Robert Goulet

One Sheet: $15 - $25

I'LL BE SEEING YOU
(1944 - United Artists) Ginger Rogers, Joseph Cotten, Shirley Temple
One Sheet: $75 - $150

I'LL BE SEEING YOU
(1956R - United Artists) Ginger Rogers
One Sheet: $15 - $30   *Re-release.*

I'LL BE YOURS
(1947 - Universal) Deanna Durbin, Tom Drake
One Sheet: $40 - $75

I'LL CRY TOMORROW
(1955 - MGM) Susan Hayward, Eddie Albert, Richard Conte
One Sheet: $75 - $125

I'LL DO ANYTHING
(1994 - Columbia) Nick Nolte, Albert Brooks
One Sheet: $3 - $5

I'LL FIX IT
(1934 - Columbia) Jack Holt, Mona Barrie
One Sheet: $100 - $200

I'LL GET BY
(1950 - 20th Century Fox) William Lundigan, June Haver
One Sheet: $15 - $35

I'LL GET HIM YET
(1919 - Paramount) Dorothy Gish, George Fawcett
One Sheet: $600 - $1,000

I'LL GET YOU
(1952 - Lippert) George Raft, Sally Gray
One Sheet: $15 - $25

I'LL GIVE A MILLION
(1938 - 20th Century Fox) Warner Baxter, Peter Lorre, John Carradine
One Sheet: $100 - $200

I'LL LOVE YOU ALWAYS
(1935 - Columbia) Nancy Carroll, George Murphy
One Sheet: $100 - $200

I'LL NAME THE MURDERER
(1936 - Puritan) Ralph Forbes, Marion Shilling
One Sheet: $50 - $100

I'LL NEVER FORGET WHAT'S 'IS NAME
(1968 - Regional) Oliver Reed, Carol White, Orson Welles
One Sheet: $15 - $25

I'LL NEVER FORGET YOU
(1951 - 20th Century Fox) Tyrone Power, Ann Blyth
One Sheet: $30 - $50

I'LL NEVER HEIL AGAIN
(1941 - Columbia) The Three Stooges (Curly)
One Sheet: $4,000 - $6,000   *Comedy short. Duotone.*

I'LL REMEMBER APRIL
(1944 - Universal) Gloria Jean, Kirby Grant
One Sheet: $40 - $75

I'LL SEE YOU IN MY DREAMS
(1951 - Warner Bros.) Doris Day, Danny Thomas
One Sheet: $30 - $50

I'LL SELL MY LIFE
(1941 - Select) Rose Hobart, Michael Whalen
One Sheet: $75 - $125

I'LL TAKE ROMANCE
(1937 - Columbia) Grace Moore, Melvyn Douglas, Stuart Erwin
One Sheet: $75 - $150

I'LL TAKE SWEDEN
(1965 - United Artists) Bob Hope, Tuesday Weld
One Sheet: $15 - $30

I'LL TELL THE WORLD
(1934 - Universal) Lee Tracy, Gloria Stuart
One Sheet: $125 - $250

I'LL TELL THE WORLD
(1945 - Universal) Lee Tracy, Brenda Joyce
One Sheet: $40 - $75

I'LL WAIT FOR YOU
(1941 - MGM) Robert Sterling, Marsha Hunt

One Sheet: $50 - $100

I'M A MONKEY'S UNCLE
(1948 - Columbia) The Three Stooges (Shemp)
One Sheet: $350 - $750   *Comedy short. Duotone.*

I'M ALL RIGHT, JACK
(1960 - Columbia) Peter Sellers, Ian Carmichael
One Sheet: $10 - $20

I'M FROM ARKANSAS
(1944 - PRC) Slim Summerville, El Brendel
One Sheet: $50 - $100

I'M FROM MISSOURI
(1939 - Paramount) Bob Burns, Gladys George
One Sheet: $75 - $150

I'M FROM THE CITY
(1938 - RKO) Joe Penner, Kay Sutton
One Sheet: $125 - $250

I'M GONNA GET YOU SUCKA
(1988 -) Keenen Ivory Wayans, Bernie Casey
One Sheet: $15 - $25

I'M NO ANGEL
(1933 - Paramount) Mae West, Cary Grant
One Sheet: $250 - $500

One Sheet

I'M NOBODY'S SWEETHEART NOW
(1940 - Universal) Dennis O'Keefe, Constance Moore
One Sheet: $75 - $150

I'M STILL ALIVE
(1940 - RKO) Kent Taylor, Linda Hayes
One Sheet: $75 - $125

I'VE ALWAYS LOVED YOU
(1946 - Republic) Philip Dorn, Catherine McLeod
One Sheet: $30 - $50

I'VE BEEN AROUND
(1934 - Universal) Chester Morris, Rochelle Hudson
One Sheet: $125 - $250

I'VE GOT YOUR NUMBER
(1934 - Warner Bros.) Glenda Farrell, Joan Blondell, Pat O'Brien
One Sheet: $75 - $150

I'VE HEARD THE MERMAIDS SINGING
(1987 -) Sheila McCarthy, Paule Baillargeon
One Sheet: $7 - $15

I'VE LIVED BEFORE
(1956 - Universal) Jock Mahoney, Leigh Snowden
One Sheet: $50 - $100

ICE CAPADES
(1941 - Republic) Dorothy Lewis, Jerry Colonna
One Sheet: $50 - $100   *Sports (Ice Skating). Sports Movie Posters #257.*

ICE CAPADES REVUE
(1942 - Republic) Ellen Drew, Richard Denning
One Sheet: $40 - $75

ICE CASTLES
(1978 - Columbia) Robby Benson, Lynn-Holly Johnson
One Sheet: $3 - $5

ICE FOLLIES OF 1939, THE
(1939 - MGM) Joan Crawford, James Stewart, Lew Ayres
One Sheet: $500 - $800   *Sports (Ice Skating). Sports Movie Posters #256.*

ICE PALACE
(1960 - Warner Bros.) Richard Burton, Robert Ryan
One Sheet: $7 - $15

ICE PIRATES, THE
(1984 - MGM/United Artists) Robert Urich, Mary Crosby
One Sheet: $3 - $5

ICE POND, THE
(1939 - 20th Century Fox) Terry-toons
One Sheet: $100 - $200   *Cartoon. Full color stone litho. Stock poster with inset title.*

ICE STATION ZEBRA
(1969 - MGM) Rock Hudson, Ernest Borgnine, Patrick McGoohan, Jim Brown
One Sheet: $15 - $30   *Price is for Style A. Style B: $30-$50. Cinerama One Sheet: $100-$200.*

ICELAND
(1942 - 20th Century Fox) Sonja Henie, John Payne
One Sheet: $75 - $150

One Sheet

ICEMAN
(1984 - Universal) Timothy Hutton, Lindsay Crouse
One Sheet: $3 - $5

ICHABOD AND MR. TOAD
(1949 - Disney) -
One Sheet: $200 - $400   *Cartoon.*

ICICLE THIEF, THE
(1989 - Bambu Cinema) Maurizio Nichetti, Caterina Sylos Labini
One Sheet: $3 - $5

IDAHO
(1943 - Republic) Roy Rogers, Virginia Grey
One Sheet: $150 - $350

IDAHO
(1955R - Republic) Roy Rogers
One Sheet: $50 - $100   *Re-release.*

IDAHO KID
(1936 - Colony) Rex Bell
One Sheet: $100 - $200

IDAHO RED
(1929 - FBO) Tom Tyler, Patricia Caron, Frankie Darro
One Sheet: $200 - $400

IDEA GIRL
(1946 - Universal) Jess Barker, Julie Bishop
One Sheet: $40 - $75

IDEAL FARM, AN
(1924 - Pathe) Animated by Paul Terry
One Sheet: $600 - $1,200   *Cartoon. An Aesop's Fables film. Cartoon Movie Posters #19.*

IDEAL HUSBAND, AN
(1948 - British-Lion) Paulette Goddard, Michael Wilding
One Sheet: $30 - $50

IDEAL MARRIAGE, THE
(1970 -) Eva Christine, Gunter Stoll
One Sheet: $5 - $10

IDEAL WIFE, AN
(1947 -) Paulette Goddard
One Sheet: $40 - $75

IDENTITY UNKNOWN
(1945 - Republic) Richard Arlen, Cheryl Walker
One Sheet: $40 - $75

IDIOT, THE
(1963 - Shochiku) Toshiro Mifune, Masayuki Mori
One Sheet: $15 - $30   *Japanese.*

IDIOT'S DELIGHT
(1939 - MGM) Norma Shearer, Clark Gable
One Sheet: $350 - $750

IDIOT'S DELUXE
(1945 - Columbia) Three Stooges (Curly)
One Sheet: $2,500 - $4,000   *Comedy short. Duotone.*

IDLE CLASS, THE
(1921 - First National) Charlie Chaplin, Edna Purviance
One Sheet: $5,000 - $8,000

IDLE RICH
(1921 - Metro) Bert Lytell, Virginia Valli
One Sheet: $200 - $400

IDLE ROOMERS
(1944 - Columbia) The Three Stooges (Curly)
One Sheet: $2,500 - $4,000   *Comedy short. Duotone.*

IDOL, THE
(1966 - Embassy) Jennifer Jones, Michael Parks
One Sheet: $5 - $10

IDOL OF THE CROWDS
(1937 - Universal) John Wayne, Sheila Bromley
One Sheet: $800 - $1,500   *Sports (Hockey). Sports Movie Posters #232.*

IDOL OF THE CROWDS
(1948R - Universal) John Wayne
One Sheet: $125 - $250   *Sports (Hockey). Re-release.*

IDOLMAKER, THE
(1980 - United Artists) Ray Sharkey, Joe Pantoliano
One Sheet: $3 - $5

IF...
(1969 - Paramount) Malcolm McDowell, David Wood, Richard Warwick
One Sheet: $10 - $20

IF A BODY MEETS A BODY
(1945 - Columbia) The Three Stooges (Curly)
One Sheet: $2,500 - $4,000   *Comedy short. Duotone.*

IF A MAN ANSWERS
(1962 - Universal) Sandra Dee, Bobby Darin
One Sheet: $15 - $30

IF HE HOLLERS, LET HIM GO
(1968 - Cinerama) Dana Wynter, Raymond St. Jacques, Kevin McCarthy
One Sheet: $15 - $30

IF I HAD A MILLION
(1932 - Paramount) Gary Cooper, W. C. Fields, Charles Laughton, George Raft
One Sheet: $150 - $300   *One Sheet is all text.*

NOW PLAYING
PUBLIX-CAPITOL

Mini Window Card

IF I HAD MY WAY
(1940 - Universal) Bing Crosby, Gloria Jean
One Sheet: $75 - $125

IF I WERE FREE
(1933 - RKO) Irene Dunne, Nils Asther, Clive Brook
One Sheet: $125 - $250

IF I WERE KING

(1920 - Fox) William Farnum
One Sheet: $500 - $800

IF I WERE KING
(1938 - Paramount Publix) Ronald Colman, Basil Rathbone, Frances Dee
One Sheet: $2,200 - $3,500

IF I'M LUCKY
(1946 - 20th Century Fox) Carmen Miranda, Perry Como, Harry James Orch.
One Sheet: $100 - $200   *Big Band musical.*

IF IT'S TUESDAY, THIS MUST BE BELGIUM
(1969 - United Artists) Suzanne Pleshette, Ian McShane, Mildred Natwick
One Sheet: $5 - $10

IF LUCY FELL
(1996 - TriStar) Sarah Jessica Parker, Eric Schaeffer, Ben Stiller
One Sheet: $5 - $12

IF THIS BE SIN
(1949 - United Artists) Myrna Loy, Richard Greene
One Sheet: $40 - $75

IF WINTER COMES
(1947 - MGM) Walter Pidgeon, Deborah Kerr
One Sheet: $20 - $40

IF YOU COULD ONLY COOK
(1935 - Columbia) Herbert Marshall, Jean Arthur
One Sheet: $800 - $1,500

IF YOU COULD SEE WHAT I HEAR
(1982 - Cypress Grove/Farley) Marc Singer, Shari Belafonte
One Sheet: $3 - $5

IF YOU KNEW SUSIE
(1948 - RKO) Eddie Cantor, Joan Davis
One Sheet: $40 - $75

IGLOO
(1932 - Universal) -
One Sheet: $100 - $200

IGNATZ & LOTTE
(1995 - Big Stick) Keith McDermott, Mary Schultz
One Sheet: $5 - $10

IL MAGNIFICO STRANIERO
(1966 - -) Clint Eastwood
One Sheet: $100 - $200   *Italian. Edited episodes from the RAWHIDE TV series (shut down by U.S. producers due to copyright infringement).*

ILLEGAL
(1932 - Warner Bros.) Margot Grahame, Isobel Elsom
One Sheet: $150 - $300

ILLEGAL
(1955 - Warner Bros.) Edward G. Robinson, Jayne Mansfield(film debut)
One Sheet: $40 - $75

ILLEGAL ENTRY
(1949 - Universal) Howard Duff, Marta Toren
One Sheet: $30 - $50

ILLEGAL TRAFFIC
(1938 - Paramount) J. Carroll Naish, Mary Carlisle, Robert Preston
One Sheet: $75 - $150

ILLEGALLY YOURS
(1988 - -) Rob Lowe, Colleen Camp
One Sheet: $3 - $5

ILLICIT
(1931 - Warner Bros.) Barbara Stanwyck, Charles Butterworth, Joan Blondell
One Sheet: $700 - $1,200

ILLUSION
(1929 - Paramount) Buddy Rogers, Nancy Carroll
One Sheet: $150 - $300

ILLUSTRATED MAN, THE
(1969 - Warner Bros.) Rod Steiger, Claire Bloom
One Sheet: $15 - $25

ILSA, SHE WOLF OF THE SS
(1974 - -) Dyanne Thorne
One Sheet: $50 - $100

IMAGE OF LOVE
(1965 - Green) Documentary
One Sheet: $3 - $5

IMAGES
(1972 - Columbia) Susannah York, Rene Auberjonois
One Sheet: $3 - $5

IMAGINARY CRIMES
(1994 - Warner Bros.) Harvey Keitel, Fairuza Balk, Kelly Lynch
One Sheet: $5 - $10

IMAGINATION
(1941 - Columbia) Color Rhapsodies
One Sheet: $150 - $350   *Cartoon. Full color semi-stock poster with inset of title.*

IMAGINE: JOHN LENNON
(1988 - -) -
One Sheet: $30 - $50   *Documentary.*

IMITATION GENERAL
(1958 - MGM) Glenn Ford, Red Buttons
One Sheet: $15 - $25

IMITATION OF LIFE
(1934 - Universal) Claudette Colbert, Warren William
One Sheet: $1,000 - $1,800

IMITATION OF LIFE
(1945R - Universal) Claudette Colbert
One Sheet: $100 - $200   *Re-release.*

IMITATION OF LIFE
(1959 - Universal) Lana Turner, John Gavin
One Sheet: $50 - $100

One Sheet

IMMEDIATE FAMILY
(1989 - Columbia) Glenn Close, James Woods, Mary Stuart Masterson
One Sheet: $3 - $5

IMMIGRANT, THE
(1917 - Mutual) Charlie Chaplin, Edna Purviance
One Sheet: $6,500 - $10,000

IMMIGRANT, THE
(1919R - Select) Charlie Chaplin, Edna Purviance
One Sheet: $1,300 - $2,000   *Re-release.*

IMMIGRANT, THE
(1921R - Select) Charlie Chaplin
One Sheet: $500 - $800   *Re-release.*

IMMORAL MR. TEAS, THE
(1959 - -) W. Ellis Teas, Dir: Russ Meyer
One Sheet: $50 - $100

IMMORTAL BELOVED
(1994 - Columbia) Gary Oldman, Isabella Rossellini
One Sheet: $5 - $12

IMMORTAL SERGEANT, THE
(1942 - 20th Century Fox) Henry Fonda, Thomas Mitchell
One Sheet: $50 - $100

IMMORTAL STORY, THE
(1969 - Altura) Orson Welles, Jeanne Moreau, Roger Coggio, Norman Ashley
One Sheet: $10 - $20

IMPACT
(1949 - United Artists) Brian Donlevy, Ella Raines
One Sheet: $40 - $75

IMPASSE
(1969 - United Artists) Burt Reynolds, Anne Francis, Lyle Bettger
One Sheet: $10 - $20

IMPATIENT MAIDEN, THE
(1932 - Universal) Lew Ayres, Mae Clark
One Sheet: $150 - $300

IMPATIENT YEARS, THE
(1944 - Columbia) Jean Arthur, Lee Bowman
One Sheet: $50 - $100

IMPERFECT LADY, THE
(1947 - Paramount) Ray Milland, Teresa Wright
One Sheet: $40 - $75

IMPORTANCE OF BEING EARNEST, THE
(1952 - Universal International) Michael Redgrave, Joan Greenwood
One Sheet: $15 - $25

IMPOSSIBLE MRS. BELLEW, THE
(1922 - Lasky) Gloria Swanson, Robert Cain, Conrad Nagel
One Sheet: $1,000 - $1,800

IMPOSSIBLE YEARS, THE
(1968 - MGM) David Niven, Chad Everett, Christina Ferrare
One Sheet: $7 - $15

IMPOSTER, THE
(1944 - Universal) Jean Gabin, Richard Whorf, Ellen Drew
One Sheet: $50 - $100

IMPROPAGANDA
(1919 - Paramount) -
One Sheet: $150 - $300

IMPROPER CHANNELS
(1981 - -) Alan Arkin, Mariette Hartley
One Sheet: $3 - $5

IMPULSE
(1974 - Conqueror) William Shatner, Ruth Roman, Harold "Odd Job" Sakata
One Sheet: $15 - $25   *Duotone.*

IMPULSE
(1983 - ABC) Tim Matheson, Meg Tilly
One Sheet: $3 - $5

IMPULSE
(1990 - Warner Bros.) Theresa Russell, Jeff Fahey
One Sheet: $3 - $5

IN A LONELY PLACE
(1950 - Santana) Humphrey Bogart, Gloria Grahame, Frank Lovejoy
One Sheet: $100 - $200

IN A SHALLOW GRAVE
(1988 - -) Michael Biehn, Maureen Mueller
One Sheet: $5 - $10

IN BED WITH MADONNA
(1991 - -) Madonna
One Sheet: $15 - $30   *Documentary. AKA: TRUTH OR DARE.*

IN CALIENTE
(1935 - Warner Bros.) Dolores Del Rio, Pat O'Brien
One Sheet: $100 - $200

IN COLD BLOOD
(1968 - Columbia) Robert Blake, Scott Wilson
One Sheet: $30 - $50

IN COUNTRY
(1989 - -) Bruce Willis, Emily Lloyd
One Sheet: $5 - $10

IN CUSTODY
(1994 - Sony) Shashi Kapoor, Shabana Azmi
One Sheet: $5 - $10   *Indian.*

IN EARLY ARIZONA
(1938 - Columbia) Bill Elliott, Dorothy Gulliver
One Sheet: $75 - $150

IN ENEMY COUNTRY
(1968 - Universal) Tony Franciosa, Anjanette Comer, Guy Stockwell
One Sheet: $3 - $5

IN FAST COMPANY
(1946 - Monogram) Bowery Boys, Judy Clark
One Sheet: $75 - $125

IN GAY MADRID
(1930 - MGM) Ramon Novarro, Claude King
One Sheet: $150 - $300

IN HARM'S WAY
(1965 - Paramount) John Wayne, Kirk Douglas
One Sheet: $50 - $100

IN HER ARMS
(1930 - -) Warner Baxter
One Sheet: $500 - $800

IN HOT BLOOD
(1968 - AFD) -
One Sheet: $15 - $25

IN LIKE FLINT
(1967 - 20th Century Fox) James Coburn, Lee J. Cobb
One Sheet: $15 - $30   *Bob Peak art.*

IN LOVE AND WAR
(1958 - 20th Century Fox) Robert Wagner, Dana Wynter
One Sheet: $15 - $25

IN LOVE AND WAR
(1996 - New Line) Sandra Bullock, Chris O'Donnell
One Sheet: $5 - $10

IN LOVE WITH LIFE
(1934 - Invincible) Lila Lee, Onslow Stevens
One Sheet: $75 - $150

IN LOVE WITH LOVE
(1924 - Fox) -
One Sheet: $700 - $1,200

IN MIZZOURA
(1919 - Paramount-Artcraft) Robert Warwick, Eileen Percy, Burr Mackintosh
One Sheet: $150 - $350

IN NAME ONLY
(1939 - RKO) Cary Grant, Carole Lombard
One Sheet: $500 - $800

IN OLD AMARILLO
(1951 - Republic) Roy Rogers, Penny Edwards
One Sheet: $50 - $100

IN OLD ARIZONA
(1929 - Fox) Warner Baxter, Edmund Lowe
One Sheet: $1,300 - $2,000   *Academy Award: Best Actor(Warner Baxter). Academy Award Movie Posters #13. Cowboy Movie Posters #75.*

IN OLD CALIENTE
(1939 - Republic) Roy Rogers, Gabby Hayes
One Sheet: $800 - $1,500   *Cowboy Movie Posters #240.*

IN OLD CALIENTE
(1948R - Republic) Roy Rogers, Gabby Hayes
One Sheet: $50 - $100   *Re-release.*

IN OLD CALIFORNIA
(1942 - Republic) John Wayne, Patsy Kelly
One Sheet: $250 - $500

Half Sheet (Style A)

IN OLD CHEYENNE
(1931 - Sono Art/World Wide) Rex Lease
One Sheet: $150 - $300

IN OLD CHEYENNE
(1941 - Republic) Roy Rogers, Gabby Hayes
One Sheet: $200 - $400

IN OLD CHICAGO
(1938 - 20th Century Fox) Tyrone Power, Alice Faye
One Sheet: $800 - $1,500   *Academy*

Award Movie Posters #56.

IN OLD CHICAGO
(1943R - 20th Century Fox) Tyrone Power, Alice Faye
One Sheet: $100 - $200   *Re-release. Full color. No indication of re-release is shown on lobby cards other than Roman numeral date.*

IN OLD COLORADO
(1941 - Paramount) William Boyd, Russell Hayden
One Sheet: $150 - $300

IN OLD KENTUCKY
(1935 - 20th Century Fox) Will Rogers, Dorothy Wilson
One Sheet: $200 - $400

IN OLD MEXICO
(1938 - Paramount) William Boyd
One Sheet: $350 - $750

IN OLD MISSOURI
(1940 - Republic) Weaver Brothers, Alan Ladd
One Sheet: $75 - $125

IN OLD MONTEREY
(1939 - Republic) Gene Autry, Smiley Burnette
One Sheet: $200 - $400

IN OLD OKLAHOMA
(1943 - Republic) John Wayne, Martha Scott
One Sheet: $250 - $500

IN OLD SACRAMENTO
(1946 - Republic) William Elliott, Constance Moore
One Sheet: $30 - $50

IN OLD SANTA FE
(1934 - Mascot) Ken Maynard, Gene Autry
One Sheet: $700 - $1,200   *Autry's film debut. Cowboy Movie Posters #172.*

IN OUR TIME
(1944 - Warner Bros.) Ida Lupino, Paul Henreid
One Sheet: $30 - $50

IN PERSON
(1935 - RKO) Ginger Rogers, George Brent
One Sheet: $500 - $800

IN SEARCH OF GREGORY
(1970 - Universal) Julie Christie, Michael Sarrazin, John Hurt
One Sheet: $2 - $3

IN SEARCH OF HISTORIC JESUS
(1979 - Sunn) John Rubinstein, John Anderson
One Sheet: $5 - $10

IN SEARCH OF NOAH'S ARK
(1976 - Sun) Brad Crandall
One Sheet: $7 - $15

IN SEARCH OF THE CASTAWAYS
(1962 - Buena Vista/Disney) Hayley Mills, Maurice Chevalier
One Sheet: $15 - $25

IN SEARCH OF THE CASTAWAYS
(1970R - Disney) Hayley Mills, Maurice Chevalier
One Sheet: $5 - $10   *Re-release.*

IN SOCIETY
(1938 - Universal) Little Tough Guys
One Sheet: $200 - $400

IN SOCIETY
(1944 - Universal) Bud Abbott, Lou Costello, Kirby Grant
One Sheet: $150 - $300

IN SOCIETY
(1953R - Realart) Bud Abbott, Lou Costello, Ann Gillis
One Sheet: $30 - $50   *Re-release.*

IN SPITE OF DANGER
(1935 - Columbia) Wallace Ford, Marian Marsh
One Sheet: $75 - $150

IN THE ARMY NOW
(1994 - Buena Vista) Pauly Shore, Andy Dick, Lori Petty
One Sheet: $5 - $10

IN THE BAG
(1956 - RKO/Disney) Humphrey Bear
One Sheet: $200 - $400   *Cartoon. Full color.*

IN THE CLUTCHES OF THE GANG
(1913 - -) Roscoe "Fatty" Arbuckle
One Sheet: $1,300 - $2,000

IN THE COOL OF THE DAY
(1963 - MGM) Jane Fonda, Peter Finch
One Sheet: $15 - $30

IN THE DAYS OF BUFFALO BILL
(1922 - Universal) Art Accord
One Sheet: $250 - $500   *Serial. Western. 18 Chapters. Cowboy Movie Posters #32.*

IN THE FOLDS OF THE FLESH
(1971 - -) -
One Sheet: $7 - $15

IN THE FRENCH STYLE
(1963 - Columbia) Jean Seberg, Stanley Baker
One Sheet: $7 - $15

IN THE GOOD OLD SUMMERTIME
(1949 - MGM) Judy Garland, Van Johnson
One Sheet: $150 - $300

IN THE HEAT OF THE NIGHT
(1967 - United Artists) Sidney Poitier, Rod Steiger
One Sheet: $15 - $30   *Academy Award: Best Picture, Best Actor(Steiger). Academy Award Movie Posters #238 & #241.*

IN THE HOUSE OF THE CHIEF
(1916 - Selig) Dir: T.N. Heffron
One Sheet: $250 - $500

IN THE LAND OF FIRE
(1913 - G.Melies) Documentary of New Zealand
One Sheet: $250 - $500   *"The Great Waidakei Geyser"*

IN THE LINE OF FIRE
(1993 - Universal) Clint Eastwood, Rene Russo, John Malkovich
One Sheet: $7 - $15

One Sheet

IN THE MEANTIME, DARLING
(1944 - 20th Century Fox) Jeanne Crain, Frank Latimore
One Sheet: $50 - $100

IN THE MONEY
(1933 - Invincible) Skeets Gallagher, Hattie McDaniel
One Sheet: $150 - $300

IN THE MONEY
(1958 - Allied Artist) Bowery Boys
One Sheet: $20 - $40

IN THE MOOD
(1987 - -) Patrick Dempsey, Talia Balsam
One Sheet: $3 - $5

IN THE MOUTH OF MADNESS
(1995 - New Line) Sam Neill, Julie Carmen, Dir: John Carpenter
One Sheet: $3 - $5

IN THE NAME OF THE FATHER
(1994 - Warner Bros.) Daniel Day-Lewis, Emma Thompson
One Sheet: $5 - $10

IN THE NAVY
(1941 - -) See ABBOTT AND COSTELLO IN THE NAVY

IN THE NEXT ROOM
(1930 - First National) Jane Winton, Crauford Kent
One Sheet: $100 - $200

IN THE PARK
(1915 - Essanay) Charlie Chaplin, Edna Purviance
One Sheet: $7,500 - $12,000

IN THE SAME BOAT
(1913 - Patheplay)
One Sheet: $250 - $500

IN THE SHADOWS OF KILIMANJARO
(1985 - -) John Rhys-Davies, Timothy Bottoms
One Sheet: $3 - $5

IN THE SWEET PIE AND PIE
(1941 - Columbia) The Three Stooges (Curly)
One Sheet: $4,000 - $6,000   *Comedy short. Duotone.*

IN THE WAKE OF A STRANGER
(1960 - Paramount) Shirley Eaton, Tony Wright
One Sheet: $5 - $10

IN THIS CORNER
(1948 - Eagle-Lion) Scott Brady, Anabel Shaw
One Sheet: $50 - $100   *Sports (Boxing). Sports Movie Posters #148.*

IN THIS OUR LIFE
(1942 - Warner Bros.) Bette Davis, Olivia de Havilland
One Sheet: $150 - $300

IN WHICH WE SERVE
(1942 - United Artists) Noel Coward, Bernard Miles
One Sheet: $50 - $100

INADMISSABLE EVIDENCE
(1968 - Paramount) Nicol Williamson, Eleanor Fazan, Jill Bennett
One Sheet: $3 - $5

INBAD THE SAILOR
(1923 - Pathe) -
One Sheet: $150 - $300

IN-BETWEEN AGE
(1958 - Allied Artists) Mary Steele, Lee Patterson
One Sheet: $15 - $25

INCENDIARY BLONDE
(1945 - Paramount) Betty Hutton, Arturo De Cordova
One Sheet: $75 - $125

INCHON
(1982 - One Way) Laurence Olivier, Jacqueline Bisset
One Sheet: $3 - $5

INCIDENT
(1948 - Monogram) Warren Douglas, Jane Frazee
One Sheet: $20 - $40

INCIDENT, THE
(1968 - 20th Century Fox) Beau Bridges, Martin Sheen
One Sheet: $10 - $20

INCIDENT AT OGLALA
(1992 - Miramax) Leonard Peltier
One Sheet: $3 - $5

INCIDENT AT PHANTOM HILL
(1966 - Universal) Robert Fuller, Dan Duryea
One Sheet: $5 - $10

INCIDENT IN AN ALLEY
(1961 - United Artists) Charles Warfield, Erin O'Donnell
One Sheet: $15 - $30

INCOME TAX SAPPY
(1954 - Columbia) The Three Stooges (Shemp)
One Sheet: $150 - $300   *Comedy short. Duotone.*

INCOMING FRESHMAN
(1974 - Ballard Pictures) Mary Moon
One Sheet: $15 - $25   *Sexploitation.*

INCORRIGIBLE DUKANE, THE
(1915 - Paramount) John Barrymore, W.T. Carleton
One Sheet: $1,300 - $2,000

INCREDIBLE HULK, THE
(1977 - -) Lou Ferrigno, Bill Bixby
One Sheet: $20 - $40   *Pilot for TV series. Comic book tie-in.*

INCREDIBLE JOURNEY, THE
(1963 - Buena Vista/Disney) Emile Genest, John Drainie
One Sheet: $15 - $30

INCREDIBLE JOURNEY OF DR. MEG LAUREL, THE
(1978 - -) Lindsay Wagner, Jane Wyman, James Woods
One Sheet: $3 - $5

INCREDIBLE MELTING MAN, THE
(1977 - AIP) Alex Rebar, Burr DeBenning
One Sheet: $15 - $25

INCREDIBLE MR. LIMPET, THE
(1964 - Warner Bros.) Don Knotts, Jack Weston
One Sheet: $30 - $50

INCREDIBLE PETRIFIED WORLD, THE
(1960 - Governor) John Carradine, Robert Clarke
One Sheet: $15 - $35

INCREDIBLE SHRINKING MAN, THE
(1957 - Universal International) Grant Williams, Randy Stuart
One Sheet: $250 - $500   *Graven Images, pg. 184.*

One Sheet

INCREDIBLE SHRINKING MAN, THE
(1964R - Universal) Grant Williams, Randy Stuart
One Sheet: $75 - $150

INCREDIBLE SHRINKING WOMAN, THE
(1981 - Universal) Lily Tomlin, Charles Grodin
One Sheet: $5 - $10

INCREDIBLE TORTURE SHOW, THE
(197? - -) O'Brien
One Sheet: $15 - $25

INCREDIBLE TWO-HEADED TRANSPLANT, THE
(1971 - AIP) Bruce Dern, Pat Priest
One Sheet: $15 - $25

INCREDIBLY STRANGE CREATURES, THE
(1964 - Fairway) Cash Flagg, Carolyn Brandt
One Sheet: $50 - $100

INCUBUS, THE
(1982 - Film Ventures) John Cassavetes, Kerrie Kane
One Sheet: $5 - $10

INDECENT PROPOSAL
(1993 - Paramount) Robert Redford, Demi Moore, Woody Harrelson
One Sheet: $5 - $10

INDEPENDENCE B'GOSH!
(1918 - Paramount) -
One Sheet: $200 - $400

INDEPENDENCE DAY
(1996 - 20th Century Fox) Will Smith, Bill Pullman, Jeff Goldblum
One Sheet: $7 - $15   *Advance Style: $12-$20. Advance Style with spaceships: $15-$20.*

INDESTRUCTIBLE MAN, THE
(1955 - C.G.K.) Lon Chaney Jr., Casey Adams
One Sheet: $50 - $100

INDIA SPEAKS
(1933 - RKO) -
One Sheet: $75 - $150

INDIAN AGENT
(1948 - RKO) Tim Holt, Nan Leslie

One Sheet: $30 - $50

INDIAN FIGHTER, THE
(1955 - United Artists) Kirk Douglas, Elsa Martinelli, Walter Matthau
One Sheet: $15 - $25

INDIAN IN THE CUPBOARD, THE
(1995 - Paramount) Hal Scardino, Litefoot
One Sheet: $5 - $12

INDIAN PAINT
(1966 - Eagle-International) Johnny Crawford, Jay Silverheels
One Sheet: $5 - $10

INDIAN RUNNER, THE
(1992 - -) Patricia Arquette (Debut), Sean Penn
One Sheet: $5 - $10

INDIAN SERENADE
(1950R - Columbia) -
One Sheet: $100 - $200   *Re-release. Cartoon. Full color stock re-release poster of a 1937 cartoon.*

INDIAN SUMMER
(1993 - Buena Vista) Alan Arkin, Diane Lane, Bill Paxton
One Sheet: $3 - $5

INDIAN TERRITORY
(1950 - Columbia) Gene Autry, Gail Davis
One Sheet: $75 - $125

INDIAN UPRISING
(1951 - Columbia) George Montgomery, Audrey Long
One Sheet: $15 - $35

INDIANA JONES AND THE LAST CRUSADE
(1989 - Lucasfilm) Harrison Ford, Sean Connery
One Sheet: $15 - $25

INDIANA JONES AND THE TEMPLE OF DOOM
(1984 - Lucasfilm) Harrison Ford, Kate Capshaw
One Sheet: $30 - $50   *Advance (Styel A):$50-75, Advance (Style B):$75-$100.*

INDIANAPOLIS SPEEDWAY
(1939 - Warner Bros.) Gale Page, Pat O'Brien, John Payne, Ann Sheridan
One Sheet: $100 - $200   *Sports (Auto racing). Sports Movie Posters #12.*

INDIANS ARE COMING, THE
(1930 - Universal) Tim McCoy, Allene Ray
One Sheet: $500 - $800   *Serial. Western. 12 Chapters.*

INDISCREET
(1931 - Feature) Gloria Swanson, Ben Lyon
One Sheet: $600 - $1,000   *Art-Cinema re-issue:$200-300.*

INDISCREET
(1958 - Warner Bros.) Ingrid Bergman, Cary Grant
One Sheet: $75 - $150

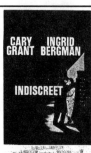

One Sheet

INDISCRETION
(1921 - Pioneer) Florence Reed, Lionel Atwill
One Sheet: $150 - $300

INDISCRETION OF AN AMERICAN WIFE
(1953 - Columbia) Jennifer Jones, Montgomery Clift
One Sheet: $50 - $100

INDOCHINE
(1992 - Sony Classics) Catherine Denueve
One Sheet: $3 - $5

INFAMOUS MISS REVELL, THE
(1921 - Metro) Alice Lake, Cullen Landis
One Sheet: $250 - $500

INFATUATION
(1926 - -) Corrine Griffith, Percy Marmont
One Sheet: $250 - $500

INFERIOR DECORATOR
(1948 - RKO/Disney) Donald Duck
One Sheet: $800 - $1,500   *Cartoon. The Disney Poster, pg. 56.*

INFERNAL MACHINE
(1933 - Fox) Chester Morris, Genevieve Tobin
One Sheet: $200 - $400

INFERNO
(1953 - 20th Century Fox) Robert Ryan, Rhonda Fleming
One Sheet: $15 - $25

INFERNO
(1980 - Fox) Irene Miracle, Leigh McCloskey
One Sheet: $15 - $25

INFORMATION RECEIVED
(1962 - Universal) Sabina Sesselman, William Sylvester
One Sheet: $3 - $5

INFORMER, THE
(1929 - British International) Lya de Putti, Lars Hansen
One Sheet: $500 - $800

INFORMER, THE
(1935 - RKO) Victor McLaglen, Heather Angel
One Sheet: $4,000 - $6,000   *Academy Award: Best Actor, Best Direction(John Ford). Academy Award Movie Posters #41, #44.*

One Sheet

INFORMER, THE
(1955R - RKO) Victor McLaglen, Heather Angel
One Sheet: $15 - $30   *Re-release. Duotone.*

INFRA-MAN
(1975 - Shaw Bros.) Li Hsiu-Hsien, Wang Hsieh
One Sheet: $7 - $15

INGAGI
(1930 - Congo) Sir Hubert Winstead, Daniel Swayne
One Sheet: $800 - $1,500

INHERIT THE WIND
(1960 - United Artists) Spencer Tracy, Fredric March
One Sheet: $50 - $100

INKWELL, THE
(1994 - Touchstone) Larenz Tate, Jada Pinkett
One Sheet: $5 - $10

IN-LAWS, THE
(1979 - Warner Bros.) Peter Falk, Alan Arkin
One Sheet: $5 - $10

INN OF SIXTH HAPPINESS, THE
(1958 - 20th Century Fox) Ingrid Bergman, Curt Jurgens, Robert Donat
One Sheet: $15 - $30

INNER CIRCLE, THE
(1946 - Republic) Warren Douglas, Lynn Roberts
One Sheet: $30 - $50

INNER MAN, THE
(1922 - Syracuse) Wyndham Standing, Dorothy Mackaill, J.Barney Sherry
One Sheet: $200 - $400

INNER SANCTUM
(1948 - United Artists) Charles Russell, Mary Beth Hughes
One Sheet: $50 - $100

INNERMOST LIMITS OF PURE FUN, THE
(197? - George Greenough) -
One Sheet: $30 - $50   *Sports (Surfing documentary).*

INNERSPACE
(1987 - Warner Bros.) Dennis Quaid, Martin Short, Meg Ryan
One Sheet: $7 - $15

INNERTUBE ANTICS
(1944 - MGM) -
One Sheet: $250 - $500   *Cartoon. Full color stone litho.*

INNOCENT, THE
(1994 - -) Anthony Hopkins, Isabella Rossellini
One Sheet: $5 - $10

INNOCENT AFFAIR, AN
(1948 - United Artists) Fred MacMurray, Madeleine Carroll
One Sheet: $30 - $50

INNOCENT BLOOD
(1992 - Warner Bros.) Anne Parillaud, Robert Loggia, Don Rickles
One Sheet: $3 - $5

INNOCENT BYSTANDERS
(1972 - Paramount) Stanley Baker, Geraldine Chaplin
One Sheet: $3 - $5

INNOCENT HUSBANDS
(1925 - Pathe) Charley Chase
One Sheet: $150 - $350

INNOCENT MAN, AN
(1989 - Touchstone) Tom Selleck, F. Murray Abraham
One Sheet: $5 - $10

INNOCENTS, THE
(1962 - 20th Century Fox) Deborah Kerr, Michael Redgrave
One Sheet: $75 - $150   *Graven Images, pg. 218.*

INNOCENTS IN PARIS
(1955 - Tudor) Alastair Sim, Claire Bloom
One Sheet: $15 - $30

INSERTS
(1976 - United Artists) Richard Dreyfuss. Jessica Harper
One Sheet: $5 - $10

INSIDE CACKLE CORNERS
(1951 - MGM) -
One Sheet: $200 - $400   *Cartoon. Full color stone litho.*

INSIDE DAISY CLOVER
(1966 - Warner Bros.) Natalie Wood, Christoper Plummer, Robert Redford
One Sheet: $10 - $20

INSIDE DETROIT
(1956 - Columbia) Dennis O'Keefe, Pat O'Brien
One Sheet: $15 - $30

INSIDE INFORMATION
(1939 - Universal) June Lang, Dick Foran
One Sheet: $75 - $125

INSIDE JOB
(1946 - Universal) Preston Foster, Ann Rutherford
One Sheet: $40 - $75

INSIDE MONKEY ZETTERLAND
(1993 - I.R.S.) Steve Antinin, Patricia Arquette
One Sheet: $3 - $5

INSIDE MOVES
(1980 - Warner Bros.) John Savage, David Morse
One Sheet: $7 - $15   *Sports (Basketball). Sports Movie Posters #97.*

INSIDE OF THE WHITE SLAVE TRAFFIC, THE
(1913 - Samuel H. London) -
One Sheet: $600 - $1,000   *Exploitation.*

INSIDE OUT
(1975 - Warner Bros.) Telly Savalas, Robert Culp

One Sheet: $5 - $10

INSIDE STORY
(1939 - 20th Century Fox) Michael Whelan, Jean Rogers
One Sheet: $100 - $200

INSIDE STORY, THE
(1948 - Republic) Marsha Hunt, William Lundigan
One Sheet: $30 - $50

INSIDE STRAIGHT
(1951 - MGM) David Brian, Arlene Dahl
One Sheet: $40 - $75

INSIDE THE LAW
(1942 - PRC) Wallace Ford, Luana Walters
One Sheet: $30 - $60

INSIDE THE LINES
(1930 - RKO) Ralph Forbes, Betty Compson
One Sheet: $150 - $300

INSIDE THE MAFIA
(1959 - United Artists) Cameron Mitchell, Elaine Edwards
One Sheet: $15 - $30

INSIDE THE WALLS OF FOLSOM PRISON
(1951 - Warner Bros.) Steve Cochran, David Brian
One Sheet: $30 - $50

INSPECTOR CALLS, AN
(1954 - British Lion) Alastair Sim, Eileen Moore
One Sheet: $10 - $20

INSPECTOR CLOUSEAU
(1968 - United Artists) Alan Arkin, Delia Boccardo, Frank Finlay
One Sheet: $15 - $25

INSPECTOR GENERAL, THE
(1949 - Warner Bros.) Danny Kaye, Walter Slezak
One Sheet: $40 - $75

INSPECTOR HORNLEIGH
(1939 - Fox) Gordon Harker, Alastair Sim
One Sheet: $75 - $125

INSPIRATION
(1931 - MGM) Greta Garbo, Lewis Stone
One Sheet: $2,500 - $4,000

INSURANCE INVESTIGATOR
(1951 - Republic) Audrey Long, Richard Denning
One Sheet: $30 - $60

INTENT TO KILL
(1958 - 20th Century Fox) Richard Todd, Betsy Drake
One Sheet: $15 - $25

INTERFERENCE
(1928 - Paramount) Evelyn Brent, Clive Brook
One Sheet: $150 - $300

INTERIORS
(1978 - United Artists) Geraldine Page, Diane Keaton
One Sheet: $10 - $20   *Woody Allen's first film as writer/director. Photo at Top Style:$20-$30.*

INTERLUDE
(1957 - Universal) June Allyson, Rossano Brazzi
One Sheet: $10 - $20

INTERLUDE
(1968 - Columbia) Oskar Werner, Barbara Ferris, Virginia Maskell
One Sheet: $3 - $5

INTERMEZZO
(1936 - Svensk) Gosta Ekman, Inga Tidblad, Ingrid Bergman
One Sheet: $250 - $600   *Swedish.*

INTERMEZZO
(1939 - United Artists) Leslie Howard, Ingrid Bergman
One Sheet: $300 - $700   *Bergman's first U.S. film.*

INTERNAL AFFAIRS
(1990 - Paramount) Richard Gere, Andy Garcia, Nancy Travis
One Sheet: $5 - $10

INTERNATIONAL BURLESQUE

(1950 - Jewel) -
One Sheet: $30 - $50   *Sexploitation.*

INTERNATIONAL COUNTERFEITERS
(1958 - -) Gordon Howard
One Sheet: $15 - $25

INTERNATIONAL CRIME, THE
(1938 - Grand National) Rod La Rocque, Astrid Allwyn
One Sheet: $50 - $100

INTERNATIONAL HOUSE
(1933 - Paramount) George Burns, Gracie Allen, W.C. Fields
One Sheet: $2,200 - $3,500

INTERNATIONAL LADY
(1941 - United Artists) Basil Rathbone, Ilona Massey, George Brent
One Sheet: $50 - $100

INTERNATIONAL SETTLEMENT
(1938 - 20th Century Fox) Dolores Del Rio, George Sanders
One Sheet: $200 - $400

INTERNATIONAL SQUADRON
(1941 - Warner Bros.) Ronald Reagan, James Stephenson
One Sheet: $150 - $350

INTERNATIONAL SWEETHEARTS OF RHYTHM
(1947 - Transvideo) All-Girl band
One Sheet: $250 - $600   *Black cast. Separate Cinema, pg. 100.*

INTERNATIONAL VELVET
(1978 - MGM) Tatum O'Neal, Christopher Plummer
One Sheet: $7 - $15   *Sports (Horse racing). Sports Movie Posters #253.*

INTERNES CAN'T TAKE MONEY
(1937 - Paramount) Joel McCrea, Barbara Stanwyck
One Sheet: $200 - $400

INTERNS, THE
(1962 - Columbia) Michael Callan, Cliff Robertson
One Sheet: $15 - $25

INTERRUPTED JOURNEY
(1950 - London) Richard Todd, Valerie Hobson
One Sheet: $7 - $15

INTERRUPTED MELODY
(1955 - MGM) Glenn Ford, Eleanor Parker
One Sheet: $15 - $30

INTERSECTION
(1994 - Paramount) Richard Gere, Sharon Stone
One Sheet: $3 - $5

INTERVAL
(1973 - Avco/Embassy) Merle Oberon, Robert Wolders
One Sheet: $3 - $5

INTERVIEW WITH THE VAMPIRE
(1994 - Warner Bros.) Tom Cruise, Brad Pitt
One Sheet: $15 - $30

INTERVISTA
(1993 - Castle Hill) Federico Fellini, Marcello Mastroianni
One Sheet: $3 - $5

INTIMACY
(1966 - Goldstone) Jack Ging, Nancy Malone
One Sheet: $3 - $5

INTO THE NIGHT
(1985 - Universal) Jeff Goldblum, Michelle Pfeiffer
One Sheet: $5 - $10

INTO THE WEST
(1992 - Miramax) Gabriel Byrne, Ellen Barkin
One Sheet: $3 - $5

INTOLERANCE
(1916 - Wark) Lillian Gish, Dir: D.W. Griffith
One Sheet: $7,500 - $12,000

INTRIGUE
(1947 - United Artists) George Raft, June Havoc
One Sheet: $40 - $75

INTRUDER, THE
(1933 - Allied) Monte Blue, Lila Lee

One Sheet: $100 - $200

INTRUDER, THE
(1955 - Associated Artists) Jack Hawkins, Dennis Price
One Sheet: $10 - $20

INTRUDER, THE
(1962 - Pathe-America) William Shatner, Frank Maxwell
One Sheet: $15 - $30   *AKA: I HATE YOUR GUTS; SHAME; Great Britain: THE STRANGER.*

INTRUDER IN THE DUST
(1949 - MGM) David Brian, Claude Jarman, Jr.
One Sheet: $50 - $100

INVADERS, THE
(1929 - Syndicate) Bob Steele, Edna Aslin
One Sheet: $150 - $300

INVADERS, THE
(1942 - Columbia) Leslie Howard, Laurence Olivier
One Sheet: $125 - $250

INVADERS FROM MARS
(1953 - 20th Century Fox) Helena Carter, Arthur Franz
One Sheet: $600 - $1,000   *Graven Images, pg. 158.*

One Sheet

INVADERS FROM MARS
(1955R - 20th Century Fox) Helena Carter, Arthur Franz
One Sheet: $200 - $400   *Re-release. One Sheet identical to original except copyright 1955.*

INVADERS FROM MARS
(1976R - 20th Century Fox) Helena Carter, Arthur Franz
One Sheet: $7 - $15   *Re-release.*

INVADERS FROM MARS
(1986 - Cannon) Karen Black, Hunter Carson
One Sheet: $7 - $15

INVASION
(1941 - Adventure) -
One Sheet: $40 - $75

INVASION 1700
(1965 - Medallion) Jeanne Crain, John Drew Barrymore
One Sheet: $15 - $35

INVASION OF THE ANIMAL PEOPLE
(1962 - ADP) Barbara Wilson, John Carradine
One Sheet: $20 - $40

INVASION OF THE ASTROS
(1970 - Maron Films) Nick Adams, Akira Takarada
One Sheet: $40 - $75   *AKA: MONSTER ZERO.*

INVASION OF THE BLOOD FARMERS
(1972 - NMO) Cynthia Fleming, Norman Kelly
One Sheet: $7 - $15

INVASION OF THE BODY SNATCHERS
(1956 - Allied Artists) Kevin McCarthy, Dana Wynter
One Sheet: $250 - $600   *Half Sheet(Style B "Spotlight Dance"):$1500-2500. Graven Images, pg. 171.*

INVASION OF THE BODY SNATCHERS
(1978 - United Artists) Donald Sutherland, Leonard Nimoy
One Sheet: $10 - $20   *Price is for either style.*

INVASION OF THE FLESH HUNTERS
(1982 - -) John Saxon, Elizabeth Turner
One Sheet: $7 - $15

INVASION OF THE SAUCER MEN
(1957 - AIP) Steve Terrell, Gloria Castillo
One Sheet: $1,300 - $2,000   *Graven Images, pg. 179.*

INVASION OF THE SAUCER-MEN/TEEN-AGE WEREWOLF
(1957 - AIP) -
One Sheet: $500 - $800   *Double feature poster.*

INVASION OF THE STAR CREATURES
(1963 - AIP) Bob Ball, Frankie Ray
One Sheet: $30 - $50

INVASION QUARTET
(1961 - MGM) Bill Travers, Spike Milligan
One Sheet: $5 - $10

INVASION U.S.A.
(1952 - Columbia) Gerald Mohr, Peggie Castle
One Sheet: $30 - $60

INVASION U.S.A.
(1985 - Cannon) Chuck Norris, Melissa Prophet
One Sheet: $5 - $10

INVENTING THE ABBOTTS
(1997 - 20th Century Fox) Liv Tyler, Billy Crudup, Joaquin Phoenix, Jennifer Connelly
One Sheet: $5 - $10

INVINCIBLE GLADIATOR, THE
(1963 - Seven Arts) Richard Harrison, Isabel Corey
One Sheet: $7 - $15

INVINCIBLE SIX, THE
(1970 - Continental) Stuart Whitman, Elke Sommer
One Sheet: $3 - $5

INVISIBLE AGENT
(1942 - Universal) Jon Hall, Ilona Massey
One Sheet: $100 - $200   *Graven Images, pg. 127.*

INVISIBLE AVENGER
(1958 - Republic) Richard Derr, Helen Westcott
One Sheet: $10 - $20

INVISIBLE BOY
(1957 - MGM) Richard Eyer, Philip Abbot, Robby The Robot
One Sheet: $200 - $450   *Graven Images, pg. 173.*

INVISIBLE BOY
(1973R - MGM) Richard Eyer, Phillip Abbot, Robby The Robot
One Sheet: $15 - $30   *Re-release.*

INVISIBLE ENEMY
(1938 - Republic) Alan Marshall, Tala Birell
One Sheet: $50 - $100

INVISIBLE GHOST
(1941 - Monogram) Bela Lugosi, Polly Ann Young, John McGuire
One Sheet: $1,300 - $2,000   *Graven Images, pg. 133.*

INVISIBLE GHOST
(194?R - Astor) Bela Lugosi
One Sheet: $150 - $300   *Re-release.*

INVISIBLE INFORMER, THE
(1946 - Republic) Linda Sterling, William Henry
One Sheet: $30 - $60

INVISIBLE INVADERS
(1959 - Premium) John Agar, Jean Byron
One Sheet: $40 - $75

INVISIBLE MAN, THE
(1933 - Universal) Claude Rains, Gloria Stuart
One Sheet: $40,000 - $50,000   *One Sheet(Advance):$25000-35000. Gravven Images, pg. 76-77.*

INVISIBLE MAN, THE
(1951R - Realart) Claude Rains, Gloria Stuart
One Sheet: $500 - $900   *Re-release.*

INVISIBLE MAN RETURNS, THE
(1940 - Universal) Vincent Price, Cedric Hardwicke
One Sheet: $3,500 - $5,000   *Graven Images, pg. 127.*

INVISIBLE MAN RETURNS, THE
(1951R - Realart) Vincent Price, Cedric Hardwicks
One Sheet: $125 - $250   *Re-release.*

INVISIBLE MAN'S REVENGE, THE
(1944 - Universal) Jon Hall, Evelyn Ankers, John Carradine
One Sheet: $200 - $400   *Graven Images, pg. 127.*

INVISIBLE MENACE, THE
(1937 - Warner Bros.) Boris Karloff, Marie Wilson
One Sheet: $250 - $500

INVISIBLE MONSTER, THE
(1950 - Republic) Richard Webb, Aline Towne
One Sheet: $100 - $200   *Serial. 12 Chapters.*

INVISIBLE RAY, THE
(1936 - Universal) Boris Karloff, Bela Lugosi
One Sheet: $16,000 - $25,000   *Graven Images, pg. 83.*

INVISIBLE STRIPES
(1939 - Warner Bros.) George Raft, William Holden, Humphrey Bogart
One Sheet: $250 - $500

INVISIBLE WALL, THE
(1947 - 20th Century Fox) Don Castle, Virginia Christine
One Sheet: $30 - $50

INVISIBLE WOMAN, THE
(1940 - Universal) John Barrymore, Virginia Bruce
One Sheet: $250 - $600   *Graven Images, pg. 127.*

INVITATION
(1951 - MGM) Dorothy McGuire, Van Johnson
One Sheet: $20 - $40

INVITATION TO A GUNFIGHTER
(1964 - United Artists) Yul Brynner, Janice Rule
One Sheet: $30 - $60   *Cowboy Movie Posters #314.*

One Sheet

INVITATION TO HAPPINESS
(1939 - Paramount) Irene Dunn, Fred MacMurray
One Sheet: $75 - $150

INVITATION TO THE DANCE
(1954 - MGM) Gene Kelly, Daphne Dale
One Sheet: $75 - $150

IPCRESS FILE, THE
(1965 - Universal) Michael Caine, Nigel Green
One Sheet: $15 - $25   *Pre-Review*
One Sheet: $100-$200.

I.Q.
(1994 - Paramount) Meg Ryan, Tim Robbins, Walter Matthau
One Sheet: $5 - $10

IRENE
(1926 - First National) Colleen Moore, Lloyd Hughes
One Sheet: $150 - $300

IRENE
(1940 - RKO) Anna Neagle, Ray Milland
One Sheet: $50 - $100

IRISH DESTINY
(1925 - Eppel) Denis O'Shea, Una Shiels
One Sheet: $250 - $500

IRISH EYES ARE SMILING
(1944 - 20th Century Fox) Dick Haymes, June Haver
One Sheet: $75 - $125

IRISH FOR LUCK
(1936 - Warner Bros.) Margaret Lockwood, Athene Seyler
One Sheet: $125 - $250

IRISH HEARTS
(1927 - Warner Bros.) May McAvoy, Jason Robards, Sr.
One Sheet: $200 - $400

IRISH IN US, THE
(1935 - Warner Bros.) James Cagney, Olivia de Havilland
One Sheet: $700 - $1,200

IRISH LUCK
(1939 - Monogram) Frankie Darro, Dick Purcell
One Sheet: $75 - $150

IRISH WHISKEY REBELLION
(1973 - Cinerama) William Devane, Anne Meara
One Sheet: $3 - $5

IRMA LA DOUCE
(1963 - Universal) Shirley MacLaine, Jack Lemmon
One Sheet: $15 - $35

IRON ANGEL
(1964 - Kennedy) Jim Davis, Margo Woode
One Sheet: $5 - $10

IRON CLAW, THE
(1941 - Columbia) Charles Quigley, Walter Sande
One Sheet: $125 - $250   *Serial. 15 Chapters.*

IRON CURTAIN, THE
(1948 - 20th Century Fox) Dana Andrews, Gene Tierney
One Sheet: $50 - $100

IRON DUKE, THE
(1934 - Gaumont) George Arliss, Ellaline Terriss
One Sheet: $75 - $150

IRON EAGLE
(1986 - TriStar) Louis Gossett, Jr., Jason Gedrick
One Sheet: $5 - $10

IRON EAGLE 2
(1988 - TriStar) Louis Gossett, Jr., Mark Humphrey
One Sheet: $3 - $5

IRON GLOVE, THE
(1954 - Columbia) Robert Stack, Ursula Thiess
One Sheet: $15 - $30

IRON HORSE, THE
(1924 - William Fox) George O'Brien, Madge Bellamy, Dir: John Ford
One Sheet: $1,300 - $2,000   *Cowboy Movie Posters #47.*

IRON JUSTICE
(1915 - Renaissance) Julian Royce, Fanny Tittell
One Sheet: $250 - $600

IRON MAJOR, THE
(1943 - RKO) Pat O'Brien, Ruth Warrick
One Sheet: $150 - $300   *Sports (Football). Sports Movie Posters #199.*

IRON MAN, THE
(1925 - Chadwick) Lionel Barrymore, Mildred Harris
One Sheet: $500 - $800

IRON MAN, THE
(1931 - Universal) Lew Ayres, Jean Harlow
One Sheet: $800 - $1,500

IRON MAN, THE
(1951 - Universal) Stephen McNally, Evelyn Keys
One Sheet: $15 - $25

IRON MASK, THE
(1929 - United Artists) Douglas Fairbanks, Belle Bennett
One Sheet: $1,300 - $2,000

IRON MASTER, THE

(1932 - Allied) Reginald Denny, Lila Lee
One Sheet: $75 - $150

IRON MISTRESS, THE
(1952 - Warner Bros.) Alan Ladd, Virginia Mayo
One Sheet: $30 - $50

IRON MONKEY, THE
(197? - -) -
One Sheet: $3 - $5   *Chinese martial arts.*

IRON MOUNTAIN TRAIL
(1953 - Republic) Rex Allen, Slim Pickens
One Sheet: $30 - $50   *Re-release.*

IRON MULE, THE
(1925 - Educational) Al St. John
One Sheet: $250 - $500

IRON PETTICOAT, THE
(1956 - MGM) Bob Hope, Katharine Hepburn
One Sheet: $30 - $50

IRON RING, THE
(1917 - World) Edward Langford, Arthur Ashley, Gerda Holmes
One Sheet: $300 - $600

IRON SHERIFF, THE
(1957 - Grand) Sterling Hayden, Constance Ford
One Sheet: $7 - $15

IRON STAIR, THE
(1933 - Real Art) Dorothy Boyd, Henry Kendall
One Sheet: $150 - $300

IRON TO GOLD
(1922 - Fox) Dustin Farnum
One Sheet: $150 - $300

IRON TRAIL, THE
(1921 - Bennett) Reginald Denny, Wyndham Standing
One Sheet: $125 - $250

IRON TRIANGLE
(1989 - Scotti Brothers) Beau Bridges, Haing S. Ngor
One Sheet: $3 - $5

IRON WARRIOR
(1987 - -) Miles O'Keefe, Savina Gersak
One Sheet: $3 - $5

IRON WILL
(1994 - Buena Vista) MacKenzie Astin
One Sheet: $3 - $5

IRONWEED
(1987 - -) Jack Nicholson, Meryl Streep
One Sheet: $7 - $15

IROQUOIS TRAIL, THE
(1950 - Reliance) George Montgomery, Brenda Marshall
One Sheet: $20 - $40

IROQUOIS TRAIL, THE
(1958R - Reliance) George Montgomery, Brenda Marshall
One Sheet: $3 - $7   *Re-release. Duotone.*

IRRECONCILABLE DIFFERENCES
(1984 - Warner Bros.) Ryan O'Neal, Shelley Long
One Sheet: $3 - $5

IRRESISTIBLE LOVER, THE
(1927 - Universal-Jewel) Norman Kerry, Lois Moran
One Sheet: $250 - $600

IS DIVORCE A FAILURE?
(1923 - Beck) Leah Baird, Richard Tucker
One Sheet: $200 - $400

IS EVERYBODY HAPPY?
(1929 - Warner Bros.) Ted Lewis, Alice Day, Ann Pennington
One Sheet: $350 - $750

IS EVERYBODY HAPPY?
(1943 - Columbia) Ted Lewis & Orch.
One Sheet: $100 - $200   *Big Band musical.*

IS LOVE EVERYTHING?
(1924 - Garrson) Alma Rubens, Frank Mayo
One Sheet: $150 - $300

IS MONEY EVERYTHING?

(1923 - Bradford) Norman Kerry, Miriam Cooper
One Sheet: $125 - $250

IS MY FACE RED?
(1932 - RKO) Helen Twelvetrees, Ricardo Cortez
One Sheet: $125 - $250

IS PARIS BURNING?
(1966 - Paramount) Jean-Paul Belmondo, Charles Boyer
One Sheet: $15 - $25

IS THERE JUSTICE?
(1931 - Sono Art/World Wide) Rex Lease, Blanche Mehaffey
One Sheet: $75 - $150

IS THIS NICE?
(1926 - FBO) George O'Hara, Doris Hill
One Sheet: $150 - $300

IS YOUR DAUGHTER SAFE?
(1927 - Chadwick) Vivian Winston, Jerome Young
Or.e Sheet: $200 - $400   *Exploitation. Venereal disease.*

IS ZAT SO?
(1927 - Fox) George O'Brien, Douglas Fairbanks, Jr.
One Sheet: $250 - $600

ISABEL
(1968 - Paramount) Genevieve Bujold, Mark Strange
One Sheet: $3 - $5

ISADORA
(1968 - Universal) Vanessa Redgrave, James Fox
One Sheet: $7 - $15

ISHTAR
(1986 - Columbia) Warren Beatty, Dustin Hoffman
One Sheet: $10 - $20

ISLAND, THE
(1962 - Zenith) Nobuko Otowa
One Sheet: $15 - $25   *Japanese. AKA: NAKED ISLAND.*

ISLAND, THE
(1980 - Universal) Michael Caine, Davis Warner
One Sheet: $3 - $5

ISLAND AT THE TOP OF THE WORLD, THE
(1974 - Disney) David Hartman, Donald Sinden
One Sheet: $7 - $15

ISLAND CAPTIVES
(1937 - Falcon) Eddie Nugent, Joan Barclay
One Sheet: $75 - $150

ISLAND CLAWS
(1981 - CBS) Robert Lansing, Nita Talbot
One Sheet: $3 - $5

ISLAND IN THE SKY
(1938 - 20th Century Fox) Gloria Stuart, Michael Whalen
One Sheet: $75 - $150

ISLAND IN THE SKY
(1953 - Warner Bros.) John Wayne, Lloyd Nolan, James Arness
One Sheet: $100 - $200

ISLAND IN THE SUN
(1957 - 20th Century Fox) Harry Belafonte, Joan Fontaine, Dorothy Dandridge
One Sheet: $30 - $60   *Separate Cinema, pg. 85.*

ISLAND OF DESIRE
(1951 - Coronado) Linda Darnell, Tab Hunter
One Sheet: $15 - $35

ISLAND OF DOOMED MEN
(1940 - Columbia) Rochelle Hudson, Peter Lorre
One Sheet: $125 - $250

ISLAND OF DOOMED MEN
(1955R - Columbia) Rochelle Hudson, Peter Lorre
One Sheet: $15 - $30   *Re-release. Duotone.*

ISLAND OF DR. MOREAU, THE
(1977 - AIP) Burt Lancaster, Michael York

One Sheet: $10 - $20

ISLAND OF LOST MEN
(1939 - Paramount) Anna May Wong, J. Carroll Naish, Anthony Quinn
One Sheet: $150 - $300

ISLAND OF LOST SOULS
(1932 - Paramount) Charles Laughton, Richard Arlen, Bela Lugosi
One Sheet: $10,000 - $15,000   *Graven Images, pg. 76.*

ISLAND OF LOST WOMEN
(1959 - Warner Bros.) Jeff Richards, Venetia Stevenson
One Sheet: $15 - $35

ISLAND OF LOVE
(1963 - Warner Bros.) Robert Preston, Tony Randall
One Sheet: $7 - $15

ISLAND OF REGENERATION, THE
(1915 - Vitagraph) Edith Storey, Antonio Moreno
One Sheet: $500 - $900

ISLAND OF TERROR
(1967 - Universal) Peter Cushing, Edward Judd
One Sheet: $15 - $30

ISLAND OF THE BLUE DOLPHINS
(1964 - Universal) Celia Kaye, Larry Domasin
One Sheet: $5 - $10

ISLAND OF THE BURNING DAMNED
(1971 - Planet) Christopher Lee, Peter Cushing
One Sheet: $7 - $15

ISLAND OF THE DAMNED
(1976 - AIP) Lewis Fiander, Prunella Ransome
One Sheet: $7 - $15

ISLAND OF THE DOOMED
(1968 - Allied Artists) Cameron Mitchell, Elisa Montes
One Sheet: $5 - $12

ISLAND RESCUE
(1951 - British Films) David Niven, Glynis Johns
One Sheet: $15 - $25

ISLAND WOMEN
(1957 - United Artists) Marie Windsor, Vince Edwards
One Sheet: $15 - $25

ISLANDS IN THE STREAM
(1977 - Paramount) George C. Scott
One Sheet: $7 - $15

ISLE OF CONQUEST
(1919 - Select) Norma Talmadge, Wyndham Standing, Hedda Hopper
One Sheet: $500 - $800

ISLE OF DESTINY
(1940 - RKO) William Gargan, Wallace Ford
One Sheet: $75 - $125

ISLE OF ESCAPE
(1930 - Warner Bros.) Monte Blue, Myrna Loy
One Sheet: $150 - $350

ISLE OF FORGOTTEN WOMEN
(1927 - Columbia) Conway Tearle, Alice Calhoun
One Sheet: $500 - $800

ISLE OF FORGOTTON SINS
(1943 - PRC) John Carradine, Gale Sondergaard
One Sheet: $50 - $100

ISLE OF FURY
(1936 - Warner Bros.) Margaret Lindsay, Humphrey Bogart
One Sheet: $600 - $1,000

ISLE OF HOPE, THE
(1925 - FBO) Richard Talmadge, Helen Ferguson
One Sheet: $200 - $400

ISLE OF LOST MEN
(1928 - Rayart) Tom Santschi, Allen Connor
One Sheet: $250 - $500

ISLE OF LOST SHIPS, THE
(1923 - First National) Anna Q. Nilsson, Milton Sills
One Sheet: $250 - $600

ISLE OF LOST SHIPS
(1929 - First National) Jason Robards, Sr., Noah Beery, Sr.
One Sheet: $250 - $600

ISLE OF MISSING MEN
(1942 - Monogram) John Howard, Gilbert Roland
One Sheet: $50 - $100

ISLE OF RETRIBUTION, THE
(1926 - FBO) Robert Frazer, Lillian Rich
One Sheet: $200 - $400

ISLE OF THE DEAD
(1945 - RKO) Boris Karloff, Ellen Drew
One Sheet: $250 - $600   *Graven Images, pg. 124.*

ISLE OF THE DEAD
(1953R - RKO) Boris Karloff, Ellen Drew
One Sheet: $50 - $100   *Re-release.*

ISLE OF THE DEAD
(1957R - Realart) Boris Karloff
One Sheet: $30 - $50   *Re-release.*

ISN'T IT ROMANTIC?
(1948 - Paramount) Veronica Lake, Mona Freeman
One Sheet: $75 - $150

ISN'T LIFE TERRIBLE?
(1925 - Pathe) Charley Chase, Oliver Hardy
One Sheet: $700 - $1,200

ISN'T LIFE WONDERFUL?
(1924 - United Artists) Carol Dempster, Neil Hamilton
One Sheet: $500 - $800

ISN'T LIFE WONDERFUL?
(1954 - Stratford) Cecil Parker, Eileem Herlie
One Sheet: $10 - $20

ISOBEL
(1920 - Davis) Jane Novak, House Peters
One Sheet: $250 - $500

ISTANBUL
(1956 - Universal) Errol Flynn, Cornell Borchers
One Sheet: $50 - $100

IT
(1927 - Paramount) Clara Bow, Gary Cooper
One Sheet: $1,900 - $3,000

IT
(1966 - Warner Bros.) Roddy McDowall, Jill Haworth
One Sheet: $7 - $15

IT AIN'T EASY
(1972 - Dandelion) Lance Henriksen, Barra Grant
One Sheet: $3 - $5

IT AIN'T HAY
(1943 - Universal) Bud Abbott, Lou Costello, Eugene Pallette
One Sheet: $150 - $300

IT AIN'T NO SIN
(1934 - Paramount) Mae West
One Sheet: $1,900 - $3,000

IT ALL CAME TRUE
(1940 - Warner Bros.) Ann Sheridan, Humphrey Bogart
One Sheet: $250 - $500

One Sheet

IT ALWAYS RAINS ON SUNDAY

(1948 - Eagle-Lion) Googie Withers, Jack Warner
One Sheet: $40 - $75

IT CAME FROM BENEATH THE SEA
(1955 - Columbia) Faith Domergue, Kenneth Tobey
One Sheet: $250 - $600   *Ray Harryhausen effects. Graven Images, pg. 165.*

IT CAME FROM HOLLYWOOD
(1982 - -) Dan Aykroyd, John Candy, Gilda Radner
One Sheet: $5 - $10

IT CAME FROM OUTER SPACE
(1953 - Universal) Richard Carlson, Barbara Rush
One Sheet: $500 - $800   *Graven Images, pg. 159. 3-D.*

One Sheet

IT CAME FROM OUTER SPACE
(1972R - Universal) Richard Carlson, Barbara Rush
One Sheet: $10 - $20   *Re-release. 3-D duotone.*

IT CAME...WITHOUT WARNING
(1980 - Filmways) Jack Palance, Martin Landau
One Sheet: $5 - $10   *AKA: WITHOUT WARNING.*

IT CAN BE DONE
(1921 - Vitagraph) Earl Williams, Jack Carlisle
One Sheet: $150 - $300

IT CAN BE DONE
(1929 - Universal) Glenn Tryon, Sue Carol
One Sheet: $200 - $400

IT CAN'T LAST FOREVER
(1937 - Columbia) Betty Furness, Ralph Bellamy
One Sheet: $75 - $150

IT COMES UP LOVE
(1942 - Universal) Gloria Jean, Ian Hunter
One Sheet: $50 - $100

IT COMES UP MURDER
(1967 - United Artists) Rex Harrison, Susan Hayward
One Sheet: $7 - $15

IT CONQUERED THE WORLD
(1956 - AIP) Peter Graves, Beverly Garland, Dir: Roger Corman
One Sheet: $200 - $400   *Graven Images, pg. 177.*

One Sheet

IT COULD HAPPEN TO YOU
(1937 - Republic) Alan Baxter, Andrea Leeds
One Sheet: $50 - $100

IT COULD HAPPEN TO YOU
(1939 - 20th Century Fox) Gloria Stuart, Stuart Erwin
One Sheet: $75 - $125

IT COULD HAPPEN TO YOU
(1952 - MGM) Pete Smith
One Sheet: $100 - $200   *One-reel exercise comedy.*

IT COULDN'T HAVE HAPPENED
(1936 - Invincible) Reginald Denny, Jack LaRue
One Sheet: $75 - $125

IT FELL FROM THE SKY
(1980 - Firebird) Mike Bonavia, Buster Crabbe
One Sheet: $5 - $10   *aka: Alien Dead.*

IT GROWS ON TREES
(1952 - Universal) Irene Dunn, Dean Jagger
One Sheet: $30 - $50

IT HAD TO BE YOU
(1947 - Columbia) Ginger Rogers, Cornel Wilde
One Sheet: $75 - $125

IT HAD TO HAPPEN
(1936 - 20th Century Fox) George Raft, Rosalind Russell
One Sheet: $125 - $250

IT HAPPENED AT THE WORLD'S FAIR
(1963 - MGM) Elvis Presley, Joan O'Brien
One Sheet: $50 - $100

One Sheet

IT HAPPENED HERE
(1966 - Lopert) Pauline Murray, Sebastian Shaw
One Sheet: $3 - $5

IT HAPPENED IN ATHENS
(1962 - 20th Century Fox) Jayne Mansfield, Trax Colton
One Sheet: $20 - $40

IT HAPPENED IN BROAD DAYLIGHT
(1960 - Continental) Heinz Ruhmann, Michel Simon
One Sheet: $3 - $5   *One Sheet is Black & White.*

IT HAPPENED IN BROOKLYN
(1947 - MGM) Frank Sinatra, Jimmy Durante, Kathryn Grayson
One Sheet: $75 - $150

IT HAPPENED IN FLATBUSH
(1942 - 20th Century Fox) Lloyd Nolan, Carole Landis
One Sheet: $150 - $300   *Sports (Baseball). Sports Movie Posters #s 50, 51.*

IT HAPPENED IN HARLEM
(1945 - -) Christopher Columbus & His Swing Crew
One Sheet: $125 - $250   *Black cast.*

IT HAPPENED IN HOLLYWOOD
(1937 - Columbia) Richard Dix, Fay Wray
One Sheet: $200 - $400

IT HAPPENED IN NEW ORLEANS
(1936 - RKO) Alan Mowbray, Benita Hume
One Sheet: $75 - $150

IT HAPPENED IN NEW YORK
(1935 - Universal) Lyle Talbot, Gertrude Michael
One Sheet: $100 - $200

IT HAPPENED IN PARIS

(1935 - Associated British) John Loder, Nancy Burne
One Sheet: $100 - $200

IT HAPPENED IN ROME
(1959 - Rank) June Laverick, Vittorio De Sica
One Sheet: $7 - $15

IT HAPPENED IN SOHO
(1948 - Associated British) Richard Murdoch, Patricia Raine
One Sheet: $40 - $75

IT HAPPENED ON 5TH AVENUE
(1947 - Allied Artists) Don DeFore, Ann Harding
One Sheet: $40 - $75

IT HAPPENED ONE NIGHT
(1934 - Columbia) Claudette Colbert, Clark Gable
One Sheet: $10,000 - $15,000   *Academy Award: Best Picture, Best Actor, Best Actress, Best Direction(Frank Capra). First film to sweep the Oscars.Academy Award Movie Posters #33-#39.*

Title Card

IT HAPPENED ONE NIGHT
(1937R - Columbia) Claudette Colbert, Clark Gable
One Sheet: $1,900 - $3,000   *Re-release.*
Note: One sheet-stone litho and identical to original except for date.

IT HAPPENED ONE NIGHT
(1948R - Columbia) Claudette Colbert, Clark Gable
One Sheet: $150 - $300   *Re-release.*

IT HAPPENED ONE SUNDAY
(1944 - Pathe) Robert Beatty, Barbara White
One Sheet: $30 - $50

IT HAPPENED OUT WEST
(1937 - Principal) Paul Kelly, Judith Allen
One Sheet: $50 - $100

IT HAPPENED TO JANE
(1959 - Columbia) Doris Day, Jack Lemmon
One Sheet: $15 - $30   *AKA: TWINKLE AND SHINE.*

IT HAPPENED TO ONE MAN
(1941 - RKO) Wilfred Lawson, Nora Swinburne
One Sheet: $50 - $100

IT HAPPENED TOMORROW
(1944 - United Artists) Dick Powell, Linda Darnell
One Sheet: $75 - $150

IT HAPPENS EVERY SPRING
(1949 - 20th Century Fox) Ray Milland, Paul Douglas
One Sheet: $75 - $125   *Sports (Baseball). Sports Movie Posters #53.*

IT HAPPENS EVERY THURSDAY
(1953 - Universal) Loretta Young, John Forsythe
One Sheet: $30 - $50

IT IS THE LAW
(1924 - Fox) Arthur Hohl, Herbert Heyes
One Sheet: $150 - $300

IT LIVES AGAIN
(1978 - Warner Bros.) Frederic Forrest, Kathleen Lloyd
One Sheet: $5 - $10   *AKA: IT'S ALIVE II.*

IT MUST BE LOVE
(1926 - First National) Colleen Moore, Jean Hersholt, Malcolm McGregor

One Sheet: $600 - $1,000

IT ONLY HAPPENS TO OTHERS
(1971 - Cinerama) Marcello Mastroianni, Catherine Deneuve
One Sheet: $7 - $15

IT PAYS TO ADVERTISE
(1931 - Paramount Publix) Carole Lombard, Preston Foster
One Sheet: $600 - $1,000

IT SEEMED LIKE A GOOD IDEA AT THE TIME
(1975 - Ambassador) Anthony Newley, Isaac Hayes
One Sheet: $5 - $10

IT SHOULD HAPPEN TO YOU
(1954 - Columbia) Judy Holliday, Jack Lemmon
One Sheet: $30 - $50

IT SHOULDN'T HAPPEN TO A DOG
(1946 - 20th Century Fox) Carole Landis, Allyn Joslyn
One Sheet: $50 - $100

IT STARTED IN NAPLES
(1960 - Paramount) Clark Gable, Sophia Loren
One Sheet: $30 - $50

IT STARTED IN PARADISE
(1952 - GFD) Ian Hunter, Martita Hunt
One Sheet: $7 - $15

IT STARTED WITH A KISS
(1959 - MGM) Glenn Ford, Debbie Reynolds
One Sheet: $15 - $30

IT STARTED WITH EVE
(1941 - Universal) Charles Laughton, Deanna Durbin, Robert Cummings
One Sheet: $75 - $150

IT TAKES A THIEF
(1960 - Valiant) Jayne Mansfield, Anthony Quale
One Sheet: $20 - $40

IT TAKES ALL KINDS
(1969 - Commonwealth) Vera Miles, Robert Lansing
One Sheet: $4 - $8

IT TAKES TWO
(1995 - Warner Bros.) Kirstie Alley, Steve Guttengerg, Olsen twins
One Sheet: $3 - $5

IT! THE TERROR FROM BEYOND SPACE
(1958 - United Artists) Marshall Thompson, Shawn Smith
One Sheet: $150 - $350   *Graven Images, pg. 178.*

IT! THE TERROR FROM BEYOND SPACE/ FACELESS MAN
(1958 - United Artists) -
One Sheet: $125 - $250   *Double feature poster.*

IT WON'T RUB OFF, BABY!
(1969 - Peppercorn-Wormser) Don Murray, Dick Gregory, Diane Varsi, Robert Hooks
One Sheet: $15 - $25   *Black cast. Duotone. Separate Cinema, pg. 154.*

IT'S A BEAR
(1919 - William Fox) Mutt & Jeff
One Sheet: $800 - $1,500   *Cartoon.*

IT'S A BET
(1935 - Wardour) Helen Chandler, Gene Gerrard
One Sheet: $75 - $125

IT'S A BIG COUNTRY
(1951 - MGM) Gary Cooper, Gene Kelly
One Sheet: $50 - $100

IT'S A BIKINI WORLD
(1967 - Trans-America) Deborah Walley, Tommy Kirk, The Animals
One Sheet: $20 - $40   *Rock 'n Roll.*

IT'S A BOY
(1934 - Gaumont) Leslie Henson, Edward E. Horton
One Sheet: $75 - $125

IT'S A COP
(1934 - United Artists) Sydney Howard, Garry Marsh
One Sheet: $100 - $200

IT'S A DATE
(1940 - Universal) Deanna Durbin, Kay Francis, Harry Owens & Royal Hawaiians
One Sheet: $100 - $200

IT'S A DEAL
(1930 - Majestic) Philip Reed, Helen Vinson
One Sheet: $100 - $200

IT'S A DOG'S LIFE
(1955 - MGM) Edmund Gwenn, Jeff Richards
One Sheet: $15 - $30

IT'S A GIFT
(1923 - Pathe) Snub Pollard
One Sheet: $150 - $300

IT'S A GIFT
(1934 - Paramount) W.C. Fields, Kathleen Howard, Baby LeRoy
One Sheet: $2,200 - $3,500

IT'S A GRAND OLD WORLD
(1937 - British Lion) Sandy Powell, Gina Malo
One Sheet: $75 - $150

IT'S A GREAT DAY
(1956 - Butcher) Edward Evans, Ruth Dunning
One Sheet: $7 - $15

IT'S A GREAT FEELING
(1949 - Warner Bros.) Dennis Morgan, Doris Day
One Sheet: $30 - $50

IT'S A GREAT LIFE
(1930 - MGM) Duncan Sisters, Lawrence Gray
One Sheet: $150 - $300

IT'S A GREAT LIFE!
(1935 - Paramount) Joe Morrison, Paul Kelly
One Sheet: $100 - $200

IT'S A GREAT LIFE!
(1943 - Columbia) Arthur Lake, Penny Singleton, Hugh Herbert
One Sheet: $75 - $150

IT'S A JOKE, SON
(1947 - Pathe) Kenny Delmar, Una Merkel
One Sheet: $30 - $60

IT'S A KING
(1933 - Gaumont) Joan Maude, Sydney Howard
One Sheet: $125 - $250

IT'S A MAD MAD MAD MAD WORLD!
(1963 - United Artists) Spencer Tracy, Milton Berle, All Star Cast
One Sheet: $40 - $75   *Price is for Style A one sheet. One Sheet (Style B, Saul Bass art):$100-$200; One Sheet(Cinerama style)$150-$300.*

IT'S A MAD MAD MAD MAD WORLD!
(1970R - United Artists) Spencer Tracy, Milton Berle
One Sheet: $15 - $25   *Re-release. Jack Davis art.*

IT'S A PLEASURE!
(1945 - RKO) Sonja Henie, Michael O'Shea, Marie McDonald
One Sheet: $75 - $125

IT'S A SMALL WORLD
(1935 - Fox) Spencer Tracy, Wendy Barrie
One Sheet: $200 - $400

IT'S A SMALL WORLD
(1950 - Eagle-Lion) Paul Dale, Lorraine Miller
One Sheet: $15 - $30

IT'S A WISE CHILD
(1931 - MGM) Marion Davies, Sidney Blackmer
One Sheet: $150 - $300

IT'S A WONDERFUL DAY
(1949 - Equity) John Blythe, Jack Hodges
One Sheet: $15 - $25

IT'S A WONDERFUL LIFE
(1946 - Liberty) James Stewart, Donna Reed, Lionel Barrymore
One Sheet: $2,500 - $4,000   *Undated One Sheets are re-releases (look identical to original but missing date). Re-release onesheet:$500-$700. Graven Images, pg. 142.*

IT'S A WONDERFUL LIFE
(195?R - M & A Alexander Productions) James Stewart
One Sheet: $250 - $500   *Re-release.*

Does not have RKO logo. Lobby Cards are printed on thin stock.

IT'S A WONDERFUL LIFE
(1991R - -) James Stewart, Donna Reed, Lionel Barrymore
One Sheet: $15 - $25   *Re-release.*

IT'S A WONDERFUL WORLD
(1939 - MGM) James Stewart, Claudette Colbert
One Sheet: $250 - $600

IT'S A WONDERFUL WORLD
(1956 - Renown) Terence Morgan, George Cole
One Sheet: $10 - $20

IT'S ALIVE
(1968 - Azalea) Tommy Kirk, Shirley Bonne
One Sheet: $7 - $15

IT'S ALIVE
(1974 - Warner Bros.) John Ryan, Sharon Farrell
One Sheet: $7 - $15

IT'S ALL IN THE STARS
(1940 - 20th Century Fox) Terry-toons
One Sheet: $100 - $200   *Cartoon. Full color stone litho. Stock poster with inset title.*

IT'S ALL OVER TOWN
(1963 - Delmore) Lance Percival, The Hollies
One Sheet: $15 - $30   *Rock 'n Roll.*

IT'S ALL YOURS
(1937 - Columbia) Francis Lederer, Madeleine Carroll
One Sheet: $75 - $150

IT'S ALWAYS FAIR WEATHER
(1955 - MGM) Gene Kelly, Dan Dailey, Cyd Charisse
One Sheet: $50 - $100

IT'S GREAT TO BE ALIVE
(1933 - Fox) Raul Roulien, Gloria Stuart
One Sheet: $100 - $200

IT'S GREAT TO BE YOUNG
(1946 - Columbia) Robert Stanton, Leslie Brooks
One Sheet: $50 - $100

IT'S GREAT TO BE YOUNG
(1956 - Pathe) John Mills, Cecil Parker
One Sheet: $10 - $20

IT'S HAPPINESS THAT COUNTS
(1918 - Butcher) Harry Drummond, Queenie Thomas
One Sheet: $200 - $400

IT'S HARD TO BE GOOD
(1950 - Rank) Anne Crawford, Jimmy Hanley
One Sheet: $10 - $20

IT'S IN THE AIR
(1935 - MGM) Jack Benny, Una Merkel
One Sheet: $150 - $350

IT'S IN THE AIR
(1940 - BSB) George Formby, Polly Ward, Garry Marsh
One Sheet: $15 - $30   *AKA: George Takes the Air.*

IT'S IN THE BAG
(1936 - Warner Bros.) Teddy Knox, Jimmy Nervo
One Sheet: $100 - $200

IT'S IN THE BAG
(1943 - Butchers) Water Sisters, Reginald Purdell
One Sheet: $30 - $50

IT'S IN THE BAG
(1945 - United Artists) Fred Allen, Jack Benny, William Bendix, Sydney Toler
One Sheet: $50 - $100

IT'S IN THE BLOOD
(1938 - Warner Bros.) Lesley Brooks, Claude Halbert
One Sheet: $75 - $150

IT'S LOVE AGAIN
(1936 - Gaumont) Jessie Matthews, Robert Young
One Sheet: $500 - $800

IT'S LOVE I'M AFTER

(1937 - Warner Bros.) Leslie Howard, Bette Davis
One Sheet: $500 - $800

IT'S MY TURN
(1980 - Columbia) Jill Clayburgh, Michael Douglas
One Sheet: $3 - $5

IT'S NEVER TOO LATE
(1956 - Associated British-Pathe) Phyllis Calvert, Patrick Barr
One Sheet: $15 - $25

IT'S NEVER TOO LATE TO MEND
(1937 - MGM) Tod Slaughter, Marjorie Taylor
One Sheet: $75 - $150

IT'S NIFTY TO BE THRIFTY
(1943 - Paramount) Little Lulu
One Sheet: ` $250 - $600   *Cartoon.*
Duotone stock poster with huge image of Little Lulu. Title sheet attached.

IT'S NO LAUGHING MATTER
(1915 - Bosworth) Macklyn Arbuckle, Herbert Standing
One Sheet: $200 - $400

IT'S NOT CRICKET
(1937 - Warner Bros.) Betty Lynne, Claude Hulbert
One Sheet: $100 - $200

IT'S NOT CRICKET
(1949 - GFD) Basil Radford, Naunton Wayne
One Sheet: $15 - $30

IT'S NOT THE SIZE THAT COUNTS
(1979 - Brenner) Leigh Lawson, Elke Sommer, Vincent Price
One Sheet: $7 - $15

IT'S ONLY MONEY
(1962 - Paramount) Jerry Lewis, Zachary Scott
One Sheet: $20 - $40

IT'S THAT MAN AGAIN
(1943 - GFD) Tommy Handley, Greta Gynt
One Sheet: $20 - $40

IT'S THE OLD ARMY GAME
(1926 - Paramount) W.C. Fields, Louise Brooks
One Sheet: $1,900 - $3,000

IT'S TOUGH TO BE FAMOUS
(1932 - First National) Douglas Fairbanks Jr., Mary Brian
One Sheet: $150 - $300

IT'S YOU I WANT
(1936 - British Lion) Seymour Hicks, Jane Carr
One Sheet: $200 - $400

ITALIAN, THE
(1915 - N.Y. Motion Picture) George Beban, Clara Williams
One Sheet: $500 - $800

ITALIAN CONNECTION, THE
(1973 - AIP) Mario Adorf, Henry Silva
One Sheet: $5 - $10

ITALIAN JOB, THE
(1969 - Paramount) Michael Caine, Noel Coward, Raf Vallone
One Sheet: $7 - $15

IVANHOE
(1913 - Imperial) King Baggot, Leah Baird
One Sheet: $800 - $1,500

IVANHOE
(1952 - MGM) Robert Taylor, Elizabeth Taylor
One Sheet: $100 - $200

IVANHOE
(1962R - MGM) Robert Taylor, Elizabeth Taylor
One Sheet: $20 - $40   *Re-release.*

IVORY HUNTER
(1951 - Universal) Anthony Steele, Dinah Sheridan
One Sheet: $15 - $35

IVORY SNUFF BOX, THE
(1915 - Brady) Holbrook Blinn, Norman Trevor
One Sheet: $500 - $800

IVORY-HANDLED GUN, THE
(1935 - Universal) Buck Jones
One Sheet: $300 - $650   *Cowboy Movie Posters #'s 176, 177.*

IVORY-HANDLED GUN, THE
(1947R - Realart) Buck Jones
One Sheet: $50 - $100   *Re-release.*

IVORY-HANDLED GUN, THE
(1957R - Universal) Buck Jones
One Sheet: $20 - $40   *Re-release.*

IVY
(1947 - Universal-International) Joan Fontaine, Patric Knowles
One Sheet: $30 - $50

JABBERWALK
(1980 - ITM) Dir: Romano Vanderbes
One Sheet: $15 - $25

JABBERWOCKY
(1977 - Cinema 5) Michael Palin, Max Wall, Dir: Terry Gilliam
One Sheet: $30 - $50   *Price is for style A one sheet. One Sheet (Style B):$20-$40; One Sheet (Style C):$40-$75.*

JACARE
(1942 - United Artists) Animal Feature
One Sheet: $50 - $100

JACK
(1996 - Hollywood) Robin Williams, Diane Lane
One Sheet: $3 - $5

JACK & SARAH
(1996 - Gramercy) Richard E. Grant, Imogen Stubbs
One Sheet: $5 - $10

JACK AHOY
(1934 - Gaumont) Jack Hulbert, Nancy O'Neil
One Sheet: $75 - $150

JACK AND JILL
(1917 - Paramount) Jack Pickford, Louise Haff
One Sheet: $500 - $800

JACK AND THE BEANSTALK
(1917 - William Fox) Francis Carpenter, Virginia Lee Corbin
One Sheet: $250 - $500   *"A Modern..."*

JACK AND THE BEANSTALK
(1933 - Celebrity) Ub Iwerks
One Sheet: $700 - $1,200   *Cartoon. First Comi-color cartoon. Full color stone litho.*

JACK AND THE BEANSTALK
(1951 - Exclusive) Bud Abbott, Lou Costello
One Sheet: $50 - $100

JACK AND THE BEANSTALK
(1970 - Cinetron) Mitchell Poalos, Chris Brooks
One Sheet: $3 - $5

JACK AND THE BEANSTALK
(1976 - Columbia) -
One Sheet: $7 - $15   *Cartoon.*

JACK ARMSTRONG
(1947 - Columbia) John Hart, Rosemary La Planche
One Sheet: $100 - $200   *Serial. 15 Chapters.*

JACK FROST
(1934 - Celebrity) Animation by Ub Werks
One Sheet: $1,400 - $2,200   *Cartoon. Full color stone litho. Cartoon Movie Posters #112.*

JACK FROST
(1966 - Embassy) Natasha Sedykh, Alexander Khvylya
One Sheet: $3 - $5

JACK KNIFE MAN, THE
(1920 - King Vidor) Fred Turner, Harry Todd
One Sheet: $250 - $500

JACK LONDON
(1943 - United Artists) Michael O'Shea, Susan Hayward
One Sheet: $75 - $125

JACK MCCALL, DESPERADO
(1953 - Columbia) George Montgomery, Angela Stevens
One Sheet: $15 - $25

JACK O' CLUBS
(1924 - Universal) Herbert Rawlinson, Ruth Dwyer
One Sheet: $250 - $500

JACK O' HEARTS
(1926 - Hartford) Cullen Landis, Bert Cumming

JACK OF DIAMOND, THE
(1949 - Exclusive) Nigel Patrick, Joan Carol
One Sheet: $7 - $15

JACK OF DIAMONDS
(1967 - MGM) George Hamilton, Joseph Cotten
One Sheet: $7 - $15

JACK RIDER
(1921 - Aywon) Guinn Williams, Thelma Worth
One Sheet: $150 - $300

JACK, SAM AND PETE
(1919 - Pollock) Percy Moran, Eddie Willey
One Sheet: $250 - $500

JACK SLADE
(1953 - Monogram) Mark Stevens, Dorothy Malone
One Sheet: $15 - $25

JACK SPURLOCK, PRODICAL
(1918 - Fox) George Walsh, Dan Mason
One Sheet: $200 - $400

JACK STRAW
(1920 - Paramount) Robert Warwick, Sylvia Ashton
One Sheet: $150 - $300

JACK TAR
(1915 - Barker) Jack Tessier, Edith Yates
One Sheet: $250 - $500

JACK THE BEAR
(1993 - 20th Century Fox) Danny DeVito, Gary Sinise
One Sheet: $3 - $5

JACK THE GIANT KILLER
(1962 - United Artists) Kerwin Mathews, Judi Meredith
One Sheet: $15 - $30   *Graven Images, pg. 221.*

JACK THE RIPPER
(1960 - Paramount) Lee Patterson, Eddie Byrne
One Sheet: $15 - $35

One Sheet

JACK'S BACK
(1988 - -) James Spader, Cynthia Gibb
One Sheet: $3 - $5

JACKALS, THE
(1967 - 20th Century Fox) Vincent Price
One Sheet: $15 - $25

JACKASS MAIL
(1942 - MGM) Wallace Beery, Marjorie Main
One Sheet: $50 - $100

JACKIE ROBINSON STORY, THE
(1950 - Eagle-Lion) Jackie Robinson, Ruby Dee
One Sheet: $600 - $1,000   *Sports (Baseball). Separate Cinema, pg. 63. Sports Movie Posters #s 55, 57.*

JACKNIFE
(1989 - -) Robert DeNiro, Kathy Baker, Ed Harris
One Sheet: $5 - $10

JACKPOT, THE
(1950 - 20th Century Fox) James Stewart, Barbara Hale
One Sheet: $40 - $75

JACKPOT
(1960 - Grand National) William Hartnell, Eddie Byrne

One Sheet: $7 - $15

JACKSON COUNTY JAIL
(1976 - New World) Yvette Mimieux, Tommy Lee Jones
One Sheet: $5 - $12

JACKTOWN
(1962 - PIP) Richard Meade, Patty McCormack
One Sheet: $5 - $10

JACOB TWO-TWO MEETS THE HOODED FANG
(1977 - Cinema Shares International) Stephen Rosenberg, Alex Karras

JACOB TWO-TWO MEETS THE HOODED FANG
(1979 - Gulkin) Stephen Rosenberg, Alex Karras
One Sheet: $5 - $10

JACOB'S LADDER
(1990 - TriStar) Tim Robbins, Danny Aiello, Elizabeth Pena
One Sheet: $7 - $15

JACQUELINE
(1957 - Rank) John Gregson, Kathleen Ryan
One Sheet: $40 - $75

JACQUELINE KENNEDY'S ASIAN JOURNEY
(1962 - -) Documentary
One Sheet: $50 - $100

JACQUELINE, OR BLAZING BARRIERS
(1923 - Arrow) Marguerite Courtot, Lew Cody
One Sheet: $150 - $300

JACQUOT
(1993 - Sony Classics) Philippe Maron, Edouard Joubeaud
One Sheet: $3 - $5   *French.*

JADE
(1995 - Paramount) David Caruso, Linda Fiorentino
One Sheet: $5 - $10

JADE BOX, THE
(1930 - Universal) Jack Perrin, Louise Morraine
One Sheet: $150 - $350   *Serial. 10 Chapters.*

JADE MASK, THE
(1944 - Monogram) Sidney Toler, Mantan Moreland
One Sheet: $100 - $200   *Charlie Chan series.*

JAGGED EDGE
(1985 - Columbia) Jeff Bridges, Glenn Close
One Sheet: $5 - $10

JAGUAR
(1955 - Republic) Sabu, Mike Connors
One Sheet: $20 - $40

JAGUAR
(1980 - Atienza) Phillip Salvador, Amy Austria
One Sheet: $3 - $6

JAGUAR LIVES
(1979 - AIP) Christopher Lee, Donald Pleasense
One Sheet: $5 - $10

JAIL BAIT
(1954 - Howco) Dolores Fuller, Lyle Talbot, Dir:Ed Wood, Jr.
One Sheet: $75 - $125

JAIL BIRD, THE
(1921 - Pathe) Snub Pollard
One Sheet: $250 - $600

JAIL BUSTERS
(1955 - Allied Artists) Leo Gorcey, Huntz Hall
One Sheet: $30 - $60

JAIL HOUSE BLUES
(1941 - Universal) Robert Paige, Ann Gwynne
One Sheet: $75 - $150

JAILBIRD, THE
(1920 - Paramount) Douglas MacLean, Doris May
One Sheet: $150 - $300

JAILBIRDS
(1939 - Butchers) Albert Burdon, Charles Hawtrey
One Sheet: $100 - $200

JAILBREAK

(1936 - Warner Bros.) Barton MacLane, June Travis
One Sheet: $75 - $150

JAILBREAKERS, THE
(1960 - AIP) Robert Hutton, Mary Castle
One Sheet: $7 - $15

JAILHOUSE ROCK
(1957 - MGM) Elvis Presley, Judy Tyler
One Sheet: $700 - $1,200

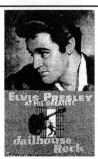
One Sheet

JAKE SPEED
(1986 - Balcor) Wayne Crawford, Dennis Christopher, Karen Kopins
One Sheet: $3 - $5

JAKE THE PLUMMER
(1927 - FBO) Sharon Lynn, Rosa Rosanova, Jess Devorska
One Sheet: $150 - $350

JALINA
(1935 - RKO) Peggy Wood, Ian Hunter
One Sheet: $75 - $150

JALOPY
(1953 - Monogram) Bowery Boys
One Sheet: $40 - $75   *Sports (Auto racing).*

JAM SESSION
(1944 - Columbia) Ann Miller, Jess Barker, Louis Armstrong
One Sheet: $75 - $150   *Jazz musical.*

JAMAICA INN
(1939 - Paramount) Charles Laughton, Robert Newton, Dir: Alfred Hitchcock
One Sheet: $1,900 - $3,000

28 x 39 (Swedish)

JAMAICA INN
(195?R - Paramount) Charles Laughton, Robert Newton, Dir: Alfred Hitchcock
One Sheet: $75 - $150   *Re-release.*

JAMAICA RUN
(1953 - Paramount) Ray Milland, Arlene Dahl, Wendell Corey
One Sheet: $15 - $35

JAMBOREE
(1944 - Republic) George Byron, Ruth Terry, Ernest Tubb
One Sheet: $100 - $200   *Country musical.*

JAMBOREE
(1957 - Warner Bros.) Kay Medford, Paul Carr, All Star Rock Cast
One Sheet: $150 - $300   *Rock and roll.*

JAMES AND THE GIANT PEACH
(1996 - Walt Disney Pictures) Voices of Paul

Terry, Miriam Margolyes
One Sheet: $10 - $20   *Children's Stop-Motion Animation. Advance Style, please note: Advance Style is a beautifulimage of all the characters: $25-$35.*

JAMES BOND 25TH ANNIVERSARY
(1993 - -) -
One Sheet: $10 - $20

JAMES BROTHERS OF MISSOURI, THE
(1949 - Republic) Keith Richards, Robert Bice
One Sheet: $40 - $75   *Serial. Western. 12 Chapters.*

JAMES DEAN: THE FIRST AMERICAN TEENAGER
(1976 - -) James Dean (Documentary)
One Sheet: $40 - $75

JAMES DEAN STORY, THE
(1957 - Warner Bros.) Documentary
One Sheet: $150 - $300

JAMESTOWN
(1923 - Pathe) Robert Gaillard, Harry Kendall
One Sheet: $200 - $400

JAMIE'S TREASURE HUNT
(1975R - Paramount) Kirk Douglas, Mark Lester, Leslie Anne Down
One Sheet: $3 - $5   *Re-titled re-release of SCALAWAG (1973).*

JAMMIN' THE BLUES
(1944 - -) -
One Sheet: $150 - $300

JANE AUSTIN IN MANHATTAN
(1980 - Contemporary) Anne Baxter, Robert Powell, Sean Young
One Sheet: $4 - $8

JANE EYRE
(1921 - Hodkinson) Norman Trevor, Mabel Ballin
One Sheet: $250 - $600

JANE EYRE
(1934 - Monogram) Virginia Bruce, Colin Clive
One Sheet: $150 - $300

JANE EYRE
(1944 - 20th Century Fox) Orson Welles, Joan Fontaine, Elizabeth Taylor
One Sheet: $350 - $750

JANE EYRE
(1971 - British Lion) George C. Scott, Susannah York
One Sheet: $7 - $15

JANE EYRE
(1996 - Miramax) Anna Paquin, William Hurt
One Sheet: $5 - $12

JANE STEPS OUT
(1938 - Associated British) -
One Sheet: $50 - $100

JANE'S TROUBLES
(1926 - Stern Bros.) -
One Sheet: $125 - $250

JANICE MEREDITH
(1924 - Metro-Goldwyn) W.C. Fields, Marion Davies, Harrison Ford
One Sheet: $1,900 - $3,000

JANIE
(1944 - Warner Bros.) Joyce Reynolds, Robert Hutton, Edward Arnold
One Sheet: $40 - $75

JANIE GETS MARRIED
(1946 - Warner Bros.) Joan Leslie, Robert Hutton
One Sheet: $30 - $50

JANUARY MAN, THE
(1989 - -) Kevin Kline, Mary Elizabeth Mastrantonio
One Sheet: $3 - $5

JAPANESE WAR BRIDE
(1951 - 20th Century Fox) Shirley Yamaguchi, Don Taylor
One Sheet: $15 - $25

JASON AND THE ARGONAUTS
(1963 - Columbia) Todd Armstrong, Nancy Kovack
One Sheet: $75 - $150   *Ray Harryhausen effects. Graven Images, pg. 221.*

JASON AND THE ARGONAUTS
(1978R - Columbia) Todd Armstrong, Nancy Kovack
One Sheet: $15 - $25   *Re-release.*

JASPER IN A JAM
(1946 - Paramount) George Pal Puppet
One Sheet: $250 - $500   *Cartoon. Cartoon Movie Posters #229.*

JASSY
(1947 - Universal) Margaret Lockwood, Basil Sydney
One Sheet: $30 - $50

JAVA HEAD
(1923 - Famous Players) Leatrice Joy, Jacqueline Logan
One Sheet: $150 - $300

JAVA HEAD
(1934 - First National-Warner Bros.) Anna May Wong, Edmund Gwenn
One Sheet: $150 - $350

JAWS
(1975 - Universal) Roy Scheider, Richard Dreyfuss
One Sheet: $40 - $75

One Sheet

JAWS 3-D
(1983 - Universal) Dennis Quaid, Bess Armstrong
One Sheet: $5 - $10

JAWS II
(1978 - Universal) Roy Scheider, Lorraine Gray
One Sheet: $7 - $15   *Advance:$15-25.*

JAWS II
(1980R - Universal) RoyScheider, Lorraine Gray
One Sheet: $5 - $10   *Re-release.*

JAWS OF HELL
(1931 - Sono Art/World Wide) -
One Sheet: $100 - $200

JAWS OF JUSTICE
(1933 - Principal) Ruth Sullivan, Kazan (The Dog)
One Sheet: $100 - $200

JAWS OF SATAN
(1980 - United Artists) Fritz Weaver, Christine Applegate
One Sheet: $7 - $15

JAWS OF STEEL
(1927 - Warner Bros.) Rin Tin-Tin, Jason Robards
One Sheet: $200 - $400

JAWS OF THE DRAGON
(1976 - World Wide) James Nam
One Sheet: $5 - $10   *Poster is black & white.*

JAWS OF THE JUNGLE
(1936 - Jay Dee Kay) Teeto, Minta
One Sheet: $75 - $150

JAWS THE REVENGE
(1987 - -) Lorraine Gary, Lance Guest
One Sheet: $5 - $10

JAYHAWKERS
(1959 - Paramount) Jeff Chandler, Fess Parker
One Sheet: $7 - $15

JAZZ AGE, THE
(1929 - RKO) Douglas Fairbanks, Jr.,

Marceline Day
One Sheet: $700 - $1,200

JAZZ AND JAILBIRDS
(1919 - Vitagraph) James Aubrey
One Sheet: $200 - $400

JAZZ BABIES
(1932 - Peerless) Madge Evans, Elizabeth Patterson
One Sheet: $250 - $500

JAZZ BALL
(1952 - -) -
One Sheet: $40 - $75

JAZZ BOAT
(1960 - Columbia) Anthony Newley, Anne Aubrey
One Sheet: $15 - $25

JAZZ CINDERELLA
(1930 - Chesterfield) Myrna Loy, Jason Robards, Sr.
One Sheet: $150 - $300

JAZZ GIRL
(1926 - Motion Picture Guild) Gaston Glass, Edith Roberts
One Sheet: $250 - $600

JAZZ HEAVEN
(1929 - RKO) John Mack Brow, Clyde Cook
One Sheet: $500 - $800

JAZZ MAD
(1928 - Universal Jewel) Jean Hersholt, Marion Nixson
One Sheet: $500 - $800

JAZZ ON A SUMMER'S DAY
(1959 - Newport Jazz Festival) Louis Armstrong, Chuck Berry, All-Star Jazz cast
One Sheet: $40 - $75   *Jazz musical.*

JAZZ SINGER, THE
(1927 - Warner Bros.) Al Jolson, May McAvoy, Warner Oland
One Sheet: $10,000 - $15,000   *First sound (2 segments) film. Special Academy Award. Separate Cinema, pg. 106.*

JAZZ SINGER, THE
(1952 - Warner Bros.) Danny Thomas, Peggy Lee
One Sheet: $20 - $40

JAZZ SINGER, THE
(1980 - Associated) Neil Diamond, Laurence Olivier
One Sheet: $7 - $15

JAZZ SOUND, THE
(1931 - -) -
One Sheet: $150 - $300

JAZZLAND
(1928 - Quality) Bryant Washburn, Vera Reynolds
One Sheet: $250 - $500

JAZZMANIA
(1923 - Metro) Mae Murray, Rod La Rocque
One Sheet: $700 - $1,200

J.D.'S REVENGE
(1976 - AIP) Glynn Turman, Lou Gossett Jr.
One Sheet: $15 - $30   *Blaxploitation horror film.*

JEALOUS HUSBANDS
(1923 - Associated First) Jane Novak, Earle Williams
One Sheet: $125 - $250

JEALOUSY
(1916 - Fox) Valeska Suratt
One Sheet: $600 - $1,000

JEALOUSY
(1929 - Paramount) Fredric March, Jeanne Eagels
One Sheet: $250 - $600

JEALOUSY
(1931 - Majestic) Mary Newland, Malcolm Keen
One Sheet: $125 - $250

JEALOUSY
(1934 - Columbia) Nancy Carroll, Donald Cook
One Sheet: $100 - $200

JEALOUSY
(1945 - Republic) John Loder, Nils Asther,

Jane Randolph
One Sheet: $30 - $60

JEANNE EAGLES
(1957 - Columbia) Kim Novak, Jeff Chandler
One Sheet: $30 - $50

JEDDA THE UNCIVILIZED
(1956 - DCA) Narla Kunough, Robert Tudewali
One Sheet: $10 - $20

JEEPERS CREEPERS
(1939 - Republic) Weaver Brothers & Elviry,
Roy Rogers
One Sheet: $125 - $250

JEEPERS CREEPERS
(1950R - Republic) Roy Rogers
One Sheet: $30 - $60   *Re-release.*

JEFFERSON IN PARIS
(1995 - Disney) Nick Nolte, Gwyneth Paltrow,
Greta Scacchi
One Sheet: $5 - $10

JEFFREY
(1995 - Orion) Steven Weber, Patrick Stewart
One Sheet: $5 - $10

JEKYLL & HYDE, TOGETHER AGAIN
(1982 - Paramount) Mark Blankfield, Bess
Armstrong
One Sheet: $5 - $10

JEKYLL'S INFERNO
(1961 - AIP) Christopher Lee, Paul Massie
One Sheet: $20 - $40   *AKA: House
Of Fright.*

JENIFER HALE
(1937 - Fox) Rene Ray, John Longden
One Sheet: $100 - $200

JENNIE
(1940 - 20th Century Fox) Virginia Gilmore,
William Henry
One Sheet: $50 - $100

JENNIE GERHARDT
(1933 - Paramount) Sylvia Sidney, Mary Astor,
Donald Cook
One Sheet: $350 - $750

JENNIFER
(1953 - Monogram) Ida Lupino, Howard Duff
One Sheet: $15 - $30

JENNIFER
(1978 - AIP) Lisa Pelikan, Bert Convy
One Sheet: $5 - $10

JENNIFER EIGHT
(1992 - Paramount) Andy Garcia, Uma
Thurman
One Sheet: $5 - $10

JENNIFER ON MY MIND
(1971 - United Artists) Michael Brandon, Tippy
Walker
One Sheet: $3 - $5

JENNY
(1970 - Cinerama) Marlo Thomas, Alan Alda
One Sheet: $2 - $3

JENNY BE GOOD
(1920 - Realart) Jay Belasco, Mary Miles
Minter
One Sheet: $125 - $250

JEOPARDY
(1952 - MGM) Barbara Stanwyck, Barry
Sullivan
One Sheet: $30 - $50

JEREMIAH JOHNSON
(1972 - Warner Bros.) Robert Redford, Will
Geer
One Sheet: $10 - $20   *Price applies
to all three styles.*

JEREMY
(1973 - United Artists) Robby Benson, Glynnis
O'Connor
One Sheet: $3 - $5

JERK, THE
(1979 - Universal) Steve Martin, Bernadette
Peters, Jackie Mason
One Sheet: $10 - $20

JERKY BOYS, THE
(1995 - Touchstone) Johnny Brennan, Kamal,
Alan Arkin

One Sheet: $4 - $8

JERKY TURKEY
(1945 - MGM) Tex Avery
One Sheet: $250 - $600   *Cartoon.
Cartoon Movie Posters #296.*

JERRY AND JUMBO
(1953 - MGM) Tom & Jerry
One Sheet: $200 - $400   *Cartoon. Full
color stone litho.*

JERRY AND THE GOLDFISH
(1951 - MGM) Tom & Jerry
One Sheet: $200 - $400   *Cartoon. Full
color stone litho.*

JERRY AND THE LION
(1950 - MGM) Tom & Jerry
One Sheet: $200 - $400   *Cartoon. Full
color stone litho.*

JERRY MAGUIRE
(1996 - TriStar) Tom Cruise, Cuba Gooding Jr.
One Sheet: $5 - $10

JERRY ON THE RAILROAD
(1918 - Mutual) George Ovey
One Sheet: $250 - $500

JERRY'S COUSIN
(1951 - MGM) Tom & Jerry
One Sheet: $200 - $400   *Cartoon. Full
color stone litho.*

JERRY'S DIARY
(1948 - MGM) Tom & Jerry
One Sheet: $250 - $500   *Cartoon. Full
color stone litho.*

JERUSALEM FILE, THE
(1972 - MGM) Bruce Davison, Nicol Williamson
One Sheet: $3 - $5

JES CALL ME JIM
(1920 - Goldwyn) Will Rogers
One Sheet: $600 - $1,000

JESSE JAMES
(1927 - Paramount) Fred Thompson, Nora Lane
One Sheet: $200 - $400

JESSE JAMES
(1939 - 20th Century Fox) Tyrone Power,
Henry Fonda
One Sheet: $1,900 - $3,000   *Cowboy
Movie Posters #251.*

JESSE JAMES
(1945R - 20th Century Fox) Tyrone Power,
Henry Fonda
One Sheet: $250 - $500   *Re-release.*

JESSE JAMES AS THE OUTLAW
(1921 - Mesco) Jesse James, Jr., Diana Reed
One Sheet: $250 - $600

JESSE JAMES AT BAY
(1941 - Republic) Roy Rogers, Gabby Hayes
One Sheet: $200 - $400

JESSE JAMES AT BAY
(1955R - Republic) Roy Rogers, Gabby Hayes
One Sheet: $50 - $100   *Re-release.*

JESSE JAMES, JR.
(1942 - Republic) Don "Red" Barry
One Sheet: $75 - $150

**JESSE JAMES MEETS FRANKENSTEIN'S
DAUGHTER**
(1966 - Embassy) John Lupton, Estelita
One Sheet: $30 - $50

JESSE JAMES RIDES AGAIN
(1947 - Republic) Clayton Moore, Linda
Sterling
One Sheet: $75 - $125   *Serial.
Western. 13 Chapters.*

JESSE JAMES RIDES AGAIN
(1955R - Republic) Clayton Moore, Linda
Stirling
One Sheet: $15 - $25   *Re-release.
Serial.*

JESSE JAMES UNDER THE FLAG
(1921 - Mesco) Jesse James, Jr., Franklin B.
Coates
One Sheet: $250 - $500

JESSE JAMES VS. THE DALTONS
(1953 - Columbia) Brett King, Barbara
Lawrence

One Sheet: $15 - $25

JESSE JAMES' WOMEN
(1954 - United Artists) Peggie Castle, Don
Barry
One Sheet: $15 - $30   *Cowboy
Movie Posters #299.*

JESSICA
(1962 - United Artists) Maurice Chevalier,
Angie Dickenson
One Sheet: $5 - $10

JESSIE'S GIRLS
(1976 - Manson) Sondra Currie, Regina Carrol,
Geoffrey Land
One Sheet: $5 - $10

JESUS
(1979 - Warner Bros.) Brian Deacon, Rivka
Norman
One Sheet: $5 - $10

JESUS CHRIST SUPERSTAR
(1973 - Universal) Ted Neeley, Carl Anderson
One Sheet: $15 - $25   *Rock musical.*

JESUS OF MONTREAL
(1989 - Max) Lothaire Bluteau, Catherine
Wilkening
One Sheet: $7 - $15

JESUS THE MAN YOU THOUGHT YOU KNEW
(1979 - Warner Bros.) -
One Sheet: $3 - $5

JESUS TRIP, THE
(1971 - Emco) Elisabeth Walker, Robert Porter
One Sheet: $5 - $10

JET ATTACK
(1958 - AIP) John Agar, Audrey Totter
One Sheet: $7 - $15

JET JOB
(1952 - Monogram) Stanley Clements, Elena
Verdugo
One Sheet: $15 - $25

JET OVER THE ATLANTIC
(1960 - Inter-Continent) Guy Madison, Virginia
Mayo
One Sheet: $3 - $5

JET PILOT
(1957 - Universal International) John Wayne,
Janet Leigh
One Sheet: $75 - $150

JET STORM
(1961 - British Lion) Richard Attenborough, Mai
Zetterling
One Sheet: $5 - $12

JETLAG
(1981 - Figaro) Jeanine Mestre, Norman Brisky
One Sheet: $3 - $6

JETSONS: THE MOVIE
(1990 - Universal) -
One Sheet: $5 - $10   *Cartoon. TV
tie-in.*

JETSTREAM
(1959 - Britannia) Richard Attenborough,
Stanley Baker
One Sheet: $7 - $15

JEWEL, THE
(1933 - Paramount) Hugh Williams, Jack
Hawkins
One Sheet: $150 - $300

JEWEL OF THE NILE
(1985 - 20th Century Fox) Michael Douglas,
Kathleen Turner
One Sheet: $5 - $10

JEWEL ROBBERY
(1932 - Warner Bros.) William Powell, Kay
Francis
One Sheet: $200 - $400

JEWELS OF BRANDENBURG
(1947 - 20th Century Fox) Richard Travis,
Micheline Cheirel
One Sheet: $30 - $50

JEWELS OF DESIRE
(1927 - Metropolitan) John Bowers, Pricilla
Dean
One Sheet: $200 - $400

JEZEBEL

(1938 - Warner Bros.) Bette Davis, Henry
Fonda, Dir: William Wyler
One Sheet: $5,000 - $8,000   *Academy
Award: Best Actress (her 2nd Oscar). Academy
Award Movie Posters #58 & #61.*

One Sheet

JEZEBEL
(1948R - Warner Bros.) Bette Davis, Henry
Fonda, Dir: William Wyler
One Sheet: $100 - $200   *Re-release.*

JFK
(1991 - Warner Bros.) Kevin Costner, Sissy
Spacek, Joe Pesci
One Sheet: $10 - $20

JIG SAW
(1979 - -) Angie Dickinson, Lino Ventura
One Sheet: $5 - $12

JIGGS AND MAGGIE IN COURT
(1948 - Monogram) Joe Yule, Renie Riano
One Sheet: $30 - $50

JIGGS AND MAGGIE IN JACKPOT JITTERS
(1949 - Monogram) Renie Riano, Joe Yule
One Sheet: $20 - $40

JIGGS AND MAGGIE IN SOCIETY
(1947 - Monogram) Joe Yule, Renie Riano
One Sheet: $20 - $40

JIGGS AND MAGGIE OUT WEST
(1950 - Monogram) Joe Yule, Renie Riano
One Sheet: $20 - $40

JIGGS IN SOCIETY
(1920 - Pathe) Johnny Ray
One Sheet: $200 - $400   *From the
Bringing Up Father Series.*

JIGSAW
(1949 - United Artists) Franchot Tone, Jean
Wallace
One Sheet: $15 - $30

JIGSAW
(1965 - Beverly) Jack Warner, Ronald Lewis
One Sheet: $5 - $12

JILT, THE
(1922 - Universal) Marguerite De la Motte,
Ralph Graves
One Sheet: $150 - $300

JIM GRIMBY'S BOY
(1916 - Triangle) Frank Keenan, Enid Markey
One Sheet: $125 - $250

JIM HARVEY, DETECTIVE
(1937 - Republic) Guy Kibbee, Tom Brown
One Sheet: $75 - $125

JIM THE CONQUEROR
(1927 - Metropolitan) William Boyd, Elinor Fair
One Sheet: $200 - $400

JIM THE PENMAN
(1921 - Bennett) Lionel Barrymore, Doris
Rankin
One Sheet: $250 - $500

JIM, THE WORLD'S GREATEST
(1976 - Universal) Gregory Harrison, Robbie
Wolcott
One Sheet: $3 - $5

JIM THORPE-ALL AMERICAN
(1951 - Warner Bros.) Burt Lancaster, Charles
Bickford
One Sheet: $75 - $150   *Sports
(Olympics, track, football). Sports Movie Posters
#286.*

JIMI PLAYS MONTEREY
(1980 - Pennebaker) Jimi Hendrix
One Sheet: $250 - $500   *Rock 'n' Roll.*

JIMMIE'S MILLIONS
(1925 - Truart) Richard Talmadge, Betty
Francisco
One Sheet: $150 - $300

JIMMY
(1916 - Gaumont) John Astley, George Tully
One Sheet: $250 - $500

JIMMY AND SALLY
(1933 - Fox) James Dunn, Claire Trevor
One Sheet: $125 - $250

JIMMY BOY
(1935 - Universal) Jimmy O'Dea, Gay
Middleton
One Sheet: $150 - $300

JIMMY HOLLYWOOD
(1994 - Paramount) Joe Pesci, Christian Slater
One Sheet: $5 - $10

JIMMY STEPS OUT
(1948 - Astor) James Stewart, Paulette
Goddard
One Sheet: $15 - $30   *Re-titled re-
release of "Pot O' Gold" (1941).*

One Sheet

JIMMY THE GENT
(1934 - Warner Bros.) James Cagney, Bette
Davis
One Sheet: $2,800 - $4,500   *Lobby Card
with both Cagney and Davis shown is the most
desirable card (100% over other lobby cards).*

JIMMY THE KID
(1982 - New World) Gary Coleman, Paul LeMat
One Sheet: $3 - $5

JINGLE ALL THE WAY
(1996 - Fox) Arnold Schwarzenegger, Sinbad
One Sheet: $7 - $15

JINX MONEY
(1948 - Monogram) Bowery Boys, Sheldon
Leonard
One Sheet: $40 - $75

JINXED!
(1982 - MGM) Bette Midler, Ken Wahl
One Sheet: $5 - $12

JITNEY ELOPEMENT, A
(1915 - Essanay) Charlie Chaplin, Edna
Purviance
One Sheet: $5,500 - $9,000

JITTERBUGS
(1943 - 20th Century Fox) Stan Laurel, Oliver
Hardy, Vivian Blaine
One Sheet: $500 - $800

Title Card

JIVARO
(1954 - Paramount) Fernando Lomas, Rhonda
Fleming
One Sheet: $15 - $30   *3-D.*

JIVE JUNCTION
(1943 - PRC) Dickie Moore, Tina Thayer
One Sheet: $40 - $75

JIVIN' IN THE BE-BOP
(1946 - Alexander) Dizzie Gilespie, The Hubba
Hubba Girls
One Sheet: $250 - $500   *Black cast.
Separate Cinema, pg. 96.*

JO, THE CROSSING SWEEPER
(1918 - Barker) Unity Moore, Rolf Leslie
One Sheet: $200 - $400

JOAN AT THE STAKE
(1954 - London) Ingrid Bergman, Tullio
Carminati
One Sheet: $40 - $75   *French/Italian.*

JOAN LOWELL, ADVENTURE GIRL
(1934 - Van Buren)
One Sheet: $100 - $200

JOAN OF ARC
(1948 - RKO) Ingrid Bergman, Dir: Walter
Wanger
One Sheet: $100 - $200   *One Sheet(on
horse):$300-400.*

JOAN OF OZARK
(1942 - RKO) Judy Canova, Joe E. Brown
One Sheet: $50 - $100

JOAN OF PARIS
(1942 - RKO) Michele Morgan, Paul Henreid
One Sheet: $50 - $100

JOAN OF PLATTSBURG
(1918 - Goldwyn) Mabel Normand, Robert
Elliott
One Sheet: $250 - $600

JOAN OF THE WOODS
(1918 - World) Walter P. Lewis, June Elvidge
One Sheet: $200 - $400

JOAN THE WOMAN
(1916 - Cardinal) Geraldine Farrar, Raymond
Hatton, Dir: Cecil B. DeMille
One Sheet: $1,300 - $2,000

JOANNA
(1925 - First National) Jack Mulhall, Dorothy
Mackaill
One Sheet: $150 - $300

JOANNA
(1968 - 20th Century Fox) Genevieve Waite,
Calvin Lockhart, Christian Doermer
One Sheet: $2 - $3

JOCKS
(1987 - -) Scott Strader, Perry Lang
One Sheet: $3 - $5

JOE
(1970 - Cannon) Peter Boyle, Susan Sarandon,
Dennis Patrick
One Sheet: $3 - $5

**JOE AND ETHEL TURP CALL ON THE
PRESIDENT**
(1939 - MGM) William Gargan, Ann Sothern
One Sheet: $75 - $150

JOE BUTTERFLY
(1957 - Universal) Audie Murphy, George
Nader
One Sheet: $30 - $60

Half Sheet

JOE DAKOTA
(1957 - Universal) Jock Mahoney, Luana
Patten
One Sheet: $15 - $25

JOE HILL
(1971 - Paramount) Thommy Berggren, Ania
Schmidt
One Sheet: $2 - $3

JOE KIDD
(1972 - Universal) Clint Eastwood, Robert
Duvall, John Saxton
One Sheet: $40 - $75

**JOE LOUIS AND MAX SCHMELING WORLD
CHAMPIONSHIP**
(1936 - Official Motion Pictures) Joe Louis, Max
Schmeling
One Sheet: $250 - $600   *Red and white
duotone.*

JOE LOUIS AND PRIMO CARNERA
(1935 - -) Heavyweight Boxing Match
One Sheet: $300 - $700

JOE LOUIS STORY, THE
(1953 - United Artists) Coley Wallace, Paul
Stewart
One Sheet: $150 - $350   *Black cast.
Sports (Boxing). Separate Cinema, pg. 61. Sports
Movie Posters #151.*

JOE LOUIS VS. BILLY CONN
(1946 - Fight Pictures) Joe Louis, Billy Conn
One Sheet: $800 - $1,500

JOE MACBETH
(1955 - Columbia) Paul Douglas, Ruth Roman
One Sheet: $10 - $20

JOE PALOOKA, CHAMP
(1946 - Monogram) Joe Kirkwood, Elyse Knox,
Joe Louis
One Sheet: $75 - $150   *Sports
(Boxing). Sports Movie Posters #145.*

Half Sheet (Style A)

JOE PALOOKA IN FIGHTING MAD
(1948 - Monogram) Leon Errol, Joe Kirkwood
One Sheet: $50 - $100   *Sports
(Boxing).*

JOE PALOOKA IN THE BIG FIGHT
(1948 - Monogram) Leon Errol, Joe Kirkwood
One Sheet: $50 - $100   *Sports
(Boxing).*

JOE PALOOKA IN THE COUNTERPUNCH
(1949 - Monogram) Joe Kirkwood, Leon Errol
One Sheet: $50 - $100   *Sports
(Boxing).*

JOE PALOOKA IN THE KNOCKOUT
(1947 - Monogram) Leon Errol, Joe Kirkwood
One Sheet: $50 - $100   *Sports
(Boxing).*

JOE PALOOKA IN THE SQUARED CIRCLE
(1950 - Monogram) Joe Kirkwood, Myrna Dell
One Sheet: $50 - $100   *Sports
(Boxing).*

JOE PALOOKA IN THE TRIPLE CROSS
(1951 - Monogram) Joe Kirkwood, Leon Errol
One Sheet: $50 - $100   *Sports
(Boxing).*

JOE PALOOKA IN WINNER TAKE ALL
(1948 - Monarch) Joe Kirkwood Jr., Elyse Knox
One Sheet: $50 - $100   *Sports
(Boxing).*

JOE PALOOKA MEETS HUMPHREY

JOE PALOOKA
(1950 - Monogram) Joe Kirkwood, Leon Errol
One Sheet: $50 - $100   *Sports
(Boxing).*

JOE PANTHER
(1976 - Artists Creation) Brian Keith, Ricardo
Montalban
One Sheet: $5 - $10

JOE SMITH, AMERICAN
(1942 - MGM) Robert Young, Marsha Hunt
One Sheet: $75 - $125

JOE VERSUS THE VOLCANO
(1990 - -) Tom Hanks, Meg Ryan, Lloyd
Bridges
One Sheet: $7 - $15

JOE'S APARTMENT
(1996 - Warner Bros.) Jerry O'Connell, Mega
Ward
One Sheet: $4 - $8

JOEY BOY
(1965 - British Lion) Harry H. Corbett, Bill
Fraser
One Sheet: $5 - $10

JOEY BREAKER
(1993 - Skourus) Richard Edson, Cedella
Marley (Debut)
One Sheet: $3 - $5

JOHANN MOUSE
(1953 - MGM) Tom & Jerry
One Sheet: $300 - $700   *Cartoon.
Academy Award: Best Cartoon Short. Full color
stone litho.*

JOHANNA ENLISTS
(1918 - Artcraft) Mary Pickford
One Sheet: $800 - $1,500

JOHN AND JULIE
(1957 - Group 3) Lesley Dudley, Peter Sellers
One Sheet: $10 - $20

JOHN AND MARY
(1969 - 20th Century Fox) Dustin Hoffman, Mia
Farrow
One Sheet: $10 - $20

JOHN BARLEYCORN
(1914 - Bosworth) Matty Roubert, Antrim Short,
Viola Barry
One Sheet: $250 - $500

JOHN GLAYDE'S HONOR
(1915 - Frohman) Mary Lawton, C. Aubrey
Smith
One Sheet: $250 - $500

JOHN GOLDFARB, PLEASE COME HOME
(1965 - 20th Century Fox) Shirley MacLaine,
Peter Ustinov
One Sheet: $15 - $30

JOHN HALIFAX, GENTLEMAN
(1938 - MGM) John Warwick, Nancy Burne,
Roddy McDowall
One Sheet: $150 - $350

JOHN HERIOT'S WIFE
(1920 - Anglo) Henry Victor, Mary Odette
One Sheet: $150 - $300

JOHN LOVES MARY
(1949 - Warner Bros.) Ronald Reagan, Jack
Carson, Wayne Morris
One Sheet: $75 - $150

JOHN MEADE'S WOMAN
(1937 - Paramount) Edward Arnold, Francine
Larrimore, Gail Patrick
One Sheet: $75 - $125

JOHN NEEDHAM'S DOUBLE
(1916 - Blue) Tyrone Power Sr., Marie
Walcamp
One Sheet: $200 - $400

**JOHN NESBITT'S PASSING PARADE "THE
GOLDEN HUNCH"**
(1945 - MGM) -
One Sheet: $150 - $300

**JOHN NESBITT'S PASSING PARADE
"STAIRWAY TO LIGHT"**
(1945 - MGM) -
One Sheet: $150 - $300

**JOHN NESBITT'S PASSING PARADE "OUR OLD
CAR"**
(1946 - MGM) -

One Sheet: $150 - $300

JOHN NESBITT'S PASSING PARADE "MAGIC ON A STICK"
(1946 - MGM) -
One Sheet: $150 - $300

JOHN OF THE FAIR
(1962 - Continental) Arthur Young, John Charles World
One Sheet: $5 - $10

JOHN PAUL JONES
(1959 - Warner Bros.) Robert Stack, Bette Davis
One Sheet: $20 - $40

JOHN SMITH
(1922 - Select) Eugene O'Brien, Viva Ogden
One Sheet: $150 - $300

JOHN, THE DRUNKARD
(1944 - PRC) -
One Sheet: $50 - $100

JOHN WESLEY
(1954 - Radio & Film) Leonard Sachs, Neil Hayes
One Sheet: $15 - $25

JOHNNY ALLEGRO
(1949 - Columbia) George Raft, Nina Foch
One Sheet: $75 - $150   *Sports (Boxing).*

One Sheet

JOHNNY ANGEL
(1945 - RKO) George Raft, Claire Trevor
One Sheet: $50 - $100

JOHNNY APOLLO
(1940 - 20th Century Fox) Tyrone Power, Dorothy Lamour
One Sheet: $250 - $600

One Sheet

JOHNNY APPLESEED
(1966R - Disney) Dennis Day (voice)
One Sheet: $20 - $40   *Re-release.*

JOHNNY BE GOOD
(1988 - -) Anthony Michael Hall, Robert Downey, Jr.
One Sheet: $3 - $5

JOHNNY BELINDA
(1948 - Warner Bros.) Jane Wyman, Lew Ayres
One Sheet: $50 - $100   *Academy Award: Best Actress. Academy Award Movie Posters #119.*

JOHNNY CASH
(1969 - Continental) Johnny Cash, June Carter
One Sheet: $40 - $75   *Country musical. Duotone.*

JOHNNY COME LATELY
(1943 - United Artists) James Cagney, Grace George
One Sheet: $75 - $150

JOHNNY COMES FLYING HOME
(1946 - 20th Century Fox) Martha Stewart, Richard Crane
One Sheet: $50 - $100

JOHNNY CONCHO
(1956 - United Artists) Frank Sinatra, Phyllis Kirk
One Sheet: $30 - $60

JOHNNY COOL
(1963 - United Artists) Henry Silva, Elizabeth Montgomery
One Sheet: $20 - $40

JOHNNY DANGEROUSLY
(1984 - 20th Century Fox) Michael Keaton, Marilu Henner, Joe Piscopo
One Sheet: $3 - $5

JOHNNY DARK
(1954 - Universal-International) Tony Curtis, Piper Laurie, Don Taylor
One Sheet: $50 - $100

One Sheet

JOHNNY DARK
(1959R - Universal) Tony Curtis, Piper Laurie, Don Taylor
One Sheet: $15 - $25   *Re-release.*

JOHNNY DOESN'T LIVE HERE ANYMORE
(1944 - Monogram) Simone Simon, James Ellison, Robert Mitchum
One Sheet: $75 - $150

JOHNNY DOUGHBOY
(1942 - Republic) Jane Withers, Spanky McFarland
One Sheet: $75 - $125

JOHNNY EAGER
(1941 - MGM) Robert Taylor, Lana Turner
One Sheet: $125 - $250   *Academy Award Movie Posters #85.*

One Sheet

JOHNNY EAGER
(1950R - MGM) Robert Taylor, Lana Turner
One Sheet: $15 - $30   *Re-release.*

JOHNNY FRENCHMAN
(1947 - Universal) Francoise Rosay, Patricia Roc
One Sheet: $20 - $40

JOHNNY GET YOUR GUN
(1919 - Paramount) Fred Stone, Noah Beery
One Sheet: $250 - $500

JOHNNY GET YOUR HAIR CUT

(1927 - MGM) Jackie Coogan, Mattie Witting
One Sheet: $250 - $600

JOHNNY GOT HIS GUN
(1971 - Cinemation) Timothy Bottoms, Jason Robards
One Sheet: $20 - $40

JOHNNY GUITAR
(1954 - Republic) Joan Crawford, Sterling Hayden
One Sheet: $125 - $250

JOHNNY HANDSOME
(1989 - TriStar) Mickey Rourke, Ellen Barkin
One Sheet: $3 - $5

JOHNNY HOLIDAY
(1949 - United Artists) William Bendix, Allen Martin Jr.
One Sheet: $30 - $50

JOHNNY IN THE CLOUDS
(1946 - United Artists) Michael Redgrave, John Mills
One Sheet: $40 - $75

JOHNNY MNEMONIC
(1995 - TriStar) Keanu Reeves, Dolph Lundgren, Ice-T
One Sheet: $5 - $10

JOHNNY NOBODY
(1965 - Medallion) Nigel Patrick, Yvonne Mitchell
One Sheet: $3 - $5

JOHNNY O'CLOCK
(1947 - Columbia) Dick Powell, Evelyn Keyes
One Sheet: $75 - $150

JOHNNY O'CLOCK
(1956R - Columbia) Dick Powell, Evelyn Keyes
One Sheet: $30 - $60   *Re-release.*

JOHNNY ON THE RUN
(1953 - Associate British) Michael Balfour, Eugene Chylek
One Sheet: $15 - $25

JOHNNY ON THE SPOT
(1919 - Metro) Hale Hamilton, Louise Lovely
One Sheet: $150 - $300

JOHNNY ON THE SPOT
(1954 - New Realm) Hugh McDermott, Elspet Gray
One Sheet: $10 - $20

JOHNNY ONE-EYE
(1949 - United Artists) Pat O'Brien, Wayne Morris
One Sheet: $30 - $50

JOHNNY RENO
(1966 - Paramount) Dana Andrews, Jane Russell
One Sheet: $10 - $20

JOHNNY ROCCO
(1958 - Allied Artists) Stephen McNally, Richard Eyer
One Sheet: $5 - $10

JOHNNY STECCHINO
(1992 - New Line) Roberto Benigni
One Sheet: $3 - $5

JOHNNY STOOL PIGEON
(1949 - Universal) Howard Duff, Shelley Winters
One Sheet: $40 - $75

JOHNNY SUEDE
(1992 - Miramax) Brad Pitt, Nick Cave
One Sheet: $7 - $15

JOHNNY THE GIANT KILLER
(1958 - Lippert) -
One Sheet: $100 - $200   *Cartoon. Full color feature.*

JOHNNY TIGER
(1966 - Universal) Robert Taylor, Geraldine Brooks, Chad Everett
One Sheet: $5 - $10

JOHNNY TREMAIN
(1957 - Disney) Hal Stalmaster, Luana Patten
One Sheet: $15 - $35

JOHNNY TROUBLE
(1957 - Warner Bros.) Ethel Barrymore, Cecil Kellaway

One Sheet: $10 - $20

JOHNNY VIK
(1973 - Nauman) Warren Hammack, Gina McCormick
One Sheet: $5 - $10

JOHNNY WEISMULLER AS TARZAN
(1945? - RKO) Johnny Weismuller
One Sheet: $250 - $500

JOHNNY, YOU'RE WANTED
(1956 - Merton) John Slater, Garry Marsh
One Sheet: $7 - $15

JOHNNY YUMA
(1967 - Clover) Mark Damon, Rosalba Neri
One Sheet: $5 - $12

JOHNNY'S ROMEO
(1916 - Mutual) -
One Sheet: $1,600 - $2,500   *Cartoon. Partial full color stone litho. Cartoon Movie Posters #3.*

JOHNSTOWN FLOOD, THE
(1926 - Fox) George O'Brien, Janet Gaynor
One Sheet: $200 - $400

JOHNSTOWN FLOOD, THE
(1943 - 20th Century Fox) Mighty Mouse
One Sheet: $250 - $600   *Cartoon. Full color stock poster with printed title. Huge image of Mighty Mouse on yellow background.*

JOIN THE MARINES
(1937 - Republic) June Travis, Paul Kelly
One Sheet: $75 - $150

JOINING THE TANKS
(1918 - Fox) Mutt 'n Jeff
One Sheet: $2,500 - $4,000   *Cartoon.*

JOINT IS JUMPIN', THE
(1948 - Soundies) -
One Sheet: $125 - $250   *Black cast. Jazz musical.*

JOJO DANCER, YOUR LIFE IS CALLING
(1986 - -) Richard Pryor, Debbie Allen
One Sheet: $5 - $10   *Pryor's life story.*

JOKER, THE
(1961 - United Artists) Francois Maistre, Anne Tonietti
One Sheet: $5 - $10

JOKER IS WILD, THE
(1957 - A.M.B.L.) Frank Sinatra, Mitzi Gaynor
One Sheet: $30 - $60

JOKERS, THE
(1967 - Universal) Michael Crawford, Oliver Reed
One Sheet: $3 - $5

JOLLY BAD FELLOW, A
(1964 - Continental) Leo McKern, Janet Munro
One Sheet: $7 - $15

JOLSON SINGS AGAIN
(1950 - Columbia) Larry Parks, Barbara Hale
One Sheet: $40 - $75

JOLSON STORY, THE
(1946 - Columbia) Larry Parks, Evelyn Keyes
One Sheet: $50 - $100

JOLT, THE
(1921 - Fox) Johnnie Walker, Edna Murphy
One Sheet: $150 - $300

JONATHAN
(1973 - New York) Jurgen Jung, Paul Albert
One Sheet: $3 - $5

JONATHAN LIVINGSTON SEAGULL
(1973 - Paramount) James Franciscus, Juliet Mills
One Sheet: $7 - $15

JONES FAMILY IN AS YOUNG AS YOU FEEL, THE
(1940 - 20th Century Fox) Jed Prouty, Spring Byington
One Sheet: $50 - $100

JONES FAMILY IN BIG BUSINESS, THE
(1937 - 20th Century Fox) Jed Prouty, Spring Byington
One Sheet: $75 - $150

JONES FAMILY IN HOLLYWOOD, THE

(1939 - 20th Century Fox) Jed Prouty, Spring
Byington
One Sheet: $100 - $200

JONES FAMILY IN HOT WATER, THE
(1937 - 20th Century Fox) Jed Prouty, Spring
Byington
One Sheet: $75 - $150

JONES FAMILY IN QUICK MILLIONS, THE
(1939 - 20th Century Fox) Jed Prouty, Spring
Byington
One Sheet: $50 - $100

JONES FAMILY ON THEIR OWN, THE
(1940 - 20th Century Fox) Jed Prouty, Spring
Byington
One Sheet: $50 - $100

JONI
(1980 - World Wide) Joni Eareckson, Bert
Remsen
One Sheet: $3 - $5

JORDON IS A HARD ROAD
(1915 - Triangle) Dorothy Gish, Owen Moore
One Sheet: $200 - $400

JORY
(1972 - Avco/Embassy) John Marley, Robby
Benson
One Sheet: $3 - $5

JOSEPH ANDREWS
(1977 - Paramount) Ann Margaret, Peter Firth
One Sheet: $10 - $20

JOSEPH IN THE LAND OF EGYPT
(1932 - Guaranteed) -
One Sheet: $125 - $250

JOSEPHINE AND MEN
(1955 - Charter) Glynis Johns, Peter Finch
One Sheet: $7 - $15

JOSETTE
(1938 - 20th Century Fox) Simone Simon, Don
Ameche, Bert Lahr
One Sheet: $100 - $200

JOSH AND S.A.M.
(1993 - Columbia) Noah Fleiss, Jacob Tierney
One Sheet: $3 - $5

JOSHUA
(1976 - Lone Star) Fred Williamson, Calvin
Bartlett
One Sheet: $10 - $20   *Black cast.*
Cowboy Movie Posters #344. Sports Movie
Posters #367.

JOSHUA THEN AND NOW
(1985 - -) James Woods, Alan Arkin
One Sheet: $4 - $8

JOSSELYN'S WIFE
(1926 - Tiffany) Holmes Herbert, Pauline
Frederick
One Sheet: $150 - $300

JOSSER IN THE ARM
(1932 - Wardour) Ernie Lotinga, Betty Norton,
Jack Hobbs
One Sheet: $100 - $200

JOSSER JOINS THE NAVY
(1932 - Wardour) Ernie Lotinga, Jack Hobbs
One Sheet: $100 - $200

JOSSER ON THE FARM
(1934 - 20th Century Fox) Ernie Lotinga, Garry
Marsh
One Sheet: $100 - $200

JOSSER ON THE RIVER
(1932 - Wardour) Ernie Lotinga, Molly Lemont
One Sheet: $100 - $200

JOUR DE FETE
(1949 - Francinex) Jacques Tati
One Sheet: $100 - $200   *French.*

JOURNAL OF A CRIME
(1934 - First National) Adolphe Menjou, Jane
Darwell
One Sheet: $100 - $200

JOURNEY, THE
(1958 - MGM) Yul Brynner, Deborah Kerr
One Sheet: $30 - $50

JOURNEY
(1977 - Quest) Genevieve Bujold, John Vernon
One Sheet: $5 - $10

JOURNEY AHEAD
(1947 - Random) John Stevens, Ruth Haven
One Sheet: $15 - $30

JOURNEY BACK TO OZ
(1974 - Filmation) -
One Sheet: $10 - $20   *Cartoon.*

JOURNEY FOR MARGARET
(1942 - MGM) Robert Young, Laraine Day,
Margaret O'Brien(film debut)
One Sheet: $75 - $150

JOURNEY INTO DARKNESS
(1968 - Hammer) Jennifer Hilary, Robert Reed
One Sheet: $10 - $20

JOURNEY INTO FEAR
(1943 - RKO) Joseph Cotten, Dolores Del Rio,
Orson Welles
One Sheet: $500 - $800

JOURNEY INTO FEAR
(1976 - Sterling) Sam Waterston, Zero Mostel
One Sheet: $5 - $10   *AKA: BURN*
OUT.

JOURNEY INTO LIGHT
(1951 - 20th Century Fox) Sterling Hayden,
Viveca Lindfors
One Sheet: $15 - $30

JOURNEY INTO MIDNIGHT
(1968 - Hammer) Julie Harris, Chad Everett
One Sheet: $10 - $20

JOURNEY OF AUGUST KING, THE
(1995 - Miramax) Jason Patric
One Sheet: $4 - $8

JOURNEY OF NATTY GANN, THE
(1985 - Disney) Meredith Salenger, John
Cusack
One Sheet: $3 - $5

JOURNEY THROUGH ROSEBUD
(1972 - Cinerama) Robert Forster, Kristoffer
Tabori
One Sheet: $5 - $10

JOURNEY TO FREEDOM
(1957 - Republic) Jacques Scott, Genevieve
Aumont
One Sheet: $10 - $20

JOURNEY TO JERUSALEM
(1941 - Maxwell Anderson) -
One Sheet: $50 - $100

JOURNEY TO SHILOH
(1968 - Universal) James Caan, Michael
Sarrazin, Brenda Scott
One Sheet: $3 - $5

JOURNEY TO THE BEGINNING OF TIME
(1966 - New Trend) Vladimir Bejval, Peter
Hermann
One Sheet: $15 - $25

JOURNEY TO THE CENTER OF THE EARTH
(1959 - 20th Century Fox) Pat Boone, James
Mason
One Sheet: $75 - $125   *Graven*
Images, pg. 176.

JOURNEY TO THE CENTER OF TIME
(1967 - Borealis) Scott Brady, Lyle Waggoner
One Sheet: $7 - $15

JOURNEY TO THE FAR SIDE OF THE SUN
(1969 - Universal) Roy Thinnes, Herbert Lom,
Patrick Wymark
One Sheet: $10 - $20

JOURNEY TO THE LOST CITY
(1960 - AIP) Debra Paget, Paul Christian
One Sheet: $50 - $100

JOURNEY TO THE SEVENTH PLANET
(1962 - AIP) John Agar, Greta Thyssen
One Sheet: $30 - $60

JOURNEY TOGETHER
(1946 - English Films) Richard Attenborough,
Edward G. Robinson
One Sheet: $75 - $125

JOURNEY'S END
(1918 - World) Ethel Clayton, John Bowers
One Sheet: $200 - $400

JOURNEY'S END, THE
(1921 - Ballin) George Bancroft, Mabel Ballin

One Sheet: $150 - $300

JOURNEY'S END
(1930 - Tiffany) Colin Clive, Ian MacLaren
One Sheet: $500 - $800

JOURNEYS FROM BERLIN
(1980 - Center) Annette Michelson, Gabor
Vernon
One Sheet: $3 - $5

JOY AND THE DRAGON
(1916 - Balboa) Marie Osborne, Cullen Landis
One Sheet: $200 - $400

JOY GIRL, THE
(1927 - Fox) Olive Bordon, Neil Hamilton
One Sheet: $250 - $600

JOY HOUSE
(1964 - MGM) Alain Delon, Jane Fonda
One Sheet: $15 - $25

JOY IN THE MORNING
(1965 - MGM) Richard Chamberlain, Yvette
Mimieux
One Sheet: $10 - $20

JOY LUCK CLUB, THE
(1993 - Buena Vista) Ming-Na Wen, Tsai Chin,
Kieu Chinh
One Sheet: $5 - $10

JOY OF LIVING
(1938 - RKO) Irene Dunne, Douglas Fairbanks
Jr.
One Sheet: $125 - $250

One Sheet

JOY OF SEX
(1984 - Paramount) Christopher Lloyd,
Cameron Dye
One Sheet: $5 - $10

JOY RIDE
(1935 - City) Gene Gerrard
One Sheet: $150 - $300

JOY RIDE
(1958 - Allied Artists) Rad Fulton, Ann Doran
One Sheet: $30 - $60   *Hot Rod*
Gang.

JOY RIDE TO NOWHERE
(1978 - -) Leslie Ackerman, Sandy Serrano
One Sheet: $15 - $25

JOY STREET
(1929 - Fox) Lois Moram, Rex Bell
One Sheet: $100 - $200

JOYLESS STREET
(1925 - Sofar) Asta Nielsen, Greta Garbo
One Sheet: $6,500 - $10,000   *German.*

JOYOUS LIAR, THE
(1919 - Brunton) J. Warren Kerrigan, Lillian
Walker
One Sheet: $250 - $500

JOYOUS TROUBLEMAKERS, THE
(1920 - Fox) William Farnum, Louise Lovely
One Sheet: $200 - $400

JOYRIDE
(1977 - AIP) Desi Arnaz Jr., Robert Carradine
One Sheet: $5 - $10

JOYSTICKS
(1983 - Jensen Farley) Joe Don Baker
One Sheet: $3 - $5   *AKA: VIDEO*
MADNESS

JU DOU
(1990 - -) Gong Li, Li Baotian

One Sheet: $7 - $15   *Chinese.*
Martial arts.

JUAREZ
(1939 - Warner Bros.) Paul Muni, Bette Davis,
Brian Aherne
One Sheet: $800 - $1,500

One Sheet

JUBAL
(1956 - Columbia) Glenn Ford, Ernest
Borgnine, Rod Steiger
One Sheet: $15 - $30

JUBILEE
(1978 - Cinegate) Jenny Runacre, Adam Ant
One Sheet: $4 - $8

JUBILEE TRAIL
(1954 - Republic) Vera Ralston, Forrest Tucker
One Sheet: $15 - $30

JUBILEE WINDOW
(1935 - Paramount) Sebastian Shaw, Ralph
Truman
One Sheet: $125 - $250

JUBILO
(1919 - Goldwyn) Will Rogers, James Mason
One Sheet: $500 - $800

JUCKLINS, THE
(1920 - Paramount) Mabel Julienne Scott,
Monte Blue
One Sheet: $200 - $400

JUD
(1971 - Maron) Joseph Kaufmann, Claudia
Jennings
One Sheet: $3 - $5

JUDAS PROJECT, THE
(1993 - RS Entertainment) -
One Sheet: $3 - $5

JUDE
(1996 - Gramercy) Kate Winslet, Christopher
Eccleston
One Sheet: $3 - $5

JUDEX
(1966 - Continental) Michael Vitold, Channing
Pollock
One Sheet: $3 - $5

JUDGE, THE
(1948 - Film Classics) Milburn Stone, Katherine
DeMille
One Sheet: $15 - $30

JUDGE AND THE ASSASSIN, THE
(1979 - Libra) Philippe Noiret, Michael Galabru
One Sheet: $3 - $5

JUDGE AND THE SINNER, THE
(1964 - Casino) Heinz Ruehmann, Karin Baal
One Sheet: $3 - $5

JUDGE DREDD
(1995 - Buena Vista) Sylvester Stallone, Diane
Lane
One Sheet: $10 - $20   *Comic book*
tie-in.

JUDGE HARDY AND SON
(1939 - MGM) Lewis Stone, Mickey Rooney
One Sheet: $75 - $150

JUDGE HARDY'S CHILDREN
(1938 - MGM) Lewis Stone, Mickey Rooney
One Sheet: $75 - $150

JUDGE NOT
(1920 - Jury) Fay Compton, George Bellamy
One Sheet: $200 - $400

JUDGE NOT or THE WOMAN OF MONA DIGGINGS
(1915 - Universal) Harry Carey, Julia Daen
One Sheet: $250 - $500

JUDGE PRIEST
(1934 - Fox) Will Rogers, Tom Brown, Anita Louise
One Sheet: $250 - $600

JUDGE STEPS OUT, THE
(1949 - RKO) Alexander Knox, Ann Sothern
One Sheet: $30 - $60

JUDGMENT AT NUREMBERG
(1961 - United Artists) Spencer Tracy, Burt Lancaster, Maximillian Schell
One Sheet: $75 - $125   *Academy Award: Best Actor(Schell). Saul Bass art. One Sheet (Academy Awards style,duotone):$15-$30. Academy Award Movie Posters #203.*

JUDGMENT DEFERRED
(1953 - Group 3) Hugh Sinclair, Joan Collins
One Sheet: $15 - $25

JUDGMENT IN BERLIN
(1988 - --) Martin Sheen, Sam Wanamaker
One Sheet: $3 - $5

JUDGMENT NIGHT
(1993 - Universal) Emilio Esteves, Cuba Gooding Jr.
One Sheet: $3 - $5

JUDGMENT OF THE HILLS
(1927 - FBO) Frankie Darro, Virginia Valli
One Sheet: $125 - $250

JUDGMENT OF THE STORM
(1924 - FBO) Lloyd Hughes, Frankie Darro
One Sheet: $150 - $300

JUDITH
(1966 - Paramount) Sophia Loren, Peter Finch
One Sheet: $15 - $25

JUDITH OF BETHULIA
(1914 - Biograph) Blanche Sweet, Lillian & Dorothy Gish
One Sheet: $700 - $1,200

JUDITH OF THE CUMBERLANDS
(1916 - Signal) Helen Holmes, Leo D. Maloney, Alma Reubens
One Sheet: $250 - $500

JUDO SAGA
(1965 - Toho) Toshiro Mifune, Yuzo Kayama
One Sheet: $10 - $20

JUDY OF ROGUES HARBOUR
(1920 - Reelart) Mary M. Minter, Charles Meredith
One Sheet: $150 - $300

JUDY'S LITTLE NO-NO
(1969 - Schooner Bay) Elisa Ingram, John Lodge
One Sheet: $5 - $12   *aka: Let's Do It.*

JUGGERNAUT, THE
(1915 - Vitagraph) Anita Stewart, Earle Williams
One Sheet: $200 - $400

JUGGERNAUT
(1937 - Grand National) Boris Karloff, Mona Goya
One Sheet: $150 - $300   *Graven Images, pg. 87.*

JUGGERNAUT
(1974 - United Artists) Richard Harris, Omar Sharif
One Sheet: $5 - $10

JUGGLER, THE
(1953 - Columbia) Kirk Douglas, Milly Vitale
One Sheet: $15 - $30

JUICE
(1992 - Paramount) Omar Epps, Jermaine Hopkins, Tupac Shakur
One Sheet: $7 - $15

JUKE BOX JENNY
(1942 - Universal) Ken Murray, Harriet Hilliard
One Sheet: $50 - $100   *Big band musical.*

JUKE BOX RACKET

(1960 - Brenner) Steve Karmen, Arlene Corwin
One Sheet: $15 - $30

JUKE BOX RHYTHM
(1959 - Columbia) Jack Jones, Jo Morrow
One Sheet: $15 - $35

JUKE GIRL
(1942 - Warner Bros.) Ronald Reagan, Ann Sheridan
One Sheet: $150 - $300

One Sheet

JUKE JOINT
(1947 - Sack Amusement) Spencer Williams, July Jones
One Sheet: $250 - $500   *Black cast. Williams's last film. Separate Cinema, pg. 24.*

JULES AND JIM
(1962 - Janus) Jeanne Moreau, Oscar Werner
One Sheet: $75 - $150   *1st U.S. release.*

JULES OF THE STRONG HEART
(1918 - Paramount) George Beban, Hellen Eddy
One Sheet: $150 - $300

JULIA
(1977 - 20th Century Fox) Jane Fonda, Vanessa Redgrave, Jason Robards.
One Sheet: $15 - $35   *Academy Award: Best Supporting Actor (Robards), Best Supporting Actress (Redgrave). Academy Award Movie Posters#300.*

JULIA AND JULIA
(1988 - --) Kathleen Turner, Gabriel Byrne, Sting
One Sheet: $10 - $20

JULIA MISBEHAVES
(1948 - MGM) Greer Garson, Walter Pidgeon, Peter Lawford
One Sheet: $30 - $50

JULIE
(1956 - MGM) Doris Day, Louis Jourdan, Barry Sullivan
One Sheet: $15 - $35

JULIE DARLING
(1982 - Cinequity) Anthony Franciosa, Sybil Danning
One Sheet: $3 - $5

JULIET DESADE
(1970 - --) -
One Sheet: $7 - $15

JULIET OF THE SPIRITS
(1965 - Rizzoli) Giulietta Masina, Sandra Milo
One Sheet: $40 - $75   *Italian. Price is for U.S. one sheet. Original Italian(39x55):$200-$300.*

JULIETTA
(1957 - Kingsley) Jean Marais, Dany Robin
One Sheet: $3 - $5

JULIUS CAESAR
(1952 - Avon) Charlton Heston, Harold Tasker, Robert Holt
One Sheet: $75 - $125

JULIUS CAESAR
(1953 - MGM) Marlon Brando, James Mason, Louis Calhern
One Sheet: $100 - $200

JULIUS CAESAR
(1962R - MGM) Marlon Brando, James Mason, Louis Calhern
One Sheet: $15 - $30   *Re-release.*

JULIUS CAESAR
(1970 - AIP) Jason Robards, John Gielgud, Charlton Heston
One Sheet: $7 - $15

JULIUS SIZZER
(1931 - RKO/Pathe) Benny Rubin
One Sheet: $100 - $200

JUMANJI
(1995 - TriStar) Robin Williams, Bonnie Hunt
One Sheet: $5 - $10

JUMBO
(1962 - MGM) Doris Day, Jimmy Durante, Martha Raye, Dean Jagger
One Sheet: $30 - $60   *AKA: BILLY ROSE'S JUMBO.*

JUMBO
(1970R - MGM) Doris Day, Jimmy Durante, Martha Raye, Dean Jagger
One Sheet: $7 - $15   *Re-release.*

JUMP
(1971 - Cannon) Tom Ligon, Sally Kirkland
One Sheet: $3 - $5

JUMP INTO HELL
(1955 - Warner Bros.) Jacques Sernas, Kurt Kasznar
One Sheet: $15 - $25

JUMPIN' JACK FLASH
(1986 - 20th Century Fox) Whoopie Goldberg, Stephen Collins
One Sheet: $5 - $10

JUMPING FOR JOY
(1956 - Rank) Frankie Howerd, Tony Wright
One Sheet: $5 - $10

JUMPING JACKS
(1952 - Paramount) Dean Martin, Jerry Lewis
One Sheet: $40 - $75

JUNCTION 88
(1940 - Sack) Noble Sissle & Orch., Pigmeat Markham
One Sheet: $250 - $500   *Black cast. Big band musical.*

JUNCTION CITY
(1952 - Columbia) Charles Starrett, Smiley Burnette
One Sheet: $15 - $25

JUNE BRIDE
(1948 - Warner Bros.) Bette Davis, Robert Montgomery
One Sheet: $50 - $100

JUNE FRIDAY
(1915 - Edison) Gertrude McCoy, Robert Conness
One Sheet: $200 - $400

JUNE MADNESS
(1922 - Metro) Viola Dana, Bryant Washburn
One Sheet: $150 - $300

JUNE MOON
(1931 - Paramount Publix) Jack Oakie, Frances Dee
One Sheet: $150 - $300

JUNGLE, THE
(1914 - All Star) George Nash, Robert Cummings
One Sheet: $250 - $500

JUNGLE, THE
(1952 - Lippert) Rod Cameron, Cesar Romero
One Sheet: $15 - $30

JUNGLE 2 JUNGLE
(1997 - Buena Vista) Tim Allen, Lolita Davidovitch, Martin Short
One Sheet: $5 - $10

JUNGLE BELLES
(1927 - Bray) Dir: Walter Lantz
One Sheet: $600 - $1,000   *Cartoon. From the Hot Dog Cartoon series.*

JUNGLE BOOK, THE
(- - -) Also see Rudyard Kipling's The Jungle Book

JUNGLE BOOK, THE
(1942 - Alexander Korda) Sabu, Joseph Calleia
One Sheet: $500 - $800

JUNGLE BOOK
(1967 - Buena Vista/Disney) Mowgli, Baloo, Bagheera
One Sheet: $75 - $150   *Cartoon. Cartoon Movie Posters #384.*

JUNGLE BOOK
(1978R - Disney) Mowgli, Baloo, Bagheera
One Sheet: $15 - $35   *Re-release. Cartoon.*

JUNGLE BOOK
(197? - Trans National) -
One Sheet: $3 - $5

JUNGLE BOOK
(1984R - Disney) Mowgli, Baloo, Bagheera
One Sheet: $15 - $25   *Re-release. Cartoon.*

JUNGLE BOOK
(1989R - Disney) Mowgli, Baloo, Bagheera
One Sheet: $7 - $15   *Re-release. Cartoon.*

JUNGLE BOOK/CHARLIE THE LONESOME COUGAR COMBO
(1967 - Buena Vista) -
One Sheet: $15 - $35   *Double feature poster.*

JUNGLE BRIDE
(1933 - Monogram) Anita Page, Charles Starrett
One Sheet: $250 - $600

JUNGLE CAPTIVE
(1944 - Universal) Otto Kruger, Rondo Hatton, Vicky Lane
One Sheet: $50 - $100

Lobby Card

JUNGLE CAT
(1960 - Buena Vista/Disney) Wildlife Feature
One Sheet: $7 - $15

JUNGLE CAVALCADE
(1941 - Compilation) Frank Buck, Armand Denis
One Sheet: $50 - $100

JUNGLE CHILD, THE
(1916 - Triangle) Dorothy Dalton, Howard Hickman
One Sheet: $200 - $400

JUNGLE DRUMS OF AFRICA
(1953 - Republic) Clayton Moore, Phyllis Coates
One Sheet: $40 - $75   *Serial. 13 Chapters.*

JUNGLE FEVER
(1991 - Universal) Wesley Snipes, Annabella Sciorra, Dir: Spike Lee
One Sheet: $10 - $20

JUNGLE FLIGHT
(1947 - Paramount) Robert Lowery, Ann Savage
One Sheet: $30 - $50

JUNGLE GENTS
(1954 - Allied Artists) Leo Gorcey, Huntz Hall
One Sheet: $30 - $60

JUNGLE GIRL
(1941 - Republic) Frances Gifford, Tom Neal
One Sheet: $100 - $200   *Serial. 15 Chapters.*

JUNGLE GODDESS
JUNGLE GIRL
(1948 - Screen Guild) George Reeves, Ralph Byrd, Wanda McKay

One Sheet: $30 - $60

JUNGLE HEADHUNTERS
(1950 - RKO) Documentary
One Sheet: $30 - $50

JUNGLE HEAT
(1957 - United Artists) Lex Barker, Mari
Blanchard
One Sheet: $15 - $35

JUNGLE HEAT
(1984 - -) Peter Fonda, Deborah Raffin
One Sheet: $3 - $5

JUNGLE JIM
(1937 - Universal) Grant Withers, Betty Jane
Rhodes
One Sheet: $600 - $1,000   *Serial. 12
Chapters.*

JUNGLE JIM
(1948 - Columbia) Johnny Weissmuller,
Virginia Grey
One Sheet: $75 - $150

JUNGLE JIM IN THE FORBIDDEN LAND
(1952 - Columbia) Johnny Weissmuller, Angela
Greene
One Sheet: $50 - $100

JUNGLE KILLER, THE
(1932 - Century) -
One Sheet: $100 - $200

JUNGLE MAN
(1941 - PRC) Buster Crabbe
One Sheet: $50 - $100

JUNGLE MAN-EATERS
(1954 - Columbia) Johnny Weissmuller
One Sheet: $75 - $125

JUNGLE MANHUNT
(1951 - Columbia) Johnny Weissmuller, Sheila
Ryan
One Sheet: $75 - $125

JUNGLE MENACE
(1937 - Columbia) Frank Buck, John St. Polis
One Sheet: $75 - $150   *Serial. 15
Episodes.*

JUNGLE MOON MEN
(1955 - Columbia) Johnny Weissmuller, Jean
Byron
One Sheet: $75 - $125

JUNGLE MYSTERY
(1932 - Universal) Tom Tyler, Cecelia Parker,
Noah Beery,Jr.
One Sheet: $200 - $400   *Serial. 12
Chapters.*

JUNGLE OF CHANG
(1951 - RKO) Leonard Bucknall Eyre, Chang
the Elephant
One Sheet: $15 - $30

JUNGLE PATROL
(1948 - 20th Century Fox) Kristine Miller,
Arthur Franz
One Sheet: $15 - $30

JUNGLE PRINCESS, THE
(1936 - Paramount) Dorothy Lamour (film
debut), Ray Milland
One Sheet: $250 - $500

JUNGLE PRINCESS, THE
(1946R - Paramount) Dorothy Lamour
One Sheet: $40 - $75   *Re-release.*

JUNGLE QUEEN
(1945 - Universal) Edward Norris, Eddie
Quillan
One Sheet: $50 - $100

JUNGLE RAIDERS
(1945 - Columbia) Kane Richmond, Eddie
Quillan
One Sheet: $40 - $75

JUNGLE SAFARI
(1954 - -) Ruth Roman
One Sheet: $7 - $15

JUNGLE SIREN
(1942 - PRC) Ann Corio, Buster Crabbe
One Sheet: $50 - $100

JUNGLE STAMPEDE
(1950 - Republic) George Breakston, Yorke
Coplen

One Sheet: $15 - $30

JUNGLE STREET GIRLS
(1963 - Ajay) David McCallum, Jill Ireland
One Sheet: $7 - $15   *aka: Jungle
Street.*

JUNGLE TRAIL, THE
(1919 - Fox) William Farnum, Lester Chambers
One Sheet: $200 - $400

JUNGLE WOMAN, THE
(1926 - Stoll) Eric Bransby, Lillian Douglas
One Sheet: $150 - $300

JUNGLE WOMAN
(1944 - Universal) Evelyn Ankers, J. Carrol
Naish
One Sheet: $75 - $150

JUNIOR
(1994 - Universal) Arnold Schwarzenegger,
Danny DeVito, Emma Thompson
One Sheet: $5 - $10

JUNIOR ARMY
(1943 - Columbia) Freddie Bartholomew, Huntz
Hall
One Sheet: $40 - $75

JUNIOR BONNER
(1972 - ABC) Steve McQueen, Ida Lupino,
Robert Preston
One Sheet: $30 - $50

JUNIOR G-MEN
(1940 - Universal) Billy Halop, Huntz Hall
One Sheet: $100 - $200   *Serial. 12
Chapters.*

JUNIOR G-MEN OF THE AIR
(1942 - Universal) Billy Halop, Gene Reynolds
One Sheet: $75 - $150   *Serial. 12
Chapters.*

JUNIOR MISS
(1945 - 20th Century Fox) Peggy Ann Garner,
Allyn Joslyn
One Sheet: $50 - $100

JUNIOR PROM
(1946 - Monogram) Freddie Stewart, June
Preisser
One Sheet: $30 - $60

JUNKET 89
(1970 - Balfour) Stephen Brassett, Linda
Robson
One Sheet: $5 - $10

JUNKMAN, THE
(1982 - Halicki) Christopher Stone, Susan
Shaw, Linda Day George
One Sheet: $3 - $5

JUNO AND THE PAYCOCK
(1930 - Waldour) Sara Allgood, Edward
Chapman, Dir: Alfred Hitchcock
One Sheet: $2,500 - $4,000   *AKA: THE
SHAME OF MARY BOYLE.*

JUPITER
(1952 - Sirius) Dany Robin, Georges Marchal
One Sheet: $10 - $20

JUPITER'S DARLING
(1954 - MGM) Esther Williams, Howard Keel
One Sheet: $40 - $75

JURASSIC PARK
(1993 - Universal) Sam Neill, Laura Dern, Jeff
Goldblum
One Sheet: $10 - $20

JUROR, THE
(1996 - Columbia) Demi Moore, Alec Baldwin
One Sheet: $5 - $10   *Courtroom
drama.*

JURY DUTY
(1995 - TriStar) Pauly Shore, Tia Carrere
One Sheet: $3 - $5

JURY OF ONE
(1975 - Avco-Embassy) Sophia Loren, Jean
Gabin
One Sheet: $40 - $75   *First U.S.
release. AKA: LE TESTAMENT.*

JURY'S EVIDENCE
(1936 - British Lion) Hartley Power, Sebastian
Shaw
One Sheet: $100 - $200

JURY'S SECRET, THE
(1938 - Universal) Fay Wray, Kent Taylor
One Sheet: $150 - $300

JUST A GIGOLO
(1931 - MGM) Ray Milland, Irene Purcell
One Sheet: $150 - $300

JUST A GIGOLO
(1979 - United Artists) David Bowie, Sydne
Rome, Kim Novak, Marlene Dietrich
One Sheet: $30 - $50

JUST A GIRL
(1916 - Moss) Owen Nares, Daisy Burrell
One Sheet: $200 - $400

JUST A SONG AT TWILIGHT
(1922 - Dixie) Richard Barthelmess, Pedro De
Cordoba
One Sheet: $125 - $250

JUST A WOMAN
(1925 - First National) Conway Tearle, Dorothy
Revier
One Sheet: $150 - $300

JUST ACROSS THE STREET
(1952 - Universal) Ann Sheridan, John Lund
One Sheet: $15 - $30

JUST ANOTHER GIRL ON THE IRT
(1993 - Miramax) Ariyan Johnson
One Sheet: $3 - $5

JUST AROUND THE CORNER
(1921 - Cosmopolitan) Margaret Seddon, Lewis
Sergent
One Sheet: $125 - $250

JUST AROUND THE CORNER
(1938 - 20th Century Fox) Shirley Temple,
Joan Davis, Charles Farrell
One Sheet: $800 - $1,500

JUST BEFORE DAWN
(1946 - Columbia) Warner Baxter, Adele
Roberts
One Sheet: $20 - $40

JUST BEFORE DAWN
(1980 - Juniper) Chris Lemmon, George
Kennedy
One Sheet: $3 - $6

JUST BETWEEN FRIENDS
(1986 - Orion) Mary Tyler Moore, Christine
Lahti, Ted Danson
One Sheet: $3 - $5

JUST CAUSE
(1995 - Warner Bros.) Sean Connery, Kate
Capshaw
One Sheet: $5 - $10

JUST DECEPTION, A
(1917 - Tiger) Robert Leonard, Blanche
Forsythe
One Sheet: $200 - $400

JUST DOGS
(1932 - United Artists) Silly Symphony
One Sheet: $11,000 - $18,000   *Cartoon. The
Disney Poster, pg. 6.*

JUST DUCKY
(1952 - MGM) Tom and Jerry
One Sheet: $200 - $400   *Cartoon.*

JUST FOR A SONG
(1930 - Sono-Art/World Wide) Roy Royston,
Lilliam Davis
One Sheet: $150 - $300

JUST FOR FUN
(1963 - Columbia) Mark Wynter, Cherry Roland
One Sheet: $5 - $10

JUST FOR THE HELL OF IT
(1968 - Argent) Rodney Bedell, Dir: Hershell
Gordon Lewis
One Sheet: $15 - $35

JUST FOR TONIGHT
(1918 - Goldwyn) Lucy Fox, Tom Moore
One Sheet: $250 - $500

JUST FOR YOU
(1952 - Paramount) Bing Crosby, Jane Wyman
One Sheet: $30 - $50

JUST IMAGINE
(1930 - Fox) Maureen O'Sullivan, John Garrick,
El Brendel

One Sheet: $800 - $1,500   *Graven
Images, pg. 75.*

JUST IN TIME
(1994 - TriStar) Marisa Tomei, Robert Downey
Jr.
One Sheet: $3 - $7

JUST JIM
(1915 - Universal) Harry Carey, Jean Taylor
One Sheet: $250 - $500

JUST JOE
(1960 - Parkside) Leslie Randall, Anna May
Wong
One Sheet: $10 - $20

JUST LIKE A WOMAN
(1923 - Haskins) Marguerite De La Motte,
George Fawcett
One Sheet: $200 - $400

JUST LIKE A WOMAN
(1938 - Alliance) Gertrude Michael, John Lodge
One Sheet: $75 - $125

JUST LIKE A WOMAN
(1967 - Monarch) Wendy Craig, John Wood
One Sheet: $7 - $15

JUST LIKE HEAVEN
(1930 - Tiffany) Anita Louise
One Sheet: $125 - $250

JUST MARRIED
(1928 - Paramount) Ruth Taylor, James Hall,
Lila Lee
One Sheet: $150 - $300

JUST MY LUCK
(1933 - British/Dominions) Ralph Lynn
One Sheet: $100 - $200

JUST MY LUCK
(1957 - Rank) Norman Wisdom, Leslie Phillips
One Sheet: $5 - $10

JUST NEIGHBORS
(1919 - Pathe) Harold Lloyd
One Sheet: $800 - $1,500

JUST OFF BROADWAY
(1924 - Fox) John Gilbert, Marian Nixon
One Sheet: $200 - $400

JUST OFF BROADWAY
(1929 - Chesterfield) Ann Christy, Donald Keith
One Sheet: $200 - $400

JUST OFF BROADWAY
(1942 - 20th Century Fox) Lloyd Nolan,
Marjorie Weaver
One Sheet: $75 - $150   *Michael
Shayne mystery.*

JUST ONE
(1950 - DIF) Maurice Chevalier, Jean Wall
One Sheet: $15 - $30

JUST ONE OF THE GUYS
(1985 - Columbia) Joyce Hyser, Clayton
Rohner
One Sheet: $7 - $15   *Sports
(Football). Sports Movie Posters #212.*

JUST OUT OF COLLEGE
(1921 - Goldwyn) Molly Malone, Jack Pickford
One Sheet: $150 - $300

JUST OUT OF REACH
(1979 - Australian Film Commission) Sam Neill,
Lorna Lesley
One Sheet: $5 - $10

JUST RAMBLING ALONG
(1919 - Pathe) Stan Laurel, Clarine Seymore
One Sheet: $600 - $1,000

JUST SUPPOSE
(1926 - First National) Richard Barthelmess,
Lois Moran
One Sheet: $150 - $300

JUST SYLVIA
(1918 - World) Barbara Castleton, Jack
Drumier
One Sheet: $200 - $400

JUST TELL ME WHAT YOU WANT
(1980 - Warner Bros.) Ali McGraw, Alan King
One Sheet: $2 - $3

JUST THE WAY YOU ARE
(1984 - MGM) Kristy McNichol, Michael

Ontkean
One Sheet: $3 - $5

JUST THIS ONCE
(1952 - MGM) Peter Lawford, Janet Leigh
One Sheet: $30 - $50

JUST TONY
(1922 - Fox) Tom Mix, Duke Lee
One Sheet: $700 - $1,200

JUST WILLIAM
(1939 - Pathe) Dicky Lupino, Roddy McDowell
One Sheet: $75 - $125

JUST WILLIAM'S LUCK
(1948 - Alliance) Garry Marsh, William Graham
One Sheet: $15 - $30

JUST YOU AND ME KID
(1979 - Columbia) George Burns, Brooke Shields
One Sheet: $10 - $20

JUSTICE
(1914 - Hepworth) Alec Worcester, Alma Taylor
One Sheet: $200 - $400

JUSTICE OF THE FAR NORTH
(1925 - Columbia) Marcia Manon, Arthur Jasmine
One Sheet: $100 - $200

JUSTICE OF THE RANGE
(1935 - Columbia) Tim McCoy, Ward Bond
One Sheet: $250 - $600

JUSTICE TAKES A HOLIDAY
(1933 - Mayfair) H. B. Warner, Huntley Gordon, Syd Saylor
One Sheet: $100 - $200

Three Sheet

JUSTIN MORGAN HAD A HORSE
(1972 - Disney) Don Murray, Lana Wood, Gary Crosby
One Sheet: $5 - $10

JUSTINE
(1969 - 20th Century Fox) Anouk Aimee, Dirk Bogarde, Robert Forster
One Sheet: $2 - $3

JUSTINE
(1969 - AIP) Klaus Kinski, Jack Palance
One Sheet: $7 - $15

JUVENILE COURT
(1938 - Columbia) Paul Kelly, Rita Hayworth
One Sheet: $150 - $300

JUVENILE JUNGLE
(1958 - Republic) Corey Allen, Rebecca Welles
One Sheet: $30 - $60   *Teen-age exploitation.*

J.W. COOP
(1972 - Columbia) Cliff Robertson, Geraldine Page
One Sheet: $3 - $5

K - THE UNKNOWN
(1924 - Universal) Virginia Valli, Percy Marmont
One Sheet: $250 - $600

K2, THE ULTIMATE HIGH
(1992 - Paramount) -
One Sheet: $2 - $3

K-33
(1936 - -) Greta Nissen, Paul Cavanagh
One Sheet: $75 - $150

K-9

(1988 - Universal) James Belushi, Mel Harris
One Sheet: $3 - $5

KACHENJUNGHA
(1966 - Edward Harrison) Chhabi Biswas, Karuna Banerji
One Sheet: $5 - $10

KAGEMUSHA (THE SHADOW WARRIOR)
(1980 - Toho) Tatsuya Nakadai, Dir: Akira Kurosawa
One Sheet: $10 - $20   *Japanese. Martial arts.*

KAISER, BEAST OF BERLIN, THE
(1918 - Jewel) Rupert Julian, Lon Chaney
One Sheet: $300 - $700

KAISER'S FINISH, THE
(1918 - Warner Bros.) Claire Whitney, Earl Schenck
One Sheet: $200 - $400

KAISER'S SHADOW, THE
(1918 - Paramount) Thurston Hall, Dorothy Dalton
One Sheet: $200 - $400

KALEIDOSCOPE
(1966 - Warner Bros.) Warren Beatty, Susannah York
One Sheet: $10 - $20

KALIFORNIA
(1993 - Gramercy) Brad Pitt, Juliette Lewis, David Duchovny
One Sheet: $15 - $25

KAMA SUTRA
(1971 - AIP) Bruno Dietrich, Persis Khambatta
One Sheet: $15 - $30

KAMA SUTRA: A TALE OF LOVE
(1997 - Trimark) Indira Varma, Sarita Choudhury
One Sheet: $5 - $10

KAMIKAZE '89
(1983 - Trio-Oase) Rainer Werner Fassbinder, Gunther Kaufmann
One Sheet: $5 - $10

KAMOURASKA
(1973 - New Line) Genevieve Bujold, Richard Jordan
One Sheet: $4 - $8

KANGAROO
(1951 - 20th Century Fox) Maureen O'Hara, Peter Lawford
One Sheet: $15 - $35

KANGAROO DETECTIVE, THE
(1927 - Fox) Animal Comedy
One Sheet: $250 - $500

KANGAROO KID, THE
(1950 - Eagle-Lion) Jock Mahoney, Veda Borg
One Sheet: $15 - $35

KANSAN, THE
(1943 - United Artists) Richard Dix, Jane Wyatt
One Sheet: $50 - $100

KANSAS
(1988 - -) Matt Dillon, Andrew McCarthy, Leslie Hope
One Sheet: $3 - $5

KANSAS CITY
(1996 - Fine Line) Jennifer Jason Leigh, Miranda Richardson
One Sheet: $5 - $12   *Gangsters.*

KANSAS CITY BOMBER
(1972 - MGM) Raquel Welch, Kevin McCarthy
One Sheet: $10 - $20   *Sports (Roller Derby). Sports Movie Posters #306.*

KANSAS CITY CONFIDENTIAL
(1952 - United Artists) John Payne, Coleen Gray
One Sheet: $15 - $25

KANSAS CITY KITTY
(1944 - Columbia) Joan Davis, Jane Frazee, Bob Crosby
One Sheet: $30 - $50   *Big band, "Bob Crosby and his Bobcats".*

KANSAS CITY PRINCESS, THE
(1934 - Warner Bros.) Joan Blondell
One Sheet: $100 - $200

KANSAS CYCLONE
(1941 - Republic) Don Barry, Lynn Merrick
One Sheet: $40 - $75

KANSAS PACIFIC
(1953 - Allied Artists) Sterling Hayden, Eve Miller
One Sheet: $10 - $20

KANSAS RAIDERS
(1950 - Universal) Audie Murphy, Marguerite Chapman
One Sheet: $30 - $60

KANSAS TERRITORY
(1939 - Republic) Three Mesquiteers, Jacqueline Wells
One Sheet: $75 - $150

KANSAS TERRITORY
(1952 - Monogram) Bill Elliott, Peggy Stewart
One Sheet: $15 - $35

KANSAS TERRORS, THE
(1939 - Republic) Raymond Halton, Robert Livingston
One Sheet: $50 - $100

KAPO
(1964 - Lionex) Susan Strasberg, Laurent Terzieff
One Sheet: $3 - $5

KARATE KID, THE
(1984 - Columbia) Ralph Macchio, Noriyuki (Pat) Morita
One Sheet: $7 - $15   *Martial arts. Sports Movie Posters #267.*

KARATE KID III, THE
(1989 - Columbia) Ralph Macchio, Noriyuki (Pat) Morita
One Sheet: $3 - $5

KARATE KID PART II, THE
(1986 - Columbia) Ralph Macchio, Noriyuki (Pat) Morita
One Sheet: $3 - $5

KARATE KILLERS, THE
(1967 - MGM) Robert Vaughn, David McCallum, Joan Crawford
One Sheet: $40 - $75   *MAN FROM UNCLE(T.V. tie in).*

KARATE, THE HAND OF DEATH
(1961 - Allied Artists) Joel Holt, Reiko Okada
One Sheet: $30 - $50   *Martial arts.*

KARTOON KARNIVAL
(1954 - MGM) Tom & Jerry
One Sheet: $75 - $150   *Cartoon.*

KATE PLUS TEN
(1938 - General Films) Genevieve Tobin, Jack Hulbert
One Sheet: $100 - $200

KATHLEEN
(1938 - Hoffberg) Tom Burke, Sally O'Neil
One Sheet: $75 - $150

KATHLEEN
(1941 - MGM) Shirley Temple, Herbert Marshall
One Sheet: $100 - $200

KATHLEEN MAVOURNEEN
(1919 - Fox) Theda Bara, Edward O'Connor
One Sheet: $200 - $400

KATHLEEN MAVOURNEEN
(1930 - Tiffany) Sally O'Neil, Charles Delaney
One Sheet: $125 - $250

KATHY O'
(1957 - Universal International) Dan Duryea, Patty McCormick
One Sheet: $30 - $50

KATIE DID IT
(1950 - Universal) Ann Blyth, Mark Stevens
One Sheet: $15 - $30

KATZENJAMMER KIDS, THE ORIGINAL
(192? - National) Hans and Fritz
One Sheet: $150 - $300   *Cartoon. One Sheet is duotone (black/green).*

KAZAAM
(1996 - Disney) Shaquille O'Neal, Frances Capra
One Sheet: $3 - $5   *Urban Fantasy.*

KAZAN
(1949 - Columbia) Stephen Dunne, Lois Maxwell
One Sheet: $15 - $30

KEEP, THE
(1983 - Paramount) Scott Glenn, Alberta Watson, Ian McKellen
One Sheet: $5 - $10

KEEP 'EM FLYING
(1941 - Universal) Bud Abbott, Lou Costello, Martha Raye
One Sheet: $200 - $400

KEEP 'EM LAUGHING
(194?R - Astor) Jack Benny, Sid Silvers
One Sheet: $40 - $75   *Re-titled re-release of "Transatlantic Merry-Go-Round".*

KEEP 'EM ROLLING
(1934 - RKO) Walter Huston, Frances Dee
One Sheet: $150 - $350

KEEP 'EM SLUGGING
(1943 - Universal) Bobby Jordan, Huntz Hall, Evelyn Ankers
One Sheet: $75 - $150

KEEP FIT
(1937 - Associated British) George Formby, Kay Walsh
One Sheet: $75 - $150

KEEP IT CLEAN
(1956 - Eros) Ronald Shiner, Ursula Howells
One Sheet: $10 - $20

KEEP IT QUIET
(1934 - MGM) Jane Carr, Frank Pettingell
One Sheet: $125 - $250

KEEP MOVING
(1915 - Kleine) Harry Watson, Jr., George Bickel
One Sheet: $200 - $400

KEEP MY GRAVE OPEN
(1980 - Century) Camilla Carr, Gene Ross
One Sheet: $5 - $10

KEEP PUNCHING
(1939 - Sack) Henry Armstrong, Francine Everett
One Sheet: $200 - $400   *Black cast. Sports (Boxing). Separate Cinema, pg. 60. Sports Movie Posters #141.*

KEEP SHOOTING
(1941 - RKO) -
One Sheet: $50 - $100

KEEP SMILING
(1925 - Associated Exhibitors) Monty Banks, Anne Cornwall
One Sheet: $150 - $300

KEEP SMILING
(1938 - 20th Century Fox) Jane Withers, Gloria Stuart
One Sheet: $75 - $150

KEEP YOUR POWDER DRY
(1945 - MGM) Lana Turner, Laraine Day
One Sheet: $100 - $200

KEEP YOUR SEATS PLEASE
(1936 - Associated British) George Formby, FLorence Desmond
One Sheet: $50 - $100

KEEPER, THE
(1976 - Lions Gate) Christopher Lee, Sally Gray
One Sheet: $5 - $10

KEEPER OF THE BEES, THE
(1935 - Monogram) Neil Hamilton, Betty Furness
One Sheet: $125 - $250

KEEPER OF THE BEES, THE
(1947 - Columbia) Michael Duane, Gloria Henry
One Sheet: $40 - $75

KEEPER OF THE DOOR
(1919 - Stoll) Basil Gill, Peggy Carlisle
One Sheet: $200 - $400

KEEPER OF THE FLAME
(1942 - MGM) Spencer Tracy, Katharine Hepburn
One Sheet: $250 - $500

KEEPERS OF YOUTH
(1931 - Wardour) Garry Marsh, Ann Todd
One Sheet: $150 - $300

KEEPING COMPANY
(1940 - MGM) Frank Morgan, Ann Rutherford
One Sheet: $75 - $125

KEEPING UP WITH LIZZIE
(1921 - Rockett) Otis Harlan, Enid Bennett
One Sheet: $150 - $300

KELLY AND ME
(1956 - Universal) Van Johnson, Piper Laurie
One Sheet: $20 - $40

KELLY OF THE SECRET SERVICE
(1936 - Principle) Lloyd Hughes, Jack Mulhall
One Sheet: $150 - $300

KELLY THE SECOND
(1936 - MGM) Charlie Chase, Patsy Kelly
One Sheet: $150 - $300   *Sports (Boxing). Sports Movie Posters #136.*

KELLY'S HEROES
(1970 - MGM) Clint Eastwood, Telly Savalas, Don Rickles
One Sheet: $50 - $100
Advance(70mm):$75-125.

KELLY'S HEROES
(1972R - MGM) Clint Eastwood, Telly Savalas, Don Rickles
One Sheet: $15 - $25   *Re-release.*

KENNEDY SQUARE
(1916 - Vitagraph) Charles Kent, Antonio Moreno
One Sheet: $200 - $400

KENNEL MURDER CASE, THE
(1933 - Warner Bros.) William Powell, Mary Astor
One Sheet: $2,500 - $4,000

KENNEL MURDER CASE, THE
(1938R - Warner Bros.) William Powell, Mary Astor
One Sheet: $150 - $350   *Re-release.*

KENNER
(1969 - MGM) Jim Brown, Madlyn Rhue, Robert Coote
One Sheet: $10 - $20   *Blaxploitation.*

KENNY AND CO.
(1976 - 20th Century Fox) Dan McCann, Mike Baldwin
One Sheet: $5 - $10

KENT, THE FIGHTING MAN
(1916 - Gaumont) Billy Wells, Arthur Rooke
One Sheet: $250 - $500

KENTUCKIAN, THE
(1955 - United Artists) Burt Lancaster, Walter Matthau(his film debut)
One Sheet: $150 - $300   *Art by Thomas Hart Benton.*

KENTUCKIANS, THE
(1921 - Paramount) Monte Blue, Wilfred Lytell
One Sheet: $200 - $400

KENTUCKY
(1938 - 20th Century Fox) Loretta Young, Richard Greene, Walter Brennan
One Sheet: $150 - $350   *Academy Award: Best Supporting Actor (Brennan, his 2nd Oscar for supporting role). Academy Award MoviePosters #62.*

KENTUCKY
(1951R - 20th Century Fox) Loretta Young, Richard Greene, Walter Brennan
One Sheet: $30 - $50   *Re-release.*

KENTUCKY BLUE STREAK
(1935 - Puritan) Pat Scott, Eddie Nugent
One Sheet: $150 - $300   *Sports (Horse racing). Sports Movie Posters #246.*

KENTUCKY BROTHERS
(1915 - Unicorn) -
One Sheet: $250 - $600

KENTUCKY CINDERELLA, A
(1917 - Blue) Harry Carter, Ruth Clifford
One Sheet: $200 - $400

KENTUCKY DAYS
(1923 - Fox) Dustin Farnum
One Sheet: $250 - $500

KENTUCKY DERBY, THE
(1922 - Universal) Reginald Denny, Lillian Rich
One Sheet: $800 - $1,500

KENTUCKY FRIED MOVIE
(1977 - United Film) Donald Sutherland, Bill Bixby, George Lazenby
One Sheet: $10 - $20

KENTUCKY HANDICAP
(1926 - Rayart) Alice Calhoun, Reed Howes
One Sheet: $200 - $400   *Sports (Horse racing).*

KENTUCKY JUBILEE
(1951 - Lippert) Jerry Colonna, Jean Porter
One Sheet: $30 - $50

KENTUCKY KERNELS
(1934 - RKO) Spanky McFarland, Wheeler & Woolsey
One Sheet: $150 - $350

KENTUCKY MINSTRELS
(1934 - Universal) Scott & Whaley, Wilson Coleman
One Sheet: $150 - $300   *Minstrel Jazz Bands (Eight Black Streaks, Harry S. Pepper and His White Coons).*

KENTUCKY MOONSHINE
(1938 - 20th Century Fox) The Ritz Brothers, Tony Martin
One Sheet: $75 - $150

KENTUCKY RIFLE
(1956 - Howco) Chill Wills, Lance Fuller
One Sheet: $15 - $25

KEPT HUSBANDS
(1931 - RKO) Joel McCrea, Ned Sparks
One Sheet: $100 - $200

KERIMA THE SHE WOLF
(1954 - Republic) May Britt (debut)
One Sheet: $20 - $40

KES
(1970 - United Artists) David Bradley, Colin Welland
One Sheet: $2 - $3

KETTLES IN THE OZARKS, THE
(1955 - Universal) Marjorie Main, Arthur Hunnicutt
One Sheet: $30 - $50

KETTLES ON OLD MACDONALD'S FARM, THE
(1957 - Universal) Marjorie Main, Parker Fennelly
One Sheet: $30 - $50

KEY, THE
(1934 - Warner Bros.) Edna Best, William Powell, Colin Clive
One Sheet: $600 - $1,000

KEY, THE
(1958 - Columbia) William Holden, Sophia Loren, Trevor Howard
One Sheet: $20 - $40

KEY LARGO
(1948 - Warner Bros.) Humphrey Bogart, Edward G. Robinson, Lauren Bacall
One Sheet: $250 - $500   *Academy Award Movie Posters #118.*

KEY LARGO/TREASURE OF THE SIERRA MADRE, THE
(1950R - Warner Bros.) Humphrey Bogart
One Sheet: $50 - $100   *Re-release double feature poster.*

KEY MAN, THE
(1957 - Anglo) Lee Patterson, Colin Gordon
One Sheet: $7 - $15

KEY TO HARMONY
(1935 - Paramount) Fred Conyngham, Belle Chrystal
One Sheet: $150 - $300

KEY TO THE CITY
(1949 - MGM) Clark Gable, Loretta Young
One Sheet: $75 - $150

KEY WITNESS
(1947 - Columbia) John Beal, Trudy Marshall
One Sheet: $40 - $75

KEY WITNESS
(1960 - MGM) Jeffrey Hunter, Pat Crowley

One Sheet: $7 - $15

KEYHOLE, THE
(1933 - Warner Bros.) George Brent, Kay Francis
One Sheet: $100 - $200

KEYS OF THE KINGDOM, THE
(1944 - 20th Century Fox) Gregory Peck, Peggy Ann Garner, Vincent Price
One Sheet: $100 - $200

KEYS OF THE KINGDOM, THE
(1954R - 20th Century Fox) Gregory Peck, Peggy Ann Garner, Vincent Price
One Sheet: $30 - $50   *Re-release.*

KHARTOUM
(1966 - United Artists) Charlton Heston, Laurence Olivier
One Sheet: $15 - $30   *Cinerama One Sheet: $100-$200.*

KHYBER PATROL
(1954 - United Artists) Richard Egan, Dawn Addams
One Sheet: $15 - $25

KIBITZER, THE
(1930 - Paramount) Harry Green, Mary Brian
One Sheet: $100 - $200

KICK BACK, THE
(1922 - FBO) Harry Carey, Henry B. Walthall
One Sheet: $250 - $500

KICK IN
(1917 - Astra) William Courtenay, Richard Taber
One Sheet: $200 - $400

KICK IN
(1922 - Paramount) Betty Compson, Bert Lytell
One Sheet: $150 - $300

KICK IN
(1931 - Paramount Publix) Clara Bow
One Sheet: $300 - $700

KICKAPOO JUICE
(1944 - Columbia) Li'l Abner
One Sheet: $250 - $600   *Cartoon. Full color poster with scene inset. Cartoon Movie Posters #42.*

KICKBOXER
(1989 - -) Jean-Claude Van Damme, Denis Alexio
One Sheet: $15 - $25   *Sports (Kick-Boxing).*

KICKING AND SCREAMING
(1995 - Trimark) Olivia d'Abo, Eric Stoltz
One Sheet: $3 - $5

KICK-OFF
(1926 - Excel) George Walsh, Leila Hyams
One Sheet: $150 - $300

KID, THE
(1916 - Vitagraph) Lillian Walker, Robert Gaillard
One Sheet: $250 - $600

KID, THE
(1921 - First National) Charles Chaplin, Jackie Coogan
One Sheet: $16,000 - $25,000   *Chaplin's first full-length feature film. Two styles one sheet exist.*

One Sheet (Style A)

KID 'N' AFRICA
(1933 - Educational) Shirley Temple
One Sheet: $250 - $600   *From the Baby Burlesk series.*

KID 'N' HOLLYWOOD
(1933 - Educational) Shirley Temple
One Sheet: $250 - $600   *From the Baby Burlesk series.*

KID AUTO RACES AT VENICE
(1914 - Keystone) Charlie Chaplin
One Sheet: $16,000 - $25,000   *Chaplin's first film as "The Tramp".*

KID BLUE
(1973 - 20th Century Fox) Dennis Hopper, Warren Oates
One Sheet: $5 - $10

KID BOOTS
(1926 - Paramount) Eddie Cantor, Clara Bow
One Sheet: $600 - $1,000   *Sports (Golf). Sports Movie Posters #219.*

KID BROTHER, THE
(1927 - Paramount) Harold Lloyd, Jobyna Ralston
One Sheet: $800 - $1,500

KID COMES BACK, THE
(1937 - Warner Bros.) Wayne Morris, Barton MacLane
One Sheet: $150 - $300   *Sports (Boxing). Sports Movie Posters #139.*

KID COURAGEOUS
(1935 - Supreme) Bob Steele, Lafe McKee
One Sheet: $150 - $300

KID DYNAMITE
(1943 - Monogram) Leo Gorcey, Huntz Hall, Pamela Blake
One Sheet: $75 - $125

KID FOR TWO FARTHINGS, A
(1954 - Lopert) Celia Johnson, Diana Dors
One Sheet: $15 - $30

KID FROM AMARILLO, THE
(1951 - Columbia) Charles Starrett, Smiley Burnette
One Sheet: $15 - $35

KID FROM ARIZONA, THE
(1931 - States Rights) Jack Perrins, Robert Walker
One Sheet: $150 - $300

KID FROM BORNEO, THE
(1933 - MGM) Our Gang
One Sheet: $1,300 - $2,000

KID FROM BROKEN GUN, THE
(1952 - Columbia) Charles Starrett
One Sheet: $15 - $35

KID FROM BROOKLYN, THE
(1946 - RKO) Danny Kaye, Virginia Mayo
One Sheet: $75 - $125

KID FROM CANADA, THE
(1957 - British Lion) Christopher Braden, Bobby Stevenson
One Sheet: $7 - $15

KID FROM CLEVELAND, THE
(1949 - Republic) Satchel Paige, Bob Feller, George Brent, Lynn Bari
One Sheet: $250 - $600   *Sports (Baseball).*

KID FROM GOWER GULCH, THE
(1949 - Astor) Spade Cooley, Wanda Cantlon
One Sheet: $40 - $75

KID FROM KANSAS, THE
(1941 - Universal) Leo Carrillo, Andy Devine
One Sheet: $50 - $100

KID FROM KOKOMO, THE
(1939 - Warner Bros.) Wayne Morris, Pat O'Brien, Joan Blondell
One Sheet: $75 - $125

KID FROM LEFT FIELD, THE
(1953 - 20th Century Fox) Dan Dailey, Anne Bancroft, George Garner
One Sheet: $50 - $100   *Sports (Baseball).*

KID FROM SANTA FE, THE
(1940 - Monogram) Jack Randall
One Sheet: $75 - $125

KID FROM SPAIN, THE
(1933 - Samuel Goldwyn) Eddie Cantor, Lyda Roberti, Robert Young

One Sheet: $500 - $800

KID FROM SPAIN, THE
(194?R - Film Classics) Eddie Cantor
One Sheet: $30 - $60   *Re-release.*

KID FROM TEXAS, THE
(1939 - MGM) Dennis O'Keefe, Buddy Ebsen
One Sheet: $100 - $200

KID FROM TEXAS, THE
(1950 - Universal) Audie Murphy, Gale Storm
One Sheet: $75 - $125

KID GALAHAD
(1937 - Warner Bros.) Edward G. Robinson,
Bette Davis, Humphrey Bogart
One Sheet: $2,200 - $3,500

Title Card

KID GALAHAD
(1962 - United Artists) Elvis Presley, Gig Young
One Sheet: $75 - $150

One Sheet

KID GLOVE KILLER
(1942 - MGM) Van Heflin, Marsha Hunt
One Sheet: $75 - $125

KID GLOVES
(1929 - Warner Bros.) Conrad Nagel
One Sheet: $150 - $350

KID HAYSEED
(1928 - Educational) Big Boy
One Sheet: $250 - $500

KID MILLIONS
(1934 - United Artists) Eddie Cantor, Ethel
Merman
One Sheet: $500 - $800

KID MONK BARONI
(1952 - Realart) Bruce Cabot, Richard Rober
One Sheet: $30 - $60

KID NIGHTINGALE
(1939 - Warner Bros.) John Payne, Jane
Wyman
One Sheet: $75 - $125

KID RANGER, THE
(1936 - Supreme) Bob Steele, William Farnum
One Sheet: $250 - $500

KID RIDES AGAIN, THE
(1943 - PRC) Buster Crabbe
One Sheet: $40 - $75

KID RODELO
(1966 - Paramount) Don Murray, Janet Leigh
One Sheet: $5 - $10

KID SISTER, THE
(1927 - Columbia) Marguerite De La Motte, Ann
Christy

One Sheet: $150 - $300

KID SISTER, THE
(1945 - PRC) Judy Clark, Roger Pryor
One Sheet: $40 - $75

KID VENGEANCE
(1977 - Golan-Globus) Jim Brown, Lee Van
Cleef
One Sheet: $5 - $12

KID'S CLEVER, THE
(1929 - Universal) Glenn Tryon, Kathryn
Crawford, Stepin Fetchit
One Sheet: $250 - $500

KID'S LAST RIDE, THE
(1941 - Monogram) The Three Mesquiteers
One Sheet: $40 - $75

KIDNAPPED
(1917 - Edison) Raymond McKee, Joseph
Burke
One Sheet: $200 - $400

KIDNAPPED
(1938 - 20th Century Fox) Warner Baxter,
Freddie Bartholomew
One Sheet: $150 - $300

KIDNAPPED
(1948 - Monogram) Roddy McDowall, Susan
England
One Sheet: $30 - $60

KIDNAPPED
(1960 - Buena Vista) Peter Finch, James
MacArthur
One Sheet: $15 - $35

KIDNAPPED
(1971 - AIP) Michael Caine, Trevor Howard
One Sheet: $7 - $15

KIDNAPPERS, THE
(1954 - United Artists) Duncan Macrae, Jean
Anderson
One Sheet: $15 - $30

KIDNAPPERS, THE
(1964 - Manson) Burgess Meredith, William
Phipps
One Sheet: $15 - $25

KIDNAPPING OF THE PRESIDENT, THE
(1980 - Crown) William Shatner, Hal Holbrook
One Sheet: $3 - $5

KIDS IN THE SHOE, THE
(1935 - Paramount) Produced by Max Fleischer
One Sheet: $600 - $1,000   *Cartoon.*
Cartoon Movie Posters #200.

KIKA
(1994 - October) Veronique Forque, Peter
Coyote
One Sheet: $5 - $10

KIKI
(1926 - First National) Norma Talmadge,
Ronald Colman
One Sheet: $600 - $1,000

KIKI
(1931 - Feature) Mary Pickford, Betty Grable
One Sheet: $250 - $500

KIKO AND THE HONEY BEARS
(1936 - Educational) Paul Terry Studio
One Sheet: $250 - $600   *Cartoon.*
Duotone. Stock poster with inset of title.

KIKO THE KANGAROO IN CLEANING DAY
(1937 - Educational) Terry Toons
One Sheet: $100 - $200   *Cartoon.*

KILDARE OF STORM
(1918 - Metro) Emily Stevens, Edward David
One Sheet: $250 - $600

KILKENNY CATS, THE
(1943 - 20th Century Fox) Mighty Mouse
One Sheet: $250 - $600   *Cartoon. Full*
color stock poster with printed title. Huge image of
Mighty Mouse on yellow background.

KILL, THE
(1968 - Canyon) Tony Brooks, Antoinette
Maynard
One Sheet: $5 - $10

KILL A DRAGON
(1967 - United Artists) Jack Palance, Fernando
Lamas

One Sheet: $15 - $25

KILL AND KILL AGAIN
(1981 - Film Ventures Int.) James Ryan,
Anneline Kriel
One Sheet: $3 - $5

KILL, BABY, KILL
(1966 - Europix) Giacomo Rossi-Stuart, Erika
Blanc, Dir: Bava
One Sheet: $50 - $100   *AKA: CURSE*
OF THE LIVING DEAD.

KILL HER GENTLY!
(1958 - Columbia) Marc Lawrence, Griffith
Jones
One Sheet: $15 - $25

KILL! KILL! KILL!
(1972 - Cinerama) Stephen Boyd, Jean Seberg
One Sheet: $10 - $20

KILL ME AGAIN
(1989 - MGM) Val Kilmer, Joanne Whalley-
Kilmer
One Sheet: $10 - $20

KILL ME TOMORROW
(1957 - Delta) Pat O'Brien, Tommy Steele, Lois
Maxwell
One Sheet: $15 - $25

KILL OR BE KILLED
(1950 - Eagle-Lion) Lawrence Tierney, George
Coulouris
One Sheet: $40 - $75

KILL OR BE KILLED
(1967 - Regal) Robert Mark, Gordon Mitchell,
Elina De Witt
One Sheet: $5 - $10

KILL OR BE KILLED
(1980 - Film Ventures) Norman Combes,
James Ryan
One Sheet: $3 - $5

KILL OR CURE
(1923 - Pathe) Stan Laurel
One Sheet: $500 - $800

KILL OR CURE
(1962 - MGM) Terry Thomas, Eric Sykes
One Sheet: $3 - $5

KILL SQUAD
(1982 - Summa Vista) Cameron Mitchell, Jeff
Risk
One Sheet: $4 - $8

KILL THE UMPIRE
(1950 - Columbia) William Bendix, Una Merkel
One Sheet: $75 - $150   *Sports*
(Baseball). Sports Movie Posters #59.

KILL THEM ALL AND COME BACK ALONE
(1970 - Fanfare) Chuck Connors, Frank Wolff
One Sheet: $5 - $10

KILLER, THE
(1921 - Pathe) Claire Adams, Jack Conway
One Sheet: $300 - $700

KILLER
(1989 - -) Dir: John Woo
One Sheet: $40 - $75   *Beware re-*
releases.

KILLER APE
(1953 - Columbia) Johnny Weissmuller, Carol
Thurston
One Sheet: $75 - $125   *Jungle Jim*
series.

KILLER AT LARGE
(1936 - Columbia) Mary Brian, Russell Hardie
One Sheet: $125 - $250

KILLER AT LARGE
(1947 - PRC) Robert Lowery, Anabel Shaw
One Sheet: $30 - $60

KILLER BAIT
(195? - Astor) Lizabeth Scott, Dan Duryea
One Sheet: $15 - $25

KILLER DILL
(1947 - Nivel) Stuart Erwin, Anne Gwynne
One Sheet: $40 - $75

KILLER ELITE, THE
(1975 - United Artists) James Caan, Robert
Duvall
One Sheet: $5 - $10

KILLER FISH
(1979 - Associated) Lee Majors, Karen Black,
James Franciscus
One Sheet: $7 - $15   *AKA:*
TREASURE OF THE PIRANHA.

KILLER FORCE
(1976 - AIP) Peter Fonda, Telly Savalas
One Sheet: $5 - $10

KILLER INSIDE ME, THE
(1976 - Warner Bros.) Stacy Keach, Susan
Tyrrell
One Sheet: $3 - $7

KILLER IS LOOSE, THE
(1955 - Crown) Joseph Cotten, Rhonda
Fleming
One Sheet: $30 - $60

KILLER KLOWNS FROM OUTER SPACE
(1988 - -) Suzanne Snyder, Grant Cramer
One Sheet: $15 - $25

KILLER LEOPARD
(1954 - Allied Artists) Johnny Sheffield, Beverly
Garland
One Sheet: $20 - $40   *Bomba series.*

KILLER MCCOY
(1947 - MGM) Mickey Rooney, Brian Donlevy
One Sheet: $40 - $75

KILLER ON A HORSE
(1967 - MGM) Henry Fonda, Janice Rule
One Sheet: $20 - $40   *Cowboy*
Movie Posters #320.

KILLER PARTY
(1986 - -) Elaine Wilkes, Paul Bartel
One Sheet: $5 - $10

KILLER SHARK
(1950 - Monogram) Roddy McDowall, Laurette
Luez
One Sheet: $15 - $30

KILLER SHREWS, THE
(1959 - AIP) James Best, Ken Curtis, Ingrid
Goude
One Sheet: $75 - $150

KILLER THAT STALKED NEW YORK, THE
(1950 - Columbia) Evelyn Keyes, Charles
Korvin
One Sheet: $100 - $200

KILLER TOMATOES STRIKE BACK
(1990 - Fox) John Astin, Rick Rockwell
One Sheet: $10 - $20

KILLER WALKS, A
(1952 - Grand National) Lawrence Harvey,
Susan Shaw
One Sheet: $15 - $25

KILLER'S KISS
(1955 - United Artists) Frank Silvera,
Dir:Stanley Kubrick
One Sheet: $75 - $150

KILLERS, THE
(1946 - Universal) Burt Lancaster (film debut),
Ava Gardner, Edmond O'Brien
One Sheet: $250 - $500

KILLERS, THE
(1956R - Realart) Burt Lancaster (film debut),
Ava Gardner, Edmond O'Brien
One Sheet: $75 - $125   *Re-release.*

KILLERS, THE
(1964 - Universal) Lee Marvin, Angie
Dickinson, Ronald Reagan(his last film)
One Sheet: $30 - $60

KILLERS ALL
(1947 - Del Cal Theaters) -
One Sheet: $30 - $50

KILLERS FROM SPACE
(1953 - Republic) Peter Graves, Barbara
Bestar
One Sheet: $125 - $250

KILLERS OF KILIMANJARO
(1960 - Columbia) Robert Taylor, Anthony
Newley
One Sheet: $15 - $25

KILLERS OF THE SEA
(1939 - Grand National) Capt. Wallace
Casewell (Documentary)

One Sheet: $75 - $125

KILLERS OF THE WILD
(1940 - Times) Joan Valeries, James Bush, Silver Wolf (The Dog)
One Sheet: $30 - $50

KILLERS THREE
(1968 - AIP) Robert Walker, Diane Varsi, Dick Clark
One Sheet: $5 - $10

KILLING, THE
(1956 - United Artists) Sterling Hayden, Coleen Gray, Dir:Stanley Kubrick
One Sheet: $125 - $250

KILLING FIELDS, THE
(1984 - Warner Bros.) Sam Waterston, Haing S. Ngor
One Sheet: $15 - $25   *Academy Award: Best Supporting Actor (Ngor). Academy Award Movie Posters #338.*

KILLING GAME
(1968 - Regional) Jean-Pierre Cassel, Claudine Auger
One Sheet: $5 - $10   *AKA: ALL WEEKEND LOVERS.*

KILLING HOUR, THE
(1982 - Lansbury) Perry King, Elisabeth Kemp
One Sheet: $5 - $10

KILLING KIND, THE
(1973 - Media) Ann Sothern, John Savage, Cindy Williams
One Sheet: $5 - $10

KILLING OF A CHINESE BOOKIE, THE
(1976 - Faces) Ben Gazzara, Meade Roberts
One Sheet: $5 - $10

KILLING OF ANGEL STREET, THE
(1983 - Satori) John Hargreaves, Liz Alexander
One Sheet: $3 - $5

KILLING OF SISTER GEORGE, THE
(1969 - Cinerama) Beryl Reid, Susannah York, Coral Browne
One Sheet: $15 - $35

KILLING TIME
(1987 - -) Beau Bridges, Kiefer Sutherland
One Sheet: $5 - $10

KILLING ZOE
(1994 - -) Eric Stoltz
One Sheet: $5 - $10

KILMENY
(1915 - Morosco) Leonore Ulrich, Herbert Standing
One Sheet: $250 - $500

KILROY WAS HERE
(1947 - Monogram) Jackie Cooper, Jackie Coogan
One Sheet: $75 - $150

KIM
(1950 - MGM) Errol Flynn, Dean Stockwell
One Sheet: $50 - $100

KIM
(1962R - MGM) Errol Flynn, Dean Stockwell
One Sheet: $10 - $20   *Re-release.*

KIMBERLY JIM
(1965 - Embassy) Jim Reeves, Madeleine Usher
One Sheet: $10 - $20

KIND HEARTS AND CORONETS
(1950 - Eagle-Lion) Dennis Price, Valerie Hobson, Alec Guinness
One Sheet: $50 - $100

KIND LADY
(1935 - MGM) Aline MacMahon, Basil Rathbone
One Sheet: $100 - $200

KIND LADY
(1951 - MGM) Ethel Barrymore, Maurice Evans, Angela Lansbury
One Sheet: $20 - $40

KIND OF LOVING, A
(1962 - Governor) Alan Bates, June Ritchie
One Sheet: $5 - $10

KINDERGARTEN COP
(1990 - Universal) Arnold Schwarzenegger

One Sheet: $7 - $15

KINDLED COURAGE
(1923 - Universal) Hoot Gibson, Beatrice Burnahm
One Sheet: $200 - $400

KINDLING
(1915 - Lasky) Thomas Meighan, Charlotte Walker
One Sheet: $250 - $500

KINDRED, THE
(1987 - -) Rod Steiger, Kim Hunter
One Sheet: $5 - $10

KINDRED OF THE DUST
(1922 - R.A. Walsh) Miriam Cooper, Ralph Graves
One Sheet: $150 - $300

KINFOLK
(1970 - Clover) Mady Maquire, Jay Scott
One Sheet: $5 - $10

KING, THE
(1933 - RKO) The Little King
One Sheet: $500 - $800   *Cartoon. Cartoon Movie Poster #141.*

KING AND COUNTRY
(1965 - Allied Artists) Dirk Bogarde, Tom Courtenay
One Sheet: $3 - $5

KING AND FOUR QUEENS, THE
(1956 - United Artists) Clark Gable, Eleanor Parker
One Sheet: $30 - $60

KING AND I, THE
(1956 - 20th Century Fox) Yul Brynner, Deborah Kerr
One Sheet: $125 - $250   *Academy Award: Best Actor. Academy Award Movie Posters #170.*

KING AND I, THE
(1961R - 20th Century Fox) Yul Brynner, Deborah Kerr
One Sheet: $15 - $30   *Re-release.*

KING AND THE CHORUS GIRL, THE
(1937 - Warner Bros.) Joan Blondell, Edward Everett Horton
One Sheet: $100 - $200

KING ARTHUR WAS A GENTLEMAN
(1942 - GFD) Arthur Askey, Peter Graves
One Sheet: $30 - $50

KING BLANK
(1983 - Metafilm) Rosemary Hochschild, Will Patton
One Sheet: $3 - $5

KING COWBOY
(1928 - FBO) Tom Mix
One Sheet: $1,300 - $2,000   *Cowboy Movie Posters #67.*

KING CREOLE
(1958 - Paramount) Elvis Presley, Carolyn Jones
One Sheet: $200 - $400

KING CREOLE
(1959R - Paramount) Elvis Presley, Carolyn Jones
One Sheet: $40 - $75   *Re-release.*

One Sheet

KING DAVID
(1985 - Paramount) Richard Gere, Edward Woodward, Alice Krige

One Sheet: $3 - $5

KING DINOSAUR
(1955 - Lippert) Bill Bryant, Wanda Curtis
One Sheet: $100 - $200

KING FOR A NIGHT
(1933 - Universal) Chester Morris, Helen Twelvetrees
One Sheet: $125 - $250

KING IN NEW YORK, A
(1957 - Attica) Charles Chaplin, Dawn Addams
One Sheet: $50 - $100

KING KELLY OF THE USA
(1934 - Monogram) Irene Ware, Edgar Kennedy
One Sheet: $100 - $200

KING KONG
(1933 - RKO) Fay Wray, Robert Armstrong
One Sheet: $45,000 - $60,000   *Graven Images, pg. 45, 70-73. Lobby Cards are undated.*

One Sheet (Style A)

One Sheet (Style B)

KING KONG
(1938R - RKO) Faye Wray, Robert Armstrong
One Sheet: $6,500 - $10,000   *First re-release. Lobby Cards are undated but different logo than original release.*

KING KONG
(1942R - RKO) Fay Wray, Robert Armstrong
One Sheet: $800 - $1,500   *Re-release. Posters and lobby cards are dated.*

KING KONG
(1947R - RKO) Fay Wray, Robert Armstrong
One Sheet: $150 - $300   *Re-release. One sheet is duotone.*

KING KONG
(1952R - RKO) Fay Wray, Robert Armstrong
One Sheet: $150 - $300   *Re-release. One Sheet is duotone.*

KING KONG
(1956R - RKO) Fay Wray, Robert Armstrong
One Sheet: $250 - $600   *Re-release. One sheet is full color.*

KING KONG
(1968R - Janus) Fay Wray, Robert Armstrong
One Sheet: $15 - $30   *Re-release.*

KING KONG
(1976 - Paramount) Jeff Brides, Jessica Lange
One Sheet: $7 - $15

KING KONG ESCAPES
(1968 - Universal) Rhodes Reason, Mie Hama, Linda Miller
One Sheet: $40 - $75

KING KONG LIVES

(1986 - -) Brian Kerwin, Linda Hamilton
One Sheet: $7 - $15

KING KONG VS. GODZILLA
(1963 - Universal) Michael Keith, James Yagi
One Sheet: $125 - $250   *Japanese poster:$600-$1000.*

One Sheet

KING KONG/LEOPARD MAN
(1950R - RKO) Fay Wray, Robert Armstrong/ Dennis O'Keefe, Jean Brooks
One Sheet: $100 - $200   *Re-release double feature poster.*

KING LEAR
(1916 - Gold Rooster) Frederick Warde, Ina Hammer
One Sheet: $500 - $800

KING LEAR
(1971 - Altura) Paul Scofield, Cyril Cusack
One Sheet: $7 - $15

KING MONSTER
(1976 - -) -
One Sheet: $10 - $20

KING MURDER, THE
(1932 - Chesterfield) Conway Tearle, Dorothy Revier
One Sheet: $100 - $200

KING NEPTUNE
(1932 - United Artists) Silly Symphony
One Sheet: $10,000 - $15,000   *Cartoon. Full color. The Disney Poster, pg. 12.*

KING OEDIPUS
(1957 - Motion Pictures) Douglas Rain, Douglas Campbell
One Sheet: $15 - $25

KING OF ALCATRAZ
(1938 - Paramount) Lloyd Nolan, Gail Patrick
One Sheet: $75 - $150

KING OF BURLESQUE
(1936 - 20th Century Fox) Warner Baxter, Alice Faye
One Sheet: $150 - $300

KING OF CARDS
(1910 - -) Harry Houdini
One Sheet: $10,000 - $15,000   *Magic. Beware reissues and reprints.*

KING OF CHINATOWN
(1939 - Paramount) Anna May Wong, Akim Tamiroff
One Sheet: $100 - $200

KING OF COMEDY, THE
(1982 - 20th Century Fox) Robert De Niro, Jerry Lewis
One Sheet: $20 - $40

KING OF DIAMONDS, THE
(1918 - Vitagraph) Betty Blythe, Harry Morey
One Sheet: $250 - $500

KING OF DODGE CITY
(1941 - Columbia) Bill Elliott, Tex Ritter
One Sheet: $75 - $150

KING OF GAMBLERS
(1937 - Paramount) Lloyd Nolan, Claire Trevor
One Sheet: $100 - $200

KING OF HEARTS
(1936 - Butcher) Will Fyffe, Googie Withers
One Sheet: $100 - $200

KING OF HEARTS
(1967 - Lopert) Alan Bates, Pierre Brasseur

One Sheet: $30 - $60

KING OF HEARTS
(1978R - United Artists) Alan Bates, Pierre
Brasseur
One Sheet: $20 - $40   *Re-release.*

KING OF HOCKEY
(1936 - Warner Bros.) Wayne Morris, Anne
Nagel
One Sheet: $150 - $300   *Sports*
(Hockey).

KING OF JAZZ
(1930 - Universal) Paul Whiteman, John Boles,
Bing Crosby
One Sheet: $250 - $600   *Big band*
musical.

KING OF JUNGLELAND
(1949R - Republic) Clyde Beatty, Manuel King
One Sheet: $15 - $30   *Serial. Re-*
titled re-release of DARKEST AFRICA. 15
Chapters.

KING OF KINGS
(1927 - Pathe) H. B. Warner, Dorothy
Cumming, Dir: Cecil B. DeMille
One Sheet: $800 - $1,500

KING OF KINGS
(1961 - MGM) Jeffrey Hunter, Siobhan
McKenna
One Sheet: $30 - $50

KING OF KONG ISLAND
(1978 - -) Brad Harris, Esmeralda Barros
One Sheet: $7 - $15

KING OF MARVIN GARDENS, THE
(1972 - Columbia) Jack Nicholson, Bruce Dern,
Ellen Burstyn
One Sheet: $15 - $30

KING OF NEW YORK
(1990 - -) Christopher Walken, Larry Fishburne
One Sheet: $7 - $15

KING OF PARIS, THE
(1934 - United Artists) Cedric Hardwicke, Ralph
Richardson
One Sheet: $100 - $200

KING OF THE ARENA
(1933 - Universal) Ken Maynard
One Sheet: $250 - $600

KING OF THE BANDITS
(1947 - Monogram) Gilbert Roland, Angela
Green
One Sheet: $40 - $75   *Cisco Kid*
series.

KING OF THE BULLWHIP
(1950 - Realart) Lash LaRue
One Sheet: $50 - $100

KING OF THE CARNIVAL
(1955 - Republic) Harry Lauter, Fran Bennett
One Sheet: $50 - $100   *Serial. 12*
Chapters.

KING OF THE CASTLE
(1925 - Stoll) Marjorie Hume, Brian Aherne
One Sheet: $200 - $400

KING OF THE CASTLE
(1936 - GFD) Claude Damper, June Clyde,
Wally Patch
One Sheet: $100 - $200

KING OF THE CIRCUS, THE
(1920 - Universal) -
One Sheet: $200 - $400   *Serial. 18*
Chapters.

KING OF THE CIRCUS
(194? - Astor) John Loder, Gregory Ratoff,
Benita Hume
One Sheet: $75 - $150

KING OF THE CONGO
(1952 - Columbia) Buster Crabbe, Gloria Dee
One Sheet: $50 - $100   *Serial. 15*
Chapters.

KING OF THE CORAL SEA
(1956 - Allied Artists) Chips Rafferty, Charles
Tingwell
One Sheet: $7 - $15

KING OF THE COWBOYS
(1943 - Republic) Roy Rogers, Smiley Burnette
One Sheet: $200 - $400

KING OF THE COWBOYS
(1955R - Republic) Roy Rogers
One Sheet: $50 - $100   *Re-release.*

KING OF THE DAMNED
(1935 - Gaumont British) Conrad Veidt, Helen
Vinson
One Sheet: $250 - $500

KING OF THE FOREST RANGERS
(1946 - Republic) Larry Thompson, Helen
Talbot
One Sheet: $200 - $400   *Serial. 12*
Chapters.

KING OF THE GAMBLERS
(1948 - Republic) Janet Martin, William Wright
One Sheet: $40 - $75

KING OF THE GRIZZLIES
(1970 - Buena Vista) John Yesno, Chris
Wiggins
One Sheet: $5 - $10

KING OF THE GYPSIES
(1978 - Paramount) Sterling Hayden, Shelly
Winters
One Sheet: $3 - $5

KING OF THE HERD
(1927 - Aywon) Raymond McKee, Bud Osborne
One Sheet: $150 - $300

KING OF THE HILL
(1993 - Gramercy) Jesse Bradford, Jerome
Krabbe
One Sheet: $3 - $5

KING OF THE JUNGLE
(1927 - Rayart) Elmo Lincoln
One Sheet: $200 - $400

KING OF THE JUNGLE
(1933 - Paramount) Buster Crabbe, Francis
Dee
One Sheet: $1,300 - $2,000

KING OF THE KHYBER RIFLES
(1953 - 20th Century Fox) Tyrone Power, Terry
Moore
One Sheet: $50 - $100

KING OF THE LUMBERJACKS
(1940 - Warner Bros.) John Payne, Gloria
Dixon
One Sheet: $50 - $100

KING OF THE MOUNTAIN
(1981 - Universal) Harry Hamlin, Dennis
Hopper
One Sheet: $3 - $6

KING OF THE MOUNTIES
(1942 - Republic) Allan Lane, Gilbert Emery
One Sheet: $75 - $125   *Serial.*
Western. 12 Chapters.

KING OF THE NEWSBOYS
(1938 - Republic) Lew Ayres, Allison Skipworth
One Sheet: $75 - $150

KING OF THE PECOS
(1936 - Republic) John Wayne, Muriel Evans
One Sheet: $1,600 - $2,500   *Cowboy*
Movie Posters #s 197, 198.

One Sheet

KING OF THE RITZ
(1933 - Regal) Stanley Lupino, Betty Stockfeld
One Sheet: $30 - $50   *One Sheet is*
black & white.

KING OF THE ROARING TWENTIES
(1961 - Allied Artists) David Jansen, Mickey

Rooney
One Sheet: $15 - $25

KING OF THE ROCKET MEN
(1949 - Republic) Tristram Coffin, Mae Clarke
One Sheet: $600 - $1,000   *Serial. 12*
Chapters. Graven Images, pg. 139.

KING OF THE ROCKET MEN
(1953R - Republic) Tristram Coffin, Mae Clarke
One Sheet: $250 - $500   *Re-release.*
Serial. 12 Chapters. One Sheet is full color and
similar to original.

KING OF THE ROCKET MEN
(1956R - Republic) Tristram Coffin, Mae Clark
One Sheet: $200 - $400   *Re-release.*
Serial. 12 Chapters. One Sheet is full color and
very similar to original.

KING OF THE RODEO
(1929 - Universal) Hoot Gibson, Jack Knapp
One Sheet: $150 - $300

KING OF THE ROYAL MOUNTED
(1936 - 20th Century Fox) Robert Kent,
Rosalind Keith
One Sheet: $75 - $150

KING OF THE ROYAL MOUNTED
(1940 - Republic) Allan Lane, Robert Strange
One Sheet: $75 - $150   *Serial.*
Western. 12 Chapters.

KING OF THE SIERRAS
(1938 - Grand National) Hobart Bosworth,
Harry Harvey, Jr.
One Sheet: $75 - $125

KING OF THE STALLIONS
(1942 - Monogram) Chief Thundercloud, David
O'Brien
One Sheet: $75 - $125

KING OF THE STALLIONS
(1958 - Allied Artists) George Montgomery,
Diane Brewster
One Sheet: $15 - $30

KING OF THE TEXAS RANGERS
(1941 - Republic) "Slingin' Sammy" Baugh, Neil
Hamilton
One Sheet: $100 - $200   *Serial.*
Western. 12 Chapters. Sports Movie Posters
#363.

KING OF THE TURF, THE
(1926 - FBO) George Irving, Al Roscoe
One Sheet: $100 - $200

KING OF THE TURF
(1939 - United Artists) Adolphe Menjou,
Delores Costello
One Sheet: $50 - $100

KING OF THE UNDERWORLD
(1939 - Warner Bros.) Humphrey Bogart, Kay
Francis
One Sheet: $800 - $1,500

KING OF THE UNDERWORLD
(194?R - Warner Bros.) Humphrey Bogart, Kay
Francis
One Sheet: $50 - $100   *Re-release.*

KING OF THE UNDERWORLD
(1952 - Ambassador) Tod Slaughter, Patrick
Barr
One Sheet: $15 - $25

KING OF THE WHITE ELEPHANT, THE
(1940 - Pridi) -
One Sheet: $30 - $50

KING OF THE WILD
(1931 - Mascot) Walter Miller
One Sheet: $125 - $250   *Serial.*
Western. 12 Chapters.

KING OF THE WILD HORSES
(1924 - Pathe) Rex, Leon Bary, Edna Murphy
One Sheet: $150 - $300

KING OF THE WILD HORSES
(1933 - Columbia) Rex, Lady, Marquis, William
Janney
One Sheet: $75 - $150

KING OF THE WILD HORSES
(1947 - Columbia) Preston Foster, Gail Patrick
One Sheet: $40 - $75

KING OF THE WILD STALLIONS
(1959 - Allied Artists) George Montgomery,

Diane Brewster
One Sheet: $15 - $25

KING OF THE ZOMBIES
(1941 - Monogram) Dick Purcell, Joan
Woodbury, Mantan Moreland
One Sheet: $150 - $300   *Graven*
Images, pg. 134.

KING, QUEEN, KNAVE
(1972 - AVCO/Embassy) Gina Lollobrigida,
David Niven
One Sheet: $7 - $15

KING RALPH
(1991 - Universal) John Goodman, Peter
O'Toole
One Sheet: $3 - $5

KING RAT
(1965 - Columbia) George Segal, Tom
Courtenay
One Sheet: $5 - $10

KING RICHARD AND THE CRUSADERS
(1954 - Warner Bros.) Rex Harrison, George
Sanders, Virginia Mayo
One Sheet: $50 - $100

KING SOLOMON OF BROADWAY
(1935 - Universal) Edmund Lowe, Dorothy
Page
One Sheet: $125 - $250

KING SOLOMON'S MINES
(1937 - Gaumont) Paul Robeson, Anna Lee,
John Loder
One Sheet: $1,300 - $2,000   *Separate*
Cinema, pg. 44.

KING SOLOMON'S MINES
(1950 - MGM) Deborah Kerr, Stewart Granger
One Sheet: $40 - $75

KING SOLOMON'S MINES
(1985 - Cannon) Richard Chamberlain, Sharon
Stone
One Sheet: $5 - $10

KING SOLOMON'S TREASURE
(1978 - Towers) David McCallum, Patrick
MacNee, Brit Ekland
One Sheet: $5 - $12

KING SPRUCE
(1920 - Dial) Mitchell Lewis, Betty Wales
One Sheet: $150 - $300

KING STEPS OUT, THE
(1936 - Columbia) Franchot Tone, Grace Moore
One Sheet: $150 - $300

KING'S CREEK LAW
(1923 - Steiner) Leo Maloney, Milton Brown
One Sheet: $200 - $400

KING'S CUP, THE
(1933 - British & Dominions) Harry Milton,
Dorothy Bouchier
One Sheet: $100 - $200

KING'S DAUGHTER, THE
(1916 - Jury) Janet Ross, Gerald Ames
One Sheet: $250 - $500

KING'S GAME, THE
(1916 - Gold Rooster) Sheldon Lewis, Pearl
White
One Sheet: $500 - $800

KING'S JESTER, THE
(1947 - Scalela) Michel Simon, Rossano Brazzi
One Sheet: $40 - $75

KING'S PIRATE, THE
(1967 - Universal) Doug McClure, Jill St. John
One Sheet: $10 - $20

KING'S RHAPSODY
(1955 - United Artists) Anna Neagle, Errol
Flynn
One Sheet: $30 - $60

KING'S ROW
(1942 - Warner Bros.) Ann Sheridan, Robert
Cummings, Ronald Reagan
One Sheet: $200 - $400

KING'S ROW
(1956R - Warner Bros.) Ann Sheridan, Robert
Cummings, Ronald Reagan
One Sheet: $40 - $75   *Re-release.*

KING'S THIEF, THE

(1955 - MGM) David Niven, Ann Blyth
One Sheet: $15 - $25

KING'S VACATION, THE
(1933 - Warner Bros.) George Arliss, Marjorie Gateson
One Sheet: $100 - $200

KINGDOM OF LOVE, THE
(1918 - Fox) Jewel Carmen, Fred Milton
One Sheet: $250 - $500

KINGDOM OF THE SPIDERS, THE
(1977 - Dimension) William Shatner, Woody Strode
One Sheet: $7 - $15

KINGDOM WITHIN, THE
(1922 - Security) Russell Simpson, Z. Wall Covington
One Sheet: $125 - $250

KINGFISH CAPER, THE
(1976 - Cavalier) David McCallum, Hayley Mills
One Sheet: $7 - $15

KINGFISHER'S ROOST, THE
(1922 - Pinnacle) Neal Hart, Ben Corbett
One Sheet: $150 - $300

KINGPIN
(1996 - MGM) Woody Harrelson, Bill Murray, Randy Quaid
One Sheet: $3 - $6   *Sports (Bowling).*

KINGS GO FORTH
(1958 - United Artists) Frank Sinatra, Tony Curtis
One Sheet: $30 - $50

Insert

KINGS OF THE OLYMPICS
(1948 - United Artists) Jesse Owens, Earle Medows
One Sheet: $200 - $400   *Sports (Olympics). Duotone photomontage. Review of 1936 Berlin Olympics.*

KINGS OF THE SUN
(1964 - United Artists) Yul Brynner, George Chakiris
One Sheet: $15 - $25

KINJITE: FORBIDDEN SUBJECTS
(1989 - -) Charles Bronson, Juan Fernandez
One Sheet: $5 - $10

KINKAID, GAMBLER
(1916 - Feather) Ruth Stonehouse, Jean Hersholt
One Sheet: $250 - $600

KINKY COACHES & THE POM POM PUSSYCATS, THE
(1981 - Summa Vista) Norman Fell
One Sheet: $15 - $25   *Sexploitation.*

KIPPS
(1921 - Stoll) George K. Arthur, Christine Rayner
One Sheet: $150 - $300

KIPPS
(1941 - 20th Century Fox) Michael Redgrave, Phillis Calvert
One Sheet: $75 - $125

KIRLIAN WITNESS, THE
(1978 - Samson/Cranor) Nancy Snyder, Mara Danziger
One Sheet: $3 - $5

KISENGA, MAN OF AFRICA

(1952 - Two Cities) Robert Adams, Eric Portman
One Sheet: $10 - $20

KISMET
(1920 - Robertson/Cole) Otis Skinner, Herschell Mayall, Elinor Fair
One Sheet: $150 - $300

KISMET
(1930 - First National) Loretta Young, Otis Skinner
One Sheet: $150 - $300

KISMET
(1944 - MGM) Ronald Colman, Marlene Dietrich
One Sheet: $100 - $200

KISMET
(1955 - MGM) Howard Keel, Ann Blyth
One Sheet: $40 - $75

KISS, THE
(1916 - Famous Players) Owen Moore, Adolphe Menjou
One Sheet: $250 - $500

KISS, THE
(1929 - MGM) Greta Garbo, Lew Ayres
One Sheet: $1,900 - $3,000   *MGM's last silent film.*

KISS AND KILL
(1969 - Commonwealth United) Christopher Lee, Richard Greene, Shirley Eaton
One Sheet: $7 - $15

KISS AND MAKE UP
(1934 - Paramount) Cary Grant, Helen Mack
One Sheet: $200 - $400

KISS AND TELL
(1945 - Columbia) Shirley Temple, Jerome Courtland
One Sheet: $75 - $150

KISS AND TELL
(1953R - Columbia) Shirley Temple, Jerome Courtland
One Sheet: $15 - $25   *Re-release. Duotone.*

KISS BARRIER, THE
(1925 - Fox) Edmund Lowe, Claire Adams
One Sheet: $150 - $300

KISS BEFORE DYING, A
(1955 - United Artists) Robert Wagner, Jeffrey Hunter
One Sheet: $20 - $40

KISS BEFORE DYING, A
(1991 - Universal) Matt Dillon, Sean Young
One Sheet: $5 - $10

KISS BEFORE THE MIRROR, THE
(1933 - Universal) Paul Lukas, Walter Pidgeon
One Sheet: $100 - $200

KISS FOR A KILLER, A
(1960 - -) -
One Sheet: $15 - $25

KISS FOR CINDERELLA, A
(1926 - Paramount) Betty Bronson, Tom Moore, Esther Ralston
One Sheet: $250 - $500

KISS FOR CORLISS, A
(1949 - United Artists) Shirley Temple, David Niven
One Sheet: $50 - $100   *Temple's last film.*

KISS FOR SUSIE, A
(1917 - Paramount) Jack Nelson, Vivian Martin
One Sheet: $150 - $300

KISS IN A TAXI
(1927 - Paramount) Bebe Daniels, Chester Conklin
One Sheet: $500 - $800

KISS IN THE DARK, A
(1925 - Paramount) Adolphe Menjou, Aileen Pringle
One Sheet: $150 - $300

KISS IN THE DARK, A
(1948 - Warner Bros.) David Niven, Jane Wyman
One Sheet: $20 - $40

KISS IN TIME, A
(1921 - Real Art) Roy Barnes, Wanda Hawley
One Sheet: $150 - $300

KISS ME AGAIN
(1925 - Warner Bros.) Clara Bow, Monte Blue, Marie Prevost, Dir: Ernst Lubitsch
One Sheet: $1,300 - $2,000

KISS ME AGAIN
(1931 - First National) Walter Pidgeon, Bernice Claire
One Sheet: $125 - $250

KISS ME DEADLY
(1955 - United Artists) Ralph Meeker, Cloris Leachman
One Sheet: $100 - $200

KISS ME GOODBYE
(1935 - Sterling) Arthur Riscoe, Magda Schneider
One Sheet: $150 - $300

KISS ME GOODBYE
(1982 - 20th Century Fox) Sally Field, James Caan, Jeff Bridges
One Sheet: $5 - $10

KISS ME KATE
(1953 - MGM) Kathryn Grayson, Howard Keel
One Sheet: $75 - $150

KISS ME, SERGEANT
(1930 - Wardour) Leslie Fuller, Mamie Holland
One Sheet: $100 - $200

KISS ME, STUPID
(1964 - Lopert) Dean Martin, Kim Novak
One Sheet: $15 - $25

KISS OF ARABY
(1933 - Freuler) Maria Alba, Walter Byron, Claire Windsor
One Sheet: $75 - $150

One Sheet

KISS OF DEATH
(1947 - 20th Century Fox) Victor Mature, Coleen Gray, Richard Widmark
One Sheet: $600 - $1,000   *Widmark's film debut.*

KISS OF DEATH
(1953R - 20th Century Fox) Victor Mature, Coleen Gray, Richard Widmark (film debut)
One Sheet: $50 - $100   *Re-release.*

KISS OF DEATH
(1995 - Fox) David Caruso, Nicolas Cage, Samuel L. Jackson
One Sheet: $5 - $10

KISS OF FIRE
(1955 - Universal) Jack Palance, Barbara Rush
One Sheet: $30 - $50

KISS OF THE SPIDER WOMAN
(1985 - Island Alive) William Hurt, Raul Julia, Sonia Braga
One Sheet: $15 - $35   *Academy Award: Best Actor(Hurt). Academy Award Movie Posters #343.*

KISS OF THE TARANTULA
(1975 - Manson International) Eric Mason, Suzanne Ling
One Sheet: $5 - $12

KISS OF THE VAMPIRE
(1963 - Universal) Clifford Evans, Noel Willman
One Sheet: $20 - $40   *Graven Images, pg. 215. AKA: KISS OF EVIL.*

KISS THE BLOOD OFF MY HANDS

(1948 - Universal International) Joan Fontaine, Burt Lancaster
One Sheet: $50 - $100

KISS THE BOYS GOODBYE
(1941 - Paramount) Don Ameche, Mary Martin, Eddie "Rochester" Anderson
One Sheet: $75 - $125

KISS THE BRIDE GOODBYE
(1944 - Butcher) Patricia Medina, Jimmy Hanley
One Sheet: $40 - $75

KISS THE GIRLS AND MAKE THEM DIE
(1967 - Columbia) Michael Connors, Dorothy Provine
One Sheet: $7 - $15

KISS THE OTHER SHEIK
(1968 - MGM) Marcello Mastroianni, Pamela Tiffin
One Sheet: $15 - $25   *French/Italian. AKA: THE BLONDE WIFE.*

KISS THEM FOR ME
(1957 - 20th Century Fox) Cary Grant, Jayne Mansfield
One Sheet: $30 - $60

KISS TOMORROW GOODBYE
(1950 - Warner Bros.) James Cagney, Barbara Payton
One Sheet: $40 - $75

KISSED
(1922 - Universal) Marie Prevost, Frank Glendon
One Sheet: $250 - $500

KISSED
(1997 - Goldwyn) Molly Parker, Peter Outerbridge
One Sheet: $3 - $5

KISSES
(1922 - Metro) Alve Lake, Harry Myers
One Sheet: $150 - $300

KISSES FOR BREAKFAST
(1941 - Warner Bros.) Dennis Morgan, Jane Wyatt
One Sheet: $50 - $100

KISSES FOR MY PRESIDENT
(1964 - Warner Bros.) Fred MacMurray, Polly Bergen
One Sheet: $15 - $25

KISSIN' COUSINS
(1964 - MGM) Elvis Presley, Glenda Farrell
One Sheet: $40 - $75

One Sheet

KISSING BANDIT, THE
(1948 - MGM) Frank Sinatra, Kathryn Grayson
One Sheet: $75 - $125

KISSING CUP'S RACE
(1920 - Butcher) Clive Brook, Violet Hopson
One Sheet: $200 - $400

KISSING CUP'S RACE
(1930 - Butcher) John Stuart, Madeleine Carroll
One Sheet: $100 - $200

KISSING TIME
(1934 - Vitaphone) Jane Froman, George Metaxa
One Sheet: $250 - $600

KIT CARSON
(1928 - Famous Players) Fred Thomson, Dorothy James
One Sheet: $250 - $600

KIT CARSON
(1940 - United Artists) Jon Hall, Lynn Bari, Clayton Moore
One Sheet: $75 - $150

KITTEN WITH A WHIP
(1964 - Universal) Ann-Margret, John Forsythe
One Sheet: $30 - $60

KITTY
(1929 - Wardour) Estelle Brody, John Stuart, Dorothy Cumming
One Sheet: $150 - $300

KITTY
(1945 - Paramount) Paulette Goddard, Ray Milland
One Sheet: $75 - $125

KITTY FOYLE
(1940 - RKO) Ginger Rogers, Dennis Morgan
One Sheet: $125 - $250   *Academy Award: Best Actress(Rogers). Academy Award Movie Posters #73.*

KITTY FROM KILLARNEY
(1926 - Pathe) Alice Day, Eddie Quillan
One Sheet: $150 - $300

One Sheet

KLANSMAN, THE
(1974 - Paramount) Lee Marvin, Richard Burton, O. J. Simpson
One Sheet: $15 - $30

KLONDIKE
(1932 - Monogram) Lyle Talbot, Thelma Todd
One Sheet: $75 - $150

KLONDIKE ANNIE
(1936 - Paramount) Mae West, Victor McLaglen
One Sheet: $1,600 - $2,500

KLONDIKE FEVER
(1980 - CFI) Rod Steiger, Angie Dickinson, Jeff East
One Sheet: $5 - $10

KLONDIKE FURY
(1942 - Monogram) Edmund Lowe, Lucille Fairbanks
One Sheet: $30 - $60

KLONDIKE KATE
(1943 - Columbia) Anne Savage, Tom Neal
One Sheet: $50 - $100

KLONDIKE KID, THE
(1932 - United Artists) Mickey Mouse
One Sheet: $40,000 - $50,000   *Cartoon. The Disney Poster, pg. 21. Cartoon Movie Posters #60.*

KLUTE
(1971 - Warner Bros.) Jane Fonda, Donald Sutherland
One Sheet: $15 - $25   *Academy Award: Best Actress(Fonda). Academy Award Movie Posters #266 & #267.*

KNACK...AND HOW TO GET IT, THE
(1965 - United Artists) Rita Tushingham, Ray Brooks
One Sheet: $5 - $10

KNAVE OF HEARTS, THE
(1919 - Harma) Evelyn Boucher, James Knight
One Sheet: $200 - $400

KNICKERBOCKER BUCKAROO, THE
(1919 - Artcraft) Douglas Fairbanks, Marjorie Dew
One Sheet: $300 - $700

KNICKERBOCKER HOLIDAY
(1944 - United Artists) Nelson Eddy, Charles Coburn, Constance Dowling
One Sheet: $50 - $100

KNIFE, THE
(1918 - Select) Frank Morgan, Alice Brady
One Sheet: $250 - $500

KNIFE IN THE WATER
(1961 - Polski) Leon Niemczyk, Dir: Roman Polanski
One Sheet: $30 - $50   *Polish.*

KNIGHT DUTY
(1933 - Educational) Harry Langdon, Vernon Dent
One Sheet: $150 - $300

KNIGHT FOR A DAY
(1946 - RKO/Disney) Goofy
One Sheet: $800 - $1,500   *Cartoon. The Disney Poster, pg. 62.*

KNIGHT OF THE PLAINS
(1939 - Spectrum) John Merton, Frank LaRue
One Sheet: $100 - $200

KNIGHT OF THE RANGE, A
(1916 - Universal) Harry Carey, Hoot Gibson
One Sheet: $200 - $400

KNIGHT OF THE WEST, A
(1921 - Blanchfield) Olin Francis, Estelle Harrison
One Sheet: $150 - $300

KNIGHT WITHOUT ARMOR
(1937 - United Artists) Marlene Dietrich, Robert Donat
One Sheet: $1,300 - $2,000

KNIGHTRIDERS
(1981 - United Film) Ed Harris, Gary Lahti
One Sheet: $7 - $15

KNIGHTRIDERS
(1981 - United Film) Ed Harris, Gary Lahti
One Sheet: $5 - $10   *Advance Style (Boris Vallejo art):$20-$30.*

KNIGHTS FOR A DAY
(1937 - Pathe) Nelson Keys, John Garrick
One Sheet: $75 - $150

KNIGHTS OF THE RANGE
(1940 - Paramount) Russell Hayden, Jean Parker
One Sheet: $50 - $100

KNIGHTS OF THE ROUND TABLE
(1953 - MGM) Robert Taylor, Ava Gardner, Mel Ferrer
One Sheet: $50 - $100

KNIVES OF THE AVENGER
(1967 - World) Cameron Mitchell, Jack Stewart
One Sheet: $15 - $30

KNOCK ON ANY DOOR
(1949 - Columbia) Humphrey Bogart, John Derek
One Sheet: $75 - $150

KNOCK ON ANY DOOR
(1959R - Columbia) Humphrey Bogart, John Derek
One Sheet: $15 - $25   *Re-release.*

KNOCK ON WOOD
(1953 - Paramount) Danny Kaye, Mai Zetterling
One Sheet: $30 - $60

KNOCKNAGOW
(1918 - Ireland Film) Fred O'Donovan, Cyril Cusack (debut)
One Sheet: $200 - $400

KNOCKOUT, THE
(1914 - Keystone) Charlie Chaplin, Roscoe "Fatty" Arbuckle
One Sheet: $11,000 - $18,000   *Sports (Boxing).*

KNOCKOUT, THE
(1923 - Jury) Rex Davis, Lilian Hall Davis
One Sheet: $250 - $500   *Sports (Boxing).*

KNOCKOUT, THE
(1925 - First National) Milton Sills, Jed Prouty
One Sheet: $250 - $500   *Sports (Boxing).*

KNOCKOUT
(1941 - Warner Bros.) Arthur Kennedy, Olympe Bradna
One Sheet: $75 - $125   *Sports (Boxing).*

KNOCKOUT
(1947 - Monogram) Leon Errol, Joe Kirkwood
One Sheet: $125 - $250   *Sports (Boxing).*

KNOCKOUT KID, THE
(1925 - Rayart) Jack Perrine, Molly Malone
One Sheet: $250 - $500   *Sports (Boxing).*

KNOCKOUT REILLY
(1927 - First National) Richard Dix, Mary Brian
One Sheet: $250 - $600   *Sports (Boxing).*

KNOW YOUR MEN
(1921 - Fox) Pearl White, Wilfred Lytell
One Sheet: $800 - $1,500

KNOWING MEN
(1930 - United Artists) Elissa Landi, Carl Brisson
One Sheet: $100 - $200

KNUTE ROCKNE, ALL AMERICAN
(1940 - Warner Bros.) Pat O'Brien, Gale Page, Ronald Reagan
One Sheet: $150 - $300   *Sports (Football). Sports Movie Posters #s 195, 197.*

KNUTZY KNIGHTS
(1954 - Columbia) The Three Stooges (Shemp)
One Sheet: $150 - $300   *Comedy short. Duotone. Remake of SQUAREHEADS OF THE ROUND TABLE.*

KOENIGSMARK
(1935 - Capital) Elissa Landi, John Lodge
One Sheet: $100 - $200

KOLYA
(1996 - Miramax) Zdenek Sverak, Andrej Chalimon
One Sheet: $3 - $5

KONA COAST
(1968 - Warner Bros./Seven Arts) Richard Boone, Vera Miles
One Sheet: $3 - $5

KONGA
(1961 - AIP) Michael Gough, Margo Johns
One Sheet: $75 - $125

KONGA, THE WILD STALLION
(1939 - Columbia) Fred Stone, Rochelle Hudson
One Sheet: $75 - $150

KONGO
(1932 - MGM) Walter Huston, Lupe Velez
One Sheet: $200 - $400

KON-TIKI
(1951 - RKO) Thor Heyerdahl
One Sheet: $15 - $25   *Documentary.*

KOREA PATROL
(1950 - Eagle-Lion) Richard Emory, Teri Duna
One Sheet: $20 - $40

KOTCH
(1971 - Cinerama) Walter Matthau, Deborah Winters
One Sheet: $3 - $5

KRAKATOA
(1943 - 20th Century Fox) Mighty Mouse
One Sheet: $250 - $600   *Cartoon. Full color stock poster with printed title. Huge image of Mighty Mouse on yellow background.*

KRAKATOA, EAST OF JAVA
(1969 - Cinerama) Maximilian Schell, Diane Baker, Brian Keith
One Sheet: $10 - $20

KRAMER VS. KRAMER
(1979 - Columbia) Dustin Hoffman, Meryl Streep
One Sheet: $15 - $30   *Academy Award: Best Picture, Best Actor, Best Supporting Actress. Academy Award Movie Posters #306 & #308.*

KRAYS, THE
(1990 - Miramax) Billie Whitelaw, Gary Kemp, Martin Kemp, Tom Bell

One Sheet: $7 - $15

KRAZY KAT STOCK POSTER
(1930 - Columbia) Krazy Kat
One Sheet: $1,900 - $3,000   *Cartoon. "Come right in and see my newest cartoon!" Cartoon Movie Posters #29.*

KRAZY KAT STOCK POSTER
(1931 - Columbia) Krazy Kat
One Sheet: $1,600 - $2,500   *Cartoon. "Step right in, folks" Cartoon Movie Posters #30.*

KRAZY'S BEAR TALE
(1936 - Columbia) Krazy Kat
One Sheet: $800 - $1,500   *Cartoon. Full color stock poster with title sheet attached.*

KREMLIN LETTER, THE
(1970 - 20th Century Fox) Bibi Andersson, Richard Boone
One Sheet: $5 - $10

KRIEMHILD'S REVENGE
(1924 - UFA) Dir: Fritz Lang
One Sheet: $3,500 - $5,000   *German. Price is for original German release poster.*

KRONOS
(1957 - 20th Century Fox) Jeff Morrow, Barbara Lawrence, John Emery
One Sheet: $50 - $100   *Graven Images, pg. 180.*

KRULL
(1983 - Columbia) Ken Marshall, Lysette Anthony
One Sheet: $5 - $10

KRUSH GROOVE
(1984 - Warner Bros.) Run DMC, The Fat Boys, Sheila E.
One Sheet: $7 - $15

KUFFS
(1992 - Universal) Christian Slater, Milla Jovovich
One Sheet: $5 - $10

L'AFFICHE DE CINEMA DE 1895
(1895 - -) -
One Sheet: $1,300 - $2,000   *French. Price is for 23x31 poster.*

L'AVVENTURA
(1960 - Janus) Monice Vitti, Gabriele Ferzetti
One Sheet: $15 - $30

L'ENFANT SAUVAGE
(1969 - -) -
One Sheet: $15 - $25   *French.*

LA BABY SITTER
(1975 - Champion) Maria Schneider, Robert Vaughn, Vic Morrow
One Sheet: $3 - $5   *AKA: BABYSITTER.*

LA BAMBA
(1985 - Columbia) Lou Diamond Phillips, Esai Morales
One Sheet: $5 - $10

LA BELLE ET LA BETE (BEAUTY AND THE BEAST)
(1946 - Dis Cina) Jean Marais, Josette Day
One Sheet: $4,000 - $6,000   *French. Price is for original French One Panel(47x63) with Beast shown. Graven Images, pg. 144-145.*

LA BELLE NOISEUSE
(1991 - -) Michel Piccoli, Jane Birkin
One Sheet: $7 - $15   *French.*

LA BELLE RUSSE
(1919 - Fox) Theda Bara, Warburton Gamble
One Sheet: $1,600 - $2,500

LA BETE HUMAINE
(1938 - Discina) Jean Gabin, Simone Simon
One Sheet: $250 - $500   *French.*

LA BOHEME
(1965 - Warner Bros.) La Seala Opera Co.
One Sheet: $15 - $35

LA BONNE SOUPE
(1964 - International Classics) Annie Girardot, Marie Bell
One Sheet: $15 - $25

LA CAGE AUX FOLLES
(1979 - United Artists) Ugo Tognazzi, Michel Serrault

One Sheet: $15 - $25   *AKA: THE*
MAD CAGE; BIRDS OF A FEATHER

LA CAGE AUX FOLLES II
(1981 - United Artists) Ugo Tognazzi
One Sheet: $5 - $10

LA CONGA NIGHTS
(1940 - Universal) Hugh Herbert, Dennis
O'Keefe, Constance Moore
One Sheet: $75 - $150

LA DOLCE VITA
(1960 - Cinertz) Marcello Mastroianni, Anita
Ekberg, Dir: Fellini
One Sheet: $2,500 - $4,000   *Italian. Price
is for original Italian one panel (39x55). Italian two
panel:$6000-$8000.*

LA DOLCE VITA
(1961 - Astor) Marcello Mastroianni, Anita
Ekberg, Dir: Fellini
One Sheet: $100 - $200   *Price is for
U.S. one sheet.*

LA DOLCE VITA
(1966R - AIP) Marcello Mastroianni, Anita
Ekberg, Dir: Fellini
One Sheet: $20 - $40   *Re-release.*

LA FEMME DE MES RIVES
(1930S - Osso) Suzy Vernon, Roland Toutain
One Sheet: $100 - $200   *French.*

LA FEMME ET LE PAUTIN
(1960 - Pathe) Brigitte Bardot
One Sheet: $600 - $1,000   *French. Price
is for original French 47x63.*

LA FEMME NIKITA
(1991 - Goldwyn) Anne Parilland
One Sheet: $15 - $30

LA FUGA
(1966 - Int.) Giovanni Ralli, Anouk Aimee
One Sheet: $10 - $20

LA GRANDE BOURGEOISE
(1974 - Atlantic) Catherine Deneuve. Giancarlo
Giannini
One Sheet: $5 - $10   *Poster is
black & white.*

LA JETEE
(1963 - -) -
One Sheet: $15 - $25   *French.*

LA MARCHE SUR ROME
(197? - -) -
One Sheet: $40 - $75   *French.*

LA MERVEILLEUSE VISTE
(1978 - -) -
One Sheet: $15 - $25

LA PARISIENNE
(1958 - -) Brigitte Bardot, Charles Boyer
One Sheet: $75 - $125

LA RONDE
(1954 - Commercial) Anton Walbrook, Simone
Signoret, Simone Simon
One Sheet: $30 - $60   *French.*

LA RONDE
(1964 - Pathe) Jane Fonda, Maurice Ronet,
Jean Sorel
One Sheet: $125 - $250   *French. Price
is for French 47x63. American title: "Circle Of
Love."*

LA SIRENE DES TROPIQUES
(1927 - Aubert) Josephine Baker
One Sheet: $6,500 - $10,000   *Baker's first
film. Price is for original French 47x63. Separate
Cinema, pg. 76.*

L.A. STORY
(1990 - TriStar) Steve Martin, Victoria Tennent
One Sheet: $7 - $15

LA STRADA
(1954 - Trans-Lux) Anthony Quinn, Richard
Basehart, Dir: Fellini
One Sheet: $30 - $50   *Italian.*

LA TOSCA
(1911 - -) Sarah Bernhardt
One Sheet: $800 - $1,500

LA TRAVIATA
(1968 - Royal) Ann Moffo, Franco Bonisolli
One Sheet: $15 - $25

LA VAMPIRE NUE
(1969 - ABC) -
One Sheet: $125 - $250   *French.*

LA VERITE
(1961 - -) See TRUTH, THE
French.

LA VIE CONTINUE
(1982 - Columbia) Annie Girardot, Jean-Pierre
Cassel
One Sheet: $3 - $5   *French.*

LA VISTA
(1966 - Promenade) Sandra Milo, Francois
Perier
One Sheet: $5 - $10

LABOUR LEADER, THE
(1917 - British Actors) Fay Compton, Fred
Groves
One Sheet: $200 - $400

LABYRINTH
(1986 - TriStar) David Bowie, Jennifer Connelly
One Sheet: $15 - $25   *Advance:$30-
40.*

LAD, THE
(1935 - Universal) Betty Stockfield, Gordon
Harker
One Sheet: $150 - $300

LAD: A DOG
(1961 - Warner Bros.) Peter Breck, Peggy
McCay
One Sheet: $10 - $20

LADDIE
(1935 - RKO) Donald Crisp
One Sheet: $100 - $200

LADDIE
(1940 - RKO) Tim Holt, Virginia Gilmore
One Sheet: $40 - $75

LADDIE BE GOOD
(1928 - Pathe) Bill Cody, Rose Blossom
One Sheet: $200 - $400

**LADIES AND GENTLEMEN, THE FABULOUS
STAINS**
(1982 - Paramount) Diane Lane, Ray Winstone
One Sheet: $3 - $5

**LADIES AND GENTLEMEN: THE ROLLING
STONES**
(1981 - -) Stones (Documentary)
One Sheet: $20 - $40   *Rock 'n Roll.*

LADIES AT EASE
(1927 - Chadwick) Pauline Garon, Lillian
Hackett
One Sheet: $150 - $300

LADIES AT PLAY
(1926 - First National) Lloyd Hughes, Doris
Kengon
One Sheet: $150 - $300

LADIES COURAGEOUS
(1944 - Universal) Loretta Young, Diana
Barrymore
One Sheet: $75 - $125

LADIES CRAVE EXCITEMENT
(1935 - Mascot) Evalyn Knapp, Norman Foster
One Sheet: $150 - $300

LADIES IN DISTRESS
(1938 - Republic) Alison Skipworth, Polly
Moran
One Sheet: $75 - $125

LADIES IN LOVE
(1930 - Chesterfield) Alice Day, Johnny Walker
One Sheet: $75 - $150

LADIES IN LOVE
(1936 - 20th Century Fox) Janet Gaynor,
Constance Bennett
One Sheet: $250 - $500

LADIES IN RETIREMENT
(1941 - Columbia) Ida Lupino, Louis Hayward
One Sheet: $75 - $125

LADIES LOVE BRUTES
(1930 - Paramount Publix) Mary Astor, Fredric
March
One Sheet: $150 - $300

LADIES LOVE DANGER
(1935 - Fox) Mona Barrie, Gilbert Roland

One Sheet: $100 - $200

LADIES MUST DRESS
(1927 - Fox) Virginia Valli, Earle Foxe,
Lawrence Gray
One Sheet: $200 - $400

LADIES MUST LIVE
(1940 - Warner Bros.) Wayne Morris,
Rosemary Lane
One Sheet: $50 - $100

LADIES MUST LOVE
(1933 - Universal) June Knight, Neil Hamilton
One Sheet: $125 - $250

LADIES MUST PLAY
(1930 - Columbia) Dorothy Sebastian, Neil
Hamilton
One Sheet: $150 - $300

LADIES OF LEISURE
(1930 - Columbia) Barbara Stanwyck, Lowell
Sherman
One Sheet: $1,600 - $2,500

LADIES OF THE BIG HOUSE
(1931 - Paramount Publix) Sylvia Sidney, Gene
Raymond
One Sheet: $200 - $400

LADIES OF THE CHORUS
(1949 - Columbia) Adele Jergens, Marilyn
Monroe (her 1st real role)
One Sheet: $150 - $300   *Monroe
appears on most posters and lobby cards.*

LADIES OF THE CHORUS
(1952R - Columbia) Marilyn Monroe, Adele
Jergens
One Sheet: $350 - $750   *Re-release.
Monroe is top-billed and featured prominently on
all posters.*

LADIES OF THE JURY
(1932 - RKO) Edna Mae Oliver, Ken Murray
One Sheet: $150 - $300

LADIES OF THE MOB
(1928 - Paramount) Clara Bow, Richard Arlen
One Sheet: $600 - $1,000

LADIES OF WASHINGTON
(1944 - 20th Century Fox) Ronald Graham,
Trudy Marshall
One Sheet: $50 - $100

LADIES SHOULD LISTEN
(1934 - Paramount) Cary Grant, Frances Drake
One Sheet: $250 - $600

LADIES THEY TALK ABOUT
(1933 - Warner Bros.) Barbara Stanwyck,
Preston Foster
One Sheet: $4,000 - $6,000   *Vargas art.*

LADIES TO BOARD
(1924 - Fox) Tom Mix, Gertrude Olmstead
One Sheet: $250 - $600

LADIES WHO DO
(1963 - Continental) Robert Morley, Peggy
Mount
One Sheet: $7 - $15

LADIES' DAY
(1943 - RKO) Lupe Velez, Eddie Albert, Patsy
Kelly
One Sheet: $50 - $100   *Sports
(Baseball).*

LADIES' MAN
(1931 - Paramount Publix) William Powell, Kay
Francis, Carole Lombard
One Sheet: $600 - $1,000

LADIES' MAN
(1947 - Paramount) Eddie Bracken, Cass Daley
One Sheet: $30 - $60

LADIES' MAN
(1961 - Paramount) Jerry Lewis, Helen Traubel
One Sheet: $30 - $50

LADRI DI BICICLETTE
(1948 - Produzione P.D.S.) Vittorio De Sica
One Sheet: $10,000 - $15,000   *Italian. Price
is for original Italian 39x55 poster. Art by E. Brini.
Beware early reissues.*

LADY AND GENT
(1932 - Paramount Publix) George Bancroft,
Charles Starrett
One Sheet: $100 - $200

LADY AND THE BANDIT, THE
(1951 - Columbia) Louis Hayward, Patricia
Medina
One Sheet: $15 - $30

LADY AND THE MOB, THE
(1939 - Columbia) Fay Bainter, Lee Bowman
One Sheet: $75 - $150

LADY AND THE MONSTER, THE
(1944 - Republic) Erich von Stroheim, Richard
Arlen, Vera Ralston
One Sheet: $100 - $200   *Graven
Images, pg. 135.*

LADY AND THE TRAMP
(1955 - RKO/Disney) -
One Sheet: $350 - $750   *Cartoon.
Cartoon Movie Posters #382.*

Three Sheet

LADY AND THE TRAMP
(1962R - Disney) -
One Sheet: $40 - $75   *Re-release.
Cartoon.*

LADY AND THE TRAMP
(1972R - Buena Vista/Disney) -
One Sheet: $40 - $75   *Re-release.
Cartoon. Full color.*

LADY AND THE TRAMP
(1980R - Disney) -
One Sheet: $30 - $50   *Re-release.
Cartoon.*

LADY AND THE TRAMP
(1985R - Disney) -
One Sheet: $15 - $30   *Re-release.
Cartoon.*

**LADY AND THE TRAMP/ALMOST ANGELS
COMBO**
(1967R - Disney) -
One Sheet: $30 - $50   *Double
feature re-release.*

LADY AT MIDNIGHT
(1948 - Eagle-Lion) Richard Denning, Frances
Rafferty
One Sheet: $20 - $40

LADY BE CAREFUL
(1936 - Paramount Publix) Lew Ayres, Buster
Crabbe
One Sheet: $100 - $200

LADY BE GOOD
(1928 - First National) Jack Mulhall, Dorothy
MacKaill
One Sheet: $150 - $300

LADY BE GOOD
(1941 - MGM) Eleanor Powell, Robert Young
One Sheet: $75 - $150

LADY BEHAVE
(1938 - Republic) Sally Eilers, Neil Hamilton
One Sheet: $75 - $125

LADY BEWARE
(1987 - -) Diane Lane, Michael Woods
One Sheet: $3 - $5

LADY BODYGUARD
(1943 - Paramount) Eddie Albert, Anne Shirley
One Sheet: $50 - $100

LADY BY CHOICE
(1934 - Columbia) Carole Lombard, May
Robson
One Sheet: $600 - $1,000

LADY CAROLINE LAMB
(1972 - United Artists) Sarah Miles, Jon Finch, Richard Chamberlain
One Sheet: $3 - $5

LADY CHASER
(1946 - PRC) Anne Savage, Robert Lowery
One Sheet: $30 - $50

LADY CHATTERLY'S LOVER
(1981 - Cannon) Sylvia Kristel, Nicholas Clay
One Sheet: $5 - $10

LADY COCOA
(1975R - Moonstone) Lola Falana, Gene Washington, "Mean" Joe Greene
One Sheet: $15 - $25   *Blaxploitation. Re-titled re-release of POP GOES THE WEASEL.*

LADY CONFESSES, THE
(1945 - PRC) Mary Beth Hughes, Hugh Beaumont
One Sheet: $100 - $200

LADY CONSENTS, THE
(1936 - RKO) Herbert Marshall, Ann Harding
One Sheet: $100 - $200

LADY CRAVED EXCITEMENT, THE
(1950 - Hammer) Hy Hazell, Sidney James
One Sheet: $40 - $75

LADY ESCAPES, THE
(1937 - 20th Century Fox) Gloria Stuart, Michael Whalen
One Sheet: $100 - $200

LADY EVE, THE
(1941 - Paramount) Barbara Stanwyck, Henry Fonda
One Sheet: $600 - $1,000

LADY EVE, THE
(1950R - Paramount) Barbara Stanwyck, Henry Fonda
One Sheet: $75 - $150   *Re-release.*

LADY FIGHTS BACK, THE
(1937 - Universal) Irene Hervey, Kent Taylor
One Sheet: $75 - $150

LADY FOR A DAY
(1933 - Columbia) Warren William, May Robson, Dir: Frank Capra
One Sheet: $1,300 - $2,000   *First Columbia Oscar nomination.*

LADY FOR A NIGHT
(1942 - Republic) Joan Blondell, John Wayne
One Sheet: $150 - $350

Insert

LADY FRANKENSTEIN
(1972 - New World) Joseph Cotton, Sarah Bay
One Sheet: $15 - $30   *AKA: DAUGHTER OF FRANKENSTEIN.*

LADY FROM CHEYENNE, THE
(1941 - Universal) Loretta Young, Robert Preston
One Sheet: $75 - $150

LADY FROM CHUNGKING
(1943 - PRC) Anna May Wong, Harold Huber
One Sheet: $50 - $100

LADY FROM HELL, THE
(1926 - Associated Exhibitors) Blanche Sweet, Roy Stewart
One Sheet: $250 - $600

LADY FROM LISBON
(1942 - Anglo) Jane Carr, Francis L. Sullivan
One Sheet: $20 - $40

LADY FROM LOUISIANA
(1941 - Republic) John Wayne, Ona Munson
One Sheet: $150 - $350

LADY FROM LOUISIANA
(1953R - Republic) John Wayne, Ona Munson
One Sheet: $40 - $75   *Re-release.*

LADY FROM NOWHERE
(1931 - Chesterfield) Alice Day, John Holland
One Sheet: $150 - $300

LADY FROM NOWHERE
(1936 - Columbia) Mary Astor, Charles Quigley
One Sheet: $150 - $350

One Sheet

LADY FROM SHANGHAI, THE
(1948 - Columbia) Rita Hayworth, Orson Welles
One Sheet: $1,300 - $2,000

One Sheet

LADY FROM TEXAS, THE
(1951 - Universal) Howard Duff, Mona Freeman
One Sheet: $30 - $50

LADY GAMBLES, THE
(1949 - Universal) Barbara Stanwyck, Robert Preston
One Sheet: $40 - $75

LADY GANGSTER
(1942 - Warner Bros.) Faye Emerson, Frank Wilcox
One Sheet: $40 - $75

LADY GODIVA
(1955 - Universal) Maureen O'Hara, George Nader
One Sheet: $20 - $40

LADY GODIVA RIDES AGAIN
(1951 - British Lion) Diana Dors, Joan Collins (her film debut)
One Sheet: $30 - $50

LADY GODIVA RIDES AGAIN
(1965 - -)
One Sheet: $20 - $40   *Cartoon.*

LADY GREY
(1980 - Maverick) David Allen Coe, Ginger Alden
One Sheet: $5 - $10

LADY HAS PLANS, THE
(1941 - Paramount) Ray Milland, Paulette Goddard
One Sheet: $75 - $150

LADY ICE
(1973 - National General) Donald Sutherland, Jennifer O'Neill
One Sheet: $3 - $5

LADY IN A CAGE

(1964 - Paramount) Olivia de Havilland, Ann Southern
One Sheet: $15 - $25

LADY IN A JAM
(1942 - Universal) Irene Dunne, Ralph Bellamy
One Sheet: $50 - $100

LADY IN CEMENT
(1968 - 20th Century Fox) Frank Sinatra, Raquel Welch, Dan Blocker
One Sheet: $15 - $30

LADY IN DANGER
(1934 - Gaumont) Tom Walls, Anne Grey
One Sheet: $100 - $200

LADY IN DISTRESS
(1939 - GFD) Paul Lukas, Michael Redgrave
One Sheet: $100 - $200

LADY IN ERMINE, THE
(1927 - First National) Corinne Griffith, Einar Hanson
One Sheet: $250 - $500

LADY IN LOVE, A
(1920 - Paramount) Harrison Ford, Ethel Clayton
One Sheet: $200 - $400

LADY IN QUESTION, THE
(1940 - Columbia) Brian Aherne, Rita Hayworth
One Sheet: $150 - $300

LADY IN RED, THE
(1979 - New World) Robert Conrad, Pamela Sue Martin
One Sheet: $5 - $10

LADY IN SCARLET, THE
(1935 - Chesterfield) Reginald Denny, Patricia Farr
One Sheet: $125 - $250

LADY IN THE CAR WITH GLASSES AND A GUN, THE
(1970 - Columbia) Samantha Eggar, Oliver Reed
One Sheet: $3 - $5

LADY IN THE DARK
(1944 - Paramount) Ginger Rogers, Ray Milland
One Sheet: $150 - $350

One Sheet

LADY IN THE DEATH HOUSE
(1944 - PRC) Lionel Atwill, Jean Parker
One Sheet: $40 - $75

LADY IN THE IRON MASK
(1952 - 20th Century Fox) Louis Hayward, Patricia Medina
One Sheet: $20 - $40

LADY IN THE LAKE
(1946 - MGM) Robert Montgomery, Audrey Totter
One Sheet: $200 - $400

LADY IN THE MORGUE, THE
(1938 - Universal) Preston Foster, Patricia Ellis
One Sheet: $100 - $200

LADY IN WHITE
(1988 - -) Lukas Haas, Len Cariou, Katherine Helmond
One Sheet: $3 - $5

LADY IS A SQUARE, THE
(1959 - Pathe) Anna Neagle, Frankie Vaughan
One Sheet: $10 - $20

LADY IS WILLING, THE

(1934 - Columbia) Leslie Howard, Nigel Bruce
One Sheet: $150 - $300

LADY IS WILLING, THE
(1942 - Columbia) Marlene Dietrich, Fred MacMurray
One Sheet: $100 - $200

LADY JANE
(1985 - -) Cary Elwes, Sara Kestelman
One Sheet: $3 - $5

LADY JANE GREY
(1936 - Gaumont) Cedric Hardwicke, John Mills
One Sheet: $75 - $150

LADY KILLER
(1933 - Warner Bros.) James Cagney, Mae Clarke
One Sheet: $1,900 - $3,000

LADY L
(1966 - MGM) Sophia Loren, Paul Newman
One Sheet: $15 - $25

LADY, LET'S DANCE
(1944 - Monogram) Belita, James Ellison, Henry Busse Orchestra
One Sheet: $30 - $60   *Sports (Ice Skating). Big Band.*

LADY LIBERTY
(1972 - United Artists) Sophia Loren, William Devane
One Sheet: $5 - $10

LADY LIES, THE
(1929 - Paramount) Walter Huston, Claudette Colbert
One Sheet: $600 - $1,000

LADY LUCK
(1936 - Chesterfield) Patricia Farr, William Bakewell
One Sheet: $75 - $150

LADY LUCK
(1941 - Dixie National) Mantan Moreland
One Sheet: $800 - $1,500   *Black cast.*

LADY LUCK
(1946 - RKO) Robert Young, Barbara Hale
One Sheet: $50 - $100

LADY MISLAID, A
(1958 - Pathe) Alan White, Phyllis Calvert
One Sheet: $7 - $15

LADY NAGGS PEERESS
(1929 - Butcher) George Bellamy, Joan Morgan
One Sheet: $150 - $300

LADY OBJECTS, THE
(1938 - Columbia) Lanny Ross, Jean Marsh
One Sheet: $75 - $125

LADY OF BURLESQUE
(1943 - United Artists) Barbara Stanwyck, Michael O'Shea
One Sheet: $100 - $200

LADY OF BURLESQUE
(1948R - United Artists) Barbara Stanwyck, Michael O'Shea
One Sheet: $30 - $50   *Re-release.*

LADY OF CHANCE, A
(1928 - MGM) Norma Shearer, John Mack Brown
One Sheet: $250 - $500

LADY OF MONZA, THE
(1970 - Tower) Anne Heywood, Antonio Sabato, Hardy Kruger
One Sheet: $3 - $5

LADY OF QUALITY, A
(1913 - Frohman) Cecelia Loftus, House Peters
One Sheet: $250 - $600

LADY OF QUALITY, A
(1924 - Universal) Virginia Valli
One Sheet: $125 - $250

LADY OF SCANDAL, THE
(1930 - MGM) Basil Rathbone, Ruth Chatterton
One Sheet: $250 - $600

LADY OF SECRETS
(1936 - Columbia) Ruth Chatterton, Otto Kruger, Lionel Atwill
One Sheet: $100 - $200

LADY OF THE LAKE, THE

(1928 - Select) Benita Hume, Percy Marmont
One Sheet: $200 - $400

LADY OF THE NIGHT
(1925 - MGM) Norma Shearer, Malcolm McGregor
One Sheet: $200 - $450

LADY OF THE NIGHT
(1933 - MGM) Loretta Young, Ricardo Cortez
One Sheet: $200 - $400

LADY OF THE PAVEMENTS
(1929 - United Artists) William Boyd, Jetta Goudel
One Sheet: $250 - $600

LADY OF THE TROPICS
(1939 - MGM) Robert Taylor, Hedy Lamarr
One Sheet: $250 - $500

LADY OF VENGEANCE
(1956 - Princess) Dennis O'Keefe, Ann Sears
One Sheet: $15 - $25

LADY ON A TRAIN
(1945 - Universal) Deanna Durbin, Ralph Bellamy
One Sheet: $75 - $150

LADY PAYS OFF, THE
(1951 - Universal) Linda Darnell, Stephen McNally
One Sheet: $15 - $35

LADY POSSESSED
(1951 - Republic) James Mason, June Havoc
One Sheet: $30 - $50

LADY REFUSES, THE
(1931 - RKO) Betty Compson, John Darrow
One Sheet: $150 - $300

LADY ROBINHOOD
(1925 - FBO) Evelyn Brent, Boris Karloff
One Sheet: $250 - $600

LADY SAYS NO, THE
(1952 - United Artists) David Niven, Joan Caulfield
One Sheet: $15 - $35

LADY SCARFACE
(1941 - RKO) Dennis O'Keefe, Francis Neal, Judith Anderson
One Sheet: $100 - $200

LADY SINGS THE BLUES
(1972 - Paramount) Diana Ross, Billy Dee Williams
One Sheet: $20 - $40 *Black cast.*
Life of blues great Billie Holiday. Three Sheet:$100-$200.

LADY SINGS THE BLUES/MAHOGANY COMBO
(1976R - Paramount) Diana Ross, Billy Dee Williams
One Sheet: $15 - $30 *Re-release*
Double feature poster.

LADY SURRENDERS, A
(1930 - Universal) Basil Rathbone, Conrad Nagel
One Sheet: $200 - $400

LADY SURRENDERS, A
(1947 - Universal-International) Margaret Lockwood, Stewart Granger
One Sheet: $30 - $60

LADY TAKES A CHANCE, A
(1933 - Grand National) Heather Angel, John King
One Sheet: $100 - $200

LADY TAKES A CHANCE, A
(1943 - RKO) John Wayne, Jean Arthur
One Sheet: $250 - $600

LADY TAKES A CHANCE, A
(1950R - RKO) John Wayne, Jean Arthur
One Sheet: $40 - $75 *Re-release.*

LADY TAKES A FLYER, THE
(1958 - Universal) Lana Turner, Jeff Chandler
One Sheet: $30 - $50

LADY TAKES A SAILOR, THE
(1949 - Warner Bros.) Jane Wyman, Dennis Morgan
One Sheet: $20 - $40

LADY TO LOVE, A
(1930 - MGM) Vilma Banky, Edward G.

Robinson
One Sheet: $200 - $400

LADY TUBBS
(1935 - Universal) Alice Brady, Douglas Montgomery
One Sheet: $100 - $200

LADY VANISHES, THE
(1938 - Gaumont-British) Margaret Lockwood, Michael Redgrave, Dir: Alfred Hitchcock
One Sheet: $5,000 - $8,000

One Sheet

LADY VANISHES, THE
(1952R - -) Margaret Lockwood, Michael Redgrave, Dir: Alfred Hitchcock
One Sheet: $150 - $300 *Re-release.*

LADY WANTS MINK, THE
(1952 - Universal) Dennis O'Keefe, Ruth Hussey
One Sheet: $15 - $30

LADY WHO DARED, THE
(1931 - First National) Billie Dove, Sidney Blackmer
One Sheet: $150 - $300

LADY WINDERMERE'S FAN
(1925 - Warner) Ronald Colman, May McAvoy
One Sheet: $800 - $1,500

LADY WITH A LAMP, THE
(1951 - British Lion) Anna Neagle, Michael Wilding
One Sheet: $15 - $35

LADY WITH A PAST
(1932 - RKO Pathe) Constance Bennett, Ben Lyon
One Sheet: $600 - $1,000

LADY WITH RED HAIR
(1940 - Warner Bros.) Claude Rains, Miriam Hopkins
One Sheet: $75 - $150

LADY WITHOUT PASSPORT, A
(1950 - MGM) Hedy Lamarr, John Hodiak
One Sheet: $75 - $125

LADY'S FROM KENTUCKY, THE
(1939 - Paramount) George Raft, Ellen Drew
One Sheet: $100 - $200

LADY'S MORALS, A
(1930 - MGM) Grace Moore, Reginald Denny
One Sheet: $150 - $300

LADY'S PROFESSION, A
(1933 - Paramount) Roland Young, Alison Skipworth
One Sheet: $100 - $200

LADYBUG, LADYBUG
(1963 - United Artists) Jane Connell, William Daniels
One Sheet: $7 - $15

LADYBUGS
(1992 - Paramount) Rodney Dangerfield
One Sheet: $3 - $5

LADYHAWKE
(1985 - Warner Bros.) Matthew Broderick, Rutger Hauer, Michelle Pfeiffer
One Sheet: $30 - $60 *Style B:$30-$50.*

LADYKILLERS, THE
(1955 - Ealing) Alec Guiness, Peter Sellers
One Sheet: $50 - $100

LADYKILLERS, THE/LAVENDER HILL MOB,

THE
(195? - Ealing) -
One Sheet: $20 - $40 *Double feature poster.*

LAFAYETTE
(1964 - Maco) Jack Hawkins, Orson Welles
One Sheet: $15 - $25

LAFAYETTE ESCADRILLE
(1958 - Warner Bros.) Tab Hunter, Clint Eastwood, Etchika Choureau
One Sheet: $30 - $60

LAFF JAMBOREE
(1945 - Toddy) Buck and Bubbles
One Sheet: $250 - $500 *Black cast.*
Separate Cinema, pg. 66.

LAIR OF THE WHITE WORM, THE
(1988 - -) Amanda Donohoe, Hugh Grant
One Sheet: $7 - $15

LAKE PLACID SERENADE
(1944 - Republic) Vera Vague, Vera Hruba Ralston, Ray Noble & Orchestra
One Sheet: $50 - $100 *Big band.*
Sports (Ice Skating).

LAMB, THE
(1915 - Triangle) Douglas Fairbanks, Seena Owen
One Sheet: $250 - $500

LAMBERT THE SHEEPISH LION
(1952 - RKO/Disney) -
One Sheet: $250 - $600 *Cartoon. Full color.*

LAMBETH WALK, THE
(1939 - MGM) Lupino Lane, Sally Gray
One Sheet: $125 - $250

LAME DUCKS
(1991 - Paramount) John Turturro
One Sheet: $3 - $5

LAMERICA
(1995 - New Yorker) Enrico Lo Verso, Michele Placido
One Sheet: $5 - $10

LANCELOT AND GUINEVERE
(1963 - Universal) Cornel Wilde, Jean Wallace
One Sheet: $15 - $30

LANCER SPY
(1937 - 20th Century Fox) George Sanders, Peter Lorre, Dolores Del Rio
One Sheet: $250 - $500

One Sheet

LAND AND FREEDOM
(1996 - Gramercy) Ian Hart
One Sheet: $5 - $12

LAND BEFORE TIME, THE
(1988 - -) Voices of Pat Hingle, Gabriel Damon, Helen Shaver
One Sheet: $7 - $15 *Cartoon.*

LAND BEYOND THE LAW
(1927 - First National) Ken Maynard, Dorothy Dwan
One Sheet: $250 - $500

LAND BEYOND THE LAW
(1937 - Warner Bros.) Dick Foran, Linda Perry
One Sheet: $50 - $100

LAND OF FIGHTING MEN
(1938 - Monogram) Jack Randall
One Sheet: $50 - $100

LAND OF FURY

(1955 - Universal) Jack Hawkins, Glynis Johns
One Sheet: $10 - $20

LAND OF HUNTED MEN
(1943 - Monogram) The Range Busters
One Sheet: $20 - $40

LAND OF JAZZ, THE
(1921 - Fox) Eileen Percy, Herbert Hayes
One Sheet: $500 - $800

LAND OF LIBERTY
(1941 - Motion Picture Prod.) Dir: Cecil B. DeMille
One Sheet: $50 - $100

LAND OF MISSING MEN, THE
(1930 - Tiffany) Bob Steele
One Sheet: $150 - $300

LAND OF THE LAWLESS
(1947 - Monogram) Johnny Mack Brown, Raymond Hatton
One Sheet: $20 - $40

LAND OF THE MINOTAUR
(1977 - Crown) Peter Cushing, Donald Pleasence
One Sheet: $10 - $20

LAND OF THE OPEN RANGE
(1942 - RKO) Tim Holt
One Sheet: $40 - $75

LAND OF THE OUTLAWS
(1944 - Monogram) Johnny Mack Brown
One Sheet: $40 - $75

LAND OF THE PHARAOHS
(1955 - Continental) Jack Hawkins, Joan Collins
One Sheet: $50 - $100

LAND OF THE SILVER FOX
(1928 - Warner Bros.) Leila Hyams, Rin Tin Tin
One Sheet: $150 - $300

LAND OF THE SIX GUNS
(1940 - Monogram) Jack Randall, Louise Stanley
One Sheet: $75 - $125

LAND RAIDERS
(1969 - Columbia) Telly Savalas, George Maharis
One Sheet: $15 - $25

LAND THAT TIME FORGOT, THE
(1975 - AIP) Doug McClure, John McEnery
One Sheet: $15 - $25

LAND UNKNOWN, THE
(1957 - Universal) Jock Mahoney, Shawn Smith
One Sheet: $75 - $150

LANDFALL
(1950 - British-Pathe) Michael Denison, Patricia Plunkett
One Sheet: $10 - $20

LANDLORD, THE
(1970 - United Artists) Beau Bridges, Lee Grant, Diana Sands, Pearl Bailey
One Sheet: $3 - $5

LANDRUSH
(1946 - Columbia) Charles Starrett, Smiley Burnette
One Sheet: $30 - $60

LARAMIE
(1949 - Columbia) Charles Starrett
One Sheet: $20 - $40

One Sheet

LARAMIE MOUNTAINS
(1952 - Columbia) Charles Starrett, Smiley
Burnette
One Sheet: $15 - $25

LARAMIE TRAIL, THE
(1944 - Republic) Bob Livingston, Smiley
Burnette
One Sheet: $20 - $40

LARCENY
(1948 - Universal-International) John Payne,
Joan Caulfield
One Sheet: $30 - $50

LARCENY IN HER HEART
(1946 - PRC) Hugh Beaumont, Cheryl Walker
One Sheet: $15 - $30

LARCENY, INC.
(1942 - Warner Bros.) Edward G. Robinson,
Jane Wyman
One Sheet: $100 - $200

One Sheet

LARCENY ON THE AIR
(1937 - Republic) Grace Bradley, Robert
Livingston
One Sheet: $75 - $125

LARCENY WITH MUSIC
(1943 - Universal) Allen Jones, Kelly Carlisle,
Alvino Rey and his Orchestra
One Sheet: $75 - $125   *Big band
musical.*

LARGER THAN LIFE
(1996 - United Artists) Bill Murray, Janeane
Garofalo
One Sheet: $4 - $8

LARIAT KID, THE
(1929 - Universal Jewel) Hoot Gibson
One Sheet: $200 - $400

LAS VEGAS HILLBILLYS
(1966 - Woolner Bros.) Ferlin Husky, Jayne
Mansfield
One Sheet: $30 - $60   *Country
musical.*

LAS VEGAS NIGHTS
(1941 - Paramount) Phil Regan, Constance
Moore, Bert Wheeler
One Sheet: $100 - $200

LAS VEGAS SHAKEDOWN
(1955 - Allied Artists) Dennis O'Keefe, Thomas
Gomez
One Sheet: $20 - $40

LAS VEGAS STORY, THE
(1952 - RKO) Jane Russell, Victor Mature
One Sheet: $75 - $150

LASCA OF THE RIO GRANDE
(1931 - Universal) Leo Carrillo, Johnny Mack
Brown
One Sheet: $125 - $250

LASERBLAST
(1978 - Irwin Yablans) Kim Milford, Cheryl
Smith, Roddy McDowall
One Sheet: $5 - $10

LASH, THE
(1930 - First National) Richard Barthelmess,
Mary Astor
One Sheet: $250 - $500

LASH OF THE PENITENTES
(1936 - Stewart) Jose Swickard, Marie de
Forest
One Sheet: $50 - $100

LASSIE
(1994 - Paramount) Thomas Guiry, Helen
Slater
One Sheet: $5 - $10

LASSIE COME HOME
(1943 - MGM) Roddy McDowall, Donald Crisp,
Elizabeth Taylor
One Sheet: $150 - $350

LASSIE COME HOME
(1971R - MGM) Roddy McDowall, Elisabeth
Taylor
One Sheet: $5 - $10   *Re-release.*

LASSIE'S GREAT ADVENTURE
(1963 - 20th Century Fox) June Lockhart, Hugh
Reilly, Jon Provost
One Sheet: $30 - $50   *TV tie-in.*

LASSITER
(1984 - Warner Bros.) Tom Selleck, Jane
Seymour
One Sheet: $5 - $10

LAST ACTION HERO, THE
(1993 - Columbia) Arnold Schwarzenegger,
Austin O'Brien
One Sheet: $5 - $10

LAST ADVENTURE, THE
(1968 - Universal) Alain Delon, Lino Ventura
One Sheet: $5 - $10

LAST ALARM, THE
(1940 - Monogram) Dolly Ann Young, Warren
Hull
One Sheet: $50 - $100

LAST AMERICAN HERO, THE
(1973 - 20th Century Fox) Jeff Bridges, Valerie
Perrine
One Sheet: $5 - $10   *Price is for
both styles.*

LAST ANGRY MAN, THE
(1959 - Columbia) Paul Muni (his last film),
David Wayne
One Sheet: $15 - $30

LAST BANDIT, THE
(1949 - Republic) Bill Elliott, Adrian Booth
One Sheet: $40 - $75

LAST BANDIT, THE
(1956R - Republic) Bill Elliott
One Sheet: $15 - $35   *Re-release.*

LAST BLITZKRIEG, THE
(1949 - Columbia) Van Johnson, Kerwin
Matthews
One Sheet: $15 - $30

LAST BOY SCOUT, THE
(1991 - Warner Bros.) Bruce Willis, Damon
Wayans
One Sheet: $7 - $15   *Sports
(Football). Sports Movie Posters #214.*

LAST BRIDGE, THE
(1957 - Union) Maria Schell, Bernhard Wicki
One Sheet: $5 - $10

LAST CHALLENGE, THE
(1967 - MGM) Glenn Ford, Angie Dickinson
One Sheet: $3 - $5

LAST CHANCE, THE
(1924 - Fox) John Gilbert
One Sheet: $600 - $1,000

LAST CHANCE, THE
(1946 - MGM) E. G. Morrison, John Hoyt
One Sheet: $20 - $40

LAST CHASE, THE
(1981 - -) Lee Majors, Chris Makepeace
One Sheet: $3 - $5

LAST COMMAND, THE
(1928 - Paramount) Emil Jannings, William
Powell
One Sheet: $1,600 - $2,500   *Academy
Award Movie Posters #8.*

LAST COMMAND, THE
(1955 - Republic) Sterling Hayden, Anna Maria
Alberghetti
One Sheet: $15 - $25

LAST CROOKED MILE, THE
(1946 - Republic) Donald Barry, Ann Savage
One Sheet: $15 - $30

LAST DANCE
(1996 - Touchstone) Sharon Stone, Rob
Morrow, Randy Quaid
One Sheet: $5 - $12

LAST DAYS OF BOOT HILL
(1947 - Columbia) Charles Starrett, Smiley
Burnette
One Sheet: $15 - $35

LAST DAYS OF DOLWYN, THE
(1949 - London) Edith Evans, Richard Burton
One Sheet: $50 - $100

LAST DAYS OF MAN ON EARTH, THE
(1975 - New World) Jon Finch, Jenny Runacre
One Sheet: $10 - $20

LAST DAYS OF POMPEII, THE
(1926 - W.& F.) Victori Varconi, Maria Corda
One Sheet: $600 - $1,000

LAST DAYS OF POMPEII, THE
(1935 - RKO) Preston Foster, Alan Hale
One Sheet: $200 - $400

LAST DAYS OF POMPEII, THE
(1948R - RKO) Preston Foster, Alan Hale
One Sheet: $30 - $50   *Re-release.*

LAST DAYS OF POMPEII, THE
(1960 - United Artists) Steve Reeves, Christine
Kaufmann
One Sheet: $15 - $30

LAST DETAIL, THE
(1973 - Columbia) Jack Nicholson, Randy
Quaid
One Sheet: $10 - $20

LAST DRAGON, THE
(1985 - TriStar) Taimak, Vanity, Chris Murney
One Sheet: $3 - $5

LAST EMBRACE
(1979 - United Artists) Roy Scheider, Janet
Margolin
One Sheet: $3 - $5

LAST EMPEROR, THE
(1987 - Columbia) John Lone, Joan Chen
One Sheet: $7 - $15   *Academy
Award: Best Picture, Best Director (Bertolucci).
Academy Award Movie Posters #353.*

LAST ESCAPE, THE
(1970 - United Artists) Stuart Whitman, John
Collin, Pinkas Braun
One Sheet: $5 - $10

LAST EXIT TO BROOKLYN
(1990 - -) Stephen Lang, Jennifer Jason Leigh
One Sheet: $10 - $20

LAST EXPRESS, THE
(1938 - Universal) Kent Taylor, Dorthea Kent
One Sheet: $100 - $200

LAST FLIGHT, THE
(1931 - First National) Richard Barthelmess,
Johnny Mack Brown, David Manners
One Sheet: $250 - $500

LAST FLIGHT OF NOAH'S ARK, THE
(1980 - Disney) Elliott Gould, Genevieve Bujold
One Sheet: $7 - $15

LAST FRONTIER, THE
(1926 - Metro) William Boyd
One Sheet: $200 - $400

LAST FRONTIER, THE
(1932 - RKO) Creighton Chaney (Lon Chaney
Jr.), Dorothy Gulliver
One Sheet: $250 - $500   *Serial. 12
Chapters.*

LAST FRONTIER, THE
(1956 - Columbia) Victor Mature, Guy Madison,
Robert Preston
One Sheet: $5 - $10

LAST FRONTIER UPRISING
(1947 - Republic) Monte Hale, Adrian Booth
One Sheet: $30 - $60

LAST GANGSTER, THE
(1937 - MGM) Edward G. Robinson, James
Stewart
One Sheet: $500 - $900   *Price is for
Style D. One Sheet(Style C):$1200-2000.*

LAST GENTLEMAN, THE
(1934 - 20th Century Fox) George Arliss, Edna

May Oliver
One Sheet: $150 - $300

LAST GOOD TIME, THE
(1995 - Samuel Goldwyn) Armin Mueller-Stahl,
Olivia d'Abo
One Sheet: $5 - $10

LAST GRENADE, THE
(1970 - Cinerama) Stanley Baker, Alex Cord
One Sheet: $2 - $3

LAST HARD MEN, THE
(1976 - 20th Century Fox) Charlton Heston,
James Coburn, Barbara Hershey
One Sheet: $5 - $10

LAST HOLIDAY
(1950 - Amalgamated-British) Alec Guiness,
Kay Walsh
One Sheet: $7 - $15

LAST HORSEMAN, THE
(1944 - Columbia) Russell Hayden, Dub Taylor
One Sheet: $30 - $60

LAST HOUSE ON DEAD END STREET
(1977 - -) Steven Morrison, Dennis Crawford
One Sheet: $5 - $12

LAST HOUSE ON THE LEFT
(1972 - AIP) David Hess, Lucy Grantham, Dir:
Wes Craven
One Sheet: $40 - $75   *An extremely
controversial cult film.*

LAST HOUSE ON THE LEFT, PART 2
(1973 - AIP) -
One Sheet: $15 - $30

**LAST HOUSE ON THE LEFT/HOUSE THAT
DRIPPED BLOOD/HOUSE BY THE LAKE**
(1978R - AIP) David Hess, Lucy Graham/
Christopher Lee, Peter Cushing
One Sheet: $15 - $25   *Re-release
triple feature poster.*

LAST HUNT, THE
(1956 - MGM) Robert Taylor, Stewart Granger
One Sheet: $15 - $25

LAST HURRAH, THE
(1958 - Columbia) Spencer Tracy, Jeffrey
Hunter
One Sheet: $15 - $25

LAST INDIAN, THE
(1937 - Educational) Paul Terry Studio
One Sheet: $250 - $500   *Cartoon.
Duotone. Stock poster with inset of title.*

LAST LAUGH, THE
(1924 - UFA) Emil Jannings
One Sheet: $2,500 - $4,000   *German.*

LAST LAUGH, THE
(1952 - -) -
One Sheet: $15 - $30

LAST MAN, THE
(1932 - Columbia) Charles Bickford, Constance
Cummings
One Sheet: $200 - $400

One Sheet

LAST MAN ON EARTH, THE
(1924 - Fox) Earle Fox, Grace Cunard
One Sheet: $3,500 - $5,000   *Graven
Images, pg. 27.*

LAST MAN ON EARTH, THE
(1964 - AIP) Vincent Price, Franca Bettoia
One Sheet: $40 - $75

LAST MAN STANDING

(1996 - New Line) Bruce Willis, Bruce Dern, Christopher Walken
One Sheet: $5 - $10

LAST MAN TO HANG, THE
(1956 - Columbia) Tom Conway, Eunice Gayson
One Sheet: $15 - $25

LAST MARRIED COUPLE IN AMERICA, THE
(1980 - Universal) George Segal, Natalie Wood
One Sheet: $3 - $5

LAST METRO, THE
(1980 - United Artists) Catherine Deneuve, Gerard Depardieu
One Sheet: $5 - $10

LAST MILE, THE
(1932 - Tiffany) Howard Phillips, Preston Foster
One Sheet: $75 - $150

LAST MILE, THE
(1959 - United Artists) Mickey Rooney, Clifford David
One Sheet: $15 - $30

LAST MOVIE, THE
(1971 - Universal) Dennis Hopper, Peter Fonda
One Sheet: $5 - $10

LAST MUSKETEER, THE
(1952 - Republic) Rex Allen, Mary Ellen Kay
One Sheet: $15 - $25

LAST OF MRS. CHEYNEY, THE
(1937 - MGM) Joan Crawford, William Powell
One Sheet: $250 - $500

LAST OF SHEILA, THE
(1973 - Warner Bros.) Richard Benjamin, James Coburn, Dyan Cannon
One Sheet: $5 - $10

LAST OF THE BADMEN, THE
(1957 - Allied Artists) George Montgomery, James Best
One Sheet: $15 - $35

LAST OF THE BUCCANEERS, THE
(1950 - Columbia) Paul Henreid, Jack Oakie
One Sheet: $15 - $30

LAST OF THE CLINTONS
(1935 - Ajax) Harry Carey
One Sheet: $75 - $150

LAST OF THE COMANCHES, THE
(1952 - Columbia) Broderick Crawford, Barbara Hale, Lloyd Bridges
One Sheet: $15 - $35

LAST OF THE DESPERADOS, THE
(1956 - Universal) James Craig, Jim Davis
One Sheet: $10 - $20

LAST OF THE DUANES, THE
(1924 - Fox) Tom Mix, Marian Nixon
One Sheet: $250 - $600   *Cowboy Movie Posters #46.*

LAST OF THE DUANES, THE
(1930 - Fox) George O'Brien, Myrna Loy, Lucile Brown
One Sheet: $250 - $500

LAST OF THE DUANES, THE
(1941 - 20th Century Fox) George Montgomery, Lynne Roberts
One Sheet: $75 - $150

LAST OF THE FAST GUNS, THE
(1958 - Universal) Jock Mahoney, Gilbert Roland
One Sheet: $15 - $30

LAST OF THE FINEST, THE
(1990 - -) Brian Dennehy, Joe Pantoliano
One Sheet: $3 - $5

LAST OF THE LONE WOLF, THE
(1930 - Columbia) Bert Lytell, Patsy Ruth Miller
One Sheet: $200 - $400

LAST OF THE MOBILE HOT-SHOTS
(1970 - Warner Bros.) James Coburn, Lynn Redgrave, Robert Hooks
One Sheet: $3 - $5

LAST OF THE MOHICANS, THE
(1932 - Mascot) Harry Carey, Edwina Booth
One Sheet: $350 - $750   *Serial. Western. 12 Chapters.*

LAST OF THE MOHICANS, THE
(1936 - United Artists) Randolph Scott, Binnie Barnes
One Sheet: $250 - $550

LAST OF THE MOHICANS, THE
(1951R - United Artists) Randolph Scott, Binnie Barnes
One Sheet: $20 - $40   *Re-release.*

LAST OF THE MOHICANS, THE
(1992 - 20th Century Fox) Daniel Day Lewis, Madeleine Stowe
One Sheet: $10 - $20   *Advance:$20-$30.*

LAST OF THE PAGANS
(1935 - MGM) Ray Mala, Lotus Long
One Sheet: $150 - $300

LAST OF THE PONY RIDERS, THE
(1953 - Columbia) Gene Autry, Smiley Burnette
One Sheet: $50 - $100

LAST OF THE RED HOT LOVERS
(1972 - Paramount) Alan Arkin, Paula Prentiss, Sally Kellerman
One Sheet: $3 - $5

LAST OF THE REDMEN
(1947 - Columbia) Jon Hall, Evelyn Ankers
One Sheet: $20 - $40

LAST OF THE RENEGADES
(1966 - Columbia) Lex Barker, Anthony Steel
One Sheet: $15 - $25

LAST OF THE SECRET AGENTS?, THE
(1966 - Paramount) Marty Allen, Steve Rossi
One Sheet: $15 - $25

LAST OF THE SKI BUMS, THE
(1969 - U.M.) Ron Funk, Mike Zuetell, Ed Ricks
One Sheet: $5 - $10   *Sports (Snow Skiing).*

LAST OF THE STAGE COACH BANDITS, THE
(192?R - -) -
One Sheet: $150 - $300   *Re-release.*

LAST OF THE STILLS, THE
(1915 - Selig) -
One Sheet: $250 - $550

LAST OF THE VIKINGS
(1962 - Medallion) Cameron Mitchell, Edmund Purdom
One Sheet: $10 - $20

LAST OF THE WARRENS
(1936 - Supreme) Bob Steele, Margaret Marquis
One Sheet: $150 - $300

LAST OF THE WILD HORSES, THE
(1948 - Screen Guild) Mary Beth Hughes, James Ellison
One Sheet: $15 - $30

LAST OUTLAW, THE
(1927 - Paramount) Gary Cooper, Jack Luden
One Sheet: $1,600 - $2,500   *One Sheet (style with horse):$600-$1000. Cowboy Movie Posters #63.*

LAST OUTLAW, THE
(1936 - RKO) Hoot Gibson, Harry Carey, Tom Tyler
One Sheet: $250 - $600

LAST OUTPOST, THE
(1935 - Paramount) Cary Grant, Claude Rains
One Sheet: $250 - $600

LAST OUTPOST, THE
(1951 - Paramount) Ronald Reagan, Rhonda Fleming
One Sheet: $75 - $150   *Reagan's first western.*

LAST PARADE, THE
(1931 - Universal) Jack Holt, Tom Moore
One Sheet: $200 - $400

LAST PARADISE, THE
(1957 - Airdart) -
One Sheet: $15 - $30

LAST PARTY, THE
(1993 - Triton) Robert Downey, Jr.
One Sheet: $3 - $5

LAST PERFORMANCE, THE

(1929 - Universal) Conrad Veidt, Mary Philbin
One Sheet: $1,900 - $3,000   *Graven images, pg. 37.*

LAST PICTURE SHOW, THE
(1971 - Columbia) Jeff Bridges, Cybill Shepherd
One Sheet: $30 - $50   *Academy Award: Best Supporting Actor(Johnson), Best Supporting Actress(Leachman). AcademyAward Movie Posters #268.*

LAST PICTURE SHOW, THE
(1973R - Columbia) Timothy Bottoms, Jeff Bridges, Cybill Shepherd, Ben Johnson
One Sheet: $10 - $20   *Re-release.*

LAST PLANE OUT
(1984 - -) Jan-Michael Vincent, Julie Carmen
One Sheet: $3 - $5

LAST POSSE, THE
(1953 - Columbia) Broderick Crawford, John Derek
One Sheet: $15 - $35

LAST REBEL, THE
(1971 - Columbia) Joe Namath, Woody Strode, Jack Elam
One Sheet: $15 - $25

LAST REMAKE OF BEAU GESTE, THE
(1977 - Universal) Marty Feldman, Ann-Margret
One Sheet: $3 - $5

LAST RIDE, THE
(1944 - Warner Bros.) Richard Travis, Eleanor Parker
One Sheet: $30 - $50

LAST ROUND-UP, THE
(1934 - Paramount) Randolph Scott
One Sheet: $150 - $300   *Cowboy Movie Posters # 163.*

LAST ROUND-UP, THE
(1947 - Columbia) Gene Autry, Jean Heather
One Sheet: $75 - $150

LAST RUN, THE
(1971 - MGM) George C. Scott, Tony Musante
One Sheet: $3 - $5

LAST SAFARI, THE
(1967 - Paramount) Kaz Garas, Stewart Granger
One Sheet: $10 - $20

LAST SEDUCTION, THE
(1994 - October) Linda Fiorentino, Peter Berg, Bill Pullman
One Sheet: $5 - $10

LAST SHOT YOU HEAR, THE
(1969 - Lippert) Hugh Marlowe, Zena Walker
One Sheet: $2 - $3

LAST STAGECOACH WEST, THE
(1957 - Republic) Jim Davis, Mary Castle
One Sheet: $7 - $15

LAST STAND, THE
(1938 - Universal) Bob Baker, Constance Moore
One Sheet: $75 - $150

LAST STARFIGHTER, THE
(1984 - Universal) Lance Guest, Dan O'Herlihy
One Sheet: $5 - $10

LAST SUMMER
(1969 - Allied Artists) Barbara Hershey, Richard Thomas, Bruce Davison, Cathy Burns
One Sheet: $3 - $5

LAST SUNSET, THE
(1961 - Universal) Rock Hudson, Kirk Douglas, Dorothy Malone
One Sheet: $20 - $40

LAST SUPPER, THE
(1996 - Sony Pictures) Cameron Diaz, Annabeth Gish
One Sheet: $5 - $10   *Comedy.*

LAST SURVIVOR
(1978 - United) Messimo Foschi, Me-Me Lei
One Sheet: $4 - $8

LAST TANGO IN PARIS
(1972 - United Artists) Marlon Brando, Maria Schneider
One Sheet: $30 - $50   *Price is for both styles.*

LAST TANGO IN PARIS
(1982R - United Artists) Marlon Brando, Maria Schneider
One Sheet: $20 - $40   *Re-release.*

LAST TEMPTATION OF CHRIST, THE
(1988 - Universal) Willem Dafoe, Harvey Keitel
One Sheet: $30 - $50

LAST TIME I SAW ARCHIE, THE
(1961 - United Artists) Robert Mitchum, Jack Webb
One Sheet: $30 - $50

LAST TIME I SAW PARIS, THE
(1954 - MGM) Elizabeth Taylor, Van Johnson
One Sheet: $75 - $150

LAST TRAIL, THE
(1921 - Fox) Maurice B. Flynn, Eva Novak
One Sheet: $250 - $500   *Cowboy Movie Posters #29.*

LAST TRAIL, THE
(1927 - Fox) Tom Mix, Carmelita Geraghty
One Sheet: $200 - $400

LAST TRAIL, THE
(1933 - Fox) George O'Brien, Claire Trevor
One Sheet: $200 - $400

LAST TRAIN FROM BOMBAY
(1952 - Columbia) Jon Hall, Lisa Ferraday
One Sheet: $15 - $30

LAST TRAIN FROM GUN HILL, THE
(1958 - Paramount) Kirk Douglas, Anthony Quinn
One Sheet: $40 - $75

LAST TRAIN FROM MADRID, THE
(1937 - Paramount) Dorothy Lamour, Lew Ayres, Gilbert Roland
One Sheet: $250 - $500

LAST TYCOON, THE
(1976 - Paramount) Robert DeNiro, Jack Nicholson
One Sheet: $15 - $25   *Price is for both styles.*

LAST UNICORN, THE
(1982 - Jensen Farley) Voices: Angela Lansbury, Alan Arkin
One Sheet: $5 - $10   *Cartoon.*

LAST VALLEY, THE
(1971 - Cinerama) Michael Caine, Omar Sharif
One Sheet: $3 - $5

LAST VOYAGE, THE
(1960 - MGM) Robert Stack, Dorothy Malone
One Sheet: $15 - $30

LAST WAGON, THE
(1956 - 20th Century Fox) Richard Widmark, Felicia Farr
One Sheet: $7 - $15

LAST WALTZ, THE
(1936 - Associated) Jarmilla Novotna, Harry Welchman
One Sheet: $100 - $200

LAST WALTZ, THE
(1978 - United Artists) Dir: M. Scorsese
One Sheet: $15 - $30   *Last concert of The Band.*

LAST WARNING, THE
(1928 - Universal) Laura La Plante, Montagu Love
One Sheet: $250 - $500   *Graven Images, pg. 31.*

LAST WARNING, THE
(1938 - Universal) Frances Robinson, Preston Foster
One Sheet: $75 - $150

LAST WILDERNESS, THE
(1934 - Du World) Jerry Fairbanks, Howard Hill
One Sheet: $100 - $200

LAST WILL OF DR. MABUSE, THE
(1943 - Goodwill) Dir: Fritz Lang
One Sheet: $125 - $250   *First American release. Graven Images, pg. 56.*

LAST WOMAN ON EARTH
(1960 - Filmgroup) Anthony Carbone, Betsy Jones-Moreland, Dir: Roger Corman
One Sheet: $15 - $35

LATE FOR DINNER
(1991 - Columbia) -
One Sheet: $3 - $5

LATE GEORGE APLEY, THE
(1947 - 20th Century Fox) Ronald Colman, Peggy Cummins
One Sheet: $100 - $200

LATE, GREAT PLANET EARTH, THE
(1976 - P.I.E.) Orson Welles
One Sheet: $10 - $20

LATE SHOW, THE
(1977 - Warner Bros.) Art Carney, Lily Tomlin
One Sheet: $15 - $30 *Amsel art.*

LATIN LOVERS
(1953 - MGM) Lana Turner, Ricardo Montalban, John Lund
One Sheet: $40 - $75

LATITUDE ZERO
(1970 - National General) Joseph Cotton, Cesar Romero
One Sheet: $10 - $20

LAUGH AND GET RICH
(1931 - RKO) Edna Mae Oliver, Hugh Herbert
One Sheet: $150 - $300

LAUGH CLOWN LAUGH
(1928 - MGM) Lon Chaney
One Sheet: $2,500 - $4,000

LAUGH IT OFF
(1939 - Universal) Constance Moore, Johnny Downs, Edgar Kennedy
One Sheet: $100 - $200

LAUGH YOUR BLUES AWAY
(1942 - Columbia) Bert Gordon, Jinx Falkenberg
One Sheet: $50 - $100

LAUGHING ANNE
(1953 - Republic) Wendell Corey, Margaret Lockwood
One Sheet: $20 - $40

LAUGHING AT DANGER
(1940 - Monogram) Mantan Moreland, Frankie Darro, George Houston
One Sheet: $100 - $200

LAUGHING AT DEATH
(1929 - FBO) Bob Steele, Natalie Joyce
One Sheet: $150 - $300

LAUGHING AT LIFE
(1933 - Mascot) Victor McLaglen, William Boyd
One Sheet: $125 - $250

LAUGHING AT TROUBLE
(1936 - 20th Century Fox) Jane Darwell, Lois Wilson
One Sheet: $75 - $150

LAUGHING BILL HYDE
(1918 - -) Will Rogers, Anne Lehr
One Sheet: $600 - $1,000

LAUGHING BOY
(1934 - MGM) Ramon Novarro, Lupe Velez
One Sheet: $150 - $300

LAUGHING GAS
(1907 - Vitagraph) -
One Sheet: $100 - $200

LAUGHING GAS
(1914 - Keystone) Charlie Chaplin
One Sheet: $7,500 - $12,000

LAUGHING GRAVY
(1931 - MGM) Laurel & Hardy
One Sheet: $2,800 - $4,500

LAUGHING IRISH EYES
(1936 - Republic) Phil Regan, Evalyn Knapp
One Sheet: $75 - $150

LAUGHING POLICEMAN, THE
(1973 - 20th Century Fox) Walter Matthau, Bruce Dern
One Sheet: $3 - $5

LAUGHING SINNERS
(1931 - MGM) Joan Crawford, Clark Gable
One Sheet: $800 - $1,500

LAUGHTER
(1930 - Paramount Publix) Nancy Carroll,

Fredric March
One Sheet: $150 - $300

LAUGHTER IN HELL
(1933 - Universal) Pat O'Brien, Tom Conlon
One Sheet: $250 - $500

LAUGHTER IN PARADISE
(1951 - Stratford) Alastair Sim, Fay Compton, Audrey Hepburn
One Sheet: $150 - $300

LAUGHTER IN THE DARK
(1969 - Lopert) Nicol Williamson, Anna Karina, Jean-Claude Drouot
One Sheet: $7 - $15

LAURA
(1944 - 20th Century Fox) Dana Andrews, Gene Tierney, Clifton Webb
One Sheet: $1,900 - $3,000

One Sheet

LAURA
(1952R - 20th Century Fox) Dana Andrews, Gene Tierney, Clifton Webb
One Sheet: $40 - $75 *Re-release.*

LAUREL AND HARDY MURDER CASE, THE
(1930 - MGM) Laurel & Hardy
One Sheet: $4,000 - $6,000

LAUREL AND HARDY PORTRAIT
(1930S - MGM) Stock Poster
One Sheet: $800 - $1,500 *Belgian. Price is for close-up portraits. Three images style (with Hardy wispering to Stan):$600.*

LAUREL AND HARDY'S LAUGHING 20'S
(1965 - MGM) Stan Laurel, Oliver Hardy
One Sheet: $15 - $35

LAVENDER HILL MOB, THE
(1951 - Universal) Alec Guinness, Stanley Holloway
One Sheet: $75 - $125

LAW AND DISORDER
(1958 - British Consolidated) Michael Redgrave, Robert Morley
One Sheet: $7 - $15

LAW AND JAKE WADE, THE
(1958 - MGM) Robert Taylor, Richard Widmark
One Sheet: $7 - $15

LAW AND LAWLESS
(1932 - Majestic) Jack Hoxie
One Sheet: $150 - $300

LAW AND ORDER
(1921 - Pathe) "Snub" Pollard
One Sheet: $500 - $800

LAW AND ORDER
(1932 - Universal) Walter Huston, Harry Carey
One Sheet: $1,300 - $2,000 *Cowboy Movie Posters # 115.*

LAW AND ORDER
(1940 - Universal) Johnny Mack Brown, Fuzzy Knight
One Sheet: $75 - $125

LAW AND ORDER
(1943 - PRC) Buster Crabbe
One Sheet: $20 - $40

LAW AND ORDER
(1953 - Universal) Ronald Reagan, Dorothy Malone
One Sheet: $150 - $300 *Cowboy Movie Posters #296.*

LAW AND THE LADY, THE

(1951 - MGM) Greer Garson, Michael Wilding
One Sheet: $15 - $30

LAW BEYOND THE RANGE
(1935 - Columbia) Tim McCoy
One Sheet: $250 - $600

LAW COMES TO GUNSIGHT, THE
(1947 - Monogram) Johnny Mack Brown, Raymond Hatton
One Sheet: $40 - $75

Insert

LAW COMES TO TEXAS, THE
(1939 - Columbia) Bill Elliott, Veda Ann Borg
One Sheet: $75 - $125

LAW COMMANDS, THE
(1938 - Crescent) Tom Keene, Lorraine Hayes
One Sheet: $150 - $350

LAW FOR TOMBSTONE
(1937 - Universal) Buck Jones, Muriel Evans
One Sheet: $300 - $700 *Cowboy Movie Posters #212.*

LAW IN HER HANDS, THE
(1936 - Warner Bros.) Margaret Lindsay, Warren Hull
One Sheet: $50 - $100

LAW MEN
(1944 - Monogram) Johnny Mack Brown
One Sheet: $40 - $75

LAW OF DESIRE
(1987 - -) Eusebio Poncela, Antonio Banderas, Carmen Maura
One Sheet: $20 - $40 *Spanish.*

LAW OF THE 45'S
(1935 - Normandy) Big Boy Williams, Al St. John
One Sheet: $100 - $200 *First 3 Mesquiteers western.*

LAW OF THE BADLANDS
(1945 - Warner Bros.) Robert Shayne
One Sheet: $30 - $60

LAW OF THE BADLANDS
(1950 - RKO) Tim Holt, Richard Martin
One Sheet: $20 - $40

LAW OF THE BARBARY COAST, THE
(1949 - Columbia) Gloria Henry, Stephen Dunne
One Sheet: $15 - $30

LAW OF THE CANYON
(1947 - Columbia) Charles Starrett, Smiley Burnette
One Sheet: $30 - $50

One Sheet

LAW OF THE GOLDEN WEST

(1949 - Republic) Monte Hale
One Sheet: $20 - $40

LAW OF THE JUNGLE, THE
(1942 - Monogram) John King, Arline Judge
One Sheet: $30 - $60

LAW OF THE LASH
(1947 - PRC) Lash LaRue, Mary Scott
One Sheet: $30 - $60

LAW OF THE LAWLESS
(1923 - Paramount) Dorothy Dalton, Charles De Roche
One Sheet: $200 - $400

LAW OF THE LAWLESS
(1964 - Paramount) Dale Robertson, Yvonne De Carlo
One Sheet: $5 - $10

LAW OF THE NORTHWEST
(1943 - Columbia) Charles Starrett, Shirley Patterson
One Sheet: $30 - $60

LAW OF THE PAMPAS
(1939 - Paramount) William Boyd (Hopalong Cassidy), Steffi Duna
One Sheet: $250 - $500

One Sheet

LAW OF THE PANHANDLE
(1950 - Monogram) Johnny Mack Brown, Myron Healy
One Sheet: $15 - $25

LAW OF THE PLAINS
(1929 - Syndicate) Tom Tyler, Natalie Joyce
One Sheet: $250 - $500

LAW OF THE PLAINS
(1938 - Columbia) Charles Starrett, Iris Meredith
One Sheet: $75 - $125

LAW OF THE RANGE, THE
(1928 - MGM) Joan Crawford, Tim McCoy
One Sheet: $1,300 - $2,000

LAW OF THE RANGE
(1941 - Universal) Johnny Mack Brown
One Sheet: $75 - $125

LAW OF THE RANGER
(1937 - Columbia) Bob Allen
One Sheet: $75 - $150

LAW OF THE SADDLE
(1943 - PRC) Bob Livingston
One Sheet: $30 - $50

LAW OF THE SEA
(1932 - Monogram) William Farnum, Rex Bell
One Sheet: $125 - $250

LAW OF THE TEXAN
(1938 - Columbia) Buck Jones, Dorothy Fay
One Sheet: $200 - $400

LAW OF THE TIMBER
(1941 - PRC) Marjorie Reynolds, Monte Blue
One Sheet: $30 - $50

LAW OF THE TROPICS
(1941 - Warner Bros.) Jeffrey Lynn, Constance Bennett
One Sheet: $30 - $60

LAW OF THE UNDERWORLD
(1938 - RKO) Chester Morris, Constance Bennett
One Sheet: $75 - $150

LAW OF THE VALLEY

(1944 - Monogram) Johnny Mack Brown
One Sheet: $20 - $40

LAW OF THE WEST
(1932 - Sono Art/World Wide) Bob Steele
One Sheet: $150 - $300

LAW OF THE WEST
(1949 - Monogram) Johnny Mack Brown
One Sheet: $40 - $75

LAW OF THE WILD
(1934 - Mascot Serials) Rex and Rin-Tin-Tin, Jr.
One Sheet: $150 - $300   *Serial. Western. 12 Chapters.*

LAW OF THE WOLF
(1940' - -) -
One Sheet: $20 - $40

LAW RIDES, THE
(1936 - Supreme) Bob Steele, Harley Wood
One Sheet: $200 - $400

LAW RIDES AGAIN, THE
(1943 - Monogram) Ken Maynard, Hoot Gibson
One Sheet: $75 - $150

LAW VS. BILLY THE KID, THE
(1954 - Columbia) Scott Brady, Betta St. John
One Sheet: $20 - $40

LAW WEST OF TOMBSTONE, THE
(1938 - RKO) Harry Carey, Tim Holt
One Sheet: $50 - $100

LAWFUL LARCENY
(1923 - Paramount) Nita Naldi, Lew Cody
One Sheet: $150 - $300

LAWFUL LARCENY
(1930 - RKO) Bebe Daniels, Lowell Sherman
One Sheet: $150 - $300

LAWLESS, THE
(1950 - Paramount) Macdonald Carey, Gail Russell
One Sheet: $15 - $30

LAWLESS BREED, THE
(1946 - Universal) Kirby Grant, Fuzzy Knight
One Sheet: $30 - $50

LAWLESS BREED, THE
(1952 - Universal) Rock Hudson, Julia Adams
One Sheet: $30 - $50

LAWLESS CODE
(1949 - Monogram) Jimmy Wakely, Cannonball Taylor
One Sheet: $40 - $75

LAWLESS COWBOYS
(1951 - Monogram) Whip Wilson
One Sheet: $30 - $50

LAWLESS EIGHTIES, THE
(1957 - Republic) Buster Crabbe, John Smith
One Sheet: $15 - $35

LAWLESS EMPIRE
(1945 - Columbia) Charles Starrett, Mildred Law
One Sheet: $40 - $75

LAWLESS FRONTIER, THE
(1935 - Monogram) John Wayne, Sheila Terry
One Sheet: $1,900 - $3,000

LAWLESS LAND
(1936 - Republic) Johnny Mack Brown
One Sheet: $100 - $200

LAWLESS NINETIES, THE
(1936 - Republic) John Wayne, Ann Rutherford
One Sheet: $2,200 - $3,500

LAWLESS PLAINSMEN
(1942 - Columbia) Charles Starrett, Russell Hayden
One Sheet: $50 - $100

LAWLESS RANGE
(1935 - Republic) John Wayne, Sheila Manners
One Sheet: $1,600 - $2,500   *Cowboy Movie Posters #187.*

LAWLESS RIDER, THE
(1954 - United Artists) Frankie Darro, Douglas Dumbrille
One Sheet: $15 - $35

LAWLESS RIDERS

(1935 - Columbia) Ken Maynard
One Sheet: $250 - $550

LAWLESS STREET, A
(1955 - Columbia) Randolph Scott, Angela Lansbury
One Sheet: $30 - $50

LAWLESS VALLEY
(1938 - RKO) George O'Brien, Kay Sutton
One Sheet: $125 - $250

LAWMAN
(1971 - United Artists) Burt Lancaster, Robert Ryan, Lee J. Cobb
One Sheet: $7 - $15

LAWMAN IS BORN, A
(1937 - Republic) Johnny Mack Brown, Iris Meredith
One Sheet: $50 - $100

LAWNMOWER MAN, THE
(1992 - New Line) Pierce Brosnan
One Sheet: $7 - $15

LAWNMOWER MAN II: BEYOND CYBERSPACE
(1996 - New Line) Matt Frewer, Patrick Bergin
One Sheet: $5 - $12

LAWRENCE OF ARABIA
(1962 - Columbia) Peter O'Toole, Sir Alec Guiness
One Sheet: $200 - $400   *Academy Award: Best Picture, Best Direction. O'Toole's first leading role. Price is for pre-Academy Award roadshow onesheet. One Sheet (AA):$50-$100. One Sheet (Parent's Magazine style):$20-$30. Academy Award Movie Posters #207.*

One Sheet

LAWRENCE OF ARABIA
(1971R - Columbia) Peter O'Toole, Sir Alec Guiness
One Sheet: $30 - $60   *Re-release.*

LAWRENCE OF ARABIA
(1984R - Columbia) Peter O'Toole, Sir Alec Guiness
One Sheet: $30 - $50   *Re-release.*

LAWRENCE OF ARABIA
(1989R - Columbia) Peter O'Toole, Sir Alec Guiness
One Sheet: $30 - $50   *Re-release.*

LAWYER, THE
(1970 - Paramount) Barry Newman, Harold Gould, Diana Muldaur
One Sheet: $10 - $20

LAWYER MAN
(1932 - Warner Bros.) William Powell, Joan Blondell
One Sheet: $800 - $1,500

Half Sheet

LAWYER'S SECRET, THE
(1931 - Paramount Publix) Richard Arlen, Jean Arthur
One Sheet: $250 - $500

LAY THAT RIFLE DOWN
(1955 - Republic) Judy Canova, Robert Lowery
One Sheet: $15 - $30

LAZY LITTLE BEAVER
(1943 - 20th Century Fox) Mighty Mouse
One Sheet: $250 - $600   *Cartoon. Full color stock poster with printed title. Huge image of Mighty Mouse on yellow background.*

LAZY RIVER
(1934 - MGM) Robert Young, Jean Parker
One Sheet: $125 - $250

LAZYBONES
(1925 - Fox) Buck Jones, Madge Bellamy
One Sheet: $150 - $300

LE BONHEUR
(1966 - Clover Films) Jean-Claude Drouot, Claire Drouot
One Sheet: $15 - $30

LE FRISSON DES VAMPIRES
(1970 - ABC) -
One Sheet: $125 - $250   *French.*

LE MANS
(1971 - Cinema Center Films) Steve McQueen
One Sheet: $40 - $80   *Sports (Auto racing). Sports Movie Posters #21.*

LE MEPRIS
(1963 - -) See CONTEMPT
French.

LE SCHPOUNTZ
(1937 - Pagnol) Leon Belieres, Robert Vattier
One Sheet: $150 - $300   *French. Price is for French 47x63.*

LE TESTAMENT D'ORPHEE
(1960 - -) See THE TESTAMENT OF ORPHEUS

LE VIOL DU VAMPIRE
(1967 - ABC) -
One Sheet: $75 - $150   *French.*

LEADBELLY
(1975 - Paramount) Roger E. Mosley, Paul Benjamin
One Sheet: $15 - $25   *Black cast. Life of the blues great.*

LEADING LIZZIE ASTRAY
(1915 - Keystone) Roscoe "Fatty" Arbuckle, Mack Swain
One Sheet: $1,900 - $3,000

LEADVILLE GUNSLINGER
(1952 - Republic) Allan "Rocky" Lane
One Sheet: $15 - $35

LEAGUE OF FRIGHTENED MEN, THE
(1937 - Columbia) Walter Connolly, Irene Hervey
One Sheet: $125 - $250

LEAGUE OF GENTLEMEN, THE
(1960 - -) Jack Hawkins, Nigel Patrick
One Sheet: $15 - $25

LEAGUE OF THEIR OWN, A
(1992 - Columbia) Geena Davis, Tom Hanks, Madonna
One Sheet: $7 - $15   *Sports (Baseball). Sports Movie Posters #82.*

LEAN ON ME
(1989 - Warner Bros.) Morgan Freeman, Beverly Todd
One Sheet: $3 - $5

LEAP OF FAITH
(1992 - Paramount) Steve Martin, Debra Winger, Liam Neeson
One Sheet: $5 - $10

LEARN POLIKENESS
(1938 - Paramount) Popeye, Fleischer Studio
One Sheet: $2,200 - $3,500   *Cartoon. Duotone. Cartoon Movie Posters #216.*

LEARNING TREE, THE
(1969 - Warner Bros.) Kyle Johnson, Alex Clarke, Estelle Evans
One Sheet: $5 - $10

LEASE OF LIFE
(1954 - Ealing) Robert Donat, Kay Walsh
One Sheet: $15 - $25

LEATHER BURNERS
(1942 - United Artists) William Boyd
One Sheet: $125 - $250   *Hopalong Cassidy series.*

LEATHER GLOVES
(1948 - Columbia) Cameron Mitchell, Virginia Grey
One Sheet: $40 - $75   *Sports (Boxing).*

LEATHER PUSHERS, THE
(1923 - Universal) Reginald Denny, Billy Sullivan
One Sheet: $350 - $750   *Serial. 24 Chapters. Sports (Boxing). Sports Movie Posters #116, 117, 118, 119.*

LEATHER SAINT, THE
(1956 - Paramount) John Derek, Paul Douglas
One Sheet: $15 - $25   *Sports (Boxing).*

LEATHERFACE: TEXAS CHAINSAW MASSACRE 3
(1990 - -) Kate Hodge, Ken Force
One Sheet: $10 - $20

LEATHERNECK, THE
(1929 - Pathe) William Boyd, Robert Armstrong, Alan Hale
One Sheet: $500 - $800

LEATHERNECKING
(1930 - RKO) Irene Dunne
One Sheet: $125 - $250

LEATHERNECKS HAVE LANDED, THE
(1936 - Republic) Lew Ayres, Isabel Jewell
One Sheet: $75 - $150

LEATHERPUSHERS, THE
(1940 - Universal) Richard Arlen, Andy Devine
One Sheet: $75 - $125   *Sports (Boxing).*

LEATHERSTOCKING
(1924 - Pathe) Edna Murphy, Harold Miller
One Sheet: $250 - $500   *Serial. 10 Chapters.*

LEAVE 'EM LAUGHING
(1928 - MGM) Laurel & Hardy
One Sheet: $4,000 - $6,000

LEAVE HER TO HEAVEN
(1946 - 20th Century Fox) Gene Tierney, Cornel Wilde, Vincent Price
One Sheet: $700 - $1,200

One Sheet

LEAVE IT TO BLONDIE
(1945 - Columbia) Arthur Lake, Penny Singleton
One Sheet: $50 - $100

LEAVE IT TO GERRY
(1924 - Grand-Asher) Billie Rhodes, William Collier
One Sheet: $100 - $200

LEAVE IT TO HENRY
(1949 - Monogram) Raymond Walburn, Walter Catlett
One Sheet: $20 - $40

LEAVE IT TO THE IRISH
(1949 - Monogram) James Dunn, Wanda McKay
One Sheet: $40 - $75

LEAVE IT TO THE MARINES
(1951 - Lippert) Sid Melton, Mara Lynn
One Sheet: $30 - $50

LEAVENWORTH CASE, THE
(1936 - Republic) Donald Cook, Jean Rouverol
One Sheet: $100 - $200

LEAVING LAS VEGAS
(1995 - -) Nicholas Cage, Elizabeth Shue
One Sheet: $10 - $20   *Academy Award: Best Actor (Cage).*

LEAVING NORMAL
(1992 - Universal) Christine Lahti, Meg Tilly
One Sheet: $3 - $5

LEECH WOMAN, THE
(1960 - Universal) Coleen Gray, Grant Williams
One Sheet: $30 - $60

One Sheet

LEFT HAND OF GOD, THE
(1955 - 20th Century Fox) Humphrey Bogart, Gene Tierney
One Sheet: $75 - $150

LEFT HANDED GUN, THE
(1958 - Warner Bros.) Paul Newman, Lita Milan
One Sheet: $15 - $30   *Dir: Arthur Penn's first film.*

LEFT-HANDED LAW
(1937 - Universal) Buck Jones
One Sheet: $250 - $600

LEFTOVER LADIES
(1931 - Tiffany) Claudia Dell, Marjorie Rambeau
One Sheet: $125 - $250

LEGAL EAGLES
(1986 - Universal) Robert Redford, Debra Winger
One Sheet: $3 - $5

LEGEND
(1986 - 20th Century Fox) Tom Cruise, Mia Sara, Tim Curry
One Sheet: $10 - $20   *Advance:$25-50.*

LEGEND OF BILLIE JEAN, THE
(1985 - TriStar) Helen Slater, Keith Gordon, Dean Stockwell
One Sheet: $3 - $5

LEGEND OF BLOOD CASTLE, THE
(1972 - Film Ventures) Ewa Aulin
One Sheet: $10 - $20

LEGEND OF BOGGY CREEK, THE
(1973 - Howco) Willie Smith, John P. Hixson (docudrama)

One Sheet: $3 - $5

LEGEND OF COYOTE ROCK, THE
(1945 - RKO/Disney) Pluto
One Sheet: $1,300 - $2,000   *Cartoon.*

LEGEND OF EARL DURAND, THE
(1974 - Howco) Martin Sheen, Slim Pickens
One Sheet: $3 - $5

LEGEND OF FRENCHIE KING, THE
(1971 - K-Tel) Brigitte Bardot, Claudia Cardinale
One Sheet: $15 - $25   *Cowboy Movie Posters #333.*

LEGEND OF HELL HOUSE, THE
(1973 - 20th Century Fox) Roddy McDowall, Pamela Franklin
One Sheet: $15 - $30

LEGEND OF HILLBILLY JOHN, THE
(1973 - Jack H. Harris Ent.) Hedge Capers, Susan Strasberg
One Sheet: $3 - $5

LEGEND OF LOBO, THE
(1962 - Buena Vista/Disney) Narrated by Rex Allen
One Sheet: $15 - $30

LEGEND OF LOBO, THE
(1972R - Walt Disney) Narrated by Rex Allen
One Sheet: $3 - $5   *Re-release.*

LEGEND OF LYLAH CLARE, THE
(1968 - MGM) Kim Novak, Peter Finch, Ernest Borgnine
One Sheet: $15 - $30

LEGEND OF NIGGER CHARLEY, THE
(1972 - Paramount) Fred Williamson, D'Urville Martin
One Sheet: $15 - $25   *Blaxploitation.*

LEGEND OF THE LONE RANGER
(1981 - Universal) Klinton Spilsbury, Michael Horse
One Sheet: $7 - $15   *Cowboy Movie Posters #352.*

LEGEND OF THE LOST
(1957 - Batjac) John Wayne, Sophia Loren
One Sheet: $75 - $150

LEGEND OF THE SEVEN GOLDEN VAMPIRES, THE
(1974 - Shaw-Hammer) David Chang, Peter Cushing
One Sheet: $7 - $15   *AKA: DRACULA AND THE SEVEN GOLDEN VAMPIRES.*

LEGEND OF TOM DOOLEY, THE
(1959 - Columbia) Michael Landon, Jack Hogan
One Sheet: $20 - $40

LEGENDARY CURSE OF LEMORA, A CHILD'S TALE OF THE SUPERNATURAL
(1973 - Blackburn) Leslie Gilb
One Sheet: $20 - $40

LEGENDS OF THE FALL
(1994 - TriStar) Brad Pitt, Anthony Hopkins, Aidan Quinn, Julia Ormond
One Sheet: $7 - $15

One Sheet

LEGENDS OF THE JUNGLE BOOK
(1994 - Disney) Jason Scott Lee, Cary Elwes
One Sheet: $5 - $12

LEGION OF LOST FLYERS
(1939 - Universal) Richard Arlen, Andy Devine
One Sheet: $75 - $150

LEGION OF MISSING MEN, THE
(1937 - Monogram) Ralph Forbes, Ben Alexander
One Sheet: $75 - $150

LEGION OF TERROR
(1936 - Columbia) Ward Bond, Marguerite Churchill
One Sheet: $125 - $250

LEGION OF THE CONDEMNED, THE
(1928 - Paramount) Gary Cooper, Fay Wray
One Sheet: $700 - $1,200

LEGION OF THE DOOMED
(1958 - Allied Artists) Bill Williams, Dawn Richard
One Sheet: $20 - $40

LEGION OF THE LAWLESS
(1940 - RKO) George O'Brien, Virginia Vale
One Sheet: $100 - $200

LEGIONNAIRES IN PARIS
(1927 - F.B.O.) Al Cooke, Kit Gaurd
One Sheet: $200 - $400

LEGIONS OF THE NILE
(1960 - 20th Century Fox) Linda Cristal, Georges Marchal
One Sheet: $15 - $25

LEGONG: DANCE OF THE VIRGINS
(1935 - Paramount) Bali Natives
One Sheet: $150 - $300

LEM HAWKINS' CONFESSION
(1935 - Micheaux) Clarence Brooks
One Sheet: $1,300 - $2,000   *Black cast. Separate Cinema, pg. 14.*

LEMON DROP KID, THE
(1934 - Paramount) Lee Tracy, Helen Mack
One Sheet: $125 - $250

LEMON DROP KID, THE
(1951 - Paramount) Bob Hope, Marilyn Maxwell
One Sheet: $30 - $50

LEMON SISTERS, THE
(1990 - Miramax) Diane Keaton, Carol Kane, Kathryn Grody
One Sheet: $3 - $5

LENA RIVERS
(1932 - Tiffany) Charlotte Henry, Beryl Mercer
One Sheet: $100 - $200

LENNY
(1974 - United Artists) Dustin Hoffman, Valerie Perrine
One Sheet: $15 - $25   *Style B:$15-30.*

LEO THE LAST
(1970 - United Artists) Marcello Mastroianni, Billie Whitelaw, Calvin Lockhart
One Sheet: $3 - $5

LEO TOLSTOY'S ANNA KARENINA
(1997 - Warner Bros.) Sophie Marceau, Sean Bean
One Sheet: $5 - $10

LEOLO
(1993 - Fine Line) Ginette Reno, Pierre Bourgault
One Sheet: $3 - $5   *French.*

LEON THE PIG FARMER
(1993 - Cinevista) Mark Frankel
One Sheet: $3 - $5

LEONARD PART 6
(1986 - Columbia) Bill Cosby, Tom Courtenay
One Sheet: $5 - $10

LEOPARD, THE
(1963 - 20th Century Fox) Burt Lancaster, Alain Delon
One Sheet: $10 - $20

LEOPARD LADY, THE
(1928 - Pathe) Jacqueline Logan, Alan Hale
One Sheet: $250 - $600

LEOPARD MAN, THE
(1943 - RKO) Dennis O'Keefe, Jean Brooks
One Sheet: $250 - $500   *Graven Images, pg. 109, 124.*

LEOPARD MAN, THE
(1957R - RKO) Dennis O'Keefe, Jean Brooks

One Sheet: $40 - $80   *Re-release.*

LEOPARD MEN OF AFRICA, THE
(1940 - Zeidman International) Dr. Eddy - Documentary
One Sheet: $100 - $200

LEOPARD WOMAN, THE
(1920 - Associated) Louise Glaum, House Peters
One Sheet: $150 - $300

LEPKE
(1974 - Warner Bros.) Tony Curtis, Anjanette Comer
One Sheet: $3 - $5

LEPRECHAUN
(1993 - Trimark) Jennifer Aniston, Ken Olandt
One Sheet: $3 - $5

LES ENFANTS DU PARADIS
(1944 - -) See CHILDREN OF PARADISE
French.

LES GIRLS
(1957 - MGM) Gene Kelly, Mitzi Gaynor
One Sheet: $75 - $125

LES MISERABLES
(1935 - 20th Century) Fredric March, Rochelle Hudson, Charles Laughton
One Sheet: $800 - $1,500

LES MISERABLES
(1952 - 20th Century Fox) Michael Rennie, Debra Paget
One Sheet: $40 - $75

LES MISERABLES
(1982 - Del Duca) Lino Ventura, Jean Carmet
One Sheet: $7 - $15

LES MYSTERES DU CIEL
(1907 - Consortium des Galas Cinematographiques)
One Sheet: $2,500 - $4,000   *French. Price is for French 47x63 poster. U.S. title: Mysteries Of The Sky.*

LES PETROLEUSES
(1971 - S.N.C.) Brigitte Bardot, Claudia Cardinale
One Sheet: $50 - $100   *French. American title: "The Legend Of Frenchie King".*

LESS THAN ZERO
(1987 - -) Andrew McCarthy, Jami Gertz
One Sheet: $7 - $15

LET 'EM HAVE IT
(1935 - Reliance) Richard Arlen, Virginia Bruce
One Sheet: $100 - $200

LET FREEDOM RING
(1939 - MGM) Nelson Eddy, Virginia Bruce
One Sheet: $100 - $200

LET IT BE
(1970 - United Artists) The Beatles
One Sheet: $125 - $250   *Rock 'n' Roll.*

LET IT RIDE
(1989 - Paramount) Richard Dreyfuss, Teri Garr
One Sheet: $3 - $5

LET NO MAN WRITE MY EPITAPH
(1960 - Columbia) Burl Ives, Shelley Winters
One Sheet: $3 - $5

LET THE GOOD TIMES ROLL
(1973 - Columbia) Chuck Berry, Little Richard, All-star rock cast
One Sheet: $15 - $30   *Rock 'n' Roll.*

LET THEM LIVE
(1937 - Universal) Nan Grey, John Howard
One Sheet: $75 - $125

LET US BE GAY
(1930 - MGM) Norma Shearer, Marie Dressler
One Sheet: $250 - $500

LET US LIVE
(1939 - Columbia) Maureen O'Sullivan, Henry Fonda
One Sheet: $75 - $150

LET US LIVE
(1947R - Columbia) Maureen O'Sullivan, Henry Fonda
One Sheet: $15 - $30   *Re-release. Duotone.*

LET'S BE HAPPY
(1956 - -) Vera Ellen, Tony Martin
One Sheet: $20 - $40

LET'S BE RITZY
(1934 - Universal) Lew Ayers, Patricia Ellis
One Sheet: $100 - $200

LET'S DANCE
(1950 - Paramount) Betty Hutton, Fred Astaire
One Sheet: $100 - $200

LET'S DO IT AGAIN
(1953 - Columbia) Jane Wyman, Ray Milland
One Sheet: $15 - $30

LET'S DO IT AGAIN
(1975 - Warner Bros.) Bill Cosby, Sidney
Poitier, Jimmie Walker
One Sheet: $15 - $25 *Black cast.*
Sequel to UPTOWN SATURDAY NIGHT.

LET'S FACE IT
(1943 - Paramount) Bob Hope, Betty Hutton
One Sheet: $100 - $200

One Sheet

LET'S FALL IN LOVE
(1934 - Columbia) Ann Sothern, Edmund Lowe
One Sheet: $100 - $200

LET'S GET HARRY
(1986 - -) Michael Schoeffling, Tom Wilson
One Sheet: $3 - $5

LET'S GET MARRIED
(1937 - Columbia) Ralph Bellamy, Ida Lupino
One Sheet: $100 - $200

LET'S GET TOUGH
(1942 - Monogram) East Side Kids, Florence
Rice
One Sheet: $50 - $100

LET'S GO
(1923 - Truart) Richard Talmadge, Eileen Percy
One Sheet: $125 - $250

LET'S GO COLLEGIATE
(1941 - Monogram) Frankie Darro, Jackie
Moran
One Sheet: $75 - $150

LET'S GO NATIVE
(1930 - Paramount Publix) Jeannette
MacDonald, Kay Francis, Jack Oakie
One Sheet: $150 - $300

LET'S GO NAVY
(1951 - Monogram) Leo Gorcey, Huntz Hall
One Sheet: $40 - $75

LET'S GO PLACES
(1930 - Fox) Joseph Wagstaff, Sharon Lynn
One Sheet: $500 - $800

LET'S GO STEADY
(1945 - Columbia) Pat Parrish, Jackie Moran,
Mel Torme
One Sheet: $30 - $60

LET'S HAVE FUN
(1943 - Columbia) Bert Gordon, Margaret
Lindsay
One Sheet: $75 - $125

LET'S KILL UNCLE
(1966 - Universal) Nigel Green, Mary Badham
One Sheet: $7 - $15

LET'S LIVE A LITTLE
(1948 - Eagle-Lion) Hedy Lamarr, Robert
Cummings
One Sheet: $30 - $50

LET'S LIVE AGAIN
(1948 - 20th Century Fox) John Emery, Hillary
Brooke
One Sheet: $30 - $60

LET'S MAKE A MILLION
(1936 - Paramount) Charlotte Wynters, Edward
Everett Horton
One Sheet: $100 - $200

LET'S MAKE A NIGHT OF IT
(1937 - Universal) Charles "Buddy" Rogers,
June Clyde
One Sheet: $100 - $200

LET'S MAKE IT LEGAL
(1951 - 20th Century Fox) Claudette Colbert,
Macdonald Carey, Marilyn Monroe
One Sheet: $150 - $350

LET'S MAKE LOVE
(1960 - 20th Century Fox) Marilyn Monroe,
Yves Montand
One Sheet: $150 - $350

LET'S MAKE MUSIC
(1941 - RKO) Bob Crosby & Orch.
One Sheet: $100 - $200 *Big Band*
musical.

LET'S MAKE UP
(1954 - United Artists) Errol Flynn, Anna Nagel
One Sheet: $40 - $75

LET'S ROCK!
(1958 - Columbia) Julius La Rosa, Phyllis
Newman, Paul Anka, Della Reese
One Sheet: $75 - $150 *Rock 'n' Roll.*

LET'S SCARE JESSICA TO DEATH
(1971 - Paramount) Zohra Lampert, Barton
Heyman
One Sheet: $7 - $15

LET'S SING AGAIN
(1936 - RKO) Bobby Breen, Henry Armetta
One Sheet: $75 - $125

LET'S SPEND THE NIGHT TOGETHER
(1983 - Embassy) The Rolling Stones
One Sheet: $30 - $60 *Rock 'n' Roll.*

LET'S TALK ABOUT WOMEN
(1964 - Embassy) Vittorio Gassman, Maria
Fiore
One Sheet: $5 - $10

LET'S TALK IT OVER
(1934 - Universal) Chester Morris, Mae Clarke
One Sheet: $125 - $250

LET'S TRY AGAIN
(1934 - RKO) Clive Brook, Irene Hervey
One Sheet: $100 - $200

LETHAL
(1986 - Cinema Group) Michael Billington,
Denise DuBarry
One Sheet: $3 - $5

LETHAL WEAPON
(1987 - Warner Bros.) Mel Gibson, Danny
Glover
One Sheet: $20 - $40 *International*
One Sheet:$30-60.

LETHAL WEAPON 3
(1992 - Warner Bros.) Mel Gibson, Danny
Glover
One Sheet: $7 - $15

LETHAL WEAPON II
(1989 - Warner Bros.) Mel Gibson, Danny
Glover
One Sheet: $7 - $15

LETTER, THE
(1940 - Warner Bros.) Bette Davis, Herbert
Marshall, James Stephenson
One Sheet: $600 - $1,000

LETTER FOR EVIE, A
(1945 - MGM) Marsha Hunt, John Carroll,
Hume Cronyn
One Sheet: $30 - $50

LETTER FROM AN UNKNOWN WOMAN
(1948 - Universal) Joan Fontaine, Louis
Jourdan
One Sheet: $200 - $400

LETTER OF INTRODUCTION
(1938 - Universal) Andrea Leeds, Adolphe
Menjou, Edgar Bergen, Charlie McCarthy
One Sheet: $150 - $300

One Sheet

LETTER TO THREE WIVES, A
(1949 - 20th Century Fox) Jeanne Crain, Linda
Darnell
One Sheet: $75 - $125 *Academy*
Award: Best Direction(Mankiewicz). Academy
Award Movie Posters #122.

LETTING IN THE SUNSHINE
(1933 - Empire/BIP) Albert Burdon, Renee
Gadd
One Sheet: $30 - $50

LETTY LYNTON
(1932 - MGM) Robert Montgomery, Joan
Crawford
One Sheet: $600 - $1,000

LEVIATHAN
(1989 - MGM) Peter Weller, Amanda Pays,
Richard Crenna
One Sheet: $5 - $10

LEW LEHR'S DRIBBLE-PUSS PARADE
(1944 - 20th Centure Fox) -
One Sheet: $100 - $200

LI'L ABNER
(1940 - RKO) Buster Keaton, Martha O'Driscoll
One Sheet: $200 - $400

LI'L ABNER
(1948R - RKO) Buster Keaton, Martha
O'Driscoll
One Sheet: $40 - $75 *Re-release.*

LI'L ABNER
(1959 - Paramount) Peter Palmer, Leslie
Parrish
One Sheet: $20 - $40

LIANE, JUNGLE GODDESS
(1958 - DCA) Marion Michaels
One Sheet: $15 - $30 *Sexploitation.*

LIAR, LIAR
(1997 - Universal) Jim Carrey, Jon Lovitz,
Amanda Donohue
One Sheet: $5 - $10

LIBEL
(1959 - MGM) Olivia de Havilland, Dirk
Bogarde
One Sheet: $15 - $30

LIBELED LADY
(1936 - MGM) Jean Harlow, William Powell,
Myrna Loy, Spencer Tracy
One Sheet: $800 - $1,500

LIBERATED WOMAN, THE
(197? - -) John Holmes
One Sheet: $75 - $125 *XXX.*

LIBERATION OF L.B. JONES, THE
(1970 - Columbia) Lee J. Cobb, Roscoe Lee
Brown, Lola Falana (film debut)
One Sheet: $10 - $20 *Director*
William Wyler's last film.

LIBERTY
(1929 - MGM) Stan Laurel, Oliver Hardy
One Sheet: $4,000 - $6,000

LICENSE TO DRIVE
(1988 - -) Corey Haim, Corey Feldman, Carol
Kane
One Sheet: $3 - $5

LICENSE TO KILL
(1989 - United Artists) Timothy Dalton, Carey
Lowell
One Sheet: $10 - $20 *Advance:$20-*
$30.

One Sheet

LIEUTENANT WORE SKIRTS, THE
(1956 - 20th Century Fox) Tom Ewell, Sheree
North
One Sheet: $20 - $40

LIFE AND ADVENTURES OF BUFFALO BILL
(1917 - -) -
One Sheet: $500 - $800

LIFE AND DEATH OF COLONEL BLIMP, THE
(1943 - United Artists) Roger Livesey, Anton
Walbrook, Deborah Kerr
One Sheet: $75 - $150

LIFE AND LOVES OF BEETHOVEN
(1938 - World) Harry Bauer, Annie Ducaux
One Sheet: $100 - $200

LIFE AND NOTHING BUT
(1989 - Hachette Premiere) Phillippe Noiret,
Sabine Azema
One Sheet: $2 - $3

LIFE AND TIMES OF GRIZZLY ADAMS, THE
(1974 - Sun Classic) Dan Haggerty
One Sheet: $3 - $5

LIFE AND TIMES OF JUDGE ROY BEAN, THE
(1972 - National General) Paul Newman, Ava
Gardner
One Sheet: $30 - $50 *Amsel art.*
Cowboy Movie Posters #336.

LIFE AT STAKE, A
(1955 - Filmakers) Angela Lansbury, Keith
Andes
One Sheet: $15 - $30

LIFE AT THE TOP
(1966 - Royal International) Laurence Harvey,
Jean Simmons
One Sheet: $3 - $5

LIFE BEGINS
(1932 - First National) Loretta Young, Eric
Linden
One Sheet: $800 - $1,500

LIFE BEGINS AT EIGHT-THIRTY
(1942 - 20th Century Fox) Monty Woolley, Ida
Lupino
One Sheet: $50 - $100

LIFE BEGINS AT FORTY
(1935 - Fox) Will Rogers, Rochelle Hudson
One Sheet: $250 - $600

LIFE BEGINS AT SEVENTEEN
(1958 - Columbia) Mark Damon, Dorothy
Johnson
One Sheet: $10 - $20

LIFE BEGINS FOR ANDY HARDY
(1941 - MGM) Mickey Rooney, Lewis Stone,
Judy Garland
One Sheet: $250 - $600

LIFE BEGINS IN COLLEGE
(1937 - 20th Century Fox) Joan Davis, Ritz
Brothers
One Sheet: $100 - $200 *Sports*
(Football). Sports Movie Posters #192.

LIFE BEGINS WITH LOVE
(1937 - Columbia) Jean Parker, Douglas
Montgomery
One Sheet: $75 - $150

LIFE GOES ON
(1938 - Paramount) Hugh Wakefield
One Sheet: $75 - $150

LIFE GOES ON
(1938B - Million Dollar) Louise Beavers
One Sheet: $250 - $600   *Black cast.*
Separate Cinema, pg. 141.

LIFE IN DANGER
(1964 - Allied Artists) Darren Nesbitt, Julie
Hopkins
One Sheet: $3 - $5

LIFE IN JOLIET PENITENTIARY
(1910 - ABO) -
One Sheet: $350 - $750

LIFE IN THE BALANCE, A
(1954 - 20th Century Fox) Ricardo Montalban,
Anne Bancroft
One Sheet: $15 - $30

LIFE IN THE RAW
(1933 - Fox) George O'Brien, Claire Trevor
One Sheet: $150 - $300

LIFE LINE, THE
(1919 - Paramount/Artcraft) Maurice Tourneur
One Sheet: $150 - $300

LIFE OF BUFFALO BILL, THE
(1914 - Pawnee) Buffalo Bill Cody
One Sheet: $600 - $1,000   *Cowboy
Movie Posters #6.*

LIFE OF EMILE ZOLA, THE
(1937 - Warner Bros.) Paul Muni, Gale
Sondergaard
One Sheet: $500 - $800   *Academy
Award: Best Picture. Academy Award Movie
Posters #51 & #55.*

LIFE OF HER OWN, A
(1950 - MGM) Lana Turner, Ray Milland
One Sheet: $50 - $100

LIFE OF JIMMY DOLAN, THE
(1933 - Warner Bros.) Douglas Fairbanks Jr.,
Loretta Young
One Sheet: $150 - $350

LIFE OF RILEY, THE
(1949 - Universal) William Bendix, James
Gleason
One Sheet: $50 - $100

LIFE OF THE PARTY, THE
(1920 - -) Fatty Arbuckle
One Sheet: $1,600 - $2,500

LIFE OF THE PARTY, THE
(1930 - Warner Bros.) Jack Whiting, Charles
Butterworth, Winnie Lightner
One Sheet: $250 - $500

One Sheet

LIFE OF THE PARTY, THE
(1937 - RKO) Gene Raymond, Harriet Hilliard
One Sheet: $75 - $125

LIFE OF VERGIE WINTERS, THE
(1934 - RKO) Ann Harding, John Boles
One Sheet: $75 - $150

LIFE ON THE HORTOBAGY
(1940 - Jewel) -
One Sheet: $50 - $100

LIFE RETURNS
(1938 - Grand National) Lois Wilson, Onslow
Stevens
One Sheet: $50 - $100

LIFE WITH BLONDIE
(1945 - Columbia) Penny Singleton, Arthur
Lake, Marc Lawrence
One Sheet: $50 - $100

LIFE WITH FATHER
(1947 - Warner Bros.) Irene Dunne, William
Powell, Elizabeth Taylor
One Sheet: $40 - $80   *Taylor does
not appear on posters.*

LIFE WITH FIDO
(1942 - 20th Century Fox) Terrytoon
One Sheet: $100 - $200   *Cartoon.
Stock poster with title inset.*

LIFE WITH HENRY
(1941 - Paramount) Jackie Cooper, Eddie
Bracken
One Sheet: $75 - $150

LIFE WITH MIKEY
(1993 - Buena Vista) Michael J. Fox, Christina
Vidal
One Sheet: $3 - $5

LIFE WITH THE LYONS
(1953 - Lippert) Bebe Daniels, Ben Lyon
One Sheet: $30 - $50

LIFE WITHOUT SOUL
(1915 - -) -
One Sheet: $3,500 - $5,000   *Graven
Images, pg. 22. Frankenstein story.*

LIFE'S GREATEST GAME
(1924 - FBO) Johnnie Walker, Tom Santschi
One Sheet: $250 - $600   *Sports
(Baseball).*

LIFEBOAT
(1944 - 20th Century Fox) Tallulah Bankhead,
William Bendix, Dir: Alfred Hitchcock
One Sheet: $1,300 - $2,000

One Sheet

LIFEFORCE
(1985 - TriStar) Steve Railsback, Peter Firth
One Sheet: $7 - $15   *International
One Sheet:$20-25.*

LIFEGUARD
(1976 - Paramount) Sam Elliott, Anne Archer
One Sheet: $7 - $15   *Sports Movie
Posters #328.*

LIGHT AT THE EDGE OF THE WORLD, THE
(1971 - National General) Kirk Douglas, Yul
Brynner
One Sheet: $5 - $10

LIGHT FINGERS
(1957 - Parkside) Guy Rolfe, Roland Culver
One Sheet: $15 - $25

LIGHT IN THE DARK
(1922 - Associated First National) Hope
Hampton, E.K. Lincoln, Lon Chaney
One Sheet: $125 - $250

LIGHT IN THE FOREST, THE
(1958 - Buena Vista) Carol Lynley, James
MacArthur
One Sheet: $15 - $30

LIGHT IN THE PIAZZA
(1962 - MGM) Olivia de Havilland, Rossano
Brazzi
One Sheet: $15 - $30

LIGHT OF DAY
(1987 - TriStar) Michael J. Fox, Gena
Rowlands
One Sheet: $5 - $10

LIGHT OF WESTERN STARS, THE
(1925 - Paramount) Jack Holt, Noah Beery,
Billie Dove
One Sheet: $600 - $1,000

LIGHT OF WESTERN STARS, THE
(1930 - Paramount) Richard Arlen
One Sheet: $250 - $500

LIGHT OF WESTERN STARS, THE
(1940 - Paramount) Victor Jory, Russell
Hayden
One Sheet: $75 - $125

LIGHT OF WESTERN STARS, THE
(1950R - Favorite) Victor Jory, Russell Hayden
One Sheet: $15 - $25   *Re-release.*

LIGHT SLEEPER
(1992 - -) Willem DaFoe, Susan Sarandon
One Sheet: $3 - $5

LIGHT THAT FAILED, THE
(1940 - Paramount) Ronald Colman, Walter
Huston
One Sheet: $250 - $600

LIGHT TOUCH, THE
(1951 - MGM) Stewart Granger, Pier Angeli
One Sheet: $40 - $75

One Sheet

LIGHT YEARS
(1988 - -) Voices: Glenn Close, Jennifer Grey
One Sheet: $7 - $15   *Cartoon.*

LIGHTHORSEMEN, THE
(1988 - -) Jon Blake, Peter Phelps
One Sheet: $5 - $10

LIGHTHOUSE
(1947 - PRC) Don Castle, June Lang
One Sheet: $40 - $75

LIGHTNIN'
(1930 - Fox) Will Rogers, Louise Dresser, Joel
McCrea
One Sheet: $250 - $600

LIGHTNIN' BILL CARSON
(1936 - Puritan) Tim McCoy, Lois January, Rex
Lease
One Sheet: $125 - $250

LIGHTNIN' CRANDALL
(1937 - Republic) Bob Steele, Lois January
One Sheet: $100 - $200

LIGHTNIN' IN THE FOREST
(1948 - Republic) Lynne Roberts, Donald Barry
One Sheet: $30 - $50

LIGHTNING BILL
(193? - -) Bill Boyd
One Sheet: $150 - $300

LIGHTNING BRYCE
(1919 - National) Ann Little, Jack Hoxie
One Sheet: $100 - $200   *Serial. 3
Chapters.*

LIGHTNING CARSON RIDES AGAIN
(1938 - Victory) Tim McCoy, Joan Barclay
One Sheet: $150 - $300

LIGHTNING EXPRESS, THE
(1930 - Universal) Lane Chandler, Louise
Lorraine
One Sheet: $150 - $300   *Serial.
Western. 10 Chapters.*

LIGHTNING FLYER, THE
(1931 - Columbia) James Hall, Dorothy
Sebastian
One Sheet: $150 - $300

LIGHTNING GUNS
(1950 - Columbia) Charles Starrett, Smiley
Burnette

One Sheet: $15 - $35

LIGHTNING RAIDER, THE
(1918 - Pathe) Pearl White, Warner Oland
One Sheet: $250 - $600   *Serial. 15
Chapters.*

LIGHTNING RAIDERS
(1945 - PRC) Buster Crabbe, Al St. John
One Sheet: $30 - $50

LIGHTNING RANGE
(1919 - -) Buddy Roosevelt
One Sheet: $250 - $500

LIGHTNING SPEED
(1928 - -) Bob Steele, Mary Mabery
One Sheet: $200 - $400

LIGHTNING STRIKES TWICE
(1934 - RKO) Ben Lyons, Thelma Todd
One Sheet: $75 - $150

LIGHTNING STRIKES TWICE
(1950 - Warner Bros.) Ruth Roman, Richard
Todd
One Sheet: $15 - $25

LIGHTNING STRIKES WEST
(1940 - Colony) Ken Maynard, Claire Rochelle
One Sheet: $100 - $200

LIGHTNING SWORDS OF DEATH
(1974 - Columbia) Tomisaburo Wakayama,
Masahiro Tomikawa
One Sheet: $15 - $25   *Re-release of
SWORD OF VENGEANCE. AKA: SHOGUN
ASSASSIN.*

LIGHTNING TRIGGERS
(1935 - William Kent) Reb Russell, Yvonne
Pelletier
One Sheet: $125 - $250

LIGHTNING WARRIOR, THE
(1931 - Mascot) Rin-Tin-Tin, Frankie Darro
One Sheet: $125 - $250   *Serial. 12
Chapters.*

LIGHTS OF NEW YORK
(1928 - Warner Bros.) Helene Costello, Cullen
Landis
One Sheet: $1,900 - $3,000   *First all-talking
film.*

LIGHTS OF OLD BROADWAY
(1925 - MGM) Marion Davies, Conrad Nagel
One Sheet: $600 - $1,000

LIGHTS OF OLD SANTA FE
(1944 - Republic) Roy Rogers, Dale Evans
One Sheet: $150 - $300

Insert

LIGHTS OF OLD SANTA FE
(1955R - Republic) Roy Rogers
One Sheet: $50 - $100   *Re-release.*

LIGHTS OUT
(1940 - 20th Century Fox) Terry-toons
One Sheet: $100 - $200   *Cartoon. Full
color stone litho. Stock poster with inset title.*

LIGHTSHIP, THE
(1986 - CBS) Robert Duvall, Klaus Maria
Brandauer
One Sheet: $3 - $5

LIKE FATHER, LIKE SON
(1987 - TriStar) Dudley Moore, Kirk Cameron

LIKE WATER FOR CHOCOLATE
(1993 - Miramax) Lumi Cavazos, Regina Torne,
Marco Leonardi

One Sheet: $15 - $25   *Spanish.*

LIKELY STORY, A
(1947 - RKO) Barbara Hale, Bill Williams
One Sheet: $20 - $40

LILAC DOMINO, THE
(1940 - Select Attractions) Michael Bartlett, June Knight
One Sheet: $50 - $100

LILAC TIME
(1928 - First National) Colleen Moore, Gary Cooper
One Sheet: $800 - $1,500

LILI
(1953 - MGM) Leslie Caron, Mel Ferrer
One Sheet: $30 - $60

LILI
(1964R - MGM) Leslie Caron, Mel Ferrer
One Sheet: $5 - $10   *Re-release.*

LILI MARLEEN
(1981 - -) Hanna Schygulia, Giancarlo Giannini
One Sheet: $10 - $20   *German.*

LILIES OF THE FIELD
(1930 - First National) Corinne Griffith, Ralph Forbes
One Sheet: $125 - $250

LILIES OF THE FIELD
(1963 - United Artists) Sidney Poitier, Lilia Skala
One Sheet: $30 - $50   *Academy Award: Best Actor. Academy Award Movie Posters #216. Separate Cinema, pg. 158.*

LILIOM
(1930 - Fox) Charles Farrell, Rose Hobart
One Sheet: $150 - $300

LILITH
(1964 - Columbia) Warren Beatty, Jean Seberg
One Sheet: $7 - $15

LILLI MARLENE
(1950 - Monarch) Lisa Daniely, Stanley Baker
One Sheet: $15 - $30

LILLIAN RUSSELL
(1940 - 20th Century Fox) Alice Faye, Henry Fonda, Don Ameche
One Sheet: $200 - $400

One Sheet

LILLIE'S NIGHTMARE
(1914 - Patheplay) -
One Sheet: $250 - $500

LILY CHRISTINE
(1932 - Paramount) Corinne Griffith, Colin Clive
One Sheet: $75 - $150

LILY OF THE DUST
(1924 - -) Pola Negri, Noah Beery
One Sheet: $600 - $1,000

LILY TURNER
(1933 - First National) George Brent, Ruth Chatterton
One Sheet: $250 - $600

LIMBO
(1972 - Universal) Kate Jackson, Katherine Justice, Kathleen Nolan
One Sheet: $3 - $5

LIMEHOUSE BLUES
(1934 - Paramount) George Raft, Jean Parker
One Sheet: $250 - $500

LIMELIGHT

(1953 - United Artists) Charles Chaplin, Claire Bloom
One Sheet: $125 - $250

LIMIT, THE
(1972 - Cannon) Yaphet Kotto, Quinn Redecker
One Sheet: $10 - $20   *Biker film.*

LIMPING MAN, THE
(1932 - Powers) Franklin Dyall, Arthur Hardy
One Sheet: $75 - $150

LIMPING MAN, THE
(1953 - Lippert) Lloyd Bridges, Moira Lister
One Sheet: $20 - $40

LINCOLN CONSPIRACY, THE
(1977 - Sunn) Bradford Dillman, John Dehner
One Sheet: $5 - $10

LINDA, BE GOOD
(1948 - Eagle-Lion) Elsye Knox, Marie Wilson
One Sheet: $40 - $75

LINDA LOVELACE FOR PRESIDENT
(1975 - General Film) Linda Lovelace
One Sheet: $7 - $15   *XXX.*

LINDBERGH FLIES ALONE
(1927 - Pathe) Charles Lindbergh
One Sheet: $250 - $500

LINEUP, THE
(1934 - Columbia) William Gargan, Marian Nixon
One Sheet: $150 - $300

LINEUP, THE
(1958 - Columbia) Eli Wallach, Robert Keith
One Sheet: $30 - $60

LINK
(1986 - Cannon) Terence Stamp, Elisabeth Shue
One Sheet: $3 - $5

LION, THE
(1962 - 20th Century Fox) William Holden, Capucine
One Sheet: $15 - $25

LION AND THE HORSE, THE
(1952 - Warner Bros.) Steve Cochran, Sherry Jackson
One Sheet: $20 - $40

LION AND THE LAMB, THE
(1931 - Columbia) Walter Byron, Carmel Myers
One Sheet: $100 - $200

LION AND THE SOUSE, THE
(1924 - Pathe) -
One Sheet: $150 - $350

LION HAS WINGS, THE
(1940 - London) Merle Oberon, Ralph Richardson
One Sheet: $50 - $100

LION HUNTERS, THE
(1951 - Monogram) Johnny Sheffield. Ann Todd
One Sheet: $30 - $50

LION IN WINTER, THE
(1968 - Avco/Embassy) Peter O'Toole, Katharine Hepburn
One Sheet: $30 - $50   *Academy Award: Best Actress(2nd year in a row). Academy Award Movie Posters #248.*

LION IN WINTER, THE
(1975R - Avco/Embassy) Peter O'Toole, Katharine Hepburn
One Sheet: $7 - $15   *Re-release.*

LION IS IN THE STREETS, A
(1953 - Warner Bros.) James Cagney, Barbara Hale
One Sheet: $30 - $60

LION KING, THE
(1994 - Disney) Voices: Matthew Broderick, Jeremy Irons, James Earl Jones
One Sheet: $15 - $25   *Cartoon.*
Advance:$25-$40.

LION MAN, THE
(1919 - Universal) Jack Perrin, Barney Sherry
One Sheet: $600 - $1,000   *Serial. 18 Episodes.*

LION OF THE DESERT
(1981 - -) Anthony Quinn, Oliver Reed, Rod Steiger

One Sheet: $3 - $5

LION'S LOVE
(1969 - Max L. Rabb) Viva, James Rado, Gerome Ragni, Shirley Clarke
One Sheet: $2 - $3

LION'S ROAR, THE
(1928 - Mack Sennett) -
One Sheet: $250 - $500

LIONHEART
(1987 - -) Eric Stoltz, Gabriel Byrne
One Sheet: $5 - $10

LIPSTICK
(1976 - Paramount) Margaux Hemingway, Anne Bancroft
One Sheet: $7 - $15

LIQUID SKY
(1983 - Z-Films) Anne Carlisle, Paula E. Sheppard
One Sheet: $15 - $35   *Outstanding one sheet design.*

LIQUIDATOR, THE
(1966 - MGM) Rod Taylor, Trevor Howard
One Sheet: $3 - $5

LISA
(1962 - 20th Century Fox) Stephen Boyd, Dolores Hart
One Sheet: $5 - $10

LISBON
(1956 - Republic) Maureen O'Hara, Ray Milland
One Sheet: $30 - $50

LIST OF ADRIAN MESSENGER, THE
(1963 - Universal) George C. Scott, Dana Wynter
One Sheet: $15 - $30

LISTEN DARLING
(1938 - MGM) Judy Garland, Freddie Bartholomew
One Sheet: $200 - $400

LISTEN JUDGE
(1952 - Columbia) The Three Stooges (Shemp)
One Sheet: $150 - $350   *Comedy short. Duotone.*

LISTEN, LET'S MAKE LOVE
(1969 - Lopert) Pierre Clementi, Beba Lancar
One Sheet: $7 - $15

LISTEN TO ME
(1989 - Columbia) Kirk Cameron, Jami Gertz, Roy Scheider
One Sheet: $3 - $5

LISTEN UP
(1990 - Warner Bros.) Quincy Jones
One Sheet: $7 - $15   *Documentary.*

LISTON VS. CLAY
(1964 - -) Sonny Liston, Cassius Clay
One Sheet: $100 - $200

LISZTOMANIA
(1975 - Warner Bros.) Roger Daltrey, Ringo Starr
One Sheet: $15 - $25   *Rock 'n' Roll opera.*

LITTLE ACCIDENT
(1930 - Universal) Douglas Fairbanks, Jr., Anita Page
One Sheet: $150 - $300

LITTLE ACCIDENT
(1939 - Universal) Baby Sandy, Hugh Herbert, Richard Carlson
One Sheet: $100 - $200

LITTLE ADVENTURESS, THE
(1938 - Columbia) Edith Fellows, Robert Paige
One Sheet: $75 - $150

LITTLE AMERICA
(1935 - Paramount) Richard E. Byrd
One Sheet: $200 - $400

LITTLE ANNIE ROONEY
(1925 - United Artists) Mary Pickford
One Sheet: $800 - $1,500

LITTLE ARK, THE
(1972 - National General) Theodore Bikel, Philip Frame
One Sheet: $2 - $3

LITTLE BIG HORN
(1951 - Lippert) John Ireland, Lloyd Bridges
One Sheet: $15 - $30

LITTLE BIG LEAGUE
(1994 - Columbia) Luke Edwards, Timothy Busfield
One Sheet: $4 - $8   *Sports (Baseball).*

LITTLE BIG MAN
(1971 - National General) Dustin Hoffman, Martin Balsam
One Sheet: $15 - $25

Half Sheet

LITTLE BIG SHOT
(1935 - Warner Bros.) Edward Everett Horton, Robert Armstrong, Glenda Farrell
One Sheet: $75 - $150

LITTLE BIT OF HEAVEN, A
(1940 - Universal) Gloria Jean, Robert Stack
One Sheet: $75 - $150

LITTLE BLACK SAMBO
(1933 - Celebrity)
One Sheet: $3,500 - $5,000   *Cartoon. Cartoon Movie Posters #110.*

LITTLE BOY BLUE
(1936 - Celebrity) By Ub Iwerks
One Sheet: $600 - $1,100   *Cartoon. A ComiColor Cartoon. Cartoon Movie Posters #122.*

LITTLE BOY BLUE AND PANCHO
(1963 - Trans-International) Prod: K. Gordon Murray
One Sheet: $3 - $5

LITTLE BOY LOST
(1953 - Paramount) Bing Crosby, Claude Dauphin
One Sheet: $40 - $75

LITTLE BOY WITH THE BIG HORN, THE
(1953 - Columbia) Jolly Frolics
One Sheet: $200 - $400   *Cartoon. Duotone.*

LITTLE BUDDHA
(1994 - Miramax) Keanu Reeves, Bridget Fonda
One Sheet: $15 - $25

LITTLE CAESAR
(1930 - First National) Edward G. Robinson, Douglas Fairbanks, Jr
One Sheet: $16,000 - $25,000

LITTLE CAESAR
(1954R - Warner Bros.) Edward G. Robinson, Douglas Fairbanks, Jr.
One Sheet: $75 - $150   *Re-release. Duotone.*

LITTLE CHURCH AROUND THE CORNER, THE
(1923 - Warner Bros.) Kenneth Harlan, Claire Windsor
One Sheet: $150 - $300

LITTLE CIGARS MOB, THE
(1973 - AIP) Angel Tompkins, Billy Curtis
One Sheet: $15 - $25

LITTLE COLONEL, THE
(1935 - Fox) Shirley Temple, Lionel Barrymore
One Sheet: $1,600 - $2,500

LITTLE DADDY
(1931 - MGM) Our Gang
One Sheet: $500 - $800

LITTLE DARLINGS
(1980 - Paramount) Tatum O'Neal, Kristy

McNichol, Matt Dillon
One Sheet: $3 - $5

LITTLE DORRIT
(1988 - Cannon) Derek Jacobi, Alec Guinness
One Sheet: $2 - $3

LITTLE DRUMMER GIRL, THE
(1984 - Warner Bros.) Diane Keaton, Yorgo Voyagis, Klaus Kinski
One Sheet: $3 - $5

LITTLE EGYPT
(1951 - Universal) Mark Stevens, Rhonda Fleming
One Sheet: $15 - $35

LITTLE EVA ASCENDS
(1921 - Metro) Eleanor Fields, Gareth Hughes
One Sheet: $150 - $300

LITTLE FAUSS AND BIG HALSY
(1970 - Paramount) Robert Redford, Michael J. Pollard
One Sheet: $5 - $10

LITTLE FLOWER OF JESUS, SAINT THERESE OF LIXIEUX
(1938 - Sunray) Semone Bourday
One Sheet: $75 - $125

LITTLE FOXES, THE
(1941 - RKO) Bette Davis, Herbert Marshall, Dir: William Wyler
One Sheet: $1,600 - $2,500

Three Sheet

LITTLE FRENCH GIRL, THE
(1925 - Paramount) Alice Joyce, Neil Hamilton
One Sheet: $200 - $400

LITTLE FRIEND
(1934 - Gaumont British) Matheson Lang, Lydia Sherwood
One Sheet: $75 - $150

LITTLE FUGITIVE, THE
(1953 - Joseph Burstyn) Richie Andrusco, Will Lee
One Sheet: $10 - $20

LITTLE GIANT
(1933 - First National) Edward G. Robinson
One Sheet: $1,300 - $2,000

LITTLE GIANT
(1946 - Universal) Abbott & Costello, Brenda Joyce
One Sheet: $125 - $250

LITTLE GIANT
(1954R - Realart) Abbott & Costello, Brenda Joyce
One Sheet: $40 - $75   *Re-release.*

LITTLE GIRL WHO LIVES DOWN THE LANE
(1977 - AIP) Jodie Foster, Martin Sheen
One Sheet: $15 - $25

LITTLE GRAVEL VOICE
(1942 - MGM) -
One Sheet: $500 - $800   *Cartoon. Cartoon Movie Posters #246.*

LITTLE GREY MOUSE, THE
(1920 - William Fox) Louise Lovely, Sam De Grasse
One Sheet: $100 - $200

LITTLE HERO, THE
(1907 - Vitagraph) -
One Sheet: $100 - $200

LITTLE HIAWATHA
(1948R - RKO/Disney) -

One Sheet: $500 - $900   *Cartoon. Full color re-release. Only one sheet for this cartoon, no original poster except 40x60.*

LITTLE HUT, THE
(1956 - MGM) Ava Gardner, Stewart Granger
One Sheet: $30 - $60

LITTLE IODINE
(1946 - Comet) Jo Ann Marlowe, Marc Cramer
One Sheet: $40 - $75

LITTLE JOE, THE WRANGLER
(1942 - Universal) Johnny Mack Brown, Tex Ritter
One Sheet: $100 - $200

LITTLE KIDNAPPERS, THE
(1954 - United Artists) John Whiteley, Vincent Winter
One Sheet: $15 - $25

LITTLE LAURA AND BIG JOHN
(1973 - Crown) Fabian Forte, Karen Black
One Sheet: $3 - $5

LITTLE LORD FAUNTLEROY
(1922 - United Artists) Mary Pickford
One Sheet: $1,600 - $2,500

LITTLE LORD FAUNTLEROY
(1936 - Selznick) Freddie Bartholomew, C. Aubrey Smith
One Sheet: $100 - $200

LITTLE LULU
(1943 - Paramount) Little LuLu
One Sheet: $250 - $600   *Cartoon. Duotone stock poster.*

LITTLE MAN TATE
(1991 - -) Jodie Foster (Dir), Adam Hann-Byrd
One Sheet: $7 - $15

LITTLE MAN, WHAT NOW?
(1934 - Universal) Margaret Sullavan, Douglass Montgomery
One Sheet: $150 - $300

LITTLE MEN
(1934 - Mascot) Ralph Morgan, Erin O'Brien Moore
One Sheet: $75 - $150

LITTLE MEN
(1941 - RKO) Jack Oakie, Jimmy Lydon
One Sheet: $40 - $75

LITTLE MERMAID, THE
(1989 - Disney) Ariel
One Sheet: $50 - $100   *Cartoon. Advance: $125-$250. The Disney Poster, pg. 89.*

LITTLE MINISTER, THE
(1934 - RKO) John Beal, Katharine Hepburn
One Sheet: $1,900 - $3,000

LITTLE MISS BIG
(1946 - Universal) Fay Holden, Frank McHugh
One Sheet: $40 - $75

LITTLE MISS BROADWAY
(1938 - 20th Century Fox) Shirley Temple, George Murphy, Jimmy Durante
One Sheet: $800 - $1,500

One Sheet

LITTLE MISS BROADWAY
(1947 - Columbia) Jean Porter, John Shelton
One Sheet: $50 - $100

LITTLE MISS MARKER
(1934 - Paramount) Shirley Temple, Adolphe Menjou
One Sheet: $1,600 - $2,500

LITTLE MISS MARKER
(1979 - Universal) Walter Matthau, Julie Andrews
One Sheet: $3 - $5

LITTLE MISS NOBODY
(1936 - 20th Century Fox) Jane Withers, Jane Darwell
One Sheet: $100 - $200

LITTLE MISS ROUGHNECK
(1938 - Columbia) Edith Fellows, Leo Carrillo
One Sheet: $50 - $100

LITTLE MISS SMILES
(1922 - Fox) Shirley Mason, Gaston Glass
One Sheet: $200 - $400

LITTLE MISS THOROUGHBRED
(1938 - Warner Bros.) Ann Sheridan, John Litel
One Sheet: $50 - $100

LITTLE MISTER JIM
(1946 - MGM) Jackie "Butch" Jenkins, James Craig
One Sheet: $30 - $50

LITTLE MOLE, THE
(1941 - MGM) -
One Sheet: $250 - $550   *Cartoon. Cartoon Movie Posters #243.*

LITTLE MOTHER
(1972 - Audubon) Christiane Kruger, Ivan Desny
One Sheet: $2 - $3

LITTLE MURDERS
(1971 - 20th Century Fox) Elliott Gould, Lou Jacobi, Alan Arkin
One Sheet: $3 - $5

LITTLE NELLIE KELLY
(1940 - MGM) Judy Garland, George Murphy
One Sheet: $200 - $400

LITTLE NIGHT MUSIC, A
(1978 - New World) Elizabeth Taylor, Diana Rigg
One Sheet: $7 - $15

LITTLE NIKITA
(1988 - -) Sidney Poitier, River Phoenix
One Sheet: $5 - $12

LITTLE OLD NEW YORK
(1940 - 20th Century Fox) Richard Greene, Alice Faye
One Sheet: $250 - $600

One Sheet

LITTLE ONES, THE
(1965 - Columbia) Dudley Foster, Carl Gonzales
One Sheet: $7 - $15

LITTLE ORPHAN, THE
(1949 - MGM) Tom & Jerry
One Sheet: $250 - $600   *Cartoon. Full color stone litho.*

LITTLE ORPHAN ANNIE
(1932 - RKO) Mitzi Green, Buster Phelps
One Sheet: $500 - $900

LITTLE ORPHAN ANNIE
(1938 - Paramount) Ann Gillis, Robert Kent
One Sheet: $125 - $250

LITTLE ORVIE
(1940 - RKO) Johnny Sheffield, Ernest True
One Sheet: $30 - $50

LITTLE PRINCE, THE

(1974 - Paramount) Steve Warner, Bob Fosse, Gene Wilder
One Sheet: $7 - $15

LITTLE PRINCESS, THE
(1939 - 20th Century Fox) Shirley Temple, Richard Greene
One Sheet: $700 - $1,200

LITTLE PRINCESS, A
(1995 - Warner Bros.) Liesel Matthews, Eleanor Bron, Liam Cunningham
One Sheet: $5 - $12

LITTLE QUACKER
(1950 - MGM) Tom & Jerry
One Sheet: $300 - $650   *Cartoon. Full color stone litho.*

LITTLE RASCALS
(1943 - Monogram) Jackie Cooper, Spanky, Stymie
One Sheet: $125 - $250

LITTLE RASCALS, THE
(1994 - Universal) Travis Tedford, Bug Hall, Brittany Ashton Holmes
One Sheet: $3 - $5

LITTLE RASCALS VARIETIES
(1959 - Allied Artists) Spanky, Alfalfa, Darla, Buckwheat
One Sheet: $50 - $100

LITTLE RED HEN, THE
(1934 - Celebrity) Ub Iwerks
One Sheet: $700 - $1,200   *Cartoon. Second Comi-color cartoon. Full color stone litho. Stock poster.*

LITTLE RED RIDING HOOD
(1963 - Murray) Maria Gracia, Manuel Valdez
One Sheet: $10 - $20   *Filmed in Mexico.*

LITTLE RED SCHOOLHOUSE, THE
(1936 - Chesterfield) Dickie Moore, Ann Doran
One Sheet: $75 - $150

LITTLE ROBINSON CORKSCREW
(1924 - Pathe) Ralph Graves
One Sheet: $200 - $400   *Sports (Bodybuilding). Sports Movie Posters #334.*

LITTLE ROBINSON CRUSOE
(1924 - MGM) Edwin Foy
One Sheet: $200 - $400

LITTLE ROMANCE, A
(1979 - Orion) Laurence Olivier, Diane Lane
One Sheet: $10 - $20

LITTLE RUNAWAY
(1952 - MGM) Tom & Jerry
One Sheet: $250 - $500   *Cartoon. Full color stone litho.*

LITTLE RURAL RIDING HOOD
(1949 - MGM) Tex Avery
One Sheet: $1,600 - $2,500   *Cartoon. Full color stone litho. Cartoon Movie Posters #308.*

LITTLE SAVAGE, THE
(1959 - 20th Century Fox) Perdo Armendariz, Rodolphe Hoyos
One Sheet: $15 - $25

LITTLE SHEPHERD OF KINGDOM COME, THE
(1920 - Goldwyn) Jack Pickford, Clara Horton
One Sheet: $150 - $300

LITTLE SHEPHERD OF KINGDOM COME, THE
(1928 - -) Richard Barthelmess
One Sheet: $150 - $300

LITTLE SHEPHERD OF KINGDOM COME, THE
(1961 - 20th Century Fox) Jimmie Rodgers, Luana Patten
One Sheet: $10 - $20

LITTLE SHOP OF HORRORS, THE
(1960 - Filmgroup) Jonathan Haze, Jack Nicholson(uncredited), Dir:Roger Corman
One Sheet: $75 - $150   *Graven Images, pg. 209.*

LITTLE SHOP OF HORRORS, THE
(1986 - Warner Bros.) Rick Moranis, Ellen Greene, Steve Martin
One Sheet: $7 - $15

LITTLE THIEF, THE
(1989 - Miramax) Charlotte Gainsbourg, Didier Bezace

One Sheet: $2 - $3

LITTLE TOKYO, USA
(1942 - 20th Century Fox) Preston Foster,
Brenda Joyce
One Sheet: $50 - $100

LITTLE TOOT
(1955 - RKO/Disney) Music by The Andrews
Sisters
One Sheet: $300 - $700   *Cartoon.*

LITTLE TOUGH GUY
(1938 - Universal) Billy Halop, Huntz Hall
One Sheet: $75 - $150

LITTLE TOUGH GUYS IN SOCIETY
(1938 - Universal) Dead End Kids, Mary Boland
One Sheet: $75 - $150

LITTLE TREASURE
(1985 - TriStar) Burt Lancaster, Ted Danson,
Margot Kidder
One Sheet: $3 - $5

LITTLE VERA
(1989 - International) Natalia Negoda, Andrei
Sokolov
One Sheet: $5 - $10   *Russian.*

LITTLE WHIRLWIND
(1941 - RKO/Disney) Mickey Mouse
One Sheet: $4,500 - $7,000   *Cartoon. The
Disney Poster, pg. 29.*

LITTLE WIDOW, THE
(1919 - Paramount) Ford Sterling, Billy
Armstrong, Myrtle Lind
One Sheet: $200 - $400

LITTLE WISE QUACKER
(1952 - MGM) Barney Bear
One Sheet: $125 - $250   *Cartoon. Full
color stone litho. Stock poster with title inset
showing Droopy, Barney Bear & others.*

LITTLE WOMEN
(1912 - William A. Brady) -
One Sheet: $500 - $800

LITTLE WOMEN
(1933 - RKO) Katharine Hepburn, Joan Bennett
One Sheet: $1,900 - $3,000

LITTLE WOMEN
(1949 - MGM) June Allyson, Peter Lawford,
Elizabeth Taylor
One Sheet: $75 - $150

LITTLE WOMEN
(1962R - MGM) June Allyson, Peter Lawford,
Elizabeth Taylor
One Sheet: $15 - $25   *Re-release.*

LITTLE WOMEN
(1994 - Columbia) Winona Ryder, Susan
Sarandon, Gabriel Byrne
One Sheet: $5 - $12

LITTLEST HOBO, THE
(1958 - Allied Artists) Buddy Hart, Wendy
Stuart
One Sheet: $15 - $25

LITTLEST HORSE THIEVES, THE
(1977 - Buena Vista) Alastair Sim, Peter
Barkworth
One Sheet: $5 - $10

LITTLEST OUTLAW, THE
(1954 - Buena Vista/Disney) Joseph Calleia,
Pedro Armendariz
One Sheet: $15 - $35

LITTLEST REBEL, THE
(1935 - 20th Century Fox) Shirley Temple,
John Boles
One Sheet: $1,900 - $3,000

LITTLEST WARRIOR, THE
(1963 - -) -
One Sheet: $15 - $25   *Cartoon.
Japanese.*

LIVE A LITTLE, LOVE A LITTLE
(1968 - MGM) Elvis Presley, Michele Carey,
Don Porter
One Sheet: $40 - $75

LIVE A LITTLE, STEAL A LOT
(1974 - Byrd) Robert Conrad, Don Stroud,
Donna Mills
One Sheet: $3 - $5   *AKA: MURPH
THE SURF.*

LIVE AND LET DIE
(1973 - United Artists) Roger Moore, Jane
Seymour
One Sheet: $125 - $250   *Moore's debut
as Bond.*

LIVE AND LET DIE
(1977R - United Artists) Roger Moore, Jane
Seymore
One Sheet: $15 - $30   *Re-release.*

LIVE FAST, DIE YOUNG
(1958 - Universal-International) Mary Murphy,
Norma Eberhardt
One Sheet: $75 - $150

LIVE FOR LIFE
(1968 - United Artists) Yves Montand, Candice
Bergen
One Sheet: $10 - $20   *French/Italian.*

LIVE GHOST, THE
(1934 - MGM) Laurel and Hardy
One Sheet: $1,600 - $2,500

LIVE, LOVE AND LEARN
(1937 - MGM) Robert Montgomery, Rosalind
Russell
One Sheet: $75 - $150

LIVE SPARKS
(1920 - Pathe) J. Warren Kerrigan, Fritzi
Brunette, Mary Talbot
One Sheet: $150 - $300

LIVE TODAY FOR TOMORROW
(1948 - Universal) Fredric March, Edmond
O'Brien
One Sheet: $50 - $100

LIVE WIRE
(1992 - New Line) Pierce Brosnan, Ron Silver
One Sheet: $3 - $5

LIVE WIRES
(1921 - Fox) Edna Murphy, Johnnie Walker
One Sheet: $150 - $300

LIVE WIRES
(1946 - Monogram) The Bowery Boys, Pamela
Blake
One Sheet: $50 - $100

LIVELY SET, THE
(1964 - Universal) James Darren, Pamela Tiffin
One Sheet: $15 - $30

LIVES OF A BENGAL LANCER, THE
(1935 - Paramount) Gary Cooper, Franchot
Tone
One Sheet: $2,200 - $3,500

LIVES OF A BENGAL LANCER, THE
(1950R - Paramount) Gary Cooper, Franchot
Tone
One Sheet: $40 - $75   *Re-release.*

LIVING DANGEROUSLY
(1936 - BIP) Leonora Corbett, Otto Kruger
One Sheet: $75 - $150

LIVING DAYLIGHTS, THE
(1987 - MGM/United Artists) Timothy Dalton,
Maryam d'Abo
One Sheet: $15 - $35

One Sheet

LIVING DEAD, THE
(1934 - First Division) Gerald DuMaurier,
George Curzon
One Sheet: $200 - $400   *Graven
Images, pg. 57.*

LIVING DEAD, THE

(1940 - Hoffberg) Paul Wegener, Eugene
Klopfer
One Sheet: $600 - $1,000   *Original 1932
German release UNHEIMLICHE GESCHICHTEN.
Graven Images, pg. 57.*

LIVING DESERT, THE
(1953 - Buena Vista/Disney) -
One Sheet: $50 - $100   *Documentary.
Disney's first true-life adventure.*

LIVING DESERT, THE
(1964R - Buena Vista/Disney) -
One Sheet: $15 - $30   *Re-release.
Documentary.*

LIVING DESERT, THE
(1971R - Disney) -
One Sheet: $5 - $10   *Re-release.
Documentary.*

LIVING DESERT/VANISHING PRAIRIE
(1971R - Disney) -
One Sheet: $5 - $10   *Documentary.
Re-release double feature poster with Academy
Awards.*

LIVING FREE
(1972 - Columbia) Nigel Davenport, Susan
Hampshire
One Sheet: $2 - $3

LIVING GHOST, THE
(1942 - Monogram) James Dunn, Joan
Woodbury
One Sheet: $75 - $125

LIVING IDOL, THE
(1957 - MGM) Steve Forrest, Lillian
Montevecchi
One Sheet: $15 - $25

LIVING IN A BIG WAY
(1947 - MGM) Gene Kelly, Marie McDonald
One Sheet: $50 - $100

LIVING IT UP
(1954 - Paramount) Jerry Lewis, Dean Martin,
Janet Leigh
One Sheet: $75 - $125

LIVING IT UP
(1965R - Paramount) Jerry Lewis, Dean Martin,
Janet Leigh
One Sheet: $15 - $30   *Re-release.*

LIVING IT UP/PARDNERS
(1965R - Paramount) Dean Martin & Jerry
Lewis
One Sheet: $15 - $30   *Re-release
double feature poster.*

LIVING ON LOVE
(1937 - RKO) James Dunn, Joan Woodbury
One Sheet: $75 - $150

LIVING ON VELVET
(1935 - First National) Warren William, Kay
Francis, George Brent
One Sheet: $350 - $750

One Sheet

LIZZIE
(1957 - MGM) Eleanor Parker, Richard Boone
One Sheet: $20 - $40

LIZZIES OF THE FIELD
(1924 - Pathe) Billy Bevan, Andy Clyde
One Sheet: $150 - $300

LLANO KID, THE
(1939 - Paramount) Tito Guizar, Gale
Sondergaard
One Sheet: $75 - $150

LLOYDS OF LONDON
(1936 - 20th Century Fox) Tyrone Power,
Freddie Bartholomew, Madeleine Carroll
One Sheet: $1,900 - $3,000   *Beware
International style.*

One Sheet (Style A)

LO, THE POOR BUFFALO
(1941 - Columbia) Color Rhapsodies
One Sheet: $150 - $300   *Cartoon. Full
color semi-stock poster with inset of title.*

LOADED
(1996 - Miramax) Catherine McCormack, Oliver
Milburn
One Sheet: $5 - $10

LOADED PISTOLS
(1948 - Columbia) Gene Autry, Barbara Britton
One Sheet: $100 - $200

LOADED PISTOLS
(1963R - Parade) Gene Autry, Barbara Britton
One Sheet: $15 - $25   *Re-release.
Duotone.*

LOAN SHARK
(1952 - Lippert) George Raft, Dorothy Hart
One Sheet: $40 - $75

LOCAL BAD MAN, THE
(1932 - Allied) Hoot Gibson, Sally Blane
One Sheet: $250 - $500

LOCAL BOY MAKES GOOD
(1931 - First National) Joe E. Brown, Dorothy
Lee
One Sheet: $150 - $300

LOCAL HERO
(1983 - Warner Bros.) Peter Riegert, Burt
Lancaster
One Sheet: $7 - $15

LOCK UP
(1989 - TriStar) Sylvester Stallone, Donald
Sutherland
One Sheet: $5 - $10

LOCK UP YOUR DAUGHTERS
(1969 - Columbia) Christopher Plummer,
Susannah York, Glynis Johns
One Sheet: $7 - $15

LOCKDOWN
(1990 - -) Joe Estevez, Richard Lynch
One Sheet: $3 - $5

LOCKET, THE
(1946 - RKO) Laraine Day, Robert Mitchum,
Brian Aherne
One Sheet: $100 - $200

LOCO BOY MAKES GOOD
(1942 - Columbia) The Three Stooges (Curly)
One Sheet: $3,500 - $5,000   *Comedy short.
Duotone.*

LOCO LOBO
(1946 - Columbia) Color Rhapsodies
One Sheet: $150 - $300   *Cartoon. Full
color semi-stock poster with inset of title.*

LODGER, THE
(1926 - Gainsborough (British)) Ivor Novello,
Malcolm Keen, Dir: Alfred Hitchcock
One Sheet: $13,000 - $20,000   *Hitchcock's
first on-screen appearance, first suspense thriller.
Graven Images, pg. 32.*

LODGER, THE
(1932 - Twickenham (British)) Ivor Novello,
Elizabeth Allan
One Sheet: $250 - $500

LODGER, THE
(1944 - 20th Century Fox) Laird Cregar, Merle Oberon, George Sanders
One Sheet: $125 - $250   *Graven Images, pg. 129.*

One Sheet

LODGER, THE
(1949R - 20th Century Fox) Laird Cregar, Merle Oberon, George Sanders
One Sheet: $30 - $50   *Re-release.*

LOGAN'S RUN
(1976 - MGM) Michael York, Jenny Agutter, Farrah Fawcett-Majors
One Sheet: $15 - $25   *Price is for both styles.*

LOLA
(1961 - Paris-Euro) Anouk Aimee
One Sheet: $30 - $50   *French/Italian.*

LOLA
(1971 - AIP) Charles Bronson, Susan George
One Sheet: $7 - $15

LOLA
(1975 - SunCoast) David Hemmings, Andrea Rau
One Sheet: $3 - $5

LOLA
(1982 - Rialto) Barbara Sukowa
One Sheet: $5 - $10   *German.*

LOLA MONTES
(1955 - Gamma) Martine Carol, Peter Ustinov
One Sheet: $15 - $25   *AKA: THE SINS OF LOLA MONTES.*

LOLITA
(1962 - MGM) James Mason, Sue Lyons
One Sheet: $200 - $400

One Sheet

LOLLY MADONNA XXX
(1973 - MGM) Season Hubley (debut), Rod Steiger
One Sheet: $7 - $15

LONDON AFTER MIDNIGHT
(1927 - MGM) Lon Chaney, Marceline Day
One Sheet: $16,000 - $25,000   *Jack the Ripper. Graven Images, pg. 36, 231.*

LONDON BLACKOUT MURDERS
(1942 - Republic) John Abbott, Mary McLeod
One Sheet: $50 - $100

LONDON BY NIGHT
(1937 - MGM) George Murphy, Rita Johnson
One Sheet: $75 - $150

LONE AVENGER, THE
(1933 - K.B.S.) Ken Maynard
One Sheet: $250 - $600

LONE BANDIT, THE
(1935 - Empire) Lane Chandler
One Sheet: $100 - $200

LONE CHANCE, THE
(1924 - Fox) John Gilbert
One Sheet: $250 - $500

One Sheet

LONE COWBOY
(1933 - Paramount) Jackie Cooper, Lila Lee
One Sheet: $125 - $250

LONE DEFENDER, THE
(1930 - Mascot) Rin-Tin-Tin, Walter Miller
One Sheet: $125 - $250   *Serial. Western. 12 Chapters.*

LONE GUN, THE
(1954 - United Artists) George Montgomery, Dorothy Malone
One Sheet: $15 - $35

LONE HAND
(1953 - Universal) Joel McCrea, Barbara Hale
One Sheet: $20 - $40

LONE HAND SAUNDERS
(1926 - FBO) Fred Thompson, Bess Flowers
One Sheet: $800 - $1,500

LONE HAND TEXAN, THE
(1947 - Columbia) Charles Starrett, Smiley Burnette
One Sheet: $30 - $60

LONE PRAIRIE, THE
(1942 - Columbia) Russell Hayden, Bob Wills & his Texas Playboys
One Sheet: $50 - $100

LONE RANGER, THE
(1938 - Republic) Lee Powell, Herman Brix, Chief Thundercloud
One Sheet: $800 - $1,500   *Serial. Western. 15 Chapters. Poster for whole serial:$2000-$4000. Cartoon Movie Posters #233.*

One Sheet

LONE RANGER, THE
(1956 - Warner Bros.) Clayton Moore, Jay Silverheels
One Sheet: $300 - $700

LONE RANGER, THE
(196?R - Warner Bros.) Clayton Moore, Jay Silverheels
One Sheet: $15 - $25   *Re-release. Western. Duotone.*

LONE RANGER AND THE LOST CITY OF GOLD, THE
(1958 - United Artists) Clayton Moore, Jay Silverheels

One Sheet: $150 - $350

LONE RANGER RIDES AGAIN, THE
(1939 - Republic) Robert Livingston, Chief Thunder Cloud
One Sheet: $600 - $1,000   *Serial. Western. 15 Chapters.*

LONE RIDER, THE
(1922 - -) Denver Dixon, Alma Rayford
One Sheet: $200 - $400

LONE RIDER, THE
(1927 - Universal) Fred Church
One Sheet: $250 - $500

LONE RIDER, THE
(1930 - Columbia) Buck Jones, Vera Reynolds
One Sheet: $700 - $1,200   *Cowboy Movie Posters # 91.*

One Sheet

LONE RIDER, THE
(1934 - -) Wally Wales, Marla Bratton
One Sheet: $100 - $200

LONE RIDER AMBUSHED, THE
(1941 - PRC) George Houston
One Sheet: $40 - $75

LONE RIDER AND THE BANDIT, THE
(1942 - PRC) George Houston
One Sheet: $40 - $75

LONE RIDER CROSSES THE RIO, THE
(1941 - PRC) George Houston
One Sheet: $40 - $75

LONE RIDER FIGHTS BACK, THE
(1941 - PRC) George Houston
One Sheet: $40 - $75

LONE RIDER IN CHEYENNE, THE
(1942 - PRC) George Houston, Al St. John
One Sheet: $40 - $75

LONE RIDER IN FRONTIER FURY, THE
(1941 - PRC) George Houston
One Sheet: $40 - $75

LONE RIDER IN GHOST TOWN, THE
(1941 - PRC) George Houston
One Sheet: $40 - $75

LONE RIDER IN TEXAS JUSTICE, THE
(1942 - PRC) George Houston, Al St. John
One Sheet: $40 - $75

LONE RIDER IN WILD HORSE RUSTLERS
(1943 - PRC) Bob Livingston, Al St. John
One Sheet: $40 - $75

LONE RIDER IN WOLVES OF THE RANGE
(1943 - PRC) Bob Livingston, Al St. John
One Sheet: $40 - $75

LONE RIDER RIDES ON, THE
(1941 - PRC) George Houston
One Sheet: $40 - $75

LONE STAR, THE
(1951 - MGM) Clark Gable, Ava Gardner
One Sheet: $75 - $150

LONE STAR LAW MEN
(1941 - Monogram) Tom Keene, Betty Miles
One Sheet: $75 - $125

LONE STAR MOONLIGHT
(1946 - Columbia) Ken Curtis, Joan Barton
One Sheet: $30 - $50

LONE STAR PIONEERS
(1939 - Columbia) Bill Elliott, Dorothy Gulliver
One Sheet: $75 - $150

LONE STAR RAIDERS
(1940 - Republic) Three Mesquiteers
One Sheet: $75 - $125

LONE STAR RANGER, THE
(1923 - Fox) Tom Mix
One Sheet: $600 - $1,000

LONE STAR RANGER, THE
(1929 - Fox) William Farnum
One Sheet: $700 - $1,200

One Sheet

LONE STAR RANGER
(1930 - Fox) George O'Brien, Sue Carol
One Sheet: $250 - $600   *O'Brien's first all-talking western.*

LONE STAR RANGER
(1942 - 20th Century Fox) John Kimbrough, Sheila Ryan
One Sheet: $75 - $125

LONE STAR TRAIL, THE
(1942 - Universal) Johnny Mack Brown
One Sheet: $50 - $100

LONE STAR VIGILANTES, THE
(1941 - Columbia) Bill Elliott, Tex Ritter
One Sheet: $75 - $125

LONE TEXAN, THE
(1958 - 20th Century Fox) Willard Parker, Grant Williams
One Sheet: $15 - $30

LONE TEXAS RANGER
(1945 - Republic) Bill Elliott, Alice Fleming
One Sheet: $75 - $125

LONE TRAIL, THE
(1932 - Syndicate) Rex Lease, Edmund Cobb
One Sheet: $75 - $150

LONE WOLF AND HIS LADY, THE
(1949 - Columbia) Ron Randell, June Vincent
One Sheet: $40 - $75

LONE WOLF IN LONDON, THE
(1947 - Columbia) Gerald Mohr, Nancy Saunders
One Sheet: $40 - $75

LONE WOLF IN MEXICO, THE
(1947 - Columbia) Gerald Mohr, Sheila Ryan
One Sheet: $40 - $75

LONE WOLF IN PARIS, THE
(1938 - Columbia) Francis Lederer, Frances Drake
One Sheet: $75 - $150

LONE WOLF KEEPS A DATE, THE
(1940 - Columbia) Warren William, Frances Robinson, Eric Blore
One Sheet: $75 - $125

LONE WOLF MCQUADE
(1982 - Orion) Chuck Norris, David Carradine
One Sheet: $5 - $10

LONE WOLF MEETS A LADY, THE
(1940 - Columbia) Warren William, Jean Muir
One Sheet: $75 - $125

LONE WOLF RETURNS, THE
(1936 - Columbia) Melvyn Douglas, Gail Patrick
One Sheet: $150 - $300

LONE WOLF SPY HUNT, THE
(1939 - Columbia) Warren William, Ida Lupino, Rita Hayworth
One Sheet: $125 - $250

LONE WOLF STRIKES, THE
(1940 - Columbia) Warren William, Joan Perry
One Sheet: $75 - $125

LONE WOLF TAKES A CHANCE, THE
(1941 - Columbia) Warren William, June Storey
One Sheet: $75 - $125

LONELINESS OF THE LONG DISTANCE RUNNER
(1963 - Continental) Michael Redgrave, Tom Cartena
One Sheet: $15 - $25   *Sports (Running).*

LONELY ARE THE BRAVE
(1962 - Universal) Kirk Douglas (his best film), Gena Rowlands
One Sheet: $75 - $125

LONELY GUY, THE
(1984 - -) Steve Martin, Judith Ivey, Charles Grodin
One Sheet: $5 - $10

LONELY HEARTS BANDITS
(1950 - Republic) Dorothy Patrick, Robert Rockwell
One Sheet: $15 - $25

LONELY LADY, THE
(1983 - Universal) Pia Zadora, Lloyd Bochner
One Sheet: $5 - $10

LONELY MAN, THE
(1956 - Paramount) Jack Palance, Anthony Perkins
One Sheet: $40 - $75

LONELY PASSION OF JUDITH HEARNE, THE
(1987 - Handmade) Maggie Smith, Bob Hoskins
One Sheet: $3 - $5

LONELY TRAIL, THE
(1936 - Republic) John Wayne
One Sheet: $1,900 - $3,000   *Cowboy Movie Posters #201.*

LONELY WIVES
(1931 - Pathe Exchange) Edward Everett Horton, Esther Ralston
One Sheet: $100 - $200

LONELYHEARTS
(1958 - United Artists) Montgomery Clift, Robert Ryan
One Sheet: $40 - $75

LONERS, THE
(1972 - Fanfare) Dean Stockwell, Pat Stich
One Sheet: $10 - $20   *Biker crime.*

LONESOME LENNY
(1946 - MGM) Screwy Squirrel, Tex Avery
One Sheet: $600 - $1,000   *Cartoon. Full color stone litho. Cartoon Movie Posters #298.*

LONESOME MOUSE, THE
(1943 - MGM) Tom & Jerry
One Sheet: $500 - $800   *Cartoon.*

LONESOME MOUSE, THE
(1949R - MGM) Tom & Jerry
One Sheet: $100 - $200   *Re-release. Cartoon. Full color stone litho.*

LONESOME TRAIL, THE
(1945 - Monogram) Jimmy Wakely, Lasses White
One Sheet: $15 - $35

LONESOME TRAIL, THE
(1955 - Lippert) Wayne Morris, John Agar
One Sheet: $7 - $15

LONG AGO TOMORROW
(1971 - Cinema 5) Malcolm McDowell, Nanette Newman
One Sheet: $7 - $15

LONG AND THE SHORT AND THE TALL, THE
(1961 - Continental) Richard Todd, Laurence Harvey
One Sheet: $5 - $10

LONG DARK HALL, THE
(1951 - United Artists) Rex Harrison, Lilli Palmer
One Sheet: $30 - $50

LONG DAY CLOSES, THE
(1993 - Sony Classics) Marjorie Yates, Leigh McCormack
One Sheet: $3 - $5

LONG DAY'S DYING, THE
(1968 - Paramount) David Hemmings, Tom Bell, Tony Beckley
One Sheet: $3 - $5

LONG DAY'S JOURNEY INTO NIGHT
(1962 - Embassy) Katharine Hepburn, Jason Robards
One Sheet: $30 - $50

LONG DUEL, THE
(1967 - Paramount) Yul Brynner, Trevor Howard
One Sheet: $7 - $15

LONG GOODBYE, THE
(1973 - United Artists) Elliott Gould, Nina Van Pallandt
One Sheet: $10 - $20   *Jack Davis art. Advance:$8-12.*

LONG GRAY LINE, THE
(1954 - Columbia) Tyrone Power, Maureen O'Hara
One Sheet: $30 - $60

LONG HAIR OF DEATH
(1964 - -) -
One Sheet: $10 - $20

LONG HAUL, THE
(1957 - Columbia) Diana Dors, Victor Mature
One Sheet: $20 - $40

LONG, HOT SUMMER, THE
(1958 - 20th Century Fox) Paul Newman, Joanne Woodward, Orson Welles
One Sheet: $40 - $75

LONG JOHN SILVER
(1954 - Treasure Island) Robert Newton, Kit Taylor
One Sheet: $15 - $30

LONG KISS GOODNIGHT, THE
(1996 - New Line) Geena Davis, Samuel L. Jackson
One Sheet: $5 - $10

LONG LIVE THE KING
(1923 - Metro) Jackie Coogan
One Sheet: $250 - $500

LONG, LONG TRAIL, THE
(1929 - Universal) Hoot Gibson
One Sheet: $250 - $600

LONG, LONG TRAILER, THE
(1954 - MGM) Lucille Ball, Desi Arnaz
One Sheet: $200 - $400

LUCILLE BALL
DESI ARNAZ
THE LONG, LONG TRAILER

One Sheet

LONG LOST FATHER
(1934 - RKO) John Barrymore, Donald Cook, Helen Chandler
One Sheet: $125 - $250

LONG MEMORY, THE
(1952 - Rank) John Mills, Elizabeth Sellars
One Sheet: $15 - $30

LONG NIGHT, THE
(1947 - RKO) Henry Fonda, Barbara Bel Geddes, Vincent Price
One Sheet: $75 - $150

LONG NIGHT, THE
(1976 - Woodie King) Dick Anthony Williams, Peggy Kirkpatrick, W. Geoffrey King
One Sheet: $5 - $10   *Black cast.*

LONG RIDE FROM HELL, A
(1970 - Cinerama) Steve Reeves (last film), Wayde Preston
One Sheet: $10 - $20

LONG RIDERS, THE
(1980 - United Artists) Stacy & James Keach, David & Keith Carradine
One Sheet: $15 - $25   *Advance One Sheet:$20-$30. Cowboy Movie Posters #355.*

The LONG RIDERS

One Sheet

LONG ROPE, THE
(1961 - 20th Century Fox) Hugh Marlowe, Alan Hale
One Sheet: $7 - $15

LONG SHIPS, THE
(1964 - Columbia) Richard Widmark, Sidney Poitier
One Sheet: $15 - $30

LONG SHOT
(1939 - Fine Arts) Marsha Hunt, Gordon Jones
One Sheet: $75 - $150

LONG TRAIL, THE
(1917 - Paramount) Lou Tellegen, Mary Fuller
One Sheet: $200 - $400

LONG VOYAGE HOME, THE
(1940 - United Artists) John Wayne, Thomas Mitchell, Dir:John Ford
One Sheet: $150 - $300

LONG WAIT, THE
(1954 - United Artists) Anthony Quinn, Peggie Castle
One Sheet: $30 - $50

LONG WALK HOME, THE
(1991 - Miramax) Whoopi Goldberg, Sissy Spacek
One Sheet: $5 - $10

LONGEST DAY, THE
(1962 - 20th Century Fox) John Wayne, Henry Fonda, plus all-star international cast
One Sheet: $40 - $75

LONGEST DAY, THE
(1969R - 20th Century Fox) John Wayne, Henry Fonda, plus all-star international cast
One Sheet: $10 - $20   *Re-release.*

LONGEST NIGHT, THE
(1936 - MGM) Robert Young, Florence Rice
One Sheet: $100 - $200

LONGEST YARD, THE
(1974 - Paramount) Burt Reynolds, Eddie Albert
One Sheet: $10 - $20

LONGHORN, THE
(1951 - Monogram) Bill Elliott, Myron Healey
One Sheet: $15 - $35

LONGSHOT, THE
(1986 - -) Tim Conway, Jack Weston
One Sheet: $3 - $5

LONGTIME COMPANION
(1990 - -) Bruce Davison, Dermot Mulroney
One Sheet: $7 - $15

LOOK BACK IN ANGER
(1959 - Warner Bros.) Richard Burton, Claire Bloom
One Sheet: $15 - $30

LOOK DOWN AND DIE
(19?? - -) Lee Majors, Art Carney
One Sheet: $3 - $7

LOOK FOR THE SILVER LINING
(1949 - Warner Bros.) June Haver, Ray Bolger
One Sheet: $50 - $100

One Sheet: $10 - $20

LOOK IN ANY WINDOW
(1961 - Allied Artists) Paul Anka, Ruth Roman
One Sheet: $15 - $30

LOOK OUT BELOW
(1918 - Pathe) Harold Lloyd
One Sheet: $800 - $1,500

LOOK OUT FOR LOVE
(1938 - Gaumont) Anna Neagle, T. Carminati
One Sheet: $75 - $150

LOOK WHO'S LAUGHING
(1941 - RKO) Charlie McCarthy, Lucille Ball, Fibber McGee and Molly
One Sheet: $150 - $350

LOOK WHO'S TALKING
(1989 - TriStar) John Travolta, Kirstie Alley
One Sheet: $7 - $15

LOOK WHO'S TALKING NOW
(1993 - TriStar) Kirstie Alley, John Travolta
One Sheet: $3 - $5

LOOK WHO'S TALKING TOO
(1990 - TriStar) John Travolta, Kirstie Alley
One Sheet: $5 - $10

LOOK YOUR BEST
(1923 - Goldwyn) Colleen Moore, Antonio Moreno
One Sheet: $200 - $400

LOOKIN' TO GET OUT
(1982 - Paramount) Jon Voight, Ann-Margret
One Sheet: $7 - $15

LOOKING FOR DANGER
(1957 - Allied Artists) Huntz Hall, Stanley Clements
One Sheet: $30 - $60

LOOKING FOR LOVE
(1964 - MGM) Connie Francis, Jim Hutton, Johnny Carson
One Sheet: $15 - $35   *Carson's only film.*

LOOKING FOR MR. GOODBAR
(1977 - Paramount) Diane Keaton, Richard Gere
One Sheet: $10 - $20

LOOKING FOR TROUBLE
(1920 - Pathe) Snub Pollard
One Sheet: $150 - $300

LOOKING FOR TROUBLE
(1934 - 20th Century Fox) Spencer Tracy, Jack Oakie, Constance Cummings
One Sheet: $200 - $400

TRACY OAKIE
LOOKING FOR TROUBLE

One Sheet

LOOKING FORWARD
(1933 - MGM) Lionel Barrymore, Lewis Stone
One Sheet: $150 - $300

LOOKING GLASS WAR, THE
(1970 - Columbia) Christopher Jones, Pia Degermark, Ralph Richardson
One Sheet: $3 - $5

LOOK-OUT SISTER
(1946 - Astor) Louis Jordan (Dir.)
One Sheet: $200 - $400   *Black cast. Separate Cinema, pg. 57.*

LOONEY TUNES STOCK
(1937 - Vitaphone Short Subject) Porky Pig
One Sheet: $800 - $1,500   *Cartoon. Porky holding "Looney Tunes" sign, blank space for title snipe lower left. Cartoon Movie Posters #99.*

LOONEY TUNES STOCK
(1940 - Vitaphone Short Subject) Daffy Duck, Porky Pig
One Sheet: $1,300 - $2,000   *Cartoon. First appearance of Daffy Duck on a poster (in car with Porky driving). Cartoon Movie Posters #97.*

One Sheet

LOONEY TUNES STOCK
(1944R - Warner Bros.) Daffy Duck, Porky Pig
One Sheet: $600 - $1,000   *Re-release of 1940 version. Cartoon.*

LOOPHOLE
(1954 - Allied Artists) Barry Sullivan, Dorothy Malone
One Sheet: $15 - $30

LOOPY DE LOOP!
(1960 - Columbia) -
One Sheet: $150 - $300   *Cartoon.*

LOOSE ANKLES
(1930 - First National) Loretta Young, Douglas Fairbanks, Jr.
One Sheet: $100 - $200

LOOSE CANNONS
(1990 - -) Gene Hackman, Dan Aykroyd
One Sheet: $3 - $5

LOOSE ENDS
(1930 - British International) Edna Best, Owen Nares
One Sheet: $100 - $200

LOOSE IN LONDON
(1953 - Monogram) The Bowery Boys
One Sheet: $40 - $75

LOOSE LOOT
(1953 - Columbia) The Three Stooges (Shemp)
One Sheet: $150 - $350   *Comedy short. Duotone.*

LOOT
(1919 - Universal) Darrell Foss
One Sheet: $150 - $300

LOOT
(1972 - Cinevision) Richard Attenborough, Lee Remick
One Sheet: $2 - $3

LOOTERS, THE
(1955 - Universal) Rory Calhoun, Julie Adams
One Sheet: $20 - $40

LORD BYRON OF BROADWAY
(1930 - MGM) Charles Kaley, Cliff Edwards
One Sheet: $100 - $200

LORD JEFF
(1938 - MGM) Freddie Bartholomew, Charles Coburn, Mickey Rooney
One Sheet: $100 - $200

LORD JIM
(1965 - Columbia) Peter O'Toole, James Mason
One Sheet: $30 - $50

LORD LOVE A DUCK
(1966 - United Artists) Roddy McDowall, Tuesday Weld
One Sheet: $15 - $25

LORD OF ILLUSIONS
(1995 - MGM/UA) Scott Bakula, Kevin J. O'Connor
One Sheet: $5 - $10

LORD OF THE FLIES
(1963 - Continental) James Aubrey, Tom

Chapin
One Sheet: $30 - $50

LORD OF THE FLIES
(1990 - Columbia) Balthazar Getty
One Sheet: $5 - $10

LORD OF THE JUNGLE
(1955 - Allied Artists) Johnny Sheffield, Wayne Morris
One Sheet: $20 - $40

LORD OF THE RINGS, THE
(1978 - United Artists) Dir: Ralph Bakshi
One Sheet: $20 - $40   *Cartoon. One Sheet (Style B):$25-$50.*

One Sheet

LORD SHANGO
(1975 - Bryanston) Lawrence Cook, Marlene Clark
One Sheet: $10 - $20   *Blaxploitation horror film.*

LORDS OF DISCIPLINE, THE
(1983 - Paramount) David Keith, Robert Prosky
One Sheet: $7 - $15

LORDS OF FLATBUSH, THE
(1974 - Columbia) Sylvester Stallone, Perry King, Henry Winkler
One Sheet: $15 - $25

LORDS OF THE DEEP
(1989 - -) Bradford Dillman, Priscilla Barnes
One Sheet: $7 - $15

LORENZO'S OIL
(1992 - Universal) Nick Nolte, Susan Sarandon
One Sheet: $3 - $5

LORNA
(1964 - -) Dir: Russ Meyer
One Sheet: $40 - $75

LORNA DOONE
(1927 - First National) Madge Bellamy, John Bowers
One Sheet: $700 - $1,200

LORNA DOONE
(1935 - Associated British) John Loder, Margaret Lockwood
One Sheet: $150 - $300

LORNA DOONE
(1951 - Columbia) Barbara Hale, Richard Greene
One Sheet: $20 - $40

LOS OLVIDADOS
(1950 - Ultramar) -
One Sheet: $250 - $500   *Spanish.*

LOSER TAKES ALL
(1956 - British Lion) Rossano Brazzi, Glynis Johns
One Sheet: $15 - $25

LOSERS, THE
(1970 - Fanfare) William Smith, Bernie Hamilton, Adam Roarke
One Sheet: $15 - $25   *Biker film.*

LOSING ISAIAH
(1995 - Paramount) Jessica Lange, Halle Berry
One Sheet: $5 - $10

LOSING IT
(1983 - Embassy) Tom Cruise, Shelley Long
One Sheet: $5 - $10

LOSS OF INNOCENCE
(1961 - Columbia) Kenneth More, Danielle Darrieux

One Sheet: $15 - $30

LOST
(1955 - Rank) David Farrar, Julie Arnall
One Sheet: $15 - $25

LOST
(1986 - -) Michael Hogan, Helen Shaver
One Sheet: $3 - $5

LOST ANGEL
(1943 - MGM) Margaret O'Brien, James Craig
One Sheet: $40 - $75

LOST BATTALION, THE
(1961 - AIP) Leopold Salcedo, Diane Jergens
One Sheet: $10 - $20

LOST BOUNDARIES
(1949 - Film Classics) Beatrice Pearson, Mel Ferrer
One Sheet: $125 - $250   *Duotone. Ferrer's film debut. Separate Cinema, pg. 150.*

LOST BOYS, THE
(1987 - Warner Bros.) Jason Patric, Dianne Wiest, Kiefer Sutherland
One Sheet: $15 - $30

LOST CANYON
(1942 - United Artists) William Boyd
One Sheet: $150 - $300

LOST CITY, THE
(1920 - Warner Bros.) Juanita Hansen
One Sheet: $600 - $1,000   *Serial. 15 Chapters. All One Sheets are full color.*

LOST CITY, THE
(1935 - Krellberg) Kane Richmond, William "Stage" Boyd
One Sheet: $150 - $300   *Serial. Chapter 1 One Sheet (full color):$400-600.*

LOST CITY OF THE JUNGLE
(1946 - Universal) Russell Hayden, Jane Adams
One Sheet: $50 - $100   *Serial. 13 Chapters.*

LOST COMMAND
(1966 - Columbia) Anthony Quinn, Alain Delon
One Sheet: $10 - $20

LOST CONTINENT, THE
(1949 - -) -
One Sheet: $30 - $50   *Documentary.*

LOST CONTINENT, THE
(1951 - Lippert) Cesar Romero, Hillary Brooke
One Sheet: $100 - $200

LOST CONTINENT, THE
(1968 - 20th Century Fox) Eric Porter, Hildegard Knef
One Sheet: $15 - $30

LOST HONEYMOON
(1947 - Pathe Ind.) Franchot Tone, Ann Richards
One Sheet: $40 - $75

LOST HORIZON
(1937 - Columbia) Ronald Colman, Jane Wyatt
One Sheet: $5,000 - $8,000   *Art by James Montgomery Flagg. Price is for style D. One Sheet(Style C):$3000-$5000. Graven Images, pg. 96.*

One Sheet

LOST HORIZON
(1948R - Columbia) Ronald Colman, Jane Wyatt
One Sheet: $100 - $200   *Re-release.*

LOST HORIZON
(1973 - Columbia) Peter Finch, Liv Ullmann, Michael York
One Sheet: $5 - $10

LOST IN A BIG CITY
(1923 - Blazed Trail) John Lowell, Baby Ivy Ward, Jane Thomas, Charles Beyer
One Sheet: $125 - $250

LOST IN A HAREM
(1944 - MGM) Bud Abbott, Lou Costello, Marilyn Maxwell
One Sheet: $150 - $300

LOST IN ALASKA
(1952 - Universal) Abbott & Costello, Mitzi Green
One Sheet: $100 - $200

LOST IN AMERICA
(1985 - -) Albert Brooks, Julie Hagerty
One Sheet: $5 - $10

LOST IN THE STRATOSPHERE
(1934 - Monogram) William Cagney
One Sheet: $200 - $400

LOST JUNGLE, THE
(1934 - Mascot) Clyde Beatty, Warner Richmond
One Sheet: $250 - $500   *Serial. 12 Chapters.*

LOST LADY, A
(1934 - First National) Barbara Stanwyck, Frank Morgan
One Sheet: $200 - $400

LOST LAGOON
(1957 - United Artists) Jeffrey Lynn, Peter Donat
One Sheet: $10 - $20

LOST, LONELY AND VICIOUS
(1958 - Howco) Ken Clayton, Barbara Wilson
One Sheet: $50 - $100   *Loosely based on the life of James Dean.*

LOST MAN, THE
(1969 - Universal) Sidney Poitier, Joanna Shimkus, Al Freeman
One Sheet: $10 - $20

LOST MISSILE, THE
(1958 - United Artists) Robert Loggila, Ellen Parker
One Sheet: $50 - $100

One Sheet

LOST MOMENT, THE
(1947 - Universal) Robert Cummings, Susan Hayward
One Sheet: $40 - $75

LOST ON THE WESTERN FRONT
(1949 - -) Paul Cavanaugh, Marcel Chantal
One Sheet: $50 - $100

LOST ONE, THE
(1951 - Columbia) Peter Lorre, Karl John
One Sheet: $50 - $100   *Lorre's only film as director.*

LOST PARADISE, THE
(1914 - Famous Players) H.B.Warner, Mabel Van Buren
One Sheet: $200 - $400

LOST PATROL, THE
(1934 - RKO) Victor McLaglen, Boris Karloff
One Sheet: $700 - $1,200   *Beware undated re-releases.*

LOST PATROL, THE

(1954R - RKO) Victor McLaglen, Boris Karloff
One Sheet: $75 - $125 *Re-release.*

LOST PLANET, THE
(1953 - Columbia) Judd Holdren, Vivian Mason
One Sheet: $50 - $100 *Serial. 15 Chapters.*

LOST PLANET AIRMEN
(1949 - Republic) Tristram Coffin, Mae Clarke
One Sheet: $125 - $250 *Feature version of "KING OF THE ROCKETMEN" serial.*

LOST RANCH
(1937 - Victory) Tom Tyler, Jeanne Martel
One Sheet: $125 - $250

LOST SPECIAL, THE
(1932 - Universal) Frank Albertson, Cecilia Parker
One Sheet: $150 - $300

LOST SQUADRON, THE
(1932 - RKO) Richard Dix, Erich von Stroheim
One Sheet: $1,300 - $2,000

One Sheet

LOST TRAIL, THE
(1945 - Monogram) Johnny Mack Brown, Raymond Hatton
One Sheet: $30 - $60

LOST TRIBE, THE
(1949 - Columbia) Johnny Weissmuller, Myrna Dell
One Sheet: $50 - $100

LOST VOLCANO, THE
(1950 - Monogram) Johnny Sheffield, Donald Woods
One Sheet: $15 - $35

LOST WEEKEND, THE
(1945 - Paramount) Ray Milland, Jane Wyman
One Sheet: $200 - $400 *Academy Award: Best Picture, Best Actor, Best Direction(Billy Wilder). Academy Award MoviePosters #99, & #100.*

LOST WORLD, THE
(1925 - First National) Wallace Beery, Willis O'Brien (stop motion animation)
One Sheet: $6,500 - $10,000 *Price is for One Sheet(Dinosaur style). One Sheet(Beery shown):$3000-$5000. Graven Images, pg.10, 24-25.*

LOST WORLD, THE
(1960 - 20th Century Fox) Michael Rennie, Jill St. John
One Sheet: $30 - $50

LOST WORLD: JURASSIC PARK, THE
(1997 - Universal) Jeff Goldblum, Richard Attenborough, Julianne Moore
One Sheet: $7 - $15

LOST WORLD OF SINBAD, THE
(1965 - AIP) Toshiro Mifume, Makoto Satoh
One Sheet: $30 - $50

LOTTERY BRIDE, THE
(1930 - Joseph M. Schenk) Jeanette MacDonald, John Garrick, Joe E. Brown
One Sheet: $250 - $500 *Beware re-releases.*

LOTTERY LOVER
(1935 - Fox) Lew Ayres, Reginald Denny
One Sheet: $150 - $300

LOTTERY MAN, THE
(1919 - Artcraft) Wallace Reid
One Sheet: $500 - $800

LOTUS EATER, THE
(1921 - First National) John Barrymore, Colleen Moore
One Sheet: $700 - $1,200

LOUDSPEAKER, THE
(1934 - Monogram) Julie Bishop, Jacqueline Wells
One Sheet: $75 - $150

LOUISA
(1950 - Universal) Ronald Reagan, Ruth Hussey
One Sheet: $75 - $150

LOUISE, QUEEN OF PRUSSIA
(1931 - European Films) -
One Sheet: $100 - $200

LOUISIANA
(1947 - Monogram) Gov. Jimmie Davis, Margaret Lindsay, Sunshine Serenaders
One Sheet: $75 - $150

LOUISIANA HAYRIDE
(1944 - Columbia) Judy Canova, Lloyd Bridges
One Sheet: $75 - $150

LOUISIANA HUSSY
(1960 - Howco) Nan Peterson, Robert Richards
One Sheet: $30 - $50

LOUISIANA PURCHASE
(1941 - Paramount) Bob Hope, Vera Zorina, Victor Moore
One Sheet: $125 - $250

LOUISIANA STORY
(1948 - Lopert) Joseph Boudreaux, Lionel Le Blanc
One Sheet: $30 - $50

LOUISIANA TERRITORY
(1953 - RKO) Val Winter, Leo Zinser
One Sheet: $30 - $50

LOULOU
(1980 - Gaumont) Gerard Depardieu, Isabelle Huppert
One Sheet: $7 - $15 *French.*

LOVABLE CHEAT, THE
(1949 - Film Classics) Charlie Ruggles, Peggy Ann Garner
One Sheet: $20 - $40

LOVE
(1919 - Paramount) Roscoe "Fatty" Arbuckle
One Sheet: $1,600 - $2,500

LOVE
(1927 - MGM) Greta Garbo, John Gilbert
One Sheet: $3,500 - $5,000

LOVE & BULLETS
(1979 - AFD) Charles Bronson, Jill Ireland
One Sheet: $5 - $10

LOVE 'EM AND WEEP
(1927 - Pathe) Laurel & Hardy
One Sheet: $4,000 - $6,000

LOVE AFFAIR
(1932 - Columbia) Humphrey Bogart, Barbara Leonard
One Sheet: $1,300 - $2,000 *Lobby Card(Bogart scene):$400-800.*

LOVE AFFAIR
(1939 - RKO) Irene Dunne, Charles Boyer
One Sheet: $500 - $800

LOVE AMONG THE MILLIONAIRES
(1930 - Paramount Publix) Clara Bow, Stuart Erwin
One Sheet: $600 - $1,000

LOVE AND DEATH
(1975 - United Artists) Woody Allen, Diane Keaton
One Sheet: $10 - $20 *Price is for Style A. Style B:$25-35; Style C:$20-30.*

LOVE AND DOUGHNUTS
(1921 - Associated) Ben Turpin
One Sheet: $500 - $800

LOVE AND HISSES
(1937 - 20th Century Fox) Simone Simon, Walter Winchell, Ben Bernie
One Sheet: $75 - $150

LOVE AND HUMAN REMAINS
(1995 - Sony Classics) Thomas Gibson, Ruth Marshall
One Sheet: $5 - $10

LOVE AND KISSES
(1965 - Universal) Rick Nelson, Jack Kelly
One Sheet: $15 - $30 *Rock 'n' Roll.*

LOVE AND LEARN
(1928 - Paramount) Esther Ralston, Lane Chandler
One Sheet: $150 - $300

LOVE AND LEARN
(1947 - Warner Bros.) Jack Carson, Robert Hutton
One Sheet: $30 - $60

LOVE AND ONIONS
(1938 - Educational) Herman Timberg Jr., Pat Rooney
One Sheet: $100 - $200

LOVE AND OTHER CATASTROPHES
(1997 - Fox Searchlight) Alice Garner, Frances O'Conner
One Sheet: $5 - $10

LOVE AND PAIN (AND THE WHOLE DAMN THING)
(1973 - Columbia) Maggie Smith, Timothy Bottoms
One Sheet: $5 - $10

LOVE AND THE DEVIL
(1929 - -) Milton Sills, Maria Corda
One Sheet: $200 - $400

LOVE AT FIRST BITE
(1950 - Columbia) The Three Stooges (Shemp)
One Sheet: $200 - $400 *Comedy short. Duotone.*

LOVE AT FIRST BITE
(1979 - AIP) George Hamilton, Susan St. James
One Sheet: $5 - $12

LOVE AT FIRST SIGHT
(1922 - Pathe) Animated by Paul Terry
One Sheet: $1,300 - $2,000 *Cartoon. An Aesop's Fables film. Cartoon Movie Posters #16.*

LOVE AT LARGE
(1990 - -) Tom Berenger
One Sheet: $3 - $5

LOVE BANDIT, THE
(1924 - -) Doris Kenyon, Victor Sutherland
One Sheet: $150 - $300

LOVE BEFORE BREAKFAST
(1936 - Universal) Carole Lombard, Preston Foster
One Sheet: $2,500 - $4,000

Lobby Card

LOVE BEGINS AT TWENTY
(1936 - Warner Bros.) Warren Hull, Hugh Herbert
One Sheet: $75 - $150

LOVE BIRDS
(1934 - Universal) Slim Summerville, ZaSu Pitts
One Sheet: $125 - $250

LOVE BRAND, THE
(1923 - Universal) Roy Stewart, Wilfrid North
One Sheet: $200 - $400

LOVE BUG, THE
(1969 - Buena Vista) Dean Jones, Michele Lee, David Tomlinson
One Sheet: $15 - $30

LOVE BUSINESS
(1931 - MGM) Our Gang
One Sheet: $500 - $800

LOVE CAPTIVE, THE
(1934 - Universal) Nils Asther, Gloria Stuart
One Sheet: $125 - $250

LOVE COMES ALONG
(1930 - RKO) Bebe Daniels, Montagu Love
One Sheet: $200 - $400

LOVE CRAZY
(1941 - MGM) William Powell, Myrna Loy
One Sheet: $150 - $300

LOVE EXPERT, THE
(1920 - -) Constance Talmadge, Arnold Lucy
One Sheet: $500 - $800

LOVE FIELD
(1992 - Orion) Michelle Pfeiffer, Dennis Haysbert
One Sheet: $5 - $10

LOVE FINDS ANDY HARDY
(1938 - MGM) Lewis Stone, Mickey Rooney, Judy Garland
One Sheet: $250 - $600

LOVE FLOWER
(1920 - United Artists) Carol Dempster, Richard Barthlemess, Dir: D.W. Griffith
One Sheet: $600 - $1,000

LOVE FROM A STRANGER
(1937 - United Artists) Ann Harding, Basil Rathbone
One Sheet: $125 - $250

LOVE FROM A STRANGER
(1947 - Pathe) John Hodiak, Sylvia Sidney
One Sheet: $40 - $75

Three Sheet

LOVE GAMBLE, THE
(1925 - Banner) Lillian Rich, Robert Frazer
One Sheet: $200 - $400

LOVE GOD?, THE
(1969 - Universal) Don Knotts, Anne Francis, Edmond O'Brien
One Sheet: $20 - $40

LOVE GODDESSES, THE
(1965 - Continental) Marilyn Monroe, Mae West, many other major female stars
One Sheet: $40 - $75

LOVE GODDESSES, THE
(1981 - -) John Holmes, Seka
One Sheet: $30 - $60 *XXX.*

LOVE HAPPY
(1950 - United Artists) Ilona Massey, Marilyn Monroe (cameo), Marx Brothers
One Sheet: $200 - $400

LOVE HAPPY
(1953R - United Artists) Ilona Massey, Marilyn Monroe (cameo), Marx Brothers
One Sheet: $250 - $600 *Re-release spotlights Monroe (only a cameo on the original release paper).*

LOVE HAS MANY FACES
(1965 - Columbia) Lana Turner, Cliff Robertson
One Sheet: $20 - $40

LOVE, HONOR, AND BEHAVE
(1938 - Warner Bros.) Wayne Morris, Priscilla Lane
One Sheet: $50 - $100

LOVE, HONOR, AND GOODBYE

(1945 - Republic) Virginia Bruce, Nils Asther
One Sheet: $50 - $100

LOVE, HONOR, AND OH BABY
(1933 - Universal) -
One Sheet: $125 - $250

LOVE, HONOR, AND OH BABY
(1940 - Universal) Donald Woods, Kathryn Adams, Wallace Ford
One Sheet: $50 - $100

LOVE IN A BUNGALOW
(1937 - Universal) Kent Taylor, Nan Grey
One Sheet: $75 - $150

LOVE IN A COTTAGE
(1940 - 20th Century Fox) Terry-toons
*Cartoon. See "Terrytoons Stock" for prices.
Cartoon Movie Posters #84.*

LOVE IN A GOLDFISH BOWL
(1961 - Paramount) Tommy Sands, Fabian
One Sheet: $15 - $30   *Rock 'n' Roll.*

LOVE IN BLOOM
(1935 - Paramount) George Burns, Gracie Allen, Dixie Lee
One Sheet: $250 - $500

LOVE IN EXILE
(1936 - Gaumont) Clive Brook, Helen Vinson
One Sheet: $125 - $250

LOVE IN LAS VEGAS
(1964 - MGM) Elvis Presley, Ann-Margret
One Sheet: $125 - $250   *British release
of Viva Las Vegas.*

LOVE IN THE AFTERNOON
(1957 - Allied Artists) Gary Cooper, Audrey Hepburn
One Sheet: $100 - $200   *Saul Bass art.*

LOVE IN THE ROUGH
(1930 - MGM) Dorothy Jordan, Robert Montgomery
One Sheet: $200 - $400

LOVE IS A BALL
(1963 - United Artists) Glenn Ford, Hope Lange
One Sheet: $20 - $40

LOVE IS A HEADACHE
(1938 - MGM) Mickey Rooney, Franchot Tone, Gladys George
One Sheet: $150 - $300

LOVE IS A MANY SPLENDORED THING
(1955 - 20th Century Fox) William Holden, Jennifer Jones
One Sheet: $40 - $75

LOVE IS A RACKET
(1932 - First National) Douglas Fairbanks Jr., Frances Dee
One Sheet: $200 - $400

LOVE IS BETTER THAN EVER
(1951 - MGM) Elizabeth Taylor, Larry Parks
One Sheet: $50 - $100

LOVE IS BETTER THAN EVER
(1962R - MGM) Elizabeth Taylor, Larry Parks
One Sheet: $30 - $50   *Re-release.*

LOVE IS MY PROFESSION
(1959 - Iena-UCIL) Jean Gabin, Bridgitte Bardot
One Sheet: $75 - $150

LOVE IS NEWS
(1937 - 20th Century Fox) Tyrone Power, Loretta Young
One Sheet: $250 - $600

One Sheet

LOVE IS ON THE AIR
(1937 - Warner Bros.) Ronald Reagan, June Travis
One Sheet: $200 - $400   *Reagan's film
debut.*

LOVE IS WHERE IT'S AT
(1967 - AFD) -
One Sheet: $10 - $20

LOVE ISLAND
(1960 - Astor) Paul Valentine, Eva Gabor
One Sheet: $20 - $40

LOVE JONES
(1997 - New Line) Larenz Tate, Nia Long, Isiah Washington
One Sheet: $4 - $8

LOVE KISS, THE
(1930 - PRC) Olive Shea, Forrest Stanley
One Sheet: $125 - $250

LOVE LAUGHS AT ANDY HARDY
(1946 - MGM) Mickey Rooney, Lewis Stone, Bonita Granville
One Sheet: $50 - $100

LOVE LETTERS
(1924 - William Fox) Shirley Mason
One Sheet: $500 - $800

LOVE LETTERS
(1945 - Paramount) Jennifer Jones, Joseph Cotten
One Sheet: $100 - $200

One Sheet

LOVE LETTERS OF A STAR
(1936 - Universal) Henry Hunter, Polly Rowles
One Sheet: $150 - $300

LOVE LIFE OF A GORILLA
(1937 - Raymond Films) Margaret Sain, Joel Bouchard
One Sheet: $250 - $500

LOVE LIGHT, THE
(1921 - United Artists) Mary Pickford
One Sheet: $1,300 - $2,000

LOVE LOTTERY, THE
(1953 - Ealing) David Niven, Peggy Cummins
One Sheet: $30 - $50

LOVE MACHINE, THE
(1971 - Columbia) John Phillip Law, Dyan Cannon, Robert Ryan
One Sheet: $7 - $15

LOVE MART, THE
(1927 - First National) Billie Dove, Gilbert Roland, Noah Beery
One Sheet: $250 - $500

LOVE MASTER, THE
(1924 - First National) Strongheart (a dog), Lillian Rich
One Sheet: $125 - $250

LOVE ME
(1918 - -) Dorothy Dalton, Jack Holt
One Sheet: $125 - $250

LOVE ME FOREVER
(1935 - Columbia) Grace Moore, Leo Carrillo
One Sheet: $150 - $300

LOVE ME MADLY
(1954 - Klayton W. Kirby) -
One Sheet: $30 - $50

LOVE ME OR LEAVE ME
(1955 - MGM) James Cagney, Doris Day

One Sheet: $100 - $200

LOVE ME TENDER
(1956 - 20th Century Fox) Elvis Presley, Richard Egan, Debra Paget
One Sheet: $250 - $500   *Presley's film
debut.*

One Sheet

LOVE ME TONIGHT
(1932 - Paramount Publix) Maurice Chevalier, Jeanette MacDonald
One Sheet: $1,300 - $2,000

LOVE MOODS
(1950 - Sonney Amusement Enterprises) Lili St. Cyr
One Sheet: $150 - $300   *Sexploitation.*

LOVE MY DOG
(1927 - Pathe) Our Gang
One Sheet: $600 - $1,000

LOVE NEST, THE
(1922 - -) Buster Keaton
One Sheet: $6,500 - $10,000

LOVE NEST
(1951 - 20th Century Fox) William Lundigan, June Haver, Marilyn Monroe
One Sheet: $150 - $350

LOVE NEST ON WHEELS
(1937 - Educational) Buster Keaton
One Sheet: $200 - $400

LOVE OF SUNYA, THE
(1927 - United Artists) Gloria Swanson, John Boles
One Sheet: $800 - $1,500

LOVE ON A BET
(1936 - RKO) Gene Raymond, Wendy Barrie
One Sheet: $150 - $300

LOVE ON A BUDGET
(1938 - 20th Century Fox) Jed Prouty, Spring Byington
One Sheet: $75 - $125

LOVE ON A PILLOW
(1964 - Royal Films) Brigitte Bardot, Robert Hossein
One Sheet: $40 - $75

LOVE ON THE DOLE
(1941 - United Artists) Deborah Kerr, Clifford Evans
One Sheet: $50 - $100

LOVE ON THE RUN
(1936 - MGM) Joan Crawford, Clark Gable
One Sheet: $700 - $1,200

LOVE ON TOAST
(1937 - Paramount) Stella Adler, John Payne
One Sheet: $75 - $150

LOVE OR HATE
(192? - -) Norma Talmadge
One Sheet: $200 - $400

LOVE OVER NIGHT
(1928 - Pathe) Rod La Rocque, Jeanette Loff
One Sheet: $150 - $300

LOVE PARADE, THE
(1930 - Paramount Famous Lasky) Maurice Chevalier, Jeanette MacDonald
One Sheet: $800 - $1,500   *MacDonald's
film debut.*

LOVE POTION #9
(1992 - 20th Century Fox) Tate Donovan, Sandra Bullock

One Sheet: $3 - $5

LOVE RACKET, THE
(1930 - First National) Dorothy Mackaill, Sidney Blackmer
One Sheet: $150 - $300

LOVE SLAVES OF THE AMAZON
(1957 - Universal International) Don Taylor, Gianna Segale
One Sheet: $40 - $75

LOVE SPECIAL, THE
(1921 - Artcraft) Wallace Reid
One Sheet: $150 - $300

LOVE, SPEED, AND THRILLS
(1915 - Keystone) Mack Swain, Chester Conklin, Keystone Kops
One Sheet: $500 - $800

LOVE STORY
(1944 - Gainsborough) Margaret Lockwood, Stewart Granger
One Sheet: $30 - $50

LOVE STORY
(1970 - Paramount) Ali MacGraw, Ryan O'Neal, John Marley, Ray Milland
One Sheet: $10 - $20

LOVE STREAMS
(1984 - MGM/UA) Gena Rowlands, John Cassavetes
One Sheet: $15 - $25

LOVE TAKES FLIGHT
(1937 - Grand National) Bruce Cabot, Beatrice Roberts
One Sheet: $100 - $200

LOVE THAT BRUTE
(1950 - 20th Century Fox) Paul Douglas, Jean Peters
One Sheet: $15 - $25

LOVE THAT PUP
(1949 - MGM) Tom & Jerry
One Sheet: $250 - $600   *Cartoon. First
Spike & Tyke. Full color stone litho.*

LOVE THRILL, THE
(1927 - Universal) Laura La Plante, Tom Moore
One Sheet: $200 - $400

LOVE THY NEIGHBOR
(1940 - Paramount) Jack Benny, Fred Allen, Mary Martin
One Sheet: $125 - $250

LOVE TIME
(1934 - Fox) Pat Paterson, Nils Asther
One Sheet: $150 - $300

LOVE TRADER, THE
(1929 - Tiffany) Leatrice Joy, Noah Beery
One Sheet: $150 - $300

LOVE UNDER FIRE
(1937 - 20th Century Fox) Loretta Young, Don Ameche
One Sheet: $200 - $400

LOVE WATCHES
(1909 - -) Billie Burke
One Sheet: $500 - $800

LOVE WITH THE PROPER STRANGER
(1964 - Paramount) Natalie Wood, Steve McQueen
One Sheet: $30 - $60

LOVE WITHOUT QUESTION
(1920 - Jans) Olive Tell
One Sheet: $150 - $300

LOVE 'EM AND WEEP
(1927 - Pathe) Mae Busch, Jimmy Finlayson
One Sheet: $200 - $400

LOVE'S BLINDNESS
(1926 - MGM) Pauline Starke, Antonio Moreno
One Sheet: $150 - $300

LOVE'S GREATEST MISTAKE
(1927 - Paramount) William Powell, Evelyn Brent
One Sheet: $250 - $600

LOVE'S MASQUERADE
(1920 - Selznick) Conway Tearle
One Sheet: $150 - $300

LOVE'S OPTION

(1928 - -) Dorothy Boyd, Pat Aherne
One Sheet: $150 - $300

LOVE'S SUNSET
(1913 - Vitagraph) Earle Williams, Clara
Kimball Young
One Sheet: $600 - $1,000

LOVED ONE, THE
(1965 - MGM) Robert Morse, Jonathan Winters
One Sheet: $30 - $50

LOVE-INS, THE
(1967 - Columbia) Richard Todd, James
MacArthur
One Sheet: $15 - $30

LOVELY BUT DEADLY
(1982 - Juniper) Lucinda Dooling, John
Randolph
One Sheet: $4 - $8

LOVELY SENORITA, THE
(1913 - Edison) -
One Sheet: $250 - $500

LOVELY TO LOOK AT
(1952 - MGM) Howard Keel, Kathryn Grayson
One Sheet: $30 - $60

LOVELY WAY TO DIE, A
(1968 - Universal) Kirk Douglas, Sylva Koscina,
Eli Wallach
One Sheet: $15 - $25

LOVEMAKERS, THE
(1962 - Titanus) Jean-Paul Belmondo, Claudia
Cardinale
One Sheet: $7 - $15

LOVER, THE
(1992 - MGM) Jane March, Tony Leung
One Sheet: $5 - $10

LOVER BOY
(1955 - 20th Century Fox) Gerard Philipe,
Valerie Hobson
One Sheet: $15 - $25

LOVER COME BACK
(1931 - Columbia) Constance Cummings, Jack
Mulhall
One Sheet: $150 - $300

LOVER COME BACK
(1946 - Universal) George Brent, Lucille Ball
One Sheet: $75 - $150

Window Card

LOVER COME BACK
(1962 - Universal) Rock Hudson, Doris Day
One Sheet: $30 - $50

LOVER DIVINE
(1934 - Gaumont) -
One Sheet: $100 - $200

LOVER OF CAMILLE, THE
(1924 - Warner Bros.) Monte Blue
One Sheet: $250 - $500

LOVERBOY
(1989 - -) Patrick Dempsey, Kate Jackson
One Sheet: $3 - $5

LOVERS AND LOLLIPOPS
(1956 - Trans-Lux) Lori March, Gerald
O'Loughlin
One Sheet: $10 - $20

LOVERS AND OTHER STRANGERS
(1970 - Cinerama) Gig Young, Anne Jackson
One Sheet: $7 - $15

LOVERS COURAGEOUS

(1932 - MGM) Robert Montgomery, Madge
Evans
One Sheet: $125 - $250

LOVES OF A DICTATOR
(1935 - Gaumont British) Clive Brook,
Madeleine Carroll
One Sheet: $100 - $200

LOVES OF AN ACTRESS
(1928 - Paramount) Pola Negri, Nils Asther
One Sheet: $500 - $800

LOVES OF CARMEN, THE
(1927 - Fox) Dolores Del Rio, Victor McLaglen
One Sheet: $1,300 - $2,000

LOVES OF CARMEN, THE
(1948 - Columbia) Rita Hayworth, Glenn Ford
One Sheet: $150 - $300

LOVES OF EDGAR ALLAN POE, THE
(1942 - 20th Century Fox) Linda Darnell, John
Shepperd
One Sheet: $75 - $150

LOVES OF ISADORA, THE
(1968 - Universal) Vanessa Redgrave, James
Fox
One Sheet: $10 - $20   *AKA:
ISADORA.*

LOVES OF SALAMMBO, THE
(1962 - 20th Century Fox) Jeanne Valerie,
Jacques Sernas
One Sheet: $3 - $5

LOVESICK
(1982 - Warner Bros.) Dudley Moore, Elizabeth
McGovern
One Sheet: $2 - $3

LOVETIME
(1921 - -) Shirley Mason, Raymond McKee
One Sheet: $125 - $250

LOVEY MARY
(1926 - MGM) Bessie Love, William Haines
One Sheet: $200 - $400

LOVIN' MOLLY
(1974 - Columbia) Anthony Perkins, Beau
Bridges
One Sheet: $7 - $15

LOVING
(1970 - Columbia) George Segal, Eva Marie
Saint
One Sheet: $5 - $10

LOVING COUPLES
(1980 - 20th Century Fox) Shirley MacLaine,
James Coburn
One Sheet: $5 - $10

LOVING THE LADIES
(1930 - RKO) Richard Dix, Lois Wilson
One Sheet: $150 - $300

LOVING YOU
(1957 - Paramount) Elvis Presley, Lizabeth
Scott
One Sheet: $200 - $400

One Sheet

LOW DOWN DIRTY SHAME, A
(1994 - Buena Vista) Keenan Ivory Wayans,
Jada Pinkett
One Sheet: $5 - $10

LOW LIFE, THE
(1995 - IRS) Rory Cochrane, Sean Astin
One Sheet: $5 - $10

L-SHAPED ROOM, THE

(1962 - Davis-Royal) Leslie Caron, Tom Bell,
Brock Peters
One Sheet: $15 - $25

LT. ROBIN CRUSOE, U.S.N.
(1966 - Buena Vista) Dick Van Dyke, Nancy
Kwan
One Sheet: $15 - $25

LUANA
(1973 - Capital) Glenn Saxon, Mei Chen
One Sheet: $15 - $30   *Classic
Frazetta art. Price is for both styles.*

LUBURNUM GROVE
(1936 - Associated British) Edmund Gwenn,
Cedric Hardwicke
One Sheet: $100 - $200

LUCAS
(1986 - -) Corey Haim, Kerri Green, Winona
Ryder
One Sheet: $5 - $10

LUCIFER RISING
(1967 - -) -
One Sheet: $15 - $30

LUCILLE LOVE, A GIRL OF MYSTERY
(1916 - Universal) Grace Cunard, Frances Ford
One Sheet: $250 - $600   *Serial. 15
Episodes.*

LUCK
(1923 - Mastodon) Violet Mersereau, Robert
Edeson
One Sheet: $250 - $600

LUCK O' THE FOOLISH
(1924 - Pathe) Harry Langdon
One Sheet: $250 - $500

LUCK OF GINGER COFFEY, THE
(1964 - Reade-Sterling) Robert Shaw, Mary
Ure
One Sheet: $3 - $5

LUCK OF JANE, THE
(1916 - Vitagraph) -
One Sheet: $250 - $600

LUCK OF ROARING CAMP, THE
(1937 - Monogram) Owen Davis Jr., Joan
Woodbury
One Sheet: $50 - $100

LUCK OF THE IRISH, THE
(1948 - 20th Century Fox) Tyrone Power, Anne
Baxter
One Sheet: $75 - $150

LUCKIEST GIRL IN THE WORLD, THE
(1936 - Universal) Jane Wyatt, Louis Hayward
One Sheet: $100 - $200

LUCKY BOY
(1929 - Tiffany-Stahl) William K. Strauss,
Margaret Quimby
One Sheet: $100 - $200

LUCKY CISCO KID
(1940 - 20th Century Fox) Cesar Romero,
Evelyn Vale
One Sheet: $100 - $200

LUCKY DEVIL, THE
(1925 - Paramount) Richard Dix, Esther
Ralston, Edna May Oliver
One Sheet: $200 - $400

LUCKY DEVILS
(1933 - RKO) William Boyd, Betty Furness
One Sheet: $200 - $400

LUCKY DEVILS
(1940 - Universal) Richard Arlen, Andy Devine
One Sheet: $75 - $125

LUCKY DUCKY
(1948 - MGM) Tex Avery
One Sheet: $350 - $750   *Cartoon. Full
color stone litho. Cartoon Movie Posters #304.*

LUCKY GAMBLERS
(1946 - All-American) Lollypop Jones
One Sheet: $150 - $300   *Black cast.
Duotone. Separate Cinema, pg. 134.*

LUCKY GHOST
(1943 - Toddy) Mantan Moreland, F. E. Miller
One Sheet: $100 - $200   *Black cast.
Separate Cinema, pg. 69.*

LUCKY HORSESHOE, THE

(1925 - Fox) Tom Mix
One Sheet: $250 - $600

LUCKY JIM
(1957 - British Lion) Ian Carmichael, Hugh
Griffith
One Sheet: $5 - $10

LUCKY JORDAN
(1943 - Paramount) Alan Ladd, Helen Walker
One Sheet: $100 - $200

LUCKY LADY
(1975 - 20th Century Fox) Gene Hackman, Burt
Reynolds, Liza Minnelli
One Sheet: $15 - $25   *Amsel Art.
Price is for both styles.*

One Sheet

LUCKY LARKIN
(1929 - Universal) Ken Maynard
One Sheet: $250 - $500

LUCKY LARRIGAN
(1933 - Monogram) Rex Bell
One Sheet: $125 - $250

LUCKY LEGS
(1942 - Columbia) Jinx Falkenburg, Kay Harris,
Leslie Brooks
One Sheet: $75 - $150

LUCKY LOSERS
(1950 - Monogram) Leo Gorcey, Huntz Hall
One Sheet: $40 - $75

LUCKY LUCIANO
(1974 - Avco-Embassy) Edmund O'Brien,
Vincent Gardenia
One Sheet: $10 - $20

LUCKY ME
(1955 - Warner Bros.) Doris Day, Robert
Cummings, Phil Silvers
One Sheet: $30 - $60

LUCKY NICK CAIN
(1951 - 20th Century Fox) George Raft, Coleen
Gray
One Sheet: $15 - $35

LUCKY NIGHT
(1939 - MGM) Robert Taylor, Myrna Loy
One Sheet: $75 - $150

LUCKY NUMBER
(195? - RKO/Disney) Donald Duck
One Sheet: $800 - $1,500   *Cartoon.*

LUCKY PARTNERS
(1940 - RKO) Ronald Colman, Ginger Rogers
One Sheet: $125 - $250

LUCKY STARS
(1925 - Pathe) Harry Langdon, Natalie
Kingston
One Sheet: $250 - $600

LUCKY STIFF, THE
(1949 - United Artists) Dorothy Lamour, Brian
Donlevy
One Sheet: $40 - $75

LUCKY STIFF
(1988 - -) Joe Alaskey, Donna Dixon
One Sheet: $3 - $5

LUCKY TERROR
(1936 - Diversion) Hoot Gibson
One Sheet: $125 - $250

LUCKY TEXAN, THE
(1934 - Monogram) John Wayne
One Sheet: $2,200 - $3,500   *Cowboy
Movie Posters # 167.*

LUCKY TEXAN, THE
(1946R - Lone Star Western) John Wayne
One Sheet: $75 - $125   *Re-release.*

LUCRETIA LOMBARD
(1923 - Warner Bros.) Irene Rich, Monte Blue
One Sheet: $250 - $500

LUCY GALLANT
(1954 - Paramount) Jane Wyman, Charlton Heston, Claire Trevor
One Sheet: $20 - $40

LUDWIG
(1973 - MGM) Helmut Berger, Trevor Howard, Romy Schneider
One Sheet: $5 - $10

LUKE AND THE BANG-TAILS
(1917 - Pathe) Harold Lloyd
One Sheet: $800 - $1,500

LULLABY OF BROADWAY
(1950 - Warner Bros.) Doris Day, Gene Nelson
One Sheet: $30 - $50

LULU BELLE
(1948 - Columbia) Dorothy Lamour, Otto Kruger
One Sheet: $50 - $100

LUM AND ABNER ABROAD
(1955 - Nasbro) Chester Lauck, Morris Goff
One Sheet: $50 - $100

LUMBER JACK-RABBIT
(1954 - Warner Bros.) Bugs Bunny
One Sheet: $1,300 - $2,000   *Cartoon. In 3 Dimension.*

LUMBERJACK
(1944 - United Artists) William Boyd
One Sheet: $125 - $250

LUMMOX
(1930 - United Artists) Winifred Westover, Dorothy Janis
One Sheet: $200 - $400

LUNA
(1979 - Fox) Jill Clayburgh, Matthew Barry
One Sheet: $7 - $15

LUNKHEAD, THE
(1929 - Educational) Harry Gribbon, Andy Clyde, Thelma Hill
One Sheet: $150 - $300

LURE OF A WOMAN, THE
(1921 - Progress) Dr. A. Porter Davis, Regina Cohee
One Sheet: $1,900 - $3,000   *Black cast. Separate Cinema, pg 7.*

LURE OF EGYPT, THE
(1921 - Pathe) Robert McKim, Claire Adams
One Sheet: $150 - $300

LURE OF GOLD, THE
(1922 - Steiner) Neal Hart, William Quinn, Ben Corbett
One Sheet: $150 - $350

LURE OF THE CIRCUS
(1918 - Universal) Eddie Polo
One Sheet: $250 - $500   *Serial. 18 Chapters.*

LURE OF THE ISLANDS
(1942 - Monogram) Margie Hart, Robert Lowery, Guinn Williams
One Sheet: $50 - $100

LURE OF THE SWAMP
(1957 - 20th Century Fox) Marshall Thompson, Joan Vohs
One Sheet: $15 - $30

LURE OF THE WILDERNESS
(1952 - 20th Century Fox) Jean Peters, Jeffrey Hunter
One Sheet: $15 - $25

LURED
(1947 - Universal) Lucille Ball, George Sanders, Boris Karloff
One Sheet: $100 - $200

LUST FOR A VAMPIRE
(1971 - Hammer) Ralph Bates, Barbara Jefford, Suzanna Leigh
One Sheet: $15 - $25

LUST FOR GOLD
(1949 - Columbia) Ida Lupino, Glenn Ford
One Sheet: $30 - $50

LUST FOR LIFE
(1956 - MGM) Kirk Douglas, Anthony Quinn
One Sheet: $50 - $100   *Academy Award: Best Supporting Actor(Quinn). Academy Award Movie Posters #172.*

LUST FOR LIFE
(1962R - MGM) Kirk Douglas, Anthony Quinn
One Sheet: $7 - $15   *Re-release.*

LUST IN THE DUST
(1985 - Fox Run) Tab Hunter, Divine, Lainie Kazan
One Sheet: $30 - $50

LUST TO KILL
(1959 - -) Jim Davis, Allison Hayes
One Sheet: $15 - $35

LUSTY MEN, THE
(1952 - RKO) Susan Hayward, Robert Mitchum
One Sheet: $75 - $150   *Cowboy Movie Posters #291.*

LUTHER
(1974 - American Film Theatre) Stacy Keach, Patrick Magee
One Sheet: $5 - $10

LUV
(1967 - Columbia) Peter Falk, Jack Lemmon, Elaine May
One Sheet: $5 - $10

LUXURY
(1921 - Lyric) Rubye DeRemer
One Sheet: $250 - $500

LUXURY GIRLS
(1953 - United Artists) Susan Stephen
One Sheet: $7 - $15

LUXURY LINER
(1933 - Paramount) George Brent, Zita Johann
One Sheet: $75 - $150

LUXURY LINER
(1948 - MGM) George Brent, Jane Powell
One Sheet: $30 - $60

LYDIA
(1941 - United Artists) Merle Oberon, Joseph Cotten
One Sheet: $50 - $100

LYDIA BAILEY
(1952 - Columbia) Dale Robertson, Anne Francis
One Sheet: $7 - $15

LYING LIPS
(1939 - Micheaux) Edna Mae Harris
One Sheet: $600 - $1,000   *Black cast. Separate Cinema, pg. 16.*

M
(1931 - Nero) Peter Lorre, Otto Wernicke, Dir: Fritz Lang
One Sheet: $7,500 - $12,000   *German. Regular German poster has Fritz Lang credited, export poster has no credits: $3500-$5000. See Graven Images, pg. 56.*

M
(1951 - Columbia) David Wayne, Howard da Silva
One Sheet: $30 - $60

M. BUTTERFLY
(1993 - Warner Bros.) Jeremy Irons, Ian Richardson, John Lone
One Sheet: $5 - $10

M'LISS
(1918 - Artcraft) Mary Pickford
One Sheet: $700 - $1,200

M'LISS
(1936 - RKO) Anne Shirley, John Beal
One Sheet: $75 - $150

M*A*S*H
(1970 - 20th Century Fox) Elliott Gould, Donald Sutherland, Sally Kellerman
One Sheet: $30 - $65

M*A*S*H
(1973R - 20th Century Fox) Elliott Gould, Donald Sutherland, Sally Kellerman
One Sheet: $15 - $25   *Re-release.*

MA AND PA KETTLE
(1949 - Universal) Marjorie Main, Percy Kilbride
One Sheet: $40 - $75

MA AND PA KETTLE AT HOME
(1954 - Universal) Marjorie Main, Percy Kilbride
One Sheet: $40 - $75

MA AND PA KETTLE AT THE FAIR
(1951 - Universal) Marjorie Main, Percy Kilbride
One Sheet: $40 - $75

MA AND PA KETTLE AT WAIKIKI
(1955 - Universal) Marjorie Main, Percy Kilbride
One Sheet: $50 - $100

MA AND PA KETTLE BACK ON THE FARM
(1951 - Universal) Marjorie Main, Percy Kilbride
One Sheet: $40 - $75

MA AND PA KETTLE GO TO TOWN
(1949 - Universal) Marjorie Main, Percy Kilbride
One Sheet: $40 - $75

MA AND PA KETTLE ON VACATION
(1952 - Universal) Marjorie Main, Percy Kilbride
One Sheet: $40 - $75

MA BARKER'S KILLER BROOD
(1960 - Film Service) Lurene Tuttle, Tris Coffin
One Sheet: $15 - $35

MA, HE'S MAKING EYES AT ME!
(1940 - Universal) Tom Brown, Constance Moore
One Sheet: $75 - $125

MABEL AND FATTY'S MARRIED LIFE
(1916 - Keystone) Roscoe "Fatty" Arbuckle
One Sheet: $1,900 - $3,000

MABEL AT THE WHEEL
(1914 - Keystone) Charlie Chaplin
One Sheet: $7,500 - $12,000   *Price assumes Chaplin is pictured on poster.*

MABEL'S BUSY DAY
(1914 - Keystone) Charlie Chaplin
One Sheet: $7,500 - $12,000   *Price assumes Chaplin is pictured on poster.*

MABEL'S MARRIED LIFE
(1914 - Keystone) Charlie Chaplin
One Sheet: $7,500 - $12,000   *Price assumes Chaplin is pictured on poster.*

MABEL'S STRANGE PREDICAMENT
(1914 - Keystone) Charlie Chaplin
One Sheet: $7,500 - $12,000   *Price assumes Chaplin is pictured on poster.*

MAC
(1993 - Samuel Goldwyn) Ellen Barkin, John Turturro
One Sheet: $3 - $5

MACABRE
(1957 - Allied Artists) William Prince, Jacqueline Scott
One Sheet: $50 - $100   *Graven Images, pg. 190.*

MACAO
(1952 - RKO) Jane Russell, Robert Mitchum
One Sheet: $100 - $200

MACARTHUR
(1977 - Universal) Gregory Peck
One Sheet: $5 - $10

MACBETH
(1948 - Republic) Orson Welles, Jeanette Nolan
One Sheet: $250 - $600

MACBETH
(1963 - Prominent) Maurice Evans, Judith Anderson
One Sheet: $15 - $35

MACBETH
(1971 - Columbia) Jon Finch, Francesca Annis
One Sheet: $5 - $10

MACHETE
(1958 - United Artists) Mari Blanchard, Albert Dekker
One Sheet: $10 - $20

MACHINE GUN KELLY
(1958 - AIP) Charles Bronson, Susan Cabot
One Sheet: $40 - $75

MACHINE GUN MAMA
(1944 - PRC) Armida, Jack LaRue, Wallace Ford
One Sheet: $50 - $100

MACHINE GUN MCCAIN
(1970 - Columbia) John Cassavetes, Peter Falk
One Sheet: $5 - $10

MACHO CALLAHAN
(1970 - Avco/Embassy) David Janssen, Jean Seberg
One Sheet: $5 - $10

MACINTOSH MAN, THE
(1973 - Warner Bros.) Paul Newman, Dominique Sandra
One Sheet: $7 - $15

MACK, THE
(1973 - Cinerama) Richard Pryor, Max Julien
One Sheet: $10 - $20   *Blaxploitation.*

MACK, THE
(1977R - Cinerama) Richard Pryor, Max Julien
One Sheet: $10 - $20   *Re-release. Blaxploitation.*

MACKENNA'S GOLD
(1969 - Columbia) Gregory Peck, Omar Sharif, Telly Savalas
One Sheet: $20 - $40

MACKINTOSH AND T.J.
(1976 - Penland) Roy Rogers, Waylon Jennings, Clay O'Brien
One Sheet: $30 - $50

MACOMBER AFFAIR, THE
(1947 - United Artists) Gregory Peck, Joan Bennett
One Sheet: $50 - $100

MACON COUNTY LINE
(1974 - AIP) Alan Vint, Cheryl Waters
One Sheet: $15 - $25

MACUMBA
(1956 - -) -
One Sheet: $15 - $30

MACUMBA LOVE
(1960 - United Artists) Ziva Rodann, William Wellman, Jr.
One Sheet: $20 - $40

MAD ABOUT MEN
(1954 - GFD) Glynis Johns, Donald Sinden
One Sheet: $15 - $30

MAD ABOUT MOONSHINE
(1941 - RKO) Edgar Kennedy, Bill Franey
One Sheet: $100 - $200

MAD ABOUT MUSIC
(1938 - Universal) Deanna Durbin, Herbert Marshall
One Sheet: $200 - $400

MAD AT THE WORLD
(1954 - Filmakers) Frank Lovejoy, Keefe Brasselle
One Sheet: $10 - $20   *Youth gangs.*

MAD ATLANTIC, THE
(1967 - Toho) Toshiro Mifune, Makoto Sato
One Sheet: $10 - $20   *Japanese.*

MAD BOMBER, THE
(1973 - Cinemation) Chuck Connors, Vince Edwards
One Sheet: $5 - $10   *AKA: POLICE CONNECTION; DETECTIVE GERONIMO.*

MAD DOCTOR, THE
(1933 - United Artists) Mickey Mouse
One Sheet: $45,000 - $60,000   *Cartoon. The Disney Poster, pg. 16. Cartoon Movie Posters #62.*

MAD DOCTOR, THE
(1940 - Paramount) Basil Rathbone, Ellen Drew
One Sheet: $150 - $300   *AKA: A DATE WITH DESTINY.*

MAD DOCTOR OF BLOOD ISLAND, THE
(1969 - Hemisphere) John Ashley, Angelique

Pettyjohn, Ronald Remy
One Sheet: $15 - $35   *AKA: BLOOD DOCTOR; TOMB OF THE LIVING DEAD.*

MAD DOCTOR OF BLOOD ISLAND/BLOOD DEMON
(1969 - Hemisphere) Christopher Lee, Lex Barker
One Sheet: $15 - $25   *Double feature poster.*

MAD DOCTOR OF MARKET STREET, THE
(1941 - Universal) Una Merkel, Lionel Atwill
One Sheet: $150 - $300

MAD DOG, THE
(1932 - Columbia) Mickey Mouse, Pluto
One Sheet: $19,000 - $30,000   *Cartoon. The Disney Poster, pg. 15.*

MAD DOG AND GLORY
(1993 - Universal) Robert DeNiro, Bill Murray, Uma Thurman
One Sheet: $5 - $10

MAD DOG COLL
(1961 - Columbia) John Davis Chandler, Telly Savalas
One Sheet: $5 - $10

MAD DOG MORGAN
(1976 - Motion Picture) Dennis Hopper, Jack Thompson
One Sheet: $5 - $10   *AKA: MAD DOG.*

MAD DOGS AND ENGLISHMEN
(1971 - MGM) Joe Cocker, Leon Russell
One Sheet: $30 - $50   *Rock 'n' Roll.*

MAD EMPEROR
(1941 - World) Harry Bauer
One Sheet: $40 - $75

MAD EMPRESS, THE
(1939 - Warner Bros.) Medea Novarro, Conrad Nagel
One Sheet: $150 - $300   *AKA: JUAREZ AND MAXIMILLIAN.*

MAD EXECUTIONERS, THE
(1965 - Paramount) Hansjorg Felmy, Maria Perschy
One Sheet: $7 - $15

MAD GAME, THE
(1933 - Fox) Spencer Tracy, Clair Trevor
One Sheet: $800 - $1,500

MAD GENIUS, THE
(1931 - Warner Bros.) John Barrymore, Marian Marsh, Boris Karloff
One Sheet: $1,900 - $3,000   *Graven Images, pg. 52.*

MAD GHOUL, THE
(1943 - Universal) George Zucco, David Bruce, Evelyn Ankers
One Sheet: $150 - $300

MAD HOLIDAY
(1936 - MGM) ZaSu Pitts, Edmund Lowe
One Sheet: $150 - $300

MAD HOUSE, THE
(1929 - Educational) Eddie Lambert
One Sheet: $100 - $200

MAD LITTLE ISLAND
(1959 - Rank) Jeannie Carson, Donald Sinden
One Sheet: $15 - $30

MAD LOVE
(1923 - Goldwyn) Pola Negri
One Sheet: $1,900 - $3,000

MAD LOVE
(1935 - MGM) Peter Lorre, Frances Drake
One Sheet: $5,000 - $7,500   *Graven Images, pg. 92.*

MAD LOVE
(1995 - Touchstone) Chris O'Donnell, Drew Barrymore
One Sheet: $5 - $10

MAD, MAD, MAD, MAD MONSTER LATE SHOW
(197? - -) -
One Sheet: $5 - $10   *Black & white poster.*

MAD MAGICIAN, THE
(1954 - Columbia) Vincent Price, Mary Murphy

One Sheet: $75 - $150   *Filmed in 3-D.*
Graven Images, pg. 162.

MAD MARTINDALES, THE
(1942 - 20th Century Fox) Jane Withers, Marjorie Weaver
One Sheet: $50 - $100

MAD MAX
(1980 - AIP) Mel Gibson
One Sheet: $40 - $75

MAD MAX BEYOND THUNDERDOME
(1985 - Warner Bros.) Mel Gibson, Tina Turner
One Sheet: $15 - $30

MAD MEN OF EUROPE
(1940 - Columbia) Edmund Gwenn, Mary Maguire
One Sheet: $50 - $100

MAD MISS MANTON, THE
(1938 - RKO) Barbara Stanwyck, Henry Fonda
One Sheet: $150 - $300

One Sheet

MAD MONSTER, THE
(1942 - PRC) George Zucco, Anne Nagel, Glenn Strange
One Sheet: $125 - $250

MAD MONSTER PARTY
(1967 - Embassy) Rankin/Bass Stop-Motion Animation
One Sheet: $15 - $25

MAD PARADE, THE
(1931 - Paramount Publix) Evelyn Brent, Irene Rich
One Sheet: $150 - $300

MAD ROOM, THE
(1969 - Columbia) Stella Stevens, Shelley Winters, Beverly Garland
One Sheet: $7 - $15

MAD WEDNESDAY
(1950 - RKO) Harold Lloyd, Frances Ramsden
One Sheet: $75 - $150   *AKA: THE SIN OF HAROLD DIDDLEBOCK.*

MADAM KITTY
(1976 - -) -
One Sheet: $15 - $25

MADAME
(1963 - Embassy) Sophia Loren
One Sheet: $20 - $40

MADAME BOVARY
(1937 - Terra) Pola Negri
One Sheet: $800 - $1,500   *German.*

MADAME BOVARY
(1949 - MGM) Jennifer Jones, James Mason
One Sheet: $40 - $75

MADAME BUTTERFLY
(1932 - Paramount) Cary Grant, Sylvia Sidney
One Sheet: $800 - $1,500

MADAME BUTTERFLY
(1956 - Toho) Karuo Yachigusa, Nicola Filacuridi
One Sheet: $50 - $100   *Japanese.*

MADAME CURIE
(1943 - MGM) Greer Garson, Walter Pidgeon
One Sheet: $75 - $150

MADAME DU BARRY
(1934 - Warner Bros.) Dolores Del Rio, Reginald Owen, Victor Jory
One Sheet: $250 - $500

MADAME MYSTERY
(1926 - Pathe) Theda Bara
One Sheet: $800 - $1,500   *AKA: MADAME LEARNED.*

MADAME POMPADOUR
(1927 - Paramount) Antonio Monero, Dorothy Gish
One Sheet: $125 - $250

MADAME RACKETEER
(1932 - Paramount Publix) George Raft, Alison Skipworth
One Sheet: $150 - $300

MADAME ROSA
(1977 - Warner Bros./Columbia) Simone Signoret, Claude Dauphin
One Sheet: $7 - $15   *French.*

MADAME SANS GENE
(1925 - Paramount) Gloria Swanson
One Sheet: $1,600 - $2,500

One Sheet

MADAME SANS JANE
(1925 - Pathe) Glenn Tryon
One Sheet: $150 - $350

MADAME SATAN
(1930 - MGM) Lillian Roth, Kay Johnson, Reginald Denny
One Sheet: $800 - $1,500

MADAME SOUSATZKA
(1988 - -) Shirley MacLaine, Peggy Ashcroft
One Sheet: $3 - $5

MADAME SPY
(1934 - Universal) Fay Wray, Nils Asther
One Sheet: $250 - $600

MADAME SPY
(1942 - Universal) Constance Bennett, Don Dorter
One Sheet: $75 - $150

MADAME X
(1920 - Goldwyn) Pauline Frederick, William Courtleigh
One Sheet: $250 - $600

MADAME X
(1929 - MGM) Ruth Chatterton, Raymond Hackett
One Sheet: $800 - $1,500

MADAME X
(1937 - MGM) Gladys George, John Beal, Warren William
One Sheet: $125 - $250

MADAME X
(1966 - Universal) Lana Turner, John Forsythe, Constance Bennett(last film)
One Sheet: $15 - $35

MADCAP AMBROSE
(1916 - Triangle) Mack Swain
One Sheet: $200 - $400

MADCAP MAGOO
(1955 - Columbia) Mr. Magoo
One Sheet: $200 - $400   *Cartoon. Duotone.*

MADCAP MODELS STOCK
(1941 - Paramount) George Pal's Puppetoons
One Sheet: $75 - $150

MADDALENA
(1971 - International Co-Prod.) Lisa Gastoni, Eric Wolfe
One Sheet: $3 - $5

MADE FOR EACH OTHER
(1939 - United Artists) Carole Lombard, James Stewart
One Sheet: $300 - $700

MADE FOR EACH OTHER
(1949R - Film Classics) Carole Lombard, James Stewart
One Sheet: $50 - $100   *Re-release.*

MADE FOR EACH OTHER
(1971 - 20th Century Fox) Renee Taylor, Joseph Bologna
One Sheet: $3 - $5

MADE IN AMERICA
(1993 - Warner Bros.) Whoopi Goldberg, Ted Danson
One Sheet: $5 - $10

MADE IN HEAVEN
(1987 - Lorimar) Timothy Hutton, Kelly McGillis
One Sheet: $3 - $5

MADE IN PARIS
(1966 - MGM) Ann-Margret, Louis Jourdan
One Sheet: $30 - $50

MADE IN U.S.A.
(1988 - -) Adrian Pasdar, Christopher Penn, Lori Singer
One Sheet: $3 - $5

MADE ON BROADWAY
(1933 - MGM) Robert Montgomery, Madge Evans
One Sheet: $200 - $400

MADELEINE
(1950 - Universal) Ann Todd, Norman Wooland
One Sheet: $125 - $250

MADEMOISELLE
(1966 - Lopert) Jeanne Moreau, Ettore Manni
One Sheet: $3 - $5

MADEMOISELLE FIFI
(1944 - RKO) Simone Simon, John Emery
One Sheet: $100 - $200

MADEMOISELLE STRIPTEASE
(1957 - DCA) Brigitte Bardot, Daniel Gelin
One Sheet: $50 - $100   *French.*

MADHOUSE
(1974 - AIP) Vincent Price, Peter Cushing
One Sheet: $15 - $25

MADHOUSE
(1990 - Orion) John Larroquette, Kirstie Alley, Dennis Miller
One Sheet: $5 - $10

MADIGAN
(1968 - Universal) Richard Widmark, Inger Stevens
One Sheet: $7 - $15

MADIGAN'S MILLIONS
(1969 - AIP) Dustin Hoffman, Elsa Martinelli
One Sheet: $10 - $20

MADISON AVENUE
(1962 - 20th Century Fox) Dana Andrews, Eleanor Parker
One Sheet: $15 - $25

MADISON SQUARE GARDEN
(1932 - Paramount Publix) Jack Oakie, William Boyd
One Sheet: $200 - $400

One Sheet

MADMAN
(1981 - Farley) Alexis Dubin, Tony Fish

One Sheet: $3 - $5

MADNESS OF KING GEORGE, THE
(1995 - Samuel Goldwyn) Nigel Hawthorne, Helen Mirren
One Sheet: $7 - $15

MADNESS OF THE HEART
(1949 - Universal) Margaret Lockwood, Paul Dupuis
One Sheet: $15 - $35

MADONNA OF THE DESERT
(1948 - Republic) Lynne Roberts, Donald Barry
One Sheet: $20 - $40

MADONNA OF THE SEVEN MOONS
(1946 - Universal) Phyllis Calvert, Stewart Granger
One Sheet: $30 - $50   *Duotone.*

One Sheet

MADONNA OF THE STREETS
(1930 - Columbia) Evelyn Brent, Robert Ames
One Sheet: $100 - $200

MADONNA'S SECRET, THE
(1946 - Republic) Francis Lederer, Gail Patrick
One Sheet: $20 - $40

MADWOMAN OF CHAILLOT, THE
(1969 - Warner Bros.) Katharine Hepburn, Charles Boyer
One Sheet: $15 - $25

MAFIOSO
(1964 - Zenith) Alberto Sordi, Norma Bengell
One Sheet: $10 - $20

MAGIC
(1978 - 20th Century Fox) Anthony Hopkins, Ann-Margret
One Sheet: $7 - $15

MAGIC BOTTLE, THE
(1925 - World) Tom Wise
One Sheet: $150 - $300

MAGIC BOW, THE
(1947 - GFD) Stewart Granger, Phyllis Calvert
One Sheet: $15 - $30

MAGIC BOX, THE
(1952 - British-Lion) Robert Donat, Maria Schell
One Sheet: $30 - $50

MAGIC BOY
(1960 - MGM) -
One Sheet: $100 - $200   *Cartoon.*
Earliest Japanese cartoon made for a U.S. audience.

MAGIC BOY
(1973R - MGM) -
One Sheet: $20 - $40   *Re-release.*
Cartoon.

MAGIC CARPET, THE
(1951 - Columbia) Lucille Ball, John Agar
One Sheet: $75 - $125

MAGIC CHRISTIAN, THE
(1970 - Commonwealth United) Peter Sellers, Ringo Starr, Raquel Welch
One Sheet: $15 - $30   *Price is for both styles.*

MAGIC FACE, THE
(1951 - Columbia) Luther Adler, Patricia Knight
One Sheet: $40 - $75

MAGIC FIRE
(1955 - Republic) Yvonne De Carlo, Carlos Thompson

One Sheet: $30 - $50

One Sheet

MAGIC FLAME, THE
(1927 - United Artists) Ronald Colman, Vilma Banky
One Sheet: $250 - $500

MAGIC GARDEN OF STANLEY SWEETHEART, THE
(1970 - MGM) Don Johnson, Diane Hull, Holly Near
One Sheet: $10 - $20

MAGIC IN THE WATER
(1995 - TriStar) Mark Harmon, Joshua Jackson
One Sheet: $3 - $5

MAGIC NIGHT
(1932 - United Artists) Jack Buchanan, Clive Currie
One Sheet: $125 - $250

MAGIC OF WALT DISNEYWORLD, THE
(1972 - Disney) Opening of Disneyworld in Florida
One Sheet: $40 - $75

One Sheet

MAGIC OF LASSIE, THE
(1978 - International) James Stewart, Mickey Rooney
One Sheet: $15 - $25

MAGIC OF THE KITE
(1974 - Paramount) -
One Sheet: $3 - $5

MAGIC PENCIL, THE
(1940 - 20th Century Fox) Terry-toons
One Sheet: $100 - $200   *Cartoon. Full color stone litho. Stock poster with inset title.*

MAGIC SHELL, THE
(1940 - 20th Century Fox) Terry-toons
One Sheet: $100 - $200   *Cartoon. Full color stone litho. Stock poster with inset title.*

MAGIC SWORD, THE
(1961 - United Artists) Basil Rathbone, Estelle Winwood
One Sheet: $20 - $40

MAGIC TOWN
(1947 - RKO) James Stewart, Jane Wyman
One Sheet: $75 - $150

MAGIC TOWN
(1955R - RKO) James Stewart, Jane Wyman
One Sheet: $20 - $40   *Re-release.*

MAGIC VOYAGE OF SINBAD, THE
(1962 - Filmgroup) Edward Stolar, Ann Larion
One Sheet: $30 - $50

MAGIC WEAVER, THE

(1965 - Allied Artists) Mikhail Kuznetsov, Ninel Myshkova
One Sheet: $5 - $10

MAGIC WORLD OF TOPO GIGIO, THE
(1965 - Columbia) Topo Gigio
One Sheet: $10 - $20   *Animated puppets.*

MAGICAL MAESTRO
(1950 - MGM) Tex Avery
One Sheet: $250 - $500   *Cartoon. Full color stone litho. Cartoon Movie Posters #313.*

MAGICIAN, THE
(1926 - MGM) Alice Terry, Paul Wegener
One Sheet: $600 - $1,000   *Graven Images, pg. 30.*

MAGICIAN MICKEY
(1937 - United Artists) Mickey Mouse, Donald Duck
One Sheet: $19,000 - $30,000   *Cartoon. 40x60 known to exist. Cartoon Movie Posters #67.*

MAGNET, THE
(1950 - Universal-International) William Fox, Kay Walsh
One Sheet: $10 - $20

MAGNETIC MONSTER, THE
(1953 - United Artists) Richard Carlson, Jean Byron
One Sheet: $50 - $100

MAGNIFICENT AMBERSONS, THE
(1942 - RKO) Joseph Cotten, Anne Baxter
One Sheet: $1,300 - $2,000   *Norman Rockwell Art.*

MAGNIFICENT ANIMATED PICTURES
(1895C - -) -
One Sheet: $600 - $1,000

MAGNIFICENT BRUTE, THE
(1936 - Universal) Victor McLaglen, Binnie Barnes, William Hall
One Sheet: $100 - $200

MAGNIFICENT BRUTE, THE
(194?R - Realart) Victor McLaglen, Binnie Barnes, William Hall
One Sheet: $10 - $20   *Re-release.*

MAGNIFICENT CONCUBINE, THE
(1964 - Shaw Bros.) Li Li-hua, Yen Chuan
One Sheet: $20 - $40

MAGNIFICENT CUCKOLD, THE
(1965 - Continental) Claudia Cardinale, Ugo Tognazzi
One Sheet: $10 - $20

MAGNIFICENT DOLL
(1946 - Universal) Ginger Rogers, David Niven
One Sheet: $75 - $150

MAGNIFICENT DOPE, THE
(1942 - 20th Century Fox) Henry Fonda, Lynn Bari
One Sheet: $75 - $150

MAGNIFICENT FRAUD, THE
(1939 - Paramount) Akim Tamiroff, Lloyd Nolan
One Sheet: $150 - $300   *One Sheet(Leader):$65-125.*

MAGNIFICENT LIE, THE
(1931 - Paramount Publix) Ralph Bellamy, Ruth Chatterton
One Sheet: $125 - $250

MAGNIFICENT MATADOR, THE
(1955 - 20th Century Fox) Maureen O'Hara, Anthony Quinn
One Sheet: $15 - $35

MAGNIFICENT OBSESSION
(1935 - Universal) Irene Dunne, Robert Taylor
One Sheet: $250 - $500

MAGNIFICENT OBSESSION
(1954 - Universal) Jane Wyman, Rock Hudson
One Sheet: $30 - $60

MAGNIFICENT ROGUE
(1946 - Republic) Lynne Roberts, Warren Douglas
One Sheet: $40 - $75

MAGNIFICENT ROUGHNECKS
(1956 - Allied Artists) Jack Carson, Mickey Rooney
One Sheet: $20 - $40

MAGNIFICENT SEVEN, THE
(1960 - United Artists) Yul Brynner, Steve McQueen, Eli Wallach
One Sheet: $125 - $250   *Cowboy Movie Posters #310.*

MAGNIFICENT SEVEN, THE
(1980R - United Artists) Yul Brynner, Steve McQueen, Eli Wallach
One Sheet: $30 - $50   *Re-release. New artwork.*

MAGNIFICENT SEVEN RIDE, THE
(1972 - United Artists) Lee Van Cleef, Michael Callan
One Sheet: $7 - $15

MAGNIFICENT YANKEE, THE
(1950 - MGM) Louis Calhern, Ann Harding
One Sheet: $20 - $40

MAGNUM FORCE
(1973 - Warner Bros.) Clint Eastwood, Hal Holbrook
One Sheet: $75 - $125

MAGOO BREAKS PAR
(1957 - Columbia) Mr. Magoo
One Sheet: $150 - $300   *Cartoon. Duotone.*

One Sheet

MAGOO EXPRESS
(1955 - Columbia) Mr. Magoo
One Sheet: $150 - $300   *Cartoon. Duotone.*

MAGUS, THE
(1968 - 20th Century Fox) Anthony Quinn, Michael Caine, Candice Bergen
One Sheet: $5 - $10

MAHOGANY
(1975 - Paramount) Diana Ross, Billy Dee Williams
One Sheet: $15 - $35   *Black cast. Excellent poster design and image of Ross.*

MAID OF SALEM
(1937 - Paramount) Claudette Colbert, Fred MacMurray
One Sheet: $150 - $300

MAID OF THE MOUNTAINS, THE
(1932 - -) Brown, Welchman, Stockfield
One Sheet: $75 - $150

MAID OF THE WEST
(1921 - Universal) Eileen Percy, William Scott
One Sheet: $150 - $300

MAID TO ORDER
(1987 - New Century) Ally Sheedy, Beverly D'Angelo
One Sheet: $3 - $5

MAID'S NIGHT OUT
(1938 - RKO) Joan Fontaine, Allan Lane
One Sheet: $50 - $100

MAIDEN FOR THE PRINCE, A
(1967 - Royal) Philippe Leroy, Vittorio Caprioli
One Sheet: $5 - $10

MAIL DOG
(1947 - RKO/Disney) Pluto
One Sheet: $600 - $1,000   *Cartoon. The Disney Poster, pg. 37.*

MAIL ORDER BRIDE
(1964 - MGM) Buddy Ebsen, Keir Dullea
One Sheet: $20 - $40

MAIL PILOT, THE

(1933 - United Artists/Disney) Mickey Mouse
One Sheet: $25,000 - $40,000 *Cartoon.*

MAIL PILOT, THE
(1974R - United Artists/Disney) Mickey Mouse
One Sheet: $15 - $25 *Re-release.*
Cartoon.

MAILBAG ROBBERY
(1958 - -) Kay Collard, Lee Patterson
One Sheet: $15 - $25

MAIN ATTRACTION, THE
(1962 - MGM) Pat Boone, Nancy Kwan
One Sheet: $20 - $40

MAIN CHANCE, THE
(1966 - Embassy) Gregoire Aslan, Tracy Reed
One Sheet: $3 - $5

MAIN EVENT, THE
(1938 - Columbia) Robert Paige, Jacqueline Wells
One Sheet: $75 - $125 *Sports (Boxing).*

MAIN EVENT, THE
(1979 - Warner Bros.) Barbra Streisand, Ryan O'Neal
One Sheet: $10 - $20 *Sports (Boxing).*

MAIN STREET AFTER DARK
(1944 - MGM) Edward Arnold, Dan Duryea
One Sheet: $30 - $50

MAIN STREET GIRL
(1938 - Syndicate) Jean Carmen, Richard Adams
One Sheet: $100 - $200 *AKA: PAROLED FROM THE BIG HOUSE.*

MAIN STREET KID, THE
(1948 - Republic) Al Pearce, Janet Martin
One Sheet: $30 - $50

MAIN STREET LAWYER
(1939 - Republic) Edward Ellis, Anita Louise
One Sheet: $100 - $200

MAIN STREET TO BROADWAY
(1953 - MGM) Lionel & Ethel Barrymore, All Star Cast
One Sheet: $30 - $60

MAISIE
(1939 - MGM) Ann Sothern, Robert Young
One Sheet: $100 - $200

MAISIE GETS HER MAN
(1942 - MGM) Ann Sothern, Red Skelton, Leo Gorcey
One Sheet: $75 - $150

MAISIE GOES TO RENO
(1944 - MGM) Ann Sothern, John Hodiak, Ava Gardner
One Sheet: $75 - $150

MAISIE WAS A LADY
(1941 - MGM) Ann Sothern, Lew Ayres
One Sheet: $50 - $100

MAITRESSE
(1976 - -) Gerard Depardieu
One Sheet: $5 - $10 *French.*

MAJOR AND THE MINOR, THE
(1942 - Paramount) Ginger Rogers, Ray Milland, Dir: Billy Wilder
One Sheet: $100 - $200 *Wilder's directorial debut.*

MAJOR BARBARA
(1941 - United Artists) Wendy Hiller, Rex Harrison, Deborah Kerr (1st film)
One Sheet: $150 - $300

MAJOR BOWES' AMATEUR THEATRE OF THE AIR
(1935 - RKO) Major Bowes
One Sheet: $150 - $300

MAJOR DUNDEE
(1965 - Columbia) Charlton Heston, James Coburn, Dir: Sam Peckinpah
One Sheet: $15 - $30

MAJOR LEAGUE
(1989 - Paramount) Tom Berenger, Charlie Sheen, Margret Whitton
One Sheet: $15 - $25 *Sports (Baseball). Sports Movie Posters #80.*

MAJOR LEAGUE II
(1994 - Warner Bros.) Charlie Sheen, Tom Berenger, Corbin Bernsen
One Sheet: $7 - $15 *Sports (Baseball).*

MAJOR PAYNE
(1995 - Universal) Damon Wayans, Karyn Parsons
One Sheet: $3 - $5 *Comedy.*

MAJORITY OF ONE, A
(1962 - Warner Bros.) Rosalind Russell, Alec Guinness
One Sheet: $15 - $30

MAKE A MILLION
(1935 - Monogram) Pauline Brooks, Charles Starrett
One Sheet: $75 - $150

MAKE A WISH
(1937 - RKO) Bobby Breen, Basil Rathbone
One Sheet: $125 - $250

One Sheet

MAKE BELIEVE BALLROOM
(1949 - Columbia) Jerome Courtland, Ruth Warrick
One Sheet: $40 - $75

MAKE HASTE TO LIVE
(1954 - Republic) Dorothy McGuire, Stephen McNally
One Sheet: $15 - $30

MAKE IT BIG
(1944 - -) Jack Haley, Harriet Hilliard
One Sheet: $50 - $100

MAKE ME A STAR
(1932 - Paramount Publix) Stuart Erwin, Joan Blondell
One Sheet: $500 - $900

MAKE ME AN OFFER
(1956 - Associated Artists) Peter Finch, Adrienne Corri
One Sheet: $7 - $15

MAKE MINE FREEDOM
(1948 - MGM) -
One Sheet: $200 - $400 *Cartoon. Full color stone litho.*

MAKE MINE LAUGHS
(1949 - RKO) Ray Bolger, Anne Shirley, Frances Langford
One Sheet: $40 - $75

MAKE MINE MINK
(1960 - Continental) Terry-Thomas, Athene Seyler
One Sheet: $5 - $10

MAKE MINE MUSIC
(1946 - RKO/Disney) Nelson Eddy, Dinah Shore, Andrews Sisters, partial animation
One Sheet: $125 - $250

MAKE WAY FOR A LADY
(1936 - RKO) Herbert Marshall, Anne Shirley
One Sheet: $125 - $250

MAKE WAY FOR TOMORROW
(1937 - Paramount) Victor Moore, Beulah Bondi
One Sheet: $100 - $200

MAKE YOUR OWN BED
(1944 - Warner Bros.) Jack Carson, Irene Manning
One Sheet: $30 - $50

MAKER OF MEN
(1931 - Columbia) Jack Holt, Richard Cromwell

One Sheet: $125 - $250

MAKING A LIVING
(1914 - Keystone) Charlie Chaplin
One Sheet: $7,500 - $12,000

MAKING CONTACT
(1985 - New World) Joshua Morell, Eve Kryll
One Sheet: $3 - $5

MAKING IT
(1971 - 20th Century Fox) Kristoffer Tabori, Marlyn Mason
One Sheet: $3 - $5

MAKING LOVE
(1982 - 20th Century Fox) Kate Jackson, Michael Ontkean
One Sheet: $3 - $5

MAKING MR. RIGHT
(1987 - -) Ann Magnuson, John Malkovich
One Sheet: $3 - $5

MAKING OF O'MALLEY, THE
(1925 - First National) Milton Sills, Dorothy Mackaill
One Sheet: $200 - $400

MAKING OUT
(1983 - SRC) Jessie St. Clair, Nona Phillips
One Sheet: $4 - $8

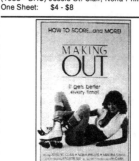
One Sheet

MAKING THE GRADE
(1984 - MGM) Judd Nelson, Gordon Jump
One Sheet: $3 - $5

MAKING THE HEADLINES
(1938 - Columbia) Jack Holt, Beverly Roberts
One Sheet: $100 - $200

MALAGA
(1962 - Cavalcade) Trevor Howard, Dorothy Dandridge
One Sheet: $7 - $15 *AKA: MOMENT OF DANGER.*

MALAMONDO
(1964 - Magna) Narrated by Marvin Miller
One Sheet: $5 - $10

MALAY NIGHTS
(1932 - Mayfair) Johnny Mack Brown, Dorothy Burgess
One Sheet: $100 - $200

MALAYA
(1949 - MGM) Spencer Tracy, James Stewart, Valentina Cortese
One Sheet: $50 - $100

MALCOLM
(1986 - -) Colin Friels, John Hargreaves
One Sheet: $3 - $5

MALCOLM X
(1972 - -) Documentary
One Sheet: $20 - $40

MALCOLM X
(1992 - Warner Bros.) Denzel Washington, Spike Lee (Dir.)
One Sheet: $10 - $20

MALE AND FEMALE
(1919 - Paramount) Gloria Swanson, Thomas Meighan, Dir: Cecil B. DeMille
One Sheet: $1,900 - $3,000

MALE ANIMAL, THE
(1942 - Warner Bros.) Henry Fonda, Olivia DeHavilland
One Sheet: $100 - $200

MALIBU BEACH
(1978 - Crown) Kim Lankford, James Daughton
One Sheet: $10 - $20

MALICE
(1993 - Columbia) Alec Baldwin, Nicole Kidman
One Sheet: $3 - $5

MALICE IN THE PALACE
(1949 - Columbia) The Three Stooges (Shemp)
One Sheet: $350 - $750 *Comedy short. Duotone.*

MALONE
(1987 - Orion) Burt Reynolds, Cliff Robertson
One Sheet: $3 - $5

MALTA STORY, THE
(1953 - United Artists) Alec Guinness, Jack Hawkins
One Sheet: $15 - $30

MALTESE BIPPY, THE
(1969 - MGM) Dan Rowan, Dick Martin, Carol Lynley
One Sheet: $15 - $30 *TV tie-in.*

MALTESE FALCON, THE
(1931 - Warner Bros.) Ricardo Cortez, Bebe Daniels
One Sheet: $1,900 - $3,000

MALTESE FALCON, THE
(1941 - Warner Bros.) Humphrey Bogart, Mary Astor, Peter Lorre
One Sheet: $3,500 - $5,000

One Sheet

MAM'ZELLE PAGELLE
(1958 - -) Brigitte Bardot
One Sheet: $75 - $125

MAMA DRACULA
(1980 - Valisa) Louise Fletcher, Maria Schneider
One Sheet: $5 - $10

MAMA LOVES PAPA
(1933 - Paramount) Charles Ruggles, Mary Boland
One Sheet: $100 - $200

MAMA LOVES PAPA
(1945 - RKO) Leon Errol, Elizabeth Risdon
One Sheet: $50 - $100

MAMA RUNS WILD
(1938 - Republic) Mary Boland, Ernest Truex
One Sheet: $50 - $100

MAMA STEPS OUT
(1937 - MGM) Guy Kibbee, Alice Brady
One Sheet: $75 - $125

MAMBA
(1930 - Tiffany) Jean Hersholt, Eleanor Boardman
One Sheet: $125 - $250

MAMBO
(1954 - Paramount) Silvana Mangano, Shelley Winters
One Sheet: $30 - $50

MAMBO KINGS
(1992 - Warner Bros.) Armand Assante, Antonio Bandero
One Sheet: $7 - $15

MAME
(1974 - Warner Bros.) Lucille Ball, Beatrice Arthur
One Sheet: $15 - $30

MAMMY

(1930 - Warner Bros.) Al Jolson, Louise Dresser
One Sheet: $1,600 - $2,500   *One Sheet(Jolson in black face style):$5000-7500.*

MAN, THE
(1972 - Paramount) James Earl Jones, Martin Balsam
One Sheet: $7 - $15

MAN ABOUT THE HOUSE, A
(1947 - 20th Century Fox) Kieron Moore, Margaret Johnstcn
One Sheet: $30 - $50

MAN ABOUT TOWN
(1923 - Pathe) Stan Laurel, James Finlayson
One Sheet: $250 - $600

MAN ABOUT TOWN
(1932 - Fox) Warner Baxter, Karen Morley
One Sheet: $150 - $300

MAN ABOUT TOWN
(1939 - Paramount) Jack Benny, Dorothy Lamour, Betty Grable
One Sheet: $500 - $800   *George Petty art.*

MAN ABOUT TOWN
(1947 - Pathe/RKO) Maurice Chevalier, Francois Perier
One Sheet: $50 - $100

MAN AFRAID
(1957 - Universal) George Nader, Phyllis Thaxter
One Sheet: $15 - $25

MAN AGAINST WOMAN
(1932 - Columbia) Jack Holt, Lillian Miles
One Sheet: $150 - $300

MAN ALIVE
(1945 - RKO) Pat O'Brien, Adolphe Menjou
One Sheet: $50 - $100

MAN ALONE, A
(1955 - Republic) Ray Milland, Mary Murphy
One Sheet: $15 - $25

MAN AND A WOMAN, A
(1966 - Allied Artists) Anouk Aimee, Jean-Louis Trintignant
One Sheet: $40 - $75

MAN AND BOY
(1972 - Levitt-Pickman) Bill Cosby, Leif Erickson
One Sheet: $5 - $10

MAN AND HIS WIFE, A
(1939 - French Film Exchange) Harry Bauer
One Sheet: $50 - $100

MAN AT LARGE
(1941 - 20th Century Fox) Marjorie Weaver, George Reeves
One Sheet: $100 - $200

MAN BAIT
(1926 - Producers) Marie Prevost, Kenneth Thompson, Douglas Fairbanks Jr.
One Sheet: $250 - $500

MAN BAIT
(1952 - Lippert) George Brent, Marguerite Chapman
One Sheet: $40 - $75

MAN BEAST
(1955 - -) Rock Madison, Virginia Maynor
One Sheet: $15 - $30

MAN BEHIND THE GUN, THE
(1952 - Warner Bros.) Randolph Scott, Patrice Wymore
One Sheet: $15 - $35

MAN BETRAYED, A
(1936 - Republic) Eddie Nugent, Kay Hughes
One Sheet: $50 - $100

MAN BETRAYED, A
(1941 - Republic) John Wayne, Frances Dee
One Sheet: $150 - $300

MAN BETRAYED, A
(1953R - Republic) John Wayne, Frances Dee
One Sheet: $30 - $60   *Re-release.*

MAN BETWEEN, THE
(1953 - United Artists) James Mason, Claire Bloom

One Sheet: $15 - $25

MAN BITES DOG
(1993 - Roxie) Benoit Poelvoorde, Remy Belvaux
One Sheet: $15 - $25   *French.*

MAN BITES LOVEBUG
(1937 - Columbia) Charlie Chase
One Sheet: $100 - $200

MAN CALLED ADAM, A
(1966 - Embassy) Sammy Davis Jr., Louis Armstrong
One Sheet: $30 - $50   *Black cast. Duotone. Separate Cinema, pg. 155.*

MAN CALLED BACK, THE
(1932 - World Wide) Conrad Nagel, Doris Kenyon
One Sheet: $100 - $200

MAN CALLED DAGGER, A
(1968 - MGM) Terry Moore, Jan Murray
One Sheet: $3 - $5

MAN CALLED FLINTSTONE, THE
(1966 - Columbia) Fred Flintstone
One Sheet: $30 - $50   *Cartoon. Cartoon Movie Posters #390.*

MAN CALLED GANNON, A
(1969 - Universal) Tony Franciosa, Michael Sarrazin, Judi West
One Sheet: $3 - $5

MAN CALLED HORSE, A
(1970 - National General) Richard Harris, Judith Anderson
One Sheet: $15 - $25

MAN CALLED NOON, THE
(1973 - National General) Richard Crenna, Stephen Boyd
One Sheet: $3 - $5

MAN CALLED PETER, A
(1955 - 20th Century Fox) Richard Todd, Jean Peters
One Sheet: $15 - $35

MAN CALLED SLEDGE, A
(1971 - Columbia) James Garner, Dennis Weaver
One Sheet: $5 - $10

MAN COULD GET KILLED, A
(1966 - Universal) James Garner, Sandra Dee
One Sheet: $15 - $30

MAN CRAZY
(1953 - 20th Century Fox) Neville Brand, Christine White
One Sheet: $50 - $100

MAN FOR ALL SEASONS, A
(1966 - Columbia) Paul Scofield, Wendy Hiller
One Sheet: $40 - $75   *Academy Award: Best Picture, Best Actor, Best Direction(Fred Zinneman). Academy Award Movie Posters #234 & #235.*

MAN FOR ALL SEASONS, A
(1972R - Columbia) Paul Scofield, Wendy Hiller
One Sheet: $5 - $10   *Re-release.*

MAN FRIDAY
(1975 - Avco) Peter O'Toole, Richard Roundtree
One Sheet: $5 - $10

MAN FROM ARIZONA, THE
(1932 - Monogram) Rex Bell
One Sheet: $150 - $300

MAN FROM BITTER RIDGE, THE
(1955 - Universal) Lex Barker, Mara Corday
One Sheet: $30 - $50

MAN FROM BLACK HILLS
(1952 - Monogram) Johnny Mack Brown, James Ellison
One Sheet: $30 - $50

MAN FROM BLANKLEYS, THE
(1930 - Warner Bros.) John Barrymore, Loretta Young
One Sheet: $150 - $300

MAN FROM BUTTON WILLOW, THE
(1965 - United Screen Arts) Voices of Dale Robertson, Edgar Buchanan
One Sheet: $15 - $35   *Cartoon. First animated western.*

MAN FROM CAIRO
(1953 - Lippert) George Raft, Irene Papas
One Sheet: $20 - $40

MAN FROM CHEYENNE
(1942 - Republic) Roy Rogers, Gabby Hayes
One Sheet: $150 - $300

MAN FROM CHICAGO
(1931 - British International) Bernard Nedell, Dodo Watts
One Sheet: $75 - $150

MAN FROM CLOVER GROVE, THE
(1978 - American Cinema) Ron Masak, Cheryl Miller, Rose Marie
One Sheet: $3 - $5

MAN FROM COLORADO, THE
(1948 - Columbia) Glenn Ford, William Holden
One Sheet: $30 - $60

MAN FROM DAKOTA, THE
(1940 - MGM) Wallace Beery, Dolores Del Rio
One Sheet: $75 - $150

MAN FROM DEATH VALLEY, THE
(1931 - Monogram) Tom Tyler, John Oscar
One Sheet: $200 - $400

MAN FROM DEEP RIVER, THE
(1977 - -) Ivan Rassimov
One Sheet: $2 - $3

MAN FROM DEL RIO
(1956 - United Artists) Anthony Quinn, Katy Jurado
One Sheet: $15 - $25

MAN FROM DOWN UNDER, THE
(1943 - MGM) Charles Laughton, Donna Reed
One Sheet: $50 - $100

One Sheet

MAN FROM FRISCO, THE
(1944 - Republic) Michael O'Shea, Anne Shirley
One Sheet: $30 - $50

MAN FROM GALVESTON, THE
(1964 - Warner Bros.) Jeffrey Hunter, Preston Foster
One Sheet: $15 - $25

MAN FROM GOD'S COUNTRY
(1958 - Allied Artists) George Montgomery, Randy Stuart
One Sheet: $10 - $20

MAN FROM GUNTOWN, THE
(1935 - Puritan) Tim McCoy
One Sheet: $150 - $300

MAN FROM HEADQUARTERS
(1942 - Monogram) Frank Albertson, Joan Woodbury
One Sheet: $30 - $60

MAN FROM HELL'S EDGES, THE
(1932 - World-Wide) Bob Steele
One Sheet: $250 - $600

MAN FROM HELL'S RIVER, THE
(1922 - -) Wallace Beery, Irving Cummings, Rin Tin Tin (1st film)
One Sheet: $200 - $400

MAN FROM HONG KONG, THE
(1975 - 20th Century Fox) Jimmy Wang Yu, George Lazenby
One Sheet: $30 - $60   *AKA: THE DRAGON FLIES.*

MAN FROM LARAMIE, THE

(1955 - Columbia) James Stewart, Arthur Kennedy
One Sheet: $75 - $150   *Cowboy Movie Posters #300.*

MAN FROM LOST RIVER
(1921 - Goldwyn) Dir: Frank Lloyd
One Sheet: $200 - $400

MAN FROM MONTANA
(1941 - Universal) Johnny Mack Brown
One Sheet: $75 - $150

MAN FROM MONTEREY
(1933 - Vitagraph) John Wayne, Ruth Hall
One Sheet: $1,900 - $3,000   *Cowboy Movie Posters # 142.*

One Sheet

MAN FROM MONTEREY
(1943R - Warner Bros.) John Wayne, Ruth Hall
One Sheet: $250 - $500   *Re-release.*

MAN FROM MONTREAL
(1939 - Universal) Richard Arlen, Andy Devine
One Sheet: $50 - $100

MAN FROM MOROCCO
(1945 - United Artists) Anton Walbrook, Margaretta Scott
One Sheet: $30 - $50

MAN FROM MUSIC MOUNTAIN
(1938 - Republic) Gene Autry, Smiley Burnette
One Sheet: $250 - $600

MAN FROM MUSIC MOUNTAIN
(1943 - Republic) Roy Rogers, Ruth Terry
One Sheet: $150 - $300

MAN FROM MUSIC MOUNTAIN
(1944R - Republic) Gene Autry, Smiley Burnette
One Sheet: $75 - $150   *Re-release.*

MAN FROM NEW MEXICO, THE
(1932 - Monogram) Tom Tyler, Caryl Lincoln
One Sheet: $250 - $500   *Astor release poster: $150-$300*

One Sheet

MAN FROM NOWHERE, THE
(1930 - Syndicate) Bob Steele, Ione Reed
One Sheet: $125 - $250   *AKA: WESTERN HONOR.*

MAN FROM NOWHERE, THE
(1968 - G.G.P.) Giuliano Gemma, Corinee Marchand
One Sheet: $3 - $5

MAN FROM OKLAHOMA
(1945 - Republic) Roy Rogers, Gabby Hayes
One Sheet: $125 - $250

MAN FROM O.R.G.Y.

(1970 - Cinemation) Robert Walker, Steve
Rossi
One Sheet: $5 - $10

MAN FROM PLANET X, THE
(1951 - United Artists) Robert Clarke, Margaret
Field
One Sheet: $1,600 - $2,500   *Graven
Images, pg 154.*

Three Sheet

MAN FROM RAINBOW VALLEY
(1946 - Republic) Monte Hale, Adrian Booth
One Sheet: $50 - $100

MAN FROM SNOWY RIVER, THE
(1982 - 20th Century Fox) Kirk Douglas, Jack
Thompson
One Sheet: $15 - $25

MAN FROM SONORA
(1951 - Monogram) Johnny Mack Brown
One Sheet: $30 - $50

MAN FROM SUNDOWN, THE
(1939 - Columbia) Charles Starrett, Iris
Meredith
One Sheet: $75 - $150

MAN FROM SUNDOWN, THE
(1952R - Columbia) Charles Starett, Iris
Meredith
One Sheet: $30 - $50   *Re-release.*

MAN FROM TANGIER
(1957 - Republic) Robert Hutton, Lisa Gastoni
One Sheet: $5 - $10

MAN FROM TEXAS, THE
(1939 - Monogram) Tex Ritter
One Sheet: $100 - $200

MAN FROM TEXAS, THE
(1948 - Eagle-Lion) James Craig, Johnnie
Johnston
One Sheet: $30 - $50

MAN FROM THE ALAMO, THE
(1953 - Universal) Glenn Ford, Julie Adams
One Sheet: $40 - $75

MAN FROM THE DINER'S CLUB, THE
(1963 - Columbia) Danny Kaye, Cara Williams
One Sheet: $15 - $30

MAN FROM THE RIO GRANDE, THE
(1943 - Republic) Don Barry, Twinkle Watts
One Sheet: $30 - $60

MAN FROM THE WEST, THE
(1926 - Blue Streak Western (Universal)) Art
Acord
One Sheet: $250 - $600

MAN FROM THUNDER RIVER, THE
(1943 - Republic) Wild Bill Elliott, George
"Gabby" Hayes
One Sheet: $50 - $100

MAN FROM THUNDER RIVER, THE
(1952R - Republic) Wild Bill Elliott, George
"Gabby" Hayes
One Sheet: $10 - $20   *Re-release.*

MAN FROM TUMBLEWEED, THE
(1940 - Columbia) Bill Elliott, Iris Meredith
One Sheet: $75 - $150

MAN FROM UTAH, THE
(1934 - Monogram) John Wayne, Gabby Hayes
One Sheet: $1,300 - $2,000

MAN FROM UTAH, THE
(194?R - Lone Star) John Wayne, Gabby
Hayes

One Sheet: $75 - $150   *Re-release.*

MAN FROM WYOMING, A
(1930 - Paramount Publix) Gary Cooper, June
Collyer
One Sheet: $500 - $800

MAN FROM YESTERDAY, THE
(1932 - Paramount Publix) Charles Boyer,
Claudette Colbert, Clive Brook
One Sheet: $300 - $700

MAN HUNT
(1933 - King) Charlotte Henry, Junior Durkin
One Sheet: $100 - $200

MAN HUNT
(1936 - Warner Bros.) William Gargan,
Marguerite Chapman
One Sheet: $50 - $100

MAN HUNT
(1942 - 20th Century Fox) Walter Pidgeon,
Joan Bennett
One Sheet: $125 - $250

MAN HUNTER, THE
(1919 - Fox) William Farnum
One Sheet: $150 - $350

MAN HUNTER, THE
(1930 - Warner Bros.) John Loder, Nora Lane
One Sheet: $125 - $250

MAN I LOVE, THE
(1947 - Warner Bros.) Ida Lupino, Robert Alda
One Sheet: $40 - $75

MAN I MARRIED, THE
(1940 - 20th Century Fox) Joan Bennett,
Francis Lederer
One Sheet: $75 - $150

MAN I MARRY, THE
(1936 - Universal) Doris Nolan, Michael
Whalen
One Sheet: $100 - $200

MAN IN A COCKED HAT
(1960 - Lion International) Terry-Thomas, Peter
Sellers
One Sheet: $20 - $40

MAN IN BLUE, THE
(1937 - Universal) Robert Wilcox, Nan Grey
One Sheet: $75 - $150

MAN IN GREY, THE
(1945 - Universal) Margaret Lockwood, James
Mason
One Sheet: $50 - $100

MAN IN HALF MOON STREET, THE
(1944 - Paramount) Nils Asther, Helen Walker
One Sheet: $30 - $60

MAN IN HIDING
(1953 - Alexander Pool Films) Paul Henreid,
Lois Maxwell
One Sheet: $7 - $15

MAN IN LOVE, A
(1987 - Cinecom) Peter Coyote, Greta Scacchi
One Sheet: $3 - $5

MAN IN POSSESSION, THE
(1931 - MGM) Robert Montgomery, Charlotte
Greenwood
One Sheet: $100 - $200

MAN IN THE ATTIC
(1953 - 20th Century Fox) Jack Palance,
Constance Smith
One Sheet: $40 - $75

MAN IN THE DARK
(1953 - Columbia) Edmond O'Brien, Audrey
Totter
One Sheet: $15 - $30

MAN IN THE DARK
(1965 - Universal) William Sylvester, Barbara
Shelley
One Sheet: $3 - $5

MAN IN THE GRAY FLANNEL SUIT, THE
(1956 - 20th Century Fox) Gregory Peck,
Jennifer Jones, Fredric March
One Sheet: $40 - $75

MAN IN THE IRON MASK, THE
(1939 - United Artists) Louis Hayward, Joan
Bennett, Warren William
One Sheet: $250 - $500

MAN IN THE MIDDLE
(1964 - 20th Century Fox) Robert Mitchum,
France Nuyen
One Sheet: $15 - $30

MAN IN THE MIRROR, THE
(1937 - Grand National) Edward E. Horton,
Genevieve Tobin
One Sheet: $50 - $100

MAN IN THE MOON
(1961 - Trans-Lux) Kenneth More, Shirley Ann
Field
One Sheet: $15 - $30

MAN IN THE NET, THE
(1959 - United Artists) Alan Ladd, Carolyn
Jones
One Sheet: $30 - $50

MAN IN THE RAINCOAT, THE
(1957 - -) Fernandel, John McGiver
One Sheet: $15 - $25

MAN IN THE ROAD, THE
(1957 - Republic) Derek Farr, Ella Raines
One Sheet: $5 - $10

MAN IN THE SADDLE
(1951 - Columbia) Randolph Scott, Joan Leslie
One Sheet: $15 - $25

MAN IN THE SADDLE
(1959R - Columbia) Randolph Scott, Joan
Leslie
One Sheet: $15 - $25   *Re-release.*

MAN IN THE SHADOW
(1957 - Universal) Jeff Chandler, Orson Welles
One Sheet: $30 - $50

Insert

MAN IN THE TRUNK, THE
(1942 - 20th Century Fox) Raymond Walburn,
Lynne Roberts
One Sheet: $50 - $100

MAN IN THE VAULT
(1955 - RKO) Anita Ekberg, William Campbell
One Sheet: $15 - $25

MAN IN THE WHITE SUIT, THE
(1951 - Universal) Alec Guinness, Joan
Greenwood
One Sheet: $20 - $40

MAN IN THE WILDERNESS
(1971 - Warner Bros.) Richard Harris, John
Bindon
One Sheet: $5 - $10

MAN INSIDE, THE
(1958 - Columbia) Jack Palance, Anita Ekberg
One Sheet: $15 - $25

MAN IS ARMED, THE
(1956 - Republic) Dane Clark, William Talman,
May Wynn
One Sheet: $10 - $20

MAN IS TEN FEET TALL, A
(1956 - MGM) John Cassavetes, Sidney Poitier
One Sheet: $40 - $75   *AKA: Edge Of
The City.*

MAN KILLER
(1933 - Warner Bros.) William Powell, Margaret
Lindsay
One Sheet: $250 - $500   *AKA:
PRIVATE DETECTIVE 62.*

MAN MADE MONSTER
(1941 - Universal) Lionel Atwill, Lon Chaney Jr.
One Sheet: $250 - $600   *Graven*

Images, pg. 114.

MAN OF A THOUSAND FACES
(1957 - Universal) James Cagney, Dorothy
Malone
One Sheet: $50 - $100

MAN OF ACTION
(1933 - Columbia) Tim McCoy
One Sheet: $500 - $800   *Cowboy
Movie Posters # 147.*

MAN OF AFFAIRS
(1936 - Gaumont) George Arliss, Rene Ray,
John Ford
One Sheet: $150 - $300

MAN OF AFRICA
(1956 - Group 3/Eden) Violet Mukabuerza,
Frederick Bijuerenda
One Sheet: $10 - $20

MAN OF ARAN
(1934 - Gaumont) Tiger King (Documentary),
Dir: Robert Flaherty
One Sheet: $150 - $300

MAN OF CONFLICT
(1953 - Atlas) Edward Arnold, John Agar
One Sheet: $15 - $25

MAN OF CONQUEST
(1939 - Republic) Richard Dix, Gail Patrick
One Sheet: $100 - $200

MAN OF COURAGE
(1943 - PRC) Barton MacLane, Charlotte
Wynters
One Sheet: $30 - $50

MAN OF EVIL
(1944 - United Artists) Phyllis Calvert, James
Mason, Stewart Granger
One Sheet: $40 - $75

MAN OF IRON
(1935 - Warner Bros.) Barton MacLane, Mary
Astor
One Sheet: $125 - $250

MAN OF LA MANCHA
(1972 - United Artists) Sophia Loren, Peter
O'Toole
One Sheet: $7 - $15

MAN OF SENTIMENT, A
(1933 - Chesterfield) Marian Marsh, Owen
Moore
One Sheet: $100 - $200

MAN OF THE EAST
(1974 - United Artists) Gregory Walcott, Harry
Carey
One Sheet: $5 - $10

MAN OF THE FOREST
(1926 - Paramount) Jack Holt, Georgia Hale,
Warner Oland
One Sheet: $150 - $300

MAN OF THE FOREST
(1933 - Paramount) Randolph Scott, Harry
Carey
One Sheet: $250 - $600

MAN OF THE HOUSE
(1996 - Buena Vista/Disney) Chevy Chase,
Jonathan Taylor Thomas, Farrah Fawcett
One Sheet: $3 - $5

MAN OF THE MOMENT
(1955 - General) Norman Wisdom, Lana Morris
One Sheet: $10 - $20

MAN OF THE PEOPLE
(1937 - MGM) Joseph Calleia, Florence Rice
One Sheet: $75 - $150

MAN OF THE WEST
(1958 - United Artists) Gary Cooper, Julie
London
One Sheet: $40 - $75   *Cowboy
Movie Posters #307.*

MAN OF THE WORLD
(1931 - Paramount) William Powell, Carole
Lombard, Wynne Gibson
One Sheet: $1,300 - $2,000

MAN OF THE YEAR
(1973 - Universal) Rossana Podesta, Lando
Buzzanca
One Sheet: $3 - $5

MAN OF TWO WORLDS
(1934 - RKO) Francis Lederer, Elissa Landi
One Sheet: $150 - $300

MAN ON A STRING
(1960 - Columbia) Ernest Borgnine, Kerwin
Matthews
One Sheet: $15 - $25

MAN ON A TIGHTROPE
(1953 - 20th Century Fox) Fredric March,
Gloria Grahame, Terry Moore
One Sheet: $40 - $75

MAN ON FIRE
(1957 - MGM) Bing Crosby, Inger Stevens
One Sheet: $15 - $25

MAN ON FIRE
(1987 - -) Scot Glen, Jade Malle, Brooke
Adams
One Sheet: $2 - $3

MAN ON THE EIFFEL TOWER, THE
(1949 - RKO) Charles Laughton, Franchot Tone
One Sheet: $40 - $75

MAN ON THE FLYING TRAPEZE, THE
(1935 - Paramount) W.C. Fields, Mary Brian
One Sheet: $1,900 - $3,000

MAN ON THE FLYING TRAPEZE, THE
(1954 - Columbia) -
One Sheet: $200 - $400   *Cartoon.*
Duotone. Cartoon Movie Posters #46.

MAN ON THE PROWL
(1957 - Stratford) Mala Powers, James Best
One Sheet: $20 - $40

MAN ON THE RUN
(1950 - Stratford) Derek Farr, Joan Hopkins
One Sheet: $15 - $25

MAN OR GUN
(1958 - Republic) Macdonald Carey, Audrey
Totter
One Sheet: $15 - $30

MAN OUTSIDE, THE
(1969 - Allied Artists) Van Heflin, Heidelinde
Weis, Pinkas Braun
One Sheet: $7 - $15

MAN POWER
(1927 - Paramount) Richard Dix, Mary Brian
One Sheet: $200 - $400

MAN RUSTLIN'
(1926 - F.B.O.) Bob Custer
One Sheet: $250 - $600

MAN THEY COULD NOT HANG, THE
(1939 - Columbia) Boris Karloff, Lorna Gray
One Sheet: $800 - $1,500   *Graven*
Images, pg. 87.

MAN THEY COULD NOT HANG, THE
(1946R - Favorite) Boris Karloff, Lorna Gray
One Sheet: $250 - $500   *Re-release.*

MAN TO MAN
(1930 - Warner Bros.) Lucille Powers, Grant
Mitchell
One Sheet: $100 - $200

MAN TO MAN
(1937 - RKO) -
One Sheet: $50 - $100

MAN TO MAN
(1937 - 20th Century Fox) Iris Adrian, George
Shelton
One Sheet: $50 - $100   *Lobby Card*
set is duotone.

MAN TO REMEMBER, A
(1938 - RKO) Edward Ellis, Anne Shirley
One Sheet: $75 - $150

MAN TRAILER, THE
(1934 - Columbia) Buck Jones
One Sheet: $250 - $600

MAN TROUBLE
(1930 - Fox) Milton Sills, Dorothy Mackaill
One Sheet: $125 - $250

MAN TROUBLE
(1992 - 20th Century Fox) Jack Nicholson,
Ellen Barkin
One Sheet: $5 - $10

MAN UPSTAIRS, THE

(1959 - Lion International) Richard
Attenborough, Bernard Lee
One Sheet: $15 - $25

MAN WANTED
(1932 - Warner Bros.) Kay Francis, Guy Kibbee
One Sheet: $100 - $200

**MAN WHO BROKE THE BANK AT MONTE
CARLO, THE**
(1935 - 20th Century Fox) Ronald Colman,
Joan Bennett
One Sheet: $800 - $1,500

MAN WHO CAME BACK, THE
(1930 - Fox) Janet Gaynor
One Sheet: $125 - $250

MAN WHO CAME TO DINNER, THE
(1942 - Warner Bros.) Monty Woolley, Bette
Davis, Ann Sheridan
One Sheet: $125 - $250

MAN WHO CHEATED HIMSELF, THE
(1950 - 20th Century Fox) Lee J. Cobb, Jane
Wyatt
One Sheet: $30 - $50

MAN WHO COULD CHEAT DEATH, THE
(1959 - Paramount) Anton Diffring, Christopher
Lee
One Sheet: $30 - $50

MAN WHO COULD WORK MIRACLES, THE
(1937 - United Artists) Roland Young, Joan
Gardner
One Sheet: $500 - $800   *Graven*
Images, pg. 96.

MAN WHO COULD WORK MIRACLES, THE
(1953R - Film Classics) Roland Young, Joan
Gardner
One Sheet: $100 - $200   *Re-release.*

MAN WHO COULDN'T WALK
(1964 - Falcon) Eric Pohlman, Peter Reynolds
One Sheet: $3 - $5

MAN WHO CRIED WOLF, THE
(1937 - Universal) Lewis Stone, Tom Brown
One Sheet: $50 - $100

MAN WHO DARED, THE
(1933 - Fox) Preston Foster, Zita Johann
One Sheet: $125 - $250

MAN WHO DARED, THE
(1939 - Warner Bros.) Charles Grapewin, Jane
Bryan
One Sheet: $40 - $75

MAN WHO DARED, THE
(1946 - Columbia) Forrest Tucker, George
Macready, Leslie Brooks
One Sheet: $30 - $50

MAN WHO DIED TWICE, THE
(1958 - Republic) Rod Cameron, Vera Ralston
One Sheet: $15 - $30

MAN WHO FELL TO EARTH, THE
(1976 - British Lion) David Bowie, Rip Torn
One Sheet: $30 - $50   *Price is for*
style B one sheet. One Sheet (Style A):$50-$100.

MAN WHO FIGHTS ALONE, THE
(1924 - Paramount) William Farnum, Lois
Wilson, Edward Everett Horton
One Sheet: $250 - $500

MAN WHO FOUND HIMSELF, THE
(1937 - RKO) John Beal, Joan Fontaine
One Sheet: $75 - $150

MAN WHO HAD POWER OVER WOMEN, THE
(1970 - Avco/Embassy) Rod Taylor, Carol
White
One Sheet: $10 - $20

MAN WHO KNEW TOO MUCH, THE
(1934 - Gaumont-British) Leslie Banks, Edna
Best, Peter Lorre, Dir: Alfred Hitchcock
One Sheet: $5,000 - $7,500

MAN WHO KNEW TOO MUCH, THE
(1956 - Paramount) James Stewart, Doris Day,
Dir: Alfred Hitchcock
One Sheet: $150 - $350

MAN WHO KNEW TOO MUCH, THE
(1963R - Paramount) James Stewart, Doris
Day, Dir: Alfred Hitchcock
One Sheet: $30 - $50   *Re-release.*

MAN WHO KNEW TOO MUCH, THE
(1983R - Universal) James Stewart, Doris Day,
Dir: Alfred Hitchcock
One Sheet: $15 - $25   *Re-release.*
Full-length sideview of Hitchcock standing.

**MAN WHO KNEW TOO MUCH/TROUBLE
WITH HARRY**
(1963R - Paramount) James Stewart, Doris
Day/John Forsythe, Edmund Gwenn
One Sheet: $30 - $60   *Re-release*
double feature poster.

MAN WHO LAUGHS, THE
(1927 - Universal) Conrad Veidt, Mary Philbin
One Sheet: $3,500 - $5,000   *Graven*
Images, pg. 37.

MAN WHO LIVED AGAIN, THE
(1936 - Gaumont) Boris Karloff, Anna Lee
One Sheet: $250 - $500   *Graven*
Images, pg. 87.

MAN WHO LIVED TWICE, THE
(1936 - Columbia) Ralph Bellamy, Marian
Marsh
One Sheet: $100 - $200

MAN WHO LOST HIMSELF, THE
(1941 - Universal) Brian Aherne, Kay Francis
One Sheet: $75 - $150

MAN WHO LOVED CAT DANCING, THE
(1973 - MGM) Burt Reynolds, Sarah Miles
One Sheet: $15 - $25

MAN WHO LOVED REDHEADS, THE
(1955 - United Artists) Moira Shearer, John
Justin
One Sheet: $20 - $40

MAN WHO LOVED WOMEN, THE
(1977 - United Artists) Leslie Caron, Charles
Denner
One Sheet: $30 - $50   *French.*

MAN WHO MARRIED HIS OWN WIFE
(1922 - Universal) Frank Mayo
One Sheet: $200 - $400

MAN WHO NEVER WAS, THE
(1955 - 20th Century Fox) Clifton Webb, Gloria
Grahame
One Sheet: $20 - $40

MAN WHO PLAYED GOD, THE
(1932 - Warner Bros.) George Arliss, Violet
Heming, Bette Davis
One Sheet: $500 - $800

MAN WHO RECLAIMED HIS HEAD, THE
(1934 - Universal) Claude Rains, Joan Bennett,
Lionel Atwill
One Sheet: $1,300 - $2,000

MAN WHO RETURNED TO LIFE, THE
(1942 - Columbia) John Howard, Ruth Ford
One Sheet: $75 - $150

MAN WHO SAW TOMORROW, THE
(1980 - -) Narrated by Orson Welles
One Sheet: $5 - $10   *Documentary.*

MAN WHO SHOT LIBERTY VALANCE, THE
(1962 - Paramount) James Stewart, John
Wayne, Dir: John Ford
One Sheet: $150 - $350   *Cowboy*
Movie Posters #313.

One Sheet

MAN WHO TALKED TOO MUCH, THE
(1940 - Warner Bros.) George Brent, Virginia
Bruce
One Sheet: $50 - $100

MAN WHO TURNED TO STONE, THE
(1957 - Columbia) Victor Jory, Ann Doran
One Sheet: $15 - $35

MAN WHO UNDERSTOOD WOMEN, THE
(1959 - 20th Century Fox) Leslie Caron, Henry
Fonda
One Sheet: $15 - $30

MAN WHO WAITED, THE
(1928 - Playgoers) -
One Sheet: $125 - $275

MAN WHO WALKED ALONE, THE
(1945 - PRC) Kay Aldrich, Dave O'Brien
One Sheet: $30 - $50

MAN WHO WAS AFRAID, THE
(1917 - Essanay) Bryant Washburn, Ernest
Maupian
One Sheet: $250 - $500

MAN WHO WON, THE
(1923 - Fox) Dustin Farnum
One Sheet: $350 - $750

MAN WHO WOULD BE KING, THE
(1975 - Allied Artists) Sean Connery, Michael
Caine, Dir:John Huston
One Sheet: $30 - $50

MAN WHO WOULDN'T DIE, THE
(1942 - 20th Century Fox) Lloyd Nolan,
Marjorie Weaver
One Sheet: $75 - $125

MAN WHO WOULDN'T TALK, THE
(1940 - 20th Century Fox) Lloyd Nolan, Jean
Rogers
One Sheet: $50 - $100

MAN WHO WOULDN'T TALK, THE
(1958 - Wilcox) Anna Neagle, Anthony Quayle,
Zsa Zsa Gabor
One Sheet: $15 - $30

MAN WITH 100 FACES
(1938 - Gaumont) Lilli Palmer, Noel Madison
One Sheet: $50 - $100

MAN WITH A CLOAK, THE
(1951 - MGM) Joseph Cotten, Barbara
Stanwyck
One Sheet: $40 - $75

MAN WITH A MILLION
(1954 - United Artists) Gregory Peck, Jane
Griffith
One Sheet: $20 - $40

MAN WITH MY FACE, THE
(1951 - United Artists) Carole Mathews, Barry
Nelson
One Sheet: $15 - $30

MAN WITH NINE LIVES, THE
(1940 - Columbia) Boris Karloff, Roger Pryor
One Sheet: $350 - $750   *Graven*
Images, pg. 130.

MAN WITH ONE RED SHOE, THE
(1985 - -) Tom Hanks, Lori Singer, Dabney
Coleman
One Sheet: $3 - $5

MAN WITH THE GOLDEN ARM, THE
(1955 - United Artists) Frank Sinatra, Kim
Novak
One Sheet: $150 - $300   *Saul Bass art.*

MAN WITH THE GOLDEN GUN, THE
(1974 - United Artists) Roger Moore,
Christopher Lee
One Sheet: $100 - $200   *Style B:$150-*
$300. Advance:$150-$250.

One Sheet

MAN WITH THE GUN
(1955 - United Artists) Robert Mitchum, Jan Sterling
One Sheet: $50 - $100

MAN WITH THE STEEL WHIP
(1954 - Republic) Richard Simmons, Barbara Bestar
One Sheet: $30 - $50 *Serial. Western. 12 Chapters.*

MAN WITH TWO BRAINS, THE
(1983 - -) Steve Martin, Kathleen Turner
One Sheet: $5 - $10

MAN WITH TWO FACES, THE
(1934 - First National) Edward G. Robinson, Mary Astor
One Sheet: $125 - $250

MAN WITH TWO LIVES
(1942 - Monogram) Edward Norris, Eleanor Lawson
One Sheet: $40 - $75

MAN WITHIN, THE
(1916 - Fox) Tom Mix
One Sheet: $500 - $800

MAN WITHIN, THE
(1948 - Eagle-Lion) Micheal Redgrave, Jean Kent
One Sheet: $15 - $30 *Re-title of: THE SMUGGLERS.*

One Sheet

MAN WITHOUT A FACE, THE
(1993 - Warner Bros.) Mel Gibson (Dir.), Nick Stahl
One Sheet: $5 - $10

MAN WITHOUT A STAR
(1955 - Universal) Kirk Douglas, Jeanne Crain
One Sheet: $100 - $200

MAN, WOMAN AND CHILD
(1983 - Paramount) Martin Sheen, Blythe Danner, Craig T. Nelson
One Sheet: $5 - $10

MAN, WOMAN AND WIFE
(1929 - Universal) Norman Kerry, Pauline Starke
One Sheet: $250 - $600

MAN'S BEST FRIEND
(1945 - Paramount) Little Lulu
One Sheet: $250 - $600 *Cartoon. See Little Lulu Stock Poster listing. Cartoon Movie Posters #228.*

MAN'S BEST FRIEND
(1993 - New Line) Ally Sheedy
One Sheet: $3 - $5

MAN'S CASTLE
(1933 - Columbia) Spencer Tracy, Loretta Young
One Sheet: $250 - $500

MAN'S COUNTRY
(1938 - Monogram) Jack Randall
One Sheet: $75 - $150

MAN'S DESIRE
(1919 - Exhibitors Mutual) Lewis S. Stone
One Sheet: $150 - $300

MAN'S FAVORITE SPORT?
(1964 - Universal) Rock Hudson, Paula Prentiss
One Sheet: $30 - $50

MAN'S GAME, A

(1934 - Columbia) Tim McCoy, Evalyn Knapp
One Sheet: $250 - $500

MAN'S GENESIS
(1912 - AB) See "History Of Posters...", pg. 12
One Sheet: $800 - $1,500

MAN'S MATE, A
(1924 - William Fox) John Gilbert
One Sheet: $350 - $750

MAN'S SIZE
(1923 - Fox) William Russell, Alma Bennett
One Sheet: $125 - $250

MAN'S WORLD, A
(1942 - Columbia) Marguerite Chapman, William Wright
One Sheet: $20 - $40

MANCHURIAN CANDIDATE, THE
(1962 - United Artists) Frank Sinatra, Laurence Harvey
One Sheet: $75 - $150 *Graven Images, pg. 225.*

MANCHURIAN CANDIDATE, THE
(1988R - United Artists) Frank Sinatra, Laurence Harvey
One Sheet: $20 - $40 *Re-release.*

MANDALAY
(1934 - First National) Kay Francis, Lyle Talbot
One Sheet: $500 - $800

MANDARIN MIXUP, A
(1924 - Selznick) Stan Laurel
One Sheet: $600 - $1,000

MANDARIN MYSTERY, THE
(1936 - Republic) Eddie Quillan, Charlotte Henry
One Sheet: $75 - $150

MANDINGO
(1975 - Paramount) James Mason, Ken Norton, Susan George
One Sheet: $10 - $20

Half Sheet

MANDRAKE THE MAGICIAN
(1939 - Columbia) Warren Hull, Doris Weston
One Sheet: $800 - $1,500 *Serial. Magic. 12 Chapters.*

MAN-EATER OF KUMAON
(1948 - Universal) Sabu, Wendell Corey, Joanne Page
One Sheet: $30 - $60

MANFISH
(1956 - United Artists) John Bromfield, Victor Jory
One Sheet: $15 - $35

MANGLER, THE
(1995 - New Line) Robert Englund, Ted Levine
One Sheet: $3 - $5

MANHANDLED
(1924 - Famous Players-Lasky) Gloria Swanson, Tom Moore
One Sheet: $700 - $1,200

MANHANDLED
(1949 - Paramount) Dorothy Lamour, Dan Duryea
One Sheet: $75 - $150

MANHATTAN
(1924 - Paramount) Richard Dix, Jacqueline Logan
One Sheet: $500 - $800

MANHATTAN

(1979 - United Artists) Woody Allen, Diane Keaton
One Sheet: $50 - $100 *Price is for "park bench" style one sheet. One Sheet(Style A):$20-30.*

MANHATTAN ANGEL
(1948 - Columbia) Gloria Jean, Ross Ford
One Sheet: $30 - $50

MANHATTAN COCKTAIL
(1928 - Paramount) Nancy Carroll, Richard Arlen
One Sheet: $900 - $1,600

MANHATTAN HEARTBEAT
(1940 - 20th Century Fox) Virginia Gilmore, Joan Davis, Robert Sterling
One Sheet: $75 - $150

MANHATTAN LOVE SONG
(1934 - Monogram) Dixie Lee, Robert Armstrong
One Sheet: $150 - $300

MANHATTAN MADNESS
(1916 - Triangle) Douglas Fairbanks
One Sheet: $800 - $1,500

MANHATTAN MELODRAMA
(1934 - MGM) Clark Gable, William Powell, Myrna Loy
One Sheet: $1,600 - $2,500 *Historical note: Film Dillinger was watching when cornered and shot.*

MANHATTAN MERRY-GO-ROUND
(1937 - Republic) Phil Regan, Ann Dvorak, Cab Calloway, Joe DiMaggio
One Sheet: $250 - $500 *Sports Movie Posters #370.*

MANHATTAN MOON
(1935 - Universal) Ricardo Cortez, Dorothy Page
One Sheet: $200 - $400

MANHATTAN MURDER MYSTERY
(1993 - TriStar) Woody Allen (Dir.) Diane Keaton
One Sheet: $7 - $15

MANHATTAN PARADE
(1932 - Warner Bros.) Winnie Lightner, Charles Butterworth
One Sheet: $150 - $300

MANHATTAN PROJECT, THE
(1986 - -) John Lithgow, Cynthia Nixon, Christopher Collet
One Sheet: $5 - $10

MANHATTAN SHAKEDOWN
(1939 - Warwick) John Gallaudet, Rosalind Keith
One Sheet: $75 - $150

MANHATTAN TOWER
(1932 - Remington) Mary Brian
One Sheet: $200 - $400

MANHUNT IN THE AFRICAN JUNGLE
(1954R - Republic) Rod Cameron, Joan Marsh
One Sheet: $20 - $40 *Serial. Re-titled re-release of "Secret Service In Darkest Africa". 10 Chapters.*

MANHUNT IN THE JUNGLE
(1958 - Warner Bros.) Robin Hughes, Luis Alvarez
One Sheet: $15 - $25

MANHUNT OF MYSTERY ISLAND
(1945 - Republic) Richard Bailey, Linda Stirling
One Sheet: $75 - $150 *Serial. 15 Chapters.*

MANHUNT OF MYSTERY ISLAND
(1956R - Republic) Richard Bailey, Linda Stirling
One Sheet: $40 - $75 *Re-release. Serial.*

MANHUNTER
(1983 - -) Earl Owensby, Elizabeth Upton
One Sheet: $3 - $5 *AKA: The Brass Ring.*

MANHUNTER
(1986 - -) William L. Peterson, Kim Greist
One Sheet: $10 - $20 *First in "Hannibal Lector" series.*

MANIA

(1961 - Triad) Peter Cushing, Donald Pleasence
One Sheet: $15 - $25 *AKA: PSYCHO KILLERS*

MANIAC
(1934 - Roadshow Attractions) Bill Woods, Ted Edwards
One Sheet: $200 - $400 *Graven Images, pg. 64.*

MANIAC
(1963 - Columbia) Kerwin Mathews, Nadia Gray
One Sheet: $15 - $25

MANIAC
(1980 - Analysis) Joe Spinell, Caroline Munro
One Sheet: $5 - $10

MANIAC COP
(1988 - -) Tom Atkins, Bruce Campbell
One Sheet: $4 - $8

MANIACS ON WHEELS
(1951 - Rank) Dirk Bogarde, Bonar Colleano
One Sheet: $30 - $60 *Motorbike racing.*

MANICURE GIRL, THE
(1925 - Paramount) Bebe Daniels, Edmund Burns
One Sheet: $250 - $500

One Sheet

MANILA CALLING
(1942 - 20th Century Fox) Lloyd Nolan, Carole Landis
One Sheet: $75 - $150

MANITOU, THE
(1978 - Avco/Embassy) Tony Curtis, Stella Stevens
One Sheet: $5 - $10

MANNEN MED JARHANDEN
(1932 - Pittaluga) Charlotte Susa
One Sheet: $200 - $400 *Swedish. U.S. title: THE MAN WITH THE IRON HAND.*

MANNEQUIN
(1938 - MGM) Joan Crawford, Spencer Tracy, Ralph Morgan
One Sheet: $250 - $500

MANNEQUIN
(1986 - 20th Century Fox) Andrew McCarthy, Kim Cattrall
One Sheet: $3 - $5

MANNEQUIN TWO ON THE MOVE
(1991 - -) Meshach Taylor
One Sheet: $5 - $10

MANPOWER
(1941 - Warner Bros.) Edward G. Robinson, Marlene Dietrich, George Raft
One Sheet: $125 - $250

MAN-PROOF
(1937 - MGM) Myrna Loy, Franchot Tone, Rosalind Russell
One Sheet: $150 - $350

MANSION OF THE DOOMED
(1976 - Group 1) Gloria Grahame, Richard Basehart
One Sheet: $10 - $20 *AKA: THE TERROR OF DR. CHANEY.*

MAN-SIZED PET
(1926 - W.C. Tuttle)
One Sheet: $150 - $300

MANSLAUGHTER

(1922 - Paramount) Thomas Meighan, Leatrice Joy
One Sheet: $600 - $1,000

MANSLAUGHTER
(1930 - Paramount Publix) Fredric March, Claudette Colbert
One Sheet: $600 - $1,000

MANSTER, THE
(1962 - United Artists) Peter Dyneley, Jane Hylton
One Sheet: $30 - $50   *Double-billed w/ Horror of Dr. Faustus.*

MANTAN MESSES UP
(1947 - Toddy) Mantan Moreland
One Sheet: $125 - $250   *Black cast. Stock poster. Beware 1960s re-release (black & white).*

One Sheet

MANTRAP
(1926 - Paramount) Clara Bow, Ernest Torrence
One Sheet: $500 - $800

MANTRAP, THE
(1943 - Republic) Lloyd Corrigan, Dorothy Lovett
One Sheet: $40 - $75

MANTRAP
(1961 - Paramount) Jeffrey Hunter, David Janssen
One Sheet: $5 - $10

MANXMAN
(1929 - British International) Carl Brisson, Anny Ondra, Dir: Alfred Hitchcock
One Sheet: $2,500 - $4,000   *Hitchcock's last silent film.*

MANY A SLIP
(1931 - Universal) Joan Bennett, Lew Ayers
One Sheet: $200 - $400

MANY ADVENTURES OF WINNIE THE POOH, THE
(1977R - Disney) Winnie The Pooh
One Sheet: $15 - $25   *Re-release. Cartoon.*

MANY HAPPY RETURNS
(1934 - Paramount) George Burns, Gracie Allen
One Sheet: $200 - $400

MANY RIVERS TO CROSS
(1955 - MGM) Robert Taylor, Eleanor Parker
One Sheet: $20 - $40

MAP OF THE HUMAN HEART
(1993 - Miramax) Jason Scott Lee, Anne Parillaud
One Sheet: $3 - $5

MARA OF THE WILDERNESS
(1965 - Allied Artists) Adam West, Linda Saunders
One Sheet: $5 - $10

MARACAIBO
(1958 - Paramount) Cornel Wilde, Jean Wallace
One Sheet: $20 - $40

MARA-MARU
(1952 - Warner Bros.) Errol Flynn, Raymond Burr, Ruth Roman
One Sheet: $50 - $100

MARAT/SADE
(1967 - United Artists) Royal Shakespeare Company, Glenda Jackson (debut)

One Sheet: $10 - $20

MARATHON MAN
(1976 - Paramount) Dustin Hoffman, Laurence Olivier
One Sheet: $20 - $40

MARAUDERS, THE
(1947 - United Artists) William Boyd, Andy Clyde
One Sheet: $50 - $100

MARAUDERS, THE
(1955 - MGM) Dan Duryea, Keenan Wynn
One Sheet: $15 - $25

MARCH OF CRIME, THE
(1936 - Road Show Attractions) Narrated by Wedgewood Nowell
One Sheet: $75 - $150

MARCH OF THE WOODEN SOLDIERS
(1950R - Film Classics) Laurel & Hardy
One Sheet: $100 - $200   *Re-titled, Re-release of BABES IN TOYLAND.*

MARCH OF TIME NEWSREEL - CRISIS IN THE ATLANTIC
(1943 - RKO) -
One Sheet: $75 - $150

MARCH OF TIME NEWSREEL - POST WAR FARMS
(1944 - 20th Century Fox) -
One Sheet: $75 - $150

MARCHING ON!
(1943 - Sack) Dir: Spencer Williams
One Sheet: $200 - $400   *Black cast. Separate Cinema, pg. 22.*

MARCIANO VS. MOORE
(1955 - Winik) Rocky Marciano, Archie Moore
One Sheet: $125 - $250   *Sports (Boxing). From the Famous Fights series.*

MARCO
(1973 - Cinerama) Desi Arnaz, Jr., Zero Mostel
One Sheet: $5 - $10

MARCO POLO
(1962 - AIP) Rory Calhoun, Yoko Tani
One Sheet: $15 - $25

MARCO THE MAGNIFICENT!
(1966 - MGM) Horst Buchholz, Anthony Quinn
One Sheet: $15 - $25

MARDI GRAS
(1958 - 20th Century Fox) Pat Boone, Tommy Sands, Sheree North
One Sheet: $30 - $50

MARE NOSTRUM
(1926 - MGM) Alice Terry, Antonio Moreno
One Sheet: $150 - $300

MARGIE
(1940 - Universal) Tom Brown, Nan Grey, Mischa Auer
One Sheet: $75 - $125

MARGIE
(1946 - 20th Century Fox) Jeanne Crain, Glenn Langan
One Sheet: $40 - $75

MARGIN FOR ERROR
(1943 - 20th Century Fox) Joan Bennett, Milton Berle, Otto Preminger
One Sheet: $50 - $100

MARIANNE
(1929 - MGM) Marion Davies (her 1st talkie), George Baxter
One Sheet: $350 - $750

MARIE
(1985 - MGM/UA) Sissy Spacek, Fred Thompson, Morgan Freeman
One Sheet: $3 - $5

MARIE ANTOINETTE
(1938 - MGM) Norma Shearer, Tyrone Power
One Sheet: $800 - $1,500

MARIE GALANTE
(1934 - Fox) Spencer Tracy
One Sheet: $200 - $400

MARIHUANA
(1936 - Road Show Attractions) Harley Wood, Pat Carlyle
One Sheet: $250 - $500   *Drug*

exploitation. Similar to "Reefer Madness".

MARILYN
(1963 - 20th Century Fox) Narrated by Rock Hudson
One Sheet: $100 - $200   *Documentary.*

MARILYN AND THE SENATOR
(196? - -) -
One Sheet: $10 - $20   *Exploitation.*

MARINE RAIDERS
(1944 - RKO) Pat O'Brien, Ruth Hussey
One Sheet: $50 - $100

MARINE RAIDERS
(1950R - RKO) Pat O'Brien, Ruth Hussey
One Sheet: $15 - $25   *Re-release.*

MARINES ARE COMING, THE
(1934 - Mascot) Conrad Nagel, William Haines, Esther Ralston
One Sheet: $125 - $250

MARINES ARE HERE, THE
(1938 - Monogram) June Travis, Gordon Oliver
One Sheet: $100 - $200

MARINES FLY HIGH, THE
(1940 - RKO) Richard Dix, Chester Morris, Lucille Ball
One Sheet: $100 - $200

MARINES, LET'S GO
(1961 - 20th Century Fox) Tom Tryon, David Hedison
One Sheet: $15 - $25

MARIUS
(1931 - Paramount) Jules Raimu, Pierre Fresnay
One Sheet: $150 - $300

MARIUS/FANNY/CESAR
(19?? - -) -
One Sheet: $10 - $20   *Re-release triple feature poster.*

MARJOE
(1972 - -) Marjoe Gortner (Documentary)
One Sheet: $3 - $5

MARJORIE MORNINGSTAR
(1958 - Warner Bros.) Gene Kelly, Natalie Wood
One Sheet: $15 - $30

MARK, THE
(1961 - Continental) Maria Schell, Stuart Whitman
One Sheet: $7 - $15

MARK OF CAIN, THE
(1948 - Rank) Sally Gray, Eric Portman
One Sheet: $40 - $75

MARK OF THE DEVIL
(1970 - Hallmark) Herbert Lom, Udo Kier
One Sheet: $10 - $20   *AKA: BURN, WITCH, BURN.*

MARK OF THE DEVIL II
(1975 - Hallmark) Erica Blanc
One Sheet: $7 - $15

MARK OF THE GORILLA
(1950 - Columbia) Johnny Weissmuller, Trudy Marshall
One Sheet: $40 - $75

MARK OF THE HAWK, THE
(1958 - Universal) Sidney Poitier, Juano Hernandez, Eartha Kitt
One Sheet: $30 - $50   *Black cast. Separate Cinema, pg. 127.*

MARK OF THE LASH
(1948 - PRC) Lash LaRue, Fuzzy St. John
One Sheet: $40 - $75

MARK OF THE RENEGADE
(1951 - Universal) Ricardo Montalban, Cyd Charisse
One Sheet: $20 - $40

MARK OF THE VAMPIRE
(1935 - MGM) Lionel Barrymore, Bela Lugosi, Dir: Tod Browning
One Sheet: $13,000 - $20,000   *Graven Images, pg. 93. Remake of "London After Midnight".*

MARK OF THE WHISTLER, THE
(1944 - Columbia) Richard Dix, Janis Carter

One Sheet: $50 - $100

MARK OF THE WITCH
(1970 - Presidio) Robert Elston, Anitra Walsh
One Sheet: $15 - $25

MARK OF ZORRO, THE
(1920 - United Artists) Douglas Fairbanks, Sr., Noah Beery
One Sheet: $4,000 - $6,000   *Cowboy Movie Posters #25.*

MARK OF ZORRO, THE
(1940 - 20th Century Fox) Tyrone Power, Linda Darnell
One Sheet: $5,500 - $9,000   *Cowboy Movie Posters #s 262, 263.*

One Sheet

MARK OF ZORRO, THE
(1946R - 20th Century Fox) Tyrone Power, Linda Darnell
One Sheet: $250 - $500   *Re-release.*

MARK OF ZORRO, THE
(1958R - 20th Century Fox) Tyrone Power, Linda Darnell
One Sheet: $100 - $200   *Re-release.*

MARKED FOR DEATH
(1990 - -) Steve Segal, Basil Wallace
One Sheet: $7 - $15

MARKED FOR MURDER
(1944 - PRC) Tex Ritter, Dave O'Brien
One Sheet: $30 - $50

MARKED MEN
(1940 - PRC) Warren Hull, Isabel Jewell
One Sheet: $30 - $50

MARKED TRAILS
(1944 - Monogram) Hoot Gibson, Veda Ann Borg
One Sheet: $50 - $100

MARKED WOMAN
(1937 - Warner Bros.) Bette Davis, Humphrey Bogart
One Sheet: $1,900 - $3,000

MARKED WOMAN
(1947R - Warner Bros.) Bette Davis, Humphrey Bogart
One Sheet: $75 - $150   *Re-release. Duotone.*

MARKED WOMAN
(1956R - Warner Bros.) Bette Davis, Humphrey Bogart
One Sheet: $30 - $50   *Re-release. Duotone.*

MARKET OF VAIN DESIRE, THE
(1916 - Triangle) H.B. Warner, Clara Williams
One Sheet: $150 - $300

MARKSMAN, THE
(1953 - Monogram) Wayne Morris, Elena Verdugo
One Sheet: $7 - $15

MARLENE
(197? - -) -
One Sheet: $15 - $30   *Documentary about Marlene Dietrich.*

MARLOWE
(1969 - MGM) James Garner, Bruce Lee, Carroll O'Connor
One Sheet: $20 - $40

MARNIE
(1964 - Universal) Tippi Hedren, Sean Connery, Dir: Alfred Hitchcock

One Sheet: $75 - $150

One Sheet

MAROC 7
(1967 - Paramount) Gene Barry, Cyd Charisse
One Sheet: $10 - $20

MAROONED
(1969 - Columbia) Gregory Peck, Richard Crenna, David Janssen
One Sheet: $15 - $25

MARRIAGE BY CONTRACT
(1928 - Tiffany-Stahl) Patsy Ruth Miller, Lawrence Gray
One Sheet: $200 - $400

MARRIAGE CHEAT, THE
(1924 - Ince) Leatrice Joy, Adolphe Menjou
One Sheet: $200 - $400

MARRIAGE CIRCLE, THE
(1924 - Warner Bros.) Florence Vidor, Monte Blue
One Sheet: $300 - $700

MARRIAGE CLAUSE, THE
(1926 - Universal) Francis X. Bushman, Billie Dove
One Sheet: $250 - $600

One Sheet

MARRIAGE FORBIDDEN
(1938 - Criterion) Pedro de Cordoba, Phyllis Barry
One Sheet: $50 - $100

MARRIAGE IN TRANSIT
(1940 - 20th Century Fox) Virginia Gilmore, Robert Skileny
One Sheet: $40 - $75

MARRIAGE IS A PRIVATE AFFAIR
(1944 - MGM) Lana Turner, John Hodiak
One Sheet: $50 - $100

MARRIAGE ITALIAN STYLE
(1964 - Embassy) Sophia Loren, Marcello Mastroianni
One Sheet: $30 - $60

MARRIAGE MAKER, THE
(1923 - Paramount) Agnes Ayers, Jack Holt
One Sheet: $150 - $300

MARRIAGE OF A YOUNG STOCKBROKER, THE
(1971 - 20th Century Fox) Richard Benjamin, Joanna Shimkus
One Sheet: $5 - $10

MARRIAGE OF CORBAL, THE
(1936 - Gaumont-British) Noah Beery, Nils Asther
One Sheet: $50 - $100

MARRIAGE OF MARIA BRAUN, THE

(1979 - Albatros) Hanna Schygulla, Klaus Lowitsch, Dir: R.W. Fassbinder
One Sheet: $15 - $30

One Sheet

MARRIAGE OF MOLLY O, THE
(1916 - Triangle) Mae Marsh, Robert Harron
One Sheet: $600 - $1,000

MARRIAGE ON APPROVAL
(1933 - Monarch) Barbara Kent, Donald Dillaway
One Sheet: $100 - $200

MARRIAGE ON THE ROCKS
(1965 - Warner Bros.) Frank Sinatra, Deborah Kerr, Dean Martin
One Sheet: $20 - $40

MARRIAGE PLAYGROUND, THE
(1929 - Paramount) Fredric March, Kay Francis
One Sheet: $500 - $800

MARRIAGE WHIRL, THE
(1925 - First National) Corinne Griffith, Kenneth Harlan, Harrison Ford
One Sheet: $250 - $600

MARRIAGE-GO-ROUND, THE
(1961 - 20th Century Fox) Susan Hayward, James Mason
One Sheet: $20 - $40

MARRIED ALIVE
(1927 - Fox) Lou Tellegen, Margaret Livingston
One Sheet: $1,300 - $2,000

MARRIED AND IN LOVE
(1940 - RKO) Alan Marshall, Barbara Reed
One Sheet: $30 - $60

MARRIED BACHELOR
(1941 - MGM) Robert Young, Ruth Hussey
One Sheet: $50 - $100

MARRIED BEFORE BREAKFAST
(1937 - MGM) Robert Young, Florence Rice
One Sheet: $75 - $150

MARRIED TO IT
(1993 - Orion) Beau Bridges, Stockard Channing
One Sheet: $3 - $5

MARRIED TO THE MOB
(1988 - Orion) Michelle Pfeiffer, Matthew Modine, Dean Stockwell
One Sheet: $10 - $20

MARRIED VIRGIN, THE
(1920 - -) Rudolph Valentino
One Sheet: $800 - $1,500

MARRIED WOMAN
(1965 - -) Macha Meril, Philippe Leroy
One Sheet: $50 - $100

MARRY ME!
(1925 - Paramount) Florence Vidor, Edward Everett Horton
One Sheet: $150 - $300

MARRY ME!
(1949 - General) Derek Bond, Zena Marshall
One Sheet: $20 - $40

MARRY ME AGAIN
(1953 - RKO) Marie Wilson, Robert Cummings
One Sheet: $15 - $30

MARRY ME! MARRY ME!
(1969 - Allied Artists) Elisabeth Wiener, Regine
One Sheet: $7 - $15

MARRY THE BOSS'S DAUGHTER

(1941 - 20th Century Fox) Brenda Joyce, Bruce Edwards
One Sheet: $100 - $200

MARRY THE GIRL
(1937 - Warner Bros.) Hugh Herbert, Mary Roland
One Sheet: $50 - $100

MARRYING KIND, THE
(1952 - Columbia) Judy Holliday, Aldo Ray
One Sheet: $20 - $40

MARRYING MAN, THE
(1991 - Touchstone) Alec Baldwin, Kim Basinger
One Sheet: $5 - $12

MARRYING WIDOWS
(1934 - Tower) Judith Allen, Minna Gombell, John Mack Brown
One Sheet: $150 - $300

MARS ATTACKS!
(1996 - Warner Bros.) Jack Nicholson, Glenn Close Dir: Tim Burton
One Sheet: $7 - $15

MARS ATTACKS THE WORLD
(1938 - Universal) Buster Crabbe, Jean Rogers
One Sheet: $250 - $500   *Feature version of FLASH GORDON'S TRIP TO MARS.*

MARS ATTACKS THE WORLD
(1950R - Filmcraft) Buster Crabbe, Jean Rogers
One Sheet: $100 - $200   *Re-release.*

MARSHAL OF AMARILLO
(1948 - Republic) Allan "Rocky" Lane
One Sheet: $30 - $50

MARSHAL OF CEDAR ROCK
(1953 - Republic) Allan "Rocky" Lane
One Sheet: $15 - $35

One Sheet

MARSHAL OF CRIPPLE CREEK
(1947 - Republic) Allan "Rocky" Lane, Bobby Blake
One Sheet: $40 - $75   *From the Red Ryder series.*

MARSHAL OF GUNSMOKE
(1943 - Universal) Tex Ritter, Russell Hayden
One Sheet: $30 - $60

MARSHAL OF HELDORADO
(1950 - Lippert) Jimmie Ellison, Russell Hayden
One Sheet: $15 - $30

MARSHAL OF LAREDO
(1945 - Republic) Bill Elliott
One Sheet: $30 - $60

MARSHAL OF MESA CITY, THE
(1939 - RKO) George O'Brien, Virginia Vale
One Sheet: $75 - $150

MARSHAL OF RENO
(1944 - Republic) Bill Elliott, Bobby Blake
One Sheet: $50 - $100   *From the Red Ryder series.*

MARSHAL'S DAUGHTER, THE
(1953 - United Artists) Ken Murray, Preston Foster, Hoot Gibson
One Sheet: $20 - $40

MARSHALS IN DISGUISE
(1952 - Allied Artists) Guy Madison, Andy Devine
One Sheet: $15 - $35   *Wild Bill Hickok series.*

MARTHA AND ETHEL
(1995 - Sony Classics) -
One Sheet: $5 - $10   *Documentary.*

MARTHA AND I
(1995 - Cinema Four) Marianne Saegebrecht, Michel Piccoli
One Sheet: $5 - $10

MARTHA'S VINDICATION
(1916 - Triangle) Norma Talmadge, Seena Owen
One Sheet: $500 - $800

MARTIN
(1978 - Libra) John Amplas, Lincoln Maazel, Dir: G. Romero
One Sheet: $50 - $100

MARTIN LUTHER
(1953 - Louis Rochemont Assoc.) Niall MacGinnis
One Sheet: $15 - $30

MARTY
(1955 - United Artists) Ernest Borgnine, Betsy Blair
One Sheet: $75 - $150   *Academy Award: Best Picture, Best Actor, Best Direction(Delbert Mann). Academy Award MoviePosters #160-#162.*

MARVIN'S ROOM
(1996 - Miramax) Meryl Streep, Leonardo DiCaprio, Diane Keaton, Hume Cronyn
One Sheet: $5 - $10

MARX BROTHERS: THE CLASSIC ZANIES
(1971 - -) The Marx Brothers
One Sheet: $15 - $30

MARY BURNS, FUGITIVE
(1935 - Paramount) Sylvia Sidney, Melvyn Douglas
One Sheet: $50 - $100

MARY HAD A LITTLE
(1961 - United Artists) Agnes Laurent
One Sheet: $5 - $10

MARY JANE'S PA
(1935 - First National) Guy Kibbee, Nan Grey
One Sheet: $75 - $150

MARY LOU
(1948 - Columbia) Robert Lowery, Joan Barton, Glenda Farrell
One Sheet: $15 - $25

MARY, MARY
(1963 - Warner Bros.) Debbie Reynolds, Barry Nelson
One Sheet: $15 - $25

MARY OF SCOTLAND
(1936 - RKO) Katharine Hepburn, Fredric March
One Sheet: $1,600 - $2,500

MARY POPPINS
(1964 - Buena Vista/Disney) Julie Andrews, Dick Van Dyke
One Sheet: $75 - $150   *Academy Award: Best Actress. Academy Award Movie Posters #224.*

One Sheet

MARY POPPINS
(1973R - Disney) Julie Andrews, Dick Van Dyke
One Sheet: $10 - $20   *Re-release.*

MARY POPPINS
(1980R - Buena Vista) Julie Andrews, Dick Van

Dyke
One Sheet: $10 - $20   *Re-release.*

MARY, QUEEN OF SCOTS
(1971 - Universal) Vanessa Redgrave, Glenda Jackson
One Sheet: $5 - $10

MARY REILLY
(1996 - TriStar) Julia Roberts, John Malkovich
One Sheet: $5 - $12

MARY RYAN, DETECTIVE
(1950 - Columbia) Marsha Hunt, John Litel
One Sheet: $20 - $40

MARY SHELLEY'S FRANKENSTEIN
(1994 - TriStar) Robert DeNiro, Kenneth Branagh
One Sheet: $10 - $20

MARY STEVENS, M.D.
(1933 - Warner Bros.) Kay Francis, Lyle Talbot
One Sheet: $200 - $400

MARYJANE
(1968 - AIP) Fabian, Diane McBain, Patty McCormack, Kevin Coughlin
One Sheet: $30 - $50   *Drug film (Marijuana).*

MARYLAND
(1940 - 20th Century Fox) Walter Brennan, Fay Bainter
One Sheet: $75 - $150

One Sheet (Style A)

MASALA
(1993 - Strand) Saeed Jaffrey, Sirvinas Krishna
One Sheet: $3 - $5

MASH - See listing under M*A*S*H

MASK, THE
(1961 - -) See EYES OF HELL

MASK
(1985 - Universal) Cher, Sam Elliot, Eric Stoltz
One Sheet: $5 - $10

MASK, THE
(1988 - Universal) Helena Bonham Carter, Michael Maloney
One Sheet: $3 - $5

MASK, THE
(1994 - New Line) Jim Carrey, Richard Leni
One Sheet: $10 - $20

One Sheet

MASK OF DIIJON, THE
(1946 - PRC) Erich von Stroheim, Jeanne Bates
One Sheet: $40 - $75

MASK OF DIMITRIOS, THE

(1944 - Warner Bros.) Peter Lorre, Sydney Greenstreet
One Sheet: $50 - $100

MASK OF FU MANCHU, THE
(1932 - MGM) Boris Karloff, Lewis Stone, Myrna Loy
One Sheet: $5,000 - $8,000   *Graven Images, pg. 58-59.*

Title Card

MASK OF THE AVENGER
(1951 - Columbia) John Derek, Jody Lawrance
One Sheet: $20 - $40

MASK OF THE DRAGON
(1951 - Lippert) Richard Travis, Sheila Ryan
One Sheet: $50 - $100

MASKED EMOTIONS
(1929 - Fox) George O'Brien
One Sheet: $250 - $600

MASKED MARVEL, THE
(1943 - Republic) William Forrest, Louise Currie
One Sheet: $200 - $400   *Serial. 12 Chapters.*

MASKED MENACE, THE
(1927 - Pathe) -
One Sheet: $250 - $600   *Serial. 10 Chapters.*

MASKED RAIDERS, THE
(1949 - RKO) Tim Holt, Marjorie Lord
One Sheet: $20 - $40

MASKED RIDER, THE
(1941 - Universal) Johnny Mack Brown
One Sheet: $75 - $125

MASKS OF THE DEVIL, THE
(1928 - MGM) John Gilbert, Alma Rubens
One Sheet: $600 - $1,000

MASQUE OF THE RED DEATH, THE
(1964 - AIP) Vincent Price, Hazel Court
One Sheet: $30 - $60   *Graven Images, pg. 209.*

MASQUE OF THE RED DEATH, THE
(1989 - -) Adrian Paul, Clare Hoak
One Sheet: $15 - $30

MASQUERADE
(1965 - United Artists) Cliff Robertson, Jack Hawkins
One Sheet: $5 - $10

MASQUERADE
(1988 - MGM/UA) Rob Lowe, Meg Tilly
One Sheet: $5 - $10

MASQUERADE IN MEXICO
(1945 - Paramount) Dorothy Lamour, Arturo de Cordova
One Sheet: $50 - $100

MASQUERADER, THE
(1914 - Keystone) Charlie Chaplin, Roscoe "Fatty" Arbuckle
One Sheet: $7,500 - $12,000

MASQUERADER, THE
(1922 - First National) Guy Bates Post
One Sheet: $250 - $600

MASQUERADER, THE
(1933 - Samuel Goldwyn) Ronald Colman, Elissa Landi
One Sheet: $600 - $1,000

MASS APPEAL
(1984 - Universal) Jack Lemmon, Zeljko Ivanek

One Sheet: $3 - $5

MASSACRE
(1934 - First National) Richard Barthelmess, Ann Dvorak
One Sheet: $75 - $150

MASSACRE
(1956 - 20th Century Fox) Dane Clark, James Craig
One Sheet: $10 - $20

MASSACRE AT CENTRAL HIGH
(1976 - Brian) Derrel Maury, Andrew Stevens
One Sheet: $3 - $5

MASSACRE CANYON
(1954 - Columbia) Phil Carey, Audrey Totter
One Sheet: $10 - $20

MASSACRE RIVER
(1949 - Allied Artists) Guy Madison, Rory Calhoun, Carole Matthews
One Sheet: $5 - $10

MASSAGE PARLOR "73"
(1973 - -) -
One Sheet: $5 - $10   *Sexploitation.*

MASTER GUNFIGHTER, THE
(1975 - Taylor-Laughlin) Tom Laughlin, Ron O'Neal
One Sheet: $3 - $5

MASTER KEY, THE
(1945 - Universal) Milburn Stone, Jan Wiley
One Sheet: $50 - $100   *Serial. 13 Chapters.*

MASTER MINDS
(1949 - Monogram) Leo Gorcey, Huntz Hall, Billy Benedict
One Sheet: $50 - $100

MASTER MYSTERY, THE
(1918 - Octagon) Harry Houdini
One Sheet: $10,000 - $15,000   *Serial. Magic. 15 Chapters. Price is for one sheet with Houdini and robot pictured.*

MASTER OF BALLANTRAE
(1952 - Warner Bros.) Errol Flynn, Anthony Steele
One Sheet: $40 - $75

MASTER OF MEN
(1933 - Columbia) Jack Holt, Fay Wray
One Sheet: $150 - $300

MASTER OF THE WORLD
(1961 - AIP) Vincent Price, Charles Bronson
One Sheet: $30 - $50

MASTER PLAN
(1955 - Astor) Wayne Morris
One Sheet: $15 - $25

MASTER RACE, THE
(1944 - RKO) George Coulouris, Stanley Ridges
One Sheet: $75 - $150

MASTER SPY
(1964 - Allied Artists) Stephen Murray, June Thorburn
One Sheet: $10 - $20

MASTER TOUCH, THE
(1974 - National General) Kirk Douglas, Giuliano Gemma
One Sheet: $3 - $5

MASTERS OF THE CONGO JUNGLE
(1960 - 20th Century Fox) Orson Welles (narrator)
One Sheet: $15 - $30

MASTERS OF THE UNIVERSE
(1987 - Cannon) Dolph Lundgren, Frank Langella
One Sheet: $7 - $15   *Advance:$10-20.*

MASTERSON OF KANSAS
(1954 - Columbia) George Montgomery, Nancy Gates
One Sheet: $7 - $15

MATA HARI
(1932 - MGM) Greta Garbo, Ramon Novarro
One Sheet: $5,000 - $7,500

MATA HARI
(1938R - MGM) Greta Garbo, Ramon Novarro

One Sheet: $250 - $500   *Re-release.*

MATA HARI THE RED DANCER
(1918 - National) -
One Sheet: $700 - $1,200

MATADOR
(1986 - -) Assumpta Serna, Antonio Banderas
One Sheet: $20 - $40   *Spanish.*

MATCH KING, THE
(1932 - First National) Warren William, Glenda Farrell
One Sheet: $100 - $200

MATCH-BREAKER, THE
(1921 - Metro) Viola Dana, Jack Perrin
One Sheet: $200 - $400

MATCHLESS
(1967 - United Artists) Ira Furstenberg, Patrick O'Neal
One Sheet: $5 - $10

MATCHMAKER, THE
(1958 - Paramount) Shirley Booth, Anthony Perkins
One Sheet: $20 - $40

MATEWAN
(1987 - Cinecom International) Chris Cooper, Mary McDonnell, Will Oldham
One Sheet: $15 - $30

MATILDA
(1978 - AIP) Elliot Gould, Robert Mitchum
One Sheet: $10 - $20   *Sports (Boxing). Film about a boxing kangaroo. Sports Movie Posters #158.*

MATILDA
(1996 - TriStar) Danny DeVito, Rhea Perlman
One Sheet: $3 - $6

MATINEE
(1993 - Universal) John Goodman, Cathy Moriarty
One Sheet: $3 - $5

One Sheet

MATING GAME, THE
(1959 - MGM) Debbie Reynolds, Tony Randall
One Sheet: $15 - $25

MATING OF MARCELLA, THE
(1918 - -) Dorothy Dalton, Thurston Hall
One Sheet: $250 - $500

MATING OF MILLIE, THE
(1948 - Columbia) Glenn Ford, Evelyn Keyes
One Sheet: $20 - $40

MATING SEASON, THE
(1950 - Paramount) Gene Tierney, John Lund, Thelma Ritter
One Sheet: $30 - $50

MATING URGE, THE
(1950 - -) -
One Sheet: $15 - $30

MATRIMONIAC, THE
(1916 - Triangle) Douglas Fairbanks, Constance Talmadge
One Sheet: $700 - $1,200

MATRIMONIAL BED, THE
(1930 - Warner Bros.) Frank Fay, Lilyan Tashman
One Sheet: $100 - $200

MATRI-PHONY
(1942 - Columbia) Three Stooges (Curly)
One Sheet: $3,500 - $5,000   *Comedy short. Duotone.*

MATTER OF INNOCENCE, A
(1968 - Universal) Hayley Mills, Trevor Howard
One Sheet: $4 - $8

MATTER OF LIFE AND DEATH, A
(1946 - Gaumont) David Niven, Roger Livesey
One Sheet: $150 - $300   *Also see U.S. release: STAIRWAY TO HEAVEN.*

MATTER OF MORALS, A
(1980 - 20th Century Fox) Patrick O'Neal
One Sheet: $15 - $30

MATTER OF TIME, A
(1976 - AIP) Liza Minnelli, Ingrid Bergman, Charles Boyer
One Sheet: $15 - $25

MATTER OF WHO, A
(1962 - MGM) Terry-Thomas
One Sheet: $10 - $20

MAU-MAU
(1950S - Rock-Price) Dir: Elwood Price
One Sheet: $100 - $200   *Black cast. Separate Cinema, pg. 126.*

MAURICE
(1987 - Cinecom) James Wilby, Hugh Grant
One Sheet: $10 - $20

MAURIE
(1973 - National General) Bernie Casey, Bo Svenson
One Sheet: $10 - $20   *Sports (Basketball). Tragic life of basketball star Maurice Stokes.*

MAUSOLEUM
(1983 - -) Marjoe Gortner, Bobby Breese
One Sheet: $7 - $15

MAVERICK, THE
(1952 - Allied Artists) Bill Elliott
One Sheet: $15 - $35

MAVERICK
(1994 - Warner Bros.) Mel Gibson, Jodie Foster, James Garner
One Sheet: $7 - $15   *Cowboy Movie Posters #363.*

MAVERICK QUEEN, THE
(1956 - Republic) Barbara Stanwyck, Barry Sullivan
One Sheet: $20 - $40

MAX BAER VS. PRIMO CARNERA
(1934 - -) Max Baer, Primo Carnera
One Sheet: $250 - $600   *Sports (Boxing).*

MAX DUGAN RETURNS
(1983 - 20th Century) Marsha Mason, Jason Robards, Matthew Broderick
One Sheet: $5 - $10

MAXIE
(1985 - Orion) Glenn Close, Mandy Patinkin
One Sheet: $3 - $5

MAXIMUM OVERDRIVE
(1986 - Dino De Laurentis) Emilio Estevez, Pat Hingle, Dir: Stephen King
One Sheet: $7 - $15

MAY ROBSON PERSONALITY POSTER
(1917 - National) May Robson
One Sheet: $100 - $200

One Sheet

MAYA
(1966 - MGM) Clint Walker, Jay North

One Sheet: $15 - $25

MAYBE IT'S LOVE
(1930 - Warner Bros.) Joan Bennett
One Sheet: $100 - $200

MAYBE IT'S LOVE
(1934 - Warner Bros.) Frank McHugh, Gloria Stuart
One Sheet: $75 - $150

MAYERLING
(1936 - Concordea) Charles Boyer, Danielle Darrieux
One Sheet: $125 - $250   *French.*

MAYERLING
(1969 - MGM) Omar Sharif, Catherine Deneuve, James Mason, Ava Gardner
One Sheet: $15 - $25

MAYOR OF 44TH STREET
(1942 - RKO) George Murphy, Freddy Martin Orch.
One Sheet: $75 - $150   *Big Band musical.*

MAYOR OF HELL, THE
(1933 - Warner Bros.) James Cagney, Madge Evans
One Sheet: $1,600 - $2,500

MAYTIME
(1923 - Preferred) Harrison Ford, Clara Bow, Ethel Shannon
One Sheet: $250 - $600

MAYTIME
(1937 - MGM) Jeanette MacDonald, Nelson Eddy, John Barrymore
One Sheet: $600 - $1,000

MAYTIME IN MAYFAIR
(1949 - Imperadio/Real Art) Anna Neagle, Michael Wilding, Peter Graves
One Sheet: $40 - $75

MAZE, THE
(1953 - Monogram) Richard Carlson, Veronica Hurst
One Sheet: $100 - $200   *Graven Images, pg. 162. Filmed in 3-D.*

MCCABE AND MRS. MILLER
(1971 - Warner Bros.) Warren Beatty, Julie Christie
One Sheet: $15 - $35   *Amsel art. Cowboy Movie Posters #331.*

MCCONNELL STORY, THE
(1955 - Warner Bros.) Alan Ladd, June Allison
One Sheet: $20 - $40

MCCULLOCHS, THE
(1975 - AIP) Forrest Tucker, Julie Adams
One Sheet: $3 - $5   *AKA: THE WILD MCCULLOCKS.*

MCFADDEN'S FLATS
(1935 - Paramount) Andy Clyde, Betty Furness
One Sheet: $75 - $150

MCGUERINS FROM BROOKLYN, THE
(1942 - United Artists) Max Baer, William Bendix
One Sheet: $30 - $50

MCGUIRE, GO HOME!
(1966 - Continental) Dirk Bogarde, George Chakiris
One Sheet: $7 - $15

MCHALE'S NAVY
(1964 - Universal) Ernest Borgnine, Joe Flynn, Tim Conway
One Sheet: $20 - $40

MCHALE'S NAVY
(1997 - Universal) Tom Arnold, David Alan Grier, Ernest Borgnine
One Sheet: $4 - $8

MCHALE'S NAVY JOINS THE AIR FORCE
(1965 - Universal) Joe Flynn, Tim Conway
One Sheet: $15 - $30

MCKENNA OF THE MOUNTED
(1932 - Columbia) Buck Jones
One Sheet: $500 - $900   *Cowboy Movie Posters # 128.*

MCKENZIE BREAK, THE
(1970 - United Artists) Brian Keith, Helmut Griem

One Sheet: $3 - $5

MCLINTOCK!
(1963 - United Artists) John Wayne, Maureen O'Hara
One Sheet: $75 - $125   *Duotone.*

MCMASTERS, THE
(1970 - Chevron) Burl Ives, Brock Peters, David Carradine
One Sheet: $3 - $5

MCQ
(1974 - Warner Bros.) John Wayne, Eddie Albert
One Sheet: $30 - $50

MCVICAR
(1981 - -) Roger Daltrey, Adam Faith, Jeremy Blake
One Sheet: $5 - $10

ME AND MY GAL
(1932 - Fox) Spencer Tracy, Joan Bennett
One Sheet: $100 - $200

ME AND MY PAL
(1933 - MGM) Laurel & Hardy
One Sheet: $1,900 - $3,000

ME AND THE COLONEL
(1958 - Lippert) Danny Kaye, Curt Jurgens
One Sheet: $20 - $40

ME AND THE KID
(1993 - Orion) Danny Aiello
One Sheet: $3 - $5

ME, NATALIE
(1969 - National General) Patty Duke, James Farentino, Salome Jens, Al Pacino (debut)
One Sheet: $15 - $30

MEAN DOG BLUES
(1977 - AIP) George Kennedy, Scatman Crothers
One Sheet: $5 - $10

MEAN JOHNNY GREEN
(1976 - Atlas) Fred Williamson, Roddy MacDowell
One Sheet: $10 - $20   *Blaxploitation.*

MEAN MOTHER
(197? - -) Clifton Brown
One Sheet: $10 - $20   *Black sexploitation.*

MEAN SEASON, THE
(1985 - Orion) Kurt Russell, Mariel Hemingway
One Sheet: $3 - $5

MEAN STREETS
(1973 - Warner Bros.) Robert De Niro, Harvey Keitel
One Sheet: $40 - $75

MEANEST GAL IN TOWN, THE
(1934 - RKO) ZaSu Pitts, James Gleason
One Sheet: $125 - $250

MEANEST MAN IN THE WORLD, THE
(1923 - First National) Bert Lytell, Blanche Sweet
One Sheet: $200 - $400

MEANEST MAN IN THE WORLD, THE
(1942 - 20th Century Fox) Jack Benny, Priscilla Lane, Eddie "Rochester" Anderson
One Sheet: $100 - $200

One Sheet

MEAT RACK
(197? - -) -
One Sheet: $7 - $15

MEATBALLS
(1979 - Paramount) Bill Murray, Harvey Atkin
One Sheet: $7 - $15

MEATBALLS II
(1984 - Paramount) Richard Mulligan, John Mengatti
One Sheet: $3 - $5

MEATBALLS III
(1987 - Dalco) Sally Kellerman, Patrick Dempsey
One Sheet: $3 - $5

MECHANIC, THE
(1972 - United Artists) Charles Bronson, Jan-Michael Vincent
One Sheet: $15 - $25

MECHANICAL OPERATION OF THE BRITISH TANKS
(1918 - Paramount) Bray-Pictograph
One Sheet: $250 - $500

MEDAL FOR BENNY, A
(1915 - Paramount) J. Carrol Naish, Dorothy Lamour
One Sheet: $50 - $100

One Sheet

MEDEA
(1959 - Euro International) Maria Callas
One Sheet: $75 - $150   *Italian.*

MEDICINE BALL CARAVAN
(1971 - Warner Bros.) B.B. King, Alice Cooper, Tom Donahue
One Sheet: $15 - $25   *Rock 'n' Roll.*

MEDICINE MAN, THE
(1930 - Tiffany) Jack Benny, Betty Bronson
One Sheet: $200 - $400

MEDICINE MAN
(1992 - Buena Vista) Sean Connery, Lorraine Bracco
One Sheet: $3 - $5

MEDICO OF PAINTED SPRINGS, THE
(1941 - Columbia) Charles Starrett
One Sheet: $50 - $100

MEDITERRANEO
(1993 - Miramax) Diego Abatantuono, Claudio Bigagli
One Sheet: $5 - $10   *Italian.*

MEDIUM, THE
(1951 - Lopert) Maria Powers, Anna Marie Alberghetti
One Sheet: $15 - $25

MEDIUM COOL
(1969 - Paramount) Robert Forster, Verna Bloom, Peter Bonerz
One Sheet: $15 - $25

MEDUSA TOUCH, THE
(1978 - ITC) Richard Burton, Lee Remick
One Sheet: $7 - $15

MEET BOSTON BLACKIE
(1941 - Columbia) Chester Morris, Rochelle Hudson
One Sheet: $75 - $150

MEET DANNY WILSON
(1951 - Universal-International) Frank Sinatra, Shelley Winters
One Sheet: $40 - $75

MEET DR. CHRISTIAN
(1939 - RKO) Jean Hersholt, Robert Baldwin, Dorothy Lovett

One Sheet: $50 - $100

MEET IN THE HEAT OF FIRECREEK
(1968 - Warner Bros.) James Stewart, Henry Fonda
One Sheet: $15 - $25

MEET JOHN DOE
(1941 - Warner Bros.) Gary Cooper, Barbara Stanwyck, Dir: Frank Capra
One Sheet: $600 - $1,000

One Sheet

MEET ME AFTER THE SHOW
(1951 - 20th Century Fox) Betty Grable, Macdonald Carey, Rory Calhoun
One Sheet: $40 - $75

MEET ME AT DAWN
(1947 - 20th Century Fox) William Eythe, Stanley Holloway
One Sheet: $20 - $40

MEET ME AT THE FAIR
(1952 - Universal) Dan Dailey, Diana Lynn
One Sheet: $30 - $50

MEET ME IN LAS VEGAS
(1956 - MGM) Dan Dailey, Cyd Charisse
One Sheet: $30 - $50

MEET ME IN ST. LOUIS
(1944 - MGM) Judy Garland, Margaret O'Brien
One Sheet: $300 - $700

MEET ME IN ST. LOUIS
(1962R - MGM) Judy Garland, Margaret O'Brien
One Sheet: $30 - $50   *Re-release.*

MEET ME ON BROADWAY
(1946 - Columbia) Majorie Reynolds, Fred Brady
One Sheet: $30 - $50

MEET MISS BOBBY SOCKS
(1944 - Columbia) Bob Crosby, Lynn Merrick
One Sheet: $30 - $50

MEET MR. LUCIFER
(1953 - General) Stanley Holloway, Peggy Cummins
One Sheet: $15 - $25

MEET NERO WOLFE
(1936 - Columbia) Rita Cansino (Hayworth), Edward Arnold, Victor Jory
One Sheet: $200 - $400

MEET THE BARON
(1933 - MGM) Jimmy Durante, Ted Healy & His Stooges (Moe, Larry & Curly)
One Sheet: $250 - $600   *Price assumes Stooges not pictured on the one sheet.*

MEET THE BOY FRIEND
(1937 - Republic) Carol Hughes, David Carlyle
One Sheet: $50 - $100

MEET THE CHUMP
(1941 - Universal) Hugh Herbert, Shemp Howard, Jeanne Kelly (Brooks)
One Sheet: $75 - $150

MEET THE GIRLS
(1938 - 20th Century Fox) June Lang, Lynn Bari
One Sheet: $75 - $150

MEET THE MISSUS
(1924 - Pathe) Glenn Tryon
One Sheet: $125 - $250

MEET THE MISSUS
(1937 - RKO) Victor Moore, Helen Broderick

One Sheet: $50 - $100

MEET THE MISSUS
(1940 - Republic) Roscoe Karns, Ruth Donnelly, Alan Ladd
One Sheet: $50 - $100

MEET THE MOB
(1942 - Monogram) ZaSu Pitts, Roger Pryor
One Sheet: $75 - $125

MEET THE PEOPLE
(1944 - MGM) Dick Powell, Lucille Ball
One Sheet: $100 - $200

MEET THE STEWARTS
(1942 - Columbia) William Holden, Frances Dee
One Sheet: $50 - $100

MEET THE WIFE
(1931 - Columbia) Laura LaPlante, Lew Cody
One Sheet: $200 - $400

MEET THE WILDCAT
(1940 - Universal) Margaret Lindsey, Ralph Bellamy
One Sheet: $75 - $125

MEETING THEDA BARA
(1918 - Fox) Mutt & Jeff
One Sheet: $6,500 - $10,000   *Cartoon. Cartoon Movie Posters #5.*

MEGA VIXENS
(198? - -) Dir: Russ Meyer
One Sheet: $7 - $15   *Sexploitation.*

MEGAFORCE
(1982 - 20th Century Fox) Micheal Beck, Persis Khambatta
One Sheet: $5 - $10

MEIN KAMPF
(1961 - Columbia) Hitler documentary
One Sheet: $15 - $30

MELANCHOLY DAME
(1929 - Paramount) -
One Sheet: $100 - $200

MELBA
(1953 - United Artists) Partice Munsel, Robert Morley
One Sheet: $5 - $10

MELINDA
(1972 - MGM) Calvin Lockhart, Vonetta McGee, Jim Kelly
One Sheet: $10 - $20   *Black cast. Outstanding poster design.*

MELLER DRAMMER, THE
(1933 - United Artists) Mickey Mouse
One Sheet: $40,000 - $50,000   *Cartoon. The Disney Poster, pg. 20.*

MELODIES IN SPRING
(1934 - Paramount) Charles Ruggles, Ann Sothern
One Sheet: $125 - $250

MELODY
(1971 - Levitt-Pickman) Jack Wild, Mark Lester
One Sheet: $2 - $3

MELODY AND MOONLIGHT
(1940 - Republic) Johnny Downs, Barbara Allen, Jerry Colonna, Jane Frazee
One Sheet: $30 - $60

MELODY CRUISE
(1933 - RKO) Charlie Ruggles, Phil Harris, Greta Nissen
One Sheet: $1,300 - $2,000

MELODY FOR THREE
(1941 - RKO) Jean Hersholt, Fay Wray
One Sheet: $75 - $150

MELODY FOR TWO
(1937 - Warner Bros.) James Melton, Patricia Ellis
One Sheet: $50 - $100

MELODY LANE
(1941 - Universal) The Merry Macs, Leon Errol
One Sheet: $50 - $100

MELODY LINGERS ON, THE
(1941 - Reliance) Josephine Hutchinson, George Houston
One Sheet: $40 - $75

MELODY MAN, THE
(1930 - Columbia) William Collier, Jr., Alice Day
One Sheet: $200 - $400

MELODY PARADE
(1943 - Monogram) Mary Beth Hughes, Eddie Quillan, Anson Weeks & Orchestra
One Sheet: $40 - $75   *Big Band musical.*

MELODY RANCH
(1940 - Republic) Gene Autry, Jimmy Durante
One Sheet: $150 - $350

MELODY TIME
(1948 - RKO/Disney) Roy Rogers, Dennis Day, Andrew Sisters
One Sheet: $200 - $400

MELODY TRAIL
(1935 - Republic) Gene Autry
One Sheet: $250 - $550

MELODY TRAIL
(1943R - Republic) Gene Autry
One Sheet: $75 - $125   *Re-release.*

MELVIN AND HOWARD
(1980 - Universal) Paul LeMat, Jason Robards, Mary Steenburger
One Sheet: $7 - $15   *Academy Award: Best Supporting Actress(Steenburgen). Academy Award Movie Posters #313.*

MEMBER OF THE WEDDING
(1953 - Columbia) Brandon de Wilde, Julie Harris, Ethel Waters
One Sheet: $15 - $30

MEMOIRS OF AN INVISIBLE MAN
(1992 - Warner Bros.) Chevy Chase, Daryl Hanna
One Sheet: $5 - $10

MEMORIES OF ME
(1988 - -) Billy Crystal, Alan King, JoBeth Williams
One Sheet: $3 - $5

MEMPHIS BELLE, THE
(1943 - War Activities Commission) -
One Sheet: $800 - $1,500   *Documentary.*

MEMPHIS BELLE
(1990 - Warner Bros.) Matthew Modine, Billy Zane
One Sheet: $10 - $20

One Sheet

MEN
(1924 - Paramount) Pola Negri, Robert Frazer
One Sheet: $500 - $800

MEN, THE
(1950 - United Artists) Marlon Brando, Teresa Wright, Jack Webb
One Sheet: $100 - $200   *Brando's film debut.*

MEN
(1985 - -) Heiner Lauterbach
One Sheet: $7 - $15

MEN AGAINST THE SKY
(1940 - RKO) Richard Dix, Edmund Lowe, Wendy Barrie
One Sheet: $50 - $100

MEN ARE CHILDREN TWICE
(1954 - Stratford) Maureen Swanson, John Fraser
One Sheet: $10 - $20

MEN ARE LIKE THAT

MEN ARE LIKE THAT
(1930 - Paramount Publix) Hal Skelly, Doris Hill
One Sheet: $100 - $200

MEN ARE LIKE THAT
(1931 - Columbia) John Wayne, Laura La Plante
One Sheet: $500 - $800

MEN ARE NOT GODS
(1937 - United Artists) Rex Harrison, Miriam Hopkins, Gertrude Lawrence
One Sheet: $75 - $150

MEN ARE SUCH FOOLS
(1932 - RKO) Una Merkel, Leo Carrillo
One Sheet: $100 - $200

MEN ARE SUCH FOOLS
(1938 - Warner Bros.) Humphrey Bogart, Priscilla Lane
One Sheet: $200 - $400

MEN AT WORK
(1990 - EPIC) Emilio Estevez, Charlie Sheen
One Sheet: $5 - $10

MEN CALL IT LOVE
(1931 - MGM) Adolphe Menjou, Hedda Hopper
One Sheet: $100 - $200

MEN DON'T LEAVE
(1990 - Warner) Jessica Lange, Arliss Howard, Joan Cusack
One Sheet: $3 - $5

MEN IN BLACK
(1934 - Columbia) The Three Stooges (Curly)
One Sheet: $10,000 - $15,000   *Comedy short. Duotone.*

MEN IN EXILE
(1937 - Warner Bros.) Dick Purcell, June Travis
One Sheet: $40 - $75

MEN IN HER DIARY
(1945 - Universal) Jon Hall. Virginia Grey
One Sheet: $50 - $100

MEN IN HER LIFE
(1931 - Columbia) Lois Moran, Charles Bickford
One Sheet: $100 - $200

MEN IN HER LIFE, THE
(1941 - Columbia) Loretta Young, Conrad Veidt
One Sheet: $100 - $200

MEN IN WAR
(1957 - United Artists) Robert Ryan, Aldo Ray
One Sheet: $15 - $30

MEN IN WHITE
(1934 - MGM) Clark Gable, Myrna Loy
One Sheet: $600 - $1,000

One Sheet (Style A)

MEN MUST FIGHT
(1933 - MGM) Robert Young, May Robson
One Sheet: $100 - $200

MEN O' WAR
(1929 - MGM) Laurel & Hardy
One Sheet: $3,500 - $5,000

MEN OF ACTION
(1937 - Conn) Frankie Darrow, Roy Mason
One Sheet: $50 - $100

MEN OF AMERICA
(1932 - RKO) William Boyd, Chic Sale
One Sheet: $125 - $250

MEN OF BOYS TOWN
(1941 - MGM) Spencer Tracy, Mickey Rooney
One Sheet: $125 - $250

MEN OF CHANCE
(1932 - RKO) Mary Astor, Ricardo Cortez
One Sheet: $75 - $150

MEN OF DARING
(1927 - -) Jack Hoxie, Ena Gregory
One Sheet: $125 - $250   *Cowboy Movie Posters #65.*

MEN OF SAN QUENTIN
(1942 - PRC) J. Anthony Hughes, George Breakston
One Sheet: $30 - $50

MEN OF SHERWOOD FOREST
(1957 - Astor) Don Taylor, Eileen Moore
One Sheet: $15 - $25

MEN OF STEEL
(1938 - Republic) Grant Withers, Beatrice Roberts
One Sheet: $75 - $125

MEN OF TEXAS
(1942 - Universal) Jackie Cooper, Anne Gwynne
One Sheet: $50 - $100

MEN OF THE FIGHTING LADY
(1954 - MGM) Van Johnson, Walter Pidgeon
One Sheet: $15 - $30

MEN OF THE HOUR
(1935 - Columbia) Richard Cromwell, Billie Seward
One Sheet: $100 - $200

MEN OF THE NIGHT
(1934 - Columbia) Bruce Cabot, Judith Allen
One Sheet: $200 - $400

MEN OF THE NORTH
(1930 - MGM) Gilbert Roland, Barbara Leonard
One Sheet: $100 - $200

MEN OF THE SEA
(1944 - PRC) Wilfred Lawson, Mary Jerrold
One Sheet: $20 - $40

MEN OF THE SKY
(1931 - First National) Irene Delroy, Jack Whiting
One Sheet: $150 - $350

MEN OF THE TIMBERLAND
(1941 - Universal) Richard Arlen, Andy Devine
One Sheet: $50 - $100

MEN OF TOMORROW
(1932 - Paramount) Merle Oberon, Robert Donat
One Sheet: $150 - $300

MEN OF TWO WORLDS
(1952 - TC/International) Phyllis Calvert, Eric Portman
One Sheet: $15 - $25   *AKA: WITCH DOCTOR; MAN OF AFRICA.*

MEN ON CALL
(1930 - Fox) Edmund Lowe, Mae Clarke
One Sheet: $125 - $250

MEN ON HER MIND
(1944 - PRC) Mary Beth Hughes, Edward Norris
One Sheet: $30 - $50

MEN WITH WINGS
(1938 - Paramount) Fred MacMurray, Ray Milland
One Sheet: $100 - $200

MEN WITHOUT LAW
(1930 - Columbia) Buck Jones
One Sheet: $700 - $1,200   *Cowboy Movie Posters # 93.*

MEN WITHOUT LAW
(1934R - Columbia) Buck Jones
One Sheet: $200 - $400   *Re-release.*

MEN WITHOUT NAMES
(1935 - Paramount) Fred MacMurray, Madge Evans
One Sheet: $125 - $250

MEN WITHOUT SOULS
(1940 - Columbia) John Litel, Rochelle Hudson
One Sheet: $75 - $150

MEN'S CLUB, THE
(1986 - -) David Dukes, Richard Jordan, Roy Scheider
One Sheet: $7 - $15

MENACE, THE
(1932 - Columbia) Bette Davis, H.B. Warner
One Sheet: $1,300 - $2,000

MENACE
(1934 - Paramount) Gertrude Michael, Paul Cavanagh
One Sheet: $75 - $150

MENACE II SOCIETY
(1993 - New Line) Allen & Albert Hughes, Tyrin Turner
One Sheet: $3 - $5

MENACE IN THE NIGHT
(1957 - United Artists) Griffith Jones, Lisa Gastoni
One Sheet: $10 - $20

MENACE OF THE RISING SUN
(1942 - Universal) Commentary by Graham McNamee
One Sheet: $150 - $300   *Documentary. Anti-Japanese propaganda film.*

MEPHISTO WALTZ, THE
(1971 - 20th Century fox) Alan Alda, Jacqueline Bisset
One Sheet: $5 - $10

MERBABIES
(1938 - RKO/Disney) Silly Symphonies
One Sheet: $3,500 - $5,000   *Cartoon. The Disney Poster, pg. 6. Cartoon Movie Posters #193.*

MERBABIES
(1951R - RKO/Disney) Silly Symphonies
One Sheet: $200 - $400   *Re-release. Cartoon.*

MERCENARY, THE
(1970 - United Artists) Franco Nero, Tony Musante, Jack Palance
One Sheet: $5 - $10

MERCY ISLAND
(1941 - Republic) Ray Middleton, Gloria Dickson
One Sheet: $40 - $75

MERELY MARY ANN
(1931 - Fox) Janet Gaynor, Charles Farrell
One Sheet: $500 - $800

MERMAIDS
(1990 - Orion) Cher, Winona Ryder, Bob Hoskins
One Sheet: $10 - $20

MERMAIDS OF TIBURON, THE
(1962 - Filmgroup) Diane Webber, George Rowe
One Sheet: $40 - $75   *AKA: THE AQUA SEX.*

MERRIE MELODIES STOCK
(1936 - Vitagraph) -
One Sheet: $800 - $1,500   *Cartoon. Stock poster.*

One Sheet (Stock 1936)

MERRIE MELODIES STOCK
(1938 - Vitaphone Short Subject) -
One Sheet: $1,600 - $2,500   *Cartoon. Stock poster. "Merrie Melodies" on music staff, "New Technicolor" on tube of paint, various characters in background.*

MERRIE MELODIES STOCK
(1940 - Vitaphone Short Subject) Elmer Fudd, Bugs Bunny (First poster image)

One Sheet: $1,300 - $2,000   *Cartoon. Cartoon Movie Posters #102. Mouse dipping paint brush in Bugs Bunny's can ofpaint.*

MERRIE MELODIES STOCK
(1941 - Vitaphone Short Subject) Bugs Bunny and other characters
One Sheet: $800 - $1,500   *Cartoon. Bugs Bunny on swing with can of paint and paint brush. Full color stock poster with 2ndappearance of Bugs Bunny. Cartoon Movie Posters #103.*

MERRILL'S MARAUDERS
(1962 - Warner Bros.) Jeff Chandler, Ty Hardin
One Sheet: $5 - $10

MERRILY WE GO TO HELL
(1932 - Paramount) Sylvia Sidney, Fredric March, Cary Grant
One Sheet: $800 - $1,500

MERRILY WE LIVE
(1938 - MGM) Constance Bennett, Brian Aherne, Billie Burke
One Sheet: $75 - $150

MERRY ANDREW
(1958 - MGM) Danny Kaye, Pier Angeli
One Sheet: $15 - $25

MERRY CHRISTMAS, MR. LAWRENCE
(1983 - Universal) Tom Conti, David Bowie
One Sheet: $7 - $15

One Sheet

MERRY FRINKS, THE
(1934 - First National) Hugh Herbert, Aline McMahon
One Sheet: $50 - $100

MERRY MAVERICKS
(1951 - Columbia) The Three Stooges (Shemp)
One Sheet: $200 - $400   *Comedy short. Duotone.*

MERRY MIRTHQUAKES
(1953 - RKO) Liberace
One Sheet: $75 - $150   *Short Subject.*

MERRY MIX-UP, A
(1957 - Columbia) The Three Stooges (Joe Besser)
One Sheet: $75 - $125   *Comedy short. Duotone.*

MERRY MONAHANS, THE
(1944 - Universal) Donald O'Connor, Peggy Ryan, Ann Blyth
One Sheet: $50 - $100

MERRY WIDOW, THE
(1925 - MGM) Mae Murray, John Gilbert, Dir: Erich Von Stroheim
One Sheet: $1,600 - $2,500

MERRY WIDOW, THE
(1934 - MGM) Maurice Chevalier, Jeanette MacDonald
One Sheet: $500 - $800

MERRY WIDOW, THE
(1952 - MGM) Lana Turner, Fernando Lamas
One Sheet: $30 - $50

MERRY WIDOW, THE
(1962R - MGM) Maurice Chevalier, Jeanette MacDonald
One Sheet: $15 - $25   *Re-release.*

MERRY WIVES OF RENO
(1934 - Warner Bros.) Glenda Farrell, Margaret Lindsay
One Sheet: $100 - $200

MERRY WIVES OF WINDSOR, THE

One Sheet: $1,300 - $2,000   *Cartoon.*

(1966 - Sigma III) Norman Foster, Colette Boxy
One Sheet: $7 - $15

MERRY XMAS AND A HAPPY NEW YEAR
(1934 - Fox) Shirley Temple
One Sheet: $1,300 - $2,000   *Special promotional poster.*

MERRY-GO-ROUND
(1923 - Universal) Mary Philbin, Norman Kerry
One Sheet: $1,300 - $2,000

MERRY-GO-ROUND OF 1938
(1938 - Universal) Bert Lahr, Alice Brady, Dave Apollon & his Orchestra
One Sheet: $75 - $150   *Big Band musical.*

MERTON OF THE MOVIES
(1924 - Paramount) Glenn Hunter, Viola Dana
One Sheet: $600 - $1,000

MERTON OF THE MOVIES
(1947 - MGM) Red Skelton, Virginia O'Brien
One Sheet: $75 - $125

MESA OF LOST WOMEN
(1952 - Howco) Jackie Coogan, Lyle Talbot
One Sheet: $125 - $250   *Graven Images, pg. 188.*

MESQUITE BUCKAROO, THE
(1939 - Metropolitan) Bob Steele
One Sheet: $150 - $300

MESSAGE FROM SPACE
(1978 - United Artists) Vic Morrow, Sonny Chiba
One Sheet: $15 - $30

MESSAGE TO GARCIA, A
(1936 - 20th Century Fox) John Boles, Barbara Stanwyck, Wallace Beery
One Sheet: $150 - $300

MESSENGER OF DEATH
(1988 - -) Charles Bronson, Trish Van Devere
One Sheet: $4 - $8

MESSET'S MUSICAL ENTERTAINERS
(1915 - -) -
One Sheet: $150 - $300

MESSIAH OF EVIL
(1974 - International Cinefilm) Michael Greer, Marianna Hill
One Sheet: $15 - $25   *AKA: DEAD PEOPLE.*

METALSTORM: THE DESTRUCTION OF JARED-SYN
(1983 - Universal) Jeffrey Byron, Mike Preston, Kelly Preston
One Sheet: $5 - $10

METEOR
(1979 - AIP) Henry Fonda, Sean Connery, Natalie Woods
One Sheet: $7 - $15

METEOR MAN, THE
(1993 - MGM) Robert Townsend, Bill Cosby
One Sheet: $3 - $5   *Advance (3-D):$20-$40.*

METRO
(1997 - Touchstone) Eddie Murphy, Michael Rapaport
One Sheet: $5 - $10

METRO-GOLDWYN-MAYER STORY, THE
(1951 - MGM) Documentary
One Sheet: $15 - $30

METROPOLIS
(1926 - UFA) Dir: Fritz Lang, Alfred Abel, Gustav Frolich
One Sheet: $75,000 - $100,000   *Price is for original German release three sheet (either style). German one sheets are not known to exist.*

METROPOLIS
(1927 - Paramount) Dir: Fritz Lang, Alfred Abel, Gustav Frolich
One Sheet: $25,000 - $40,000   *Graven Images, pg. 19, 20, 21. First American release. Full color posters.*

METROPOLIS
(1984R - -) Dir: Fritz Lang, Alfred Abel, Gustav Frolich
One Sheet: $40 - $75   *Re-release.*

METROPOLITAN

(1935 - 20th Century Fox) Cesar Romero, Jane Darwell, Lawrence Tibbett
One Sheet: $100 - $200

METROPOLITAN
(1990 - -) Carolyn Farina, Edward Clements
One Sheet: $5 - $10

MEXICALI KID
(1938 - Monogram) Jack Randall
One Sheet: $75 - $150

MEXICALI ROSE
(1929 - Columbia) Barbara Stanwyck, Sam Hardy
One Sheet: $1,600 - $2,500   *Stanwyck's third film.*

MEXICALI ROSE
(1939 - Republic) Gene Autry, Smiley Burnette
One Sheet: $200 - $450

MEXICALI ROSE
(1942R - Republic) Gene Autry, Smiley Burnette
One Sheet: $75 - $150   *Re-release.*

MEXICAN HAYRIDE
(1948 - Universal) Bud Abbott, Lou Costello, Virginia Grey
One Sheet: $100 - $200

MEXICAN MANHUNT
(1953 - Monogram) George Brent, Hillary Brooke
One Sheet: $15 - $25

MEXICAN SPITFIRE
(1940 - RKO) Lupe Velez, Leon Errol
One Sheet: $50 - $100

MEXICAN SPITFIRE AT SEA
(1942 - RKO) Lupe Velez, Leon Errol, Charles "Buddy" Rogers
One Sheet: $40 - $75

MEXICAN SPITFIRE OUT WEST
(1940 - RKO) Lupe Velez, Leon Errol
One Sheet: $50 - $100

MEXICAN SPITFIRE SEES A GHOST
(1942 - RKO) Lupe Velez, Leon Errol
One Sheet: $40 - $75

MEXICAN SPITFIRE'S BABY, THE
(1941 - RKO) Lupe Velez, Leon Errol
One Sheet: $40 - $75

MEXICAN SPITFIRE'S BLESSED EVENT
(1943 - RKO) Lupe Velez, Leon Errol
One Sheet: $30 - $50

MEXICAN SPITFIRE'S ELEPHANT
(1942 - RKO) Lupe Velez, Leon Errol
One Sheet: $40 - $75

MEXICANA
(1945 - Republic) Constance Moore, Tito Guizar
One Sheet: $30 - $60

MGM CARTOONS STOCK
(1955 - MGM) Tom & Jerry & friends
One Sheet: $100 - $200   *Cartoon.*

MGM KARTOON KARNIVAL
(1954 - MGM) -
One Sheet: $100 - $200   *Cartoon. Full color stock poster.*

MGM SIXTY YEARS OF GREAT ENTERTAINMENT DIAMOND JUBILEE
(1984 - MGM/UA) -
One Sheet: $10 - $20

MGM'S BIG PARADE OF COMEDY
(1964 - MGM) Stars of Past and Present
One Sheet: $15 - $30

MI VIDA LOCA
(1994 - -) Angel Aviles, Seidy Lopez
One Sheet: $5 - $10

MIAMI BLUES
(1990 - Orion) Fred Ward, Alec Baldwin, Jennifer Jason Leigh
One Sheet: $7 - $15

MIAMI EXPOSE
(1956 - Columbia) Lee J. Cobb, Patricia Medina
One Sheet: $15 - $30

MIAMI RHAPSODY

(1995 - Disney) Sarah Jessica Parker, Antonio Banderas, Mia Farrow
One Sheet: $5 - $12

MIAMI STORY, THE
(1954 - Columbia) Barry Sullivan, Beverly Garland
One Sheet: $20 - $40

MICHAEL
(1996 - New Line) John Travolta, Andie McDowell
One Sheet: $7 - $15

MICHAEL AND HELGA
(1969 - AIP) Ruth Gassmann, Felix Franchy
One Sheet: $3 - $5

MICHAEL AND MARY
(1932 - Gainsborough) Herbert Marshall
One Sheet: $75 - $125

MICHAEL COLLINS
(1996 - Warner Bros.) Liam Neeson, Julia Roberts
One Sheet: $5 - $10

MICHAEL O'HALLORAN
(1937 - Republic) Wynne Gibson, Warren Hull
One Sheet: $30 - $60

MICHAEL O'HALLORAN
(1948 - Windsor) Scotty Beckett, Allene Roberts
One Sheet: $15 - $30

MICHAEL SHAYNE, PRIVATE DETECTIVE
(1941 - 20th Century Fox) Lloyd Nolan, Marjorie Weaver
One Sheet: $75 - $150

MICHAEL STROGOFF
(1926 - Universal) Ivan Moskine
One Sheet: $300 - $700

MICHELIN DEALERS' 007 SWEEPSTAKES
(1985 - Michelin/MGM/UA) Roger Moore
One Sheet: $10 - $20   *Cross-promotional poster for A VIEW TO A KILL.*

MICHIGAN KID
(1928 - Laemmle) Renee Adoree, Conrad Nagel
One Sheet: $350 - $750

MICHIGAN KID
(1947 - Universal) Jon Hall, Rita Johnson, Andy Devine
One Sheet: $40 - $75

MICKEY
(1919 - Mack Sennett) Mabel Normand, Lew Cody
One Sheet: $600 - $1,000

MICKEY
(1920R - -) Mabel Normand, Lew Cody
One Sheet: $250 - $500   *Re-release.*

MICKEY
(1948 - Pathe) Lois Butler, Bill Goodwin
One Sheet: $15 - $30

MICKEY AND THE SEAL
(1948 - RKO/Disney) Mickey Mouse
One Sheet: $1,900 - $3,000   *Cartoon. The Disney Poster, pg. 29.*

MICKEY DOWN UNDER
(1948 - RKO/Disney) Mickey Mouse
One Sheet: $1,900 - $3,000   *Cartoon. The Disney Poster, pg. 29.*

MICKEY IN ARABIA
(1932 - Columbia) Mickey & Minnie Mouse
One Sheet: $19,000 - $30,000   *Cartoon. Duotone. The Disney Poster, pg. 19.*

MICKEY MOUSE AND SILLY SYMPHONIES
(1932 - United Atrists) Mickey Mouse
One Sheet: $1,300 - $2,000   *Cartoon. Campaign Book for all Single-Reel Disney features from 1932 (48 pages).*

MICKEY MOUSE ANNIVERSARY SHOW, THE
(1970 - Disney) Mickey Mouse
One Sheet: $10 - $20

MICKEY MOUSE DISCO
(1979 - Disney) Mickey Mouse
One Sheet: $15 - $30   *Cartoon.*

MICKEY MOUSE FILM FESTIVAL
(1965 - Disney) Mickey Mouse

One Sheet: $30 - $50

MICKEY MOUSE IN HIS 8TH BIRTHDAY CELEBRATION
(1936 - United Artists) Mickey Mouse
One Sheet: $16,000 - $25,000   *Cartoon. 40x60 known to exist. Cartoon Movie Posters #65.*

MICKEY MOUSE STANDEE
(1937 - RKO/Disney) Mickey Mouse
One Sheet: $10,000 - $15,000   *Cartoon. 5 ft. tall, full color silkscreen lobby standee. This standee was used with 14x28 full color silkscreen cards. Cartoon Movie Posters #143.*

MICKEY MOUSE STOCK
(1931 - Columbia) Mickey Mouse, Disney Studio
One Sheet: $2,500 - $4,000   *Cartoon. Two color 14" x 28" stock poster.*

One Sheet

MICKEY MOUSE STOCK
(1935 - United Artists) Mickey Mouse
One Sheet: $13,000 - $20,000   *Cartoon. Full color. Released in conjunction with "Mickey's Rand Concert". States "Now In Technicolor" at top.*

MICKEY MOUSE STOCK
(1958 - Disney) Mickey Mouse
One Sheet: $250 - $500   *Cartoon. Special advertising poster (French). "Le Journal De Mickey"*

MICKEY ONE
(1965 - Columbia) Warren Beatty, Hurd Hatfield, Alexandra Stewart
One Sheet: $15 - $30

MICKEY THE KID
(1939 - Republic) Bruce Cabot, Ralph Byrd, ZaSu Pitts
One Sheet: $75 - $125

MICKEY THE MOUSE
(1929 - -) Mickey Mouse
One Sheet: $2,200 - $3,500   *Cartoon. Australian Stock Poster. Cartoon Movie Posters #28.*

MICKEY'S BARGAIN
(1930 - RKO) Mickey McGuire (Rooney)
One Sheet: $250 - $600

MICKEY'S BIG BROADCAST
(1930 - RKO) Mickey McGuire (Rooney)
One Sheet: $150 - $300

MICKEY'S BIRTHDAY PARTY
(1942 - RKO/Disney) Mickey Mouse
One Sheet: $4,000 - $6,000   *Cartoon.*

MICKEY'S BIRTHDAY PARTY
(1978R - Disney) Mickey Mouse
One Sheet: $10 - $20   *Re-release. Cartoon.*

MICKEY'S CHRISTMAS CAROL
(1983 - Disney) Mickey Mouse
One Sheet: $15 - $25

MICKEY'S CHRISTMAS CAROL/RESCUERS
(1983R - Disney) -
One Sheet: $10 - $20   *Re-release double feature poster. Cartoon.*

MICKEY'S CRUSADERS
(1931 - RKO) Mickey McGuire (Rooney)
One Sheet: $150 - $300

MICKEY'S GOOD DEED
(1932 - United Artists) Mickey Mouse
One Sheet: $45,000 - $60,000   *Cartoon. The Disney Poster, pg. 14. Cartoon Movie Posters*

#61.

MICKEY'S GOOD DEED
(1974R - Buena Vista/Disney) Mickey Mouse
One Sheet: $10 - $20   *Re-release. Cartoon. One Sheet is black & white.*

MICKEY'S IN LOVE
(1928 - FBO) Mickey McGuire (Rooney)
One Sheet: $500 - $850

MICKEY'S NIGHTMARE
(1932 - United Artists) Mickey Mouse
One Sheet: $45,000 - $60,000   *Cartoon. The Disney Poster, pg. 26.*

MICKEY'S PAL PLUTO
(1933 - United Artists) Mickey Mouse
One Sheet: $25,000 - $40,000   *Cartoon. The Disney Poster, pg. 27.*

MICKEY'S REVUE
(1932 - Columbia) Mickey Mouse
One Sheet: $19,000 - $30,000   *Cartoon. Duotone. The Disney Poster, pg. 19.*

MICKEY'S STAMPEDE
(1931 - RKO) Mickey McGuire (Rooney)
One Sheet: $500 - $850   *Sports (Football). Sports Movie Posters #178.*

MICKEY'S TRIUMPH
(1928 - FBO) Mickey McGuire (Rooney)
One Sheet: $500 - $850

MICKI AND MAUDE
(1984 - Columbia) Dudley Moore, Amy Irving
One Sheet: $3 - $5

MICRO-PHONIES
(1945 - Columbia) The Three Stooges (Curly)
One Sheet: $2,500 - $4,000   *Comedy short. Duotone.*

MIDAS RUN
(1969 - Cinerama) Richard Crenna, Anne Heywood, Fred Astaire
One Sheet: $15 - $25

MIDDLE AGE CRAZY
(1980 - 20th Century Fox) Bruce Dern, Ann-Margret
One Sheet: $5 - $10

MIDDLE OF THE NIGHT
(1959 - Columbia) Kim Novak, Fredric March
One Sheet: $15 - $25

MIDDLE WATCH, THE
(1930 - British International) Owen Nares, Jacqueline Logan
One Sheet: $75 - $150

MIDDLE WATCH
(1939 - Pathe) Jack Buchanan
One Sheet: $30 - $50

MIDNIGHT
(1934 - Universal) Sidney Fox, Humphrey Bogart
One Sheet: $1,300 - $2,000

MIDNIGHT
(1939 - Paramount) John Barrymore, Claudette Colbert, Don Ameche, Mary Astor
One Sheet: $250 - $600

MIDNIGHT ALARM
(1923 - Vitagraph) Alice Calhoun, Percy Marmont
One Sheet: $150 - $300

MIDNIGHT ALIBI
(1934 - First National) Richard Barthelmess
One Sheet: $150 - $300

MIDNIGHT CLEAR, A
(1992 - -) Ethan Hawke, Kevin Dillon
One Sheet: $10 - $20

MIDNIGHT CLUB
(1933 - Paramount) George Raft, Alison Skipworth
One Sheet: $250 - $600

MIDNIGHT COURT
(1937 - Warner Bros.) Ann Dvorak, John Litel
One Sheet: $75 - $125

MIDNIGHT COWBOY
(1969 - United Artists) Dustin Hoffman, Jon Voight
One Sheet: $50 - $100   *Academy Award: Best Picture, Best Direction(John*

Schlesinger). One Sheet (X-Rated):$100-$200.
Academy Award Movie Posters#252 & #254.

One Sheet

MIDNIGHT COWBOY
(1980R - United Artists) Dustin Hoffman, Jon Voight
One Sheet: $30 - $50 *Re-release.*

MIDNIGHT CROSSING
(1988 - Vestron) Faye Dunaway, Daniel J. Travanti
One Sheet: $5 - $10

MIDNIGHT DADDIES
(1930 - Sono Art/World Wide) Harry Gribbon, Andy Clyde
One Sheet: $100 - $200

MIDNIGHT EXPRESS
(1978 - Columbia) Brad Davis, Randy Quaid
One Sheet: $10 - $20

MIDNIGHT FROLICS
(1938 - Columbia) Color Rhapsodies, Ub Iwerks
One Sheet: $800 - $1,500 *Cartoon. Full color. The concept of Casper came from this cartoon. Cartoon Movie Posters #44.*

MIDNIGHT FROLICS
(1949 - Sonney Roadshows) -
One Sheet: $30 - $60 *Sexploitation.*

MIDNIGHT INTRUDER
(1938 - Monogram) Marjorie Reynolds, John King
One Sheet: $50 - $100

MIDNIGHT KISS
(1993 - Academy) Michelle Owens, Gregory A. Greer
One Sheet: $3 - $5

MIDNIGHT LACE
(1960 - Universal) Doris Day, Rex Harrison
One Sheet: $20 - $40

MIDNIGHT MADNESS
(1980 - Buena Vista) Debra Clinger, David Naughton, Michael J. Fox
One Sheet: $5 - $10

MIDNIGHT MADONNA
(1937 - Paramount) Warren William, Mady Correll
One Sheet: $50 - $100

MIDNIGHT MAN, THE
(1919 - Universal) James J. Corbett
One Sheet: $600 - $1,000 *Sports Movie Posters #355.*

MIDNIGHT MAN, THE
(1974 - Universal) Burt Lancaster, Cameron Mitchell
One Sheet: $5 - $10

MIDNIGHT MANHUNT
(1945 - Paramount) Ann Savage, William Gargan
One Sheet: $30 - $50

MIDNIGHT MARY
(1933 - MGM) Loretta Young, Andy Devine
One Sheet: $200 - $400

MIDNIGHT MENACE
(1946 - All-American) Lollipop Jones
One Sheet: $100 - $200 *Black cast. Duotone. Separate Cinema, pg. 134.*

MIDNIGHT MORALS
(1932 - Mayfair) Beryl Mercer, De Witt Jennings

One Sheet: $100 - $200

MIDNIGHT MYSTERY
(1930 - RKO) Lowell Sherman, Betty Compson
One Sheet: $150 - $300

MIDNIGHT PATROL, THE
(1933 - MGM) Laurel & Hardy
One Sheet: $1,900 - $3,000

MIDNIGHT PHANTOM
(1933 - Reliable) Reginald Denny, Claudia Dell
One Sheet: $150 - $300

MIDNIGHT RUN
(1988 - Universal) Robert DeNiro, Charles Grodin
One Sheet: $5 - $10

MIDNIGHT SPECIAL, THE
(1931 - Chesterfield) Glenn Tryon
One Sheet: $150 - $350

MIDNIGHT STORY, THE
(1957 - Universal) Tony Curtis, Marisa Pavan
One Sheet: $15 - $30

MIDNIGHT TAXI
(1937 - 20th Century Fox) Brian Donlevy, Frances Drake
One Sheet: $100 - $200

MIDNIGHT WARNING
(1932 - Mayfair) William Boyd, Claudia Dell
One Sheet: $100 - $200

MIDSHIPMAN, THE
(1925 - MGM) Ramon Novarro
One Sheet: $300 - $700

MIDSHIPMAN JACK
(1933 - RKO) Bruce Cabot, Betty Furness
One Sheet: $125 - $250

MIDSUMMER NIGHT'S DREAM, A
(1935 - Warner Bros.) James Cagney, Joe E. Brown, Olivia de Havilland (film debut)
One Sheet: $1,600 - $2,500

One Sheet

MIDSUMMER NIGHT'S DREAM, A
(1962 - Columbia) Suzanne Farrell, Edward Villella
One Sheet: $7 - $15

MIDSUMMER NIGHT'S DREAM, A
(1969 - Eagle) Derek Godfrey
One Sheet: $7 - $15

MIDSUMMER NIGHT'S SEX COMEDY, A
(1982 - Warner Bros.) Woody Allen, Mia Farrow
One Sheet: $5 - $10

MIDWAY
(1976 - Universal) Charlton Heston, Henry Fonda, Robert Mitchum
One Sheet: $5 - $10

MIDWINTER'S TALE, A
(1996 - Sony Classics) Joan Collins, Dir: Kenneth Branagh
One Sheet: $5 - $12

MIGHTY APHRODITE
(1995 - Miramax) Helena Bonham-Carter, Mira Sorvino, Woody Allen
One Sheet: $7 - $15 *Academy Award: Best Supporting Actress (Sorvino).*

MIGHTY BARNUM, THE
(1935 - 20th Century Fox) Wallace Beery, Adolphe Menjou, Virginia Bruce
One Sheet: $125 - $250

MIGHTY DUCKS, THE

(1992 - Disney) Emilio Estevez, Joss Ackland
One Sheet: $5 - $10 *Sports (Hockey). Sports Movie Posters #235.*

MIGHTY JOE YOUNG
(1949 - RKO) Joseph Young, Terry Moore, Ben Johnson
One Sheet: $250 - $600 *Harryhausen Effects. Graven Images, pg. 120.*

MIGHTY JOE YOUNG
(1953R - RKO) Joseph Young, Terry Moore
One Sheet: $150 - $300 *Re-release. Harryhausen effects.*

MIGHTY JOE YOUNG
(1959R - RKO) Joseph Young, Terry Moore, Ben Johnson
One Sheet: $75 - $125 *Re-release.*

MIGHTY JUNGLE
(1965 - Parade) Marshall Thompson, David Dalie
One Sheet: $5 - $10

MIGHTY LAK' A ROSE
(1923 - First National) James Rennie, Sam Hardy
One Sheet: $125 - $250

MIGHTY LIKE A MOOSE
(1926 - Pathe) Vivien Oakland, Charley Chase
One Sheet: $200 - $400

MIGHTY MCGURK, THE
(1946 - MGM) Wallace Beery, Edward Arnold
One Sheet: $50 - $100

MIGHTY MORPHIN POWER RANGERS: THE MOVIE
(1995 - 20th Century Fox) John Bosch, Steven Cardenas
One Sheet: $5 - $10

One Sheet

MIGHTY MOUSE MEETS BAD BILL BUNION
(1945 - 20th Century Fox) Mighty Mouse
One Sheet: $250 - $600 *Cartoon. Full color stock poster with printed title. Huge image of Mighty Mouse on yellow background.*

MIGHTY MOUSE MEETS JECKYLL AND HYDE CAT
(1944 - 20th Century Fox) Mighty Mouse
One Sheet: $250 - $600 *Cartoon. Full color stock poster with printed title. Huge image of Mighty Mouse on yellow background.*

MIGHTY MOUSE STOCK POSTER
(1944 - 20th Century Fox) (Blue background, yellow costume)
One Sheet: $250 - $600 *Cartoon. "...And Terry-Toons"*

MIGHTY MOUSE STOCK POSTER
(1945 - 20th Century Fox) Mighty Mouse
One Sheet: $250 - $600 *Cartoon. Mighty Mouse in blue costume, yellow background, Mighty Mouse in red letters across top. Cartoon Movie Posters#89. Graven Images, pg. 137.*

MIGHTY MOUSE STOCK POSTER
(195? - 20th Century Fox) Mighty Mouse
One Sheet: $200 - $400 *Cartoon.*

MIGHTY QUINN, THE
(1989 - MGM) Denzel Washington, Robert Townsend
One Sheet: $5 - $10

MIGHTY TREVE, THE
(1937 - Universal) Noah Beery, Jr., Barbara Reed
One Sheet: $75 - $150

MIGHTY URSUS
(1962 - United Artists) Ed Fury, Cristina Gajoni
One Sheet: $15 - $30

MIKADO, THE
(1939 - Universal) Kenny Baker, Jean Colin
One Sheet: $75 - $125

MIKADO, THE
(1967 - Warner Bros.) D'Oyly Carte Opera Company
One Sheet: $10 - $20

MIKE'S MURDER
(1982 - Warner Bros.) Debra Winger, Mark Keyloun
One Sheet: $3 - $5

MILAGRO BEANFIELD WAR, THE
(1988 - Universal) Ruben Blades, Richard Bradford, Robert Redford (Dir.)
One Sheet: $5 - $10

MILDRED PIERCE
(1945 - Warner Bros.) Joan Crawford, Jack Carson
One Sheet: $250 - $500 *Academy Award: Best Actress. Academy Award Movie Posters #101.*

MILDRED PIERCE
(1956R - Dominant) Joan Crawford, Jack Carson
One Sheet: $50 - $100 *Re-release.*

MILE-A-MINUTE KENDALL
(1918 - Famous Players/Lasky) Jack Pickford, Louise Huff
One Sheet: $150 - $300

MILITARY ACADEMY
(1940 - Columbia) Tommy Kelly, Bobby Jordan
One Sheet: $50 - $100

MILITARY ACADEMY WITH THAT TENTH AVENUE GANG
(1950 - Columbia) Stanley Clements, Myron Welton
One Sheet: $30 - $50

MILK MONEY
(1994 - Paramount) Melanie Griffith, Ed Harris
One Sheet: $5 - $10

MILKMAN, THE
(1950 - Universal) Donald O'Connor, Jimmy Durante
One Sheet: $50 - $100

MILKY WAY, THE
(1936 - Paramount) Harold Lloyd, Adolphe Menjou
One Sheet: $600 - $1,000

MILKY WAY, THE
(1969 - U-M) Paul Frankeur, Laurent Terzieff
One Sheet: $3 - $5

MILL OF THE STONE WOMEN
(1963 - Parade) Pierre Brice, Scilla Gabel
One Sheet: $15 - $25

One Sheet

MILL ON THE FLOSS, THE
(1939 - Morgan) Frank Lawton, Geraldine Fitzgerald, James Mason
One Sheet: $100 - $200

MILLENNIUM
(1989 - 20th Century Fox) Kris Kristofferson, Cheryl Ladd
One Sheet: $3 - $5

MILLER'S CROSSING

(1990 - 20th Century Fox) Albert Finney, Gabriel Byrne, John Turturro
One Sheet: $15 - $25

MILLERSON CASE, THE
(1947 - Columbia) Warner Baxter, Nancy Saunders
One Sheet: $40 - $75   *Crime Doctor series.*

MILLIE
(1931 - RKO) Joan Blondell, Helen Twelvetrees
One Sheet: $150 - $300

MILLIE'S DAUGHTER
(1947 - Columbia) Gladys George, Gay Nelson
One Sheet: $30 - $60

MILLION DOLLAR BABY
(1934 - Monogram) Arline Judge, Ray Walker
One Sheet: $150 - $300

MILLION DOLLAR BABY
(1941 - Warner Bros.) Jeffrey Lynn, Priscilla Lane, Ronald Reagan
One Sheet: $75 - $150

MILLION DOLLAR CAT, THE
(1944 - MGM) Tom & Jerry
One Sheet: $500 - $800   *Cartoon. Full color stone litho. Cartoon Movie Posters #269.*

MILLION DOLLAR COLLAR, THE
(1929 - Warner Bros.) Rin-Tin-Tin
One Sheet: $250 - $500

MILLION DOLLAR KID
(1943 - Monogram) East Side Kids, Noah Beery
One Sheet: $75 - $125

MILLION DOLLAR LEGS
(1932 - Paramount Publix) W. C. Fields, Jack Oakie
One Sheet: $700 - $1,200

MILLION DOLLAR LEGS
(1939 - Paramount) Betty Grable, Jackie Coogan
One Sheet: $250 - $500

MILLION DOLLAR MANHUNT
(1956 - Anglo) Richard Denning, Carole Mathews
One Sheet: $15 - $25   *AKA: ASSIGNMENT REDHEAD.*

MILLION DOLLAR MERMAID
(1952 - MGM) Esther Williams, Victor Mature
One Sheet: $50 - $100

MILLION DOLLAR MYSTERY, THE
(1914 - Thanhouser) -
One Sheet: $350 - $750   *Serial. 4 Chapters.*

MILLION DOLLAR MYSTERY
(1987 - -) Eddie Deezen, Penny Baker
One Sheet: $2 - $3

MILLION DOLLAR PURSUIT
(1951 - Republic) Penny Edwards, Steve Flagg
One Sheet: $15 - $30

MILLION DOLLAR RACKET
(1937 - Victory) Herman Brix, Joan Barclay
One Sheet: $50 - $100

MILLION DOLLAR RANSOM
(1934 - Universal) Phillips Holmes, Edward Arnold
One Sheet: $75 - $150

MILLION DOLLAR WEEKEND
(1948 - Eagle-Lion) Gene Raymond, Stephanie Paull
One Sheet: $30 - $60

MILLION EYES OF SU-MURU, THE
(1967 - AIP) Frankie Avalon, Shirley Eaton
One Sheet: $10 - $20

MILLIONAIRE, THE
(1919 - King Bee) Billy West
One Sheet: $250 - $500

MILLIONAIRE, THE
(1931 - Warner Bros.) George Arliss, Evalyn Knapp, James Cagney
One Sheet: $500 - $800   *Cagney not pictured on One Sheet or Lobby Cards.*

MILLIONAIRE FOR CHRISTY, A
(1951 - 20th Century Fox) Fred MacMurray, Eleanor Parker

One Sheet: $15 - $30

MILLIONAIRE PLAYBOY
(1949 - RKO) Joe Penner, Linda Hayes, Richard Lane
One Sheet: $30 - $60

MILLIONAIRES IN PRISON
(1940 - RKO) Lee Tracy, Linda Hayes
One Sheet: $50 - $100

MILLIONAIRESS, THE
(1961 - 20th Century Fox) Sophia Loren, Peter Sellers
One Sheet: $15 - $30

MILLIONS IN THE AIR
(1935 - Paramount) John Howard, Wendy Barrie
One Sheet: $50 - $100

MILLIONS LIKE US
(1943 - Gainsborough) Eric Portman, Patricia Roc
One Sheet: $30 - $60

MILLS BROTHERS ON PARADE
(1956 - Universal) Mills Brothers
One Sheet: $75 - $150   *Musical short.*

MILLS OF THE GODS
(1934 - Columbia) May Robson, Fay Wray
One Sheet: $200 - $400

MIMI
(1934 - First Division) Gertrude Lawrence, Douglas Fairbanks Jr.
One Sheet: $100 - $200

MIN AND BILL
(1930 - MGM) Marie Dressler, Wallace Beery
One Sheet: $500 - $800   *Academy Award: Best Actress. Academy Award Movie Posters #22.*

MINA TANNENBAUM
(1995 - New Yorker) Romane Bohringer, Elsa Zyiberstein
One Sheet: $5 - $10

MIND BENDERS, THE
(1963 - AIP) Dirk Bogarde, Mary Ure
One Sheet: $10 - $20

MIND NEEDER
(1938 - Columbia) Charley Chase, Ann Doran
One Sheet: $100 - $200   *Comedy short. Duotone.*

MIND OF MR. SOAMES, THE
(1970 - Columbia) Terence Stamp, Robert Vaughn
One Sheet: $3 - $5

MIND READER, THE
(1933 - First National) Constance Cummings, Warren William
One Sheet: $125 - $250

MIND SNATCHERS, THE
(1972 - Cinerama) Christopher Walken, Ronny Cox
One Sheet: $7 - $15   *AKA: THE HAPPINESS CAGE.*

MIND WARP
(1981 - New World) Edward Albert, Erin Moran
One Sheet: $15 - $25

MIND YOUR OWN BUSINESS
(1937 - Paramount) Charlie Ruggles, Alice Brady
One Sheet: $75 - $125

MINDFIELD
(1989 - Image) Michael Ironside, Lisa Langlois
One Sheet: $3 - $5

MINE OWN EXECUTIONER
(1947 - 20th Century Fox) Burgess Meredith, Dulcie Gray
One Sheet: $30 - $60

MINE WITH THE IRON DOOR, THE
(1936 - Columbia) Richard Arlen
One Sheet: $100 - $200

MINESWEEPER
(1943 - Paramount) Richard Arlen, Jean Parker
One Sheet: $30 - $60

MINI-SKIRT MOB, THE
(1968 - AIP) Jeremy Slate, Sherry Jackson
One Sheet: $15 - $35   *Biker gang.*

MINISTRY OF FEAR
(1944 - Paramount) Ray Milland, Marjorie Reynolds
One Sheet: $250 - $500

One Sheet

MINIVER STORY, THE
(1950 - MGM) Greer Garson, Walter Pidgeon
One Sheet: $30 - $60

MINNIE
(1922 - First National) Marshall Neilan, Leatrice Loy
One Sheet: $250 - $500

MINNIE AND MOSKOWITZ
(1971 - Universal) Gena Rowlands, Seymour Cassel
One Sheet: $3 - $5

MINOTAUR, THE
(1961 - United Artists) Bob Mathias, Rosanna Schiaffino
One Sheet: $15 - $30

MINSTREL MAN
(1944 - PRC) Benny Fields, Gladys George
One Sheet: $75 - $150   *Separate Cinema, pg. 110.*

MINUTE TO PRAY, A SECOND TO DIE, A
(1968 - Cinerama) Alex Cord, Robert Ryan
One Sheet: $10 - $20

MINX, THE
(1969 - Cambist Films) Jan Sterling, Robert Rodan
One Sheet: $10 - $20

MIRACLE, THE
(1959 - Warner Bros.) Carroll Baker, Roger Moore
One Sheet: $15 - $25

MIRACLE IN HARLEM
(1948 - Screen Guild) Stepin Fetchit, Sheila Guyse
One Sheet: $150 - $300   *Black cast. Separate Cinema, pg. 143.*

MIRACLE IN SOHO
(1957 - Rank) John Gregson, Belinda Lee
One Sheet: $15 - $25

MIRACLE IN THE RAIN
(1956 - Warner Bros.) Jane Wyman, Van Johnson
One Sheet: $15 - $35

MIRACLE KID, THE
(1941 - PRC) Tom Neal, Carol Hughes
One Sheet: $30 - $50   *Sports (Boxing).*

MIRACLE MAN, THE
(1919 - Paramount) Lon Chaney, Betty Compson, Thomas Meighan
One Sheet: $900 - $1,600

MIRACLE MAN, THE
(1932 - Paramount Publix) Sylvia Sidney, Boris Karloff
One Sheet: $700 - $1,200

MIRACLE MILE
(1989 - -) Anthony Edwards, Mare Winningham
One Sheet: $5 - $10

MIRACLE OF LOVE, THE
(1969 - Times) Biggi Freyer, Katarina Haertel
One Sheet: $3 - $5

MIRACLE OF MANHATTAN, THE
(1921 - Selznick) Elaine Hammerstein

One Sheet: $350 - $750

MIRACLE OF MORGAN'S CREEK, THE
(1944 - Paramount) Eddie Bracken, Betty Hutton
One Sheet: $200 - $400

MIRACLE OF OUR LADY OF FATIMA, THE
(1952 - Warner Bros.) Gilbert Roland, Angela Clark
One Sheet: $50 - $100

MIRACLE OF SISTER BEATRICE, THE
(1939 - Park Lane) -
One Sheet: $30 - $50

MIRACLE OF THE BELLS, THE
(1948 - RKO) Fred MacMurray, Valli, Frank Sinatra
One Sheet: $75 - $150

MIRACLE OF THE HILLS, THE
(1959 - 20th Century Fox) Rex Reason, Jay North
One Sheet: $15 - $30

MIRACLE OF THE WHITE REINDEER, THE
(1960 - -) -
One Sheet: $15 - $25   *Cartoon.*

MIRACLE OF THE WHITE STALLIONS
(1963 - Buena Vista) Robert Taylor, Lilli Palmer
One Sheet: $15 - $25

MIRACLE ON 34TH STREET
(1947 - 20th Century Fox) Maureen O'Hara, John Payne, Natalie Wood, Edmund Gwenn
One Sheet: $600 - $1,000   *Academy Award: Best Supporting Actor(Gwenn). Academy Award Movie Posters #114.*

MIRACLE ON 34TH STREET
(1994 - 20th Century Fox) Richard Attenborough
One Sheet: $5 - $10

MIRACLE ON MAIN STREET
(1939 - Columbia) Margo, Walter Abel
One Sheet: $40 - $75

Three Sheet

MIRACLE RIDER
(1934 - Mascot) Tom Mix, Jean Gale
One Sheet: $300 - $700   *Serial. 15 Chapters.*

MIRACLE WOMAN, THE
(1931 - Columbia) Barbara Stanwyck, David Manners
One Sheet: $2,200 - $3,500

MIRACLE WORKER, THE
(1962 - United Artists) Anne Bancroft, Patty Duke
One Sheet: $40 - $75   *Academy Award: Best Actress(Bancroft), Best Supporting Actress(Duke). Academy Award Movie Posters #210 & #212.*

MIRACLES FOR SALE
(1939 - MGM) Robert Young, Frank Craven, Florence Rice
One Sheet: $125 - $250   *Graven Images, pg. 94.*

MIRACLES OF THE JUNGLE
(1921 - Warner Bros.) -
One Sheet: $250 - $500   *Serial. 15 Chapters.*

MIRACULOUS JOURNEY
(1948 - Film Classics) Rory Calhoun, Andrew Long
One Sheet: $20 - $40

MIRAGE
(1965 - Universal) Gregory Peck, Diane Baker
One Sheet: $15 - $30

MIRANDA
(1948 - Eagle-Lion) Glynis Johns, Googie
Withers
One Sheet: $15 - $25

MIRROR CRACK'D, THE
(1980 - AFD) Elizabeth Taylor, Tony Curtis,
Angela Lansbury
One Sheet: $7 - $15

MIRROR HAS TWO FACES, THE
(1996 - TriStar) Barbara Streisand, Jeff
Bridges, Lauren Bacall
One Sheet: $5 - $12

MISADVENTURES OF MERLIN JONES
(1964 - Buena Vista/Disney) Tommy Kirk,
Annette Funicello
One Sheet: $30 - $50

MISBEHAVING HUSBANDS
(1940 - PRC) Harry Langdon, Ralph Byrd
One Sheet: $75 - $125

MISBEHAVING LADIES
(1931 - First National) Lila Lee, Ben Lyon
One Sheet: $100 - $200

MISCHIEF
(1985 - 20th Century Fox) Catherine Mary
Stewart, Doug McKeon, Jami Gertz
One Sheet: $3 - $5

MISERY
(1990 - Columbia) James Caan, Kathy Bates
One Sheet: $7 - $15   *Academy
Award: Best Actress(Bates). Academy Award
Movie Posters #372.*

MISFIT SAILOR, A
(1926 - Educational) Billy Dooley, Vera
Steadman
One Sheet: $125 - $250

MISFITS, THE
(1961 - United Artists) Clark Gable, Marilyn
Monroe
One Sheet: $150 - $300   *Price is for
style A one sheet. One Sheet (Style B,
puzzle):$200-$400. Cowboy Movie Posters #311.*

MISHIMA
(1985 - M Film) Ken Ogata, Narrated by Roy
Scheider
One Sheet: $2 - $3

MISLEADING LADY
(1932 - Paramount Publix) Claudette Colbert,
Edmund Lowe
One Sheet: $350 - $750

MISLEADING WIDOW, THE
(1919 - Paramount-Artcraft) Billie Burke
One Sheet: $350 - $750

MISS ANNIE ROONEY
(1942 - United Artists) Shirley Temple, William
Gargan
One Sheet: $75 - $150

MISS FANE'S BABY IS STOLEN
(1934 - Paramount) Jack LaRue, Baby Leroy
One Sheet: $100 - $200

MISS FIRECRACKER
(1989 - -) Holly Hunter, Mary Steenburben
One Sheet: $7 - $15

MISS GRANT TAKES RICHMOND
(1949 - Columbia) Lucille Ball, William Holden,
James Gleason
One Sheet: $75 - $125

MISS LULU BETT
(1921 - Paramount) Lois Wilson, Milton Sills
One Sheet: $150 - $300

MISS MARY
(1986 - New World) Julie Christie, Nacha
Guevara
One Sheet: $2 - $3

MISS MINK OF 1949
(1949 - 20th Century Fox) Jimmy Lydon, Lois
Collier
One Sheet: $30 - $50

MISS PACIFIC FLEET
(1935 - Warner Bros.) Joan Blondell, Warren
Hull

MISS PINKERTON
(1932 - First National) Joan Blondell, George
Brent
One Sheet: $75 - $150

MISS POLLY
(1941 - United Artists) ZaSu Pitts, Slim
Summerville
One Sheet: $75 - $125

MISS ROBIN CRUSOE
(1952 - 20th Century Fox) Amanda Blake,
George Nader
One Sheet: $20 - $40

MISS ROBIN HOOD
(1952 - Group 3) Margaret Rutherford, Richard
Hearne
One Sheet: $15 - $25

MISS SADIE THOMPSON
(1953 - Columbia) Rita Hayworth, Jose Ferrer
One Sheet: $125 - $250

MISS SUSIE SLAGLE'S
(1946 - Paramount) Lillian Gish, Veronica Lake
One Sheet: $100 - $200

One Sheet

MISS TATLOCK'S MILLIONS
(1948 - Paramount) John Lund, Wanda Hendrix
One Sheet: $20 - $40

MISS V FROM MOSCOW
(1942 - PRC) Lola Lane, Noel Madison
One Sheet: $30 - $50

MISSED FORTUNE, A
(1952 - Columbia) The Three Stooges (Shemp)
One Sheet: $200 - $400   *Comedy short.
Duotone. Remake of HEALTHY, WEALTHY, AND
DUMB.*

One Sheet

MISSILE MONSTERS
(1958 - Republic) Walter Reed, Lois Collier
One Sheet: $75 - $125

MISSILE TO THE MOON
(1959 - Astor) Richard Travis, Cathy Downs
One Sheet: $50 - $100

MISSILES FROM HELL
(1960 - Eros) Michael Rennie, Particia Medina
One Sheet: $30 - $50   *AKA:
UNSEEN HEROES; V1; BATTLE OF THE V1.*

MISSING
(1982 - Universal) Jack Lemmon, Sissy Spacek
One Sheet: $2 - $3

MISSING CORPSE, THE
(1945 - PRC) J. Edward Bromberg, Frank
Jenks

MISSING DAUGHTERS
(1939 - Columbia) Richard Arlen, Rochelle
Hudson
One Sheet: $75 - $150

MISSING EVIDENCE
(1939 - Universal) Preston Foster, Irene
Hervey
One Sheet: $50 - $100

MISSING GIRLS
(1936 - Chesterfield) Muriel Evans, Sidney
Blackmer
One Sheet: $50 - $100

MISSING GUEST, THE
(1936 - Universal) Paul Kelly, Constance
Moore
One Sheet: $75 - $125

MISSING HEAD, THE
(1953R - Realart) Lon Chaney, Brenda Joyce
One Sheet: $50 - $100   *Re-release.*

MISSING IN ACTION
(1984 - Cannon) Chuck Norris, M. Emmet
Walsh
One Sheet: $5 - $10

MISSING IN ACTION 2: THE BEGINNING
(1985 - Cannon) Chuck Norris, Soon-Tek Oh
One Sheet: $3 - $5

MISSING JUROR, THE
(1944 - Columbia) Jim Bannon, Janis Carter
One Sheet: $30 - $50

MISSING LADY, THE
(1946 - Monogram) Kane Richmond, Barbara
Reed
One Sheet: $30 - $50

MISSING MOUSE, THE
(1953 - MGM) Tom & Jerry
One Sheet: $250 - $500   *Cartoon. Full
color stone litho.*

MISSING PEOPLE
(1940 - Monogram) Will Fyffe
One Sheet: $50 - $100

MISSING TEN DAYS
(1941 - Columbia) Rex Harrison, Karen Verne
One Sheet: $75 - $125

MISSING WITNESSES
(1937 - First National) Dick Purcell, John Litel
One Sheet: $50 - $100

MISSING WOMEN
(1951 - Republic) Penny Edwards, James
Millican
One Sheet: $15 - $30

MISSION, THE
(1986 - Warner Bros.) Robert DeNiro, Jeremy
Irons
One Sheet: $10 - $20

MISSION GALACTICA: THE CYLON ATTACK
(1979 - Universal) Richard Hatch, Dirk
Benedict
One Sheet: $30 - $50   *Battlestar
Galactica TV tie-in.*

MISSION: IMPOSSIBLE
(1968 - Paramount) Peter Graves, Martin
Landau
One Sheet: $75 - $125   *Foreign film
release of an American TV program.*

MISSION: IMPOSSIBLE
(1996 - Paramount) Tom Cruise, Jon Voight
One Sheet: $7 - $15   *Action-thriller.
Advance Style: $12-$20.*

MISSION MARS
(1968 - Sagittarius) Darren McGavin, Nick
Adams
One Sheet: $10 - $20

MISSION OF JUSTICE
(1992 - -) Brigitte Nielson, Jeff Wincott
One Sheet: $3 - $5

MISSION OVER KOREA
(1953 - Columbia) John Hodiak, Audrey Totter
One Sheet: $15 - $25

MISSION STARDUST
(1968 - Times) Essy Persson, Lang Jeffries,
John Karelsen

MISSION TO MOSCOW
(1943 - Warner Bros.) Walter Huston, Ann
Harding
One Sheet: $40 - $75

MISSIONARY, THE
(1982 - -) Michael Palin, Maggie Smith
One Sheet: $3 - $5

MISSISSIPPI
(1935 - Paramount) Bing Crosby, W. C. Fields
One Sheet: $1,300 - $2,000

One Sheet

MISSISSIPPI BURNING
(1988 - Orion) Gene Hackman, Willem Dafoe
One Sheet: $5 - $12

MISSISSIPPI GAMBLER, THE
(1929 - Universal) Joseph Schildkraut, Joan
Bennett
One Sheet: $250 - $600

MISSISSIPPI GAMBLER
(1942 - Universal) Kent Taylor, Frances
Langford
One Sheet: $40 - $80

MISSISSIPPI GAMBLER, THE
(1953 - Universal) Tyrone Power, Piper Laurie
One Sheet: $75 - $125

MISSISSIPPI MASALA
(1992 - Goldwyn) Denzel Washington
One Sheet: $5 - $10

MISSISSIPPI MERMAID
(1970 - United Artists) Jean Paul Belmondo,
Catherine Deneuve
One Sheet: $10 - $20

MISSISSIPPI MOODS
(1940 - Sack) Hattie McDaniel, Willie Best
One Sheet: $250 - $500   *Black cast.
Separate Cinema, pg. 132.*

MISSISSIPPI RHYTHM
(1949 - Monogram) Jimmie Davis, Lee "Lasses"
White, James Flavin
One Sheet: $30 - $50

MISSOURI BREAKS, THE
(1976 - United Artists) Marlon Brando, Jack
Nicholson
One Sheet: $20 - $40   *Cowboy
Movie Posters #s 345, 346.*

MISSOURI OUTLAW
(1941 - Republic) Don "Red" Barry
One Sheet: $30 - $60

MISSOURI TRAVELER, THE
(1957 - Buena Vista) Brandon de Wilde, Lee
Marvin
One Sheet: $15 - $25

MISSOURIANS, THE
(1950 - Republic) Monte Hale, Paul Hurst
One Sheet: $40 - $75

MISTAKEN IDENTITY
(1919 - Triangle) Anita King
One Sheet: $100 - $200

MISTAKEN IDENTITY
(1941 - -) -
One Sheet: $50 - $100

MISTER 880
(1950 - 20th Century Fox) Burt Lancaster,
Edmund Gwenn
One Sheet: $30 - $50

MISTER BIG
(1943 - Universal) Donald O'Connor, Gloria Jean
One Sheet: $50 - $100

MISTER BUDDWING
(1966 - MGM) James Garner, Jean Simmons
One Sheet: $7 - $15

MISTER CORY
(1957 - Universal) Tony Curtis, Martha Hyer
One Sheet: $20 - $40

MISTER DRAKE'S DUCK
(1951 - United Artists) Douglas Fairbanks Jr., Yolande Donlan
One Sheet: $15 - $30

MISTER FROST
(1990 - -) Jeff Goldblum, Alan Bates, Kathy Baker
One Sheet: $3 - $5

MISTER HOBO
(1935 - Gaumont) George Arliss, Gene Garrard
One Sheet: $75 - $150

MISTER MOSES
(1965 - United Artists) Robert Mitchum, Carroll Baker
One Sheet: $15 - $25

MISTER ROBERTS
(1955 - Warner Bros.) Henry Fonda, James Cagney, William Powell (his last film)
One Sheet: $75 - $150   *Academy Award Movie Posters #165.*

MISTER ROCK AND ROLL
(1957 - Paramount) Alan Freed, Lionel Hampton, All-star rock cast
One Sheet: $150 - $300   *Rock 'n' Roll.*

MISTER SCOUTMASTER
(1953 - 20th Century Fox) Clifton Webb, Edmund Gwenn
One Sheet: $15 - $30

MISTER UNIVERSE
(1950 - -) See MR. UNIVERSE

MISTER V
(1941 - United Artists) Leslie Howard, Mary Morris
One Sheet: $40 - $75

MISTRESS
(1991 - International Rainbow) Robert DeNiro, Danny Aiello, Eli Wallach
One Sheet: $5 - $10

MISTRESS OF THE SEAS
(1993 - Columbia) -
One Sheet: $3 - $5

MISTRESS OF THE WORLD, THE
(1922 - Paramount) Mia May
One Sheet: $200 - $400   *Serial. 4 Chapters.*

MISTY
(1961 - 20th Century Fox) David Ladd, Arthur O'Connell
One Sheet: $7 - $15

MITCHELL
(1975 - Allied Artists) Joe Don Baker, Martin Balsam
One Sheet: $3 - $5

MITT THE PRINCE
(1920 - Pathe) Snub Pollard
One Sheet: $150 - $300

MIX ME A PERSON
(1962 - Wessex) Anne Baxter, Donald Sinden
One Sheet: $7 - $15

MIXED COMPANY
(1974 - United Artists) Barbara Harris, Joseph Bologna
One Sheet: $3 - $5

MIXED NUTS
(1994 - TriStar) Steve Martin, Juliette Lewis
One Sheet: $3 - $5

MNASIDIKA
(1969 - AFD) -
One Sheet: $5 - $10

MO' BETTER BLUES
(1990 - Universal) Denzel Washington, Spike Lee

One Sheet: $10 - $20   *Black cast.*

MO' MONEY
(1992 - Columbia) Daman Wayans, Marlon
One Sheet: $5 - $10   *Black cast.*

MOANA
(1926 - -) Ta'avale Fa'amgase, T'ugaita, Dir: Robert Flaherty
One Sheet: $150 - $300

MOB, THE
(1951 - Columbia) Broderick Crawford, Betty Buehler
One Sheet: $20 - $40

MOB TOWN
(1941 - Universal) The Dead End Kids, The Little Tough Guys, Dick Foran
One Sheet: $75 - $150

MOBSTERS
(1991 - Universal) Patrick Dempsey, Christian Slater
One Sheet: $5 - $10

MOBY DICK
(1930 - Warner Bros.) John Barrymore, Joan Bennett
One Sheet: $800 - $1,500

MOBY DICK
(1956 - Warner Bros.) Gregory Peck, Orson Welles, Richard Basehart
One Sheet: $75 - $125

MOCKERY
(1927 - MGM) Lon Chaney
One Sheet: $600 - $1,000

MODEL AND THE MARRIAGE BROKER, THE
(1952 - 20th Century Fox) Jeanne Crain, Thelma Ritter
One Sheet: $15 - $30

MODEL FOR MURDER
(1960 - Parroch) Keith Andes, Hazel Court
One Sheet: $10 - $20

MODEL MURDER CASE, THE
(1964 - Cinema 5) Ian Hendry, Ronald Fraser
One Sheet: $5 - $10

MODEL SHOP, THE
(1969 - Columbia) Anouk Aimee, Gary Lockwood, Alexandra Hay
One Sheet: $3 - $5

MODEL WIFE
(1941 - Universal) Dick Powell, Lee Bowman, Joan Blondell
One Sheet: $50 - $100

MODERN GIRLS
(1986 - -) Daphne Zuniga, Virginia Madsen, Cynthia Gibb
One Sheet: $3 - $5

MODERN HERO, A
(1934 - Warner Bros.) Richard Barthelmess, Jean Muir
One Sheet: $75 - $150

MODERN LOVE
(1929 - Universal) Jean Hersholt, Charley Chase, Kathryn Crawford
One Sheet: $250 - $500

MODERN MARRIAGE, A
(1950 - Monogram) Reed Hadley, Margaret Field
One Sheet: $15 - $25

MODERN MINSTRELS
(1930 - A. D. W) Cliff Nazzarro
One Sheet: $250 - $600   *Black cast. Separate Cinema, pg. 108.*

MODERN MOTHERHOOD
(1934 - Roadshow Attractions) -
One Sheet: $100 - $200   *Exploitation.*

MODERN MUSKETEER, A
(1917 - Artcraft) Douglas Fairbanks
One Sheet: $250 - $600

MODERN PROBLEMS
(1981 - 20th Century Fox) Chevy Chase, Patti D'Arbanville
One Sheet: $3 - $5

MODERN ROMANCE
(1981 - Columbia) Albert Brooks, George Kennedy

One Sheet: $3 - $5

MODERN TIMES
(1936 - United Artists) Charlie Chaplin, Paulette Goddard
One Sheet: $7,500 - $12,000   *Chaplin's last silent film. One Sheet(Leader Press):$400-$800.*

Title Card

MODERN TIMES
(1959R - United Artists) Charlie Chaplin, Paulette Goddard
One Sheet: $100 - $200   *Re-release.*

MODERN TIMES
(1972R - United Artists) Charlie Chaplin, Paulette Goddard
One Sheet: $20 - $40   *Re-release.*

MODERNS, THE
(1988 - -) Keith Carradine, Linda Fiorentino
One Sheet: $10 - $20

MODESTY BLAISE
(1966 - 20th Century Fox) Monica Vitti, Terence Stamp
One Sheet: $30 - $50   *Bob Peak art.*

MOGAMBO
(1953 - MGM) Clark Gable, Ava Gardner, Grace Kelly
One Sheet: $125 - $250

One Sheet

MOHAWK
(1955 - 20th Century Fox) Scott Brady, Rita Gam
One Sheet: $10 - $20

MOJAVE FIREBRAND
(1944 - Republic) Gabby Hayes, Bill Elliott
One Sheet: $30 - $60

MOJAVE KID, THE
(1927 - R-C Pictures) Bob Steele, Lillian Gilmore
One Sheet: $100 - $200

MOKEY
(1942 - MGM) Donna Reed, Dan Dailey, Bobby Blake
One Sheet: $30 - $50

MOLE PEOPLE, THE
(1956 - Universal) John Agar, Cynthia Patrick
One Sheet: $250 - $600   *Graven Images, pg. 184.*

MOLE PEOPLE, THE
(1964R - Universal) John Agar, Cynthia Patrick
One Sheet: $75 - $125   *Re-release.*

MOLESTER, THE
(1963 - Hammer/Pathe) Gwen Watford, Patrick Allen
One Sheet: $50 - $100   *AKA: NEVER*

One Sheet: $3 - $5

TAKE CANDY FROM A STRANGER (British).

MOLLY
(1950 - Paramount) Gertrude Berg, Philip Loeb
One Sheet: $15 - $25

MOLLY AND LAWLESS JOHN
(1972 - Malibu) Vera Miles, Sam Elliott, Cynthia Myers
One Sheet: $5 - $10

MOLLY AND ME
(1945 - 20th Century Fox) Gracie Fields, Monty Woolley
One Sheet: $50 - $100

MOLLY CURES A COWBOY
(1940 - RKO) Ray Whitley, Lee "Lasses" White
One Sheet: $40 - $75

MOLLY MAGUIRES, THE
(1970 - Paramount) Richard Harris, Sean Connery, Samantha Eggar
One Sheet: $5 - $10

MOLLY O
(1921 - Associated Producers) Mabel Normand
One Sheet: $800 - $1,500

MOLLYCODDLE, THE
(1920 - United Artists) Douglas Fairbanks, Ruth Renick
One Sheet: $600 - $1,000

MOM AND DAD
(1948 - Hallmark) Hardie Albright, Sarah Blake
One Sheet: $50 - $100   *Controversial sex education film.*

MOM AND DAD SAVE THE WORLD
(1992 - Warner Bros.) Teri Garr, John Lovitz
One Sheet: $3 - $5

MOMENT BY MOMENT
(1978 - Universal) Lily Tomlin, John Travolta
One Sheet: $15 - $25

MOMENT OF DANGER
(1961 - Warner Bros.) Trevor Howard, Dorothy Dandridge
One Sheet: $15 - $30

MOMENT TO MOMENT
(1966 - Universal) Jean Seberg, Honor Blackman
One Sheet: $15 - $30

MOMMIE DEAREST
(1981 - Paramount) Faye Dunaway, Steve Forrest
One Sheet: $7 - $15

MONA LISA
(1986 - Handmade) Bob Hoskins, Cathy Tyson, Michael Caine
One Sheet: $7 - $15

MONARCH OF THE MOUNTAINS
(196? - Mountain West) Narrator: Slim Pickens
One Sheet: $3 - $7   *Documentary.*

MONARCH OF THE MOUNTAINS
(1982 - Western Cinema) -
One Sheet: $5 - $10

MONDO CANE
(1963 - Times) -
One Sheet: $75 - $150   *Documentary on eccentric human behavior.*

MONDO PAZZO
(1965 - Rizzoli) -
One Sheet: $30 - $50   *Documentary.*

MONDO TRASHO
(1970 - Dreamland) Divine, Mink Stole
One Sheet: $75 - $150

MONEY AND THE WOMAN
(1940 - Warner Bros.) Jeffrey Lynn, Brenda Marshall
One Sheet: $30 - $50

MONEY FOR NOTHING
(1993 - Buena Vista) John Cusack, Michael Madsen, Debi Mazar
One Sheet: $3 - $5

MONEY FROM HOME
(1953 - Paramount) Dean Martin, Jerry Lewis, Pat Crowley
One Sheet: $75 - $125

MONEY JUNGLE, THE

(1968 - Commonwealth United) John Ericson, Lola Albright, Leslie Parrish
One Sheet: $3 - $5

MONEY MADNESS
(1948 - Film Classics) Hugh Beaumont, Frances Rafferty
One Sheet: $30 - $50

MONEY MEANS NOTHING
(1934 - Monogram) Wallace Ford, Gloria Shea
One Sheet: $100 - $200

MONEY MONEY MONEY
(1972 - Cinerama) Lino Ventura, Jacques Brel
One Sheet: $5 - $10

MONEY ON YOUR LIFE
(1938 - Educational) Danny Kaye, Charles Kemper
One Sheet: $100 - $200

MONEY PIT, THE
(1986 - Universal) Shelley Long, Tom Hanks
One Sheet: $5 - $10

MONEY TALKS
(1926 - —) Clair Windsor, Owen Moore, Bert Roach
One Sheet: $150 - $300

MONEY TALKS
(1972 - United Artists) Allen Funt
One Sheet: $10 - $20   *Candid camera TV tie-in.*

MONEY TO BURN
(1926 - Gotham) Dorothy Devore, Malcome McGregor
One Sheet: $350 - $750

MONEY TO BURN
(1939 - Republic) James Gleason, Lucille Gleason, Russell Gleason
One Sheet: $40 - $75

MONEY TRAIN
(1995 - Columbia) Wesley Snipes, Woody Harrelson
One Sheet: $5 - $10   *Either style.*

MONEY TRAP, THE
(1966 - MGM) Glenn Ford, Elke Sommer, Rita Hayworth
One Sheet: $20 - $40

MONEY, WOMEN AND GUNS
(1958 - Universal) Jock Mahoney, Kim Hunter
One Sheet: $40 - $75

MONGOLS, THE
(1962 - Colorama) Anita Ekberg, Jack Palance
One Sheet: $15 - $25

MONIQUE
(1970 - Avco/Embassy) Sibylia Kay, Joan Alcom
One Sheet: $5 - $10

MONITORS, THE
(1969 - Commonwealth United) Guy Stockwell, Susan Oliver
One Sheet: $5 - $10

MONKEY BUSINESS
(1924 - Pathe Exchange) An Aesop Fable, Paul Terry - Animator
One Sheet: $1,600 - $2,500   *Cartoon. Full color stone litho.*

MONKEY BUSINESS
(1926 - Pathe) Our Gang
One Sheet: $1,300 - $2,000

MONKEY BUSINESS
(1931 - Paramount Publix) The Marx Brothers
One Sheet: $5,000 - $7,500

MONKEY BUSINESS
(1952 - 20th Century Fox) Cary Grant, Marilyn Monroe, Ginger Rogers
One Sheet: $200 - $450

MONKEY BUSINESSMEN
(1946 - Columbia) The Three Stooges (Curly)
One Sheet: $2,500 - $4,000   *Comedy short. Duotone.*

MONKEY HUSTLE, THE
(1976 - AIP) Yaphet Kotto, Rudy Ray Moore
One Sheet: $10 - $20   *Black cast.*

MONKEY IN WINTER
(1963 - MGM) Jean Gabin, Jean-Paul

Belmondo
One Sheet: $5 - $12

MONKEY ON MY BACK
(1957 - United Artists) Cameron Mitchell, Dianne Foster
One Sheet: $15 - $25   *Drug addiction.*

MONKEY SHINES
(1988 - Orion) Jason Beghe, John Pankow, Melanie Parker
One Sheet: $5 - $10

MONKEY TALKS, THE
(1927 - Fox) Olive Borden, Jacques Lerner
One Sheet: $3,500 - $5,000   *Graven Images, pg. 30.*

MONKEY TROUBLE
(1994 - New Line) Thora Birch, Mimi Rogers, Harvey Keitel
One Sheet: $5 - $10

MONKEY'S PAW, THE
(1932 - RKO) Ivan Simpson, Louise Carter
One Sheet: $350 - $750   *Graven Images, pg. 64.*

MONKEY'S UNCLE, THE
(1965 - Buena Vista/Disney) Tommy Kirk, Annette Funicello
One Sheet: $15 - $30

MONKEYS, GO HOME!
(1967 - Buena Vista/Disney) Maurice Chevalier (his last film), The Monkees
One Sheet: $40 - $75   *T.V. tie-in. Rock 'n' Roll.*

MONNA VANNA
(1923 - Fox) Lee Parry, Paul Wegener
One Sheet: $600 - $1,000

MONOLITH MONSTERS, THE
(1957 - Universal) Grant Williams, Lola Albright
One Sheet: $125 - $250   *Graven Images, pg. 178.*

MONSIEUR BEAUCAIRE
(1924 - Paramount) Rudolph Valentino, Bebe Daniels
One Sheet: $2,500 - $4,000

Title Card

MONSIEUR BEAUCAIRE
(1946 - Paramount) Bob Hope, Joan Caulfield
One Sheet: $100 - $200

MONSIEUR VERDOUX
(1947 - United Artists) Charles Chaplin, Martha Raye
One Sheet: $100 - $200

MONSIEUR VINCENT
(1948 - Lopert) Pierre Fresnay, Aime Clairiond
One Sheet: $30 - $50   *French. Academy Award: Best Foreign film.*

MONSIGNOR
(1982 - 20th Century Fox) Christopher Reeve, Genevieve Bujold
One Sheet: $5 - $10

MONSOON
(1952 - United Artists) Ursula Theiss, Diana Douglas
One Sheet: $7 - $15

MONSTER, THE
(1925 - Metro-Goldwyn) Lon Chaney, Gertrude Olmstead
One Sheet: $3,500 - $5,000   *Graven Images, pg. 33.*

MONSTER A GO-GO
(1965 - B.I.& L) Phil Morton, June Travis, Dir: H. Gordon Lewis
One Sheet: $40 - $80

MONSTER AND THE APE, THE
(1945 - Columbia) Robert Lowery, George Macready
One Sheet: $125 - $250   *Serial. 15 Chapters.*

MONSTER AND THE APE, THE
(1956R - Columbia) Robert Lowery, George Macready
One Sheet: $30 - $50   *Re-release. Serial.*

MONSTER AND THE GIRL, THE
(1941 - Paramount) Ellen Drew, Robert Paige, George Zucco
One Sheet: $50 - $100

MONSTER CLUB, THE
(1981 - ITC) Vincent Price, John Carradine, Britt Ekland
One Sheet: $20 - $40

MONSTER FROM GREEN HELL/HALF HUMAN
(1958 - DCA) -
One Sheet: $40 - $75   *Double feature poster. "MONSTER" does not exist as a separate poster.*

MONSTER FROM THE OCEAN FLOOR, THE
(1954 - Lippert) Anne Kimball, Stuart Wade, Dir:Roger Corman (his 1st film)
One Sheet: $150 - $350   *Graven Images, pg. 169.*

MONSTER IN THE CLOSET
(1987 - -) Donald Grant, Denise DuBarry
One Sheet: $15 - $25

MONSTER MAKER, THE
(1944 - PRC) J. Carrol Naish, Wanda McKay
One Sheet: $75 - $150

MONSTER OF PIEDRAS BLANCAS, THE
(1959 - Film Service) Jeanne Carmen, Lee Tremayne
One Sheet: $200 - $400

One Sheet

MONSTER OF THE ISLAND
(1953 - Romana) Boris Karloff, Franco Marzi
One Sheet: $30 - $50   *Italian.*

MONSTER OF ZOMBOR, THE
(1941 - Universal) Boris Karloff, Bela Lugosi Abandoned project. Posters do not exist. Promotional items exist. Graven Images, pg. 115.

MONSTER ON THE CAMPUS
(1958 - Universal) Arthur Franz, Troy Donahue, Joanna Moore
One Sheet: $75 - $150

Daybill

MONSTER SQUAD, THE
(1987 - TriStar) Andre Gower, Robby Kiger
One Sheet: $7 - $15

MONSTER THAT CHALLENGED THE WORLD/ THE VAMPIRE
(1957 - United Artists) -
One Sheet: $50 - $120   *Double feature poster.*

MONSTER THAT CHALLENGED THE WORLD, THE
(1957 - United Artists) Tim Holt, Audrey Dalton
One Sheet: $100 - $200   *Graven Images, pg. 169.*

MONSTER WALKS, THE
(1932 - Action) Rex Lease, Vera Reynolds, Mischa Auer
One Sheet: $150 - $300

MONSTER WALKS, THE
(1946R - Astor) Rex Lease, Vera Reynolds, Mischa Auer
One Sheet: $75 - $125   *Re-release.*

MONSTER ZERO/WAR OF THE GARGANTUAS
(1966 - Maron) Godzilla, Rodan, Ghidrah
One Sheet: $40 - $80   *Double feature poster.*

MONSTERS FROM THE UNKNOWN PLANET
(1973 - Toho) Katsuhiko Sasaki
One Sheet: $40 - $75   *AKA: TERROR OF GODZILLA.*

MONSTERS OF THE SEA
(1932 - United Screen Associates) -
One Sheet: $40 - $75   *Documentary. Duotone .*

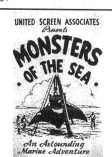

One Sheet

MONSTROSITY
(1964 - Emerson) Frank Gerstle, Erika Peters
One Sheet: $15 - $30   *AKA: THE ATOMIC BRAIN.*

MONTANA
(1950 - Warner Bros.) Errol Flynn, Alexis Smith
One Sheet: $50 - $100

MONTANA BELLE
(1951 - RKO) Jane Russell, George Brent
One Sheet: $50 - $100

MONTANA DESPERADO
(1951 - Monogram) Johnny Mack Brown
One Sheet: $15 - $35

MONTANA INCIDENT
(1952 - Monogram) Whip Wilson
One Sheet: $20 - $40

MONTANA MOON
(1930 - MGM) Joan Crawford, Johnny Mack Brown
One Sheet: $800 - $1,500

MONTANA TERRITORY
(1952 - Columbia) Lon McCallister, Wanda Hendrix
One Sheet: $7 - $15

MONTE CARLO
(1930 - Paramount Publix) Jeanette MacDonald, Jack Buchanan
One Sheet: $600 - $1,000

MONTE CARLO BABY
(1954 - Filmakers) Audrey Hepburn, Jules Munshin
One Sheet: $100 - $200

MONTE CARLO MADNESS

(1931 - UFA) Hans Albers, Anna Sten, Peter Lorre
One Sheet: $800 - $1,500

MONTE CARLO NIGHTS
(1934 - Monogram) Mary Brian, John Darrow
One Sheet: $75 - $150

MONTE CARLO STORY, THE
(1957 - United Artists) Marlene Dietrich, Vittorio De Sica
One Sheet: $40 - $75

MONTE WALSH
(1970 - National General) Lee Marvin, Jeanne Moreau
One Sheet: $7 - $15

MONTEREY POP
(1969 - -) Jimi Hendrix, Janis Joplin, The Who, etc.
One Sheet: $100 - $200   *Documentary. Rock 'n' Roll. First major rock concert film.*

MONTH IN THE COUNTRY, A
(1987 - -) Colin Firth, Kenneth Branagh
One Sheet: $3 - $5

MONTY PYTHON AND THE HOLY GRAIL
(1974 - Cinema 5) Graham Chapman, John Cleese
One Sheet: $50 - $100

One Sheet

MONTY PYTHON LIVE AT THE HOLLYWOOD BOWL
(1982 - -) John Cleese, Eric Idle
One Sheet: $15 - $30

MONTY PYTHON'S LIFE OF BRIAN
(1979 - Warner Bros.) Graham Chapman, John Cleese, Monty Python
One Sheet: $15 - $35   *Either style.*

MONTY PYTHON'S THE MEANING OF LIFE
(1983 - Universal) John Cleese, Graham Chapman, Eric Idle
One Sheet: $15 - $30

MOO COW BOOGIE
(1943 - -) -
One Sheet: $75 - $150

MOOCHIE OF THE LITTLE LEAGUE
(1959 - -) James Brown, Stu Erwin
One Sheet: $15 - $25   *Sports (Baseball).*

MOOCHING THROUGH GEORGIA
(1939 - Columbia) Buster Keaton
One Sheet: $350 - $750   *Comedy short.*

MOON AND SIXPENCE, THE
(1942 - United Artists) George Sanders, Herbert Marshall
One Sheet: $40 - $75

MOON IS BLUE, THE
(1953 - United Artists) William Holden, David Niven, Maggie McNamara
One Sheet: $15 - $30

MOON IS DOWN, THE
(1943 - 20th Century Fox) Cedric Hardwicke, Lee J. Cobb
One Sheet: $75 - $125

MOON OF ISRAEL
(1927 - R-C) Maria Corda, Adelqui Millar
One Sheet: $700 - $1,200   *French. Price for original French 47 x 63.*

MOON OVER BURMA
(1940 - Paramount) Dorothy Lamour, Robert Preston, Preston Foster

One Sheet: $100 - $200

MOON OVER HARLEM
(1939 - Meteor) Bud Harris, Cora Green
One Sheet: $150 - $300   *Black cast. Duotone. Separate Cinema, pg. 141.*

MOON OVER HER SHOULDER
(1941 - 20th Century Fox) Dan Dailey, Lynn Bari, John Sutton
One Sheet: $30 - $60

MOON OVER LAS VEGAS
(1944 - Universal) Anne Gwynne, David Bruce
One Sheet: $50 - $100

MOON OVER MIAMI
(1941 - 20th Century Fox) Don Ameche, Betty Grable
One Sheet: $3,500 - $5,000   *24 Sheet is Vargas art. Other posters with Vargas-like art were drawn by his staff. Above price is for Style A one sheet. One Sheet(Style B, not Vargas-like):$1200-$2000.*

MOON OVER MONTANA
(1946 - Monogram) Jimmy Wakely, Lee "Lasses" White
One Sheet: $50 - $100

MOON OVER PARADOR
(1988 - -) Richard Dreyfuss, Sonia Braga, Raul Julia
One Sheet: $5 - $10

MOON PILOT
(1962 - Buena Vista/Disney) Tom Tryon, Brian Keith
One Sheet: $20 - $40

MOON RIDERS, THE
(1920 - Universal) Art Acord
One Sheet: $200 - $400   *Serial. 18 Chapters.*

MOON WOLF
(1966 - Allied Artists) Carl Moehner, Ann Savo
One Sheet: $5 - $10

MOON ZERO TWO
(1970 - Warner Bros.) James Olson, Catherina Von Schell
One Sheet: $7 - $15

MOON'S OUR HOME, THE
(1936 - Paramount) Margaret Sullavan, Henry Fonda
One Sheet: $250 - $600

MOONFLEET
(1955 - MGM) Stewart Granger, Viveca Lindfors
One Sheet: $15 - $30

MOONLIGHT AND CACTUS
(1943 - Universal) The Andrews Sisters, Eylse Knox, Mitch Ayers Orchestra
One Sheet: $100 - $200   *Big Band musical.*

MOONLIGHT AND HONEYSUCKLE
(1921 - Realart) Mary Miles Minter, Monte Blue
One Sheet: $250 - $500

MOONLIGHT AND NOSES
(1925 - Pathecomedy) Clyde Cook
One Sheet: $200 - $400

MOONLIGHT AND PRETZELS
(1933 - Universal) Leo Carrillo, Mary Brian, Jack Denny's Orchestra
One Sheet: $500 - $800   *Big Band musical.*

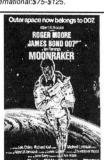
One Sheet

MOONLIGHT IN HAVANA
(1942 - Universal) Allan Jones, Jane Frazee
One Sheet: $75 - $150   *Sports (Baseball).*

MOONLIGHT IN HAWAII
(1941 - Universal) Mischa Auer, Jane Frazee, Maria Montez
One Sheet: $125 - $250

MOONLIGHT IN VERMONT
(1943 - Universal) Gloria Jean, Fay Helm
One Sheet: $50 - $100

MOONLIGHT MASQUERADE
(1942 - Republic) Betty Kean, Eddie Foy Jr.
One Sheet: $20 - $40

MOONLIGHT MURDER
(1936 - MGM) Leo Carrillo, Madge Evans, Chester Morris
One Sheet: $100 - $200

MOONLIGHT ON THE PRAIRIE
(1935 - Warner Bros.) Dick Foran, George Stone
One Sheet: $50 - $100

MOONLIGHT SONATA
(1938 - United Artists) Ignace Jan Paderewski, Charles Farrell
One Sheet: $125 - $250   *Classical music.*

MOONLIGHTER, THE
(1953 - Warner Bros.) Barbara Stanwyck, Fred MacMurray
One Sheet: $50 - $100   *3-D.*

MOONRAKER
(1958 - Pathe) George Baker, Sylvia Syms
One Sheet: $15 - $25

MOONRAKER
(1979 - United Artists) Roger Moore, Lois Chiles
One Sheet: $40 - $75   *Advance:$60-$100; International:$75-$125.*

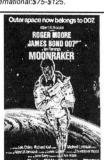
One Sheet (Advance)

MOONRISE
(1948 - Republic) Dane Clark, Gail Russell
One Sheet: $20 - $40

MOONRUNNERS
(1974 - United Artists) James Mitchum, Waylon Jennings
One Sheet: $5 - $10

MOONSHINE COUNTY EXPRESS
(1977 - New World) John Saxon, William Conrad, Maureen McCormick
One Sheet: $15 - $25

MOONSHINE MOUNTAIN
(1967 - Creative) Chuck Scott, Adam Sorg, Dir: Herschell Gordon Lewis
One Sheet: $30 - $65   *Country musical.*

MOONSHINE WAR, THE
(1970 - MGM) Patrick McGoohan, Richard Widmark
One Sheet: $7 - $15

MOON-SPINNERS, THE
(1964 - Buena Vista/Disney) Hayley Mills, Peter McEnery, Pola Negri
One Sheet: $15 - $25

MOONSTONE
(1934 - Monogram) David Manners, Phyllis Barry
One Sheet: $75 - $150

MOONSTRUCK
(1987 - MGM) Cher, Nicholas Cage, Olympia Dukakis
One Sheet: $10 - $20   *Academy Award: Best Actress(Cher), Best Supporting Actress(Dukakis). Academy Award Movie Posters #355, #357 & #358.*

MOONTIDE
(1942 - 20th Century Fox) Jean Gabin, Ida Lupino
One Sheet: $75 - $125

MOONWALKER
(1988 - Warner Brothers) Michael Jackson
One Sheet: $75 - $150

MOOSE HUNT, THE
(1931 - Columbia) Mickey Mouse
One Sheet: $25,000 - $40,000   *Cartoon.*

MOPPING UP
(1942 - 20th Century Fox) Terry-toons
Cartoon. See "Terrytoons Stock" for prices. Cartoon Movie Posters #88.

MORALS
(1921 - Paramount) May McAvoy, William P. Carleton
One Sheet: $300 - $700

MORALS FOR WOMEN
(1931 - Tiffany) Bessie Love, Conway Tearle
One Sheet: $150 - $300

MORALS OF MARCUS
(1935 - Gaumont British) Lupe Velez, Ian Hunter
One Sheet: $100 - $200

MORALS SQUAD
(1960 - Brenner) Bob O'Connell, Beverly Bennett
One Sheet: $7 - $15

MORAN OF THE LADY LETTY
(1922 - Paramount) Rudolph Valentino (unbilled)
One Sheet: $350 - $750

MORAN OF THE MARINES
(1928 - Paramount) Richard Dix, Ruth Elder
One Sheet: $250 - $600

MORAN OF THE MOUNTED
(1928 - Paramount) Reed Howes, Ruth Elder
One Sheet: $200 - $400

MORE
(1969 - Cinema 5) Mimsy Farmer, Heinz Engelmann, Klaus Grunberg
One Sheet: $3 - $5

MORE AMERICAN GRAFFITI
(1979 - Universal) Paul LeMat, Ron Howard
One Sheet: $15 - $25   *Sequel.*

MORE DEAD THAN ALIVE
(1968 - United Artists) Clint Walker, Vincent Price
One Sheet: $15 - $30

MORE THAN A MIRACLE
(1967 - MGM) Sophia Loren, Omar Sharif
One Sheet: $15 - $25

MORE THAN A SECRETARY
(1936 - Columbia) Jean Arthur, George Brent
One Sheet: $125 - $250

MORE THAN JUST A BREATH OF SCANDAL
(1960 - Paramount) Sophia Loren, John Gavin
One Sheet: $15 - $30

MORE THE MERRIER, THE
(1943 - Columbia) Jean Arthur, Joel McCrea
One Sheet: $100 - $200   *Academy Award Movie Posters #91.*

MORGAN
(1966 - Cinema 5) Vanessa Redgrave, David Warner
One Sheet: $5 - $10

MORGAN STEWART'S COMING HOME
(1987 - Kings Road) Jon Cryer, Lynn Redgrave
One Sheet: $2 - $3

MORGAN THE PIRATE
(1961 - MGM) Steve Reeves, Valerie Lagrange
One Sheet: $15 - $35

MORITURI
(1965 - 20th Century Fox) Marlon Brando, Yul

Brynner
One Sheet: $15 - $35

MORNING AFTER, THE
(1986 - 20th Century Fox) Jane Fonda, Jeff Bridges
One Sheet: $3 - $5

MORNING CALL
(1957 - Republic) Ron Randell, Greta Gynt
One Sheet: $15 - $25

MORNING GLORY
(1933 - RKO) Katharine Hepburn, Douglas Fairbanks, Jr.
One Sheet: $2,800 - $4,500 *Academy Award: Best Actress. Academy Award Movie Posters #30.*

One Sheet

MORNING GLORY
(1993 - -) Christopher Reeve, Deborah Raffin
One Sheet: $3 - $5

MORO WITCH DOCTOR
(1964 - Fox) Jock Mahoney, Margia Dean
One Sheet: $15 - $35

MOROCCO
(1930 - Paramount Publix) Gary Cooper, Marlene Dietrich
One Sheet: $7,500 - $12,000 *Dietrich's first U.S. film.*

MORON THAN OFF
(1946 - Columbia) Sterling Holloway
One Sheet: $50 - $100 *Comedy short. Duotone.*

MORRIS THE MIDGET MOOSE
(1950 - RKO/Disney) -
One Sheet: $500 - $800 *Cartoon. Full color.*

MORTAL KOMBAT
(1995 - New Line) Christopher Lambert
One Sheet: $5 - $10

One Sheet (Advance)

MORTAL STORM, THE
(1940 - MGM) Margaret Sullavan, James Stewart
One Sheet: $200 - $400

MORTAL THOUGHTS
(1991 - Columbia) Demi Moore, Bruce Willis
One Sheet: $5 - $10

MORTUARY
(1984 - -) Christopher George, Lynda Day George
One Sheet: $5 - $10

MOSCOW NIGHTS
(194? - Guaranteed) Laurence Olivier
One Sheet: $75 - $150

MOSCOW ON THE HUDSON
(1984 - Columbia) Robin Williams, Alejandro Ray
One Sheet: $3 - $5

MOSES
(1976 - Avco Embassy) Burt Lancaster, Anthony Quayle
One Sheet: $5 - $10

MOSQUITO COAST, THE
(1986 - -) Harrison Ford, Helen Mirren
One Sheet: $5 - $10

MOSQUITO SQUADRON
(1970 - United Artists) David McCallum, Suzanne Neve
One Sheet: $3 - $5

MOSS ROSE
(1947 - 20th Century Fox) Peggy Cummins, Victor Mature, Vincent Price
One Sheet: $50 - $100

MOST DANGEROUS GAME, THE
(1932 - RKO) Leslie Banks, Joel McCrea, Fay Wray
One Sheet: $5,000 - $7,500 *Graven Images, pg. 60.*

MOST DANGEROUS MAN ALIVE
(1961 - Columbia) Ron Randell, Debra Paget
One Sheet: $10 - $20

MOST PRECIOUS THING IN LIFE
(1934 - Columbia) Jean Arthur, Anita Louise
One Sheet: $100 - $200

MOTEL HELL
(1980 - United Artists) Rory Calhoun, Paul Linke
One Sheet: $20 - $40 *Cannibalism.*

MOTH, THE
(1934 - Screencraft) Sally O'Neil, Paul Page
One Sheet: $75 - $150

MOTH AND THE FLAME
(1938 - Disney) A Silly Symphony
One Sheet: $1,900 - $3,000 *Cartoon.*

MOTH AND THE FLAME
(1950R - RKO/Disney) Silly Symphony
One Sheet: $350 - $750 *Re-release. Cartoon. Full color.*

MOTHER
(1996 - Paramount) Albert Brooks, Debbie Reynolds
One Sheet: $5 - $10

MOTHER AND THE LAW
(1919R - -) Dir: D.W. Griffith
One Sheet: $1,300 - $2,000 *Re-titled re-release of INTOLERANCE.*

MOTHER CAREY'S CHICKENS
(1938 - RKO) Fay Bainter, Ruby Keeler, Anne Shirley
One Sheet: $50 - $100

One Sheet

MOTHER DIDN'T TELL ME
(1950 - 20th Century Fox) Dorothy McGuire, William Lundigan
One Sheet: $15 - $25

MOTHER GOOSE GOES HOLLYWOOD
(1938 - RKO/Disney) Silly Symphony
One Sheet: $13,000 - $20,000 *Cartoon. The Disney Poster, pg. 6. Cartoon Movie Posters #194.*

MOTHER GOOSE NIGHTMARE

(1940 - 20th Century Fox) Terry-toons
One Sheet: $100 - $200 *Cartoon. Full color stone litho. Stock poster with inset title.*

MOTHER IS A FRESHMAN
(1949 - 20th Century Fox) Loretta Young, Van Johnson
One Sheet: $30 - $60

MOTHER, JUGS & SPEED
(1976 - Fox) Raquel Welch, Bill Cosby, Harvey Keitel
One Sheet: $10 - $20

MOTHER LODE
(1983 - Agamemnon) Charlton Heston, Kim Basinger
One Sheet: $7 - $15

MOTHER MACHREE
(1927 - Fox Film) Belle Bennett, Neil Hamilton
One Sheet: $150 - $300

MOTHER O' MINE
(1921 - Associated) Lloyd Hughes, Betty Ross, Betty Blythe
One Sheet: $150 - $350

MOTHER WORE TIGHTS
(1947 - 20th Century Fox) Betty Grable, Dan Dailey
One Sheet: $150 - $350

MOTHER'S BOYS
(1993 - Miramax) Jamie Lee Curtis, Peter Gallagher
One Sheet: $3 - $5

MOTHER'S DAY
(1980 - -) Nancy Hendrickson, Deborah Luce
One Sheet: $3 - $5

MOTHER'S MILLIONS
(1931 - Universal) May Robson, James Hall
One Sheet: $200 - $400

MOTHERS CRY
(1930 - First National) Dorothy Peterson, Helen Chandler
One Sheet: $75 - $175

MOTHRA
(1962 - Columbia) Franky Sakai, Hiroshi Koizumi
One Sheet: $75 - $150 *Japanese poster:$500-$700.*

MOTOR MANIA
(1950 - RKO/Disney) Goofy
One Sheet: $250 - $500 *Cartoon.*

MOTOR PATROL
(1950 - Lippert) Don Castle, Jane Nigh
One Sheet: $15 - $25

MOTOR PSYCHO
(1965 - Eve) Haji, Alex Rocco, Dir: Russ Meyer
One Sheet: $50 - $100

MOTORCYCLE GANG
(1957 - AIP) John Ashley, Anne Neyland
One Sheet: $50 - $100 *Biker gang.*

MOULIN ROUGE
(1934 - 20th Century Fox) Constance Bennett, Franchot Tone
One Sheet: $2,800 - $4,500

One Sheet

MOULIN ROUGE
(1952 - Romulus) Jose Ferrer, Zsa Zsa Gabor
One Sheet: $50 - $100

MOUNTAIN, THE
(1956 - Paramount) Spencer Tracy, Robert

Wagner, Claire Trevor
One Sheet: $15 - $35

MOUNTAIN FAMILY ROBINSON
(1979 - Pacific Intl.) Robert F. Logan, Susan Damante Shaw
One Sheet: $3 - $5

MOUNTAIN JUSTICE
(1915 - Universal) Elsie Jane Wilson, Lon Chaney, Arthur Shirley
One Sheet: $800 - $1,500

MOUNTAIN JUSTICE
(1930 - Universal) Ken Maynard
One Sheet: $250 - $600

MOUNTAIN JUSTICE
(1936 - Warner Bros.) Josephine Hutchinson, George Brent
One Sheet: $50 - $100

MOUNTAIN MEN, THE
(1980 - Columbia) Charlton Heston, Brian Keith
One Sheet: $5 - $10

MOUNTAIN MOONLIGHT
(1941 - Republic) Weaver Bros. & Elviry
One Sheet: $20 - $40

MOUNTAIN MUSIC
(1937 - Paramount) Bob Burns, Martha Raye
One Sheet: $75 - $150 *Country musical.*

MOUNTAIN RHYTHM
(1939 - Republic) Gene Autry, Smiley Burnette, June Storey
One Sheet: $150 - $350

MOUNTAIN RHYTHM
(1943 - Republic) Weaver Bros. & Elviry
One Sheet: $15 - $35

MOUNTAIN ROAD, THE
(1960 - Columbia) James Stewart, Lisa Lu
One Sheet: $15 - $30

MOUNTAIN ROMANCE, A
(1937 - 20th Century Fox) Terry Toons
One Sheet: $100 - $200 *Cartoon.*

MOUNTAIN WOMAN, THE
(1921 - Fox) Pearl White, Corliss Giles
One Sheet: $250 - $600

MOUNTAINS OF MANHATTAN
(1927 - Gotham) Dorothy Devore, Charles Delaney, Kate Price
One Sheet: $600 - $1,000

MOUNTAINS OF THE MOON
(1990 - Columbia) Patrick Bergin, Iain Glen
One Sheet: $7 - $15

MOUNTED FURY
(1931 - Sono Art/World Wide) John Bowers
One Sheet: $75 - $125

MOUNTED STRANGER, THE
(1930 - Universal) Hoot Gibson
One Sheet: $250 - $500

MOURNING BECOMES ELECTRA
(1947 - RKO) Rosalind Russell, Michael Redgrave
One Sheet: $75 - $150 *Academy Award: Best Actress.*

MOUSE CLEANING
(1948 - MGM) Tom & Jerry
One Sheet: $350 - $750 *Cartoon. Full color stone litho.*

MOUSE COMES TO DINNER, THE
(1945 - MGM) Tom & Jerry
One Sheet: $350 - $750 *Cartoon. Full color stone litho.*

MOUSE COMES TO DINNER, THE
(1951R - MGM) Tom & Jerry
One Sheet: $150 - $300 *Re-release. Cartoon. Full color stone litho.*

MOUSE IN MANHATTAN
(1945 - MGM) Tom & Jerry
One Sheet: $350 - $750 *Cartoon. Cartoon Movie Posters #271.*

MOUSE IN THE HOUSE, A
(1947 - MGM) Tom & Jerry
One Sheet: $300 - $650 *Cartoon.*

MOUSE MEETS LION

(1939 - Columbia) Fables
One Sheet: $100 - $200   *Cartoon. Full color stock poster with paper title attached.*

MOUSE ON THE MOON, THE
(1963 - United Artists) Margaret Rutherford, Terry-Thomas
One Sheet: $10 - $20

MOUSE THAT ROARED, THE
(1959 - Columbia) Peter Sellers, Jean Seberg
One Sheet: $20 - $40

MOUTHPIECE, THE
(1932 - Warner Bros.) Warren William, Sidney Fox
One Sheet: $250 - $600

MOVE
(1970 - 20th Century Fox) Elliott Gould, Genevieve Waite, Paula Prentiss
One Sheet: $3 - $5

MOVE OVER DARLING
(1963 - 20th Century Fox) Doris Day, James Garner
One Sheet: $20 - $40

MOVIE CRAZY
(1932 - Paramount) Harold Lloyd, Constance Cummings
One Sheet: $1,900 - $3,000

MOVIE CRAZY
(1949R - Paramount) Harold Lloyd, Constance Cummings
One Sheet: $125 - $250   *Re-release.*

MOVIE MANIACS
(1936 - Columbia) The Three Stooges (Curly)
One Sheet: $10,000 - $16,000   *Comedy short. Duotone.*

MOVIE MOVIE
(1978 - Warner Bros.) George C. Scott, Trish Van Devere, Barbara Harris
One Sheet: $5 - $10

MOVIE STRUCK
(194?R - Astor) Jack Haley, Patsy Kelly, Laurel & Hardy
One Sheet: $50 - $100   *Re-release of PICK A STAR.*

MOVIE-MANIA
(1937 - Vitaphone/Broadway Brevity) Dave Apollon
One Sheet: $50 - $100   *Lobby Card set is duotone.*

MOVIETONE FOLLIES OF 1930
(1930 - Fox) El Brendel, Marjorie White
One Sheet: $200 - $400

MOVING
(1988 - Warner Bros.) Richard Pryor, Beverly Todd, Randy Quaid
One Sheet: $3 - $5

MOVING THE MOUNTAIN
(1995 - October) Dir: Michael Apted
One Sheet: $5 - $10   *Documentary.*

MOVING VIOLATION
(1976 - -) Stephen McHattie, Kay Lenz
One Sheet: $3 - $5

MOVING VIOLATIONS
(1985 - 20th Century Fox) John Murray, Jennifer Tilly
One Sheet: $2 - $3

MOZAMBIQUE
(1966 - Seven Arts) Steve Cochran, Hildegarde Neff
One Sheet: $7 - $15

MOZART STORY, THE
(1948 - Patrician) Winnie Markus, Irene V. Mayendorf
One Sheet: $15 - $35

MR. ACE
(1946 - United Artists) George Raft, Sylvia Sidney
One Sheet: $40 - $75

MR. AND MRS. BRIDGE
(1990 - Miramax) Paul Newman, Joanne Woodward
One Sheet: $5 - $10

MR. AND MRS. NORTH
(1941 - MGM) Gracie Allen, William Post Jr.

One Sheet: $75 - $150

MR. AND MRS. SMITH
(1941 - RKO) Carole Lombard, Robert Montgomery, Dir: Alfred Hitchcock
One Sheet: $500 - $900

One Sheet

MR. ARKADIN
(1955 - Talbot) Orson Wells, Michael Redgrave
One Sheet: $150 - $300   *AKA: CONFIDENTIAL REPORT.*

MR. BASEBALL
(1992 - Universal) Tom Selleck, Ken Takakura
One Sheet: $7 - $15   *Sports (Baseball). Sports Movie Posters #81.*

MR. BELDEN'S AMAZING GASMOBILE
(1973R - MGM) Red Skelton, Sally Forrest
One Sheet: $5 - $10   *Re-titled re-release of EXCUSE MY DUST.*

MR. BELVEDERE GOES TO COLLEGE
(1949 - 20th Century Fox) Clifton Webb, Shirley Temple
One Sheet: $50 - $100

MR. BELVEDERE RINGS THE BELL
(1951 - 20th Century Fox) Clifton Webb, Joanne Dru
One Sheet: $15 - $30

MR. BILLION
(1977 - 20th Century Fox) Terence Hill, Valerie Perrine, Jackie Gleason
One Sheet: $3 - $5

MR. BLANDINGS BUILDS HIS DREAM HOUSE
(1948 - RKO) Cary Grant, Myrna Loy
One Sheet: $100 - $200

MR. BLANDINGS BUILDS HIS DREAM HOUSE
(1954R - RKO) Cary Grant, Myrna Loy
One Sheet: $30 - $50   *Re-release.*

MR. BOGGS STEPS OUT
(1937 - Grand National) Stuart Erwin, Helen Chandler
One Sheet: $50 - $100

MR. BROADWAY
(1933 - Broadway Hollywood) Dir: Johnnie Walker
One Sheet: $250 - $500

MR. BUG GOES TO TOWN
(1941 - Paramount) Animation by D. Fleischer
One Sheet: $500 - $800   *Cartoon. Graven Images, pg. 113. Cartoon Movie Posters #234.*

Half Sheet

MR. CELEBRITY
(1941 - PRC) Buzzy Henry, James Shea
One Sheet: $30 - $50

MR. CHUMP
(1938 - Warner Bros.) Johnnie Davis, Lola Lane
One Sheet: $50 - $100

MR. CINDERELLA
(1936 - MGM) Jack Haley, Betty Furness
One Sheet: $75 - $150

MR. CREEPS
(1938 - -) -
One Sheet: $50 - $100

MR. DEEDS GOES TO TOWN
(1936 - Columbia) Gary Cooper, Jean Arthur, Dir:Frank Capra
One Sheet: $2,200 - $3,500   *Academy Award: Best Direction(Frank Capra). Academy Award Movie Posters #46.*

MR. DEEDS GOES TO TOWN
(1950R - Columbia) Gary Cooper, Jean Arthur, Dir: Frank Capra
One Sheet: $75 - $150   *Re-release.*

MR. DENNING DRIVES NORTH
(1951 - British Lion) John Mills, Phyllis Calvert
One Sheet: $10 - $20

MR. DESTINY
(1990 - Buena Vista) Jim Belushi, Michael Caine
One Sheet: $10 - $20

MR. DISTRICT ATTORNEY
(1941 - Republic) Dennis O'Keefe, Peter Lorre, Florence Rice
One Sheet: $150 - $300

MR. DISTRICT ATTORNEY
(1947 - Columbia) Dennis O'Keefe, Adolphe Menjou, Marguerite Chapman
One Sheet: $75 - $125

MR. DISTRICT ATTORNEY IN THE CARTER CASE
(1941 - Republic) James Ellison, Virginia Gilmore
One Sheet: $50 - $100

MR. DODD TAKES THE AIR
(1937 - Warner Bros.) Kenny Baker, Jane Wyman
One Sheet: $75 - $125

MR. DOODLE KICKS OFF
(1938 - RKO) Joe Penner, June Travis
One Sheet: $75 - $150   *Sports (Football).*

MR. DUCK STEPS OUT
(1940 - RKO/Disney) Donald Duck, Daisy Duck
One Sheet: $2,500 - $4,000   *Cartoon. Cartoon Movie Posters #164.*

MR. DYNAMITE
(1935 - Universal) Jean Dixon, Edmund Lowe
One Sheet: $75 - $150

MR. DYNAMITE
(1941 - Universal) Lloyd Nolan, Irene Hervey, J. Carrol Naish
One Sheet: $50 - $100

MR. EMMANUEL
(1945 - United Artists) Felix Aylmer, Greta Gynt
One Sheet: $15 - $30

MR. HEX
(1946 - Monogram) Leo Gorcey, Huntz Hall, Bobby Jordan
One Sheet: $50 - $100

MR. HOBBS TAKES A VACATION
(1962 - 20th Century Fox) James Stewart, Maureen O'Hara
One Sheet: $15 - $30

MR. HOLLAND'S OPUS
(1996 - Hollywood) Richard Dreyfuss, Glenne Headly, Jay Thomas
One Sheet: $7 - $15

MR. HULOT'S HOLIDAY
(1954 - Cady/Gaumont) Jacques Tati, Nathalie Pascaud
One Sheet: $15 - $30   *French. AKA: MONSIEUR HULOT'S HOLIDAY.*

MR. IMPERIUM
(1950 - MGM) Ezio Pinza, Lana Turner
One Sheet: $20 - $40

MR. JONES
(1993 - TriStar) Richard Gere, Lena Olin
One Sheet: $3 - $5

MR. LEMON OF ORANGE
(1931 - Fox) El Brendel, Fifi Dorsay
One Sheet: $100 - $200

MR. LOGAN, U.S.A.
(1918 - Fox) Tom Mix, Kathleen O'Connor
One Sheet: $600 - $1,000

MR. LORD SAYS "NO"
(1951 - Souvaine Selective) Stanley Holloway, Kathleen Harrison
One Sheet: $15 - $25

MR. LUCKY
(1943 - RKO) Cary Grant, Laraine Day
One Sheet: $250 - $600

One Sheet

MR. MAGOO'S HOLIDAY FESTIVAL
(1970 - UPA) Mr. Magoo
One Sheet: $15 - $25   *Cartoon. Duotone . Two Magoo cartoons.*

MR. MAJESTYK
(1974 - United Artists) Charles Bronson, Al Lettieri
One Sheet: $7 - $15

MR. MARI'S GIRLS
(1967 - AFD) -
One Sheet: $15 - $30

MR. MEAN
(197? - -) Fred Williamson
One Sheet: $10 - $20   *Blaxploitation.*

MR. MOM
(1983 - -) Michael Keaton, Teri Garr, Ann Jillian
One Sheet: $3 - $5

MR. MOOCHER
(1943 - Columbia) Fox & Crow
One Sheet: $200 - $400   *Cartoon. Full color poster with scene inset.*

MR. MOTO IN DANGER ISLAND
(1939 - 20th Century Fox) Peter Lorre, Jean Hersholt
One Sheet: $200 - $400

MR. MOTO TAKES A CHANCE
(1938 - 20th Century Fox) Peter Lorre, Rochelle Hudson
One Sheet: $200 - $400

MR. MOTO TAKES A VACATION
(1939 - 20th Century Fox) Peter Lorre, Joseph Schildkraut, Lionel Atwill
One Sheet: $200 - $400

MR. MOTO'S GAMBLE
(1938 - 20th Century Fox) Peter Lorre, Keye Luke, Dick Baldwin
One Sheet: $200 - $400

MR. MOTO'S LAST WARNING
(1939 - 20th Century Fox) Peter Lorre, Richardo Cortez
One Sheet: $200 - $400

MR. MOUSE TAKES A TRIP
(1940 - RKO/Disney) Mickey Mouse
One Sheet: $5,000 - $8,000   *The Disney Poster, pg. 28. Cartoon Movie Posters #147.*

MR. MOUSE TAKES A TRIP
(1953R - RKO/Disney) Mickey Mouse
One Sheet: $125 - $250   *Re-release. Duotone one sheet.*

MR. MUGGS RIDES AGAIN

(1945 - Monogram) The East Side Kids, Nancy
Brinckman
One Sheet: $75 - $125

MR. MUGGS STEPS OUT
(1943 - Monogram) East Side Kids
One Sheet: $75 - $125

MR. MUSIC
(1950 - Paramount) Bing Crosby, Nancy Olson,
Groucho Marx
One Sheet: $30 - $50

MR. NANNY
(1993 - New Line) Hulk Hogan
One Sheet: $5 - $10

MR. NOISY
(1946 - Columbia) Shemp Howard
One Sheet: $100 - $200   *Duotone short
subject.*

MR. NORTH
(1988 - Samuel Goldwyn) Anthony Edwards,
Robert Mitchum, Lauren Bacall
One Sheet: $10 - $20

MR. PAYBACK
(1995 - Advanced Exhibition) Billy Warlock,
Christopher Lloyd
One Sheet: $5 - $10

MR. PEABODY AND THE MERMAID
(1948 - Universal International) William Powell,
Ann Blyth
One Sheet: $50 - $100

MR. PEEK-A-BOO
(1951 - United Artists) Bourvil, Joan
Greenwood
One Sheet: $7 - $15

MR. PERRIN AND MR. TRAILL
(1948 - Eagle-Lion) David Farrar, Greta Gynt
One Sheet: $10 - $20

MR. POTTS GOES TO MOSCOW
(1953 - Stratford) Oscar Homolka, Nadia Gray,
George Cole
One Sheet: $15 - $25

MR. RECKLESS
(1948 - Paramount) William Eythe, Barbara
Britton
One Sheet: $20 - $40

MR. RICCO
(1975 - MGM/UA) Dean Martin, Eugene Roche
One Sheet: $5 - $10

MR. ROBINSON CRUSOE
(1932 - United Artists) Douglas Fairbanks,
William Farnum, Maria Alba
One Sheet: $100 - $200

MR. ROBINSON CRUSOE
(1953R - United Artists) Douglas Fairbanks,
William Farnum, Maria Alba
One Sheet: $30 - $50   *Re-release.*

MR. SARDONICUS
(1961 - Columbia) Oscar Homolka, Ronald
Lewis
One Sheet: $40 - $75   *Graven
Images, pg. 206.*

MR. SATURDAY NIGHT
(1992 - Columbia) Billy Crystal, David Paymer
One Sheet: $5 - $10

MR. SKEFFINGTON
(1944 - Warner Bros.) Bette Davis, Claude
Rains
One Sheet: $250 - $500

MR. SKITCH
(1933 - Fox) Will Rogers, ZaSu Pitts
One Sheet: $200 - $400

MR. SMITH GOES TO WASHINGTON
(1939 - Columbia) James Stewart, Jean Arthur
One Sheet: $1,000 - $1,800   *Price is for
Style A. One Sheet(Style B):$2500-4000.*

MR. SOFT TOUCH
(1949 - Columbia) Glenn Ford, Evelyn Keyes
One Sheet: $20 - $40

MR. SUPERVISIBLE
(197? - K-Tel) Dean Jones, Gastone Moschin
One Sheet: $3 - $5

MR. TOPAZE
(1961 - 20th Century Fox) Peter Sellers, Nadia

Gray
One Sheet: $15 - $30   *AKA: I LIKE
MONEY.*

MR. UNIVERSE
(1951 - Eagle-Lion) Jack Carson, Janis Paige,
Robert Alda
One Sheet: $30 - $50   *Sports
(Wrestling).*

MR. WALKIE TALKIE
(1952 - Lippert) Joe Sawyer, William Tracy
One Sheet: $15 - $30

MR. WASHINGTON GOES TO TOWN
(1941 - --) Mantan Moreland
One Sheet: $150 - $300   *Black cast.*

MR. WHITNEY HAD A NOTION
(1949 - MGM) Lloyd Bridges, Erville Anderson
One Sheet: $15 - $25

MR. WINKLE GOES TO WAR
(1944 - Columbia) Edward G. Robinson, Ruth
Warrick
One Sheet: $50 - $100

MR. WISE GUY
(1942 - Monogram) The East Side Kids, Billy
Gilbert
One Sheet: $75 - $125

MR. WONDERFUL
(1993 - Warner Bros.) Matt Dillon, Annabella
Sciorra
One Sheet: $3 - $5

MR. WONG, DETECTIVE
(1938 - Monogram) Boris Karloff, Grant
Withers, Maxine Jennings
One Sheet: $500 - $900

MR. WONG IN CHINATOWN
(1939 - Monogram) Boris Karloff, Marjorie
Reynolds
One Sheet: $250 - $500

MR. WRONG
(1996 - Touchstone) Ellen DeGeneres, Bill
Pullman
One Sheet: $3 - $6

MR. WU
(1927 - MGM) Lon Chaney, Renee Adoree
One Sheet: $2,200 - $3,500

**MRS. BROWN, YOU'VE GOT A LOVELY
DAUGHTER**
(1968 - MGM) Herman's Hermits
One Sheet: $30 - $60   *Rock 'n' Roll.*

MRS. DOUBTFIRE
(1993 - 20th Century Fox) Robin Williams, Sally
Fields
One Sheet: $7 - $15

MRS. MIKE
(1949 - United Artists) Dick Powell, Evelyn
Keyes
One Sheet: $20 - $40

MRS. MINIVER
(1942 - MGM) Greer Garson, Walter Pidgeon,
Teresa Wright
One Sheet: $150 - $350   *Academy
Award: Best Picture, Best Actress(Garson), Best
Supporting Actress(Wright), Best Director(William
Wyler).Academy Award Movie Posters #82, #83,
& #86.*

One Sheet

MRS. O'LEARY'S COW
(1937 - 20th Century Fox) Terry-toons
*Cartoon. See "Terrytoons Stock" for prices.
Cartoon Movie Posters #83.*

MRS. O'MALLEY AND MR. MALONE
(1950 - MGM) Marjorie Main, James Whitmore
One Sheet: $15 - $25

MRS. PARKER AND THE VICIOUS CIRCLE
(1994 - Fine Line) Jennifer Jason Leigh,
Campbell Scott, Matthew Broderick
One Sheet: $7 - $15

MRS. PARKINGTON
(1944 - MGM) Greer Garson, Walter Pidgeon
One Sheet: $40 - $75

MRS. POLLIFAX - SPY
(1971 - United Artists) Rosalind Russell,
Darren McGavin
One Sheet: $15 - $25   *Frank Frazetta
art.*

MRS. SOFFEL
(1984 - MGM/UA) Diane Keaton, Mel Gibson
One Sheet: $7 - $15

MRS. WIGGS OF THE CABBAGE PATCH
(1934 - Paramount) Pauline Lord, W. C. Fields
One Sheet: $800 - $1,500

MRS. WIGGS OF THE CABBAGE PATCH
(1942 - Paramount) Fay Bainter, Hugh Herbert
One Sheet: $40 - $75

MUCH ADO ABOUT NOTHING
(1939 - 20th Century Fox) Terrytoons
One Sheet: $100 - $200   *Cartoon.*

MUCH ADO ABOUT NOTHING
(1993 - Columbia) Kenneth Branagh, Emma
Thompson, Michael Keaton
One Sheet: $10 - $20

MUDLARK, THE
(1951 - 20th Century Fox) Irene Dunne, Alec
Guinness
One Sheet: $15 - $35

MUG TOWN
(1942 - Universal) The Dead End Kids, The
Little Tough Guys, Grace McDonald
One Sheet: $75 - $150

MUGGER, THE
(1958 - United Artists) Kent Smith, Nan Martin
One Sheet: $15 - $30

MULE TRAIN
(1950 - Columbia) Gene Autry, Sheila Ryan
One Sheet: $75 - $150

MULHOLLAND FALLS
(1995 - MGM) Nick Nolte, Melanie Griffith
One Sheet: $4 - $8

MULTIPLE MANIACS
(1971 - --) Divine, Mink Stole
One Sheet: $50 - $100

MULTIPLICITY
(1996 - Columbia) Michael Keaton, Andie
McDowell
One Sheet: $5 - $12

MUM'S THE WORD
(1926 - Pathe) Charlie Chase
One Sheet: $350 - $750

MUMMY, THE
(1932 - Universal) Boris Karloff, Zita Johann
One Sheet: $75,000 - $200,000   *Graven
Images, pg. 69. Two one sheet styles exist.*

MUMMY, THE
(1951R - Realart) Boris Karloff, Zita Johann
One Sheet: $700 - $1,200   *Re-release.*

MUMMY, THE
(1959 - Universal-International) Peter Cushing,
Christopher Lee
One Sheet: $100 - $200   *Graven
Images, pg. 196.*

MUMMY'S BOYS
(1936 - RKO) Wheeler and Woolsey, Barbara
Pepper
One Sheet: $125 - $250

MUMMY'S CURSE, THE
(1944 - Universal) Lon Chaney, Jr., Virginia
Christine, Peter Coe
One Sheet: $1,300 - $2,000   *Graven
Images, pg. 126.*

MUMMY'S CURSE, THE
(1951R - Realart) Peter Coe, Lon Chaney Jr.

One Sheet: $150 - $300   *Re-release*

MUMMY'S DUMMIES
(1948 - Columbia) Three Stooges (Shemp)
One Sheet: $350 - $750   *Comedy short.
Duotone.*

MUMMY'S GHOST, THE
(1943 - Universal) Lon Chaney Jr., John
Carradine, Ramsay Ames
One Sheet: $1,600 - $2,500   *Graven
Images, pg. 126.*

MUMMY'S GHOST, THE
(1949R - Realart) Lon Chaney Jr., John
Carradine, Ramsay Ames
One Sheet: $150 - $300   *Re-release.*

MUMMY'S HAND, THE
(1940 - Universal) Dick Foran, George Zucco,
Tom Tyler
One Sheet: $1,300 - $2,000   *Graven
Images, pg. 126.*

MUMMY'S SHROUD, THE
(1967 - 20th Century Fox) Andre Morell, John
Phillips
One Sheet: $15 - $30

MUMMY'S TOMB, THE
(1942 - Universal) Lon Chaney, Jr., Turhan
Bey, John Hubbard
One Sheet: $2,500 - $4,000   *Graven
Images, pg. 126.*

MUMMY'S TOMB, THE
(1949R - Realart) Lon Chaney, Jr., Turhan Bey,
John Hubbard
One Sheet: $250 - $500   *Re-release.*

MUMSY, NANNY, SONNY, AND GIRLY
(1970 - Cinerama) Michael Bryant, Ursula
Howells
One Sheet: $3 - $5

MUNSTER, GO HOME
(1966 - Universal) Fred Gwynne, Yvonne De
Carlo
One Sheet: $100 - $200   *TV tie-in.*

MUPPET CHRISTMAS CAROL, THE
(1992 - Buena Vista/Disney) Michael Caine,
Miss Piggy
One Sheet: $7 - $15

MUPPET MOVIE, THE
(1979 - ITC) Miss Piggy, Kermit
One Sheet: $15 - $35   *Price is for
Style A one sheet. One Sheet (Style B):$20-$40.*

One Sheet (Style A)

MUPPET TREASURE ISLAND
(1996 - Buena Vista) Kermit The Frog, Fozzie
Bear
One Sheet: $5 - $10

MUPPETS TAKE MANHATTAN, THE
(1984 - TriStar) Miss Piggy, Kermit
One Sheet: $10 - $20

MURDER!
(1930 - BIP) Herbert Marshall, Norah Baring,
Dir: Alfred Hitchcock
One Sheet: $3,500 - $5,000

MURDER AHOY!
(1964 - MGM) Margaret Rutherford, Lionel
Jeffries
One Sheet: $20 - $40

MURDER AMONG FRIENDS
(1941 - 20th Century Fox) Marjorie Weaver,
John Hubbard
One Sheet: $40 - $75

MURDER AT 1600
(1997 - Warner Bros.) Wesley Snipes, Diane Lane
One Sheet: $4 - $8

MURDER AT DAWN
(1932 - Big 4) Jack Mulhall, Josephine Dunn
One Sheet: $100 - $200

MURDER AT GLEN ATHOL
(1935 - Invincible) John Miljan, Irene Ware
One Sheet: $100 - $200

MURDER AT MIDNIGHT
(1931 - Tiffany) Hale Hamilton, Aileen Pringle
One Sheet: $125 - $250

MURDER AT MONTE CARLO
(1935 - First National) Errol Flynn
One Sheet: $250 - $600

MURDER AT THE GALLOP
(1963 - MGM) Margaret Rutherford, Robert Morley
One Sheet: $20 - $40

MURDER AT THE VANITIES
(1934 - Paramount) Jack Oakie, Victor McLaglen, Kitty Carlisle
One Sheet: $150 - $350

MURDER BY ARISTOCRAT
(1936 - Warner Bros.) Marguerite Churchill, Lyle Talbot
One Sheet: $75 - $150

MURDER BY CONTRACT
(1958 - Columbia) Vince Edwards, Herschel Bernardi
One Sheet: $7 - $15

MURDER BY DEATH
(1976 - Columbia) Peter Sellers, Truman Capote
One Sheet: $15 - $25

MURDER BY DECREE
(1979 - Ambassador) Christopher Plummer, James Mason
One Sheet: $10 - $20

MURDER BY INVITATION
(1941 - Monogram) Wallace Ford, Marian Marsh
One Sheet: $40 - $75

MURDER BY TELEVISION
(1935 - Cameo) Bela Lugosi, George Meeker
One Sheet: $2,500 - $4,000   *Graven Images, pg. 88. AKA: THE HOUGHLAND MURDER CASE.*

MURDER BY THE CLOCK
(1931 - Paramount Publix) William "Stage" Boyd, Irving Pichel
One Sheet: $250 - $600   *Graven Images, pg. 55.*

MURDER CAN BE DEADLY
(1963 - Shoenfeld) Liz Fraser, Kenneth Griffith
One Sheet: $7 - $15

MURDER GAME, THE
(1966 - 20th Century Fox) Ken Scott, Marla Landi
One Sheet: $3 - $5

MURDER GOES TO COLLEGE
(1937 - Paramount) Roscoe Karns, Marsha Hunt
One Sheet: $75 - $150

MURDER, HE SAYS
(1945 - Paramount) Fred MacMurray, Helen Walker
One Sheet: $100 - $200

MURDER IN GREENWICH VILLAGE
(1937 - Columbia) Fay Wray, Richard Arlen
One Sheet: $150 - $350

MURDER IN HARLEM
(1935 - Micheaux) Clarence Brooks, Laura Bowman
One Sheet: $1,900 - $3,000   *Black cast. Separate Cinema, pg. 15.*

MURDER IN REVERSE
(1947 - Four Continent) William Hartnell, Jimmy Hanley
One Sheet: $20 - $40

MURDER IN THE AIR
(1940 - Warner Bros.) Ronald Reagan, John Litel
One Sheet: $100 - $200

MURDER IN THE BIG HOUSE
(1942 - Warner Bros.) Van Johnson, Faye Emerson
One Sheet: $40 - $75

MURDER IN THE BLUE ROOM
(1944 - Universal) Grace McDonald, Donald Cook, Anne Gwynne
One Sheet: $40 - $75

MURDER IN THE CLOUDS
(1934 - First National) Lyle Talbot, Ann Dvorak
One Sheet: $100 - $200

MURDER IN THE CLOUDS
(1951 - 20th Century Fox) Stuart Whitman, May Britt
One Sheet: $15 - $25

MURDER IN THE FIRST
(1995 - Warner Bros.) Christian Slater, Kevin Bacon, Gary Oldman
One Sheet: $5 - $10

MURDER IN THE FLEET
(1935 - MGM) Robert Taylor, Jean Parker, Ted Healy
One Sheet: $100 - $200

MURDER IN THE MUSIC HALL
(1946 - Republic) Vera Hruba Ralston, William Marshall
One Sheet: $30 - $50

MURDER IN THE OLD RED BARN
(1936 - Sound City/Olympic) Tod Slaughter, Sophie Stewart
One Sheet: $50 - $100

MURDER IN THE PRIVATE CAR
(1934 - MGM) Charles Ruggles, Una Merkel
One Sheet: $100 - $200

MURDER IN THORNTON SQUARE, THE
(1950R - MGM) Dir: Alfred Hitchcock
One Sheet: $40 - $75   *British re-release of GASLIGHT.*

MURDER IN TIMES SQUARE
(1943 - Columbia) Edmund Lowe, Marguerite Chapman, Sidney Blackmer
One Sheet: $100 - $200

MURDER IN TRINIDAD
(1934 - Fox) Nigel Bruce, Heather Angel
One Sheet: $75 - $150

MURDER, INC.
(1960 - 20th Century Fox) Stuart Whitman, May Britt
One Sheet: $15 - $25

MURDER IS MY BEAT
(1955 - Allied Artists) Barbara Payton, Paul Langton
One Sheet: $40 - $75

MURDER IS MY BUSINESS
(1946 - PRC) Hugh Beaumont, Cheryl Walker
One Sheet: $30 - $50

MURDER IS NEWS
(1939 - Warwick) John Gallaudet, Iris Meredith
One Sheet: $75 - $125

MURDER MAN, THE
(1935 - MGM) Spencer Tracy, Virginia Bruce, James Stewart (1st feature)
One Sheet: $500 - $800

MURDER MOST FOUL
(1964 - MGM) Margaret Rutherford, Stringer Davis
One Sheet: $20 - $40

MURDER, MY SWEET
(1945 - RKO Radio) Dick Powell, Claire Trevor
One Sheet: $700 - $1,200

MURDER OF DR. HORRIGAN, THE
(1935 - Warner Bros.) Mary Astor, Ricardo Cortez
One Sheet: $75 - $150

MURDER ON A HONEYMOON
(1935 - RKO) Lola Lane, Edna May Oliver
One Sheet: $150 - $300

MURDER ON APPROVAL
(1956 - RKO) Tom Conway, Delphi Lawrence
One Sheet: $10 - $20

MURDER ON DIAMOND ROW
(1937 - London) Edmund Lowe, Ann Todd
One Sheet: $75 - $125

MURDER ON LENOX AVENUE
(1941 - Colonnade) Mamie Smith, Alec Lovejoy
One Sheet: $250 - $500   *Black cast. Separate Cinema, pg. 142.*

MURDER ON THE BLACKBOARD
(1934 - RKO) Edna May Oliver, Bruce Cabot
One Sheet: $150 - $300

MURDER ON THE BRIDLE PATH
(1936 - RKO) Helen Broderick, James Gleason
One Sheet: $150 - $300

MURDER ON THE CAMPUS
(1934 - Chesterfield) Shirley Grey, Charles Starrett
One Sheet: $150 - $300

MURDER ON THE CAMPUS
(1963 - Colorama) Terence Longdon, Donald Gray
One Sheet: $7 - $15

MURDER ON THE ORIENT EXPRESS
(1974 - Paramount) Albert Finney, Ingrid Bergman, Sean Connery
One Sheet: $15 - $30   *Academy Award: Best Supporting Actress (Bergman). Amsel art. Academy Award Movie Posters #285.*

MURDER ON THE ROOF, THE
(1930 - Columbia) Joseph Walker
One Sheet: $100 - $200

MURDER ON THE WATERFRONT
(1943 - Warner Bros.) John Loder, Ruth Todd
One Sheet: $40 - $75

MURDER ON THE YUKON
(1940 - Monogram) James Newill, Dave O'Brien
One Sheet: $75 - $150

MURDER ONE
(1988 - -) Henry Thomas, James Wilder
One Sheet: $3 - $5

MURDER OVER NEW YORK
(1940 - 20th Century Fox) Sidney Toler, Marjorie Weaver, Robert Lowery
One Sheet: $125 - $250

MURDER REPORTED
(1956 - Columbia) Paul Carpenter, Melissa Stribling
One Sheet: $10 - $20

MURDER, SHE SAID
(1962 - MGM) Margaret Rutherford, Arthur Kennedy
One Sheet: $7 - $15

MURDER WILL OUT
(1930 - Warner Bros.) Hedda Hopper, Noah Beery
One Sheet: $100 - $200

MURDER WILL OUT
(1939 - Warner Bros.) John Loder, Roddy McDowall
One Sheet: $50 - $100

MURDER WILL OUT
(1953 - Eros) Valerie Hobson, Ian Fleming
One Sheet: $15 - $30

MURDER WITH MUSIC
(1945 - -) -
One Sheet: $30 - $50

MURDER WITH PICTURES
(1936 - Paramount) Lew Ayres, Gail Patrick
One Sheet: $100 - $200

MURDER WITHOUT CRIME
(1951 - Strafford) Dennis Price, Derek Farr
One Sheet: $10 - $20

MURDER WITHOUT TEARS
(1953 - Columbia) Craig Stevens, Joyce Holden
One Sheet: $15 - $25

MURDERERS' ROW
(1966 - Columbia) Dean Martin, Ann-Margret
One Sheet: $15 - $35

MURDERS IN THE RUE MORGUE
(1932 - Universal) Bela Lugosi, Sidney Fox, Leon Ames
One Sheet: $13,000 - $20,000   *Graven Images, pg. 53.*

Window Card

MURDERS IN THE RUE MORGUE
(1948R - Realart) Bela Lugosi, Sidney Fox
One Sheet: $150 - $300   *Re-release.*

MURDERS IN THE RUE MORGUE
(1971 - AIP) Jason Robards, Christine Kaufmann, Herbert Lom
One Sheet: $10 - $20

MURDERS IN THE ZOO
(1933 - Paramount) Lionel Atwill, Randolph Scott
One Sheet: $250 - $600   *Graven Images, pg. 66.*

MURIEL
(1963 - Lopert) Delphine Seyrig, Jean-Pierre Kerien
One Sheet: $3 - $5

MURIEL'S WEDDING
(1995 - Miramax) Toni Collette, Bill Hunter
One Sheet: $5 - $10

MURIETA
(1965 - Warner Bros.) Jeffrey Hunter, Arthur Kennedy
One Sheet: $7 - $15

MURMUR OF THE HEART
(1971 - Reade/Palomar) Lea Massari, Benoit Ferreux
One Sheet: $3 - $5

MURPH THE SURF
(1974 - Byrd) Robert Conrad, Don Stroud, Donna Mills
One Sheet: $3 - $5   *AKA: LIVE A LITTLE, STEAL A LOT.*

MURPHY'S LAW
(1986 - Cannon) Charles Bronson, Kathleen Wilhoite
One Sheet: $3 - $5

MURPHY'S ROMANCE
(1985 - Columbia) Sally Field, James Garner
One Sheet: $5 - $10

MURPHY'S WAR
(1971 - Paramount) Peter O'Toole, Sian Phillips
One Sheet: $3 - $5

MUSCLE BEACH PARTY
(1964 - AIP) Frankie Avalon, Annette Funicello
One Sheet: $50 - $100   *Rock 'n' Roll. Surfing.*

One Sheet

MUSCLE UP A LITTLE CLOSER

(1957 - Columbia) The Three Stooges (Joe Besser)
One Sheet: $75 - $125   *Comedy short. Duotone.*

MUSIC BOX, THE
(1932 - MGM) Stan Laurel, Oliver Hardy
One Sheet: $5,000 - $7,500   *Academy Award: Best Comedy short.*

MUSIC BOX
(1989 - TriStar) Jessica Lange, Lukas Haas
One Sheet: $5 - $10

MUSIC BOX KID, THE
(1960 - United Artists) Ronald Foster, Luana Patten
One Sheet: $10 - $20

MUSIC FOR MADAME
(1937 - RKO) Nino Martini, Joan Fontaine
One Sheet: $50 - $100

MUSIC FOR MILLIONS
(1944 - MGM) Margaret O'Brien, Jimmy Durante, June Allyson, Jose Iturbi
One Sheet: $75 - $125

MUSIC GOES 'ROUND, THE
(1936 - Columbia) Rochelle Hudson, Harry Richman, Onyx Club Band
One Sheet: $75 - $150   *Big Band musical.*

MUSIC IN MANHATTAN
(1944 - RKO) Dennis Day, Anne Shirley, Charlie Barnet Orchestra
One Sheet: $75 - $150   *Big Band musical.*

MUSIC IN MY HEART
(1939 - Columbia) Tony Martin, Rita Hayworth
One Sheet: $125 - $300

MUSIC IN THE AIR
(1934 - Fox) Gloria Swanson, John Boles
One Sheet: $250 - $500

MUSIC IS MAGIC
(1935 - 20th Century Fox) Alice Faye, Ray Walker
One Sheet: $200 - $400

MUSIC LAND
(1955 - RKO/Disney) -
One Sheet: $100 - $200

MUSIC LOVERS, THE
(1971 - United Artists) Richard Chamberlain, Glenda Jackson
One Sheet: $3 - $5

MUSIC MAN, THE
(1948 - Monogram) Phil Brito, Freddie Stewart
One Sheet: $20 - $40

MUSIC MAN, THE
(1962 - Warner Bros) Robert Preston, Shirley Jones
One Sheet: $30 - $50

MUSIC OF CHANCE, THE
(1993 - I.R.S.) Mandy Patinkin, James Spader
One Sheet: $3 - $5

MUSICAL BANDIT, THE
(1941 - RKO) Ray Whitley, Virginia Vale
One Sheet: $30 - $60

MUSICAL FARMER, THE
(1932 - Columbia) Mickey Mouse
One Sheet: $25,000 - $40,000   *Cartoon. The Disney Poster, pg. 19.*

MUSIQUIZ
(1952 - MGM) Pete Smith Specialty
One Sheet: $150 - $300

MUSKETEERS OF THE SEA
(1962 - -) -
One Sheet: $10 - $20

MUSS 'EM UP
(1936 - RKO) Preston Foster, Margaret Callahan
One Sheet: $150 - $300

MUSSOLINI SPEAKS!
(1933 - -) Narrated by Lowell Thomas
One Sheet: $500 - $800   *Documentary.*

MUSTANG
(1959 - United Artists) Jack Beutel
One Sheet: $7 - $15

MUSTANG COUNTRY
(1976 - Universal) Robert Fuller, Patrick Wayne, Joel McCrea
One Sheet: $5 - $10

MUSTY MUSKETEERS
(1954 - Columbia) The Three Stooges (Shemp)
One Sheet: $150 - $300   *Comedy short. Duotone.*

MUTANT
(1983 - -) Wings Hauser, Bo Hopkins
One Sheet: $5 - $10

MUTATIONS, THE
(1974 - Columbia) Donald Pleasence, Tom Baker
One Sheet: $7 - $15

MUTE WITNESS
(1995 - Sony Classics) Marina Sudina
One Sheet: $3 - $5

MUTINEERS, THE
(1949 - Columbia) Jon Hall, Adele Jergens
One Sheet: $30 - $60

MUTINY
(1951 - United Artists) Patric Knowles, Angela Lansbury
One Sheet: $15 - $30

MUTINY AHEAD
(1935 - Majestic) Leon Ames, Neil Hamilton
One Sheet: $75 - $125

MUTINY IN OUTER SPACE
(1964 - Allied Artists) Glenn Langan, Dolores Faith
One Sheet: $15 - $35

MUTINY IN THE ARCTIC
(1941 - Universal) Richard Arlen, Andy Devine
One Sheet: $40 - $75

MUTINY IN THE BIG HOUSE
(1939 - Monogram) Charles Bickford, Barton MacLane
One Sheet: $50 - $100

MUTINY ON THE BLACKHAWK
(1939 - Universal) Richard Arlen, Andy Devine
One Sheet: $50 - $100

MUTINY ON THE BLACKHAWK
(1948R - Universal) Richard Arlen, Andy Devine
One Sheet: $15 - $25   *Re-release.*

MUTINY ON THE BOUNTY
(1935 - MGM) Clark Gable, Charles Laughton
One Sheet: $800 - $1,500   *Academy Award: Best Picture. Academy Award Movie Posters #40 & #42.*

One Sheet

MUTINY ON THE BOUNTY
(1957R - MGM) Clark Gable, Charles Laughton
One Sheet: $100 - $200   *Re-release. Full color.*

MUTINY ON THE BOUNTY
(1962 - MGM) Marlon Brando, Trevor Howard
One Sheet: $40 - $75

MUTT AND JEFF IN HAVANA
(1916 - Bud Fisher) Mutt and Jeff
One Sheet: $1,300 - $2,000   *Cartoon. Full color stone litho.*

MUTTS TO YOU
(1938 - Columbia) The Three Stooges (Curly)
One Sheet: $7,500 - $12,000   *Comedy short. Duotone.*

MY AMERICAN COUSIN
(1986 - Spectra) Margaret Langrick, John Wildman
One Sheet: $2 - $3

MY AMERICAN WIFE
(1922 - Paramount) Gloria Swanson
One Sheet: $1,900 - $3,000

MY AMERICAN WIFE
(1936 - Paramount) Ann Sothern, Billie Burke
One Sheet: $100 - $200

MY BABY
(1912 - Biograph) Mary Pickford, Lionel Barrymore
One Sheet: $1,600 - $2,500

MY BABY IS BLACK!
(1965 - Athos) Gordon Heath, Francoise Giret
One Sheet: $20 - $40

MY BEAUTIFUL LAUNDRETTE
(1986 - -) Daniel Day Lewis, Saeed Jaffrey
One Sheet: $5 - $10

MY BEST GAL
(1944 - Republic) Jane Withers, Jimmy Lydon
One Sheet: $50 - $100

MY BEST GIRL
(1927 - United Artists) Mary Pickford
One Sheet: $1,300 - $2,000

MY BILL
(1938 - Warner Bros.) Kay Francis, Bonita Granville, Dickie Moore
One Sheet: $50 - $100

MY BLOOD RUNS COLD
(1965 - Warner Bros.) Troy Donahue, Joey Heatherton
One Sheet: $10 - $20

MY BLOODY VALENTINE
(1981 - Paramount) Paul Kelman, Lori Hallier
One Sheet: $5 - $10

MY BLUE HEAVEN
(1950 - 20th Century Fox) Betty Grable, Dan Dailey
One Sheet: $75 - $125

MY BLUE HEAVEN
(1990 - Warner Bros.) Steve Martin, Rick Moranis
One Sheet: $5 - $10

MY BODYGUARD
(1980 - 20th Century Fox) Chris Makepeace, Ruth Gordon
One Sheet: $3 - $5

MY BOY
(1921 - First National) Jackie Coogan
One Sheet: $600 - $1,000

MY BOYFRIEND'S BACK
(1993 - Buena Vista) Edward Hermann, Mary Beth Hurt
One Sheet: $3 - $5

MY BROTHER JONATHAN
(1949 - Allied Artists) Michael Denison, Dulcie Gray
One Sheet: $10 - $20

MY BROTHER TALKS TO HORSES
(1946 - MGM) Peter Lawford, Butch Jenkins
One Sheet: $50 - $100

MY BROTHER'S KEEPER
(1947 - Eagle-Lion) Jack Warner, Jane Hylton
One Sheet: $15 - $30

MY BUDDY
(1944 - Republic) Don "Red" Barry, Ruth Terry
One Sheet: $15 - $35

MY CHAUFFEUR
(1986 - -) Deborah Foreman, Sam Jones
One Sheet: $3 - $5

MY COUNTRY FIRST
(1917 - Terriss) -
One Sheet: $150 - $300

MY COUSIN RACHEL
(1952 - 20th Century Fox) Olivia de Havilland, Richard Burton
One Sheet: $30 - $60

MY COUSIN VINNY

MY COUSIN VINNY
(1992 - 20th Century Fox) Joe Pesci, Ralph Macchio, Marisa Tomei
One Sheet: $7 - $15   *Academy Award: Best Supporting Actress(Tomei). Academy Award Movie Posters #384.*

MY DARLING CLEMENTINE
(1946 - 20th Century Fox) Henry Fonda, Linda Darnell, Victor Mature
One Sheet: $800 - $1,500   *Cowboy Movie Posters #s 278, 279.*

MY DARLING CLEMENTINE
(1953R - 20th Century Fox) Henry Fonda, Linda Darnell, Victor Mature
One Sheet: $100 - $200   *Re-release.*

MY DAUGHTER JOY
(1950 - London) Edward G. Robinson, Peggy Cummins
One Sheet: $15 - $25

MY DEAR MISS ALDRICH
(1937 - MGM) Edna May Oliver, Maureen O'Sullivan
One Sheet: $75 - $125

MY DEAR SECRETARY
(1948 - United Artists) Laraine Day, Kirk Douglas
One Sheet: $20 - $40

MY DEMON LOVER
(1987 - -) Scott Valentine, Michelle Little
One Sheet: $5 - $12

MY DOG BUDDY
(1960 - Columbia) Ken Curtis
One Sheet: $7 - $15

MY DOG RUSTY
(1948 - Columbia) Ted Donaldson, John Litel
One Sheet: $15 - $30

MY DOG SHEP
(1946 - Screen Guild) Tom Neal, Helen Chapman, Flame
One Sheet: $20 - $40

MY DREAM IS YOURS
(1949 - Warner Bros.) Jack Carson, Doris Day
One Sheet: $40 - $75

MY ECSTASY
(1948 - Pix) -
One Sheet: $15 - $30

MY FAIR LADY
(1964 - Warner Bros.) Audrey Hepburn, Rex Harrison
One Sheet: $75 - $150   *Academy Award: Best Picture, Best Actor, Best Direction(George Cukor). Bob Peak art. Academy Award Movie Posters #220-#223.*

One Sheet

MY FAIR LADY
(1971R - Warner Bros.) Audrey Hepburn, Rex Harrison
One Sheet: $40 - $75   *Re-release.*

MY FAIR LADY
(1994R - Warner Bros.) Audrey Hepburn, Rex Harrison
One Sheet: $15 - $30   *Re-release.*

MY FAMILY
(1995 - New Line) Jimmy Smits, Edward James Olmos
One Sheet: $5 - $10

MY FATHER, THE HERO
(1994 - Touchstone) Gerard Depardieu, Katherine Heigl
One Sheet: $3 - $5

MY FAVORITE BLONDE
(1942 - Paramount) Bob Hope, Madeleine Carroll
One Sheet: $100 - $200

One Sheet

MY FAVORITE BRUNETTE
(1947 - Paramount) Bob Hope, Dorothy Lamour, Peter Lorre, Lon Chaney, Jr.
One Sheet: $75 - $150

MY FAVORITE SPY
(1942 - RKO) Kay Kyser, Ellen Drew
One Sheet: $75 - $150   *Big Band musical.*

MY FAVORITE SPY
(1951 - Paramount) Bob Hope, Hedy Lamarr
One Sheet: $50 - $100

MY FAVORITE WIFE
(1940 - RKO) Irene Dunne, Cary Grant, Randolph Scott
One Sheet: $600 - $1,000

One Sheet

MY FAVORITE YEAR
(1982 - MGM) Peter O'Toole, Mark Linn-Baker
One Sheet: $7 - $15

MY FELLOW AMERICANS
(1996 - Warner Bros.) Jack Lemmon, James Garner, Dan Aykroyd
One Sheet: $5 - $10

MY FOOLISH HEART
(1949 - RKO) Dana Andrews, Susan Hayward
One Sheet: $30 - $50

MY FORBIDDEN PAST
(1950 - RKO) Robert Mitchum, Ava Gardner
One Sheet: $75 - $150

One Sheet

MY FOUR YEARS IN GERMANY
(1918 - Warner Bros.) Ambassador James W.

Gerard
One Sheet: $1,600 - $2,500   *Warner Bros. first major feature film.*

MY FRIEND FLICKA
(1943 - 20th Century Fox) Roddy McDowall, Preston Foster
One Sheet: $100 - $200

MY FRIEND FLICKA
(1951R - 20th Century Fox) Roddy McDowell, Preston Foster
One Sheet: $40 - $75   *Re-release.*

MY FRIEND IRMA
(1949 - Paramount) Marie Wilson, Dean Martin, Jerry Lewis (their film debut)
One Sheet: $75 - $150

MY FRIEND IRMA GOES WEST
(1950 - Paramount) Marie Wilson, John Lund, Dean Martin, Jerry Lewis
One Sheet: $50 - $100

MY GAL LOVES MUSIC
(1944 - Universal) Bob Crosby, Grace McDonald
One Sheet: $50 - $100

MY GAL SAL
(1942 - 20th Century Fox) Victor Mature, Rita Hayworth
One Sheet: $250 - $600

One Sheet

MY GEISHA
(1962 - Paramount) Shirley MacLaine, Yves Montand
One Sheet: $15 - $30

MY GIRL
(1991 - Columbia) Macauley Culkin, Anna Chlumsky, Dan Aykroyd
One Sheet: $3 - $5

MY GIRL TISA
(1948 - United States Pictures) Lilli Palmer, Sam Wanamaker
One Sheet: $15 - $30

MY GUN IS QUICK
(1957 - United Artists) Robert Bray, Pamela Duncan
One Sheet: $20 - $40

MY HEART BELONGS TO DADDY
(1943 - Paramount) Richard Carlson, Martha O'Driscoll
One Sheet: $50 - $100

MY HEART GOES CRAZY
(1953 - United Artists) Sid Field, Greta Gynt
One Sheet: $15 - $25

MY HEART IS CALLING
(1934 - Gaumont-British) Sonnie Hale, Marta Eggerth
One Sheet: $50 - $100

MY HEROES HAVE ALWAYS BEEN COWBOYS
(1991 - -) Scott Glenn, Mickey Rooney
One Sheet: $5 - $10   *Sports (Rodeo).*

MY HUSBAND'S WIVES
(1924 - William Fox) Shirley Mason, Bryant Washburn, Evelyn Brent
One Sheet: $500 - $900

MY KINGDOM FOR A COOK
(1943 - Columbia) Charles Coburn, Isbel Elsom
One Sheet: $50 - $100

MY LADY OF WHIMS
(1925 - -) Clara Bow, Donald Keith

One Sheet: $1,300 - $2,000

MY LEFT FOOT
(1989 - Miramax) Daniel Day-Lewis, Brenda Fricker
One Sheet: $7 - $15   *Academy Award: Best Actor(Day-Lewis), Best Supporting Actress(Fricker). Academy Award Movie Posters #365 & #367.*

MY LIFE
(1949 - Pix) -
One Sheet: $15 - $30

MY LIFE
(1993 - Columbia) Michael Keaton, Nicole Kidman
One Sheet: $3 - $5

MY LIFE AS A DOG
(1987 - Skouras) Anton Glanzelius, Tomas von Bromssen
One Sheet: $7 - $15

MY LIFE TO LIVE
(1963 - Union-Pathe) Anna Karina, Saddy Rebbot, Dir: Jean-Luc Godard
One Sheet: $75 - $125

MY LIFE WITH CAROLINE
(1941 - RKO) Ronald Colman, Anna Lee
One Sheet: $50 - $100

MY LIPS BETRAY
(1933 - Fox) Lillian Harvey, John Boles
One Sheet: $600 - $1,000

MY LITTLE CHICKADEE
(1939 - Universal) W. C. Fields, Mae West
One Sheet: $800 - $1,500   *Price is for white-background one sheet. One sheet(red background, portrait):$4000-5000. (See photo Camden House 6/92, pg. 63).*

MY LITTLE CHICKADEE
(1947R - Realart) W.C. Fields, Mae West
One Sheet: $125 - $250   *Re-release.*

MY LOVE CAME BACK
(1940 - Warner Bros.) Olivia de Havilland, Jeffrey Lynn
One Sheet: $50 - $100

MY LOVER, MY SON
(1970 - MGM) Romy Schneider, Donald Houston
One Sheet: $5 - $10

MY LUCKY STAR
(1938 - 20th Century Fox) Sonja Henie, Cesar Romero
One Sheet: $250 - $600

MY MAN
(1924 - Vitagraph) Patsy Ruth Miller, Dustin Farnum
One Sheet: $250 - $500

MY MAN AND I
(1952 - MGM) Shelley Winters, Wendell Corey
One Sheet: $15 - $30

MY MAN GODFREY
(1936 - Universal) William Powell, Carole Lombard
One Sheet: $4,500 - $7,000

MY MAN GODFREY
(1940R - Universal) William Powell, Carole Lombard
One Sheet: $500 - $800   *Re-release.*

One Sheet

MY MAN GODFREY
(1957 - Universal) June Allyson, David Niven

One Sheet: $20 - $40

MY MARRIAGE
(1936 - 20th Century Fox) Claire Trevor, Kent Taylor
One Sheet: $100 - $200

MY NAME IS BILL W.
(1989 - -) -
One Sheet: $3 - $5

MY NAME IS JULIA ROSS
(1945 - Columbia) Nina Foch, Dame May Whitty
One Sheet: $40 - $75

MY NAME IS NOBODY
(1974 - Universal) Henry Fonda, Terrence Hill
One Sheet: $10 - $30   *Spaghetti Western.*

MY OFFICIAL WIFE
(1914 - Vitagraph) Rudolph Valentino
One Sheet: $600 - $1,000

MY OLD DUTCH
(1926 - Universal) May McAvoy
One Sheet: $150 - $300

MY OLD KENTUCKY HOME
(1938 - Monogram) Grant Richards, Evelyn Venable
One Sheet: $75 - $150

MY OLD KENTUCKY HOME
(1943 - 20th Century Fox) Mighty Mouse
One Sheet: $250 - $600   *Cartoon. Full color stock poster with printed title. Huge image of Mighty Mouse on yellow background.*

MY OUTLAW BROTHER
(1951 - Eagle Lion Classics) Mickey Rooney, Wanda Hendrix
One Sheet: $15 - $30

MY OWN PRIVATE IDAHO
(1991 - -) River Phoenix, Keanu Reeves
One Sheet: $7 - $15

MY OWN TRUE LOVE
(1949 - Paramount) Phyllis Calvert, Melvyn Douglas, Wanda Hendrix
One Sheet: $20 - $40

MY PAL GUS
(1952 - 20th Century Fox) Richard Widmark, Joanne Dru
One Sheet: $10 - $20

MY PAL THE KING
(1932 - Universal) Tom Mix, Mickey Rooney
One Sheet: $1,300 - $2,000   *Cowboy Movie Posters # 134.*

MY PAL TRIGGER
(1946 - Republic) Roy Rogers, Gabby Hayes, Dale Evans
One Sheet: $250 - $500

MY PAL WOLF
(1944 - RKO) Sharyn Moffett, Jill Esmond, Una O'Connor
One Sheet: $20 - $40

MY PAST
(1931 - Warner Bros.) Joan Blondell, Bebe Daniels
One Sheet: $125 - $250

MY REPUTATION
(1946 - Warner Bros.) Barbara Stanwyck, George Brent
One Sheet: $75 - $150

MY SCIENCE PROJECT
(1985 - Touchstone) John Stockwell, Danielle Von Zerneck
One Sheet: $3 - $5

MY SIDE OF THE MOUNTAIN
(1969 - Paramount) Teddy Eccles, Theodore Bikel
One Sheet: $3 - $5

MY SIN
(1931 - Paramount Publix) Tallulah Bankhead, Fredric March
One Sheet: $600 - $1,000

MY SISTER EILEEN
(1942 - Columbia) Rosalind Russell, Janet Blair, Three Stooges (Curly)
One Sheet: $75 - $150   *Price assumes Stooges not pictured on the one sheet.*

MY SISTER EILEEN
(1955 - Columbia) Janet Leigh, Jack Lemmon
One Sheet: $30 - $50

MY SIX CONVICTS
(1952 - Columbia) John Beal, Gilbert Roland
One Sheet: $15 - $25

MY SIX LOVES
(1963 - Paramount) Debbie Reynolds, Cliff
Robertson
One Sheet: $10 - $20

MY SON IS A CRIMINAL
(1939 - Columbia) Alan Baxter, Jacqueline
Wells
One Sheet: $75 - $150

MY SON IS GUILTY
(1939 - Columbia) Jacqueline Wells, Bruce
Cabot, Glenn Ford
One Sheet: $75 - $150

MY SON JOHN
(1952 - Paramount) Helen Hayes, Van Heflin,
Robert Walker
One Sheet: $20 - $40

MY SON, MY SON
(1940 - United Artists) Madeleine Carroll, Brian
Aherne
One Sheet: $40 - $75

MY SON THE HERO
(1943 - PRC) Patsy Kelly, Roscoe Karns
One Sheet: $50 - $100

MY SON THE HERO
(1963 - United Artists) Pedro Armendariz,
Jacqueline Sassard
One Sheet: $10 - $20

MY SONG FOR YOU
(1934 - Gaumont-British) Jan Kiepura, Sonnie
Hale
One Sheet: $50 - $100

MY STARS
(1926 - Educational) Johnny Arthur
One Sheet: $250 - $500

MY STEPMOTHER IS AN ALIEN
(1989 - Weintraub) Dan Aykroyd, Kim Basinger
One Sheet: $5 - $10

MY SWEET CHARLIE
(1970 - Universal) Patty Duke, Al Freeman Jr
One Sheet: $3 - $5

MY TRUE STORY
(1951 - Columbia) Helen Walker, Willard
Parker
One Sheet: $10 - $20

MY TUTOR
(1983 - Crown) Kevin McCarthy, Caren Kaye
One Sheet: $3 - $5

MY UNCLE
(1958 - Continental) Jacques Tati, Jean-Pierre
Zola
One Sheet: $100 - $200   *French.
Academy Award: Best Foreign Film. AKA: MY
UNCLE, MR. HULOT.*

MY WEAKNESS
(1933 - Fox) Lillian Harvey, Lew Ayres
One Sheet: $125 - $250

MY WIFE'S AN ANGEL
(1943 - Columbia) -
One Sheet: $50 - $100

MY WIFE'S BEST FRIEND
(1952 - 20th Century Fox) Anne Baxter,
Macdonald Carey
One Sheet: $15 - $25

MY WIFE'S FAMILY
(1932 - BIP America) Gene Gerrard, Muriel
Angelus
One Sheet: $100 - $200

MY WIFE'S FAMILY
(1958 - Associated British/Pathe) Greta Gynt,
Ted Roy
One Sheet: $5 - $10

MY WIFE'S RELATIONS
(1922 - Comique) Buster Keaton
One Sheet: $5,500 - $9,000

MY WIFE'S RELATIVES

(1939 - Republic) James, Lucille, and Russell
Gleason
One Sheet: $50 - $100

MY WILD IRISH ROSE
(1947 - Warner Bros.) Dennis Morgan, Andrea
King
One Sheet: $30 - $50

MY WOMAN
(1933 - Columbia) Helen Twelvetrees, Victory
Jory
One Sheet: $150 - $300

MY WORLD DIES SCREAMING
(1958 - Howco) Gerald Mohr, Cathy O'Donnell
One Sheet: $15 - $30

MYRA BRECKINRIDGE
(1970 - 20th Century Fox) Mae West, Raquel
Welch, John Huston
One Sheet: $15 - $25

MYRT AND MARGE
(1933 - Universal) Myrtle Vail, Eddie Foy, Jr.,
The Three Stooges (Curly)
One Sheet: $250 - $500   *Price
assumes Stooges not pictured on one sheet. One
Lobby Card features the Stooges:$1000-$1500.*

MYSTERIANS, THE
(1959 - MGM or RKO) Kenji Sahara, Yumi
Shirakawa
One Sheet: $75 - $125   *Japanese
poster:$300-$500.*

One Sheet

MYSTERIES FROM BEYOND EARTH
(1975 - American National) Lawrence Dobkin
One Sheet: $7 - $15

MYSTERIOUS AVENGER, THE
(1936 - Columbia) Charles Starrett, Joan Perry,
Roy Rogers (minor role)
One Sheet: $250 - $600

MYSTERIOUS CROSSING
(1936 - Universal) James Dunn, Jean Rogers
One Sheet: $150 - $300

MYSTERIOUS DESPERADO, THE
(1949 - RKO) Tim Holt, Richard Martin
One Sheet: $30 - $60

MYSTERIOUS DOCTOR, THE
(1943 - Warner Bros.) John Loder, Eleanor
Parker
One Sheet: $40 - $75

MYSTERIOUS DR. FU MANCHU, THE
(1929 - Paramount) Warner Oland, Jean Arthur
One Sheet: $1,300 - $2,000   *Graven
Images, pg. 38.*

MYSTERIOUS DR. SATAN
(1940 - Republic) Eduardo Ciannelli, Robert
Wilcox
One Sheet: $150 - $300   *Serial. 15
Chapters. Chapter One(one sheet):$350.*

MYSTERIOUS INTRUDER
(1946 - Columbia) Richard Dix, Nina Vale
One Sheet: $30 - $50

MYSTERIOUS ISLAND
(1929 - MGM) Lionel Barrymore, Lloyd Hughes
One Sheet: $1,600 - $2,500   *Graven
Images, pg. 39.*

MYSTERIOUS ISLAND
(1951 - Columbia) Richard Crane, Marshall
Reed
One Sheet: $40 - $75   *Serial. 15
Chapters.*

MYSTERIOUS ISLAND
(1961 - Columbia) Michael Craig, Joan
Greenwood
One Sheet: $40 - $75   *Ray
Harryhausen effects.*

One Sheet

MYSTERIOUS ISLAND OF CAPTAIN NEMO
(1974 - Cinerama) Omar Sharif
One Sheet: $5 - $10

MYSTERIOUS LADY, THE
(1927 - MGM) Greta Garbo, Conrad Nagel
One Sheet: $2,500 - $4,000

MYSTERIOUS MISS X, THE
(1939 - Republic) Michael Whalen, Mary Hart
One Sheet: $50 - $100

MYSTERIOUS MONSTERS, THE
(1975 - Sun) Narrator: Peter Graves
One Sheet: $5 - $10   *Documentary.*

MYSTERIOUS MR. M, THE
(1946 - Universal) Richard Martin, Pamela
Blake
One Sheet: $50 - $100   *Serial. 13
Chapters.*

MYSTERIOUS MR. MOTO
(1938 - 20th Century Fox) Peter Lorre, Mary
Maguire
One Sheet: $300 - $700

One Sheet

MYSTERIOUS MR. REEDER, THE
(1940 - Monogram) Will Fyffe, Kay Walsh
One Sheet: $30 - $60

MYSTERIOUS MR. VALENTINE, THE
(1946 - Republic) Willima Henry, Linda Stirling
One Sheet: $20 - $40

MYSTERIOUS MR. WONG, THE
(1935 - Monogram) Bela Lugosi, Arline Judge
One Sheet: $350 - $750   *Graven
Images, pg. 88.*

MYSTERIOUS PILOT, THE
(1937 - Columbia) Frank Hawks, Dorothy
Sebastian
One Sheet: $125 - $250   *Serial. 15
Chapters.*

MYSTERIOUS RIDER, THE
(1933 - Paramount) Kent Taylor
One Sheet: $150 - $300

MYSTERIOUS RIDER, THE
(1938 - Paramount) Russell Hayden, Weldon
Heyburn
One Sheet: $75 - $150

MYSTERIOUS RIDER, THE
(1943 - PRC) Buster Crabbe, Al "Fuzzy" St.
John

One Sheet: $30 - $60

MYSTERIOUS RIDER, THE
(1950R - Paramount) Russell Hayden, Weldon
Heyburn
One Sheet: $30 - $50   *Re-release.*

MYSTERY AT THE BURLESQUE
(1950 - Monogram) Garry Marsh, Jon Pertwee
One Sheet: $40 - $75

MYSTERY BROADCAST
(1943 - Republic) Ruth Terry, Frank Albertson
One Sheet: $40 - $75

MYSTERY HOUSE
(1937 - Warner Bros.) Dick Purcell, Ann
Sheridan
One Sheet: $50 - $100

MYSTERY IN MEXICO
(1948 - RKO) William Lundigan, Jacqueline
White
One Sheet: $20 - $40

MYSTERY IN SWING
(1940 - International) F.E. Miller, Monte Hawley
One Sheet: $50 - $100

MYSTERY LINER
(1934 - Monogram) Noah Beery, Astrid Allwyn
One Sheet: $100 - $200

MYSTERY MAN, THE
(1935 - Monogram) Robert Armstrong, Maxine
Doyle
One Sheet: $75 - $150

MYSTERY MAN, THE
(1944 - United Artists) William Boyd, Andy
Clyde
One Sheet: $150 - $300   *Hopalong
Cassidy series. Cowboy Movie Posters #274.*

One Sheet

MYSTERY MAN, THE
(1948R - United Artists) William Boyd
One Sheet: $50 - $100   *Re-release.*

MYSTERY MOUNTAIN
(1934 - Mascot) Ken Maynard, Verna Hillie
One Sheet: $250 - $500   *Serial.
Western. 12 Chapters.*

MYSTERY OF EDWIN DROOD, THE
(1935 - Universal) Claude Rains, Valerie
Hobson
One Sheet: $500 - $800   *Graven
Images, pg. 94.*

MYSTERY OF LIFE
(1931 - Universal)
One Sheet: $150 - $300

MYSTERY OF MARIE ROGET, THE
(1942 - Universal) Maria Montez, Patric
Knowles
One Sheet: $125 - $250

MYSTERY OF MR. WONG, THE
(1939 - Monogram) Boris Karloff, Dorothy Tree
One Sheet: $150 - $300

MYSTERY OF MR. X
(1934 - MGM) Robert Montgomery, Lewis
Stone
One Sheet: $100 - $200

MYSTERY OF RAMPO, THE
(1995 - Goldwyn) Masahiro Motoki, Michiko
Hada, Naoto Takenaka
One Sheet: $5 - $10

MYSTERY OF ROOM 13
(1940 - Film Alliance) Gibb McLaughlin

One Sheet: $40 - $75

MYSTERY OF THE 13TH GUEST, THE
(1943 - Monogram) Dick Purcell, Helen Parrish
One Sheet: $50 - $100

MYSTERY OF THE BLACK JUNGLE
(1954 - Republic) Lex Barker, Jane Maxwell
One Sheet: $30 - $50

MYSTERY OF THE DOUBLE CROSS
(1917 - Pathe) Molly King
One Sheet: $250 - $600   *Serial. 15 Episodes.*

MYSTERY OF THE DOWNS
(1956 - Associated British-Pathe) -
One Sheet: $5 - $10

MYSTERY OF THE HOODED HORSEMEN
(1937 - Grand National) Tex Ritter, Iris Meredith
One Sheet: $125 - $250

MYSTERY OF THE RIVER BOAT
(1944 - Universal) Robert Lowery, Eddie Quillan
One Sheet: $50 - $100   *Serial. 13 Chapters.*

MYSTERY OF THE WAX MUSEUM, THE
(1933 - Warner Bros.) Lionel Atwill, Fay Wray
One Sheet: $7,500 - $12,000   *Graven Images, pg. 67.*

Title Card

MYSTERY OF THE WHITE ROOM
(1939 - Universal) Bruce Cabot, Helen Mack
One Sheet: $75 - $150

MYSTERY OF THUG ISLAND, THE
(1966 - Columbia) Guy Madison, Peter Van Eyck
One Sheet: $5 - $10

MYSTERY PLANE
(1939 - Monogram) John Trent, Marjorie Reynolds
One Sheet: $50 - $100

MYSTERY RANCH
(1932 - Fox) George O'Brien
One Sheet: $200 - $400

MYSTERY RANCH
(1934 - Reliable) Tom Tyler
One Sheet: $250 - $500

One Sheet

MYSTERY RANGE
(1937 - Victory) Tom Tyler
One Sheet: $125 - $250

MYSTERY SCIENCE THEATER 3000
(1996 - Gramercy) Mike Nelson, Trace Beaulieu

One Sheet: $10 - $20

MYSTERY SEA RAIDER
(1940 - Paramount) Henry Wilcoxon, Carole Landis
One Sheet: $30 - $60

MYSTERY SHIP
(1941 - Columbia) Paul Kelly, Larry Parks
One Sheet: $75 - $150

MYSTERY SQUADRON
(1933 - Mascot) Bob Steele, "Big Boy" Williams
One Sheet: $500 - $800   *Serial. 12 Chapters.*

MYSTERY STREET
(1950 - MGM) Ricardo Montalban, Sally Forrest
One Sheet: $30 - $50

MYSTERY SUBMARINE
(1950 - Universal) Macdonald Carey, Marta Toren
One Sheet: $15 - $30

MYSTERY SUBMARINE
(1963 - Universal) Edward Judd, James Robertson Justice
One Sheet: $10 - $20

MYSTERY TRAIN
(1989 - -) Youki Kaudoh, Masatochi Nagase, Joe Strummer
One Sheet: $30 - $50

MYSTERY WOMAN, THE
(1935 - Fox) Mona Barrie, Gilbert Roland
One Sheet: $200 - $400

MYSTIC, THE
(1925 - MGM) Aileen Pringle, Conway Tearle
One Sheet: $250 - $600

MYSTIC PIZZA
(1988 - -) Julia Roberts, Annabeth Gish, Lili Taylor
One Sheet: $15 - $35

MYTH OF THE WHITE WOLF, THE
(1994 - Walt Disney) Scott Bairstow, Charmaine Craig
One Sheet: $4 - $8

NABONGA
(1944 - PRC) Buster Crabbe, Fifi D'Orsay
One Sheet: $100 - $200

NADINE
(1987 - TriStar) Kim Basinger, Jeff Bridges
One Sheet: $5 - $10

NAGANA
(1933 - Universal) Tala Birell, Melvyn Douglas
One Sheet: $100 - $200

NAKED
(1994 - Fine Line) David Thewlis
One Sheet: $3 - $5

NAKED AFRICA
(1957 - AIP) Quentin Reynolds
One Sheet: $10 - $20

NAKED ALIBI
(1954 - Universal) Sterling Hayden, Gloria Grahame
One Sheet: $40 - $75

NAKED AMAZON
(195? - -) -
One Sheet: $7 - $15

NAKED AND THE DEAD, THE
(1958 - Warner Bros.) Aldo Ray, Cliff Robertson
One Sheet: $15 - $25

NAKED ANGELS
(1969 - Favorite) Michael Greene, Jennifer Gan
One Sheet: $7 - $15

NAKED APE, THE
(1973 - Universal) Johnny Crawford, Victoria Principal
One Sheet: $3 - $5

NAKED BRIGADE, THE
(1965 - Universal) Shirley Eaton, Ken Scott
One Sheet: $7 - $15

NAKED CAGE, THE
(1986 - -) Shari Shattuck, Angel Tompkins
One Sheet: $3 - $5

NAKED CITY, THE
(1948 - Universal) Barry Fitzgerald, Howard Duff
One Sheet: $40 - $75

NAKED CITY, THE
(1956R - Universal) Barry Fitzgerald, Howard Duff
One Sheet: $15 - $25   *Re-release.*

NAKED CIVIL SERVANT, THE
(1976 - -) John Hurt
One Sheet: $5 - $10

NAKED DAWN, THE
(1955 - Universal) Arthur Kennedy, Betta St. John
One Sheet: $7 - $15

NAKED EARTH
(1957 - 20th Century Fox) Richard Todd, Juliette Greco
One Sheet: $5 - $10

NAKED EDGE, THE
(1961 - United Artists) Gary Cooper, Deborah Kerr
One Sheet: $20 - $40   *Cooper's final film.*

NAKED EYE, THE
(1960S - Film Representations) Raymond Massey
One Sheet: $30 - $50

NAKED FACE
(1984 - Cannon) Roger Moore, Anne Archer, Rod Steiger
One Sheet: $5 - $10

NAKED GUN, THE
(1956 - Associated) Willard Parker, Mara Corday
One Sheet: $10 - $20

NAKED GUN, THE
(1988 - Paramount) Leslie Nielsen, Priscilla Presley, George Kennedy
One Sheet: $10 - $20

NAKED GUN 2 1/2, THE
(1991 - Paramount) Leslie Nielsen, Priscilla Presley, Robert Goulet
One Sheet: $5 - $10

NAKED GUN 33 1/3
(1994 - Paramount) Leslie Nielson, O.J. Simpson
One Sheet: $5 - $10

NAKED HEART, THE
(1955 - Associated Artists) Michele Morgan, Kieron Moore
One Sheet: $5 - $10

NAKED HILLS, THE
(1956 - Allied Artists) David Wayne, Keenan Wynn
One Sheet: $5 - $10

NAKED IN NEW YORK
(1993 - New Line) Eric Stoltz, Mary-Louise Parker
One Sheet: $3 - $5

NAKED IN THE SUN
(1957 - Allied Artists) James Craig, Barton MacLane
One Sheet: $10 - $20

NAKED JUNGLE, THE
(1953 - Paramount) Charlton Heston, Eleanor Parker
One Sheet: $30 - $50

NAKED KISS, THE
(1964 - Allied Artists) Constance Towers, Anthony Eisley
One Sheet: $40 - $75

NAKED LUNCH
(1992 - 20th Century Fox) Peter Weller
One Sheet: $15 - $25

NAKED MAJA, THE
(1959 - United Artists) Ava Gardner, Anthony Franciosa
One Sheet: $15 - $35

NAKED PARADISE
(1957 - AIP) Richard Denning, Beverly Garland
One Sheet: $30 - $50   *Aka: Thunder Over Hawaii.*

NAKED PREY, THE
(1966 - Paramount) Cornel Wilde, Gert Van Den Bergh
One Sheet: $10 - $20

NAKED RUNNER, THE
(1967 - Warner Bros.) Frank Sinatra, Peter Vaughan
One Sheet: $15 - $25

NAKED SEA
(1954 - RKO) Narrated by William Conrad
One Sheet: $10 - $20

NAKED SPUR, THE
(1953 - MGM) James Stewart, Janet Leigh
One Sheet: $125 - $250

NAKED SPUR, THE
(1962R - MGM) James Stewart, Janet Leigh
One Sheet: $30 - $50   *Re-release.*

NAKED STREET, THE
(1955 - United Artists) Farley Granger, Anne Bancroft, Anthony Quinn
One Sheet: $15 - $35

NAKED UNDER LEATHER
(1970 - Mid-Atlantic) Alain Delon, Marianne Faithful
One Sheet: $7 - $15

NAKED WYTCHE
(1972 - -) -
One Sheet: $10 - $20

NAKED YOUNG LADY, THE
(197? - Pro Int'l) Ann Michelle, Harlee McBride
One Sheet: $5 - $10

NAKED YOUTH
(1961 - Cinema Associates) Carol Ohmart, Robert Hutton
One Sheet: $15 - $30   *AKA: WILD YOUTH.*

NAME FOR EVIL, A
(1973 - Cinerama) Robert Culp, Samantha Eggar
One Sheet: $3 - $5

NAME OF THE GAME IS KILL, THE
(1968 - Fanfare) Jack Lord, Susan Strasberg
One Sheet: $5 - $10

NAME OF THE ROSE, THE
(1986 - 20th Century Fox) Sean Connery, F. Murray Abraham, Christian Slater
One Sheet: $10 - $20

NAME THE WOMAN
(1934 - Columbia) Richard Cromwell, Arline Judge
One Sheet: $75 - $150

NAMU THE KILLER WHALE
(1966 - United Artists) Robert Lansing, John Anderson
One Sheet: $5 - $10

NANA
(1934 - Samuel Goldwyn) Anna Sten, Phillips Holmes
One Sheet: $150 - $300

NANCY DREW - DETECTIVE
(1938 - Warner Bros.) Bonita Granville, Frankie Thomas, James Stephenson
One Sheet: $125 - $250

NANCY DREW - REPORTER
(1939 - Warner Bros.) Bonita Granville, Frankie Thomas, John Litel
One Sheet: $100 - $200

NANCY DREW AND THE HIDDEN STAIRCASE
(1939 - Warner Bros.) Bonita Granville, Frankie Thomas, Frank Orth
One Sheet: $100 - $200

NANCY DREW, TROUBLESHOOTER
(1939 - Warner Bros.) Bonita Granville, Frankie Thomas, John Litel
One Sheet: $100 - $200

NANCY GOES TO RIO
(1949 - MGM) Ann Sothern, Jane Powell, Barry Sullivan
One Sheet: $40 - $75

NANCY STEELE IS MISSING
(1937 - 20th Century Fox) Victor McLaglen, June Lang, Peter Lorre
One Sheet: $100 - $200

NANNY, THE
(1965 - 20th Century Fox) Bette Davis
One Sheet: $20 - $40

NANOOK OF THE NORTH
(1921 - Pathe) -
One Sheet: $3,500 - $5,000 *Documentary.*

NAPOLEON
(1927 - Gaumont/Metro-Goldwyn) Albert Dieudonne, Dir: Abel Gance
One Sheet: $10,000 - $15,000

One Sheet

NAPOLEON
(1935R - Paramount) Albert Dieudonne, Dir: Abel Gance
One Sheet: $3,500 - $5,000 *Re-release.*

NAPOLEON
(1981R - -) Albert Dieudonne, Dir: Abel Gance
One Sheet: $15 - $30 *Re-release.*
Style B (borderless):$25-$40.

NAPOLEON AND JOSEPHINE
(1924 - R-C) Dir: Alexander Butler
One Sheet: $250 - $600

NAPOLEON AND SAMANTHA
(1972 - Buena Vista/Disney) Michael Douglas, Jodie Foster (film debut)
One Sheet: $15 - $30

NARROW CORNER, THE
(1933 - Warner Bros.) Douglas Fairbanks Jr., Patricia Ellis
One Sheet: $100 - $200

NARROW MARGIN, THE
(1952 - RKO) Charles McGraw, Marie Windsor
One Sheet: $100 - $200

NARROW MARGIN, THE
(1990 - TriStar) Gene Hackman, Anne Archer
One Sheet: $3 - $5

NARROW TRAIL, THE
(1919 - Hart) William S. Hart
One Sheet: $1,300 - $2,000

NASHVILLE
(1975 - Paramount) Henry Gibson, Karen Black, Dir: Robert Altman
One Sheet: $40 - $75

NASHVILLE REBEL
(1966 - AIP) Tex Ritter, Sonny James, Loretta Lynn
One Sheet: $30 - $60 *Country musical.*

NASHVILLE SOUND, THE
(1972 - Conestaga) Johnny Cash
One Sheet: $15 - $25 *Country musical.*

NASTY RABBIT, THE
(1964 - Fairway) Micha Terr, Arch Hall, Jr.
One Sheet: $7 - $15

NAT "KING" COLE MUSICAL STORY, THE
(1955 - Universal-International Featurette) Nat King Cole
One Sheet: $100 - $200 *Separate Cinema, pg. 99.*

NATE AND HAYES
(1983 - Paramount) Tommy Lee Jones, Michael O'Keefe
One Sheet: $3 - $5

NATIONAL BARN DANCE, THE
(1944 - Paramount) Jean Heather, Charles Quigley
One Sheet: $75 - $150 *Country*

musical. "America's Favorite Radio Show!"

NATIONAL LAMPOON'S CHRISTMAS VACATION
(1989 - Warner Bros.) Chevy Chase
One Sheet: $5 - $10

NATIONAL LAMPOON'S CLASS REUNION
(1982 - 20th Century Fox) Gerrit Graham, Stephen Furst
One Sheet: $7 - $15

NATIONAL LAMPOON'S EUROPEAN VACATION
(1985 - Warner Bros.) Chevy Chase, Beverly D'Angelo
One Sheet: $5 - $10

NATIONAL LAMPOON'S LOADED WEAPON 1
(1993 - New Line) Emilio Estevez, Samuel L. Jackson
One Sheet: $3 - $5

NATIONAL LAMPOON'S MOVIE MADNESS
(1982 - United Artists) Richard Widmark
One Sheet: $5 - $10

NATIONAL LAMPOON'S SENIOR TRIP
(1995 - New Line) Matt Frewer, Valerie Mahaffey, Tommy Chong
One Sheet: $7 - $15

NATIONAL LAMPOON'S VACATION
(1983 - Warner Bros.) Chevy Chase, Beverly D'Angelo
One Sheet: $15 - $30 *Boris Vallejo art.*

NATIONAL VELVET
(1944 - MGM) Elizabeth Taylor, Mickey Rooney
One Sheet: $200 - $400 *Sports (Horse Racing). Sports Movie Posters #252.*

NATIVE LAND
(1942 - Frontier) Documentary on civil liberties, Narrator: Paul Robeson
One Sheet: $15 - $30

NATIVE SON
(1951 - Classic) Richard Wright, Jean Wallace
One Sheet: $200 - $400 *Separate Cinema, pg. 151.*

NATIVE SON
(1986 - -) Victor Love, Matt Dillon, Oprah Winfrey
One Sheet: $3 - $5

NATURAL, THE
(1984 - TriStar) Robert Redford, Robert Duvall
One Sheet: $30 - $50 *Sports (Baseball). Style B:$40-65. Sports Movie Posters #s 74,75.*

NATURAL BORN KILLERS
(1994 - Warner Bros.) Woody Harrelson, Juliette Lewis
One Sheet: $7 - $15

NATURE GIRL AND THE SLAYER
(1959 - United Producers) -
One Sheet: $15 - $30

NATZY NUISANCE
(1942 - United Artists) Bobby Watson, Joe Devlin
One Sheet: $50 - $100 *Hitler spoof.*

NAUGHTY ARLETTE
(1950 - Eagle-Lion) Mai Zetterling, Hugh Williams
One Sheet: $5 - $10

NAUGHTY BUT NICE
(1939 - Warner Bros.) Dick Powell, Gale Page, Ronald Reagan
One Sheet: $125 - $250

NAUGHTY CHEERLEADERS
(1970S - -) -
One Sheet: $10 - $20 *Sexploitation.*

NAUGHTY CO-EDS
(1975 - -) -
One Sheet: $10 - $20 *Sexploitation.*

NAUGHTY FLIRT, THE
(1930 - First National) Myrna Loy, Alice White
One Sheet: $200 - $400

NAUGHTY MARIETTA
(1935 - MGM) Jeanette MacDonald, Nelson Eddy
One Sheet: $700 - $1,200 *Their first film*

as a team.

One Sheet

NAUGHTY MARIETTA
(1944R - MGM) Jeanette MacDonald, Nelson Eddy
One Sheet: $100 - $200 *Re-release.*

NAUGHTY MARIETTA
(1962R - MGM) Jeanette MacDonald, Nelson Eddy
One Sheet: $20 - $40 *Re-release.*

NAUGHTY NEW ORLEANS
(195? - Rebel Pictures) Rita Parker, Monmartre Kitty
One Sheet: $15 - $30 *Sexploitation.*

NAUGHTY NEW YORK
(1959 - -) -
One Sheet: $20 - $40

NAUGHTY NINETIES, THE
(1945 - Universal) Bud Abbott, Lou Costello, Alan Curtis
One Sheet: $200 - $400 *The film that features the classic "Who's On First" routine.*

Three Sheet

NAVAJO
(1951 - Lippert) Navajo Indian Cast
One Sheet: $15 - $25

NAVAJO JOE
(1967 - United Artists) Burt Reynolds, Aldo Sanbrell
One Sheet: $10 - $20

NAVAJO KID
(1945 - PRC) Bob Steele, Caren March
One Sheet: $30 - $50

NAVAJO RUN
(1964 - AIP) Johnny Seven, Virginia Vincent
One Sheet: $5 - $10

NAVAJO TRAIL
(1946 - Monogram) Johnny Mack Brown
One Sheet: $40 - $75

NAVAJO TRAIL RAIDERS
(1949 - Republic) Allan "Rocky" Lane, Eddy Waller
One Sheet: $30 - $50

NAVAL ACADEMY
(1941 - Columbia) Jimmy Lydon, Freddie Bartholomew, Joe Brown Jr.
One Sheet: $40 - $75

NAVIGATOR, THE
(1924 - MGM) Buster Keaton
One Sheet: $7,500 - $12,000

NAVIGATOR, THE
(1988 - -) Hamish McFarlane, Bruce Lyons

One Sheet: $5 - $10

NAVY AIR PATROL
(1955 - Allied Artists) John Derek, Diana Lyon
One Sheet: $15 - $25 *AKA: AN ANNAPOLIS STORY.*

NAVY BEANS
(1928 - Educational) Big Boy
One Sheet: $250 - $500

NAVY BLUE AND GOLD
(1937 - MGM) Lionel Barrymore, Robert Young, James Stewart
One Sheet: $200 - $400

NAVY BLUES
(1930 - MGM) William Haines, Anita Page
One Sheet: $100 - $200

NAVY BLUES
(1937 - Republic) Mary Brian, Dick Purcell
One Sheet: $40 - $75

NAVY BLUES
(1941 - Warner Bros.) Jack Oakie, Jack Haley, Ann Sheridan
One Sheet: $30 - $60

NAVY BORN
(1936 - Republic) William Gargan, Claire Dodd
One Sheet: $50 - $100

NAVY BOUND
(1951 - Monogram) Tom Neal, Regis Toomey
One Sheet: $15 - $25

NAVY COMES THROUGH, THE
(1942 - RKO) Pat O'Brien, George Murphy
One Sheet: $75 - $150

NAVY SEALS
(1990 - Orion) Charlie Sheen, Michael Biehn
One Sheet: $5 - $10

NAVY SECRETS
(1939 - Monogram) Fay Wray, Grant Withers
One Sheet: $100 - $200

NAVY SPY
(1937 - Grand National) Conrad Nagel, Eleanor Hunt
One Sheet: $75 - $125

NAVY VS. THE NIGHT MONSTERS, THE
(1965 - Realart) Anthony Eisley, Mamie Van Doren
One Sheet: $50 - $100 *Duotone.*

NAVY WAY, THE
(1944 - Paramount) Jean Parker, Robert Lowery
One Sheet: $40 - $75 *Sports (Boxing).*

NAVY WIFE
(1935 - 20th Century Fox) Ralph Bellamy, Claire Trevor
One Sheet: $100 - $200

NAVY WIFE
(1956 - Allied Artists) Joan Bennett, Gary Merrill, Shirley Yamaguchi
One Sheet: $15 - $25

NAZI AGENT
(1942 - MGM) Conrad Veidt, Frank Reicher, Anne Ayars
One Sheet: $150 - $300

NEAL OF THE NAVY
(1915 - Pathe/Balboa) Lillian Lorraine, William Courtleigh
One Sheet: $250 - $500 *Serial. 14 Episodes.*

NEANDERTHAL MAN, THE
(1953 - United Artists) Robert Shayne, Doris Merrick
One Sheet: $40 - $75

NEAR DARK
(1987 - -) Bill Paxton, Lance Henrikson, Jenny Wright
One Sheet: $30 - $50

NEAR THE RAINBOW'S END
(1931 - Tiffany) Bob Steele, Louise Lorraine
One Sheet: $100 - $200

NEAR THE TRAIL'S END
(1931 - Tiffany) Bob Steele
One Sheet: $200 - $400

NEARLY A NASTY ACCIDENT
(1962 - Universal) Jimmy Edwards, Kenneth Connor
One Sheet: $5 - $10

NEARLY EIGHTEEN
(1943 - Monogram) Gale Storm, Bill Henry
One Sheet: $50 - $100

NEAR-SIGHTED MISTER MAGOO, THE
(1950 - Columbia) Mr. Magoo
One Sheet: $250 - $600   *Cartoon.*

NEATH ARIZONA SKIES
(1935 - Monogram) John Wayne
One Sheet: $1,900 - $3,000

NEATH BROOKLYN BRIDGE
(1942 - Monogram) East Side Kids, Noah Beery Jr.
One Sheet: ` $75 - $125

NEATH CANADIAN SKIES
(1946 - Golden Gate) Russell Hayden, Inez Cooper
One Sheet: $20 - $40

NEBRASKAN, THE
(1953 - Columbia) Phil Carey, Roberta Haynes
One Sheet: $10 - $20

NECK AND NECK
(1931 - Sono Art/World Wide) Walter Brennan, Vera Reynolds
One Sheet: $125 - $250

NECK AND NECK
(1940 - 20th Century Fox) Terry-toons
One Sheet: $100 - $200   *Cartoon. Full color stone litho. Stock poster with inset title.*

NECROMANCY
(1972 - Cinerama) Orson Welles, Pamela Franklin
One Sheet: $15 - $25

NECROPOLIS
(1986 - -) Leeanne Baker, Michael Conte
One Sheet: $5 - $10

NED KELLY
(1970 - United Artists) Mick Jagger, Clarissa Kaye
One Sheet: $15 - $30

NEEDFUL THINGS
(1993 - Columbia) Ed Harris, Max von Sydow, Bonnie Bedelia
One Sheet: $3 - $5

NEGATIVES
(1968 - Continental) Peter McEnery, Glenda Jackson
One Sheet: $3 - $5

NEGRO SOLDIER, THE
(1944 - -) -
One Sheet: $100 - $200   *Documentary. Black cast.*

NEIGHBOR'S WIVES
(1933 - Fanchon Royer) Dorothy Mackaill, Tom Moore
One Sheet: $100 - $200

NEIGHBORS
(1920 - Metro) Buster Keaton
One Sheet: $7,500 - $12,000

NEIGHBORS
(1981 - Columbia) John Belushi, Dan Aykroyd
One Sheet: $5 - $10

NEIL SIMON'S LOST IN YONKERS
(1993 - Columbia) Mercedes Reuhl, Richard Dreyfuss
One Sheet: $3 - $5

NELL
(1994 - 20th Century Fox) Jodie Foster
One Sheet: $7 - $15

NELL GWYN
(1935 - United Artists) Anna Neagle, Cedric Hardwicke
One Sheet: $75 - $150

NELSON AFFAIR, THE
(1972 - Universal) Glenda Jackson, Peter Finch
One Sheet: $3 - $5

NELSON TOUCH, THE
(1936 - Gaumont-British) George Arliss
One Sheet: $75 - $150

NEMESIS
(1913 - European Feature) -
One Sheet: $250 - $600

NEMESIS
(1993 - Imperial Enterprise) Olivier Gruner, Gary-Hiroyuki Tagawa
One Sheet: $3 - $5

NEPTUNE FACTOR, THE
(1973 - 20th Century Fox) Ben Gazzara, Yvette Mimieux
One Sheet: $7 - $15

NEPTUNE'S DAUGHTER
(1914 - Universal) Annette Kellermann, William E. Shay
One Sheet: $350 - $750

NEPTUNE'S DAUGHTER
(1949 - MGM) Esther Williams, Red Skelton, Ricardo Montalban
One Sheet: $75 - $125

NEPTUNE'S STEPDAUGHTER
(1925 - Fox) -
One Sheet: $600 - $1,000

NERO
(1922 - Fox) Dir: J. Gordon Edwards
One Sheet: $350 - $750

NEST, THE
(1988 - -) Robert Lansing, Lisa Langlois
One Sheet: $7 - $15

NEST UNFEATHERED, A
(1914 - Biograph) -
One Sheet: $250 - $600

NET, THE
(1995 - Columbia) Sandra Bullock, Dennis Miller
One Sheet: $5 - $10

NETWORK
(1977 - MGM/United Artists) Peter Finch, Faye Dunaway, Beatice Straight
One Sheet: $15 - $25   *Academy Award: Best Actor(Finch), Best Actress(Dunaway), Best Supporting Actress(Straight). Academy AwardMovie Posters #293, #294 & #296.*

NEVADA
(1927 - Paramount) Gary Cooper, Thelma Todd, William Powell
One Sheet: $1,300 - $2,000

NEVADA
(1935 - Paramount) Buster Crabbe
One Sheet: $75 - $150   *Cowboy Movie Posters #205.*

NEVADA
(1944 - RKO) Bob (Robert) Mitchum, Anne Jeffreys
One Sheet: $125 - $250

NEVADA
(1951R - RKO) Bob (Robert) Mitchum, Anne Jeffreys
One Sheet: $50 - $100   *Re-release.*

NEVADA BADMEN
(1951 - Monogram) Whip Wilson, Fuzzy Knight
One Sheet: $30 - $50

NEVADA BUCKAROO
(1931 - Tiffany) Bob Steele
One Sheet: $200 - $400

NEVADA CITY
(1941 - Republic) Roy Rogers, Sally Payne
One Sheet: $150 - $350

NEVADA SMITH
(1966 - Paramount) Steve McQueen, Karl Malden
One Sheet: $40 - $75

NEVADAN, THE
(1950 - Columbia) Randolph Scott, Dorothy Malone
One Sheet: $15 - $30

NEVER A DULL MOMENT
(1943 - Universal) Ritz Brothers, Frances Langford
One Sheet: $75 - $150

NEVER A DULL MOMENT
(1950 - RKO) Fred MacMurray, Irene Dunne

One Sheet: $15 - $35

NEVER A DULL MOMENT
(1968 - Walt Disney) Dick Van Dyke, Dorothy Provine
One Sheet: $5 - $10

NEVER A DULL MOMENT
(1976R - Disney) Dick Van Dyke, Dorothy Provine
One Sheet: $3 - $5   *Re-release.*

NEVER CRY WOLF
(1982 - Disney) Charles Martin Smith, Brian Dennehy
One Sheet: $3 - $5

NEVER FEAR
(1949 - Eagle-Lion) Sally Forrest, Keefe Brasselle
One Sheet: $15 - $35

NEVER GIVE A SUCKER A BREAK
(1933 - MGM) Lee Tracy, Madge Evans, Frank Morgan
One Sheet: $100 - $200   *AKA: THE NUISANCE.*

NEVER GIVE A SUCKER AN EVEN BREAK
(1941 - Universal) W. C. Fields (his last starring role), Gloria Jean
One Sheet: $250 - $600

NEVER LET GO
(1963 - Continental) Richard Todd, Peter Sellers
One Sheet: $5 - $10

NEVER LET ME GO
(1953 - MGM) Clark Gable, Gene Tierney
One Sheet: $40 - $75

NEVER LOVE A STRANGER
(1958 - Allied Artists) John Drew Barrymore, Steve McQueen
One Sheet: $20 - $40

NEVER ON SUNDAY
(1960 - Lopert) Melina Mercouri, Jules Dassin
One Sheet: $15 - $25

NEVER PUT IT IN WRITING
(1964 - Allied Artists) Pat Boone, Fidelma Murphy
One Sheet: $5 - $10

NEVER SAY DIE
(1939 - Paramount) Bob Hope, Martha Raye
One Sheet: $125 - $250

Mini Window Card (Trimmed)

NEVER SAY GOODBYE
(1946 - Warner Bros.) Errol Flynn, Eleanor Parker
One Sheet: $50 - $100

NEVER SAY GOODBYE
(1955 - Universal) Rock Hudson, Cornell Borchers
One Sheet: $30 - $60

NEVER SAY NEVER AGAIN
(1983 - Taliafilm) Sean Connery, Klaus Maria Brandauer
One Sheet: $15 - $30

NEVER SO FEW
(1959 - MGM) Frank Sinatra, Gina Lollobrigida
One Sheet: $30 - $60

NEVER STEAL ANYTHING SMALL
(1958 - Universal-International) James Cagney, Shirley Jones
One Sheet: $15 - $35

NEVER TAKE CANDY FROM A STRANGER
(1961 - Hammer Films) Gwen Watford, Patrick Allen
One Sheet: $100 - $200   *British.*

NEVER TALK TO STRANGERS
(1995 - TriStar) Rebecca De Mornay, Antonio Banderas
One Sheet: $5 - $10

NEVER THE TWAIN SHALL MEET
(1925 - MGM) Anita Stewart, Bert Lytell
One Sheet: $100 - $200

NEVER THE TWAIN SHALL MEET
(1931 - MGM) Leslie Howard, C. Aubrey Smith
One Sheet: $150 - $300

NEVER TOO LATE
(1965 - Warner Bros.) Paul Ford, Maureen O'Sullivan
One Sheet: $10 - $20

NEVER TOO OLD TO WOO
(1917 - Universal) Jack Nelson, Marjorie Ellison
One Sheet: $250 - $500

NEVER TRUST A GAMBLER
(1951 - Columbia) Dane Clark, Cathy O'Donnell
One Sheet: $15 - $30

NEVER WAVE AT A WAC
(1952 - RKO) Rosalind Russell, Paul Douglas
One Sheet: $15 - $25

NEVERENDING STORY, THE
(1984 - Warner Bros.) Barret Oliver, Gerald McRaney
One Sheet: $7 - $15

NEVERENDING STORY II, THE
(1991 - Warner Bros.) Jonathan Brandis, Kenny Morrison
One Sheet: $5 - $10

NEW ADVENTURES OF GET RICH QUICK WALLINGFORD
(1931 - MGM) William Haines, Jimmy Durante, Ernest Torrence
One Sheet: $125 - $250

NEW ADVENTURES OF PIPPI LONGSTOCKING
(1988 - Columbia) Melissa Gilbert
One Sheet: $5 - $10

NEW ADVENTURES OF TARZAN, THE
(1935 - Dearholt-Stout and Cohen) Herman Brix, Ula Holt
One Sheet: $350 - $750   *Serial. 12 Chapters.*

NEW ADVENTURES OF TARZAN, THE
(1935 - Republic) Herman Brix, Ula Holt
One Sheet: $600 - $1,000   *Feature version. AKA: TARZAN AND THE GREEN GODDESS.*

NEW AGE, THE
(1994 - Warner Bros.) Peter Weller, Judy Davis
One Sheet: $5 - $10

NEW CENTURIONS, THE
(1972 - Columbia) George C. Scott, Stacy Keach, Jane Alexander
One Sheet: $15 - $30

NEW CHAMP, THE
(1925 - Winkler) Krazy Kat
One Sheet: $2,200 - $3,500   *Cartoon. Cartoon Movie Posters #7.*

NEW FACES
(1953 - 20th Century Fox) Eartha Kitt, Robert Clary
One Sheet: $75 - $125   *Separate Cinema, pg. 86.*

NEW FACES OF 1937
(1937 - RKO) Milton Berle, Ann Miller, Harriet Hilliard (Nelson)
One Sheet: $150 - $300

NEW FRONTIER, THE
(1935 - Republic) John Wayne, Jennifer Jones
One Sheet: $3,500 - $5,000   *Cowboy Movie Posters #s 184, 186.*

NEW FRONTIER, THE
(1939 - Republic) John Wayne (The Three Mesquiteers)
One Sheet: $300 - $700

NEW FRONTIER, THE

(1953R - Republic) John Wayne
One Sheet: $50 - $100 *Re-release.*

NEW HALFBACK, THE
(1929 - Educational) Harry Gribbon, Andy Clyde
One Sheet: $250 - $500

NEW INTERNS, THE
(1964 - Columbia) Michael Callan, Barbara Eden
One Sheet: $7 - $15

NEW INVISIBLE MAN, THE
(1958 - Calderon) Arturo de Cordova, Raul Meraz
One Sheet: $50 - $100 *Mexican.*
Original Title: El Hombre Invisible.

NEW JACK CITY
(1991 - Warner Bros.) Wesley Snipes, Dir: Mario Van Peebles
One Sheet: $7 - $15

NEW JANITOR, THE
(1914 - Keystone) Charlie Chaplin
One Sheet: $7,500 - $12,000

NEW JERSEY DRIVE
(1995 - Gramercy) Sharron Corley, Gabriel Casseus
One Sheet: $5 - $10 *Black cast.*

NEW KIND OF LOVE, A
(1963 - Paramount) Paul Newman, Joanne Woodward
One Sheet: $15 - $25

NEW KLONDIKE, THE
(1926 - Paramount) Thomas Meighan, Lila Lee
One Sheet: $250 - $500 *Sports (Baseball). Sports Movie Posters #34.*

NEW LAND, THE
(1973 - Warner Bros.) Max von Sydow, Liv Ullmann
One Sheet: $2 - $3

NEW LEAF, A
(1971 - Paramount) Walter Matthau, Elaine May
One Sheet: $3 - $5

NEW LIFE, A
(1988 - -) Alan Alda, Ann-Margret
One Sheet: $3 - $5

NEW LIVES FOR OLD
(1925 - Paramount) Betty Compson, Wallace MacDonald
One Sheet: $150 - $350

NEW MARILYN MONROE, THE
(1959 - S.E. Post) Marilyn Monroe
One Sheet: $500 - $800 *Promo poster.*

NEW MEXICO
(1951 - United Artists) Lew Ayres, Marilyn Maxwell
One Sheet: $15 - $25

NEW MOON
(1931 - MGM) Grace Moore, Adolphe Menjou, Lawrence Tibbett
One Sheet: $125 - $250

NEW MOON
(1940 - MGM) Jeanette MacDonald, Nelson Eddy
One Sheet: $250 - $500

NEW MORALS FOR OLD
(1932 - MGM) Robert Young, Myrna Loy
One Sheet: $150 - $300

NEW MOVIETONE FOLLIES OF 1930
(1930 - -) See FOX MOVIETONE FOLLIES OF 1930

NEW NEIGHBOR, THE
(1953 - RKO/Disney) Donald Duck
One Sheet: $250 - $600 *Cartoon. The Disney Poster, pg. 57.*

NEW NOVELTOON, A
(1949 - Paramount) -
One Sheet: $150 - $300 *Cartoon. Duotone. Stock poster with many characters, including a very early Casper and Little Audry.*

NEW ORLEANS
(1929 - Tiffany) Ricardo Cortez, William Collier, Jr., Alma Bennett
One Sheet: $250 - $600

NEW ORLEANS
(1947 - Majestic) Arturo de Cordova, Louis Armstrong, Billie Holiday (cameo)
One Sheet: $75 - $150

NEW ORLEANS AFTER DARK
(1958 - Allied Artists) Stacy Harris, Louis Sirgo
One Sheet: $15 - $30

NEW ORLEANS UNCENSORED
(1955 - Columbia) Arthur Franz, Beverly Garland
One Sheet: $30 - $50

NEW SCHOOL TEACHER, THE
(1923 - Mastodon) Charles "Chic" Sale, Irvin S. Cobb
One Sheet: $125 - $250

NEW SPIRIT, THE
(1942 - RKO/Disney) Donald Duck
One Sheet: $1,900 - $3,000 *Cartoon.*

NEW WINE
(1941 - United Artists) Llona Massey, Binnie Barnes, Alan Curtis
One Sheet: $40 - $75

NEW YEAR'S EVIL
(1981 - Cannon) Roz Kelly, Kip Niven
One Sheet: $3 - $5

NEW YEARS EVE
(1929 - Fox) Mary Astor
One Sheet: $250 - $600

NEW YORK
(1927 - Paramount) Ricardo Cortez, Lois Wilson
One Sheet: $600 - $1,000

NEW YORK - BY HECK!
(1918 - Universal) -
One Sheet: $250 - $600

NEW YORK CONFIDENTIAL
(1955 - Warner Bros.) Broderick Crawford, Marilyn Maxwell
One Sheet: $15 - $35

NEW YORK, NEW YORK
(1977 - United Artists) Liza Minnelli, Robert DeNiro
One Sheet: $30 - $50

Half Sheet

NEW YORK NIGHTS
(1930 - United Artists) Norma Talmadge
One Sheet: $250 - $600 *One Sheet(Art Cinema re-release):$150-300.*

NEW YORK STORIES
(1989 - Touchstone) Woody Allen
One Sheet: $7 - $15

NEW YORK TOWN
(1941 - Paramount) Fred MacMurray, Mary Martin, Akim Tamiroff
One Sheet: $100 - $200

NEWCOMER, THE
(1938 - 20th Century Fox) Terry-toons
One Sheet: $100 - $200 *Cartoon. Full color stone litho. Stock poster with inset of title.*

NEWLYWEDS CAMP OUT
(1929 - Universal) -
One Sheet: $150 - $300

NEWLYWEDS' PESTS, THE
(1929 - Universal) -
One Sheet: $125 - $250

NEWMAN'S LAW

(1974 - Universal) George Peppard, Roger Robinson
One Sheet: $3 - $5

NEWS HOUNDS
(1947 - Monogram) The Bowery Boys, Christine McIntyre
One Sheet: $75 - $125

NEWS IS MADE AT NIGHT
(1939 - 20th Century Fox) Preston Foster, Lynn Bari
One Sheet: $75 - $150

NEWSBOYS HOME
(1938 - Universal) Jackie Cooper, Wendy Barrie
One Sheet: $75 - $150

NEWSIES
(1992 - Disney) Ann-Margret, Robert Duvall
One Sheet: $3 - $5

NEXT AISLE OVER
(1918 - Pathe) Harold Lloyd
One Sheet: $800 - $1,500

NEXT AISLE OVER
(1922R - Pathe) Harold Lloyd
One Sheet: $350 - $750 *Re-release.*

NEXT KARATE KID, THE
(1994 - Columbia) Pat Morita, Hilary Swank
One Sheet: $5 - $10

NEXT MAN, THE
(1976 - Allied Artists) Sean Connery, Cornelia Sharpe
One Sheet: $5 - $10

NEXT OF KIN, THE
(1943 - Universal) Mervyn Johns, David Hutcheson
One Sheet: $50 - $100

Window Card

NEXT OF KIN
(1989 - -) Patrick Swayze, Liam Neeson, Helen Hunt
One Sheet: $7 - $15

NEXT STOP, GREENWICH VILLAGE
(1976 - 20th Century Fox) Lenny Baker, Shelley Winters, Christopher Walken
One Sheet: $7 - $15

NEXT TIME I MARRY
(1938 - RKO) Lucille Ball, James Ellison
One Sheet: $125 - $250

NEXT TIME WE LOVE
(1936 - Universal) Margaret Sullavan, James Stewart
One Sheet: $200 - $400

NEXT TO NO TIME
(1960 - Cornelius) Kenneth More, Betsy Drake
One Sheet: $7 - $15

NEXT VOICE YOU HEAR, THE
(1950 - MGM) James Whitmore, Nancy Davis
One Sheet: $15 - $30

NE'ER DO WELL, THE
(1923 - -) Thomas Meighan, Lila Lee
One Sheet: $150 - $300

NIAGARA
(1953 - 20th Century Fox) Marilyn Monroe, Joseph Cotten
One Sheet: $500 - $900

NIAGARA FALLS
(1941 - United Artists) Marjorie Woodworth, Tom Brown

One Sheet: $75 - $150

NICE GIRL?
(1941 - Universal) Deanna Durbin, Franchot Tone
One Sheet: $75 - $175

NICE GIRL LIKE ME, A
(1969 - Avco/Embassy) Barbara Ferris, Harry Andrews, Gladys Cooper
One Sheet: $3 - $5

NICE GIRLS DON'T EXPLODE
(1987 - -) Barbara Harris, Michelle Meyrink
One Sheet: $3 - $5

NICE LITTLE BANK THAT SHOULD BE ROBBED, A
(1958 - 20th Century Fox) Tom Ewell, Mickey Rooney
One Sheet: $10 - $20

NICE PEOPLE
(1922 - Paramount) Wallace Reid, Bebe Daniels
One Sheet: $350 - $750

NICE WOMAN
(1931 - Universal) Sidney Fox, Frances Dee
One Sheet: $200 - $400

NICHOLAS AND ALEXANDRA
(1971 - Columbia) Michael Jayston, Janet Suzman
One Sheet: $3 - $5

NICHOLAS NICKLEBY
(1947 - Universal-International) Cedric Hardwicke, Derek Bond
One Sheet: $15 - $35

NICK CARTER, MASTER DETECTIVE
(1939 - MGM) Walter Pidgeon, Rita Johnson
One Sheet: $100 - $200

NICK OF TIME
(1995 - Paramount) Johnny Depp, Christopher Walken
One Sheet: $5 - $10

NICK'S COFFEE POT
(1938 - 20th Century Fox) Terry-toons
One Sheet: $100 - $200 *Cartoon. Full color stone litho. Stock poster with inset title.*

NICKELODEON
(1976 - Columbia) Ryan O'Neal, Burt Reynolds, Tatum O'Neal
One Sheet: $7 - $15

NIFTY NINETIES, THE
(1941 - RKO/Disney) Mickey Mouse
One Sheet: $4,500 - $7,000 *Cartoon. Cartoon Movie Posters #148.*

NIFTY NINETIES, THE
(1953R - RKO/Disney) Mickey Mouse
One Sheet: $150 - $300 *Re-release. Cartoon. Special 25th Anniversary poster.*

NIGGER, THE
(1915 - William Fox) William Farnum, Claire Whitney
One Sheet: $1,300 - $2,000

NIGHT AFTER NIGHT
(1932 - Paramount Publix) Mae West, Constance Cummings, George Raft
One Sheet: $1,600 - $2,500 *West's film debut.*

NIGHT ALARM
(1934 - Majestic) Bruce Cabot, Judith Allen
One Sheet: $100 - $200

One Sheet

NIGHT AMBUSH
(1958 - Rank) Dirk Bogarde, Marius Goring
One Sheet: $10 - $20

NIGHT AND DAY
(1946 - Warner Bros.) Cary Grant, Alexis Smith
One Sheet: $75 - $150

NIGHT AND THE CITY
(1950 - 20th Century Fox) Richard Widmark,
Gene Tierney
One Sheet: $50 - $100

NIGHT AND THE CITY
(1992 - 20th Century Fox) Robert De Niro,
Jessica Lange
One Sheet: $5 - $10

NIGHT ANGEL, THE
(1931 - Paramount) Nancy Carroll, Fredric
March
One Sheet: $250 - $500

NIGHT ANGEL, THE
(1935 - MGM) -
One Sheet: $100 - $200

NIGHT AT EARL CARROLL'S, A
(1940 - Paramount) Ken Murray, Lillian Cornell
One Sheet: $100 - $200

NIGHT AT THE FOLLIES, A
(1947 - Roadshow Attractions) Evelyn West,
Amalia Aguilar
One Sheet: $30 - $60

NIGHT AT THE OPERA, A
(1935 - MGM) Marx Brothers, Kitty Carlisle
One Sheet: $3,500 - $5,000

NIGHT AT THE OPERA, A
(1948R - MGM) Marx Brothers, Kitty Carlisle
One Sheet: $150 - $350   *Re-release.*

NIGHT AT THE OPERA, A
(1962R - MGM) Marx Brothers
One Sheet: $15 - $30   *Re-release.*

NIGHT BEAT
(1932 - Action) Jack Mulhall
One Sheet: $150 - $300

NIGHT BEAT
(1949 - London) Anne Crawford, Maxwell Reed
One Sheet: $10 - $20

NIGHT BEFORE, THE
(1921 - Fox) Sunshine Comedy
One Sheet: $250 - $500

NIGHT BEFORE, THE
(1988 - -) Keanu Reeves, Lori Loughlin
One Sheet: $3 - $5

NIGHT BEFORE CHRISTMAS, THE
(1941 - MGM) Tom & Jerry
One Sheet: $1,600 - $2,500   *Cartoon.*
Cartoon Movie Posters #261.

NIGHT BEFORE THE DIVORCE, THE
(1942 - 20th Century Fox) Lynn Bari, Joseph
Allen Jr.
One Sheet: $75 - $150

NIGHT BIRDS
(1931 - British International) Muriel Angelus,
Jack Raine
One Sheet: $75 - $150

NIGHT BREED
(1989 - -) Craig Sheffer, David Cronenberg
One Sheet: $5 - $10

NIGHT CALL NURSES
(1972 - New World) Patricia T. Bryne, Alana
Collins
One Sheet: $5 - $10

NIGHT CALLER
(1975 - World) Charles Denner
One Sheet: $3 - $5

NIGHT CARGO
(1932 - Peerless) Lloyd Hughes, Jacqueline
Wells
One Sheet: $150 - $300

NIGHT CLUB GIRL
(1944 - Universal) Vivian Austin, Edward
Norris, Delta Rhythm Boys
One Sheet: $30 - $50   *Big Band*
musical.

NIGHT CLUB LADY
(1932 - Columbia) Adolphe Menjou, Mayo
Methot
One Sheet: $200 - $400

NIGHT CLUB SCANDAL
(1937 - Paramount) John Barrymore, Lynne
Overman
One Sheet: $150 - $300

NIGHT COURT
(1932 - MGM) Walter Huston, Lewis Stone
One Sheet: $250 - $500

NIGHT CREATURES
(1962 - Universal) Peter Cushing, Yvonne
Romain
One Sheet: $30 - $60

One Sheet

NIGHT CROSSING
(1982 - Buena Vista/Disney) John Hurt, Jane
Alexander
One Sheet: $5 - $12

NIGHT CRY, THE
(1926 - Warner Bros.) Rin-Tin-Tin
One Sheet: $300 - $700

NIGHT DIGGER, THE
(1971 - MGM) Patricia Neal, Pamela Brown
One Sheet: $3 - $5

NIGHT EDITOR
(1946 - Columbia) William Gargan, Janis Carter
One Sheet: $40 - $75

**NIGHT EVELYN CAME OUT OF THE GRAVE,
THE**
(1972 - Phase One) Anthony Steffen, Marina
Malfatti
One Sheet: $7 - $15

NIGHT FALLS ON MANHATTAN
(1996 - Paramount) Andy Garcia, Richard
Dreyfuss
One Sheet: $4 - $8

NIGHT FIGHTERS
(1960 - Allied Artists) Robert Mitchum, Dan
O'Herlihy
One Sheet: $30 - $50

NIGHT FLIGHT
(1933 - MGM) John Barrymore, Clark Gable,
Lionel Barrymore
One Sheet: $1,600 - $2,500

One Sheet

NIGHT FOR CRIME, A
(1942 - PRC) Glenda Farrell, Lyle Talbot
One Sheet: $200 - $400

NIGHT FREIGHT
(1955 - Allied Artists) Forrest Tucker, Barbara
Britton

One Sheet: $15 - $35

NIGHT GALLERY
(1969 - Universal) Rod Serling, Roddy
McDowall, Joan Crawford
One Sheet: $40 - $75   *TV pilot.*

NIGHT GAME
(1989 - -) Roy Scheider, Karen Young
One Sheet: $5 - $10

NIGHT GAMES
(1980 - Avco Embassy) Cindy Pickett, Joanna
Cassidy
One Sheet: $3 - $5

NIGHT HAS A THOUSAND EYES, THE
(1948 - Paramount) Edward G. Robinson, Gail
Russell
One Sheet: $150 - $300

One Sheet

NIGHT HAS EYES, THE
(1942 - Pathe) James Mason, Joyce Howard
One Sheet: $75 - $150   *AKA:*
TERROR HOUSE.

NIGHT HAWK
(1938 - Republic) Robert Livingston, June
Travis
One Sheet: $50 - $100

NIGHT HEAVEN FELL, THE
(1958 - Kingsley) Brigitte Bardot
One Sheet: $50 - $100

NIGHT HOLDS TERROR, THE
(1955 - Columbia) Jack Kelly, Vince Edwards
One Sheet: $15 - $25

NIGHT HORSEMEN, THE
(1921 - Fox) Tom Mix, May Hopkins
One Sheet: $500 - $800

NIGHT IN CASABLANCA, A
(1946 - United Artists) Marx Brothers, Lois
Collier
One Sheet: $250 - $500

NIGHT IN CASABLANCA, A
(1962R - MGM) Marx Brothers, Lois Collier
One Sheet: $15 - $30   *Re-release.*

NIGHT IN HEAVEN, A
(1983 - 20th Century Fox) Christopher Atkins,
Lesley Ann Warren
One Sheet: $5 - $10

NIGHT IN HOLLYWOOD, A
(1953 - Broadway Roadshows) -
One Sheet: $20 - $40

NIGHT IN NEW ORLEANS, A
(1942 - Paramount) Preston Foster, Patricia
Morison
One Sheet: $50 - $100

NIGHT IN PARADISE, A
(1946 - Universal) Merle Oberon, Turhan Bey
One Sheet: $30 - $50

NIGHT IN THE LIFE OF JIMMY REARDON, A
(1988 - -) River Phoenix, Ann Magnuson,
Meredith Salenger
One Sheet: $15 - $25

NIGHT IN THE SHOW, A
(1915 - Essanay) Charlie Chaplin, Edna
Purviance
One Sheet: $6,500 - $10,000   *Beware re-*
release posters.

NIGHT INTO MORNING
(1951 - MGM) Ray Milland, Nancy Davis
One Sheet: $15 - $25

NIGHT IS MY FUTURE
(1947 - -) Mai Zetherling, Birgen Malursten, Dir:
Ingmar Bergman
One Sheet: $50 - $100   *AKA: Music in*
Darkness.

NIGHT IS MY FUTURE
(1947 - Embassy) Mai Zetterling, Birger
Malmsten, Dir: Ingmar Bergman
One Sheet: $75 - $150   *Swedish.*
Price is for Swedish one sheet. AKA: MUSIC IN
DARKNESS.

NIGHT IS YOUNG, THE
(1935 - MGM) Ramon Novarro, Evelyn Laye
One Sheet: $75 - $150

NIGHT KEY
(1937 - Universal) Boris Karloff, Jean Rogers
One Sheet: $600 - $1,000

One Sheet

NIGHT KEY
(1954R - Realart) Boris Karloff, Jean Rogers
One Sheet: $75 - $150   *Re-release.*

NIGHT LIFE IN RENO
(1931 - Artclass) Virginia Valli, Jameson
Thomas
One Sheet: $150 - $300

NIGHT LIFE OF THE GODS
(1935 - Universal) Alan Mowbray, Florine
McKinney
One Sheet: $75 - $150

NIGHT LIKE THIS, A
(1932 - Woodfall) Ralph Lynn, Tom Walls
One Sheet: $100 - $200

NIGHT MAIL
(1935 - MGM) Henry Oscar, Hope Davy
One Sheet: $150 - $300

NIGHT MAYOR, THE
(1932 - Columbia) Lee Tracy, Evalyn Knapp
One Sheet: $125 - $250

NIGHT MONSTER
(1942 - Universal) Bela Lugosi, Lionel Atwill
One Sheet: $250 - $600   *Graven*
Images, pg. 114.

NIGHT MOTHER
(1986 - Universal) Sissy Spacek, Anne
Bancroft
One Sheet: $5 - $10

NIGHT MOVES
(1975 - Warner Bros.) Gene Hackman, Susan
Clark
One Sheet: $5 - $10

NIGHT MUST FALL
(1937 - MGM) Robert Montgomery, Rosalind
Russell
One Sheet: $150 - $350

NIGHT MUST FALL
(1962R - MGM) Robert Montgomery, Rosalind
Russell
One Sheet: $15 - $25   *Re-release.*

NIGHT MUST FALL
(1964 - MGM) Albert Finney, Susan Hampshire
One Sheet: $10 - $20

NIGHT MY NUMBER CAME UP, THE
(1955 - Rank) Michael Redgrave, Alexander
Knox
One Sheet: $50 - $100

NIGHT NURSE
(1931 - Warner Bros.) Barbara Stanwyck, Joan

Blondell, Clark Gable
One Sheet: $1,600 - $2,500

NIGHT OF ADVENTURE, A
(1944 - RKO) Tom Conway, Nancy Gates
One Sheet: $40 - $75

One Sheet

NIGHT OF BLOODY HORROR
(1969 - Howco) Gerald McRaney, Gaye Yellen
One Sheet: $20 - $40

NIGHT OF DARK SHADOWS
(1971 - MGM) David Shelby, Grayson Hall
One Sheet: $30 - $60   *TV tie-in.*

NIGHT OF JANUARY 16TH, THE
(1941 - Paramount) Ellen Drew, Robert Preston
One Sheet: $75 - $150

NIGHT OF JUNE 13
(1932 - Paramount Publix) Clive Brook, Mary Boland
One Sheet: $125 - $250

NIGHT OF MYSTERY
(1937 - Paramount) Roscoe Karns, Ruth Coleman, Grant Richards
One Sheet: $75 - $125

NIGHT OF NIGHTS, THE
(1939 - Paramount) Pat O'Brien, Olympe Bradna
One Sheet: $50 - $100

NIGHT OF TERROR
(1933 - Columbia) Bela Lugosi, Wallace Ford
One Sheet: $700 - $1,200   *Graven Images, pg. 55.*

NIGHT OF TERROR, A
(1945R - Guaranteed) Basil Rathbone, Ann Harding
One Sheet: $30 - $50   *Re-titled, re-release (possibly 1st American release) of LOVE FROM A STRANGER (1937, British).*

One Sheet

NIGHT OF THE BLOOD BEAST
(1958 - AIP) Michael Emmet, Angela Greene
One Sheet: $100 - $200

NIGHT OF THE BLOOD MONSTER
(1972 - -) Christopher Lee
One Sheet: $15 - $30

NIGHT OF THE COBRA WOMAN
(1972 - New World) Joy Bang, Marlene Clark
One Sheet: $5 - $10

NIGHT OF THE COMET
(1984 - -) Catherine Mary Stewart, Kelli Maroney
One Sheet: $5 - $10

NIGHT OF THE CREEPS

(1986 - -) Jason Lively, Steve Marchall
One Sheet: $5 - $10

NIGHT OF THE DEMON
(1957 - Columbia) Dana Andrews, Peggy Cummins
One Sheet: $75 - $150   *AKA: CURSE OF THE DEMON. Graven Images, pg. 197.*

NIGHT OF THE DEMONS
(1989 - -) William Gallo
One Sheet: $7 - $15

NIGHT OF THE FOLLOWING DAY, THE
(1969 - Universal) Marlon Brando, Rita Moreno, Richard Boone
One Sheet: $15 - $30

NIGHT OF THE GARTER, A
(1934 - British/Dominions) Sydney Howard, Winifred Shotter
One Sheet: $75 - $150

NIGHT OF THE GENERALS, THE
(1967 - Columbia) Peter O'Toole, Omar Sharif
One Sheet: $10 - $20

NIGHT OF THE GRIZZLY
(1966 - Paramount) Clint Walker, Martha Hyer
One Sheet: $10 - $20

NIGHT OF THE HUNTER, THE
(1955 - United Artists) Robert Mitchum, Shelley Winters, Lillian Gish
One Sheet: $150 - $350   *Graven Images, pg. 198.*

NIGHT OF THE IGUANA, THE
(1964 - MGM) Richard Burton, Ava Gardner
One Sheet: $30 - $60

NIGHT OF THE JUGGLER
(1980 - Columbia) James Brolin, Cliff Gorman
One Sheet: $7 - $15

NIGHT OF THE LEPUS
(1972 - MGM) Stuart Whitman, Janet Leigh
One Sheet: $7 - $15

NIGHT OF THE LIVING DEAD
(1968 - Continental) Judith O'Dea, Russell Streiner
One Sheet: $150 - $300   *Graven Images, pg. 202, 219.*

NIGHT OF THE LIVING DEAD, THE
(1990 - Columbia) Tony Todd, Patricia Tallman
One Sheet: $7 - $15

NIGHT OF THE QUARTER MOON
(1959 - MGM) Julie London, John Drew Barrymore
One Sheet: $15 - $30

NIGHT OF THE SHOOTING STARS, THE
(1982 - United Artists) Omero Antonutti, Margarita Lozano
One Sheet: $5 - $10

NIGHT OF THE ZOMBIES
(1984 - -) Frank Garfield, Selan Karay
One Sheet: $7 - $15

NIGHT ON EARTH
(1992 - Columbia/TriStar) Winona Ryder, Gena Rowlands
One Sheet: $5 - $10

NIGHT OUT, A
(1915 - Essanay) Charlie Chaplin, Edna Purviance
One Sheet: $7,500 - $12,000

NIGHT OWLS
(1930 - MGM) Laurel & Hardy
One Sheet: $2,800 - $4,500

NIGHT PASSAGE
(1957 - Universal) James Stewart, Audie Murphy
One Sheet: $50 - $100

NIGHT PATROL
(1985 - -) Linda Blair, Pat Paulsen
One Sheet: $3 - $5

NIGHT PEOPLE
(1954 - 20th Century Fox) Gregory Peck, Broderick Crawford
One Sheet: $30 - $60

NIGHT PLANE FROM CHUNGKING
(1943 - Paramount) Ellen Drew, Robert Preston
One Sheet: $50 - $100

(1986 - -)
One Sheet: $125 - $250

NIGHT PORTER, THE
(1974 - Avco/Embassy) Dirk Bogarde, Charlotte Rampling
One Sheet: $7 - $15

NIGHT RAIDERS
(1952 - Monogram) Whip Wilson
One Sheet: $20 - $40

NIGHT RIDE
(1930 - Universal) Joe Schildkraut, Barbara Kent, Edward G. Robinson
One Sheet: $150 - $300

NIGHT RIDER, THE
(1932 - Weiss) Harry Carey
One Sheet: $150 - $300

NIGHT RIDERS, THE
(1939 - Republic) John Wayne, Ray Corrigan, Max Terhune
One Sheet: $500 - $800

NIGHT RIDERS, THE
(1953R - Republic) John Wayne, Ray Corrigan, Max Terhune
One Sheet: $30 - $50   *Re-release.*

NIGHT RIDERS OF MONTANA
(1951 - Republic) Allan "Rocky" Lane
One Sheet: $20 - $40

NIGHT RUNNER, THE
(1957 - Universal) Ray Danton, Colleen Miller
One Sheet: $15 - $30

NIGHT SHADOWS
(1984 - -) Wings Hauser, Bo Hopkins, Jennifer Warren
One Sheet: $5 - $10

NIGHT SHIFT
(1982 - Warner Bros.) Henry Winkler, Michael Keaton, Shelley Long
One Sheet: $5 - $10

NIGHT SHIP, THE
(1925 - Lumas) Mary Carr, Tom Santschi
One Sheet: $150 - $300

NIGHT SONG
(1947 - RKO) Dana Andrews, Merle Oberon, Ethel Barrymore
One Sheet: $30 - $60

NIGHT SPOT
(1938 - RKO) Allan Lane, Joan Woodbury
One Sheet: $50 - $100

NIGHT STAGE TO GALVESTON
(1952 - Columbia) Gene Autry, Pat Buttram
One Sheet: $75 - $125

NIGHT STALKER, THE
(1986 - -) Charles Napier, Michelle Reese
One Sheet: $5 - $10

NIGHT THE LIGHTS WENT OUT IN GEORGIA, THE
(1981 - Avco/Embassy) Kristy McNichol, Dennis Quaid, Mark Hamill
One Sheet: $5 - $10

NIGHT THE WORLD EXPLODED, THE
(1957 - Columbia) Kathryn Grant, William Leslie
One Sheet: $30 - $50

NIGHT THEY KILLED RASPUTIN, THE
(1962 - Brigadier) Edmund Purdom, John Drew Barrymore
One Sheet: $10 - $20

NIGHT THEY RAIDED MINSKY'S, THE
(1968 - United Artists) Jason Robards, Britt Ekland
One Sheet: $20 - $40   *Frazetta art.*

NIGHT TIDE
(1963 - AIP) Dennis Hopper, Linda Lawson
One Sheet: $75 - $150   *Price is for style B one sheet. Graven Images, pg. 211.*

NIGHT TIME IN NEVADA
(1948 - Republic) Roy Rogers, Andy Devine
One Sheet: $150 - $300

NIGHT TO REMEMBER, A
(1943 - Columbia) Loretta Young, Brian Aherne
One Sheet: $75 - $150

NIGHT TO REMEMBER, A
(1959 - Rank) Kenneth More, Honor Blackman

One Sheet: $125 - $250

NIGHT TRAIN TO MEMPHIS
(1946 - Republic) Roy Acuff, Smoky Mountain Boys, Allan Lane
One Sheet: $75 - $150   *Country musical.*

NIGHT TRAIN TO MUNICH
(1940 - 20th Century Fox) Margaret Lockwood, Rex Harrison
One Sheet: $250 - $500

NIGHT TRAIN TO PARIS
(1964 - 20th Century Fox) Leslie Nelson, Alzia Gur
One Sheet: $15 - $25

NIGHT UNTO NIGHT
(1947 - Warner Bros.) Ronald Reagan, Viveca Lindfors
One Sheet: $75 - $150

NIGHT VISITOR, THE
(1971 - UMC) Max von Sydow, Trevor Howard
One Sheet: $5 - $10

NIGHT WAITRESS
(1936 - RKO) Margot Grahame, Don Barry
One Sheet: $150 - $300

NIGHT WALKER, THE
(1965 - Universal) Robert Taylor, Barbara Stanwyck
One Sheet: $50 - $100

NIGHT WATCH
(1973 - Avco/Embassy) Elizabeth Taylor, Lauren Harvey
One Sheet: $10 - $20

NIGHT WATCH
(1997 - Miramax) Ewan McGregor, Josh Brolin
One Sheet: $4 - $8

NIGHT WE NEVER MET, THE
(1993 - Miramax) Matthew Broderick, Annabella Sciorra
One Sheet: $3 - $5

NIGHT WIND
(1948 - 20th Century Fox) Charles Russell, Virginia Christine
One Sheet: $30 - $60

NIGHT WITHOUT SLEEP
(1952 - 20th Century Fox) Gary Merrill, Linda Darnell
One Sheet: $15 - $35

NIGHT WITHOUT STARS
(1952 - RKO) David Farrar, Nadia Gray
One Sheet: $15 - $25

NIGHT WORK
(1930 - Pathe) Eddie Quillan, Sally Starr
One Sheet: $100 - $200

NIGHT WORK
(1939 - Paramount) Mary Boland, Charles Ruggles
One Sheet: $50 - $100

NIGHT WORLD
(1932 - Universal) Lew Ayres, Boris Karloff
One Sheet: $600 - $1,000

NIGHTCOMERS, THE
(1972 - Avco/Embassy) Marlon Brando, Stephanie Beacham
One Sheet: $7 - $15

NIGHTFALL
(1956 - Columbia) Aldo Ray, Anne Bancroft, Brian Keith
One Sheet: $10 - $20

NIGHTFALL
(1988 - -) David Birney, Sarah Douglas
One Sheet: $10 - $20

NIGHTFLYERS
(1987 - -) Catherine Mary Stewart, Michael Praed
One Sheet: $5 - $10

NIGHTFORCE
(1986 - -) Linda Blair, James Van Patten
One Sheet: $3 - $5

NIGHTHAWKS
(1981 - Universal) Sylvester Stallone, Billy Dee Williams
One Sheet: $5 - $10

NIGHTMARE
(1942 - Universal) Diana Barrymore, Brian Donlevy
One Sheet: $50 - $100

NIGHTMARE
(1956 - United) Edward G. Robinson, Kevin McCarthy, Connie Russell
One Sheet: $30 - $50

NIGHTMARE
(1964 - Universal) David Knight, Moyra Redmond
One Sheet: $10 - $20

NIGHTMARE
(1981 - Century) C. J. Cooke, Mik Cribben
One Sheet: $5 - $10

NIGHTMARE ALLEY
(1947 - 20th Century Fox) Tyrone Power, Joan Blondell
One Sheet: $150 - $300

NIGHTMARE ALLEY
(1955R - 20th Century Fox) Tyrone Power, Joan Blondell
One Sheet: $30 - $50   *Re-release.*

NIGHTMARE BEFORE CHRISTMAS
(1993 - Buena Vista/Disney) Stop-motion puppets
One Sheet: $15 - $30   *Lenticular 3-D Style:$300-$600. Three Sheet (3 styles, "Meet Jack", "Meet Sally", "Meet The Mayor"): $40-$80.*

One Sheet

NIGHTMARE CASTLE
(1966 - Allied Artists) Barbara Steele, Paul Mueller
One Sheet: $15 - $30

NIGHTMARE HONEYMOON
(1973 - MGM) Dack Rambo
One Sheet: $10 - $20

NIGHTMARE IN THE SUN
(1965 - Zodiak) Ursula Andress, John Derek
One Sheet: $15 - $25

NIGHTMARE IN WAX
(1969 - Crown) Scott Brady, Cameron Mitchell
One Sheet: $10 - $20

NIGHTMARE ON ELM STREET, A
(1984 - New Line Cinema) John Saxon, Robert Englund, Ronee Blakely, Johnny Depp
One Sheet: $30 - $50

NIGHTMARE ON ELMSTREET 2: FREDDY'S REVENGE
(1985 - New Line Cinema) Mark Patton, Robert Englund, Kim Myers
One Sheet: $10 - $20

NIGHTMARE ON ELMSTREET 3: DREAM WARRIORS
(1987 - New Line Cinema) Heather Langenkamp, Robert Englund
One Sheet: $10 - $20

NIGHTMARE ON ELMSTREET 4: THE DREAM MASTER
(1988 - New Line Cinema) Robert Englund, Lisa Wilcox
One Sheet: $5 - $10

NIGHTMARE ON ELMSTREET 5: THE DREAM CHILD
(1989 - New Line Cinema) Robert Englund, Lisa Wilcox
One Sheet: $5 - $10

NIGHTMARES

(1983 - -) Cristina Raines, Timothy James
One Sheet: $3 - $7

NIGHTMARES
(1983 - Universal) Emilio Estevez, Moon Unit Zappa
One Sheet: $5 - $10

NIGHTS OF CABIRIA
(1957 - Lopert) Giulietta Masina, Francois Perier, Dir: Fellini
One Sheet: $40 - $75   *Italian. Academy Award: Best Foreign film. AKA: CABIRIA.*

NIGHTS OF LUCRETIA BORGIA, THE
(1960 - Columbia) Belinda Lee, Jacques Sernas
One Sheet: $7 - $15

NIGHTWING
(1979 - Columbia) Nick Mancuso
One Sheet: $3 - $5

NIJINSKY
(1980 - Paramount) Alan Bates, George De La Pena, Leslie Browne
One Sheet: $5 - $10   *Amsel art.*

One Sheet

NIKKI, WILD DOG OF THE NORTH
(1961 - Buena Vista) Jean Coutu, Emile Genest
One Sheet: $7 - $15

NINA TAKES A LOVER
(1994 - Triumph) Laura San Giacomo, Paul Rhys
One Sheet: $3 - $5

9 1/2 WEEKS
(1985 - Jonesfilm) Mickey Rourke, Kim Basinger
One Sheet: $15 - $25

NINE DAYS A QUEEN
(1936 - Gaumont) Nova Pilbeam, Cedric Hardwicke
One Sheet: $100 - $200

NINE GIRLS
(1944 - Columbia) Ann Harding, Evelyn Keyes
One Sheet: $40 - $75

NINE HOURS TO RAMA
(1963 - 20th Century Fox) Horst Buchholz, Jose Ferrer
One Sheet: $5 - $10

NINE LIVES ARE NOT ENOUGH
(1941 - Warner Bros.) Ronald Reagan, Joan Perry
One Sheet: $200 - $400

NINE LIVES OF FRITZ THE CAT, THE
(1974 - AIP) -
One Sheet: $15 - $35   *Cartoon. R-rated.*

9 MILES TO NOON
(1964 - Falcon) Renato Baldini, Peter Lazer
One Sheet: $5 - $10

NINE MONTHS
(1995 - Fox) Hugh Grant, Julianne Moore, Tom Arnold
One Sheet: $5 - $10

976-EVIL
(1989 - New Line) Pat O'Bryan
One Sheet: $3 - $5

NINE TO FIVE
(1980 - 20th Century Fox) Dolly Parton, Jane Fonda, Lily Tomlin
One Sheet: $7 - $15

NINETEEN AND PHYLLIS
(1921 - First National) Charles Ray, Cora Drew
One Sheet: $150 - $300

1984
(1955 - Columbia) Edmund O'Brien, Jan Sterling
One Sheet: $150 - $300   *Graven Images, pg. 170.*

1984
(1984 - Atlantic) John Hurt, Richard Burton
One Sheet: $15 - $25

1941
(1979 - Columbia/Universal) John Belushi, Dan Aykroyd
One Sheet: $30 - $50   *Price is for all styles.*

One Sheet

1900
(1977 - Paramount/United Artists) Burt Lancaster, Robert DeNiro, Dir: Bernardo Bertolucci
One Sheet: $30 - $50

1990: THE BRONX WARRIORS
(1983 - United Film Dist.) Vic Morrow, Christopher Connolly
One Sheet: $5 - $10

90 DEGREES IN THE SHADE
(1966 - Landau/Unger) Anne Heywood, James Booth
One Sheet: $5 - $10

99 RIVER STREET
(1953 - United Artists) John Payne, Evelyn Keyes
One Sheet: $30 - $50

99 WOMEN
(1969 - Commonwealth United) Maria Schell, Mercedes McCambridge
One Sheet: $5 - $10

99 AND 44/100% DEAD
(1974 - 20th Century Fox) Richard Harris, Edmund O'Brien
One Sheet: $15 - $35

92 IN THE SHADE
(1975 - United Artists) Peter Fonda, Warren Oates
One Sheet: $7 - $15

NINJA 3: THE DOMINATION
(1984 - -) Lucinda Dickey, Sho Kosugi, Jordan Bennett
One Sheet: $3 - $5

NINJA MISSION, THE
(1985 - -) Christopher Kohlberg, Curt Brober, Hana Pola
One Sheet: $5 - $10

NINOTCHKA
(1939 - MGM) Greta Garbo, Melvyn Douglas, Bela Lugosi
One Sheet: $600 - $1,000   *One Sheet(Smiling portrait style):$600-1200.*

NINOTCHKA
(1947R - MGM) Greta Garbo, Melvyn Douglas, Bela Lugosi
One Sheet: $100 - $200   *Re-release.*

NINOTCHKA
(1962R - MGM) Greta Garbo
One Sheet: $15 - $30   *Re-release.*

NINTH GUEST, THE
(1934 - Columbia) Donald Cook, Genevieve

Tobin
One Sheet: $200 - $400

NIT WITTY KITTY
(1950 - MGM) Tom and Jerry
One Sheet: $200 - $400   *Cartoon.*

NITWITS, THE
(1935 - RKO) Bert Wheeler, Robert Woolsey, Betty Grable
One Sheet: $150 - $350

Mini Window Card (Trimmed)

NIXON
(1995 - Hollywood) Anthony Hopkins, James Woods, Dir: Oliver Stone
One Sheet: $5 - $12

NO BLADE OF GRASS
(1970 - MGM) Nigel Davenport, Jean Wallace
One Sheet: $3 - $5

NO CENSUS NO FEELING
(1940 - Columbia) The Three Stooges (Curly)
One Sheet: $5,000 - $7,500   *Comedy short. Duotone. Lobby cards have switched name tags, Larry is called Moe, Moe is called Larry.*

NO DEPOSIT, NO RETURN
(1975 - Disney/Buena Vista) David Niven, Darren McGavin, Don Knotts
One Sheet: $10 - $20

NO DOUGH, BOYS
(1944 - Columbia) The Three Stooges (Curly)
One Sheet: $2,500 - $4,000   *Comedy short. Duotone.*

NO DOWN PAYMENT
(1957 - 20th Century Fox) Joanne Woodward, Sheree North
One Sheet: $15 - $30

NO DRUMS, NO BUGLES
(1971 - Cinerama) Martin Sheen
One Sheet: $3 - $5

NO ESCAPE
(1953 - United Artists) Lew Ayres, Sonny Tufts
One Sheet: $7 - $15

NO ESCAPE
(1994 - Savoy) Ray Liotta
One Sheet: $5 - $10

NO FATHER TO GUIDE HIM
(1925 - Pathe) Charley Chase
One Sheet: $200 - $400

NO FUNNY BUSINESS
(1933 - Principal) Gertrude Lawrence, Laurence Olivier
One Sheet: $200 - $400

NO GREATER GLORY
(1934 - Columbia) George Breakston, Jimmy Butler, Frankie Darro
One Sheet: $125 - $250

NO GREATER LOVE
(1932 - Columbia) Dickie Moore, Richard Bennett, Beryl Mercer
One Sheet: $125 - $250

NO GREATER SIN
(1941 - Universal) Leon Ames, Luana Walters
One Sheet: $50 - $100

NO GUN MAN, THE
(1924 - -) Lefty Flynn
One Sheet: $250 - $500

NO HANDS ON THE CLOCK
(1941 - Paramount) Chester Morris, Jean Parker

One Sheet: $75 - $125

NO HIGHWAY IN THE SKY
(1951 - 20th Century Fox) James Stewart,
Marlene Dietrich
One Sheet: $100 - $200

NO HOLDS BARRED
(1952 - Monogram) Bowery Boys
One Sheet: $40 - $75

NO HOLDS BARRED
(1989 - New Line) Hulk Hogan
One Sheet: $10 - $20   *Sports
(Wrestling).*

NO HUNTING
(1954 - Disney) Donald Duck
One Sheet: $600 - $1,000   *Cartoon.*

NO LEAVE, NO LOVE
(1946 - MGM) Van Johnson, Keenan Wynn
One Sheet: $30 - $50

NO LIMIT
(1931 - Paramount Publix) Clara Bow, Norman
Foster
One Sheet: $700 - $1,200

NO LIVING WITNESS
(1932 - Mayfair) Gilbert Roland, Noah Beery
One Sheet: $100 - $200

NO MAN IS AN ISLAND
(1962 - Universal) Jeffrey Hunter, Marshall
Thompson
One Sheet: $15 - $25

NO MAN OF HER OWN
(1933 - Paramount) Clark Gable, Carole
Lombard
One Sheet: $5,000 - $7,500

NO MAN OF HER OWN
(1937R - Paramount) Clark Gable, Carole
Lombard
One Sheet: $600 - $1,000   *Re-release.*

NO MAN OF HER OWN
(1950 - Paramount) Barbara Stanwyck, John
Lund
One Sheet: $50 - $100

NO MAN'S GOLD
(1926 - Fox) Tom Mix
One Sheet: $700 - $1,200   *Cowboy
Movie Posters #54.*

NO MAN'S LAND
(1987 - Orion) Charlie Sheen, D.B. Sweeney
One Sheet: $3 - $5

NO MAN'S RANGE
(1935 - Supreme) Bob Steele, Roberta Gale
One Sheet: $125 - $250

NO MAN'S WOMAN
(1955 - Republic) Marie Windsor, Patric
Knowles
One Sheet: $15 - $25

NO MARRIAGE TIES
(1933 - RKO) Richard Dix, Elizabeth Allen
One Sheet: $150 - $300

NO MERCY
(1986 - TriStar) Richard Gere, Kim Basinger
One Sheet: $5 - $10

NO MINOR VICES
(1948 - MGM) Dana Andrews, Lilli Palmer
One Sheet: $30 - $50

NO MORE EXCUSES
(1968 - Impact) Robert Downey, Allen Noel
One Sheet: $5 - $10

NO MORE LADIES
(1935 - Paramount Publix) Joan Crawford,
Robert Montgomery
One Sheet: $500 - $800

NO MORE ORCHIDS
(1932 - Columbia) Carole Lombard
One Sheet: $3,500 - $5,000

NO MORE WEST
(1934 - Van Bueren) -
One Sheet: $50 - $100

NO MORE WOMEN
(1934 - Paramount) Victor McLaglen, Edmund
Lowe
One Sheet: $100 - $200

NO, MY DARLING DAUGHTER
(1964 - Zenith) Michael Redgrave, Michael
Craig
One Sheet: $5 - $10

NO NAME ON THE BULLET
(1959 - Universal) Audie Murphy, Charles
Drake
One Sheet: $40 - $75

One Sheet

NO, NO, NANETTE
(1930 - First National) Bernice Claire,
Alexander Gray, Lucien Littlefield
One Sheet: $100 - $200

NO, NO, NANETTE
(1940 - RKO) Anne Neagle, Richard Carlson
One Sheet: $50 - $100

NO NUKES
(1980 - -) Gil Scott-Heron, Bruce Springsteen
One Sheet: $15 - $30

NO ONE MAN
(1932 - Paramount Publix) Carole Lombard,
Ricardo Cortez, Paul Lukas
One Sheet: $700 - $1,200

NO ORCHIDS FOR MISS BLANDISH
(1951 - Eagle-Lion) Jack LaRue, Linden
Travers
One Sheet: $15 - $30

NO OTHER WOMAN
(1928 - Fox) Dolores Del Rio, Don Alvarado
One Sheet: $250 - $500

NO OTHER WOMAN
(1933 - RKO) Irene Dunne, Charles Bickford,
Gwill Andre
One Sheet: $200 - $400

NO PLACE FOR A LADY
(1943 - Columbia) William Gargan, Dick
Purcell, Margaret Lindsay
One Sheet: $50 - $100

NO PLACE FOR JENNIFER
(1950 - British-Pathe) Leo Genn, Rosamund
John
One Sheet: $5 - $10

NO PLACE TO GO
(1939 - Warner Bros.) Fred Stone, Gloria
Dickson
One Sheet: $40 - $75

NO PLACE TO HIDE
(1955 - Allied Artists) David Brian, Marsha Hunt
One Sheet: $15 - $25

NO PLACE TO LAND
(1958 - Republic) John Ireland, Mari Blanchard
One Sheet: $10 - $20

NO QUESTIONS ASKED
(1951 - MGM) Arlene Dahl, Barry Sullivan
One Sheet: $15 - $30

NO RANSOM
(1934 - Liberty) Leila Hyams, Phillips Holmes
One Sheet: $75 - $150

NO RETREAT, NO SURRENDER
(1986 - New World) Kurt McKinney, Jean-
Claude Van Damme
One Sheet: $7 - $15   *Sports (Kick-
Boxing). Sports Movie Posters #164.*

NO ROAD BACK
(1957 - RKO) Sean Connery (Debut), Skip
Homeier
One Sheet: $15 - $30

NO ROOM AT THE INN
(1950 - Stratford) Freda Jackson, Hermione
Baddeley
One Sheet: $15 - $25

NO ROOM FOR THE GROOM
(1952 - Universal) Tony Curtis, Piper Laurie
One Sheet: $30 - $50

NO SAD SONGS FOR ME
(1950 - Columbia) Margaret Sullavan, Wendell
Corey
One Sheet: $20 - $40   *Sullavan's
final film.*

NO SAIL
(1945 - RKO/Disney) Donald Duck and Goofy
One Sheet: $1,300 - $2,000   *Cartoon. Full
color. The Disney Poster, pg. 59.*

NO SLEEP ON THE DEEP
(1934 - Educational) Betty Compson, Robert
Warwick
One Sheet: $100 - $200   *A Mermaid
Comedy.*

NO SMOKING
(1951 - RKO/Disney) Goofy
One Sheet: $500 - $800   *Cartoon. The
Disney Poster, pg. 73.*

NO SOUP
(1915 - Universal) Ernest Shields, Eddie
Boland
One Sheet: $350 - $750

NO TIME FOR COMEDY
(1940 - Warner Bros.) James Stewart, Rosalind
Russell
One Sheet: $150 - $300

One Sheet

NO TIME FOR FLOWERS
(1952 - RKO) Viveca Lindfors, Paul Christian
One Sheet: $10 - $20

NO TIME FOR LOVE
(1943 - Paramount) Claudette Colbert, Fred
MacMurray
One Sheet: $75 - $150

One Sheet

NO TIME FOR SERGEANTS
(1958 - Warner Bros.) Andy Griffith, Nick
Adams, Don Knotts
One Sheet: $40 - $75

NO TIME TO BE YOUNG
(1957 - Columbia) Robert Vaughn, Roger Smith
One Sheet: $15 - $25

NO TIME TO MARRY
(1938 - Columbia) Mary Astor, Richard Arlen
One Sheet: $100 - $200

NO TREES IN THE STREET
(1964 - Seven Arts) Sylvia Syms, Herbert Lom
One Sheet: $5 - $10

NO WAY OUT
(1950 - 20th Century Fox) Richard Widmark,
Linda Darnell, Sidney Poitier
One Sheet: $75 - $150   *Separate
Cinema, pg. 156. Poitier's film debut.*

NO WAY OUT
(1987 - Orion) Kevin Costner, Gene Hackman
One Sheet: $7 - $15

NO WAY TO TREAT A LADY
(1968 - Paramount) Rod Steiger, Lee Remick
One Sheet: $10 - $20

NOAH'S ARK
(1929 - Warner Bros.) Dolores Costello,
George O'Brien
One Sheet: $150 - $350

NOAH'S ARK
(1957R - Dominant) Dolores Costello, George
O'Brien
One Sheet: $7 - $15   *Re-release.*

NOB HILL
(1945 - 20th Century Fox) George Raft, Joan
Bennett
One Sheet: $125 - $250

NOBODY LIVES FOREVER
(1946 - Warner Bros.) John Garfield, Geraldine
Fitzgerald
One Sheet: $50 - $100

NOBODY WAVED GOODBYE
(1965 - Cinema 5) Peter Kastner, Julie Biggs
One Sheet: $3 - $5

NOBODY'S BABY
(1937 - MGM) Patsy Kelly, Robert Armstrong
One Sheet: $50 - $100

NOBODY'S CHILDREN
(1940 - Columbia) Edith Fellows, Lois Wilson
One Sheet: $50 - $100

NOBODY'S DARLING
(1943 - Republic) Mary Lee, Gladys George
One Sheet: $50 - $100

NOBODY'S FOOL
(1921 - Universal) Marie Provost, Helen Harris
One Sheet: $200 - $400

NOBODY'S FOOL
(1936 - Universal) Edward Everett Horton,
Glenda Farrell, Cesar Romero
One Sheet: $75 - $150

Mini Window Card (Trimmed)

NOBODY'S FOOL
(1994 - Paramount) Paul Newman, Jessica
Tandy, Melanie Griffith
One Sheet: $5 - $10

NOBODY'S MONEY
(1923 - Paramount) Jack Holt, Wanda Hawley
One Sheet: $150 - $300

NOBODY'S PERFECT
(1968 - Universal) James Whitmore, Doug
McClure
One Sheet: $5 - $10

NOCTURNE
(1947 - RKO) George Raft, Lynn Bari
One Sheet: $50 - $100

NOISES OFF
(1992 - Buena Vista) Carol Burnett, Michael
Caine

One Sheet: $20 - $40   *Hirschfeld art.*

NOMADS
(1986 - PSO) Lesley-Anne Down, Pierce Brosnan, Adam Ant
One Sheet: $5 - $10

NONE BUT THE BRAVE
(1965 - Warner Bros.) Frank Sinatra, Clint Walker
One Sheet: $30 - $50

NONE BUT THE LONELY HEART
(1944 - RKO) Cary Grant, Ethel Barrymore
One Sheet: $125 - $250   *Academy Award Movie Posters #98.*

NONE SHALL ESCAPE
(1944 - Columbia) Alexander Knox, Marsha Hunt
One Sheet: $75 - $150

NON-STOP NEW YORK
(1937 - Gaumont British) Anna Lee, Desmond Tester
One Sheet: $600 - $1,000

NOON WHISTLE, THE
(1923 - Pathe) Stan Laurel
One Sheet: $350 - $750

NOOSE FOR A GUNMAN
(1960 - United Artists) Jim Davis, Lyn Thomas
One Sheet: $15 - $25

NOOSE HANGS HIGH, THE
(1948 - Pathe) Bud Abbott, Lou Costello
One Sheet: $75 - $150

NORA PRENTISS
(1947 - Warner Bros.) Ann Sheridan, Kent Smith
One Sheet: $30 - $60

NORMA RAE
(1979 - 20th Century Fox) Sally Field, Ron Liebman
One Sheet: $15 - $25   *Academy Award: Best Actress(Fields). Price is for both styles. Academy Award Movie Posters #307.*

NORMAN CONQUEST
(1953 - Lippert) Tom Conway, Eva Bartok
One Sheet: $10 - $20

NORMAN...IS THAT YOU?
(1976 - MGM/UA) Redd Foxx, Pearl Bailey
One Sheet: $15 - $25   *Black cast.*

NORSEMAN, THE
(1978 - AIP) Lee Majors, Cornel Wilde
One Sheet: $3 - $5

NORTH
(1994 - Columbia) Bruce Willis, Elijah Wood
One Sheet: $3 - $5

NORTH AVENUE IRREGULARS, THE
(1979 - Disney) Edward Herrmann, Barbara Harris
One Sheet: $5 - $10

NORTH BY NORTHWEST
(1959 - MGM) Cary Grant, Eva Marie Saint, Dir: Alfred Hitchcock
One Sheet: $250 - $500   *Price is for full color one sheet. One Sheet(duotone):$75-$150.*

One Sheet

NORTH BY NORTHWEST
(1966R - MGM) Cary Grant, Eva Marie Saint, James Mason, Dir: Hitchcock
One Sheet: $75 - $150   *Re-release.*

NORTH DALLAS FORTY

(1979 - Paramount) Nick Nolte, Mac Davis, Charles Durning
One Sheet: $10 - $20   *Sports (Football). Sports Movie Posters #210.*

NORTH FROM THE LONE STAR
(1941 - Columbia) Bill Elliott
One Sheet: $40 - $75

NORTH OF 36
(1924 - Paramount) Jack Holt, Ernest Torrence, Noah Beery
One Sheet: $200 - $400

NORTH OF ARIZONA
(1935 - Steiner) Jack Perrin
One Sheet: $100 - $200

NORTH OF HUDSON BAY
(1924 - Fox) Tom Mix
One Sheet: $500 - $800

NORTH OF NEVADA
(1924 - Monogram) Fred Thomson, Hazel Keener, Chester Conklin
One Sheet: $200 - $400

NORTH OF NOME
(1936 - Columbia) Jack Holt, Evelyn Venable
One Sheet: $75 - $150

NORTH OF SHANGHAI
(1939 - Columbia) Betty Furness, James Craig
One Sheet: $50 - $100

NORTH OF THE BORDER
(1946 - Golden Gate) Russell Hayden, Inez Cooper
One Sheet: $20 - $40

NORTH OF THE GREAT DIVIDE
(1950 - Republic) Roy Rogers, Penny Edwards
One Sheet: $75 - $150

NORTH OF THE RIO GRANDE
(1922 - Paramount) Jack Holt, Bebe Daniels
One Sheet: $200 - $400

NORTH OF THE RIO GRANDE
(1937 - Paramount) William Boyd, Gabby Hayes
One Sheet: $250 - $500   *Hopalong Cassidy Series.*

NORTH OF THE ROCKIES
(1942 - Columbia) Bill Elliott, Tex Ritter
One Sheet: $75 - $125

NORTH OF THE YUKON
(1939 - Columbia) Charles Starrett, Linda Winters
One Sheet: $75 - $150

NORTH SHORE
(1987 - -) Matt Adler, Nia Peeples
One Sheet: $7 - $15   *Sports (Surfing). Sports Movie Posters #321.*

NORTH STAR, THE
(1943 - RKO) Walter Huston, Dana Andrews, Anne Baxter
One Sheet: $75 - $150

One Sheet

NORTH TO ALASKA
(1960 - 20th Century Fox) John Wayne, Stewart Granger
One Sheet: $50 - $100

NORTH TO THE KLONDIKE
(1942 - Universal) Broderick Crawford, Lon Chaney
One Sheet: $75 - $125

NORTHERN FRONTIER

(1935 - Ambassador) Kermit Maynard
One Sheet: $75 - $150

NORTHERN PATROL
(1953 - Monogram) Kirby Grant
One Sheet: $15 - $35

NORTHERN PURSUIT
(1943 - Warner Bros.) Errol Flynn, Helmut Dantine, Julie Bishop
One Sheet: $125 - $250

NORTHWEST HOUNDED POLICE
(1946 - MGM) Droopy, Dir: Tex Avery
One Sheet: $250 - $600   *Cartoon. Cartoon Movie Posters #300.*

NORTHWEST MOUNTED POLICE
(1940 - Paramount) Gary Cooper, Madeleine Carroll
One Sheet: $350 - $750

NORTHWEST MOUNTED POLICE
(1945R - Paramount) Gary Cooper, Madeleine Carroll
One Sheet: $40 - $75   *Re-release.*

NORTHWEST MOUNTED POLICE
(1958R - Paramount) Gary Cooper, Madeleine Carroll
One Sheet: $15 - $30   *Re-release.*

NORTHWEST OUTPOST
(1947 - Republic) Nelson Eddy, Ilona Massey
One Sheet: $40 - $75

NORTHWEST PASSAGE
(1940 - MGM) Spencer Tracy, Robert Young
One Sheet: $250 - $500

NORTHWEST PASSAGE
(1956R - MGM) Spencer Tracy, Robert Young
One Sheet: $40 - $75   *Re-release.*

NORTHWEST RANGERS
(1942 - MGM) James Craig, Patricia Dane
One Sheet: $30 - $50

NORTHWEST STAMPEDE
(1948 - Pathe) Joan Leslie, James Craig
One Sheet: $15 - $25

NORTHWEST TERRITORY
(1945 - Action) Bob Steele
One Sheet: $40 - $75

NORTHWEST TERRITORY
(1951 - Monogram) Kirby Grant
One Sheet: $15 - $35

NORWOOD
(1970 - Paramount) Glen Campbell, Kim Darby, Joe Namath
One Sheet: $5 - $10

NOSFERATU
(1922 - Prana) Max Schreck
One Sheet: $60,000 - $80,000   *German. Virtually no German posters in any size are known to exist.*

NOSFERATU, THE VAMPIRE
(1979 - Fox) Klaus Kinski, Isabelle Adjani
One Sheet: $40 - $75   *French/ German.*

NOSTRADAMUS
(1994 - Orion) Tcheky Karyo, Amanda Plummer
One Sheet: $5 - $10

NOT A LADIES' MAN
(1942 - Columbia) Paul Kelly, Fay Wray
One Sheet: $75 - $150

NOT AS A STRANGER
(1955 - United Artists) Robert Mitchum, Olivia de Havilland, Frank Sinatra
One Sheet: $40 - $75

NOT DAMAGED
(1930 - Fox) Lois Morgan, Walter Byron
One Sheet: $125 - $250

NOT EXACTLY GENTLEMEN
(1931 - Fox) Victor Mclaglen, Fay Wray, Lew Cody
One Sheet: $150 - $300

NOT GUILTY
(1921 - First National) Sylvia Breamer, Richard Dix
One Sheet: $150 - $300

NOT GUILTY

(1926 - Universal) Texas Guinan
One Sheet: $150 - $350

NOT NOW DARLING
(1975 - Dimension) Leslie Phillips, Ray Cooney
One Sheet: $5 - $10

NOT OF THIS EARTH
(1956 - Allied Artists) Paul Birch, Beverly Garland
One Sheet: $250 - $600   *Graven Images, pg. 177.*

Half Sheet

NOT OF THIS EARTH
(1988 - Concorde) Traci Lords, Arthur Roberts
One Sheet: $20 - $40

NOT SO DUMB
(1930 - MGM) Marion Davies, Elliott Nugent
One Sheet: $150 - $300

NOT SO QUIET ON THE WESTERN FRONT
(1930 - British International) Leslie Fuller, Mona Goya
One Sheet: $75 - $150

NOT WANTED
(1949 - Film Classics) Sally Forrest, Keefe Brasselle
One Sheet: $15 - $30

NOT WITH MY WIFE YOU DON'T!
(1966 - Warner Bros.) Tony Curtis, Virna Lisi, George C. Scott
One Sheet: $15 - $30

NOT WITHOUT MY DAUGHTER
(1991 - MGM) Sally Field
One Sheet: $3 - $5

NOTHING BUT A MAN
(1963 - Cinema V) Ivan Dixon, Abbey Lincoln
One Sheet: $30 - $60   *Black cast. Duotone. Separate Cinema, pg. 155.*

NOTHING BUT THE BEST
(1964 - Columbia) Alan Bates, Millicent Martin
One Sheet: $15 - $30

NOTHING BUT THE TRUTH
(1941 - Paramount) Bob Hope, Paulette Goddard
One Sheet: $100 - $200

NOTHING BUT TROUBLE
(1944 - MGM) Stan Laurel, Oliver Hardy, Mary Boland
One Sheet: $250 - $500

NOTHING BUT TROUBLE
(1991 - Warner Bros.) Dan Aykroyd, Chevy Chase, John Candy, Demi Moore
One Sheet: $3 - $5

NOTHING IN COMMON
(1986 - TriStar) Tom Hanks, Jackie Gleason
One Sheet: $3 - $5

NOTHING LIKE A DANE
(1973 - Universal) -
One Sheet: $5 - $10   *Exploitation.*

NOTHING PERSONAL
(1980 - Purple Heart) Donald Sutherland, Suzanne Somers
One Sheet: $3 - $5

NOTHING SACRED
(1937 - United Artists) Carole Lombard, Fredric March
One Sheet: $500 - $800   *Duotone.*

NOTHING SACRED

(1947R - Film Classics) Carole Lombard,
Fredric March
One Sheet: $50 - $100   *Re-release.*
One Sheet more colorful than duotone original.

NOTORIETY
(1922 - Weber & North) Maurine Powers, Mary
Alden
One Sheet: $125 - $250

NOTORIOUS
(1946 - RKO) Cary Grant, Ingrid Bergman, Dir:
Alfred Hitchcock
One Sheet: $1,300 - $2,000

One Sheet

NOTORIOUS
(1956R - RKO) Cary Grant, Ingrid Bergman,
Dir: Alfred Hitchcock
One Sheet: $75 - $150   *Re-release.*

NOTORIOUS AFFAIR, A
(1930 - First National) Basil Rathbone, Kay
Francis
One Sheet: $150 - $300

NOTORIOUS BUT NICE
(1933 - Chesterfield) Marian Marsh, Donald
Dillaway
One Sheet: $100 - $200

NOTORIOUS ELINOR LEE, THE
(194? - -) Robert Earl Jones, Edna Mae Harris
One Sheet: $125 - $250

NOTORIOUS GENTLEMAN, A
(1935 - Universal) Charles Bickford, Sidney
Blackmer
One Sheet: $100 - $200

NOTORIOUS GENTLEMAN
(1946 - Universal) Rex Harrison, Lilli Palmer
One Sheet: $50 - $100

NOTORIOUS LANDLADY, THE
(1962 - Columbia) Kim Novak, Jack Lemmon,
Fred Astaire
One Sheet: $15 - $25

NOTORIOUS LONE WOLF, THE
(1946 - Columbia) Gerald Mohr, Janis Carter,
Eric Blore
One Sheet: $40 - $75

NOTORIOUS MISS LISLE, THE
(1921 - First National) Katherine MacDonald,
Nigel Barrie
One Sheet: $250 - $500

NOTORIOUS MR. MONKS, THE
(1958 - Republic) Vera Ralston, Don Kelly
One Sheet: $30 - $60

NOTORIOUS SOPHIE LANG
(1934 - Paramount) Gertrude Michael, Paul
Cavanagh
One Sheet: $125 - $250

NOVEL AFFAIR, A
(1957 - Continental) Ralph Richardson,
Maragret Leighton
One Sheet: $15 - $25   *AKA: THE*
PASSIONATE STRANGER.

NOVELTOON CARTOON
(1943 - Paramount) -
One Sheet: $250 - $500   *Cartoon.*
*Duotone. Stock poster with 1st image of Jack-in-
the-box clown that became the Harvey Comics
trade mark.*

NOW AND FOREVER
(1934 - Paramount) Gary Cooper, Carole
Lombard, Shirley Temple
One Sheet: $1,900 - $3,000

NOW AND FOREVER
(1956 - Associated British-Pathe) Janette
Scott, Vernon Gray
One Sheet: $5 - $10

NOW AND THEN
(1995 - New Line) Demi Moore, Rosie
O'Donnell, Melanie Griffith
One Sheet: $5 - $10

NOW I'LL TELL
(1934 - Fox) Spencer Tracy, Helen
Twelvetrees, Alice Faye
One Sheet: $250 - $600

NOW I'LL TELL ONE
(192? - Pathecomedy) Charley Chase, Stan
Laurel
One Sheet: $600 - $1,000

NOW OR NEVER
(1921 - Pathe) Harold Lloyd
One Sheet: $500 - $800

NOW OR NEVER
(1923 - Ajax) Dick Talmadge, Janet Chandler
One Sheet: $100 - $200

NOW, VOYAGER
(1942 - Warner Bros.) Bette Davis, Paul
Henreid, Claude Rains
One Sheet: $250 - $500   *Duotone.*

One Sheet

NOW WE'RE IN THE AIR
(1927 - Paramount) Wallace Beery, Raymond
Hatton, Louise Brooks
One Sheet: $800 - $1,500

NOW YOU SEE HIM, NOW YOU DON'T
(1972 - Buena Vista/Disney) Kurt Russell,
Cesar Romero, Joe Flynn
One Sheet: $5 - $10

NOWHERE TO GO
(1958 - MGM) George Nader, Bernard Lee,
Maggie Smith (film debut)
One Sheet: $10 - $20

NOWHERE TO HIDE
(1987 - New Century/Vista) Amy Madigan,
Daniel Hugh Kelly
One Sheet: $3 - $5

NOWHERE TO RUN
(1993 - Columbia) Jean-Claude Van Damme,
Rosanna Arquette
One Sheet: $7 - $15

NTH COMMANDMENT, THE
(1923 - Paramount) Colleen Moore, James
Morrison
One Sheet: $250 - $600

NUDE BOMB, THE
(1980 - Universal) Don Adams, Sylvia Kristel
One Sheet: $15 - $30   *TV tie-in.*
AKA: THE RETURN OF MAXWELL SMART.

NUDE CAMERA
(196? - -) Joe Syrno
One Sheet: $50 - $100

NUISANCE, THE
(1920 - Universal) Bartine Burkett
One Sheet: $200 - $400   *A Star*
Comedy.

NUISANCE, THE
(1921 - Vitagraph) Jimmy Aubrey
One Sheet: $250 - $500

NUISANCE, THE
(1933 - MGM) Frank Morgan, Madge Evans

One Sheet: $125 - $250

NUMBER ONE
(1969 - United Artists) Charlton Heston,
Jessica Walter, Bruce Dern
One Sheet: $15 - $30

NUMBER ONE
(1984 - -) Bob Geldof, Mel Smith
One Sheet: $15 - $30   *Sports*
(Billiards).

NUMBER ONE WITH A BULLET
(1987 - Cannon) Robert Carradine, Billy Dee
Williams
One Sheet: $3 - $5

NUMBER SEVENTEEN
(1932 - Wardour) Leon M. Lion, Anne Grey,
Dir: Hitchcock
One Sheet: $1,900 - $3,000

NUMBERED MEN
(1930 - First National) Conrad Nagel, Bernice
Claire
One Sheet: $100 - $200

NUMBERED WOMAN
(1938 - Monogram) Sally Blane, Lloyd Hughes
One Sheet: $75 - $125

NUN AND THE SERGEANT, THE
(1962 - United Artists) Robert Webber, Anna
Sten
One Sheet: $7 - $15

NUN AT THE CROSSROADS, A
(1970 - Universal) Rosanna Schiaffino, John
Richardson
One Sheet: $5 - $10

NUN'S STORY, THE
(1959 - Warner Bros.) Audrey Hepburn, Peter
Finch
One Sheet: $75 - $150

NUNS ON THE RUN
(1990 - -) Eric Idle, Robbie Coltrane
One Sheet: $5 - $10

NURSE EDITH CAVELL
(1939 - Imperadio) Anna Neagle, Edna May
Oliver
One Sheet: $40 - $75

NURSE FROM BROOKLYN
(1938 - Universal) Sally Eilers, Paul Kelly
One Sheet: $75 - $125

NURSE MARJORIE
(1920 - Realart) Mary Miles Minter, Clyde
Fillmore
One Sheet: $500 - $800

NURSE ON WHEELS
(1963 - Janus) Juliet Mills, Ronald Lewis
One Sheet: $10 - $20

NURSE'S SECRET, THE
(1941 - Warner Bros.) Lee Patrick, Julie
Bishop, Regis Toomey
One Sheet: $40 - $75

NURSE-MATES
(1940 - Paramount) Popeye, Brutus, Swee' Pea
One Sheet: $1,600 - $2,500   *Cartoon.*
Duotone.

NURSERY RHYME MYSTERIES
(1943 - MGM) -
One Sheet: $250 - $500   *Cartoon. Full*
color stone litho.

NURSES FOR SALE
(1977 - -) Curt Jurgens, Joan Kozian
One Sheet: $10 - $20

NURSING A VIPER
(1909 - Biograph) -
One Sheet: $600 - $1,000

NUT, THE
(1921 - United Artists) Douglas Fairbanks,
Marguerite De La Motte
One Sheet: $500 - $800

NUT FARM, THE
(1935 - Monogram) Wallace Ford, Joan Gale
One Sheet: $75 - $150

NUTCRACKER
(1986 - -) Hugh Bigney, Vanessa Sharp
One Sheet: $3 - $5

NUTS
(1987 - Warner Bros.) Barbra Streisand,
Richard Dreyfuss
One Sheet: $7 - $15

NUTTY BUT NICE
(1940 - Columbia) The Three Stooges (Curly)
One Sheet: $5,000 - $7,500   *Comedy short.*
Duotone.

NUTTY, NAUGHTY CHATEAU, THE
(1964 - Lopert) Monica Vitti, Curt Jurgens
One Sheet: $7 - $15

NUTTY NETWORK, THE
(1939 - 20th Century Fox) Terry-toons
One Sheet: $100 - $200   *Cartoon. Full
color stone litho. Stock poster with inset title.*

NUTTY NOTES
(1929 - Universal) Oswald (the Lucky Rabbit)
One Sheet: $600 - $1,000   *Cartoon.*
*Animated by Walter Lantz. Cartoon Movie Posters
#47.*

NUTTY PROFESSOR, THE
(1963 - Paramount) Jerry Lewis, Stella Stevens
One Sheet: $30 - $50   *Graven
Images, pg. 223.*

NUTTY PROFESSOR, THE
(1996 - Universal) Eddie Murphy, Jada Pinkett
One Sheet: $7 - $15

O DE CONDUITE
(1946 - Franfilmdis) Jean Daste
One Sheet: $200 - $400   *French.*

O. HENRY'S FULL HOUSE
(1952 - 20th Century Fox) Fred Allen, Anne
Baxter, Marilyn Monroe, Charles Laughton
One Sheet: $125 - $250

O LUCKY MAN
(1973 - Warner Bros.) Malcolm McDowell,
Ralph Richardson, Rachel Roberts
One Sheet: $3 - $5

O, MY DARLING CLEMENTINE
(1943 - Republic) Frank Albertson, Lorna Gray,
Roy Acuff
One Sheet: $50 - $100   *Country
musical.*

O. S. S.
(1947 - Paramount) Alan Ladd, Geraldine
Fitzgerald
One Sheet: $75 - $150

O'MALLEY OF THE MOUNTED
(1921 - Paramount) William S. Hart
One Sheet: $1,300 - $2,000   *Cowboy
Movie Posters #27.*

O'MALLEY OF THE MOUNTED
(1936 - 20th Century Fox) George O'Brien
One Sheet: $125 - $250

O'SHAUGHNESSY'S BOY
(1935 - MGM) Wallace Beery, Jackie Cooper
One Sheet: $350 - $750

O'VOUTIE O'ROONEY
(1947 - Astor) Slim Gaillard
One Sheet: $150 - $300   *Black cast.*
Separate Cinema, pg. 98.

OASIS
(1956 - 20th Century Fox) Michele Morgan,
Cornell Borchers
One Sheet: $5 - $10

OATH OF VENGEANCE
(1944 - PRC) Buster Crabbe, Al St. John
One Sheet: $40 - $75

OATHBOUND
(1922 - Fox) Dustin Farnum
One Sheet: $150 - $300

OBEY THE LAW
(1933 - Columbia) Leo Carrillo, Dickie Moore
One Sheet: $100 - $200

OBJECTIVE BURMA
(1945 - Warner Bros.) Errol Flynn, James
Brown
One Sheet: $100 - $200

OBLIGING YOUNG LADY
(1941 - RKO) Joan Carroll, Edmond O'Brien,
Ruth Warrick
One Sheet: $40 - $75

OBLONG BOX, THE
(1969 - AIP) Vincent Price, Christopher Lee
One Sheet: $20 - $40

OBSESSED, THE
(1951 - United Artists) David Farrar, Geraldine Fitzgerald
One Sheet: $10 - $20

OBSESSION
(1976 - Columbia) Cliff Robertson, Genevieve Bujold
One Sheet: $3 - $5

OCEAN DRIVE
(1959 - Columbia) Edmund O'Brien, Joanne Dru
One Sheet: $15 - $30

OCEAN'S ELEVEN
(1960 - Warner Bros.) Frank Sinatra, Dean Martin
One Sheet: $100 - $200

OCTAMAN
(1971 - Filmers Guild) Kerwin Matthews, Jeff Morrow, Pier Angeli
One Sheet: $5 - $10

OCTOBER
(1927 - Sovkino) Nikandraf, N. Popov
One Sheet: $1,900 - $3,000   *Russian. AKA: TEN DAYS THAT SHOOK THE WORLD.*

OCTOBER MAN, THE
(1948 - Eagle-Lion) John Mills, Joan Greenwood
One Sheet: $15 - $30

OCTOBER MOTH
(1960 - Rank) Lee Patterson, Lana Morris
One Sheet: $15 - $25

OCTOPUSSY
(1982 - MGM/United Artists) Roger Moore, Maud Adams
One Sheet: $20 - $40   *Advance:$30-$50.*

One Sheet

ODD ANGRY SHOT, THE
(1979 - -) John Hargreaves, Bryan Brown
One Sheet: $3 - $5

ODD COUPLE, THE
(1968 - Paramount) Jack Lemmon, Walter Matthau
One Sheet: $20 - $40

ODD COUPLE/ROSEMARY'S BABY COMBO
(1969R - Paramount) -
One Sheet: $15 - $25   *Re-release double feature poster.*

ODD JOB, THE
(1978 - Columbia) Graham Chapman
One Sheet: $3 - $5

ODD MAN OUT
(1947 - GFD) James Mason, Kathleen Ryan
One Sheet: $15 - $25

ODD SPORTS
(1939 - Columbia) -
One Sheet: $100 - $200   *Sports. (News World Of Sports)*

ODDO
(1967 - Montgomery) Martin Donley, Nicki Holt
One Sheet: $5 - $10

ODDS AGAINST TOMORROW
(1959 - United Artists) Harry Belafonte, Robert Ryan, Shelly Winters
One Sheet: $75 - $150   *Separate*

Cinema, pg. 153.

ODE TO BILLY JOE
(1976 - Warner Bros.) Robby Benson, Glynnis O'Connor
One Sheet: $5 - $10

ODESSA FILE, THE
(1974 - Columbia) Jon Voight, Maximillian Schell
One Sheet: $7 - $15

ODETTE
(1950 - Lopert) Anna Neagle, Trevor Howard
One Sheet: $7 - $15

ODONGO
(1956 - Columbia) Macdonald Carey, Rhonda Fleming
One Sheet: $15 - $25

ODYSSEY OF THE NORTH, AN
(1914 - Paramount) Howard Bosworth, Rhea Haines
One Sheet: $600 - $1,000

ODYSSEY OF THE PACIFIC
(1983 - CinePacific) Mickey Rooney, Jonathan Starr
One Sheet: $3 - $5

OEDIPUS REX
(1957 - Motion Pictures) Douglas Rain, Eric House
One Sheet: $15 - $25   *AKA: KING OEDIPUS.*

OEDIPUS THE KING
(1968 - Universal) Christopher Plummer, Orson Welles, Lilli Palmer
One Sheet: $10 - $20

OF CASH AND HASH
(1955 - Columbia) The Three Stooges (Shemp)
One Sheet: $150 - $300   *Comedy short. Duotone.*

OF HUMAN BONDAGE
(1934 - RKO) Leslie Howard, Bette Davis
One Sheet: $5,000 - $8,000

One Sheet

OF HUMAN BONDAGE
(1946 - Warner Bros.) Eleanor Parker, Paul Henreid
One Sheet: $30 - $60

OF HUMAN BONDAGE
(1964 - MGM) Kim Novak, Laurence Harvey
One Sheet: $15 - $30

OF HUMAN HEARTS
(1938 - MGM) Walter Huston, James Stewart
One Sheet: $200 - $400

OF LOVE AND DESIRE
(1963 - 20th Century Fox) Merle Oberon, Steve Cochran
One Sheet: $15 - $25

OF LOVE AND SHADOWS
(1996 - Miramax) Antonio Banderas, Jennifer Connelly
One Sheet: $7 - $15   *Drama.*

OF MICE AND MEN
(1940 - United Artists) Lon Chaney Jr., Betty Field, Burgess Meredith
One Sheet: $300 - $700

OF MICE AND MEN
(1992 - MGM) John Malkovich, Gary Sinise, Sherilyn Fenn
One Sheet: $5 - $10

OF ONE BLOOD
(1944 - Sack) Dir: Spencer Williams
One Sheet: $150 - $300   *Black cast. Separate Cinema, pg. 22.*

OFF BEAT
(1986 - Buena Vista) Judge Reinhold, Meg Tilly, Cleavant Derricks
One Sheet: $3 - $5

OFF LIMITS
(1952 - Paramount) Bob Hope, Marilyn Maxwell
One Sheet: $40 - $75

OFF LIMITS
(1988 - -) Willem Dafoe, Gregory Hines, Amanda Pays
One Sheet: $5 - $10

OFF THE HIGHWAY
(1925 - Producers Distributing) -
One Sheet: $150 - $300

OFF THE RECORD
(1939 - Warner Bros.) Pat O'Brien, Joan Blondell
One Sheet: $50 - $100

OFF TO THE RACES
(1937 - 20th Century Fox) Jed Prouty, Shirley Deane
One Sheet: $50 - $100   *Sports (Horse racing).*

OFFENCE, THE
(1973 - United Artists) Sean Connery, Trevor Howard
One Sheet: $5 - $10

OFFICE GIRL, THE
(1931 - RKO) Renate Muller, Jack Hulbert
One Sheet: $600 - $1,000

OFFICE WIFE, THE
(1930 - Warner Bros.) Joan Blondell, Lewis Stone
One Sheet: $150 - $300

OFFICER 666
(1914 - Kleine) Howard Estabrook, Sidney Seaward
One Sheet: $250 - $500

OFFICER AND A GENTLEMAN, AN
(1982 - Paramount) Richard Gere, Debra Winger, Louis Gossett Jr.
One Sheet: $10 - $20   *Academy Award: Best Supporting Actor (Gossett).*

OFFICER AND THE LADY, THE
(1941 - Columbia) Bruce Bennett, Dorothy Mackaill
One Sheet: $40 - $75

OFFICER DUCK
(1939 - RKO/Disney) Donald Duck
One Sheet: $2,500 - $4,000   *Cartoon. Cartoon Movie Posters #156.*

OFFICER O'BRIEN
(1930 - Pathe) William Boyd, Ernest Torrence
One Sheet: $100 - $200

OFFICER OF THE DAY
(1926 - Fox) -
One Sheet: $150 - $300

OFFICER THIRTEEN
(1932 - Allied) Monte Blue, Lila Lee
One Sheet: $100 - $200

OFFICIAL UNITED STATES WAR FILMS
(1917 - -) -
One Sheet: $500 - $800   *Documentary.*

OFFICIAL URBAN MOVIE CHATS...
(1929 - Kineto) -
One Sheet: $100 - $200

OFFSPRING, THE
(1986 - -) Vincent Price, Ted Whittenbarger
One Sheet: $7 - $15   *AKA: FROM A WHISPER TO A SCREAM.*

OH, BABY!
(1944 - Columbia) Hugh Herbert, Esther Howard, Bud Jamison
One Sheet: $50 - $100   *Comedy short. Duotone.*

OH BILLY, BEHAVE
(1926 - Rayart) Billy West
One Sheet: $250 - $500

OH! CALCUTTA!
(1972 - Cinemation) Raina Barrett, Mark Dempsey
One Sheet: $5 - $10

OH DAD, POOR DAD, MAMA'S HUNG YOU IN THE CLOSET AND I'M FEELIN SO SAD
(1967 - Paramount) Rosalind Russell, Robert Morse
One Sheet: $7 - $15

OH, DOCTOR
(1924 - Universal) Mary Astor, Reginald Denny
One Sheet: $200 - $400

OH, DOCTOR
(1937 - Universal) Edward Everett Horton
One Sheet: $75 - $150

OH, FOR A MAN
(1930 - Fox) Jeanette MacDonald, Bela Lugosi, Reginald Denny
One Sheet: $250 - $600

OH GENTLE SPRING
(1940 - 20th Century Fox) Terry-toons
One Sheet: $100 - $200   *Cartoon. Full color stone litho. Stock poster with inset title.*

OH, GOD!
(1977 - Warner Bros.) George Burns, John Denver
One Sheet: $7 - $15

One Sheet

OH GOD! BOOK II
(1980 - Warner Bros.) George Burns, Susan Pleshette
One Sheet: $3 - $5

OH GOD, YOU DEVIL!
(1984 - Warner Bros.) George Burns, Ted Wass
One Sheet: $3 - $5

OH, JOHNNY, HOW YOU CAN LOVE!
(1940 - Universal) Peggy Moran, Tom Brown
One Sheet: $75 - $125

OH, MEN! OH, WOMEN!
(1957 - 20th Century Fox) Ginger Rogers, Dan Dailey, Tony Randall
One Sheet: $20 - $40

OH! MY PA-PA
(1956 - 20th Century Fox) -
One Sheet: $10 - $20

OH, SAILOR BEHAVE
(1930 - Warner Bros.) Olsen & Johnson
One Sheet: $200 - $400   *The team's first film.*

OH SUSANNAH!
(1936 - Republic) Gene Autry
One Sheet: $500 - $900   *Cowboy Movie Posters #194.*

OH SUSANNAH!
(1941R - Republic) Gene Autry
One Sheet: $75 - $150   *Re-release. Full color.*

OH SUSANNAH!
(1951 - Republic) Rod Cameron, Adrian Booth
One Sheet: $15 - $30

OH! WHAT A LOVELY WAR
(1969 - Paramount) Laurence Olivier, Michael Redgrave, Maggie Smith
One Sheet: $10 - $20

OH, WHAT A NIGHT!
(1944 - Monogram) Edmund Lowe, Jean Parker
One Sheet: $40 - $75

OH YEAH!
(1929 - Pathe) Robert Armstrong, James Gleason
One Sheet: $125 - $250

OH, YOU BEAUTIFUL DOLL
(1949 - 20th Century Fox) June Haver, Mark Stevens
One Sheet: $30 - $50

OH, YOU TONY!
(1924 - Fox) Tom Mix, Claire Adams
One Sheet: $500 - $800

OIL FOR THE LAMPS OF CHINA
(1935 - First National) Pat O'Brien, Josephine Hutchinson
One Sheet: $150 - $300

OIL RAIDER, THE
(1934 - Mayfair) Buster Crabbe, Gloria Shea
One Sheet: $75 - $150

OIL'S WELL THAT ENDS WELL
(1958 - Columbia) The Three Stooges (Joe Besser)
One Sheet: $75 - $125   *Comedy short. Duotone. Remake of OILY TO BED, OILY TO RISE.*

OILY SCOUNDREL, AN
(1916 - Triangle/Keystone) Fred Mace
One Sheet: $600 - $1,000

OILY TO BED, OILY TO RISE
(1939 - Columbia) The Three Stooges (Curly)
One Sheet: $7,500 - $12,000   *Comedy short. Duotone.*

OKAY AMERICA
(1932 - Universal) Lew Ayres, Maureen O'Sullivan
One Sheet: $150 - $300

OKINAWA
(1952 - Columbia) Pat O'Brien, Richard Denning
One Sheet: $15 - $25

OKLAHOMA!
(1955 - Magna) Shirley Jones, Gordon MacRae, Gene Nelson
One Sheet: $75 - $125   *Jones' film debut.*

OKLAHOMA!
(1963R - Magna) Shirley Jones, Gordon MacRae
One Sheet: $10 - $20   *Re-release.*

OKLAHOMA!
(1982R - Magna) Shirley Jones, Gordon MacRae
One Sheet: $5 - $10   *Re-release.*

OKLAHOMA ANNIE
(1952 - Republic) Judy Canova, John Russell
One Sheet: $15 - $30

OKLAHOMA BADLANDS
(1948 - Republic) Allan "Rocky" Lane
One Sheet: $40 - $75

OKLAHOMA BLUES
(1948 - Monogram) Jimmy Wakely
One Sheet: $50 - $100

OKLAHOMA CRUDE
(1973 - Columbia) George C. Scott, Faye Dunaway
One Sheet: $3 - $5

OKLAHOMA CYCLONE
(1930 - Tiffany) Bob Steele, Al St. John
One Sheet: $100 - $200

OKLAHOMA FRONTIER
(1939 - Universal) Johnny Mack Brown
One Sheet: $75 - $150

OKLAHOMA JUSTICE
(1951 - Monogram) Johnny Mack Brown
One Sheet: $20 - $40

OKLAHOMA KID, THE
(1928 - Syndicate) Bob Custer
One Sheet: $150 - $300

OKLAHOMA KID, THE
(1939 - Warner Bros.) James Cagney, Humphrey Bogart
One Sheet: $800 - $1,500   *Cowboy Movie Posters #s 241-245.*

OKLAHOMA KID, THE
(1942R - Warner Bros.) James Cagney, Humphrey Bogart
One Sheet: $75 - $125   *Re-release. One Sheet is duotone and features Bogart and Cagney prominently.*

Half Sheet (1942R)

OKLAHOMA KID, THE
(1956R - Warner Bros.) James Cagney, Humphrey Bogart
One Sheet: $40 - $75   *Re-release.*

OKLAHOMA OUTLAWS
(1943 - Warner Bros.) Robert Shayne, Juanita Stark
One Sheet: $30 - $60

OKLAHOMA RAIDERS
(1943 - Universal) Tex Ritter, Fuzzy Knight
One Sheet: $50 - $100

OKLAHOMA RENEGADES
(1940 - Republic) Three Mesquiteers (Livingston, Hatton, Renaldo)
One Sheet: $40 - $75

OKLAHOMA SHERIFF, THE
(1930 - Syndicate) Bob Steele, Jean Reno
One Sheet: $100 - $200

OKLAHOMA TERRITORY
(1960 - Premium/United Artists) Bill Williams, Gloria Talbott
One Sheet: $10 - $20

OKLAHOMA TERROR
(1939 - Monogram) Jack Randall
One Sheet: $50 - $100

OKLAHOMA WOMAN, THE
(1956 - American Releasing) Richard Denning, Peggie Castle
One Sheet: $10 - $20

OKLAHOMAN, THE
(1957 - Allied Artists) Joel McCrea, Barbara Hale
One Sheet: $15 - $30

OLAF LAUGHS LAST
(1942 - Columbia) El Brendel
One Sheet: $100 - $200   *Comedy short. Duotone.*

OLD ACQUAINTANCE
(1943 - Warner Bros.) Bette Davis, Miriam Hopkins
One Sheet: $100 - $200

One Sheet

OLD BARN DANCE, THE
(1938 - Republic) Gene Autry, Smiley Burnette
One Sheet: $200 - $400

OLD BLACKOUT JOE
(1939 - Columbia) Phantasy
One Sheet: $200 - $400   *Cartoon. Full color stock poster with paper title attached.*

OLD BOYFRIENDS
(1979 - Avco/Embassy) Talia Shire, John Belushi
One Sheet: $15 - $25

OLD CHISHOLM TRAIL, THE
(1942 - Universal) Tex Ritter, Johnny Mack Brown
One Sheet: $50 - $100

OLD CLOTHES
(1925 - Metro-Goldwyn) Joan Crawford, Jackie Coogan
One Sheet: $250 - $500

OLD CORRAL, THE
(1936 - Republic) Gene Autry, Roy Rogers (Leonard Slye)
One Sheet: $250 - $500

OLD DARK HOUSE, THE
(1932 - Universal) Melvyn Douglas, Charles Laughton, Boris Karloff
One Sheet: $16,000 - $25,000   *Graven Images, pg. 51.*

OLD DARK HOUSE, THE
(1939R - Universal) Melvyn Douglas, Charles Laughton, Boris Karloff
One Sheet: $600 - $1,000   *First re-release. One Sheet is yellow/blue duotone.*

OLD DARK HOUSE, THE
(1943R - Universal) Melvyn Douglas, Charles Laughton, Boris Karloff
One Sheet: $250 - $500   *Re-release.*

OLD DARK HOUSE, THE
(1963 - Columbia) Tom Poston, Robert Morley
One Sheet: $7 - $15

OLD DRACULA
(1975 - AIP) David Niven, Teresa Graves
One Sheet: $10 - $20

OLD ENGLISH
(1930 - Warner Bros.) George Arliss, Doris Lloyd
One Sheet: $150 - $300

OLD ENOUGH
(1984 - Orion) Sarah Boyd, Danny Aiello, Alyssa Milano
One Sheet: $3 - $5

OLD FASHIONED BOY, AN
(1920 - Paramount) Charles Ray, Ethel Shannon
One Sheet: $150 - $300

OLD FASHIONED GIRL, AN
(1949 - Pathe) Gloria Jean, Jimmy Lydon
One Sheet: $20 - $40

OLD FASHIONED WAY, THE
(1934 - Paramount) W.C. Fields, Joe Morrison
One Sheet: $1,900 - $3,000

OLD FIRE HORSE, THE
(1939 - 20th Century Fox) Terry-toons
One Sheet: $100 - $200   *Cartoon. Full color stone litho. Stock poster with inset title.*

OLD FRONTIER, THE
(1950 - Republic) Monte Hale
One Sheet: $30 - $50

OLD GRAD
(1937 - Universal) Charles Grapewin
One Sheet: $75 - $125

OLD GRINGO
(1989 - Columbia) Gregory Peck, Jane Fonda
One Sheet: $5 - $10

OLD HOME WEEK
(1925 - Paramount) Thomas Meighan
One Sheet: $150 - $300

OLD HOMESTEAD, THE
(1922 - Paramount) Theodore Roberts, Harrison Ford
One Sheet: $150 - $300

OLD HOMESTEAD, THE
(1935 - Liberty) Mary Carlisle, Lawrence Gray
One Sheet: $75 - $125

OLD HOMESTEAD, THE

OLD HUTCH
(1936 - MGM) Wallace Beery, Elizabeth Patterson
One Sheet: $75 - $150

OLD IRONSIDES
(1926 - Paramount) Esther Ralston, Wallace Beery
One Sheet: $250 - $500

OLD LOS ANGELES
(1948 - Republic) Wild Bill Elliott, Andy Devine
One Sheet: $40 - $75

OLD LOUISIANA
(1937 - Crescent) Tom Keene, Rita Cansino (Hayworth)
One Sheet: $200 - $400

OLD MAID, THE
(1939 - Warner Bros.) Bette Davis, Miriam Hopkins
One Sheet: $350 - $750   *Duotone.*

One Sheet

OLD MAN AND THE SEA, THE
(1958 - Warner Bros.) Spencer Tracy, Felipe Pazos
One Sheet: $75 - $150

OLD MAN RHYTHM
(1935 - RKO) Buddy Rogers, Betty Grable
One Sheet: $250 - $500

OLD MILL, THE
(1950R - RKO/Disney) Silly Syphony
One Sheet: $800 - $1,500   *Re-release. Cartoon. Cartoon Movie Posters #198.*

OLD MOTHER HUBBARD
(1935 - Celebrity) By Ub Iwerks
One Sheet: $800 - $1,400   *Cartoon. A ComiColor Cartoon.*

OLD MOTHER RILEY, DETECTIVE
(1943 - British National) Arthur Lucan, Kitty McShane
One Sheet: $15 - $35

OLD NEST, THE
(1921 - Goldwyn) Dwight Crittenden, Mary Alden
One Sheet: $200 - $400

OLD OAKEN BUCKET, THE
(1940 - 20th Century Fox) Terry-toons
One Sheet: $100 - $200   *Cartoon. Full color stone litho. Stock poster with inset title.*

OLD OKLAHOMA PLAINS
(1952 - Republic) Rex Allen
One Sheet: $15 - $35

OLD OVERLAND TRAIL
(1952 - Republic) Rex Allen
One Sheet: $40 - $75

OLD ROCKIN' CHAIR TOM
(1948 - MGM) Tom & Jerry
One Sheet: $300 - $650   *Cartoon.*

OLD SEQUOIA
(1945 - RKO/Disney) Donald Duck
One Sheet: $1,300 - $2,000   *Cartoon. The Disney Poster, pg. 53.*

OLD SOAK, THE
(1926 - Universal) Jean Hersholt, George Lewis
One Sheet: $150 - $300

(1942 - Republic) Weaver Bros. & Elviry
One Sheet: $50 - $100

OLD SPANISH CUSTOM, AN
(1936 - J. H. Hoffberg Co.) Buster Keaton
One Sheet: $700 - $1,200

OLD SWIMMIN' HOLE
(1940 - Monogram) Marcia Mae Jones, Jackie Moran
One Sheet: $40 - $75

OLD SWIMMING HOLE, THE
(1921 - First National) Charles Ray
One Sheet: $250 - $500

OLD TEXAS TRAIL, THE
(1944 - Universal) Rod Cameron, Fuzzy Knight
One Sheet: $40 - $75

OLD WEST, THE
(1952 - Columbia) Gene Autry, Pat Buttram
One Sheet: $50 - $100

OLD WYOMING TRAIL, THE
(1937 - Columbia) Charles Starrett, Barbara Weeks
One Sheet: $75 - $150

OLD YELLER
(1957 - Buena Vista/Disney) Dorothy McGuire, Fess Parker
One Sheet: $30 - $60

OLD YELLER
(1965R - Walt Disney) Dorothy McGuire, Fess Parker
One Sheet: $7 - $15   *Re-release.*

OLD YELLER
(1974R - Buena Vista/Disney) Dorothy McGuire, Fess Parker
One Sheet: $5 - $10   *Re-release.*

OLDEST PROFESSION, THE
(1968 - Goldstone) Raquel Welch, Jeanne Moreau
One Sheet: $15 - $30

OLEANNA
(1994 - Goldwyn) William H. Macy, Debra Eisenstadt
One Sheet: $3 - $5

OLGA'S HOUSE OF SHAME
(1964 - AFD) Audrey Campbell
One Sheet: $15 - $30

OLIVER
(1969 - Columbia) Mark Lester, Ron Moody, Oliver Reed
One Sheet: $20 - $40   *Academy Award: Best Picture. Academy Award Movie Posters #246.*

OLIVER & COMPANY
(1988 - Disney) Oliver
One Sheet: $7 - $15   *Cartoon. The Disney Poster, pg. 88.*

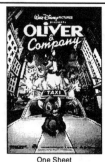
One Sheet

OLIVER THE EIGHTH
(1933 - MGM) Laurel & Hardy
One Sheet: $1,900 - $3,000

OLIVER TWIST
(1912 - -) -
One Sheet: $800 - $1,500   *French. D. Angelo art.*

OLIVER TWIST
(1922 - First National) Jackie Coogan, Lon Chaney
One Sheet: $800 - $1,500

OLIVER TWIST
(1933 - Monogram) Dickie Moore, Irving Pichel
One Sheet: $125 - $250

OLIVER TWIST
(1948 - United Artists) John Howard Davies, Alec Guinness
One Sheet: $30 - $50

OLIVER'S STORY
(1978 - Paramount) Ryan O'Neal, Candice Bergen
One Sheet: $10 - $20

OLIVIER OLIVIER
(1993 - Sony Classics) Francois Cluzet, Brigette Rouan
One Sheet: $3 - $5   *French.*

OLLY OLLY OXEN FREE
(1978 - Rico-Lion) Katherine Hepburn
One Sheet: $10 - $20

OLSEN'S BIG MOMENT
(1933 - Fox) El Brendel, Walter Catlett
One Sheet: $100 - $200

OLYMPIA
(1936 - Tobis) Dir: Leni Riefenstahl
One Sheet: $7,500 - $12,000   *German. Rare documentary. Price is for original German poster measuring 56"x38". Sports Movie Posters #281.*

OLYMPIA
(1958R - Tobis) Dir: Leni Riefenstahl
One Sheet: $1,900 - $3,000   *Re-release. German. Price is for second release poster measuring 56"x38".*

OLYMPIC CAVALCADE
(1948 - Westport International) Documentary
One Sheet: $75 - $125   *Sports.*

OLYMPIC GAMES, THE
(1925 - Universal) Dir: Bryan Foy
One Sheet: $150 - $350   *Sports.*

OLYMPIC GAMES
(1927 - Pathe) Our Gang
One Sheet: $600 - $1,000   *Sports (Boxing). Full color stone litho. Sports Movie Posters #124.*

OMAHA TRAIL, THE
(1942 - MGM) James Craig, Dean Jagger
One Sheet: $30 - $50

OMAR KHAYYAM
(1924 - Universal) Dir: Bryan Foy
One Sheet: $100 - $200   *An "Hysterical History Comedy."*

OMAR KHAYYAM
(1956 - Paramount) Cornel Wilde, Michael Rennie
One Sheet: $10 - $20

OMEGA MAN, THE
(1971 - Warner Bros.) Charlton Heston, Rosalind Cash, Anthony Zerbe
One Sheet: $15 - $25

OMEN, THE
(1976 - 20th Century Fox) Gregory Peck, Lee Remick
One Sheet: $7 - $15

OMOO-OMOO, THE SHARK GOD
(1949 - Elsa) Ron Randell, Devera Burton
One Sheet: $15 - $25

ON A CLEAR DAY YOU CAN SEE FOREVER
(1970 - Paramount) Barbra Streisand, Yves Montand, Bob Newhart
One Sheet: $15 - $30

ON AGAIN-OFF AGAIN
(1937 - RKO) Wheeler & Woolsey
One Sheet: $100 - $200

ON AN ISLAND WITH YOU
(1948 - MGM) Esther Williams, Peter Lawford, Ricardo Montalban
One Sheet: $75 - $125

ON ANY SUNDAY
(1971 - Cinema 5) Steve McQueen, Dir: Bruce Brown (Endless Summer)
One Sheet: $50 - $100   *Sports (Motocross racing). One Sheet features full-color motocross racers.*

ON APPROVAL
(1945 - English) Clive Brook, Beatrice Lillie
One Sheet: $15 - $30

ON BORROWED TIME

(1939 - MGM) Lionel Barrymore, Beulah Bondi
One Sheet: $200 - $400   *Graven Images, pg. 90.*

ON DANGEROUS GROUND
(1951 - RKO) Ida Lupino, Robert Ryan
One Sheet: $75 - $150

ON DEADLY GROUND
(1994 - Warner Bros.) Steven Seagal, Michael Caine, Joan Chen
One Sheet: $4 - $8

ON DRESS PARADE
(1939 - Warner Bros.) The Dead End Kids, John Litel
One Sheet: $75 - $125

ON GOLDEN POND
(1981 - Universal) Katharine Hepburn, Henry Fonda
One Sheet: $15 - $30   *Academy Award: Best Actor (Fonda), Best Actress (Hepburn). Preview Style:$10-15. Academy Award Movie Posters #318-#320.*

ON HER MAJESTY'S SECRET SERVICE
(1969 - United Artists) George Lazenby, Diana Rigg, Telly Savalas
One Sheet: $40 - $75   *Price is for skiing style; other styles:$30-$60. One Sheet (advance):$75-$150.*

One Sheet (Style B)

ON HER MAJESTY'S SECRET SERVICE
(1980R - United Artists/Transamerica) George Lazenby, Diana Rigg, Telly Savalas
One Sheet: $15 - $30   *Re-release. Poster is NSS stamped "For. 'A' 70/9" on back and dated 1969 onlower left front but "Entertainment from Transamerica" on lower right means that poster was produced after 1979 when Transamerica was formed.*

ON MOONLIGHT BAY
(1951 - Warner Bros.) Doris Day, Gordon MacRae
One Sheet: $30 - $60

ON MY WAY TO THE CRUSADES I MET A GIRL WHO
(1969 - Warner Bros.) Tony Curtis, Monica Vitti
One Sheet: $7 - $15

ON OUR MERRY WAY
(1948 - United Artists) Paulette Goddard, James Stewart
One Sheet: $50 - $100

ON RECORD
(1917 - Paramount) Mae Murray
One Sheet: $200 - $400

ON STAGE EVERYBODY
(1945 - Universal) Jack Oakie, Peggy Ryan, King Sisters
One Sheet: $50 - $100

ON SUCH A NIGHT
(1937 - Paramount) Karen Morley, Grant Richards
One Sheet: $75 - $150

ON THE AVENUE
(1937 - 20th Century Fox) Dick Powell, Madeleine Carroll, Alice Faye
One Sheet: $700 - $1,200

ON THE BANKS OF THE WABASH
(1923 - Vitagraph) Mary Carr, Burt McIntosh
One Sheet: $150 - $300

ON THE BEACH
(1959 - United Artists) Gregory Peck, Ava Gardner, Anthony Perkins, Fred Astaire
One Sheet: $50 - $100   *Other style*

(red):$60-$125. Graven Images, pg. 170.

ON THE BORDER
(1930 - Warner Bros.) Rin-Tin-Tin, John Litel, Armida
One Sheet: $200 - $400

ON THE DOUBLE
(1961 - Paramount) Danny Kaye, Dana Wynter
One Sheet: $15 - $30

ON THE GREAT WHITE TRAIL
(1938 - Grand National) James Newill, Terry Walker
One Sheet: $100 - $200   *AKA: Renfrew Of The Royal Mounted On The Great White Trail.*

ON THE HIGH SEAS
(1922 - Paramount) Dorothy Dalton, Jack Holt
One Sheet: $100 - $200

ON THE ISLE OF SAMOA
(1950 - Columbia) Jon Hall, Susan Cabot
One Sheet: $15 - $25

ON THE LEVEL
(1930 - Fox) Victor McLaglen, Fifi D'Orsay
One Sheet: $75 - $150

ON THE LINE
(1972 - Interwest) -
One Sheet: $7 - $15   *Sports (Dirt Bike Racing).*

ON THE LOOSE
(1951 - RKO) Joan Evans, Melvyn Douglas
One Sheet: $15 - $30

ON THE MESA OF LOST WOMEN
(1952 - -) See MESA OF LOST WOMEN

ON THE NIGHT STAGE
(1915 - -) William S. Hart
One Sheet: $1,900 - $3,000

ON THE NIGHT STAGE
(192?R - -) William S. Hart
One Sheet: $500 - $800   *Re-release.*

ON THE OLD SPANISH TRAIL
(1947 - Republic) Roy Rogers, Jane Frazee
One Sheet: $125 - $250

ON THE OLD SPANISH TRAIL
(1952R - Republic) Roy Rogers
One Sheet: $50 - $100   *Re-release.*

ON THE RIGHT TRACK
(1981 - 20th Century) Gary Coleman, Maureen Stapleton
One Sheet: $2 - $3

ON THE RIVIERA
(1951 - 20th Century Fox) Danny Kaye, Gene Tierney
One Sheet: $30 - $50

ON THE SPOT
(1940 - Monogram) Frankie Darro, Mary Korman
One Sheet: $40 - $75

ON THE SUNNY SIDE
(1941 - 20th Century Fox) Roddy McDowall, Jane Darwell
One Sheet: $50 - $100

ON THE THRESHOLD OF SPACE
(1956 - 20th Century Fox) Guy Madison, Virginia Leith
One Sheet: $15 - $25

ON THE TOWN
(1949 - MGM) Gene Kelly, Frank Sinatra
One Sheet: $200 - $400

One Sheet

ON THE TOWN
(1962R - MGM) Gene Kelly, Frank Sinatra
One Sheet: $15 - $30   *Re-release.*

ON THE WATERFRONT
(1954 - Columbia) Marlon Brando, Karl Malden, Eva Marie Saint
One Sheet: $150 - $350   *Academy Award: Best Picture, Best Actor(Brando), Best Supp. Actress(Saint), Best Direction(Elia Kazan).Academy Award Movie Posters #154-#156 & #159.*

Lobby Card

ON THE WATERFRONT
(1959R - Columbia) Marlon Brando, Karl Malden, Eva Marie Saint
One Sheet: $200 - $400   *Re-release. One Sheet image is superior to original.*

ON THEIR OWN
(1940 - 20th Century Fox) Spring Byington, Marguerite Chapman
One Sheet: $40 - $75

ON TOP OF OLD SMOKEY
(1953 - Columbia) Gene Autry
One Sheet: $100 - $200   *Full color stone litho.*

ON TRIAL
(1939 - Warner Bros.) John Litel, Margaret Lindsay
One Sheet: $40 - $75

ON WITH THE DANCE
(1920 - Paramount) Mae Murray, David Powell
One Sheet: $150 - $300

ON WITH THE SHOW
(1929 - Warner Bros.) Betty Compson, Louise Fazenda
One Sheet: $600 - $1,000   *First film in all natural color.*

Insert

ON YOUR BACK
(1930 - Fox) Irene Rich, Raymond Hackett
One Sheet: $200 - $400

ON YOUR TOES
(1939 - Warner Bros.) Eddie Albert, Vera Zorina
One Sheet: $40 - $75

ONCE A DOCTOR
(1936 - Warner Bros.) Donald Woods, Jean Muir
One Sheet: $75 - $150

ONCE A GENTLEMAN
(1930 - World Wide) Edward Everett Horton
One Sheet: $100 - $200

ONCE A LADY

(1931 - Paramount Publix) Ruth Chatterton, Jill Edmond
One Sheet: $125 - $250

ONCE A SINNER
(1930 - Fox) Dorothy Mackaill, Joel McCrea
One Sheet: $150 - $300

ONCE A THIEF
(1950 - United Artists) June Havoc, Cesar Romero
One Sheet: $15 - $25

ONCE A THIEF
(1965 - MGM) Alain Delon, Ann-Margret
One Sheet: $15 - $25

ONCE BITTEN
(1985 - -) Lauren Hutton, Jim Carrey
One Sheet: $5 - $10

ONCE IN A BLUE MOON
(1935 - Paramount) Jimmy Sano, Cecilia Loftus
One Sheet: $100 - $200

ONCE IN A LIFETIME
(1932 - Universal) Jack Oakie, Sidney Fox
One Sheet: $150 - $300

ONCE IN A MILLION
(1936 - British International) Buddy Rogers, Mary Brian
One Sheet: $75 - $150

ONCE IS NOT ENOUGH
(1975 - Paramount) Kirk Douglas, Alexis Smith
One Sheet: $3 - $5

ONCE MORE, MY DARLING
(1949 - Universal) Robert Montgomery, Ann Blyth
One Sheet: $20 - $40

ONCE MORE WITH FEELING
(1960 - Columbia) Yul Brynner, Kay Kendall (her last film)
One Sheet: $10 - $20

ONCE TO EVERY BACHELOR
(1934 - Liberty) Marian Nixon, Neil Hamilton
One Sheet: $75 - $150

ONCE TO EVERY WOMAN
(1920 - Universal) Rudolph Valentino, Dorothy Phillips
One Sheet: $800 - $1,500

ONCE TO EVERY WOMAN
(1934 - Columbia) Ralph Bellamy, Fay Wray
One Sheet: $250 - $500

ONCE UPON A DREAM
(1949 - Eagle-Lion) Googie Withers, Griffith Jones
One Sheet: $15 - $30

ONCE UPON A FOREST
(1993 - 20th Century) -
One Sheet: $5 - $10   *Cartoon.*

ONCE UPON A GIRL
(1976 - -) Richmond Johnson, Carol Piacente
One Sheet: $5 - $12

ONCE UPON A HONEYMOON
(1942 - RKO) Ginger Rogers, Cary Grant
One Sheet: $250 - $500

ONCE UPON A HORSE
(1958 - Universal) Dan Rowan, Dick Martin, plus old-time western star cast
One Sheet: $30 - $50

ONCE UPON A TIME
(1944 - Columbia) Cary Grant, Janet Blair
One Sheet: $100 - $200

ONCE UPON A TIME
(1976 - G.G. Communications) -
One Sheet: $7 - $15   *Cartoon.*

ONCE UPON A TIME IN AMERICA
(1984 - -) Robert De Niro, James Woods
One Sheet: $5 - $10

ONCE UPON A TIME IN THE WEST
(1969 - Paramount) Henry Fonda, Charles Bronson, Dir: Sergio Leone
One Sheet: $100 - $200   *Spaghetti Western. Cowboy Movie Posters #s 328, 330.*

ONCE WERE WARRIORS
(1994 - -) Rena Owen, Temuera Morrison
One Sheet: $5 - $10

ONCE YOU KISS A STRANGER
(1969 - Warner Bros.) Paul Burke, Carol Lynley, Martha Hyer
One Sheet: $5 - $10

ONE A.M.
(1916 - Mutual) Charlie Chaplin
One Sheet: $7,500 - $12,000   *Beware re-issues.*

ONE AND ONLY, THE
(1978 - Paramount) Henry Winkler, Kim Darby
One Sheet: $5 - $10   *Sports (Wrestling). Sports Movie Posters #343.*

ONE AND ONLY GENUINE, ORIGINAL FAMILY BAND, THE
(1968 - Walt Disney) Walter Brennan, Buddy Ebsen, Goldie Hawn (debut)
One Sheet: $15 - $25

ONE ARABIAN NIGHT
(1920 - First National) Dir: Ernst Lubitsch, Pola Negri
One Sheet: $700 - $1,200

ONE BIG AFFAIR
(1952 - United Artists) Dennis O'Keefe, Evelyn Keyes
One Sheet: $10 - $20

ONE BODY TOO MANY
(1944 - Paramount) Jack Haley, Jean Parker, Bela Lugosi
One Sheet: $100 - $200

ONE CAB'S FAMILY
(1951 - MGM) Tex Avery
One Sheet: $200 - $400   *Cartoon.*

ONE CHANCE IN A HUNDRED
(1914 - General Film) Helen Gibson
One Sheet: $350 - $750

ONE CHANCE TO WIN
(1976 - -) -
One Sheet: $7 - $15   *Sports (Motocross racing).*

ONE CRAZY SUMMER
(1986 - -) John Cusack, Demi Moore
One Sheet: $5 - $10

ONE CROWDED NIGHT
(1940 - RKO) William Hoade, Billie Seward
One Sheet: $50 - $100

ONE DANGEROUS NIGHT
(1942 - Columbia) Warren William, Marguerite Chapman, Eric Blore
One Sheet: $50 - $100

ONE DARK NIGHT
(1939 - Million Dollar) Mantan Moreland, Betty Treadville
One Sheet: $125 - $250   *Black cast.*

ONE DAY IN THE LIFE OF IVAN DENISOVICH
(1971 - Cinerama) Tom Courtenay, Alfred Burke
One Sheet: $3 - $5

ONE DESIRE
(1955 - Universal) Anne Baxter, Rock Hudson
One Sheet: $40 - $75

ONE DOWN, TWO TO GO!
(1983 - -) Jim Brown, Fred Williamson, Jim Kelly
One Sheet: $7 - $15   *Black cast.*

ONE EMBARRASSING NIGHT
(1930 - MGM) Ralph Lynn, Tom Walls
One Sheet: $125 - $250

ONE EVERY MINUTE
(1918 - Paramount) -
One Sheet: $150 - $300

ONE EXCITING ADVENTURE
(1934 - Universal) Binnie Barnes, Neil Hamilton
One Sheet: $100 - $200

ONE EXCITING NIGHT
(1922 - United Artists) Carol Dempster, Henry Hull, Dir: D.W. Griffith
One Sheet: $3,500 - $5,000   *First haunted-house film. Graven Images, pg. 28.*

ONE EXCITING WEEK
(1946 - Republic) Al Pearce, Arline Harris
One Sheet: $30 - $50

ONE FINE DAY
(1996 - 20th Century Fox) Michelle Pfeiffer, George Clooney
One Sheet: $3 - $5

ONE FLEW OVER THE CUCKOO'S NEST
(1975 - United Artists) Jack Nicholson, Louise Fletcher
One Sheet: $100 - $200   *AA: Best Picture, Best Actor(Nicholson), Best Actress(Fletcher), Best Director(Forman). Price is for regular style. One Sheet (Academy Awards review style):$10-$20; Rare style (with cast under basketball net):$150-$300.*

One Sheet

ONE FOOT IN HEAVEN
(1941 - Warner Bros.) Fredric March, Martha Scott
One Sheet: $50 - $100

ONE FOOT IN HELL
(1960 - 20th Century Fox) Alan Ladd, Don Murray
One Sheet: $15 - $30

ONE FRIGHTENED NIGHT
(1935 - Mascot) Mary Carlisle, Wallace Ford
One Sheet: $150 - $300

ONE FROGGY EVENING
(1956 - Warner Bros.) Dir: Chuck Jones
One Sheet: $250 - $600   *Cartoon.*

ONE FROM THE HEART
(1982 - Columbia) Frederic Forrest, Teri Garr
One Sheet: $3 - $5

ONE GIRL'S CONFESSION
(1953 - Columbia) Hugo Haas, Cleo Moore
One Sheet: $40 - $75

ONE GOOD COP
(1991 - Hollywood) Michael Keaton
One Sheet: $5 - $10

ONE GOOD TURN
(1931 - MGM) Laurel & Hardy
One Sheet: $1,900 - $3,000

ONE GOOD TURN
(1955 - Two Cities) Norman Wisdom, Joan Rice
One Sheet: $15 - $25

ONE GUN GARY IN THE NICK OF TIME
(1938 - 20th Century Fox) Terry-toons
One Sheet: $100 - $200   *Cartoon. Full color stone litho. Stock poster with inset title.*

ONE HAM'S FAMILY
(1943 - MGM) Dir: Tex Avery
One Sheet: $300 - $700   *Cartoon. Cartoon Movie Posters #288.*

ONE HEAVENLY NIGHT
(1930 - United Artists) Evelyn Laye, John Boles
One Sheet: $100 - $200

ONE HOUR LATE
(1934 - Paramount) Helen Twelvetrees, Conrad Nagel
One Sheet: $100 - $200

ONE HOUR MARRIED
(1926 - Pathe) Mable Normand
One Sheet: $150 - $300

ONE HOUR TO LIVE
(1939 - Universal) Charles Bickford, Doris Nolan
One Sheet: $75 - $125

ONE HOUR WITH YOU
(1932 - Paramount Publix) Maurice Chevalier, Jeanette MacDonald

One Sheet: $700 - $1,200

ONE HUNDRED AND ONE DALMATIONS
(1961 - Buena Vista/Disney) Perdita & Pongo
One Sheet: $250 - $600   *Cartoon. The Disney Poster, pg. 87. Cartoon Movie Posters #386.*

ONE HUNDRED AND ONE DALMATIONS
(1965R - Disney) Perdita & Pongo
One Sheet: $50 - $100   *Re-release. Cartoon.*

ONE HUNDRED AND ONE DALMATIONS
(1969R - Disney) Perdita & Pongo
One Sheet: $30 - $50   *Re-release. Cartoon.*

ONE HUNDRED AND ONE DALMATIONS
(1972R - Disney) Perdita & Pongo
One Sheet: $15 - $35   *Re-release. Cartoon.*

ONE HUNDRED AND ONE DALMATIONS
(1979R - Disney) Perdita & Pongo
One Sheet: $15 - $30   *Re-release. Cartoon.*

ONE HUNDRED AND ONE DALMATIONS
(1985R - Disney) Perdita & Pongo
One Sheet: $10 - $20   *Re-release. Cartoon.*

ONE HUNDRED AND ONE DALMATIONS
(1990R - Buena Vista/Disney) Perdita & Pongo
One Sheet: $10 - $20   *Re-release. Cartoon.*

101 DALMATIONS
(1996 - Disney) Glenn Close, Jeff Daniels
One Sheet: $5 - $10

One Sheet

ONE HUNDRED MEN AND A GIRL
(1937 - Universal) Deanna Durbin, Leopold Stokowski
One Sheet: $150 - $300

100 RIFLES
(1969 - 20th Century Fox) Jim Brown, Raquel Welch, Burt Reynolds
One Sheet: $15 - $25   *Sports Movie Posters #359.*

ONE HYSTERICAL NIGHT
(1929 - Universal) Reginald Denny
One Sheet: $150 - $300

ONE IN A MILLION
(1934 - Invincible) Dorothy Wilson, Charles Starrett
One Sheet: $50 - $100

ONE IN A MILLION
(1937 - 20th Century Fox) Sonja Henie, Adolphe Nenjou
One Sheet: $200 - $400   *Sports (Ice Skating). Henie's film debut. One Sheet(Full Length style):$600-$1000. Sports Movie Posters #255.*

ONE IS A LONELY NUMBER
(1972 - MGM) Trish Van-Denere, Janet Leigh
One Sheet: $7 - $15

ONE IS GUILTY
(1934 - Columbia) Ralph Bellamy, Shirley Grey
One Sheet: $150 - $300

ONE LAST FLING
(1949 - Warner Bros.) Alexis Smith, Zachary Scott
One Sheet: $30 - $50

ONE LAW FOR THE WOMAN

(1924 - Vitagraph) Cullen Landis, Mildred Harris
One Sheet: $125 - $250

ONE LITTLE INDIAN
(1973 - Walt Disney) James Garner, Vera Miles
One Sheet: $7 - $15

ONE MAD KISS
(1930 - Fox) Don Jose Mojica, Mona Maris
One Sheet: $150 - $300

ONE MAGIC CHRISTMAS
(1985 - Disney) Mary Steenburgen, Gary Basaraba, Harry Dean Stanton
One Sheet: $3 - $5

ONE MAN IN A MILLION
(1921 - RC) George Beban, Helen Jerome Eddy
One Sheet: $200 - $400

ONE MAN JUSTICE
(1937 - Columbia) Charles Starrett, Barbara Weeks
One Sheet: $75 - $150

ONE MAN LAW
(1932 - Columbia) Buck Jones
One Sheet: $500 - $800   *Cowboy Movie Posters # 97.*

ONE MAN'S JOURNEY
(1933 - RKO) Lionel Barrymore, May Robson
One Sheet: $100 - $200

ONE MAN'S LAW
(1940 - Republic) Don "Red" Barry, Janet Waldo
One Sheet: $40 - $75

ONE MAN'S WAY
(1964 - United Artists) Don Murray, Diana Hyland
One Sheet: $5 - $10

ONE MILE FROM HEAVEN
(1937 - 20th Century Fox) Claire Trevor, Sally Blane
One Sheet: $100 - $200

ONE MILLION B.C.
(1940 - United Artists) Victor Mature, Carole Landis, Lon Chaney Jr.
One Sheet: $500 - $900   *Graven Images, pg. 120.*

$1,000,000 DUCK
(1971 - Buena Vista/Disney) Dean Jones, Sandy Duncan
One Sheet: $15 - $25

ONE MILLION YEARS B.C.
(1966 - 20th Century Fox) Raquel Welch, John Richardson
One Sheet: $50 - $100   *Ray Harryhausen effects.*

ONE MILLION YEARS B.C./SHE
(1966 - Hammer) Raquel Welch/Ursula Andress
One Sheet: $30 - $60   *Double feature poster. Graven Images, pg. 221.*

Half Sheet

ONE MINUTE TO PLAY
(1926 - FBO) Red Grange
One Sheet: $1,900 - $3,000   *Sports (Football).*

ONE MINUTE TO TWELVE
(1950 - Eagle-Lion) -
One Sheet: $15 - $25

ONE MINUTE TO ZERO
(1952 - RKO) Ann Blyth, Robert Mitchum

One Sheet: $40 - $75

ONE MORE RIVER
(1934 - Universal) Diane Wynyard, Colin Clive
One Sheet: $75 - $150

ONE MORE SPRING
(1935 - Fox) Janet Gaynor, Warner Baxter
One Sheet: $125 - $250

ONE MORE TIME
(1970 - United Artists) Sammy Davis, Jr., Peter Lawford, Esther Anderson
One Sheet: $5 - $10

ONE MORE TOMORROW
(1946 - Warner Bros.) Ann Sheridan, Dennis Morgan
One Sheet: $50 - $100

One Sheet

ONE MORE TRAIN TO ROB
(1971 - Universal) George Peppard, Diana Muldaur
One Sheet: $3 - $5

ONE MYSTERIOUS NIGHT
(1944 - Columbia) Chester Morris, Janis Carter
One Sheet: $50 - $100

ONE NEW YORK NIGHT
(1935 - MGM) Franchot Tone
One Sheet: $75 - $150

ONE NIGHT AT SUSIE'S
(1930 - First National) Billie Dove, Douglas Fairbank's, Jr. Helen Ware
One Sheet: $100 - $200

ONE NIGHT IN LISBON
(1941 - Paramount) Fred MacMurray, Madeleine Carroll
One Sheet: $50 - $100

ONE NIGHT IN PARIS
(1938 - Alliance) John Lodge
One Sheet: $50 - $100

ONE NIGHT IN THE TROPICS
(1940 - Universal) Robert Cummings, Bud Abbott, Lou Costello
One Sheet: $150 - $350

ONE NIGHT OF LOVE
(1934 - Columbia) Grace Moore, Tullio Carminati
One Sheet: $75 - $150

Mini Window Card (Trimmed)

ONE NIGHT STAND
(1995 - New Horizon) Ally Sheedy, A Martinez
One Sheet: $3 - $5

ONE NIGHT WITH YOU
(1948 - Universal) Nino Martini, Patricia Roc
One Sheet: $20 - $40

ONE OF OUR AIRCRAFT IS MISSING
(1942 - United Artists) Godfrey Tearle, Eric Portman
One Sheet: $40 - $75

ONE OF OUR DINOSAURS IS MISSING!
(1975 - Disney) Peter Ustinov, Helen Hays
One Sheet: $7 - $15

ONE OF THE FINEST
(1919 - Goldwyn) Tom Moore, Seena Owen
One Sheet: $150 - $350

ONE OF THE FINEST
(1936 - PRC) -
One Sheet: $40 - $75

ONE ON ONE
(1977 - Warner Bros.) Robby Benson, Annette O'Toole, Melanie Griffith
One Sheet: $5 - $10

ONE POTATO, TWO POTATO
(1964 - Cinema 5) Barbara Barrie, Bernie Hamilton
One Sheet: $50 - $100   *Duotone. Separate Cinema, pg. 154.*

ONE RAINY AFTERNOON
(1936 - United Artists) Frances Lederer, Ida Lupino
One Sheet: $75 - $150

ONE ROMANTIC NIGHT
(1930 - United Artists) Lillian Gish, Marie Dressler
One Sheet: $250 - $600

ONE ROMANTIC NIGHT
(1941R - Astor) Ilona Massey, Alan Curtis
One Sheet: $15 - $25   *Re-titled, reissue of NEW WINE.*

ONE RUN ELMER
(1935 - Fox) Buster Keaton, Lona Andre
One Sheet: $250 - $500

ONE SPY TOO MANY
(1966 - MGM) Robert Vaughn, David McCallum
One Sheet: $30 - $50   *TV tie-in (Man From U.N.C.L.E.)*

ONE STEP TO ETERNITY
(1955 - -) Danielle Dameux, Corinne Calvet
One Sheet: $15 - $25

ONE STEP TO HELL
(1969 - World) Ty Hardin, Pier Angeli, Rossano Brazzi
One Sheet: $10 - $20

ONE SUMMER LOVE
(1976 - AIP) Beau Bridges, Susan Sarandon
One Sheet: $7 - $15

ONE SUNDAY AFTERNOON
(1933 - Paramount) Gary Cooper, Fay Wray
One Sheet: $600 - $1,000

ONE SUNDAY AFTERNOON
(1949 - Warner Bros.) Dennis Morgan, Janis Paige
One Sheet: $15 - $25

ONE TERRIBLE DAY
(1922 - Pathecomedy) Our Gang
One Sheet: $1,300 - $2,000   *Classic image of black boy and white girl sitting on the back of a truck.*

ONE THAT GOT AWAY, THE
(1958 - Rank) Hardy Kruger, Colin Gordon
One Sheet: $10 - $20

ONE THIRD OF A NATION
(1939 - Paramount) Sylvia Sidney, Leif Erickson
One Sheet: $150 - $300

1001 ARABIAN NIGHTS
(1959 - Columbia) Mr. Magoo
One Sheet: $125 - $250   *Cartoon. Feature-length.*

1000 CONVICTS AND A WOMAN
(1971 - AIP) Alexandra Hay, Sandor Eles
One Sheet: $10 - $20

$1000 A MINUTE
(1935 - Republic) Roger Pryor, Leila Hyams
One Sheet: $50 - $100

$1000 A TOUCHDOWN

(1939 - Paramount) Joe E. Brown, Martha Raye
One Sheet: $50 - $100

1,000 PLANE RAID, THE
(1969 - United Artists) Christopher George, J.D. Cannon
One Sheet: $3 - $5

ONE THRILLING NIGHT
(1942 - Monogram) John Beal, Wanda McKay
One Sheet: $30 - $50

ONE TOO MANY
(1951 - Hallmark) Ruth Warrick, Richard Travis
One Sheet: $15 - $30

ONE TOUCH OF VENUS
(1948 - Universal) Robert Walker, Ava Gardner
One Sheet: $75 - $150

ONE, TWO, THREE
(1962 - United Artists) James Cagney, Horst Buchholz
One Sheet: $30 - $50 *Saul Bass art.*
Cagney's last film for 20 years.

One Sheet

1-2-3-GO!
(1941 - MGM) Our Gang
One Sheet: $500 - $850

ONE WAY OUT
(1957 - Rank) Jill Adams, Lyndon Brook
One Sheet: $5 - $10

ONE WAY PASSAGE
(1932 - Vitagraph) William Powell, Kay Francis
One Sheet: $1,300 - $2,000 *Beware*
Warner Bros. re-release.

ONE WAY PENDULUM
(1965 - Lopert) Eric Sykes, George Cole
One Sheet: $3 - $5

ONE WAY STREET
(1950 - Universal) James Mason, Marta Toren
One Sheet: $15 - $35

ONE WAY TICKET
(1935 - Columbia) Lloyd Nolan, Peggy Conklin
One Sheet: $125 - $250

ONE WAY TICKET TO HELL
(1955 - Eden) Barbara Marks, Bamlet L. Price Jr.
One Sheet: $50 - $100 *Drug*
exploitation.

ONE WAY TO LOVE
(1945 - Columbia) Willard Parker, Marguerite Chapman
One Sheet: $30 - $50

ONE WAY TRAIL, THE
(1931 - Columbia) Tim McCoy
One Sheet: $250 - $500

ONE WEEK
(1920 - Metro) Buster Keaton
One Sheet: $5,500 - $9,000

ONE WILD NIGHT
(1938 - 20th Century Fox) June Lang, Dick Baldwin, Sidney Toler
One Sheet: $50 - $100

ONE WILD RIDE
(1925 - Pathe) Our Gang
One Sheet: $800 - $1,500

ONE WOMAN'S STORY
(1948 - Universal) Ann Todd, Claude Rains
One Sheet: $15 - $35

ONE YEAR LATER

(1933 - Allied) Mary Brian, Russell Hampton
One Sheet: $75 - $125

ONE-EYED JACKS
(1961 - Paramount) Marlon Brando, Karl Malden
One Sheet: $100 - $225

ONE-EYED JACKS
(1966R - Paramount) Marlon Brando, Karl Malden
One Sheet: $150 - $350 *Re-release.*
One sheet design is superior to original release.

ONE-ROUND JONES
(194? - -) Eddie Green
One Sheet: $50 - $100

ONION FIELD, THE
(1979 - Avco Embassy) John Savage, James Woods, Ted Danson
One Sheet: $3 - $5

ONION PACIFIC
(1940 - Paramount) Popeye
One Sheet: $1,300 - $2,000 *Cartoon.*
Duotone. Cartoon Movie Posters #215.

ONIONHEAD
(1958 - Warner Bros.) Andy Griffith, Felicia Farr
One Sheet: $30 - $50

ONLY ANGELS HAVE WINGS
(1939 - Columbia) Cary Grant, Jean Arthur, Rita Hayworth
One Sheet: $1,600 - $2,500

Mini Window Card (Trimmed)

ONLY GAME IN TOWN, THE
(1969 - 20th Century Fox) Elizabeth Taylor, Warren Beatty
One Sheet: $15 - $25

ONLY SAPS WORK
(1930 - Paramount Publix) Richard Arlen, Mary Brian
One Sheet: $100 - $200

ONLY THE BRAVE
(1930 - Paramount Famous Lasky) Gary Cooper, Mary Brian
One Sheet: $600 - $1,000

ONLY THE FRENCH CAN
(1955 - Franco/London) Jean Gabin, Edith Piaf
One Sheet: $15 - $25 *French/Italian.*
AKA: FRENCH CAN CAN.

ONLY THE STRONG
(1993 - 20th Century Fox) Mark Dacascos, Stacy Travis
One Sheet: $3 - $5

ONLY THE VALIANT
(1951 - Warner Bros.) Gregory Peck, Barbara Payton
One Sheet: $15 - $35

ONLY THING, THE
(1925 - MGM) Joan Crawford
One Sheet: $1,600 - $2,500

ONLY TWO CAN PLAY
(1962 - Columbia) Peter Sellers, Mai Zetterling
One Sheet: $10 - $20

ONLY WHEN I LARF
(1969 - Paramount) Richard Attenborough, David Hemmings, Alexandra Stewart
One Sheet: $3 - $5

ONLY WHEN I LAUGH
(1981 - Columbia) Kristy McNichol, Marsha Mason

One Sheet: $3 - $5

ONLY WOMAN, THE
(1924 - First National) Norma Talmadge, Eugene O'Brien
One Sheet: $250 - $600

ONLY YESTERDAY
(1933 - Universal) Margaret Sullavan(film debut), John Boles
One Sheet: $250 - $600 *Price is for*
portrait style, other style is 1/2 the price listed.

ONLY YOU
(1994 - TriStar) Marisa Tomei, Robert Downey Jr.
One Sheet: $5 - $10

OPEN CITY
(1946 - Excelsa) Anna Magnani, Aldo Fabrizi
One Sheet: $50 - $100 *Italian. AKA:*
ROME, OPEN CITY.

OPEN RANGE
(1927 - Paramount) Betty Bronson, Lane Chandler
One Sheet: $150 - $300

OPEN SEASON
(1986 - -) -
One Sheet: $3 - $5

OPEN SEASON
(1995 - New Line) Robert Wuhl
One Sheet: $5 - $10

OPEN SECRET
(1948 - Pathe) John Ireland, Jane Randolph
One Sheet: $15 - $25

OPEN THE DOOR AND SEE ALL THE PEOPLE
(1964 - Pitkin) Maybelle Nash, Alec Wilder
One Sheet: $5 - $10

OPENED BY MISTAKE
(1940 - Paramount) Charles Ruggles, Janice Logan, Robert Paige
One Sheet: $30 - $50

OPENING NIGHT
(1977 - Faces) Gene Rowlands, John Cassavetes
One Sheet: $10 - $20

OPERA
(1987 - -) Dario Argento
One Sheet: $5 - $10 *Italian.*

OPERATION AMSTERDAM
(1960 - 20th Century Fox) Peter Finch, Eva Bartok
One Sheet: $5 - $10

OPERATION BIKINI
(1963 - AIP) Tab Hunter, Frankie Avalon
One Sheet: $15 - $30

OPERATION BOTTLENECK
(1961 - United Artists) Ron Foster, Miiko Taka
One Sheet: $4 - $8

OPERATION CAMEL
(1961 - AIP) Nora Hayden, Louis Reynard
One Sheet: $3 - $5

OPERATION C.I.A.
(1955 - Allied Artists) Burt Reynolds, John Hoyt
One Sheet: $15 - $30

OPERATION CONSPIRACY
(1957 - Republic) Phillip Friend, Mary Mackenzie
One Sheet: $5 - $10

OPERATION CROSSBOW
(1965 - MGM) George Peppard, Sophia Loren
One Sheet: $10 - $20

OPERATION DAMES
(1958 - AIP) Eve Meyer, Chuck Henderson
One Sheet: $20 - $40

OPERATION DAYBREAK
(1976 - Warner Bros.) Timothy Bottoms, Martin Shaw
One Sheet: $5 - $10

OPERATION DISASTER
(1950 - Universal-International) John Mills, Helen Cherry
One Sheet: $7 - $15

OPERATION DUMBO DROP
(1995 - Disney) Danny Glover, Ray Liotta,

Denis Leary
One Sheet: $3 - $6

One Sheet (Advance)

OPERATION EICHMANN
(1961 - Allied Artists) Werner Klemperer, Ruta Lee
One Sheet: $10 - $20

OPERATION HAYLIFT
(1950 - Lippert) Bill Williams, Ann Rutherford
One Sheet: $15 - $30

OPERATION KID BROTHER
(1967 - United Artists) Neil Connery, Daniela Bianchi
One Sheet: $10 - $20

OPERATION MAD BALL
(1957 - Columbia) Jack Lemmon, Ernie Kovacs, Mickey Rooney
One Sheet: $20 - $40

OPERATION MALAYA
(1955 - American Releasing) -
One Sheet: $10 - $20 *Documentary.*

OPERATION MANHUNT
(1954 - United Artists) Ira Jensen, Harry Townes
One Sheet: $5 - $10

OPERATION PACIFIC
(1951 - Warner Bros.) John Wayne, Patricia Neal
One Sheet: $75 - $150

OPERATION PETTICOAT
(1959 - Universal) Cary Grant, Tony Curtis
One Sheet: $30 - $50

OPERATION SECRET
(1952 - Warner Bros.) Cornel Wilde, Phyllis Thaxter
One Sheet: $10 - $20

OPERATION SNAFU
(1965 - AIP) Sean Connery, Stanley Holloway
One Sheet: $15 - $25

OPERATION SNATCH
(1962 - Continental) Terry-Thomas, George Sanders
One Sheet: $5 - $10

OPERATION X
(1951 - Columbia) Edward G. Robinson, Peggy Cummins
One Sheet: $20 - $40

OPERATOR 13
(1934 - MGM) Gary Cooper, Marion Davies, Jean Parker
One Sheet: $600 - $1,000

OPPORTUNITY KNOCKS
(1990 - -) Dana Carvey, Robert Loggia
One Sheet: $3 - $5

OPPOSITE SEX, THE
(1956 - MGM) June Allyson, Joan Collins, Ann Sheridan
One Sheet: $15 - $25

OPTIMISTS, THE
(1973 - Paramount) Peter Sellers
One Sheet: $7 - $15

ORANGES AND LEMONS
(1923 - Pathe) Stan Laurel
One Sheet: $100 - $200

ORCA-KILLER WHALE
(1977 - Paramount) Richard Harris, Bo Derek, Dir: Dino De Laurentis

One Sheet: $5 - $10

ORCHESTRA WIVES
(1942 - 20th Century Fox) George Montgomery, Ann Rutherford, Glenn Miller & Orch.
One Sheet: $200 - $400   *Big Band musical.*

One Sheet

ORCHIDS TO CHARLIE
(1941 - -) Elizabeth Arden
One Sheet: $30 - $50

ORCHIDS TO YOU
(1935 - Fox) John Boles, Spring Byington
One Sheet: $100 - $200

ORDERS ARE ORDERS
(1959 - Group 3) Margot Grahame, Peter Sellers
One Sheet: $10 - $20

ORDERS TO KILL
(1958 - Lynx) Eddie Albert, Lillian Gish
One Sheet: $10 - $20

ORDET
(1957 - Kingsley) Henrik Malberg, Emil Hass Christensen
One Sheet: $10 - $20   *Danish. AKA: THE WORD.*

ORDINARY PEOPLE
(1980 - Paramount) Donald Sutherland, Mary Tyler Moore, Timothy Hutton
One Sheet: $15 - $25   *Academy Award: Best Picture, Best Director (Redford), Best Supporting Actor (Hutton). Academy AwardMovie Posters #310, #314 & #315.*

One Sheet

OREGON PASSAGE
(1958 - Allied Artists) John Ericson, Lola Albright
One Sheet: $5 - $10

OREGON TRAIL
(1923 - Universal) Art Acord
One Sheet: $200 - $400   *Serial. Western. 18 Chapters.*

OREGON TRAIL, THE
(1936 - Republic) John Wayne
One Sheet: $5,500 - $9,000   *Cowboy Movie Posters #200.*

OREGON TRAIL
(1939 - Universal) Johnny Mack Brown
One Sheet: $125 - $250   *Serial. 15 Chapters.*

OREGON TRAIL
(1945 - Republic) Sunset Carson
One Sheet: $40 - $75

OREGON TRAIL, THE

(1959 - 20th Century Fox) Fred MacMurray, William Bishop
One Sheet: $15 - $25

OREGON TRAIL SCOUTS
(1947 - Republic) Allan "Rocky" Lane, Martha Wentworth
One Sheet: $50 - $100

ORGANIZATION, THE
(1971 - United Artists) Sidney Poitier, Barbara McNair
One Sheet: $7 - $15

ORGY OF THE DEAD
(1965 - Astra) Criswell, Pat Barringer
One Sheet: $15 - $30

ORGY OF THE LIVING DEAD
(1972 - -) -
One Sheet: $15 - $35

ORGY OF THE VAMPIRES
(1973 - IAC) Jack Taylor, Charo Soriano
One Sheet: $15 - $30   *AKA: The Vampires Night Orgy.*

ORIENT EXPRESS
(1934 - Fox) Heather Angel, Norman Foster
One Sheet: $125 - $250

ORIENTAL VANITIES
(1952 - Broadway Roadshow) -
One Sheet: $15 - $35   *Sexploitation.*

ORIGINAL GANGSTAS
(1996 - Orion) Fred Williamson, Jim Brown, Pam Grier
One Sheet: $7 - $15   *Black cast.*

ORLANDO
(1993 - Sony Classics) Tilda Swinton, Billy Zane
One Sheet: $3 - $5

ORPHAN OF THE SAGE
(1928 - FBO) Buzz Barton, Frank Rice
One Sheet: $300 - $700

ORPHANS
(1987 - Lorimar) Albert Finney, Matthew Modine
One Sheet: $3 - $5

ORPHANS OF THE NORTH
(1940 - Monogram) Bob Webster, Mary Joyce
One Sheet: $15 - $35

ORPHANS OF THE PECOS
(1937 - Victory) Tom Tyler
One Sheet: $100 - $200

ORPHANS OF THE STORM
(1922 - United Artists) Lillian Gish, Dorothy Gish, Dir: D.W. Griffith
One Sheet: $5,000 - $7,500

ORPHANS OF THE STREET
(1938 - Republic) Robert Livingston, June Storey
One Sheet: $50 - $100

ORPHEE
(1950 - -) Jean Marais
One Sheet: $200 - $400   *French. Price is for French (47x63). See Graven Images, pg. 198.*

ORPHEUS
(1950 - -) See ORPHEE   *French.*

OSCAR, THE
(1966 - Embassy) Stephen Boyd, Elke Sommer
One Sheet: $10 - $20

OSCAR
(1991 - Buena Vista) Sly Stallone, Vincent Spano, Tim Curry
One Sheet: $5 - $10

OSS 117 - MISSION FOR A KILLER
(1966 - Embassy) Frederick Stafford, Mylene Demongeot
One Sheet: $7 - $15

O.S.S. 117 IS NOT DEAD
(1959 - Republic) Magali Noel, Ivan Desney
One Sheet: $15 - $30

OSSESSIONE
(1959 - Roma) Clara Calamai, Massimo Girotti
One Sheet: $10 - $20   *Italy.*

OSTERMAN WEEKEND, THE
(1983 - 20th Century Fox) Rutger Hauer, John Hurt, Burt Lancaster

OSWALD THE LUCKY RABBIT STOCK
(1934 - Universal) A Walter Lantz Cartoon Comedy
One Sheet: $600 - $1,000   *Cartoon. Large image of Oswald waving with smaller characters surrounding him on both sides. Red background.*

OTELLO
(1986 - -) Placido Domingo, Katia Ricciarelli
One Sheet: $7 - $15

OTHELLO
(1955 - United Artists) Orson Welles, Suzanne Cloutier
One Sheet: $125 - $250

OTHELLO
(1966 - Warner Bros.) Laurence Olivier, Maggie Smith, Frank Finlay
One Sheet: $15 - $35

OTHELLO
(1982 - -) William Marshall, Ron Moody
One Sheet: $7 - $15

OTHELLO
(1995 - Columbia) Laurence Fishburne, Irene Jacob, Kenneth Branagh
One Sheet: $10 - $20

OTHER, THE
(1972 - 20th Century Fox) Uta Hagen, Christopher and Martin Udvarnoky
One Sheet: $5 - $10

OTHER HALF, THE
(1919 - Exhibitors Mutual) Florence Vidor, ZaSu Pitts, Charles Meredith
One Sheet: $500 - $800

OTHER LOVE, THE
(1947 - Enterprise Studios) Barbara Stanwyck, David Niven
One Sheet: $40 - $75

OTHER MAN, THE
(1916 - Triangle/Keystone) Roscoe Arbuckle
One Sheet: $1,300 - $2,000

OTHER MEN'S WOMEN
(1931 - Warner Bros.) Grant Withers, James Cagney, Mary Astor
One Sheet: $1,300 - $2,000   *Lobby Card(with Cagney):$500-1000.*

OTHER SIDE OF MIDNIGHT, THE
(1977 - Fox) Marie-France Pisier, John Beck, Susan Sarandon
One Sheet: $7 - $15

OTHER SIDE OF THE MOUNTAIN, THE
(1975 - Universal) Marilyn Hassett, Beau Bridges
One Sheet: $5 - $10

OTHER SIDE OF THE MOUNTAIN - PART 2, THE
(1978 - Universal) Marilyn Hassett, Timothy Bottoms
One Sheet: $3 - $5

OTHER TOMORROW, THE
(1930 - First National) Billie Dove, Kenneth Thomson
One Sheet: $75 - $150

OTHER WOMAN, THE
(1954 - 20th Century Fox) Hugo Haas, Cleo Moore
One Sheet: $15 - $30

OTLEY
(1969 - Columbia) Tom Courtenay, Romy Schneider, Alan Badel
One Sheet: $3 - $5

OUR AMERICAN BOYS IN THE EUROPEAN WAR
(1916 - Triangle) Victor Tardieu
One Sheet: $250 - $600

OUR BETTERS
(1933 - RKO) Constance Bennett, Gilbert Roland
One Sheet: $150 - $300

OUR BLUSHING BRIDES
(1930 - MGM) Joan Crawford, Anita Page

One Sheet: $700 - $1,200   *Price is for full color stone litho one sheet. One Sheet(rotogravure style):$400-$800.*

One Sheet (Style B)

OUR DAILY BREAD
(1934 - United Artists) Karen Morley, Tom Keene
One Sheet: $250 - $600

OUR DANCING DAUGHTERS
(1928 - MGM) Joan Crawford, Johnny Mack Brown
One Sheet: $1,900 - $3,000

OUR GANG
(1922 - Pathe) Our Gang
One Sheet: $1,600 - $2,500

OUR GANG FOLLIES OF 1938
(1938 - MGM) Spanky McFarland, Alfalfa, Buckwheat
One Sheet: $250 - $600

OUR HEARTS WERE GROWING UP
(1946 - Paramount) Gail Russell, Diana Lynn
One Sheet: $50 - $100

OUR HEARTS WERE YOUNG AND GAY
(1944 - Paramount) Gail Russell, Diana Lynn
One Sheet: $40 - $75

OUR HOSPITALITY
(1923 - Metro) Buster Keaton
One Sheet: $7,500 - $12,000

Title Card

OUR LEADING CITIZEN
(1923 - Paramount) Thomas Meighan, Lois Wilson
One Sheet: $250 - $500

OUR LEADING CITIZEN
(1939 - Paramount) Bob Burns, Gene Lockhart, Susan Hayward
One Sheet: $75 - $150

OUR LITTLE GIRL
(1935 - Fox) Shirley Temple, Rosemary Ames, Joel McCrea
One Sheet: $1,600 - $2,500   *Price is for Style A One Sheet. One Sheet(Style B):$400-$800.*

OUR MAN FLINT
(1966 - 20th Century Fox) James Coburn, Lee J. Cobb
One Sheet: $30 - $50   *Bob Peak art.*

OUR MAN IN HAVANA
(1960 - Columbia) Alec Guinness, Maureen O'Hara
One Sheet: $10 - $20

OUR MISS BROOKS
(1956 - Warner Bros.) Eve Arden, Gale Gordon

One Sheet: $20 - $40

OUR MODERN MAIDENS
(1929 - MGM) Joan Crawford
One Sheet: $1,600 - $2,500

OUR MOTHER'S HOUSE
(1967 - MGM) Dirk Bogarde, Margaret Brooks
One Sheet: $3 - $5

OUR NEIGHBORS, THE CARTERS
(1939 - Paramount) Faye Bainter, Frank Craven
One Sheet: $30 - $60

OUR NEW POSSESSIONS
(1898C - Sears Roebuck) -
One Sheet: $150 - $300   *Special Moving Picture exhibition poster.*

OUR RELATIONS
(1936 - MGM) Stan Laurel, Oliver Hardy
One Sheet: $2,200 - $3,500   *Hirschfeld art.*

OUR RUSSIAN FRONT
(1942 - -) Narrated by Walter Huston
One Sheet: $30 - $50   *Documentary. Russian propaganda film.*

OUR TEDDY
(1918 - First National) Teddy Roosevelt
One Sheet: $800 - $1,500

OUR TOWN
(1940 - United Artists) William Holden, Martha Scott
One Sheet: $75 - $150

OUR VERY OWN
(1949 - RKO) Ann Blyth, Farley Granger
One Sheet: $15 - $35

OUR VINES HAVE TENDER GRAPES
(1945 - MGM) Edward G. Robinson, Margaret O'Brien
One Sheet: $40 - $75

OUR WIFE
(1931 - MGM) Laurel & Hardy
One Sheet: $2,200 - $3,500

OUR WIFE
(1941 - Columbia) Melvyn Douglas, Ruth Hussey
One Sheet: $50 - $100

OUT ALL NIGHT
(1933 - Universal) ZaSu Pitts, Slim Summerville
One Sheet: $75 - $150

OUT CALIFORNIA WAY
(1946 - Republic) Monte Hale, Adrian Booth
One Sheet: $30 - $60

OUT COLD
(1989 - Hemdale) Terri Garr, Randy Quaid
One Sheet: $3 - $5

OUT OF AFRICA
(1985 - Universal) Meryl Streep, Robert Redford
One Sheet: $15 - $30   *Academy Award: Best Picture, Best Director(Pollack). Academy Award Movie Posters #340-#342.*

OUT OF BOUNDS
(1986 - -) Anthony Michael Hall, Jenny Wright
One Sheet: $3 - $5

OUT OF IT
(1969 - United Artists) Barry Gordon, Jon Voight, Lada Edmund, Jr.
One Sheet: $5 - $10

OUT OF LUCK
(1919 - Paramount) Rudolph Valentino, Dorothy Gish, Ralph Graves
One Sheet: $1,300 - $2,000

OUT OF LUCK
(1923 - Universal) Hoot Gibson, Laura La Plante
One Sheet: $250 - $600

OUT OF SIGHT
(1966 - Universal) Gary Lewis and the Playboys, Freddie and the Dreamers
One Sheet: $30 - $50   *Rock 'n' Roll.*

OUT OF SINGAPORE
(1932 - Goldsmith) Noah Beery
One Sheet: $75 - $150

OUT OF THE BLUE
(1947 - Pathe) George Brent, Virginia Mayo
One Sheet: $15 - $35

OUT OF THE BLUE
(1982 - -) Dennis Hopper, Linda Manz
One Sheet: $3 - $5

OUT OF THE CLOUDS
(1957 - Rank) Anthony Steel, Bernard Lee
One Sheet: $5 - $10

OUT OF THE DARKNESS
(1979 - -) Donald Pleasence
One Sheet: $5 - $10

OUT OF THE DEPTHS
(1945 - Columbia) Jim Bannon, Robert Williams
One Sheet: $15 - $35

OUT OF THE FOG
(1919 - Metro) Nazimova
One Sheet: $500 - $800

OUT OF THE FOG
(1941 - Warner Bros.) Ida Lupino, John Garfield
One Sheet: $75 - $150

OUT OF THE NIGHT
(1945 - PRC) Jimmy Lydon, Sally Eilers
One Sheet: $30 - $50

OUT OF THE PAST
(1947 - RKO) Robert Mitchum, Jane Greer, Kirk Douglas
One Sheet: $1,600 - $2,500

One Sheet

OUT OF THE PAST
(1953R - RKO) Robert Mitchum, Jane Greer, Kirk Douglas
One Sheet: $200 - $400   *Re-release.*

OUT OF THE STORM
(1948 - Republic) James Lydon, Lois Collier
One Sheet: $15 - $25

OUT OF THE WEST
(1926 - FBO) Tom Tyler
One Sheet: $200 - $400   *Cowboy Movie Posters #64.*

OUT OF THIS WORLD
(1945 - Paramount) Eddie Bracken, Veronica Lake
One Sheet: $75 - $150

OUT WEST
(1918 - Paramount) Roscoe "Fatty" Arbuckle
One Sheet: $3,500 - $5,000

OUT WEST
(1947 - Columbia) The Three Stooges (Shemp)
One Sheet: $600 - $1,000   *Comedy short. Duotone.*

OUT WEST WITH THE HARDYS
(1938 - MGM) Lewis Stone, Mickey Rooney
One Sheet: $75 - $150

OUT WEST WITH THE PEPPERS
(1940 - Columbia) Edith Fellows, Tommy Bond
One Sheet: $30 - $50

OUTBACK
(1971 - United Artists) Donald Pleasence, Gary Bond
One Sheet: $3 - $5

OUTBREAK
(1995 - Warner Bros.) Dustin Hoffman, Rene Russo, Morgan Freeman
One Sheet: $5 - $10

OUTCAST
(1937 - Paramount) Warren William, Karen Morley
One Sheet: $50 - $100

OUTCAST
(1954 - Republic) John Derek, Joan Davis
One Sheet: $15 - $25

OUTCAST LADY
(1934 - MGM) Constance Bennett, Herbert Marshall
One Sheet: $75 - $150

OUTCAST OF BLACK MESA
(1950 - Columbia) Charles Starrett, Smiley Burnette
One Sheet: $15 - $35

OUTCAST OF THE ISLANDS
(1951 - British Lion) Trevor Howard, Ralph Richardson
One Sheet: $10 - $20

OUTCAST SOULS
(1927 - Sterling) Priscilla Bonner, Charles Delaney
One Sheet: $100 - $200

OUTCASTS OF POKER FLAT, THE
(1919 - Universal) Harry Carey, Cullen Landis
One Sheet: $200 - $400

OUTCASTS OF POKER FLAT, THE
(1937 - RKO) Preston Foster, Jean Muir, Van Heflin
One Sheet: $50 - $100

OUTCASTS OF POKER FLAT, THE
(1952 - 20th Century Fox) Dale Robertson, Anne Baxter
One Sheet: $15 - $25

OUTCASTS OF THE CITY
(1958 - Republic) Osa Massen, Robert Hutton
One Sheet: $20 - $40

OUTCASTS OF THE TRAIL
(1949 - Republic) Monte Hale, Jeff O'Donnell
One Sheet: $15 - $35

OUTCRY, THE
(1962 - Astor) Steve Cochran, Alida Valli
One Sheet: $10 - $20   *Italian. Original Title: IL GRIDO.*

OUTER GATE, THE
(1937 - Monogram) Ralph Morgan, Kay Linaker
One Sheet: $40 - $75

OUTER SPACE CONNECTION, THE
(1975 - Sun) Narrator: Rod Sterling
One Sheet: $15 - $30

OUTER SPACE JITTERS
(1957 - Columbia) The Three Stooges (Joe Besser)
One Sheet: $75 - $125   *Comedy short. Duotone.*

OUTFIT, THE
(1973 - MGM) Robert Duvall, Karen Black
One Sheet: $3 - $5

OUT-FOXED
(1948 - MGM) Droopy, Tex Avery
One Sheet: $600 - $1,000   *Cartoon. Full color stone litho. Cartoon Movie Posters #309.*

OUTLAND
(1981 - Warner Bros.) Sean Connery, Peter Boyle
One Sheet: $10 - $20

OUTLAW, THE
(1941 - 20th Century Fox) Walter Huston, Jack Beutel, Jane Russell
One Sheet: $5,000 - $8,000   *Cowboy Movie Posters #264. Original release banned after only a few weeks. Posters and Lobby Cards are dated.*

OUTLAW, THE
(1946 - RKO) Jane Russell, Jack Beutel, Dir: Howard Hughes
One Sheet: $500 - $900   *First national release.*

OUTLAW, THE
(1950R - RKO) Jane Russell, Jack Beutel, Dir: Howard Hughes
One Sheet: $75 - $150   *Re-release.*

OUTLAW BLUES

(1977 - Warner Bros.) Peter Fonda, Susan St. James
One Sheet: $5 - $10

OUTLAW BRAND
(1948 - Monogram) Jimmy Wakely, Cannonball Taylor
One Sheet: $30 - $50

OUTLAW COUNTRY
(1948 - PRC) Lash LaRue, Fuzzy St. John
One Sheet: $30 - $60

OUTLAW DEPUTY, THE
(1935 - Puritan) Tim McCoy
One Sheet: $250 - $500

OUTLAW EXPRESS
(1938 - Universal) Johnny Mack Brown, Jane Adams, Bob Baker
One Sheet: $75 - $150

OUTLAW GIRL
(1955 - -) -
One Sheet: $15 - $25

OUTLAW GOLD
(1950 - Monogram) Johnny Mack Brown, Jane Adams
One Sheet: $20 - $40

OUTLAW JOSEY WALES
(1976 - Warner Bros.) Clint Eastwood
One Sheet: $100 - $200   *Cowboy Movie Posters #s 347, 349.*

One Sheet

OUTLAW JUSTICE
(1933 - Majestic) Jack Hoxie, Dorothy Gulliver, Kermit Maynard
One Sheet: $150 - $300

OUTLAW OF THE PLAINS
(1946 - PRC) Buster Crabbe, Al St. John
One Sheet: $15 - $35

OUTLAW RIDERS
(1971 - Ace) Darlene Duralia, Bambi Allen
One Sheet: $15 - $35   *Biker gang.*

OUTLAW ROUNDUP
(1944 - PRC) Dave O'Brien, Jim Newill
One Sheet: $15 - $35

OUTLAW RULE
(1935 - Kent) Reb Russell, Betty Mack
One Sheet: $75 - $125

OUTLAW SAFARI
(1956 - -) -
One Sheet: $5 - $10

OUTLAW STALLION, THE
(1954 - Columbia) Phil Carey, Dorothy Patrick
One Sheet: $10 - $20

OUTLAW TAMER, THE
(1935 - Kinematrade) Lane Chandler
One Sheet: $75 - $125

OUTLAW TERRITORY
(1953 - -) Joanne Dru, John Ireland
One Sheet: $15 - $30   *Originally shot in 3-D. AKA: HANNAH LEE.*

OUTLAW TRAIL
(1944 - Monogram) Bob Steele, Hoot Gibson
One Sheet: $50 - $100

OUTLAW TREASURE
(1955 - American Releasing) John Forbes, Frank "Red" Carpenter
One Sheet: $5 - $10

OUTLAW WOMEN

(1951 - Lippert) Marie Windsor, Richard Rober
One Sheet: $15 - $30

OUTLAW'S DAUGHTER, THE
(1954 - 20th Century Fox) Bill Williams, Kelly Ryan
One Sheet: $15 - $25

OUTLAW'S HIGHWAY
(1935 - -) John King, Tom London
One Sheet: $100 - $200   *AKA: FIGHTING FURY.*

OUTLAW'S PARADISE
(1939 - Victory) Tim McCoy, Benny Corbett
One Sheet: $100 - $200

OUTLAW'S SON
(1957 - United Artists) Dane Clark, Lori Nelson
One Sheet: $7 - $15

OUTLAWED
(1929 - FBO) Tom Mix, Sally Blane
One Sheet: $800 - $1,500

OUTLAWED GUNS
(1935 - Universal) Buck Jones
One Sheet: $250 - $500

OUTLAWS IS COMING, THE
(1965 - Columbia) The Three Stooges, Adam West
One Sheet: $50 - $100   *Teams final film.*

OUTLAWS OF BOULDER PASS
(1943 - PRC) George Houston, Al St. John
One Sheet: $15 - $35

OUTLAWS OF CHEROKEE TRAIL
(1941 - Republic) Three Mesquiteers
One Sheet: $40 - $75

OUTLAWS OF PINE RIDGE
(1942 - Republic) Don Barry, Lynn Merrick
One Sheet: $20 - $40

OUTLAWS OF RED RIVER
(1927 - Fox) Tom Mix, Marjorie Daw
One Sheet: $250 - $600

OUTLAWS OF SANTA FE
(1944 - Republic) Don Barry, Wally Vernon
One Sheet: $30 - $50

OUTLAWS OF SONORA
(1938 - Republic) Bob Livingston, Ray Corrigan
One Sheet: $40 - $75

OUTLAWS OF STAMPEDE PASS
(1943 - Monogram) Johnny Mack Brown
One Sheet: $30 - $60

OUTLAWS OF TEXAS
(1950 - Monogram) Whip Wilson, Andy Clyde
One Sheet: $15 - $35

OUTLAWS OF THE DESERT
(1941 - Paramount) Bill Boyd, Andy Clyde
One Sheet: $75 - $150

OUTLAWS OF THE ORIENT
(1937 - Columbia) Jack Holt, Mae Clarke
One Sheet: $75 - $125

OUTLAWS OF THE PANHANDLE
(1941 - Columbia) Charles Starrett, Frances Robinson
One Sheet: $30 - $50

OUTLAWS OF THE PLAINS
(1946 - PRC) -
One Sheet: $15 - $35

OUTLAWS OF THE PRAIRIE
(1937 - Columbia) Charles Starrett, Donald Grayson
One Sheet: $75 - $125

OUTLAWS OF THE RIO GRANDE
(1941 - PRC) Tim McCoy
One Sheet: $50 - $100

OUTLAWS OF THE ROCKIES
(1945 - Columbia) Charles Starrett, Tex Harding
One Sheet: $30 - $50

OUT-OF-TOWNERS, THE
(1970 - Paramount) Sandy Dennis, Jack Lemmon
One Sheet: $3 - $5

OUTPOST IN MALAYA

(1952 - United Artists) Claudette Colbert, Jack Hawkins
One Sheet: $20 - $40

OUTPOST IN MOROCCO
(1949 - United Artists) George Raft, Marie Windsor
One Sheet: $15 - $30

OUTPOST OF THE MOUNTIES
(1939 - Columbia) Charles Starrett, Iris Meredith
One Sheet: $75 - $150

OUTRAGE
(1950 - RKO) Mala Powers, Tod Andrews, Dir: Ida Lupino
One Sheet: $75 - $125

OUTRAGE, THE
(1964 - MGM) Paul Newman, Laurence Harvey
One Sheet: $15 - $25

OUTRAGEOUS FORTUNE
(1987 - Touchstone) Bette Midler, Shelley Long
One Sheet: $5 - $10

OUTRIDERS, THE
(1949 - MGM) Joel McCrea, Arlene Dahl
One Sheet: $30 - $50

OUTSIDE CHANCE OF MAXIMILIAN GLICK, THE
(1988 - -) Noam Zylberman, Fairuza Balk
One Sheet: $2 - $3

OUTSIDE IN
(1972 - Robbins International) Darrell Larson, Heather Menzies
One Sheet: $3 - $5

OUTSIDE MAN, THE
(1973 - United Artists) Roy Scheider, Ann-Margret
One Sheet: $7 - $15

OUTSIDE OF PARADISE
(1938 - Republic) Phil Regan, Penny Singleton
One Sheet: $50 - $100

OUTSIDE THE LAW
(1921 - Universal) Priscilla Dean, Lon Chaney
One Sheet: $3,500 - $5,000   *Price is for style showing Chaney. One Sheet(no Chaney):$1000-$2000.*

OUTSIDE THE LAW
(1930 - Universal) Edward G. Robinson, Mary Nolan
One Sheet: $250 - $500

OUTSIDE THE LAW
(1956 - Universal) Ray Danton, Leigh Snowden
One Sheet: $10 - $20

OUTSIDE THE WALL
(1950 - Universal) Richard Basehart, Marilyn Maxwell
One Sheet: $7 - $15

OUTSIDE THESE WALLS
(1939 - Columbia) Dolores Costello, Michael Whalen
One Sheet: $40 - $75

OUTSIDER, THE
(1933 - MGM) Joan Barry, Harold Huth
One Sheet: $75 - $150

OUTSIDER, THE
(1962 - Universal) Tony Curtis, James Franciscus
One Sheet: $15 - $30

OUTSIDERS, THE
(1983 - Warner Bros.) Tom Cruise, Patrick Swayze, Dir: F. Ford Coppola
One Sheet: $15 - $30   *Advance:$20-$30; International:$30-$40.*

OUTWARD BOUND
(1930 - Warner Bros.) Leslie Howard, Douglas Fairbanks, Jr.
One Sheet: $250 - $600

OVER 21
(1945 - Columbia) Irene Dunne, Alexander Knox
One Sheet: $30 - $50

OVER MY DEAD BODY
(1942 - 20th Century Fox) Milton Berle, Mary Beth Hughes
One Sheet: $50 - $100

OVER NIGHT
(1934 - London) Robert Donat, Pearl Argyle
One Sheet: $50 - $100

OVER THE BORDER
(1950 - Monogram) Johnny Mack Brown, Myron Healey
One Sheet: $15 - $35

OVER THE EDGE
(1979 - Warner Bros.) Michael Kramer, Matt Dillon (Debut), Vincent Spano
One Sheet: $10 - $20

OVER THE GOAL
(1937 - Warner Bros.) William Hopper, June Travis
One Sheet: $75 - $150

OVER THE HILL
(1931 - Fox) James Dunn, Sally Eilers
One Sheet: $125 - $250

OVER THE MOON
(1937 - United Artists) Rex Harrison, Merle Oberon
One Sheet: $75 - $150

OVER THE SANTA FE TRAIL
(1947 - Columbia) Ken Curtis, Jennifer Holt
One Sheet: $15 - $35

OVER THE TOP
(1918 - Vitagraph) Arthur Guy Empey, Lois Meredith
One Sheet: $200 - $400

OVER THE TOP
(1987 - Cannon) Sylvester Stallone, Robert Loggia
One Sheet: $15 - $25   *Sports (Arm Wrestling). Sports Movie Posters #5.*

OVER THE WALL
(1937 - Warner Bros.) Dick Foran, June Travis
One Sheet: $75 - $150

OVERBOARD
(1987 - -) Goldie Hawn, Kurt Russell
One Sheet: $5 - $10

OVERCOAT, THE
(1965 - Lenfilm/Cinemaster) Roland Bykov, Yuriy Tolubeyev
One Sheet: $30 - $50   *Russian.*

OVER-EXPOSED
(1956 - Columbia) Cleo Moore, Richard Crenna
One Sheet: $15 - $35

OVERLAND BOUND
(1929 - -) Wally Wales, Jack Perrin
One Sheet: $150 - $300

OVERLAND EXPRESS
(1923 - Capital) Helen Gibson
One Sheet: $250 - $500

OVERLAND EXPRESS
(1938 - Columbia) Buck Jones, Marjorie Reynolds
One Sheet: $250 - $600

OVERLAND MAIL
(1939 - Monogram) Jack Randall
One Sheet: $40 - $75

OVERLAND MAIL
(1942 - Universal) Lon Chaney, Jr., Helen Parrish
One Sheet: $50 - $100   *Serial. Western. 15 Chapters.*

OVERLAND MAIL ROBBERY
(1943 - Republic) Bill Elliott, Anne Jeffreys
One Sheet: $30 - $50

OVERLAND PACIFIC
(1954 - United Artists) Jock Mahoney, Peggie Castle
One Sheet: $15 - $35

OVERLAND RIDERS
(1948 - PRC) Buster Crabbe
One Sheet: $20 - $40

OVERLAND STAGE, THE
(1927 - First National) Ken Maynard, Kathleen Collins
One Sheet: $200 - $400

OVERLAND STAGE RAIDERS
(1938 - Republic) John Wayne, Three Mesquiteers, Louise Brooks
One Sheet: $300 - $700

OVERLAND STAGE RAIDERS
(1953R - Republic) John Wayne, Three Mesquiteers, Louise Brooks
One Sheet: $100 - $200   *Re-release. Full color.*

OVERLAND STAGECOACH
(1943 - PRC) Robert Livingston
One Sheet: $20 - $40

OVERLAND TELEGRAPH
(1951 - RKO) Tim Holt, Richard Martin
One Sheet: $15 - $30

OVERLAND TO DEADWOOD
(1942 - Columbia) Charles Starrett, Russell Hayden
One Sheet: $30 - $50

OVERLAND TO DEADWOOD
(1955R - Columbia) Charles Starrett, Russell Hayden
One Sheet: $7 - $15   *Re-release.*

OVERLAND TRAIL
(1948 - Monogram) Johnny Mack Brown, Virginia Belmont
One Sheet: $15 - $35

OVERLAND WITH KIT CARSON
(1939 - Columbia) Bill Elliott, Iris Meredith
One Sheet: $100 - $200   *Serial. 15 Chapters.*

OVERNIGHT HAUL
(1956 - -) -
One Sheet: $15 - $30

OVERTURE TO GLORY
(1940 - G & L) Moishe Oysher, Florence Weiss
One Sheet: $30 - $50

OWL AND THE PUSSYCAT, THE
(1938 - 20th Century Fox) Terry-toons
One Sheet: $100 - $200   *Cartoon. Full color stone litho. Stock poster with inset title.*

OWL AND THE PUSSYCAT, THE
(1970 - Columbia) Barbra Streisand, George Segal
One Sheet: $15 - $30

OX-BOW INCIDENT, THE
(1942 - 20th Century Fox) Henry Fonda, Dana Andrews
One Sheet: $250 - $500   *Cowboy Movie Posters #271.*

One Sheet

OXFORD BLUES
(1984 - MGM) Rob Lowe, Ally Sheedy
One Sheet: $3 - $5

OYSTER DREDGER, THE
(1915 - Universal) J. Warren Kerrigan
One Sheet: $700 - $1,200   *Produced by Lon Chaney.*

P. J.
(1968 - Universal) George Peppard, Gayle Hunicutt
One Sheet: $3 - $5

P. K. KID
(1982 - Castle Hill) Paul LeMat, Molly Ringwald
One Sheet: $15 - $25   *Sports (Arm wrestling). Sports Movie Posters #4.*

P. O. BOX 303
(1959 - Allied Artists) Van Johnson, Vera Miles
One Sheet: $10 - $20

P. T. RAIDERS
(1955 - Continental) Richard Attenborough, George Baker
One Sheet: $5 - $10

PACE THAT KILLS, THE
(1936 - Willis Kent) -
One Sheet: $75 - $125 *Exploitation.*

PACE THAT THRILLS, THE
(1952 - RKO) Bill Williams, Carla Balenda
One Sheet: $15 - $30 *Sports*
(Motorcycle racing).

PACIFIC ADVENTURE
(1947 - Columbia) Ron Randell, Muriel Steinbeck
One Sheet: $15 - $35

PACIFIC BLACKOUT
(1941 - Paramount) Robert Preston, Eva Gabor
One Sheet: $30 - $50

PACIFIC DESTINY
(1956 - British Lion) Demholm Elliott, Susan Stephen
One Sheet: $10 - $20

PACIFIC HEIGHTS
(1990 - 20th Century Fox) Michael Keaton, Matthew Modine, Melanie Griffith
One Sheet: $5 - $10

PACIFIC LINER
(1939 - RKO) Victor McLaglen, Chester Morris
One Sheet: $75 - $150

PACIFIC RENDEZVOUS
(1942 - MGM) Lee Bowman, Jean Rogers
One Sheet: $30 - $50

PACIFIC VIBRATIONS
(1971 - AIP) Jock Sutherland, Corky Carroll
One Sheet: $20 - $40 *Sports*
documentary (Surfing). Sports Movie Posters #322.

PACK, THE
(1977 - Warner Bros.) Joe Don Baker, Hope Alexander-Willis
One Sheet: $5 - $10

PACK TRAIN
(1953 - Columbia) Gene Autry, Smiley Burnette
One Sheet: $40 - $75

PACK UP YOUR TROUBLES
(1932 - 20th Century Fox) Stan Laurel, Oliver Hardy, Grady Sutton
One Sheet: $2,500 - $4,000

PACK UP YOUR TROUBLES
(1939 - 20th Century Fox) The Ritz Brothers, Jane Withers
One Sheet: $75 - $150

PACK UP YOUR TROUBLES/PARDON US
(1940S - Hal Roach) Laurel & Hardy
One Sheet: $100 - $200 *Double*
feature Indian release poster.

PACKAGE, THE
(1989 - -) Gene Hackman, Joanna Cassidy
One Sheet: $3 - $5

PAD (AND HOW TO USE IT), THE
(1966 - Universal) Brian Bedford, James Farentino, Julie Sommars
One Sheet: $5 - $10

PADDY
(1933 - Fox) Janet Gaynor, Warner Baxter
One Sheet: $200 - $400

PADDY
(1970 - Allied Artists) Milo O'Shea, Des Cave, Dearbhla Molloy
One Sheet: $3 - $5

PADDY O'DAY
(1936 - 20th Century Fox) Jane Withers, Rita Hayworth
One Sheet: $150 - $350

PADDY, THE NEXT BEST THING
(1933 - Fox) Janet Gaynor, Warner Baxter
One Sheet: $100 - $200

PAGAN HELLCAT
(1963 - Victoria) Tumata Teuiau
One Sheet: $30 - $50

PAGAN LADY
(1931 - Columbia) Evelyn Brent, Conrad Nagel

One Sheet: $200 - $400

PAGAN LOVE SONG
(1950 - MGM) Esther Williams, Howard Keel
One Sheet: $40 - $75

PAGANS, THE
(1958 - Allied Artists) Pierre Cressoy, Helen Remy
One Sheet: $10 - $20

PAGE MISS GLORY
(1935 - Warner Bros.) Dick Powell, Marion Davies
One Sheet: $200 - $400

PAGEMASTER, THE
(1994 - 20th Century Fox) Macaulay Culkin, Christopher Lloyd
One Sheet: $5 - $10 *Cartoon/Live Action.*

PAID
(1930 - MGM) Joan Crawford, Robert Armstrong
One Sheet: $1,300 - $2,000

PAID IN FULL
(1950 - Paramount) Robert Cummings, Lizabeth Scott
One Sheet: $30 - $50

PAID TO DANCE
(1937 - Columbia) Don Terry, Jacqueline Wells, Rita Hayworth
One Sheet: $250 - $600

PAID TO KILL
(1954 - Lippert) Dane Clark, Thea Gregory
One Sheet: $15 - $30

PAIN IN THE PULLMAN, A
(1936 - Columbia) The Three Stooges (Curly)
One Sheet: $10,000 - $16,000 *Comedy short. Duotone.*

PAINT YOUR WAGON
(1969 - Paramount) Clint Eastwood, Lee Marvin
One Sheet: $40 - $75 *One Sheet*
(Gold foil, Peter Maxx art):$50-$100; One Sheet
(Silver foil, Peter Maxx art):$50-$100; One Sheet
(Nitty Gritty Dirt Band style):$75-$150; One Sheet
(other Peter Maxx sheets):$40-$80. Cowboy
Movie Posters #329.

One Sheet

PAINTED BOATS
(1945 - Ealing) Jenny Caird
One Sheet: $100 - $200

PAINTED DESERT, THE
(1931 - Pathe) William Boyd, Clark Gable (his talkie debut)
One Sheet: $600 - $1,000 *Only one*
Lobby Card features Gable.

PAINTED DESERT
(1938 - RKO) George O'Brien, Laraine (Day) Johnson
One Sheet: $200 - $400

PAINTED DESERT
(1947R - RKO) George O'Brien
One Sheet: $40 - $75 *Re-release.*

PAINTED FACES
(1929 - Tiffany-Stahl) Joe E. Brown
One Sheet: $600 - $1,000

PAINTED HILLS, THE
(1950 - MGM) Lassie, Bruce Cowling, Gary Grey
One Sheet: $50 - $100

PAINTED PONIES

(1927 - Universal) Hoot Gibson, William Dunn
One Sheet: $250 - $500

PAINTED STALLION, THE
(1937 - Republic) Ray "Crash" Corrigan
One Sheet: $150 - $300 *Serial.*
Western. 12 Chapters.

PAINTED TRAIL
(1938 - Monogram) Tom Keene
One Sheet: $75 - $150

PAINTED VEIL, THE
(1934 - MGM) Greta Garbo, Herbert Marshall
One Sheet: $1,900 - $3,000 *Two styles*
One Sheet exist, price is for full color stone litho.
One Sheet(photographic):$800-$1500.

One Sheet (Style B)

PAINTED WOMAN, THE
(1932 - Fox) Spencer Tracy, Peggy Shannon
One Sheet: $500 - $800

PAINTING THE CLOUDS WITH SUNSHINE
(1951 - Warner Bros.) Dennis Morgan, Virginia Mayo
One Sheet: $15 - $25

PAIR O' DICE, A
(1930C - A.D.W.) Lee "Bud" Harrison, Peenie Elmo
One Sheet: $250 - $600 *Black cast.*
Separate Cinema, pg. 109.

PAIR OF BRIEFS, A
(1963 - 20th Century Fox) Michael Craig, Mary Peach
One Sheet: $5 - $10

PAISAN
(1948 - Mayer-Burstyn) Bill Tubbs, Carmela Sazio
One Sheet: $30 - $50 *Italian.*

PAJAMA GAME, THE
(1957 - Warner Bros.) Doris Day, John Raitt
One Sheet: $30 - $50

PAJAMA MARRIAGE, A
(1925 - Special) Neely Edwards
One Sheet: $125 - $250

PAJAMA PARTY
(1964 - AIP) Tommy Kirk, Annette Funicello, Buster Keaton
One Sheet: $30 - $50

PAL FROM TEXAS
(1939 - Metropolitan) Bob Steele, Claire Rochelle
One Sheet: $125 - $250

PAL JOEY
(1957 - Columbia) Frank Sinatra, Rita Hayworth, Kim Novak
One Sheet: $40 - $75

Insert

PAL'S RETURN
(1948 - RKO) Gary Gray, John Ridgely, Anne Nagel
One Sheet: $15 - $30

PALACE OF PLEASURE
(1920 - Fox) Betty Compson, Edmund Lowe
One Sheet: $200 - $400

PALE RIDER
(1985 - Warner Bros.) Clint Eastwood, Michael Moriarty
One Sheet: $30 - $60 *Cowboy*
Movie Posters #357.

PALEFACE, THE
(1922 - First National) Buster Keaton
One Sheet: $7,500 - $12,000

PALEFACE, THE
(1948 - Paramount) Bob Hope, Jane Russell
One Sheet: $100 - $200

PALLBEARER, THE
(1996 - Miramax) David Schwimmer, Gwyneth Paltrow, Barbara Hershey
One Sheet: $5 - $10

PALM BEACH GIRL, THE
(1926 - Paramount) Bebe Daniels
One Sheet: $250 - $600

PALM BEACH STORY, THE
(1942 - Paramount) Claudette Colbert, Joel McCrea
One Sheet: $600 - $1,000

PALM SPRINGS
(1936 - Paramount) Frances Langford, David Niven
One Sheet: $100 - $200

PALM SPRINGS WEEKEND
(1963 - Warner Bros.) Troy Donahue, Connie Stevens
One Sheet: $15 - $30

PALMY DAYS
(1931 - United Artists) Eddie Cantor, Charlotte Greenwood, George Raft
One Sheet: $500 - $800

PALOMINO, THE
(1950 - Columbia) Jerome Courtland, Beverly Tyler
One Sheet: $15 - $25

PALOOKA
(1934 - Reliance) Jimmy Durante, Stu Erwin, Lupe Velez
One Sheet: $150 - $350

PALS AND GALS
(1954 - Columbia) The Three Stooges (Shemp)
One Sheet: $150 - $300 *Comedy short. Duotone.*

PALS IN BLUE
(1915 - Fox) Tom Mix
One Sheet: $700 - $1,200

PALS IN BLUE
(192?R - Fox) Tom Mix
One Sheet: $150 - $300

PALS OF THE GOLDEN WEST
(1951 - Republic) Roy Rogers, Dale Evans
One Sheet: $100 - $200 *Roy's last B Western.*

PALS OF THE PECOS
(1941 - Republic) Bob Livingston, Bob Steele
One Sheet: $50 - $100

PALS OF THE PRAIRIE
(1929 - F.B.O.) Buzz Barton
One Sheet: $150 - $350

PALS OF THE SADDLE
(1938 - Republic) John Wayne, Ray Corrigan, Max Terhune
One Sheet: $600 - $1,000

PALS OF THE SADDLE
(1953R - Republic) John Wayne
One Sheet: $75 - $175 *Re-release. Full color.*

PALS OF THE SILVER SAGE
(1940 - Monogram) Tex Ritter
One Sheet: $75 - $150

PAN AMERICANA

(1945 - RKO) Phillip Terry, Eve Arden, Robert Benchley
One Sheet: $20 - $40

PANAMA AND THE CANAL FROM AN AEROPLANE
(1914 - Dudley & Cosby) -
One Sheet: $250 - $600

PANAMA FLO
(1932 - RKO) Charles Bickford, Robert Armstrong
One Sheet: $150 - $300

PANAMA HATTIE
(1942 - MGM) Ann Sothern, Dan Dailey, Red Skelton
One Sheet: $75 - $125

One Sheet

PANAMA LADY
(1939 - RKO) Lucille Ball, Allan "Rocky" Lane
One Sheet: $150 - $300

PANAMA PATROL
(1939 - Fine Arts) Leon Ames, Charlotte Wynters
One Sheet: $40 - $75

PANAMA SAL
(1957 - Republic) Elena Verdugo, Ed Kemmer
One Sheet: $10 - $20

PANAMINT'S BAD MAN
(1938 - 20th Century Fox) Smith Ballew
One Sheet: $75 - $150

PANCHO VILLA RETURNS
(1950 - Hispano Continental) Leo Carrillo
One Sheet: $15 - $35

PANDA BEAR IN THE NEWCOMER
(1938 - 20th Century Fox) TerryToons
One Sheet: $100 - $200   Cartoon.
Stock poster.

PANDORA AND THE FLYING DUTCHMAN
(1950 - MGM) Ava Gardner, James Mason
One Sheet: $75 - $125

PANDORA'S BOX
(1929 - Nero) Louise Brooks, Franz Lederer
One Sheet: $40,000 - $50,000   German.

PANDORA'S BOX
(1970R - Nero) Louise Brooks, Franz Lederer
One Sheet: $15 - $25   German Re-release.

PANHANDLE
(1948 - Monogram) Rod Cameron, Cathy Downs
One Sheet: $15 - $35

PANHANDLE TRAIL
(1944 - Eagle-Lion) Buster Crabbe
One Sheet: $20 - $40

PANIC
(1946 - Tricolore) Michael Simon, Viviane Romance
One Sheet: $15 - $30

PANIC BUTTON
(1964 - Gorton) Maurice Chevalier, Jayne Mansfield
One Sheet: $20 - $40

PANIC IN NEEDLE PARK, THE
(1971 - 20th Century Fox) Al Pacino, Kitty Winn
One Sheet: $7 - $15   Heroin addiction.

PANIC IN THE PARLOR
(1957 - DCA) Peggy Mount, Gordon Jackson

One Sheet: $5 - $10

PANIC IN THE STREETS
(1950 - 20th Century Fox) Richard Widmark, Paul Douglas
One Sheet: $50 - $100

PANIC IN YEAR ZERO
(1962 - AIP) Ray Milland, Jean Hagen
One Sheet: $20 - $40

One Sheet

PANIC ON THE AIR
(1936 - Columbia) Lew Ayres, Florence Rice
One Sheet: $150 - $300

PANORAMA BLUE
(1973 - -) John Holmes, Rene Bond
One Sheet: $30 - $50

PANTHER
(1995 - Gramercy) Kadeem Hardison, Courtney Vance
One Sheet: $7 - $15   Black cast.
Controversial look at the Black Panther party.

PANTHER GIRL OF THE CONGO
(1955 - Republic) Phyllis Coates, Myron Healey
One Sheet: $40 - $75   Serial. 12 Chapters.

PANTHER'S CLAW, THE
(1942 - PRC) Sidney Blackmer, Lynn Starr
One Sheet: $30 - $50

PAPA'S DELICATE CONDITION
(1963 - Paramount) Jackie Gleason, Glynis Johns
One Sheet: $15 - $35

PAPER, THE
(1994 - -) Michael Keaton, Marissa Tomei
One Sheet: $5 - $10

PAPER BULLETS
(1941 - PRC) Joan Woodbury, Jack LaRue
One Sheet: $20 - $40

PAPER CHASE, THE
(1973 - 20th Century Fox) Timothy Bottoms, Lindsay Wagner, John Houseman
One Sheet: $10 - $20   Academy Award: Best Supporting Actor(Houseman). Academy Award Movie Posters #278.

PAPER LION
(1968 - United Artists) Alan Alda, Lauren Hutton, The Detroit Lions
One Sheet: $15 - $35   Sports (Football). Sports Movie Posters #203.

PAPER MOON
(1973 - Paramount) Ryan O'Neal, Tatum O'Neal
One Sheet: $15 - $30   Tatum O'Neal's film debut. Academy Award: Best Supporting Actress(Tatum). Academy Award Movie Posters #279.

PAPERBACK HERO
(1973 - Agincourt International) Elizabeth Ashley, John Beck
One Sheet: $4 - $8

PAPERHANGER, THE
(192?R - -) Charlie Chaplin
One Sheet: $700 - $1,200   Re-release. Formerly titled "WORK".

PAPILLON
(1974 - Allied Artists) Steve McQueen, Dustin Hoffman
One Sheet: $30 - $60

PAPILLON

(1977R - Allied Artists) Steve McQueen, Dustin Hoffman
One Sheet: $15 - $25   Re-release.

PARACHUTE BATALLION
(1941 - RKO) Robert Preston, Edmond O'Brien
One Sheet: $40 - $75

PARACHUTE JUMPER
(1933 - Warner Bros.) Bette Davis, Douglas Fairbanks Jr.
One Sheet: $1,300 - $2,000

PARACHUTE NURSE
(1942 - Columbia) William Wright, Kay Harris
One Sheet: $30 - $50

PARADE OF THE WEST
(1929 - Universal) Ken Maynard
One Sheet: $250 - $600

PARADINE CASE, THE
(1947 - United Artists) Gregory Peck, Charles Laughton, Dir:Alfred Hitchcock
One Sheet: $125 - $250

One Sheet

PARADINE CASE, THE
(1956R - United Artists) Gregory Peck, Charles Laughton, Dir:Alfred Hitchcock
One Sheet: $50 - $100   Re-release.

PARADISE
(1926 - First National) Milton Sills, Betty Bronson
One Sheet: $200 - $400

PARADISE
(1991 - Touchstone) Don Johnson, Melanie Griffith
One Sheet: $5 - $10

PARADISE ALLEY
(1962 - Pathe) Marie Windsor, Billy Gilbert
One Sheet: $7 - $15   AKA: STARS IN THE BACK YARD.

PARADISE ALLEY
(1978 - Universal) Sylvester Stallone, Kevin Conway
One Sheet: $7 - $15

PARADISE CANYON
(1935 - Monogram) John Wayne
One Sheet: $2,800 - $4,500   Cowboy Movie Posters #s 183, 185.

One Sheet

PARADISE CANYON
(1948R - Monogram) John Wayne
One Sheet: $75 - $150   Re-release.

PARADISE EXPRESS
(1937 - Republic) Grant Withers, Dorothy Appelby
One Sheet: $75 - $125

PARADISE FOR THREE
(1938 - MGM) Robert Young, Frank Morgan, Mary Astor
One Sheet: $75 - $150

PARADISE, HAWAIIAN STYLE
(1966 - Paramount) Elvis Presley, Suzanna Leigh
One Sheet: $75 - $125

One Sheet

PARADISE IN HARLEM
(1939 - International Roadshow) Mamie Smith
One Sheet: $250 - $600   Black cast. Separate Cinema, pg. 143.

PARADISE ISLAND
(1930 - Tiffany) Kenneth Harlan, Marceline Day
One Sheet: $150 - $350

PARADISE ISLE
(1937 - Monogram) Warren Hull, Movita
One Sheet: $50 - $100

PARADISE LAGOON
(1958 - Columbia) Kenneth More, Diane Cilento
One Sheet: $5 - $10

PARADISIO
(1962 - Fanfare) Arthur Howard, Eva Wagner
One Sheet: $15 - $35

PARALLAX VIEW, THE
(1974 - Paramount) Warren Beatty, Paula Prentiss
One Sheet: $5 - $10

PARAMOUNT CHAMPION SHORT SUBJECT, A
(1949 - Paramount) -
One Sheet: $100 - $200   Cartoon.
Duotone stock poster with various characters, including Popeye and Raggedy Ann.

PARAMOUNT NEWS
(1927 - Paramount) Newsreel
One Sheet: $250 - $500

PARAMOUNT ON PARADE
(1930 - -) Jean Arthur, Clara Bow, Gary Gooper, All Star Cast
One Sheet: $1,300 - $2,000

PARAMOUNT PICTURES
(1915 - Paramount) Stock poster
One Sheet: $500 - $900

PARAMOUNT TRAVEL PICTURES
(- - -) See individual titles.

PARANOIA
(1969 - Commonwealth United) Carroll Baker, Lou Castel
One Sheet: $15 - $25

PARANOIAC
(1963 - Universal) Oliver Reed, Janette Scott
One Sheet: $15 - $30

PARASITE
(1982 - Embassy) Robert Glaudini, Demi Moore, Luca Bercovici
One Sheet: $10 - $20   3-D.

PARASITE MURDERS, THE
(1976 - AIP) Marilyn Chambers, Dir: David Cronenberg
One Sheet: $15 - $25   AKA: THEY CAME FROM WITHIN; RABID. Chamber's first non-porno film.

PARATROOP COMMAND
(1958 - AIP) Richard Bakalyan, Ken Lynch
One Sheet: $10 - $20

PARATROOPER
(1953 - Columbia) Alan Ladd, Susan Stephen
One Sheet: $30 - $50

PARDNERS
(1956 - Paramount) Dean Martin, Jerry Lewis, Lon Chaney, Jr.
One Sheet: $40 - $75

PARDNERS
(1965R - Paramount) Dean Martin, Jerry Lewis, Lon Chaney, Jr.
One Sheet: $10 - $20   *Re-release.*

PARDON MY BACKFIRE
(1953 - Columbia) The Three Stooges (Shemp)
One Sheet: $150 - $350   *Comedy short.*
Duotone. 3-D.

PARDON MY BLOOPER
(1974 - K-Tel) Kermit Schaffer
One Sheet: $5 - $10   *Based on*
Radio & T.V. Bloopers.

PARDON MY CLUTCH
(1948 - Columbia) The Three Stooges (Shemp)
One Sheet: $350 - $750   *Comedy short.*
Duotone.

PARDON MY FRENCH
(1951 - United Artists) Merle Oberon, Paul Henreid
One Sheet: $15 - $25

PARDON MY GUN
(1930 - Pathe) Tom Keene
One Sheet: $150 - $300

PARDON MY GUN
(1942 - Columbia) Charles Starrett
One Sheet: $40 - $75

PARDON MY NERVE
(1922 - Fox) Charles "Buck" Jones, Eileen Percy
One Sheet: $250 - $600

PARDON MY PAST
(1945 - Columbia) Fred MacMurray, Marguerite Chapman
One Sheet: $75 - $150

PARDON MY PUPS
(193? - -) Shirley Temple
One Sheet: $150 - $300   *Short Subject.*

PARDON MY RHYTHM
(1944 - Universal) Gloria Jean, Patric Knowles, Bob Crosby & his Orchestra
One Sheet: $30 - $50   *Big Band*
musical.

PARDON MY SARONG
(1942 - Universal) Bud Abbott, Lou Costello
One Sheet: $150 - $350

PARDON MY SCOTCH
(1935 - Columbia) The Three Stooges (Curly)
One Sheet: $13,000 - $20,000   *Comedy short.*
Duotone.

PARDON MY STRIPES
(1942 - Republic) Bill Henry, Sheila Ryan
One Sheet: $20 - $40

PARDON OUR NERVE
(1939 - 20th Century Fox) Michael Whalen, Lynn Bari
One Sheet: $75 - $150

PARDON US
(1931 - MGM) Stan Laurel, Oliver Hardy (their 1st starring feature)
One Sheet: $4,000 - $6,000

PARENT TRAP, THE
(1961 - Buena Vista) Hayley Mills, Maureen O'Hara
One Sheet: $15 - $35

PARENT TRAP, THE
(1968R - Beuna Vista/Disney) Hayley Mills, Brian Keith, Maureen O'Hara
One Sheet: $10 - $20   *Re-release.*

PARENTHOOD
(1989 - -) Steve Martin, Mary Steenburgen
One Sheet: $5 - $10

PARENTS ON TRIAL
(1939 - Columbia) Jean Parker, Johnny Downs
One Sheet: $75 - $125

PARIS

PARIS
(1926 - MGM) Charles Ray, Joan Crawford
One Sheet: $1,600 - $2,500

PARIS
(1929 - First National) Irene Bordoni, Jack Buchanan, ZaSu Pitts
One Sheet: $500 - $800

PARIS AFTER DARK
(1943 - 20th Century Fox) George Sanders, Brenda Marshall
One Sheet: $30 - $50

PARIS BLUES
(1961 - United Artists) Paul Newman, Joanne Woodward
One Sheet: $20 - $40

PARIS BOUND
(1929 - Pathe) Ann Harding, Fredric March
One Sheet: $250 - $500

PARIS CALLING
(1941 - Universal) Elisabeth Bergner, Randolph Scott, Basil Rathbone
One Sheet: $50 - $100

PARIS DOES STRANGE THINGS
(1957 - Warner Bros) Ingrid Bergman, Mel Ferrer
One Sheet: $30 - $50

PARIS EXPRESS, THE
(1953 - George Schuefer) Claude Rains, Marta Toren
One Sheet: $15 - $35

PARIS FOLLIES OF 1956
(1956 - Allied Artists) Forrest Tucker, Margaret Whiting
One Sheet: $15 - $35

PARIS HOLIDAY
(1958 - United Artists) Bob Hope, Anita Ekberg
One Sheet: $20 - $40

PARIS HONEYMOON
(1939 - Paramount) Bing Crosby, Shirley Ross
One Sheet: $150 - $300

PARIS IN SPRING
(1935 - Paramount) Tullio Carminati, Mary Ellis
One Sheet: $75 - $150

PARIS IN THE MONTH OF AUGUST
(1968 - Trans-Lux) Charles Aznavour, Susan Hampshire
One Sheet: $3 - $5

PARIS INTERLUDE
(1934 - MGM) Robert Young, Una Merkel
One Sheet: $75 - $150

PARIS IS BURNING
(1991 - -) Dorian Corey, Pepper Labeija
One Sheet: $5 - $10

PARIS MODEL
(1953 - Columbia) Marilyn Maxwell, Paulette Goddard
One Sheet: $15 - $30

PARIS PLAYBOYS
(1954 - Monogram) The Bowery Boys
One Sheet: $40 - $75

PARIS, TEXAS
(1984 - 20th Century Fox) Harry Dean Stanton, Nastassia Kinski
One Sheet: $20 - $40

PARIS UNDERGROUND
(1945 - United Artists) Grace Fields, Constance Bennett
One Sheet: $30 - $50

PARIS WHEN IT SIZZLES
(1964 - Paramount) William Holden, Audrey Hepburn
One Sheet: $50 - $100

PARIS-CHAMPAGNE
(1960 - -) -
One Sheet: $150 - $300   *French.*

PARISIAN ROMANCE, A
(1932 - Allied) Gilbert Roland
One Sheet: $75 - $125

PARK AVENUE LOGGER
(1937 - RKO) George O'Brien, Beatrice Roberts
One Sheet: $50 - $100

PARK ROW
(1952 - United Artists) Gene Evans, Mary Welch
One Sheet: $30 - $50

PARLOR, BEDROOM, AND BATH
(1931 - MGM) Buster Keaton, Sally Eilers
One Sheet: $1,300 - $2,000

PARNELL
(1937 - MGM) Clark Gable, Myrna Loy
One Sheet: $350 - $750

PAROLE
(1936 - Universal) Henry Hunter, Ann Preston, Anthony Quinn (minor role)
One Sheet: $75 - $150

PAROLE FIXER
(1940 - Paramount) William Henry, Virginia Dale, Robert Paige
One Sheet: $40 - $75

PAROLE GIRL
(1933 - Columbia) Ralph Bellamy, Mae Clarke
One Sheet: $100 - $200

PAROLE, INC.
(1948 - Eagle-Lion) Michael O'Shea, Turhan Bey
One Sheet: $15 - $30

PAROLE RACKET
(1937 - Columbia) Paul Kelly, Rosalind Keith
One Sheet: $50 - $100

PAROLED FROM THE BIG HOUSE
(1938 - Syndicate) Jean Carmen, Milburn Stone
One Sheet: $75 - $125   *AKA: MAIN*
STREET GIRL.

PAROLED TO DIE
(1937 - Republic) Bob Steele, Kathleen Elliott
One Sheet: $75 - $150

PARRISH
(1961 - Warner Bros.) Troy Donahue, Claudette Colbert
One Sheet: $15 - $30

PARSON AND THE OUTLAW, THE
(1957 - Columbia) Anthony Dexter, Marie Windsor
One Sheet: $10 - $20

PARSON OF PANAMINT, THE
(1941 - Paramount) Phillip Terry, Ellen Drew
One Sheet: $30 - $50

PART TIME PAL
(1947 - MGM) Tom & Jerry
One Sheet: $250 - $600   *Cartoon. Full*
color stone litho.

PARTNERS
(1932 - RKO) Tom Keene
One Sheet: $200 - $400   *Cowboy*
Movie Posters # 135.

PARTNERS IN CRIME
(1937 - Paramount) Lynne Overman, Roscoe Karns, Anthony Quinn
One Sheet: $50 - $100

PARTNERS IN TIME
(1946 - RKO) Pamela Blake, John James, Lum & Abner
One Sheet: $50 - $100

PARTNERS OF THE PLAINS
(1938 - Paramount) William Boyd
One Sheet: $200 - $400

PARTNERS OF THE SUNSET
(1948 - Monogram) Jimmy Wakely, Dub Taylor
One Sheet: $15 - $35

PARTNERS OF THE TRAIL
(1944 - Monogram) Johnny Mack Brown
One Sheet: $20 - $40

PARTS: THE CLONUS HORROR
(1979 - Group I) Dick Sargent, Peter Graves, Tim Donnelly
One Sheet: $5 - $10   *AKA: THE*
CLONUS HORROR.

PART-TIME WIFE
(1930 - Fox) Edmund Lowe, Leila Hyams
One Sheet: $150 - $300

PARTY, THE
(1968 - United Artists) Peter Sellers, Claudine

Longet
One Sheet: $10 - $20

PARTY CRASHERS, THE
(1958 - Paramount) Mark Damon, Frances Farmer (her last film)
One Sheet: $30 - $50

PARTY GIRL
(1930 - Victory) Douglas Fairbanks, Jr., Jeanette Loff
One Sheet: $100 - $200

PARTY GIRL
(1958 - MGM) Robert Taylor, Cyd Charisse, Lee J. Cobb
One Sheet: $40 - $75

PARTY GIRL
(1995 - First Look) Parker Posey, Omar Townsend
One Sheet: $3 - $5

PARTY HUSBAND
(1931 - First National) Dorothy Mackaill, James Rennie
One Sheet: $100 - $200

PARTY LINE
(1988 - -) Richard Hatch, Shawn Weatherly
One Sheet: $5 - $10

PARTY WIRE
(1935 - Columbia) Jean Arthur, Victor Jory
One Sheet: $150 - $300

PARTY'S OVER, THE
(1934 - Columbia) Stuart Erwin, Ann Sothern
One Sheet: $150 - $300

PASS THE AMMO
(1988 - -) Bill Paxton, Linda Kozlowski, Tim Curry
One Sheet: $3 - $5

PASS THE DUMPLINGS
(1927 - Pathe) Alice Day
One Sheet: $125 - $250

PASSAGE, THE
(1979 - United Artists) Anthony Quinn, James Mason, Malcolm McDowell
One Sheet: $10 - $20

PASSAGE FROM HONG KONG
(1941 - Warner Bros.) Keye Luke, Keith Douglas
One Sheet: $40 - $75

PASSAGE HOME
(1955 - GFD) Anthony Steel, Peter Finch
One Sheet: $15 - $25

PASSAGE TO INDIA, A
(1984 - Columbia) Victor Banerjee, Peggy Ashcroft
One Sheet: $7 - $15   *Academy*
Award: Best Supporting Actress(Ashcroft).
Academy Award Movie Posters #339.

PASSAGE TO MARSEILLES
(1944 - Warner Bros.) Humphrey Bogart, Claude Rains, Michele Morgan, Peter Lorre
One Sheet: $125 - $250

One Sheet

PASSAGE WEST
(1951 - Paramount) John Payne, Arleen Whelan
One Sheet: $15 - $30

PASSAGES FROM FINNEGAN'S WAKE
(1967 - Grove Press) Martin J.Kelly, Jane Reilly
One Sheet: $3 - $5

PASSED AWAY
(1992 - Buena Vista) Tim Curry, Bob Hopkins
One Sheet: $3 - $5

PASSENGER, THE
(1975 - United Artists) Jack Nicholson, Maria Schneider
One Sheet: $10 - $20

PASSENGER 57
(1992 - Warner Bros.) Wesley Snipes, Bruce Payne
One Sheet: $3 - $5

PASSING OF THE OKLAHOMA OUTLAWS
(1915 - Eagle) -
One Sheet: $250 - $500

PASSING OF THE THIRD FLOOR BACK, THE
(1935 - Gaumont British) Conrad Veidt, Anna Lee
One Sheet: $200 - $400

PASSING OF WOLF MACLEAN, THE
(1924 - Ermine) Jack Meehan, Frank Fenton
One Sheet: $150 - $350

PASSING PARADE
(1955 - -) -
One Sheet: $15 - $35

PASSION
(1920 - First National) Pola Negri, Dir: Ernst Lubitsch
One Sheet: $800 - $1,500   *German.*

PASSION
(1954 - RKO) Cornel Wilde, Yvonne De Carlo, Lon Chaney, Jr.
One Sheet: $40 - $75

PASSION FISH
(1993 - Miramax) Mary McDonnell, Alfie Woodard
One Sheet: $5 - $10

One Sheet

PASSION FLOWER, THE
(1930 - MGM) Charles Bickford, Kay Francis
One Sheet: $250 - $500

PASSION OF JOAN OF ARC, THE
(1929 - Societe Generale Des Films) Mlle Falconetti
One Sheet: $250 - $500

PASSION PLAY, THE
(1900C - Edison) -
One Sheet: $2,500 - $4,000

PASSION PLAY, THE
(1930 - Quality Amusement) -
One Sheet: $250 - $500

PASSION'S PLAYGROUND
(1920 - First National) Rudolph Valentino
One Sheet: $600 - $1,000

PASSIONATE FRIENDS, THE
(1949 - Universal) Ann Todd, Claude Rains, Trevor Howard
One Sheet: $30 - $50   *AKA: ONE WOMAN'S STORY.*

PASSIONATE PLUMBER, THE
(1932 - MGM) Buster Keaton, Jimmy Durante
One Sheet: $1,300 - $2,000

PASSIONATE SENTRY, THE
(1952 - Fine Arts) Nigel Patrick, Peggy Cummins
One Sheet: $15 - $25   *AKA: WHO GOES THERE?*

PASSKEY TO DANGER
(1946 - Republic) Stephanie Bachelor, Kane Richmond
One Sheet: $15 - $30

PASSPORT HUSBAND
(1938 - 20th Century Fox) Stuart Erwin, Pauline Moore
One Sheet: $50 - $100

PASSPORT TO ALCATRAZ
(1940 - Columbia) Jack Holt, Noah Beery
One Sheet: $40 - $75

PASSPORT TO CHINA
(1961 - Columbia) Richard Basehart, Alan Gifford
One Sheet: $5 - $10

PASSPORT TO DESTINY
(1944 - RKO) Elsa Lanchester, Gordon Oliver
One Sheet: $20 - $40

PASSPORT TO HEAVEN
(1933 - Film Classics) Albert Basserman, Eric Blore
One Sheet: $75 - $150

PASSPORT TO HELL, A
(1932 - Fox) Paul Lukas, Donald Crisp, Elissa Landi
One Sheet: $150 - $300

PASSPORT TO PIMLICO
(1949 - Eagle-Lion) Stanley Holloway, Betty Warren
One Sheet: $15 - $30

PASSPORT TO SUEZ
(1943 - Columbia) Warren William, Ann Savage
One Sheet: $30 - $60   *Lone Wolf series.*

PASSWORD IS COURAGE, THE
(1963 - MGM) Dirk Bogarde, Maria Perschy
One Sheet: $5 - $10

PAST OF MARY HOLMES, THE
(1933 - RKO) Helen MacKellar, Eric Linden
One Sheet: $500 - $900

PASTOR HALL
(1940 - United Artists) Wilfred Lawson, Nova Pilbeam, Seymour Hicks
One Sheet: $20 - $40

PAT AND MIKE
(1952 - MGM) Spencer Tracy, Katharine Hepburn
One Sheet: $75 - $150

PAT GARRETT AND BILLY THE KID
(1973 - MGM) James Coburn, Bob Dylan, Dir:Sam Peckinpah
One Sheet: $20 - $40   *Cowboy Movie Posters #338.*

PATCH MAH BRITCHES
(1935 - Columbia) Barney Google
One Sheet: $800 - $1,500   *Cartoon. Cartoon Movie Posters #37.*

PATCH OF BLUE, A
(1966 - MGM) Sidney Poitier, Shelley Winters
One Sheet: $15 - $30   *Academy Award Movie Posters #233.*

PATENT LEATHER KID, THE
(1927 - First National) Richard Barthelmess
One Sheet: $250 - $600

PATHER PANCHALI
(1958 - West Bengal) Kanu Banerji, Karuna Naerji
One Sheet: $15 - $30   *AKA: THE SONG OF THE ROAD.*

PATHFINDER, THE
(1952 - Columbia) George Montgomery, Helena Carter, Jay Silverheels
One Sheet: $15 - $30

PATHS OF GLORY
(1957 - United Artists) Kirk Douglas, Ralph Meeker, Dir: Stanley Kubrick
One Sheet: $75 - $150

PATHS TO PARADISE
(1925 - Paramount) Betty Compson, Raymond Griffith
One Sheet: $250 - $500

PATIENT IN ROOM 18, THE
(1937 - Warner Bros.) Patric Knowles, Ann Sheridan
One Sheet: $50 - $100

PATIENT VANISHES, THE
(1947 - Film Classics) James Mason, Mary Clare
One Sheet: $15 - $30

PATRIA
(1916 - -) Rudolph Valentino
One Sheet: $800 - $1,500

PATRICK THE GREAT
(1944 - Universal) Donald O'Connor, Peggy Ryan
One Sheet: $30 - $50

PATRIOT, THE
(1928 - Paramount) Emil Jannings
One Sheet: $500 - $800

PATRIOT GAMES
(1992 - Paramount) Harrison Ford
One Sheet: $7 - $15

PATSY, THE
(1964 - Paramount) Jerry Lewis, Ina Balin, Peter Lorre (his last film)
One Sheet: $20 - $40

PATTERN FOR PLUNDER
(1963 - Rank) Keenan Wynn, Mai Zetterling
One Sheet: $7 - $15

PATTERNS
(1956 - United Artists) Van Heflin, Ed Begley, Everett Sloane
One Sheet: $10 - $20

PATTERSON VS. JOHANSSON
(1961 - Turn of the Century Fights) Floyd Patterson, Ingemar Johansson
One Sheet: $75 - $125   *Sports (Boxing).*

PATTI ROCKS
(1988 - -) Chris Mulkey, John Jenkins, Karen Landry
One Sheet: $5 - $10

PATTON
(1970 - 20th Century Fox) George C. Scott, Karl Malden
One Sheet: $40 - $75   *Academy Award: Best Picture, Best Actor(Scott), Best Direction(Franklin J. Schaffner). Academy Award Movie Posters #258-#260.*

One Sheet

PAUL AND MICHELLE
(1974 - Paramount) Anicee Alvina, Keir Dullea
One Sheet: $3 - $5

PAUL McCARTNEY AND WINGS - ROCKSHOW
(1979 - -) Paul McCartney & Wings
One Sheet: $15 - $25   *Rock 'n' Roll concert film.*

PAULA
(1952 - Columbia) Loretta Young, Kent Smith
One Sheet: $20 - $40

PAWNBROKER, THE
(1965 - Allied Artists) Rod Steiger, Geraldine Fitzgerald
One Sheet: $20 - $40   *Price is for Non-Review sheet.*

PAWNEE
(1957 - Republic) George Montgomery, Lola Albright
One Sheet: $15 - $30

PAWNSHOP, THE
(1916 - Mutual) Charlie Chaplin, Edna Purviance
One Sheet: $7,500 - $12,000

PAY AS YOU ENTER
(1928 - -) Louise Fazenda, Clyde Cook, William Demarest
One Sheet: $150 - $300

PAY DAY
(1922 - First National) Charlie Chaplin, Edna Purviance
One Sheet: $5,000 - $8,000

PAY OR DIE
(1960 - Allied Artists) Ernest Borgnine, Zohra Lampert
One Sheet: $7 - $15

PAYDAY
(1973 - Cinerama) Rip Torn, Anna Capri
One Sheet: $3 - $5

PAYMENT DEFERRED
(1932 - MGM) Charles Laughton, Maureen O'Sullivan
One Sheet: $150 - $300

PAYMENT IN BLOOD
(1968 - Columbia) Guy Madison, Edd Byrnes
One Sheet: $15 - $25

PAYMENT ON DEMAND
(1951 - RKO) Bette Davis, Barry Sullivan
One Sheet: $75 - $150

One Sheet

PAYOFF, THE
(1930 - RKO) Lowell Sherman, Marian Nixon
One Sheet: $150 - $300

PAYOFF, THE
(1935 - Warner Bros.) James Dunn, Claire Dodd
One Sheet: $100 - $200

PAYOFF, THE
(1943 - PRC) Lee Tracy, Tina Thayer, Tom Brown
One Sheet: $15 - $35

PAYROLL
(1962 - Allied Artists) Michael Craig, Francoise Prevost
One Sheet: $3 - $5

PEACEMAKER, THE
(1956 - United Artists) James Mitchell, Rosemarie Bowe
One Sheet: $5 - $10

PEACH O'RENO
(1931 - RKO) Wheeler & Woolsey
One Sheet: $200 - $400

PEACHY COBBLER, THE
(1950 - MGM) Tex Avery
One Sheet: $250 - $600   *Cartoon. Full color stone litho.*

PEACOCK ALLEY
(1929 - Tiffany) Mae Murray
One Sheet: $150 - $300

PEAKS OF DESTINY
(1927 - -) Leni Riefenstahl, Louis Trenker
One Sheet: $600 - $1,000   *German. First German sound film.*

PEANUT BUTTER SOLUTION, THE
(1985 - -) Matthew Mackay
One Sheet: $3 - $5

PEANUT MAN, THE
(1947 - Consolidated) Clarence Muse
One Sheet: $150 - $300   *Black cast.*

Duotone. Separate Cinema, pg. 130.

PEARL, THE
(1947 - RKO) Pedro Armendariz, Maria Elena Marques
One Sheet: $20 - $40

PEARL OF DEATH, THE
(1944 - Universal) Basil Rathbone, Nigel Bruce
One Sheet: $500 - $800   *Sherlock Holmes series. Graven Images, pg. 141.*

One Sheet

PEARL OF THE ARMY
(1916 - Pathe) Pearl White
One Sheet: $700 - $1,200

PEARL OF THE SOUTH PACIFIC
(1955 - RKO) Dennis Morgan, Virginia Mayo
One Sheet: $30 - $50

PECK'S BAD BOY
(1921 - First National) Jackie Coogan, Raymond James Corrigan
One Sheet: $600 - $1,000

PECK'S BAD BOY
(1934 - 20th Century Fox) Thomas Meighan, Jackie Cooper
One Sheet: $150 - $300

PECK'S BAD BOY WITH THE CIRCUS
(1938 - RKO) Tommy Kelly, Billy Gilbert, Spanky MacFarland
One Sheet: $100 - $200

PECK'S BAD GIRL
(1918 - Goldwyn) Mabel Normand, Earle Foxe
One Sheet: $300 - $700

PECOS BILL
(1949R - RKO/Disney) Roy Rogers
One Sheet: $150 - $300   *Cartoon/Live action. Western. Special One Sheet from the feature "Melody Time".*

PECOS BILL
(1954 - RKO/Disney) Roy Rogers
One Sheet: $250 - $500   *Cartoon/Live action short. Western. Previously part of MELODY TIME (1948).*

PECOS KID
(1935 - Commodore) Fred Kohler Jr.
One Sheet: $75 - $150

PECOS RIVER
(1951 - Columbia) Charles Starrett, Smiley Burnette
One Sheet: $15 - $35

PEEPER
(1975 - 20th Century Fox) Michael Caine, Natalie Wood
One Sheet: $3 - $5   *AKA: FAT CHANCE.*

PEEPING TOM
(1960 - Astor) Karl Boehm, Anna Massey
One Sheet: $50 - $100   *AKA: FACE OF FEAR. Graven Images, pg. 205.*

PEER GYNT
(1965 - Brandon) Charlton Heston
One Sheet: $10 - $20

PEE-WEE'S BIG ADVENTURE
(1985 - Warner Bros.) Pee-Wee Herman (Paul Reubens), Dir: Tim Burton
One Sheet: $30 - $50   *Burton's directorial debut.*

PEG O' MY HEART
(1919 - National) Wanda Hawley, Thomas Meighan

One Sheet: $200 - $400   *Film never released due to Supreme Court ruling. One poster known to exist.*

PEG O' MY HEART
(1923 - -) Laurette Taylor, Mahlon Hamilton, Dir: King Vidor
One Sheet: $150 - $300

PEG O' MY HEART
(1933 - MGM) Marion Davies, Alan Mowbray
One Sheet: $75 - $150

PEG OF OLD DRURY
(1936 - British/Dominion) Anna Neagle
One Sheet: $75 - $125

PEGGY
(1950 - Universal) Diana Lynn, Charles Coburn
One Sheet: $15 - $25

PEGGY SUE GOT MARRIED
(1986 - -) Kathleen Turner, Nicolas Cage
One Sheet: $5 - $10

PEKING EXPRESS
(1951 - Paramount) Joseph Cotten, Corinne Calvet
One Sheet: $15 - $30

PELICAN BRIEF, THE
(1993 - Warner Bros.) Julia Roberts, Denzel Washington
One Sheet: $5 - $10

PELICAN'S BILL, THE
(1923 - Bray Productions) Directed by Walter Lantz
One Sheet: $500 - $800   *Cartoon. Cartoon Movie Posters #23.*

PELLE THE CONQUEROR
(1988 - -) Max von Sydow, Pelle Hvenegaard
One Sheet: $10 - $20   *Swedish.*

PENAL CODE
(1934 - Monarch) Regis Toomey
One Sheet: $150 - $350

PENALTY, THE
(1920 - Goldwyn) Gouverneur Morris, Lon Chaney
One Sheet: $800 - $1,500

PENALTY, THE
(1941 - MGM) Edward Arnold, Lionel Barrymore
One Sheet: $40 - $75

PENDULUM
(1969 - Columbia) George Peppard, Jean Seberg
One Sheet: $7 - $15

PENELOPE
(1966 - MGM) Natalie Wood, Ian Bannen
One Sheet: $10 - $20

PENGUIN POOL MURDER, THE
(1932 - RKO) Edna May Oliver, James Gleason
One Sheet: $600 - $1,000

PENITENTIARY
(1938 - Columbia) Walter Connolly, Jean Parker
One Sheet: $125 - $250

PENITENTIARY
(1979 - -) Leon Issac Kennedy, Thommy Pollard
One Sheet: $3 - $5

PENITENTIARY II
(1982 - -) Leon Issac Kennedy, Ernie Hudson
One Sheet: $3 - $5

PENITENTIARY III
(1987 - -) Leon Issac Kennedy, Anthony Geary
One Sheet: $3 - $5

PENNIES FROM HEAVEN
(1936 - Columbia) Bing Crosby, Madge Evans
One Sheet: $200 - $400

PENNIES FROM HEAVEN
(1981 - MGM) Steve Martin, Bernadette Peters
One Sheet: $7 - $15

PENNY PRINCESS, THE
(1952 - Universal International) Yolande Donlan, Dirk Bogarde
One Sheet: $10 - $20

PENNY SERENADE

(1941 - Columbia) Irene Dunne, Cary Grant
One Sheet: $500 - $800

One Sheet

PENROD
(1924 - First National) Freckles Barry, Marshall Neilan
One Sheet: $200 - $400

PENROD AND HIS TWIN BROTHER
(1938 - Warner Bros.) Bobby & Billy Mauch, Spring Byington
One Sheet: $30 - $50

PENROD AND SAM
(1931 - First National) ZaSu Pitts, Leon Janney
One Sheet: $150 - $300

PENROD AND SAM
(1937 - Warner Bros.) Billy Mauch, Spring Byington
One Sheet: $30 - $50

PENROD'S DOUBLE TROUBLE
(1938 - Warner Bros.) Billy & Bobby Mauch, Gene Lockhart
One Sheet: $30 - $50

PENTHOUSE
(1933 - MGM) Myrna Loy, Warner Baxter
One Sheet: $500 - $800

PENTHOUSE, THE
(1967 - Paramount) Suzy Kendall, Terence Morgan
One Sheet: $5 - $10

PENTHOUSE RHYTHM
(1944 - Universal) Kirby Grant, Lois Collier
One Sheet: $20 - $40

PEOPLE AGAINST O'HARA, THE
(1951 - MGM) Spencer Tracy, Diana Lynn, Pat O'Brien
One Sheet: $40 - $75

PEOPLE ARE FUNNY
(1946 - Paramount) Jack Haley, Ozzie Nelson, Rudy Vallee, Art Linkletter
One Sheet: $30 - $50

PEOPLE NEXT DOOR, THE
(1970 - Avco/Embassy) Julie Harris, Eli Wallach
One Sheet: $3 - $5

PEOPLE THAT TIME FORGOT, THE
(1977 - AIP) Patrick Wayne, Doug McClure
One Sheet: $10 - $20

PEOPLE VS. DR. KILDARE, THE
(1941 - MGM) Lew Ayres, Lionel Barrymore, Red Skelton
One Sheet: $30 - $50

PEOPLE VS. LARRY FLINT, THE
(1996 - Columbia) Woody Harrelson, Courtney Love
One Sheet: $5 - $10

PEOPLE WILL TALK
(1935 - Paramount) Mary Boland, Charles Ruggles
One Sheet: $100 - $200

PEOPLE WILL TALK
(1951 - 20th Century Fox) Cary Grant, Jeanne Crain
One Sheet: $40 - $75

PEOPLE'S ENEMY, THE
(1935 - RKO) Melvyn Douglas, Preston Foster
One Sheet: $75 - $150

PEPE

(1960 - Columbia) Cantinflas, Dan Dailey
One Sheet: $15 - $30

PEPE LE MOKO
(1937 - Mayer/Burstyn) Jean Gabin, Gabriel Gabiro
One Sheet: $150 - $300   *French.*

PEPPER
(1936 - Fox) Jane Withers, Slim Summerville
One Sheet: $100 - $200

PERCY
(1971 - MGM) Hywel Bennett, Elke Sommer
One Sheet: $3 - $5

PEREZ FAMILY, THE
(1995 - Goldwyn) Alfred Molina, Marisa Tomei
One Sheet: $3 - $5

PERFECT
(1985 - Columbia) John Travolta, Jamie Lee Curtis
One Sheet: $7 - $15

PERFECT 36, A
(1918 - Goldwyn) Mabel Normand
One Sheet: $800 - $1,500

PERFECT ALIBI
(1931 - RKO) Frank Lawton, Robert Loraine
One Sheet: $100 - $200

PERFECT CLOWN, THE
(1925 - Chadwick) Larry Semon, Oliver Hardy, Kate Price
One Sheet: $250 - $600

PERFECT CLUE, THE
(1935 - Majestic) David Manners, Skeets Gallagher
One Sheet: $100 - $200

PERFECT COUPLE, A
(1979 - 20th Century Fox) Paul Dooley, Marta Heflin
One Sheet: $3 - $5

PERFECT CRIME, THE
(1928 - FBO) Clive Brook, Irene Rich
One Sheet: $800 - $1,500

One Sheet

PERFECT DAY, THE
(1929 - MGM) Laurel & Hardy
One Sheet: $3,500 - $5,000

PERFECT FLAPPER, THE
(1924 - -) Colleen Moore
One Sheet: $150 - $300

PERFECT FRIDAY
(1970 - Chevron) Stanley Baker, Ursula Andress
One Sheet: $3 - $5

PERFECT FURLOUGH, THE
(1958 - Universal-International) Tony Curtis, Janet Leigh
One Sheet: $15 - $35

PERFECT GENTLEMAN, A
(1928 - -) Monty Banks
One Sheet: $125 - $250

PERFECT GENTLEMAN, THE
(1935 - MGM) Frank Morgan, Heather Angel
One Sheet: $75 - $150

PERFECT MARRIAGE, THE
(1946 - Paramount) Loretta Young, David Niven
One Sheet: $40 - $75

PERFECT SNOB, THE

(1941 - 20th Century Fox) Lynn Bari, Cornel Wilde
One Sheet: $40 - $75

PERFECT SPECIMEN, THE
(1937 - Warner Bros.) Errol Flynn, Joan Blondell, Hugh Herbert
One Sheet: $250 - $500

One Sheet

PERFECT STRANGERS
(1950 - Warner Bros.) Ginger Rogers, Dennis Morgan
One Sheet: $30 - $50

PERFECT TRIBUTE, THE
(1935 - MGM) -
One Sheet: $75 - $125

PERFECT UNDERSTANDING
(1933 - United Artists) Gloria Swanson, Laurence Olivier
One Sheet: $600 - $1,000

PERFECT WEAPON
(1991 - -) Jeff Speakman, Mako
One Sheet: $3 - $5

PERFECT WOMAN, THE
(1920 - -) Constance Talmadge, Charles Meredith
One Sheet: $250 - $600

PERFECT WOMAN, THE
(1949 - Eagle-Lion) Patricia Roc, Stanley Holloway
One Sheet: $15 - $30

PERFECT WORLD, A
(1993 - Warner Bros.) Clint Eastwood, Kevin Costner
One Sheet: $7 - $15

PERFECTLY FIENDISH FLANAGAN
(1918 - Paramount) -
One Sheet: $150 - $350

PERFIDIA
(1939 - RKO) -
One Sheet: $50 - $100

PERFORMANCE
(1970 - Warner Bros.) James Fox, Mick Jagger
One Sheet: $40 - $85

PERILOUS HOLIDAY
(1946 - Columbia) Pat O'Brien, Ruth Warrick
One Sheet: $15 - $30

PERILOUS JOURNEY, A
(1953 - Republic) Vera Ralston, David Brian
One Sheet: $10 - $20

PERILOUS WATERS
(1948 - Monogram) Don Castle, Audrey Long
One Sheet: $10 - $20

PERILS OF NYOKA
(1942 - Republic) Kay Aldridge, Clayton Moore
One Sheet: $150 - $300   *Serial. 15 Chapters. Chapter 1 One Sheet:$300-$500.*

PERILS OF P. K.
(1986 - -) Sammy Davis Jr.
One Sheet: $7 - $15

PERILS OF PAULINE, THE
(1914 - Eclectic) Pearl White
One Sheet: $4,000 - $6,000   *Serial. 15 Chapters. Price is for best graphics chapters. One Sheet(Lesser Chapters):$3000-4000. One Sheet(no Pauline):$500-1200.*

PERILS OF PAULINE, THE
(1934 - Universal) Evalyn Knapp, Robert Allen

One Sheet: $200 - $400   *Serial. 12 Chapters.*

PERILS OF PAULINE, THE
(1947 - Paramount) Betty Hutton, John Lund, William Demarest
One Sheet: $50 - $100

PERILS OF PAULINE, THE
(1967 - Universal) Pat Boone, Pamela Austin
One Sheet: $7 - $15

PERILS OF PETERSBORO
(1926 - Pathe) Alice Day, Eddie Quillan
One Sheet: $200 - $400

PERILS OF THE JUNGLE
(1953 - Lippert) Clyde Beatty, Stanley Farrar
One Sheet: $20 - $40

PERILS OF THE ROYAL MOUNTED
(1942 - Columbia) Robert Stevens, Kenneth MacDonald
One Sheet: $50 - $100   *Serial. Western. 15 Chapters.*

PERILS OF THE WILD
(1925 - Universal) Joe Bonomo, Margaret Quimby
One Sheet: $150 - $300   *Serial. Western. 15 Chapters.*

One Sheet

PERILS OF THE WILDERNESS
(1956 - Columbia) Dennis Moore, Richard Emory
One Sheet: $40 - $75   *Serial. Western. 15 Chapters.*

PERILS OF THE YUKON
(1922 - Universal) -
One Sheet: $200 - $400   *Serial. Western. 15 Chapters.*

PERIOD OF ADJUSTMENT
(1962 - MGM) Tony Franciosa, Jane Fonda
One Sheet: $15 - $25

PERMANENT RECORD
(1988 - Paramount) Alan Boyce, Keanu Reeves
One Sheet: $2 - $3

PERMISSION TO KILL
(1975 - Avco Embassy) Dirk Bogard, Ava Gardner, Timothy Dalton
One Sheet: $7 - $15

PERRI
(1957 - Buena Vista/Disney) Narrated by Winston Hibler
One Sheet: $15 - $25

PERRY RHODAN
(1966 - -) Lang Jeffries, Essy Persson
One Sheet: $7 - $15   *German. AKA: MISSION STARDUST.*

PERSECUTION
(1974 - Tyburn) Lana Turner, Trevor Howard
One Sheet: $20 - $40   *AKA: TERROR OF SHEBA.*

PERSONA
(1967 - -) Liv Ullmann, Bibi Andersson
One Sheet: $30 - $50

PERSONAL AFFAIR
(1953 - United Artists) Gene Tierney, Leo Genn
One Sheet: $15 - $35

PERSONAL BEST
(1982 - Warner Bros.) Mariel Hemingway, Scott Glenn
One Sheet: $3 - $5

PERSONAL COLUMN
(1947 - United Artists) George Sanders, Lucille Ball
One Sheet: $75 - $150

PERSONAL MAID
(1931 - Paramount Publix) Nancy Carroll, Gene Raymond
One Sheet: $150 - $300

PERSONAL MAID'S SECRET
(1935 - Warner Bros.) Warren Hull, Margaret Lindsay
One Sheet: $75 - $125

PERSONAL PROPERTY
(1937 - MGM) Jean Harlow, Robert Taylor
One Sheet: $350 - $750

PERSONAL SECRETARY
(1938 - Universal) William Gargan, Joy Hodges
One Sheet: $50 - $100

PERSONAL SERVICES
(1987 - Vestron) Julie Walters, Alec McCowen
One Sheet: $3 - $5

PERSONALITY
(1930 - Columbia) Sally Starr, Johnny Arthur
One Sheet: $100 - $200

PERSONALITY KID, THE
(1934 - Warner Bros.) Pat O'Brien, Glenda Farrell
One Sheet: $100 - $200

PERSONALITY KID, THE
(1946 - Columbia) Anita Louise, Michael Duane
One Sheet: $15 - $25

PERSONS IN HIDING
(1939 - Paramount) Lynne Overman, Patricia Morison
One Sheet: $40 - $75

PERSUADER, THE
(1957 - Allied Artists) James Craig, William Talman
One Sheet: $15 - $25

PEST, THE
(1997 - TriStar) John Leguizamo, Jeffrey Jones
One Sheet: $3 - $5

PEST FROM THE WEST
(1939 - Columbia) Buster Keaton
One Sheet: $150 - $300

PEST MAN WINS, THE
(1951 - Columbia) The Three Stooges (Shemp)
One Sheet: $200 - $400   *Comedy short. Duotone. Remake of ANTS IN THE PANTRY.*

PESTS OF THE WEST
(1950 - RKO/Disney) Pluto
One Sheet: $500 - $800   *Cartoon. The Disney Poster, pg. 32.*

PET SEMATARY
(1989 - Paramount) Dale Midkiff, Denise Crosby, Fred Gwynne
One Sheet: $10 - $20

PET SEMATARY 2
(1992 - Paramount) Anthony Edwards, Clancy Brown, Edward Furlong
One Sheet: $3 - $5

PETE 'N' TILLIE
(1972 - Universal) Carol Burnett, Walter Matthau
One Sheet: $5 - $10

PETE KELLY'S BLUES
(1955 - Warner Bros.) Jack Webb, Janet Leigh
One Sheet: $30 - $60

PETE, PEARL AND THE POLE
(1973 - National General) Tony Anthony, Adolfo Celi
One Sheet: $3 - $5

PETE SMITH SPECIALTY, A
(- - -) See individual titles.

PETE'S DRAGON
(1977 - Buena Vista/Disney) Helen Reddy, Jim Dale, partial animation
One Sheet: $15 - $25

PETER IBBETSON
(1935 - Paramount) Gary Cooper, Ann Harding
One Sheet: $500 - $800

PETER PAN
(1924 - Paramount) Betty Bronson, Dir: Herbert Brenon
One Sheet: $800 - $1,500   *Graven Images, pg. 26.*

PETER PAN
(1953 - RKO/Disney) -
One Sheet: $250 - $600   *Cartoon. Cartoon Movie Posters #379.*

PETER PAN
(1958R - RKO/Disney) -
One Sheet: $75 - $150   *Re-release. Cartoon.*

PETER PAN
(1960R - Disney) -
One Sheet: $40 - $75   *Re-release. Cartoon.*

PETER PAN
(1969R - Disney) -
One Sheet: $15 - $25   *Re-release. Cartoon.*

PETER PAN
(1976R - Buena Vista/Disney) -
One Sheet: $15 - $25   *Re-release. Cartoon.*

PETER PAN
(1982R - Disney) -
One Sheet: $15 - $25   *Re-release. Cartoon.*

PETER PAN
(1989R - Disney) -
One Sheet: $15 - $25   *Re-release. Cartoon.*

PETER RABBIT AND TALES OF BEATRIX POTTER
(1971 - MGM) British Royal Ballet Company
One Sheet: $15 - $35   *Dancing (Ballet).*

PETER THE TRAMP
(1922 - -) Greta Garbo
One Sheet: $3,500 - $5,000

PETER'S FRIENDS
(1992 - Samuel Goldwyn) Kenneth Branagh, Emma Thompson
One Sheet: $5 - $10

PETERING-OUT
(1927 - Bray Productions) Directed by Walt Lantz
One Sheet: $250 - $600   *Cartoon. Cartoon Movie Posters #25.*

PETEY WHEATSTRAW
(1977 - Generation) Rudy Ray Moore, Jimmy Lynch
One Sheet: $5 - $10

PETRIFIED FOREST, THE
(1936 - Warner Bros.) Leslie Howard, Bette Davis, Humphrey Bogart
One Sheet: $6,500 - $10,000

PETRIFIED FOREST, THE
(1946R - Warner Bros.) Leslie Howard, Bette Davis, Humphrey Bogart
One Sheet: $100 - $200   *Re-release.*

PETTICOAT FEVER
(1936 - MGM) Robert Montgomery, Myrna Loy
One Sheet: $150 - $300

PETTICOAT LARCENY
(1943 - RKO) Ruth Warrick, Joan Carroll
One Sheet: $15 - $35

PETTICOAT POLITICS
(1941 - Republic) Roscoe Karns, Ruth Donnelly, Alan Ladd
One Sheet: $30 - $50

PETTY GIRL
(1950 - Columbia) Robert Cummings, Joan Caulfield
One Sheet: $125 - $250   *Petty art.*

PETTY GIRL
(1955R - Columbia) Robert Cummings, Joan Caulfield
One Sheet: $50 - $100   *Re-release.*

PETULIA
(1968 - Warner Bros.) Julie Christie, George C. Scott, Shirley Knight
One Sheet: $7 - $15

PEYTON PLACE
(1957 - 20th Century Fox) Lana Turner, Lloyd Nolan
One Sheet: $40 - $75

PHAEDRA
(1962 - United Artists) Melina Mercouri, Anthony Perkins
One Sheet: $5 - $10

PHANEIDON
(1905 - -) -
One Sheet: $1,000 - $1,800   *French. Price is for French 47x63.*

PHANTASM
(1979 - Avco Embassy) Michael Baldwin, Bill Thornbury
One Sheet: $15 - $25

PHANTASM II
(1988 - -) James Le Gros, Angus Scrimm
One Sheet: $5 - $10

PHANTOM, THE
(1943 - Columbia) Tom Tyler, Kenneth MacDonald
One Sheet: $250 - $500   *Serial. 15 Chapters.*

PHANTOM, THE
(1996 - Paramount) Billy Zane, Treat Williams, Kristy Swanson
One Sheet: $5 - $10

PHANTOM BROADCAST, THE
(1933 - Monogram) Ralph Forbes, Gail Patrick
One Sheet: $150 - $300

PHANTOM BULLET, THE
(1926 - Universal) Hoot Gibson
One Sheet: $150 - $300

PHANTOM COWBOY, THE
(1935 - -) Ted Wells
One Sheet: $150 - $300

PHANTOM COWBOY, THE
(1941 - Republic) Don Barry, Lynn Merrick
One Sheet: $30 - $60

PHANTOM CREEPS, THE
(1939 - Universal) Bela Lugosi, Robert Kent
One Sheet: $350 - $750   *Serial. 12 Chapters. Graven Images, pg. 99.*

PHANTOM EMPIRE, THE
(1935 - Mascot) Gene Autry, Frank Darro
One Sheet: $1,900 - $3,000   *Serial. Western. Sci-Fi. 12 Chapters. Cowboy Movie Posters #s 179, 182. Graven Images, pg. 99.*

PHANTOM EXPRESS, THE
(1932 - Majestic) J. Farrell MacDonald, Sally Blane
One Sheet: $100 - $200

PHANTOM FIEND, THE
(1932 - Olympia) Ivor Novello, Elizabeth Alan
One Sheet: $100 - $200

PHANTOM FROM 10,000 LEAGUES
(1956 - AIP) Kent Taylor, Cathy Downs
One Sheet: $75 - $150

One Sheet

PHANTOM FROM SPACE
(1953 - United Artists) Noreen Nash, Ted Cooper
One Sheet: $75 - $150

PHANTOM GOLD
(1938 - Columbia) Jack Luden, Beth Marion
One Sheet: $75 - $150

PHANTOM KILLER
(1942 - Monogram) Dick Purcell, Joan Woodbury
One Sheet: $40 - $75

PHANTOM LADY
(1944 - Universal) Ella Raines, Franchot Tone
One Sheet: $125 - $250

PHANTOM OF 42ND STREET
(1945 - PRC) Dave O'Brien, Kay Aldrich
One Sheet: $40 - $75

PHANTOM OF CHINATOWN
(1940 - Universal) Keye Luke, Grant Withers
One Sheet: $125 - $250

PHANTOM OF CRESTWOOD, THE
(1932 - RKO) Ricardo Cortez, Anita Louise
One Sheet: $250 - $600   *Graven Images, pg. 64.*

PHANTOM OF KENWOOD
(1933 - -) -
One Sheet: $100 - $200

PHANTOM OF PARIS, THE
(1931 - MGM) John Gilbert, Lewis Stone
One Sheet: $200 - $400

PHANTOM OF PARIS, THE
(1951R - MGM) John Gilbert, Lewis Stone
One Sheet: $40 - $75   *Re-release.*

PHANTOM OF SANTA FE
(1936 - Burroughs-Tarzan) Thomas Gerridy, Nina Quartaro
One Sheet: $100 - $200

PHANTOM OF THE AIR, THE
(1933 - Universal) Tom Tyler, Gloria Shea
One Sheet: $350 - $750   *Serial. 12 Chapters.*

PHANTOM OF THE JUNGLE
(1954 - Lippert) Jon Hall, Ray Montgomery
One Sheet: $15 - $35

PHANTOM OF THE MALL: ERIC'S REVENGE
(1988 - Fries) Derek Rydall, Jonathan Goldsmith
One Sheet: $3 - $5

PHANTOM OF THE OPERA, THE
(1925 - Universal) Lon Chaney, Norman Kerry
One Sheet: $22,000 - $35,000   *Price is for best two styles. One Sheet(lesser style):$10,000-$15,000. Graven Images, pg. 35.*

One Sheet

PHANTOM OF THE OPERA, THE
(1929R - Universal) Lon Chaney, Norman Kerry
One Sheet: $5,000 - $7,500   *Re-release with sound segments.*

PHANTOM OF THE OPERA, THE
(1943 - Universal) Nelson Eddy, Susanna Foster, Claude Rains
One Sheet: $700 - $1,200   *Graven Images, pg. 140.*

PHANTOM OF THE OPERA, THE
(1962 - Universal) Herbert Lom, Heather Sears
One Sheet: $50 - $100   *Graven Images, pg. 216.*

PHANTOM OF THE OPERA, THE
(1989 - 21st Century) Robert England, Jill Schoelen
One Sheet: $5 - $10

PHANTOM OF THE PARADISE
(1974 - 20th Century Fox) Paul Williams, Jessica Harper(debut), Dir: De Palma

One Sheet: $15 - $25   *Rock 'n' Roll.*

PHANTOM OF THE PLAINS
(1945 - Republic) William Elliott, Bobby Blake
One Sheet: $30 - $50   *Red Ryder series.*

PHANTOM OF THE RANGE
(1936 - Victory) Tom Tyler
One Sheet: $150 - $300

PHANTOM OF THE RUE MORGUE
(1954 - Warner Bros.) Karl Malden, Patricia Medina
One Sheet: $50 - $100   *Originally shot in 3-D. Graven Images, pg. 162.*

PHANTOM OF THE WEST, THE
(1931 - Mascot) Tom Tyler, Dorothy Gulliver
One Sheet: $200 - $400   *Serial. Western. 10 Chapters. Cowboy Movie Posters #'s 102-111.*

One Sheet

PHANTOM PATROL
(1936 - Ambassador) Kermit Maynard, Joan Barclay
One Sheet: $100 - $200

PHANTOM PLAINSMEN, THE
(1942 - Republic) Bob Steele, Tom Tyler
One Sheet: $50 - $100

PHANTOM PLANET, THE
(1962 - Four Crown) Dean Fredericks, Coleen Gray
One Sheet: $30 - $50

PHANTOM PRESIDENT, THE
(1932 - Paramount Publix) George M. Cohan, Jimmy Durante, Claudette Colbert
One Sheet: $600 - $1,000

PHANTOM RAIDERS
(1940 - MGM) Walter Pidgeon, Florence Rice
One Sheet: $40 - $75   *Nick Carter Detective series.*

PHANTOM RANGER
(1938 - Monogram) Tim McCoy
One Sheet: $150 - $300

PHANTOM RIDER, THE
(1936 - Universal) Buck Jones
One Sheet: $250 - $500   *Serial. Western. 15 chapters.*

PHANTOM RIDER, THE
(1946 - Republic) Robert Kent, Peggy Stewart
One Sheet: $125 - $250   *Serial. Western. 12 Chapters.*

PHANTOM SHIP
(1936 - Guaranteed) Bela Lugosi, Shirley Grey
One Sheet: $350 - $750

PHANTOM SPEAKS, THE
(1945 - Republic) Richard Arlen, Lynne Roberts
One Sheet: $40 - $75

PHANTOM STAGE, THE
(1939 - Universal) Bob Baker
One Sheet: $50 - $100

PHANTOM STAGE, THE
(1950R - Universal) Bob Baker
One Sheet: $15 - $35   *Re-release.*

PHANTOM STAGECOACH, THE
(1957 - Columbia) William Bishop, Richard Webb
One Sheet: $5 - $10

PHANTOM STALLION
(1954 - Republic) Rex Allen

One Sheet: $15 - $35

One Sheet

PHANTOM STRIKES, THE
(1939 - Monogram) Wilfrid Lawson
One Sheet: $75 - $125

PHANTOM SUBMARINE, THE
(1940 - Columbia) Anita Louise, Bruce Bennett
One Sheet: $30 - $50

PHANTOM THIEF, THE
(1946 - Columbia) Chester Morris, Jeff Donnell
One Sheet: $30 - $50   *Boston Blackie series*

PHANTOM THUNDERBOLT
(1933 - World Wide) Ken Maynard
One Sheet: $200 - $400

PHANTOM VALLEY
(1947 - Columbia) Charles Starrett, Virginia Hunter
One Sheet: $20 - $40

PHAR LAP
(1983 - 20th Century Fox) Tom Burlinson, Martin Vaughan
One Sheet: $5 - $10   *Sports (Horse Racing). Sports Movie Posters #254.*

PHARAOH'S CURSE
(1956 - United Artists) Mark Dana, Ziva Rodann
One Sheet: $30 - $50

PHARAOH'S WOMAN, THE
(1961 - Universal) John Drew Barrymore, Linda Cristal
One Sheet: $15 - $30

PHASE IV
(1974 - Paramount) Michael Murphy, Lynne Fredrick, Dir: Saul Bass
One Sheet: $7 - $15

PHENIX CITY STORY, THE
(1955 - Allied Artists) Richard Kiley, John McIntire
One Sheet: $15 - $35

PHENOMENA
(1985 - -) -
One Sheet: $10 - $20   *Italian.*

PHENOMENON
(1996 - Touchstone) John Travolta, Robert Duvall, Kyra Sedgwick
One Sheet: $7 - $15   *Fantasy.*

PHFFFT!
(1954 - Columbia) Judy Holliday, Jack Lemmon, Kim Novak
One Sheet: $15 - $30

PHILADELPHIA
(1993 - TriStar) Tom Hanks, Denzel Washington
One Sheet: $10 - $20   *Academy Award: Best Actor (Hanks). Academy Award Movie Posters #387.*

PHILADELPHIA EXPERIMENT, THE
(1984 - New World) Michael Pare, Nancy Allen
One Sheet: $3 - $5

PHILADELPHIA EXPERIMENT II, THE
(1993 - Trimark) Brad Johnson
One Sheet: $3 - $5

PHILADELPHIA STORY, THE
(1940 - MGM) Cary Grant, Katharine Hepburn, James Stewart
One Sheet: $1,900 - $3,000   *Academy Award: Best Actor(Stewart). Academy Award*

Movie Posters #75.

PHILBERT
(1963 - Warner Bros.) William Schallert
One Sheet: $5 - $10

PHILO VANCE RETURNS
(1947 - Pathe) William Wright, Terry Austin
One Sheet: $40 - $75

PHILO VANCE'S GAMBLE
(1947 - Pathe) Alan Curtis, Terry Austin
One Sheet: $40 - $75

PHILO VANCE'S SECRET MISSION
(1947 - Pathe Industries) Alan Curtis, Sheila Ryan
One Sheet: $40 - $75

PHOBIA
(1988 - Jadee) Gosia Dobrowolska, Sean Scully
One Sheet: $5 - $10

PHONE CALL FROM A STRANGER
(1952 - 20th Century Fox) Gary Merrill, Shelley Winters, Bette Davis
One Sheet: $40 - $75

PHONEY BALONEY
(1943 - Columbia) Fox & Crow
One Sheet: $350 - $750   *Cartoon. Full color poster with scene inset.*

PHONY AMERICAN, THE
(1963 - Signal) Christine Kaufmann, William Bendix
One Sheet: $7 - $15

PHONY EXPRESS
(1943 - Columbia) The Three Stooges (Curly)
One Sheet: $2,500 - $4,000   *Comedy short. Duotone.*

PHYNX, THE
(1970 - Warner Bros.) Michael Miller, Ray Chippeway
One Sheet: $3 - $5

PHYSICAL EVIDENCE
(1989 - Columbia) Burt Reynolds, Theresa Russell
One Sheet: $5 - $10

PIANO, THE
(1993 - Miramax) Holly Hunter, Harvey Keitel, Anna Paquin
One Sheet: $15 - $25   *Academy Award: Best Actress (Hunter), Best Supporting Actress (Paquin). Academy Award Movie Posters #386 & #389.*

PICADILLY INCIDENT
(1948 - MGM) Anna Neagle, Michael Wilding
One Sheet: $40 - $75   *AKA: THEY MET AT MIDNIGHT.*

PICCADILLY JIM
(1936 - MGM) Robert Montgomery, Madge Evans
One Sheet: $75 - $125

PICK A STAR
(1937 - MGM) Jack Haley, Patsy Kelly, Laurel & Hardy
One Sheet: $500 - $800

PICK AND SHOVEL
(1923 - Pathe) Stan Laurel
One Sheet: $800 - $1,500

PICK UP ON 101
(1972 - AIP) Lesley Ann Warren, Martin Sheen
One Sheet: $5 - $10

PICKANINNY, THE
(1921 - Pathe) Our Gang
One Sheet: $800 - $1,500

PICKING ON GEORGE
(1927 - Stern Bros.) -
One Sheet: $100 - $200

PICKING PEACHES
(1924 - Pathe) Harry Langdon
One Sheet: $900 - $1,600

PICKLE, THE
(1993 - Columbia) Danny Aiello, Dyan Cannon, Chris Penn
One Sheet: $3 - $5

PICKPOCKET
(1969 - New Yorker) Marin Lassalle, Pierre

Leymarie
One Sheet: $40 - $75   *French original:$200-$300.*

PICK-UP
(1933 - Paramount) Sylvia Sidney, George Raft
One Sheet: $600 - $1,000

PICKUP
(1951 - Columbia) Beverly Michaels, Hugo Haas
One Sheet: $50 - $100

PICK-UP
(1975 - Crown) Jill Senter, Alan Long
One Sheet: $5 - $10

PICKUP ALLEY
(1957 - Columbia) Victor Mature, Anita Ekberg
One Sheet: $20 - $40

PICK-UP ARTIST
(1987 - -) Molly Ringwald, Robert Downey, Jr.
One Sheet: $3 - $5

PICKUP ON SOUTH STREET
(1953 - 20th Century Fox) Richard Widmark, Jean Peters
One Sheet: $75 - $175

PICKWICK PAPERS
(1952 - Mayer-Kingsley) James Donald, Hermione Baddeley
One Sheet: $15 - $25

PICNIC
(1956 - Columbia) Kim Novak, William Holden, Cliff Robertson (film debut)
One Sheet: $125 - $250

PICNIC
(1961R - Columbia) Kim Novak, William Holden, Cliff Robertson
One Sheet: $15 - $25   *Re-release.*

PICNIC AT HANGING ROCK
(1975 - Atlantic) Rachel Robert, Dominic Guard, Dir: Peter Weir
One Sheet: $30 - $50

PICTURE BRIDE
(1995 - Miramax) Tamlyn Tomita, Youki Kudoh
One Sheet: $5 - $12

PICTURE BRIDES
(1933 - Allied) Regis Toomey, Alan Hale
One Sheet: $100 - $200

PICTURE MOMMY DEAD
(1966 - Embassy) Don Ameche, Martha Hyer
One Sheet: $7 - $15

PICTURE OF DORIAN GRAY, THE
(1945 - MGM) Hurd Hatfield, George Sanders
One Sheet: $100 - $200   *Graven Images, pg. 128.*

PICTURE SNATCHER
(1933 - Warner Bros.) James Cagney, Ralph Bellamy
One Sheet: $1,600 - $2,500

PIE COVERED WAGON, THE
(1932 - Educational) Shirley Temple
One Sheet: $150 - $300   *From the Baby Burlesk series.*

PIE IN THE SKY
(1996 - Fine Line) Josh Charles, John Goodman
One Sheet: $5 - $12

PIECE OF THE ACTION, A
(1977 - First Artists) Bill Cosby, Sidney Poitier, James Earl Jones
One Sheet: $10 - $20   *Black cast.*

PIECES OF DREAMS
(1970 - United Artists) Robert Forster, Lauren Hutton
One Sheet: $3 - $5

PIED PIPER, THE
(1942 - 20th Century Fox) Monty Woolley, Roddy McDowall
One Sheet: $40 - $75

PIED PIPER, THE
(1972 - Paramount) Donovan, Jack Wild, Donald Pleasence
One Sheet: $3 - $5

PIED PIPER OF HAMELIN, THE
(1917 - Thomas A. Edison) -

One Sheet: $300 - $700

PIER 13
(1940 - 20th Century Fox) Lynn Bari, Lloyd Nolan
One Sheet: $30 - $60

PIER 23
(1951 - Lippert) Hugh Beaumont, Richard Travis
One Sheet: $10 - $20

PIER 5, HAVANA
(1959 - United Artists) Cameron Mitchell, Allison Hayes
One Sheet: $10 - $20

PIERRE OF THE PLAINS
(1942 - MGM) John Carroll, Ruth Hussey
One Sheet: $15 - $35

PIES AND GUYS
(1958 - Columbia) The Three Stooges (Joe Besser)
One Sheet: $75 - $125   *Comedy short. Duotone. Remake of HALF-WITS' HOLIDAY.*

PIG'S CURLY TAIL, THE
(1926 - Bray) -
One Sheet: $800 - $1,500   *Cartoon. Cartoon Movie Posters #24.*

PIGEON THAT TOOK ROME, THE
(1962 - Paramount) Charlton Heston, Elsa Martinelli
One Sheet: $5 - $10

PIGEONS
(1970 - MGM) Jordan Christopher, Jill O'Hara
One Sheet: $3 - $5

PIGMEAT'S LAFF JAMBOREE
(194? - -) Pigmeat Markham
One Sheet: $50 - $100   *Black cast.*

PIGSKIN PALOOKA
(1952R - Monogram) Little Rascals
One Sheet: $50 - $100   *Re-release.*

PIGSKIN PARADE
(1936 - 20th Century Fox) Stuart Erwin, Patsy Kelly, Judy Garland, Betty Grable
One Sheet: $250 - $600   *Sports (Football). Garland's first feature film.*

PIKER'S DREAM, THE
(1907 - Vitagraph) -
One Sheet: $150 - $300

PILGRIM, THE
(1923 - First National) Charlie Chaplin, Edna Purviance
One Sheet: $5,000 - $7,500

PILGRIM LADY, THE
(1946 - Republic) Adele Mara, Warren Douglas
One Sheet: $15 - $30

PILGRIMAGE
(1933 - Fox) Henrietta Crosman, Heather Angel, Dir: John Ford
One Sheet: $250 - $500

PILLARS OF THE SKY
(1956 - Universal) Jeff Chandler, Dorothy Malone, Lee Marvin
One Sheet: $15 - $25

PILLOW OF DEATH
(1945 - Universal) Lon Chaney Jr., Brenda Joyce
One Sheet: $100 - $200

PILLOW TALK
(1959 - Universal) Rock Hudson, Doris Day
One Sheet: $75 - $125

PILLOW TO POST
(1945 - Warner Bros.) Ida Lupino, William Prince, Sydney Greenstreet
One Sheet: $40 - $75

PILOT NO. 5
(1943 - MGM) Franchot Tone, Marsha Hunt, Gene Kelly
One Sheet: $40 - $75

PILOT X
(1930 - Puritan) Lona Andre, John Carrol
One Sheet: $100 - $200

PIMPERNEL SMITH
(1942 - United Artists) Leslie Howard, Francis L. Sullivan

One Sheet: $50 - $100   *AKA: MISTER V.*

PINCH HITTER, THE
(1917 - Triangle) Charles Ray, Sylvia Breamer
One Sheet: $350 - $750   *Sports (Baseball). Sports Movie Posters #30.*

PINCHED IN THE FINISH
(1922 - Triangle) Ford Sterling, Mary Thurman
One Sheet: $250 - $600

PIN-DOWN GIRL
(1951 - Arena) -
One Sheet: $15 - $25   *Sexploitation.*

PINK ANGELS, THE
(1971 - Crown) John Alderman, Tom Basham
One Sheet: $5 - $10

PINK CADILLAC
(1989 - -) Clint Eastwood, Bernadette Peters
One Sheet: $15 - $25

PINK FLAMINGOS
(1972 - -) Divine, Mink Stole
One Sheet: $100 - $200

PINK FLOYD-THE WALL
(1982 - MGM) Bob Geldof, Christine Hargreaves
One Sheet: $30 - $60   *Rock 'n' Roll.*

PINK ICE
(1965 - United Artists) The Pink Panther
One Sheet: $40 - $75   *Cartoon.*

PINK JUNGLE, THE
(1968 - Univeral) James Garner, Eva Renzi
One Sheet: $5 - $10

PINK MOTEL
(1982 - New Image) -
One Sheet: $7 - $15

PINK PANTHER, THE
(1964 - United Artists) David Niven, Peter Sellers
One Sheet: $50 - $100

PINK PANTHER STRIKES AGAIN, THE
(1976 - United Artists) Peter Sellers, Herbert Lom
One Sheet: $7 - $15

PINK PHINK
(1965 - United Artists) The Pink Panther
One Sheet: $50 - $100   *Cartoon. First Pink Panther cartoon. Duotone stock poster with title inset. Huge image of the Pink Panther. Cartoon Movie Posters #389.*

PINKY
(1949 - 20th Century Fox) Jeanne Crain, Ethel Barrymore
One Sheet: $40 - $75   *Separate Cinema, pg. 82.*

PINOCCHIO
(1940 - RKO/Disney) -
One Sheet: $3,500 - $5,000   *Cartoon. Cartoon Movie Posters #326-#336. The Disney Poster, pg. 80.*

Half Sheet

PINOCCHIO
(1945R - RKO/Disney) -
One Sheet: $200 - $450   *Re-release. Cartoon.*

PINOCCHIO
(1954R - Disney) -
One Sheet: $100 - $200   *Re-release. Cartoon.*

PINOCCHIO
(1962R - Disney) -
One Sheet: $40 - $75 *Re-release.*
Cartoon.

PINOCCHIO
(1969 - Childhood Productions) Martin Florchinger, (Live Action & Puppets)
One Sheet: $5 - $10

PINOCCHIO
(1971R - Disney) -
One Sheet: $15 - $35 *Re-release.*
Cartoon.

PINOCCHIO
(1978R - Disney) -
One Sheet: $15 - $25 *Re-release.*
Cartoon.

PINOCCHIO
(1984R - Disney) -
One Sheet: $10 - $20 *Re-release.*
Cartoon.

PINOCCHIO
(1992R - Disney) -
One Sheet: $7 - $15 *Re-release.*
Cartoon. Advance:$30-40.

PINOCCHIO IN OUTER SPACE
(1965 - Universal) -
One Sheet: $30 - $50 *Cartoon.*

PINOCCHIO'S BIRTHDAY PARTY
(1974 - K-Tel) Nancy Belle Fuller, Sean Sullivan
One Sheet: $2 - $3

PINTO BANDIT, THE
(1944 - PRC) Jim Newill, Dave O'Brien
One Sheet: $20 - $40

PINTO CANYON
(1940 - Metropolitan) Bob Steele
One Sheet: $100 - $200

PINTO KID, THE
(1940 - Columbia) Charles Starrett
One Sheet: $40 - $75

PINTO RUSTLERS
(1937 - Reliable) Tom Tyler, George Walsh
One Sheet: $150 - $300

PINTO RUSTLERS
(194?R - -) Tom Tyler, George Walsh
One Sheet: $20 - $40 *Re-release.*

PIN-UP GIRL
(1944 - 20th Century Fox) Betty Grable, Martha Raye
One Sheet: $250 - $500

One Sheet

PIN-UP PLAYMATES
(197? - SRC) Janie Meyers, Candy Lace
One Sheet: $15 - $25 *Sexploitation.*

PIONEER DAYS
(1940 - Monogram) Jack Randall
One Sheet: $40 - $75

PIONEER JUSTICE
(1947 - Pathe) Lash LaRue
One Sheet: $30 - $60

PIONEER MARSHALL
(1949 - Republic) Monte Hale
One Sheet: $20 - $40

PIONEER TRAIL
(1938 - Columbia) Jack Luden
One Sheet: $40 - $75

PIONEER TRAILS
(1923 - -) Cullen Landis, Alice Calhoun
One Sheet: $150 - $300

PIONEERS, THE
(1941 - Monogram) Tex Ritter
One Sheet: $100 - $200

PIONEERS GOLD
(1924 - -) Pete Morrison
One Sheet: $250 - $600

PIONEERS OF THE FRONTIER
(1940 - Columbia) Bill Elliott
One Sheet: $40 - $75

PIONEERS OF THE WEST
(1940 - Republic) Three Mesquiteers (Bob Livingston, R. Hatton, D. Renaldo)
One Sheet: $40 - $75

PIPE DREAMS
(1976 - -) Gladys Knight
One Sheet: $15 - $25

PIPER, THE
(1919 - Fox) -
One Sheet: $200 - $400

PIPPI GOES ON BOARD
(1975 - G.G. Communications) Inger Nilsson
One Sheet: $7 - $15

PIPPI IN THE SOUTH SEAS
(1974 - G.G. Communications) Inger Nilsson
One Sheet: $7 - $15

PIPPI LONGSTOCKINGS
(1969 - -) Inger Nilsson
One Sheet: $10 - $20

PIPPI ON THE RUN
(1977 - G.G. Communications) Inger Nilsson
One Sheet: $5 - $10

PIRANHA
(1978 - New World) Heather Menzies, Kevin McCarthy
One Sheet: $7 - $15

PIRANHA 2: THE SPAWNING
(1983 - -) Tricia O'Neil, Steve Marachuk
One Sheet: $5 - $10

PIRATE, THE
(1948 - MGM) Judy Garland, Gene Kelly
One Sheet: $125 - $250

PIRATE AND THE SLAVE GIRL
(1961 - Crest) Lex Barker, Chelo Alonso
One Sheet: $15 - $25 *French/Italian.*

PIRATE MOVIE
(1982 - 20th Century Fox) Kristy McNichol, Christopher Atkins
One Sheet: $3 - $5

One Sheet

PIRATE PARTY ON CATALINA ISLE
(1936 - MGM) Davies, Grant, Errol, Morris
One Sheet: $250 - $500

PIRATE SUBMARINE
(1951 - Lippert) -
One Sheet: $10 - $20

PIRATE TREASURE
(1934 - Universal) Richard Talmadge, Lucille Lund
One Sheet: $300 - $700 *Serial. 12 Chapters.*

PIRATES
(1986 - Cannon) Walter Matthau, Damien Thomas

PIRATES OF BLOOD RIVER, THE
(1962 - Columbia) Kerwin Mathews, Glenn Corbett, Christopher Lee
One Sheet: $15 - $25

PIRATES OF CAPRI, THE
(1949 - Film Classics) Louis Hayward, Binnie Barnes
One Sheet: $15 - $25

PIRATES OF MONTEREY
(1947 - Universal) Maria Montez, Rod Cameron, Gilbert Roland
One Sheet: $30 - $60

PIRATES OF PENZANCE
(1982 - Universal) Kevin Kline, Linda Ronstadt
One Sheet: $5 - $10

PIRATES OF THE HIGH SEAS
(1950 - Columbia) Buster Crabbe, Lois Hall
One Sheet: $40 - $75 *Serial. 15 Chapters.*

PIRATES OF THE PRAIRIE
(1942 - RKO) Tim Holt
One Sheet: $30 - $50

PIRATES OF THE SEVEN SEAS
(1941 - Film Alliance) John Lodge, Judy Kelly
One Sheet: $75 - $125

PIRATES OF THE SKIES
(1939 - Universal) Kent Taylor, Rochelle Hudson
One Sheet: $75 - $125

PIRATES OF TORTUGA
(1961 - 20th Century Fox) Ken Scott, Letitia Roman
One Sheet: $3 - $5

PIRATES OF TRIPOLI
(1954 - Columbia) Paul Henreid, Paul Newland
One Sheet: $15 - $30

PIRATES ON HORSEBACK
(1941 - Paramount) William Boyd
One Sheet: $200 - $400

PIRATES' HARBOR
(1951R - Republic) Kane Richmond, Kay Aldridge
One Sheet: $10 - $20 *Serial. Re-titled re-release of HAUNTED HARBOR. 15 Chapters.*

PISTOL
(1970' - -) -
One Sheet: $4 - $8

PISTOL FOR RINGO, A
(1966 - Embassy) Montgomery Wood, Fernando Sancho
One Sheet: $3 - $5

PISTOL HARVEST
(1951 - RKO) Tim Holt, Richard Martin
One Sheet: $20 - $40

PISTOL PACKIN' MAMA
(1943 - Republic) Ruth Terry, Bob Livingston, Nat "King" Cole
One Sheet: $30 - $50

PISTON PACKIN' NITWITS
(1945 - Columbia) Harry Langdon
One Sheet: $30 - $50

PIT AND THE PENDULUM, THE
(1961 - AIP) Vincent Price, John Kerr
One Sheet: $30 - $60 *One Sheet is black and white. Graven Images, pg. 208.*

PIT AND THE PENDULUM, THE
(1991 - -) Lance Henriksen, Rona De Ricci
One Sheet: $5 - $10

PIT OF DARKNESS
(1962 - Butchers) William Franklyn, Nigel Green
One Sheet: $15 - $35

PIT STOP
(1969 - Crown) Brian Donlevy
One Sheet: $7 - $15 *Sports (Auto racing).*

PITCHING EDGE
(1966 - -) Jack Nicklaus
One Sheet: $40 - $75 *Sports (Golf). Film about golf techniques by golf-great Jack*

One Sheet: $3 - $5

Nicklaus.

PITFALL, THE
(1948 - United Artists) Dick Powell, Lizabeth Scott
One Sheet: $75 - $125

PITFALLS OF A BIG CITY
(1923 - Pathe) Ben Turpin
One Sheet: $250 - $600

PITTSBURGH
(1942 - Universal) Marlene Dietrich, John Wayne, Randolph Scott
One Sheet: $350 - $750

PITTSBURGH KID, THE
(1941 - Republic) Billy Conn, Jean Parker
One Sheet: $40 - $75 *Sports Movie Posters #358.*

P.K. AND THE KID
(1982 - Castle Hill) Paul LeMat, Molly Ringwald
One Sheet: $5 - $10 *Sports (Arm Wrestling). Sports Movie Posters #4.*

PLACE CALLED GLORY, A
(1966 - Embassy) Lex Barker, Pierre Brice
One Sheet: $5 - $10

PLACE FOR LOVERS, A
(1969 - MGM) Faye Dunaway, Marcello Mastroianni
One Sheet: $10 - $20

PLACE IN THE SUN, A
(1951 - Paramount) Montgomery Clift, Elizabeth Taylor, Shelley Winters
One Sheet: $350 - $750 *Academy Award: Best Direction(George Stevens). Academy Award Movie Posters #135 & #136.*

One Sheet

PLACE IN THE SUN, A
(1959R - Paramount) Montgomery Clift, Elizabeth Taylor, Shelley Winters
One Sheet: $50 - $100 *Re-release.*

PLACE OF ONE'S OWN, A
(1945 - Eagle) James Mason, Margaret Lockwood
One Sheet: $40 - $75

PLACES IN THE HEART
(1984 - TriStar) Sally Field, Lindsay Crouse
One Sheet: $10 - $20 *Academy Award: Best Actress (Fields). Academy Award Movie Posters #337.*

PLAGUE
(1978 - Group 1) Daniel Pilon, Kate Reid
One Sheet: $10 - $20

PLAGUE OF THE ZOMBIES, THE
(1966 - 20th Century Fox) Andre Morell, Diane Clare
One Sheet: $15 - $35

PLAINSMAN, THE
(1937 - Paramount) Gary Cooper, Jean Arthur
One Sheet: $1,600 - $2,500 *Cowboy Movie Posters #s 207, 208, 209.*

PLAINSMAN, THE
(1942R - Paramount) Gary Cooper, Jean Arthur
One Sheet: $100 - $200 *Re-release.*

PLAINSMAN, THE
(1964 - Universal) Robert Culp, Brian Keith
One Sheet: $10 - $20 *AKA: THE RAIDERS.*

PLAINSMAN, THE
(1966 - Universal) Don Murray, Guy Stockwell
One Sheet: $10 - $20

PLAINSMAN AND THE LADY, THE
(1946 - Republic) William Elliott, Vera Ralston
One Sheet: $20 - $40

PLAN 9 FROM OUTER SPACE
(1959 - 20th Century Fox) Gregory Walcott,
Mona McKinnon, Bela Lugosi
One Sheet: $700 - $1,200   *Graven Images, pg. 189. Lugosi's last film.*

PLAN FOR DESTRUCTION
(1943 - MGM) Lewis Stone, Frank Reicher,
George Lynn
One Sheet: $200 - $400

PLANE NUTS
(1933 - MGM) Ted Healy and His Stooges
(Moe, Larry & Curly)
One Sheet: $10,000 - $15,000   *Comedy musical short.*

PLANES, TRAINS AND AUTOMOBILES
(1987 - Paramount) Steve Martin, John Candy
One Sheet: $5 - $10

PLANET OF THE APES
(1968 - 20th Century Fox) Charlton Heston,
Roddy McDowall
One Sheet: $125 - $250   *Graven Images, pg. 226.*

PLANET OF THE APES/BENEATH THE PLANET OF THE APES COMBO
(1971R - 20th Century Fox) Charlton Heston
One Sheet: $40 - $75   *Re-release double feature.*

PLANET OF THE VAMPIRES
(1965 - AIP) Barry Sullivan, Norma Bengell
One Sheet: $30 - $60

One Sheet

PLANET OUTLAWS
(1940? - Goodwill) Larry (Buster) Crabbe
One Sheet: $100 - $200   *Feature length re-release.*

PLASTICS INVENTOR, THE
(1944 - RKO/Disney) Donald Duck
One Sheet: $1,300 - $2,000   *Cartoon. The Disney Poster, pg. 60.*

PLATINUM BLONDE
(1931 - Columbia) Jean Harlow, Loretta Young
One Sheet: $2,200 - $3,500

PLATINUM HIGH SCHOOL
(1960 - MGM) Mickey Rooney, Terry Moore
One Sheet: $20 - $40

PLATOON
(1986 - Orion) Tom Berenger, Willem Dafoe
One Sheet: $20 - $40   *Academy Award: Best Picture, Best Director(Stone). Price is for non-review style. Academy Award Movie Posters #347 & #348.*

PLATOON LEADER
(1988 - -) Michael Dudikoff, Brian Libby
One Sheet: $3 - $5

PLAY DIRTY
(1969 - United Artists) Michael Caine, Nigel Green
One Sheet: $5 - $10

PLAY GIRL
(1941 - RKO) Kay Francis, James Ellison
One Sheet: $50 - $100

PLAY IT AGAIN, SAM
(1972 - Paramount) Woody Allen, Diane Keaton
One Sheet: $15 - $30

PLAY IT AGAIN, SAM
(1976R - Paramount) Woody Allen, Diane Keaton
One Sheet: $10 - $20   *Re-release.*

PLAY IT AS IT LAYS
(1972 - Universal) Tuesday Weld, Anthony Perkins
One Sheet: $5 - $10

PLAY IT COOL
(1963 - Allied Artists) Billy Fury, Dennis Price
One Sheet: $7 - $15

PLAY MISTY FOR ME
(1971 - Universal) Clint Eastwood, Jessica Walter, Donna Mills
One Sheet: $15 - $35

PLAYBOY OF PARIS
(1930 - Paramount Publix) Maurice Chevalier, Frances Dee
One Sheet: $350 - $750

PLAYBOY OF THE WESTERN WORLD, THE
(1963 - Janus) Siobhan McKenna, Gary Raymond
One Sheet: $7 - $15

PLAYER, THE
(1992 - Fine Line) Tim Robbins, Anjelica Huston, Cher
One Sheet: $10 - $20   *Style B:$20-35. Style C:$15-30.*

PLAYERS
(1979 - Paramount) Ali MacGraw, Dean Paul Martin
One Sheet: $5 - $10

PLAYGIRL
(1932 - Warner Bros.) Loretta Young, Norman Foster
One Sheet: $200 - $400

PLAYGIRL
(1954 - Universal) Shelley Winters, Barry Sullivan
One Sheet: $20 - $40

PLAYGIRL AFTER DARK
(1962 - Topaz) Jayne Mansfield
One Sheet: $40 - $75   *AKA: TOO HOT TO HANDLE.*

PLAYGIRL AND THE WAR MINISTER, THE
(1963 - Union) Joan Greenwood, Cecil Parker
One Sheet: $3 - $5

PLAYGIRLS AND THE VAMPIRE
(1964 - Nord) Lyla Rocco, Walter Brandi, Maria Giovannini
One Sheet: $20 - $40

PLAYHOUSE, THE
(1922 - First National) Buster Keaton
One Sheet: $7,500 - $12,000

PLAYING AROUND
(1930 - First National) Alice White, Chester Morris
One Sheet: $100 - $200

PLAYING THE GAME
(1918 - Paramount) Charles Ray, Doris Dee
One Sheet: $150 - $300

PLAYING THE PONIES
(1937 - Columbia) The Three Stooges (Curly)
One Sheet: $8,500 - $14,000   *Comedy short. Duotone.*

PLAYMATES
(1941 - RKO) John Barrymore, Lupe Velez
One Sheet: $75 - $150   *Barrymore's final film.*

PLAZA SUITE
(1971 - Paramount) Walter Matthau, Maureen Stapleton
One Sheet: $3 - $5

PLEASE BELIEVE ME
(1949 - MGM) Deborah Kerr, Robert Walker
One Sheet: $15 - $35

PLEASE DON'T EAT THE DAISIES
(1960 - MGM) Doris Day, David Niven
One Sheet: $20 - $40

PLEASE! MR. BALZAC
(1957 - Hoche) Brigitte Bardot, Daniel Gelin
One Sheet: $50 - $100   *French. AKA: MADEMOISELLE STRIPTEASE; WHILE*

PLUCKING THE DAISY.

PLEASE MURDER ME
(1956 - DCA) Angela Lansbury, Raymond Burr
One Sheet: $15 - $30

PLEASE, NOT NOW
(1963 - 20th Century Fox) Brigitte Bardot
One Sheet: $30 - $60

PLEASE TURN OVER
(1960 - Columbia) Ted Ray, Jean Kent
One Sheet: $5 - $10

PLEASURE BOUND
(1925 - Educational) Lige Conley
One Sheet: $125 - $250

PLEASURE CRUISE
(1933 - Fox) Genevieve Tobin, Roland Young
One Sheet: $150 - $300

PLEASURE GARDEN, THE
(1925 - Gainsborough) Virginia Valli, Dir: Alfred Hitchcock
One Sheet: $10,000 - $15,000   *Hitchcock's first film as director. U.S. posters released by Artlee Pictures.*

PLEASURE MAD
(1923 - Metro) Norma Shearer, Huntley Gordon
One Sheet: $200 - $400

PLEASURE OF HIS COMPANY, THE
(1961 - Paramount) Fred Astaire, Debbie Reynolds
One Sheet: $30 - $60

PLEASURE PIT, THE
(1971 - -) Pascale Audret, Elsa Martinelli
One Sheet: $3 - $5

PLEASURE SEEKERS, THE
(1965 - 20th Century Fox) Ann-Margret, Tony Franciosa
One Sheet: $15 - $30

PLENTY
(1985 - 20th Century Fox) Meryl Streep, Charles Dance, Tracey Ullman
One Sheet: $3 - $5

PLOT THICKENS, THE
(1936 - RKO) ZaSu Pitts, Louise Latimer
One Sheet: $200 - $400

PLOT TO KILL ROOSEVELT, THE
(1948 - Selected) Derek Farr, Marta Labarr
One Sheet: $30 - $50

PLOUGH AND THE STARS, THE
(1937 - RKO) Barbara Stanwyck, Preston Foster, Dir: John Ford
One Sheet: $250 - $600

PLUMBER, THE
(1924 - Pathe) Ralph Graves
One Sheet: $150 - $300

PLUMBER'S DAUGHTER, THE
(1926 - Pathe) Alice Day
One Sheet: $200 - $400

PLUNDER
(1922 - Pathe) Pearl White
One Sheet: $200 - $400   *Serial. 15 Chapters.*

PLUNDER IN THE SUN
(1953 - Warner Bros.) Glenn Ford, Diana Lynn
One Sheet: $20 - $40

PLUNDER ROAD
(1957 - 20th Century Fox) Gene Raymond, Wayne Morris
One Sheet: $15 - $25

PLUNDERERS, THE
(1948 - Republic) Rod Cameron, Adrian Booth
One Sheet: $20 - $40

PLUNDERERS, THE
(1954R - Republic) Rod Cameron, Adrian Booth
One Sheet: $7 - $15   *Re-release.*

PLUNDERERS, THE
(1960 - Allied Artists) Jeff Chandler, John Saxon
One Sheet: $7 - $15

PLUNDERERS OF PAINTED FLATS
(1959 - Republic) Corinne Calvet, John Carroll
One Sheet: $5 - $10

PLUTO AT THE ZOO
(1942 - RKO/Disney) Pluto
One Sheet: $800 - $1,500   *Cartoon. Duotone. Cartoon Movie Posters #188.*

PLUTO JUNIOR
(1942 - RKO/Disney) Pluto
One Sheet: $1,600 - $2,500   *Cartoon. Full color. Cartoon Movie Posters #187.*

PLUTO'S BLUE NOTE
(1947 - RKO/Disney) Pluto
One Sheet: $250 - $500   *Cartoon. The Disney Poster, pg. 43.*

PLUTO'S CHRISTMAS TREE
(1952 - RKO/Disney) Pluto, Mickey Mouse, Chip & Dale
One Sheet: $700 - $1,200   *Cartoon. Full color. The Disney Poster, pg. 34.*

PLUTO'S DREAM HOUSE
(1940 - RKO/Disney) Pluto, Mickey Mouse
One Sheet: $5,000 - $7,500   *Cartoon. The Disney Poster, pg. 28.*

PLUTO'S FLEDGLING
(1948 - RKO/Disney) Pluto
One Sheet: $500 - $900   *Cartoon.*

PLUTO'S HEART THROB
(1949 - RKO/Disney) Pluto
One Sheet: $700 - $1,200   *Cartoon.*

PLUTO'S HOUSEWARMING
(1946 - RKO) Pluto
One Sheet: $600 - $1,000   *Cartoon. The Disney Poster, pg. 33.*

PLUTO'S KID BROTHER
(1946 - RKO/Disney) Pluto
One Sheet: $600 - $1,000   *Cartoon. Full color. Cartoon Movie Posters #191.*

PLUTO'S PARTY
(1952 - RKO/Disney) Pluto, Mickey Mouse
One Sheet: $250 - $600   *Cartoon. The Disney Poster, pg. 38.*

PLUTO'S QUINTUPLETS
(1937 - Disney) Pluto
One Sheet: $1,900 - $3,000   *Cartoon.*

PLUTO'S SURPRISE PACKAGE
(1949 - RKO/Disney) Pluto
One Sheet: $500 - $800   *Cartoon. Full color.*

PLUTO'S SWEATER
(1949 - RKO/Disney) Pluto
One Sheet: $500 - $800   *Cartoon. The Disney Poster, pg. 42.*

PLUTOPIA
(1951 - RKO/Disney) Pluto, Mickey Mouse
One Sheet: $800 - $1,500   *Cartoon. The Disney Poster, pg. 35.*

PLYMOUTH ADVENTURE
(1952 - MGM) Spencer Tracy, Gene Tierney
One Sheet: $40 - $75

POACHER'S DAUGHTER, THE
(1960 - Show Corp. of America) Julie Harris, Harry Brogan
One Sheet: $7 - $15

POCAHONTAS
(1995 - Buena Vista) Voices of Mel Gibson, Irene Bedard
One Sheet: $15 - $25   *Cartoon. Advance Style: $20-$30.*

One Sheet

POCATELLO KID, THE
(1931 - Tiffany) Ken Maynard
One Sheet: $200 - $400   *One Sheet*
(re-release by Albert Dezel Prod.): $150-250.

POCKET MONEY
(1972 - National General) Paul Newman, Lee
Marvin
One Sheet: $15 - $25

POCKETFUL OF MIRACLES
(1961 - United Artists) Glenn Ford, Bette Davis,
Dir: Frank Capra
One Sheet: $40 - $75

One Sheet

POE'S TALES OF TERROR
(1962 - AIP) Vincent Price, Peter Lorre
One Sheet: $30 - $60

POETIC JUSTICE
(1993 - Universal) Janet Jackson, Tupar
Shakur, Dir: John Singleton
One Sheet: $7 - $15

One Sheet

POINT, THE
(1971 - -) Narrated by Ringo Starr
One Sheet: $5 - $10   *Cartoon.*
Made for TV Movie.

POINT BLANK
(1967 - MGM) Lee Marvin, Angie Dickinson
One Sheet: $50 - $100

POINT OF NO RETURN
(1993 - Warner Bros.) Bridget Fonda, Dermot
Mulroney
One Sheet: $7 - $15

POINT OF ORDER
(1964 - Point Films) McCarthy hearings
One Sheet: $20 - $45

POINT OF TERROR
(1971 - Crown) Peter Carpenter
One Sheet: $3 - $5

POINTED HEELS
(1930 - Paramount) William Powell, Fay Wray
One Sheet: $700 - $1,200

POINTER, THE
(1939 - RKO/Disney) Mickey Mouse
One Sheet: $5,500 - $9,000   *Cartoon.*

POINTS WEST
(1929 - Universal) Hoot Gibson
One Sheet: $250 - $600

POISONED PARADISE
(1924 - -) Kenneth Harlan, Carmel Myers, Clara
Bow
One Sheet: $1,300 - $2,000

POLAR PLAYMATES
(1941 - Columbia) Color Rhapsodies
One Sheet: $150 - $350   *Cartoon. Full
color semi-stock poster with inset of title.*

POLICE
(1916 - Essanay) Charlie Chaplin, Edna
Purviance
One Sheet: $6,500 - $10,000

POLICE ACADEMY
(1984 - Columbia) Steve Guttenberg, G.W.
Bailey
One Sheet: $7 - $15

**POLICE ACADEMY 2: THEIR FIRST
ASSIGNMENT**
(1985 - -) Steve Guttenberg, Bubba Smith
One Sheet: $3 - $5

POLICE ACADEMY 3: BACK IN TRAINING
(1986 - -) Steve Guttenberg, Bubba Smith
One Sheet: $3 - $5

POLICE ACADEMY 4: CITIZENS ON PATROL
(1987 - -) Steve Guttenberg, Bubba Smith
One Sheet: $3 - $5

**POLICE ACADEMY 5: ASSIGNMENT AT MIAMI
BEACH**
(1988 - -) Bubba Smith, G.W. Bailey, George
Gaynes
One Sheet: $3 - $5

POLICE ACADEMY 6: CITY UNDER SEIGE
(1989 - -) Bubba Smith, David Graf
One Sheet: $3 - $5

POLICE BULLETS
(1942 - Monogram) John Archer, Joan Marsh,
Milburn Stone
One Sheet: $30 - $50

POLICE CALL
(1933 - Showmen's) Nick Stuart, Merna
Kennedy
One Sheet: $100 - $200   *Sports
(Boxing). Sports Movie Posters #132.*

One Sheet

POLICE CAR 17
(1933 - Columbia) Tim McCoy
One Sheet: $200 - $400

POLICE DOG STORY, THE
(1961 - United Artists) Jim Brown, Merry
Anders
One Sheet: $7 - $15

POLICE NURSE
(1963 - 20th Century Fox) Ken Scott, Merry
Anders
One Sheet: $7 - $15

POLICY MAN
(1938 - Creative) Jimmie Baskette, Count
Basie (debut)
One Sheet: $300 - $650   *Black cast.
Separate Cinema, pg. 139.*

POLITICS
(1931 - MGM) Marie Dressler, Roscoe Ates
One Sheet: $250 - $500

POLKA-DOT PUSS
(1949 - MGM) Tom & Jerry
One Sheet: $300 - $700   *Cartoon. Full
color stone litho.*

POLLY OF THE CIRCUS
(1932 - MGM) Clark Gable, Marion Davies
One Sheet: $600 - $1,000

POLLY OF THE STORM COUNTRY
(1920 - First National) Mildred Harris Chaplin

One Sheet: $800 - $1,400

POLLY TIX IN WASHINGTON
(1933 - Educational) Shirley Temple
One Sheet: $150 - $300   *From the
Baby Burlesk series.*

POLLYANA
(1920 - United Artists) Mary Pickford
One Sheet: $1,900 - $3,000

POLLYANA
(1960 - Buena Vista) Hayley Mills, Jane
Wyman
One Sheet: $20 - $40

One Sheet

POLO JOE
(1936 - Warner Bros.) Joe E. Brown, Carol
Hughes
One Sheet: $75 - $150   *Sports Movie
Posters #291.*

POLO JOE
(194?R - Warner Bros.) Joe E. Brown
One Sheet: $30 - $50   *Re-release.*

POLTERGEIST
(1982 - MGM) JoBeth Williams, Craig T. Nelson
One Sheet: $10 - $20   *Advance:$25-
30.*

POLTERGEIST II: THE OTHER SIDE
(1986 - MGM/United Artists) JoBeth Williams,
Craig T. Nelson
One Sheet: $5 - $10

POLTERGEIST III
(1988 - MGM/UA) Tom Skerritt, Nancy Allen
One Sheet: $5 - $10

POLYESTER
(1981 - New Line) Divine, Tab Hunter
One Sheet: $40 - $75   *Filmed in
"Odorama".*

POLYGAMY
(1936 - Unusual) Wade Sain, Ti Ti Delma
One Sheet: $50 - $100

POM POM GIRLS, THE
(1976 - Crown International) Robert Carradine,
Jennifer Ashley
One Sheet: $15 - $30

PONJOLA
(1923 - -) Anna Q. Nilsson, James Kirkwood
One Sheet: $125 - $250

PONTIAC MOON
(1994 - Paramount) Ted Danson, Mary
Steenburgen, Eric Schweig
One Sheet: $3 - $5

PONY EXPRESS
(1925 - Paramount) Betty Compson, Ricardo
Cortez, Wallace Beery
One Sheet: $200 - $400

PONY EXPRESS
(1953 - Paramount) Charlton Heston, Rhonda
Fleming
One Sheet: $20 - $40

PONY EXPRESS DAYS
(1940 - Warner Bros.) George Reeves
One Sheet: $40 - $75

PONY EXPRESS RIDER
(1976 - Doty-Dayton) Stewart Petersen,
Maureen McCormick, Ken Curtis
One Sheet: $7 - $15

PONY POST
(1940 - Universal) Johnny Mack Brown, Fuzzy

Night
One Sheet: $40 - $75

PONY SOLDIER
(1952 - 20th Century Fox) Tyrone Power,
Cameron Mitchell
One Sheet: $30 - $50

POOL OF LONDON
(1950 - Universal) Susan Show, Bonar
Colleano
One Sheet: $7 - $15

POOL SHARKS
(1915 - -) W.C. Fields
One Sheet: $5,000 - $7,500

POOR BUT BEAUTIFUL
(1957 - Trans Lux) -
One Sheet: $15 - $25

POOR COW
(1968 - National General) Terence Stamp,
Carol White
One Sheet: $5 - $10

POOR LITTLE RICH GIRL
(1917 - Artcraft) Mary Pickford
One Sheet: $1,900 - $3,000

POOR LITTLE RICH GIRL
(1936 - 20th Century Fox) Shirley Temple,
Alice Faye
One Sheet: $1,600 - $2,500

POOR LITTLE RICH GIRL
(1965 - Warhol) Edie Sedgewick
One Sheet: $40 - $75

POOR NUT, THE
(1927 - First National) Jack Mulhall, Charlie
Murray
One Sheet: $150 - $300

POOR RICH, THE
(1934 - Universal) Edward Everett Horton,
Edna May Oliver
One Sheet: $125 - $250

POP ALWAYS PAYS
(1940 - RKO) Leon Errol, Dennis O'Keefe
One Sheet: $40 - $75

POP GOES THE EASEL
(1935 - Columbia) The Three Stooges (Curly)
One Sheet: $13,000 - $20,000   *Comedy short.
Duotone.*

POPCORN
(1970 - Sherpix) Mick Jagger, Jimi Hendrix
One Sheet: $30 - $60   *Rock 'n' Roll.*

POPCORN
(1991 - -) Jill Schoelen, Tom Villard
One Sheet: $5 - $10

POPE OF GREENWICH VILLAGE, THE
(1984 - MGM/United Artists) Eric Roberts,
Mickey Rourke, Daryl Hannah
One Sheet: $15 - $25

POPEYE
(1980 - Paramount) Robin Williams, Shelley
Duvall
One Sheet: $5 - $10

POPEYE FOLLIES
(1960' - Paramount) Popeye
One Sheet: $20 - $40   *Cartoon.*

POPEYE STOCK POSTER
(1941 - Paramount) Popeye
One Sheet: $500 - $800   *Cartoon.
Duotone. Popeye with can of spinach (with blank
space for title).*

POPEYE STOCK POSTER
(1943 - Paramount) Popeye
One Sheet: $150 - $300   *Cartoon.
Duotone. Popeye flexing muscle. Title sheets are
often attached to the One Sheet.*

POPEYE STOCK POSTER
(1949 - Paramount) Popeye
One Sheet: $125 - $250   *Cartoon.
Popeye (left-handed) punching thug while Olive
dances.*

POPEYE STOCK POSTER
(1950 - Paramount) Popeye
One Sheet: $100 - $200   *Cartoon.
Popeye at top (smaller scene of punching Popeye
& dancing Olive below). Cartoon Movie Posters
#225.*

POPEYE, THE ACE OF SPACE
(1953 - Paramount) Popeye
One Sheet: $600 - $1,100 *Cartoon. 3-D.*
Cartoon Movie Posters #226.

POPEYE THE SAILOR
(1933 - Paramount) Popeye
One Sheet: $10,000 - $15,000 *Cartoon. First*
Popeye cartoon (released in Betty Boop series).

**POPEYE THE SAILOR MEETS ALI BABA'S
FORTY THIEVES**
(1937 - Paramount) Popeye
One Sheet: $3,500 - $5,000 *Cartoon.*
Second Popeye feature cartoon. Full color.
Cartoon Movie Posters #222.

**POPEYE THE SAILOR MEETS SINDBAD THE
SAILOR**
(1936 - Paramount) Popeye
One Sheet: $3,500 - $5,000 *Cartoon. Full*
color. Cartoon Movie Posters #221.

POPI
(1969 - United Artists) Alan Arkin, Rita Moreno
One Sheet: $5 - $10

POPPY
(1917 - Selznick) Norma Talmadge
One Sheet: $500 - $800

One Sheet

POPPY
(1936 - Paramount) W.C. Fields, Rochelle
Hudson
One Sheet: $800 - $1,500

POPPY GIRL'S HUSBAND, THE
(1919 - Artcraft) William S. Hart, Juanita
Hansen
One Sheet: $600 - $1,000

POPPY IS ALSO A FLOWER, THE
(1966 - Comet) Senta Berger, Stephen Boyd
One Sheet: $10 - $20

PORGY AND BESS
(1959 - Columbia) Sidney Poitier, Dorothy
Dandridge
One Sheet: $250 - $500 *Separate*
Cinema, pg. 37.

PORK CHOP HILL
(1959 - United Artists) Gregory Peck, Harry
Guardino
One Sheet: $30 - $50

PORKULIAR PIGGY
(1944 - Columbia) Li'l Abner
One Sheet: $250 - $500 *Cartoon. Full*
color poster with scene inset.

PORKY'S
(1982 - 20th Century Fox) Kim Cattrall, Scott
Colomby
One Sheet: $10 - $20

PORKY'S II: THE NEXT DAY
(1983 - 20th Century Fox) Dan Monahan, Wyatt
Knight
One Sheet: $3 - $5

PORKY'S REVENGE
(1985 - 20th Century Fox) Dan Monahan, Wyatt
Knight
One Sheet: $3 - $5

PORT AFRIQUE
(1956 - Columbia) Pier Angeli, Phil Carey
One Sheet: $7 - $15

PORT OF FORTY THIEVES
(1944 - Republic) Richard Powers, Stephanie
Bachelor

One Sheet: $15 - $30

PORT OF HELL
(1954 - Allied Artists) Wayne Morris, Carole
Mathews
One Sheet: $10 - $20

PORT OF LOST DREAMS
(1935 - Chesterfield) William Boyd, Lola Lane
One Sheet: $150 - $300

PORT OF MISSING GIRLS
(1938 - Monogram) Judith Allen, Milburn Stone
One Sheet: $50 - $100

PORT OF MISSING MICE
(1943 - 20th Century Fox) Mighty Mouse
Cartoon. See "Terrytoon Stock" for prices.
Cartoon Movie Posters #89.

PORT OF NEW YORK
(1949 - Eagle-Lion) Scott Brady, Richard
Rober, Yul Brynner
One Sheet: $50 - $100

PORT OF SEVEN SEAS
(1938 - Warner Bros.) Wallace Beery, Maureen
O'Sullivan
One Sheet: $200 - $400

PORT SAID
(1948 - Columbia) William Bishop, Edgar
Barrier
One Sheet: $15 - $25

PORT SINISTER
(1952 - RKO) James Warren, Lynn Roberts
One Sheet: $10 - $20

PORTIA ON TRIAL
(1937 - Republic) Frieda Inescort, Walter Abel
One Sheet: $40 - $75

PORTLAND EXPOSE
(1957 - Allied Artists) Edward Binns, Carolyn
Craig
One Sheet: $5 - $10

PORTNOY'S COMPLAINT
(1972 - Warner Bros) Richard Benjamin, Karen
Black
One Sheet: $5 - $10

PORTRAIT IN BLACK
(1960 - Universal) Lana Turner, Anthony Quinn
One Sheet: $20 - $40

PORTRAIT OF A LADY, THE
(1996 - Gramercy) Nicole Kidman, John
Malkovich, Barbara Hershey
One Sheet: $3 - $5

PORTRAIT OF A MOBSTER
(1961 - Warner Bros.) Vic Morrow, Leslie
Parrish
One Sheet: $15 - $25

PORTRAIT OF A SINNER
(1959 - AIP) Nadja Tiller, Tony Britton
One Sheet: $5 - $10

PORTRAIT OF AN UNKNOWN WOMAN
(1958 - Universal) Ruth Leuwerik, O.W. Fisher
One Sheet: $5 - $10

PORTRAIT OF CLARE
(1950 - British-Pathe) Margaret Johnston,
Richard Todd
One Sheet: $7 - $15

PORTRAIT OF JENNIE
(1949 - Vanguard) Jennifer Jones, Joseph
Cotten, Ethel Barrymore
One Sheet: $150 - $300

PORTRAIT OF JENNIE
(1956R - Vanguard) Jennifer Jones, Joseph
Cotten, Ethel Barrymore
One Sheet: $30 - $50 *Re-release.*

PORTS OF CALL
(1924 - Fox) Edmund Lowe
One Sheet: $150 - $300

POSEIDON ADVENTURE, THE
(1972 - 20th Century Fox) Gene Hackman,
Shelley Winters
One Sheet: $30 - $50 *Kustler art.*
Price is for style showing cast diving off deck;
other styles:$15-25.

POSITIVE I.D.
(1987 - -) Stephanie Rasloe, John Davies
One Sheet: $5 - $10

POSSE
(1975 - Paramount) Kirk Douglas, Bruce Dern
One Sheet: $7 - $15

POSSE
(1993 - Gramercy) Mario Van Peebles, Stephen
Baldwin
One Sheet: $15 - $30 *Black cast.*

POSSE FROM HELL
(1961 - Universal) Audie Murphy, John Saxon
One Sheet: $30 - $50

One Sheet

POSSESSED
(1931 - MGM) Joan Crawford, Clark Gable
One Sheet: $1,300 - $2,000

POSSESSED
(1947 - Warner Bros.) Joan Crawford, Van
Heflin
One Sheet: $75 - $150

POSSESSION
(1983 - Limelight International) Isabelle Adjani,
Sam Neill
One Sheet: $10 - $20

POSSESSION OF JOEL DELANEY, THE
(1972 - Paramount) Shirley MacLaine, Perry
King
One Sheet: $3 - $5

POST OFFICE INVESTIGATOR
(1949 - Republic) Audrey Long, Warren
Douglas
One Sheet: $15 - $30

POSTAL INSPECTOR
(1936 - Universal) Ricardo Cortez, Patricia
Ellis, Bela Lugosi
One Sheet: $100 - $200

POSTCARDS FROM THE EDGE
(1990 - Columbia) Meryl Streep, Shirley
MacLaine
One Sheet: $7 - $15

POSTMAN, THE
(1995 - Miramax) Massimo Troisi, Philippe
Noiret
One Sheet: $10 - $20 *Italian.*

POSTMAN ALWAYS RINGS TWICE, THE
(1946 - MGM) Lana Turner, John Garfield
One Sheet: $1,300 - $2,000

One Sheet

POSTMAN ALWAYS RINGS TWICE, THE
(1981 - Paramount) Jack Nicholson, Jessica
Lange
One Sheet: $15 - $30

POSTMAN DIDN'T RING, THE
(1942 - 20th Century Fox) Richard Travis,

Brenda Joyce
One Sheet: $30 - $50

POSTMAN GOES TO WAR, THE
(1968 - Les Films) Charles Aznavour, Daniel
Ceccaldi
One Sheet: $10 - $20

POSTMAN'S KNOCK
(1962 - MGM) Spike Milligan, Barbara Shelley
One Sheet: $10 - $20

POSTMARK FOR DANGER
(1955 - RKO) Terry Moore, Robert Beatty
One Sheet: $10 - $20

POT O' GOLD
(1941 - United Artists) Paulette Goddard,
James Stewart
One Sheet: $100 - $200

POTEMKIN
(1925 - Russian) See BATTLESHIP POTEMKIN

POTTERS, THE
(1927 - Paramount) W.C. Fields, Mary Alden
One Sheet: $1,600 - $2,500

POUND
(1970 - United Artists) Joe Madden, James
Green
One Sheet: $3 - $5

P.O.W. THE ESCAPE
(1986 - -) David Carradine, Charles R. Floyd
One Sheet: $3 - $5

POWDER
(1995 - Buena Vista) Sean Patrick Flanery,
Mary Steenburgen, Jeff Goldblum
One Sheet: $5 - $10

POWDER RIVER
(1953 - 20th Century Fox) Rory Calhoun,
Corinne Calvet
One Sheet: $10 - $20

POWDER RIVER GUNFIRE
(1948 - Universal) Kenne Duncan, Paula
Raymond, The Santa Fe Rangers
One Sheet: $15 - $25

POWDER RIVER RUSTLERS
(1949 - Republic) Allan "Rocky" Lane, Eddie
Waller
One Sheet: $30 - $50

POWDER TOWN
(1942 - RKO) Victor McLaglen, Edmond
O'Brien, June Havoc
One Sheet: $50 - $100

POWDERSMOKE RANGE
(1935 - RKO) Harry Carey, Hoot Gibson, Tom
Tyler, Bob Steele
One Sheet: $600 - $1,000 *Western. First*
appearance 3 Mesquiteers (rare).

POWER
(1928 - Pathe) William Boyd, Alan Hale
One Sheet: $200 - $400

POWER, THE
(1934 - Gaumont) Conrad Veidt, Benita Hume
One Sheet: $125 - $250

POWER, THE
(1968 - MGM) George Hamilton, Suzanne
Pleshette
One Sheet: $7 - $15

POWER, THE
(1986 - 20th Century Fox) Richard Gere, Julie
Christie, Gene Hackman
One Sheet: $3 - $5

POWER AND THE GLORY, THE
(1933 - Fox) Spencer Tracy, Colleen Moore
One Sheet: $600 - $1,000

POWER AND THE PRIZE, THE
(1956 - MGM) Robert Taylor, Burl Ives
One Sheet: $15 - $25

POWER DIVE
(1941 - Paramount) Jean Parker, Richard Arlen
One Sheet: $40 - $75

POWER OF ONE
(1992 - Warner Bros.) Stephen Dorff, John
Gielgud
One Sheet: $3 - $5

POWER OF THE PRESS

(1928 - Columbia) Douglas Fairbanks, Jr., Jobyna Ralston
One Sheet: $1,300 - $2,000

POWER OF THE PRESS
(1943 - Columbia) Lee Tracy, Guy Kibbee
One Sheet: $50 - $100

POWER OF THE WHISTLER, THE
(1945 - Columbia) Richard Dix, Janis Carter
One Sheet: $40 - $75

POWER WITHIN, THE
(1921 - Pathe) William Tooker, Nellie P. Spaulding
One Sheet: $150 - $300

POWERS GIRL, THE
(1943 - United Artists) George Murphy, Anne Shirley, Benny Goodman
One Sheet: $75 - $125

PRACTICAL PIG, THE
(1938 - RKO/Disney) Silly Symphony
One Sheet: $5,000 - $8,000   *Cartoon. Cartoon Movie Posters #196.*

One Sheet

PRACTICAL PIG, THE
(1951R - Disney) Silly Symphony
One Sheet: $250 - $600   *Re-release. Cartoon.*

PRACTICALLY YOURS
(1944 - Paramount) Claudette Colbert, Fred MacMurray
One Sheet: $75 - $125

PRAIRIE, THE
(1948 - Screen Guild) Alan Baxter, Lenore Aubert
One Sheet: $15 - $25

PRAIRIE BADMEN
(1946 - PRC) Buster Crabbe, Al "Fuzzy" St. John
One Sheet: $30 - $50

PRAIRIE CHICKENS
(1942 - United Artists) Jimmy Rogers, Noah Beery Jr.
One Sheet: $30 - $60

PRAIRIE EXPRESS
(1947 - Monogram) Johnny Mack Brown, Raymond Hatton
One Sheet: $15 - $35

PRAIRIE GUNSMOKE
(1942 - Columbia) Bill Elliott, Tex Ritter
One Sheet: $50 - $100

PRAIRIE JUSTICE
(1938 - Universal) Bob Baker
One Sheet: $75 - $125

PRAIRIE KING
(1927 - Universal Jewel) Hoot Gibson
One Sheet: $250 - $600

PRAIRIE LAW
(1940 - RKO) George O'Brien
One Sheet: $100 - $200

PRAIRIE MOON
(1938 - Republic) Gene Autry
One Sheet: $250 - $500

PRAIRIE OUTLAWS
(1948 - PRC) Eddie Dean, Roscoe Ates
One Sheet: $15 - $35

PRAIRIE PALS
(1943 - PRC) Bill Boyd, Lee Powell
One Sheet: $15 - $35

PRAIRIE PIONEERS
(1941 - Republic) Three Mesquiteers
One Sheet: $30 - $50

PRAIRIE PIRATES, THE
(192? - Producers) Harry Carey
One Sheet: $150 - $300

PRAIRIE PIRATES
(1949 - Universal) Tex Williams
One Sheet: $20 - $40

PRAIRIE RAIDERS
(1947 - Columbia) Charles Starrett, Smiley Burnette
One Sheet: $20 - $40

PRAIRIE ROUNDUP
(1951 - Columbia) Charles Starrett, Smiley Burnette
One Sheet: $15 - $35

PRAIRIE RUSTLERS
(1945 - PRC) Buster Crabbe
One Sheet: $15 - $35

PRAIRIE SCHOONER
(1940 - Columbia) Bill Elliott
One Sheet: $40 - $75

PRAIRIE SPOONERS
(1941 - RKO) Ron Whitley
One Sheet: $40 - $75

PRAIRIE STRANGER
(1941 - Columbia) Charles Starrett
One Sheet: $30 - $50

PRAIRIE THUNDER
(1937 - Warner Bros.) Dick Foran
One Sheet: $40 - $75

PRANCER
(1989 - Orion) Sam Elliott, Rebecca Harrell
One Sheet: $5 - $10

PRAY FOR DEATH
(1986 - American Dist.) Sho Kosugi, James Booth
One Sheet: $5 - $10

PRAY TV
(1981 - Filmways) John Ritter, Ned Beatty
One Sheet: $3 - $5

PRAYER FOR THE DYING, A
(1987 - Samuel Goldwyn) Mickey Rourke, Bob Hoskins
One Sheet: $7 - $15

PREACHER'S WIFE, THE
(1996 - Touchstone) Denzel Washington, Whitney Houston
One Sheet: $4 - $8

PREACHERMAN
(197? - Carolina Film) Amos Huxley, Adam Hesse
One Sheet: $3 - $5

PREDATOR
(1987 - 20th Century Fox) Arnold Schwarzenegger, Carl Weathers
One Sheet: $15 - $25

PREDATOR 2
(1990 - -) Danny Glover, Gary Busey, Ruben Blades
One Sheet: $7 - $15

One Sheet (Advance)

PRE-HISTORIC MAN, THE
(1924 - Universal) -
One Sheet: $100 - $200

PREHISTORIC WOMEN
(1966 - 20th Century Fox) Martine Beswicke, Edina Ronay
One Sheet: $15 - $30

PRELUDE TO A KISS
(1992 - 20th Century Fox) Alec Baldwin, Meg Ryan
One Sheet: $3 - $5

PRELUDE TO FAME
(1950 - Universal) Guy Rolfe, Kathleen Byron
One Sheet: $10 - $20

PRELUDE TO KOREA
(1950 - Pathe) -
One Sheet: $30 - $50   *Documentary. Lobby Card(Babe Ruth at bat):$50-$100.*

PRELUDE TO WAR
(1943 - Office of War Information) Narrated by Walter Huston
One Sheet: $100 - $200   *Documentary.*

PREMATURE BURIAL
(1962 - AIP) Ray Milland, Hazel Court
One Sheet: $30 - $50

PREMONITION
(1975 - Avco) Sharon Farrell, Richard Lynch
One Sheet: $7 - $15   *Duotone.*

PRESCOTT KID, THE
(1934 - Columbia) Tim McCoy, Sheila Mannors
One Sheet: $600 - $1,000   *Cowboy Movie Posters #168.*

PRESCRIPTION FOR ROMANCE
(1937 - Universal) Wendy Barrie, Kent Taylor
One Sheet: $75 - $125

PRESENTING LILY MARS
(1943 - MGM) Judy Garland, Van Heflin
One Sheet: $125 - $250

PRESIDENT VANISHES, THE
(1935 - Paramount) Arthur Buron, Janet Beecher
One Sheet: $100 - $200

PRESIDENT'S ANALYST, THE
(1967 - Paramount) James Coburn, Godfrey Cambridge
One Sheet: $7 - $15

PRESIDENT'S LADY, THE
(1953 - 20th Century Fox) Susan Hayward, Charlton Heston
One Sheet: $20 - $40

PRESIDENT'S MYSTERY, THE
(1936 - Republic) Sidney Blackmer, Betty Furness
One Sheet: $75 - $125

PRESIDIO, THE
(1988 - -) Sean Connery, Mark Harmon, Meg Ryan
One Sheet: $5 - $10

PRESSURE POINT
(1962 - United Artists) Sidney Poitier, Bobby Darin, Peter Falk
One Sheet: $15 - $25

One Sheet

PRESTIGE
(1932 - RKO/Pathe) Ann Harding, Melvyn Douglas, Adolph Menjou
One Sheet: $150 - $300

PRESUMED INNOCENT
(1990 - Warner Bros.) Harrison Ford, Brian Dennehy

● One Sheet: $7 - $15

PRET-A-PORTER
(1995 - Miramax) Sophia Loren, Lauren Bacall, Julia Roberts, Tim Robbins
One Sheet: $7 - $15   *Regular Style with American translation: $10-$15. Advance nude Style: $15-$25.*

PRETENDER, THE
(1947 - Republic) Albert Dekker, Catherine Craig
One Sheet: $15 - $25

PRETTY BABY
(1950 - Warner Bros.) Dennis Morgan, Betsy Drake
One Sheet: $15 - $25

PRETTY BABY
(1978 - Paramount) Keith Carradine, Brooke Shields
One Sheet: $15 - $30

PRETTY CLOTHES
(1928 - Sterling) Jobyna Ralston, Johnny Walker
One Sheet: $125 - $250

PRETTY IN PINK
(1986 - Paramount) Molly Ringwald, Jon Cryer, Andrew McCarthy
One Sheet: $20 - $40

PRETTY LADIES
(1925 - Metro-Goldwyn) Joan Crawford (as Lucille LeSueur), ZaSu Pitts
One Sheet: $1,300 - $2,000

PRETTY MAIDS ALL IN A ROW
(1971 - MGM) Rock Hudson, Angie Dickinson
One Sheet: $5 - $10

PRETTY POISON
(1968 - 20th Century Fox) Anthony Perkins, Tuesday Weld
One Sheet: $15 - $25

PRETTY WOMAN
(1990 - Touchstone) Richard Gere, Julia Roberts
One Sheet: $10 - $20

PREVIEW MURDER MYSTERY, THE
(1936 - Paramount) Reginald Denny, Gail Patrick
One Sheet: $100 - $200

PRICE OF FEAR, THE
(1956 - Universal) Merle Oberon, Lex Barker
One Sheet: $15 - $30

PRICE OF SILENCE, THE
(1918 - Bluebird Photoplays) Dorothy Phillips, Lon Chaney
One Sheet: $700 - $1,200

PRICK UP YOUR EARS
(1987 - Zenith) Gary Oldman, Vanessa Redgrave, Alfred Molina
One Sheet: $15 - $25

PRIDE AND PREJUDICE
(1940 - MGM) Greer Garson, Laurence Olivier
One Sheet: $200 - $400

PRIDE AND PREJUDICE
(1962R - MGM) Greer Garson, Laurence Olivier
One Sheet: $15 - $25   *Re-release.*

PRIDE AND THE PASSION, THE
(1957 - United Artists) Cary Grant, Frank Sinatra, Sophia Loren
One Sheet: $30 - $50

PRIDE OF MARYLAND
(1950 - Republic) Frankie Darro, Stanley Clements
One Sheet: $15 - $30

PRIDE OF NEW YORK, THE
(1917 - Fox) George Walsh
One Sheet: $250 - $600

PRIDE OF PALOMOR, THE
(1922 - Paramount) Forrest Stanley, Marjorie Daw
One Sheet: $150 - $300

PRIDE OF ST. LOUIS, THE
(1952 - 20th Century Fox) Dan Dailey, Joanne Dru
One Sheet: $100 - $200   *Sports (Baseball). Life story of baseball legend Dizzy*

Dean. Sports Movie Posters #61.

PRIDE OF THE BLUE GRASS
(1939 - Warner Bros.) Edith Fellows, James McCallion
One Sheet: $40 - $75

PRIDE OF THE BLUE GRASS
(1954 - Monogram) Lloyd Bridges, Vera Miles
One Sheet: $15 - $30

PRIDE OF THE BOWERY
(1940 - Monogram) The East Side Kids
One Sheet: $75 - $125

PRIDE OF THE LEGION, THE
(1932 - Mascot) Victor Jory, Rin Tin Tin Jr.
One Sheet: $75 - $150

PRIDE OF THE MARINES
(1936 - Columbia) Ward Bond, Charles Bickford
One Sheet: $75 - $125

PRIDE OF THE MARINES
(1945 - Warner Bros.) John Garfield, Eleanor Parker
One Sheet: $40 - $75

PRIDE OF THE NAVY
(1939 - Republic) James Dunn, Rochelle Hudson
One Sheet: $30 - $50

PRIDE OF THE PLAINS
(1943 - Republic) Bob Livingston, Smiley Burnette
One Sheet: $15 - $35

PRIDE OF THE WEST
(1938 - Paramount) William Boyd, Gabby Hayes
One Sheet: $250 - $600   *Hopalong Cassidy series.*

PRIDE OF THE YANKEES, THE
(1942 - RKO) Gary Cooper, Teresa Wright
One Sheet: $600 - $1,000   *Sports (Baseball). Original release posters do not feature Ruth. Sports Movie Posters #s 46, 47.*

One Sheet

PRIDE OF THE YANKEES, THE
(1949R - RKO) Gary Cooper, Teresa Wright
One Sheet: $600 - $1,000   *Re-release. Sports (Baseball). Posters and lobbies feature Ruth. Sports Movie Posters #s 48, 49.*

PRIEST OF LOVE
(1981 - Filmways) Ava Garner, Jorge Rivero, John Gielgud
One Sheet: $5 - $10

PRIEST'S WIFE, THE
(1971 - Warner Bros) Marcello Mastroianni, Sophia Loren
One Sheet: $5 - $10

PRIMAL FEAR
(1996 - Paramount) Richard Gear, Laura Linney
One Sheet: $5 - $12

PRIMAL LAW, THE
(1921 - Fox) Dustin Farnum
One Sheet: $600 - $1,000

PRIME CUT
(1972 - National General) Gene Hackman, Lee Marvin
One Sheet: $3 - $5

PRIME OF MISS JEAN BRODIE, THE
(1969 - 20th Century Fox) Maggie Smith, Robert Stephens

One Sheet: $15 - $25   *Academy Award: Best Actress. Academy Award Movie Posters #255.*

PRIME TIME, THE
(1960 - Essanjay) JoAnn LeCompte, Frank Roche, Dir:H. Gordon Lewis
One Sheet: $20 - $40

PRIMITIVE LOVE
(1966 - American) Jayne Mansfield, Franco Franchi
One Sheet: $30 - $50

PRIMITIVE LOVER
(1922 - First National) Constance Talmadge
One Sheet: $250 - $500

PRIMITIVE MAN
(1913 - Kalem) -
One Sheet: $300 - $700

PRIMITIVE PLUTO
(1950 - RKO/Disney) Pluto
One Sheet: $250 - $600   *Cartoon. Full color.*

PRIMROSE PATH, THE
(1925 - Arrow) Clara Bow, Wallace MacDonald
One Sheet: $600 - $1,000

PRIMROSE PATH, THE
(1940 - RKO) Ginger Rogers, Joel McCrea
One Sheet: $100 - $200

One Sheet

PRINCE AND THE PAUPER, THE
(1937 - Warner Bros.) Errol Flynn, Bobby & Billy Mauch
One Sheet: $300 - $700

PRINCE AND THE PAUPER, THE
(1978 - Warner Bros.) Charlton Heston, Mark Lester, Oliver Reed
One Sheet: $5 - $10   *AKA: CROSSED SWORDS.*

PRINCE AND THE PAUPER, THE
(1990 - Disney) Mickey Mouse
One Sheet: $15 - $30   *Cartoon.*

PRINCE AND THE SHOWGIRL, THE
(1957 - Warner Bros.) Marilyn Monroe, Laurence Olivier
One Sheet: $250 - $600

One Sheet

PRINCE OF DARKNESS
(1914 - Cromelin) -
One Sheet: $500 - $900

PRINCE OF DARKNESS
(1987 - -) Donald Pleasence, Lisa Blount, Jameson Parker
One Sheet: $5 - $10

PRINCE OF DIAMONDS
(1930 - Columbia) Aileen Pringle, Ian Keith
One Sheet: $100 - $200

PRINCE OF FOXES
(1949 - 20th Century Fox) Tyrone Power, Orson Welles
One Sheet: $200 - $400

PRINCE OF PIRATES
(1952 - Columbia) John Derek, Barbara Rush
One Sheet: $15 - $25

PRINCE OF PLAYERS
(1955 - 20th Century Fox) Richard Burton, Maggie McNamara
One Sheet: $20 - $40

PRINCE OF THE CITY
(1981 - Warner Bros.) Treat Williams
One Sheet: $3 - $5

PRINCE OF THE PLAINS
(1949 - Republic) Monte Hale, Paul Hurst
One Sheet: $15 - $35

PRINCE OF THIEVES, THE
(1948 - Columbia) Jon Hall, Adele Jergens
One Sheet: $15 - $30

PRINCE OF TIDES
(1991 - Columbia) Barbra Streisand, Nick Nolte
One Sheet: $7 - $15

PRINCE PISTACHIO
(1921 - Pathe) Eddie Boland, The Vanuty Fair Girls
One Sheet: $150 - $300

PRINCE VALIANT
(1954 - 20th Century Fox) Robert Wagner, James Mason, Janet Leigh
One Sheet: $100 - $200

PRINCE WHO WAS A THIEF, THE
(1950 - Universal) Tony Curtis, Piper Laurie
One Sheet: $30 - $50

PRINCESS AND THE PIRATE, THE
(1944 - RKO) Bob Hope, Virginia Mayo
One Sheet: $125 - $250

PRINCESS AND THE PLUMBER, THE
(1930 - Fox) Charles Farrell, Maureen O'Sullivan
One Sheet: $125 - $250

PRINCESS BRIDE, THE
(1987 - 20th Century Fox) Carey Elwes, Mandy Patinkin, Peter Falk
One Sheet: $40 - $75

PRINCESS CARABOO
(1994 - TriStar) Phoebe Cates, Stephen Rea, Wendy Hughes
One Sheet: $5 - $10

PRINCESS CHARMING
(1934 - Gaumont) Evelyn Laye, Henry Wilcoxon
One Sheet: $50 - $100

PRINCESS COMES ACROSS, THE
(1936 - Paramount) Carole Lombard, Fred MacMurray
One Sheet: $350 - $750

PRINCESS O'HARA
(1935 - Universal) Jean Parker, Chester Morris
One Sheet: $150 - $300

PRINCESS O'ROURKE
(1943 - Warner Bros.) Olivia de Havilland, Robert Cummings
One Sheet: $40 - $75   *Duotone.*

PRINCESS OF THE NILE
(1954 - 20th Century Fox) Jeffrey Hunter, Debra Paget
One Sheet: $15 - $25

PRINCESS TAM-TAM
(1935 - Les Films) Josephine Baker
One Sheet: $3,500 - $5,000   *Price is for original French 47x63. Separate Cinema, pg. 79.*

PRINCIPAL, THE
(1987 - -) James Belushi, Louis Gossett, Jr.
One Sheet: $3 - $5

PRIORITIES ON PARADE
(1942 - Paramount) Ann Miller, Jerry Colonna
One Sheet: $30 - $50

PRISON

(1988 - -) Lane Smith, Viggo Mortensen
One Sheet: $5 - $10

PRISON BAIT
(1939 - Million Dollar) Louise Beavers
One Sheet: $150 - $300   *Black cast. Separate Cinema, pg. 118.*

PRISON BREAK
(1938 - Universal) Barton MacLane, Glenda Farrell
One Sheet: $40 - $75

PRISON FARM
(1938 - Paramount) Lloyd Nolan, Shirley Ross
One Sheet: $50 - $100

PRISON GIRLS
(1972 - United Producers) Robin Whitting, Maria Arnold
One Sheet: $15 - $25   *Sexploitation. Full color image of prison girls disrobing.*

One Sheet

PRISON NURSE
(1938 - Republic) Henry Wilcoxon, Marian Marsh
One Sheet: $75 - $150

PRISON SHADOWS
(1936 - Puritan) Eddie Nugent, Lucille Lund
One Sheet: $100 - $200

PRISON SHIP
(1945 - Columbia) Nina Foch, Robert Lowery
One Sheet: $15 - $35

PRISON TRAIN
(1938 - Malcolm-Browne) Fred Keating, Linda Winters
One Sheet: $40 - $75

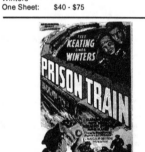
One Sheet

PRISON WARDEN
(1949 - Columbia) Warner Baxter, Anna Lee
One Sheet: $15 - $35

PRISON WITHOUT BARS
(1938 - United Artists) Corinne Luchaire, Edna Best
One Sheet: $40 - $75

PRISONER, THE
(1955 - Columbia) Alec Guinness, Jack Hawkins
One Sheet: $15 - $25

PRISONER OF CORBAL
(1939 - Capitol) Nils Asther, Hugh Sinclair, Noah Beery
One Sheet: $125 - $250

PRISONER OF JAPAN
(1942 - PRC) Gertrude Michael, Alan Baxter
One Sheet: $30 - $50

PRISONER OF SECOND AVENUE, THE
(1975 - Warner Bros.) Jack Lemmon, Anne Bancroft
One Sheet: $3 - $5

PRISONER OF SHARK ISLAND, THE
(1938 - 20th Century Fox) Warner Baxter, Gloria Stuart
One Sheet: $150 - $350

PRISONER OF THE IRON MASK, THE
(1969 - AIP) Michael Lemoine, Wandisa Guida
One Sheet: $7 - $15

PRISONER OF THE MOUNTAINS
(1997 - Orion) Oleg Menshikov, Sergei Bodrov Jr.
One Sheet: $3 - $5

PRISONER OF THE VOLGA
(1960 - Paramount) John Derek, Elsa Martinelli
One Sheet: $5 - $10

PRISONER OF WAR
(1954 - MGM) Ronald Reagan, Steve Forrest
One Sheet: $50 - $100

PRISONER OF ZENDA, THE
(1922 - Metro) Lewis Stone, Alice Terry
One Sheet: $800 - $1,500

PRISONER OF ZENDA, THE
(1937 - United Artists) Ronald Colman, Madeleine Carroll, Douglas Fairbanks Jr.
One Sheet: $1,900 - $3,000

PRISONER OF ZENDA, THE
(1945R - Casanve-Artlee) Ronald Colman
One Sheet: $75 - $150 *Re-release.*

PRISONER OF ZENDA, THE
(1952 - MGM) Stewart Granger, James Mason
One Sheet: $40 - $75

PRISONER OF ZENDA, THE
(1979 - Universal) Peter Seller, Elke Sommer
One Sheet: $5 - $10

PRISONERS
(1929 - First National) Bela Lugosi
One Sheet: $1,300 - $2,000

PRISONERS IN PETTICOATS
(1950 - Republic) Dorothy Patrick, Robert Rockwell
One Sheet: $15 - $30

PRISONERS OF THE CASBAH
(1953 - Columbia) Gloria Grahame, Cesar Romero
One Sheet: $15 - $35

PRIVATE AFFAIRS
(1940 - Universal) Nancy Kelly, Roland Young
One Sheet: $40 - $75

PRIVATE AFFAIRS OF BEL AMI, THE
(1947 - MGM) George Sanders, Angela Lansbury
One Sheet: $30 - $50

PRIVATE BENJAMIN
(1980 - Warner Bros.) Goldie Hawn, Eileen Brennan
One Sheet: $7 - $15

PRIVATE BUCKAROO
(1942 - Universal) The Andrews Sisters, Joe E. Brown
One Sheet: $75 - $175 *Big Band musical.*

PRIVATE DETECTIVE
(1939 - Warner Bros.) Jane Wyman, Dick Foran
One Sheet: $40 - $75

PRIVATE DETECTIVE 62
(1933 - Warner Bros.) William Powell, Margaret Lindsay
One Sheet: $500 - $900

PRIVATE EYES
(1953 - Monogram) The Bowery Boys, Myron Healey
One Sheet: $40 - $75

PRIVATE EYES, THE
(1980 - TriStar) Tim Conway, Don Knotts
One Sheet: $7 - $15

PRIVATE FILES OF J. EDGAR HOOVER, THE
(1977 - AIP) Broderick Crawford, Jose Ferrer
One Sheet: $3 - $5

PRIVATE HELL 36
(1954 - Filmakers) Ida Lupino, Howard Duff
One Sheet: $75 - $125

PRIVATE JONES
(1933 - Universal) Lee Tracy, Donald Cook, Gloria Stuart
One Sheet: $125 - $250

PRIVATE LESSONS
(1981 - -) Eric Brown, Sylvia Kristel
One Sheet: $5 - $10

PRIVATE LIFE OF DON JUAN, THE
(1934 - United Artists) Douglas Fairbanks
One Sheet: $250 - $500 *Fairbanks' final film.*

PRIVATE LIFE OF HELEN OF TROY, THE
(1928 - First National) Maria Corda, Lewis Stone
One Sheet: $600 - $1,000

PRIVATE LIFE OF HENRY VIII, THE
(1933 - United Artists) Charles Laughton, Robert Donat
One Sheet: $2,500 - $4,000 *Academy Award: Best Actor(Laughton). Academy Award Movie Posters #31 & #32.*

PRIVATE LIFE OF HITLER
(1962 - -) -
One Sheet: $7 - $15

PRIVATE LIFE OF SHERLOCK HOLMES, THE
(1970 - United Artists) Robert Stephens, Colin Blakely
One Sheet: $7 - $15

PRIVATE LIVES
(1931 - MGM) Norma Shearer, Reginald Denny
One Sheet: $500 - $800

PRIVATE LIVES OF ADAM AND EVE, THE
(1960 - Universal) Mickey Rooney, Mamie Van Doren
One Sheet: $30 - $50

PRIVATE LIVES OF ELIZABETH AND ESSEX, THE
(1939 - Warner Bros.) Bette Davis, Errol Flynn, Olivia de Havilland
One Sheet: $1,600 - $2,500

One Sheet

PRIVATE NAVY OF SGT. O'FARRELL, THE
(1968 - United Artists) Bob Hope, Phyllis Diller
One Sheet: $15 - $25

PRIVATE NUMBER
(1936 - 20th Century Fox) Robert Taylor, Loretta Young, Basil Rathbone
One Sheet: $250 - $600

PRIVATE NURSE
(1941 - 20th Century Fox) Brenda Joyce, Ann Todd
One Sheet: $30 - $50

PRIVATE PARTS
(1972 - MGM) Ann Ruymen, Lucille Benson
One Sheet: $7 - $15

PRIVATE PLUTO
(1943 - RKO/Disney) Pluto
One Sheet: $1,300 - $2,000 *Cartoon. The Disney Poster, pg. 30.*

PRIVATE PROPERTY
(1960 - Citation) Kate Manx, Corey Allen
One Sheet: $5 - $10

PRIVATE SCANDAL, A
(1931 - Headline) Mary Brian, ZaSu Pitts
One Sheet: $100 - $200

PRIVATE SCANDAL
(1934 - Paramount) Zasu Pitts, Phillips Holmes, Lew Cody
One Sheet: $75 - $150

PRIVATE SCHOOL
(1983 - Universal) Phoebe Cates, Betsy Russell, Matthew Modine
One Sheet: $5 - $10

PRIVATE SECRETARY, THE
(1935 - Twickenham) Edward Everett Horton, Barry Mackay
One Sheet: $100 - $200

PRIVATE SNUFFY SMITH
(1942 - Capital) Bud Duncan, Edgar Kennedy
One Sheet: $50 - $100

PRIVATE WAR OF MAJOR BENSON, THE
(1955 - Universal) Charlton Heston, Julie Adams
One Sheet: $15 - $25

PRIVATE WORLDS
(1935 - Paramount) Claudette Colbert, Charles Boyer
One Sheet: $250 - $500

PRIVATE'S AFFAIR, A
(1959 - 20th Century Fox) Sal Mineo, Christine Carere
One Sheet: $7 - $15

PRIVATE'S PROGRESS
(1956 - Charter) Richard Attenborough, Terry-Thomas
One Sheet: $15 - $25

PRIVILEGE
(1967 - Universal) Paul Jones, Jean Shrimpton
One Sheet: $3 - $5

PRIZE, THE
(1963 - MGM) Paul Newman, Edward G. Robinson
One Sheet: $15 - $25

PRIZE FIGHTER, THE
(1979 - TriStar) Tim Conway, Don Knotts
One Sheet: $10 - $20 *Sports (Boxing). Sports Movie Posters #159.*

PRIZE OF GOLD, A
(1955 - Columbia) Richard Widmark, Mai Zetterling
One Sheet: $15 - $25

PRIZEFIGHTER AND THE LADY, THE
(1933 - MGM) Myrna Loy, Walter Huston, Max Baer, Jack Dempsey
One Sheet: $350 - $750 *Sports (Boxing).*

PRIZZI'S HONOR
(1985 - ABC) Jack Nicholson, Kathleen Turner, Anjelica Huston
One Sheet: $10 - $20 *Academy Award: Best Supporting Actress(Huston). Academy Award Movie Posters #346.*

PRO FOOTBALL
(1934 - MGM) Featuring Red Grange, explanations by Pete Smith
One Sheet: $250 - $600 *Sports (Football). Printed on Sport Champions stock poster. Sports Movie Posters #182.*

PROBLEM CHILD
(1990 - Universal) John Ritter, Michael Oliver
One Sheet: $3 - $5

PROBLEM GIRLS
(1953 - Columbia) Helen Walker, Ross Elliott
One Sheet: $100 - $200

PRODIGAL, THE
(1955 - MGM) Edmund Purdom, Lana Turner
One Sheet: $40 - $75

PRODIGAL, THE
(1984 - World Wide) John Hammond, Hope Lange, Morgan Brittany
One Sheet: $5 - $10

PRODIGAL DAUGHTERS
(1923 - Paramount) Gloria Swanson
One Sheet: $700 - $1,200

PRODIGAL JUDGE, THE
(1922 - -) Jean Paige, Maclyn Arbuckle
One Sheet: $150 - $300

PRODIGAL SON, THE
(1923 - Stoll) Stewart Rome
One Sheet: $800 - $1,500 *British.*

PRODUCERS, THE
(1968 - Embassy) Zero Mostel, Gene Wilder, Dir: Mel Brooks' 1st film
One Sheet: $40 - $90 *Price is for full color one sheet. Style B black & white poster: $15-$30.*

PROFESSIONAL, THE
(1994 - Columbia) Jean Reno, Natalie Portman, Gary Oldman
One Sheet: $7 - $15

PROFESSIONAL SOLDIER
(1936 - 20th Century Fox) Victor McLaglen, Freddie Bartholomew
One Sheet: $100 - $200

PROFESSIONAL SWEETHEART
(1933 - RKO) Ginger Rogers, Norman Foster
One Sheet: $500 - $800

One Sheet

PROFESSIONALS, THE
(1961 - AIP) William Lucas, Andrew Faulds
One Sheet: $3 - $5

PROFESSIONALS, THE
(1966 - Columbia) Burt Lancaster, Lee Marvin, All star cast
One Sheet: $20 - $40

PROFESSOR BEWARE
(1938 - Paramount) Harold Lloyd, William Frawley
One Sheet: $250 - $600

PROFESSOR CREEPS
(1941 - Toddy) Mantan Moreland, F.E. Miller
One Sheet: $250 - $600 *Black cast. Separate Cinema, pg. 68.*

PROFESSOR OFFKEYSKI
(1939 - 20th Century Fox) Terry-toons
One Sheet: $100 - $200 *Cartoon. Full color stone litho. Stock poster with inset title.*

PROFESSOR SMALL AND MR. TALL
(1941 - Columbia) Color Rhapsodies
One Sheet: $150 - $350 *Cartoon. Full color semi-stock poster with inset of title.*

PROFESSOR TIM
(1959 - RKO) Ray MacAnally, Maire Keane
One Sheet: $5 - $10

PROFESSOR TOM
(1948 - MGM) Tom & Jerry
One Sheet: $350 - $750 *Cartoon. Full color stone litho.*

PROGRAM, THE
(1993 - Buena Vista) James Caan, Halle Berry
One Sheet: $5 - $10 *Sports (Football). Sports Movie Posters #217.*

PROGRAMMED TO KILL
(1987 - -) Sandahl Bergman, Robert Ginty
One Sheet: $3 - $5

PROJECT M-7
(1953 - Universal) Phyllis Calvert, James Donald
One Sheet: $15 - $30

PROJECT MOONBASE
(1953 - Lippert) Donna Martell, Hayden Rorke
One Sheet: $75 - $150

PROJECT X
(1949 - Film Classics) Keith Andes, Rita Colton
One Sheet: $40 - $75

PROJECT X
(1968 - Paramount) Christopher George, Greta Baldwin
One Sheet: $10 - $20

PROJECT X
(1987 - -) Matthew Broderick, Helen Hunt
One Sheet: $3 - $5

PROJECTED MAN, THE
(1967 - Universal) Bryant Halliday, Mary Peach
One Sheet: $15 - $35

PROJECTED MAN, THE/ISLAND OF TERROR COMBO
(1967 - Universal) Bryant Haliday/Peter Cushing
One Sheet: $10 - $20   *Double feature.*

PROJECTIONIST, THE
(1971 - Maron) Chuck McCann, Ina Balin
One Sheet: $3 - $5

PROM NIGHT
(1980 - -) Jamie Lee Curtis, Leslie Nielsen
One Sheet: $10 - $20

PROM NIGHT III: LAST KISS
(1989 - -) Tom Contin, Cyndy Preston
One Sheet: $3 - $5

PROMISE AT DAWN
(1970 - Paramount) Melina Mercouri, Assaf Dayan
One Sheet: $3 - $5

PROMISE HER ANYTHING
(1966 - Paramount) Warren Beatty, Leslie Caron
One Sheet: $15 - $25

PROMISED LAND
(1988 - -) Jason Gedrick, Kiefer Sutherland, Meg Ryan
One Sheet: $7 - $15

PROMISES, PROMISES
(1963 - NTD) Jayne Mansfield, Marie McDonald
One Sheet: $40 - $80

PROMOTER, THE
(1952 - Universal) Alec Guiness, Glynis Johns
One Sheet: $15 - $30

PROPER TIME, THE
(1960 - Lopert) Tom Laughlin, Nira Monsour
One Sheet: $7 - $15

PROPERTY MAN, THE
(1914 - Keystone) Charlie Chaplin
One Sheet: $7,500 - $12,000

PROPHECY
(1979 - Paramount) Talia Shire, Robert Foxworth
One Sheet: $5 - $10

PROPHECY, THE
(1995 - Dimension) Christopher Walken, Eric Stoltz, Virginia Madsen
One Sheet: $3 - $5

PROSPERITY
(1932 - MGM) Marie Dressler, Anita Page
One Sheet: $200 - $400

PROTEK THE WEAKEREST
(1937 - Paramount) Popeye The Sailor
One Sheet: $2,200 - $3,500   *Cartoon. Duotone. Cartoon Movie Posters #213.*

One Sheet

PROTOCOL

(1984 - Warner Bros.) Goldie Hawn, Chris Sarandon
One Sheet: $5 - $10

PROUD AND THE DAMNED, THE
(1972 - Columbia) Chuck Connors, Aron Kincaid
One Sheet: $5 - $10

PROUD AND THE PROFANE, THE
(1955 - Paramount) William Holden, Deborah Kerr
One Sheet: $15 - $35

PROUD ONES, THE
(1956 - 20th Century Fox) Robert Ryan, Virginia Mayo
One Sheet: $15 - $25

PROUD REBEL, THE
(1958 - MGM) Alan Ladd, Olivia de Havilland
One Sheet: $15 - $35

PROWL CAR
(1950 - Columbia) -
One Sheet: $15 - $25

PROWLER, THE
(1951 - United Artists) Van Heflin, Evelyn Keyes
One Sheet: $30 - $50

PROWLERS OF THE EVERGLADES
(1953 - Buena Vista/Disney) -
One Sheet: $10 - $20   *Documentary.*

PRUDENCE AND THE PILL
(1968 - 20th Century Fox) Deborah Kerr, David Niven
One Sheet: $7 - $15

PRUDENCE ON BROADWAY
(1919 - Triangle) Olive Thomas, Francis McDonald
One Sheet: $250 - $500

PRUNELLA
(1918 - Paramount) Marguerite Clark, Jules Raycourt
One Sheet: $600 - $1,000

PSYCHE' 59
(1964 - Royal) Curt Jurgens, Patricia Neal
One Sheet: $15 - $25

PSYCHIC, THE
(1977 - -) Jennifer O'Neill, Marc Porel
One Sheet: $5 - $10

PSYCHIC KILLER
(1975 - Avco Embassy) Jim Hutton, Julie Adams
One Sheet: $15 - $25

PSYCHO
(1960 - Paramount) Anthony Perkins, Janet Leigh, Dir: Hitchcock
One Sheet: $250 - $600   *Graven Images, pg. 200, 204.*

One Sheet

PSYCHO
(1965R - Paramount) Anthony Perkins, Janet Leigh, Dir: Alfred Hitchcock
One Sheet: $75 - $150   *Re-release.*

PSYCHO
(1969R - Paramount) Anthony Perkins, Janet Leigh, Dir: Alfred Hitchcock
One Sheet: $50 - $100   *Re-release.*

PSYCHO 2
(1983 - Universal) Anthony Perkins, Vera Miles
One Sheet: $10 - $20

PSYCHO 3
(1986 - Universal) Anthony Perkins, Diana Scarwid
One Sheet: $5 - $10   *Advance:$10-15.*

PSYCHO LOVER, THE
(197? - Medford) Lawrence Montaigne, Joanne Meredith
One Sheet: $15 - $25   *Sexploitation. Pseudo-psychedelic graphics portrays woman clawing killer's face.*

PSYCHO-CIRCUS
(1967 - AIP) Christopher Lee, Leo Genn
One Sheet: $15 - $30

PSYCHOMANIA
(1976 - Victoria) Lee Philips, Shepperd Strudwick
One Sheet: $15 - $35   *Sexploitation. Graphic shows nude woman and other scantilly-clad women.*

PSYCHOPATH, THE
(1966 - Paramount) Patrick Wymark, Margaret Johnson
One Sheet: $15 - $25

PSYCH-OUT
(1968 - AIP) Jack Nicholson, Bruce Dern
One Sheet: $30 - $50

PSYCHOUT FOR MURDER
(1971 - Times Films) Rossano Brazzi, Adrienne LaRussa
One Sheet: $3 - $5

PT 109
(1963 - Warner Bros.) Cliff Robertson, Ty Hardin
One Sheet: $40 - $75   *J.F.K. story. Price is for JFK portrait style.*

PUBLIC COWBOY NO. 1
(1937 - Republic) Gene Autry, William Farnum
One Sheet: $250 - $500   *Cowboy Movie Posters #215.*

PUBLIC DEB. NO. 1
(1940 - 20th Century Fox) George Murphy, Brenda Joyce, Ralph Bellamy
One Sheet: $40 - $75

PUBLIC DEFENDER
(1931 - RKO) Boris Karloff, Richard Dix
One Sheet: $250 - $600

PUBLIC ENEMIES
(1941 - Republic) Phillip Terry, Wendy Barrie
One Sheet: $30 - $50

PUBLIC ENEMY
(1931 - Warner Bros.) James Cagney, Jean Harlow
One Sheet: $19,000 - $30,000

PUBLIC ENEMY
(1956R - Warner Bros.) James Cagney, Jean Harlow
One Sheet: $100 - $200   *Re-release. Duotone.*

PUBLIC ENEMY'S WIFE
(1936 - Warner Bros.) Pat O'Brien, Margaret Lindsay
One Sheet: $75 - $150

PUBLIC EYE, THE
(1972 - Universal) Mia Farrow, Topol
One Sheet: $5 - $10

PUBLIC EYE, THE
(1992 - Universal) Joe Pesci, Barbara Hershey
One Sheet: $3 - $5

PUBLIC HERO NO. 1
(1935 - MGM) Lionel Barrymore, Jean Arthur, Chester Morris
One Sheet: $250 - $500

PUBLIC MENACE, THE
(1935 - Columbia) Jean Arthur, George Murphy
One Sheet: $200 - $400

PUBLIC OPINION
(1935 - Invincible) Lois Wilson, Crane Wilbur
One Sheet: $75 - $150

PUBLIC PIGEON NO. 1
(1956 - RKO) Red Skelton, Vivian Blaine
One Sheet: $40 - $75

PUBLIC STENOGRAPHER

(1933 - Screencraft) Lola Lane, William Collier, Jr.
One Sheet: $75 - $150

PUBLIC WEDDING
(1937 - Warner Bros.) Jane Wyman, William Hopper
One Sheet: $40 - $75

PUDDIN' HEAD
(1941 - Republic) Judy Canova, Francis Lederer
One Sheet: $30 - $50

PUFNSTUF
(1970 - Universal) Jack Wild, Billie Hayes
One Sheet: $30 - $50

PULP
(1972 - United Artists) Michael Caine, Mickey Rooney
One Sheet: $5 - $10

PULP FICTION
(1994 - Miramax) John Travolta, Uma Thurman, Bruce Willis
One Sheet: $10 - $20

PULSE
(1988 - Columbia) Cliff DeYoung, Roxanne Hart
One Sheet: $10 - $20

PUMP UP THE VOLUME
(1990 - New Line) Christian Slater
One Sheet: $15 - $25

PUMPING IRON
(1977 - -) Arnold Schwarzenegger, Lou Ferrigno
One Sheet: $150 - $300   *Sports documentary (Bodybuilding). Arm style: $200-$400. Sports Movie Posters #s 335, 336.*

PUMPING IRON II: THE WOMEN
(1985 - Cinecom) Lori Bowen, Rachel McLish
One Sheet: $15 - $30   *Sports documentary (Bodybuilding). Sports Movie Posters #337.*

PUMPKIN EATER, THE
(1964 - Royal) Anne Bancroft, Peter Finch
One Sheet: $15 - $25

PUMPKINHEAD
(1989 - -) Lance Henriksen, Jeff East
One Sheet: $10 - $20   *Advance One Sheet:$20-30.*

PUNCH DRUNKS
(1934 - Columbia) The Three Stooges (Curly)
One Sheet: $16,000 - $25,000   *Comedy short. Duotone.*

PUNCHES AND PERFUME
(1926 - Bray) -
One Sheet: $125 - $250

PUNCHLINE
(1988 - -) Sally Field, Tom Hanks, John Goodman
One Sheet: $5 - $10

PUNCHY COWPUNCHERS
(1950 - Columbia) The Three Stooges (Shemp)
One Sheet: $200 - $400   *Comedy short. Duotone.*

PUNISHER, THE
(1990 - -) Dolph Lundgren, Louis Gossett Jr.
One Sheet: $5 - $12

PUPPET ON A CHAIN
(1972 - Cinerama) Sven-Bertil Taube, Barbara Parkins
One Sheet: $3 - $5

PUPPETOON
(1944 - Paramount) George Pal's Puppetoons
One Sheet: $250 - $500

PUPPETS OF FATE
(1921 - Metro) Viola Dana
One Sheet: $200 - $400

PURCHASE PRICE, THE
(1932 - Warner Bros.) Barbara Stanwyck, George Brent
One Sheet: $600 - $1,000

PURE COUNTRY
(1993 - Warner Bros.) George Strait, Lesley-Anne Downs
One Sheet: $7 - $15

PURPLE "V", THE
(1943 - Republic) John Archer, Mary McLeod
One Sheet: $30 - $50   *Nazi film.*

PURPLE GANG, THE
(1960 - Allied Artists) Barry Sullivan, Robert Blake
One Sheet: $15 - $25

PURPLE HEART, THE
(1944 - 20th Century Fox) Dana Andrews, Richard Conte
One Sheet: $75 - $150

PURPLE HEART DIARY
(1951 - Columbia) Judd Holdren, Frances Langford
One Sheet: $15 - $30

PURPLE HIGHWAY, THE
(1923 - Paramount) Madge Kennedy
One Sheet: $150 - $350

PURPLE HILLS, THE
(1961 - 20th Century Fox) Gene Nelson, Joanna Barnes
One Sheet: $10 - $20

PURPLE MASK, THE
(1955 - Universal) Tony Curtis, Colleen Miller
One Sheet: $20 - $40

PURPLE MONSTER STRIKES, THE
(1945 - Republic) Dennis Moore, Linda Stirling
One Sheet: $600 - $1,000   *Serial. 15 Chapters.*

PURPLE NOON
(1961 - Times Film) Alain Delon, Marie Laforet
One Sheet: $40 - $75

PURPLE PEOPLE EATER
(1988 - -) Ned Beatty, Shelley Winters
One Sheet: $5 - $10

PURPLE PLAIN, THE
(1954 - United Artists) Gregory Peck, Wim Min Than
One Sheet: $15 - $25

PURPLE RAIN
(1984 - —) Prince
One Sheet: $15 - $30   *Rock 'n' Roll.*

PURPLE ROSE OF CAIRO
(1985 - Orion) Mia Farrow, Jeff Daniels, Dir: Woody Allen
One Sheet: $10 - $20

PURPLE TAXI, THE
(1977 - TFI) Fred Astaire, Peter Ustinov, Charlotte Rampling
One Sheet: $10 - $20

PURPLE VIGILANTES, THE
(1938 - Republic) Three Mesquiteers (Bob Livingston,Ray Corrigan, Max Terhune)
One Sheet: $75 - $125

PURSUED
(1934 - Fox) Rosemary Ames, Victor Jory
One Sheet: $100 - $200

PURSUED
(1947 - Hemisphere) Teresa Wright, Robert Mitchum
One Sheet: $75 - $125   *Cowboy Movie Posters #280.*

PURSUIT
(1935 - MGM) Chester Morris, Sally Eilers, Scotty Beckett
One Sheet: $75 - $150

PURSUIT OF THE GRAF SPEE
(1957 - Rank) John Gregson, Anthony Quayle
One Sheet: $40 - $75

PURSUIT OF D.B. COOPER
(1981 - Universal) Robert Duvall, Treat Williams
One Sheet: $3 - $5

PURSUIT OF HAPPINESS, THE
(1934 - Paramount) Francis Lederer, Joan Bennett
One Sheet: $150 - $300

PURSUIT OF HAPPINESS, THE
(1971 - Columbia) Michael Sarrazin, Barbara Hershey
One Sheet: $3 - $5

PURSUIT TO ALGIERS
(1945 - Universal) Basil Rathbone, Nigel Bruce, Marjorie Riordan
One Sheet: $200 - $400

One Sheet

PUSHER, THE
(1960 - United Artists) Kathy Carlyle, Felice Orlandi
One Sheet: $15 - $35   *Drug abuse.*

PUSHOVER
(1954 - Columbia) Fred MacMurray, Kim Novak(debut)
One Sheet: $40 - $75

PUSS IN BOOTS
(1934 - Celebrity) -
One Sheet: $700 - $1,200   *Cartoon.*

PUSS N' BOOTS
(1963 - K. Gordon Murray) Rafael Munoz
One Sheet: $3 - $5

PUSS N' BOOTS
(1967 - Forster) Margitta Sonke, Christa Oenicke
One Sheet: $5 - $10

PUSS-CAFE
(1950 - RKO/Disney) Pluto
One Sheet: $500 - $800   *Cartoon. The Disney Poster, pg. 30.*

PUSSYCAT, PUSSYCAT, I LOVE YOU
(1970 - United Artists) Ian McShane, John Gavin
One Sheet: $5 - $10

PUTNEY SWOPE
(1969 - Cinema 5) Antonio Fargas, Allen Garfield
One Sheet: $75 - $125

PUTTIN' ON THE DOG
(1944 - MGM) Tom & Jerry
One Sheet: $500 - $800   *Cartoon. Full color stone litho. Cartoon Movie Posters #270.*

PUTTIN' ON THE RITZ
(1930 - United Artists) Harry Richman, Joan Bennett
One Sheet: $250 - $500

PUTTIN' ON THE RITZ
(194?R - Art Cinema) Harry Richman, Joan Bennett
One Sheet: $75 - $150   *Re-release.*

PUTTING PANTS ON PHILIP
(1927 - MGM) Laurel & Hardy
One Sheet: $2,500 - $4,000

PUZZLE OF A DOWNFALL CHILD
(1970 - Universal) Faye Dunaway, Barry Primus
One Sheet: $5 - $10

PYGMALION
(1938 - MGM) Leslie Howard
One Sheet: $700 - $1,200   *Hirschfeld art.*

PYGMY ISLAND
(1950 - Columbia) Johnny Weissmuller, Ann Savage
One Sheet: $30 - $50

PYRO
(1964 - AIP) Barry Sullivan, Martha Hyer
One Sheet: $10 - $20

PYROMANIAC'S LOVE STORY, A
(1995 - Hollywood) William Baldwin, John Leguizamo
One Sheet: $5 - $12

Q
(1982 - United Film Dist.) David Carradine, Michael Moriarty
One Sheet: $15 - $25   *Boris art. One Sheet(B&W):$6*

Q & A
(1990 - TriStar) Nick Nolte, Timothy Hutton
One Sheet: $3 - $5

Q PLANES
(1939 - Columbia) Lawrence Olivier, Ralph Richardson
One Sheet: $150 - $300   *AKA: CLOUDS OVER EUROPE.*

Q-QUETZALCOATL
(1982 - -) -
One Sheet: $3 - $5

QUACKSER FORTUNE HAS A COUSIN IN THE BRONX
(1970 - UMC) Gene Wilder, Margot Kidder
One Sheet: $10 - $20

QUADRANGLE
(1976 - Avco Embassy) Jacqueline Bisset
One Sheet: $5 - $10

QUADROON
(1971 - -) Kathrine McKee, Tim Kincaid
One Sheet: $15 - $35

QUADROPHENIA
(1979 - Who Films) Phil Daniels, Sting, The Who
One Sheet: $30 - $50   *Rock'n'Roll.*

QUALITY STREET
(1927 - MGM) Marion Davies, Conrad Nagel
One Sheet: $600 - $1,000

QUALITY STREET
(1937 - RKO) Katharine Hepburn, Franchot Tone
One Sheet: $1,300 - $2,000

QUANTEZ
(1957 - Universal) Fred MacMurray, Dorothy Malone
One Sheet: $10 - $20

QUANTRILL'S RAIDERS
(1958 - Allied Artists) Steve Cochran, Diane Brewster
One Sheet: $10 - $20

QUARE FELLOW, THE
(1966 - Ajay) Patrick McGoohan, Sylvia Syms
One Sheet: $3 - $5

QUARTERBACK
(1940 - Paramount) Wayne Morris, Virginia Dale
One Sheet: $75 - $150   *Sports (Football).*

QUARTET
(1949 - Eagle Lion) Ian Fleming, Mai Zetterling
One Sheet: $50 - $100

QUARTET
(1981 - 20th Century Fox) Alan Bates, Maggie Smith, Isabelle Adjani
One Sheet: $5 - $10

QUATERMASS AND THE PIT
(1968 - Hammer) James Donald, Andrew Keir
One Sheet: $30 - $50   *AKA: FIVE MILLIONS YEARS TO EARTH. Price is for British Quad. Graven Images, pg. 224.*

QUATERMASS EXPERIMENT, THE
(1955 - Hammer) Brian Donlevy, Jack Warner
One Sheet: $100 - $200   *AKA: THE CREEPING UNKNOWN. Price is for British Quad. Graven Images, pg. 192.*

QUATERMASS II
(1957 - Hammer) Brian Donlevy, Sidney James
One Sheet: $75 - $125   *AKA: ENEMY FROM SPACE. Price is for British Quad. Graven Images, pg. 192.*

QUEBEC
(1950 - Paramount) John Barrymore, Jr., Corinne Calvet
One Sheet: $10 - $20

QUEEN BEE
(1955 - Columbia) Joan Crawford, Barry Sullivan
One Sheet: $40 - $75

QUEEN CHRISTINA
(1934 - MGM) Greta Garbo, John Gilbert
One Sheet: $4,000 - $6,000   *One Sheet(Leader Press):$500-$1,000.*

QUEEN ELIZABETH
(1912 - Famous Players) Sarah Bernhardt
One Sheet: $3,500 - $5,000

QUEEN HIGH
(1930 - Paramount Publix) Ginger Rogers, Charles Ruggles
One Sheet: $600 - $1,000

QUEEN IS CROWNED, A
(1952 - Universal) Narrated By Laurence Olivier
One Sheet: $30 - $60   *Documentary.*

QUEEN KELLY
(1929 - United Artists) Gloria Swanson, Seena Owen
One Sheet: $1,600 - $2,500

QUEEN MARGOT
(1995 - Miramax) Isabelle Adjani, Daniel Auteuil
One Sheet: $10 - $20

QUEEN O' DIAMONDS
(1926 - FBO) Evelyn Brent, Elsa Lorimer
One Sheet: $200 - $400

QUEEN OF BABYLON
(1956 - 20th Century Fox) Rhonda Fleming, Ricardo Montalban
One Sheet: $15 - $25

QUEEN OF BLOOD
(1966 - AIP) John Saxon, Basil Rathbone
One Sheet: $30 - $50

Lobby Card

QUEEN OF BROADWAY
(1943 - PRC) Rochelle Hudson, Buster Crabbe
One Sheet: $30 - $50

QUEEN OF BURLESQUE
(1946 - PRC) Evelyn Ankers, Carleton Young
One Sheet: $40 - $75

QUEEN OF DESTINY
(1938 - RKO) Anna Neagle, Anton Walbrook, C. Aubrey Smith
One Sheet: $75 - $150

QUEEN OF HEARTS, THE
(1934 - Celebrity) UB Iwerks
One Sheet: $1,300 - $2,000   *Cartoon.*

QUEEN OF HEARTS
(1989 - -) Vittorio Duse, Joseph Long, Anit Zagaria
One Sheet: $3 - $5

QUEEN OF OUTER SPACE
(1958 - Allied Artists) Zsa Zsa Gabor, Eric Fleming
One Sheet: $250 - $600   *Graven Images, pg. 187.*

QUEEN OF SHEBA
(1921 - Fox) Dir: J. Gordon Edwards
One Sheet: $800 - $1,500

QUEEN OF SHEBA
(1953 - Lippert) Leonora Ruffo
One Sheet: $15 - $25

QUEEN OF SPADES
(1950 - Associated British-Pathe) Anton Walbrook, Edith Evans
One Sheet: $7 - $15

QUEEN OF THE AMAZONS
(1946 - Screen Art) Robert Lowery, Patricia Morison
One Sheet: $15 - $35

QUEEN OF THE JUNGLE
(1930 - Screen Attractions) Reed Howes, Mary Kornman
One Sheet: $75 - $150   *Serial. 15 Chapters.*

QUEEN OF THE JUNGLE
(1931 - Screen Attractions) Mary Komman, Reed Howes
One Sheet: $200 - $400   *Feature version of serial of same name.*

QUEEN OF THE MOB
(1940 - Paramount) Blanche Yurka, Ralph Bellamy
One Sheet: $40 - $75

QUEEN OF THE NILE
(1964 - Colorama) Jeanne Crain, Vincent Price
One Sheet: $15 - $30   *Italian.*

QUEEN OF THE PIRATES
(1961 - Columbia) Gianna Maria Canale, Massimo Serato
One Sheet: $15 - $25

QUEEN OF THE YUKON
(1940 - Monogram) Charles Bickford, Irene Rich
One Sheet: $30 - $50

QUENTIN DURWARD
(1955 - MGM) Robert Taylor, Kay Kendall
One Sheet: $15 - $35

QUERELLE
(1982 - Planet) Brad Davis, Franco Nero, Jeanne Moreau
One Sheet: $15 - $30   *German.*

QUEST, THE
(1986 - -) Henry Thomas, Tony Barry, Rachel Friend
One Sheet: $3 - $5

QUEST, THE
(1996 - Universal) Jean-Claude Van Damme, Roger Moore
One Sheet: $5 - $10

QUEST FOR FIRE
(1981 - ICC) Everett McGill, Rae Dawn Chong, Ron Perlman
One Sheet: $10 - $20

QUEST FOR PEACE, THE
(1987 - Warner Bros.) -
One Sheet: $2 - $3

QUEST FOR THE LOST CITY
(1955 - RKO) Dana and Ginger Lamb
One Sheet: $15 - $25

QUESTION OF ADULTERY, A
(1959 - -) Julie London, Anthony Steel
One Sheet: $10 - $20   *AKA: THE CASE OF MRS. LORING.*

QUICK AND THE DEAD, THE
(1963 - Manson) Larry D. Mann, Victor French
One Sheet: $7 - $15

QUICK AND THE DEAD, THE
(1995 - TriStar) Sharon Stone, Gene Hackman
One Sheet: $7 - $15

QUICK BEFORE IT MELTS
(1965 - MGM) George Maharis, Robert Morse
One Sheet: $5 - $10

QUICK CHANGE
(1990 - Warner Bros.) Bill Murray, Geena Davis
One Sheet: $3 - $5

QUICK GUN, THE
(1964 - Columbia) Audie Murphy, Merry Anders
One Sheet: $15 - $30

QUICK, LET'S GET MARRIED
(1971 - Adrian Weiss) Ginger Rogers, Elliott Gould (Debut)
One Sheet: $10 - $20   *AKA: SEVEN DIFFERENT WAYS.*

QUICK MILLIONS
(1931 - Fox) Spencer Tracy, Marguerite Churchill, George Raft
One Sheet: $250 - $500

QUICK MILLIONS
(1939 - 20th Century Fox) Spring Byington, Jed Prouty
One Sheet: $50 - $100

QUICK MONEY
(1937 - RKO) Fred Stone, Dorothy Moore
One Sheet: $50 - $100

QUICK ON THE TRIGGER
(1948 - Columbia) Charles Starrett
One Sheet: $20 - $40

QUICK TRIGGER LEE
(1931 - Big 4) Bob Custer
One Sheet: $125 - $250

QUICKSAND
(1949 - United Artists) Mickey Rooney, Jeanne Cagney, Peter Lorre
One Sheet: $40 - $75

QUICKSANDS
(1923 - -) Helene Chadwick, Richard Dix
One Sheet: $250 - $500

QUICKSILVER
(1986 - Columbia) Kevin Bacon, Jami Gertz
One Sheet: $3 - $5

QUIET AMERICAN, THE
(1958 - United Artists) Audie Murphy, Michael Redgrave
One Sheet: $30 - $50

QUIET DAY IN BELFAST, A
(1978 - Ambassador) Barry Foster, Margot Kidder
One Sheet: $5 - $10

QUIET EARTH, THE
(1985 - -) Bruno Lawrence, Alison Routledge
One Sheet: $10 - $20

QUIET GUN, THE
(1957 - 20th Century Fox) Forrest Tucker, Joan Davis
One Sheet: $15 - $30

QUIET MAN, THE
(1952 - Republic) John Wayne, Maureen O'Hara
One Sheet: $500 - $800   *Academy Award: Best Direction(John Ford). Academy Award Movie Posters #143.*

One Sheet

QUIET MAN, THE
(1957R - Republic) John Wayne, Maureen O'Hara
One Sheet: $50 - $100   *Re-release.*

QUIET ONE, THE
(1948 - Film Documents) Donald Thompson, Clarence Cooper
One Sheet: $15 - $30

QUIET PLACE IN THE COUNTRY, A
(1970 - Lopert) Franco Nero, Vanessa Redgrave
One Sheet: $3 - $5

QUIET PLEASE
(1945 - MGM) Tom & Jerry
One Sheet: $500 - $800   *Cartoon. Academy Award: Best Cartoon Short. Full color stone litho. Cartoon Movie Posters #272.*

QUIET PLEASE, MURDER
(1942 - 20th Century Fox) George Sanders, Gail Patrick
One Sheet: $50 - $100

QUIET ROOM, THE
(1997 - Fine Line) Chloe Ferguson, Celine O'Leary, Paul Blackwell
One Sheet: $3 - $5

QUIET WEDDING
(1941 - Universal) Margaret Lockwood, Derek Farr
One Sheet: $30 - $50

QUIGLEY DOWN UNDER
(1990 - MGM) Tom Selleck
One Sheet: $5 - $10

QUILLER MEMORANDUM, THE
(1967 - 20th Century Fox) George Segal, Alec Guinness
One Sheet: $5 - $10

QUINCANNON, FRONTIER SCOUT
(1956 - -) Tony Martin, Peggie Castle
One Sheet: $7 - $15

QUINTET
(1979 - 20th Century Fox) Paul Newman, Vittorio Gassman
One Sheet: $7 - $15

QUITTER, THE
(1929 - Columbia) Ben Lyon, Dorothy Revier
One Sheet: $200 - $400

QUITTER, THE
(1934 - Chesterfield) Charles Grapewin, Emma Dunn
One Sheet: $75 - $150

QUIZ SHOW
(1994 - Buena Vista) Ralph Fiennes, Rob Morrow, Dir: Robert Redford
One Sheet: $5 - $12

QUIZ WHIZ
(1958 - Columbia) The Three Stooges (Joe Besser)
One Sheet: $75 - $125   *Comedy short. Duotone.*

QUO VADIS?
(1925 - Unione) Emil Jannings, Lillian Hall Davis
One Sheet: $500 - $800   *Italian.*

QUO VADIS?
(1951 - MGM) Robert Taylor, Deborah Kerr
One Sheet: $75 - $150   *Advance One Sheet: $100-$200.*

R & B REVUE
(1955 - -) -
One Sheet: $40 - $75

RABBIT, RUN
(1970 - Warner Bros) James Caan, Anjanette Comer
One Sheet: $3 - $5

RABBIT TEST
(1978 - Avco/Embassy) Billy Crystal
One Sheet: $5 - $10

RABBIT TEST/KENTUCKY FRIED MOVIE
(1978R - -) Billy Crystal/Donald Sutherland, Bill Bixby
One Sheet: $5 - $10   *Re-release double feature poster.*

RABBIT TRAP, THE
(1959 - United Artists) Ernest Borgnine, David Brian
One Sheet: $5 - $10

RABID
(1976 - New World) Dir: David Cronenberg, Marilyn Chambers
One Sheet: $15 - $25

RACE FOR LIFE
(1954 - Lippert) Richard Conte, Mari Aldon
One Sheet: $5 - $10

RACE FOR YOUR LIFE, CHARLIE BROWN
(1977 - Paramount) Charlie Brown
One Sheet: $15 - $25   *Cartoon.*

RACE STREET
(1948 - RKO) George Raft, William Bendix, Marilyn Maxwell
One Sheet: $50 - $100

RACE SUICIDE
(1937 - Real Life Dramas) -
One Sheet: $40 - $75

RACE WILD
(1926 - Ellbee) Rex Lease, David Torrence
One Sheet: $250 - $500

RACE WITH THE DEVIL
(1975 - 20th Century Fox) Peter Fonda, Warren Oates
One Sheet: $15 - $25

RACERS, THE
(1955 - 20th Century Fox) Kirk Douglas, Bella Darvi
One Sheet: $40 - $75   *Sports (Auto racing).*

RACETRACK
(1933 - World Wide) Leo Carrillo, Junior Coghlan
One Sheet: $150 - $300   *Sports (Horse racing).*

RACHAEL PAPERS, THE
(1989 - MGM/United Artists) Damian Harris
One Sheet: $3 - $5

RACHEL AND THE STRANGER
(1948 - RKO) Loretta Young, William Holden
One Sheet: $75 - $150

RACHEL, RACHEL
(1968 - Warner Bros.) Joanne Woodward, James Olson
One Sheet: $7 - $15   *Paul Newman's first film as director.*

RACING BLOOD
(1928 - FBO) Alberta Vaughn, Al Cooke
One Sheet: $250 - $600   *Serial. 12 Chapters.*

RACING BLOOD
(1938 - Conn) Frankie Darro, Kane Richmond
One Sheet: $75 - $150   *Sports (Horse racing).*

RACING BLOOD
(1954 - 20th Century Fox) Bill Williams, Jean Porter
One Sheet: $20 - $40   *Sports (Horse racing).*

RACING FEVER
(1965 - Allied Artists) Joe Morrison, Charles Martin
One Sheet: $7 - $15   *Sports (Boat racing).*

RACING KID, THE
(1924 - Universal) Buddy Messinger
One Sheet: $200 - $400

RACING LADY
(1937 - RKO) Ann Dvorak, Smith Ballew
One Sheet: $75 - $150   *Sports (Horse racing).*

RACING LUCK
(1935 - Republic) William Boyd, Barbara Worth
One Sheet: $150 - $300   *Sports (Horse racing).*

RACING LUCK
(1948 - Columbia) Gloria Henry, Stanley Clements
One Sheet: $15 - $30   *Sports (Horse racing).*

RACING ROMEO, THE
(1927 - FBO) Harold "Red" Grange, Jobyna Ralston
One Sheet: $250 - $600   *Sports (Auto racing).*

RACING STRAIN, THE
(1933 - Maxim) Wally Reid, Jr., Dickie Moore
One Sheet: $100 - $200   *Sports (Auto racing). Sports Movie Posters #9.*

One Sheet

RACING WITH THE MOON
(1984 - Paramount) Sean Penn, Elizabeth McGovern, Nicolas Cage
One Sheet: $5 - $10

RACING YOUTH
(1932 - Universal) Frank Albertson, June Clyde
One Sheet: $200 - $400   *Sports (Auto racing).*

RACK, THE
(1956 - MGM) Paul Newman, Wendell Corey
One Sheet: $15 - $35

RACKET, THE
(1928 - Paramount) Thomas Meighan, Marie Prevost
One Sheet: $250 - $500

RACKET, THE
(1951 - RKO) Robert Mitchum, Lizabeth Scott, Robert Ryan
One Sheet: $100 - $200

RACKET BUSTERS
(1938 - Warner Bros.) George Brent, Humphrey Bogart
One Sheet: $250 - $500

RACKET DOCTOR
(194?R - Toddy) Ralph Cooper
One Sheet: $30 - $50   *Black cast. Duotone. Re-release of AM I GUILTY? Separate Cinema, pg. 138.*

RACKET MAN, THE
(1944 - Columbia) Tom Neal, Hugh Beaumont
One Sheet: $30 - $50

RACKETEERS
(1945R - Guaranteed) Melvyn Douglas, Preston Foster
One Sheet: $15 - $35   *Re-titled, re-release of THE PEOPLE'S ENEMY (1935, RKO).*

One Sheet

RACKETEERS IN EXILE
(1937 - Columbia) George Bancroft, Evelyn Venable
One Sheet: $200 - $400

One Sheet

RACKETEERS OF THE RANGE
(1939 - RKO) George O'Brien
One Sheet: $100 - $200

RACKETY RAX
(1932 - Fox) Victor McLaglen, Greta Nissen
One Sheet: $100 - $200   *Sports (Football). Sports Movie Posters #187.*

RAD
(1986 - -) Bart Connor, Lori Laughlin
One Sheet: $2 - $3

RADAR MEN FROM THE MOON

(1952 - Republic) George Wallace, Aline Towne
One Sheet: $75 - $150   *Serial. 12 Chapters.*

RADAR PATROL VS. SPY KING
(1950 - Republic) Kirk Alyn, Jean Dean
One Sheet: $75 - $150   *Serial. 12 Chapters.*

RADIO CITY REVELS
(1938 - RKO) Bob Burns, Jack Oakie, Ann Miller, Hal Kemp & his Orchestra
One Sheet: $150 - $300   *Big Band musical.*

RADIO DAYS
(1987 - Orion) Mia Farrow, Seth Green
One Sheet: $10 - $20

RADIO DETECTIVE, THE
(1926 - Universal) Jack Daugherty, Margaret Quimby
One Sheet: $150 - $350   *Serial. 10 Chapters.*

RADIO FLYER
(1992 - Columbia) Lorraine Bracco
One Sheet: $5 - $10

RADIO FOLLIES
(1935 - BIP) Will Hay, Helen Chandler
One Sheet: $50 - $100

RADIO PATROL
(1932 - Universal) Sidney Toler
One Sheet: $200 - $400   *Serial.*

RADIO PATROL
(1937 - Universal) Grant Withers, Catherine Hughes
One Sheet: $200 - $400   *Serial. 12 Chapters. Stock color One Sheet: $500-$1000.*

RADIO RANCH
(1940 - Mascot) Gene Autry, Smiley Burnette
One Sheet: $200 - $400

RADIO SECRET SERVICE
(1950 - Lippert) -
One Sheet: $7 - $15

RADIO STARS ON PARADE
(1945 - RKO) Wally Brown, Alan Carney, Frances Langford
One Sheet: $30 - $50

RADIOACTIVE DREAMS
(1986 - -) John Stockwell, Michael Dudikoff
One Sheet: $5 - $10

RADIOLAND MURDERS
(1994 - Universal) Mary Stuart Masterson, Brian Benben
One Sheet: $5 - $10

RAFFERTY AND THE GOLD DUST TWINS
(1975 - Warner Bros) Alan Arkin, Sally Kellerman
One Sheet: $3 - $5

RAFFLES
(1917 - -) John Barrymore
One Sheet: $1,600 - $2,500

RAFFLES
(1930 - Samuel Goldwyn) Ronald Colman, Kay Francis
One Sheet: $1,600 - $2,500

RAFFLES
(1940 - Samuel Goldwyn) David Niven, Olivia de Havilland
One Sheet: $1,600 - $2,500

RAFFLES, THE AMATEUR CRACKSMAN
(1925 - -) House Peters
One Sheet: $250 - $600

RAFTER ROMANCE
(1933 - RKO) Ginger Rogers, Norman Foster
One Sheet: $200 - $400

RAG MAN, THE
(1925 - Metro Goldwyn) Jackie Coogan
One Sheet: $250 - $550

RAGE
(1966 - Columbia) Glenn Ford, Stella Stevens
One Sheet: $5 - $10

RAGE
(1972 - Warner Bros.) George C.Scott, R. Basehart

One Sheet: $3 - $5   *Scott's directorial debut.*

RAGE AT DAWN
(1955 - RKO) Randolph Scott, Mala Powers
One Sheet: $15 - $30

RAGE IN HEAVEN
(1941 - MGM) Robert Montgomery, Ingrid Bergman, George Sanders
One Sheet: $75 - $150

RAGE OF PARIS, THE
(1938 - Universal) Danielle Darrieux, Douglas Fairbanks, Jr.
One Sheet: $75 - $150

RAGE OF THE BUCCANEERS
(1963 - Max) Ricardo Montalban, Vincent Price
One Sheet: $15 - $30   *AKA: BLACK BUCCANEER, THE.*

RAGE TO LIVE, A
(1965 - United Artists) Suzanne Pleshette, Ben Gazzara
One Sheet: $3 - $5

RAGGEDY MAN
(1981 - Universal) Sissy Spacek, Eric Roberts
One Sheet: $5 - $10

RAGGEDY ROSE
(1926 - Pathe) Mabel Normand, Jimmie Finlayson
One Sheet: $350 - $750

RAGING BULL
(1980 - United Artists) Robert De Niro, Cathy Moriarty
One Sheet: $40 - $75   *Sports (Boxing). Life of Jake LaMotta. Academy Award: Best Actor(DeNiro). Advance:$50-$100. Academy Award Movie Posters#311. Sports Movie Posters #160.*

RAGING TIDE, THE
(1951 - Universal) Richard Conte, Shelley Winters
One Sheet: $10 - $20

RAGS
(1915 - Famous Players) Mary Pickford, Marshall Neilan
One Sheet: $1,600 - $2,500

RAGS TO RICHES
(1922 - Warner Bros.) Wesley Barry, Niles Welch
One Sheet: $150 - $300

RAGS TO RICHES
(1941 - Republic) Alan Baxter, Mary Carlisle
One Sheet: $40 - $75

RAGTIME
(1981 - Ragtime) James Cagney, Elizabeth McGovern
One Sheet: $5 - $10

RAGTIME COWBOY JOE
(1940 - Universal) Johnny Mack Brown, Fuzzy Knight
One Sheet: $40 - $75

RAGTIME COWBOY JOE
(1947R - Universal) Johnny Mack Brown, Fuzzy Knight
One Sheet: $15 - $25   *Re-release.*

RAID, THE
(1954 - 20th Century Fox) Van Heflin, Anne Bancroft, Lee Marvin
One Sheet: $10 - $20

RAID ON ROMMEL
(1971 - Universal) Richard Burton, Wolfgang Preiss
One Sheet: $3 - $5

RAIDERS, THE
(1921 - Canyon) Franklyn Farnum, Bud Osborne
One Sheet: $150 - $300

RAIDERS, THE
(1952 - Universal) Richard Conte, Viveca Lindfors
One Sheet: $5 - $10

RAIDERS, THE
(1964 - Universal) Robert Culp, Brian Keith
One Sheet: $3 - $5

RAIDERS FROM BENEATH THE SEA, THE

(1965 - 20th Century Fox) Ken Scott, Merry Anders
One Sheet: $10 - $20

RAIDERS OF GHOST CITY
(1944 - Universal) Dennis Moore, Wanda McKay
One Sheet: $75 - $150   *Serial. Western. 13 Chapters.*

RAIDERS OF LEYTE GULF, THE
(1963 - Hemisphere) Jennings Sturgeon, Efren Reyes
One Sheet: $5 - $10

RAIDERS OF OLD CALIFORNIA
(1957 - Republic) Jim Davis, Arleen Whelan
One Sheet: $15 - $25

RAIDERS OF RED GAP
(1948 - PRC) Bob Livingston
One Sheet: $15 - $35

RAIDERS OF RED ROCK
(1951R - PRC) Buster Crabbe, Al (Fuzzy) St. John
One Sheet: $15 - $25   *Re-titled re-release of FUGITIVE OF THE PLAINS.*

RAIDERS OF SAN JOAQUIN
(1942 - Universal) Johnny Mack Brown, Tex Ritter
One Sheet: $50 - $100

RAIDERS OF SAN JOAQUIN
(1949R - Universal) Johnny Mack Brown, Tex Ritter
One Sheet: $7 - $15   *Re-release. Western. Duotone.*

RAIDERS OF SUNSET PASS
(1943 - Republic) Eddie Dew, Smiley Burnette
One Sheet: $15 - $35

RAIDERS OF THE BORDER
(1944 - Monogram) Johnny Mack Brown
One Sheet: $20 - $40

RAIDERS OF THE DESERT
(1941 - Universal) Richard Arlen, Andy Devine, Maria Montez
One Sheet: $40 - $75

RAIDERS OF THE EAST
(1958 - Howco) Lee Wu Chin, George Sain
One Sheet: $15 - $25

RAIDERS OF THE LOST ARK
(1981 - Paramount) Harrison Ford, Karen Allen, Wolf Kahler
One Sheet: $50 - $100

One Sheet

RAIDERS OF THE LOST ARK
(1982R - Paramount) Harrison Ford, Karen Allen, Wolf Kahler
One Sheet: $30 - $50   *Re-release.*

RAIDERS OF THE LOST ARK
(1991R - Paramount) Harrison Ford, Karen Allen, Wolf Kahler
One Sheet: $10 - $20   *Re-release. 10th Anniversary poster.*

RAIDERS OF THE LOST ARK/INDIANA JONES AND THE TEMPLE OF DOOM COMBO
(1984R - Paramount) Harrison Ford
One Sheet: $20 - $40   *Re-release. Double feature poster.*

RAIDERS OF THE NORTH
(1921 - Metro) Rudolph Valentino, Rebecca Hite
One Sheet: $200 - $400

RAIDERS OF THE RANGE
(1942 - Republic) Three Mesquiteers
One Sheet: $20 - $40

RAIDERS OF THE SEVEN SEAS
(1953 - United Artists) John Payne, Donna
Reed, Lon Chaney, Jr.
One Sheet: $15 - $30

RAIDERS OF THE SOUTH
(1947 - Monogram) Johnny Mack Brown,
Raymond Hatton
One Sheet: $15 - $35

RAIDERS OF THE WEST
(1942 - PRC) Bill Boyd, Art Davis, Lee Powell
One Sheet: $15 - $35

RAIDERS OF TOMAHAWK CREEK
(1950 - Columbia) Charles Starrett, Smiley
Burnette
One Sheet: $15 - $35

RAILROAD CONSPIRACY, A
(1914 - Kalem) -
One Sheet: $250 - $600

RAILROAD RAIDERS, THE
(1917 - Signal) Helen Holmes
One Sheet: $200 - $400

RAILROAD SPECIAL AGENT
(1951 - -) -
One Sheet: $20 - $40

RAILROADED
(1923 - Universal) Herbert Rawlinson, Esther
Ralston
One Sheet: $250 - $500

RAILROADED
(1947 - Pathe) John Ireland, Sheila Ryan
One Sheet: $15 - $35

RAILS INTO LARAMIE
(1954 - Universal) John Payne, Mari Blanchard
One Sheet: $15 - $35

RAILWAY CHILDREN, THE
(1971 - Universal) Dinah Sheridan, Bernard
Cribbins
One Sheet: $3 - $5

RAIN
(1932 - United Artists) Joan Crawford, Walter
Huston
One Sheet: $1,600 - $2,500

RAIN
(1938R - Atlantic) Joan Crawford, Walter
Huston
One Sheet: $125 - $250   *Re-release.*

RAIN MAN
(1988 - MGM/UA) Dustin Hoffman, Tom Cruise
One Sheet: $20 - $40   *Academy
Award: Best Picture, Best Actor(Hoffman), Best
Director(Levinson). Academy Award Movie
Posters #359.*

RAIN OR SHINE
(1930 - Columbia) Joe Cook, Louise Fazenda
One Sheet: $75 - $150

RAIN PEOPLE, THE
(1969 - Warner Bros.) James Caan, Shirley
Knight, Robert Duvall
One Sheet: $10 - $20   *Written/
Directed by Francis Ford Coppola.*

RAINBOW, THE
(1989 - -) Sammi Davis, Amanda Donohoe
One Sheet: $5 - $10

RAINBOW 'ROUND MY SHOULDER
(1952 - Columbia) Frankie Laine, Charlotte
Austin
One Sheet: $15 - $30

RAINBOW BRIGHT AND THE STAR STEALER
(1985 - Warner Bros.) -
One Sheet: $7 - $15   *Cartoon.*

RAINBOW ISLAND
(1944 - Paramount) Dorothy Lamour, Eddie
Bracken
One Sheet: $75 - $150

RAINBOW ON THE RIVER
(1936 - RKO) Bobby Breen, May Robson
One Sheet: $100 - $200

RAINBOW OVER BROADWAY
(1933 - Chesterfield) Joan Marsh, Frank

Albertson
One Sheet: $75 - $150

RAINBOW OVER TEXAS
(1946 - Republic) Roy Rogers, Dale Evans
One Sheet: $200 - $400

RAINBOW OVER THE RANGE
(1940 - Monogram) Tex Ritter
One Sheet: $75 - $150

RAINBOW OVER THE ROCKIES
(1946 - Monogram) Jimmy Wakely, Lee
"Lasses" White
One Sheet: $20 - $40

RAINBOW PARADE
(1935 - RKO) -
One Sheet: $75 - $150

RAINBOW RANCH
(1933 - Monogram) Rex Bell, Cecelia Parker
One Sheet: $500 - $800   *Cowboy
Movie Posters # 153.*

RAINBOW TRAIL, THE
(1918 - Fox) William Farnum, Ann Forrest
One Sheet: $350 - $750

RAINBOW TRAIL, THE
(1925 - Fox) Tom Mix, George Bancroft
One Sheet: $500 - $800

RAINBOW TRAIL
(1931 - Fox) George O'Brien, Cecilia Parker
One Sheet: $200 - $400   *Cowboy
Movie Posters #101.*

RAINBOW VALLEY
(1935 - Monogram) John Wayne, George
Hayes
One Sheet: $1,300 - $2,000

RAINBOW'S END
(1935 - First Division) Hoot Gibson, Buddy
Roosevelt
One Sheet: $250 - $500

RAINMAKER, THE
(1956 - Paramount) Burt Lancaster, Katharine
Hepburn
One Sheet: $30 - $60

RAINMAKERS, THE
(1935 - RKO) Wheeler and Woolsey, Dorothy
Lee
One Sheet: $125 - $250

RAINS CAME, THE
(1939 - 20th Century Fox) Myrna Loy, Tyrone
Power, George Brent
One Sheet: $150 - $300

RAINS CAME, THE
(1943R - 20th Century Fox) Tyrone Power,
Myrna Loy
One Sheet: $75 - $150   *Re-release.*

RAINS OF RANCHIPUR, THE
(1955 - 20th Century Fox) Lana Turner,
Richard Burton
One Sheet: $30 - $50

RAINTREE COUNTY
(1957 - MGM) Elizabeth Taylor, Montgomery
Clift, Eva Marie Saint
One Sheet: $75 - $175

RAINY DAY WITH THE BEAR FAMILY, A
(1940 - MGM) Barney Bear
One Sheet: $500 - $800   *Cartoon. Full
color stone litho.*

RAISE THE RED LANTERN
(1991 - Orion) Gongli, Ma Jingwu
One Sheet: $5 - $10   *Mandarin.*

RAISE THE TITANIC
(1980 - Associated) Jason Robards, Richard
Jordan
One Sheet: $10 - $20

RAISIN IN THE SUN, A
(1961 - Columbia) Sidney Poitier, Claudia
McNeil
One Sheet: $50 - $100   *Separate
Cinema, pg. 158.*

RAISING ARIZONA
(1987 - 20th Century Fox) Nicholas Cage, Holly
Hunter, Dir: Coen Bros.
One Sheet: $15 - $35

RAISING CAIN

(1992 - Universal) John Lithgow, Lolita
Davidovich
One Sheet: $2 - $3

RALLY 'ROUND THE FLAG, BOYS!
(1958 - 20th Century Fox) Paul Newman,
Joanne Woodward
One Sheet: $15 - $25

RAMBLIN' KID, THE
(1923 - Universal) Hoot Gibson, Laura La
Plante
One Sheet: $200 - $400

RAMBLING ROSE
(1991 - New Line) Laura Dern, Diane Ladd,
Robert Duvall
One Sheet: $5 - $10

RAMBO: FIRST BLOOD PART II
(1985 - TriStar) Sylvester Stallone, Richard
Crenna
One Sheet: $7 - $15

RAMBO III
(1988 - TriStar) Sylvester Stallone, Richard
Crenna
One Sheet: $7 - $15

RAMONA
(1916 - Clune) Adda Gleason, Monroe
Salisbury, Richard Sterling
One Sheet: $250 - $500

RAMONA
(1928 - United Artists) Delores Del Rio, Warner
Baxter
One Sheet: $250 - $500

Title Card

RAMONA
(1936 - 20th Century Fox) Loretta Young, Don
Ameche, Kent Taylor
One Sheet: $800 - $1,500   *Cowboy
Movie Posters #204.*

RAMPAGE
(1963 - Warner Bros) Robert Mitchum, Elsa
Martinelli
One Sheet: $15 - $30

RAMPARTS OF CLAY
(1971 - Cinema 5) Leila Schenna
One Sheet: $5 - $10

RAMPARTS WE WATCH, THE
(1940 - Time) -
One Sheet: $40 - $75   *Documentary.*

RAMROD
(1947 - United Artists) Joel McCrea, Veronica
Lake
One Sheet: $100 - $200

RAN
(1985 - Orion) Tatsuya Nakadai, Satoshi Terao,
Dir: Akira Kurosawa
One Sheet: $30 - $50

RANCH HOUSE BLUES
(1930 - Pathe) -
One Sheet: $250 - $500   *A Rodeo
Comedies short subject.*

RANCH HOUSE ROMEO
(1939 - RKO) Ray Whitley, Mary Parker
One Sheet: $40 - $75

RANCH OF HOODOOS
(1924 - -) Fred Church
One Sheet: $250 - $500

RANCHO DELUXE
(1975 - United Artists) Jeff Bridges, Sam
Waterston

One Sheet: $7 - $15   *Cowboy
Movie Posters #342.*

RANCHO GRANDE
(1940 - Republic) Gene Autry
One Sheet: $150 - $300

RANCHO GRANDE
(194?R - Republic) Gene Autry
One Sheet: $50 - $100   *Re-release.*

RANCHO NOTORIOUS
(1952 - RKO) Marlene Dietrich, Arthur Kennedy
One Sheet: $150 - $300   *Cowboy
Movie Posters #292.*

RANDOLPH FAMILY, THE
(1945 - English Films) Margaret Lockwood,
Michael Wilding
One Sheet: $10 - $20

RANDOM HARVEST
(1942 - MGM) Ronald Colman, Greer Garson
One Sheet: $75 - $150

RANDY RIDES ALONE
(1934 - Monogram) John Wayne
One Sheet: $1,600 - $2,500

RANGE BEYOND THE BLUE
(1947 - Pathe) Eddie Dean
One Sheet: $15 - $35

RANGE BUSTERS, THE
(1940 - Monogram) Ray Corrigan, John King,
Max Terhune
One Sheet: $40 - $75

RANGE DEFENDERS
(1947 - Republic) Three Mesquiteers
One Sheet: $15 - $35

RANGE FEUD, THE
(1931 - Columbia) Buck Jones, John Wayne
One Sheet: $600 - $1,000   *Price
assumes Wayne is not pictured.*

RANGE FIGHTER, THE
(1926 - Exhibitors) Ken Maynard
One Sheet: $200 - $400   *Serial.
Western.*

RANGE JUSTICE
(1949 - Monogram) Johnny Mack Brown
One Sheet: $15 - $35

RANGE LAND
(1949 - Monogram) Whip Wilson
One Sheet: $20 - $40

RANGE LAW
(1944 - Monogram) Johnny Mack Brown
One Sheet: $30 - $50

RANGE RENEGADES
(1948 - Monogram) Jimmy Wakely
One Sheet: $15 - $35

RANGE RHYTHM
(1942 - RKO) Ray Whitley, Virginia Vale
One Sheet: $30 - $50

RANGE WAR
(1939 - Paramount) William Boyd
One Sheet: $350 - $750   *Hopalong
Cassidy series. Cowboy Movie Posters #236.*

RANGELAND
(1922 - William Steiner) Neal Hart, Ben Corbett
One Sheet: $300 - $700

RANGER AND THE LADY, THE
(1940 - Republic) Roy Rogers
One Sheet: $150 - $300

RANGER COURAGE
(1936 - Columbia) Bob Allen
One Sheet: $50 - $100

RANGER OF CHEROKEE STRIP
(1949 - Republic) Monte Hale
One Sheet: $20 - $40

RANGER OF THE NORTH
(1927 - FBO) Hugh Trevor, Lina Basquette,
Ranger the Dog
One Sheet: $150 - $350

RANGER'S CODE
(1933 - Monogram) Bob Steele
One Sheet: $200 - $400

RANGER'S ROUNDUP, THE
(1938 - Spectrum) Fred Scott, Al St. John

One Sheet: $75 - $125

RANGERS OF FORTUNE
(1940 - Paramount) Fred MacMurray, Gilbert Roland
One Sheet: $50 - $100

RANGERS RIDE, THE
(1948 - Monogram) Jimmy Wakely
One Sheet: $15 - $30

RANGERS STEP IN, THE
(1937 - Columbia) Bob Allen
One Sheet: $50 - $100

RANGERS TAKE OVER, THE
(1943 - PRC) Dave O'Brien, Jim Newell
One Sheet: $15 - $35

RANGLE RIVER
(1939 - Columbia) Victor Jory, Margaret Dare
One Sheet: $100 - $200

RANGO
(1931 - Paramount Publix) Claude King, Douglas Scott
One Sheet: $75 - $150

RANSOM
(1955 - MGM) Glenn Ford, Donna Reed
One Sheet: $15 - $25

RANSOM
(1996 - Buena Vista) Mel Gibson, Rene Russo, Gary Sinise
One Sheet: $5 - $10

RAP, THE
(1927 - Pathe) Laurel & Hardy
One Sheet: $4,000 - $6,000

RAPA NUI
(1994 - Warner Bros.) Jason Scott Lee
One Sheet: $5 - $10

RAPID FIRE
(1992 - 20th Century Fox) Brandon Lee, Powers Booth
One Sheet: $15 - $25

RAPPIN
(1985 - Cannon) Mario Van Peebles, Tasia Valenza
One Sheet: $5 - $10

RAPTURE
(1949 - Film Classics) Glenn Langan, Elsy Albin
One Sheet: $15 - $25

RAPTURE
(1965 - International Classics) Melvyn Douglas, Dean Stockwell
One Sheet: $3 - $5

RARE BREED, THE
(1966 - Universal) James Stewart, Maureen O'Hara
One Sheet: $50 - $100   *Cowboy Movie Posters #319.*

RASCAL
(1938 - 20th Century Fox) Jane Withers, Rochelle Hudson
One Sheet: $75 - $150

RASCAL
(1969 - Buena Vista) Steve Forrest, Bill Mumy
One Sheet: $5 - $10

RASHOMON
(1951 - RKO) Toshiro Mifune, Machiko Kyo, Dir: Akira Kurosawa
One Sheet: $100 - $200   *Academy Award: Best Foreign film. Aka: In The Woods.*

RASPUTIN AND THE EMPRESS
(1933 - MGM) John, Ethel & Lionel Barrymore (their only film together)
One Sheet: $1,600 - $2,500   *Graven Images, pg. 52.*

RASPUTIN, DAMON DER FRAUEN
(1932 - Gottschalk) Conrad Veidt
One Sheet: $3,500 - $5,000   *German. Graven Images, pg. 57.*

RASPUTIN THE MAD MONK/THE REPTILE
(1966 - 20th Century Fox) Christopher Lee, Barbara Shelley, Noel Willman, Ray Barrett
One Sheet: $15 - $30   *Double feature. Graven Images, pg. 213.*

RASPUTIN-THE MAD MONK

(1966 - 20th Century Fox) Christopher Lee, Barbara Shelley
One Sheet: $15 - $35

RASTUS
(1910 - -) -
One Sheet: $300 - $700

RAT, THE
(1938 - RKO) Ruth Chatterton, Anton Walbrook
One Sheet: $75 - $150

RAT FINK
(1966 - Cinema) Schuyler Hayden, The Futuras
One Sheet: $7 - $15   *Rock 'n' Roll.*

RAT RACE, THE
(1960 - Paramount) Tony Curtis, Debbie Reynolds
One Sheet: $15 - $30

RATBOY
(1986 - Warner Bros.) Sondra Locke, Robert Townsend
One Sheet: $3 - $5

RATIONING
(1944 - MGM) Wallace Beery, Marjorie Main
One Sheet: $30 - $50

RATON PASS
(1951 - Warner Bros.) Patricia Neal, Dennis Morgan
One Sheet: $15 - $25

RATTLE OF A SIMPLE MAN
(1964 - Reade-Sterling) Harry H.Corbett, Diane Cilento
One Sheet: $3 - $5

RAVAGED
(196? - -) -
One Sheet: $20 - $40   *Nazi exploitation.*

RAVAGERS, THE
(1965 - Hemisphere) John Saxon, Fernando Poe, Jr.
One Sheet: $5 - $10

RAVAGERS, THE
(1979 - Columbia) Richard Harris, Ann Turkel, Art Carney
One Sheet: $3 - $5

RAVE REVIEW
(1995 - Gnu/Bergman) Jeff Seymour, Ed Begley Jr.
One Sheet: $5 - $10

RAVEN, THE
(1912 - Eclair) -
One Sheet: $5,000 - $8,000   *Graven Images, pg. 22.*

RAVEN, THE
(1935 - Universal) Bela Lugosi, Boris Karloff
One Sheet: $19,000 - $30,000   *Graven Images, pg. 81-82.*

RAVEN, THE
(1943 - Paramount) -
One Sheet: $700 - $1,200   *Cartoon.*

RAVEN, THE
(1948R - Realart) Boris Karloff, Bela Lugosi
One Sheet: $250 - $500   *Re-release.*

RAVEN, THE
(1963 - Universal International) Vincent Price, Peter Lorre, Boris Karloff
One Sheet: $75 - $150   *Graven Images, pg. 209.*

One Sheet

RAW DEAL
(1948 - Reliance) Dennis O'Keefe, Claire Trevor, Raymond Burr
One Sheet: $40 - $75

RAW DEAL
(1986 - De Laurentis) Arnold Schwarzenegger, Kathryn Harrold
One Sheet: $7 - $15

RAW EDGE
(1956 - Universal) Rory Calhoun, Yvonne De Carlo
One Sheet: $15 - $25

RAW MEAT
(1973 - AIP) Donald Pleasence, Christopher Lee
One Sheet: $7 - $15   *AKA: DEATHLINE.*

RAW TIMBER
(1937 - Cresent) Tom Keene, Peggy Keys
One Sheet: $125 - $250

RAW WIND IN EDEN
(1958 - Universal) Esther Williams, Jeff Chandler
One Sheet: $20 - $40

RAWHEAD REX
(1986 - Empire) David Dukes, Kelly Piper
One Sheet: $5 - $10

One Sheet

RAWHIDE
(1938 - 20th Century Fox) Smith Ballew, Lou Gehrig
One Sheet: $150 - $300   *Cowboy Movie Posters #235. Sports Movie Posters #369. Beware re-issues by Principal worth $30-50.*

RAWHIDE
(1951 - 20th Century Fox) Tyrone Power, Susan Hayward
One Sheet: $40 - $75

RAWHIDE BREED
(1958 - Allied Artists) Rex Reason, Nancy Gates
One Sheet: $5 - $10

RAWHIDE KID, THE
(1928 - Universal-Jewel) Hoot Gibson, Georgia Hale
One Sheet: $250 - $500

RAWHIDE MAIL
(1934 - -) Jack Perrin, Nelson McDowell
One Sheet: $100 - $200

RAWHIDE RANGERS
(1941 - Universal) Johnny Mack Brown
One Sheet: $50 - $100

RAWHIDE TRAIL, THE
(1958 - Allied Artists) Rex Reason, Nancy Gates
One Sheet: $15 - $25

RAWHIDE YEARS, THE
(1955 - Universal) Tony Curtis, Colleen Miller
One Sheet: $15 - $35

RAYMIE
(1960 - Allied Artists) David Ladd, Julie Adams
One Sheet: $5 - $10

RAZOR'S EDGE, THE
(1946 - 20th Century Fox) Tyrone Power, Gene Tierney, John Payne, Anne Baxter
One Sheet: $1,600 - $2,500   *Academy Award Movie Posters #108. Price is for one sheet with Norman Rockwell art. OneSheet(not*

Rockwell):$150-300.

One Sheet

RAZOR'S EDGE, THE
(1984 - Columbia) Bill Murray, Theresa Russell
One Sheet: $5 - $10

RAZZBERRIES
(1931 - Educational) Paul Terry Studio
One Sheet: $800 - $1,500   *Cartoon. Duotone. Cartoon Movie Posters #74.*

RCA STUDIO PARTY
(1933 - RCA Cunningham Radiotron) -
One Sheet: $3,500 - $5,000   *Art by Viale.*

REACH FOR GLORY
(1963 - Royal) Harry Andrews, Kay Walsh
One Sheet: $3 - $5

REACH FOR THE SKY
(1957 - Rank) Kenneth More
One Sheet: $30 - $50

REACHING FOR THE MOON
(1931 - Feature) Douglas Fairbanks, Bebe Daniels, Bing Crosby
One Sheet: $150 - $300

REACHING FOR THE SUN
(1941 - Paramount) Joel McCrea, Ellen Drew
One Sheet: $30 - $50

READY FOR LOVE
(1934 - Paramount) Ida Lupino, Richard Arlen
One Sheet: $200 - $400

READY FOR THE PEOPLE
(1964 - Warner Bros.) Simon Oakland, Everett Sloane
One Sheet: $7 - $15

READY MONEY
(1914 - Paramount) Edward Abeles, Monroe Salisbury
One Sheet: $250 - $500

READY TO WEAR
(1994 - Miramax) Sophia Loren, Marcello Mastroianni
One Sheet: $4 - $8

READY, WILLING, AND ABLE
(1937 - Warner Bros.) Lee Dixon, Ruby Keeler
One Sheet: $125 - $250

READY, WILLING, AND ABLE
(1977 - -) -
One Sheet: $5 - $10

REAL GENIUS
(1985 - TriStar) Val Kilmer, Gabe Jarret, Michelle Meyrink
One Sheet: $10 - $20

REAL GLORY, THE
(1939 - United Artists) Gary Cooper, Andrea Leeds
One Sheet: $250 - $500

REAL LIFE
(1979 - Paramount) Dick Haynes, Albert Brooks, Charles Grodin
One Sheet: $5 - $10

REAL MCCOY, THE
(1993 - Universal) Kim Basinger, Val Kilmer
One Sheet: $5 - $10

REAL MEN
(1987 - MGM/UA) James Belushi, John Ritter, Barbara Barrie
One Sheet: $5 - $10

REALITY BITES

(1994 - Universal) Winona Ryder, Ethan Hawke
One Sheet: $3 - $5

RE-ANIMATOR
(1985 - Empire) Jeffery Combs, Bruce Abbott,
Barbara Crampton
One Sheet: $15 - $25

RE-ANIMATOR II
(1991 - -) Jeffrey Combs
One Sheet: $5 - $10

REAP THE WILD WIND
(1942 - Paramount) John Wayne, Paulette
Goddard
One Sheet: $250 - $600

REAR WINDOW
(1954 - Paramount) James Stewart, Grace
Kelly, Dir: Alfred Hitchcock
One Sheet: $300 - $700

One Sheet

REAR WINDOW
(1962R - Paramount) James Stewart, Grace
Kelly, Dir: Alfred Hitchcock
One Sheet: $75 - $150   *Re-release.*

REAR WINDOW
(1983R - Paramount) James Stewart, Grace
Kelly, Dir: Alfred Hitchcock
One Sheet: $10 - $20   *Re-release.*

REASON AND EMOTION
(1943 - RKO/Disney) -
One Sheet: $600 - $1,100   *Cartoon.*

REASON TO LIVE, A REASON TO DIE, A
(1974 - Heritage) James Coburn, Telly Savalas
One Sheet: $5 - $10

REBECCA
(1940 - United Artists) Laurence Olivier, Joan
Fontaine, Dir: Alfred Hitchcock
One Sheet: $1,900 - $3,000   *Academy
Award: Best Picture. Hitchcock's first American
film. Academy Award Movie Posters #70.*

One Sheet

REBECCA
(1946R - United Artists) Laurence Olivier, Joan
Fontaine, Dir: Alfred Hitchcock
One Sheet: $150 - $300   *Re-release.*

REBECCA
(1956R - 20th Century Fox) Laurence Olivier,
Joan Fontaine, Dir: Alfred Hitchcock
One Sheet: $50 - $100   *Re-release.*

REBECCA OF SUNNYBROOK FARM
(1917 - Artcraft) Mary Pickford
One Sheet: $800 - $1,500

REBECCA OF SUNNYBROOK FARM
(1932 - Fox) Mae Marsh
One Sheet: $250 - $600

REBECCA OF SUNNYBROOK FARM
(1938 - 20th Century Fox) Shirley Temple,
Randolph Scott
One Sheet: $800 - $1,500

REBEL, THE
(1933 - Universal) Vilma Banky, Victor Varconi
One Sheet: $125 - $250

REBEL
(1985 - -) Matt Dillon, Debbie Byrne
One Sheet: $5 - $10

REBEL CASTRO
(1958 - -) -
One Sheet: $50 - $100   *Documentary.*

REBEL CITY
(1953 - Monogram) Bill Elliott
One Sheet: $15 - $25

REBEL GIRLS
(1957 - Transworld) -
One Sheet: $40 - $75

REBEL IN TOWN
(1956 - United Artists) John Payne, Ruth
Roman
One Sheet: $10 - $20

REBEL ROUSERS
(1970 - Paragon) Cameron Mitchell, Jack
Nicholson, Bruce Dern
One Sheet: $15 - $35

REBEL SET, THE
(1959 - Allied Artists) Gregg Palmer, Kathleen
Crowley
One Sheet: $30 - $50   *Beatnik.*

REBEL WITHOUT A CAUSE
(1955 - Warner Bros.) James Dean, Natalie
Wood, Sal Mineo
One Sheet: $1,300 - $2,000

One Sheet

REBEL WITHOUT A CAUSE
(1957R - Warner Bros.) James Dean, Natalie
Wood, Sal Mineo
One Sheet: $250 - $500   *Re-release.
One Sheet is identical to original except for date.
Beware reprints and fakes.*

REBELLION
(1936 - Crescent Pictures) Tom Keene
One Sheet: $125 - $250

REBELLIOUS DAUGHTERS
(1938 - Progressive) Verna Hills, Marjorie
Reynolds
One Sheet: $75 - $150

REBOUND
(1931 - RKO/Pathe) Ina Claire, Myrna Loy,
Hedda Hopper
One Sheet: $250 - $500

RECAPTURED LOVE
(1930 - Warner Bros.) Belle Bennett, John
Halliday
One Sheet: $100 - $200

RECKLESS
(1935 - MGM) Jean Harlow, William Powell
One Sheet: $1,900 - $3,000

RECKLESS
(1984 - -) Aidan Quinn, Daryl Hannah
One Sheet: $5 - $10

RECKLESS
(1995 - Samuel Goldwyn) Mia Farrow
One Sheet: $5 - $12

RECKLESS AGE
(1944 - Universal) Gloria Jean, Marshall
Thompson
One Sheet: $30 - $50

RECKLESS HOUR, THE
(1931 - First National) Conrad Nagel
One Sheet: $150 - $300

RECKLESS LIVING
(1931 - Universal) Ricardo Cortez, Mae Clark
One Sheet: $100 - $200

RECKLESS LIVING
(1938 - Universal) Robert Wilcox, Nan Grey
One Sheet: $75 - $150

RECKLESS MOMENT, THE
(1949 - Columbia) James Mason, Joan Bennett
One Sheet: $15 - $30

RECKLESS RANGER
(1937 - Columbia) Bob Allen
One Sheet: $75 - $150   *Cowboy
Movie Posters #225.*

RECKLESS ROADS
(1935 - Majestic) Regis Toomey, Judith Allen
One Sheet: $100 - $200

RECKONING, THE
(1969 - Columbia) Nicol Williamson, Rachel
Roberts
One Sheet: $15 - $30

RECORD CITY
(1977 - AIP) Ruth Buzzi, Michael Callan
One Sheet: $7 - $15

RECREATION
(1914 - Keystone) Charlie Chaplin
One Sheet: $3,500 - $5,000   *Split-reel
short.*

RED
(1995 - Miramax) Irene Jacob, Jean-Louis
Trintignant
One Sheet: $15 - $30

RED BADGE OF COURAGE, THE
(1951 - MGM) Audie Murphy, Bill Mauldin
One Sheet: $125 - $250

RED BALL EXPRESS
(1952 - Universal) Jeff Chandler, Sidney
Poitier, Jack Kelly
One Sheet: $15 - $25

RED BARRY
(1938 - Universal) Larry "Buster" Crabbe,
Frances Robinson
One Sheet: $250 - $500   *Serial. 13
Chapters. Price is for duotone chapters. One
Sheet(full color Chapter One):$500-$800.*

RED BEARD
(1965 - -) Toshiro Mifune, Dir: Akira Kurasawa
One Sheet: $30 - $50

RED BLOOD OF COURAGE
(1935 - Ambassador) Kermit Maynard, Ann
Sheridan
One Sheet: $75 - $150

RED CANYON
(1949 - Universal) Ann Blyth, Howard Duff
One Sheet: $15 - $30

RED DANCE, THE
(1928 - -) Charles Farrell, Delores Del Rio
One Sheet: $150 - $300

RED DANUBE, THE
(1949 - MGM) Walter Pidgeon, Peter Lawford,
Janet Leigh
One Sheet: $30 - $50

RED DAWN
(1984 - MGM/United Artists) Patrick Swayze,
Lea Thompson, C. Thomas Howell
One Sheet: $5 - $10

RED DESERT
(1949 - Lippert) Don Barry, Jack Holt, Tom
Neal
One Sheet: $15 - $30

RED DESERT
(1965 - Rizzoli) Monica Vitti, Richard Harris,
Dir: Antonioni
One Sheet: $30 - $50

RED DRAGON, THE
(1945 - Monogram) Sidney Toler, Fortunio
Bonanova, Benson Fong
One Sheet: $50 - $100   *Charlie Chan
series.*

RED DRAGON, THE
(1967 - Woolner Bros.) Stewart Granger,
Rosanna Schiaffino
One Sheet: $5 - $10

RED DUST
(1932 - MGM) Clark Gable, Jean Harlow
One Sheet: $5,000 - $7,500

One Sheet

RED FIRECRACKER, GREEN FIRECRACKER
(1994 - October) Ning Jing, Wu Gang, Zhao
Xiaorui
One Sheet: $7 - $15   *Chinese.*

RED FORK RANCH
(1931 - Big 4) Wally Wales
One Sheet: $100 - $200

RED GARTERS
(1954 - Paramount) Rosemary Clooney, Jack
Carson
One Sheet: $20 - $40

RED HAIR
(1928 - Paramount) Clara Bow, Lane Chandler
One Sheet: $1,300 - $2,000

RED HEAT
(1988 - -) Arnold Schwarzenegger, James
Belushi
One Sheet: $5 - $10

RED, HOT, AND BLUE
(1949 - Paramount) Betty Hutton, Victor Mature
One Sheet: $30 - $50

RED HOT RANGERS
(1947 - MGM) Tex Avery
One Sheet: $300 - $700   *Cartoon. Full
color stone litho. Cartoon Movie Posters #302.*

RED HOT RHYTHM
(1930 - Pathe) Alan Hale, Kathryn Crawford
One Sheet: $200 - $400

RED HOT RIDING HOOD
(1942 - MGM) Animated by Tex Avery
One Sheet: $3,500 - $5,000   *Cartoon.
Cartoon Movie Posters #290.*

RED HOT RIDING HOOD
(1952R - MGM) Animated by Tex Avery
One Sheet: $75 - $150   *Re-release
(on stock poster). Cartoon.*

RED HOT TIRES
(1935 - First National) Mary Astor, Frankie
Darro
One Sheet: $75 - $150

RED HOT WHEELS
(1962R - MGM) -
One Sheet: $15 - $30   *Re-release of
HOW TO PLEASE A LADY.*

RED HOUSE, THE
(1947 - United Artists) Edward G. Robinson,
Lon McCallister
One Sheet: $50 - $100

RED IMPS, THE
(1923 - Georgian) -
One Sheet: $700 - $1,300   *Russian.*

RED LANTERN, THE
(1919 - Metro) Alla Nazimova, Frank Currier
One Sheet: $500 - $800

RED LIGHT
(1949 - United Artists) George Raft, Virginia

Mayo, Gene Lockhart
One Sheet: $40 - $75

RED LIGHTS AHEAD
(1937 - Chesterfield) Andy Clyde, Paula Stone
One Sheet: $50 - $100

RED LINE 7000
(1965 - Paramount) James Caan, Laura Devon
One Sheet: $40 - $75   *Sports (Auto racing).*

RED MENACE, THE
(1949 - Republic) Robert Rockwell, Hanne Axman
One Sheet: $15 - $35   *Communist theme.*

RED MILL, THE
(1927 - MGM) Marion Davies
One Sheet: $500 - $800

RED MORNING, THE
(1934 - RKO) Regis Toomey, Steffi Duna
One Sheet: $150 - $300

RED MOUNTAIN
(1951 - Paramount) Alan Ladd, Lizabeth Scott
One Sheet: $30 - $50

RED NOSES
(1932 - MGM) Zasu Pitts
One Sheet: $500 - $900

RED PLANET MARS
(1952 - United Artists) Peter Graves, Andrea King
One Sheet: $75 - $150

RED PONY, THE
(1949 - Republic) Myrna Loy, Robert Mitchum
One Sheet: $75 - $125

RED RIDER, THE
(1934 - Universal) Buck Jones, Grant Withers
One Sheet: $350 - $750   *Serial. Western. 15 Chapters.*

RED RIDINGHOOD RIDES AGAIN
(1939 - Columbia) Color Rhapsodies
One Sheet: $200 - $400   *Cartoon. Full color semi-stock poster with inset of title.*

RED RIVER
(1948 - United Artists) John Wayne, Walter Brennan, Dir: Howard Hawks
One Sheet: $600 - $1,000   *Cowboy Movie Posters #281.*

RED RIVER RANGE
(1938 - Republic) Three Mesquiteers, John Wayne
One Sheet: $300 - $700

RED RIVER RANGE
(1953R - Republic) Three Mesquiteers, John Wayne
One Sheet: $50 - $100   *Re-release. Full color.*

RED RIVER RENEGADES
(1946 - Republic) Sunset Carson
One Sheet: $30 - $50

RED RIVER ROBIN HOOD
(1942 - RKO) Tim Holt
One Sheet: $40 - $75

RED RIVER SHORE
(1953 - Republic) Rex Allen
One Sheet: $15 - $35

One Sheet

RED RIVER VALLEY
(1936 - Republic) Gene Autry, Smiley Burnette

One Sheet: $250 - $600   *Cowboy Movie Posters #192.*

RED RIVER VALLEY
(1940R - Republic) Gene Autry, Smiley Burnette
One Sheet: $75 - $150   *Re-release.*

RED RIVER VALLEY
(1942 - Republic) Roy Rogers, Gale Storm
One Sheet: $250 - $500   *Cowboy Movie Posters #267.*

RED RIVER VALLEY
(1948R - Republic) Rog Rogers, Gale Storm
One Sheet: $50 - $100   *Re-release.*

RED ROCK WEST
(1993 - -) -
One Sheet: $7 - $15

RED ROPE, THE
(1937 - Republic) Bob Steele, Lois January
One Sheet: $100 - $200

RED ROSES FOR THE FUHRER
(1967 - -) -
One Sheet: $7 - $15

RED SALUTE
(1935 - Reliance) Barbara Stanwyck, Robert Young
One Sheet: $200 - $400

RED SCORPION
(1989 - -) Dolph Lundgren, M. Emmet Walsh
One Sheet: $5 - $10

RED SHADOW, THE
(1932 - Universal) -
One Sheet: $250 - $500   *From the Shadow Detective Series.*

RED SHOES, THE
(1948 - Eagle-Lion) Anton Walbrook, Marius Goring
One Sheet: $250 - $500

Three Sheet

RED SKIES OF MONTANA
(1952 - 20th Century Fox) Richard Widmark, Constance Smith
One Sheet: $15 - $35

RED SKY AT MORNING
(1971 - Universal) Richard Thomas, Catherine Burns
One Sheet: $3 - $5

RED SNOW
(1952 - Columbia) Guy Madison, Ray Mala
One Sheet: $10 - $20

RED SONJA
(1985 - MGM/UA) Brigitte Nielsen, Arnold Schwarzenegger
One Sheet: $7 - $15

RED SORGHUM
(1988 - -) Gong Li, Jiang Wen
One Sheet: $15 - $30

RED STALLION, THE
(1947 - Pathe) Robert Paige, Ted Donaldson
One Sheet: $15 - $25

RED STALLION IN THE ROCKIES
(1949 - Pathe) Jean Heather, Arthur Franz
One Sheet: $15 - $30

RED SUN
(1972 - National General) Charles Bronson, Ursula Andress
One Sheet: $7 - $15

RED SUNDOWN
(1955 - Universal) Rory Calhoun, Martha Hyer
One Sheet: $15 - $30

RED TENT, THE
(1971 - Paramount) Sean Connery, Peter Finch
One Sheet: $7 - $15

RED TOMAHAWK
(1966 - Paramount) Howard Keel, Joan Caulfield
One Sheet: $10 - $20

RED WAGON
(1935 - First Division) Charles Bickford, Raquel Torres, Greta Nissen
One Sheet: $50 - $100

RED WARNING, THE
(1923 - Universal) Jack Hoxie, Elinor Field
One Sheet: $250 - $500

REDEMPTION
(1917 - Triumph) Evelyn Nesbit, Russell Thaw
One Sheet: $300 - $700

REDEMPTION
(1930 - MGM) John Gilbert, Conrad Nagel
One Sheet: $150 - $350

REDHEAD
(1934 - Monogram) Bruce Cabot, Grace Bradley
One Sheet: $75 - $150

REDHEAD
(1941 - Monogram) June Lang, Johnny Downs
One Sheet: $30 - $60

REDHEAD AND THE COWBOY, THE
(1951 - Paramount) Glenn Ford, Rhonda Fleming
One Sheet: $15 - $30

REDHEAD FROM MANHATTAN
(1943 - Columbia) Lupe Velez, Michael Duane
One Sheet: $40 - $75

REDHEAD FROM WYOMING, THE
(1953 - Universal) Maureen O'Hara, Alex Nichol
One Sheet: $15 - $30

RED-HEADED STRANGER
(1986 - -) Willie Nelson, Morgan Fairchild
One Sheet: $7 - $15

RED-HEADED WOMAN
(1932 - MGM) Jean Harlow, Chester Morris
One Sheet: $6,500 - $10,000   *Price is for portrait style one sheet. One Sheet(other Style):$3500-5000.*

REDHEADS ON PARADE
(1935 - 20th Century Fox) John Boles, Dixie Lee
One Sheet: $200 - $400

REDS
(1981 - Paramount) Warren Beatty, Maureen Stapleton
One Sheet: $15 - $25   *Academy Award: Best Director (Beatty), Best Supporting Actress (Stapleton). Academy Award Movie Posters #317 & #321.*

REDSKIN
(1929 - Paramount) Richard Dix
One Sheet: $250 - $500

REDUCING
(1931 - MGM) Marie Dressler, Anita Page
One Sheet: $800 - $1,500   *Hirschfeld art.*

REDWOOD FOREST TRAIL
(1950 - Republic) Rex Allen, Dorothy Patrick
One Sheet: $15 - $30

REED CASE, THE
(1917 - Butterfly) Allen Holubar, Louise Lovely
One Sheet: $250 - $500

REEFER MADNESS
(1936 - -) Dorothy Short, Dave O'Brien
One Sheet: $150 - $300

REEFER MADNESS
(194?R - -) Dorothy Short, Dave O'Brien
One Sheet: $75 - $150

REET-PETITE AND GONE
(1947 - Astor) Louis Jordan
One Sheet: $250 - $500   *Black cast. Separate Cinema, pg. 94.*

REFLECTING SKIN, THE
(1991 - -) Viggo Mortensen, Lindsay Duncan
One Sheet: $5 - $10

REFLECTIONS IN A GOLDEN EYE
(1967 - Warner Bros.) Elizabeth Taylor, Marlon Brando
One Sheet: $15 - $25

REFORM SCHOOL
(1938 - -) Louise Beavers, Harlem Tuff Kids
One Sheet: $250 - $500   *Black cast.*

REFORM SCHOOL GIRL
(1957 - AIP) Gloria Castillo, Ross Ford
One Sheet: $50 - $100   *Exploitation.*

One Sheet

REFORM SCHOOL GIRL
(1986 - -) Linda Carol, Wendy O. Williams
One Sheet: $15 - $30

REFORMATORY
(1938 - Columbia) Jack Holt, Charlotte Wynters
One Sheet: $75 - $150

REFORMED SALOONS/NARCISSUS
(1919 - Goldwyn-Bray) Bray Studios
One Sheet: $600 - $1,000   *Cartoon. Full color stone litho. Cartoon Movie Posters #4.*

REFORMER AND THE REDHEAD, THE
(1949 - MGM) June Allyson, Dick Powell
One Sheet: $30 - $50

REFUGE
(1923 - First National) Katherine MacDonald
One Sheet: $700 - $1,200

REG'LAR FELLERS
(1941 - PRC) Billy Lee, Alfalfa Switzer
One Sheet: $75 - $150   *Based on famous cartoon strip.*

REGARDING HENRY
(1991 - Paramount) Harrison Ford, Annette Bening
One Sheet: $7 - $15

REGENERATES
(1917 - Triangle) Walt Whitman, Alma Rubens
One Sheet: $250 - $500

REGENERATION
(1923 - Norman Film) Stella Mayo, M.C. Maxwell
One Sheet: $5,000 - $8,000   *Black cast. Separate Cinema, pg. 6.*

REGGIE MIXES IN
(1916 - Triangle) Douglas Fairbanks, Bessie Love
One Sheet: $600 - $1,000

REGISTERED NURSE
(1934 - First National) Bebe Daniels, Lyle Talbot
One Sheet: $100 - $200

REIGN OF TERROR
(1949 - Eagle-Lion) Robert Cummings, Richard Basehart
One Sheet: $15 - $35

REINCARNATION OF PETER PROUD, THE
(1975 - AIP) Michael Sarrazin, Jennifer O'Neill
One Sheet: $3 - $5

REIVERS, THE
(1969 - National General) Steve McQueen, Sharon Farrell
One Sheet: $30 - $60

REJUVENATION OF AUNT MARY, THE

(1927 - Metropolitan) Harrison Ford
One Sheet: $125 - $250

RELATIVITY AND RELATIVES
(1929 - Vitaphone) Dr. Rockwell
One Sheet: $125 - $250

RELENTLESS
(1948 - Columbia) Robert Young, Marguerite
Chapman
One Sheet: $15 - $35

RELENTLESS
(1989 - -) Judd Nelson, Robert Loggia
One Sheet: $3 - $5

RELIC, THE
(1996 - Paramount) Penelope Ann Miller, Tom
Sizemore
One Sheet: $5 - $12   *Thriller.*

RELUCTANT ASTRONAUT, THE
(1967 - Universal) Don Knotts, Leslie Nielsen
One Sheet: $30 - $60

RELUCTANT DEBUTANTE, THE
(1958 - MGM) Rex Harrison, Kay Kendall
One Sheet: $15 - $25

RELUCTANT DRAGON, THE
(1941 - RKO/Disney) Robert Benchley
One Sheet: $500 - $800   *Cartoon.*
Cartoon Movie Posters #374.

RELUCTANT SAINT, THE
(1962 - Columbia) Maximilian Schell, Ricardo
Montalban
One Sheet: $7 - $15

REMAINS OF THE DAY, THE
(1993 - Columbia) Anthony Hopkins, Emma
Thompson
One Sheet: $7 - $15

REMAINS TO BE SEEN
(1952 - MGM) June Allyson, Van Johnson,
Angela Lansbury
One Sheet: $15 - $35

REMARKABLE ANDREW, THE
(1942 - Paramount) William Holden, Brian
Donlevy, Ellen Drew
One Sheet: $30 - $50

REMARKABLE MR. PENNYPACKER, THE
(1958 - 20th Century Fox) Clifton Webb,
Dorothy McGuire, Jill St. John
One Sheet: $15 - $25

REMBRANDT
(1936 - United Artists) Charles Laughton,
Gertrude Lawrence, Elsa Lanchester
One Sheet: $1,900 - $3,000

REMEDY FOR RICHES
(1940 - RKO) Jean Hersholt, Dorothy Lovett
One Sheet: $30 - $50

REMEMBER?
(1939 - MGM) Robert Taylor, Greer Garson,
Lew Ayres
One Sheet: $75 - $150

REMEMBER LAST NIGHT?
(1935 - Universal) Robert Young, Constance
Cummings
One Sheet: $75 - $150

REMEMBER MY NAME
(1978 - -) Geraldine Chaplin, Anthony Perkins
One Sheet: $5 - $10

REMEMBER PEARL HARBOR
(1942 - Republic) Don "Red" Barry, Alan Curtis
One Sheet: $75 - $150

REMEMBER THE DAY
(1941 - 20th Century Fox) Claudette Colbert,
John Payne
One Sheet: $75 - $125

REMEMBER THE NIGHT
(1940 - Paramount) Barbara Stanwyck, Fred
MacMurray
One Sheet: $200 - $400

REMO WILLIAMS: THE ADVENTURE BEGINS
(1985 - Orion) Fred Ward, Joel Grey
One Sheet: $3 - $5

REMOTE CONTROL
(1930 - MGM) William Haines, Charles King
One Sheet: $150 - $300

REMOTE CONTROL
(1987 - -) Kevin Dillon, Deborah Goodrich,
Jennifer Tilly
One Sheet: $3 - $5

RENAISSANCE MAN
(1994 - Buena Vista) Danny DeVito, Gregory
Hines, Marky Mark
One Sheet: $5 - $10

RENDEZVOUS
(1935 - MGM) William Powell, Rosalind Russell
One Sheet: $250 - $500

RENDEZVOUS 24
(1946 - 20th Century Fox) William Gargan,
Marie Palmer
One Sheet: $15 - $30

RENDEZVOUS AT MIDNIGHT
(1935 - Universal) Ralph Bellamy, Valerie
Hobson
One Sheet: $100 - $200

RENDEZVOUS WITH ANNIE
(1946 - Republic) Eddie Albert, Faye Marlowe
One Sheet: $15 - $30

RENEGADE, THE
(1943 - PRC) Buster Crabbe, Al St. John
One Sheet: $20 - $40

RENEGADE GIRL
(1946 - Screen Guild) Alan Curtis, Ann Savage
One Sheet: $15 - $35

RENEGADE RANGER
(1938 - RKO) George O'Brien, Tim Holt, Rita
Hayworth
One Sheet: $125 - $250

RENEGADE TRAIL
(1939 - Paramount) William Boyd
One Sheet: $200 - $400   *Hopalong*
Cassidy series.

RENEGADES
(1930 - Fox) Warner Baxter, Myrna Loy, Bela
Lugosi
One Sheet: $600 - $1,000

RENEGADES
(1946 - Columbia) Evelyn Keyes, Willard
Parker
One Sheet: $15 - $35

RENEGADES OF SONORA
(1948 - Republic) Allan "Rocky" Lane
One Sheet: $20 - $40

RENEGADES OF THE RIO GRANDE
(1944 - Universal) Rod Cameron
One Sheet: $15 - $35

RENEGADES OF THE SAGE
(1949 - Columbia) Charles Starrett
One Sheet: $20 - $40

RENEGADES OF THE WEST
(1932 - RKO) Tom Keene
One Sheet: $150 - $300

RENFREW OF THE ROYAL MOUNTED
(1937 - Grand National) Jim Newill, Carol
Hughes
One Sheet: $100 - $200

**RENFREW OF THE ROYAL MOUNTED IN
CRASHING THRU**
(1939 - Monogram) Jim Newill
One Sheet: $50 - $100

**RENFREW OF THE ROYAL MOUNTED IN
FIGHTING MAD**
(1939 - Monogram) Jim Newill
One Sheet: $50 - $100

**RENFREW OF THE ROYAL MOUNTED IN SKY
BANDITS**
(1940 - Monogram) Jim Newill
One Sheet: $50 - $100

**RENFREW OF THE ROYAL MOUNTED IN
MURDER ON THE YUKON**
(1940 - Monogram) Jim Newill
One Sheet: $50 - $100

**RENFREW OF THE ROYAL MOUNTED IN
YUKON FLIGHT**
(1940 - Monogram) Jim Newill
One Sheet: $50 - $100

**RENFREW OF THE ROYAL MOUNTED IN
DANGER AHEAD**

(1940 - Monogram) Jim Newill
One Sheet: $50 - $100

RENO
(1939 - RKO) Richard Dix, Gail Patrick
One Sheet: $75 - $150

RENT COLLECTOR, THE
(1921 - Vitagraph) Dir: Larry Semon
One Sheet: $200 - $450

RENT-A-COP
(1988 - -) Burt Reynolds, Liza Minnelli
One Sheet: $3 - $5

REPEAT PERFORMANCE
(1947 - Eagle-Lion) Louis Hayward, Joan Leslie
One Sheet: $20 - $40

REPENT AT LEISURE
(1941 - RKO) Kent Taylor, Wendy Barrie
One Sheet: $40 - $75

REPO MAN
(1984 - Universal) Emilo Estevez, Harry Dean
Stanton
One Sheet: $50 - $100

REPORT FROM THE ALEUTIANS
(1943 - Office Of War Information) United
States Army Signal Corps
One Sheet: $40 - $75   *Documentary.*

REPORT TO THE COMMISSIONER
(1975 - United Artists) Michael Moriarty,
Yaphet Kotto
One Sheet: $3 - $5

REPORTED MISSING
(1922 - Selznick) Owen Moore, Pauline Garon
One Sheet: $200 - $400

REPORTED MISSING
(1937 - Universal) William Gargan, Jean
Rogers
One Sheet: $75 - $150

REPOSSESSED
(1990 - -) Linda Blair, Leslie Nielsen, Ned
Beatty
One Sheet: $3 - $5

REPRIEVE
(1962 - Allied Artists) Ben Gazzara, Stuart
Whitman
One Sheet: $3 - $5

REPRISAL!
(1956 - Columbia) Guy Madison, Felicia Farr
One Sheet: $15 - $25

REPTILE, THE
(1966 - 20th Century Fox) Noel Willman,
Jennifer Daniels
One Sheet: $20 - $40

REPTILICUS
(1961 - AIP) Ann Smyrner, Carl Ottosen
One Sheet: $75 - $150

REPULSION
(1965 - Royal) Catherine Deneuve, Ian Hendry
One Sheet: $50 - $100   *Graven*
Images, pg. 207.

REQUIEM FOR A GUNFIGHTER
(1965 - Embassy) Rod Cameron, Stephen
McNally
One Sheet: $10 - $20

REQUIEM FOR A HEAVYWEIGHT
(1962 - Columbia) Anthony Quinn, Jackie
Gleason
One Sheet: $15 - $35   *Sports*
(Boxing).

RESCUE, THE
(1929 - United Artists) Ronald Colman, Lily
Damita
One Sheet: $250 - $500

RESCUE, THE
(1988 - -) Kevin Dillon, Christina Harnos
One Sheet: $2 - $3

RESCUE DOG
(1947 - RKO/Disney) Pluto
One Sheet: $300 - $700   *Cartoon. Full*
color. The Disney Poster, pg. 36.

RESCUE SQUAD
(1935 - Empire) Ralph Forbes, Sheila Terry
One Sheet: $75 - $150

RESCUERS, THE
(1977 - Disney) -
One Sheet: $15 - $30   *Cartoon.*

RESCUERS, THE
(1989R - Disney) -
One Sheet: $7 - $15   *Re-release.*
Cartoon.

RESCUERS DOWN UNDER, THE
(1990 - Disney) -
One Sheet: $15 - $25   *Cartoon. The*
Disney Poster, pg. 91.

One Sheet

RESERVED FOR LADIES
(1932 - Paramount) Leslie Howard, George
Grossmith, Benita Hume
One Sheet: $250 - $500

RESERVOIR DOGS
(1992 - Miramax) Harvey Keitel, Tim Roth, Dir:
Quentin Tarantino
One Sheet: $30 - $60   *Tarentino's*
directorial debut.

RESPECTFUL PROSTITUTE
(1957 - -) -
One Sheet: $15 - $30

RESTLESS BREED, THE
(1957 - 20th Century Fox) Scott Brady, Anne
Bancroft
One Sheet: $10 - $20

RESTLESS KNIGHTS
(1935 - Columbia) The Three Stooges (Curly)
One Sheet: $13,000 - $20,000   *Comedy short.*
Duotone.

RESTLESS NATIVES
(1986 - -) Vincent Friell, Ned Beatty
One Sheet: $3 - $5

RESTLESS NIGHT, THE
(1965 - Casino) Bernhard Wicke, Ulla Jacobson
One Sheet: $3 - $5

RESTLESS YEARS, THE
(1958 - Universal-International) John Saxon,
Sandra Dee
One Sheet: $15 - $30

RESTORATION
(1996 - Miramax) Robert Downey Jr., Sam
Neill, Meg Ryan
One Sheet: $5 - $10

RESURRECTION
(1927 - United Artists) Rod La Rocque, Dolores
Del Rio
One Sheet: $250 - $500

RESURRECTION
(1931 - Universal) John Boles, Lupe Velez
One Sheet: $200 - $400

RESURRECTION
(1980 - Universal) Ellen Burstyn, Sam Shepard
One Sheet: $3 - $5

RETIK, THE MOON MENACE
(1952 - -) Clayton Moore, Roy Bancroft
One Sheet: $75 - $150   *Feature*
version of serial Radar Men From The Moon.

RETREAT, HELL!
(1952 - Warner Bros.) Frank Lovejoy, Richard
Carlson
One Sheet: $10 - $20

RETRIBUTION
(1988 - -) Dennis Lipscomb, Leslie Wing
One Sheet: $5 - $10

RETURN FROM THE ASHES
(1965 - United Artists) Maximilian Schell, Samantha Eggar
One Sheet: $5 - $10

RETURN FROM THE SEA
(1954 - Allied Artists) Jan Sterling Neville Brand
One Sheet: $10 - $20

RETURN FROM WITCH MOUNTAIN
(1978 - Disney) Bette Davis, Christopher Lee
One Sheet: $10 - $20   *Sequel to: ESCAPE TO WITCH MOUNTAIN.*

RETURN OF A MAN CALLED HORSE, THE
(1976 - United Artists) Richard Harris
One Sheet: $3 - $5

RETURN OF BULLDOG DRUMMOND, THE
(1935 - British International) Ralph Richardson, Ann Todd
One Sheet: $100 - $200

RETURN OF CAPTAIN MARVEL, THE
(1953R - Republic) Tom Tyler, Frank Coghlan, Jr.
One Sheet: $100 - $200   *Serial. Re-release of "Adventures Of Captain Marvel". 12 Chapters.*

RETURN OF CASEY JONES, THE
(1933 - Monogram) Charles Starrett, Ruth Hall
One Sheet: $125 - $250

RETURN OF CHANDU, THE
(1934 - Principal) Bela Lugosi, Maria Alba
One Sheet: $250 - $600   *Serial. 12 Chapters. Graven Images, pg. 88.*

RETURN OF COUNT YORGA
(1971 - AIP) Robert Quarry, Mariette Hartley
One Sheet: $15 - $25

RETURN OF DANIEL BOONE, THE
(1941 - Columbia) Bill Elliott
One Sheet: $75 - $125

RETURN OF DOCTOR X, THE
(1939 - Warner Bros.) Humphrey Bogart, Rosemary Lane, Wayne Morris
One Sheet: $300 - $700   *Graven Images, pg. 102.*

RETURN OF DR. FU MANCHU, THE
(1930 - Paramount Publix) Warner Oland
One Sheet: $1,300 - $2,000   *Graven Images, pg. 58.*

RETURN OF DRACULA, THE
(1958 - United Artists) Francis Lederer, Norma Eberhardt
One Sheet: $75 - $150   *AKA: THE FANTASTIC DISAPPEARING MAN. Retitled for T.V. "THE CURSE OF DRACULA".*

RETURN OF FRANK JAMES, THE
(1940 - 20th Century Fox) Henry Fonda, Gene Tierney (film debut), Jackie Cooper
One Sheet: $350 - $750   *Cowboy Movie Posters #259.*

Mini Window Card (Trimmed)

RETURN OF FRANK JAMES, THE
(1945R - 20th Century Fox) Henry Fonda, Gene Tierney
One Sheet: $75 - $125   *Re-release.*

RETURN OF FRANK JAMES, THE
(1946R - 20th Century Fox) Henry Fonda, Gene Tierney
One Sheet: $40 - $75   *Re-release.*

RETURN OF JACK SLADE, THE
(1955 - Allied Artists) John Ericson, Mari

Blanchard
One Sheet: $10 - $20

RETURN OF JESSE JAMES, THE
(1950 - Lippert) John Ireland, Reed Hadley
One Sheet: $15 - $35

RETURN OF JIMMY VALENTINE, THE
(1936 - Republic) Roger Pryor, Charlotte Henry
One Sheet: $75 - $150

RETURN OF MANDY'S HUSBAND, THE
(194? - -) Mantan Moreland, Flourney E. Miller
One Sheet: $100 - $200   *Black cast.*

RETURN OF MONTE CRISTO, THE
(1946 - Columbia) Louis Hayward, Barbara Britton
One Sheet: $30 - $50

RETURN OF MR. MOTO, THE
(1965 - 20th Century Fox) Henry Silva, Terence Longdon
One Sheet: $10 - $20

RETURN OF OCTOBER, THE
(1948 - Columbia) Glenn Ford, Terry Moore
One Sheet: $40 - $75

RETURN OF PETER GRIMM, THE
(1935 - RKO) Lionel Barrymore, Helen Mack
One Sheet: $150 - $350

RETURN OF RIN TIN TIN, THE
(1947 - Romay) Donald Woods, Bobby Blake
One Sheet: $30 - $50

RETURN OF SABATA
(1972 - United Artists) Lee Van Cleef, Reiner Schone
One Sheet: $5 - $10

RETURN OF SOPHIE LANG, THE
(1936 - Paramount) Ray Milland, Gertrude Michael
One Sheet: $75 - $150

RETURN OF SUPERFLY, THE
(1990 - -) Nathan Purdee, Margaret Avery
One Sheet: $7 - $15   *Blaxploitation.*

RETURN OF SWAMP THING, THE
(1989 - -) Dick Durock, Heather Locklear
One Sheet: $7 - $15

RETURN OF TARZAN, THE
(1920 - -) Elmo Lincoln
One Sheet: $3,500 - $5,000

RETURN OF THE APE MAN
(1944 - Monogram) Bela Lugosi, John Carradine, George Zucco
One Sheet: $100 - $200   *Graven Images, pg. 132.*

RETURN OF THE BAD MEN
(1948 - RKO) Randolph Scott, Gabby Hayes
One Sheet: $40 - $75

RETURN OF THE CISCO KID, THE
(1939 - 20th Century Fox) Warner Baxter
One Sheet: $200 - $400

RETURN OF THE DRAGON
(1958 - United Artists) Frances Lederer, Norma Eberhardt
One Sheet: $15 - $25

RETURN OF THE DRAGON
(1974 - Bryanston) Bruce Lee, Chuck Norris
One Sheet: $40 - $75

RETURN OF THE DURANGO KID, THE
(1945 - Columbia) Charles Starrett
One Sheet: $40 - $75

RETURN OF THE FLY, THE
(1959 - 20th Century Fox) Vincent Price, Brett Halsey
One Sheet: $40 - $75

RETURN OF THE FRONTIERSMAN
(1950 - Warner Bros.) Gordon MacRae, Jack Holt
One Sheet: $15 - $25

RETURN OF THE JEDI
(1983 - 20th Century Fox) Mark Hamill, Harrison Ford
One Sheet: $30 - $50   *One Sheet(Style B):$40-$75.*

RETURN OF THE JEDI
(1985R - 20th Century Fox) Mark Hamill,

Harrison Ford
One Sheet: $15 - $30   *Re-release.*

One Sheet (1985R)

RETURN OF THE JEDI
(1993R - 20th Century Fox) Mark Hamill, Harrison Ford
One Sheet: $15 - $30   *Re-release.*

RETURN OF THE KILLER TOMATOES
(1988 - New World) Anthony Starke, John Astin
One Sheet: $10 - $20

RETURN OF THE LASH
(1947 - PRC) Lash LaRue
One Sheet: $30 - $60

RETURN OF THE LIVING DEAD
(1985 - Orion) Clu Gulager, James Karen
One Sheet: $7 - $15

RETURN OF THE LIVING DEAD II
(1988 - -) James Karen, Thom Mathews
One Sheet: $7 - $15

RETURN OF THE LIVING DEAD III
(199? - -) -
One Sheet: $7 - $15

RETURN OF THE MOHICANS, THE
(1940R - -) -
One Sheet: $40 - $75   *Re-titled re-release of 1931 version LAST OF THE MOHICANS.*

RETURN OF THE PINK PANTHER, THE
(1975 - United Artists) Peter Sellers, Christopher Plummer
One Sheet: $7 - $15

RETURN OF THE RANGERS
(1943 - PRC) Dave O'Brien, James Newill
One Sheet: $15 - $35

RETURN OF THE SCARLET PIMPERNEL, THE
(1938 - United Artists) Barry K. Barnes, Sophie Stewart, James Mason
One Sheet: $75 - $150

RETURN OF THE SCARLET PIMPERNEL, THE
(1948R - United Artists) Barry K. Barnes, Sophie Stewart, James Mason
One Sheet: $30 - $60   *Re-release.*

RETURN OF THE SEVEN
(1966 - United Artists) Yul Brynner, Robert Fuller
One Sheet: $15 - $25

RETURN OF THE TERROR, THE
(1934 - First National) Mary Astor
One Sheet: $250 - $500   *Graven Images, pg. 65.*

RETURN OF THE TEXAN
(1952 - 20th Century Fox) Dale Robertson, Joanne Dru
One Sheet: $15 - $30

RETURN OF THE VAMPIRE, THE
(1943 - Columbia) Bela Lugosi, Frieda Inescort
One Sheet: $250 - $600   *Graven Images, pg. 130.*

RETURN OF THE WHISTLER, THE
(1948 - Columbia) Michael Duane, Lenore Aubert
One Sheet: $20 - $40

RETURN OF THE WILDFIRE, THE
(1948 - Screen Guild) Richard Arlen, Mary Beth Hughes
One Sheet: $15 - $25

RETURN OF WILD BILL, THE

(1940 - Columbia) Wild Bill Elliott
One Sheet: $40 - $75

RETURN TO HORROR HIGH
(1987 - -) Vince Edward, Alex Rocco
One Sheet: $10 - $20

RETURN TO MACON COUNTY
(1975 - AIP) Don Johnson, Nick Nolte
One Sheet: $7 - $15

RETURN TO OZ
(1984 - Disney) Nicol Williamson, Fairuza Balk, Piper Laurie
One Sheet: $7 - $15   *Drew art.*

One Sheet

RETURN TO PARADISE
(1953 - United Artists) Gary Cooper, Roberta Haynes
One Sheet: $30 - $60

RETURN TO PEYTON PLACE
(1961 - 20th Century Fox) Carol Lynley, Jeff Chandler
One Sheet: $15 - $25

RETURN TO SNOWY RIVER
(1988 - 20th Century Fox) Tom Burlinson, Sigrid Thornton
One Sheet: $5 - $10

RETURN TO TREASURE ISLAND
(1954 - United Artists) Tab Hunter, Dawn Addams
One Sheet: $15 - $25

RETURN TO WARBOW
(1958 - Columbia) Phil Carey, Catherine McLeod
One Sheet: $10 - $20

REUNION
(1936 - 20th Century Fox) Dionne Quints, Jean Hersholt, Rochelle Hudson
One Sheet: $250 - $600

REUNION IN FRANCE
(1942 - MGM) Joan Crawford, John Wayne
One Sheet: $150 - $350

REUNION IN RENO
(1951 - Universal) Mark Stevens, Peggy Dow
One Sheet: $10 - $20

REUNION IN VIENNA
(1933 - MGM) John Barrymore, Diana Wynyard, Frank Morgan
One Sheet: $200 - $400

REVEILLE WITH BEVERLY
(1943 - Columbia) Ann Miller, Larry Parks, Frank Sinatra, Bob Crosby
One Sheet: $100 - $200   *Big Band musical. (Count Basie & his Orchestra, Duke Ellington & his Orchestra, Bob Crosby & his Orchestra, Freddie Slack & his Orchestra).*

REVELATION
(1918 - -) Alla Nazimova, Charles Bryant
One Sheet: $250 - $500

REVENGE
(1926 - United Artists) Dolores Del Rio
One Sheet: $250 - $500

REVENGE
(1990 - -) Kevin Costner, Anthony Quinn, Madeline Stowe
One Sheet: $7 - $15

REVENGE AT MONTE CARLO
(1933 - Mayfair) June Collyer, Jose Crespo
One Sheet: $100 - $200

REVENGE OF FRANKENSTEIN, THE
(1958 - Columbia) Peter Cushing, Francis
Matthews
One Sheet: $100 - $200   *Graven*
Images, pg. 196.

Title Card

REVENGE OF TARZAN, THE
(1920 - Goldwyn) Dir: Harry Revier
One Sheet: $3,500 - $5,000

REVENGE OF THE CHEERLEADERS
(1976 - Monarch) Jerri Woods
One Sheet: $15 - $25

REVENGE OF THE CONQUERED
(1964 - AIP) Burt Nelson, Wandisa Guida
One Sheet: $15 - $25

REVENGE OF THE CREATURE
(1955 - Universal) John Agar, Lori Nelson, Clint
Eastwood (his 1st film)
One Sheet: $700 - $1,200   *Originally*
filmed in 3-D. Graven Images, pg. 161.

One Sheet

REVENGE OF THE DEAD
(1960 - Crown) Tor Johnson, Lon Chaney, Jr.,
Dir: E. Wood, Jr.
One Sheet: $75 - $150   *AKA: NIGHT*
OF THE GHOULS.

REVENGE OF THE DEAD
(1984 - -) Gabriele Lavia, Anne Canoras
One Sheet: $7 - $15

REVENGE OF THE GLADIATORS
(1965 - Paramount) Roger Browne, Scilla
Gabel
One Sheet: $5 - $10

REVENGE OF THE JEDI
(1983 - 20th Century Fox) Mark Hamill,
Harrison Ford, Carrie Fisher
One Sheet: $200 - $400   *Special error*
poster released before title change. Beware of
unfolded reprints. Originals are folded. One
Sheet(rolled reprint):$15-$25.

REVENGE OF THE NERDS
(1984 - -) Robert Carradine, Anthony Edwards
One Sheet: $5 - $10

**REVENGE OF THE NERDS 2: NERDS IN
PARADISE**
(1987 - -) Robert Carradine, Curtis Armstrong
One Sheet: $3 - $5

REVENGE OF THE NINJA
(1983 - MGM/United Artists) Sho Kosugi, Keith
Vitali
One Sheet: $3 - $5

REVENGE OF THE PINK PANTHER
(1978 - United Artists) Peter Sellers, Herbert
Lom, Dyan Cannon

One Sheet: $7 - $15

REVENGE OF THE ZOMBIES
(1943 - Monogram) John Carradine, Gale
Storm, Mantan Moreland
One Sheet: $125 - $250

REVENGE RIDER, THE
(1935 - Columbia) Tim McCoy
One Sheet: $250 - $500

REVENGERS, THE
(1972 - National General) William Holden,
Ernest Borgnine, Susan Hayward (last film)
One Sheet: $7 - $15

REVENUE AGENT
(1951 - Columbia) Douglas Kennedy, Jean
Willes
One Sheet: $10 - $20

REVERSAL OF FORTUNE
(1990 - Warner Bros.) Jeremy Irons, Glenn
Close
One Sheet: $7 - $15   *Academy*
Award: Best Actor(Irons). Academy Award Movie
Posters #371.

REVOLT AT FORT LARAMIE
(1957 - United Artists) John Dehner, Gregg
Palmer
One Sheet: $10 - $20

REVOLT IN THE BIG HOUSE
(1958 - Allied Artists) Gene Evans, Robert
Blake
One Sheet: $15 - $35

REVOLT OF MAMIE STOVER, THE
(1956 - 20th Century Fox) Jane Russell,
Richard Egan
One Sheet: $30 - $50

REVOLT OF THE SLAVES
(1961 - United Artists) Rhonda Fleming, Lang
Jeffries
One Sheet: $15 - $30

REVOLT OF THE ZOMBIES
(1936 - Filmcraft) Dean Jagger, Dorothy Stone
One Sheet: $250 - $500   *Graven*
Images, pg. 95.

REVOLUTION
(1968 - Lopert) Today Malone
One Sheet: $30 - $50   *Documentary.*
Shows "Weird Rites of the Hippies."

REVOLUTION
(1985 - Warner Bros.) Al Pacino, Donald
Sutherland
One Sheet: $5 - $10

REVOLUTIONARY, THE
(1970 - United Artists) Jon Voight, Jennifer Salt
One Sheet: $5 - $10

REWARD, THE
(1965 - 20th Century Fox) Max von Sydow,
Yvette Mimieux
One Sheet: $5 - $10

RHAPSODY
(1953 - MGM) Elizabeth Taylor, Vittorio
Gassman
One Sheet: $75 - $125

RHAPSODY IN BLUE
(1945 - Warner Bros.) Robert Alda, Joan
Leslie, Paul Whiteman & his Orchestra
One Sheet: $40 - $75   *Big Band*
musical.

RHINESTONE
(1984 - 20th Century Fox) Dolly Parton,
Sylvester Stallone
One Sheet: $5 - $10

RHINO!
(1964 - MGM) Harry Guardino, Robert Culp
One Sheet: $3 - $5

RHINOCEROS
(1974 - Cinevision) Zero Mostel, Gene Wilder
One Sheet: $5 - $10

RHODES
(1936 - Gaumont) Walter Huston
One Sheet: $250 - $500

RHODES OF AFRICA
(1936 - Gaumont) Walter Huston, Oscar
Homolka
One Sheet: $500 - $800

AKA:RHODES.

RHUBARB
(1951 - Paramount) Ray Milland, Jan Sterling
One Sheet: $30 - $50

RHYTHM AND BLUES REVUE
(1955 - Studio Films) Count Basie, Lionel
Hampton
One Sheet: $150 - $300   *Black cast.*
Separate Cinema, pg. 103.

RHYTHM AND WEEP
(1946 - Columbia) The Three Stooges (Curly)
One Sheet: $2,500 - $4,000   *Comedy short.*
Duotone.

RHYTHM IN A RIFF
(1947 - Astor) Billy Eckstine and Band, Babe
Wallace
One Sheet: $250 - $600   *Black cast.*
Separate Cinema, pg. 100.

RHYTHM IN THE CLOUDS
(1937 - Republic) Warren Hull, Patricia Ellis
One Sheet: $75 - $150

RHYTHM INN
(1951 - Monogram) Jane Frazee, Kirby Grant,
Anson Weeks & Orchestra
One Sheet: $15 - $35   *Big Band*
musical.

RHYTHM MASTERS
(1948 - -) -
One Sheet: $75 - $125

RHYTHM OF THE ISLANDS
(1943 - Universal) Allan Jones, Jane Frazee
One Sheet: $40 - $75

RHYTHM OF THE RIO GRANDE
(1940 - Monogram) Tex Ritter
One Sheet: $125 - $250

RHYTHM OF THE SADDLE
(1938 - Republic) Gene Autry
One Sheet: $200 - $400

RHYTHM OF THE SADDLE
(1944R - Republic) Gene Autry
One Sheet: $75 - $150   *Re-release.*
Full color.

RHYTHM ON THE RANGE
(1936 - Paramount) Bing Crosby, Frances
Farmer
One Sheet: $500 - $800

RHYTHM ON THE RIVER
(1940 - Paramount) Bing Crosby, Mary Martin,
Basil Rathbone
One Sheet: $125 - $250

RHYTHM PARADE
(1942 - Monogram) Gale Storm, Robert
Lowery, Ted Fio Rito's Orchestra
One Sheet: $50 - $100   *Big Band*
musical.

RHYTHM RODEO
(1938 - Randol) Troy Brown
One Sheet: $250 - $600   *Black cast.*
Separate Cinema, pg. 54.

RHYTHM ROUND-UP
(1945 - Columbia) Ken Curtis, Cheryl Walker
One Sheet: $40 - $75

RICE GIRL
(1963 - Ultra Pictures) Elsa Martinelli
One Sheet: $15 - $25

RICH AND FAMOUS
(1981 - MGM) Jacqueline Bisset, Candice
Bergen
One Sheet: $4 - $8

RICH AND STRANGE
(1932 - Power Pictures) Henry Kendall, Joan
Barry, Dir: Hitchcock
One Sheet: $2,500 - $4,000   *AKA: EAST*
OF SHANGHAI.

RICH ARE ALWAYS WITH US, THE
(1932 - First National) George Brent, Ruth
Chatterton, Bette Davis
One Sheet: $800 - $1,500

RICH GIRL, POOR GIRL
(1921 - -) Gladys Walton, Gordon McGregor
One Sheet: $200 - $400

RICH IN LOVE

(1993 - MGM) Albert Finney, Jill Clayburgh
One Sheet: $3 - $5

RICH KIDS
(1979 - United Artists) Trini Alvarado, Jeremy
Levy, John Lithgow
One Sheet: $3 - $5

RICH MAN, POOR GIRL
(1938 - MGM) Robert Young, Lew Ayres, Ruth
Hussey, Lana Turner
One Sheet: $100 - $200

RICH MAN'S FOLLY
(1931 - Paramount Publix) George Bancroft,
Frances Dee
One Sheet: $100 - $200

RICH MAN'S WIFE, THE
(1996 - Hollywood) Halle Berry, Christopher
McDonald
One Sheet: $3 - $5

RICH MEN'S WIVES
(1922 - Preferred) House Peters, Claire
Windsor
One Sheet: $250 - $600

RICH, YOUNG AND PRETTY
(1951 - MGM) Jane Powell, Vic Damone
One Sheet: $15 - $30

RICHARD III
(1955 - Lopert) Laurence Olivier, John Gielgud
One Sheet: $500 - $800

One Sheet

RICHARD III
(1967?R - Lopert) Laurence Olivier, John
Gielgud
One Sheet: $30 - $50   *Re-release.*

RICHARD III
(1995 - United Artists) Ian McKellen, Maggie
Smith, Annette Bening
One Sheet: $10 - $20

RICHARD PRYOR - LIVE IN CONCERT
(1979 - Special Event) Richard Pryor
One Sheet: $7 - $15

RICHARD PRYOR HERE AND NOW
(1983 - -) Concert
One Sheet: $7 - $15

RICHARD PRYOR LIVE ON THE SUNSET STRIP
(1982 - Columbia) Richard Pryor
One Sheet: $7 - $15

RICHEST GIRL IN THE WORLD, THE
(1934 - RKO) Joel McCrea, Fay Wray, Miriam
Hopkins
One Sheet: $200 - $400

RICHEST MAN IN THE WORLD, THE
(1930 - MGM) Robert Montgomery
One Sheet: $150 - $300

RICHEST MAN IN TOWN, THE
(1941 - Columbia) Frank Craven, Eileen
O'Hearn
One Sheet: $40 - $75

RICHIE RICH
(1994 - Warner Bros.) Macaulay Culkin, John
Larroquette
One Sheet: $5 - $10

RICOCHET
(1991 - Warner Bros.) Denzel Washington,
John Lithgow
One Sheet: $5 - $10

RICOCHET ROMANCE
(1954 - Universal) Marjorie Main, Chill Wills

One Sheet: $15 - $25

RIDDLE GAWNE
(1918 - Artcraft) William S. Hart, Lambert Hillyer
One Sheet: $800 - $1,500

RIDE 'EM COWBOY
(1930 - Pathe)
One Sheet: $200 - $400

RIDE 'EM COWBOY
(1936 - Universal) Buck Jones
One Sheet: $600 - $1,000   *Sports (Auto racing). Western. Cowboy Movie Posters #203. Sports Movie Posters #11.*

RIDE 'EM COWBOY
(1941 - Universal) Abbott & Costello, Dick Foran
One Sheet: $200 - $400

Half Sheet

RIDE 'EM COWGIRL
(1939 - Grand National) Dorothy Page
One Sheet: $40 - $75

RIDE A CROOKED MILE
(1938 - Paramount) Akim Tamiroff, Frances Farmer
One Sheet: $150 - $300

RIDE A CROOKED TRAIL
(1958 - Universal International) Audie Murphy, Gia Scala, Walter Matthau
One Sheet: $50 - $100

RIDE A VIOLENT MILE
(1957 - 20th Century Fox) John Agar, Penny Edwards
One Sheet: $15 - $25

RIDE A WILD PONY
(1975 - Disney) Michael Craig, John Meillon
One Sheet: $5 - $10

RIDE BACK, THE
(1957 - United Artists) Anthony Quinn, Lita Milan
One Sheet: $7 - $15

RIDE BEYOND VENGEANCE
(1966 - Columbia) Chuck Connors, Michael Rennie
One Sheet: $7 - $15

RIDE CLEAR OF DIABLO
(1953 - Universal) Audie Murphy, Susan Cabot
One Sheet: $30 - $50

RIDE FOR YOUR LIFE
(1924 - Universal) Hoot Gibson, Laura La Plante
One Sheet: $250 - $500

RIDE HIM, COWBOY
(1932 - Vitagraph) John Wayne
One Sheet: $2,200 - $3,500

RIDE HIM, COWBOY
(1955R - -) John Wayne
One Sheet: $30 - $50   *Re-release. Duotone.*

RIDE, KELLY, RIDE
(1941 - 20th Century Fox) Marvin Stephens, Rita Quigley
One Sheet: $50 - $100   *Sports (Horse Racing). Sports Movie Posters #251.*

RIDE LONESOME
(1959 - Columbia) Randolph Scott, Lee Van Cleef
One Sheet: $15 - $35   *Cowboy Movie Posters #304.*

RIDE ON VAQUERO
(1941 - 20th Century Fox) Cisco Kid, Cesar Romero
One Sheet: $50 - $100

RIDE OUT FOR REVENGE
(1958 - United Artists) Rory Calhoun, Gloria Grahame
One Sheet: $10 - $20

RIDE, RANGER, RIDE
(1936 - Republic) Gene Autry
One Sheet: $250 - $500

RIDE, RANGER, RIDE
(1942R - Republic) Gene Autry
One Sheet: $50 - $100   *Re-release. Western. Full color.*

RIDE, RYDER, RIDE
(1948 - Eagle-Lion) Jim Bannon
One Sheet: $20 - $40   *Red Ryder series.*

RIDE TENDERFOOT, RIDE
(1940 - Republic) Gene Autry
One Sheet: $150 - $300

RIDE TENDERFOOT, RIDE
(1943R - Republic) Gene Autry
One Sheet: $50 - $100   *Re-release. Western. Full color.*

RIDE THE HIGH COUNTRY
(1962 - MGM) Randolph Scott, Joel McCrea
One Sheet: $40 - $75   *Scott's final film.*

RIDE THE HIGH IRON
(1956 - Columbia) Don Taylor, Raymond Burr
One Sheet: $7 - $15

RIDE THE MAN DOWN
(1952 - Republic) Brian Donlevy, Rod Cameron
One Sheet: $15 - $25

RIDE THE PINK HORSE
(1947 - Universal) Robert Montgomery, Wanda Hendrix
One Sheet: $50 - $100

RIDE THE WILD SURF
(1964 - Columbia) Fabian, Shelly Fabares, Barbara Eden
One Sheet: $30 - $60   *Sports (Surfing).*

RIDE TO HANGMAN'S TREE, THE
(1967 - Universal) Jack Lord, James Farentino
One Sheet: $5 - $10

RIDE VAQUERO!
(1953 - MGM) Robert Taylor, Ava Gardner
One Sheet: $30 - $50

RIDE VAQUERO!
(1962R - MGM) Robert Taylor, Ava Gardner
One Sheet: $7 - $15   *Re-release.*

RIDER FROM TUCSON
(1950 - RKO) Tim Holt
One Sheet: $15 - $35

RIDER OF DEATH VALLEY
(1932 - Universal) Tom Mix
One Sheet: $1,300 - $2,000

RIDER OF THE KING LOG
(1921 - -) Frank Sheridan, Irene Boyle
One Sheet: $250 - $500

RIDER OF THE PURPLE COWS
(1924 - Pathecomedy) Ralph Graves
One Sheet: $150 - $350

RIDER ON A DEAD HORSE
(1962 - Allied Artists) John Vivyan, Lisa Lu
One Sheet: $7 - $15

RIDER ON THE RAIN
(1970 - Avco) Charles Bronson, Marlene Jobert
One Sheet: $15 - $30

RIDERS FROM NOWHERE
(1940 - Monogram) Jack Randall
One Sheet: $75 - $150   *Full color stone litho.*

RIDERS IN THE SKY
(1949 - Columbia) Gene Autry, Gloria Henry
One Sheet: $75 - $150

RIDERS OF BLACK MOUNTAIN

(1940 - PRC) Tim McCoy
One Sheet: $75 - $150

RIDERS OF BLACK RIVER
(1939 - Columbia) Charles Starrett
One Sheet: $75 - $150

One Sheet

RIDERS OF DEATH VALLEY
(1941 - Universal) Dick Foran, Leo Carrillo
One Sheet: $50 - $100   *Serial. Western. 15 Chapters. Price is for duotone chapters. One Sheet(Color Chapter One):$150-250.*

RIDERS OF DESTINY
(1934 - Lone Star) John Wayne, Cecilia Parker
One Sheet: $2,500 - $4,000   *Cowboy Movie Posters # 166.*

RIDERS OF DESTINY
(1944R - Lone Star) John Wayne
One Sheet: $75 - $150   *Re-release. Western.*

RIDERS OF PASCO BASIN
(1939 - Universal) Johnny Mack Brown
One Sheet: $75 - $125

RIDERS OF THE BADLANDS
(1941 - Columbia) Charles Starrett
One Sheet: $40 - $75

RIDERS OF THE BLACK HILLS
(1938 - Republic) Three Mesquiteers
One Sheet: $75 - $125

RIDERS OF THE DAWN
(1937 - Monogram) Jack Randall
One Sheet: $75 - $150

RIDERS OF THE DAWN
(1945 - Monogram) Jimmy Wakely
One Sheet: $30 - $50

RIDERS OF THE DEADLINE
(1943 - United Artists) William Boyd, Robert Mitchum
One Sheet: $150 - $350   *Hopalong Cassidy series. Cowboy Movie Posters #273. Mitchum's last B Western.*

One Sheet

RIDERS OF THE DESERT
(1932 - Sono Art/World Wide) Bob Steele
One Sheet: $150 - $300

RIDERS OF THE DUSK
(1949 - Monogram) Whip Wilson
One Sheet: $20 - $40

RIDERS OF THE FRONTIER
(1939 - Monogram) Tex Ritter, Jack Rutherford, Mantan Moreland
One Sheet: $100 - $200

RIDERS OF THE LONE STAR
(1947 - Columbia) Charles Starrett
One Sheet: $20 - $40

RIDERS OF THE NORTHLAND
(1942 - Columbia) Charles Starrett, Russell Hayden
One Sheet: $40 - $75

RIDERS OF THE NORTHWEST MOUNTED
(1943 - Columbia) Russell Hayden
One Sheet: $30 - $50

RIDERS OF THE PONY EXPRESS
(1949 - Screen-Craft) Ken Curtis
One Sheet: $15 - $35

RIDERS OF THE PURPLE COWS
(1924 - Pathe) Ralph Graves
One Sheet: $125 - $250

RIDERS OF THE PURPLE SAGE
(1918 - Fox) William Farnum, Mary Mersch, William Scott
One Sheet: $250 - $600

RIDERS OF THE PURPLE SAGE
(1925 - Fox) Tom Mix
One Sheet: $600 - $1,000

RIDERS OF THE PURPLE SAGE
(1931 - Fox) George O'Brien
One Sheet: $200 - $400

RIDERS OF THE PURPLE SAGE
(1941 - 20th Century Fox) George Montgomery
One Sheet: $75 - $125

RIDERS OF THE PURPLE SAGE
(1954R - 20th Century Fox) George Montgomery
One Sheet: $15 - $25   *Re-release.*

RIDERS OF THE RANGE
(1949 - RKO) Tim Holt
One Sheet: $15 - $35

RIDERS OF THE RIO GRANDE
(1943 - Republic) Three Mesquiteers
One Sheet: $40 - $75

RIDERS OF THE ROCKIES
(1937 - Grand National) Tex Ritter
One Sheet: $100 - $200

RIDERS OF THE SAGE
(1939 - Metropolitan) Bob Steele
One Sheet: $125 - $250

RIDERS OF THE SANTA FE
(1944 - Universal) Rod Cameron
One Sheet: $20 - $40

RIDERS OF THE TIMBERLINE
(1941 - Paramount) William Boyd
One Sheet: $150 - $300   *Hopalong Cassidy series.*

RIDERS OF THE WEST
(1942 - Monogram) Buck Jones, Tim McCoy
One Sheet: $100 - $200

RIDERS OF THE WEST
(1954R - Monogram) Buck Jones, Tim McCoy
One Sheet: $15 - $25   *Re-release.*

RIDERS OF THE WHISTLING SKULL
(1937 - Republic) Three Mesquiteers
One Sheet: $75 - $150

RIDERS OF WHISTLING PINES
(1949 - Columbia) Gene Autry, Patricia White
One Sheet: $75 - $150

RIDERS TO THE STARS
(1953 - United Artists) William Lundigan, Herbert Marshall
One Sheet: $20 - $40

RIDIN' DOWN THE CANYON
(1942 - Republic) Roy Rogers
One Sheet: $125 - $250

RIDIN' DOWN THE TRAIL
(1947 - Monogram) Jimmy Wakely
One Sheet: $20 - $40

RIDIN' FOOL, THE
(1931 - Tiffany) Bob Steele
One Sheet: $150 - $300

RIDIN' FOR JUSTICE
(1931 - Columbia) Buck Jones, Mary Doran
One Sheet: $1,900 - $3,000   *Cowboy*

Movie Posters #'s 94, 98.

RIDIN' MAD
(1924 - Arrow) Yakima Canutt, Lorraine Eason
One Sheet: $250 - $500

RIDIN' ON
(1936 - Reliable) Tom Tyler
One Sheet: $125 - $250

RIDIN' ON A RAINBOW
(1941 - Republic) Gene Autry
One Sheet: $150 - $300

RIDIN' ROMEO, THE
(1921 - Fox) Tom Mix
One Sheet: $500 - $800

RIDIN' THE CHEROKEE TRAIL
(1941 - Monogram) Tex Ritter
One Sheet: $100 - $200

RIDIN' THE LONE TRAIL
(1937 - Republic) Bob Steele
One Sheet: $100 - $200

RIDIN' THE OUTLAW TRAIL
(1951 - Columbia) Charles Starrett
One Sheet: $15 - $30

RIDIN' THRU
(1935 - Reliable) Tom Tyler
One Sheet: $200 - $400

One Sheet

RIDIN' WILD
(1922 - Universal) Hoot Gibson, Edna Murphy
One Sheet: $250 - $500

RIDING AVENGER, THE
(1936 - Diversion) Hoot Gibson, Ruth Mix
One Sheet: $150 - $300

RIDING HIGH
(1943 - Paramount) Dorothy Lamour, Dick Powell
One Sheet: $75 - $125

RIDING HIGH
(1950 - Paramount) Bing Crosby, Coleen Gray
One Sheet: $15 - $35

RIDING ON AIR
(1937 - RKO) Joe E. Brown
One Sheet: $125 - $250

RIDING ON AIR
(194?R - Trinity) Joe E. Brown
One Sheet: $30 - $50   *Re-release.*

RIDING RENEGADE, THE
(1928 - FBO) Bob Steele, Lafe McKee
One Sheet: $250 - $500

RIDING SHOTGUN
(1954 - Warner Bros.) Randolph Scott, Wayne Morris
One Sheet: $40 - $75

RIDING THE CALIFORNIA TRAIL
(1947 - Monogram) Gilbert Roland
One Sheet: $20 - $40

RIDING THE LONE TRAIL
(1937 - Republic) Bob Steele
One Sheet: $100 - $200

RIDING THE LONE TRAIL
(1947R - Republic) Bob Steele
One Sheet: $30 - $50   *Re-release.*

RIDING THE SUNSET TRAIL
(1941 - Monogram) Tom Keene
One Sheet: $75 - $125

RIDING THE WIND
(1941 - RKO) Tim Holt
One Sheet: $40 - $75

RIDING THROUGH NEVADA
(1942 - Columbia) Charles Starrett
One Sheet: $30 - $50

RIDING TORNADO, THE
(1932 - Columbia) Tim McCoy
One Sheet: $500 - $800

RIDING WEST
(1944 - Columbia) Charles Starrett
One Sheet: $30 - $50

RIDING WILD
(1935 - Columbia) Tim McCoy
One Sheet: $700 - $1,200   *Cowboy Movie Posters #180.*

RIDING WITH BUFFALO BILL
(1954 - Columbia) Marshall Reed, Rick Vallin
One Sheet: $40 - $75   *Serial. Western. 15 Chapters.*

RIDING WITH DEATH
(1921 - Fox) Charles "Buck" Jones, Betty Francisco
One Sheet: $700 - $1,200

RIFF RAFF GIRLS
(1962 - Techno Stampa) Nadja Tiller, Robert Hossein
One Sheet: $15 - $30   *French/Italian. AKA: RIFIFI FOR GIRLS.*

RIFFRAFF
(1935 - MGM) Jean Harlow, Spencer Tracy
One Sheet: $700 - $1,200   *AKA: RIFF-RAFF.*

RIFFRAFF
(1947 - RKO) Pat O'Brien, Walter Slezak
One Sheet: $40 - $75

RIFIFI
(1956 - -) Jean Servais, Carl Mohner
One Sheet: $15 - $30   *French.*

RIFIFI IN TOKYO
(1963 - Cipra/MGM) Karl Boehm, Michel Vitold
One Sheet: $10 - $20   *French/Italian. AKA: RIFIFI A TOKYO.*

RIGHT APPROACH, THE
(1961 - 20th Century Fox) Frankie Vaughan, Juliet Prowse
One Sheet: $5 - $10

RIGHT CROSS
(1950 - MGM) June Allyson, Dick Powell, Marilyn Monroe (cameo)
One Sheet: $50 - $100

RIGHT OF WAY, THE
(1931 - First National) Conrad Nagel, Loretta Young
One Sheet: $250 - $600

RIGHT STUFF, THE
(1982 - Warner Bros.) Sam Shepard, Scott Glenn, Ed Harris
One Sheet: $15 - $25   *Advance:$20-40.*

RIGHT THAT FAILED, THE
(1922 - Metro) Bert Lytell, Virginia Valli
One Sheet: $250 - $550

RIGHT TO LIVE, THE
(1935 - Warner Bros.) George Brent, Peggy Wood
One Sheet: $75 - $150

RIGHT TO LOVE, THE
(1930 - Paramount Publix) Ruth Chatterton, Paul Lukas
One Sheet: $150 - $300

RIGHT TO ROMANCE, THE
(1933 - RKO) Ann Harding, Robert Young
One Sheet: $150 - $300

RIGHT TO THE HEART
(1942 - 20th Century Fox) Brenda Joyce, Joseph Allen Jr.
One Sheet: $30 - $50

RIM OF THE CANYON
(1949 - Columbia) Gene Autry, Nan Leslie
One Sheet: $75 - $150

RIMFIRE

(1949 - Screen Guild) James Millican, Mary Beth Hughes
One Sheet: $15 - $25

RING, THE
(1927 - British International) Carl Brisson, Dir: Alfred Hitchcock
One Sheet: $5,000 - $7,500   *Sports (Boxing). Sports Movie Posters #122.*

RING, THE
(1952 - King Bros.) Gerald Mohr, Rita Moreno
One Sheet: $75 - $150   *Sports (Boxing).*

RING AROUND THE MOON
(1936 - Chesterfield) Donald Cook, John Qualen
One Sheet: $75 - $150

RING OF BRIGHT WATER
(1969 - Cinerama) Bill Travers, Virginia McKenna
One Sheet: $3 - $5

RING OF FEAR
(1954 - Warner Bros.) Clyde Beatty, Pat O'Brien
One Sheet: $30 - $50

RING OF FIRE
(1961 - MGM) David Janssen, Joyce Taylor
One Sheet: $7 - $15

RING OF TERROR
(1962 - Ashcroft) George Mathers, Esther Furst
One Sheet: $15 - $25

RING OF TREASON
(1964 - Paramount) Bernard Lee, Margaret Tyzack
One Sheet: $5 - $10

RING-A-DING RHYTHM
(1962 - Columbia) Helen Shapiro, Craig Douglas, Chubby Checker, Del Shannon
One Sheet: $15 - $30   *Rock 'n' Roll.*

RINGER, THE
(1932 - First Anglo) Patric Curwen, Franklin Dyall
One Sheet: $150 - $300

RINGER, THE
(1953 - Regent) Herbert Lom, Mai Zetterling
One Sheet: $15 - $35

RINGS AROUND THE WORLD
(1966 - Columbia) Don Ameche
One Sheet: $7 - $15

RINGS ON HER FINGERS
(1942 - 20th Century Fox) Henry Fonda, Gene Tierney
One Sheet: $250 - $500

RINGSIDE
(1949 - Lippert) Don Barry, Tom Brown
One Sheet: $15 - $35

RINGSIDE MAISIE
(1941 - MGM) Ann Sothern, George Murphy, Robert Sterling
One Sheet: $40 - $75

RINK, THE
(1916 - Mutual) Charlie Chaplin, Edna Purviance
One Sheet: $6,500 - $10,000

RIN-TIN-TIN, JR.
(1933 - Mascot) Stock poster
One Sheet: $200 - $450

RINTY OF THE DESERT
(1928 - Warner Bros.) Rin-Tin-Tin, Audrey Ferris
One Sheet: $200 - $400

RIO
(1939 - Universal) Basil Rathbone, Victor McLaglen
One Sheet: $75 - $150

RIO
(1949R - Realart) Basil Rathbone, Victor McLaglen
One Sheet: $20 - $40   *Re-release.*

RIO BRAVO
(1959 - Warner Bros.) John Wayne, Dean Martin
One Sheet: $200 - $400

RIO CONCHOS
(1964 - 20th Century Fox) Richard Boone, Stuart Whitman
One Sheet: $10 - $20

RIO GRANDE
(1938 - Columbia) Charles Starrett
One Sheet: $75 - $150

RIO GRANDE
(1950 - Republic) John Wayne, Maureen O'Hara
One Sheet: $500 - $900   *Cowboy Movie Posters #288.*

RIO GRANDE PATROL
(1950 - RKO) Tim Holt
One Sheet: $15 - $35

RIO GRANDE RAIDERS
(1946 - Republic) Sunset Carson
One Sheet: $20 - $40

RIO GRANDE RANGER
(1936 - Columbia) Bob Allen
One Sheet: $75 - $150

RIO GRANDE ROMANCE
(1936 - Victory) Eddie Nugent
One Sheet: $50 - $100

RIO LOBO
(1971 - Cinema Center) John Wayne, Jorge Rivero, Dir: Howard Hawks
One Sheet: $40 - $80   *Hawks' final film.*

RIO RATTLER
(1935 - Bernard Ray Presents) Tom Tyler
One Sheet: $200 - $400   *Cowboy Movie Posters #188.*

RIO RITA
(1929 - RKO) Bebe Daniels, John Boles
One Sheet: $800 - $1,500

RIO RITA
(1942 - MGM) Bud Abbott, Lou Costello, Kathryn Grayson
One Sheet: $150 - $300

Half Sheet

RIOT
(1969 - Paramount) Jim Brown, Gene Hackman
One Sheet: $15 - $25   *Poster depicts Brown behind bars.*

RIOT IN CELL BLOCK 11
(1954 - Monogram) Neville Brand, Emile Meyer
One Sheet: $20 - $40

RIOT IN JUVENILE PRISON
(1958 - United Artists) Jerome Thor, Marcia Henderson
One Sheet: $15 - $30

RIOT ON SUNSET STRIP
(1967 - AIP) Aldo Ray, Mimsy Farmer
One Sheet: $20 - $40

RIOT SQUAD
(1933 - Mayfair) Madge Bellamy, Pat O'Malley
One Sheet: $75 - $125

RIOT SQUAD
(1941 - Monogram) Richard Cromwell, Rita Quigley
One Sheet: $20 - $40

RIP OFF
(1972 - Cinemax) Don Scardino, Ralph Endersby
One Sheet: $3 - $5

RIP ROARIN' BUCKAROO

(1936 - Victory) Tom Tyler, Beth Marion, Sammy Cohen
One Sheet: $100 - $200

RIP ROARING RILEY
(1935 - Puritan) Lloyd Hughes, Grant Withers
One Sheet: $50 - $100

RIP, SEW AND STITCH
(1953 - Columbia) The Three Stooges (Shemp)
One Sheet: $150 - $350   *Comedy short. Duotone.*

RIPTIDE
(1934 - MGM) Norma Shearer, Robert Montgomery
One Sheet: $250 - $600

RISE AND FALL OF LEGS DIAMOND, THE
(1960 - Warner Bros.) Ray Danton, Karen Steele
One Sheet: $15 - $25

RISE AND SHINE
(1941 - 20th Century Fox) Jack Oakie, Milton Berle, Linda Darnell
One Sheet: $75 - $150   *Sports (Football).*

RISING OF THE MOON, THE
(1957 - Warner Bros.) Cyril Cusack, Noel Purcell
One Sheet: $10 - $20

RISING SUN
(1993 - 20th Century Fox) Sean Connery, Wesley Snipes
One Sheet: $5 - $10

RISKY BUSINESS
(1939 - Universal) George Murphy, Dorothy Kent
One Sheet: $75 - $150

RISKY BUSINESS
(1983 - Warner Bros.) Tom Cruise, Rebecca DeMornay
One Sheet: $20 - $40

RITA, SUE AND BOB TOO!
(1986 - Orion Classics) George Costigan, Michelle Holmes
One Sheet: $3 - $5

RITZ, THE
(1976 - Warner Bros.) Jack Weston, Rita Moreno
One Sheet: $5 - $10

RIVALS
(1972 - Avco/Embassy) Joan Hackett, Scott Jacoby
One Sheet: $3 - $5

RIVER, THE
(1951 - United Artists) Patricia Walters, Arthur Shields
One Sheet: $20 - $40

RIVER, THE
(1984 - Universal) Sissy Spacek, Mel Gibson
One Sheet: $10 - $20

RIVER BEAT
(1954 - Lippert) Phyllis Kirk, John Bentley
One Sheet: $15 - $25

RIVER CHANGES, THE
(1955 - Warner Bros.) Rosanna Rory, Harold Maresch
One Sheet: $5 - $10

RIVER GANG
(1945 - Universal) Gloria Jean, Bill Goodwin
One Sheet: $20 - $40

RIVER LADY
(1948 - Universal) Rod Cameron, Dan Duryea, Yvonne De Carlo
One Sheet: $15 - $30

RIVER NIGER, THE
(1976 - Cine Artists) Cecily Tyson, James Earl Jones, Lou Gossett
One Sheet: $10 - $20   *Black cast.*

RIVER OF DEATH
(1989 - Cannon) Michael Dudikoff, Donald Pleasence
One Sheet: $7 - $15

RIVER OF NO RETURN
(1954 - 20th Century Fox) Marilyn Monroe, Robert Mitchum

One Sheet: $250 - $500

RIVER OF NO RETURN
(1961R - 20th Century Fox) Marilyn Monroe, Robert Mitchum
One Sheet: $100 - $200   *Re-release.*

RIVER OF UNREST
(1936 - Gaumont) John Lodge, John Loder
One Sheet: $75 - $150

RIVER PIRATE, THE
(1928 - Fox) Victor McLaglen, Lois Moran
One Sheet: $250 - $500

RIVER RIBBER
(1941 - Columbia) Color Rhapsodies
One Sheet: $150 - $350   *Cartoon. Full color semi-stock poster with inset of title.*

RIVER RUNS THROUGH IT, A
(1992 - Columbia) Craig Sheffer, Brad Pitt
One Sheet: $15 - $30

One Sheet

RIVER WILD, THE
(1994 - Universal) Meryl Streep, Kevin Bacon
One Sheet: $5 - $10

RIVER'S EDGE, THE
(1957 - 20th Century Fox) Ray Milland, Anthony Quinn
One Sheet: $7 - $15

RIVER'S EDGE, THE
(1986 - Island) Crispin Glover, Keanu Reaves
One Sheet: $15 - $25

RIVER'S END
(1930 - Warner Bros.) Charles Bickford, Evalyn Knapp
One Sheet: $200 - $400

RIVER'S END
(1940 - Warner Bros.) Dennis Morgan, Victor Jory
One Sheet: $30 - $50

RIVERBOAT RHYTHM
(1946 - RKO) Leon Errol, Glenn Vernon, Frankie Carle & his Orchestra
One Sheet: $30 - $50   *Big Band musical.*

RIVERRUN
(1970 - Columbia) John McLiam, Louise Ober, Mark Jenkins
One Sheet: $3 - $5

RIVETER, THE
(1940 - RKO/Disney) Donald Duck
One Sheet: $4,500 - $7,000   *Cartoon. The Disney Poster, pg. 51. Cartoon Movie Posters #159.*

ROAD AGENT
(1941 - Universal) Dick Foran, Leo Carrillo
One Sheet: $30 - $50

ROAD AGENT
(1952 - RKO) Tim Holt
One Sheet: $15 - $35

ROAD BACK, THE
(1937 - Universal) John King, Richard Cromwell
One Sheet: $125 - $250

ROAD DEMON, THE
(1921 - Fox) Tom Mix
One Sheet: $250 - $600

ROAD DEMON
(1938 - 20th Century Fox) Henry Arthur, Joan Valerie

One Sheet: $50 - $100

ROAD GAMES
(1981 - Quest) Stacy Keach, Jamie Lee Curtis
One Sheet: $7 - $15

ROAD GANG
(1936 - Warner Bros.) Donald Woods, Kay Linaker
One Sheet: $75 - $150

ROAD HOUSE
(1948 - 20th Century Fox) Ida Lupino, Cornel Wilde, Richard Widmark
One Sheet: $100 - $200

ROAD HOUSE
(1989 - United Artists) Patrick Swayze, Kelly Lynch
One Sheet: $10 - $20

ROAD HUSTLERS, THE
(1968 - Saturn) Jim Davis, Scott Brady
One Sheet: $15 - $25

ROAD SCHOLAR
(1993 - Samuel Goldwyn) Andrei Codrescu
One Sheet: $3 - $5

ROAD SHOW
(1941 - United Artists) Carole Landis, Adolphe Menjou
One Sheet: $50 - $100

Window Card (Trimmed)

ROAD TO ALCATRAZ
(1945 - Republic) Robert Lowery, June Storey
One Sheet: $20 - $40

ROAD TO BALI
(1952 - Paramount) Bing Crosby, Bob Hope, Dorothy Lamour
One Sheet: $100 - $200   *Only color "ROAD" film.*

ROAD TO DENVER, THE
(1955 - Republic) John Payne, Mona Freeman
One Sheet: $10 - $20

ROAD TO FORT ALAMO, THE
(1966 - World Entertainment) Ken Clark, Jany Clair
One Sheet: $5 - $10

ROAD TO GLORY, THE
(1936 - 20th Century Fox) Fredric March, Warner Baxter, Lionel Barrymore
One Sheet: $250 - $600

ROAD TO HAPPINESS
(1942 - Monogram) John Boles, Mona Barrie
One Sheet: $20 - $40

ROAD TO HONG KONG
(1962 - United Artists) Bing Crosby, Bob Hope, Peter Sellers
One Sheet: $30 - $50   *Last "ROAD" film.*

ROAD TO MANDALAY, THE
(1926 - MGM) Lon Chaney, Lois Moran, Owen Moore
One Sheet: $2,500 - $4,000

ROAD TO MOROCCO
(1942 - Paramount) Bob Hope, Bing Crosby, Dorothy Lamour
One Sheet: $200 - $400

ROAD TO NASHVILLE
(1967 - -) Marty Robbins, Connie Smith
One Sheet: $30 - $50   *Country musical.*

ROAD TO PARADISE

(1930 - First National) Loretta Young, Jack Mulhall
One Sheet: $250 - $600

ROAD TO RENO
(1931 - Paramount Publix) Buddy Rogers, Peggy Shannon
One Sheet: $100 - $200

ROAD TO RENO
(1938 - Universal) Hope Hampton, Randolph Scott
One Sheet: $100 - $200

ROAD TO RIO
(1947 - Paramount) Bing Crosby, Bob Hope, Dorothy Lamour
One Sheet: $100 - $200

ROAD TO SALINA
(1971 - Avco/Embassy) Rita Hayworth, Robert Walker
One Sheet: $15 - $35

ROAD TO SINGAPORE, THE
(1931 - Warner Bros.) William Powell, Miriam Marsh
One Sheet: $250 - $600

ROAD TO SINGAPORE
(1940 - Paramount) Bing Crosby, Bob Hope, Dorothy Lamour
One Sheet: $250 - $500   *First "Road" film.*

ROAD TO THE BIG HOUSE
(1947 - Sumerset) John Shelton, Ann Doran
One Sheet: $20 - $40

ROAD TO UTOPIA
(1946 - Paramount) Bing Crosby, Bob Hope, Dorothy Lamour
One Sheet: $125 - $250

ROAD TO WELLVILLE, THE
(1994 - Columbia) Anthony Hopkins, Bridget Fonda, Matthew Broderick
One Sheet: $5 - $10

ROAD TO YESTERDAY
(1925 - -) Jetta Goudal, Dir: Cecil B. DeMille
One Sheet: $500 - $800

ROAD TO ZANZIBAR
(1941 - Paramount) Bing Crosby, Bob Hope, Dorothy Lamour
One Sheet: $200 - $400

ROAD WARRIOR, THE
(1982 - Warner Bros.) Mel Gibson
One Sheet: $20 - $40   *One Sheet(Style B):$30-$60; One Sheet:(Style C/ photo review):$30-50. One Sheet(Style C/art review):$20-30.*

ROADBLOCK
(1951 - Monogram) Charles McGraw, Milburn Stone
One Sheet: $40 - $75

ROADHOUSE GIRL
(1953 - Butchers) Maxwell Reed, Sandra Dorne
One Sheet: $30 - $50   *AKA: MARILYN.*

ROADHOUSE MURDER
(1932 - RKO) Bruce Cabot, Dorothy Jordan
One Sheet: $100 - $200

ROADIE
(1980 - United Artists) "Roadie" Meat Loaf, Alice Cooper, Blondie, Art Carney
One Sheet: $15 - $25

ROADRACERS, THE
(1959 - AIP) Joel Lawrence, Marian Collier
One Sheet: $10 - $20   *Sports (Auto racing).*

ROADSIDE PROPHETS
(1992 - Fine Line) John Doe, David Carradine
One Sheet: $3 - $5

ROAMING LADY
(1936 - Columbia) Fay Wray, Ralph Bellamy
One Sheet: $125 - $250

ROAR OF THE CROWD
(1953 - Monogram) Howard Duff, Helene Stanley
One Sheet: $40 - $75   *Sports (Boxing). Documentary on the career of Joe Louis. Separate Cinema, pg. 58,61.*

ROAR OF THE DRAGON
(1932 - RKO) Richard Dix, ZaSu Pitts
One Sheet: $150 - $300

ROAR OF THE IRON HORSE
(1951 - Columbia) Jock O'Mahoney, Virginia Herrick
One Sheet: $40 - $75   *Serial.*
Western. 15 Chapters. Cowboy Movie Posters #290.

ROAR OF THE PRESS
(1941 - Monogram) Jean Parker, Wallace Ford
One Sheet: $30 - $50

ROARIN' LEAD
(1936 - Republic) Three Mesquiteers
One Sheet: $75 - $125

ROARIN' LEAD
(1948R - Republic) Three Mesquiteers
One Sheet: $20 - $40   *Re-release.*

ROARING CITY
(1951 - Lippert) Hugh Beaumont, Richard Travis
One Sheet: $15 - $25

ROARING FRONTIERS
(1941 - Columbia) Bill Elliott, Tex Ritter
One Sheet: $75 - $125

ROARING GUNS
(1936 - Puritan) Tim McCoy, Rex Lease
One Sheet: $150 - $300

ROARING GUNS
(1944 - Warner Bros.) Robert Shayne
One Sheet: $15 - $30

ROARING LIONS ON THE MIDNIGHT EXPRESS
(1918 - William Fox) -
One Sheet: $500 - $800

ROARING RANCH
(1930 - Universal) Hoot Gibson
One Sheet: $200 - $400

ROARING RANGERS
(1946 - Columbia) Charles Starrett
One Sheet: $15 - $35

ROARING SIX GUNS
(1937 - Ambassador) Kermit Maynard
One Sheet: $40 - $75

One Sheet

ROARING TIMBER
(1936 - Samuel Goldwyn) Frances Farmer, Walter Brennan
One Sheet: $75 - $125   *Reissue of COME AND GET IT.*

ROARING TIMBER
(1937 - Columbia) Jack Holt
One Sheet: $100 - $200

ROARING TWENTIES, THE
(1939 - Warner Bros.) James Cagney, Humphrey Bogart, Priscilla Lane
One Sheet: $2,200 - $3,500

ROARING TWENTIES, THE
(1950R - Warner Bros.) James Cagney, Humphrey Bogart, Priscilla Lane
One Sheet: $50 - $100   *Re-release.*
Duotone.

ROARING WEST
(1935 - Universal) Buck Jones
One Sheet: $250 - $600   *Serial.*
Western. 15 Chapters.

ROARING WESTWARD
(1949 - Monogram) Jimmy Wakely

One Sheet: $15 - $35

ROB ROY
(1995 - United Artists) Liam Neeson, Jessica Lange, Tim Roth
One Sheet: $7 - $15

ROB ROY, THE HIGHLAND ROGUE
(1953 - RKO/Disney) Richard Todd, Glynis Johns
One Sheet: $30 - $50   *AKA: ROB ROY.*

ROBBER'S ROOST
(1932 - Fox) George O'Brien, Maureen O'Sullivan
One Sheet: $250 - $600

ROBBER'S ROOST
(1955 - United Artists) George Montgomery, Richard Boone
One Sheet: $15 - $30

ROBBERS OF THE RANGE
(1941 - RKO) Tim Holt
One Sheet: $40 - $75

ROBBERY
(1967 - Embassy) Stanley Baker, Joanna Pettet
One Sheet: $3 - $5

ROBBERY UNDER ARMS
(1958 - Rank) Peter Finch, Ronald Lewis
One Sheet: $5 - $10

ROBE, THE
(1953 - 20th Century Fox) Richard Burton, Jean Simmons
One Sheet: $100 - $200   *First CinemaScope film.*

ROBE, THE
(1963R - 20th Century Fox) Richard Burton, Jean Simmons
One Sheet: $15 - $25   *Re-release.*

ROBERTA
(1935 - RKO) Fred Astaire, Ginger Rogers, Irene Dunne
One Sheet: $2,200 - $3,500

ROBIN AND MARIAN
(1976 - Columbia) Sean Connery, Audrey Hepburn
One Sheet: $20 - $40

ROBIN AND THE SEVEN HOODS
(1964 - Warner Bros.) Frank Sinatra, Dean Martin, Sammy Davis Jr.
One Sheet: $30 - $60

ROBIN HOOD
(1922 - United Artists) Douglas Fairbanks
One Sheet: $10,000 - $15,000

One Sheet

ROBIN HOOD
(1973 - Buena Vista/Disney) Robin Hood
One Sheet: $15 - $30   *Cartoon.*

ROBIN HOOD
(1977R - Buena Vista/Disney) Robin Hood
One Sheet: $10 - $20   *Re-release. Cartoon.*

ROBIN HOOD
(1982R - Disney) Robin Hood
One Sheet: $7 - $15   *Re-release. Cartoon.*

ROBIN HOOD: MEN IN TIGHTS
(1993 - 20th Century) Cary Elwes, Richard Lewis
One Sheet: $3 - $5

ROBIN HOOD OF EL DORADO, THE
(1936 - MGM) Warner Baxter, Ann Loring, Bruce Cabot
One Sheet: $125 - $250

ROBIN HOOD OF MONTEREY
(1947 - Monogram) Gilbert Roland
One Sheet: $30 - $50   *Cisco Kid series.*

ROBIN HOOD OF TEXAS
(1947 - Republic) Gene Autry, Lynne Roberts
One Sheet: $75 - $150

ROBIN HOOD OF TEXAS
(1953R - Republic) Gene Autry, Lynne Roberts
One Sheet: $30 - $50   *Re-release. Full color.*

ROBIN HOOD OF THE PECOS
(1941 - Republic) Roy Rogers
One Sheet: $150 - $300

ROBIN HOOD OF THE RANGE
(1943 - Columbia) Charles Starrett
One Sheet: $40 - $75

ROBIN HOOD: PRINCE OF THIEVES
(1991 - 20th Century Fox) Kevin Costner, Alan Rickman, Christian Slater
One Sheet: $7 - $15   *Advance: $20-$35.*

ROBIN HOOD-WINKED
(1943 - Paramount) -
One Sheet: $150 - $300

ROBINSON CRUSOE
(1916 - Henry W. Savage) Robert P. Gibbs
One Sheet: $600 - $1,000

ROBINSON CRUSOE
(1936 - Guaranteed) Uncle Don
One Sheet: $75 - $150   *Radio show tie-in.*

One Sheet

ROBINSON CRUSOE
(197? - K-Tel) Robinson Crusoe
One Sheet: $3 - $5   *Cartoon.*

ROBINSON CRUSOE, LTD.
(1928 - -) Lloyd "Ham" Hamilton
One Sheet: $200 - $400

ROBINSON CRUSOE OF CLIPPER ISLAND
(1936 - Republic) Mala, Rex, Buck, Mamo Clark
One Sheet: $125 - $250   *Serial. 6 Chapters. Chapter 1 One Sheet: $200-$350.*

ROBINSON CRUSOE OF MYSTERY ISLAND
(1936 - -) Mala, Rex, Buck, Mamo Clark
One Sheet: $100 - $200   *Feature version of: ROBINSON CRUSOE OF CLIPPER ISLAND.*

ROBINSON CRUSOE ON MARS
(1964 - Paramount) Paul Mantee, Victor Lundin
One Sheet: $30 - $50

ROBINSON CRUSOE'S BROADCAST
(1937 - Educational) Paul Terry Studio
One Sheet: $150 - $300   *Cartoon. Duotone. Stock poster with inset of title.*

ROBINSON CRUSOELAND
(1952 - -) Laurel & Hardy
One Sheet: $250 - $500   *Their last film together.*

ROBOCOP
(1987 - Orion) Peter Weller, Nancy Allen
One Sheet: $15 - $25

ROBOCOP 2
(1990 - Orion) Peter Weller, Nancy Allen
One Sheet: $5 - $10

ROBOCOP 3
(1993 - Orion) Robert Burke, Nancy Allen, Rip Torn
One Sheet: $5 - $10

ROBOT MONSTER
(1954 - Paramount) George Nader, Selena Royle
One Sheet: $500 - $900   *Graven Images, pg. 188.*

ROBOT VS. THE AZTEC MUMMY
(1959 - Calderon) Ramon Gay, Rosita Arenas
One Sheet: $125 - $250   *Mexican.*

ROCCO AND HIS BROTHERS
(1960 - Titanus) Alain Delon, Annie Girardot, Claudia Cardinale
One Sheet: $250 - $500   *Italian.*

ROCCO BLUES
(1943 - Soundies) Louis Jordan and Orchestra
One Sheet: $125 - $250   *Black cast.*

ROCK, THE
(1996 - Hollywood) Sean Connery, Nicholas Cage
One Sheet: $7 - $15

ROCK 'N ROLL REVUE
(1955 - Studio) Duke Ellington, Nat King Cole
One Sheet: $150 - $300   *Black cast. Rock 'n' Roll. Separate Cinema, pg. 103.*

ROCK ALL NIGHT
(1957 - AIP) Dick Miller, Russell Johnson, The Platters, The Blockbusters
One Sheet: $125 - $250   *Rock 'n' Roll.*

ROCK AND RULE
(1983 - -) -
One Sheet: $5 - $10   *Cartoon.*

ROCK AROUND THE CLOCK
(1957 - Columbia) Johnny Johnston, The Platters, All star rock cast
One Sheet: $150 - $300   *Rock 'n' Roll.*

ROCK AROUND THE WORLD
(1957 - AIP) Tommy Steele, Dennis Price
One Sheet: $50 - $100   *Rock 'n' Roll.*

ROCK BABY, ROCK IT
(1957 - Freebar) The Five Stars, Kay Wheeler, All-star rock cast
One Sheet: $75 - $175   *Rock 'n' Roll.*

ROCK ISLAND TRAIL
(1950 - Republic) Forrest Tucker, Adele Mara
One Sheet: $15 - $30

ROCK ISLAND TRAIL
(1956R - Republic) Forrest Tucker, Adele Mara
One Sheet: $7 - $15   *Re-release.*

ROCK N ROLL HIGH SCHOOL
(1979 - New World) P.J. Soles, Vincent Van Patten, The Ramones
One Sheet: $15 - $30   *Rock 'n' Roll.*

ROCK, PRETTY BABY
(1957 - Universal) Sal Mineo, John Saxon, Fay Wray
One Sheet: $50 - $100   *Rock 'n' Roll.*

ROCK RIVER RENEGADES
(1942 - Monogram) The Three Mesquiteers
One Sheet: $20 - $40

ROCK, ROCK, ROCK
(1956 - DCA) Alan Freed, Tuesday Weld, All-star cast
One Sheet: $200 - $400   *Rock 'n' Roll.*

ROCKABILLY BABY
(1957 - 20th Century Fox) Virginia Field, Irene Ryan
One Sheet: $50 - $100

ROCKABYE
(1932 - RKO) Constance Bennett, Joel McCrea
One Sheet: $500 - $800

ROCK-A-BYE BABY
(1958 - 20th Century Fox) Jerry Lewis, Marilyn Maxwell
One Sheet: $30 - $60

ROCK-A-BYE BABY
(1963R - Paramount) Jerry Lewis, Marilyn

Maxwell
One Sheet: $15 - $25   *Re-release.*

ROCK-A-BYE BEAR
(1952 - MGM) Barney Bear
One Sheet: $200 - $400   *Cartoon.*

ROCK-A-DOODLE
(1992 - Samuel Goldwyn) Voices of Glen
Campbell, Sandy Duncan
One Sheet: $5 - $10   *Cartoon.*

ROCKET ATTACK, U.S.A.
(1959 - Exploit) Monica Davis, John McKay
One Sheet: $30 - $50

ROCKET FROM CALABUCH, THE
(1956 - Trans-Lux) Edmund Gwenn, Valentina
Cortesa
One Sheet: $10 - $20

ROCKET GIBRALTAR
(1988 - -) Burt Lancaster, Suzy Amis
One Sheet: $3 - $5

ROCKET MAN, THE
(1954 - 20th Century Fox) Charles Coburn,
George Winslow
One Sheet: $40 - $75   *Screenplay by
Lenny Bruce.*

ROCKET SHIP
(1940S - Filmcraft) Larry "Buster" Crabbe
One Sheet: $150 - $300   *Feature length
version of Flash Gordon serial.*

One Sheet

ROCKETEER, THE
(1991 - Disney) Bill Campbell, Timothy Dalton,
Jennifer Connelly
One Sheet: $15 - $30

ROCKETSHIP X-M
(1950 - Lippert) Lloyd Bridges, Osa Massen
One Sheet: $200 - $400   *Graven
Images, pg. 152.*

ROCKIN' IN THE ROCKIES
(1945 - Columbia) Mary Beth Hughes, Jay
Kirby, Three Stooges (Curly) cameo
One Sheet: $200 - $400   *Lobby Card
with Stooges:$300-$400.*

ROCKIN' THE BLUES
(1955 - -) The Wanderers, Hurricanes, Hal
Jackson, M. Moreland
One Sheet: $150 - $350   *Black cast.
Rock 'n' Roll.*

ROCKIN' THRU THE ROCKIES
(1940 - Columbia) The Three Stooges (Curly)
One Sheet: $5,000 - $7,500   *Comedy short.
Duotone.*

ROCKING HORSE WINNER, THE
(1949 - Universal-International) Valerie
Hobson, John Howard Davis
One Sheet: $15 - $35

ROCKING MOON
(1926 - PDC) Lilyan Tashman, John Bowers
One Sheet: $125 - $250

ROCKY
(1948 - Monogram) Roddy McDowall, Edgar
Barrier
One Sheet: $15 - $35

ROCKY
(1977 - United Artists) Sylvester Stallone, Talia
Shire
One Sheet: $40 - $75   *Sports
(Boxing). Academy Award: Best Picture, Best
Director(Avildsen). Academy Award Movie
Posters #292. Sports Movie Posters#157.*

ROCKY HORROR PICTURE SHOW, THE
(1975 - 20th Century Fox) Tim Curry, Susan
Sarandon, Barry Bostwick
One Sheet: $30 - $50   *Cult classic.
Price is for "Lips" style. One Sheet (Leg
style):$30-$60.*

ROCKY II
(1979 - United Artists) Sylvester Stallone,
Burgess Meredith
One Sheet: $15 - $25   *Sports
(Boxing).*

ROCKY III
(1982 - United Artists) Sylvester Stallone, Talia
Shire
One Sheet: $10 - $20   *Sports
(Boxing). Advance:$25-50. Sports Movie Posters
161.*

ROCKY IV
(1985 - MGM/UA) Sylvester Stallone, Talia
Shire, Dolph Lundgren
One Sheet: $7 - $15   *Sports
(Boxing). Advance:$10-20. Sports Movie Posters
#s 162, 163.*

ROCKY MOUNTAIN
(1950 - Warner Bros.) Errol Flynn, Patrice
Wymore
One Sheet: $40 - $75

ROCKY MOUNTAIN MYSTERY
(1935 - Adolph Zukor) Randolph Scott
One Sheet: $150 - $300   *Cowboy
Movie Posters #189.*

ROCKY MOUNTAIN RANGERS
(1940 - Republic) Three Mesquiteers
One Sheet: $50 - $100

ROCKY RHODES
(1934 - Universal) Buck Jones
One Sheet: $350 - $750

ROCKY V
(1990 - MGM/Pathe) Sylvester Stallone, Talia
Shire
One Sheet: $5 - $10   *Sports
(Boxing). Advance:$10-20. Sports Movie Posters
#s 167, 168.*

ROCKY/ROCKY II
(1980 - -) -
One Sheet: $15 - $30   *Re-release
double feature poster. Duotone.*

RODAN! THE FLYING MONSTER
(1957 - DCA and RKO) Kenji Sawara, Akihiko
Hirata
One Sheet: $125 - $250   *Half Sheet
(best style):$150-$250. RKO Card #1:$50-$100.
Graven Images, pg. 167.*

RODEO
(1952 - Monogram) John Archer, Jane Nigh
One Sheet: $20 - $40

RODEO DOUGH
(1931 - Columbia) Krazy Kat
One Sheet: $1,900 - $3,000   *Cartoon.*

RODEO DOUGH
(1940 - MGM) Sally Payne
One Sheet: $40 - $75

RODEO KING AND THE SENORITA, THE
(1951 - Republic) Rex Allen
One Sheet: $15 - $35

RODEO RHYTHM
(1941 - Del Cal Theatres) Fred Scott
One Sheet: $50 - $100

ROGER AND ME
(1989 - Warner Bros.) -
One Sheet: $7 - $15   *Documentary.*

ROGER TOUHY, GANGSTER
(1944 - 20th Century Fox) Preston Foster,
Victor McLaglen
One Sheet: $30 - $50

ROGUE COP
(1954 - MGM) Robert Taylor, Janet Leigh
One Sheet: $15 - $35

ROGUE OF THE RANGE
(1937 - Supreme) Johnny Mack Brown, Lois
January
One Sheet: $75 - $175

ROGUE OF THE RIO GRANDE

(1930 - Sono Art/World Wide) Myrna Loy, Jose
Bohr, Raymond Hatton
One Sheet: $250 - $600

ROGUE RIVER
(1950 - Eagle Lion) Rory Calhoun, Peter
Graves
One Sheet: $10 - $20

ROGUE SONG, THE
(1930 - MGM) Lawrence Tibbett, Catherine
Dale Owen, Laurel & Hardy
One Sheet: $1,300 - $2,000

ROGUE'S GALLERY
(1945 - PRC) Frank Jenks, Robin Raymond
One Sheet: $15 - $25

ROGUE'S MARCH
(1952 - MGM) Peter Lawford, Janice Rule
One Sheet: $15 - $25

ROGUE'S REGIMENT
(1948 - Universal) Dick Powell, Marta Toren
One Sheet: $15 - $25

ROGUE'S ROMANCE, A
(1919 - Vitagraph) Rudolph Valentino
One Sheet: $1,300 - $2,000

ROGUE'S ROMANCE, A
(1921R - Vitagraph) Rudolph Valentino
One Sheet: $250 - $500   *Re-release.*

ROGUE'S TAVERN, THE
(1936 - Puritan) Wallace Ford, Joan Woodbury
One Sheet: $75 - $125

ROGUES OF SHERWOOD FOREST
(1950 - Columbia) John Derek, Diana Lynn
One Sheet: $15 - $30

ROLL ALONG COWBOY
(1937 - 20th Century Fox) Smith Ballew, Bill
Elliott
One Sheet: $100 - $200

ROLL ALONG COWBOY
(194?R - Principal Releasing) Smith Ballew, Bill
Elliott
One Sheet: $15 - $30   *Re-release.*

ROLL ON TEXAS MOON
(1946 - Republic) Roy Rogers
One Sheet: $150 - $300

ROLL, THUNDER, ROLL!
(1949 - Eagle-Lion) Jim Bannon
One Sheet: $15 - $25

ROLL WAGONS ROLL
(1940 - Monogram) Tex Ritter
One Sheet: $100 - $200

ROLLER BOOGIE
(1979 - United Artists) Linda Blair, Jimmy Van
Patten
One Sheet: $5 - $10

ROLLER COASTER
(1977 - Universal) Henry Fonda, George Segal
One Sheet: $5 - $10

ROLLER COASTER RABBIT
(1989 - -) -
One Sheet: $7 - $15   *Cartoon.*

ROLLERBALL
(1975 - United Artists) James Caan, John
Houseman, Maud Adams
One Sheet: $15 - $25   *Sports Movie
Posters #379.*

One Sheet

ROLLIN' PLAINS

(1938 - Grand National) Tex Ritter
One Sheet: $125 - $250

ROLLIN' WESTWARD
(1939 - Monogram) Tex Ritter
One Sheet: $125 - $250

ROLLING CARAVANS
(1938 - Columbia) Jack Luden
One Sheet: $100 - $200

ROLLING DOWN THE GREAT DIVIDE
(1942 - PRC) Bill "Cowboy Rambler" Boyd, Art
Davis
One Sheet: $15 - $35

ROLLING HOME
(1946 - Screen Guild) Jean Parker, Russell
Hayden
One Sheet: $15 - $35

ROLLING STONES AT THE MAX
(1991 - IMAX) Rolling Stones
One Sheet: $30 - $50   *Rock 'n' Roll
concert film.*

ROLLING THUNDER
(1977 - AIP) William Devane, Tommy Lee
Jones
One Sheet: $10 - $20

ROLLOVER
(1981 - Warner Bros.) Jane Fonda, Kris
Kristofferson
One Sheet: $5 - $10

ROMA
(1972 - Ultra) Frederico Fellini, Pia De Doses
One Sheet: $150 - $300   *Italian. Price
is for 39x55.*

ROMAN HOLIDAY
(1953 - Paramount) Gregory Peck, Audrey
Hepburn
One Sheet: $200 - $400   *Academy
Award: Best Actress. Hepburn's U.S. film debut.
Academy Award Movie Posters #152.*

ROMAN HOLIDAY
(1960R - Paramount) Gregory Peck, Audrey
Hepburn
One Sheet: $150 - $300   *Re-release.
Price is for style A (coliseum style). One Sheet
(Style B, embracing):$100-$200.*

ROMAN HOLIDAY
(1962R - Paramount) Gregory Peck, Audrey
Hepburn
One Sheet: $50 - $100   *Re-release.*

ROMAN SCANDAL, A
(1926 - Short Films Syndicate) Mutt & Jeff
One Sheet: $800 - $1,500   *Cartoon.
Cartoon Movie Posters #9.*

ROMAN SCANDALS
(1933 - United Artists) Eddie Cantor, Ruth
Etting
One Sheet: $600 - $1,000

ROMAN SCANDALS
(1946R - United Artists) Eddie Cantor, Ruth
Etting
One Sheet: $50 - $100   *Re-release.*

ROMAN SPRING OF MRS. STONE, THE
(1961 - Warner Bros.) Vivien Leigh, Warren
Beatty
One Sheet: $40 - $75

ROMANCE
(1930 - MGM) Greta Garbo, Lewis Stone,
Gavin Gordon
One Sheet: $3,500 - $5,000

ROMANCE AND RHYTHM
(1940 - Republic) Kenny Baker, Frances
Langford
One Sheet: $40 - $75

ROMANCE AND RICHES
(1937 - Grand National) Cary Grant, Mary Brian
One Sheet: $250 - $600

ROMANCE IN MANHATTAN
(1935 - RKO) Ginger Rogers, Frances Lederer
One Sheet: $600 - $1,000

ROMANCE IN THE DARK
(1938 - Paramount) Gladys Swarthout, John
Boles
One Sheet: $100 - $200

ROMANCE IN THE RAIN

(1934 - Universal) Roger Pryor, Heather Angel, Victor Moore
One Sheet: $125 - $250

ROMANCE LAND
(1923 - Fox) Tom Mix, Barbara Bedford
One Sheet: $500 - $800

ROMANCE OF A HORSETHIEF
(1971 - Allied Artists) Yul Brynner, Eli Wallach
One Sheet: $5 - $10

ROMANCE OF ELAINE
(1915 - Pathe) -
One Sheet: $250 - $600

ROMANCE OF ROSY RIDGE, THE
(1947 - MGM) Van Johnson, Thomas Mitchell, Janet Leigh(film debut)
One Sheet: $30 - $60

ROMANCE OF TARZAN
(1918 - -) Elmo Lincoln
One Sheet: $5,000 - $7,500

ROMANCE OF THE LIMBERLOST
(1938 - Monogram) Jean Parker, Eric Linden
One Sheet: $50 - $100

ROMANCE OF THE REDWOODS
(1917 - Artcraft) Mary Pickford, Dir: Cecil B. Demille
One Sheet: $1,900 - $3,000

ROMANCE OF THE REDWOODS
(1939 - Columbia) Jean Parker, Charles Bickford
One Sheet: $75 - $125

ROMANCE OF THE RIO GRANDE
(1941 - 20th Century Fox) Cesar Romero
One Sheet: $40 - $75   *Cisco Kid series.*

ROMANCE OF THE ROCKIES
(1937 - Monogram) Tom Keene
One Sheet: $100 - $200

ROMANCE OF THE WEST
(1930 - Arthur Hammond Presents) Jack Perrin
One Sheet: $200 - $400   *Cowboy Movie Posters #86.*

ROMANCE OF THE WEST
(1946 - PRC) Eddie Dean
One Sheet: $15 - $35

ROMANCE ON THE HIGH SEAS
(1948 - Warner Bros.) Jack Carson, Janis Paige, Don Defore, Doris Day
One Sheet: $40 - $75   *Day's film debut.*

ROMANCE ON THE RANGE
(1942 - Republic) Roy Rogers, Gabby Hayes
One Sheet: $150 - $300

ROMANCE ON THE RUN
(1938 - Republic) Donald Woods, Patricia Ellis
One Sheet: $30 - $50

ROMANCE RIDES THE RANGE
(1936 - Spectrum) Fred Scott, Cliff Nazarro
One Sheet: $100 - $200

ROMANCING THE STONE
(1984 - Columbia) Michael Douglas, Kathleen Turner
One Sheet: $10 - $20

ROMANOFF AND JULIET
(1961 - Universal) John Gavin, Sandra Dee, Peter Ustinov
One Sheet: $10 - $20

ROMANTIC COMEDY
(1983 - MGM/United Artists) Dudley Moore, Mary Steenburgen
One Sheet: $3 - $5

ROME ADVENTURE
(1962 - Warner Bros.) Troy Donahue, Angie Dickinson
One Sheet: $7 - $15

ROME EXPRESS
(1932 - Universal) Esther Ralston, Conrad Veidt, Joan Barry
One Sheet: $250 - $600

ROMEO AND JULIET
(1936 - MGM) Norma Shearer, Leslie Howard, John Barrymore
One Sheet: $600 - $1,000

ROMEO AND JULIET
(1954 - United Artists) Laurence Harvey, Susan Shentall
One Sheet: $50 - $100

ROMEO AND JULIET
(1962R - MGM) Laurence Harvey, Susan Shentall
One Sheet: $10 - $20   *Re-release.*

ROMEO AND JULIET
(1966 - Embassy) Margot Fonteyn, Rudolf Nureyev, Royal Ballet Performance
One Sheet: $10 - $20

ROMEO AND JULIET
(1968 - Paramount) Leonard Whiting, Olivia Hussey
One Sheet: $15 - $30

ROMEO AND JULIET
(1973R - Paramount) Leonard Whiting, Olivia Hussey
One Sheet: $3 - $5   *Re-release.*

ROMEO IS BLEEDING
(1994 - Gramercy) Gary Oldman, Lena Olin
One Sheet: $5 - $10

ROMY AND MICHELE'S HIGH SCHOOL REUNION
(1997 - Touchstone) Mira Sorvino, Lisa Kudrow, Janeane Garofalo
One Sheet: $4 - $8

RONNY
(1932 - UFA) -
One Sheet: $50 - $100

ROOF TREE, THE
(1921 - -) William Russell
One Sheet: $125 - $250

ROOFTOPS
(1989 - New Visions) Jason Gedrick, Troy Beyer, Tisha Campbell
One Sheet: $1 - $2

ROOGIE'S BUMP
(1954 - Republic) Roy Campanella, Carl Erskine, Brooklyn Dodgers
One Sheet: $200 - $400   *Sports (Baseball). Sports Movie Posters #62.*

ROOKIE, THE
(1960 - 20th Century Fox) Tommy Noonan, Pete Marshall
One Sheet: $10 - $20

ROOKIE, THE
(1990 - Warner Bros.) Clint Eastwood, Charlie Sheen, Raul Julia
One Sheet: $7 - $15

ROOKIE BEAR, THE
(1941 - MGM) Barney Bear
One Sheet: $700 - $1,200   *Cartoon. Cartoon Movie Posters #253.*

ROOKIE COP, THE
(1939 - RKO) Tim Holt, Virginia Weidler, Ace the Wonder Dog
One Sheet: $40 - $75

ROOKIE FIREMAN
(1950 - Columbia) Bill Williams, Barton MacLane
One Sheet: $15 - $30

ROOKIE OF THE YEAR
(1993 - 20th Century Fox) Thomas Ian Nicholas, Gary Busey, Dir: Daniel Stern
One Sheet: $3 - $5   *Stern's directorial debut.*

ROOKIE'S COOKIE, A
(1943 - Columia) El Brendel
One Sheet: $75 - $150   *Short subject. Duotone.*

ROOKIES IN BURMA
(1943 - RKO) Alan Carney, Wally Brown, Joan Barclay
One Sheet: $15 - $35

ROOKIES ON PARADE
(1941 - Republic) Bob Crosby, Ruth Terry
One Sheet: $20 - $40

ROOKIES RETURN
(1920 - Paramount) Douglas MacLean
One Sheet: $250 - $500

ROOM 43
(1959 - Cory Film) Diana Dors, Herbert Lom
One Sheet: $15 - $25

ROOM AND BORED
(1943 - Columbia) Fox & Crow
One Sheet: $250 - $500   *Cartoon. First Fox & Crow series poster. Full color with scene inset. Cartoon Movie Posters #41.*

ROOM AT THE TOP
(1959 - Continental) Laurence Harvey, Simone Signoret
One Sheet: $15 - $30   *Academy Award: Best Actress. Academy Award Movie Posters #191.*

ROOM FOR ONE MORE
(1951 - Warner Bros.) Cary Grant, Betsy Drake
One Sheet: $30 - $50

ROOM SERVICE
(1938 - RKO) The Marx Brothers, Lucille Ball
One Sheet: $800 - $1,500

ROOM WITH A VIEW
(1986 - Cinecom) Maggie Smith, Helena Bonham Carter
One Sheet: $20 - $40

ROOMMATES
(1995 - Hollywood) Peter Falk, D.B. Sweeney
One Sheet: $3 - $5

ROONEY
(1958 - Rank) Barry Fitzgerald, John Gregson
One Sheet: $15 - $25

ROOSEVELT STORY, THE
(1947 - -) -
One Sheet: $40 - $75   *Documentary.*

ROOSTER COGBURN
(1975 - Universal) John Wayne, Katherine Hepburn
One Sheet: $50 - $100

ROOTIN' TOOTIN' RHYTHM
(1937 - Republic) Gene Autry, Smiley Burnette
One Sheet: $200 - $400

ROOTIN' TOOTIN' RHYTHM
(1942R - Republic) Gene Autry, Smiley Burnette
One Sheet: $75 - $150   *Re-release. Full color.*

ROOTS IN THE SOIL
(1949 - -) Richard Travis, Michael Whalen, Rochelle Hudson
One Sheet: $10 - $20

ROOTS OF HEAVEN, THE
(1958 - 20th Century Fox) Errol Flynn, Juliette Greco
One Sheet: $15 - $35

ROPE
(1948 - Warner Bros.) James Stewart, John Dall, Dir: Alfred Hitchcock
One Sheet: $150 - $350   *Hitchcock's first color film.*

Three Sheet

ROPE
(1958R - Warner Bros.) James Stewart, John Dall, Dir: Alfred Hitchcock
One Sheet: $40 - $75   *Re-release.*

ROPE OF SAND
(1949 - Paramount) Burt Lancaster, Paul Henreid, Claude Rains, Peter Lorre
One Sheet: $40 - $75

ROSA DE FRANCIA

(1935 - 20th Century Fox) -
One Sheet: $100 - $200   *French. U.S. title: Rose of France.*

ROSALIE
(1937 - MGM) Eleanor Powell, Nelson Eddy
One Sheet: $150 - $300

ROSARY, THE
(1915 - Unicorn) Kathlyn Williams
One Sheet: $125 - $250

ROSARY MURDERS, THE
(1987 - Samuel Goldwyn) Donald Sutherland, Charles Durning
One Sheet: $3 - $5

ROSE, THE
(1979 - 20th Century Fox) Bette Midler, Alan Bates
One Sheet: $15 - $25

ROSE BOWL
(1936 - Paramount) Buster Crabbe, Tom Brown
One Sheet: $150 - $300   *Sports (Football). Sports Movie Posters #188.*

Mini Window Card

ROSE BOWL STORY, THE
(1952 - Monogram) Marshall Thompson, Vera Miles
One Sheet: $50 - $100   *Sports (Football). Sports Movie Posters #200.*

ROSE FOR EVERYONE, A
(1967 - Royal) Claudia Cardinale, Nino Manfredi, Akim Tamiroff
One Sheet: $15 - $25

ROSE MARIE
(1928 - MGM) Joan Crawford, James Murray
One Sheet: $1,300 - $2,000

ROSE MARIE
(1936 - MGM) Jeannette MacDonald, Nelson Eddy
One Sheet: $600 - $1,000

ROSE MARIE
(1954 - MGM) Ann Blyth, Howard Keel
One Sheet: $15 - $35

ROSE MARIE
(1962R - MGM) Jeanette MacDonald, Nelson Eddy
One Sheet: $15 - $30   *Re-release.*

ROSE OF CIMARRON
(1952 - 20th Century Fox) Jack Beutel, Mala Powers
One Sheet: $10 - $20

ROSE OF SANTA ROSA
(1947 - Columbia) Patricia White, Eduardo Moriega, The Hoosier Hot Shots
One Sheet: $20 - $40

ROSE OF THE RIO GRANDE
(1938 - Monogram) John Carroll
One Sheet: $40 - $75

ROSE OF THE YUKON
(1949 - Republic) Steve Brodie, Myrna Dell
One Sheet: $15 - $35

ROSE OF WASHINGTON SQUARE
(1939 - 20th Century Fox) Tyrone Power, Alice Faye, Al Jolson
One Sheet: $600 - $1,000

ROSE TATTOO, THE
(1955 - Paramount) Anna Magnani, Burt Lancaster
One Sheet: $20 - $40   *Academy Award: Best Actress. Academy Award Movie*

Posters #163 & #164.

ROSEANNA MCCOY
(1949 - RKO) Farley Granger, Charles Bickford
One Sheet: $15 - $30

ROSEANNA'S GRAVE
(1997 - Fine Line) Jean Reno, Mercedes Ruehl
One Sheet: $4 - $8

ROSEMARY'S BABY
(1968 - Paramount) Mia Farrow, John
Cassavetes
One Sheet: $50 - $100   *Academy
Award Movie Posters #251. Graven Images, pg.
207.*

**ROSENCRANTZ AND GUILDENSTERN ARE
DEAD**
(1991 - -) Gary Oldman, Tim Roth, Richard
Dreyfuss
One Sheet: $7 - $15

ROSES ARE RED
(1947 - 20th Century Fox) Don Castle, Peggy
Knudsen
One Sheet: $15 - $35

ROSEWOOD
(1996 - Warner Bros.) Jon Voight, Ving
Rhames
One Sheet: $3 - $5

ROSIE!
(1967 - Universal) Rosalind Russell, Brian
Aherne
One Sheet: $10 - $20

ROSIE, THE RIVETER
(1944 - Republic) Jane Frazee, Frank
Albertson
One Sheet: $20 - $40

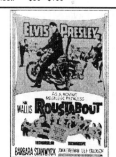

One Sheet

ROSITA
(1923 - United Artists) Mary Pickford, Holbrook
Blinn
One Sheet: $2,200 - $3,500

ROUGED LIPS
(1923 - Metro) Viola Dana
One Sheet: $250 - $500

ROUGH AND READY
(1924 - Educational) Stan Laurel & Oliver
Hardy?
One Sheet: $200 - $400

ROUGH COMPANY
(1954 - Columbia) Glenn Ford, Barbara
Stanwyck, Edward G. Robinson
One Sheet: $30 - $50   *AKA: THE
VIOLENT MEN (Great Britain title).*

ROUGH CUT
(1980 - Paramount) Burt Reynolds, Lesley-Ann
Down
One Sheet: $7 - $15

ROUGH DIAMOND, THE
(1920 - Fox) Tom Mix, Eva Novak
One Sheet: $500 - $800

ROUGH HOUSE ROSIE
(1927 - Paramount) Clara Bow
One Sheet: $600 - $1,000

ROUGH NIGHT IN JERICHO
(1967 - Universal) George Peppard, Dean
Martin
One Sheet: $15 - $30

ROUGH RIDERS, THE
(1927 - Paramount) Charles Farrell, Mary Astor
One Sheet: $200 - $400

ROUGH RIDERS OF CHEYENNE
(1945 - Republic) Sunset Carson, Monte Hale
One Sheet: $30 - $50

ROUGH RIDERS OF DURANGO
(1951 - Republic) Allan "Rocky" Lane
One Sheet: $15 - $35

ROUGH RIDERS ROUND-UP
(1939 - Republic) Roy Rogers, Mary Hart
One Sheet: $200 - $450

ROUGH RIDIN' JUSTICE
(1945 - Columbia) Charles Starrett, Jimmy
Wakely
One Sheet: $30 - $50

ROUGH RIDIN' RED
(1928 - -) Buzz Barton, Frank Rice
One Sheet: $250 - $600

ROUGH RIDING RANGER
(1935 - Superior) Rex Lease, Bobby Nelson
One Sheet: $100 - $200

ROUGH RIDING RHYTHM
(1937 - Ambassador) Kermit Maynard
One Sheet: $75 - $125

ROUGH RIDING ROMANCE
(1919 - Fox) Tom Mix, Juanita Hansen
One Sheet: $700 - $1,200

ROUGH ROMANCE
(1930 - Fox) George O'Brien, Helen Chandler
One Sheet: $150 - $300

ROUGH, TOUGH, AND READY
(1945 - Columbia) Chester Morris, Victor
McLaglen
One Sheet: $30 - $60

ROUGH, TOUGH WEST, THE
(1952 - Columbia) Charles Starrett
One Sheet: $15 - $35

ROUGH WATERS
(1930 - Warner Bros.) Rin-Tin-Tin, Lane
Chandler
One Sheet: $150 - $300

ROUGHEST AFRICA
(1924 - -) Stan Laurel
One Sheet: $800 - $1,500

ROUGHLY SPEAKING
(1945 - Warner Bros.) Rosalind Russell, Jack
Carson
One Sheet: $15 - $35

ROUGHNECK, THE
(1925 - -) George O'Brien, Billie Dove
One Sheet: $500 - $800

ROUGHSHOD
(1922 - Fox) Charles "Buck" Jones, Helen
Ferguson
One Sheet: $250 - $600

ROUGHSHOD
(1949 - RKO) Robert Sterling, Gloria Grahame
One Sheet: $20 - $40

ROUND MIDNIGHT
(1986 - Warner Bros.) Dexter Gordon, Francois
Cluzet
One Sheet: $10 - $20

ROUND TRIP
(1967 - Continental) Venantino Venantini, Ellen
Faison
One Sheet: $3 - $5

ROUNDERS, THE
(1914 - Keystone) Charlie Chaplin, Roscoe
"Fatty" Arbuckle
One Sheet: $11,000 - $18,000   *Price
assumes Chaplin is pictured prominently on
poster.*

ROUNDERS, THE
(1965 - MGM) Glenn Ford, Henry Fonda
One Sheet: $10 - $20

ROUND-UP, THE
(1920 - Paramount) Roscoe "Fatty" Arbuckle
One Sheet: $2,500 - $4,000   *Cowboy
Movie Posters #24.*

ROUND-UP, THE
(1941 - Paramount) Richard Dix, Patricia
Morison
One Sheet: $50 - $100

ROUND-UP TIME IN TEXAS
(1937 - Republic) Gene Autry, Smiley Burnette
One Sheet: $200 - $450

ROUSTABOUT
(1964 - Paramount) Elvis Presley, Barbara
Stanwyck
One Sheet: $50 - $100

One Sheet

ROVER DANGERFIELD
(1991 - Warner Bros.) Voice of Rodney
Dangerfield
One Sheet: $3 - $5   *Cartoon.*

ROVIN' TUMBLEWEEDS
(1939 - Republic) Gene Autry, Smiley Burnette
One Sheet: $150 - $350

One Sheet

ROXANNE
(1986 - Columbia) Steve Martin, Daryl Hannah
One Sheet: $5 - $10

ROXIE HART
(1942 - 20th Century Fox) Ginger Rogers,
Adolphe Menjou
One Sheet: $150 - $350

ROY COLT & WINCHESTER JACK
(1970 - -) -
One Sheet: $3 - $5

ROYAL AFRICAN RIFLES, THE
(1953 - Monogram) Louis Hayward, Veronica
Hurst
One Sheet: $15 - $30

ROYAL BED, THE
(1930 - RKO) Mary Astor, Lowell Sherman
One Sheet: $200 - $400

ROYAL BOX, THE
(1930 - Warner Bros.) Alexander Moissi,
Camilla Horn
One Sheet: $100 - $200

ROYAL FAMILY OF BROADWAY, THE
(1931 - Paramount Publix) Fredric March, Mary
Brian, Ina Claire
One Sheet: $500 - $800

ROYAL FLASH
(1975 - Fox) Malcolm McDowell, Britt Ekland
One Sheet: $7 - $15

ROYAL HUNT OF THE SUN
(1969 - National General) Robert Shaw,
Christopher Plummer
One Sheet: $5 - $10

ROYAL JOURNEY
(1952 - -) Documentary
One Sheet: $30 - $50

ROYAL MOUNTED PATROL, THE
(1941 - Columbia) Charles Starrett, Russell
Hayden
One Sheet: $40 - $75

ROYAL MOUNTED RIDES AGAIN, THE
(1945 - Universal) George Dolenz, Bill Kennedy
One Sheet: $40 - $75   *Serial.
Western. 13 Chapters.*

ROYAL ROGUE, A
(1917 - Keystone) Billy Armstrong, Juanita
Hansen
One Sheet: $200 - $400

ROYAL ROMANCE, A
(1930 - Columbia) William Collier, Jr., Pauline
Starke, Clarence Muse
One Sheet: $75 - $150

ROYAL SCANDAL, A
(1945 - 20th Century Fox) Tallulah Bankhead,
Charles Coburn
One Sheet: $50 - $100

One Sheet

ROYAL WEDDING
(1950 - MGM) Fred Astaire, Jane Powell
One Sheet: $75 - $175

R.P.M.
(1970 - Columbia) Anthony Quinn, Ann-Margret
One Sheet: $5 - $10

RUBBER RACKETEERS
(1942 - Monogram) Rochelle Hudson, Ricardo
Cortez
One Sheet: $30 - $50

RUBBER TIRES
(1927 - DeMille) Harrison Ford, Bessie Love
One Sheet: $150 - $350

RUBIN AND ED
(1992 - I.R.S.) Crispin Glover, Howard
Hesseman
One Sheet: $3 - $5

RUBY
(1977 - Dimension) Piper Laurie, Stuart
Whitman, Roger Davis
One Sheet: $5 - $10

RUBY
(1991 - -) Danny Aiello, Sherilyn Fenn
One Sheet: $5 - $10

RUBY CAIRO
(1993 - Miramax) Andie MacDowell, Liam
Neeson
One Sheet: $3 - $5

RUBY GENTRY
(1952 - 20th Century Fox) Jennifer Jones,
Charlton Heston
One Sheet: $30 - $50

RUBY IN PARADISE
(1993 - October Films) Ashley Judd, Todd Field
One Sheet: $3 - $5

RUDE AWAKENING
(1989 - -) Cheech Marin, Eric Roberts, Julie
Hagerty
One Sheet: $3 - $5

RUDE BOY
(1980 - Buzzy) Ray Gange, The Clash, John
Green
One Sheet: $50 - $100   *Rock 'n' Roll.*

RUDOLPH THE RED-NOSED REINDEER
(1948 - Jam Handy) Dir: Max Fleischer
One Sheet: $150 - $300   *Cartoon.*

RUDY
(1993 - TriStar) Sean Astin, Ned Beatty
One Sheet: $7 - $15   *Sports*
(Football). Sports Movie Posters #215.

RUDYARD KIPLING'S THE JUNGLE BOOK
(1942 - United Artists) Sabu, Rosemary
DeCamp, Dir: Zoltan Korda
One Sheet: $200 - $400

RUDYARD KIPLING'S THE JUNGLE BOOK
(1994 - Disney) Jason Scott Lee, John Cleese
One Sheet: $5 - $10

RUFUS JONES FOR PRESIDENT
(1933 - -) Sammy Davis Jr., Ethel Waters
One Sheet: $250 - $500

RUGGED BEAR
(1953 - RKO/Disney) Donald Duck
One Sheet: $125 - $250   *Cartoon.*

RUGGED O'RIORDANS, THE
(1950 - Universal) John O'Malley, Thelma Scott
One Sheet: $10 - $20

RUGGLES OF RED GAP
(1923 - Paramount) Edward Horton, Ernest
Torrence
One Sheet: $600 - $1,000

RUGGLES OF RED GAP
(1935 - Paramount) Charles Laughton, Charlie
Ruggles
One Sheet: $600 - $1,000   *Cowboy*
Movie Posters #190.

RULERS OF THE SEA
(1939 - Paramount) Douglas Fairbanks, Jr.,
Margaret Lockwood
One Sheet: $125 - $250

RULES OF THE GAME
(1939 - Janus) Marcel Dalio, Jean Revoir (dir)
One Sheet: $75 - $150   *French.*

RULING CLASS, THE
(1972 - Avco/Embassy) Peter O'Toole, Alastair
Sim
One Sheet: $7 - $15

RULING PASSIONS
(1922 - Select) Julia Dean, Edwin Arden
One Sheet: $150 - $300

RULING VOICE, THE
(1931 - First National) Walter Huston, Loretta
Young
One Sheet: $300 - $700

RUMBA
(1935 - Paramount) George Raft, Carole
Lombard
One Sheet: $1,600 - $2,500

RUMBLE FISH
(1983 - Universal) Matt Dillon, Mickey Rourke
One Sheet: $7 - $15

RUMBLE IN THE BRONX
(1996 - New Line) Jackie Chan, Anita Mui, Bill
Tung
One Sheet: $15 - $25

RUMBLE ON THE DOCKS
(1956 - Columbia) James Darren, Laurie
Carroll
One Sheet: $30 - $50   *Gang*
exploitation.

RUMORS FOR RENT
(1927 - William Fox) -
One Sheet: $250 - $500

RUMPELSTILTSKIN
(1965 - K. Gordon Murray) -
One Sheet: $7 - $15

RUMPELSTILTSKIN
(1974R - K. Gordon Murray) -
One Sheet: $3 - $5   *Re-release.*

RUMPELSTILTSKIN
(1986 - VanLamsweerde) -
One Sheet: $5 - $10   *Cartoon.*

RUMPELSTILTSKIN
(1987 - Cannon) Amy Irving, Billy Barty
One Sheet:

RUMPUS IN THE HAREM
(1956 - Columbia) The Three Stooges (Shemp)
One Sheet: $150 - $300   *Comedy short.*
Duotone.

RUN
(1990 - Hollywood) Patrick Dempsey
One Sheet: $3 - $5

RUN, ANGEL, RUN!
(1969 - Fanfare) William Smith, Valerie Starett,
Gene Shane
One Sheet: $7 - $15

RUN, COUGAR, RUN!
(1972 - Disney) Stuart Whitman, Alfonso Arau
One Sheet: $7 - $15

RUN FOR COVER
(1955 - Paramount) James Cagney, Viveca
Lindfors
One Sheet: $30 - $50

RUN FOR THE HILLS
(1953 - Kinego) Sonny Tufts, Barbara Payton
One Sheet: $10 - $20

RUN FOR THE SUN
(1956 - United Artists) Richard Widmark,
Trevor Howard
One Sheet: $15 - $25

RUN FOR YOUR MONEY, A
(1949 - Universal International) Donald
Houston, Meredith Edwards
One Sheet: $15 - $30

RUN FOR YOUR WIFE
(1966 - Allied Artists) Ugo Tognazzi, Marina
Vlady
One Sheet: $3 - $5

RUN OF THE ARROW
(1957 - RKO) Rod Steiger, Brian Keith
One Sheet: $15 - $25

RUN SILENT, RUN DEEP
(1958 - United Artists) Clark Gable, Burt
Lancaster
One Sheet: $40 - $75

RUN, VIRGIN, RUN
(197? - International Producers) Cheryl Ross
One Sheet: $5 - $10

RUN WILD, RUN FREE
(1969 - Columbia) John Mills, Sylvia Syms,
Mark Lester
One Sheet: $3 - $5

RUNAROUND, THE
(1931 - RKO) Geoffrey Kerr, Mary Brian, Marie
Prevost
One Sheet: $125 - $250

One Sheet

RUNAROUND, THE
(1946 - Universal) Broderick Crawford, Rod
Cameron, Ella Raines
One Sheet: $15 - $25

RUNAWAY, THE
(1926 - Paramount) Clara Bow, Warner Baxter
One Sheet: $1,300 - $2,000

RUNAWAY, THE
(1972 - Group One) Gilda Texter, Bill Smith
One Sheet: $3 - $5

RUNAWAY
(1984 - —) Tom Selleck, Kirstie Alley
One Sheet: $7 - $15

RUNAWAY BRAIN
(1995 - Buena Vista) Mickey Mouse
One Sheet: $15 - $25   *Cartoon.*

RUNAWAY BRIDE, THE
(1930 - RKO) Mary Astor

RUNAWAY DAUGHTERS
(1956 - AIP) Marla English, Anna Sten
One Sheet: $30 - $50

RUNAWAY FREIGHT, THE
(1913 - Kalem) -
One Sheet: $200 - $400

RUNAWAY GIRLS
(1928 - Columbia) Shirley Mason, Arthur
Rankin, Hedda Hopper
One Sheet: $250 - $500

RUNAWAY QUEEN, THE
(1934 - British & Dominions) Anna Neagle,
Fernand Graavey
One Sheet: $50 - $100

RUNAWAY TRAIN
(1985 - Cannon) Jon Voight, Eric Roberts,
Rebecca DeMornay
One Sheet: $7 - $15

RUNNER STUMBLES, THE
(1979 - -) Dick Van Dyke, Kathleen Quinlan
One Sheet: $2 - $3

RUNNING
(1979 - Universal) Michael Douglas, Susan
Anspach
One Sheet: $3 - $5

RUNNING BRAVE
(1983 - Englander) Robby Benson, Pat Hingle
One Sheet: $3 - $5

RUNNING MAN, THE
(1963 - Columbia) Laurence Harvey, Lee
Remick
One Sheet: $15 - $25

RUNNING MAN, THE
(1987 - -) Arnold Schwarzenegger, Maria
Conchita Alonso
One Sheet: $7 - $15

RUNNING ON EMPTY
(1988 - Lorimar) Christine Lahti, River Phoenix
One Sheet: $7 - $15

RUNNING SCARED
(1986 - MGM/United Artists) Gregory Hines,
Billy Crystal
One Sheet: $5 - $10

RUNNING TARGET
(1956 - United Artists) Arthur Franz, Doris
Dowling
One Sheet: $5 - $10

RUNNING WILD
(1927 - Paramount) W.C. Fields
One Sheet: $1,900 - $3,000

RUNNING WILD
(1955 - Universal) William Campbell, Mamie
Van Doren
One Sheet: $40 - $75

RUSH
(1992 - MGM/Pathe) Jason Patric, Jennifer
Jason Leigh
One Sheet: $5 - $10

RUSS MEYER'S VIXEN
(1969 - Eve) Erica Gavin, Harrison Page
One Sheet: $50 - $100   *Sexploitation.*

RUSSIA HOUSE, THE
(1990 - MGM/Pathe) Sean Connery, Michelle
Pfeiffer
One Sheet: $7 - $15

**RUSSIANS ARE COMING! THE RUSSIANS ARE
COMING!, THE**
(1966 - United Artists) Carl Reiner, Eva Marie
Saint, Alan Arkin
One Sheet: $15 - $25   *Arkin's first*
starring role.

RUSSKIES
(1987 - -) Whip Hubley, Leaf Phoenix, Peter
Billingsley
One Sheet: $5 - $10

**RUST NEVER SLEEPS: NEIL YOUNG &
CRAZYHORSE**
(1979 - -) Concert film
One Sheet: $40 - $75   *Rock 'n' Roll.*

RUSTLER'S PARADISE
(1935 - Ajax) Harry Carey, Edmund Cobb

One Sheet: $150 - $300

RUSTLER'S RHAPSODY
(1985 - Paramount) Tom Berenger, Marilu
Henner
One Sheet: $3 - $5

RUSTLER'S VALLEY
(1937 - Paramount) William Boyd, Gabby
Hayes
One Sheet: $250 - $600   *Hopalong*
Cassidy series. Rare.

RUSTLERS, THE
(1949 - RKO) Tim Holt
One Sheet: $15 - $35

RUSTLERS OF DEVIL'S CANYON
(1947 - Republic) Allan "Rocky" Lane
One Sheet: $15 - $35

RUSTLERS OF RED DOG
(1935 - Universal) John Mack Brown, Joyce
Compton
One Sheet: $250 - $500   *Serial.*
Western. 12 Chapters.

RUSTLERS OF THE BADLANDS
(1945 - Columbia) Charles Starrett
One Sheet: $30 - $50

RUSTLERS ON HORSEBACK
(1950 - Republic) Allan "Rocky" Lane
One Sheet: $15 - $25

RUSTLERS' HIDEOUT
(1944 - PRC) Buster Crabbe
One Sheet: $30 - $50

RUSTLERS' ROUNDUP
(1933 - Universal) Tom Mix, Diane Sinclair
One Sheet: $800 - $1,500

RUSTLERS' ROUNDUP
(1946 - Universal) Kirby Grant
One Sheet: $15 - $35

RUSTY LEADS THE WAY
(1948 - Columbia) Ted Donaldson, Sharyn
Moffet
One Sheet: $15 - $25

RUSTY RIDES ALONE
(1933 - Columbia) Tim McCoy, Barbara Weeks
One Sheet: $600 - $1,000   *Cowboy*
Movie Posters #'s 143, 144.

RUSTY ROMEOS
(1957 - Columbia) The Three Stooges (Joe
Besser)
One Sheet: $75 - $125   *Comedy short.*
Duotone. Remake of CORNY CASANOVAS.

RUSTY SAVES A LIFE
(1948 - Columbia) Ted Donaldson, Gloria
Henry
One Sheet: $10 - $20

RUSTY'S BIRTHDAY
(1949 - Columbia) Ted Donaldson, John Litel
One Sheet: $15 - $25

RUTH OF THE RANGE
(1923 - Pathe) Ruth Roland
One Sheet: $150 - $300   *Serial.*
Western. 15 Episodes.

RUTHLESS
(1948 - PRC) Zachary Scott, Diana Lynn
One Sheet: $15 - $35

RUTHLESS MEN
(1953R - -) Zachary Scott, Diana Lynn
One Sheet: $15 - $25   *Re-titled, re-*
release of RUTHLESS from 1948.

RUTHLESS PEOPLE
(1986 - Touchstone) Danny DeVito, Bette
Midler
One Sheet: $10 - $20

RUTLES, THE
(1978 - -) Eric Idle, Neil Innes, George
Harrison, John Belushi
One Sheet: $30 - $50   *AKA: ALL*
YOU NEED IS CASH. Made for TV movie (parody
of The Beatles).

RX MURDER
(1958 - 20th Century Fox) Rick Jason, Marius
Goring
One Sheet: $15 - $25

RYAN'S DAUGHTER

(1970 - MGM) Robert Mitchum, Trevor Howard, John Mills, Sarah Miles
One Sheet: $30 - $50   *Academy Award Movie Posters #262.*

S'MATTER PETE
(1927 - Bray Productions) Directed by Walt Lantz
One Sheet: $500 - $800   *Cartoon. Cartoon Movie Posters #26.*

SAADIA
(1953 - MGM) Cornel Wilde, Rita Gam, Mel Ferrer
One Sheet: $7 - $15

SABAKA
(1954 - United Artists) Boris Karloff, Reginald Denny
One Sheet: $20 - $40   *AKA: THE HINDU.*

SABATA
(1970 - United Artists) Lee Van Cleef, William Berger
One Sheet: $7 - $15

SABOTAGE
(1936 - Gaumont) Sylvia Sidney, Oscar Homolka, Dir: Alfred Hitchcock
One Sheet: $2,200 - $3,500   *AKA: A WOMAN ALONE.*

SABOTAGE
(1939 - Republic) Arleen Whelan, Gordon Oliver
One Sheet: $40 - $80

SABOTAGE AT SEA
(1942 - Anglo-American) Jane Carr, Dave Hutcheson
One Sheet: $30 - $50

SABOTAGE SQUAD
(1942 - Columbia) Bruce Bennett, Kay Harris
One Sheet: $15 - $35

SABOTEUR
(1942 - Universal) Robert Cummings, Priscilla Lane, Director: Alfred Hitchcock
One Sheet: $300 - $700

One Sheet

SABOTEUR
(1952R - Realart) Robert Cummings, Priscilla Lane, Dir: Alfred Hitchcock
One Sheet: $75 - $150   *Re-release.*

SABOTEUR CODE-NAME MORITURI, THE
(1965 - -) Marlon Brando, Yul Brynner
One Sheet: $7 - $15

SABRE JET
(1953 - United Artists) Robert Stack, Coleen Gray
One Sheet: $7 - $15

SABRINA
(1954 - Paramount) Audrey Hepburn, Humphrey Bogart, William Holden
One Sheet: $150 - $300   *Half Sheet (Style A): $500-$1000.*

SABRINA
(1962R - Paramount) Audrey Hepburn, Humphrey Bogart, William Holden
One Sheet: $100 - $200   *Re-release. Price is for style A (white) one sheet. One Sheet (Style B, pink): $75-$150.*

SABRINA
(1965R - Paramount) Audrey Hepburn, Humphrey Bogart
One Sheet: $50 - $100   *Re-release.*

SABRINA
(1995 - Paramount) Harrison Ford, Julia Ormond
One Sheet: $5 - $12

SABU AND THE MAGIC RING
(1957 - Allied Artists) Sabu, Daria Massey
One Sheet: $15 - $35

SACCO AND VANZETTI
(1971 - UMC) Gian Maria Volonte, Riccardo Cucciolla
One Sheet: $5 - $10

SACRED AND PROFANE LOVE
(1921 - Paramount) Elsie Ferguson, Conrad Nagel, Helen Dunbar
One Sheet: $250 - $500

SACRED GROUND
(1983 - Pacific International) Jack Elam, Tim McIntire
One Sheet: $3 - $5

SACRED KNIVES OF VENGEANCE, THE
(1973 - Warner Bros.) Chin Han, Tsung Hua
One Sheet: $15 - $25   *AKA: THE KILLER.*

SAD HORSE, THE
(1959 - 20th Century Fox) David Ladd, Chill Wills
One Sheet: $7 - $15

SAD SACK, THE
(1957 - Paramount) Jerry Lewis, David Wayne
One Sheet: $15 - $35

SADDLE ACES
(1935 - Resolute) Rex Bell, Ruth Mix
One Sheet: $125 - $250

SADDLE BUSTER, THE
(1932 - RKO) Tom Keene
One Sheet: $125 - $250

SADDLE LEATHER LAW
(1944 - Columbia) Charles Starrett, Vi Athens
One Sheet: $20 - $40

SADDLE LEGION
(1950 - RKO) Tim Holt, Dorothy Malone
One Sheet: $15 - $35

SADDLE MOUNTAIN ROUNDUP
(1941 - Monogram) Ray Corrigan, John King, Max Terhune (Three Mesquiteers)
One Sheet: $50 - $100

SADDLE PALS
(1947 - Republic) Gene Autry, Lynne Roberts
One Sheet: $75 - $150

SADDLE SERENADE
(1945 - Monogram) Jimmy Wakely
One Sheet: $30 - $50

SADDLE THE WIND
(1957 - MGM) Robert Taylor, Julie London, Screenplay: Rod Serling
One Sheet: $15 - $30

SADDLE TRAMP
(1950 - Universal) Joel McCrea, Wanda Hendrix
One Sheet: $15 - $25

SADDLEMATES
(1941 - Republic) Three Mesquiteers
One Sheet: $40 - $75

SADDLES AND SAGEBRUSH
(1943 - Columbia) Russell Hayden, Bob Willis
One Sheet: $30 - $60

SADIE LOVE
(1919 - Paramount/Artcraft) Billie Burke
One Sheet: $300 - $700

SADIE McKEE
(1934 - MGM) Joan Crawford, Gene Raymond
One Sheet: $1,300 - $2,000

SADIE THOMPSON
(1928 - United Artists) Gloria Swanson
One Sheet: $2,800 - $4,500

SADIST, THE
(1963 - Fairway Intl.) Arch Hall Jr., Helen Hovey
One Sheet: $15 - $30

SAFARI
(1940 - Paramount) Madeleine Carroll, Douglas Fairbanks, Jr.
One Sheet: $50 - $100

SAFARI
(1956 - Columbia) Victor Mature, Janet Leigh
One Sheet: $15 - $30

SAFARI DRUMS
(1953 - Monogram) Johnny Sheffield, Douglas Kennedy
One Sheet: $20 - $40

SAFE
(1995 - Sony Classics) Julianne Moore
One Sheet: $5 - $12

SAFE AT HOME
(1962 - Columbia) Mickey Mantle, Roger Maris
One Sheet: $200 - $400   *Sports (Baseball). Sports Movie Posters #s 68, 69, 70.*

One Sheet

SAFE IN HELL
(1931 - First National) Donald Cook, Dorothy Mackail
One Sheet: $200 - $400

SAFE PASSAGE
(1995 - New Line) Sam Shepard, Susan Sarandon
One Sheet: $5 - $12

SAFE PLACE, A
(1971 - Columbia) Tuesday Weld, Orson Welles
One Sheet: $15 - $30

SAFECRACKER, THE
(1957 - MGM) Ray Milland, Barry Jones
One Sheet: $15 - $25

SAFEGUARDED
(1924 - -) Eva Novak
One Sheet: $100 - $225

SAFETY IN NUMBERS
(1930 - Paramount Publix) Carole Lombard
One Sheet: $600 - $1,000

SAFETY IN NUMBERS
(1938 - 20th Century Fox) Jed Prouty, Spring Byington
One Sheet: $30 - $50

SAFETY LAST
(1923 - Pathe) Harold Lloyd
One Sheet: $1,600 - $2,500

SAFETY SECOND
(1950 - MGM) Tom & Jerry
One Sheet: $250 - $600   *Cartoon. Full color stone litho.*

SAGA OF ANATAHAN, THE
(1954 - -) -
One Sheet: $15 - $30   *AKA: ANATAHAN.*

SAGA OF DEATH VALLEY
(1939 - Republic) Roy Rogers, George Hayes
One Sheet: $500 - $800   *Cowboy Movie Posters #239.*

SAGA OF DEATH VALLEY
(1949R - Republic) Roy Rogers, George Hayes
One Sheet: $50 - $100   *Re-release.*

SAGA OF HEMP BROWN, THE
(1958 - Universal) Rory Calhoun, Beverly Garland
One Sheet: $10 - $20

SAGEBRUSH HEROES
(1945 - Columbia) Charles Starrett, Constance Worth
One Sheet: $15 - $30

SAGEBRUSH LAW
(1942 - RKO) Tim Holt
One Sheet: $15 - $35

SAGEBRUSH TRAIL
(1933 - Monogram) John Wayne, Nancy Shubert
One Sheet: $1,900 - $3,000

SAGEBRUSH TRAIL
(1943R - Lone Star) John Wayne, Nancy Shubert
One Sheet: $125 - $250   *Re-release.*

SAGEBRUSH TROUBADOUR, THE
(1935 - Republic) Gene Autry, Smiley Burnette
One Sheet: $300 - $700

SAGINAW TRAIL
(1953 - Columbia) Gene Autry, Smiley Burnette
One Sheet: $50 - $100

SAHARA
(1943 - Columbia) Humphrey Bogart, Bruce Bennett
One Sheet: $200 - $400

SAHARA
(1984 - -) Brooke Shields, Lambert Wilson
One Sheet: $7 - $15

SAIGON
(1948 - Paramount) Alan Ladd, Veronica Lake
One Sheet: $100 - $200

SAIL A CROOKED SHIP
(1961 - Columbia) Robert Wagner, Ernie Kovacs
One Sheet: $7 - $15

SAILING ALONG
(1938 - Gaumont) Jessie Matthews, Roland Young
One Sheet: $50 - $100

SAILOR BE GOOD
(1933 - RKO) Jack Oakie, Vivian Osborne
One Sheet: $150 - $300

SAILOR BEWARE
(1951 - Paramount) Dean Martin, Jerry Lewis, Betty Hutton
One Sheet: $50 - $100

SAILOR BEWARE
(1968R - Paramount) Dean Martin, Jerry Lewis, Betty Hutton
One Sheet: $10 - $20   *Re-release.*

SAILOR FROM GIBRALTAR, THE
(1967 - Lopert) Jeanne Moreau, Orson Welles, Vanessa Redgrave
One Sheet: $7 - $15

SAILOR OF THE KING
(1953 - 20th Century Fox) Jeffrey Hunter, Michael Rennie, Wendy Hiller
One Sheet: $15 - $35

SAILOR PAPA, A
(1925 - Pathe) Glenn Tryon
One Sheet: $250 - $500

SAILOR TAKES A WIFE, THE
(1945 - MGM) Robert Walker, June Allyson
One Sheet: $30 - $50

SAILOR'S HOLIDAY
(1944 - Columbia) Arthur Lake, Jane Lawrence
One Sheet: $30 - $50

SAILOR'S HOME, THE
(1936 - Educational) Paul Terry Studio
Cartoon. See "Terrytoons Stock" for prices. Cartoon Movie Posters #81.

SAILOR'S LADY
(1940 - 20th Century Fox) Nancy Kelly, Dana Andrews
One Sheet: $40 - $75

SAILOR'S LUCK
(1933 - Fox) James Dunn, Sally Eilers
One Sheet: $100 - $200

SAILOR-MADE MAN, A
(1921 - Pathe) Harold Lloyd
One Sheet: $600 - $1,000

SAILORS BEWARE!
(1927 - Pathecomedy) Stan Laurel
One Sheet: $1,300 - $2,000

SAILORS ON LEAVE
(1941 - Republic) William Lundigan, Shirley Ross
One Sheet: $20 - $40

SAINT, THE
(1997 - Paramount) Val Kilmer, Elisabeth Shue
One Sheet: $7 - $15

SAINT IN LONDON, THE
(1939 - RKO) George Sanders, Sally Gray
One Sheet: $150 - $300

SAINT IN NEW YORK, THE
(1938 - RKO) Louis Hayward, Kay Sutton
One Sheet: $150 - $350

SAINT IN PALM SPRINGS, THE
(1941 - RKO) George Sanders, Wendy Barrie
One Sheet: $125 - $250

SAINT JACK
(1979 - New World) Ben Gazzara, Denholm Elliott
One Sheet: $5 - $10

SAINT JOAN
(1957 - United Artists) Richard Widmark, Richard Todd, Jean Seberg
One Sheet: $150 - $300   *Saul Bass art.*

SAINT MEETS THE TIGER, THE
(1943 - Republic) Hugh Sinclair, Jean Gillie
One Sheet: $100 - $200

SAINT OF FORT WASHINGTON, THE
(1993 - Warner Bros.) Danny Glover, Matt Dillon
One Sheet: $3 - $5

SAINT STRIKES BACK, THE
(1939 - RKO) George Sanders, Wendy Barrie
One Sheet: $200 - $400

SAINT TAKES OVER, THE
(1940 - RKO) George Sanders, Wendy Barrie
One Sheet: $125 - $250

SAINT'S DOUBLE TROUBLE, THE
(1940 - RKO) George Sanders, Helene Whitney, Bela Lugosi
One Sheet: $150 - $300

SAINT'S GIRL FRIDAY, THE
(1953 - RKO) Louis Hayward, Naomi Chance
One Sheet: $30 - $50

SAINT'S VACATION, THE
(1941 - RKO) Hugh Sinclair, Sally Gray
One Sheet: $125 - $250

SAINTED DEVIL, THE
(1924 - Paramount) Rudolph Valentino
One Sheet: $4,500 - $7,000

SAINTED SISTERS, THE
(1948 - Paramount) Veronica Lake, Joan Caulfield
One Sheet: $50 - $100

SAINTLY SINNERS
(1962 - United Artists) Don Beddoe, Ellen Corby
One Sheet: $5 - $10

SAINTS AND SINNERS
(1949 - London) Kieron Moore, Christine Norden
One Sheet: $15 - $25

SALEM'S LOT
(1979 - -) David Soul, James Mason, Bonnie Bedelia
One Sheet: $15 - $30

SALESLADY
(1939 - Monogram) Anna Neagle, Weldon Heuburn
One Sheet: $40 - $75

SALESMAN
(1969 - Maysles) Paul Brennan, Charles McDevitt, James Baker
One Sheet: $3 - $5

SALLY
(1925 - First National) Colleen Moore, Lloyd Hughes
One Sheet: $500 - $900

SALLY
(1930 - First National) Marilyn Miller, Alexander Gray, Joe E. Brown
One Sheet: $250 - $600

SALLY AND SAINT ANNE
(1952 - Universal) Ann Blyth, Edmund Gwenn
One Sheet: $15 - $35

SALLY, IRENE, AND MARY
(1925 - MGM) Joan Crawford, Constance Bennett
One Sheet: $1,900 - $3,000

SALLY, IRENE, AND MARY
(1938 - 20th Century Fox) Alice Faye, Jimmy Durante, Tony Martin
One Sheet: $250 - $600

SALLY OF THE SAWDUST
(1925 - United Artists) W.C. Fields, Carol Dempster, Dir: D.W. Griffith
One Sheet: $1,900 - $3,000

SALLY SWING
(1938 - Paramount) Betty Boop, Fleischer Studio
One Sheet: $600 - $1,000   *Cartoon. Duotone. Betty is not on poster. Cartoon Movie Posters #206.*

SALLY'S SHOULDERS
(1928 - FBO) Lois Wilson
One Sheet: $100 - $200

SALOME
(1922 - Allied) Alla Nazimova
One Sheet: $3,500 - $5,000   *Beardsley art.*

SALOME
(1953 - Columbia) Rita Hayworth, Stewart Granger, Charles Laughton
One Sheet: $100 - $200

SALOME, WHERE SHE DANCED
(1945 - Universal) Yvonne De Carlo, David Bruce
One Sheet: $40 - $75

SALOME'S LAST DANCE
(1988 - -) Glenda Jackson, Stratford Johns
One Sheet: $10 - $20

SALOMY JANE
(1923 - Paramount) Jacqueline Logan, George Fawcett
One Sheet: $125 - $250

SALSA
(1988 - -) Robby Rosa, Magali Alvarado
One Sheet: $3 - $5

SALT AND PEPPER
(1968 - United Artists) Sammy Davis, Jr., Peter Lawford
One Sheet: $15 - $25   *Jack Davis art.*

SALT LAKE RAIDERS
(1950 - Republic) Allan "Rocky" Lane, Eddy Waller
One Sheet: $15 - $35

SALT OF THE EARTH
(1954 - -) Will Geer, Juan Chacon
One Sheet: $100 - $200

SALT OF THE EARTH
(1965R - -) Will Geer, Juan Chacon
One Sheet: $15 - $30   *Re-release.*

SALT TO THE DEVIL
(1949 - Eagle-Lion) Sam Wanamaker, Lea Padovani
One Sheet: $15 - $25

SALT WATER TABBY
(1947 - MGM) Tom & Jerry
One Sheet: $250 - $600   *Cartoon. Full color stone litho.*

SALTY O'ROURKE
(1945 - Paramount) Alan Ladd, Gail Russell, Stanley Clements
One Sheet: $75 - $150

SALUDOS AMIGOS
(1943 - RKO/Disney) Donald Duck
One Sheet: $500 - $800   *Cartoon. The Disney Poster, pg. 84. Cartoon Movie Posters #375.*

SALUTE
(1929 - Fox) George O'Brien, Dir: John Ford
One Sheet: $250 - $500

SALUTE FOR THREE
(1943 - Paramount) Macdonald Carey, Betty

Rhodes
One Sheet: $30 - $50

SALUTE TO DUKE ELLINGTON
(1950 - Universal) Duke Ellington, Johhny Hodges
One Sheet: $1,300 - $2,000   *Black cast. Big Band.*

SALUTE TO THE MARINES
(1943 - MGM) Marilyn Maxwell, Wallace Beery
One Sheet: $30 - $60

SALVADOR
(1986 - Hemdale) James Woods, James Belushi
One Sheet: $7 - $15

SALVATION
(1986 - -) Stephen McHattie, Dominique Davalos
One Sheet: $3 - $5

SALVATION NELL
(1931 - RCA Photophone) Ralph Graves, Helen Chandler, Dir: James Cruze
One Sheet: $200 - $400

SALZBURG CONNECTION, THE
(1972 - 20th Century Fox) Barry Newman, Anna Karina
One Sheet: $3 - $5

SAM WHISKEY
(1969 - United Artists) Burt Reynolds, Clint Walker, Ossie Davis
One Sheet: $10 - $20

SAMAR
(1962 - Warner Bros.) George Montgomery, Gilbert Roland
One Sheet: $15 - $35

SAMARANG
(1933 - United Artists) -
One Sheet: $75 - $125

SAME TIME NEXT YEAR
(1978 - Universal) Ellen Burstyn, Alan Alda
One Sheet: $3 - $5

SAMMY AND ROSIE GET LAID
(1987 - Cinecom) Sashi Kapoor, Claire Bloom
One Sheet: $5 - $10

SAMMY, THE WAY-OUT SEAL
(1962 - Disney) Jack Carson, Robert Culp
One Sheet: $15 - $30   *Originally telecast on Walt Disney's Wonderful World of Color.*

SAMSON AND DELILAH
(1949 - Paramount) Victor Mature, Hedy Lamarr, George Sanders
One Sheet: $75 - $150

SAMSON AND DELILAH
(1959R - Paramount) Victor Mature, Hedy Lamarr
One Sheet: $50 - $100   *Re-release.*

SAMSON AND DELILAH
(1968R - Paramount) Victor Mature, Hedy Lamarr
One Sheet: $20 - $40   *Re-release.*

SAMSON AND THE SEVEN MIRACLES OF THE WORLD
(1963 - AIP) Gordon Scott, Yoko Tani
One Sheet: $20 - $40

SAMSON AND THE SLAVE QUEEN
(1964 - AIP) Alan Steel, Pierre Brice
One Sheet: $15 - $25

SAMURAI ASSASSIN
(1965 - Toho/Mifune) Toshiro Mifune, Keiju Kobayashi
One Sheet: $30 - $50

SAN ANTONE
(1953 - Republic) Rod Cameron, Arleen Whelan
One Sheet: $15 - $30

SAN ANTONE AMBUSH
(1949 - Republic) Monte Hale, Paul Hurst
One Sheet: $15 - $35

SAN ANTONIO
(1945 - Warner Bros.) Errol Flynn, Alexis Smith
One Sheet: $200 - $400

SAN ANTONIO KID, THE

(1944 - Republic) Bill Elliott, Bobby Blake
One Sheet: $30 - $50   *Red Ryder series.*

SAN ANTONIO ROSE
(1941 - Universal) Robert Paige, Jane Frazee, Shemp Howard
One Sheet: $40 - $75

SAN DIEGO, I LOVE YOU
(1944 - Universal) Jon Hall, Buster Keaton, Edward Everett Horton
One Sheet: $50 - $100

SAN FERNANDO VALLEY
(1944 - Republic) Roy Rogers, Dale Evans
One Sheet: $150 - $350

SAN FRANCISCO
(1936 - MGM) Clark Gable, Jeanette MacDonald, Spencer Tracy
One Sheet: $1,600 - $2,500

SAN FRANCISCO
(1948R - MGM) Clark Gable, Jeanette McDonald
One Sheet: $100 - $200   *Re-release.*

SAN FRANCISCO DOCKS
(1940 - Universal) Burgess Meredith, Irene Hervey
One Sheet: $50 - $100

SAN FRANCISCO STORY, THE
(1952 - Warner Bros.) Yvonne De Carlo, Joel McCrea
One Sheet: $15 - $30

SAN QUENTIN
(1937 - Warner Bros.) Pat O'Brien, Humphrey Bogart
One Sheet: $600 - $1,000

SAN QUENTIN
(1946 - RKO) Lawrence Tierney, Marian Carr
One Sheet: $50 - $100

SAN QUENTIN
(1950R - Warner Bros.) Humphrey Bogart
One Sheet: $30 - $50   *Re-release.*

SAN QUENTIN
(1956R - Warner Bros.) Humphrey Bogart
One Sheet: $20 - $40   *Re-release.*

SANCTUARY
(1961 - 20th Century Fox) Lee Remick, Yves Montand
One Sheet: $7 - $15

SAND
(1949 - 20th Century Fox) Mark Stevens, Coleen Gray
One Sheet: $15 - $25

SAND CASTLE, THE
(1960 - Contemporary) Barry Cardwell, Alec Wilder
One Sheet: $7 - $15

SAND PEBBLES, THE
(1966 - 20th Century Fox) Steve McQueen, Richard Attenborough
One Sheet: $30 - $60

SANDERS OF THE RIVER
(1935 - United Artists) Paul Robeson, Leslie Banks
One Sheet: $500 - $800   *Roberson not pictured on One Sheet. Separate Cinema, pg. 42.*

SANDFLOW
(1936 - Universal) Buck Jones, Lita Chevret
One Sheet: $800 - $1,500

SANDLOT, THE
(1993 - 20th Century Fox) Tom Guiry, Karen Allen, James Earl Jones
One Sheet: $7 - $15   *Sports (Baseball). Sports Movie Posters #84.*

SANDPIPER, THE
(1965 - MGM) Elizabeth Taylor, Richard Burton
One Sheet: $30 - $50

SANDS OF BEERSHEBA
(1966 - Landauunger) Diane Baker, David Opatoshu
One Sheet: $7 - $15

SANDS OF IWO JIMA
(1949 - Republic) John Wayne, John Agar
One Sheet: $250 - $500

SANDS OF IWO JIMA
(1976R - Republic) John Wayne, John Agar
One Sheet: $15 - $25   *Re-release.*

SANDS OF THE KALAHARI
(1965 - Paramount) Stuart Whitman, Stanley Baker
One Sheet: $5 - $10

SANDY GETS HER MAN!
(1940 - Universal) Baby Sandy, Stuart Erwin
One Sheet: $30 - $50

SANDY IS A LADY
(1940 - Universal) Baby Sandy, Nan Grey
One Sheet: $30 - $50

SANGAREE
(1953 - Paramount) Fernando Lamas, Arlene Dahl
One Sheet: $30 - $50   *Filmed in 3-D.*

SANSHO THE BAILIFF
(1969 - Daiei/Kyoto) Kinuyo Tanaka, Yoshiaki Hanayagi
One Sheet: $15 - $25   *Japanese.*
AKA: THE BAILIFF.

SANTA CLAUS
(1960 - K. Gordon Murray) Joseph Elias Moreno, Ken Smith(narrator)
One Sheet: $10 - $20

SANTA CLAUS
(1974R - -) Joseph Elias Moreno, Ken Smith (narrator)
One Sheet: $2 - $3   *Re-release.*

SANTA CLAUS CONQUERS THE MARTIANS
(1964 - Embassy) John Call, Leonard Hicks, Pia Zadora
One Sheet: $75 - $125   *Zadora's film debut.*

SANTA CLAUS: THE MOVIE
(1985 - TriStar) Dudley Moore, John Lithgow
One Sheet: $5 - $10

SANTA CLAUSE, THE
(1994 - Buena Vista) Tim Allen, Judge Reinhold, Wendy Crewson
One Sheet: $5 - $10   *Advance 3-D Style $12-$20.*

SANTA FE
(1951 - PRC) Randolph Scott, Janis Carter
One Sheet: $15 - $35

SANTA FE
(1959R - PRC) Randolph Scott, Janis Carter
One Sheet: $5 - $10   *Re-release.*

SANTA FE BOUND
(1937 - Reliable) Tom Tyler, Jeanne Martel
One Sheet: $200 - $400

SANTA FE MARSHAL
(1940 - Paramount) William Boyd, Russell Hayden
One Sheet: $200 - $400   *Hopalong Cassidy series.*

SANTA FE PASSAGE
(1955 - Republic) John Payne, Faith Domergue
One Sheet: $15 - $30

SANTA FE SADDLEMATES
(1945 - Republic) Sunset Carson, Linda Stirling
One Sheet: $30 - $50

SANTA FE SCOUTS
(1943 - Republic) Three Mesquiteers (Tom Tyler, Bob Steele, Jimmie Dodd)
One Sheet: $50 - $100

SANTA FE STAMPEDE
(1938 - Republic) Three Mesquiteers, June Martel, John Wayne
One Sheet: $350 - $750

SANTA FE STAMPEDE
(1953R - Republic) Three Mesquiteers, John Wayne
One Sheet: $40 - $75   *Re-release.*

SANTA FE TRAIL
(1930 - Paramount Publix) Richard Arlen
One Sheet: $150 - $350

SANTA FE TRAIL
(1940 - Warner Bros.) Errol Flynn, Olivia de Havilland, Ronald Reagan
One Sheet: $250 - $500   *Cowboy Movie Posters #257.*

SANTA FE UPRISING
(1946 - Republic) Rocky Lane, Robert Blake
One Sheet: $30 - $50   *From the Red Ryder series.*

SANTA SANGRE
(1990 - -) Axel Jodorowsky, Guy Stockwell
One Sheet: $5 - $10   *Italian.*

SANTA'S WORKSHOP
(1932 - United Artists) Silly Symphony
One Sheet: $10,000 - $15,000   *Cartoon. The Disney Poster, pg. 7.*

SANTE FE UPRISING
(1946 - Republic) Allan Lane, Bobby Blake
One Sheet: $20 - $40   *Red Ryder series.*

SANTEE
(1973 - Crown) Glenn Ford, Dana Wynter
One Sheet: $3 - $5

SANTERELLA
(1954 - -) -
One Sheet: $40 - $75

SANTIAGO
(1956 - Warner Bros.) Alan Ladd, Lloyd Nolan
One Sheet: $20 - $40

SANTO AND THE BLUE DEMON VS. THE MONSTERS
(1968 - Sotomayor) Santo, Alejandro Cruz
One Sheet: $75 - $150   *Mexican.*

SANTO IN THE WAX MUSEUM
(1963 - Panamericana) Santo, Claudio Brook
One Sheet: $75 - $150   *Mexican.*
AKA: SAMSON IN THE WAX MUSEUM.

SANTO VERSUS THE MARTIAN INVASION
(1966 - Cinematograficas) Santo, Maura Monti
One Sheet: $50 - $100   *Mexican.*

SANTO VS. FRANKENSTEIN'S DAUGHTER
(1971 - Calderon) Santo, Gina Romand
One Sheet: $75 - $150   *Mexican.*
AKA: SANTO VS THE DAUGHTER OF FRANKENSTEIN.

SANTO VS. THE VAMPIRE WOMEN
(1962 - Santo) -
One Sheet: $75 - $150   *Mexican.*

SAP FROM SYRACUSE, THE
(1930 - Paramount Publix) Jack Oakie, Ginger Rogers
One Sheet: $300 - $700

SAPHEAD, THE
(1920 - Metro) Buster Keaton, Carol Holloway
One Sheet: $5,500 - $9,000

SAPPHIRE
(1959 - Universal) Nigel Patrick, Yvonne Mitchell
One Sheet: $7 - $15

SAPPY BIRTHDAY
(1942 - Columbia) Andy Clyde
One Sheet: $75 - $150   *Comedy short. Duotone.*

SAPPY BULLFIGHTERS
(1958 - Columbia) The Three Stooges (Joe Besser)
One Sheet: $75 - $125   *Comedy short. Duotone. Remake of WHAT'S THE MATADOR.*

SAPS AT SEA
(1940 - United Artists) Stan Laurel, Oliver Hardy
One Sheet: $350 - $750

SAPS AT SEA
(1946R - Favorite) Stan Laurel, Oliver Hardy
One Sheet: $40 - $75   *Re-release.*

SARABAND
(1949 - Eagle-Lion) Stewart Granger, Joan Greenwood
One Sheet: $15 - $25

SARACEN BLADE, THE
(1954 - Columbia) Ricardo Montalban, Betta St. John
One Sheet: $10 - $20

SARAFINA!
(1992 - Miramax) Whoopi Goldberg
One Sheet: $7 - $15

SARAH AND SON
(1930 - Paramount) Ruth Chatterton, Fredric March
One Sheet: $500 - $800

SARAH VAUGHN AND HERB JEFFRIES
(1950 - -) -
One Sheet: $125 - $250   *Black cast.*

SARATOGA
(1937 - MGM) Clark Gable, Jean Harlow
One Sheet: $500 - $900   *Harlow's final film.*

One Sheet (Other Company)

SARATOGA TRUNK
(1946 - Warner Bros.) Gary Cooper, Ingrid Bergman
One Sheet: $100 - $200

SARATOGA TRUNK
(1954R - Warner Bros.) Gary Cooper, Ingrid Bergman
One Sheet: $30 - $50   *Re-release. Duotone.*

SARGE GOES TO COLLEGE
(1947 - Monogram) Alan Hale, Jr., Freddie Stewart
One Sheet: $15 - $25

SARONG GIRL
(1943 - Monogram) Anne Corio, Tim & Irene
One Sheet: $30 - $50

SASKATCHEWAN
(1954 - Universal) Alan Ladd, Shelley Winters
One Sheet: $15 - $35

SASKATCHEWAN
(1962R - Universal) Alan Ladd, Shelley Winters
One Sheet: $10 - $20   *Re-release.*

SASQUATCH
(1978 - North American) George Lauris
One Sheet: $3 - $5

SATAN BUG, THE
(1965 - United Artists) George Maharis, Richard Basehart
One Sheet: $7 - $15

SATAN IN HIGH HEELS
(1962 - -) Meg Myles, Grayson Hall
One Sheet: $15 - $25   *Sexploitation.*

SATAN MET A LADY
(1936 - Warner Bros.) Warren William, Bette Davis
One Sheet: $2,200 - $3,500

SATAN NEVER SLEEPS
(1962 - 20th Century Fox) William Holden, Clifton Webb, France Nuyen
One Sheet: $15 - $25

SATAN'S CHEERLEADERS
(1977 - World Amusements) Yvonne De Carlo, John Carradine
One Sheet: $15 - $25

SATAN'S CRADLE
(1949 - United Artists) Duncan Renaldo, Leo Carrillo
One Sheet: $30 - $50   *Cisco Kid series.*

SATAN'S SATELLITES
(1958 - Republic) Judd Holdren, Aline Towne, Leonard Nimoy
One Sheet: $75 - $150   *Feature version of ZOMBIES OF THE STRATOSPHERE.*

SATANIC RITES OF DRACULA, THE
(1973 - Hammer) Christopher Lee, Peter

Cushing
One Sheet: $20 - $40   *AKA: COUNT DRACULA AND HIS VAMPIRE BRIDE.*

SATCHMO THE GREAT
(1956 - United Artists) Louis Armstrong, Leonard Bernstein
One Sheet: $100 - $200   *Separate Cinema, pg. 105.*

SATELLITE IN THE SKY
(1956 - Warner Bros.) Kieron Moore, Lois Maxwell
One Sheet: $40 - $75

Insert

SATISFACTION
(1988 - -) Justine Bateman, Liam Neeson
One Sheet: $7 - $15

SATURDAY AFTERNOON
(1926 - Pathe) Harry Langdon, Alice Ward
One Sheet: $250 - $600

SATURDAY NIGHT
(1922 - Paramount) Leatrice Joy, Conrad Nagel, Dir: Cecil B. DeMille
One Sheet: $250 - $600

SATURDAY NIGHT AND SUNDAY MORNING
(1961 - Continental) Albert Finney, Shirley Anne Field
One Sheet: $5 - $10

SATURDAY NIGHT FEVER
(1977 - Paramount) John Travolta, Karen Lynn Gorney
One Sheet: $30 - $60

SATURDAY NIGHT FEVER/GREASE
(1979R - Paramount) John Travolta
One Sheet: $15 - $25   *Re-release double feature poster.*

SATURDAY NIGHT KID, THE
(1929 - Paramount) Clara Bow
One Sheet: $1,600 - $2,500

SATURDAY NIGHT OUT
(1964 - Compton/Tekli) Heather Sears, Bernard Lee
One Sheet: $10 - $20

SATURDAY THE 14TH
(1981 - -) Richard Benjamin, Paula Prentiss
One Sheet: $10 - $20

SATURDAY THE 14TH STRIKES BACK
(1988 - -) -
One Sheet: $10 - $20

SATURDAY'S CHILDREN
(1940 - Warner Bros.) John Garfield, Anne Shirley, Claude Rains
One Sheet: $75 - $125

SATURDAY'S HERO
(1951 - Columbia) John Derek, Donna Reed
One Sheet: $10 - $20

SATURDAY'S HEROES
(1937 - RKO) Van Heflin, Marian Marsh
One Sheet: $50 - $100

SATURDAY'S LESSON
(1929 - MGM) Our Gang
One Sheet: $500 - $800

SATURDAY'S MILLIONS
(1933 - Universal) Robert Young, Johnny Mack Brown, Lelia Hyams
One Sheet: $100 - $200

SATURN THREE
(1980 - Associated) Farrah Fawcett, Kirk

Douglas
One Sheet: $5 - $10

SAVAGE, THE
(1952 - Paramount) Charlton Heston, Susan
Morrow
One Sheet: $30 - $50

SAVAGE, THE
(1973 - New World) James Inglehart, Carol
Speed
One Sheet: $3 - $5   *Blaxploitation.*

SAVAGE BRIDE
(1948 - H.K.S.) -
One Sheet: $10 - $20

SAVAGE DAWN
(1984 - Media) George Kennedy, Lance
Henriksen
One Sheet: $3 - $5

SAVAGE DRUMS
(1951 - Lippert) Sabu, Lita Baron
One Sheet: $15 - $35

SAVAGE FRONTIER
(1953 - Republic) Allan "Rocky" Lane
One Sheet: $15 - $35

SAVAGE GIRL
(1932 - Monarch) Rochelle Hudson, Walter
Byron
One Sheet: $125 - $250   *Hudson's first
leading role.*

SAVAGE GOLD
(1933 - -) George M. Wyatt
One Sheet: $100 - $200

SAVAGE GUNS
(1962 - MGM) Richard Basehart, Don Taylor
One Sheet: $5 - $10

SAVAGE HORDE, THE
(1950 - Republic) William Elliott, Adrian Booth
One Sheet: $15 - $25

SAVAGE INNOCENTS, THE
(1961 - Paramount) Anthony Quinn, Peter
O'Toole
One Sheet: $7 - $15

SAVAGE MESSIAH
(1972 - MGM) Dorothy Tutin, Scott Antony
One Sheet: $3 - $5

SAVAGE MUTINY
(1953 - Columbia) Johnny Weissmuller, Angela
Stevens
One Sheet: $30 - $50   *Jungle Jim
series.*

SAVAGE RED, OUTLAW WHITE
(1976 - Embassy) Padilla
One Sheet: $5 - $10

SAVAGE SAM
(1963 - Buena Vista) Brian Keith, Tommy Kirk
One Sheet: $7 - $15

SAVAGE SEVEN, THE
(1968 - AIP) Robert Walker, Adam Roarke
One Sheet: $5 - $10

SAVAGE SISTERS
(1974 - -) Cheri Caffaro, Gloria Hendry
One Sheet: $7 - $15   *Sexploitation.*

SAVAGE SPLENDOR
(1949 - RKO) Denis Cotlow
One Sheet: $15 - $35

SAVAGE STREETS
(1984 - -) Linda Blair, John Vernon
One Sheet: $5 - $10

SAVAGE WILD, THE
(1970 - AIP) Gordon Eastman, Carl Spore
One Sheet: $5 - $10

SAVANNAH SMILES
(1982 - Embassy) Mark Miller, Bridgette
Andersen (film debut)
One Sheet: $5 - $10

SAVE THE CHILDREN
(1973 - Paramount) Gladys Knight, Jackson 5
One Sheet: $30 - $60   *Black cast. All
star soul music documentary.*

SAVE THE SHIP
(1925 - Pathe) Stan Laurel
One Sheet: $600 - $1,000

SAVE THE TIGER
(1972 - Paramount) Jack Lemmon, Jack Gilford
One Sheet: $10 - $20   *Academy
Award: Best Actor(Lemmon). Academy Award
Movie Posters #276.*

SAVED BY THE BELLE
(1939 - Columbia) The Three Stooges (Curly)
One Sheet: $7,500 - $12,000   *Comedy short.
Duotone.*

SAWDUST
(1923 - Universal) Glady Walton, Niles Welch
One Sheet: $200 - $400

SAWDUST AND TINSEL
(1956 - Sandrew/Times) Harriet Andersson,
Ake Groenberg, Dir: I. Bergman
One Sheet: $100 - $200   *Swedish.
AKA: THE NAKED NIGHT; SUNSET OF THE
CLOWN.*

SAWDUST PARADISE, THE
(1928 - Paramount Famous Players Lasky)
Esther Ralston, Reed Howes
One Sheet: $125 - $250

SAWDUST RING, THE
(1917 - -) Bessie Love, Harold Goodwin
One Sheet: $200 - $400

SAWDUST TRAIL
(1924 - Universal) Hoot Gibson, Josie
Sedgwick
One Sheet: $250 - $600

SAWING A LADY IN HALF
(1922 - Weiss Bros.) -
One Sheet: $700 - $1,200

SAXON CHARM, THE
(1948 - Universal) Robert Montgomery, Susan
Hayward
One Sheet: $20 - $40

SAY AMEN SOMEBODY
(1982 - -) Willie Mae Ford Smith, Thomas A.
Forsey
One Sheet: $10 - $20   *Black cast.*

SAY ANYTHING...
(1989 - -) John Cusack, Ione Skye, Joan
Cusack
One Sheet: $15 - $30

SAY HELLO TO YESTERDAY
(1971 - Cinerama) Jean Simmons, Leonard
Whiting
One Sheet: $3 - $5

SAY IT IN FRENCH
(1938 - Paramount) Ray Milland, Olympe
Bradna
One Sheet: $50 - $100

SAY IT WITH SONGS
(1929 - Warner Bros.) Al Jolson
One Sheet: $1,900 - $3,000

SAY ONE FOR ME
(1959 - 20th Century Fox) Bing Crosby, Debbie
Reynolds
One Sheet: $20 - $40

SAYONARA
(1957 - Warner Bros.) Marlon Brando, Miyoshi
Umeki, Red Buttons
One Sheet: $30 - $60   *Academy
Award Movie Posters #178.*

SAYONARA
(1962R - Warner Bros.) Marlon Brando,
Miyoshi Umeki, Red Buttons
One Sheet: $7 - $15   *Re-release.*

SCALAWAG
(1973 - Paramount) Kirk Douglas, Mark Lester
One Sheet: $5 - $10

SCALPEL
(1976 - Avco Embassy) Robert Lansing, Judith
Chapman
One Sheet: $7 - $15

SCALPHUNTERS, THE
(1968 - United Artists) Burt Lancaster, Ossie
Davis
One Sheet: $7 - $15   *Cowboy
Movie Posters #323.*

SCANDAL
(1929 - Universal) Laura LaPlante, John Boles
One Sheet: $350 - $750

SCANDAL
(1989 - Miramax) John Hurt, Joanne Whalley-
Kilmer, Ian McKellen
One Sheet: $7 - $15

SCANDAL AT SCOURIE
(1952 - MGM) Greer Garson, Walter Pidgeon
One Sheet: $15 - $30

SCANDAL FOR SALE
(1932 - Universal) Charles Bickford, Rose
Hobart
One Sheet: $200 - $400

SCANDAL IN PARIS
(1946 - United Artists) George Sanders, Signe
Hasso
One Sheet: $20 - $40

SCANDAL IN SORRENTO
(1956 - DCA) Sophia Loren, Vittorio De Sica
One Sheet: $30 - $50

SCANDAL INC.
(1956 - Republic) Robert Hutton, Paul Richards
One Sheet: $15 - $30

SCANDAL SHEET
(1931 - Paramount Publix) George Bancroft,
Kay Francis
One Sheet: $150 - $300

SCANDAL SHEET
(1951 - Columbia) Broderick Crawford, Donna
Reed
One Sheet: $15 - $25

SCANDAL STREET
(1938 - Paramount) Lew Ayres, Louise
Campbell
One Sheet: $75 - $150

SCANDALOUS
(1984 - Hemdale) Robert Hays, John Gielgud
One Sheet: $3 - $5

SCANDALOUS JOHN
(1971 - Buena Vista/Disney) Brian Keith,
Alfonso Arau
One Sheet: $5 - $10

Insert

SCANNERS
(1981 - Avco) Jennifer O'Neal, Stephen Lack
One Sheet: $10 - $20   *Advance One
Sheet:$15-$30.*

SCAPEGOAT, THE
(1958 - MGM) Alec Guinness, Bette Davis
One Sheet: $15 - $25

SCAR, THE
(1948 - Eagle-Lion) Paul Henreid, Joan Bennett
One Sheet: $40 - $75   *AKA:
HOLLOW TRIUMPH.*

SCAR OF SHAME
(1927 - -) Harry Henderson, Lucia Lynn Moses
One Sheet: $150 - $300

SCARAB
(1982 - Tesauro) Rip Torn, Robert Ginty
One Sheet: $5 - $10   *US/Spanish.*

SCARAB MURDER CASE, THE
(1936 - Paramount) Kathleen Kelly, Wilfrid
Hyde-White
One Sheet: $250 - $500   *Philo Vance
Series.*

SCARAMOUCHE
(1923 - Metro) Ramon Novarro, Alice Terry
One Sheet: $600 - $1,000

SCARAMOUCHE
(1952 - MGM) Stewart Granger, Janet Leigh
One Sheet: $50 - $100

SCARECROW, THE
(1920 - Metro) Buster Keaton
One Sheet: $5,500 - $9,000

SCARECROW
(1973 - Warner Bros.) Gene Hackman, Al
Pacino
One Sheet: $10 - $20

SCARED PINK
(1921 - Paramount) Anna Cornwall
One Sheet: $150 - $300

SCARED STIFF
(1945 - Paramount) Jack Haley, Ann Savage
One Sheet: $30 - $50

SCARED STIFF
(1952 - Paramount) Dean Martin, Jerry Lewis,
Lizabeth Scott, Carmen Miranda
One Sheet: $75 - $175

SCARED TO DEATH
(1946 - Golden Gate) Bela Lugosi, George
Zucco, Joyce Compton
One Sheet: $125 - $250

SCARF, THE
(1950 - United Artists) John Ireland, Mercedes
McCambridge
One Sheet: $10 - $20

SCARFACE
(1932 - Warner Bros.) Paul Muni, Ann Dvorak,
Boris Karloff, George Raft
One Sheet: $5,500 - $9,000

SCARFACE
(1938R - Astor) Paul Muni, Ann Dvorak, Boris
Karloff, George Raft
One Sheet: $150 - $300   *Re-release.*

SCARFACE
(1983 - Universal) Al Pacino, Michelle Pfeiffer
One Sheet: $20 - $40   *Advance:$20-
$50.*

SCARFACE MOB
(1962 - Desilu) Robert Stack, Keenan Wynn
One Sheet: $30 - $60   *Theatrical
release of TV series "The Untouchables".*

SCARLET ANGEL
(1952 - Universal) Yvonne De Carlo, Rock
Hudson
One Sheet: $15 - $35

SCARLET BRAND, THE
(1932 - Big 4) Bob Custer, Betty Mack
One Sheet: $150 - $350

SCARLET CLAW, THE
(1944 - Universal) Basil Rathbone, Nigel Bruce,
Paul Cavanagh
One Sheet: $500 - $800

One Sheet

SCARLET CLUE, THE
(1945 - Monogram) Sidney Toler, Benson
Fong, Mantan Moreland
One Sheet: $150 - $350

SCARLET COAT, THE
(1955 - MGM) Cornel Wilde, Michael Wilding,
Anne Francis
One Sheet: $15 - $25

SCARLET DAYS
(1919 - Paramount-Artcraft) Richard
Barthelmess, Carol Dempster, Dir: D.W. Griffith
One Sheet: $600 - $1,000   *Cowboy*

Movie Posters #16.

SCARLET EMPRESS, THE
(1934 - Paramount) Marlene Dietrich, John Lodge, Sam Jaffe
One Sheet: $6,500 - $10,000

SCARLET HORSEMAN, THE
(1946 - Universal) Paul Guilfoyle, Peter Cookson
One Sheet: $100 - $200   *Serial. 13 Chapters.*

SCARLET HOUR, THE
(1955 - Paramount) Carol Ohmart, Tom Tryon, Jody Lawrance
One Sheet: $7 - $15

SCARLET LETTER, THE
(1927 - MGM) Lillian Gish, Lars Hanson
One Sheet: $1,900 - $3,000

SCARLET LETTER, THE
(1934 - Majestic) Colleen Moore, Hardie Albright
One Sheet: $250 - $600

SCARLET LETTER, THE
(1996 - Buena Vista) Demi Moore, Gary Oldman, Robert Duvall
One Sheet: $3 - $5

SCARLET PAGES
(1930 - First National) Elsie Ferguson, John Halliday
One Sheet: $100 - $200

SCARLET PIMPERNEL, THE
(1935 - London) Leslie Howard, Merle Oberon
One Sheet: $1,900 - $3,000

SCARLET RIVER
(1933 - RKO) Tom Keene, Betty Furness
One Sheet: $100 - $200

SCARLET SEAS
(1928 - First National) Richard Barthlemess, Betty Compson
One Sheet: $250 - $500

SCARLET SPEAR, THE
(1954 - United Artists) John Bentley, Martha Hyer
One Sheet: $7 - $15

SCARLET STREAK
(1925 - Universal) -
One Sheet: $250 - $600   *Serial. 10 Chapters.*

SCARLET STREET
(1945 - Universal) Edward G. Robinson, Joan Bennett
One Sheet: $100 - $200

SCARLET WEEK, THE
(1956 - Sonney) -
One Sheet: $7 - $15

SCARLET WEEK-END, A
(1932 - Maxium) Dorothy Revier, Theodore Von Eltz
One Sheet: $150 - $300

SCARS OF DRACULA, THE
(1970 - American Continental) Christopher Lee, Dennis Waterman
One Sheet: $75 - $125

SCARS OF DRACULA/HORROR OF FRANKENSTEIN
(1971R - American Continental) Christopher Lee/Ralph Bates
One Sheet: $30 - $50   *Re-release double feature poster.*

SCARS OF JEALOUSY
(1923 - First National) Frank Keenan, Lloyd Hughes
One Sheet: $200 - $400

SCARY CROWS
(1937 - Columbia) Color Rhapsodies
One Sheet: $250 - $500   *Cartoon. Full color. Cartoon Movie Posters #39.*

SCATTERBRAIN
(1940 - Republic) Judy Canova, Alan Mowbray
One Sheet: $30 - $50

SCATTERGOOD BAINES
(1940 - RKO) Guy Kibbee, Carol Hughes, John Archer
One Sheet: $50 - $100

SCATTERGOOD MEETS BROADWAY
(1941 - RKO) Guy Kibbee
One Sheet: $30 - $60

SCATTERGOOD PULLS THE STRING
(1941 - RKO) Guy Kibbee, Dink Trout
One Sheet: $30 - $60

SCATTERGOOD RIDES HIGH
(1942 - RKO) Guy Kibbee, Dorothy Moore
One Sheet: $30 - $60

SCATTERGOOD SURVIVES A MURDER
(1942 - RKO) Guy Kibbee, Margaret Hayes
One Sheet: $30 - $60

SCAVENGER HUNT
(1979 - 20th Century Fox) Richard Benjamin, Roddy McDowall
One Sheet: $5 - $10

SCAVENGERS, THE
(1959 - Roach) Vince Edwards, Carol Ohmart
One Sheet: $10 - $20

SCEICCO BIANCO
(1951 - P.D.C.) Alberto Sordi, Brunella Bovo, Dir: Federico Fellini
One Sheet: $500 - $800   *Italian. Price is for original Italian poster.*

SCENE OF THE CRIME
(1949 - MGM) Van Johnson, Gloria DeHaven
One Sheet: $15 - $30

SCENES FROM A MALL
(1991 - Touchstone) Woody Allen, Bette Midler
One Sheet: $3 - $5

SCENT OF A WOMAN
(1992 - Universal) Al Pacino, Chris O'Donnell
One Sheet: $15 - $25   *Academy Award: Best Actor(Pacino). Academy Award Movie Posters #382.*

SCHEMING SCHEMERS
(1956 - Columbia) The Three Stooges (Shemp)
One Sheet: $150 - $300   *Comedy short. Duotone. Remake of VAGABOND LOAFERS and A-PLUMBING WE WILL GO.*

SCHINDLER'S LIST
(1993 - Universal) Liam Neeson, Ben Kingsley, Dir: Steven Spielberg
One Sheet: $15 - $25   *Academy Award: Best Picture, Best Director. Academy Award Movie Posters #385.*

SCHIZOID
(1972 - AIP) Florinda Bolkan, Stanley Baker
One Sheet: $10 - $20

SCHLOCK
(1971 - Gazotskie) John Landis, Saul Kahan, Dir: John Landis
One Sheet: $15 - $35   *Landis' film debut.*

SCHOCK
(1980 - -) Daria Nicolodi, Dir: Mario Bava
One Sheet: $5 - $10

SCHOOL DAYS
(1920 - Vitagraph) Dir: Larry Semon
One Sheet: $250 - $600

SCHOOL DAZE
(1942 - 20th Century Fox) Nancy & Sluggo
One Sheet: $1,000 - $1,900   *Cartoon.*

SCHOOL DAZE
(1988 - Columbia) Larry Fishburne, Giancarlo Esposito, Dir: Spike Lee
One Sheet: $7 - $15

SCHOOL FOR GIRLS
(1934 - Liberty) Sidney Fox, Paul Kelly
One Sheet: $75 - $150

SCHOOL FOR SCOUNDRELS
(1960 - Continental) Ian Carmichael, Terry Thomas
One Sheet: $7 - $15

SCHOOL FOR UNCLAIMED GIRLS
(1973 - AIP) Renee Asherson, Dennis Waterman
One Sheet: $10 - $20   *Sexploitation.*

SCHOOL TEACHER AND THE WAIF, THE
(1912 - Biograph) Dir: D.W. Griffith
One Sheet: $250 - $500

SCHOOL TIES
(1992 - Paramount) Brendan Fraser, Matt Damon
One Sheet: $2 - $3

SCHOOLHOUSE SCANDAL, THE
(1919 - William Fox) -
One Sheet: $200 - $450

SCHTONK!
(1993 - -) Gotz George, Uwe Ochsenknecht
One Sheet: $3 - $5

SCIENTIFIC CARDPLAYER, THE
(1972 - Dino De Laurentis) Bette Davis, Joseph Cotton, Alberto Sordi
One Sheet: $15 - $25

SCORCHY
(1976 - AIP) Connie Stevens, Cesare Danova
One Sheet: $7 - $15

SCORPIO
(1973 - United Artists) Burt Lancaster, Alain Delon
One Sheet: $7 - $15

SCORPION
(1986 - Crown) Don Murray, Robert Logan
One Sheet: $3 - $5

SCOTCHED IN SCOTLAND
(1954 - Columbia) The Three Stooges (Shemp)
One Sheet: $150 - $300   *Comedy short. Duotone.*

SCOTLAND YARD
(1930 - Fox) Edmund Lowe, Joan Bennett
One Sheet: $250 - $500

SCOTLAND YARD
(1941 - 20th Century Fox) Nancy Kelly, Edmund Gwenn, John Loder
One Sheet: $40 - $75

SCOTLAND YARD COMMANDS
(1937 - Grand National) Clive Brook, Vera Hopper
One Sheet: $75 - $150

SCOTLAND YARD DRAGNET
(1956 - Republic) Roland Dulver, Patricia Roc
One Sheet: $15 - $25

SCOTLAND YARD INSPECTOR
(1952 - Lippert) Cesar Romero, Lois Maxwell
One Sheet: $15 - $35

SCOTLAND YARD INVESTIGATOR
(1945 - Republic) C. Aubrey Smith, Erich von Stroheim
One Sheet: $40 - $75

SCOTT OF THE ANTARCTIC
(1949 - Eagle-Lion) John Mills, Derek Bond
One Sheet: $10 - $20

SCOUNDREL, THE
(1935 - Paramount) Noel Coward, Julie Haydon
One Sheet: $800 - $1,500   *Coward's first lead role.*

Mini Window Card

SCOUT, THE
(1994 - 20th Century Fox) Albert Brooks, Brendan Fraser, Dianne Wiest
One Sheet: $7 - $15   *Sports (Baseball). Sports Movie Posters #87.*

SCOUTS TO THE RESCUE
(1939 - Universal) Jackie Cooper, Vondell Darr
One Sheet: $100 - $200   *Serial. 12 Chapters.*

SCRAM

(1932 - MGM) Laurel & Hardy
One Sheet: $2,500 - $4,000

SCRAMBLED BRAINS
(1951 - Columbia) The Three Stooges (Shemp)
One Sheet: $200 - $400   *Comedy short. Duotone.*

SCRAMBLED WIVES
(1921 - First National) Marguerite Clark
One Sheet: $250 - $500

SCRAP FOR VICTORY
(1942 - 20th Century Fox) Terry-toons
One Sheet: $200 - $400   *Cartoon. Full color stock poster with inset title. Large image of Supermouse and Gandy Goose.*

SCRAPPY STOCK POSTER
(1933 - Columbia) Scrappy
One Sheet: $2,200 - $3,500   *Cartoon. Cartoon Movie Posters #33, #34.*

SCRATCH HARRY
(1969 - Cannon) Harry Walker Staff, Victoria Wilde, Christine Kelly
One Sheet: $3 - $5

SCREAM
(1996 - Miramax) Drew Barrymore, Neve Campbell
One Sheet: $5 - $10

One Sheet

SCREAM AND SCREAM AGAIN
(1970 - AIP) Vincent Price, Christopher Lee, Peter Cushing
One Sheet: $15 - $25

SCREAM, BLACULA, SCREAM!
(1973 - AIP) William Marshall, Don Mitchell
One Sheet: $30 - $50   *Blaxploitation.*

SCREAM IN THE DARK, A
(1943 - Republic) Robert Lowery, Marie McDonald
One Sheet: $125 - $250

SCREAM IN THE NIGHT
(1943 - Astor) Lon Chaney Jr., Zara Tasil
One Sheet: $100 - $200   *Originally filmed in 1935, released in 1943.*

SCREAM OF FEAR
(1961 - Columbia) Susan Strasberg, Christopher Lee
One Sheet: $15 - $25   *Graven Images, pg. 205.*

SCREAMERS
(1996 - Triumph) Peter Weller, Jennifer Rubin
One Sheet: $5 - $10

SCREAMING EAGLES
(1956 - Allied Artists) Tom Tryon, Jan Merlin
One Sheet: $15 - $25

SCREAMING MIMI, THE
(1958 - Columbia) Anita Ekberg, Phil Carey
One Sheet: $40 - $75

SCREAMING SKULL, THE
(1958 - AIP) Alex Nicol, John Hudson
One Sheet: $50 - $100

SCREAMING SKULL, THE/TERROR FROM THE YEAR 5,000
(1958 - AIP) Alex Nicol, Joyce Holden
One Sheet: $30 - $50   *Double feature poster.*

SCREEN SONG
(1949 - Paramount) -
One Sheet: $800 - $1,500   *Cartoon.*

SCREWY TRUANT, THE
(1945 - MGM) Screwy Squirrel, Dir: Tex Avery
One Sheet: $250 - $600   *Cartoon.*
Cartoon Movie Posters #293.

SCROOGE
(1935 - Paramount) Sir Seymour Hicks,
Maurice Evans
One Sheet: $125 - $250

Mini Window Card (Trimmed)

SCROOGE
(1970 - National General) Albert Finney, Alec
Guinness
One Sheet: $5 - $10

SCROOGED
(1988 - Paramount) Bill Murray, Karen Allen
One Sheet: $3 - $5

SCUDDA HOO! SCUDDA HAY!
(1948 - 20th Century Fox) June Haver, Lon
McAllister
One Sheet: $40 - $75

SEA AROUND US, THE
(1953 - -) Narrated by Dan Forbes
One Sheet: $10 - $20   *Documentary.*

SEA BAT, THE
(1930 - MGM) Charles Bickford, Nils Asther
One Sheet: $150 - $300

SEA BEAST, THE
(1926 - Warner Bros.) John Barrymore, Dolores
Costello
One Sheet: $1,600 - $2,500

SEA CHASE, THE
(1955 - RKO) John Wayne, Lana Turner
One Sheet: $75 - $150

SEA DEVILS
(1931 - Continental) Walter Long, Edmund
Burns
One Sheet: $75 - $150

SEA DEVILS
(1937 - RKO) Victor McLaglen, Preston Foster
One Sheet: $50 - $100

SEA DEVILS
(1952 - RKO) Yvonne De Carlo, Rock Hudson
One Sheet: $15 - $25

SEA FEAST, THE
(193? - -) -
One Sheet: $150 - $300

SEA FURY
(1959 - Rank) Stanley Baker, Victor McLaglen
One Sheet: $75 - $150

SEA GOD, THE
(1930 - Paramount Publix) Richard Arleng, Fay
Wray
One Sheet: $250 - $500

SEA GULL, THE
(1968 - Warner Bros.) James Mason, Simone
Signoret, Vanessa Redgrave
One Sheet: $10 - $20

SEA HAWK, THE
(1924 - -) Milton Sills, Enid Bennett
One Sheet: $150 - $300

SEA HAWK, THE
(1940 - Warner Bros.) Errol Flynn, Brenda
Marshall
One Sheet: $2,500 - $4,000

SEA HAWK, THE
(1947R - Warner Bros.) Errol Flynn
One Sheet: $200 - $400   *Re-release.*

SEA HAWK, THE
(1956R - Warner Bros.) Erroll Flynn, Brenda
Marshall
One Sheet: $50 - $100   *Re-release.*

SEA HORNET, THE
(1951 - Republic) Rod Cameron, Adele Mara
One Sheet: $10 - $20

SEA HOUND, THE
(1947 - Columbia) Buster Crabbe, Jimmy Lloyd
One Sheet: $50 - $100   *Serial. 15
Chapters.*

SEA LEGS
(1930 - Paramount Publix) Jack Oakie, Lillian
Roth
One Sheet: $125 - $250

SEA OF GRASS, THE
(1946 - MGM) Spencer Tracy, Katharine
Hepburn
One Sheet: $150 - $300

SEA OF LOST SHIPS
(1953 - Republic) John Derek, Wanda Hendrix
One Sheet: $10 - $20

SEA OF LOVE
(1988 - Universal) Al Pacino, Ellen Barkin
One Sheet: $7 - $15

SEA PIRATE, THE
(1967 - Paramount) Antonella Lualdi, Terence
Morgan
One Sheet: $3 - $5

SEA RACKETEERS
(1937 - Republic) Weldon Heyburn, Jeanne
Madden
One Sheet: $40 - $75

SEA RAIDERS
(1941 - Universal) Billy Halop, Huntz Hall
One Sheet: $50 - $100   *Serial. 12
Chapters.*

SEA SALTS
(1949 - RKO/Disney) Donald Duck
One Sheet: $800 - $1,500   *Cartoon.*
Cartoon Movie Posters #179.

SEA SCOUTS
(1937 - Disney) Donald Duck
One Sheet: $5,000 - $7,500   *Cartoon.*
Cartoon Movie Posters #154.

SEA SPOILERS
(1936 - Universal) John Wayne, Nan Grey
One Sheet: $700 - $1,200

SEA SQUAWK, THE
(1924 - Pathe) Harry Langdon
One Sheet: $800 - $1,500

SEA TIGER
(1952 - Monogram) John Archer, Marguerite
Chapman
One Sheet: $7 - $15

SEA WIFE
(1957 - 20th Century Fox) Richard Burton,
Joan Collins
One Sheet: $15 - $30

SEA WOLF, THE
(1930 - Fox) Milton Sills, Jane Keith
One Sheet: $250 - $500

SEA WOLF, THE
(1941 - Warner Bros.) Edward G. Robinson,
John Garfield
One Sheet: $100 - $200

One Sheet

SEALED CARGO
(1951 - RKO) Dana Andrews, Claude Rains
One Sheet: $30 - $50

SEALED HEARTS
(1919 - Selznick) Eugene O'Brien
One Sheet: $125 - $250

SEALED LIPS
(1941 - Universal) William Gargan, June Clyde
One Sheet: $30 - $50

SEALED VERDICT
(1948 - Paramount) Ray Milland, Florence
Marly
One Sheet: $20 - $40

SEANCE ON A WET AFTERNOON
(1964 - Artixo) Kim Stanley, Richard
Attenborough
One Sheet: $15 - $35

SEARCH, THE
(1948 - MGM) Montgomery Clift, Aline
MacMahon
One Sheet: $30 - $50

SEARCH AND DESTROY
(1981 - -) Perry King, Don Stroud
One Sheet: $5 - $10

SEARCH FOR BEAUTY
(1934 - Paramount) Ida Lupino, Larry "Buster"
Crabbe
One Sheet: $500 - $900

SEARCH FOR BRIDEY MURPHY, THE
(1956 - Paramount) Louis Hayward, Teresa
Wright
One Sheet: $15 - $25

SEARCH FOR DANGER
(1949 - Film Classics) John Calvert, Albert
Dekker
One Sheet: $15 - $25

SEARCH FOR PARADISE
(1957 - Cinerama) -
One Sheet: $10 - $20

SEARCHERS, THE
(1956 - Warner Bros.) John Wayne, Jeffrey
Hunter, Natalie Wood
One Sheet: $600 - $1,000   *Cowboy
Movie Posters #303.*

SEARCHING FOR BOBBY FISHER
(1993 - Paramount) Ben Kingsley, Larry
Fishburne
One Sheet: $7 - $15

SEARCHING WIND, THE
(1946 - -) Robert Young, Sylvia Sidney
One Sheet: $30 - $60

SEAS BENEATH
(1931 - Fox) George O'Brien, Marion Lessing
One Sheet: $125 - $250

SEASON OF PASSION
(1961 - United Artists) Ernest Borgnine, Anne
Baxter
One Sheet: $15 - $25

SEBASTIAN
(1968 - Paramount) Dirk Bogarde, Susannah
York
One Sheet: $5 - $10

SECOND 100 YEARS, THE
(1927 - MGM) Laurel & Hardy
One Sheet: $3,500 - $5,000

SECOND BEST
(1994 - Warner Bros.) William Hurt, Chris
Cleary Miles
One Sheet: $5 - $10

**SECOND BEST SECRET AGENT IN THE WHOLE
WIDE WORLD, THE**
(1965 - Embassy) Tom Adams, Veronica Hurst
One Sheet: $5 - $10

SECOND CHANCE
(1947 - 20th Century Fox) Kent Taylor, Louise
Currie
One Sheet: $15 - $25

SECOND CHANCE
(1953 - RKO) Robert Mitchum, Linda Darnell,
Jack Palance
One Sheet: $50 - $100   *Filmed in 3-D.*

SECOND CHORUS
(1941 - Paramount) Fred Astaire, Paulette
Goddard
One Sheet: $200 - $400

SECOND FACE, THE
(1950 - Eagle Lion Classics) Ella Raines, Bruce
Bennett
One Sheet: $15 - $30

SECOND FIDDLE
(1923 - Hodkinson) Mary Astor, Glenn Hunter
One Sheet: $250 - $500

SECOND FIDDLE
(1939 - 20th Century Fox) Sonja Henie, Tyrone
Power
One Sheet: $200 - $400

SECOND FIDDLE TO A STEEL GUITAR
(1965 - Marathon) Arnold Stang, Leo Gorcey,
Huntz Hall, Minnie Pearl
One Sheet: $40 - $75   *Country
musical.*

SECOND FLOOR MYSTERY, THE
(1930 - Warner Bros.) Grant Withers, Loretta
Young
One Sheet: $250 - $600

SECOND GREATEST SEX, THE
(1955 - Universal) Jeanne Crain, George
Nader, Mamie van Doren
One Sheet: $30 - $50

SECOND HAND WIFE
(1932 - Fox) Sally Eilers, Ralph Bellamy
One Sheet: $100 - $200

SECOND HONEYMOON
(1930 - Rayart) Josephine Dunn, Edward Earle
One Sheet: $100 - $200

SECOND HONEYMOON
(1937 - 20th Century Fox) Tyrone Power,
Loretta Young
One Sheet: $250 - $500

SECOND SIGHT
(1989 - Warner Bros.) John Larroquette,
Bronson Pinochot, Bess Armstrong
One Sheet: $3 - $5

SECOND TIME AROUND, THE
(1961 - 20th Century Fox) Debbie Reynolds,
Steve Forrest, Andy Griffith
One Sheet: $15 - $30

SECOND WIFE
(1930 - RKO) Conrad Nagel, Lila Lee
One Sheet: $100 - $200

SECOND WIFE
(1936 - RKO) Gertrude Michael, Walter Abel
One Sheet: $75 - $150

SECOND WIND
(1976 - Olympic/Ambassador) James
Naughton, Lindsay Wagner
One Sheet: $3 - $5

SECOND WOMAN, THE
(1950 - United Artists) Robert Young, Betsy
Drake
One Sheet: $15 - $25

SECONDS
(1966 - Paramount) Rock Hudson, Salome
Jens
One Sheet: $30 - $50

SECRET 4, THE
(1940 - Monogram) H. Sinclair, F. Lawton, A.
Lee

One Sheet: $40 - $75

SECRET 7, THE
(1966 - MGM) Tony Russell, Helga Line
One Sheet: $5 - $10

SECRET ADMIRER
(1985 - Orion) C. Thomas Howell, Lori Laughlin
One Sheet: $2 - $3

SECRET AGENT
(1936 - Gaumont) Peter Lorre, Robert Young,
Dir: Alfred Hitchcock
One Sheet: $2,500 - $4,000

Half Sheet

SECRET AGENT
(1965 - AIP) Richard Harrison, Dominique
Boschero
One Sheet: $10 - $20

SECRET AGENT
(1966 - United Screen Arts) Ray Danton,
Marisa Mell
One Sheet: $10 - $20

SECRET AGENT FIREBALL
(1966 - AIP) Richard Harrison
One Sheet: $7 - $15

SECRET AGENT OF JAPAN
(1942 - 20th Century Fox) Lynn Bari, Preston
Foster
One Sheet: $30 - $50

SECRET AGENT X-9
(1937 - Universal) Scott Kolk,, Jean Rogers
One Sheet: $600 - $1,000   Serial. 12
Chapters.

SECRET AGENT X-9
(1945 - Universal) Lloyd Bridges, Keye Luke
One Sheet: $150 - $350   Serial. 13
Chapters.

SECRET BEYOND THE DOOR
(1948 - Universal International) Joan Bennett,
Michael Redgrave
One Sheet: $30 - $50

SECRET BRIDE, THE
(1934 - Warner Bros.) Barbara Stanwyck,
Warren William
One Sheet: $600 - $1,000

One Sheet

SECRET CALL, THE
(1931 - Paramount Publix) Richard Arlen,
Peggy Shannon
One Sheet: $100 - $200

SECRET CEREMONY
(1969 - Universal) Elizabeth Taylor, Mia
Farrow, Robert Mitchum
One Sheet: $15 - $25

SECRET CODE, THE

(1942 - Columbia) Paul Kelly, Anne Nagel
One Sheet: $150 - $300   Serial. 15
Chapters.

SECRET CODE, THE
(1953R - Columbia) Paul Kelly, Anne Nagel
One Sheet: $30 - $50   Re-release.
Serial. 15 Chapters.

SECRET COMMAND
(1944 - Columbia) Pat O'Brien, Carole Landis
One Sheet: $40 - $75

SECRET DOOR, THE
(1963 - Allied Artists) Robert Hutton, Sandra
Dorne
One Sheet: $5 - $10

SECRET ENEMIES
(1942 - Warner Bros.) Craig Stevens, Faye
Emerson
One Sheet: $20 - $40

SECRET EVIDENCE
(1941 - PRC) Marjorie Reynolds, Charles
Quigley
One Sheet: $20 - $40

SECRET FILE: HOLLYWOOD
(1962 - Crown International) Robert Clarke,
Francine York
One Sheet: $15 - $25   AKA:
SECRET FILE OF HOLLYWOOD.

SECRET FURY, THE
(1950 - RKO) Claudette Colbert, Robert Ryan
One Sheet: $15 - $35

SECRET GARDEN, THE
(1949 - MGM) Margaret O'Brien, Dean
Stockwell
One Sheet: $30 - $50

SECRET GARDEN, THE
(1993 - Warner Bros.) Kate Maberry, Heydon
Prowse
One Sheet: $3 - $5

SECRET HEART, THE
(1946 - MGM) Claudette Colbert, Walter
Pidgeon
One Sheet: $30 - $50

SECRET HOUR, THE
(1928 - Paramount) Pola Negri, Jean Hersholt
One Sheet: $250 - $500

SECRET INVASION, THE
(1964 - United Artists) Stewart Granger, Raf
Vallone
One Sheet: $15 - $30   Directed by
Roger Corman.

SECRET LAND, THE
(1948 - MGM) Robert Montgomery, Robert
Taylor
One Sheet: $30 - $50

SECRET LIFE OF AN AMERICAN WIFE, THE
(1968 - 20th Century Fox) Walter Matthau,
Anne Jackson
One Sheet: $10 - $20

SECRET LIFE OF WALTER MITTY, THE
(1947 - Samuel Goldwyn) Danny Kaye, Virginia
Mayo, Boris Karloff
One Sheet: $75 - $150

SECRET MISSION
(1945 - Excelsior) Hugh Williams, Carla
Lehmann
One Sheet: $15 - $35

SECRET OF BLOOD ISLAND
(1965 - Universal) Jack Hedley, Barbara
Shelley
One Sheet: $15 - $35

SECRET OF CONVICT LAKE, THE
(1951 - 20th Century Fox) Ethel Barrymore,
Glenn Ford, Gene Tierney
One Sheet: $20 - $40

SECRET OF DR. KILDARE, THE
(1939 - MGM) Lionel Barrymore, Lew Ayres,
Laraine Day
One Sheet: $50 - $100

SECRET OF MADAME BLANCHE, THE
(1933 - MGM) Irene Dunne, Lionel Atwill
One Sheet: $150 - $300

SECRET OF MAGIC ISLAND
(1965 - Embassy) Narrated by Phil Tonkin

One Sheet: $3 - $5

SECRET OF MONTE CRISTO, THE
(1961 - MGM) Rory Calhoun, Patricia Bredin
One Sheet: $5 - $10

SECRET OF MY SUCCESS, THE
(1965 - MGM) Shirley Jones, Stella Stevens
One Sheet: $20 - $40   Frazetta art.

SECRET OF MY SUCCESS, THE
(1987 - Universal) Michael J. Fox, Helen Slater
One Sheet: $7 - $15

SECRET OF NIMH, THE
(1982 - Aurora) Voices of Elizabeth Hartman,
Derek Jacobi
One Sheet: $7 - $15   Cartoon.

SECRET OF OUTLAW FLATS
(1953 - Allied Artists) Guy Madison, Andy
Devine
One Sheet: $15 - $35   Wild Bill
Hickok series.

SECRET OF ROAN INISH, THE
(1995 - First Look) Jeni Courtney, Mick Lally,
Eileen Colgan
One Sheet: $5 - $10

SECRET OF SANTA VITTORIA, THE
(1969 - United Artists) Anthony Quinn, Anna
Magnani, Virna Lisi
One Sheet: $7 - $15

SECRET OF ST. IVES, THE
(1949 - Columbia) Richard Ney, Vanessa
Brown
One Sheet: $15 - $25

SECRET OF THE BLUE ROOM
(1934 - Universal) Lionel Atwill, Gloria Stuart
One Sheet: $250 - $500   Graven
Images, pg. 66.

SECRET OF THE CHATEAU
(1934 - Universal) Jack LaRue, Claire Dodd
One Sheet: $200 - $400

SECRET OF THE INCAS
(1954 - Paramount) Charlton Heston, Nicole
Maurey
One Sheet: $30 - $50

SECRET OF THE PURPLE REEF, THE
(1960 - 20th Century Fox) Jeff Richards,
Margia Dean
One Sheet: $7 - $15

SECRET OF THE STORM COUNTRY, THE
(1917 - -) Norma Talmadge, Herbert Frank
One Sheet: $300 - $700

SECRET OF THE WASTELANDS
(1941 - Paramount) Bill Boyd, Andy Clyde
One Sheet: $75 - $150   Hopalong
Cassidy series.

SECRET OF THE WHISTLER
(1946 - Columbia) Richard Dix, Leslie Brooks,
Mary Currier
One Sheet: $50 - $100

SECRET OF TREASURE ISLAND, THE
(1938 - Columbia) Don Terry, Gwen Gaze
One Sheet: $250 - $500   Serial. 15
Chapters.

SECRET OF TREASURE MOUNTAIN
(1956 - Columbia) Raymond Burr, William
Prince
One Sheet: $15 - $30

SECRET PARTNER, THE
(1961 - MGM) Stewart Granger, Haya Harareet
One Sheet: $15 - $25

SECRET PASSION, THE
(1962 - Universal) Montgomery Clift, Susannah
York
One Sheet: $10 - $20   AKA: FREUD.

SECRET PATROL
(1936 - Columbia) Charles Starrett, Henry
Mollison
One Sheet: $75 - $150

SECRET PEOPLE, THE
(1951 - Lippert) Valentina Cortese, Audrey
Hepburn
One Sheet: $100 - $200

SECRET PLACE, THE
(1958 - Rank) Belinda Lee, Ronald Lewis

One Sheet: $7 - $15

SECRET POLICEMAN'S OTHER BALL, THE
(1982 - -) John Cleese, Peter Cook, Michael
Palin, Sting
One Sheet: $15 - $30   Rock 'n' Roll
concert film.

SECRET SERVICE
(1931 - RKO) Richard Dix, Shirley Grey
One Sheet: $125 - $250

SECRET SERVICE IN DARKEST AFRICA
(1943 - Republic) Rod Cameron, Joan Marsh
One Sheet: $75 - $150   Serial. 10
Chapters.

SECRET SERVICE INVESTIGATOR
(1948 - Republic) Lynne Roberts, Lloyd Bridges
One Sheet: $15 - $35

SECRET SERVICE OF THE AIR
(1939 - Warner Bros.) Ronald Reagan, John
Litel
One Sheet: $200 - $400

SECRET SEVEN, THE
(1940 - Columbia) Bruce Bennett, Florence
Rice
One Sheet: $30 - $50

SECRET SIN, THE
(1915 - Paramount) Blanche Sweet
One Sheet: $250 - $500

SECRET SINNERS
(1933 - Mayfair) Jack Mulhall, Sue Carol
One Sheet: $75 - $175

SECRET SIX, THE
(1931 - MGM) Wallace Beery, Jean Harlow,
Clark Gable
One Sheet: $1,600 - $2,500   Price
assumes Harlow and Gable are pictured.

SECRET VALLEY
(1937 - Principal) Richard Arlen, Virginia Grey
One Sheet: $50 - $100

SECRET VENTURE
(1954 - Republic) Kent Taylor, Jane Hylton
One Sheet: $10 - $20

SECRET WAR OF HARRY FRIGG, THE
(1968 - Universal) Paul Newman, Sylva
Koscina
One Sheet: $7 - $15

SECRET WAYS, THE
(1961 - Universal) Richard Widmark, Sonja
Ziemann
One Sheet: $10 - $20

SECRET WITNESS, THE
(1931 - Columbia) Una Merkel, William Collier,
Jr.
One Sheet: $350 - $750

SECRET WORLD
(1969 - 20th Century Fox) Jacqueline Bisset,
Jean-Francois Maurin
One Sheet: $7 - $15

SECRETARY, THE
(1971 - United Film) Josh Gamble, Angela Gale
One Sheet: $5 - $10

SECRETS
(1924 - -) Norma Talmadge, Eugene O'Brien
One Sheet: $300 - $700

SECRETS
(1933 - United Artists) Mary Pickford, Leslie
Howard
One Sheet: $125 - $250

One Sheet

SECRETS OF A BEAUTY PARLOR
(1918 - Mack Sennett) Hugh Fay, Bobby Dunn
One Sheet: $250 - $500

SECRETS OF A CO-ED
(1943 - PRC) Otto Kruger, Tina Thayer
One Sheet: $30 - $50

SECRETS OF A MODEL
(1939 - Continental) Sharon Lee, Harold
Daniels
One Sheet: $100 - $200   *Sexploitation.*

SECRETS OF A NURSE
(1938 - Universal) Edmund Lowe, Helen Mack
One Sheet: $50 - $100

SECRETS OF A SECRETARY
(1931 - Paramount Publix) Claudette Colbert,
Herbert Marshall
One Sheet: $150 - $350

SECRETS OF A SORORITY GIRL
(1946 - PRC) Mary Ware, Rick Vallin
One Sheet: $30 - $50

SECRETS OF A SOUL
(1926 - -) Lily Damita, Werner Krass
One Sheet: $500 - $800

SECRETS OF AN ACTRESS
(1938 - Warner Bros.) Kay Francis, George
Brent
One Sheet: $150 - $350

SECRETS OF LIFE
(1956 - Buena Vista/Disney) True-life
adventure, narrated by Winston Hibler
One Sheet: $15 - $35

SECRETS OF MONTE CARLO
(1951 - Republic) Warren Douglas, Lois Hall
One Sheet: $15 - $25

SECRETS OF MONTE CARLO
(1961 - MGM) Rory Calhoun
One Sheet: $10 - $20

SECRETS OF SCOTLAND YARD
(1944 - Republic) Edgar Barrier, C. Aubrey
Smith, Lionel Atwill
One Sheet: $30 - $50

SECRETS OF THE FRENCH POLICE
(1932 - RKO) Gwilli Andre, Frank Morgan
One Sheet: $100 - $200   *Graven
Images, pg. 64.*

SECRETS OF THE LONE WOLF
(1941 - Columbia) Warren William, Ruth Ford
One Sheet: $50 - $100

SECRETS OF THE UNDERGROUND
(1942 - Republic) John Hubbard, Virginia Grey
One Sheet: $15 - $30

SECRETS OF WU SIN, THE
(1933 - Chesterfield) Lois Wilson, Grant
Withers
One Sheet: $100 - $200

SECT, THE
(1991 - -) Dir: Dario Argento
One Sheet: $7 - $15

SECURITY RISK
(1954 - Allied Artists) John Ireland, Dorothy
Malone
One Sheet: $15 - $30

SEDUCTION, THE
(1982 - -) Morgan Fairchild, Michael Sarrazin
One Sheet: $5 - $10

SEDUCTION OF JOE TYNAN, THE
(1979 - Universal) Alan Alda, Barbara Harris,
Meryl Streep
One Sheet: $3 - $5

SEE AMERICA THIRST
(1930 - Universal) Harold Langdon, George
"Slim" Summerville
One Sheet: $250 - $600

SEE HERE, PRIVATE HARGROVE
(1944 - MGM) Robert Walker, Donna Reed
One Sheet: $30 - $50

SEE MY LAWYER
(1921 - -) T. Roy Barnes, Grace Darmond
One Sheet: $150 - $300

SEE MY LAWYER

(1944 - Universal) Ole Olsen, Chic Johnson,
Grace McDonald
One Sheet: $40 - $75

SEE NO EVIL
(1971 - Columbia) Mia Farrow, Dorothy Alison
One Sheet: $5 - $10

SEE NO EVIL, HEAR NO EVIL
(1989 - -) Richard Pryor, Gene Wilder
One Sheet: $5 - $10

SEE YOU IN THE MORNING
(1989 - Warner Bros.) Jeff Bridges, Alice Krige
One Sheet: $3 - $5

SEED
(1931 - Universal) John Boles, Genevieve
Tolbin, Bette Davis (cameo)
One Sheet: $250 - $500

SEEMS LIKE OLD TIMES
(1980 - Columbia) Goldie Hawn, Chevy Chase
One Sheet: $5 - $10

SEIZURE
(1974 - AIP) Jonathan Frid, Martine Beswick,
Herve Villechaize
One Sheet: $5 - $10

SELENA
(1997 - Warner Bros.) Jennifer Lopez, Edward
James Olmos
One Sheet: $3 - $5

SELF-DEFENSE
(1933 - Monogram) -
One Sheet: $75 - $125

SELFISH YATES
(1919 - -) William S. Hart
One Sheet: $1,300 - $2,000

SELF-MADE MAIDS
(1950 - Columbia) The Three Stooges (Shemp)
One Sheet: $200 - $400   *Comedy short.
Duotone.*

SELF-MADE MAN, THE
(1922 - -) William Russell
One Sheet: $200 - $400

SELLOUT, THE
(1951 - MGM) Walter Pidgeon, Audrey Totter
One Sheet: $15 - $30

SELLS-FLOTO CIRCUS PRESENTS TOM MIX
(1931 - -) Tom Mix
One Sheet: $500 - $800   *Promo poster.*

SEMINOLE
(1953 - Universal) Rock Hudson, Barbara Hale
One Sheet: $20 - $40

SEMINOLE UPRISING
(1955 - Columbia) George Montgomery, Karin
Booth
One Sheet: $15 - $30

SEMI-TOUGH
(1977 - United Artists) Burt Reynolds, Kris
Kristofferson
One Sheet: $10 - $20   *Sports
(Football). Sports Movie Posters #s 206, 207, 208.*

One Sheet

SEMURG THE MAGIC BIRD
(196? - -) Tamara Kokova, Tamara Shahirova
One Sheet: $15 - $25

SENATOR WAS INDISCREET, THE
(1948 - Universal-International) William Powell,
Ella Raines
One Sheet: $40 - $75

SEND ME NO FLOWERS
(1964 - Universal) Rock Hudson, Doris Day
One Sheet: $30 - $50

SENDER, THE
(1982 - -) Kathryn Harrold, Zeliko Ivanek
One Sheet: $3 - $5

SENECHAL THE MAGNIFICENT
(1958 - DCA) Fernandel, Nadia Gray
One Sheet: $7 - $15

SENIOR PROM
(1958 - Columbia) Jill Corey, Paul Hampton
One Sheet: $15 - $30

SENOR DAREDEVIL
(1926 - First National) Ken Maynard, Dorothy
Devore
One Sheet: $500 - $800

SENOR DROOPY
(1948 - MGM) Tex Avery
One Sheet: $800 - $1,500   *Cartoon.
Cartoon Movie Posters #306.*

SENORITA FROM THE WEST
(1945 - Universal) Allan Jones, Bonita Granville
One Sheet: $20 - $40

SENSATION HUNTERS
(1933 - Monogram) Arline Judge, Preston
Foster
One Sheet: $75 - $150

SENSATION HUNTERS
(1945 - Monogram) Doris Merrick, Robert
Lowery
One Sheet: $20 - $40

SENSATIONS OF 1945
(1944 - United Artists) Dennis O'Keefe, Eleanor
Powell, W. C. Fields (his last film)
One Sheet: $150 - $300   *Cab Calloway
and Orch. featured on one lobby card.*

SENSE AND SENSIBILITY
(1995 - Columbia) Emma Thompson, Kate
Winslet, Hugh Grant
One Sheet: $10 - $20

SENSE OF LOSS, A
(1972 - Cinema 5) -
One Sheet: $3 - $5

SENSUOUS NURSE, THE
(1978 - Mid Broadway) Ursula Andress, Jack
Palance
One Sheet: $15 - $25   *Italian.*

SENTIMENTAL JOURNEY
(1946 - 20th Century Fox) John Payne,
Maureen O'Hara
One Sheet: $100 - $200

SENTINEL, THE
(1977 - Universal) Chris Sarandon, Cristina
Raines
One Sheet: $3 - $5

SEPARATE PEACE, A
(1972 - Paramount) John Heyl, Parker
Stevenson
One Sheet: $5 - $10

SEPARATE TABLES
(1958 - United Artists) David Niven, Deborah
Kerr, Rita Hayworth, Burt Lancaster
One Sheet: $30 - $60   *Academy
Award: Best Actor(Niven). Academy Award Movie
Posters #182 & #185.*

SEPIA CINDERELLA
(1947 - Herald) Billy Daniels, Sheila Guyse
One Sheet: $150 - $300   *Black cast.*

SEPTEMBER
(1987 - Orion) Denholm Elliott, Mia Farrow
One Sheet: $5 - $10

SEPTEMBER 30, 1955
(1977 - Universal) Richard Thomas, Susan
Tyrell
One Sheet: $5 - $10

SEPTEMBER AFFAIR
(1951 - Paramount) Joan Fontaine, Joseph
Cotten
One Sheet: $20 - $40

SEPTEMBER STORM
(1960 - 20th Century Fox) Joanne Dru, Mark
Stevens
One Sheet: $15 - $25   *Filmed in 3-D*

CinemaScope.

SEQUOIA
(1935 - MGM) Jean Parker, Russell Hardie
One Sheet: $75 - $150

SERENADE
(1927 - -) Adolphe Menjou, Kathryn Carver
One Sheet: $125 - $250

SERENADE
(1956 - Warner Bros.) Mario Lanza, Joan
Fontaine, Sarita Montiel
One Sheet: $20 - $40

SERENGETI
(1960 - Allied Artists) -
One Sheet: $15 - $25   *Documentary.
Academy Award: Best Documentary. Film about
Africa.*

SERGEANT, THE
(1969 - Warner Bros.) Rod Steiger, John Phillip
Law, Ludmila Mikael
One Sheet: $10 - $20

SERGEANT AND THE SPY
(1954 - Princess) -
One Sheet: $5 - $10

SERGEANT DEADHEAD
(1965 - AIP) Frankie Avalon, Deborah Walley
One Sheet: $15 - $30

SERGEANT MADDEN
(1939 - MGM) Wallace Beery, Laraine Day
One Sheet: $75 - $150

SERGEANT MIKE
(1944 - Columbia) Larry Parks, Jim Bannon
One Sheet: $15 - $35

SERGEANT MURPHY
(1937 - Warner Bros.) Ronald Reagan, Mary
Maguire
One Sheet: $100 - $200

SERGEANT RUTLEDGE
(1960 - Warner Bros.) Jeffrey Hunter, Woody
Strode
One Sheet: $15 - $25

SERGEANT RYKER
(1968 - Universal) Lee Marvin, Vera Miles
One Sheet: $10 - $20

SERGEANT WAS A LADY, THE
(1961 - Universal) Martin West, Venetia
Stevenson
One Sheet: $7 - $15

SERGEANT YORK
(1941 - Warner Bros.) Gary Cooper, Walter
Brennan
One Sheet: $250 - $500   *Academy
Award: Best Actor(Cooper). Duotone. Academy
Award Movie Posters #77.*

SERGEANT YORK
(1958R - Warner Bros.) Gary Cooper, Walter
Brennan
One Sheet: $30 - $60   *Re-release.*

SERGEANTS 3
(1962 - United Artists) Frank Sinatra, Dean
Martin, Sammy Davis, Jr.
One Sheet: $20 - $40

SERIAL
(1980 - Paramount) Tuesday Weld, Sally
Kellerman
One Sheet: $5 - $10

SERIAL MOM
(1994 - -) Kathleen Turner, Ricki Lake
One Sheet: $5 - $10

SERIE NOIRE
(1955 - Pathe) Sidney Bechet, Erich Von
Stroheim
One Sheet: $100 - $200   *French. Black
cast.*

SERPENT, THE
(1973 - Avco) Henry Fonda, Yul Brynner
One Sheet: $5 - $10

SERPENT AND THE RAINBOW, THE
(1988 - -) Bill Pullman, Cathy Tyson
One Sheet: $5 - $10

SERPENT OF THE NILE
(1953 - Columbia) Rhonda Fleming, William
Lundigan

One Sheet: $15 - $30

SERPENT'S EGG, THE
(1977 - Paramount) Liv Ullmann, David Carradine
One Sheet: $15 - $25

SERPENTS OF THE PIRATE MOON, THE
(1973 - Planfilm) Sylvia Morales, Sahdji
One Sheet: $10 - $20

SERPICO
(1974 - Paramount) Al Pacino, John Randolph
One Sheet: $15 - $25

SERVANT, THE
(1964 - Landau) Dirk Bogarde, James Fox
One Sheet: $5 - $10

SERVANT'S ENTRANCE
(1934 - Fox) Janet Gaynor, Lew Ayres
One Sheet: $75 - $150

SERVES YOU RIGHT
(1936 - Vitaphone) Shemp Howard, Nell O'Day
One Sheet: $150 - $300

SERVICE DE LUXE
(1938 - Universal) Constance Bennett, Charles Ruggles, Vincent Price
One Sheet: $150 - $300   *Price's film debut.*

SERVICE FOR LADIES
(1927 - -) Adolphe Menjou, Kathryn Carver
One Sheet: $150 - $350

SET IT OFF
(1996 - New Line) Jada Pinkett, Queen Latifah
One Sheet: $5 - $10

SET-UP, THE
(1949 - RKO) Robert Ryan, Audrey Totter
One Sheet: $50 - $100   *Sports (Boxing). Sports Movie Posters #149.*

SET-UP, THE
(1963 - Merton Park) Maurice Denham, John Carson
One Sheet: $7 - $15

SEVEN
(1979 - AIP) William Smith
One Sheet: $5 - $10

SEVEN ALONE
(1975 - Doty) Dewey Martin, Aldo Ray
One Sheet: $3 - $5

SEVEN ANGRY MEN
(1955 - Allied Artists) Raymond Massey, Debra Paget
One Sheet: $7 - $15

SEVEN BLOWS OF THE DRAGON
(1973 - New World) David Chang
One Sheet: $15 - $30

SEVEN BRIDES FOR SEVEN BROTHERS
(1954 - MGM) Jane Powell, Howard Keel
One Sheet: $75 - $125

SEVEN BRIDES FOR SEVEN BROTHERS
(1962R - MGM) Jane Powell, Howard Keel
One Sheet: $15 - $30   *Re-release.*

SEVEN BROTHERS MEET DRACULA, THE
(1973 - Shaw-Hammer) Peter Cushing, David Chaing, Julie Ege
One Sheet: $15 - $30

One Sheet

SEVEN CHANCES
(1925 - Metro Goldwyn) Buster Keaton
One Sheet: $6,500 - $10,000

SEVEN CITIES OF GOLD
(1955 - 20th Century Fox) Richard Egan, Michael Rennie, Jeffrey Hunter
One Sheet: $15 - $25

SEVEN DAYS ASHORE
(1944 - RKO) Wally Brown, Alan Carney, Virginia Mayo, Gordon Oliver
One Sheet: $30 - $50

SEVEN DAYS IN MAY
(1964 - Paramount) Burt Lancaster, Kirk Douglas, Fredric March, Ava Gardner
One Sheet: $15 - $35

SEVEN DAYS TO NOON
(1950 - London) Barry Jones, Andre Morrell
One Sheet: $10 - $20

SEVEN DAYS' LEAVE
(1930 - Paramount Famous Lasky) Gary Cooper, Beryl Mercer
One Sheet: $500 - $800

SEVEN DAYS' LEAVE
(1942 - RKO) Victor Mature, Lucille Ball
One Sheet: $100 - $200

SEVEN DOORS TO DEATH
(1944 - PRC) Chick Chandler, June Clyde
One Sheet: $20 - $40

SEVEN DWARFS TO THE RESCUE, THE
(1965 - Childhood) Rossana Podesta, Roberto Risso
One Sheet: $3 - $5

711 OCEAN DRIVE
(1950 - Columbia) Edmond O'Brien, Joanne Dru
One Sheet: $50 - $100

SEVEN FACES OF DR. LAO
(1964 - MGM) Tony Randall, Arthur O'Connell
One Sheet: $30 - $50   *Graven Images, pg. 220.*

SEVEN FOOTPRINTS TO SATAN
(1929 - First National) Thelma Todd, Creighton Hale
One Sheet: $2,500 - $4,000   *Graven Images, pg. 38.*

SEVEN GOLDEN MEN
(1969 - Warner Bros.) Rossana Podesta, Philippe Leroy, Gastone Moschin
One Sheet: $3 - $5

SEVEN GUNS TO MESA
(1958 - Allied Artists) Lola Albright, Charles Quinlivan
One Sheet: $7 - $15

SEVEN HILLS OF ROME, THE
(1957 - MGM) Mario Lanza, Peggie Castle
One Sheet: $15 - $30

SEVEN JOURNEYS
(1947 - Vogue) -
One Sheet: $30 - $50

SEVEN KEYS TO BALDPATE
(1930 - RKO) Richard Dix, Miriam Sezgar
One Sheet: $300 - $700

SEVEN KEYS TO BALDPATE
(1935 - RKO) Gene Raymond, Margaret Callahan, Eric Blore
One Sheet: $150 - $300

SEVEN KEYS TO BALDPATE
(1947 - RKO) Philip Terry, Jacqueline White
One Sheet: $40 - $75

SEVEN LITTLE FOYS, THE
(1954 - Paramount) Bob Hope, James Cagney
One Sheet: $40 - $75

SEVEN MEN FROM NOW
(1956 - Warner Bros.) Randolph Scott, Gail Russell, Lee Marvin
One Sheet: $30 - $50

SEVEN MILES FROM ALCATRAZ
(1943 - RKO) James Craig, Bonita Granville
One Sheet: $50 - $100

SEVEN MINUTES, THE
(1971 - 20th Century Fox) Wayne Maunder, Marianne McAndrew
One Sheet: $5 - $10

SEVEN PERCENT SOLUTION, THE

(1976 - Universal) Alan Arkin, Vanessa Redgrave
One Sheet: $3 - $5

SEVEN SAMURAI, THE
(1954 - Toho/Columbia) Toshiro Mifune, Takashi Shimura
One Sheet: $250 - $500   *Japanese. Kurosawa's classic "eastern western" on which THE MAGNIFICENT SEVEN was based. Japanese poster: $2000-$3000.*

SEVEN SEAS TO CALAIS
(1963 - MGM) Rod Taylor, Keith Mitchell
One Sheet: $10 - $20

SEVEN SINNERS
(1936 - Gaumont British) Edmund Lowe, Constance Cummings
One Sheet: $250 - $500

SEVEN SINNERS
(1940 - Universal) Marlene Dietrich, John Wayne
One Sheet: $300 - $700

SEVEN SINNERS
(1948R - Universal) Marlene Dietrich, John Wayne
One Sheet: $75 - $125   *Re-release.*

SEVEN SURPRISES
(1964 - Quartet International) Claude Jutra, Wallace Jensen
One Sheet: $3 - $5

SEVEN SWEETHEARTS
(1942 - MGM) Kathryn Grayson, Van Heflin
One Sheet: $30 - $50

SEVEN THIEVES
(1960 - 20th Century Fox) Edward G. Robinson, Rod Steiger
One Sheet: $15 - $25

SEVEN-UPS, THE
(1974 - 20th Century Fox) Roy Scheider, Tony Lobianco
One Sheet: $7 - $15

One Sheet

SEVEN WAYS FROM SUNDOWN
(1960 - Universal) Audie Murphy, Barry Sullivan
One Sheet: $15 - $35

SEVEN WERE SAVED
(1947 - Paramount) Richard Denning, Catherine Craig
One Sheet: $10 - $20

SEVEN WOMEN
(1966 - MGM) Anne Bancroft, Sue Lyon, Dir:John Ford (last film)
One Sheet: $15 - $35

SEVEN WOMEN FROM HELL
(1961 - 20th Century Fox) Patricia Owens, Denise Darcel
One Sheet: $10 - $20

SEVEN YEAR ITCH, THE
(1955 - 20th Century Fox) Marilyn Monroe, Tom Ewell, Dir: Billy Wilder
One Sheet: $800 - $1,500

SEVENTEEN
(1916 - Paramount) Louise Huff, Jack Pickford
One Sheet: $100 - $200

SEVENTEEN
(1940 - Paramount) Jackie Cooper, Betty Field
One Sheet: $30 - $50

SEVENTEEN

(1968 - -) Ole Soltoft, Ghita Norby
One Sheet: $5 - $10

1776
(1972 - Columbia) William Daniels, Howard Da Silva, Ken Howard
One Sheet: $5 - $10

7TH CAVALRY
(1956 - Columbia) Randolph Scott, Barbara Hale
One Sheet: $30 - $50

SEVENTH COIN, THE
(1993 - Hemdale) Peter O'Toole
One Sheet: $3 - $5

SEVENTH COMMANDMENT, THE
(1928 - Dwain Esper) -
One Sheet: $200 - $400

SEVENTH CROSS, THE
(1944 - MGM) Spencer Tracy, Signe Hasso
One Sheet: $50 - $100

7TH DAWN, THE
(1964 - United Artists) William Holden, Susannah York
One Sheet: $10 - $20

SEVENTH DAY, THE
(1922 - First National) Richard Barthelmess, Frank Losee
One Sheet: $200 - $400

SEVENTH HEAVEN
(1927 - Fox) Janet Gaynor, Charles Farrell
One Sheet: $800 - $1,500   *Academy Award: Best Actress, Best Direction(Frank Borzage). Academy Award Movie Posters #4 & #5.*

SEVENTH HEAVEN
(1937 - 20th Century Fox) Simone Simon, James Stewart
One Sheet: $600 - $1,000

SEVENTH SEAL, THE
(1957 - Svensk) Max von Sydow, Bibi Andersson
One Sheet: $1,600 - $2,500   *Swedish. Graven Images, pg. 198.*

SEVENTH SIGN, THE
(1988 - -) Demi Moore, Michael Biehn
One Sheet: $7 - $15

SEVENTH SIN, THE
(1957 - MGM) Eleanor Parker, Bill Travers
One Sheet: $15 - $25

SEVENTH VEIL, THE
(1946 - Universal) James Mason, Ann Todd
One Sheet: $20 - $40

SEVENTH VICTIM, THE
(1943 - RKO) Tom Conway, Kim Hunter, Dir:Val Lewton
One Sheet: $125 - $250   *Graven Images, pg. xiv, 124.*

SEVENTH VOYAGE OF SINBAD
(1958 - Columbia) Kerwyn Matthews, Kathryn Grant
One Sheet: $100 - $200   *Ray Harryhausen effects. Graven Images, pg. 183.*

SEVENTH VOYAGE OF SINBAD
(1975R - Columbia) Kerwyn Matthews, Kathryn Grant
One Sheet: $15 - $30   *Re-release.*

70,000 WITNESSES
(1932 - Paramount Publix) Philip Holmes, Dorothy Jordan
One Sheet: $200 - $400   *Sports (Football). Sports Movie Posters #183.*

SEVERED HEAD, A
(1971 - Columbia) Lee Remick, Richard Attenborough
One Sheet: $10 - $20

SEX
(1920 - Pathe) Louise Glaum, Peggy Pearce
One Sheet: $250 - $500

SEX AND THE SINGLE GIRL
(1965 - Warner Bros.) Tony Curtis, Natalie Wood
One Sheet: $15 - $25

SEX DRUGS ROCK AND ROLL
(1991 - Avenue) Eric Bogosian

One Sheet: $10 - $20

SEX KITTENS GO TO COLLEGE
(1960 - Allied Artists) Mamie Van Doren,
Tuesday Weld
One Sheet: $30 - $50

SEX, LIES, AND VIDEOTAPE
(1989 - Miramax) James Spader, Andie
MacDowell
One Sheet: $15 - $30

SEX OF ANGELS, THE
(1969 - Lopert) Rosemarie Dexter, Laura
Troschel
One Sheet: $7 - $15

SEXTETTE
(1978 - -) Mae West, Timothy Dalton, Alice
Cooper, Ringo Starr
One Sheet: $20 - $40   *West's final
film.*

SEXTON BLAKE AND THE HOODED TERROR
(1938 - MGM) George Curzon, Tod Slaughter
One Sheet: $50 - $100

SEZ O'REILLY TO MACNAB
(1937 - Gaumont) Will Fyffe, Will Mahoney
One Sheet: $40 - $75

S.F.W.
(1994 - Gramercy) Stephen Dorff, Reese
Witherspoon
One Sheet: $5 - $10

SGT. BILKO
(1996 - Universal) Steve Martin
One Sheet: $3 - $5

SGT. PEPPER'S LONELY HEARTS CLUB BAND
(1978 - Universal) Peter Frampton, BeeGees,
Steve Martin
One Sheet: $15 - $25   *Rock 'n' Roll.*

SH! THE OCTOPUS
(1937 - Warner Bros.) Hugh Herbert, Allen
Jenkins
One Sheet: $150 - $300   *Graven
Images, pg. 95.*

SHACK OUT ON 101
(1955 - Allied Artists) Terry Moore, Frank
Lovejoy
One Sheet: $30 - $50

SHACKLES OF GOLD
(1922 - Fox) William Farnum, Myrtyle Bonillas
One Sheet: $250 - $600

SHADOW, THE
(1937 - Columbia) Charles Quigley, Rita
Hayworth
One Sheet: $500 - $800   *First film with
Hayworth top-billed.*

SHADOW, THE
(1940 - Columbia) Victor Jory, Veda Ann Borg
One Sheet: $1,900 - $3,000   *Serial. 15
Chapters.*

SHADOW, THE
(1994 - Universal) Alec Baldwin, John Lone
One Sheet: $7 - $15

One Sheet

SHADOW BETWEEN, THE
(1932 - Powers) Godfrey Tearle, Kathleen
O'Regan
One Sheet: $75 - $150

SHADOW CONSPIRACY, THE
(1997 - Hollywood) Charlie Sheen, Linda
Hamilton
One Sheet: $4 - $8

SHADOW IN THE SKY
(1951 - MGM) Nancy Davis, James Whitmore
One Sheet: $20 - $40

SHADOW LAUGHS, THE
(1933 - Trojan) Hal Skelly, Rose Hobart
One Sheet: $500 - $800

SHADOW MAN, THE
(1953 - Lippert) Cesar Romero, Kay Kendall
One Sheet: $15 - $30

SHADOW OF A DOUBT
(1935 - MGM) Ricardo Cortez, Virginia Bruce
One Sheet: $100 - $200

SHADOW OF A DOUBT
(1942 - Universal) Teresa Wright, Joseph
Cotten, Dir: Hitchcock
One Sheet: $500 - $800

One Sheet

SHADOW OF A DOUBT
(1946R - Realart) Teresa Wright, Joseph
Cotten, Dir: Hitchcock
One Sheet: $100 - $200   *Re-release.*

SHADOW OF A DOUBT
(1950R - Realart) Teresa Wright, Joseph
Cotten, Dir: Hitchcock
One Sheet: $50 - $100   *Re-release.*

SHADOW OF A WOMAN
(1946 - Warner Bros.) Helmut Dantine, Andrea
King
One Sheet: $15 - $30

SHADOW OF CHINATOWN
(1936 - Victory) Bela Lugosi, Joan Barclay
One Sheet: $250 - $600   *Serial. 15
Chapters.*

SHADOW OF EVIL
(1966 - Seven Arts) Kerwin Matthews
One Sheet: $15 - $30

SHADOW OF FEAR
(1956 - United Artists) Mona Freeman, Jean
Kent
One Sheet: $15 - $30

SHADOW OF HER PAST
(1910 - -) Lina Cavalieri
One Sheet: $300 - $650

SHADOW OF SUSPICION
(1944 - Monogram) Marjorie Weaver, Peter
Cookson
One Sheet: $15 - $35

SHADOW OF TERROR
(1945 - PRC) Dick Fraser, Cy Kendall
One Sheet: $15 - $35

SHADOW OF THE CAT, THE
(1961 - Universal) Andre Morell, Barbara
Shelley
One Sheet: $30 - $50

SHADOW OF THE EAGLE, THE
(1932 - Mascot) John Wayne, Dorothy Gulliver
One Sheet: $1,300 - $2,000   *Serial.
Western.*

SHADOW OF THE EAGLE
(1955 - Valiant/UA) Richard Greene, Valentina
Cortesa
One Sheet: $10 - $20

SHADOW OF THE HAWK
(1976 - Columbia) Jan-Michael Vincent, Marilyn
Hassett
One Sheet: $5 - $10

SHADOW OF THE LAW
(1930 - Paramount Publix) William Powell,
Natalie Moorehead
One Sheet: $600 - $1,000

SHADOW OF THE THIN MAN
(1941 - MGM) William Powell, Myrna Loy
One Sheet: $250 - $500

One Sheet

SHADOW OF THE WOLF
(1993 - Vision International) Lou Diamond
Phillips, Toshiro Mifune
One Sheet: $3 - $5

SHADOW ON THE WALL
(1949 - MGM) Ann Sothern, Zachary Scott
One Sheet: $15 - $35

SHADOW ON THE WINDOW
(1956 - Columbia) Phil Carey, Betty Garrett
One Sheet: $7 - $15

SHADOW RANCH
(1930 - Columbia) Buck Jones, Marguerite De
La Motte
One Sheet: $1,900 - $3,000   *Cowboy
Movie Posters #'s 92, 95.*

SHADOW RETURNS, THE
(1946 - Monogram) Kane Richmond, Barbara
Reed
One Sheet: $75 - $150

SHADOW RIDERS
(1982 - -) Tom Selleck, Sam Elliott
One Sheet: $15 - $25   *Made for TV
western released theatrically.*

SHADOW STRIKES, THE
(1937 - Grand National) Rod La Rocque, Lynn
Anders
One Sheet: $150 - $300

One Sheet

SHADOW VALLEY
(1947 - PRC) Eddie Dean, Roscoe Ates
One Sheet: $15 - $35

SHADOWED
(1946 - Columbia) Anita Louise, Robert Scott
One Sheet: $15 - $30

SHADOWLANDS
(1993 - Savoy) Anthony Hopkins, Debra Winger
One Sheet: $5 - $10

SHADOWS
(1922 - Preferred) Lon Chaney, Margueritte De
La Motte
One Sheet: $1,300 - $2,000

SHADOWS
(1960 - Lion) Hugh Hurd, Lelia Goldini
One Sheet: $100 - $200   *John
Cassavetes' first film as director.*

SHADOWS AND FOG
(1992 - Orion) Woody Allen, Mia Farrow
One Sheet: $7 - $15

SHADOWS IN THE NIGHT
(1944 - Columbia) Nina Foch, Warner Baxter,
George Zucco
One Sheet: $30 - $50   *Crime Doctor
series.*

SHADOWS OF DEATH
(1945 - PRC) Buster Crabbe, Al St. John
One Sheet: $30 - $50

SHADOWS OF PARIS
(1924 - Paramount) Pola Negri
One Sheet: $350 - $750

SHADOWS OF SING SING
(1933 - Columbia) Mary Brian, Bruce Cabot
One Sheet: $150 - $300

SHADOWS OF THE NIGHT
(1928 - MGM) Lawrence Gray, Louise Lorraine,
Flash
One Sheet: $250 - $600

SHADOWS OF THE ORIENT
(1937 - Monogram) Regis Toomey, Esther
Ralston
One Sheet: $50 - $100

SHADOWS OF THE WEST
(1949 - Monogram) Whip Wilson, Andy Clyde
One Sheet: $30 - $50

SHADOWS OF TOMBSTONE
(1953 - Republic) Rex Allen
One Sheet: $20 - $40

SHADOWS ON THE RANGE
(1946 - Monogram) Johnny Mack Brown,
Raymond Hatton
One Sheet: $20 - $40

SHADOWS ON THE SAGE
(1942 - Republic) Three Mesquiteers (Tom
Tyler, Bob Steele, Ruse Davis)
One Sheet: $75 - $125

SHADOWS ON THE SNOW
(1949 - Warner Bros.) -
One Sheet: $10 - $20

SHADOWS ON THE STAIRS
(1941 - Warner Bros.) Freida Inescort, Paul
Cavanagh
One Sheet: $30 - $50

SHADOWS OVER CHINATOWN
(1946 - Monogram) Sidney Toler, Mantan
Moreland
One Sheet: $150 - $300   *Charlie Chan
series.*

SHADOWS OVER SHANGHAI
(1938 - Grand National) James Dunn, Ralph
Morgan
One Sheet: $50 - $100

SHADY LADY
(1945 - Universal) Ginny Simms, Charles
Coburn, Robert Paige
One Sheet: $30 - $60

SHAFT
(1971 - MGM) Richard Roundtree, Gwenn
Mitchell
One Sheet: $30 - $50   *Blaxploitation.*

One Sheet

SHAFT IN AFRICA
(1973 - MGM) Richard Roundtree, Frank Finlay
One Sheet: $15 - $25   *Blaxploitation.*

SHAFT'S BIG SCORE!
(1972 - MGM) Richard Roundtree, Moses Gunn
One Sheet: $15 - $30   *Blaxploitation.*

One Sheet

SHAG
(1989 - Hemdale) Phoebe Cates, Scott Coffey
One Sheet: $3 - $5

SHAGGY
(1948 - Paramount) George Nokes, Brenda
Joyce
One Sheet: $15 - $30

SHAGGY D.A., THE
(1976 - Disney/Buena Vista) Dean Jones,
Suzanne Pleshette
One Sheet: $7 - $15

SHAGGY D.A., THE
(1977R - Disney) Dean Jones, Suzanne
Pleshette
One Sheet: $5 - $10   *Re-release.*

SHAGGY DOG, THE
(1959 - Buena Vista/Disney) Fred MacMurray,
Jean Hagen
One Sheet: $30 - $50

SHAGGY DOG, THE
(1967R - Buena Vista/Disney) Fred MacMurray,
Jean Hagen
One Sheet: $7 - $15   *Re-release.*

SHAGGY DOG, THE
(1974R - Buena Vista/Disney) Fred MacMurray,
Jean Hagen
One Sheet: $5 - $10   *Re-release.*

SHAKE HANDS WITH MURDER
(1944 - PRC) Iris Adrian, Frank Jenks
One Sheet: $20 - $40

SHAKE HANDS WITH THE DEVIL
(1959 - United Artists) James Cagney, Don
Murray
One Sheet: $20 - $40

SHAKE, RATTLE AND ROCK
(1956 - AIP) Fats Domino, Lisa Gaye
One Sheet: $100 - $200   *Rock 'n' Roll.*

SHAKEDOWN, THE
(1929 - Universal) James Murray, Barbara Kent
One Sheet: $250 - $500

SHAKEDOWN
(1936 - RKO) Lew Ayres, Joan Perry
One Sheet: $100 - $200

SHAKEDOWN
(1950 - Universal) Howard Duff, Brian Donlevy
One Sheet: $15 - $25

SHAKEDOWN, THE
(1961 - Universal) Terence Morgan, Hazel
Court
One Sheet: $15 - $25

SHAKEDOWN
(1988 - -) Peter Weller, Sam Elliott
One Sheet: $5 - $10

SHAKESPEARE WALLAH
(1966 - -) Shashi Kapoor, Felicity Kendal
One Sheet: $5 - $10

SHAKESPEARIAN SPINACH
(1940 - Paramount) Popeye the Sailor
One Sheet: $800 - $1,500   *Cartoon.*
Duotone.

SHAKIEST GUN IN THE WEST, THE
(1968 - Universal) Don Knotts, Barbara

Rhoades
One Sheet: $30 - $50

SHALAKO
(1968 - Cinerama) Sean Connery, Brigitte
Bardot, Stephen Boyd
One Sheet: $10 - $20

SHALL WE DANCE
(1937 - RKO) Fred Astaire, Ginger Rogers
One Sheet: $3,500 - $5,000   *Price is for
Style A(dancing) one sheet. Style
B(heads):$2000-$3000.*

SHALL WE DANCE
(1997 - Miramax) Koji Yakusho, Tamiyo
Kusakari
One Sheet: $5 - $10

SHALLOW GRAVE
(1994 - Gramercy) Kerry Fox, Christopher
Eccleston
One Sheet: $3 - $5

SHAM
(1921 - Paramount) Ethel Clayton
One Sheet: $150 - $300

SHAM BATTLE SHENANIGANS
(1940 - 20th Century Fox) Terry-toons
One Sheet: $100 - $200   *Cartoon. Full
color stone litho. Stock poster with inset title.*

SHAME
(1968 - Lopert) Liv Ullmann, Max von Sydow,
Dir: Ingmar Bergman
One Sheet: $40 - $75   *Swedish.*

SHAME OF THE SABINE WOMEN
(1962 - United Producers) Lex Johnson, Lorena
& Teresa Doude
One Sheet: $15 - $35   *Mexican.
AKA: THE MATING OF THE SABINE WOMEN;
THE RAPE OF THE SABINES.*

SHAMEFUL BEHAVIOR
(1925 - Preferred) Edith Roberts, Richard
Tucker
One Sheet: $200 - $400

SHAMELESS OLD LADY
(1966 - Continental) Sylvie
One Sheet: $10 - $20

SHAMPOO
(1975 - Columbia) Warren Beatty, Goldie
Hawn, Lee Grant
One Sheet: $10 - $20   *Academy
Award: Best Supporting Actress (Grant). Academy
Award Movie Posters #291.*

SHAMROCK AND THE ROSE, THE
(1927 - -) Mack Swain, William Strauss
One Sheet: $250 - $500

SHAMROCK HILL
(1949 - Eagle-Lion) Peggy Ryan, Ray
McDonald
One Sheet: $15 - $35

SHAMUS
(1973 - Columbia) Burt Reynolds, Dyan
Cannon
One Sheet: $7 - $15

SHANE
(1953 - Paramount) Alan Ladd, Jean Arthur
One Sheet: $500 - $800   *Cowboy
Movie Posters #297.*

One Sheet

SHANE
(1959R - Paramount) Alan Ladd, Jean Arthur
One Sheet: $50 - $100   *Re-release.*

SHANE
(1966R - Paramount) Alan Ladd, Jean Arthur
One Sheet: $20 - $40   *Re-release.*

SHANGHAI
(1935 - Paramount) Charles Boyer, Loretta
Young
One Sheet: $250 - $500

SHANGHAI CHEST, THE
(1948 - Monogram) Roland Winters, Mantan
Moreland
One Sheet: $75 - $150   *Charlie Chan
series.*

SHANGHAI COBRA, THE
(1945 - Monogram) Sidney Toler, Benson
Fong, Mantan Moreland
One Sheet: $125 - $250   *Charlie Chan
series.*

SHANGHAI EXPRESS
(1932 - Paramount) Marlene Dietrich, Clive
Brook
One Sheet: $4,000 - $6,000

SHANGHAI GESTURE, THE
(1941 - United Artists) Gene Tierney, Walter
Huston
One Sheet: $700 - $1,200

SHANGHAI KILLERS, THE
(197? - AIP) -
One Sheet: $5 - $10   *Kung-Fu,
Karate Movie.*

SHANGHAI LADY
(1929 - Universal) Mary Nolan
One Sheet: $250 - $500

SHANGHAI MADNESS
(1933 - Fox) Fay Wray, Spencer Tracy
One Sheet: $500 - $800

SHANGHAI STORY, THE
(1954 - Republic) Ruth Roman, Edmond
O'Brien
One Sheet: $15 - $30

SHANGHAI SURPRISE
(1986 - -) Sean Penn, Madonna
One Sheet: $10 - $20

SHANGHAI TRIAD
(1995 - Sony Classics) Gong Li, Li Baotian
One Sheet: $5 - $12

SHANGHAIED
(1915 - Essanay) Charlie Chaplin, Edna
Purviance
One Sheet: $7,500 - $12,000

SHANGHAIED
(1934 - United Artists/Disney) Mickey Mouse
One Sheet: $19,000 - $30,000 *Cartoon.*

SHANGHAIED
(1974R - United Artists/Disney) Mickey Mouse
One Sheet: $15 - $35   *Re-release.
Cartoon.*

SHANGHAIED LOVE
(1931 - Columbia) Richard Cromwell, Noah
Beery, Sr.
One Sheet: $150 - $300

SHANGHAIED LOVERS
(1924 - Pathe) Harry Langdon
One Sheet: $300 - $700

SHANTYTOWN
(1943 - Republic) Mary Lee, John Archer
One Sheet: $15 - $30

SHAPE OF THINGS TO COME, THE
(- - -) See H.G. WELLS' "THE SHAPE OF
THINGS TO COME"

SHARAD OF ATLANTIS
(1936 - -) Crash Corrigan, Lon Chaney, Jr.
One Sheet: $250 - $500   *Feature
version of Undersea Kingdom.*

SHARK
(1969 - Excelsior) Burt Reynolds, Barry
Sullivan
One Sheet: $5 - $10

SHARK MONROE
(1918 - Artcraft) William S. Hart, Katherine
MacDonald
One Sheet: $1,300 - $2,000

SHARK RIVER

(1953 - United Artists) Steve Cochran, Carole
Mathews
One Sheet: $10 - $20

SHARK'S TREASURE
(1975 - United Artists) Cornel Wilde, Yaphet
Kotto
One Sheet: $3 - $5

SHARKFIGHTERS, THE
(1956 - United Artists) Victor Mature, Karen
Steele
One Sheet: $15 - $30

SHARKY'S MACHINE
(1981 - Orion) Burt Reynolds, Rachel Ward
One Sheet: $5 - $10

SHARPSHOOTERS
(1928 - Fox) George O'Brien, Lois Moran
One Sheet: $250 - $500

SHARPSHOOTERS
(1938 - 20th Century Fox) Brian Donlevy, Lynn
Bari
One Sheet: $75 - $150

SHATTERED
(1991 - MGM) Tom Berenger, Corbin Bernsen,
Bob Hoskins
One Sheet: $3 - $5

SHATTERED LIVES
(1925 - Lumis) Edith Roberts, Robert Gordon
One Sheet: $200 - $400

SHAWSHANK REDEMPTION, THE
(1994 - Columbia) Tim Robbins, Morgan
Freeman
One Sheet: $15 - $25

SHE
(1925 - -) Betty Blythe, Carlyle Blackwell
One Sheet: $800 - $1,500   *Graven
Images, pg. 27.*

SHE
(1935 - RKO) Helen Gahagan, Randolph Scott
One Sheet: $800 - $1,500   *Graven
Images, pg. 96.*

SHE
(1965 - MGM) Ursula Andress, Peter Cushing,
Christopher Lee
One Sheet: $30 - $50

SHE ASKED FOR IT
(1937 - Paramount) William Gargan, Orien
Hayward
One Sheet: $50 - $100

SHE BEAST, THE
(1966 - Europix) Barbara Steele, Ian Ogilvy
One Sheet: $15 - $30

SHE BEAST, THE/EMBALMER, THE
(1966 - Europix) Barbara Steele, Maureen
Brown
One Sheet: $30 - $50   *Double
feature poster.*

SHE CAME TO THE VALLEY
(1979 - R.G.V.) Dean Stockwell, Scott Glenn
One Sheet: $5 - $10

SHE COULDN'T HELP IT
(1921 - Realart) Bebe Daniels, Emory Johnson,
Wade Boteler
One Sheet: $600 - $1,000

SHE COULDN'T SAY NO
(1930 - Warner Bros.) Winnie Lightner, Chester
Morris
One Sheet: $150 - $300

SHE COULDN'T SAY NO
(1940 - Warner Bros.) Roger Pryor, Eve Arden
One Sheet: $30 - $50

SHE COULDN'T SAY NO
(1954 - RKO) Jean Simmons, Robert Mitchum
One Sheet: $30 - $50   *AKA:
BEAUTIFUL, BUT DANGEROUS.*

SHE COULDN'T SAY YES
(1945 - -) Roz Russell
One Sheet: $75 - $125

SHE COULDN'T TAKE IT
(1935 - Columbia) George Raft, Joan Bennett
One Sheet: $150 - $300

SHE CREATURE, THE
(1956 - AIP) Chester Morris, Marla English

One Sheet: $200 - $400   *Graven Images, pg. 186.*

SHE DEMONS
(1958 - Astor) Irish McCalla, Tod Griffin
One Sheet: $50 - $100

SHE DEVIL, THE
(1918 - -) Theda Bara
One Sheet: $1,300 - $2,000

SHE DEVIL
(1940 - Sack) Laura Bowman, Gus Smith
One Sheet: $150 - $300   *Black cast.*
Separate Cinema, pg. 123.

SHE DEVIL
(1957 - 20th Century Fox) Mari Blanchard,
Albert Dekker
One Sheet: $15 - $35

SHE DEVIL
(1989 - Orion) Meryl Streep, Roseanne Barr
One Sheet: $4 - $8

SHE DONE HIM WRONG
(1933 - Paramount) Mae West, Cary Grant
One Sheet: $2,500 - $4,000

SHE FREAK
(1967 - Sonney) Claire Brennan, Harry Thomas
One Sheet: $75 - $150   *Sexploitation.*

SHE GETS HER MAN
(1935 - Universal) ZaSu Pitts, Hugh O'Connell
One Sheet: $125 - $250

SHE GETS HER MAN
(1945 - Universal) Joan Davis, Leon Errol
One Sheet: $20 - $40

SHE GODS OF SHARK REEF
(1958 - AIP) Don Durant, Lisa Montell
One Sheet: $40 - $75

SHE GOES TO WAR
(1929 - United Artists) Eleanor Boardman, John
Holland
One Sheet: $200 - $400

SHE GOT WHAT SHE WANTED
(1930 - Tiffany) Betty Compson, Alan Hale, Lee
Tracy
One Sheet: $100 - $200

SHE HAD TO CHOOSE
(1934 - Majestic) Larry "Buster" Crabbe
One Sheet: $75 - $150

SHE HAD TO EAT
(1937 - 20th Century Fox) Rochelle Hudson,
Jack Haley
One Sheet: $75 - $150

SHE HAD TO SAY YES
(1933 - First National) Loretta Young, Lyle
Talbot
One Sheet: $250 - $500

SHE HAD WHAT IT TAKES
(1943 - Columbia) Jinx Falkenburg, Tom Neal
One Sheet: $30 - $50

SHE KNEW ALL THE ANSWERS
(1941 - Columbia) Joan Bennett, Franchot
Tone
One Sheet: $20 - $40

SHE LEARNED ABOUT SAILORS
(1934 - Fox) Alice Faye, Lew Ayres
One Sheet: $250 - $500

SHE LOVED A FIREMAN
(1937 - Warner Bros.) Dick Foran, Ann
Sheridan
One Sheet: $50 - $100   *Duotone.*

SHE LOVES AND LIES
(1920 - Select) Norma Talmadge, Conway
Tearle
One Sheet: $500 - $800

SHE LOVES ME NOT
(1934 - Paramount) Bing Crosby, Miriam
Hopkins
One Sheet: $250 - $500

SHE MADE HER BED
(1934 - Paramount) Richard Arlen, Sally Eilers
One Sheet: $75 - $150

SHE MAN, THE
(1967 - Southeastern) Dorian Wayne, Wendy
Roberts

One Sheet: $15 - $25

SHE MARRIED A COP
(1939 - Republic) Phil Regan, Jean Parker
One Sheet: $40 - $75

SHE MARRIED AN ARTIST
(1938 - Columbia) John Boles, Luli Deste,
Frances Drake
One Sheet: $50 - $110

SHE MARRIED HER BOSS
(1935 - Columbia) Claudette Colbert, Melvyn
Douglas
One Sheet: $1,600 - $2,500

SHE PLAYED WITH FIRE
(1958 - Columbia) Jack Hawkins, Arlene Dahl
One Sheet: $15 - $30

SHE SHALL HAVE MURDER
(1950 - International) Rosamund John, Derrick
de Marney
One Sheet: $10 - $20

SHE SHALL HAVE MUSIC
(1935 - Twickenham) June Clyde, Claude
Dampier
One Sheet: $50 - $100

SHE SHOULDA SAID NO
(1949 - -) Lila Leeds
One Sheet: $75 - $150

SHE WANTED A MILLIONAIRE
(1932 - Fox) Joan Bennett, Spencer Tracy
One Sheet: $350 - $750

SHE WAS A LADY
(1934 - Fox) Helen Twelvetrees, Donald Woods
One Sheet: $100 - $200

SHE WENT TO THE RACES
(1945 - MGM) James Craig, Frances Gifford,
Ava Gardner
One Sheet: $30 - $60

SHE WOLVES
(1925 - Fox) Alma Rubens, Jack Mulhall
One Sheet: $125 - $250

SHE WORE A YELLOW RIBBON
(1949 - RKO) John Wayne, Joanne Dru, Dir:
John Ford
One Sheet: $500 - $800   *Cowboy
Movie Posters #s 283, 284.*

One Sheet

SHE WORE A YELLOW RIBBON
(1957R - RKO) John Wayne, Joanne Dru Dir:
John Ford
One Sheet: $100 - $200   *Re-release.*

SHE WOULDN'T SAY YES
(1945 - Columbia) Rosalind Russell, Lee
Bowman
One Sheet: $50 - $100

SHE WROTE THE BOOK
(1946 - Universal) Joan Davis, Jack Oakie
One Sheet: $40 - $75

SHE'S A SHEIK
(1927 - Paramount) Bebe Daniels, Richard
Arlen
One Sheet: $250 - $600

SHE'S A SOLDIER TOO
(1944 - Columbia) Nina Foch, Beulah Bondi,
Lloyd Bridges
One Sheet: $15 - $35

SHE'S A SWEETHEART
(1944 - Columbia) Larry Parks, Jane Frazee
One Sheet: $15 - $35

SHE'S BACK ON BROADWAY
(1953 - Warner Bros.) Virginia Mayo, Gene
Nelson
One Sheet: $15 - $30

SHE'S DANGEROUS
(1937 - Universal) Cesar Romero, Tala Birell
One Sheet: $125 - $250

SHE'S FOR ME
(1943 - Universal) Grace McDonald, David
Bruce
One Sheet: $20 - $40

SHE'S GOT EVERYTHING
(1938 - RKO) Gene Raymond, Ann Sothern
One Sheet: $75 - $150

SHE'S GOTTA HAVE IT
(1986 - -) Tracy Camilla, Spike Lee
One Sheet: $40 - $80

SHE'S HAVING A BABY
(1988 - -) Kevin Bacon, Elizabeth McGovern
One Sheet: $3 - $5

SHE'S IN THE ARMY
(1942 - Monogram) Veda Ann Borg, Lyle Talbot
One Sheet: $20 - $40

SHE'S MY WEAKNESS
(1930 - RKO) Sue Carol, Arthur Lake
One Sheet: $125 - $250

SHE'S NINETEEN AND READY
(1980 - Martin) Sabine Woolen, Ekke Belle
One Sheet: $5 - $10

SHE'S OIL MINE
(1941 - -) Buster Keaton
One Sheet: $75 - $150

SHE'S OUT OF CONTROL
(1989 - -) Tony Danza, Catherine Hicks
One Sheet: $3 - $5

SHE'S TOO MEAN FOR ME
(1938 - Toddy) Mantan Moreland, Johnny Lee
One Sheet: $100 - $200   *Black cast.
Separate Cinema, pg. 69.*

**SHE'S WORKING HER WAY THROUGH
COLLEGE**
(1952 - Warner Bros.) Virginia Mayo, Ronald
Reagan
One Sheet: $75 - $125

SHEBA BABY
(1975 - AIP) Pam Grier, Austin Stoker
One Sheet: $30 - $50   *Blaxploitation.*

SHED NO TEARS
(1948 - Eagle-Lion) Wallace Ford, June Vincent
One Sheet: $30 - $50

SHE-DEVIL ISLAND
(1936 - First Division) Carmen Guerrero, J.J.
Martinez Casado
One Sheet: $250 - $600

SHE-DEVILS ON WHEELS
(1968 - Mayflower) Betty Connell, Pat Poston
One Sheet: $30 - $50   *Biker film.*

SHEENA
(1984 - Columbia) Tanya Roberts, Ted Wass
One Sheet: $5 - $10

SHEEPMAN, THE
(1958 - MGM) Glenn Ford, Shirley MacLaine
One Sheet: $15 - $30

SHEIK, THE
(1921 - Paramount) Rudolph Valentino
One Sheet: $10,000 - $15,000   *Price is for
Style B showing Valentino. One Sheet(Style A
with Agnes Ayres):$2000-$2500.*

SHEIK, THE
(1938R - Paramount) Rudolph Valentino
One Sheet: $250 - $600   *Re-release.*

SHEIK STEPS OUT, THE
(1937 - Republic) Ramon Navarro, Lola Lane
One Sheet: $75 - $150

SHELL SHOCK
(1964 - Parade) Beach Dickerson, Carl Crow
One Sheet: $3 - $5

SHELTERING SKY, THE
(1990 - Warner Bros.) John Malkovich, Debra
Winger

One Sheet: $3 - $5

SHENANDOAH
(1965 - Universal) James Stewart, Doug
McClure
One Sheet: $30 - $60   *Cowboy
Movie Posters #315.*

SHENANDOAH
(1974R - Universal) James Stewart, Doug
McClure
One Sheet: $5 - $10   *Re-release.*

SHEP COMES HOME
(1948 - Screen Guild) Robert Lowery, Billy
Kimbley
One Sheet: $10 - $20

SHEPHERD KING, THE
(1923 - Fox) -
One Sheet: $500 - $800

SHEPHERD OF THE HILLS
(1941 - Paramount) John Wayne, Betty Field,
Harry Carey
One Sheet: $300 - $700

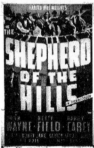

One Sheet

SHEPHERD OF THE HILLS
(1955R - Paramount) John Wayne, Betty Field,
Harry Carey
One Sheet: $40 - $75   *Re-release.*

SHEPHERD OF THE OZARKS
(1942 - Republic) Weaver Brothers & Elviry
One Sheet: $30 - $50   *Country
musical.*

SHERIFF OF CIMARRON
(1945 - Republic) Sunset Carson, Linda
Sterling
One Sheet: $30 - $50

SHERIFF OF FRACTURED JAW, THE
(1958 - 20th Century Fox) Kenneth More,
Jayne Mansfield
One Sheet: $20 - $40   *Cowboy
Movie Posters #306.*

Insert

SHERIFF OF LAS VEGAS
(1944 - Republic) Wild Bill Elliott, Bobby Blake
One Sheet: $30 - $50   *Red Ryder
series.*

SHERIFF OF MEDICINE BOW, THE
(1948 - Monogram) Johnny Mack Brown,
Raymond Hatton
One Sheet: $15 - $35

SHERIFF OF REDWOOD VALLEY
(1946 - Republic) "Wild Bill" Elliott, Alice
Fleming
One Sheet: $20 - $40

SHERIFF OF SAGE VALLEY

(1943 - PRC) Buster Crabbe
One Sheet: $30 - $50

SHERIFF OF SUNDOWN
(1944 - Republic) Allan "Rocky" Lane
One Sheet: $30 - $50

SHERIFF OF TOMBSTONE
(1941 - Republic) Roy Rogers, Gabby Hayes
One Sheet: $150 - $300   *Duotone.*

SHERIFF OF WICHITA
(1949 - Republic) Allan "Rocky" Lane, Lyn Wilde
One Sheet: $15 - $35

SHERIFF'S SISTER, THE
(1911 - American) Pauleen Bush, J. Warren Kerrigan, Dir: Alan Dwan
One Sheet: $300 - $700

SHERIFF'S SON, THE
(1919 - -) Charles Ray, Seena Owen
One Sheet: $200 - $400

SHERLOCK HOLMES
(1922 - Goldwyn) John Barrymore
One Sheet: $7,500 - $12,000   *Price is for full color one sheet. One sheet(Style B duotone):$3000-4000.*

SHERLOCK HOLMES
(1932 - Fox) Clive Brook, Reginald Owen, Ernest Torrence
One Sheet: $2,200 - $3,500

SHERLOCK HOLMES AND THE SECRET WEAPON
(1942 - Universal) Basil Rathbone, Nigel Bruce
One Sheet: $250 - $600

SHERLOCK HOLMES AND THE SPIDER WOMAN
(1944 - -) See SPIDER WOMAN

SHERLOCK HOLMES AND THE VOICE OF TERROR
(1942 - Universal) Basil Rathbone, Nigel Bruce
One Sheet: $500 - $800

One Sheet

SHERLOCK HOLMES FACES DEATH
(1943 - Universal) Basil Rathbone, Nigel Bruce
One Sheet: $250 - $600

SHERLOCK HOLMES IN WASHINGTON
(1942 - Universal) Basil Rathbone, Nigel Bruce, Henry Daniell
One Sheet: $250 - $600

SHERLOCK HOLMES STOCK
(194?R - -) -
One Sheet: $30 - $50   *Re-release. Duotone.*

SHERLOCK HOLMES' FATAL HOUR
(1931 - First Division) Arthur Wontner, Ian Fleming
One Sheet: $800 - $1,500   *AKA: THE SLEEPING CARDINAL.*

SHERLOCK HOLMES' SMARTER BROTHER
(1975 - See THE ADVENTURES OF SHERLOCK HOLMES' SMARTER BROTHER)

SHERLOCK JUNIOR
(1924 - Metro) Buster Keaton, Kathryn McGuire
One Sheet: $6,500 - $10,000

SHERMAN'S MARCH
(1986 - -) Dir: Ross McElwee
One Sheet: $5 - $10

SHE-WOLF, THE
(1931 - Universal) May Robson, James Hall

One Sheet: $350 - $750

SHE-WOLF OF LONDON
(1946 - Universal) June Lockhart, Don Porter
One Sheet: $150 - $350

SHIELD FOR MURDER
(1954 - United Artists) Edmond O'Brien, Mara English
One Sheet: $15 - $25

SHIELDING SHADOW, THE
(1916 - Pathe) Grace Darmond, Ralph Kellard
One Sheet: $250 - $500   *Serial. 15 Chapters.*

SHINBONE ALLEY
(1971 - Allied Artists) -
One Sheet: $10 - $20   *Cartoon.*

SHINE
(1996 - Fine Line) Geoffrey Rush, Noah Taylor
One Sheet: $4 - $8

SHINE ON HARVEST MOON
(1938 - Republic) Roy Rogers, Gabby Hayes
One Sheet: $300 - $700

SHINE ON HARVEST MOON
(1944 - Warner Bros.) Ann Sheridan, Dennis Morgan
One Sheet: $40 - $75   *Duotone.*

SHINING, THE
(1980 - Warner Bros.) Jack Nicholson, Shelley Duvall
One Sheet: $10 - $20

SHINING HOUR, THE
(1938 - MGM) Joan Crawford, Robert Young, Melvyn Douglas
One Sheet: $250 - $500

SHINING THROUGH
(1934 - -) -
One Sheet: $200 - $400   *French.*

SHINING THROUGH
(1992 - 20th Century Fox) Melanie Griffith, Michael Douglas
One Sheet: $3 - $5

SHINING VICTORY
(1941 - Warner Bros.) James Stephenson, Geraldine Fitzgerald
One Sheet: $15 - $35

SHIP AHOY
(1942 - MGM) Eleanor Powell, Red Skelton, Tommy Dorsey Orch.
One Sheet: $100 - $200   *Big Band musical.*

SHIP CAFE
(1935 - Paramount) Carl Brisson, Arline Judge
One Sheet: $75 - $150

SHIP COMES IN, A
(1928 - Pathe) Rudolph Schildkraut, Louise Dresser
One Sheet: $100 - $200

SHIP FROM SHANGHAI, THE
(1930 - MGM) Conrad Nagel, Kay Johnson
One Sheet: $125 - $250

SHIP OF FOOLS
(1965 - Columbia) Oskar Werner, Simone Signoret, Vivien Leigh
One Sheet: $15 - $35   *Leigh's final film.*

SHIP OF WANTED MEN, THE
(1933 - Screencraft) Dorothy Sebastian, Fred Kohler
One Sheet: $75 - $125

SHIP THAT DIED OF SHAME, THE
(1956 - General/Continental) Richard Attenborough
One Sheet: $75 - $150

SHIP WAS LOADED, THE
(1959 - -) David Tomlinson, Peggy Cummins
One Sheet: $7 - $15

SHIPMATES
(1931 - MGM) Robert Montgomery, Dorothy Jordan
One Sheet: $100 - $200

SHIPMATES FOREVER
(1935 - Warner Bros.) Dick Powell, Ruby Keeler

One Sheet: $250 - $500

SHIPS WITH WINGS
(1942 - United Artists) John Clements, Leslie Banks
One Sheet: $30 - $50

SHIPWRECKED
(1991 - Disney) Gabriel Byrne, Stian Smestad, Bjorn Sundquist
One Sheet: $3 - $5

SHIR HASHIRIM (SONG OF SONGS)
(1935 - Globe) Howard Daniels, Bruce Gordon, Betty Sain
One Sheet: $50 - $100

SHIRALEE, THE
(1957 - MGM) Peter Finch, Elizabeth Sellars
One Sheet: $10 - $20

SHIRLEY VALENTINE
(1989 - Paramount) Pauline Collins, Tom Conti
One Sheet: $2 - $3

SHIVERING SHERLOCKS
(1948 - Columbia) The Three Stooges (Shemp)
One Sheet: $350 - $750   *Comedy short. Duotone.*

SHIVERING SPOOKS
(1926 - Pathe) Our Gang
One Sheet: $500 - $800

SHIVERS
(1976 - AIP) Paul Hampton, Joe Silver, Dir: David Cronenberg
One Sheet: $15 - $30   *AKA: They Came From Within.*

SHOCK, THE
(1923 - Universal-Jewel) Virginia Valli
One Sheet: $200 - $400

SHOCK
(1934 - Monogram) Ralph Forbes, Gwenillian Gill
One Sheet: $125 - $250

SHOCK
(1946 - 20th Century Fox) Vincent Price, Lynn Bari
One Sheet: $75 - $150

SHOCK CORRIDOR
(1963 - Allied Artists) Peter Breck, Constance Towers
One Sheet: $15 - $30

SHOCK PUNCH, THE
(1925 - Paramount) Richard Dix
One Sheet: $150 - $300

SHOCK TO THE SYSTEM, A
(1990 - Corsair) Michael Caine, Elizabeth McGovern
One Sheet: $3 - $5

SHOCK TREATMENT
(1964 - 20th Century Fox) Stuart Whitman, Lauren Bacall
One Sheet: $15 - $30

SHOCK TREATMENT
(1973 - New Line) Alain Delon, Annie Girardot
One Sheet: $3 - $5

SHOCK TREATMENT
(1981 - 20th Century Fox) Jessica Harper, Cliff DeYoung
One Sheet: $7 - $15

SHOCK TROOPS
(1968 - United Artists) Bruno Cremer, Gerard Blain
One Sheet: $7 - $15

SHOCK WAVES
(1977 - Cinima Shares) Peter Cushing, Brooke Adams
One Sheet: $10 - $20

SHOCKER
(1989 - Universal) Mitch Pileggi, Michael Murphy
One Sheet: $5 - $10

SHOCKING MISS PILGRIM, THE
(1946 - 20th Century Fox) Betty Grable, Dick Haymes
One Sheet: $150 - $300

SHOCKPROOF
(1949 - Columbia) Cornel Wilde, Patricia Knight

One Sheet: $30 - $50

SHOE SHINE
(1947 - Lopert) Rinaldo Smordoni, Anielo Mele
One Sheet: $75 - $150   *Italian. AKA: SHOESHINE; SHOE-SHINE. Won Special Oscar.*

SHOE SHINE BOY
(1944 - MGM) Melvin Bryant, Sam Levene, Walter Catlett
One Sheet: $500 - $800

SHOES OF THE FISHERMAN, THE
(1968 - MGM) Anthony Quinn, David Janssen, Laurence Olivier
One Sheet: $15 - $35

SHOGUN ASSASSIN
(1980 - New World) Tomisaburo Wakayama, Kayo Matsuo
One Sheet: $15 - $25   *Japanese. AKA: LIGHTNING SWORDS OF DEATH.*

One Sheet

SHOOT FIRST
(1953 - United Artists) Joel McCrea, Evelyn Keyes
One Sheet: $15 - $30

SHOOT THE MOON
(1982 - MGM) Albert Finney, Diane Keaton
One Sheet: $7 - $15

SHOOT THE PIANO PLAYER
(1962 - Cocinor) Charles Aznavour, Marie DuBois
One Sheet: $30 - $50   *French. Price is for French 47 x 63.*

SHOOT THE WORKS
(1934 - Paramount) Jack Oakie, Ben Bernie
One Sheet: $75 - $150

SHOOT TO KILL
(1947 - Screen Guild) Russell Wade, Susan Walters
One Sheet: $30 - $50

SHOOT TO KILL
(1987 - Touchstone) Sidney Poitier, Tom Berenger, Kirstie Alley
One Sheet: $7 - $15

SHOOTIN' IRONS
(1927 - Paramount) Jack Luden, Sally Blane
One Sheet: $250 - $600

SHOOTING, THE
(1971 - Proteus) Jack Nicholson, Warren Oates
One Sheet: $15 - $25

SHOOTING HIGH
(1940 - 20th Century Fox) Jane Withers, Gene Autry
One Sheet: $150 - $350

Mini Window Card (Trimmed)

SHOOTING OF DAN MCGOO, THE
(1945 - MGM) Droopy, Tex Avery
One Sheet: $600 - $1,000   *Cartoon. Full color stone litho. Droopy's second appearance. Cartoon Movie Posters #297.*

SHOOTING OF DAN MCGOO, THE
(1951R - MGM) Droopy, Tex Avery
One Sheet: $250 - $500   *Re-release. Cartoon. Full color stone litho.*

SHOOTING OF DAN MCGREW, THE
(1924 - Metro) Barbara La Marr, Lew Cody, Mae Busch
One Sheet: $500 - $800

SHOOTING STAR, THE
(1924 - Universal-Jewel) Billy Sullivan
One Sheet: $150 - $300   *#3 in the Fast Steppers series.*

SHOOTING STRAIGHT
(1930 - RKO) Richard Dix, Mary Lawlor
One Sheet: $125 - $250

SHOOTIST
(1976 - Paramount) John Wayne, Lauren Bacall, James Stewart
One Sheet: $75 - $150   *Wayne's last film. Amsel art. Cowboy Movie Posters #348.*

SHOOTOUT
(1971 - Universal) Gregory Peck, Robert F. Lyons
One Sheet: $5 - $10

SHOOTOUT AT BIG SAG
(1962 - Parallel) Walter Brennan, Leif Erickson
One Sheet: $10 - $20

SHOOTOUT AT MEDICINE BEND
(1957 - Warner Bros.) Randolph Scott, James Craig
One Sheet: $15 - $35

SHOP ANGEL
(1932 - Tower) Holmes Herbert, Marion Shilling
One Sheet: $100 - $200

SHOP AROUND THE CORNER, THE
(1940 - MGM) Margaret Sullavan, James Stewart
One Sheet: $600 - $1,000

SHOP ON MAIN STREET, THE
(1966 - Prominent) Jozef Kroner, Ida Kaminska
One Sheet: $15 - $25
Czechoslovakian. Academy Award: Best Foreign film. AKA: THE SHOP ON HIGH STREET.

SHOPWORN
(1932 - Columbia) Barbara Stanwyck, Regis Toomey
One Sheet: $800 - $1,500

SHOPWORN ANGEL, THE
(1928 - Paramount) Nancy Carroll, Gary Cooper
One Sheet: $600 - $1,000

SHOPWORN ANGEL, THE
(1938 - MGM) Margaret Sullavan, James Stewart, Walter Pidgeon
One Sheet: $300 - $700

One Sheet

SHORE LEAVE
(1925 - First National) Richard Barthelmess, Dorothy Mackaill
One Sheet: $200 - $400

SHORT CIRCUIT
(1986 - -) Ally Sheedy, Steve Guttenberg
One Sheet: $5 - $10

SHORT CIRCUIT II
(1988 - TriStar) Fisher Stevens, Michael McKean
One Sheet: $3 - $5

SHORT CUT TO HELL
(1957 - Paramount) Robert Ivers, Georgann Johnson
One Sheet: $5 - $10

SHORT CUTS
(1993 - New Line) Tim Robbins, Robert Downey, Jr., Dir: Robert Altman
One Sheet: $3 - $5

SHORT EYES
(1977 - Paramount) Bruce Davison
One Sheet: $3 - $5   *AKA: THE SLAMMER.*

SHORT GRASS
(1950 - Allied Artists) Rod Cameron, Cathy Downs
One Sheet: $15 - $35

SHORT LIFE AND A MERRY ONE, A
(1913 - Edison) -
One Sheet: $250 - $600

SHORT SNORTS ON SPORTS
(1948 - Columbia) -
One Sheet: $100 - $200   *Cartoon. Sports.*

SHORT TIME
(1990 - -) Dabney Coleman, Matt Frewer, Teri Garr
One Sheet: $3 - $5

SHORT WEIGHT
(1922 - Universal) Johnny Fox, Brownie the Wonder Dog
One Sheet: $200 - $400

SHORTY REDUCES THE HIGH COST OF LIVING
(1920 - Sunnywest) Shorty Hamilton
One Sheet: $350 - $750

SHOT IN THE DARK, A
(1935 - Chesterfield) Charles Starrett, Robert Warwick
One Sheet: $100 - $200

SHOT IN THE DARK, THE
(1941 - Warner Bros.) William Lundigan, Nan Wynn
One Sheet: $50 - $100

SHOT IN THE DARK, A
(1964 - United Artists) Peter Sellers, Elke Sommer
One Sheet: $30 - $50

SHOT IN THE FRONTIER
(1954 - Columbia) The Three Stooges (Shemp)
One Sheet: $150 - $300   *Comedy short. Duotone.*

SHOTGUN
(1955 - Allied Artists) Sterling Hayden, Yvonne De Carlo
One Sheet: $10 - $20

SHOTGUN PASS
(1931 - Columbia) Tim McCoy, Virginia Lee Corbin
One Sheet: $250 - $600

SHOULD A GIRL MARRY
(1939 - Monogram) Anne Nagel, Warren Hull
One Sheet: $75 - $125

SHOULD A WIFE FORGIVE?
(1915 - Equitable) Lillian Lorraine, Mabel Van Buren
One Sheet: $250 - $500

SHOULD HUSBANDS MARRY?
(1926 - Pathe) Alice Day, Eddie Quillan
One Sheet: $500 - $800

SHOULD HUSBANDS WORK?
(1939 - Republic) Lucille, Russell and James Gleason
One Sheet: $40 - $75

SHOULD LADIES BEHAVE?
(1933 - MGM) Lionel Barrymore, Alice Brady
One Sheet: $100 - $200

SHOULD MARRIED MEN GO HOME?
(1928 - MGM) Laurel & Hardy
One Sheet: $3,500 - $5,000

SHOULD SAILORS MARRY?
(1925 - Pathe) Clyde Cook
One Sheet: $250 - $600

SHOULD SECOND HUSBANDS COME FIRST?
(1927 - Pathecomedy) Max Davidson
One Sheet: $150 - $300

SHOULD TALL MEN MARRY?
(1927 - Pathe) Laurel & Hardy
One Sheet: $3,500 - $5,000

SHOULDER ARMS
(1918 - First National) Charlie Chaplin, Edna Purviance
One Sheet: $5,000 - $8,000

SHOUT
(1991 - Universal) James Walters, Heather Graham, John Travolta
One Sheet: $3 - $5

SHOUT AT THE DEVIL
(1976 - AIP) Lee Marvin, Roger Moore
One Sheet: $7 - $15

SHOUT AT THE SUN
(1976 - -) See SHOUT AT THE DEVIL

SHOW, THE
(1927 - MGM) John Gilbert
One Sheet: $250 - $500

SHOW BOAT
(1936 - Universal) Irene Dunne, Allan Jones, Paul Robeson
One Sheet: $800 - $1,500

SHOW BOAT
(1951 - MGM) Kathryn Grayson, Howard Keel, Ava Gardner
One Sheet: $75 - $150

SHOW BOAT
(1963R - MGM) Kathryn Grayson, Howard Keel, Ava Gardner
One Sheet: $20 - $40   *Re-release.*

SHOW BUSINESS
(1944 - RKO) Eddie Cantor, Joan Davis
One Sheet: $75 - $125

SHOW FOLKS
(1928 - Pathe) -
One Sheet: $250 - $600

SHOW GIRL, THE
(1927 - Rayart) Mildred Harris, Gaston Glass, Mary Carr
One Sheet: $150 - $300

SHOW GOES ON, THE
(1938 - Gaumont) Anna Neagle, Tulio Carminatio
One Sheet: $75 - $125   *British.*

SHOW LIFE
(1928 - Warbour) Anna May Wong, Henry George, Mary Kid
One Sheet: $600 - $1,000

SHOW PEOPLE
(1928 - MGM) Marion Davies, William Haines

SHOW THEM NO MERCY
(1935 - 20th Century Fox) Rochelle Hudson, Cesar Romero, Bruce Cabot
One Sheet: $150 - $300

SHOW THEM NO MERCY
(1949R - 20th Century Fox) Rochelle Hudson, Cesar Romero, Bruce Cabot
One Sheet: $30 - $50   *Re-release.*

SHOWDOWN, THE
(1928 - Paramount) George Bancroft, Evelyn Brent
One Sheet: $150 - $300

SHOWDOWN, THE
(1940 - Paramount) William Boyd, Russell Hayden
One Sheet: $200 - $400   *Hopalong Cassidy series. Cowboy Movie Posters #260.*

SHOWDOWN, THE
(1950 - Republic) William Elliott, Marie Windsor
One Sheet: $15 - $35

SHOWDOWN
(1963 - Universal) Audie Murphy, Kathleen Crowley

SHOWDOWN
One Sheet: $20 - $40

SHOWDOWN
(1973 - Universal) Dean Martin, Rock Hudson
One Sheet: $7 - $15

SHOWDOWN AT ABILENE
(1956 - Universal) Jock Mahoney, Martha Hyer
One Sheet: $15 - $30

SHOWDOWN AT BOOT HILL
(1958 - 20th Century Fox) Charles Bronson, Robert Hutton
One Sheet: $15 - $25

SHOWGIRL
(1920 - Rayart) Mary Carr, Eddie Borden
One Sheet: $150 - $300

SHOWGIRL IN HOLLYWOOD
(1930 - First National) Alice White, Jack Mulhall
One Sheet: $200 - $400

SHOWGIRLS
(1995 - MGM/UA) Elizabeth Berkley, Gina Gershon
One Sheet: $15 - $25

SHOW-OFF, THE
(1934 - MGM) Spencer Tracy, Madge Evans
One Sheet: $200 - $400

SHOW-OFF, THE
(1946 - MGM) Red Skelton, Marilyn Maxwell
One Sheet: $50 - $100

SHRIEK IN THE NIGHT, A
(1933 - Allied) Ginger Rogers, Lyle Talbot
One Sheet: $200 - $400

SHRIEK OF ARABY, THE
(1923 - -) Ben Turpin, Kathryn McGuire
One Sheet: $250 - $500

SHRIKE, THE
(1955 - Universal) Jose Ferrer, June Allyson
One Sheet: $10 - $20

SHUT MY BIG MOUTH
(1942 - Columbia) Joe E. Brown, Adele Mara
One Sheet: $50 - $100

SHUTTERED ROOM, THE
(1968 - Warner Bros.) Gig Young, Carol Lynley
One Sheet: $7 - $15

SHY PEOPLE
(1987 - -) Jill Clayburgh, Barbara Hershey
One Sheet: $3 - $5

SIBLING RIVALRY
(1990 - Columbia) Kirstie Alley, Carrie Fisher
One Sheet: $3 - $5

SICILIAN, THE
(1987 - Gladden) Christopher Lambert, Terence Stamp
One Sheet: $3 - $5

SICILIAN CLAN, THE
(1970 - 20th Century Fox) Jean Gabin, Alain Deion
One Sheet: $3 - $5

SID AND NANCY
(1986 - Zenith) Gary Oldman, Chloe Webb
One Sheet: $15 - $30   *Rock 'n' Roll.*

SIDDHARTHA
(1973 - Columbia) Shashi Kapoor, Simi Garewal
One Sheet: $10 - $20

SIDE KICKS
(1993 - Columbia) Chuck Norris, Jonathan Brandis
One Sheet: $3 - $5

SIDE SHOW
(1931 - Warner Bros.) Charles Butterworth, Winnie Lightner
One Sheet: $125 - $250

SIDE SHOW
(1950 - Monogram) Don McGuire, Tracey Roberts
One Sheet: $10 - $20

SIDE STREET
(1949 - MGM) Farley Granger, Cathy O'Donnell
One Sheet: $40 - $75

SIDE STREETS

(1934 - First National) Paul Kelly, Ann Dvorak
One Sheet: $75 - $150

SIDECAR RACERS
(1975 - Universal) Ben Murphy, Peter Graves
One Sheet: $15 - $25   *Sports*
(Motorcycle racing).

SIDEHACKERS, THE
(1969 - Crown) Ross Hagen, Diane McBain
One Sheet: $15 - $30   *AKA: FIVE THE HARD WAY.*

SIDEWALKS OF LONDON
(1940 - Paramount) Charles Laughton, Vivien Leigh, Rex Harrison
One Sheet: $600 - $1,000   *AKA: ST. MARTIN'S LANE.*

SIDEWALKS OF LONDON
(1949R - Paramount) Charles Laughton, Vivien Leigh, Rex Harrison
One Sheet: $100 - $200   *Re-release.*

SIDEWALKS OF NEW YORK
(1931 - MGM) Buster Keaton, Anita Page
One Sheet: $1,300 - $2,000

SIDEWINDER ONE
(1977 - Avco/Embassy) Marjoe Gortner, Michael Parks
One Sheet: $5 - $10

SIEGE AT RED RIVER
(1954 - 20th Century Fox) Van Johnson, Joanne Dru
One Sheet: $10 - $20

SIEGE OF SYRACUSE
(1962 - Paramount) Rossano Brazzi, Tina Louise
One Sheet: $7 - $15

SIEGE OF THE SAXONS
(1963 - Columbia) Janette Scott, Ronald Lewis
One Sheet: $3 - $5

SIEGFRIED
(1925 - UFA) Dir: Fritz Lang
One Sheet: $5,000 - $8,000   *German.*

SIERRA
(1950 - Universal) Audie Murphy, Wanda Hendrix
One Sheet: $30 - $60

SIERRA BARON
(1958 - 20th Century Fox) Brian Keith, Rick Jason
One Sheet: $7 - $15

SIERRA PASSAGE
(1950 - Monogram) Wayne Morris, Lois Albright
One Sheet: $15 - $25

SIERRA STRANGER
(1957 - Columbia) Howard Duff, Gloria McGhee
One Sheet: $10 - $20

SIERRA SUE
(1941 - Republic) Gene Autry, Smiley Burnette
One Sheet: $125 - $250

SIESTA
(1987 - -) Ellen Barkin, Gabriel Byrne
One Sheet: $10 - $20

SIGN O' THE TIMES
(1987 - -) Prince, Sheila E., Sheena Easton
One Sheet: $15 - $30   *Rock 'n' Roll concert film.*

SIGN OF FOUR, THE
(1932 - World Wide) Arthur Wontner, Isla Bevan, Ian Hunter
One Sheet: $250 - $500

SIGN OF THE CROSS, THE
(1932 - Paramount Publix) Fredric March, Elissa Landi, Claudette Colbert
One Sheet: $1,900 - $3,000

SIGN OF THE CROSS, THE
(1944R - Paramount) Fredric March, Elissa Landi, Claudette Colbert
One Sheet: $150 - $300   *Re-release.*

SIGN OF THE GLADIATOR
(1959 - AIP) Anita Ekberg, Georges Marchal
One Sheet: $15 - $25

SIGN OF THE PAGAN
(1954 - Universal) Jeff Chandler, Jack Palance
One Sheet: $10 - $20

SIGN OF THE RAM, THE
(1948 - Columbia) Susan Peters, Aleander Knox
One Sheet: $15 - $30

SIGN OF THE WOLF
(1931 - Metropolitan) Rex Lease, Virginia Brown Faire
One Sheet: $50 - $100   *Serial. 10 Chapters. Duotone.*

SIGN OF THE WOLF
(1941 - Monogram) Michael Whalen, Grace Bradley
One Sheet: $40 - $75

SIGN OF ZORRO, THE
(1960 - Buena Vista) Guy Williams, Lisa Gaye
One Sheet: $40 - $75

SIGNPOST TO MURDER
(1965 - MGM) Joanne Woodward, Stuart Whitman
One Sheet: $10 - $20

SILENCE
(1931 - Paramount Publix) Clive Brook, Marjorie Rambeau
One Sheet: $125 - $250

SILENCE
(1963 - Janus) Ingrid Thulin, Dir: Ingmar Bergman
One Sheet: $30 - $50   *Price is for non-review version.*

SILENCE
(1974 - -) Will Geer, Ian Geer Flanders
One Sheet: $3 - $5

SILENCE OF THE LAMBS, THE
(1991 - Orion) Jodie Foster, Anthony Hopkins
One Sheet: $15 - $25   *Academy Award: Best Picture, Best Actor(Hopkins), Best Actress(Foster), Best Director(Jonathan Demme).Advance(Hopkins only):$20-$25. Advance(Foster only):$20-$25. One Sheet(Moth):$30-$50. Academy Award Movie Posters #375-#377.*

SILENCE OF THE NORTH
(1981 - Universal) Tom Skerritt, Ellen Burstyn
One Sheet: $5 - $10

SILENCERS, THE
(1966 - Columbia) Dean Martin, Stella Stevens
One Sheet: $15 - $30

SILENT AVENGER, THE
(1920 - Vitagraph) Charles Delaney, Duane Thompson, David Kirby
One Sheet: $150 - $300   *Serial. 15 Chapters.*

SILENT BARRIERS
(1937 - Gaumont) Richard Arlen, Lili Palmer
One Sheet: $150 - $300   *Cowboy Movie Posters #216.*

SILENT CODE
(1932 - International) Kane Richmond, Blanche Mehaffey
One Sheet: $100 - $200

SILENT COMMAND, THE
(1923 - Fox) Bela Lugosi, Edmund Lowe
One Sheet: $700 - $1,200

SILENT CONFLICT
(1948 - United Artists) William Boyd, Andy Clyde
One Sheet: $50 - $100

SILENT DUST
(1950 - Stratford) Stephen Murray, Beatrice Campbell
One Sheet: $7 - $15

SILENT ENEMY, THE
(1930 - Paramount Publix) -
One Sheet: $100 - $200

SILENT ENEMY, THE
(1957 - Universal International) Laurence Harvey, Dawn Addams
One Sheet: $15 - $25

SILENT FALL
(1994 - Warner Bros.) Richard Dreyfuss, Ben Faulkner, Liv Tyler
One Sheet: $5 - $10

SILENT FEAR

(1933 - Gibraltar) -
One Sheet: $50 - $100

SILENT MADNESS
(1984 - -) Belinda Montgomery, Viveca Lindfors
One Sheet: $7 - $15   *3-D.*

SILENT MAN, THE
(1919 - -) William S. Hart
One Sheet: $1,300 - $2,000

SILENT MASTER, THE
(1917 - Selznick) Robert Warwick
One Sheet: $300 - $700

One Sheet

SILENT MEN
(1933 - Columbia) Tim McCoy, Florence Britton
One Sheet: $700 - $1,200   *Cowboy Movie Posters #148.*

SILENT MOVIE
(1976 - 20th Century Fox) Mel Brooks, Dom DeLuise, Marty Feldman
One Sheet: $15 - $25

SILENT NIGHT, BLOODY NIGHT
(1974 - Cannon) Patick O'Neal, John Carradine
One Sheet: $15 - $25   *AKA: DEATH HOUSE.*

SILENT NIGHT, DEADLY NIGHT
(1984 - TriStar) Robert Brian Wilson, Toni Nero
One Sheet: $10 - $20

SILENT NIGHT, DEADLY NIGHT PART II
(1987 - -) Eric Freeman, James L. Newman
One Sheet: $5 - $10

SILENT NIGHT, EVIL NIGHT
(1975 - Warner Bros.) Olivia Hussey, Keir Dullea
One Sheet: $10 - $20   *AKA: BLACK CHRISTMAS.*

SILENT PARTNER
(1923 - Paramount) Leatrice Joy, Owen Moore
One Sheet: $150 - $300

SILENT PARTNER
(1944 - Republic) William Henry, Beverly Loyd
One Sheet: $15 - $30

SILENT PARTNER, THE
(1979 - Embassy) Elliott Gould, Susannah York
One Sheet: $5 - $10

SILENT POWER, THE
(1926 - Gotham) Ralph Lewis
One Sheet: $250 - $600

SILENT RAGE
(1982 - -) Chuck Norris, Ron Silver
One Sheet: $5 - $10

SILENT RAIDERS
(1954 - Lippert) Richard Bartlett, Earle Lyon
One Sheet: $10 - $20

SILENT RUNNING
(1972 - Universal) Bruce Dern, Cliff Potts
One Sheet: $15 - $25

SILENT SCREAM
(1980 - American Cinema) Rebecca Balding, Cameron Mitchell
One Sheet: $3 - $5

SILENT STRANGER, THE
(1924 - R-C Pictures) Fred Thomson, Hazel Keener
One Sheet: $200 - $400

SILENT STRANGER, THE
(1975 - United Artists) Tony Anthony, Lloyd

Barrista
One Sheet: $5 - $10

SILENT TONGUE
(1993 - -) Alan Bates, Richard Harris, River Phoenix
One Sheet: $10 - $20

SILENT TOUCH, THE
(1993 - Castle Hill) Max von Sydow, Sarah Miles
One Sheet: $3 - $5

SILENT WITNESS, THE
(1932 - Fox) Lionel Atwill, Greta Nissen
One Sheet: $125 - $250

SILENT WITNESS
(1943 - Monogram) Frank Albertson, Maris Wrixon
One Sheet: $15 - $35

SILENT WORLD
(1956 - Columbia) Jacques Cousteau
One Sheet: $15 - $25

SILK EXPRESS, THE
(1933 - Warner Bros.) Neil Hamilton, Allen Jerkins
One Sheet: $75 - $150

SILK HAT KID
(1935 - Fox) Lew Ayres, Mae Clarke
One Sheet: $100 - $200

SILK HOSIERY
(1920 - Paramount) Enid Bennett
One Sheet: $250 - $500

SILK NOOSE, THE
(1950 - Monogram) Carole Landis, Joseph Calleia
One Sheet: $15 - $35

SILK STOCKINGS
(1957 - MGM) Fred Astaire, Cyd Charisse
One Sheet: $75 - $150

SILKEN AFFAIR, THE
(1957 - RKO) David Niven, Genevieve Page
One Sheet: $15 - $25

SILKS AND SADDLES
(1928 - Universal) Richard Walling, Marion Nixon
One Sheet: $150 - $300   *Sports (Horse racing).*

SILKS AND SADDLES
(1938 - Victory) Herman Brix, Toby Wing, Fuzzy Knight
One Sheet: $75 - $150   *Sports (Horse racing).*

SILKWOOD
(1983 - ABC) Meryl Streep, Kurt Russell
One Sheet: $5 - $10

SILLY BILLIES
(1936 - RKO) Wheeler and Woolsey
One Sheet: $150 - $350

SILLY SYMPHONY
(1933 - United Artists) Donald Duck, Disney Studio
One Sheet: $5,000 - $7,500   *Cartoon. First image of Donald Duck. Full color stone litho. Stock poster. Cartoon Movie Posters #71.*

One Sheet

SILVER BANDIT, THE
(1947 - -) Spade Cooley
One Sheet: $40 - $75

SILVER BEARS
(1977 - Columbia) Michael Caine, Cybil Shepherd
One Sheet: $3 - $5

SILVER BULLET
(1935 - -) Tom Tyler, Jayne Regan
One Sheet: $200 - $400

SILVER BULLET
(1942 - Universal) Johnny Mack Brown
One Sheet: $30 - $60

SILVER BULLET
(1985 - Paramount) Gary Busey, Everett McGill
One Sheet: $5 - $10

SILVER BUTTE
(1949 - Universal) Tex Williams, Smokey Rogers
One Sheet: $20 - $40

SILVER CANYON
(1951 - Columbia) Gene Autry, Gail Davis
One Sheet: $40 - $75

SILVER CHALICE, THE
(1954 - Warner Bros.) Virginia Mayo, Jack Palance, Paul Newman
One Sheet: $40 - $75   *Newman's film debut.*

SILVER CITY
(1951 - Paramount) Yvonne De Carlo, Barry Fitzgerald
One Sheet: $15 - $30

SILVER CITY BONANZA
(1951 - Republic) Rex Allen, Mary Ellen Kay
One Sheet: $15 - $35

SILVER CITY KID
(1944 - Republic) Allan "Rocky" Lane
One Sheet: $15 - $35

SILVER CITY RAIDERS
(1943 - Columbia) Russell Haydon, Bob Wills
One Sheet: $30 - $50

SILVER CORD, THE
(1933 - RKO) Irene Dunne, Joel McCrea
One Sheet: $200 - $400

SILVER DOLLAR
(1933 - First National) Edward G. Robinson, Bebe Daniels
One Sheet: $600 - $1,000

SILVER HORDE, THE
(1930 - RKO) Joel McCrea, Jean Arthur
One Sheet: $250 - $500

SILVER LINING, THE
(1931 - United Artists) Maureen O'Sullivan, Betty Compson
One Sheet: $150 - $350

SILVER LODE
(1954 - RKO) John Payne, Lizabeth Scott
One Sheet: $15 - $35

SILVER ON THE SAGE
(1939 - Paramount) William Boyd, George Hayes
One Sheet: $200 - $400   *Hopalong Cassidy series. Cowboy Movie Posters #238.*

SILVER QUEEN
(1942 - United Artists) George Brent, Priscilla Lane
One Sheet: $30 - $50

SILVER RAIDERS
(1950 - Monogram) Whip Wilson, Andy Clyde
One Sheet: $20 - $40

SILVER RANGE
(1946 - Monogram) Johnny Mack Brown, Raymond Hatton
One Sheet: $20 - $40

SILVER RIVER
(1948 - Warner Bros.) Errol Flynn, Ann Sheridan
One Sheet: $100 - $200

SILVER SKATES
(1943 - Monogram) Patricia Morison, Kenny Baker
One Sheet: $30 - $50   *Sports (Ice skating). Sports Movie Posters #258.*

SILVER SLAVE, THE
(1927 - Warner Bros.) Irene Rich, Holmes Herbert
One Sheet: $250 - $600

SILVER SPURS
(1936 - Universal) Buck Jones, Muriel Evans
One Sheet: $500 - $800   *Cowboy Movie Posters #193.*

SILVER SPURS
(1943 - Republic) Roy Rogers, Smiley Burnette
One Sheet: $150 - $300

SILVER STALLION
(1941 - Monogram) David Sharpe, Janet Waldo
One Sheet: $20 - $40

SILVER STAR, THE
(1955 - Lippert) Edgar Buchanan, Marie Windsor
One Sheet: $15 - $30

SILVER STREAK, THE
(1934 - RKO) Arthur Lake, Sally Blane
One Sheet: $200 - $400

SILVER STREAK, THE
(1943 - 20th Century Fox) Mighty Mouse
One Sheet: $250 - $600   *Cartoon. Full color stock poster with printed title. Huge image of Mighty Mouse on yellow background.*

SILVER STREAK
(1976 - 20th Century Fox) Gene Wilder, Richard Pryor
One Sheet: $10 - $20

SILVER THREADS AMONG THE GOLD
(1915 - Kingsley & Roberts) Richard J. Jose, Dora Dean
One Sheet: $250 - $500

SILVER TRAIL, THE
(1937 - Reliable) Rex Lease
One Sheet: $75 - $150

SILVER TRAILS
(1948 - Monogram) Jimmy Wakely, Whip Wilson (film debut)
One Sheet: $40 - $75

SILVER VALLEY
(1927 - Fox) Tom Mix, Dorothy Dwan
One Sheet: $600 - $1,000   *Cowboy Movie Posters #66.*

One Sheet

SILVER WHIP, THE
(1953 - 20th Century Fox) Rory Calhoun, Dale Robertson
One Sheet: $15 - $25

SILVER WINGS
(1922 - Fox) Mary Carr
One Sheet: $150 - $300

SILVERADO
(1985 - Columbia) Kevin Kline, Scott Glenn, Kevin Costner
One Sheet: $15 - $30   *Cowboy Movie Posters #358. International:$20-$30.*

SIMBA
(1955 - Lippert) Dirk Bogarde, Virginia McKenna
One Sheet: $5 - $10   *Separate Cinema, pg. 124.*

SIMON AND LAURA
(1955 - Universal International) Peter Finch, Kay Kendell
One Sheet: $7 - $15

SIMON, KING OF THE WITCHES
(1971 - Fanfare) Andrew Prine, Brenda Scott
One Sheet: $5 - $10

SIMPLE SIMON
(1935 - Celebrity) Ub Iwerks
One Sheet: $700 - $1,200   *Cartoon. Full color stone litho. Cartoon Movie Posters #117.*

SIMPLE THINGS, THE
(1953 - RKO/Disney) Mickey Mouse, Donald Duck, Pluto
One Sheet: $800 - $1,500   *Cartoon. The Disney Poster, pg. 28.*

SIMPLE TWIST OF FATE, A
(1994 - Touchstone) Steve Martin, Gabriel Byrne, Catherine O'Hara
One Sheet: $5 - $10

SIN OF HAROLD DIDDLEBOCK, THE
(1947 - United Artists) Harold Lloyd
One Sheet: $100 - $200   *AKA: MAD WEDNESDAY.*

SIN OF MADELON CLAUDET, THE
(1931 - MGM) Helen Hayes, Lewis Stone
One Sheet: $800 - $1,500   *Academy Award: Best Actress. Academy Award Movie Posters #27.*

SIN OF NORA MORAN, THE
(1933 - Majestic) Zita Johann, John Miljan
One Sheet: $3,500 - $5,000

SIN SHIP, THE
(1931 - RKO) Louis Wollheim, Mary Astor
One Sheet: $200 - $400

SIN SISTER, THE
(1929 - Fox) Nancy Carroll, Lawrence Gray
One Sheet: $200 - $400

SIN TAKES A HOLIDAY
(1930 - Pathe Exchange) Constance Bennett, Basil Rathbone
One Sheet: $200 - $400

SIN TOWN
(1942 - Universal) Constance Bennett, Broderick Crawford
One Sheet: $40 - $75

SIN WOMAN, THE
(1917 - Four Square) Irene Fenwick, Rene Davies, Clifford Bruce
One Sheet: $250 - $500

SINBAD AND THE EYE OF THE TIGER
(1977 - Columbia) Patrick Wayne, Jane Seymour, Harryhausen effects
One Sheet: $20 - $40

SINBAD THE SAILOR
(1935 - Celebrity) ComiColor Cartoon by Ub Iwerks
One Sheet: $250 - $600   *Cartoon. Full color stone litho. Cartoon Movie Posters #114.*

SINBAD THE SAILOR
(1946 - RKO) Douglas Fairbanks Jr., Maureen O'Hara
One Sheet: $100 - $200

SINCE YOU WENT AWAY
(1944 - United Artists) Claudette Colbert, Jennifer Jones, Shirley Temple
One Sheet: $50 - $100

SINCERELY YOURS
(1955 - Warner Bros.) Liberace, Joanne Dru
One Sheet: $30 - $50

SINFUL DAVEY
(1969 - United Artists) John Hurt, Pamela Franklin, Nigel Davenport
One Sheet: $3 - $5

SING
(1989 - -) Lorraine Bracco, Peter Dobson
One Sheet: $2 - $3

SING A JINGLE
(1943 - Universal) Allan Jones, June Vincent
One Sheet: $15 - $30

SING A SONG OF SIX PANTS
(1947 - Columbia) The Three Stooges (Shemp)
One Sheet: $350 - $750   *Comedy short. Duotone.*

SING AND BE HAPPY
(1937 - 20th Century Fox) Tony Martin, Dixie Dunbar
One Sheet: $75 - $150

SING AND LIKE IT
(1934 - RKO) ZaSu Pitts, Pert Kelton
One Sheet: $75 - $150

SING AND SWING
(1964 - Universal) David Hemmings, John Pike
One Sheet: $5 - $10

SING ANOTHER CHORUS
(1941 - Universal) Johnny Downs, Jane Frazee
One Sheet: $15 - $35

SING, BABY, SING
(1936 - 20th Century Fox) Alice Faye, Adolphe Menjou, Ritz Brothers (film debut)
One Sheet: $150 - $300

SING BOY SING
(1958 - 20th Century Fox) Tommy Sands, Lili Gentle
One Sheet: $15 - $30

SING, COWBOY, SING
(1937 - Grand National) Tex Ritter, Louise Stanley
One Sheet: $150 - $300

SING, DANCE, PLENTY HOT
(1940 - Republic) Johnny Downs, Ruth Terry

SING FOR YOUR SUPPER
(1941 - Columbia) Jinx Falkenburg, Buddy Rogers
One Sheet: $30 - $50

SING ME A LOVE SONG
(1936 - Warner Bros.) James Melton, Patricia Ellis
One Sheet: $75 - $125

SING ME A SONG OF TEXAS
(1945 - Columbia) Rosemary Lane, Tom Tyler
One Sheet: $40 - $75

SING, NEIGHBOR, SING
(1944 - Republic) Ruth Terry, Lulubelle & Scotty
One Sheet: $15 - $35

SING SING NIGHTS
(1934 - Monogram) Conway Tearle, Boots Mallory
One Sheet: $75 - $150

SING WHILE YOU DANCE
(1946 - Columbia) Ellen Drew, Robert Stanton
One Sheet: $30 - $50

SING WHILE YOU'RE ABLE
(1937 - Melody) Pinky Tomlin, Toby King
One Sheet: $50 - $100

SING YOU SINNERS
(1938 - Paramount) Bing Crosby, Fred MacMurray, Ellen Drew
One Sheet: $125 - $250

SING YOUR WAY HOME
(1945 - RKO) Jack Haley, Anne Jeffreys
One Sheet: $30 - $50

SING YOUR WORRIES AWAY
(1942 - RKO) Bert Lahr, Buddy Ebsen, June Havoc
One Sheet: $30 - $50

SINGAPORE
(1947 - Universal) Fred MacMurray, Ava Gardner
One Sheet: $50 - $100

SINGAPORE MUTINY
(1928 - FBO) Ralph Ince, Estelle Taylor
One Sheet: $150 - $300

SINGAPORE WOMAN
(1941 - Warner Bros.) Brenda Marshall, David Bruce, Virginia Field
One Sheet: $15 - $35

SINGER NOT THE SONG, THE
(1962 - Paramount) John Mills, Dirk Bogarde
One Sheet: $7 - $15

SINGIN' IN THE CORN
(1946 - Columbia) Judy Canova, Allen Jenkins
One Sheet: $30 - $50

SINGIN' IN THE RAIN
(1951 - MGM) Gene Kelly, Debbie Reynolds, Jean Hagen
One Sheet: $700 - $1,200

SINGIN' IN THE RAIN

(1962R - MGM) Gene Kelly, Debbie Reynolds
One Sheet: $30 - $50   *Re-release.*

SINGIN' IN THE RAIN
(1975R - MGM) Gene Kelly, Debbie Reynolds,
Jean Hagen
One Sheet: $15 - $25   *Re-release.*

SINGIN' SPURS
(1948 - Columbia) Hoosier Hot Shots, Pat
White
One Sheet: $30 - $60

SINGING BUCKAROO, THE
(1937 - Spectrum) Fred Scott
One Sheet: $75 - $125

SINGING COWBOY, THE
(1936 - Republic) Gene Autry, Smiley Burnette
One Sheet: $1,300 - $2,000   *Cowboy
Movie Posters #191. Rare; many consider this
one sheet to be Gene's best poster.*

SINGING COWGIRL, THE
(1939 - Coronado) Dorothy Page
One Sheet: $50 - $100

SINGING FOOL, THE
(1928 - Warner Bros.) Al Jolson
One Sheet: $5,000 - $7,500

One Sheet

SINGING GUNS
(1950 - Republic) Vaughn Monroe, Ella Raines
One Sheet: $15 - $30

One Sheet

SINGING HILL, THE
(1941 - Republic) Gene Autry, Smiley Burnette
One Sheet: $150 - $300

SINGING IN THE AIR
(1937 - RKO) -
One Sheet: $100 - $200

SINGING KID, THE
(1936 - Warner Bros.) Al Jolson, Sybil Jason
One Sheet: $1,300 - $2,000

SINGING MARINE, THE
(1937 - Warner Bros.) Dick Powell, Doris
Weston
One Sheet: $75 - $150   *Duotone.*

SINGING NUN, THE
(1966 - MGM) Debbie Reynolds, Ricardo
Montalban
One Sheet: $15 - $25

SINGING ON THE TRAIL
(1946 - Columbia) Ken Curtis, Jeff Donnell
One Sheet: $15 - $30

SINGING OUTLAW
(1937 - Universal) Bob Baker, Joan Barclay
One Sheet: $50 - $100

SINGING SHERIFF, THE
(1944 - Universal) Bob Crosby, Fay McKenzie
One Sheet: $30 - $50

SINGING SPURS
(1948 - Columbia) The Hoosier Hotshots, Kirby
Grant
One Sheet: $30 - $60

SINGING VAGABOND, THE
(1935 - Republic) Gene Autry, Smiley Burnette
One Sheet: $500 - $800   *Cowboy
Movie Posters #'s 178, 181.*

SINGLE GIRLS, THE
(1973 - Dimension) Claudia Jennings, Jean
Marie Engels
One Sheet: $7 - $15   *Sexploitation.*

One Sheet

SINGLE ROOM FURNISHED
(1968 - Crown) Jayne Mansfield
One Sheet: $30 - $50   *Mansfield's
final film.*

SINGLE SIN, THE
(1931 - Tiffany) Kay Johnson, Bert Lytell
One Sheet: $100 - $200

SINGLE STANDARD, THE
(1929 - MGM) Greta Garbo, Nils Asther
One Sheet: $1,900 - $3,000

SINGLE WHITE FEMALE
(1992 - Columbia) Bridget Fonda, Jennifer
Jason Leigh
One Sheet: $5 - $10

SINGLE-HANDED SANDERS
(1932 - Monogram) Tom Tyler, Margaret Morris
One Sheet: $500 - $800

SINGLE-HANDED SANDERS
(194?R - Astor) Tom Tyler, Margaret Morris
One Sheet: $100 - $200   *Re-release.*

SINGLES
(1992 - Warner Bros.) Matt Dillon, Bridget
Fonda
One Sheet: $5 - $10

SINISTER JOURNEY
(1948 - United Artists) William Boyd, Andy
Clyde
One Sheet: $50 - $100   *Hopalong
Cassidy series.*

SINISTER URGE, THE
(1961 - Headliner) Kenne Duncan, James
Moore, Dir: Ed Wood Jr.
One Sheet: $75 - $125

SINK THE BISMARCK!
(1960 - 20th Century Fox) Kenneth More, Dana
Wynter
One Sheet: $10 - $20

SINNER TAKE ALL
(1936 - MGM) Bruce Cabot, Margaret Lindsay
One Sheet: $50 - $100

SINNER'S HOLIDAY
(1930 - Warner Bros.) Grant Withers, James
Cagney, Joan Blondell
One Sheet: $2,500 - $4,000   *Cagney's first
film, he is third billed.*

SINNERS, THE
(1952 - -) Dir: Julien Duvivier
One Sheet: $30 - $50

SINNERS IN HEAVEN
(1924 - Paramount) Bebe Daniels, Richard Dix
One Sheet: $300 - $700

SINNERS IN PARADISE
(1938 - Universal) John Boles, Madge Evans
One Sheet: $75 - $150

SINNERS IN THE SUN
(1932 - Paramount Publix) Carole Lombard,
Chester Morris, Cary Grant
One Sheet: $1,300 - $2,000

SINS OF JEZEBEL
(1953 - Lippert) Paulette Goddard, George
Nader
One Sheet: $20 - $40

SINS OF MADELEINE
(195?R - Astor) Hedy Lamarr, Dennis O'Keefe,
John Loder
One Sheet: $20 - $40   *Re-titled re-
release of Dishonored Lady.*

SINS OF MAN
(1936 - 20th Century Fox) Jean Hersholt, Don
Ameche
One Sheet: $100 - $200

SINS OF RACHEL CADE, THE
(1961 - Warner Bros.) Angie Dickinson, Peter
Finch
One Sheet: $10 - $20

SINS OF THE BORGIAS
(1955 - Ariane) Martine Carol, Pedro
Armendariz
One Sheet: $10 - $20   *AKA:
LURETIA BORGIA.*

SINS OF THE CHILDREN
(1930 - MGM) Robert Montgomery, Louis Mann
One Sheet: $125 - $250

SINS OF THE CHILDREN
(1936 - Grand National) Eric Linden, Cecilia
Parker
One Sheet: $50 - $100

SINS OF THE FATHERS
(1928 - Paramount) Emil Jannings, Ruth
Chatterton
One Sheet: $1,900 - $3,000

SINS OF THE MOTHERS, THE
(1919 - Vitagraph) Anita Stewart
One Sheet: $200 - $400

SINS OF YOUTH, THE
(1960 - -) Agnes Laurent, Gil Videl
One Sheet: $10 - $20

SIOUX CITY SUE
(1946 - Republic) Gene Autry, Lynne Roberts
One Sheet: $100 - $200

SIOUX CITY SUE
(1953R - Republic) Gene Autry, Lynne Roberts
One Sheet: $40 - $75   *Re-release.*

SIREN CALL, THE
(1921 - Paramount) Dorothy Dalton
One Sheet: $500 - $900

SIREN OF ATLANTIS
(1948 - United Artists) Maria Montez, Jean-
Pierre Aumont, Dennis O'Keefe
One Sheet: $50 - $100

SIREN OF BAGDAD
(1953 - Columbia) Paul Henreid, Patricia
Medina
One Sheet: $15 - $30

SIRENS
(1994 - Miramax) Hugh Grant, Tara Fitzgerald
One Sheet: $5 - $10

SIROCCO
(1951 - Columbia) Humphrey Bogart, Marta
Toren
One Sheet: $75 - $125

SIS HOPKINS
(1919 - Goldwyn) Mabel Normand, John
Bowers
One Sheet: $250 - $500

SIS HOPKINS
(1941 - Republic) Judy Canova, Bob Crosby,
Charles Butterworth
One Sheet: $30 - $50

SISTER ACT
(1992 - Buena Vista) Whoopi Goldberg, Maggie
Smith
One Sheet: $3 - $5

SISTER ACT 2
(1993 - Buena Vista) Whoopi Goldberg, Kathy
Najimy
One Sheet: $3 - $5

SISTER IN-LAW, THE
(1974 - Crown) John Savage, Anne Saxon
One Sheet: $3 - $5

SISTER KENNY
(1946 - RKO) Rosalind Russell, Dean Jagger
One Sheet: $75 - $150   *James
Montgomery Flagg art.*

SISTER, SISTER
(1987 - -) Diahann Carroll, Rosalind Cash,
Irene Cara
One Sheet: $3 - $5

SISTER TO JUDAS
(1933 - Mayfair) -
One Sheet: $100 - $200

SISTERS, THE
(1914 - Monopol) Lillian and Dorothy Gish
One Sheet: $250 - $600

SISTERS
(1930 - Columbia) Sally O'Neil, Molly O'Day
One Sheet: $150 - $300

SISTERS, THE
(1938 - Warner Bros.) Bette Davis, Errol Flynn
One Sheet: $2,500 - $4,000

One Sheet

SISTERS
(1973 - AIP) Margot Kidder, Jennifer Salt, Dir:
De Palma
One Sheet: $15 - $30

SISTERS OF DEATH
(1976 - World Wide) Arthur Franz, Claudia
Jennings
One Sheet: $15 - $25

SISTERS UNDER THE SKIN
(1934 - Columbia) Elissa Landi, Frank Morgan
One Sheet: $50 - $100

SIT TIGHT
(1931 - Warner Bros.) Joe E. Brown, Winnie
Brown
One Sheet: $150 - $300

SITTER-DOWNERS, THE
(1937 - Columbia) The Three Stooges (Curly)
One Sheet: $8,500 - $14,000   *Comedy short.
Duotone.*

SITTING BULL
(1960 - United Artists) Dale Robertson, Mary
Murphy
One Sheet: $15 - $30

SITTING BULL AT THE "SPIRIT LAKE MASSACRE"
(1927 - -) Bryant Washburn, Ann Schaeffer
One Sheet: $150 - $300

SITTING ON THE MOON
(1936 - Republic) Roger Pryor, Grace Bradley
One Sheet: $50 - $100

SITTING PRETTY
(1933 - Paramount) Jack Oakie, Jack Haley, Ginger Rogers
One Sheet: $200 - $400

SITTING PRETTY
(1948 - 20th Century Fox) Robert Young, Maureen O'Hara
One Sheet: $15 - $35

SITTING TARGET
(1972 - MGM) Oliver Reed, Jill St. John
One Sheet: $3 - $5

SITUATION HOPELESS-BUT NOT SERIOUS
(1965 - Paramount) Alec Guinness, Michael Connors
One Sheet: $5 - $10

SIX BLACK HORSES
(1962 - Universal) Audie Murphy, Dan Duryea
One Sheet: $20 - $40

SIX BRIDGES TO CROSS
(1955 - Universal) Tony Curtis, Julie Adams, Sal Mineo
One Sheet: $30 - $50   *Mineo's film debut.*

SIX CYLINDER LOVE
(1923 - Fox) Ernest Treux
One Sheet: $250 - $500

SIX CYLINDER LOVE
(1931 - Fox) Spencer Tracy, Edward Everett Horton
One Sheet: $200 - $400

SIX DAY BIKE RIDER
(1934 - Warner Bros.) Joe E. Brown, Maxine Doyle
One Sheet: $200 - $400   *Sports (Bicycle racing). Sports Movie Posters #106.*

SIX DAYS, SIX NIGHTS
(1995 - Fine Line) Anne Parillaud, Beatrice Dalle
One Sheet: $5 - $10

SIX DEGREES OF SEPARATION
(1993 - MGM) Donald Sutherland, Stockard Channing
One Sheet: $5 - $10

SIX GUN DECISION
(1953 - Allied Artists) Guy Madison, Andy Devine
One Sheet: $15 - $35   *Wild Bill Hickok series.*

SIX GUN MAN
(1946 - PRC) Bob Steele, Jean Carlin
One Sheet: $30 - $60

SIX GUN MESA
(1950 - Monogram) Johnny Mack Brown, Gail Davis
One Sheet: $15 - $25

SIX GUN MUSIC
(1949 - Universal) Tex Williams, Lina Romay
One Sheet: $15 - $35

SIX HOURS TO LIVE
(1932 - Fox) Warner Baxter, Irene Ware
One Sheet: $150 - $300

633 SQUADRON
(1964 - United Artists) Cliff Robertson, George Chakiris
One Sheet: $10 - $20

SIX LESSONS FROM MADAME LA ZONGA
(1941 - Universal) Lupe Velez, Leon Errol
One Sheet: $50 - $100

SIX OF A KIND
(1934 - Paramount) Charlie Ruggles, Mary Boland, W. C. Fields
One Sheet: $800 - $1,500

SIX PACK
(1982 - 20th Century Fox) Kenny Rogers, Diane Lane

One Sheet: $15 - $30   *Sports (stock car racing). Sports Movie Posters #25.*

SIX PACK ANNIE
(1975 - AIP) Lindsay Bloom, Jana Bellan, Bruce Boxleitner
One Sheet: $15 - $25

SIX SHE'S AND A HE
(1964 - -) -
One Sheet: $7 - $15

SIX WEEKS
(1982 - Universal) Dudley Moore, Mary Tyler Moore
One Sheet: $3 - $5

SIX-GUN GOLD
(1941 - RKO) Tim Holt
One Sheet: $20 - $40

SIX-GUN GOSPEL
(1943 - Monogram) Johnny Mack Brown, Raymond Hatton
One Sheet: $20 - $40

SIX-GUN JUSTICE
(1935 - Spectrum) Bill Cody
One Sheet: $75 - $150

SIX-GUN LAW
(1947 - Columbia) Charles Starrett, Smiley Burnette
One Sheet: $15 - $35

SIX-GUN RHYTHM
(1939 - Grand National) Tex Fletcher, Joan Barclay
One Sheet: $40 - $75

One Sheet

SIX-GUN SERENADE
(1947 - Monogram) Jimmy Wakely, Kay Morely
One Sheet: $15 - $35

6000 DOLLAR NIGGER
(197? - -) -
One Sheet: $20 - $40   *Blaxploitation.*

6000 ENEMIES
(1939 - MGM) Walter Pidgeon, Rita Johnson
One Sheet: $75 - $150

SIXTEEN CANDLES
(1984 - Universal) Molly Ringwold, Paul Dooley
One Sheet: $15 - $25

SIXTEEN FATHOMS DEEP
(1934 - Monogram) Lon Chaney Jr., Sally O'Neil
One Sheet: $125 - $250

SIXTEEN FATHOMS DEEP
(1948 - Monogram) Lon Chaney Jr., Arthur Lake, Lloyd Bridges
One Sheet: $40 - $75

6TH MAN, THE
(1997 - Touchstone) Marlon Wayans, Kadeem Hardison
One Sheet: $4 - $8   *Sports (Basketball).*

SIXTY GLORIOUS YEARS
(1938 - RKO) Anna Neagle, Anton Walbrook
One Sheet: $100 - $200   *AKA: QUEEN OF DESTINY.*

SKABENGA
(1955 - Allied Artists) -
One Sheet: $15 - $30   *Documentary.*

SKATETOWN U.S.A.
(1979 - Columbia) Scott Baio, Patrick Swayze
One Sheet: $10 - $20   *Sports Movie*

Posters #307.

SKELETON DANCE, THE
(1929 - Columbia) Silly Symphony
One Sheet: $16,000 - $25,000   *Cartoon. The Disney Poster, pg. 8.*

SKI BUM, THE
(1971 - Avco/Embassy) Zalman King, Charlotte Rampling
One Sheet: $5 - $10

SKI CHASE, THE
(1937 - World) Hannes Schneider
One Sheet: $40 - $75

SKI FEVER
(1969 - Allied Artists) Martin Milner, Claudia Martin
One Sheet: $7 - $15

SKI ON THE WILD SIDE
(1967 - Sigma III) -
One Sheet: $7 - $15

SKI PARTY
(1965 - AIP) Frankie Avalon, Dwayne Hickman
One Sheet: $30 - $50

SKI PATROL
(1940 - Universal) Luli Deste, Phillip Dorn
One Sheet: $40 - $75

SKI PATROL
(1981 - Triumph) -
One Sheet: $7 - $15

SKI TROOP ATTACK
(1960 - The Film Group) Frank Wolff, Michael Forrest
One Sheet: $15 - $35   *Dir: Roger Corman*

SKID ROW
(1934 - Real Life Dramas) -
One Sheet: $75 - $125   *Exploitation. AKA: Wages Of Sin.*

SKIDOO
(1969 - Paramount) Jackie Gleason, Carol Channing, Groucho Marx
One Sheet: $20 - $40   *Marx's final film.*

SKIN DEEP
(1929 - Warner Bros.) Monte Blue, Davey Lee
One Sheet: $150 - $300

Insert

SKIN DEEP
(1989 - -) John Ritter, Vincent Gardenia
One Sheet: $3 - $5

SKIN GAME, THE
(1931 - BIP) Edmund Gwenn, Helen Hayes, Dir: Hitchcock
One Sheet: $1,600 - $2,500   *British.*

SKIN GAME, THE
(1971 - Warner Bros.) James Garner, Lou Gossett
One Sheet: $10 - $20

SKINNER'S DRESS SUIT
(1917 - Essanay) Reginald Denny, Laura La Plante
One Sheet: $150 - $300

SKINNY THE MOOCHER
(1939 - Columbia) Charley Chase
One Sheet: $75 - $150   *Comedy short. Red and black duotone.*

SKIPALONG ROSENBLOOM
(1951 - Eagle Lion Classics) Max Baer, Maxie

Rosenbloom
One Sheet: $15 - $30

SKIPPER SURPRISED HIS WIFE, THE
(1950 - MGM) Robert Walker, Joan Leslie
One Sheet: $15 - $25

SKIPPY
(1931 - Paramount Publix) Jackie Cooper, Jackie Searle
One Sheet: $700 - $1,200   *Academy Award Movie Posters #21.*

SKIRT SHY
(1929 - MGM) Harry Langdon, Nancy Dover
One Sheet: $350 - $750

SKIRTS AHOY
(1952 - MGM) Esther Williams, Keefe Brasselle
One Sheet: $30 - $60

SKULL, THE
(1965 - Paramount) Peter Cushing, Patrick Wymark, Christopher Lee
One Sheet: $30 - $50

SKULLDUGGERY
(1970 - Universal) Burt Reynolds, Susan Clark
One Sheet: $7 - $15

SKY BANDITS
(1986 - London Front) Scott McGinnis, Jeff Osterhage
One Sheet: $3 - $5

SKY BRIDE
(1932 - Paramount) Richard Arlen, Jack Oakie
One Sheet: $75 - $150

SKY COMMANDO
(1953 - Columbia) Dan Duryea, Frances Gifford
One Sheet: $15 - $30

SKY DEVILS
(1932 - United Artists) Spencer Tracy, Ann Dvorak
One Sheet: $150 - $350

Three Sheet

SKY DEVILS
(194?R - Astor) Spencer Tracy
One Sheet: $50 - $100   *Re-release.*

SKY DRAGON
(1949 - Monogram) Roland Winters, Keye Luke
One Sheet: $50 - $100   *Charlie Chan series.*

SKY FULL OF MOON
(1952 - MGM) Carleton Carpenter, Jan Sterling
One Sheet: $10 - $20

SKY GIANT
(1938 - RKO) Richard Dix, Joan Fontaine, Chester Morris
One Sheet: $150 - $300

SKY HAWK
(1929 - Fox) Helen Chandler, John Garrick
One Sheet: $500 - $800

SKY HIGH
(1922 - Fox) Tom Mix, Eva Novak
One Sheet: $500 - $800

SKY HIGH
(1951 - Lippert) Sid Melton, Mara Lynn
One Sheet: $10 - $20

SKY HIGH CORRAL
(1926 - Universal) Art Acord, Marguerite Clayton
One Sheet: $300 - $650

SKY IS FALLING, THE

(1943 - 20th Century Fox) Mighty Mouse
One Sheet: $250 - $600   *Cartoon. Full color stock poster with printed title. Huge image of Mighty Mouse on yellow background.*

SKY IS RED, THE
(1952 - Realart) Marina Berti, Jacques Sernas
One Sheet: $15 - $30

SKY LINER
(1949 - Screen Guild) Richard Travis, Pamela Blake, Rochelle Hudson
One Sheet: $15 - $30

SKY MURDER
(1940 - MGM) Walter Pidgeon, Donald Meek
One Sheet: $40 - $75   *Nick Carter Detective Series.*

SKY PARADE
(1936 - Paramount) Jimmie Allen, William Gargan
One Sheet: $75 - $150

SKY PATROL
(1939 - Monogram) John Trent, Marjorie Reynolds
One Sheet: $75 - $125

SKY RAIDERS, THE
(1931 - Columbia) Lloyd Hughes, Marceline Day
One Sheet: $100 - $200

SKY RAIDERS
(1941 - Universal) Donald Woods, Billy Halop
One Sheet: $50 - $100   *Serial. 12 Chapters.*

SKY RIDERS
(1976 - 20th Century Fox) James Coburn, Susannah York
One Sheet: $3 - $5

SKY SPIDER, THE
(1931 - Action) Glenn Tryon, Beryl Mercer
One Sheet: $200 - $400

SKY'S THE LIMIT, THE
(1943 - RKO) Fred Astaire, Joan Leslie
One Sheet: $125 - $250

SKYBOUND
(1935 - Puritan) Eddie Nugent, Lloyd Hughes
One Sheet: $50 - $100

SKYDIVERS
(1963 - Crown) Kevin Casey, Eric Tomlin
One Sheet: $5 - $10

SKYJACKED
(1972 - MGM) Charlton Heston, Yvette Mimieux
One Sheet: $5 - $10

SKYLARK
(1941 - Paramount) Claudette Colbert, Ray Milland, Brian Aherne
One Sheet: $50 - $100

SKYLINE
(1931 - Fox) Maureen O'Sullivan, Thomas Meighan
One Sheet: $200 - $400

SKYLINE SERENADE
(1941 - Universal) -
One Sheet: $40 - $75

SKYSCRAPER
(1928 - -) William Boyd, Alan Hale
One Sheet: $250 - $600

SKYSCRAPER SOULS
(1932 - MGM) Maureen O'Sullivan, Warren William
One Sheet: $250 - $600

SKYTROOPER
(1942 - RKO/Disney) Donald Duck
One Sheet: $3,500 - $5,000   *Cartoon. Cartoon Movie Posters #168.*

SKYWAY
(1933 - Monogram) Ray Walker, Katherine Crawford
One Sheet: $75 - $150

SKYWAYMAN, THE
(1920 - William Fox) Ormer Locklear, Louise Lovely
One Sheet: $600 - $1,000

SLACKER, THE
(1917 - -) Emily Stevens

One Sheet: $250 - $500

SLAGET OM ENGLAND
(1943 - United Artists) Dir: Frank Capra
One Sheet: $125 - $250   *Danish.*

SLAMDANCE
(1987 - -) Tom Hulce, Mary Elizabeth Mastrantonio
One Sheet: $15 - $25

SLAMS, THE
(1973 - MGM) Jim Brown, Judy Pace
One Sheet: $10 - $20   *Blaxploitation.*

SLANDER
(1956 - MGM) Van Johnson, Ann Blyth
One Sheet: $15 - $25

SLANDER HOUSE
(1938 - Progressive) Adrienne Ames, George Meeker
One Sheet: $50 - $100

SLAP SHOT
(1977 - Universal) Paul Newman, Lindsay Crouse
One Sheet: $15 - $30   *Sports (Hockey). Sports Movie Posters # 234. Review:$10-$20.*

SLAP-HAPPY SLEUTHS
(1950 - Columbia) The Three Stooges (Shemp)
One Sheet: $200 - $400   *Comedy short. Duotone.*

SLASHER
(1952 - Lippert) James Kennedy, Joan Collins
One Sheet: $15 - $35

SLATTERY'S HURRICANE
(1949 - 20th Century Fox) Richard Widmark, Linda Darnell, Veronica Lake
One Sheet: $40 - $75

SLAUGHTER
(1972 - AIP) Jim Brown, Stella Stevens, Rip Torn
One Sheet: $15 - $30   *Blaxploitation.*

SLAUGHTER HOTEL
(1971 - American International) Klaus Kinski, Rosalba Neri
One Sheet: $10 - $20   *AKA: ASYLUM EROTICA.*

SLAUGHTER OF THE INNOCENT
(1993 - Shapiro) Scott Glenn
One Sheet: $3 - $5

SLAUGHTER ON TENTH AVENUE
(1957 - Universal) Richard Egan, Jan Sterling
One Sheet: $10 - $20

SLAUGHTER TRAIL
(1951 - RKO) Brian Donlevy, Virginia Grey
One Sheet: $15 - $30

SLAUGHTER'S BIG RIP-OFF
(1973 - AIP) Jim Brown, Brock Peters
One Sheet: $15 - $30   *Blaxploitation.*

SLAUGHTERHOUSE
(1987 - -) Joe Barton, Sherry Rendorf
One Sheet: $5 - $10

SLAUGHTERHOUSE-FIVE
(1972 - Universal) Michael Sacks, Ron Leibman
One Sheet: $15 - $25

SLAVE, THE
(1963 - MGM) Steve Reeves, Jacques Sernas
One Sheet: $20 - $40

SLAVE GIRL
(1947 - Universal) Yvonne De Carlo, George Brent
One Sheet: $30 - $50

SLAVE GIRLS FROM BEYOND INFINITY
(1987 - -) Brinke Stevens, Cindy Beal, Elizabeth Cyton
One Sheet: $15 - $25

SLAVE OF THE CANNIBAL GOD
(1979 - New Line) Ursula Andress, Stacy Keach
One Sheet: $10 - $20

SLAVE SHIP
(1937 - 20th Century Fox) Warner Baxter, Wallace Beery
One Sheet: $200 - $400

SLAVE TRADE IN THE WORLD TODAY
(1964 - Reade-Sterling) -
One Sheet: $15 - $25

SLAVES
(1969 - Continental) Stephen Boyd, Dionne Warwick, Ossie Davis
One Sheet: $5 - $10

SLAVES IN BONDAGE
(1937 - Jay-Dee-Kay) -
One Sheet: $75 - $150   *Sexploitation.*

SLAVES OF BABYLON
(1953 - Columbia) Richard Conte, Linda Christian
One Sheet: $15 - $30

SLAVES OF NEW YORK
(1989 - -) Bernadette Peters, Adam Coleman Howard
One Sheet: $7 - $15

SLAVES OF THE INVISIBLE MONSTER
(1950 - -) Richard Webb, Alice Towne
One Sheet: $50 - $100   *Feature version of THE INVISIBLE MONSTER.*

SLAY IT WITH FLOWERS
(1941 - Columbia) Fox & Crow
One Sheet: $150 - $300   *Cartoon.*

SLEEP, MY LOVE
(1948 - United Artists) Claudette Colbert, Robert Cummings
One Sheet: $40 - $75

SLEEP WALKER
(1942 - Disney) -
One Sheet: $150 - $300   *Cartoon.*

SLEEPER
(1974 - United Artists) Woody Allen, Diane Keaton
One Sheet: $15 - $30

One Sheet

SLEEPERS
(1996 - Warner Bros.) Brad Pitt, Jason Patric, Robert DeNiro, Dustin Hoffman
One Sheet: $5 - $10

SLEEPERS EAST
(1934 - Fox) Wynne Gibson, Preston Foster
One Sheet: $100 - $200

SLEEPERS WEST
(1941 - 20th Century Fox) Lloyd Nolan, Lynn Bari
One Sheet: $50 - $100

One Sheet

SLEEPING BEAUTY
(1959 - Buena Vista/Disney) -
One Sheet: $250 - $500   *Cartoon. Price*

is for Style A one sheet. One Sheet(Style B):$600-$1,000. Cartoon Movie Posters #383 and #385. The Disney Poster, pg. 86.

SLEEPING BEAUTY
(1966 - Royal Films) Alla Sizova
One Sheet: $7 - $15   *Dancing (Ballet).*

SLEEPING BEAUTY
(1970R - Buena Vista/Disney) -
One Sheet: $40 - $75   *Re-release. Cartoon.*

SLEEPING BEAUTY
(1979R - Buena Vista/Disney) -
One Sheet: $15 - $30   *Re-release. Cartoon.*

SLEEPING BEAUTY
(1986R - Buena Vista/Disney) -
One Sheet: $15 - $30   *Re-release. Cartoon.*

SLEEPING CAR TO TRIESTE
(1949 - Eagle Lion) Jean Kent, Albert Lieven
One Sheet: $10 - $20

SLEEPING CARDINAL, THE
(1931 - Warner Bros.) Arthur Wontner, Ian Fleming
One Sheet: $250 - $600   *AKA: SHERLOCK HOLMES' FATAL HOUR.*

SLEEPING CITY, THE
(1950 - Universal) Richard Conte, Coleen Gray
One Sheet: $40 - $75

SLEEPING PARTNERS
(1930 - BIP) Seymour Hicks, Edna Best
One Sheet: $75 - $125

SLEEPING TIGER, THE
(1954 - Famous) Alexis Smith, Dirk Bogarde
One Sheet: $40 - $75

SLEEPING WITH THE ENEMY
(1991 - 20th Century Fox) Julia Roberts, Patrick Bergin
One Sheet: $5 - $10

SLEEPLESS IN SEATTLE
(1993 - TriStar) Tom Hanks, Meg Ryan
One Sheet: $10 - $20

SLEEPLESS NIGHTS
(1933 - British International) Stanley Lupino, Polly Walker
One Sheet: $500 - $800

SLEEPY LAGOON
(1943 - Republic) Judy Canova, Dennis Day
One Sheet: $30 - $50

SLEEPY-TIME DONALD
(1947 - RKO/Disney) Donald Duck
One Sheet: $1,900 - $3,000   *Cartoon. Cartoon Movie Posters #173.*

SLEEPYTIME GAL
(1942 - Republic) Judy Canova, Tom Brown
One Sheet: $30 - $50

SLEEPY-TIME TOM
(1951 - MGM) Tom & Jerry
One Sheet: $300 - $700   *Cartoon. Full color stone litho.*

SLENDER THREAD, THE
(1966 - Paramount) Sidney Poitier, Anne Bancroft
One Sheet: $15 - $25

SLEUTH
(1972 - 20th Century Fox) Laurence Olivier, Michael Caine
One Sheet: $10 - $20

SLICKED-UP PUP
(1951 - MGM) Tom & Jerry
One Sheet: $300 - $700   *Cartoon. Full color stone litho.*

SLIDE DONALD SLIDE
(1949 - RKO/Disney) Donald Duck
One Sheet: $2,200 - $3,500   *Cartoon.*

SLIDE, KELLY, SLIDE
(1927 - MGM) William Haines, Sally O'neil
One Sheet: $1,300 - $2,000   *Sports (Baseball). Sports Movie Posters #35.*

SLIGHT CASE OF LARCENY, A
(1953 - MGM) Mickey Rooney, Eddie Bracken

One Sheet: $15 - $25

SLIGHT CASE OF MURDER, A
(1938 - Warner Bros.) Edward G. Robinson,
Jane Bryan
One Sheet: $75 - $150

SLIGHTLY DANGEROUS
(1943 - MGM) Lana Turner, Robert Young
One Sheet: $100 - $200

One Sheet

SLIGHTLY FRENCH
(1949 - Columbia) Dorothy Lamour, Don
Ameche
One Sheet: $30 - $50

SLIGHTLY HONORABLE
(1940 - United Artists) Pat O'Brien, Broderick
Crawford
One Sheet: $40 - $75

SLIGHTLY SCANDALOUS
(1946 - Universal) Sheila Ryan, Fred Brady
One Sheet: $30 - $50

SLIGHTLY SCARLET
(1930 - Paramount Famous Lasky) Evelyn
Brent, Clive Brook
One Sheet: $100 - $200

SLIGHTLY SCARLET
(1955 - RKO) John Payne, Arlene Dahl
One Sheet: $30 - $50

SLIGHTLY TEMPTED
(1940 - Universal) Hugh Herbert, Peggy Moran
One Sheet: $40 - $75

SLIGHTLY TERRIFIC
(1944 - Universal) Leon Errol, Anne Rooney
One Sheet: $20 - $40

SLIM
(1937 - Warner Bros.) Pat O'Brien, Henry
Fonda
One Sheet: $150 - $300

SLIM CARTER
(1957 - Universal) Jock Mahoney, Julie Adams
One Sheet: $15 - $25

SLIM SHOULDERS
(1922 - Hodkinson) Irene Castle, Rod La
Rocque
One Sheet: $200 - $400

SLIME PEOPLE, THE
(1963 - Hansen) Robert Hutton, Susan Hart
One Sheet: $30 - $50

SLING BLADE
(1996 - Miramax) Billy Bob Thornton, Dwight
Yoakam
One Sheet: $5 - $10

SLINGSHOT KID, THE
(1927 - -) Buzz Barton, Frank Rice
One Sheet: $500 - $800

SLIP AT THE SWITCH, A
(1932 - RKO) Chic Sale, George Hay
One Sheet: $100 - $200

SLIPPERY SILKS
(1936 - Columbia) The Three Stooges (Curly)
One Sheet: $10,000 - $16,000   _Comedy short._
Duotone.

SLIPPING WIVES
(1926 - Pathe) Laurel & Hardy
One Sheet: $5,000 - $8,000   _Their first film_
together.

SLIPPY MCGEE

(1948 - Republic) Donald Barry, Dale Evans
One Sheet: $15 - $35

SLITHER
(1973 - MGM) James Caan, Peter Boyle, Sally
Kellerman
One Sheet: $10 - $20

SLITHIS
(1978 - Fabtrak) Alan Blanchard, Judy
Motulsky
One Sheet: $15 - $25

One Sheet

SLIVER
(1993 - Paramount) Sharon Stone, William
Baldwin, Tom Berenger
One Sheet: $5 - $10

SLOW DANCING IN THE BIG CITY
(1978 - United Artists) Paul Sorvino, Anne
Ditchburn
One Sheet: $10 - $20

SLUGGER'S WIFE, THE
(1985 - Columbia) Michael O'Keefe, Rebecca
DeMornay
One Sheet: $3 - $5

SLUMBER PARTY '57
(1977 - Cannon) Debra Winger, Noelle North
One Sheet: $7 - $15

SLUMBER PARTY MASSACRE
(1982 - -) Michele Michaels, Robin Stille
One Sheet: $10 - $20

SMALL BACK ROOM, THE
(1949 - London) David Farrar, Jack Hawkins
One Sheet: $15 - $25

SMALL CHANGE
(1976 - New World) Geary Desmouceaux,
Phillippe Goldman
One Sheet: $125 - $250   _French._

SMALL FACES
(1996 - October Films) Claire Higgins, Iain
Robertson
One Sheet: $4 - $8

SMALL ONE, THE
(1978 - Buena Vista/Disney) -
One Sheet: $7 - $15   _Cartoon._

SMALL TOWN BOY
(1937 - Grand National) Stuart Erwin, Joyce
Compton
One Sheet: $50 - $100

SMALL TOWN DEB
(1941 - 20th Century Fox) Jane Withers, Jane
Darwell
One Sheet: $50 - $100

SMALL TOWN GIRL
(1936 - MGM) Janet Gaynor, Robert Taylor,
James Stewart
One Sheet: $125 - $250

SMALL TOWN GIRL
(1952 - MGM) Jane Powell, Farley Granger
One Sheet: $15 - $35

SMALL TOWN IN TEXAS, A
(1976 - AIP) Timothy Bottoms, Susan George
One Sheet: $5 - $10

SMALL VOICE, THE
(1947 - London) Valerie Hobson, James Donald
One Sheet: $15 - $30

SMALL WORLD OF SAMMY LEE, THE
(1963 - Seven Arts) Anthony Newley, Julie
Foster

One Sheet: $5 - $10

SMALLEST SHOW ON EARTH, THE
(1957 - Times) Bill Travers, Virginia McKenna
One Sheet: $30 - $50

SMART ALECKS
(1942 - Monogram) East Side Kids, Maxie
Rosenbloom
One Sheet: $50 - $100

SMART BLONDE
(1936 - Warner Bros.) Glenda Farrell, Barton
MacLane
One Sheet: $75 - $150

SMART GIRL
(1935 - Paramount) Ida Lupino, Kent Taylor,
Gail Patrick
One Sheet: $100 - $200

SMART GIRLS DON'T TALK
(1948 - Warner Bros.) Virginia Mayo, Bruce
Bennett
One Sheet: $15 - $35

SMART GUY
(1943 - Monogram) Rick Vallin, Wanda McKay
One Sheet: $15 - $25

SMART MONEY
(1931 - Warner Bros.) Edward G. Robinson,
James Cagney, Boris Karloff
One Sheet: $2,200 - $3,500

SMART POLITICS
(1948 - Monogram) Freddie Stewart, June
Preisser
One Sheet: $15 - $35

SMART WOMAN
(1931 - RKO) Mary Astor, Robert Ames
One Sheet: $150 - $300

SMART WOMAN
(1948 - Allied Artists) Brian Aherne, Constance
Bennett
One Sheet: $30 - $50

SMARTEST GIRL IN TOWN
(1936 - RKO) Ann Sothern, Gene Raymond
One Sheet: $500 - $800

SMARTY
(1934 - Warner Bros.) Joan Blondell, Warren
William
One Sheet: $75 - $150

SMASHING BARRIERS
(1919 - Vitagraph) William Duncan
One Sheet: $150 - $350   _Serial. 15_
Chapters.

SMASHING THE MONEY RING
(1939 - Warner Bros.) Ronald Reagan, Margot
Stevenson
One Sheet: $200 - $400

SMASHING THE RACKETS
(1938 - RKO) Chester Morris, Frances Mercer
One Sheet: $75 - $150

SMASHING THE SPY RINGS
(1938 - RKO) Fay Wray, Ralph Bellamy
One Sheet: $150 - $300

SMASHING THE VICE TRUST
(1937 - Willis Kent) -
One Sheet: $50 - $100   _Exploitation._

SMASHING TIME
(1968 - Paramount) Lynn Redgrave, Michael
York
One Sheet: $3 - $5

SMASH-UP
(1947 - Universal) Susan Hayward, Lee
Bowman, Eddie Albert
One Sheet: $250 - $600

SMASH-UP ALLEY
(1973 - Victory Lane) Richard Petty, Darren
McGavin
One Sheet: $20 - $40   _Sports (Auto_
Racing).

SMIC, SMAC, SMOC
(1972 - Cinerama) Catherine Allegret, Amidou
One Sheet: $5 - $10

SMILE
(1975 - Universal) Bruce Dern, Barbara Feldon
One Sheet: $5 - $10

SMILE PLEASE
(1924 - Pathecomedy) Harry Langdon
One Sheet: $350 - $750

SMILE WINS, THE
(1923 - Pathe) Our Gang
One Sheet: $600 - $1,000

SMILEY
(1956 - 20th Century Fox) Ralph Richardson,
Colin Peterson
One Sheet: $7 - $15

SMILEY GETS A GUN
(1958 - 20th Century Fox) Keith Calvert, Dame
Sybil Thorndike
One Sheet: $7 - $15

SMILIN' GUNS
(1928 - Universal Jewel) Hoot Gibson
One Sheet: $250 - $600   _Cowboy_
Movie Posters #69.

SMILIN' THROUGH
(1922 - First National) Norma Talmadge
One Sheet: $500 - $800

SMILIN' THROUGH
(1932 - MGM) Norma Shearer, Leslie Howard,
Fredric March
One Sheet: $500 - $800

SMILIN' THROUGH
(1941 - MGM) Jeanette MacDonald, Brian
Aherne
One Sheet: $75 - $150

SMILING GHOST, THE
(1941 - Warner Bros.) Wayne Morris, Alexis
Smith, Brenda Marshall
One Sheet: $40 - $75

SMILING IRISH EYES
(1929 - -) Colleen Moore
One Sheet: $100 - $200

SMILING LIEUTENANT, THE
(1931 - Paramount Publix) Maurice Chevalier,
Claudette Colbert
One Sheet: $600 - $1,000

SMILLA'S SENSE OF SNOW
(1997 - Fox Searchlight) Julia Ormand, Gabriel
Byrne, Vanessa Redgrave
One Sheet: $4 - $8

SMITH!
(1969 - Buena Vista) Glenn Ford, Nancy Olson,
Dean Jagger
One Sheet: $10 - $20

SMITH OF MINNESOTA
(1942 - Columbia) Bruce Smith, Arline Judge
One Sheet: $75 - $150   _Sports_
(Football). Sports Movie Posters #198.

SMITH'S NEW HOME
(1927 - Pathecomedy) Raymond McKee
One Sheet: $250 - $600

SMITH'S PICNIC
(1926 - Pathe) Baby Mary Anne Jackson,
Raymond McKee, Ruth Hiatt
One Sheet: $150 - $300

SMITHY
(1924 - Pathe) Stan Laurel, James Finlayson
One Sheet: $250 - $600

SMITTEN KITTEN
(1951 - MGM) Tom & Jerry
One Sheet: $250 - $600   _Cartoon._
Cartoon Movie Posters #284.

SMOKE LIGHTNING
(1933 - Fox) George O'Brien, Virginia Sale
One Sheet: $150 - $300   _Cowboy_
Movie Posters # 159.

SMOKE SIGNAL
(1955 - Universal International) Rex Reason,
William Talman
One Sheet: $7 - $15

SMOKE TREE RANGE
(1937 - Universal) Buck Jones, Muriel Evans
One Sheet: $250 - $600

SMOKEY AND THE BANDIT
(1977 - Universal) Burt Reynolds, Sally Field,
Jackie Gleason
One Sheet: $15 - $30

SMOKEY AND THE BANDIT II

(1980 - Universal) Burt Reynolds, Jackie Gleason
One Sheet: $5 - $10

SMOKEY AND THE BANDIT III
(1983 - Universal) Jackie Gleason, Jerry Reed
One Sheet: $5 - $10

SMOKEY JOE
(1940 - 20th Century Fox) Terry-toons
One Sheet: $100 - $200   *Cartoon. Full color stone litho. Stock poster with inset title.*

SMOKEY SMITH
(1935 - -) -
One Sheet: $75 - $150

SMOKING GUNS
(1934 - Universal) Ken Maynard, Gloria Shea
One Sheet: $350 - $750

SMOKING GUNS
(194?R - Film Classics) Ken Maynard, Gloria Shea
One Sheet: $15 - $25   *Re-release. Western.*

SMOKY
(1933 - Fox) Victor Jory, Irene Manning
One Sheet: $500 - $800   *Cowboy Movie Posters #'s 158, 161.*

SMOKY
(1946 - 20th Century Fox) Fred MacMurray, Anne Baxter
One Sheet: $30 - $50

SMOKY
(1951R - 20th Century Fox) Fred MacMurray, Anne Baxter
One Sheet: $5 - $10   *Re-release.*

SMOKY
(1966 - 20th Century Fox) Fess Parker, Diana Hyland
One Sheet: $5 - $10

SMOKY CANYON
(1951 - Columbia) Charles Starrett, Smiley Burnette
One Sheet: $15 - $35

SMOKY MOUNTAIN MELODY
(1948 - Columbia) Roy Acuff, Smoky Mountain Boys
One Sheet: $75 - $150   *Country musical.*

SMOKY RIVER SERENADE
(1947 - Columbia) Paul Campbell, Ruth Terry
One Sheet: $15 - $35

SMOKY TRAILS
(1939 - Aurora) Bob Steele
One Sheet: $75 - $150

SMOOTH AS SILK
(1946 - Universal) Kent Taylor, Virginia Grey
One Sheet: $20 - $40

SMOOTH TALK
(1985 - Goldrest) Treat Williams, Laura Dern
One Sheet: $7 - $15

SMORGASBORD
(1983 - Warner Bros.) Jerry Lewis, Herb Edelman
One Sheet: $5 - $10   *AKA: CRACKING UP.*

SMOULDERING FIRES
(1925 - Universal) Pauline Frederick, Laura La Plante
One Sheet: $250 - $500

SMUGGLED CARGO
(1939 - Republic) Rochelle Hudson, Barry MacKay
One Sheet: $30 - $50

SMUGGLER'S GOLD
(1951 - Columbia) Cameron Mitchell, Amanda Blake
One Sheet: $10 - $20

SMUGGLER'S ISLAND
(1950 - Universal) Jeff Chandler, Evelyn Keyes
One Sheet: $15 - $30

SMUGGLERS, THE
(1948 - GFD) Michael Redgrave, Jean Kent
One Sheet: $15 - $25

SMUGGLERS' COVE

(1948 - Monogram) Leo Gorcey, Huntz Hall
One Sheet: $30 - $50

SNAFU
(1945 - Columbia) Conrad Janis, Robert Benchley
One Sheet: $20 - $40

SNAKE PEOPLE, THE
(1970 - Columbia) Boris Karloff, Tongolele
One Sheet: $15 - $35

SNAKE PIT, THE
(1948 - 20th Century Fox) Olivia de Havilland, Mark Stevens, Celeste Holm
One Sheet: $50 - $100

SNAKE PIT, THE
(1953R - 20th Century Fox) Olivia DeHavilland, Mark Stevens, Celeste Holm
One Sheet: $20 - $40   *Re-release.*

SNAKE RIVER DESPERADOES
(1951 - Columbia) Charles Starrett, Smiley Burnette
One Sheet: $15 - $35

SNAKE WOMAN, THE
(1961 - United Artists) John McCarthy, Susan Travers
One Sheet: $15 - $35

SNAPPER, THE
(1994 - -) Colm Meaney, Tina Kellegher
One Sheet: $3 - $5

SNAPPY SNEEZER
(1929 - MGM) Charley Chase, Thelma Todd
One Sheet: $250 - $600

SNEAKERS
(1992 - Universal) Sidney Poitier, Robert Redford
One Sheet: $3 - $5

SNIPER, THE
(1952 - Columbia) Adolphe Menjou, Arthur Franz
One Sheet: $30 - $50

SNIPER
(1993 - TriStar) Tom Berenger, Billy Zane
One Sheet: $3 - $5

SNIPER'S RIDGE
(1961 - 20th Century Fox) Jack Ging, Stanley Clements
One Sheet: $7 - $15

SNITCH IN TIME, A
(1950 - Columbia) The Three Stooges (Shemp)
One Sheet: $200 - $400   *Comedy short. Duotone.*

SNOOPY COME HOME
(1972 - Cinema Center) Snoopy, Charlie Brown
One Sheet: $15 - $35   *Cartoon. Cartoon Movie Posters #388.*

One Sheet

SNORKEL, THE
(1958 - Columbia) Peter Van Eyck, Betta St. John
One Sheet: $5 - $10

SNOW CREATURE, THE
(1954 - United Artists) Paul Langton, Leslie Denison
One Sheet: $30 - $50

SNOW DEVILS, THE
(1965 - MGM) Giacomo Rossi-Stuart, Ombretta Colli
One Sheet: $10 - $20

SNOW DOG
(1950 - Monogram) Kirby Grant, Elena Verdugo
One Sheet: $15 - $30

SNOW JOB
(1972 - Warner Bros.) Jean-Claude Killy, Daniele Gaubert
One Sheet: $7 - $15   *Sports (Skiing). Sports Movie Posters #312.*

SNOW QUEEN, THE
(1960 - Universal) Narrated by Art Linkletter
One Sheet: $40 - $80   *Cartoon. Full color.*

SNOW TREASURE
(1968 - Allied Artists) James Franciscus, Bente Nielsen, Paul Austad
One Sheet: $3 - $5

SNOW WHITE
(1965 - -) K. Gordon Murray
One Sheet: $4 - $8

SNOW WHITE AND THE SEVEN DWARFS
(1937 - RKO/Disney) -
One Sheet: $7,500 - $12,000   *Cartoon. First Disney feature. Price is for Style B one sheet.Style A(no Snow White):$2,000-$3,000. Style C(Snow White in forest, veryrare)$20,000-$30,000. Cartoon Movie Posters #314-#325. The Disney Poster, pg. 78.*

One Sheet (Style A)

SNOW WHITE AND THE SEVEN DWARFS
(1943R - RKO/Disney) Snow White
One Sheet: $500 - $800   *First re-release. Cartoon.*

SNOW WHITE AND THE SEVEN DWARFS
(1951R - RKO/Disney) Snow White
One Sheet: $200 - $400   *Re-release. Cartoon.*

SNOW WHITE AND THE SEVEN DWARFS
(1958R - Buena Vista) Snow White
One Sheet: $50 - $100   *Re-release. Cartoon.*

SNOW WHITE AND THE SEVEN DWARFS
(1967R - Disney) Snow White
One Sheet: $15 - $30   *Re-release. Cartoon.*

SNOW WHITE AND THE SEVEN DWARFS
(1975R - Disney) Snow White
One Sheet: $30 - $50   *Re-release. Cartoon.*

SNOW WHITE AND THE SEVEN DWARFS
(1983R - Disney) Snow White
One Sheet: $15 - $35   *Re-release. Cartoon.*

SNOW WHITE AND THE SEVEN DWARFS
(1987R - Disney) Snow White
One Sheet: $15 - $30   *Re-release. Cartoon. 50th Anniversary poster. Gold foil (raised):$50-75; Silver logo:$25-40.*

SNOW WHITE AND THE SEVEN DWARFS
(1993R - Disney) Snow White
One Sheet: $15 - $30   *Re-release. Cartoon. Advance Mylar:$60-$100.*

SNOW WHITE AND THE THREE STOOGES
(1961 - 20th Century Fox) Three Stooges (Curly Joe)
One Sheet: $40 - $75

SNOWBALL EXPRESS
(1972 - Buena Vista/Disney) Dean Jones, Nancy Olson
One Sheet: $5 - $10

SNOWBOUND
(1949 - Universal) Robert Newton, Dennis Price
One Sheet: $15 - $30

SNOWDRIFT
(1923 - Fox) Charles Jones
One Sheet: $150 - $350

SNOWED IN
(1926 - Pathe) Allene Ray, Walter Miller
One Sheet: $150 - $300   *Serial. 10 Chapters.*

SNOWED UNDER
(1936 - Warner Bros.) George Brent, Glenda Farrell
One Sheet: $50 - $100

SNOWFIRE
(1957 - Allied Artists) Don McGowan
One Sheet: $7 - $15

SNOWS OF KILIMANJARO, THE
(1952 - 20th Century Fox) Gregory Peck, Susan Hayward
One Sheet: $50 - $100

SNUFFY SMITH, YARD BIRD
(1942 - Monogram) Bud Duncan, Edgar Kennedy
One Sheet: $100 - $200

SO BIG
(1932 - Warner Bros.) Barbara Stanwyck, Earl Foxe, Bette Davis
One Sheet: $100 - $200   *One Sheet is all text.*

One Sheet

SO BIG
(1954 - Warner Bros.) Jane Wyman, Sterling Hayden
One Sheet: $15 - $25

SO DARK THE NIGHT
(1946 - Columbia) Steven Geray, Micheline Cheirel
One Sheet: $15 - $25

SO DEAR TO MY HEART
(1948 - Disney) Burl Ives, Bobby Driscoll, Some Animation
One Sheet: $100 - $200

One Sheet

SO DEAR TO MY HEART
(1964R - Disney) Burl Ives, Bobby Driscoll, Some Animation
One Sheet: $15 - $35   *Re-release.*

SO DOES AN AUTOMOBILE
(1939 - Paramount) Betty Boop
One Sheet: $5,000 - $7,500   *Cartoon.*

SO ENDS OUR NIGHT

(1941 - United Artists) Fredric March, Margaret
Sullavan, Glenn Ford
One Sheet: $40 - $75

SO EVIL MY LOVE
(1948 - Paramount) Ray Milland, Ann Todd
One Sheet: $30 - $50

SO EVIL SO YOUNG
(1961 - United Artists) Jill Ireland, Ellen Pollock
One Sheet: $5 - $10

SO FINE
(1981 - Warner Bros.) Ryan O'Neal, Jack
Warden
One Sheet: $3 - $5

SO GOES MY LOVE
(1946 - Universal) Myrna Loy, Don Ameche
One Sheet: $30 - $60

SO LONG, MR. CHUMPS
(1941 - Columbia) The Three Stooges (Curly)
One Sheet: $4,000 - $6,000   *Comedy short.*
Duotone.

SO PROUDLY WE HAIL!
(1943 - Paramount) Claudette Colbert, Paulette
Goddard, George Reeves
One Sheet: $150 - $300

Half Sheet

SO RED THE ROSE
(1935 - Paramount) Margaret Sullavan, Walter
Connolly
One Sheet: $200 - $400

SO THIS IS AFRICA
(1933 - Columbia) Robert Woolsey, Bert
Wheeler
One Sheet: $100 - $200

SO THIS IS COLLEGE
(1929 - MGM) Elliott Nugent, Robert
Montgomery
One Sheet: $1,300 - $2,000   *Sports Movie*
Posters #350.

SO THIS IS LONDON
(1930 - Fox) Will Rogers, Irene Rich
One Sheet: $500 - $800

SO THIS IS LOVE
(1953 - Warner Bros.) Kathryn Grayson, Merv
Griffin
One Sheet: $15 - $25

SO THIS IS NEW YORK
(1948 - United Artists) Henry Morgan, Rudy
Vallee
One Sheet: $30 - $50

SO THIS IS PARIS
(1926 - Warner Bros.) Monte Blue, Myrna Loy
One Sheet: $700 - $1,200

SO THIS IS PARIS
(1954 - Universal) Tony Curtis, Gloria De
Haven
One Sheet: $15 - $25

SO THIS IS WASHINGTON!
(1943 - RKO) Lum 'n' Abner, Mildred Coles
One Sheet: $75 - $125

SO WELL REMEMBERED
(1947 - RKO) John Mills, Martha Scott, Trevor
Howard
One Sheet: $15 - $35

SO YOU WON'T TALK
(1940 - Columbia) Joe E. Brown, Frances
Robinson
One Sheet: $75 - $150

SO YOUNG, SO BAD
(1950 - United Artists) Paul Henreid, Catherine
McLeod
One Sheet: $15 - $25

SO'S YOUR AUNT EMMA!
(1942 - Monogram) ZaSu Pitts, Roger Pryor
One Sheet: $30 - $50

SO'S YOUR OLD MAN
(1926 - Famous Players Lasky) W.C. Fields
One Sheet: $1,600 - $2,500

SO'S YOUR UNCLE
(1943 - Universal) Donald Woods, Elyse Knox
One Sheet: $30 - $50

SOAK THE RICH
(1936 - Paramount) Walter Connolly, John
Howard
One Sheet: $100 - $200

SOAPDISH
(1991 - Paramount) Sally Field, Kevin Kline,
Whoopi Goldberg
One Sheet: $3 - $5

S.O.B.
(1981 - Lorimar) Julie Andrews, William
Holden, All Star Cast
One Sheet: $5 - $10

SOB SISTER
(1931 - Fox) James Dunn, Linda Watkins
One Sheet: $150 - $300

SOCIAL BRIARS
(1918 - -) Mary Miles Minter, Alan Forrest
One Sheet: $300 - $700

SOCIAL CELEBRITY, A
(1926 - Paramount) Adolphe Menjou, Louise
Brooks
One Sheet: $1,600 - $2,500

SOCIAL JUSTICE
(1936 - Golden Arrow) -
One Sheet: $50 - $100

SOCIAL LION, THE
(1930 - Paramount Publix) Jack Oakie, Mary
Brian
One Sheet: $150 - $300

SOCIAL LION
(1954 - RKO/Disney) -
One Sheet: $100 - $200   *Cartoon.*

SOCIAL REGISTER, THE
(1934 - Columbia) Colleen Moore, Charles
Winninger
One Sheet: $125 - $250

SOCIETY DOCTOR
(1935 - MGM) Chester Morris, Robert Taylor
One Sheet: $125 - $250

SOCIETY DOG SHOW
(1939 - RKO/Disney) Mickey Mouse, Pluto
One Sheet: $6,500 - $10,000   *Cartoon.*
Cartoon Movie Posters #145.

SOCIETY FEVER
(1935 - Chesterfield) Lois Wilson, Lloyd
Hughes
One Sheet: $50 - $100

SOCIETY GIRL
(1932 - Fox) James Dunn, Peggy Shannon,
Spencer Tracy
One Sheet: $150 - $300   *Sports Movie*
Posters #131.

SOCIETY LAWYER
(1939 - MGM) Walter Pidgeon, Virginia Bruce
One Sheet: $50 - $100

SOCIETY SCANDAL, A
(1924 - Paramount) Gloria Swanson
One Sheet: $600 - $1,000

SOCIETY SENSATION, A
(1918 - Universal) Rudolph Valentino
One Sheet: $800 - $1,500

SOCIETY SMUGGLERS
(1939 - Universal) Preston Foster, Irene
Hervey
One Sheet: $50 - $100

SOCK-A-BYE BABY
(1942 - Columbia) The Three Stooges (Curly)
One Sheet: $2,500 - $4,000   *Comedy short.*
Duotone.

SODOM AND GOMORRAH
(1963 - 20th Century Fox) Stewart Granger,
Pier Angeli
One Sheet: $20 - $40

SOFIA
(1948 - Film Classics) Gene Raymond, Sigrid
Gurie
One Sheet: $10 - $20

SOFT BOILED
(1923 - Fox) Tom Mix, Billie Dove
One Sheet: $500 - $800

SOFT BOILED
(192?R - Fox) Tom Mix, Billie Dove
One Sheet: $125 - $250   *Re-release.*

SOFT CUSHIONS
(1927 - Paramount) Douglas MacLean
One Sheet: $150 - $300

SOGGY BOTTOM, U.S.A.
(1981 - Gaylord) Ben Johnson, Anne
Wedgeworth, Don Johnson
One Sheet: $7 - $15   *AKA: SOGGY*
BOTTOM GANG.

SOILED
(1924 - Truart) Kenneth Harlan, Vivian Martin
One Sheet: $500 - $800

SOILERS, THE
(1923 - Pathe) Stan Laurel, James Finlayson
One Sheet: $250 - $600

SOL MADRID
(1968 - MGM) David McCallum, Stella Stevens
One Sheet: $15 - $25

SOLAR CRISIS
(1990 - Boss) Charlton Heston, Jack Palance
One Sheet: $7 - $15   *Japanese.*

SOLARBABIES
(1986 - -) Richard Jordan, Jami Gertz
One Sheet: $3 - $5

SOLARIS
(1972 - -) Donatas Banionis, Natalya
Bondarchuk
One Sheet: $40 - $75   *Russian.*

SOLDIER, THE
(1982 - -) Ken Wahl, Klaus Kinski
One Sheet: $3 - $5

SOLDIER AND THE LADY, THE
(1937 - RKO) Anton Walbrook, Margaret
Grahame
One Sheet: $100 - $200

SOLDIER BLUE
(1970 - Avco/Embassy) Candice Bergen, Peter
Strauss
One Sheet: $5 - $10

SOLDIER IN THE RAIN
(1963 - Allied Artists) Jackie Gleason, Steve
McQueen
One Sheet: $15 - $25

SOLDIER OF FORTUNE
(1955 - 20th Century Fox) Clark Gable, Susan
Hayward
One Sheet: $40 - $75

SOLDIER'S PLAYTHING, A
(1930 - Warner Bros.) Lotti Loder, Harry
Langdon
One Sheet: $150 - $350

SOLDIER'S STORY, A
(1984 - Columbia) Howard E. Rollins, Jr.,
Adolph Caesar
One Sheet: $5 - $10

SOLDIERS AND WOMEN
(1930 - Columbia) Aileen Pringle, Grant
Withers
One Sheet: $125 - $250

SOLDIERS OF THE STORM
(1933 - Columbia) Regis Toomey, Anita Page
One Sheet: $125 - $250

SOLDIERS THREE
(1951 - MGM) Stewart Granger, Walter
Pidgeon
One Sheet: $15 - $35

SOLID GOLD CADILLAC, THE
(1956 - Columbia) Judy Holliday, Paul Douglas

One Sheet: $40 - $75

SOLID SERENADE
(1946 - MGM) Tom & Jerry
One Sheet: $200 - $400   *Cartoon.*

SOLITAIRE MAN, THE
(1933 - MGM) Herbert Marshall, Mary Boland
One Sheet: $75 - $150

SOLOMON AND SHEBA
(1959 - United Artists) Yul Brynner, Gina
Lollobrigida, Tyrone Power
One Sheet: $30 - $50   *Power's last*
film.

SOLOMON KING
(197? - -) Written, directed & starring Sal Watts
One Sheet: $15 - $25   *Blaxploitation.*

SOMBRA, THE SPIDER WOMAN
(1947 - -) Ramsey Ames, Carol Forman
One Sheet: $30 - $50   *Feature*
version of THE BLACK WIDOW.

SOMBRERO
(1952 - MGM) Pier Angeli, Ricardo Montalban
One Sheet: $15 - $30

SOMBRERO KID, THE
(1942 - Republic) Don Barry, John James
One Sheet: $15 - $30

SOME BLONDES ARE DANGEROUS
(1937 - Universal) Noah Beery Jr., Dorothea
Kent
One Sheet: $75 - $150

SOME CAME RUNNING
(1958 - MGM) Frank Sinatra, Shirley MacLaine,
Dean Martin
One Sheet: $30 - $50

SOME KIND OF A NUT
(1969 - United Artists) Dick Van Dyke, Angie
Dickinson
One Sheet: $10 - $20

SOME KIND OF HERO
(1982 - Paramount) Richard Pryor, Margot
Kidder
One Sheet: $7 - $15

SOME KIND OF WONDERFUL
(1987 - -) Eric Stoltz, Lea Thompson
One Sheet: $15 - $25

SOME LIKE IT COOL
(1979 - Pro International) Tony Curtis, Britt
Ekland
One Sheet: $5 - $10

SOME LIKE IT HOT
(1939 - Paramount) Bob Hope, Shirley Ross
One Sheet: $150 - $300

SOME LIKE IT HOT
(1959 - United Artists) Marilyn Monroe, Tony
Curtis, Jack Lemmon, Dir: Billy Wilder
One Sheet: $350 - $750

One Sheet

SOME MORE OF SAMOA
(1941 - Columbia) The Three Stooges (Curly)
One Sheet: $4,000 - $6,000   *Comedy short.*
Duotone.

SOME MOTHER'S BOY
(1929 - Rayart) Mary Carr, Jason Robards,
Jobyna Ralston
One Sheet: $200 - $400

SOME OF THE BEST
(1949 - MGM) -
One Sheet: $15 - $35

SOMEBODY KILLED HER HUSBAND
(1978 - Columbia) Farrah Fawcett-Majors, Jeff Bridges
One Sheet: $7 - $15

SOMEBODY LOVES ME
(1952 - Paramount) Betty Hutton, Ralph Meeker
One Sheet: $30 - $50

SOMEBODY UP THERE LIKES ME
(1956 - MGM) Paul Newman, Pier Angeli, Steve McQueen
One Sheet: $40 - $75   *Sports (Boxing). McQueen's film debut. Sports Movie Posters #153.*

SOMEONE BEHIND THE DOOR
(1971 - Cinerama) Charles Bronson, Anthony Perkins
One Sheet: $10 - $20

SOMEONE TO LOVE
(1928 - Paramount) Charles "Buddy" Rogers
One Sheet: $125 - $250

SOMEONE TO REMEMBER
(1943 - Republic) Richard Crane, Mabel Paige
One Sheet: $15 - $35

SOMEONE TO WATCH OVER ME
(1987 - Columbia) Tom Berenger, Mimi Rogers
One Sheet: $5 - $10

SOMETHING BIG
(1971 - National General) Dean Martin, Brian Keith
One Sheet: $5 - $10

SOMETHING FOR EVERYONE
(1970 - National General) Angela Lansbury, Michael York
One Sheet: $5 - $10

SOMETHING FOR THE BIRDS
(1953 - 20th Century Fox) Victor Mature, Patricia Neal
One Sheet: $10 - $20

SOMETHING FOR THE BOYS
(1944 - 20th Century Fox) Carmen Miranda, Michael O'Shea
One Sheet: $100 - $200   *Earl Moran art.*

One Sheet

SOMETHING IN THE WIND
(1947 - Universal) Deanna Durbin, Donald O'Connor
One Sheet: $50 - $100

SOMETHING MONEY CAN'T BUY
(1952 - GFD) Anthony Steele, Patricia Roc
One Sheet: $5 - $10

SOMETHING OF VALUE
(1957 - MGM) Rock Hudson, Sidney Poitier
One Sheet: $15 - $30

SOMETHING SHORT OF PARADISE
(1979 - AIP) Susan Sarandon, David Steinberg
One Sheet: $5 - $10

SOMETHING TO LIVE FOR
(1951 - Paramount) Joan Fontaine, Ray Milland
One Sheet: $15 - $35

SOMETHING TO SHOUT ABOUT
(1943 - Columbia) Don Ameche, Janet Blair
One Sheet: $30 - $50

SOMETHING TO SING ABOUT
(1937 - Grand National) James Cagney, Evelyn Daw
One Sheet: $150 - $300

SOMETHING TO THINK ABOUT
(1920 - Paramount) Elliott Dexter, Gloria Swanson, Dir: Cecil B. DeMille
One Sheet: $600 - $1,000

SOMETHING WEIRD
(1967 - Hur-Lew) Tony McCabe, Elizabeth Lee
One Sheet: $20 - $40   *Dir: Herschel Gordon Lewis.*

SOMETHING WICKED THIS WAY COMES
(1982 - Disney) Jason Robards, Jonathan Price
One Sheet: $7 - $15

SOMETHING WILD
(1961 - United Artists) Carroll Baker, Ralph Meeker
One Sheet: $15 - $25

SOMETHING WILD
(1986 - Orion) Jeff Daniels, Melanie Griffith
One Sheet: $10 - $20

SOMETIMES A GREAT NOTION
(1971 - Universal) Paul Newman, Henry Fonda, Lee Remick
One Sheet: $7 - $15

SOMEWHERE I'LL FIND YOU
(1942 - MGM) Clark Gable, Lana Turner
One Sheet: $100 - $200

One Sheet

SOMEWHERE IN FRANCE
(1943 - United Artists) Constance Cummings, Tommy Trinder
One Sheet: $30 - $50

SOMEWHERE IN SONORA
(1933 - Vitagraph) John Wayne, Ann Fay
One Sheet: $2,800 - $4,500   *Cowboy Movie Posters #138.*

SOMEWHERE IN THE NIGHT
(1946 - 20th Century Fox) John Hodiak, Nancy Guild
One Sheet: $200 - $400

One Sheet

SOMEWHERE IN TIME
(1980 - Universal) Christopher Reeve, Jane Seymour
One Sheet: $50 - $100

SOMMERSBY
(1993 - Warner Bros.) Jodie Foster, Richard Gere
One Sheet: $7 - $15

SON COMES HOME, A
(1936 - Paramount) Mary Boland, Julie Hayden
One Sheet: $100 - $200

SON IN LAW, THE
(1993 - Buena Vista) Pauly Shore, Carla Gugino
One Sheet: $3 - $5

SON OF A BAD MAN
(1949 - Screen Guild) Lash LaRue, Fuzzy St. John
One Sheet: $30 - $50

SON OF A GUNFIGHTER
(1966 - MGM) Russ Tamblyn, Kieron Moore
One Sheet: $5 - $10

SON OF A SAILOR
(1933 - First National) Joe E. Brown, Thelma Todd
One Sheet: $250 - $500

SON OF ALI BABA
(1952 - Universal) Tony Curtis, Piper Laurie
One Sheet: $20 - $40

SON OF BELLE STARR
(1953 - Allied Artists) Keith Larsen, Peggie Castle
One Sheet: $15 - $25

SON OF BILLY THE KID
(1949 - Screen Guild) Lash LaRue, Fuzzy St. John
One Sheet: $30 - $50

SON OF CAPTAIN BLOOD, THE
(1962 - Paramount) Sean Flynn, Alessandra Panaro
One Sheet: $10 - $20

SON OF DAVY CROCKETT, THE
(1941 - Columbia) Bill Elliott, Iris Meredith
One Sheet: $40 - $75

SON OF DEMOCRACY
(1918 - Paramount) Benjamin Chapin
One Sheet: $250 - $500

SON OF DR. JEKYLL, THE
(1951 - Columbia) Louis Hayward, Alexander Knox
One Sheet: $50 - $100

SON OF DRACULA
(1943 - Universal) Lon Chaney Jr., Robert Paige
One Sheet: $1,900 - $3,000   *Graven Images, pg. 110, 116.*

One Sheet

SON OF DRACULA
(1950R - Realart) Lon Chaney, Louise Allbritton
One Sheet: $150 - $300   *Re-release.*

SON OF DRACULA
(1974 - Cinemation) Harry Nilsson, Ringo Starr
One Sheet: $30 - $50   *AKA: YOUNG DRACULA.*

SON OF FLUBBER
(1963 - Buena Vista/Disney) Fred MacMurray, Nancy Olson
One Sheet: $15 - $25

SON OF FLUBBER
(1970R - Disney) Fred MacMurray, Nancy Olson
One Sheet: $5 - $10   *Re-release.*

SON OF FLUBBER
(1974R - Disney) Fred MacMurray, Nancy Olson
One Sheet: $5 - $10   *Re-release.*

SON OF FRANKENSTEIN
(1939 - Universal) Basil Rathbone, Boris Karloff, Bela Lugosi
One Sheet: $13,000 - $20,000   *Graven Images, pg. 100-101. Price is for Style A one sheet. One Sheet(Style B):$4,000-$7,500.*

SON OF FRANKENSTEIN
(1953R - Realart) Basil Rathbone, Boris Karloff, Bela Lugosi
One Sheet: $125 - $250   *Re-release.*

One Sheet (1953R)

SON OF FRANKENSTEIN/BRIDE OF FRANKENSTEIN
(1953R - Film Classics) Basil Rathbone, Boris Karloff/Boris Karloff, Colin Clive
One Sheet: $100 - $200   *Re-release double feature poster.*

SON OF FURY
(1941 - 20th Century Fox) Tyrone Power, Gene Tierney, Frances Farmer
One Sheet: $600 - $1,000

SON OF GERONIMO
(1952 - Columbia) Clayton Moore, Bud Osborne
One Sheet: $40 - $75   *Serial. Western. 15 Chapters.*

SON OF GOD'S COUNTRY
(1948 - Republic) Monte Hale, Pamela Blake
One Sheet: $15 - $35

SON OF GODZILLA
(1968 - AIP) Akira Kubo, Beverly Maeda
One Sheet: $50 - $100

SON OF INDIA
(1931 - MGM) Ramon Novarro
One Sheet: $200 - $400

SON OF INGAGI
(1940 - Sack) Zack Williams, Laura Bowman
One Sheet: $800 - $1,500   *First Black cast horror film. Separate Cinema, pg. 21.*

SON OF KONG
(1933 - RKO) Robert Armstrong, Helen Mack
One Sheet: $25,000 - $40,000   *Graven Images, pg. 74. Kong does not appear on the one sheet.*

Title Card

SON OF LASSIE
(1945 - MGM) Peter Lawford, June Lockhart, Lassie
One Sheet: $75 - $150

SON OF MONTE CRISTO
(1940 - United Artists) Louis Hayward, Joan Bennett
One Sheet: $50 - $100

SON OF OKLAHOMA
(1932 - World-Wide) Bob Steele, Josie Sedgwick
One Sheet: $200 - $400

SON OF PALEFACE
(1952 - Paramount) Bob Hope, Jane Russell, Roy Rogers
One Sheet: $75 - $125

SON OF ROARING DAN
(1940 - Universal) Johnny Mack Brown, Bob Baker
One Sheet: $40 - $75

SON OF ROBIN HOOD
(1958 - 20th Century Fox) David Hedison, June Laverick
One Sheet: $10 - $20

SON OF RUSTY, THE
(1947 - Columbia) Ted Donaldson, Stephen Dunne
One Sheet: $15 - $25

SON OF SAMSON
(1961 - Medallion) Mark Forest, Chelo Alonso
One Sheet: $7 - $15

SON OF SATAN, A
(1924 - -) Andrew S. Bishop, Ida Anderson
One Sheet: $150 - $300

SON OF SINBAD
(1955 - RKO) Dale Robertson, Sally Forrest
One Sheet: $15 - $35

SON OF SPARTACUS
(1963 - MGM) Steve Reeves, Jacques Sernas
One Sheet: $30 - $50   *AKA: The Slave.*

SON OF TARZAN
(1920 - National) Kamuela C. Searle
One Sheet: $800 - $1,500   *Serial. 15 Chapters.*

SON OF THE BORDER
(1933 - RKO) Tom Keene, Julie Hayden
One Sheet: $150 - $300   *Cowboy Movie Posters # 141.*

SON OF THE GODS
(1930 - First National) Richard Barthelmess, Constance Bennett
One Sheet: $200 - $400

SON OF THE GOLDEN WEST
(1928 - FBO) Tom Mix, Sharon Lynn
One Sheet: $600 - $1,000   *Cowboy Movie Posters #72.*

SON OF THE GUARDSMAN
(1946 - Columbia) Robert Shaw, Daun Kennedy
One Sheet: $40 - $75   *Serial. 15 Chapters.*

SON OF THE NAVY
(1940 - Monogram) Jean Parker, James Dunn
One Sheet: $15 - $35

SON OF THE PINK PANTHER
(1993 - MGM) Roberto Begnini, Herbert Lom
One Sheet: $3 - $5

SON OF THE RENEGADE
(1953 - United Artists) John Carpenter, Lori Irving
One Sheet: $15 - $35

SON OF THE SHEIK, THE
(1926 - United Artists) Rudolph Valentino, Vilma Banky
One Sheet: $6,500 - $10,000   *Valentino's last film.*

One Sheet

SON OF WALLINGFORD
(1921 - Vitagraph) Wilfrid North, Tom Gallery

One Sheet: $200 - $400

SON OF ZORRO
(1947 - Republic) George Turner, Peggy Stewart
One Sheet: $50 - $100   *Serial. Western. 13 Chapters.*

SON-DAUGHTER, THE
(1932 - MGM) Helen Hayes, Ramon Novarro
One Sheet: $200 - $400

SONG AND DANCE MAN
(1936 - 20th Century Fox) Claire Trevor, Paul Kelly
One Sheet: $150 - $300

SONG AND THE SILENCE, THE
(1969 - Coverhouse) Annita Koutsoveli, Narry Rubin, Jim Murphy
One Sheet: $3 - $5

SONG FOR MISS JULIE, A
(1945 - Republic) Shirley Ross, Barton Hepburn
One Sheet: $15 - $35

SONG IS BORN, A
(1947 - RKO) Danny Kaye, Virginia Mayo, Benny Goodman, Tommy Dorsey
One Sheet: $50 - $100   *Big Band musical.*

SONG OF ARIZONA
(1946 - Republic) Roy Rogers, Gabby Hayes
One Sheet: $150 - $300

SONG OF ARIZONA
(1954R - Republic) Roy Rogers, Gabby Hayes
One Sheet: $40 - $75   *Re-release.*

SONG OF BERNADETTE, THE
(1943 - 20th Century Fox) Jennifer Jones, William Eythe
One Sheet: $300 - $700   *Academy Award Movie Posters #89. Art by Norman Rockwell.*

One Sheet

SONG OF FREEDOM
(1936 - Treo Exchange) Paul Robeson
One Sheet: $800 - $1,500   *Separate Cinema, pg. 41.*

SONG OF IDAHO
(1948 - Columbia) Kirby Grant, June Vincent
One Sheet: $15 - $35

SONG OF INDIA
(1949 - Columbia) Sabu, Gail Russell
One Sheet: $30 - $50

SONG OF LIFE, THE
(1922 - -) -
One Sheet: $150 - $300

SONG OF LOVE
(1923 - Columbia) Norma Talmadge, Joseph Schildkraut
One Sheet: $200 - $400

SONG OF LOVE
(1947 - MGM) Katharine Hepburn, Paul Henreid
One Sheet: $75 - $150

SONG OF MEXICO
(1945 - Republic) Edgar Barrier, Adele Mara
One Sheet: $15 - $30

SONG OF MY HEART
(1930 - Fox) -
One Sheet: $100 - $200

SONG OF MY HEART

(1947 - Allied Artists) Frank Sundstrom, Audrey Long, Sir Cedric Hardwicke
One Sheet: $15 - $30

SONG OF NEVADA
(1941 - Republic) Roy Rogers, Mary Lee
One Sheet: $150 - $300

Insert

SONG OF NORWAY
(1970 - Cinerama) Florence Henderson, Edward G. Robinson
One Sheet: $7 - $15

SONG OF OLD WYOMING
(1945 - PRC) Eddie Dean, Jennifer Holt, Lash Larne
One Sheet: $20 - $40

SONG OF RUSSIA
(1944 - MGM) Robert Taylor, Susan Peters
One Sheet: $30 - $50

SONG OF SCHEHERAZADE
(1947 - Universal) Yvonne De Carlo, Brian Donlevy
One Sheet: $30 - $50

SONG OF SOHO
(1930 - BIP) Carl Brisson, Edna Davies
One Sheet: $150 - $300   *British.*

SONG OF SONGS
(1933 - Paramount) Marlene Dietrich, Brian Aherne, Lionel Atwill
One Sheet: $3,500 - $5,000

SONG OF SURRENDER
(1949 - Paramount) Wanda Hendrix, Claude Rains
One Sheet: $15 - $35

SONG OF TEXAS
(1943 - Republic) Roy Rogers, Sheila Ryan
One Sheet: $125 - $250

SONG OF THE BUCKAROO
(1938 - Monogram) Tex Ritter, Jinx Falkenberg
One Sheet: $150 - $350

One Sheet

SONG OF THE CABALLERO
(1930 - Universal) Ken Maynard, Doris Hill
One Sheet: $250 - $600

SONG OF THE CITY
(1937 - MGM) Dean Jeffries, Margaret Lindsay
One Sheet: $50 - $100

SONG OF THE DAMNED
(1935 - Columbia) -
One Sheet: $75 - $150

SONG OF THE DRIFTER
(1948 - Monogram) Jimmy Wakely, "Cannonball" Taylor

One Sheet: $15 - $35

SONG OF THE EAGLE
(1933 - Paramount) Richard Arlen, Mary Brian
One Sheet: $150 - $300

SONG OF THE FLAME
(1930 - First National) Alexander Gray, Noah Beery, Sr.
One Sheet: $100 - $200

SONG OF THE GRINGO
(1936 - Grand National) Tex Ritter, Monte Blue
One Sheet: $125 - $250

SONG OF THE ISLANDS
(1942 - 20th Century Fox) Betty Grable, Victor Mature, Jack Oakie
One Sheet: $150 - $300

SONG OF THE OPEN ROAD
(1944 - United Artists) Jane Powell, Edgar Bergen, W.C. Fields
One Sheet: $100 - $200   *Big Band musical. Sammy Kaye Orch. Powell's film debut.*

SONG OF THE PRAIRIE
(1945 - Columbia) Ken Curtis, Jeff Donnell
One Sheet: $15 - $35

SONG OF THE RANGE
(1944 - Monogram) Jimmy Wakely
One Sheet: $15 - $35

SONG OF THE ROAD
(1937 - UK) Bransby Williams, Ernest Butcher, Tod Slaughter
One Sheet: $30 - $50

SONG OF THE SADDLE
(1936 - Warner Bros.) Dick Foran, Alma Lloyd
One Sheet: $75 - $150

SONG OF THE SARONG
(1945 - Universal) William Gargan, Nancy Kelly
One Sheet: $15 - $35

SONG OF THE SIERRAS
(1946 - Monogram) Jimmy Wakely, Lee "Lasses" White
One Sheet: $15 - $35

SONG OF THE SOUTH
(1946 - RKO/Disney) Ruth Warrick, Bobby Driscoll, James Baskett
One Sheet: $150 - $300   *Cartoon/Live action. Cartoon Movie Posters #377.*

SONG OF THE SOUTH
(1956R - Buena Vista/Disney) Ruth Warrick, Bobby Driscoll, James Baskett
One Sheet: $40 - $75   *Re-release. Cartoon/Live Action.*

SONG OF THE SOUTH
(1972R - Buena Vista/Disney) Ruth Warrick, Bobby Driscoll, James Baskett
One Sheet: $15 - $35   *Re-release. Cartoon/Live action.*

SONG OF THE SOUTH
(1980R - Disney) Ruth Warrick, Bobby Driscoll, James Baskett
One Sheet: $10 - $20   *Re-release. Cartoon/Live action.*

SONG OF THE SOUTH
(1986R - Disney) Ruth Warrick, Bobby Driscoll, James Baskett
One Sheet: $10 - $20   *Re-release. Cartoon/Live action.*

SONG OF THE THIN MAN
(1947 - MGM) William Powell, Myrna Loy
One Sheet: $250 - $500

SONG OF THE TRAIL
(1936 - Ambassador) Kermit Maynard, Evelyn Brent
One Sheet: $75 - $150

SONG OF THE VOLGA BOATMAN
(1926 - -) William Boyd
One Sheet: $150 - $300

SONG OF THE WASTELAND
(1947 - Monogram) Jimmy Wakely, Lee "Lasses" White
One Sheet: $15 - $35

SONG OF THE WEST
(1930 - Warner Bros.) John Boles, Vivienne Segal
One Sheet: $150 - $300   *Cowboy*

Movie Posters # 89.

SONG OVER MOSCOW
(1964 - Artkino) Herbert Rappaport, Olga Zabotinka
One Sheet: $7 - $15 *Russian.*

SONG REMAINS THE SAME, THE
(1976 - -) Led Zeppelin
One Sheet: $30 - $50 *Rock'n'Roll concert film.*

SONG TO REMEMBER, A
(1944 - Columbia) Merle Oberon, Paul Muni, Cornel Wilde
One Sheet: $75 - $150

One Sheet

SONG WITHOUT END
(1960 - Columbia) Dirk Bogarde, Capucine
One Sheet: $10 - $20

SONG YOU GAVE ME, THE
(1934 - Columbia) Bebe Daniels, Victor Varconi
One Sheet: $100 - $200

SONGS AND BULLETS
(1938 - Spectrum Pictures) Fred Scott
One Sheet: $150 - $300 *Cowboy Movie Posters #232.*

SONGWRITER
(1984 - TriStar) Willie Nelson, Kris Kristofferson
One Sheet: $15 - $25

SONNY LISTON VS. CASSIUS CLAY
(1967 - 20th Century Fox) -
One Sheet: $150 - $300 *Sports (Boxing). Film covering the Feb. 25, 1964 bout.*

SONORA STAGECOACH
(1944 - Monogram) Hoot Gibson, Bob Steele
One Sheet: $50 - $100

SONS AND LOVERS
(1960 - 20th Century Fox) Trevor Howard, Dean Stockwell
One Sheet: $15 - $25

SONS O' GUNS
(1936 - Warner Bros.) Joan Blondell, Joe E. Brown
One Sheet: $500 - $800

SONS OF ADVENTURE
(1948 - Republic) Lynne Roberts, Russ Hayden
One Sheet: $15 - $35

SONS OF KATIE ELDER, THE
(1965 - Paramount) John Wayne, Dean Martin
One Sheet: $50 - $100

SONS OF NEW MEXICO
(1950 - Columbia) Gene Autry, Gail Davis
One Sheet: $75 - $150

SONS OF STEEL
(1935 - Chesterfield) Charles Starrett
One Sheet: $75 - $125

SONS OF THE DESERT
(1933 - MGM) Stan Laurel, Oliver Hardy, Charlie Chase
One Sheet: $6,500 - $10,000

SONS OF THE DESERT
(194?R - Film Classics) Stan Laurel, Oliver Hardy, Charlie Chase
One Sheet: $250 - $500 *Re-release.*

SONS OF THE LEGION
(1938 - Paramount) Donald O'Connor, Billy Lee
One Sheet: $75 - $125

SONS OF THE PIONEERS
(1942 - Republic) Roy Rogers, Gabby Hayes
One Sheet: $150 - $350

SONS OF THE PIONEERS
(1955R - Republic) Roy Rogers, Gabby Hayes
One Sheet: $50 - $100 *Re-release.*

SONS OF THE SADDLE
(1930 - Universal) Ken Maynard, Doris Hill
One Sheet: $200 - $400

SONS OF THE SEA
(1942 - Warner Bros.) Michael Redgrave, Valerie Hobson
One Sheet: $15 - $35

SOOKY
(1932 - Paramount Publix) Jackie Cooper, Jackie Searl
One Sheet: $150 - $300

SOPHIE LANG GOES WEST
(1937 - Paramount) Gertrude Michael, Larry Crabbe
One Sheet: $75 - $150

SOPHIE'S CHOICE
(1982 - Universal) Meryl Streep, Kevin Kline
One Sheet: $7 - $15 *Academy Award Movie Posters #326. Advance:$20-$40.*

SORCERER
(1977 - Universal/Paramount) Roy Scheider, Bruno Cremer
One Sheet: $3 - $5

SORCERERS, THE
(1968 - Allied Artists) Boris Karloff, Catherine Lacey
One Sheet: $15 - $35

SORCERESS
(1983 - -) Leigh and Lynett Harris
One Sheet: $7 - $15

SORORITY GIRL
(1957 - AIP) Susan Cabot, Dick Miller
One Sheet: $30 - $60

SORORITY HOUSE
(1939 - RKO) Anne Shirley, James Ellison
One Sheet: $75 - $150

SORRELL AND SON
(1934 - United Artists) H.B. Warner, Peter Penrose
One Sheet: $75 - $150

SORROWFUL JONES
(1949 - Paramount) Bob Hope, Lucille Ball, William Demarest
One Sheet: $75 - $150

SORROWS OF SATAN, THE
(1926 - Paramount) Adolphe Menjou, Ricardo Cortez
One Sheet: $4,000 - $6,000 *Graven Images, pg. 28.*

SORRY, WRONG NUMBER
(1948 - Paramount) Barbara Stanwyck, Burt Lancaster
One Sheet: $250 - $500

S.O.S. COAST GUARD
(1937 - Republic) Ralph Byrd, Bela Lugosi
One Sheet: $250 - $500 *Serial. 12 Chapters. One Sheet (Chapter One):$600-$700.*

S.O.S. COAST GUARD
(1942 - Republic) Bela Lugosi, Ralph Byrd
One Sheet: $125 - $250 *Feature version.*

S.O.S. ICEBERG
(1933 - Universal) Rod La Rocque, Leni Riefenstahl
One Sheet: $700 - $1,200

S.O.S. PACIFIC
(1960 - Universal) Eddie Constantine, Pier Angeli
One Sheet: $7 - $15

S.O.S. TIDAL WAVE
(1939 - Republic) Ralph Byrd, Kay Sutton
One Sheet: $50 - $100

SOUL MAN
(1986 - -) C. Thomas Howell, Arye Gross, Rae Dawn Chong
One Sheet: $7 - $15

SOUL OF A MONSTER, THE
(1944 - Columbia) George Macready, Rose Hobart
One Sheet: $75 - $150

SOUL OF NIGGER CHARLEY, THE
(1973 - Paramount) Fred Williamson, Denise Nicholas
One Sheet: $10 - $20 *Blaxploitation.*

SOUL OF THE BEAST
(1923 - Metro) Madge Bellamy, Oscar the Elephant
One Sheet: $200 - $400

SOUL OF THE SLUMS
(1931 - Action) William Collier Jr.
One Sheet: $125 - $250

SOUL PATROL
(197? - Cinematic) Nigel Davenport, Ken Gampu
One Sheet: $10 - $20 *Blaxploitation. Yellow duotone.*

SOUL SOLDIERS
(1970 - Hirschman) Robert DoQui, Janee Michelle, Rafer Johnson
One Sheet: $30 - $50 *Blaxploitation. AKA: THE RED, WHITE AND BLACK. Sports Movie Posters #375.*

SOULS AT SEA
(1937 - Paramount) Gary Cooper, George Raft
One Sheet: $500 - $900

SOULS AT SEA
(1943R - Paramount) Gary Cooper, George Raft
One Sheet: $50 - $100 *Re-release.*

SOULS FOR SALE
(1923 - Goldwyn) Mae Busch, Barbara Lamar, Lew Cody
One Sheet: $100 - $200

SOULS IN PAWN
(1917 - Universal) Gail Kane, Douglas MacLean
One Sheet: $200 - $400

SOULS OF SIN
(1949 - Alexander) Savannah Churchill, Jimmy Wright
One Sheet: $100 - $200 *Black cast. Duotone. Separate cinema, pg. 145.*

SOUND AND THE FURY, THE
(1959 - 20th Century Fox) Yul Bryner, Joanne Woodward
One Sheet: $7 - $15

SOUND OF FURY, THE
(1950 - United Artists) Frank Lovejoy, Kathleen Ryan, Richard Carlson
One Sheet: $15 - $35

SOUND OF LAUGHTER, THE
(1963 - Union) Danny Kaye, Bob Hope, Bing Crosby & All Star Comedy Cast
One Sheet: $15 - $35

SOUND OF MUSIC, THE
(1965 - 20th Century Fox) Julie Andrews, Christopher Plummer
One Sheet: $150 - $350 *AA:Best Picture, Best Direction(Robert Wise). One Sheet (Advance):$50-$100; One Sheet (AcademyAwards):$20-$40; One Sheet (Road Show pre-Oscar):$300-$600. Academy Award Movie Posters #227-229.*

SOUND OF MUSIC, THE
(1973R - 20th Century Fox) Julie Andrews, Christopher Plummer
One Sheet: $20 - $40 *Re-release. Academy Awards style.*

SOUND OFF
(1952 - Columbia) Mickey Rooney, Ann James
One Sheet: $15 - $25

SOUNDER
(1972 - 20th Century Fox) Cicely Tyson, Paul Winfield
One Sheet: $15 - $25 *Black cast. Review:$8-$12.*

SOUP FOR NUTS
(1934 - Universal) Bob Hope, Al Goodman Orchestra
One Sheet: $150 - $350

SOUP TO NUTS
(1930 - Fox) Frances McCoy, Ted Healy and His Stooges (Moe, Larry, Shemp)
One Sheet: $1,900 - $3,000 *Price assumes Stooges not pictured on the one sheet. First appearance of The Stooges in film.*

SOUP'S ON
(1948 - RKO/Disney) Donald Duck
One Sheet: $3,500 - $5,500 *Cartoon.*

SOUTH BRONX HEROES
(1984 - -) Mario & Megan Van Peebles
One Sheet: $10 - $20 *Black cast.*

SOUTH OF ARIZONA
(1938 - Columbia) Charles Starrett, Iris Meredith
One Sheet: $75 - $125

SOUTH OF CALIENTE
(1951 - Republic) Roy Rogers, Dale Evans
One Sheet: $75 - $150

SOUTH OF DEATH VALLEY
(1949 - Columbia) Smiley Burnette, Charles Starrett
One Sheet: $15 - $35

SOUTH OF DIXIE
(1944 - Universal) Anne Gwynne, David Bruce
One Sheet: $30 - $50

SOUTH OF MONTEREY
(1946 - Monogram) Gilbert Roland, Frank Yacanelli
One Sheet: $15 - $35

SOUTH OF PAGO PAGO
(1940 - United Artists) Victor McLaglen, Frances Farmer
One Sheet: $200 - $400

SOUTH OF PAGO PAGO
(1947R - PRC) Victor McLaglen, Frances Farmer
One Sheet: $15 - $30 *Re-release.*

SOUTH OF PANAMA
(1928 - Chesterfield) Edouard Raquello
One Sheet: $150 - $300

SOUTH OF PANAMA
(1941 - PRC) Roger Pryor, Virginia Vale
One Sheet: $15 - $35

SOUTH OF RIO
(1949 - Republic) Monte Hale, Kay Christopher
One Sheet: $15 - $30

SOUTH OF SANTA FE
(1932 - Sono Art/World Wide) Bob Steele, Janis Elliott
One Sheet: $150 - $300

SOUTH OF SANTA FE
(1942 - Republic) Roy Rogers, Gabby Hayes
One Sheet: $150 - $300

SOUTH OF ST. LOUIS
(1949 - Warner Bros.) Joel McCrea, Alexis Smith
One Sheet: $15 - $35

SOUTH OF SUEZ
(1940 - Warner Bros.) George Brent, Brenda Marshall
One Sheet: $30 - $50

SOUTH OF TAHITI
(1941 - Universal) Brian Donlevy, Broderick Crawford
One Sheet: $30 - $50

SOUTH OF THE BORDER
(1939 - Republic) Gene Autry, Smiley Burnette
One Sheet: $200 - $450

SOUTH OF THE BOUDOIR
(1940 - Columbia) Charley Chase
One Sheet: $100 - $200 *Comedy short. Duotone.*

SOUTH OF THE CHISHOLM TRAIL
(1947 - Columbia) Charles Starrett, Smiley Burnette
One Sheet: $15 - $35

SOUTH OF THE RIO GRANDE
(1932 - Columbia) Buck Jones, Mona Maris
One Sheet: $2,500 - $4,000 *Cowboy Movie Posters #121.*

SOUTH OF THE RIO GRANDE
(1945 - Monogram) Duncan Renaldo, Armida

One Sheet: $30 - $50   *Cisco Kid series.*

SOUTH PACIFIC
(1959 - 20th Century Fox) Rossano Brazzi, Mitzi Gaynor, John Kerr
One Sheet: $30 - $50

Window Card

SOUTH PACIFIC
(1964R - 20th Century Fox) Rossano Brazzi, Mitzi Gaynor, John Kerr
One Sheet: $15 - $25   *Re-release.*

SOUTH PACIFIC TRAIL
(1952 - Republic) Rex Allen
One Sheet: $15 - $35

SOUTH RIDING
(1938 - London) Ralph Richardson, Edna Best
One Sheet: $50 - $100

SOUTH SEA SINNER
(1949 - Universal) Macdonald Carey, Shelley Winters
One Sheet: $15 - $35

SOUTH SEA WOMAN
(1953 - Warner Bros.) Burt Lancaster, Virginia Mayo
One Sheet: $30 - $50

SOUTH TO KARANGA
(1940 - Universal) Charles Bickford, James Craig, Luli Deste
One Sheet: $30 - $50

SOUTHERN COMFORT
(1981 - EMI) Keith Carradine, Powers Boothe
One Sheet: $15 - $25

SOUTHERN STAR, THE
(1969 - Columbia) George Segal, Ursula Andress, Orson Welles
One Sheet: $15 - $30

SOUTHERN YANKEE, A
(1948 - MGM) Red Skelton, Brian Donlevy
One Sheet: $40 - $75

SOUTHERNER, THE
(1931 - MGM) Lawrence Tibbett, Esther Ralston
One Sheet: $125 - $250

SOUTHERNER, THE
(1945 - United Artists) Zachary Scott, Betty Field
One Sheet: $75 - $150

SOUTHERNERS, THE
(1914 - Edison) -
One Sheet: $600 - $1,000

SOUTHSIDE 1-1000
(1950 - Monogram) Don Defore, Andrea King
One Sheet: $15 - $35

SOUTHWARD, HO!
(1939 - Republic) Roy Rogers, Mary Hart, Gabby Hayes
One Sheet: $600 - $1,000

SOUTHWEST PASSAGE
(1954 - United Artists) Rod Cameron, Joanne Dru
One Sheet: $15 - $35

SOWERS AND REAPERS
(1917 - Metro) Emmy Wehlen
One Sheet: $200 - $400

SOYLENT GREEN
(1973 - MGM) Charlton Heston, Leigh Taylor-Young, Edward G. Robinson

One Sheet: $15 - $25

SPACE CHILDREN, THE
(1958 - Paramount) Michel Ray, Adam Williams, Peggy Webber
One Sheet: $75 - $125

SPACE GODZILLA
(1979 - -) -
One Sheet: $30 - $60

SPACE JAM
(1996 - Warner Bros.) Bugs Bunny, Michael Jordan
One Sheet: $7 - $15   *One sheet (Jordan):$15-$25.*

One Sheet (Advance - Michael)

SPACE MASTER X-7
(1958 - 20th Century Fox) Bill Williams, Lyn Thomas
One Sheet: $40 - $75

SPACE MISSION TO THE LOST PLANET
(19?? - -) John Carradine
One Sheet: $5 - $10

SPACE RAIDERS
(1983 - Millennium) Vince Edwards, David Mendenhall
One Sheet: $7 - $15

One Sheet

SPACE SHIP SAPPY
(1957 - Columbia) The Three Stooges (Joe Besser)
One Sheet: $75 - $125   *Comedy short. Duotone.*

SPACEBALLS
(1987 - MGM) Mel Brooks, John Candy
One Sheet: $10 - $20

SPACECAMP
(1986 - -) Kate Capshaw, Lea Thompson
One Sheet: $3 - $5

SPACED INVADERS
(1990 - -) Douglas Barr, Royal Dano
One Sheet: $3 - $5

SPACEFLIGHT IC-1
(1965 - 20th Century Fox) Bill Williams, John Cairney
One Sheet: $15 - $30

SPACEHUNTER: ADVENTURES IN THE FORBIDDEN ZONE
(1983 - Columbia) Peter Strauss, Molly Ringwald
One Sheet: $7 - $15

SPACESHIP
(1981 - -) Leslie Nielsen, Cindy Williams
One Sheet: $5 - $10

SPACEWAYS
(1952 - Lippert) Howard Duff, Eva Bartok
One Sheet: $40 - $75

SPANISH AFFAIR
(1957 - Paramount) Richard Kiley, Carmen Sevilla
One Sheet: $10 - $20

SPANISH CAPE MYSTERY, THE
(1935 - Republic) Donald Cook, Helen Twelvetrees
One Sheet: $150 - $300

SPANISH DANCER, THE
(1923 - -) Pola Negri
One Sheet: $600 - $1,000

SPANISH GARDENER, THE
(1957 - Rank) Dirk Bogarde, Jon Whiteley
One Sheet: $50 - $100

SPANISH MAIN, THE
(1945 - RKO) Paul Henreid, Maureen O'Hara
One Sheet: $50 - $100

SPANKY McFARLAND
(1951R - Monogram) Little Rascals
One Sheet: $50 - $100   *Re-release.*

SPARE THE ROD
(1954 - RKO/Disney) Donald Duck
One Sheet: $600 - $1,000   *Cartoon.*

SPARKLE
(1976 - Warner Bros.) Lonetta McGee, Irene Cara, Philip Michael Thomas
One Sheet: $7 - $15   *Black cast musical.*

SPARROWS
(1926 - United Artists) Mary Pickford
One Sheet: $700 - $1,200

SPARROWS CAN'T SING
(1963 - Janus) James Booth, Barbara Windsor
One Sheet: $5 - $10

SPARTACUS
(1914 - George Kleine Attractions) -
One Sheet: $700 - $1,200

SPARTACUS
(1960 - Universal) Kirk Douglas, Laurence Olivier
One Sheet: $75 - $150   *Academy Award Movie Posters #199. Sports Movie Posters #3. One Sheet(Academy Awards):$30-50.*

SPARTACUS
(1967R - Universal) Kirk Douglas, Laurence Olivier
One Sheet: $7 - $15   *Re-release.*

SPARTACUS
(1991R - Universal) Kirk Douglas, Laurence Olivier
One Sheet: $15 - $25   *Re-release.*

SPAWN
(1997 - New Line) Michael Jai White, John Leguizamo
One Sheet: $15 - $25   *Based on the comic book character.*

SPAWN OF THE NORTH
(1938 - Paramount) George Raft, Henry Fonda
One Sheet: $250 - $500

SPEAK EASILY
(1931 - MGM) Buster Keaton, Sidney Toler, Jimmy Durante
One Sheet: $1,600 - $2,500

SPEAKEASY
(1929 - Fox) Paul Puge, Lola Lane
One Sheet: $800 - $1,500

SPECIAL AGENT
(1935 - Warner Bros.) Bette Davis, George Brent
One Sheet: $800 - $1,500

SPECIAL AGENT
(1949 - Paramount) William Eythe, George Reeves
One Sheet: $40 - $75

SPECIAL AGENT K-7
(1937 - Syndicate) Walter McGrail, Queenie Smith
One Sheet: $75 - $150

SPECIAL DELIVERY

(1927 - Paramount) Eddie Cantor
One Sheet: $250 - $600

SPECIAL DELIVERY
(1955 - Columbia) Joseph Cotten, Eva Bartok
One Sheet: $15 - $35

SPECIAL DELIVERY
(1976 - AIP) Bo Svenson, Cybill Shepherd
One Sheet: $7 - $15

SPECIAL INSPECTOR
(1939 - Warwick) Charles Quigley, Rita Hayworth
One Sheet: $150 - $300

SPECIAL INVESTIGATOR
(1936 - RKO) Richard Dix, Margaret Callahan
One Sheet: $150 - $300

SPECIALIST, THE
(1930 - Sale) Charles "Chic" Sale
One Sheet: $75 - $150

SPECIALIST, THE
(1975 - Crown) Adam West, John Anderson
One Sheet: $7 - $15

SPECIALIST, THE
(1994 - Warner Bros.) Sylvester Stallone, Sharon Stone, James Woods
One Sheet: $5 - $10

SPECIES
(1995 - MGM/UA) Ben Kingsley, Michael Madsen, Natasha Henstridge
One Sheet: $7 - $15   *Style that shows monster: $12-$15. Style that shows woman as part of monster: $12-$20.*

SPECKLED BAND, THE
(1931 - First Division) Raymond Massey, Lyn Harding
One Sheet: $800 - $1,500   *Sherlock Holmes. Massey's film debut.*

SPECTACLE MAKER, THE
(1934 - MGM) Dir: John Villiers Farrow
One Sheet: $100 - $200

SPECTER OF THE ROSE
(1946 - Republic) Ivan Kirov, Viola Essenf, Judith Anderson
One Sheet: $15 - $30

SPECTRE OF EDGAR ALLAN POE, THE
(1974 - Cinerama) Robert Walker, Jr., Cesar Romero
One Sheet: $7 - $15

SPEECHLESS
(1994 - MGM/UA) Michael Keaton, Gina Davis
One Sheet: $5 - $10

SPEED
(1922 - Pathe) Charles Hutchinson, Lucy Fox
One Sheet: $250 - $600   *Serial. 15 Episodes.*

SPEED
(1936 - MGM) James Stewart, Wendy Barrie
One Sheet: $250 - $500   *Sports (Auto racing).*

SPEED
(1994 - 20th Century Fox) Keanu Reeves, Dennis Hopper
One Sheet: $10 - $20

SPEED BOYS
(1924 - Universal) The Century Kids
One Sheet: $250 - $500

SPEED CRAZY
(1958 - Allied Artists) Brett Halsey, Yvonne Lime
One Sheet: $50 - $100   *Sports (Auto racing). Sports Movie Posters #15.*

SPEED DEMON, THE
(1932 - Columbia) -
One Sheet: $75 - $125

SPEED DEVILS
(1935 - Syndicate) Paul Kelly, Marguerite Churchill, Russell Hardie
One Sheet: $200 - $400   *Sports (Auto racing). Sports Movie Posters #10.*

SPEED GIRL, THE
(1921 - Reelart) Bebe Daniels, Teodore von Eltz
One Sheet: $200 - $400

SPEED IN THE GAY NINETIES
(192? - Educational) Andy Clyde
One Sheet: $100 - $200

SPEED LIMITED
(1940 - Regent) Ralph Graves, Evelyn Brent
One Sheet: $50 - $100

SPEED MANIAC, THE
(1919 - Fox) Tom Mix
One Sheet: $800 - $1,500   *Cowboy Movie Posters #17.*

SPEED REPORTER, THE
(1935 - Reliable) Richard Talmadge, Luana Walters
One Sheet: $125 - $250

SPEED SPOOK, THE
(1924 - East Coast) Johnny Hines
One Sheet: $200 - $400

SPEED TO BURN
(1938 - 20th Century Fox) Lynn Bari, Michael Whalen
One Sheet: $75 - $125

SPEED TO SPARE
(1937 - Columbia) Dorothy Wilson, Charles Quigley
One Sheet: $75 - $150

SPEED TO SPARE
(1948 - Paramount) Richard Arlen, Jean Rogers
One Sheet: $40 - $75

SPEED WINGS
(1934 - Columbia) Tim McCoy, Evalyn Knapp
One Sheet: $150 - $350

SPEED ZONE
(1989 - Orion) Peter Boyle, Donna Dixon, Melody Anderson
One Sheet: $5 - $10

SPEEDWAY
(1968 - MGM) Elvis Presley, Nancy Sinatra
One Sheet: $50 - $100   *Sports (Auto racing). Rock 'n' Roll.*

SPEEDY
(1928 - Paramount) Harold Lloyd, Ann Christy, Babe Ruth
One Sheet: $1,600 - $2,500   *Sports (Baseball). Sports Movie Posters #368.*

SPELL OF THE CIRCUS
(1931 - Universal) Francis X. Bushman, Jr., Alberta Vaughn
One Sheet: $150 - $300   *Serial. 10 Chapters.*

SPELLBINDER, THE
(1939 - RKO) Lee Tracy, Barbara Reed
One Sheet: $50 - $100

SPELLBOUND
(1945 - United Artists) Ingrid Bergman, Gregory Peck, Dir: Alfred Hitchcock
One Sheet: $1,000 - $1,800

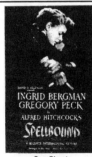

One Sheet

SPELLBOUND
(1955R - United Artists) Ingrid Bergman, Gregory Peck, Dir: Alfred Hitchcock
One Sheet: $100 - $200   *Re-release.*

SPENCER'S MOUNTAIN
(1963 - Warner Bros.) Henry Fonda, Maureen O'Hara
One Sheet: $15 - $30

SPEND A NIGHT WITH JAMES BOND!
(1972R - United Artists) Sean Connery

One Sheet: $40 - $75   *Triple feature re-release of FROM RUSSIA WITH LOVE/ GOLDFINGER/DR. NO.*

SPENDTHRIFT
(1936 - Paramount) Henry Fonda, Pat Patterson
One Sheet: $100 - $200

SPHINX, THE
(1933 - Monogram) Lionel Atwill, Sheila Terry
One Sheet: $350 - $750   *Graven Images, pg. 67.*

SPHINX
(1981 - Warner Bros.) Lesley-Anne Down, Frank Langella
One Sheet: $5 - $10

SPIDER, THE
(1931 - Fox) Edmund Lowe, Howard Phillips
One Sheet: $250 - $500

SPIDER, THE
(1945 - 20th Century Fox) Richard Conte, Faye Marlowe
One Sheet: $50 - $100

SPIDER, THE
(1958 - AIP) Ed Kemmer, June Kenny
One Sheet: $75 - $125

SPIDER BABY
(1968 - American General) Lon Chaney, Jr., Carol Ohmart
One Sheet: $20 - $40

SPIDER RETURNS, THE
(1941 - Columbia) Warren Hull
One Sheet: $250 - $500   *Serial. 15 Chapters. Based on "The Spider" magazine stories.*

Lobby Card

SPIDER WOMAN, THE
(1943 - Universal) Basil Rathbone, Nigel Bruce
One Sheet: $600 - $1,000   *AKA: SHERLOCK HOLMES AND THE SPIDER WOMAN.*

SPIDER WOMAN STRIKES BACK, THE
(1946 - Universal) Gale Sondergaard, Brenda Joyce, Rondo Hatton
One Sheet: $150 - $300

SPIDER'S WEB, THE
(1927 - -) Evelyn Preer, Lorenzo McLane
One Sheet: $250 - $600

SPIDER'S WEB, THE
(1938 - Columbia) Warren Hull, Iris Meredith
One Sheet: $800 - $1,500   *Serial. 15 Chapters. Based on "The Spider" magazine stories.*

SPIDER'S WEB, THE
(1961 - United Artists) Glynis Johns, John Justin
One Sheet: $15 - $35

SPIDER-MAN STRIKES BACK
(1978 - Columbia) Nicholas Hammond
One Sheet: $30 - $50   *Based on T.V. series and comic book characters.*

SPIELER, THE
(1929 - Pathe) Alan Hale, Renee Adoree
One Sheet: $150 - $300

SPIES
(1929 - MGM) Dir: Fritz Lang
One Sheet: $1,900 - $3,000   *German.*

SPIES LIKE US
(1985 - Warner Bros.) Chevy Chase, Dan

Aykroyd
One Sheet: $3 - $5

SPIKED SWITCH, THE
(1914 - Kalem) Helen Gibson
One Sheet: $250 - $600   *An episode of the Hazards Of Helen railroad series.*

SPIN A DARK WEB
(1955 - Columbia) Faith Domergue, Martin Benson
One Sheet: $15 - $35

SPINOUT
(1966 - MGM) Elvis Presley, Shelley Fabares
One Sheet: $40 - $75   *Sports (Auto racing). Rock 'n' Roll.*

One Sheet

SPIRAL ROAD, THE
(1962 - Universal) Rock Hudson, Burl Ives
One Sheet: $15 - $25

SPIRAL STAIRCASE, THE
(1945 - RKO) Dorothy McGuire, George Brent
One Sheet: $100 - $200   *Graven Images, pg. 128.*

SPIRIT AWAKENED, THE
(1912 - Biograph) Dir: D.W. Griffith
One Sheet: $250 - $500

SPIRIT IS WILLING, THE
(1967 - Paramount) Sid Caesar, Vera Miles
One Sheet: $7 - $15

SPIRIT OF 1976, THE
(1935 - RKO) -
One Sheet: $75 - $150

SPIRIT OF CULVER
(1939 - Universal) Jackie Cooper, Freddie Bartholomew
One Sheet: $75 - $125

SPIRIT OF NOTRE DAME
(1931 - Universal) Lew Ayres, The Four Horsemen
One Sheet: $1,900 - $3,000   *Sports (Football). Duotone. Sports Movie Posters #s 180, 181.*

SPIRIT OF NOTRE DAME
(1950R - Universal) Lew Ayres, Andy Devine
One Sheet: $125 - $250   *Re-release. Sports (Football). Price assumes football players on poster.*

SPIRIT OF ST. LOUIS, THE
(1957 - Warner Bros.) James Stewart, Murray Hamilton
One Sheet: $200 - $400

SPIRIT OF STANFORD, THE
(1942 - Columbia) Frankie Albert, Marguerite Chapman
One Sheet: $50 - $100

SPIRIT OF THE WEST, THE
(1932 - Allied) Hoot Gibson, Doris Hill
One Sheet: $100 - $200   *Duotone.*

SPIRIT OF WEST POINT, THE
(1947 - Bro-Rog) Felix "Doc" Blanchard, Glenn Davis
One Sheet: $50 - $100

SPIRIT OF YOUTH
(1937 - Grand National) Joe Louis, Mantan Moreland
One Sheet: $200 - $400   *Black cast. Sports (Boxing). Sports Movie Posters #138. Louis' film debut.*

SPIRITS OF THE DEAD

(1969 - AIP) Brigitte Bardot, Alain Delon, Jane Fonda
One Sheet: $30 - $50

SPIRITUALIST, THE
(1948 - Eagle-Lion) Turhan Bey, Lynn Bari
One Sheet: $15 - $30

SPITE MARRIAGE
(1929 - MGM) Buster Keaton, Dorothy Sebastian
One Sheet: $5,000 - $8,000

SPITFIRE
(1934 - RKO) Katharine Hepburn, Robert Young
One Sheet: $1,900 - $3,000

SPITFIRE
(1943 - RKO) Leslie Howard, David Niven
One Sheet: $50 - $100   *Howard's final film.*

SPITFIRE GRILL, THE
(1996 - Columbia) Alison Elliott, Marcia Gay Harden, Ellen Burstyn
One Sheet: $5 - $12

SPLASH
(1984 - -) Daryl Hannah, Tom Hanks
One Sheet: $7 - $15

SPLENDID ROAD, THE
(1925 - First National) Anna Q. Nilsson, Lionel Barrymore
One Sheet: $250 - $600

SPLENDOR
(1935 - Samuel Goldwyn) Miriam Hopkins, Joel McCrea
One Sheet: $250 - $500

SPLENDOR IN THE GRASS
(1961 - Warner Bros.) Natalie Wood, Pat Hingle, Warren Beatty
One Sheet: $30 - $50   *Beatty's film debut.*

SPLIT, THE
(1968 - MGM) Jim Brown, Diahann Carroll, Gene Hackman
One Sheet: $10 - $20

SPLIT DECISION
(1988 - -) Gene Hackman, Craig Sheffer
One Sheet: $3 - $5

SPLIT SECOND
(1953 - RKO) Alexis Smith, Stephen McNally
One Sheet: $15 - $25

SPLITTING HEIRS
(1993 - Universal) Rick Moranis, Eric Idle
One Sheet: $3 - $5

SPLITTING THE BREEZE
(1927 - FBO) Tom Tyler, Peggy Montgomery
One Sheet: $600 - $1,000

SPOILERS, THE
(1914 - Selig) William Farnum
One Sheet: $700 - $1,200   *Cowboy Movie Posters #5.*

One Sheet

SPOILERS, THE
(1930 - Paramount Publix) Gary Cooper
One Sheet: $1,300 - $2,000   *Cowboy Movie Posters # 90.*

SPOILERS, THE
(1942 - Universal) Marlene Dietrich, John Wayne, Randolph Scott
One Sheet: $250 - $600

SPOILERS, THE
(1948R - Realart) John Wayne, Marlene
Dietrich
One Sheet: $75 - $150   *Re-release.*
Full color.

SPOILERS, THE
(1955 - Universal) Jeff Chandler, Anne Baxter
One Sheet: $15 - $25

SPOILERS OF THE FOREST
(1957 - Republic) Rod Cameron, Vera Ralston
One Sheet: $15 - $25

SPOILERS OF THE NORTH
(1947 - Republic) Paul Kelly, Adrian Booth
One Sheet: $15 - $30

SPOILERS OF THE PLAINS
(1951 - Republic) Roy Rogers, Penny Edwards
One Sheet: $75 - $150

SPOILERS OF THE RANGE
(1939 - Columbia) Charles Starrett, Iris
Meredith
One Sheet: $75 - $125

SPONTANEOUS COMBUSTION
(1990 - -) Brad Dourif, Cynthia Bain
One Sheet: $5 - $10

SPOOK BUSTERS
(1946 - Monogram) The Bowery Boys, Douglas
Dumbrille
One Sheet: $75 - $125

SPOOK CHASERS
(1957 - Allied Artists) Huntz Hall, Stanley
Clements
One Sheet: $30 - $50

SPOOK LOUDER
(1943 - Columbia) The Three Stooges (Curly)
One Sheet: $2,500 - $4,000   *Comedy short.*
Duotone.

SPOOK SPEAKS, THE
(1949R - Columbia) -
One Sheet: $75 - $150   *Re-release.*
Duotone.

SPOOK TOWN
(1944 - PRC) David O'Brien, Jim Newill
One Sheet: $30 - $50

SPOOK WHO SAT BY THE DOOR, THE
(1973 - United Artists) Lawrence Cook, Paula
Kelly
One Sheet: $30 - $50   *Controversial*
Black cast film.

One Sheet

SPOOKS
(1954 - Columbia) Three Stooges (Shemp)
One Sheet: $150 - $350   *Comedy short.*
Duotone.

SPOOKS RUN WILD
(1941 - Monogram) The East Side Kids, Bela
Lugosi
One Sheet: $500 - $800   *Graven*
Images, pg. 134.

SPORT OF KINGS
(1947 - Columbia) Paul Campbell, Gloria Henry
One Sheet: $20 - $40   *Sports (Horse*
racing).

SPORT PARADE, THE
(1932 - RKO) Joel McCrea, Marion Marsh
One Sheet: $150 - $300

SPORT REVIEW, THE
(1922 - Goldwyn) -
One Sheet: $300 - $700

SPORTING BLOOD
(1931 - MGM) Clark Gable, Madge Evans
One Sheet: $1,600 - $2,500   *Sports (Horse*
racing). Gable's first featured-player role. Sports
Movie Posters #244.

SPORTING BLOOD
(1940 - MGM) Robert Young, Lewis Stone,
Maureen O'Sullivan
One Sheet: $75 - $125   *Sports (Horse*
racing).

SPORTING CHANCE, THE
(1925 - Tiffany) Lou Tellegen, Dorothy Phillips
One Sheet: $200 - $400

SPORTING CHANCE
(1931 - Peerless) Buster Collier, Jr., Claudia
Dell
One Sheet: $100 - $200   *Sports (Horse*
racing).

SPORTING CHANCE, A
(1945 - Republic) Jane Randolph, John
O'Malley
One Sheet: $15 - $25

SPORTING CLUB, THE
(1971 - Avco/Embassy) Robert Fields, Maggie
Blye
One Sheet: $5 - $10

SPORTING VENUS, THE
(1925 - MGM) Blanche Sweet, Ronald Colman
One Sheet: $350 - $750

SPORTING YOUTH
(1924 - Universal) Reginald Denny
One Sheet: $250 - $500   *Sports Movie*
Posters #6.

SPORTSMAN, THE
(1920 - Vitagraph) Larry Semon
One Sheet: $250 - $500

SPOTLIGHT SCANDALS
(1943 - Monogram) Billy Gilbert, Frank Fay,
Herb Miller Orch.
One Sheet: $50 - $100

SPREAD EAGLE
(1961R - Citation) John Payne, Rhonda
Fleming
One Sheet: $5 - $10   *Re-release.*

SPREE
(1967 - United) Vic Damone, Jayne Mansfield
One Sheet: $30 - $50

One Sheet

SPRING BREAK
(1983 - Columbia) David Knell, Steve Bassett
One Sheet: $5 - $10

SPRING FEVER
(1927 - MGM) Joan Crawford
One Sheet: $800 - $1,500

SPRING IN PARK LANE
(1948 - London) Anna Neagle, Michael Wilding
One Sheet: $250 - $500

SPRING IS HERE
(1930 - First National) Lawrence Gray,
Alexander Gray, Bernice Claire
One Sheet: $100 - $200

SPRING MADNESS
(1938 - MGM) Maureen O'Sullivan, Lew Ayres,
Burgess Meredith
One Sheet: $75 - $150

SPRING PARADE
(1940 - Universal) Deanna Durbin, Robert

Cummings
One Sheet: $75 - $150

SPRING REUNION
(1956 - United Artists) Betty Hutton, Dana
Andrews
One Sheet: $15 - $25

SPRING TONIC
(1935 - Fox) Lew Ayres, ZaSu Pitts, Claire
Trevor
One Sheet: $100 - $200

SPRINGFIELD RIFLE
(1952 - Warner Bros.) Gary Cooper, Phyllis
Thaxter
One Sheet: $125 - $250

SPRINGTIME FOR HENRY
(1934 - Fox) Otto Kruger, Nancy Carroll,
Heather Angel
One Sheet: $75 - $150

SPRINGTIME FOR PLUTO
(1944 - RKO/Disney) Pluto
One Sheet: $1,300 - $2,000   *Cartoon.*

SPRINGTIME FOR THOMAS
(1946 - MGM) Tom & Jerry
One Sheet: $250 - $600   *Cartoon. Full*
color stone litho. Cartoon Movie Posters #274.

SPRINGTIME IN TEXAS
(1945 - Monogram) Jimmy Wakely, Lee
"Lasses" White
One Sheet: $15 - $35

SPRINGTIME IN THE ROCKIES
(1937 - Republic) Gene Autry, Smiley Burnette
One Sheet: $200 - $450

SPRINGTIME IN THE ROCKIES
(1942 - 20th Century Fox) Betty Grable, John
Payne, Carmen Miranda
One Sheet: $200 - $400

SPRINGTIME IN THE ROCKIES
(1945R - Republic) Gene Autry, Smiley
Burnette
One Sheet: $75 - $150   *Re-release.*

SPRINGTIME IN THE SIERRAS
(1947 - Republic) Roy Rogers, Jane Frazee
One Sheet: $100 - $200

SPRINGTIME IN THE SIERRAS
(1952R - Republic) Roy Rogers, Jane Frazee
One Sheet: $40 - $75   *Re-release.*

SPURS
(1930 - Universal) Hoot Gibson, Helen Wright
One Sheet: $600 - $1,000   *Cowboy*
Movie Posters #'s 87, 88.

SPY, THE
(1931 - Fox) Kay Johnson, Neil Hamilton
One Sheet: $150 - $300

SPY 77
(1934 - Alliance) Greta Nissen, Carl Ludwig
Diehl
One Sheet: $50 - $100

SPY CHASERS
(1955 - Allied Artists) Leo Gorcey, Huntz Hall
One Sheet: $30 - $60

SPY HARD
(1996 - Hollywood) Leslie Nielsen, Charles
Durning
One Sheet: $5 - $10

SPY HUNT
(1950 - Universal) Howard Duff, Marta Toren
One Sheet: $15 - $25

SPY IN BLACK, THE
(1939 - Columbia) Conrad Veidt, Valerie
Hobson
One Sheet: $200 - $400   *AKA: U-BOAT*
29.

SPY IN THE GREEN HAT, THE
(1966 - MGM) Robert Vaughn, David McCallum
One Sheet: $30 - $50   *MAN FROM*
U.N.C.L.E. TV tie-in.

SPY IN THE SKY
(1958 - Allied Artists) Steve Brodie, Sandra
Francis
One Sheet: $40 - $75

SPY IN YOUR EYE
(1965 - AIP) Brett Halsey, Pier Angeli

One Sheet: $10 - $20

SPY RING, THE
(1938 - Universal) William Hall, Jane Wyman
One Sheet: $50 - $100

SPY SHIP
(1942 - Warner Bros.) Craig Stevens, Irene
Manning
One Sheet: $20 - $40

SPY SMASHER
(1942 - Republic) Kane Richmond, Marguerite
Chapman
One Sheet: $250 - $500   *Serial. 12*
chapters. One Sheet(Chapter one):$600-$1000.

One Sheet

SPY TRAIN
(1943 - Monogram) Richard Travis, Catherine
Craig
One Sheet: $15 - $35

SPY WHO CAME IN FROM THE COLD, THE
(1966 - Paramount) Richard Burton, Claire
Bloom
One Sheet: $20 - $40

SPY WHO CAME OUT OF THE WATER, THE
(1966 - MGM) Doris Day, Rod Taylor
One Sheet: $15 - $30

SPY WHO LOVED ME, THE
(1977 - United Artists) Roger Moore, Barbara
Bach
One Sheet: $40 - $75   *Bob Peak art.*

SPY WITH A COLD NOSE, THE
(1966 - Embassy) Laurence Harvey, Lionel
Jeffries
One Sheet: $3 - $5

SPY WITH MY FACE, THE
(1966 - MGM) Robert Vaughn, Senta Berger,
David McCallum
One Sheet: $30 - $50   *MAN FROM*
UNCLE TV tie-in.

SPY WITHIN, THE
(1995 - New Horizons) Theresa Russell, Scott
Glenn
One Sheet: $5 - $10

SPYS
(1974 - 20th Century Fox) Elliot Gould, Donald
Sutherland
One Sheet: $5 - $10

SQUAD CAR
(1960 - 20th Century Fox) Paul Bryar, Vici Raaf
One Sheet: $15 - $25

SQUADRON LEADER X
(1943 - RKO) Eric Portman, Beatrice Varley
One Sheet: $15 - $35

SQUADRON OF HONOR
(1937 - Columbia) Don Terry, Mary Russell
One Sheet: $50 - $100

SQUALL, THE
(1929 - First National) Myrna Loy, Zasu Pitts,
Alice Joyce, Richard Tucker
One Sheet: $500 - $800

SQUANTO: A WARRIOR'S TALE
(1994 - Buena Vista) Adam Beach, Mandy
Patinkin
One Sheet: $5 - $10

SQUARE DANCE JUBILEE
(1949 - Screen Guild) Don Barry, Mary Beth
Hughes
One Sheet: $30 - $50   *Country*
musical.

SQUARE DANCE KATY
(1950 - Monogram) Vera Vague, Phil Brito
One Sheet: $15 - $35 *Country musical.*

SQUARE DEAL SANDERSON
(1917 - Artcraft) William S. Hart
One Sheet: $1,300 - $2,000

SQUARE JUNGLE, THE
(1955 - Universal) Tony Curtis, Ernest Borgnine
One Sheet: $15 - $35

SQUARE RING, THE
(1953 - Republic) Jack Warner, Robert Beatty
One Sheet: $15 - $35 *Sports (Boxing).*

SQUARE SHOOTER
(1934 - Columbia) Tim McCoy
One Sheet: $250 - $600

SQUAREHEADS OF THE ROUND TABLE
(1948 - Columbia) The Three Stooges (Shemp)
One Sheet: $350 - $750 *Comedy short. Duotone.*

SQUAW MAN, THE
(1907 - Liebler & Co.) William Faversham
One Sheet: $250 - $600 *Cowboy Movie Posters #1 (theatrical poster).*

SQUAW MAN, THE
(1914 - Lasky) Dustin Farnum, Winifred Kingston, Dir: Cecil B. DeMille
One Sheet: $1,900 - $3,000

SQUAW MAN, THE
(1918 - Paramount) Elliott Dexter, Ann Little, Jack Holt
One Sheet: $600 - $1,000

SQUAW MAN, THE
(1931 - Fox) Warner Baxter, Lupe Velez
One Sheet: $250 - $600

SQUEAKER, THE
(1937 - United Artist) Edmund Lowe, Sebastian Shaw, Ann Todd
One Sheet: $100 - $200 *AKA: MURDER ON DIAMOND ROW.*

SQUEEZE, THE
(1987 - -) Michael Keaton, Rae Dawn Chong
One Sheet: $3 - $5

SQUEEZE PLAY
(1980 - Troma) Jenni, Jim Harris
One Sheet: $10 - $20

SQUIRM
(1976 - AIP) Don Scardino, Patricia Pearcy
One Sheet: $7 - $15

SSSSSS
(1973 - Universal) Strother Martin, Dirk Benedict
One Sheet: $15 - $25

SSSSSS/BOY WHO CRIED WEREWOLF, THE
(1973 - Universal) Strother Martin, Dirk Benedict, Kerwin Mathews
One Sheet: $7 - $15 *Double feature poster.*

One Sheet

ST. BENNY THE DIP
(1951 - United Artists) Dick Haymes, Freddie Bartholomew, Nina Foch
One Sheet: $15 - $25 *AKA: ESCAPE IF YOU CAN.*

ST. ELMO
(1923 - Fox) John Gilbert, Barbara La Marr, Warner Baxter
One Sheet: $250 - $600

ST. ELMO'S FIRE
(1985 - Columbia) Rob Lowe, Demi Moore, Ally Sheedy
One Sheet: $15 - $25

ST. IVES
(1976 - Warner Bros.) Charles Bronson, Jacqueline Bisset
One Sheet: $5 - $10

ST. LOUIS BLUES
(1929 - Sack) Bessie Smith
One Sheet: $1,900 - $3,000 *Black cast. Separate Cinema, pg. 91.*

ST. LOUIS BLUES
(1939 - Paramount) Lloyd Nolan, Dorothy Lamour
One Sheet: $100 - $200

ST. LOUIS BLUES
(1950 - Sonney Amusement) Bessie Smith
One Sheet: $200 - $400 *Black cast.*

ST. LOUIS BLUES
(1958 - Paramount) Nat King Cole, Cab Calloway, Ella Fitzgerald
One Sheet: $40 - $75 *Black cast. Separate Cinema, pg. 35.*

ST. LOUIS KID
(1934 - Warner Bros.) James Cagney, Patricia Ellis
One Sheet: $1,900 - $3,000 *Duotone.*

ST. LOUIS WOMAN
(1934 - Screencraft) Johnny Mack Brown, Jeanette Loff
One Sheet: $50 - $100

ST. MARTIN'S LANE
(1938 - Mayflower) Charles Laughton, Vivien Leigh
One Sheet: $600 - $1,000 *British. AKA: SIDEWALKS OF LONDON.*

ST. VALENTINE'S DAY MASSACRE, THE
(1967 - 20th Century Fox) Jason Robards Jr., George Segal
One Sheet: $15 - $25

STABLEMATES
(1938 - MGM) Wallace Beery, Mickey Rooney
One Sheet: $75 - $150

STABLEMATES
(1973R - MGM) Wallace Beery, Mickey Rooney
One Sheet: $10 - $20 *Re-release.*

STACEY
(1973 - New World) Anne Randall, Anitra Ford
One Sheet: $3 - $5

STACKING
(1987 - -) Christine Lahti, Frederic Forrest, Megan Follows
One Sheet: $15 - $25

STAGE COACH BANDIT
(1927R - -) -
One Sheet: $150 - $300 *Re-release.*

STAGE COACH DRIVER, THE
(1924 - Fox) Tom Mix
One Sheet: $500 - $800

STAGE DOOR
(1937 - RKO) Katharine Hepburn, Ginger Rogers
One Sheet: $1,600 - $2,500

One Sheet

STAGE DOOR
(1953R - RKO) Katharine Hepburn, Ginger Rogers
One Sheet: $75 - $125 *Re-release.*

STAGE DOOR CANTEEN
(1943 - United Artists) Lon McCallister, Sunset Carson, All-Star Cast
One Sheet: $75 - $150

STAGE FRIGHT
(1923 - Pathe) Our Gang
One Sheet: $800 - $1,400

STAGE FRIGHT
(1949 - Warner Bros.) Jane Wyman, Marlene Dietrich, Director: Alfred Hitchcock
One Sheet: $125 - $250

One Sheet

STAGE MOTHER
(1933 - MGM) Franchot Tone, Alice Brady
One Sheet: $75 - $125

STAGE STRUCK
(1925 - -) Gloria Swanson
One Sheet: $800 - $1,500

STAGE STRUCK
(1936 - Warner Bros.) Dick Powell, Joan Blondell, Warren William
One Sheet: $200 - $400

STAGE STRUCK
(1948 - Monogram) Kane Richmond, Audrey Long
One Sheet: $15 - $30

STAGE STRUCK
(1957 - RKO) Henry Fonda, Susan Strasberg
One Sheet: $15 - $30

STAGE TO BLUE RIVER
(1951 - Monogram) Whip Wilson
One Sheet: $15 - $35

STAGE TO CHINO
(1940 - RKO) George O'Brien, Virginia Vale
One Sheet: $75 - $125

STAGE TO MESA CITY
(1947 - PRC) Al "Fuzzy" St. John, Jennifer Holt
One Sheet: $15 - $35

STAGE TO THUNDER ROCK
(1964 - Paramount) Barry Sullivan, Marilyn Maxwell
One Sheet: $15 - $25

STAGE TO TUCSON
(1950 - Columbia) Rod Cameron, Wayne Morris
One Sheet: $15 - $35 *Cowboy Movie Posters #285.*

STAGECOACH
(1939 - United Artists) John Wayne, Claire Trevor, Dir: John Ford
One Sheet: $7,500 - $12,000 *Academy Award Movie Posters #68. Cowboy Movie Posters #s 246-250.*

STAGECOACH
(1944R - United Artists) John Wayne, Claire Trevor, Dir: John Ford
One Sheet: $700 - $1,200 *Re-release.*

STAGECOACH
(1948R - United Artists) John Wayne, Claire Trevor, Dir: John Ford
One Sheet: $350 - $750 *Re-release.*

STAGECOACH
(1966 - 20th Century Fox) Ann-Margret, Red Buttons, Bing Crosby

One Sheet: $20 - $40 *Norman Rockwell art.*

STAGECOACH BUCKAROO
(1941 - Universal) Johnny Mack Brown
One Sheet: $50 - $100

STAGECOACH DAYS
(1938 - Columbia) Jack Luden, Eleanor Stewart
One Sheet: $50 - $100

STAGECOACH DRIVER
(1951 - Monogram) Whip Wilson
One Sheet: $15 - $35

STAGECOACH EXPRESS
(1942 - Republic) Lynn Merrick, Don "Red" Barry
One Sheet: $30 - $50

STAGECOACH KID
(1949 - RKO) Tim Holt, Richard Martin
One Sheet: $15 - $35

STAGECOACH OUTLAWS
(1945 - PRC) Buster Crabbe
One Sheet: $20 - $40

STAGECOACH TO DANCERS' ROCK
(1962 - Universal) Warren Stevens, Martin Landau
One Sheet: $10 - $20

STAGECOACH TO DENVER
(1946 - Republic) Allan Lane, Bobby Blake
One Sheet: $20 - $40 *Red Ryder series.*

STAGECOACH TO FURY
(1956 - 20th Century Fox) Forrest Tucker, Mari Blanchard
One Sheet: $15 - $25

STAGECOACH TO MONTEREY
(1944 - Republic) Allan Lane, Peggy Stewart
One Sheet: $30 - $50

STAGECOACH WAR
(1940 - Paramount) William Boyd, Russell Hayden
One Sheet: $250 - $600 *Hopalong Cassidy series. Cowboy Movie Posters #261.*

STAGECOACH WAR
(1948R - Paramount) William Boyd, Russell Hayden
One Sheet: $50 - $100 *Re-release.*

STAIRCASE
(1969 - 20th Century Fox) Richard Burton, Rex Harrison
One Sheet: $7 - $15

STAIRS OF SAND
(1929 - Paramount) Jean Arthur, Wallace Beery
One Sheet: $200 - $400

STAIRWAY TO HEAVEN
(1946 - Universal) David Niven, Raymond Massey, Kim Hunter
One Sheet: $100 - $200 *Graven Images, pg. 142. Also see MATTER OF LIFE AND DEATH (British title).*

STAKEOUT
(1987 - Touchstone) Richard Dreyfuss, Emilio Estevez
One Sheet: $2 - $3

STAKEOUT ON DOPE STREET
(1957 - Warner Bros.) Yale Wexler, Jonathan Haze
One Sheet: $15 - $35

STALAG 17
(1953 - Paramount) William Holden, Don Taylor
One Sheet: $50 - $100 *Academy Award: Best Actor(Holden). Academy Award Movie Posters #150 & #151.*

STALAG 17
(1957R - Paramount) William Holden, Don Taylor
One Sheet: $30 - $50 *Re-release.*

STALAG 17
(1959R - Paramount) William Holden, Don Taylor
One Sheet: $20 - $40 *Re-release.*

STALKING MOON, THE
(1969 - National General) Eva Marie Saint, Gregory Peck, Robert Forster
One Sheet: $15 - $25

STALLION ROAD
(1947 - Warner Bros.) Ronald Reagan, Alexis Smith, Zachary Scott
One Sheet: $75 - $150

STAMBOUL QUEST
(1934 - MGM) Myrna Loy, George Brent
One Sheet: $150 - $300

STAMPEDE
(1936 - Columbia) Charles Starrett, Finis Barton
One Sheet: $50 - $100

STAMPEDE
(1949 - Allied Artists) Rod Cameron, Gale Storm
One Sheet: $15 - $35

STAND AND DELIVER
(1928 - Pathe) Rod La Rocque, Lupe Velez
One Sheet: $350 - $700

One Sheet

STAND AND DELIVER
(1987 - -) Edward James Olmos, Lou Diamond Phillips
One Sheet: $3 - $5

STAND AT APACHE RIVER, THE
(1953 - Universal) Stephen McNally, Julia Adams
One Sheet: $15 - $30

STAND BY ALL NETWORKS
(1942 - Columbia) John Beal, Florence Rice
One Sheet: $20 - $40

STAND BY FOR ACTION
(1942 - MGM) Robert Taylor, Charles Laughton
One Sheet: $40 - $75

STAND BY ME
(1986 - Columbia) Wil Wheaton, River Phoenix, Jerry O'Connell
One Sheet: $30 - $50

STAND UP AND BE COUNTED
(1972 - Columbia) Jacqueline Bisset, Stella Stevens
One Sheet: $5 - $10

STAND UP AND CHEER
(1934 - Fox) Warner Baxter, Madge Evans, Shirley Temple
One Sheet: $500 - $800   *Temple not shown on one sheet.*

STAND UP AND FIGHT
(1939 - MGM) Robert Taylor, Wallace Beery
One Sheet: $75 - $150

STAND-IN
(1937 - United Artists) Leslie Howard, Humphrey Bogart, Joan Blondell
One Sheet: $200 - $400

STANDING ROOM ONLY
(1944 - Paramount) Paulette Goddard, Fred MacMurray, Edward Arnold
One Sheet: $50 - $100

STANLEY
(1972 - Crown) Chris Robinson, Alex Rocco
One Sheet: $3 - $5

STANLEY AND IRIS
(1990 - MGM) Jane Fonda, Robert De Niro
One Sheet: $3 - $5

STANLEY AND LIVINGSTONE
(1939 - 20th Century Fox) Spencer Tracy, Nancy Kelly
One Sheet: $250 - $500

STAR, THE
(1952 - 20th Century Fox) Bette Davis, Sterling Hayden
One Sheet: $75 - $125

STAR!
(1968 - 20th Century Fox) Julie Andrews, Richard Crenna
One Sheet: $15 - $35   *Price is for style "A". One Sheet (Style B, collage):$100-$200; One Sheet (Road show):$150-$350.*

STAR 80
(1983 - Warner Bros.) Mariel Hemmingway, Cliff Robertson
One Sheet: $5 - $10

STAR BOARDER, THE
(1914 - Keystone) Charlie Chaplin
One Sheet: $7,500 - $12,000

STAR BOARDER, THE
(1919 - -) Louise Fazenda, Billy Armstrong
One Sheet: $250 - $500

STAR CHAMBER, THE
(1983 - 20th Century Fox) Michael Douglas, Hal Holbrook, Yaphet Kotto
One Sheet: $3 - $5

STAR CRASH
(1978 - -) Marjoe Gortner, Caroline Munro
One Sheet: $5 - $10

STAR DUST
(1940 - 20th Century Fox) Linda Darnell, John Payne
One Sheet: $200 - $400

STAR FOR A NIGHT
(1936 - 20th Century Fox) Claire Trevor, Jane Darwell
One Sheet: $200 - $400

STAR IN THE DUST
(1956 - Universal) John Agar, Mamie Van Doren
One Sheet: $20 - $40

STAR IS BORN, A
(1937 - United Artists) Janet Gaynor, Fredric March
One Sheet: $250 - $500   *Caution: re-release posters are difficult to identify.*

STAR IS BORN, A
(1954 - Warner Bros.) Judy Garland, James Mason
One Sheet: $200 - $400

STAR IS BORN, A
(1977 - Warner Bros.) Barbra Streisand, Kris Kristofferson
One Sheet: $15 - $25   *Artwork style:$20-35.*

STAR IS BORN, A
(1983R - Warner Bros.) Judy Garland
One Sheet: $15 - $30   *Re-release.*

STAR MAKER, THE
(1939 - Paramount) Bing Crosby, Louise Campbell
One Sheet: $75 - $150

STAR MAKER, THE
(1996 - Miramax) Dir: Giuseppe Tornatore
One Sheet: $5 - $12

STAR OF INDIA
(1956 - United Artists) Cornel Wilde, Jean Wallace
One Sheet: $15 - $25

STAR OF MIDNIGHT
(1935 - RKO) William Powell, Ginger Rogers
One Sheet: $1,900 - $3,000

STAR OF TEXAS
(1953 - Allied Artists) Wayne Morris
One Sheet: $15 - $35

STAR OVER NIGHT, A
(1919 - Universal) David Belasco
One Sheet: $250 - $500

STAR PACKER, THE
(1934 - Monogram) John Wayne
One Sheet: $1,900 - $3,000

STAR PACKER, THE
(1940R - Lone Star) John Wayne
One Sheet: $200 - $400   *Re-release.*

STAR REPORTER
(1939 - Monogram) Warren Hull, Marsha Hunt
One Sheet: $40 - $75

STAR SPANGLED GIRL
(1971 - Paramount) Sandy Duncan, Tony Roberts
One Sheet: $5 - $10

STAR SPANGLED RHYTHM
(1942 - Paramount) Bing Crosby, Bob Hope, All-Star Cast
One Sheet: $100 - $200

One Sheet

STAR TREK - THE MOTION PICTURE
(1979 - Paramount) William Shatner, Leonard Nimoy
One Sheet: $30 - $50   *Advance:$40-$80.*

STAR TREK - THE MOTION PICTURE
(1992R - Paramount) William Shatner, Leonard Nimoy
One Sheet: $10 - $20   *25th Anniversary Poster.*

STAR TREK: FIRST CONTACT
(1996 - Paramount) Patrick Stewart, Jonathan Frakes
One Sheet: $7 - $15

STAR TREK: GENERATIONS
(1994 - Paramount) Patrick Stewart, William Shatner
One Sheet: $15 - $25   *Advance 45" x 60" (Duraflex): $50-$75.*

STAR TREK II: THE WRATH OF KHAN
(1982 - Paramount) William Shatner, Leonard Nimoy, Ricardo Montalban
One Sheet: $15 - $30

STAR TREK III: THE SEARCH FOR SPOCK
(1984 - Paramount) William Shatner, Leonard Nimoy
One Sheet: $15 - $30

STAR TREK IV: THE VOYAGE HOME
(1986 - Paramount) William Shatner, Leonard Nimoy
One Sheet: $15 - $30   *Advance:$15-$25.*

STAR TREK V: THE FINAL FRONTIER
(1989 - Paramount) William Shatner, Leonard Nimoy
One Sheet: $15 - $25

STAR TREK VI: THE UNDISCOVERED COUNTRY
(1991 - Paramount) William Shatner, Leonard Nimoy
One Sheet: $5 - $10

STAR WARS
(1977 - 20th Century Fox) Mark Hamill, Harrison Ford, Carrie Fisher
One Sheet: $75 - $125   *Above price is for style "A" or "B". Beware rolled reprint one sheets ($10). One Sheet(Style C):$150-$300. OneSheet(Style D):$100-$200. One Sheet(Mylar Advance, either "W"):$800-$1,500. Half Sheet:$150-$300. Insert: $100-$200.*

STAR WARS
(1979R - 20ty Century Fox) Mark Hamill, Harrison Ford, Carrie Fisher
One Sheet: $100 - $200   *First re-release.*

STAR WARS
(1981R - 20th Century Fox) Mark Hamill, Harrison Ford, Carrie Fisher
One Sheet: $30 - $50   *Re-release.*

STAR WARS
(1982R - 20th Century Fox) Mark Hamill, Harrison Ford, Carrie Fisher
One Sheet: $30 - $50   *Re-release. REVENGE OF THE JEDI banner strip is on this year re-issue.*

One Sheet (1982R)

STAR WARS
(1987R - 20th Century Fox) Mark Hamill, Harrison Ford, Carrie Fisher
One Sheet: $30 - $50   *Re-release.*

STAR WARS
(1993R - 20th Century Fox) Mark Hamill, Harrison Ford, Carrie Fisher
One Sheet: $7 - $15   *Re-release. Price Is for Style B. One Sheet (New Hope): $15-$20.*

STAR WARS SAGA CHECKLIST
(1985 - Kilian) -
One Sheet: $15 - $30   *American One Sheet Poster Checklist. Two-sided.*

STAR WARS/THE EMPIRE STRIKES BACK/ RETURN OF THE JEDI
(1985R - 20th Century Fox) Mark Hamil, Harrison Ford
One Sheet: $20 - $40   *Re-release triple feature.*

STAR WITNESS, THE
(1931 - Warner Bros.) Walter Huston, Dickie Moore
One Sheet: $250 - $600

STARBIRD AND SWEET WILLIAM
(1975 - Howco) A. Martinez, Louise Fitch, Don Haggerty
One Sheet: $5 - $10

STARCHASER: THE LEGEND OF ORIN
(1985 - Atlantic) -
One Sheet: $7 - $15   *Cartoon.*

STARDUST MEMORIES
(1980 - United Artists) Woody Allen, Tony Roberts
One Sheet: $5 - $10

STARDUST ON THE SAGE
(1942 - Republic) Gene Autry, Smiley Burnette
One Sheet: $125 - $250   *Cowboy Movie Posters #270.*

STARGATE
(1994 - MGM/UA) Kurt Russell, James Spader, Jaye Davidson
One Sheet: $7 - $15

STARK LOVE
(1927 - -) Helen Munday, Forrest James
One Sheet: $125 - $250

STARK MAD
(1929 - Warner Bros.) H. B. Warner, Louise Fazenda
One Sheet: $1,900 - $3,000   *Graven Images, pg. 32.*

STARLIFT
(1951 - Warner Bros.) Janice Rule, Richard Webb, Doris Day
One Sheet: $15 - $35

STARLIGHT OVER TEXAS
(1938 - Monogram) Tex Ritter, Carmen LaRoux
One Sheet: $125 - $250

STARLIGHT THE UNTAMED
(1925 - Rayart) Jack Perrin
One Sheet: $250 - $500

STARLIGHT'S REVENGE
(1926 - Rayart) Jack Perrin
One Sheet: $250 - $600

STARMAN
(1984 - Columbia) Jeff Bridges, Karen Allen
One Sheet: $5 - $10

STARRING IN WESTERN STUFF
(1916 - Selig) -

STARS AND GUITARS
(1951R - Republic) Roy Rogers, Tito Guizar
One Sheet: $50 - $100   *Re-release of BRAZIL.*

STARS AND STRIPES FOREVER
(1952 - 20th Century Fox) Clifton Webb, Ruth Hussey
One Sheet: $30 - $50

STARS ARE SINGING, THE
(1952 - Paramount) Rosemary Clooney, Lauritz Melchior
One Sheet: $15 - $30

STARS IN MY CROWN
(1950 - MGM) Joel McCrea, Ellen Drew
One Sheet: $15 - $35

STARS LOOK DOWN, THE
(1941 - MGM) Michael Redgrave, Margaret Lockwood
One Sheet: $30 - $50

STARS ON PARADE
(1944 - Columbia) Lynn Merrick, Larry Parks
One Sheet: $30 - $50

STARS OVER ARIZONA
(1937 - Monogram) Jack Randall, Kathleen Elliott
One Sheet: $50 - $100

STARS OVER BROADWAY
(1935 - Warner Bros.) Pat O'Brien, James Melton, Jane Froman
One Sheet: $75 - $150

STARS OVER TEXAS
(1946 - PRC) Eddie Dean, Shirley Patterson
One Sheet: $15 - $35

STARSHIP INVASIONS
(1977 - Warner Bros.) Robert Vaughn, Christopher Lee
One Sheet: $10 - $20

START CHEERING
(1937 - Columbia) Charles Starrett, Jimmy Durante, Three Stooges (Curly)
One Sheet: $150 - $300

START THE REVOLUTION WITHOUT ME
(1970 - Warner Bros.) Gene Wilder, Donald Sutherland
One Sheet: $5 - $10

STARTING OVER
(1979 - Paramount) Burt Reynolds, Jill Clayburgh
One Sheet: $5 - $10

STARVATION BLUES
(1925 - Pathe) Clyde Cook
One Sheet: $250 - $600

STATE DEPARTMENT - FILE 649
(1949 - Film Classics) William Lundigan, Virginia Bruce
One Sheet: $15 - $30

STATE FAIR
(1933 - Fox) Will Rogers, Janet Gaynor
One Sheet: $350 - $750   *Beware 20th Century Fox re-releases. See next listing.*

STATE FAIR
(1936R - 20th Century Fox) Will Rogers, Janet Gaynor
One Sheet: $50 - $100   *Re-release.*

STATE FAIR
(1945 - 20th Century Fox) Charles Winninger, Fay Bainter, Jeanne Crain, Dana Andrews
One Sheet: $75 - $125

STATE FAIR
(1962 - 20th Century Fox) Pat Boone, Bobby Darin, Ann-Margret
One Sheet: $30 - $50

STATE OF DEATH
(1975 - -) Charles Bronson, Ralph Waite
One Sheet: $5 - $10

STATE OF GRACE
(1990 - -) Sean Penn, Ed Harris
One Sheet: $3 - $5

STATE OF SIEGE
(1973 - Cinema 5) Yves Montand, Renato Salvatori
One Sheet: $5 - $10

STATE OF THE UNION
(1948 - MGM) Spencer Tracy, Katharine Hepburn
One Sheet: $125 - $250

STATE PENITENTIARY
(1950 - Columbia) Warner Baxter, Karin Booth
One Sheet: $15 - $35

STATE SECRET
(1950 - Columbia) Douglas Fairbanks, Jr., Glynis Johns
One Sheet: $15 - $30

STATE TROOPER
(1933 - Columbia) Regis Toomey, Evalyn Knapp
One Sheet: $150 - $300

STATE'S ATTORNEY
(1932 - RKO) John Barrymore, Helen Twelvetrees
One Sheet: $250 - $500

STATION SIX-SAHARA
(1964 - Allied Artists) Carroll Baker, Ian Bannen
One Sheet: $15 - $25

STATION WEST
(1948 - RKO) Dick Powell, Jane Greer
One Sheet: $50 - $100

STATIONMASTER'S WIFE, THE
(1977 - -) Dir: R.W. Fassbinder
One Sheet: $10 - $20   *German.*

STATUE, THE
(1971 - Cinerama) David Niven, Virna Lisi
One Sheet: $3 - $5

STAY AWAY, JOE
(1968 - MGM) Elvis Presley, Burgess Meredith
One Sheet: $30 - $50

One Sheet

STAY HUNGRY
(1976 - United Artists) Jeff Bridges, Sally Field, Arnold Schwarzenegger
One Sheet: $15 - $25

STAY TUNED
(1992 - Warner Bros.) John Ritter, Pam Dawber
One Sheet: $2 - $3

STAYING ALIVE
(1983 - Paramount) John Travolta, Cynthia Rhodes
One Sheet: $15 - $30

STAYING TOGETHER
(1989 - Hemdale) Sean Astin, Stockard Channing
One Sheet: $2 - $3

STEADY COMPANY
(1932 - Universal) Norman Foster, June Clyde, ZaSu Pitts
One Sheet: $75 - $150

STEAGLE, THE
(1971 - Avco/Embassy) Richard Benjamin, Chill

Wills, Cloris Leachman
One Sheet: $3 - $5

STEALIN' AIN'T HONEST
(1940 - Paramount) Popeye, Fleischer Studio
One Sheet: $1,600 - $2,500   *Cartoon. Duotone.*

STEALING BEAUTY
(1996 - Fox Searchlight) Liv Tyler, Jeremy Irons
One Sheet: $5 - $12

STEALING HOME
(1988 - -) Mark Harmon, Jodie Foster
One Sheet: $5 - $10

STEAMBOAT BILL JUNIOR
(1927 - United Artists) Buster Keaton, Ernest Torrence, Marion Byron
One Sheet: $6,500 - $10,000

STEAMBOAT ROUND THE BEND
(1935 - 20th Century Fox) Will Rogers, Anne Shirley
One Sheet: $700 - $1,200

Title Card

STEAMBOAT WILLIE
(1928 - Disney) Mickey Mouse
One Sheet: $45,000 - $60,000   *Cartoon. First Mickey Mouse cartoon. May exist only as a stock one sheet with printed title inset.*

STEEL AGAINST THE SKY
(1941 - Warner Bros.) Alexis Smith, Craig Stevens, Lloyd Nolan
One Sheet: $15 - $35

STEEL BAYONET
(1956 - United Artists) Leo Genn, Kieron Moore
One Sheet: $15 - $25

STEEL CAGE, THE
(1953 - United Artists) Paul Kelly, Maureen O'Sullivan
One Sheet: $15 - $30

STEEL CLAW, THE
(1961 - Warner Bros.) George Montgomery, Charito Luna
One Sheet: $15 - $25

STEEL DAWN
(1987 - Vestron) Patrick Swayze, Lisa Niemi
One Sheet: $7 - $15

STEEL FIST, THE
(1952 - Monogram) Roddy McDowall, Kristine Miller
One Sheet: $15 - $30

STEEL HELMET, THE
(1951 - Lippert) Gene Evans, Steve Brodie
One Sheet: $20 - $40

STEEL JUNGLE, THE
(1956 - Warner Bros.) Perry Lopez, Beverly Garland
One Sheet: $20 - $40

STEEL LADY, THE
(1953 - United Artists) Rod Cameron, Tab Hunter
One Sheet: $15 - $30

STEEL MAGNOLIAS
(1989 - TriStar) Sally Field, Dolly Parton
One Sheet: $10 - $20

STEEL TOWN
(1952 - Universal) Ann Sheridan, John Lund
One Sheet: $15 - $30

STEEL TRAP, THE

(1953 - 20th Century Fox) Joseph Cotten, Teresa Wright
One Sheet: $15 - $30

STEELYARD BLUES
(1973 - Warner Bros.) Jane Fonda, Peter Boyle
One Sheet: $5 - $10

STELLA
(1950 - 20th Century Fox) Ann Sheridan, Victor Mature
One Sheet: $15 - $25

STELLA
(1990 - Touchstone) Bette Midler, John Goodman
One Sheet: $5 - $10

STELLA DALLAS
(1925 - United Artists) Ronald Colman, Belle Bennett
One Sheet: $600 - $1,000

STELLA DALLAS
(1937 - United Artists) Barbara Stanwyck, John Boles
One Sheet: $700 - $1,200

STELLA MARIS
(1918 - Artcraft) Mary Pickford, Conway Tearle
One Sheet: $1,300 - $2,000

STEP BY STEP
(1946 - RKO) Lawrence Tierney, Anne Jeffreys
One Sheet: $40 - $75

STEP DOWN TO TERROR
(1958 - Universal-International) Colleen Miller, Charles Drake
One Sheet: $15 - $25

STEP FAST
(1925 - Educational) -
One Sheet: $150 - $300

STEP LIVELY
(1944 - RKO) Frank Sinatra, George Murphy
One Sheet: $75 - $125

STEP LIVELY, JEEVES!
(1937 - 20th Century Fox) Arthur Treacher, Patricia Ellis
One Sheet: $75 - $150

STEP ON IT
(1922 - Universal) Hoot Gibson, Edith Yorke, Barbara Bedford
One Sheet: $250 - $600

STEPCHILD
(1947 - Pathe) Brenda Joyce, Donald Woods
One Sheet: $20 - $40

STEPFATHER, THE
(1987 - New World) Terry O'Quinn, Jill Schoelen
One Sheet: $7 - $15

STEPFATHER II, THE
(1989 - Millimeter) Terry O'Quinn, Meg Foster
One Sheet: $3 - $5

STEPFORD WIVES, THE
(1975 - Columbia) Katharine Ross, Paula Prentiss
One Sheet: $10 - $20

STEPHEN KING'S THINNER
(1996 - Paramount) Robert John Burke, Joe Mantegna
One Sheet: $5 - $12

STEPHEN STEPS OUT
(1923 - Paramount) Douglas Fairbanks Jr., Noah Beery
One Sheet: $250 - $500

STEPMOTHER
(1972 - Crown) Alejandro Rey, John Anderson
One Sheet: $15 - $25

STEPPENWOLF
(1974 - D. R. Films) Dir: Fred Haines, Max Von Sydow
One Sheet: $7 - $15

STEPPIN' IN SOCIETY
(1945 - Republic) Edward Everett Horton, Ruth Terry
One Sheet: $30 - $50

STEPPING LIVELY
(1924 - Carlos) Richard Talmadge
One Sheet: $150 - $300

STEPPING OUT
(1931 - MGM) Reginald Denny, Charlotte Greenwood
One Sheet: $150 - $300

STEPPING OUT
(1991 - Paramount) Liza Minnelli
One Sheet: $5 - $10

STEPPING SISTERS
(1931 - Fox) Louise Dresser, Minna Gombell
One Sheet: $125 - $250

STERILE CUCKOO, THE
(1969 - Paramount) Liza Minelli, Wendell Burton
One Sheet: $15 - $25

STEWARDESSES, THE
(1970 - Sherpix) Christina Hart, Michael Garrett
One Sheet: $5 - $10

STICK
(1983 - Universal) Burt Reynolds, Candice Bergen
One Sheet: $3 - $5

STICK TO YOUR GUNS
(1941 - Paramount) Bill Boyd, Andy Clyde
One Sheet: $125 - $250   *Hopalong Cassidy series.*

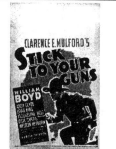

Window Card

STICKY FINGERS
(1988 - -) Helen Slater, Melanie Mayron
One Sheet: $2 - $3

STIGMA, THE
(1914 - Essanay) Francis X. Bushman
One Sheet: $300 - $650

STIGMA
(1972 - Cinerama) Philip M. Thomas, Harlan Poe
One Sheet: $3 - $5

STILETTO
(1969 - Avco/Embassy) Alex Cord, Britt Ekland, Patrick O'Neal
One Sheet: $7 - $15

STILL ALARM, THE
(1926 - Universal) Helena Chadwick, William Russell
One Sheet: $250 - $500

STILL ALARM
(1930 - Vitaphone) -
One Sheet: $100 - $200

STILL OF THE NIGHT
(1982 - MGM/United Artists) Roy Scheider, Meryl Streep
One Sheet: $5 - $10

STILL SMOKIN'
(1983 - -) Cheech Martin, Thomas Chong
One Sheet: $5 - $10

STING, THE
(1973 - Universal) Paul Newman, Robert Redford
One Sheet: $75 - $125   *Academy Award: Best Picture, Best Director(Hill). Amsel art. Academy Award Movie Posters #274 & #275.*

STING, THE
(1977R - Universal) Paul Newman, Robert Redford
One Sheet: $15 - $35   *Re-release.*

STING II, THE
(1982 - Universal) Jackie Gleason, Mac Davis
One Sheet: $5 - $10

STING OF THE WEST, THE
(1970S - Ventures International) Jack Palance, Timothy Brent
One Sheet: $7 - $15

STINGAREE
(1934 - RKO) Irene Dunne, Richard Dix
One Sheet: $200 - $400

STINGRAY
(1978 - Avco Embassy) Christopher Mitchum, Les Lannom, Sherry Jackson
One Sheet: $7 - $15

STIR CRAZY
(1980 - Columbia) Gene Wilder, Richard Pryor
One Sheet: $5 - $10

STOCK CAR
(1955 - Balblair) Paul Carpenter, Rona Anderson
One Sheet: $50 - $100   *Sports (Stock Car racing).*

STOLEN CHILDREN, THE
(1993 - Samuel Goldwyn) Enrico LoVerso, Valentina Scalici
One Sheet: $5 - $10   *Italian.*

STOLEN FACE
(1952 - Lippert) Paul Henreid, Lizabeth Scott
One Sheet: $125 - $250

STOLEN HARMONY
(1935 - Paramount) George Raft, Ben Bernie
One Sheet: $100 - $200

STOLEN HEAVEN
(1931 - Paramount Publix) Nancy Carroll, Phillip Holmes
One Sheet: $100 - $200

STOLEN HEAVEN
(1938 - Paramount) Gene Raymond, Olympe Bradna
One Sheet: $50 - $100

STOLEN HOLIDAY
(1937 - Warner Bros.) Kay Francis, Claude Rains
One Sheet: $75 - $150

STOLEN HOURS
(1963 - United Artists) Susan Hayward, Michael Craig
One Sheet: $15 - $25

STOLEN IDENTITY
(1953 - Ainsworth) Francis Lederer, Donald Buka
One Sheet: $50 - $100

STOLEN JOOLS, THE
(1931 - -) Laurel & Hardy, Buster Keaton, Our Gang, Joan Crawford, etc.
One Sheet: $1,300 - $2,000   *Comedy short.*

STOLEN KISSES
(1968 - Lopert) Jean-Pierre Leaud, Delphine Seyrig
One Sheet: $30 - $50   *French.*

STOLEN LIFE
(1939 - Paramount) Elizabeth Bergner, Michael Redgrave
One Sheet: $40 - $75

STOLEN LIFE, A
(1946 - Warner Bros.) Bette Davis, Glenn Ford
One Sheet: $75 - $150

STOLEN LOVE
(1928 - FBO) Owen Moore, Marceline Day
One Sheet: $1,300 - $2,000

STOLEN MOMENTS
(1920 - American Cinema) Rudolph Valentino
One Sheet: $700 - $1,200

STOLEN TRIUMPH, THE
(1916 - Barolfe) Julius Steger
One Sheet: $200 - $400

STONE AGE ROMEOS
(1955 - Columbia) The Three Stooges (Shemp)
One Sheet: $150 - $300   *Comedy short. Duotone. Remake of I'M A MONKEY'S UNCLE.*

STONE BOY, THE
(1984 - -) Robert Duvall, Glenn Close, Jason Presson
One Sheet: $3 - $5

STONE COLD
(1991 - Columbia) Brian Bosworth
One Sheet: $3 - $5

STONE KILLER
(1973 - Columbia) Charles Bronson
One Sheet: $15 - $25

STONE OF SILVER CREEK
(1935 - Universal) Buck Jones, Niles Welch
One Sheet: $250 - $600

STOOGE, THE
(1951 - Paramount) Dean Martin, Jerry Lewis
One Sheet: $40 - $75

STOOGEMANIA
(1986 - -) 3 Stooges
One Sheet: $15 - $25

STOP! OR MY MOM WILL SHOOT
(1992 - Universal) Sly Stallone, Estelle Getty
One Sheet: $3 - $5

STOP FLIRTING
(1925 - -) John T. Murray, Wanda Hawley
One Sheet: $200 - $400

STOP! LOOK! AND LAUGH!
(1960 - Columbia) The Three Stooges
One Sheet: $75 - $125   *Excerpts from old comedy shorts.*

STOP, LOOK, AND LOVE
(1939 - 20th Century Fox) Jean Rogers, Robert Kellard
One Sheet: $50 - $100

STOP MAKING SENSE
(1984 - -) David Byrne, Talking Heads
One Sheet: $15 - $35   *Rock 'n' Roll concert film.*

STOP ME BEFORE I KILL!
(1961 - Columbia) Claude Dauphin, Diane Cilento
One Sheet: $15 - $25

STOP THAT CAB
(1951 - Lippert) Sid Melton, Iris Adrian
One Sheet: $30 - $50

STOP THE WORLD - I WANT TO GET OFF
(1966 - Warner Bros.) Tony Tanner, Millicent Martin
One Sheet: $5 - $10

STOP TRAIN 349
(1964 - Allied Artists) Jose Ferrer, Sean Flynn
One Sheet: $5 - $10

STOP, YOU'RE KILLING ME
(1952 - Warner Bros.) Broderick Crawford, Claire Trevor
One Sheet: $15 - $25

STOPOVER TOKYO
(1957 - 20th Century Fox) Robert Wagner, Joan Collins
One Sheet: $15 - $25

STORK BITES MAN
(1947 - United Artists) Jackie Cooper, Gene Roberts
One Sheet: $15 - $30

STORK BROUGHT IT, THE
(1926 - Bray) Written by Walter Lantz
One Sheet: $500 - $800   *Cartoon. Cartoon Movie Posters #22.*

STORK CLUB, THE
(1945 - Paramount) Betty Hutton, Barry Fitzgerald
One Sheet: $50 - $100

STORK PAYS OFF, THE
(1941 - Columbia) Maxie Rosenbloom, Rochelle Hudson
One Sheet: $40 - $75

STORK'S HOLIDAY, THE
(1943 - MGM) -
One Sheet: $500 - $800   *Cartoon. Cartoon Movie Posters #250.*

STORM, THE
(1930 - Universal) Lupe Velez, Paul Cavanagh
One Sheet: $700 - $1,200

STORM, THE
(1938 - Universal) Charles Bickford, Barton MacLane
One Sheet: $50 - $100

STORM AT DAYBREAK
(1933 - MGM) Kay Francis, Walter Huston
One Sheet: $100 - $200

STORM CENTER
(1956 - Columbia) Bette Davis, Kim Hunter
One Sheet: $30 - $50

STORM FEAR
(1955 - United Artists) Cornel Wilde, Jean Wallace
One Sheet: $15 - $25

STORM IN A TEACUP
(1937 - United Artists) Rex Harrison, Vivien Leigh
One Sheet: $800 - $1,500

STORM OVER BENGAL
(1938 - Republic) Patric Knowles, Richard Cromwell
One Sheet: $50 - $100

STORM OVER LISBON
(1944 - Republic) Vera Hruba Ralston, Richard Arlen, Erich von Stroheim
One Sheet: $30 - $50

STORM OVER THE ANDES
(1935 - Universal) Jack Holt, Gene Lockhart
One Sheet: $75 - $125

STORM OVER THE NILE
(1956 - Columbia) Anthony Steel, Laurence Harvey
One Sheet: $15 - $25

STORM OVER TIBET
(1951 - Columbia) Diana Douglas, Rex Reason
One Sheet: $10 - $20

STORM OVER WYOMING
(1949 - RKO) Tim Holt, Richard Martin
One Sheet: $15 - $35

STORM RIDER, THE
(1957 - 20th Century Fox) Scott Brady, Mala Powers
One Sheet: $15 - $25

STORM WARNING
(1950 - Warner Bros.) Ginger Rogers, Ronald Reagan, Doris Day
One Sheet: $75 - $150

STORMBOUND
(1951 - Republic) Constance Dowling, Andrea Chechi
One Sheet: $15 - $25

STORMCHASERS
(1996 - MacGillivray Freeman) -
One Sheet: $5 - $10   *IMAX Documentary.*

STORMSWEPT
(1923 - FBO) Wallace and Noah Beery
One Sheet: $600 - $1,000

STORMY
(1935 - Universal) Noah Beery Jr.
One Sheet: $75 - $150

One Sheet

STORMY MONDAY
(1988 - -) Melanie Griffith, Tommy Lee Jones, Sting
One Sheet: $15 - $25

STORMY SEAS
(1920 - Pathe) J. P. McGowan, Helen Holmes
One Sheet: $150 - $350

STORMY WEATHER

(1943 - 20th Century Fox) Lena Horne, Bill Robinson
One Sheet: $1,600 - $2,500   *Black cast. Separate Cinema, pg. 33. One Sheet(text only):$200-$300.*

Three Sheet

STORY OF A WOMAN
(1970 - Universal) Bibi Andersson, Robert Stack, James Farentino
One Sheet: $3 - $5

STORY OF ADELE H., THE
(1975 - Les Films) Isabelle Adjani, Bruce Robinson
One Sheet: $15 - $25   *French.*

STORY OF ALEXANDER GRAHAM BELL, THE
(1939 - 20th Century Fox) Don Ameche, Loretta Young
One Sheet: $200 - $400

STORY OF ANYBURG U.S.A.
(1957 - Disney)
One Sheet: $30 - $50   *Cartoon.*

STORY OF BOB AND SALLY, THE
(1948 - Social Guidance Enterprises)
One Sheet: $50 - $100   *Exploitation.*

STORY OF DR. WASSELL, THE
(1944 - Paramount) Gary Cooper, Dir: Cecil B. DeMille
One Sheet: $100 - $200

One Sheet

STORY OF EARIEN LITTLE, THE
(1987 - Warren Bros.) Elizabeth Binks, Suzanna Que, Jonathan Critter
One Sheet: $15 - $25

STORY OF ESTHER COSTELLO, THE
(1957 - Columbia) Joan Crawford, Rossano Brazzi
One Sheet: $15 - $35

STORY OF G.I. JOE, THE
(1945 - United Artists) Burgess Meredith, Robert Mitchum
One Sheet: $75 - $150

STORY OF GILBERT AND SULLIVAN, THE
(1953 - United Artists) Robert Morley, Maurice Evans
One Sheet: $15 - $35

STORY OF LIFE, THE
(1948 - -) Joseph Creehan, Wanda McKay
One Sheet: $20 - $40

STORY OF LOUIS PASTEUR, THE
(1936 - Warner Bros.) Paul Muni, Josephine Hutchinson
One Sheet: $600 - $1,000   *Academy Award: Best Actor. Academy Award Movie Posters #47.*

STORY OF MANDY, THE
(1952 - GFD) Phyllis Calvert, Jack Hawkins
One Sheet: $7 - $15

STORY OF MANKIND, THE
(1957 - Warner Bros.) Ronald Colman, Hedy Lamarr, Marx Brothers
One Sheet: $30 - $50

STORY OF MOLLY X, THE
(1949 - Universal) June Havoc, John Russell
One Sheet: $15 - $30

STORY OF O, THE
(1975 - -) Udo Kier, Corienne Clery
One Sheet: $20 - $40

STORY OF PERRI
(1957 - Disney) -
One Sheet: $15 - $35

STORY OF QIUJU, THE
(1992 - Sony) Gong Li
One Sheet: $3 - $5

STORY OF ROBIN HOOD, THE
(1952 - RKO/Disney) Richard Todd, Joan Rice
One Sheet: $40 - $75

STORY OF RUTH, THE
(1960 - 20th Century Fox) Stuart Whitman, Tom Tryon, Elana Eden
One Sheet: $5 - $10

STORY OF SEABISCUIT, THE
(1950 - Warner Bros.) Shirley Temple, Barry Fitzgerald
One Sheet: $40 - $75

STORY OF TEMPLE DRAKE, THE
(1933 - Paramount) Miriam Hopkins, Jack LaRue
One Sheet: $1,300 - $2,000   *This film bears the dubious distinction of being the chief reason for the establishment of the Roman CatholicChurch's Legion Of Decency.*

STORY OF THE COUNT OF MONTE CRISTO, THE
(1962 - Warner Bros.) Louis Jourdan, Yvonne Forneau
One Sheet: $5 - $10

STORY OF THE INIMITABLE SARAH SIDDONS, THE
(1938 - John Nathaniel Ruffin) -
One Sheet: $40 - $75

STORY OF THREE LOVES, THE
(1952 - MGM) Kirk Douglas, Pier Angeli
One Sheet: $30 - $50

STORY OF VERNON AND IRENE CASTLE, THE
(1939 - RKO) Fred Astaire, Ginger Rogers
One Sheet: $1,300 - $2,000   *Price is for Style A(photographic). One Sheet(Style B, stone litho):$2,500-$3,500.*

One Sheet

STORY OF VICKIE, THE
(1953 - Buena Vista) Romy Schneider, Adrian Haven
One Sheet: $15 - $25

STORY OF WILL ROGERS, THE
(1952 - Warner Bros.) Jane Wyman, Will Rogers Jr.
One Sheet: $30 - $50

STORY ON PAGE ONE, THE
(1960 - 20th Century Fox) Rita Hayworth, Anthony Franciosa
One Sheet: $20 - $40

STOWAWAY
(1932 - Universal) Fay Wray, Betty Francisco, Leon Waycoff
One Sheet: $200 - $400

STOWAWAY
(1936 - 20th Century Fox) Shirley Temple, Robert Young, Alice Faye
One Sheet: $800 - $1,500

STOWAWAY GIRL
(1957 - Paramount) Trevor Howard, Pedro Armendariz
One Sheet: $15 - $25

STOWAWAY IN THE SKY
(1962 - United Artists) Jack Lemmon, Andre Gille
One Sheet: $10 - $20

STRAIGHT FROM THE HEART
(1935 - Universal) Mary Astor
One Sheet: $150 - $300

STRAIGHT FROM THE SHOULDER
(1936 - Paramount) Ralph Bellamy, Katherine Locke
One Sheet: $75 - $150

STRAIGHT IS THE WAY
(1934 - MGM) Franchot Tone, Karen Morley
One Sheet: $75 - $150

STRAIGHT ON TILL MORNING
(1974 - Hammer) Rita Tushingham, Shane Briant
One Sheet: $20 - $40

STRAIGHT, PLACE AND SHOW
(1938 - 20th Century Fox) The Ritz Bros., Ethel Merman
One Sheet: $150 - $300   *Sports (Horse Racing). Sports Movie Posters #249.*

Mini Window Card (Trimmed)

STRAIGHT SHOOTER
(1940 - Victory) Tim McCoy, Julie Sheldon
One Sheet: $100 - $200

STRAIGHT TALK
(1992 - Hollywood) Dolly Parton, James Woods
One Sheet: $7 - $15

STRAIGHT TIME
(1978 - Warner Bros.) Dustin Hoffman, Harry Dean Stanton
One Sheet: $10 - $20

STRAIGHT TO HEAVEN
(1939 - Sack) Nina Mae McKinney
One Sheet: $100 - $200   *Black cast. Duotone. Separate Cinema, pg. 136.*

STRAIGHT TO HELL
(1987 - Island) Sy Richardson, Dennis Hopper
One Sheet: $10 - $20

STRAIGHTAWAY
(1934 - Columbia) Tim McCoy, Sue Carol
One Sheet: $250 - $500

STRAIT-JACKET
(1964 - Columbia) Joan Crawford, Diane Baker
One Sheet: $15 - $35   *Graven Images, pg. 206.*

STRANDED
(1935 - Warner Bros.) George Brent, Kay Francis
One Sheet: $75 - $150

STRANDED
(1987 - -) Ione Skye, Joe Morton, Maureen O'Sullivan
One Sheet: $3 - $5

STRANGE ADVENTURE
(1932 - Monogram) Regis Toomey, June Clyde
One Sheet: $125 - $250

STRANGE ADVENTURE, A
(1956 - Republic) Ben Cooper, Marla English
One Sheet: $10 - $20

STRANGE AFFAIR
(1944 - Columbia) Allyn Joslyn, Evelyn Keyes
One Sheet: $15 - $35

STRANGE AFFAIR
(1968 - Paramount) Michael York, Jeremy Kemp, Susan George
One Sheet: $5 - $10

STRANGE AFFAIR OF UNCLE HARRY, THE
(1945 - Universal) George Sanders, Ella Raines
One Sheet: $15 - $35

STRANGE AFFECTION
(1959 - Brenner) Richard Attenborough, Jill Adams
One Sheet: $5 - $10

STRANGE ALIBI
(1941 - Warner Bros.) Arthur Kennedy, Joan Perry
One Sheet: $30 - $50

STRANGE BARGAIN
(1949 - RKO) Martha Scott, Jeffrey Lynn, Harry Morgan
One Sheet: $15 - $35

STRANGE BEDFELLOWS
(1965 - Universal) Rock Hudson, Gina Lollobrigida
One Sheet: $30 - $50

STRANGE BOARDERS
(1938 - Gaumont) Tom Walls, Renee Saint Cyr
One Sheet: $50 - $100

STRANGE BREW
(1983 - MGM) Rick Moranis, Dave Thomas
One Sheet: $10 - $20   *SCTV TV tie-in.*

STRANGE CARGO
(1940 - MGM) Joan Crawford, Clark Gable
One Sheet: $500 - $800

STRANGE CASE OF CAPTAIN RAMPER
(1928 - First National) Paul Wegener, Mary Johnson
One Sheet: $3,500 - $5,000   *Graven Images, pg. 18.*

STRANGE CASE OF CLARA DEANE, THE
(1932 - Paramount Publix) Pat O'Brien, Frances Dee
One Sheet: $100 - $200

STRANGE CASE OF DOCTOR MEADE, THE
(1938 - Columbia) Jack Holt, Beverly Roberts
One Sheet: $75 - $150

STRANGE CASE OF DR. MANNING, THE
(1959 - States Rights Republic) Ron Randall, Greta Gynt
One Sheet: $15 - $25

STRANGE CASE OF DR. RX, THE
(1942 - Universal) Lionel Atwill, Anne Gwynne
One Sheet: $75 - $150

STRANGE CASE OF THE COSMIC, A
(1957 - N.W. Ayer & Son) -
One Sheet: $15 - $25

STRANGE CONFESSIONS
(1945 - Universal) Lon Chaney Jr., Brenda Joyce
One Sheet: $125 - $250

STRANGE CONQUEST
(1946 - Universal) Jane Wyatt, Lowell Gilmore
One Sheet: $20 - $40

STRANGE DAYS
(1995 - 20th Century Fox) Ralph Fiennes, Angela Bassett
One Sheet: $3 - $5

STRANGE DEATH OF ADOLF HITLER, THE
(1943 - Universal) Gale Sondergaard, Ludwig Donath
One Sheet: $50 - $100

STRANGE DOOR, THE

(1951 - Universal) Charles Laughton, Boris Karloff
One Sheet: $75 - $125

STRANGE FACES
(1938 - Universal) Dorothea Kent, Frank Jenks
One Sheet: $50 - $100

STRANGE FASCINATION
(1952 - Columbia) Hugo Haas, Cleo Moore
One Sheet: $30 - $50

STRANGE GAMBLE
(1948 - United Artists) William Boyd, Andy Clyde
One Sheet: $50 - $100 *Hopalong Cassidy series.*

STRANGE HOLIDAY
(1945 - PRC) Claude Rains, Barbara Bates
One Sheet: $30 - $50

STRANGE ILLUSION
(1945 - PRC) James Lydon, Sally Eilers, Warren William
One Sheet: $30 - $60 *AKA: OUT OF THE NIGHT.*

STRANGE IMPERSONATION
(1946 - Republic) Brenda Marshall, William Gargan
One Sheet: $15 - $35

STRANGE INTERLUDE
(1932 - MGM) Norma Shearer, Clark Gable
One Sheet: $800 - $1,500

STRANGE INTRUDER
(1956 - Allied Artists) Ida Lupino, Edmund Purdom
One Sheet: $15 - $30

STRANGE INVADERS
(1983 - EMI) Paul LeMat, Nancy Allen
One Sheet: $7 - $15

STRANGE JOURNEY
(1946 - 20th Century Fox) Paul Kelly, Osa Massen
One Sheet: $15 - $35

STRANGE JUSTICE
(1932 - RKO) Marian Marsh, Norman Foster
One Sheet: $50 - $100

STRANGE LADY IN TOWN
(1955 - Warner Bros.) Greer Garson, Dana Andrews
One Sheet: $10 - $20

STRANGE LOVE OF MARTHA IVERS, THE
(1946 - Paramount) Barbara Stanwyck, Van Heflin, Kirk Douglas
One Sheet: $150 - $350 *Douglas' film debut.*

STRANGE MR. GREGORY, THE
(1945 - Monogram) Edmund Lowe, Jean Rogers
One Sheet: $30 - $50

STRANGE MRS. CRANE, THE
(1948 - Eagle-Lion) Marjorie Lord, Robert Shayne
One Sheet: $15 - $35

STRANGE ONE, THE
(1957 - Columbia) Ben Gazzara, George Peppard
One Sheet: $5 - $10 *Gazzara's and Peppard's film debut.*

STRANGE PEOPLE
(1933 - Chesterfield) John Darrow, Gloria Shea
One Sheet: $75 - $150

STRANGE SHADOWS IN AN EMPTY ROOM
(1977 - AIP) Stuart Whitman, John Saxon
One Sheet: $7 - $15

STRANGE TRAITS OF SERPENTS
(1913 - Pathe) -
One Sheet: $250 - $500

STRANGE TRIANGLE
(1946 - 20th Century Fox) Preston Foster, Signe Hasso, John Shepperd
One Sheet: $40 - $75

STRANGE VENGEANCE OF ROSALIE, THE
(1972 - 20th Century Fox) Bonnie Bedelia, Ken Howard
One Sheet: $3 - $5

STRANGE VOYAGE
(1946 - Monogram) Eddie Albert, Forrest Taylor
One Sheet: $15 - $25

STRANGE WIVES
(1934 - Universal) Roger Pryor, June Clayworth
One Sheet: $100 - $200

STRANGE WOMAN, THE
(1946 - United Artists) Hedy Lamarr, George Sanders, Louis Hayward
One Sheet: $50 - $100

STRANGE WORLD
(1952 - United Artists) Angelica Hauff, Alexandro Carlos
One Sheet: $10 - $20

STRANGER, THE
(1924 - -) Billy West
One Sheet: $150 - $300

STRANGER, THE
(1946 - RKO) Orson Welles, Loretta Young, Edward G. Robinson
One Sheet: $250 - $500

STRANGER, THE
(1968 - Paramount) Marcello Mastroianni, Anna Karina
One Sheet: $5 - $10

STRANGER AMONG US, A
(1992 - Buena Vista) Melanie Griffith, Eric Thal
One Sheet: $3 - $5

STRANGER AND THE GUNFIGHTER, THE
(1976 - Columbia) Lee Van Cleef, Lo Lieh
One Sheet: $7 - $15

STRANGER AT MY DOOR
(1956 - Republic) Macdonald Carey, Patricia Medina
One Sheet: $15 - $25

STRANGER FROM ARIZONA, THE
(1938 - Columbia) Buck Jones, Dorothy Fay
One Sheet: $200 - $400

STRANGER FROM PECOS, THE
(1943 - Monogram) Johnny Mack Brown
One Sheet: $50 - $100

STRANGER FROM PONCA CITY, THE
(1947 - Columbia) Charles Starrett, Smiley Burnette
One Sheet: $20 - $40

STRANGER FROM SANTA FE
(1945 - Monogram) Johnny Mack Brown
One Sheet: $30 - $50

STRANGER FROM TEXAS, THE
(1939 - Columbia) Charles Starrett, Lorna Gray
One Sheet: $75 - $150

STRANGER FROM TEXAS, THE
(1953R - Columbia) Charles Starrett, Lorna Gray
One Sheet: $20 - $40 *Re-release.*

STRANGER IN BETWEEN, THE
(1952 - Universal) Dirk Bogarde, Elizabeth Sellars
One Sheet: $5 - $10

STRANGER IN MY ARMS
(1958 - Universal) June Allyson, Jeff Chandler
One Sheet: $15 - $30

STRANGER IN TOWN
(1932 - Warner Bros.) Charles "Chic" Sale, Ann Dvorak
One Sheet: $75 - $150

STRANGER IN TOWN, A
(1943 - MGM) Frank Morgan, Richard Carlson
One Sheet: $15 - $35

STRANGER IN TOWN
(1957 - Astor) Alex Nicol, Colin Tapley
One Sheet: $5 - $10

STRANGER IN TOWN, A
(1968 - MGM) Tony Anthony, Yolanda Modio
One Sheet: $7 - $15

STRANGER IS WATCHING, A
(1982 - MGM/United Artists) Kate Mulgrew, Rip Torn
One Sheet: $3 - $5

STRANGER ON HORSEBACK
(1955 - United Artists) Joel McCrea, Miroslava

One Sheet: $15 - $30

STRANGER ON THE PROWL
(1953 - United Artists) Paul Muni, Joan Lorring
One Sheet: $15 - $30

STRANGER ON THE RUN
(1967 - -) -
One Sheet: $5 - $10

STRANGER ON THE THIRD FLOOR
(1940 - RKO) Peter Lorre, John McGuire, Margaret Tallichet
One Sheet: $250 - $600 *Graven Images, pg. 131.*

STRANGER RETURNS, THE
(1968 - MGM) Tony Anthony, Dan Vadis, Daniele Vargas
One Sheet: $5 - $10

STRANGER RIDES AGAIN, THE
(1938 - 20th Century Fox) Terry-toons
One Sheet: $100 - $200 *Cartoon. Full color stone litho. Stock poster with inset of title.*

STRANGER THAN PARADISE
(1984 - -) John Lurie, Eszter Balint, Cecilia Stark
One Sheet: $15 - $30

STRANGER WORE A GUN, THE
(1953 - Columbia) Randolph Scott, Claire Trevor
One Sheet: $20 - $40 *Originally filmed in 3-D.*

STRANGER'S RETURN, THE
(1933 - MGM) Lionel Barrymore, Franchot Tone, Miriam Hopkins
One Sheet: $125 - $250

STRANGERS ALL
(1935 - RKO) May Robson, Preston Foster
One Sheet: $100 - $200

STRANGERS IN LOVE
(1932 - Paramount Publix) Fredric March, Kay Francis, Sidney Toler
One Sheet: $125 - $250

STRANGERS IN THE NIGHT
(1944 - Republic) William Terry, Virginia Grey
One Sheet: $10 - $20

STRANGERS MAY KISS
(1931 - MGM) Norma Shearer, Robert Montgomery
One Sheet: $125 - $250

STRANGERS OF THE EVENING
(1932 - Tiffany) ZaSu Pitts, Eugene Pallette
One Sheet: $75 - $150

STRANGERS OF THE NIGHT
(1923 - Metro) Matt Moore, Enid Bennett
One Sheet: $150 - $300

STRANGERS ON A HONEYMOON
(1936 - Gaumont) Constance Cummings, Hugh Sinclair
One Sheet: $50 - $100

STRANGERS ON A TRAIN
(1951 - Warner Bros.) Farley Granger, Robert Walker, Dir: Alfred Hitchcock
One Sheet: $125 - $250

One Sheet

STRANGERS ON A TRAIN
(1961R - Warner Bros.) Farley Granger, Robert Walker, Dir: Alfred Hitchcock
One Sheet: $30 - $50 *Re-release.*

STRANGERS WHEN WE MEET

(1960 - Columbia) Kirk Douglas, Kim Novak
One Sheet: $15 - $30

STRANGLER, THE
(1941 - PRC) Judy Campbell, Sebastian Shaw
One Sheet: $50 - $100

STRANGLER, THE
(1964 - Allied Artists) Victor Buono, David McLean
One Sheet: $15 - $30

STRANGLER OF THE SWAMP
(1946 - PRC) Rosemary LaPlanche, Robert Barrett
One Sheet: $125 - $250 *Graven Images, pg. 135.*

One Sheet

STRANGLERS OF BOMBAY, THE
(1960 - Columbia) Guy Rolfe, Allan Cuthbertson
One Sheet: $30 - $50

STRAPHANGER, THE
(1921 - Century) Lee Moran
One Sheet: $250 - $500

STRATEGIC AIR COMMAND
(1954 - Paramount) James Stewart, June Allyson
One Sheet: $40 - $75

STRATEGY OF TERROR
(1968 - Universal) Hugh O'Brian, Barbra Rush
One Sheet: $7 - $15 *AKA: IN DARKNESS WAITING.*

STRATTON STORY, THE
(1949 - MGM) James Stewart, June Allyson
One Sheet: $75 - $150 *Sports (Baseball). Sports Movie Posters #56.*

STRAUSS' GREAT WALTZ
(1934 - Gaumont) Jessie Matthew, Fay Compton
One Sheet: $100 - $200 *AKA: WALTZES FROM VIENNA.*

STRAW DOGS
(1972 - Cinerama) Dustin Hoffman, Susan George, Dir: Sam Peckinpah
One Sheet: $10 - $20

STRAWBERRY AND CHOCOLATE
(1994 - Miramax) Jorge Perrugoria, Vladimir Cruz
One Sheet: $7 - $15 *Spanish.*

STRAWBERRY BLONDE, THE
(1941 - Warner Bros.) James Cagney, Rita Hayworth, Olivia de Havilland
One Sheet: $125 - $250

Lobby Cards (2)

STRAWBERRY BLONDE, THE

(1957R - Warner Bros.) James Cagney, Rita Hayworth, Olivia de Havilland
One Sheet: $40 - $75   *Re-release.*

STRAWBERRY ROAN, THE
(1933 - Universal) Ken Maynard, Ruth Hall
One Sheet: $200 - $400

STRAWBERRY ROAN, THE
(1948 - Columbia) Gene Autry, Gloria Henry
One Sheet: $75 - $150

STRAWBERRY STATEMENT, THE
(1970 - MGM) Bruce Davison, Kim Darby
One Sheet: $3 - $5

STRAY DOG
(1949 - Toho) Toshiro Mifune, Takashi Shimura, Dir: Kurosawa
One Sheet: $100 - $200   *Japanese.*

STREAMERS
(1984 - -) Matthew Modine, Michael Wright
One Sheet: $3 - $5

STREAMLINE EXPRESS
(1935 - Mascot) Victor Jory, Evelyn Venable
One Sheet: $75 - $125

STREAMLINED DONKEY, THE
(1939 - Columbia) -
One Sheet: $125 - $250   *Cartoon.*

STREET ANGEL
(1928 - Fox) Jaynet Gaynor, Charles Farrell
One Sheet: $700 - $1,200   *Academy Award: Best Actress. Academy Award Movie Posters #7.*

STREET BANDITS
(1951 - Republic) Penny Edwards, Robert Clarke
One Sheet: $10 - $20

STREET CORNER
(1948 - Wilshire) Joseph Crehan, Marcia Mae Jones
One Sheet: $15 - $25

STREET FIGHTER
(1959 - Savage-Brenner) Vic Savage, Ann Atmar
One Sheet: $7 - $15

STREET FIGHTER
(1975 - -) Sonny Chiba
One Sheet: $7 - $15

STREET FIGHTER
(1994 - Universal) Jean-Claude Van Damme, Raul Julia
One Sheet: $5 - $10

STREET GIRL
(1929 - RKO) Betty Compson, John Harron
One Sheet: $600 - $1,000

STREET KNIGHT
(1993 - Warner Bros.) Jeff Speakman
One Sheet: $3 - $5

STREET OF CHANCE
(1930 - Paramount Famous Lasky) William Powell, Jean Arthur, Kay Francis
One Sheet: $3,500 - $5,000

STREET OF CHANCE
(1942 - Paramount) Burgess Meredith, Claire Trevor
One Sheet: $150 - $300

STREET OF DARKNESS
(1958 - Republic) Robert Keys, John Close
One Sheet: $5 - $10

STREET OF MEMORIES
(1940 - 20th Century Fox) Lynne Roberts, Guy Kibbee, John McGuire
One Sheet: $30 - $50

STREET OF MISSING MEN
(1939 - Republic) Charles Bickford, Nana Bryant
One Sheet: $40 - $75

STREET OF SHAME
(1956 - Toho) Machioko Kyo, Aiko Mimosu
One Sheet: $75 - $150   *Japanese.*

STREET OF SIN, THE
(1928 - Paramount) Emil Jannings, Fay Wray
One Sheet: $800 - $1,500

STREET OF SINNERS

(1957 - United Artists) George Montgomery, Geraldine Brooks
One Sheet: $15 - $35

STREET OF WOMEN
(1932 - Warner Bros.) Roland Young, Kay Francis
One Sheet: $150 - $300

STREET PEOPLE
(1976 - AIP) Roger Moore, Stacy Keach
One Sheet: $5 - $10

STREET QUEEN, THE
(1975 - Worldwide Enterprises) -
One Sheet: $5 - $10   *Sexploitation.*

STREET SCENE
(1931 - United Artists) Sylvia Sidney, William Collier, Jr.
One Sheet: $300 - $700

STREET SMART
(1987 - Cannon) Christopher Reeve, Kathy Baker
One Sheet: $10 - $20

STREET TRASH
(1987 - -) Bill Chepil, Mike Lackey
One Sheet: $7 - $15

STREET WITH NO NAME, THE
(1948 - 20th Century Fox) Mark Stevens, Richard Widmark, Lloyd Nolan
One Sheet: $75 - $150

STREETCAR NAMED DESIRE, A
(1951 - Warner Bros.) Vivien Leigh, Marlon Brando, Karl Malden, Kim Hunter
One Sheet: $200 - $400   *Academy Award Movie Posters #138-#140.*

STREETCAR NAMED DESIRE, A
(1958R - Warner Bros.) Vivien Leigh, Marlon Brando, Karl Malden, Kim Hunter
One Sheet: $30 - $50   *Re-release.*

STREETCAR NAMED DESIRE, A
(1970R - Warner Bros.) Vivien Leigh, Marlon Brando
One Sheet: $15 - $35   *Re-release.*

STREETS
(1990 - -) Christina Applegate, David Mendenhall
One Sheet: $5 - $10

STREETS OF FIRE
(1984 - Universal/RKO) Michael Pare, Diane Lane, Rick Moranis
One Sheet: $10 - $20   *Advance:$20-$25.*

STREETS OF GHOST TOWN
(1950 - Columbia) Charles Starrett, Smiley Burnette
One Sheet: $20 - $40

STREETS OF GOLD
(1986 - 20th Century Fox) Wesley Snipes, Adrian Pasdar
One Sheet: $10 - $20   *Sports (Boxing). Sports Movie Posters #165.*

STREETS OF LAREDO
(1949 - Paramount) Macdonald Carey, William Holden
One Sheet: $30 - $50

STREETS OF NEW YORK
(1939 - Monogram) Jackie Cooper, Marjorie Reynolds
One Sheet: $50 - $100

STREETS OF SAN FRANCISCO
(1949 - Republic) Robert Armstrong, Mae Clarke, Wally Cassell
One Sheet: $15 - $35

STRICTLY BALLROOM
(1993 - Touchstone) Paul Mercurio, Tara Morice
One Sheet: $3 - $5

STRICTLY DISHONORABLE
(1931 - Universal) Sidney Toler
One Sheet: $100 - $200

STRICTLY DISHONORABLE
(1951 - MGM) Ezio Pinza, Janet Leigh
One Sheet: $15 - $30

STRICTLY DYNAMITE
(1934 - RKO) Jimmy Durante, Lupe Velez, Mills

Brothers
One Sheet: $200 - $400

STRICTLY IN THE GROOVE
(1942 - Universal) Leon Errol, Mary Healy
One Sheet: $30 - $50

STRICTLY MODERN
(1930 - First National) Dorothy Mackaill, Sidney Blackmer
One Sheet: $100 - $200

STRICTLY PERSONAL
(1933 - Paramount) Marjorie Rambeau, Dorothy Jordan
One Sheet: $100 - $200

Mini Window Card (Trimmed)

STRICTLY UNCONVENTIONAL
(1930 - MGM) Catherine Dale Owen, Paul Cavanaugh
One Sheet: $100 - $200

STRIKE
(1924 - -) Maxim Strauch
One Sheet: $700 - $1,200   *Russian. S. Elsenstein's first film.*

STRIKE!
(1934 - Gaumont) Leslie Banko, Carol Goodner
One Sheet: $125 - $250   *AKA: Red Ensign.*

STRIKE IT RICH
(1948 - Allied Artists) Rod Cameron, Bonita Granville, Don Castle
One Sheet: $15 - $30

STRIKE IT RICH
(1990 - Miramax) Molly Ringwald, John Lindsay
One Sheet: $3 - $5

STRIKE ME PINK
(1936 - United Artists) Eddie Cantor, Ethel Merman
One Sheet: $100 - $200

STRIKE UP THE BAND
(1940 - MGM) Mickey Rooney, Judy Garland
One Sheet: $250 - $500

STRIKING DISTANCE
(1993 - Columbia) Bruce Willis, Sarah Jessica Parker
One Sheet: $3 - $5

STRIP, THE
(1951 - MGM) Mickey Rooney, Sally Forrest, Louis Armstrong
One Sheet: $30 - $50

STRIP TEASE GIRL
(1949 - Mack-Sonney) Tempest Storm
One Sheet: $75 - $150   *Sexploitation.*

STRIP TEASE MURDER CASE
(1950 - Futurity) -
One Sheet: $40 - $75

STRIPES
(1981 - Columbia) Bill Murray, Warren Oates
One Sheet: $15 - $25

STRIPORAMA
(1950' - -) Betty Page
One Sheet: $125 - $250   *Sexploitation.*

STRIPPED TO KILL
(1987 - -) Kay Lenz, Greg Evigan
One Sheet: $15 - $25

STRIPPED TO KILL II
(1989 - -) Maria Ford, Eb Lottimer
One Sheet: $15 - $25

STRIPPER, THE
(1963 - 20th Century Fox) Joanne Woodward, Richard Beymer
One Sheet: $15 - $25

STRIPTEASE
(1996 - Columbia) Demi Moore, Burt Reynolds
One Sheet: $7 - $15

One Sheet (Advance)

STRIPTEASE GIRL
(1952 - -) -
One Sheet: $40 - $75   *Sexploitation.*

STROKER ACE
(1983 - Universal) Burt Reynolds, Ned Beatty
One Sheet: $15 - $30   *Sports (Auto Racing). Sports Movie Posters #27.*

One Sheet

STROMBOLI
(1950 - RKO) Ingrid Bergman, Mario Vitale
One Sheet: $75 - $125

STRONG MAN, THE
(1926 - First National) Harry Langdon, Dir: Frank Capra
One Sheet: $1,600 - $2,500   *Langdon's classic.*

STRONGER THAN DESIRE
(1939 - MGM) Virginia Bruce, Walter Pidgeon
One Sheet: $40 - $75

STRONGEST, THE
(1920 - William Fox) Renee Adoree, Carlo Liten
One Sheet: $150 - $300

STRONGEST MAN IN THE WORLD, THE
(1975 - Disney) Kurt Russell, Joe Flynn
One Sheet: $5 - $10

STRONGHOLD
(1952 - Lippert) Veronica Lake, Zachary Scott
One Sheet: $40 - $75

STRUGGLE, THE
(1931 - United Artists) Hal Skelly, Zita Johann
One Sheet: $75 - $150

STUART SAVES HIS FAMILY
(1995 - Paramount) Al Franken, Laura San Giacomo
One Sheet: $3 - $5

STUD, THE
(1979 - Trans-American) Joan Collins, Oliver Tobias
One Sheet: $5 - $10

STUDENT BODIES
(1981 - Paramount) Kristen Riter, Matthew Goldsby
One Sheet: $3 - $5

STUDENT NURSES, THE

(1970 - New World) Elaine Gittos, Karen
Carlson
One Sheet: $5 - $10   *Sexploitation.*

STUDENT OF PRAGUE, THE
(1927 - Sokal) Conrad Veidt
One Sheet: $1,900 - $3,000   *German. Price
is for original German poster. Graven Images, pg.
15.*

STUDENT PRINCE, THE
(1928 - MGM) Ramon Novarro, Norma Shearer
One Sheet: $700 - $1,200

STUDENT PRINCE, THE
(1954 - MGM) Ann Blyth, Edmund Purdom
One Sheet: $15 - $30

STUDENT PRINCE IN OLD HEIDELBERG
(1927 - -) Ramon Novarro, Norma Shearer
One Sheet: $200 - $400   *AKA: OLD
HEIDELBERG.*

STUDENT TEACHERS, THE
(1973 - New World) Susan Damante, Brooke
Mills
One Sheet: $5 - $10   *Sexploitation.*

STUDENT TOUR
(1934 - MGM) Jimmy Durante, Betty Grable
One Sheet: $200 - $400

STUDENT'S ROMANCE, THE
(1936 - BIP) Patric Knowles
One Sheet: $40 - $75

STUDIO RUBE, THE
(1922 - Fox) Al St. John
One Sheet: $250 - $500

STUDIO STOOPS
(1950 - Columbia) The Three Stooges (Shemp)
One Sheet: $200 - $400   *Comedy short.
Duotone.*

STUDS LONIGAN
(1960 - United Artists) Christopher Knight,
Venetia Stevenson, Jack Nicholson
One Sheet: $20 - $40

STUDY IN SCARLET, A
(1933 - World Wide) Reginald Owen, Anna May
Wong
One Sheet: $800 - $1,500   *Sherlock
Holmes.*

STUDY IN TERROR, A
(1966 - Columbia) John Neville, Donald
Houston
One Sheet: $20 - $40

STUFF, THE
(1985 - New World) Michael Moriarty, Andrea
Marcovicci
One Sheet: $7 - $15

STUNT MAN, THE
(1980 - 20th Century Fox) Peter O'Toole,
Barbara Hershey
One Sheet: $7 - $15

STUNT PILOT
(1939 - Monogram) John Trent, Marjorie
Reynolds
One Sheet: $40 - $75

STUPIDS, THE
(1996 - New Line) Tom Arnold, Jessica Lundy
One Sheet: $4 - $8

SUBJECT WAS ROSES, THE
(1968 - MGM) Patricia Neal, Jack Albertson,
Martin Sheen
One Sheet: $15 - $25   *Academy
Award Movie Posters #250.*

SUBMARINE ALERT
(1943 - Paramount) Richard Arlen, Wendy
Barrie
One Sheet: $15 - $35

SUBMARINE BASE
(1943 - PRC) John Litel, Alan Baxter
One Sheet: $15 - $35

SUBMARINE COMMAND
(1951 - Paramount) William Holden, Nancy
Olson
One Sheet: $15 - $35

SUBMARINE D-1
(1937 - Warner Bros.) Pat O'Brien, George
Brent
One Sheet: $50 - $100

SUBMARINE PATROL
(1938 - 20th Century Fox) Richard Greene,
Nancy Kelly
One Sheet: $100 - $200

SUBMARINE PIRATE, A
(1915 - Triangle) Sydney Chaplin
One Sheet: $500 - $800   *Charlie's half-
brother.*

SUBMARINE RAIDER
(1942 - Columbia) John Howard, Larry Parks
One Sheet: $15 - $35

SUBMARINE SEAHAWK
(1958 - AIP) John Bentley, Jan Brooks
One Sheet: $15 - $25

SUBMARINE X-1
(1969 - United Artists) James Caan, David
Summer
One Sheet: $10 - $20

SUBSTANCE OF FIRE, THE
(1996 - Miramax) Tony Goldwyn, Timothy
Hutton, Sarah Jessica Parker
One Sheet: $3 - $5

SUBTERRANEANS, THE
(1960 - MGM) Leslie Caron, George Peppard
One Sheet: $30 - $50

SUBURBIA
(1997 - Sony) Steve Zahn, Parker Posey
One Sheet: $3 - $5

SUBWAY
(1985 - TFI) Isabelle Adjani, Christopher
Lambert
One Sheet: $15 - $25

SUBWAY EXPRESS
(1931 - Columbia) Jack Holt, Aileen Pringle
One Sheet: $100 - $200

SUBWAY IN THE SKY
(1959 - United Artists) Van Johnson,
Hildegarde Neff
One Sheet: $7 - $15

SUCCESS AT ANY PRICE
(1934 - RKO) Douglas Fairbanks, Jr.,
Genevieve Tobin
One Sheet: $100 - $200

SUCCESSFUL CALAMITY, A
(1932 - Warner Bros.) George Arliss, Mary
Astor, Randolph Scott
One Sheet: $125 - $250

One Sheet

SUCCESSFUL FAILURE
(1934 - Monogram) William Collier Sr., Lucille
Gleason
One Sheet: $75 - $150

SUCH A GORGEOUS KID LIKE ME
(1973 - Columbia) Bernadette Lafont, Claude
Brasseur
One Sheet: $3 - $5

SUCH GOOD FRIENDS
(1971 - Paramount) Dyan Cannon, James
Coco, Lawrence Luckinbill
One Sheet: $7 - $15   *Saul Bass art.*

SUCH MEN ARE DANGEROUS
(1930 - Fox) Warner Baxter, Catherine Dale
Owen
One Sheet: $125 - $250

SUCH WOMEN ARE DANGEROUS
(1934 - Fox) Warner Baxter, Rosemary Ames
One Sheet: $125 - $250

SUCKER, THE
(1966 - Royal Films) Bourvil, Louis De Funes
One Sheet: $3 - $5

SUCKER MONEY
(1933 - Willis Kent) Mischa Auer, Phyllis
Barrington
One Sheet: $100 - $200

SUDAN
(1945 - Universal) Maria Montez, Jon Hall,
Turhan Bey
One Sheet: $50 - $100

SUDDEN BILL DORN
(1937 - Universal) Buck Jones, Evelyn Brent
One Sheet: $600 - $1,000   *Cowboy
Movie Posters #210.*

SUDDEN DANGER
(1955 - Allied Artists) Bill Elliott, Tom Drake
One Sheet: $15 - $30

SUDDEN DEATH
(1986 - Marvin) Denise Coward, Frank
Runyeon
One Sheet: $5 - $10

SUDDEN DEATH
(1995 - Universal) Jean-Claude Van Damme,
Powers Boothe
One Sheet: $5 - $10

SUDDEN FEAR
(1952 - RKO) Joan Crawford, Jack Palance
One Sheet: $75 - $125

SUDDEN IMPACT
(1983 - Warner Bros.) Clint Eastwood, Sondra
Locke
One Sheet: $15 - $30

SUDDEN MONEY
(1939 - Paramount) Billy Lee, Charles Ruggles
One Sheet: $40 - $75

SUDDEN TERROR
(1971 - National General) Mark Lester, Lionel
Jeffries
One Sheet: $3 - $5

SUDDENLY
(1954 - United Artists) Frank Sinatra, Sterling
Hayden
One Sheet: $50 - $100

SUDDENLY, A WOMAN!
(1967 - pmk) Lailla Andersson, Jorgen Buckhoj
One Sheet: $15 - $30

SUDDENLY IT'S SPRING
(1946 - Paramount) Fred MacMurray, Paulette
Goddard
One Sheet: $150 - $300   *Vargas art.*

One Sheet

SUDDENLY, LAST SUMMER
(1960 - Columbia) Elizabeth Taylor, Katharine
Hepburn, Montgomery Clift
One Sheet: $125 - $250

SUDS
(1920 - United Artists) Mary Pickford
One Sheet: $800 - $1,500

SUED FOR LIBEL
(1939 - RKO) Kent Taylor, Linda Hayes
One Sheet: $50 - $100

SUEZ
(1939 - 20th Century Fox) Tyrone Power,
Loretta Young
One Sheet: $800 - $1,500

SUFFERIN' CATS
(1949 - MGM) Tom & Jerry
One Sheet: $300 - $700   *Cartoon. Full
color stone litho. Cartoon Movie Posters #267.*

**SUGAR CHILE ROBINSON, BILLIE HOLIDAY,
COUNT BASIE AND HIS SEXTET**
(1951 - Universal-International Featurette)
Count Basie
One Sheet: $125 - $250   *Black cast.
Big Band musical. Separate Cinema, pg. 102.*

SUGAR COOKIES
(1973 - General) George Shannon
One Sheet: $3 - $5

SUGAR DADDIES
(1927 - MGM) Laurel & Hardy
One Sheet: $4,000 - $6,000

SUGAR HILL
(1974 - AIP) Marki Bey, Robert Quarry
One Sheet: $15 - $25   *Blaxploitation.*

SUGAR HILL
(1994 - 20th Century) Wesley Snipes, Michael
Wright
One Sheet: $3 - $5

**SUGAR RAY ROBINSON VS. RANDOLPH
TURPIN**
(1951 - H.J. Yates) Narrated by Jimmy Powers
One Sheet: $75 - $150   *Sports
(Boxing).*

SUGARFOOT
(1950 - Warner Bros.) Randolph Scott, Adele
Jergens
One Sheet: $15 - $35

SUGARLAND EXPRESS
(1974 - Universal) Goldie Hawn, Ben Johnson,
Dir: Steven Spielberg
One Sheet: $20 - $40   *Spielburg's
directorial debut.*

SUICIDE BATTALION
(1958 - AIP) Michael Connors, Jewell Lain
One Sheet: $15 - $25

SUICIDE FLEET
(1931 - RKO) William Boyd, Ginger Rogers
One Sheet: $350 - $750

SUICIDE MISSION
(1956 - Columbia) Leif Larsen, Michael
Aldridge
One Sheet: $5 - $10

SUICIDE SQUAD
(1936 - Puritan) -
One Sheet: $50 - $100

SUICIDE SQUADRON
(1942 - Republic) Anton Walbrook, Sally Gray
One Sheet: $30 - $50

SUITOR, THE
(1920 - Vitagraph) Larry Semon
One Sheet: $600 - $1,000

SULLIVAN'S EMPIRE
(1967 - Universal) Martin Milner, Linden Chiles
One Sheet: $5 - $10

SULLIVAN'S TRAVELS
(1941 - Paramount) Joel McCrea, Veronica
Lake, Alan Ladd
One Sheet: $2,500 - $4,000   *Price is for
hands-on-hips style one sheet. One Sheet
(caricature style):$1,500-$2,500.*

One Sheet (hands-on-hips)

SULLIVANS, THE
(1944 - 20th Century Fox) Anne Baxter,

Thomas Mitchell
One Sheet: $30 - $50

SULTAN'S BIRTHDAY, THE
(1943 - Fox) Mighty Mouse
One Sheet: $250 - $600   *Cartoon.*

SULTAN'S CAT, THE
(1931 - Educational) Terrytoons
One Sheet: $600 - $1,000   *Cartoon.*

SULTAN'S DAUGHTER, THE
(1944 - Monogram) Ann Corio, Charles
Butterworth
One Sheet: $15 - $35

SUM OF US, THE
(1995 - Samuel Goldwyn) Russell Crowe, Jack
Thompson
One Sheet: $5 - $10

SUMMER AND SMOKE
(1962 - Paramount) Geraldine Page, Laurence
Harvey
One Sheet: $20 - $40

SUMMER CAMP NIGHTMARE
(1987 - Concorde) Chuck Connors, Charles
Stratton
One Sheet: $7 - $15

SUMMER HOLIDAY
(1947 - MGM) Mickey Rooney, Gloria De
Haven
One Sheet: $30 - $50

SUMMER HOUSE, THE
(1994 - Samuel Goldwyn) Joan Plowright, Julie
Walters
One Sheet: $3 - $5

SUMMER LOVE
(1957 - Universal) John Saxon, Molly Bee
One Sheet: $15 - $30

SUMMER LOVERS
(1982 - -) Peter Gallagher, Daryl Hannah
One Sheet: $5 - $10

SUMMER MAGIC
(1963 - Buena Vista/Disney) Hayley Mills, Burl
Ives
One Sheet: $15 - $30

SUMMER OF '42
(1971 - Warner Bros.) Jennifer O'Neill, Gary
Grimes
One Sheet: $10 - $20

SUMMER PLACE, A
(1959 - Warner Bros.) Richard Egan, Dorothy
McGuire, Sandra Dee
One Sheet: $20 - $40

SUMMER RENTAL
(1985 - -) John Candy, Karen Austin
One Sheet: $3 - $5

SUMMER SCHOOL
(1987 - -) Mark Harmon, Kirstie Alley
One Sheet: $3 - $5

SUMMER STOCK
(1950 - MGM) Judy Garland, Gene Kelly
One Sheet: $125 - $250

SUMMER STORM
(1944 - United Artists) George Sanders, Linda
Darnell
One Sheet: $75 - $150

SUMMER STORM
(1950R - United Artists) George Sanders, Linda
Darnell
One Sheet: $30 - $50   *Re-release.*

SUMMER WITH MONIKA
(1952 - -) Harriet Andersson, Lars Ekborg
One Sheet: $125 - $250   *Swedish.*

SUMMERTIME
(1935 - Celebrity) By Ub Iwerks
One Sheet: $600 - $1,000   *Cartoon.*
Cartoon Movie Posters #111.

SUMMERTIME
(1955 - United Artists) Katharine Hepburn,
Rossano Brazzi
One Sheet: $100 - $200

SUMMERTIME BLUE
(197? - -) John Holmes, Samantha Fox, Serena
One Sheet: $40 - $75   *XXX.*

SUMMERTIME KILLER
(1973 - Avco/Embassy) Karl Malden, Olivia
Hussey, Christopher Mitchum
One Sheet: $7 - $15

SUMMERTREE
(1971 - Columbia) Michael Douglas, Jack
Warden, Brenda Vaccaro
One Sheet: $3 - $5

SUN ALSO RISES, THE
(1957 - 20th Century Fox) Tyrone Power, Ava
Gardner, Errol Flynn
One Sheet: $100 - $200

SUN COMES UP, THE
(1948 - MGM) Jeanette MacDonald, Lloyd
Nolan, Lassie
One Sheet: $75 - $125   *MacDonald's
final film.*

SUN NEVER SETS, THE
(1939 - Paramount) Douglas Fairbanks, Jr.,
Basil Rathbone
One Sheet: $75 - $150

SUN SETS AT DAWN, THE
(1950 - Eagle-Lion) Sally Parr, Phillip Shawn
One Sheet: $10 - $20

SUN SHINES BRIGHT, THE
(1953 - Republic) Charles Winninger, Arleen
Whelan, Dir: John Ford
One Sheet: $30 - $50

SUN VALLEY CYCLONE
(1946 - Republic) "Red Ryder" Elliott, Bobby
Blake
One Sheet: $50 - $100

SUN VALLEY CYCLONE
(1951R - Republic) Bill "Red Ryder" Elliott
One Sheet: $30 - $50   *Re-release.*

SUN VALLEY SERENADE
(1941 - 20th Century Fox) John Payne, Sonja
Henie, Glenn Miller & Orch.
One Sheet: $125 - $250

SUN VALLEY SERENADE
(1954R - 20th Century Fox) John Payne, Sonja
Henie, Glenn Miller & Orch.
One Sheet: $30 - $50   *Re-release.*

SUNBEAM, THE
(1916 - Metro) Mabel Taliaferro
One Sheet: $700 - $1,200

SUNBONNET SUE
(1945 - Monogram) Gale Storm, Phil Regan
One Sheet: $30 - $50

SUNBURN
(1979 - Paramount) Farrah Fawcett Majors, Art
Carney
One Sheet: $10 - $20

SUNDAY BLOODY SUNDAY
(1971 - United Artists) Peter Finch, Glenda
Jackson, Murray Head
One Sheet: $40 - $75

SUNDAY CALM
(1923 - Pathe) Our Gang
One Sheet: $1,300 - $2,000

SUNDAY DINNER FOR A SOLDIER
(1944 - 20th Century Fox) Anne Baxter, John
Hodiak
One Sheet: $30 - $60

SUNDAY IN NEW YORK
(1963 - MGM) Cliff Robertson, Jane Fonda,
Rod Taylor
One Sheet: $15 - $25

SUNDAY IN THE COUNTRY
(1974 - Cinerama) Ernest Borgnine, Michael J.
Pollard
One Sheet: $3 - $5

SUNDAY LOVERS
(1980 - MGM/UA) Lino Ventura, Gene Wilder,
Roger Moore
One Sheet: $7 - $15

SUNDAY PUNCH
(1942 - MGM) William Lundigan, Jean Rogers,
Dan Dailey Jr.
One Sheet: $30 - $50   *Sports
(Boxing).*

SUNDAY SINNERS
(1940 - International Road Show) Mamie Smith

One Sheet: $250 - $600   *Black cast.*
*Price is for full color one sheet. One Sheet
(duotone):$100-$150. Separate Cinema, pg. 144.*

SUNDOWN
(1941 - United Artists) Gene Tierney, Bruce
Cabot, George Sanders
One Sheet: $150 - $350

SUNDOWN IN SANTA FE
(1948 - Republic) Allan "Rocky" Lane, Eddie
Waller
One Sheet: $15 - $35

SUNDOWN JIM
(1942 - 20th Century Fox) John Kimbrough
One Sheet: $30 - $50

SUNDOWN KID
(1942 - Republic) Don Barry, Linda Johnson
One Sheet: $15 - $35

SUNDOWN ON THE PRAIRIE
(1939 - Monogram) Tex Ritter, Dorothy Fay
One Sheet: $125 - $250

SUNDOWN RIDER
(1932 - Columbia) Buck Jones, Barbara Weeks
One Sheet: $300 - $700

SUNDOWN SAUNDERS
(1937 - Supreme) Bob Steele, Catherine Cotter
One Sheet: $125 - $250

SUNDOWN TRAIL
(1931 - RKO) Tom Keene
One Sheet: $125 - $250

SUNDOWN VALLEY
(1944 - Columbia) Charles Starrett, Jeanne
Bates
One Sheet: $15 - $35

SUNDOWNERS, THE
(1949 - Nuys Theatre) Robert Preston, Robert
Sterling
One Sheet: $15 - $25

SUNDOWNERS, THE
(1960 - Warner Bros.) Deborah Kerr, Robert
Mitchum
One Sheet: $15 - $30

SUNFLOWER
(1970 - Avco/Embassy) Sophia Loren, Marcello
Mastroianni
One Sheet: $10 - $20

SUNKIST STARS AT PALM SPRINGS
(1936 - MGM) All Star cast
One Sheet: $250 - $500

SUNNY
(1930 - First National) Marilyn Miller, Lawrence
Gray
One Sheet: $100 - $200

SUNNY
(1941 - RKO) Anna Neagle, Ray Bolger,
Elizabeth Warren
One Sheet: $40 - $75

SUNNY SIDE
(1979 - AIP) Joey Travolta, John Lansing
One Sheet: $7 - $15

SUNNY SIDE OF THE STREET
(1951 - Columbia) Frankie Laine, Terry Moore
One Sheet: $15 - $35

SUNNY SIDE UP
(1929 - 20th Century Fox) Janet Gaynor,
Charles Ferrell, El Brendel
One Sheet: $200 - $400

SUNNY SKIES
(1930 - Tiffany) Benny Rubin, Marceline Day
One Sheet: $100 - $200

SUNNYSIDE
(1919 - First National) Charlie Chaplin, Edna
Purviance
One Sheet: $5,000 - $7,500

SUNNYSIDE
(1924R - Pathe) Charlie Chaplin, Edna
Purviance
One Sheet: $250 - $500   *Re-release.*

SUNRISE
(1927 - Fox) Jaynet Gaynor, George O'Brien
One Sheet: $700 - $1,200   *Academy
Award: Best Actress. Academy Award Movie
Posters #9.*

SUNRISE AT CAMPOBELLO
(1960 - Warner Bros.) Ralph Bellamy, Greer
Garson
One Sheet: $15 - $25

SUNRISE TRAIL, THE
(1931 - Tiffany) Bob Steele, Blanche Mehaffey
One Sheet: $200 - $400   *Cowboy
Movie Posters #113.*

SUNSET
(1988 - -) Bruce Willis, James Garner
One Sheet: $3 - $5

SUNSET BOULEVARD
(1950 - Paramount) Gloria Swanson, William
Holden
One Sheet: $1,900 - $3,000   *Price is for
Style A(Swanson pictured). One Sheet Style B(no
Swanson):$200-$400.*

One Sheet (Style A)

SUNSET CARSON RIDES AGAIN
(1948 - Astor) Sunset Carson
One Sheet: $30 - $50

SUNSET IN EL DORADO
(1945 - Republic) Roy Rogers, Dale Evans
One Sheet: $150 - $300

Insert

SUNSET IN EL DORADO
(1954R - Republic) Roy Rogers, Dale Evans
One Sheet: $30 - $50   *Re-release.
Duotone.*

SUNSET IN THE WEST
(1950 - Republic) Roy Rogers, Estrelita
Rodriguez
One Sheet: $75 - $150

SUNSET IN WYOMING
(1941 - Republic) Gene Autry, Smiley Burnette
One Sheet: $150 - $300

SUNSET JONES
(1921 - American Film) Charles Clary, Kathleen
O'Connor
One Sheet: $125 - $250

SUNSET OF POWER
(1935 - Universal) Buck Jones, Dorothy Dix
One Sheet: $250 - $600

SUNSET OF POWER
(1957R - Universal) Buck Jones, Dorothea Dix
One Sheet: $15 - $25   *Re-release.*

SUNSET ON THE DESERT
(1942 - Republic) Roy Rogers, Gabby Hayes
One Sheet: $150 - $300

SUNSET PARK
(1996 - TriStar) Rhea Perlman, Fredro Starr,
Carol Kane

One Sheet: $5 - $10   *Drama.*

SUNSET PASS
(1933 - Paramount) Randolph Scott, Tom
Keene
One Sheet: $100 - $200

SUNSET PASS
(1946 - RKO) James Warren, Nan Leslie
One Sheet: $15 - $30

SUNSET RANGE
(1935 - First Division) Hoot Gibson, Mary
Doran
One Sheet: $150 - $300

SUNSET SERENADE
(1942 - Republic) Roy Rogers, Gabby Hayes
One Sheet: $150 - $300

SUNSET SKIES
(1930 - Tiffany) -
One Sheet: $100 - $200

SUNSET STRIP CASE, THE
(1938 - Grand National) -
One Sheet: $50 - $100

SUNSET TRAIL
(1939 - Paramount) William Boyd, George
Hayes
One Sheet: $250 - $600   *Hopalong
Cassidy series. Rare.*

SUNSHINE BOYS, THE
(1975 - MGM/United Artists) George Burns,
Walter Matthau
One Sheet: $10 - $20   *Academy
Award: Best Supporting Actor(Burns). Academy
Award Movie Posters #290.*

One Sheet

SUNSHINE TRAIL, THE
(1923 - Thomas Ince) Douglas MacLean, Edith
Roberts
One Sheet: $125 - $250

SUPER, THE
(1991 - 20th Century Fox) Joe Pesci
One Sheet: $3 - $5

SUPER BUG
(1975 - Barbara) Robert Mark
One Sheet: $3 - $5

SUPER DUDE
(1975 - -) William Elliott, Marki Bey, Cliff Potts
One Sheet: $10 - $20   *Blaxploitation.*

SUPER FUZZ
(1981 - Avco/Embassy) Terence Hill, Ernest
Borgnine
One Sheet: $5 - $10

SUPER MARIO BROS.
(1993 - Buena Vista/Disney) Bob Hopkins,
John Leguizamo, Dennis Hopper
One Sheet: $5 - $10

SUPER SLEUTH
(1937 - RKO) Ann Sothern, Jack Oakie
One Sheet: $75 - $125

SUPER SPOOK
(1975 - -) Leonard Jackson, Bill Jay
One Sheet: $15 - $25   *Blaxploitation.*

SUPER STOOGES VS. THE WONDER WOMEN
(1974 - American International) Nick Jordan,
Marc Hannibal, Malisa Longo
One Sheet: $30 - $50

SUPER VAN
(1977 - Empire) Mark Schneider, Katie Saylor
One Sheet: $10 - $20   *Muscle autos.*

SUPER VIXENS
(1975 - -) Shari Eubank, Charles Napier, Dir:
Russ Meyer
One Sheet: $30 - $50   *Sexploitation.*

SUPER WOLF
(1949 - Columbia) Hugh Herbert, Christine
McIntyre
One Sheet: $50 - $100   *Comedy short.
Duotone.*

SUPERARGO
(1968 - -) Ken Wood, Guy Madison
One Sheet: $30 - $50   *Sports
(Muscleman/Wrestling).*

SUPERARGO VERSUS DIABOLICUS
(1966 - -) Ken Wood, Gerard Tichy
One Sheet: $30 - $50   *Sports
(Muscleman/Wrestling).*

SUPERBEAST
(1972 - United Artists) Craig Littler, Antoinette
Bower
One Sheet: $3 - $5

SUPERCHICK
(1973 - Crown) Joyce Jillson, Louis Quinn,
Dagart
One Sheet: $15 - $25

SUPERCOP
(1996 - Miramax) Jackie Chan, Michelle Yeoh
One Sheet: $7 - $15   *Martial Arts/
Action.*

SUPERCOPS, THE
(1974 - MGM) Ron Leibman, David Selby
One Sheet: $3 - $5

SUPERDAD
(1974 - Disney) Bob Crane, Barbara Rush, Kurt
Russell
One Sheet: $5 - $10

SUPERFLY
(1972 - Warner Bros.) Ron O'Neal, Carl Lee
One Sheet: $40 - $75   *Blaxploitation.*

One Sheet

SUPERFLY T.N.T.
(1973 - Paramount) Ron O'Neal, Roscoe Lee
Browne
One Sheet: $15 - $35   *Blaxploitation.*

SUPERGIRL
(1984 - Cantharus) Faye Dunaway, Helen
Slater, Brenda Vaccaro
One Sheet: $5 - $10

SUPERINTENDENTS
(1918 - William Fox) Mutt & Jeff
One Sheet: $1,600 - $2,500   *Cartoon.
Cartoon Movie Posters #8.*

SUPERMAN
(1940 - Paramount) Fleischer Animation
One Sheet: $5,000 - $8,000   *Cartoon.
Graven Images, pg. 137.*

SUPERMAN
(1948 - Columbia) Kirk Alyn, Noel Neill
One Sheet: $800 - $1,500   *Serial. 15
Chapters. Graven Images, pg. 137.*

SUPERMAN
(1978 - Warner Bros.) Christopher Reeve,
Margot Kidder
One Sheet: $15 - $35   *Advance style
A: $40-$80. Advance style B: $30-$60.*

SUPERMAN AND THE JUNGLE DEVIL
(1954 - 20th Century Fox) George Reeves
One Sheet: $200 - $400

SUPERMAN AND THE MOLE MEN
(1951 - Lippert) George Reeves, Phyllis Coates
One Sheet: $1,600 - $2,500   *Graven
Images, pg. 182.*

SUPERMAN CHU
(1973 - Capital) Chang Yi, Tien Mi, Honey Field
One Sheet: $20 - $40

SUPERMAN FLIES AGAIN
(1954 - 20th Century Fox) George Reeves
One Sheet: $250 - $600

SUPERMAN II
(1980 - Warner Bros.) Christopher Reeve,
Gene Hackman
One Sheet: $15 - $30   *Advance:$20-
$35.*

SUPERMAN III
(1983 - Warner Bros.) Christopher Reeve,
Richard Pryor
One Sheet: $10 - $20

SUPERMAN IN EXILE
(1954 - 20th Century Fox) George Reeves
One Sheet: $250 - $500

SUPERMAN IN SCOTLAND YARD
(1954 - 20th Century Fox) George Reeves
One Sheet: $250 - $500

SUPERMAN IS HERE!
(1941 - Paramount) Superman
One Sheet: $5,000 - $8,000   *Cartoon.
Stock poster, Superman running, yellow
background. Cartoon Movie Posters #237.*

SUPERMAN IV: THE QUEST FOR PEACE
(1987 - Cannon) Christopher Reeve, Gene
Hackman
One Sheet: $10 - $20

SUPERMAN'S PERIL
(1954 - 20th Century Fox) George Reeves
One Sheet: $200 - $400

SUPERNATURAL
(1933 - Paramount) Carole Lombard, Randolph
Scott
One Sheet: $5,000 - $7,500   *Graven
Images, pg. 63.*

SUPERSPEED
(1935 - Columbia) Norman Foster, Florence
Rice
One Sheet: $100 - $200

SUPERZAN AND THE SPACE BOY
(1972 - Tikal) Giovanni Lanuza, Caro Laniesti
One Sheet: $40 - $75   *Mexican.*

SUPPORT YOUR LOCAL GUNFIGHTER
(1971 - United Artists) James Garner, Suzanne
Pleshette
One Sheet: $7 - $15

SUPPORT YOUR LOCAL SHERIFF
(1969 - United Artists) James Garner, Joan
Hackett, Walter Brennan
One Sheet: $15 - $25

**SUPPOSE THEY GAVE A WAR AND NOBODY
CAME**
(1970 - Cinerama) Tony Curtis, Brian Keith,
Ernest Borgnine
One Sheet: $5 - $10

SURE FIRE
(1921 - Universal) Hoot Gibson, Molly Malone
One Sheet: $250 - $500

SURE THING, THE
(1985 - Embassy) John Cusack, Daphne
Zuniga
One Sheet: $7 - $15

SURE-MIKE
(1925 - Pathe) Martha Sleeper, Jimmie
Finlayson
One Sheet: $125 - $250

SURF NAZIS MUST DIE
(1987 - Troma) Barry Brenner, Gail Neely
One Sheet: $15 - $30

SURF NINJAS
(1993 - New Line) Leslie Nielsen, Tone Loc
One Sheet: $5 - $10

SURF PARTY
(1964 - 20th Century Fox) Bobby Vinton,
Patricia Morrow

One Sheet: $30 - $50   *Surfing.*

SURPRISE PACKAGE
(1960 - Columbia) Yul Brynner, Mitzi Gaynor
One Sheet: $15 - $25

SURPRISED PARTIES
(1942 - MGM) Our Gang
One Sheet: $250 - $600

SURPRISING SUZIE
(1953 - Universal) Abbe Lane, Hugh O'Brien
One Sheet: $20 - $40

SURRENDER
(1931 - Fox) Warner Baxter, Leila Hyams,
Ralph Bellamy
One Sheet: $150 - $300

SURRENDER
(1950 - Republic) Vera Ralston, John Carroll
One Sheet: $15 - $30

SURRENDER
(1987 - -) Sally Field, Michael Caine
One Sheet: $3 - $5

SURRENDER - HELL!
(1959 - Allied Artists) Keith Andes, Susan
Cabot
One Sheet: $10 - $20

SURVIVE!
(1976 - Paramount) Pablo Ferrel, Hugo Stiglitz
One Sheet: $3 - $5

SURVIVING PICASSO
(1996 - Warner Bros.) Anthony Hopkins,
Natascha McElhone
One Sheet: $5 - $10

SURVIVING THE GAME
(1994 - New Line) Ice-T, Rutger Hauer
One Sheet: $5 - $10

SURVIVORS, THE
(1983 - Columbia) Walter Matthau, Robin
Williams
One Sheet: $3 - $5

SUSAN AND GOD
(1940 - MGM) Joan Crawford, Fredric March
One Sheet: $150 - $300

SUSAN LENOX
(1931 - MGM) Greta Garbo, Clark Gable, Jean
Hersholt
One Sheet: $2,200 - $3,500

SUSAN SLADE
(1961 - Warner Bros.) Troy Donahue, Connie
Stevens
One Sheet: $15 - $25

SUSAN SLEPT HERE
(1954 - RKO) Dick Powell, Debbie Reynolds
One Sheet: $20 - $40

SUSANA
(1951 - Columbia) Fernando Soler, Rosita
Quintana
One Sheet: $100 - $200   *Mexican.*

SUSANNA PASS
(1949 - Republic) Roy Rogers, Dale Evans
One Sheet: $75 - $175

SUSANNA PASS
(1956R - Republic) Roy Rogers, Dale Evans
One Sheet: $30 - $50   *Re-release.*

SUSANNAH OF THE MOUNTIES
(1939 - 20th Century Fox) Shirley Temple,
Randolph Scott
One Sheet: $500 - $800

One Sheet

SUSANNAH OF THE MOUNTIES
(1958R - 20th Century Fox) Shirley Temple, Randolph Scott
One Sheet: $40 - $75   *Re-release.*

SUSIE STEPS OUT
(1946 - -) David Bruce, Cleatus Caldwell
One Sheet: $15 - $25

SUSPECT, THE
(1945 - Universal) Charles Laughton, Ella Raines
One Sheet: $200 - $400

SUSPECT
(1987 - TriStar) Cher, Dennis Quaid
One Sheet: $7 - $15

SUSPENSE
(1930 - British International) Mickey Branford, Cyril McLaglen
One Sheet: $150 - $300

SUSPENSE
(1946 - Monogram) Barry Sullivan, Belita
One Sheet: $30 - $50

SUSPICION
(1941 - RKO) Cary Grant, Joan Fontaine, Dir: Alfred Hitchcock
One Sheet: $700 - $1,200   *Academy Award Movie Posters #78.*

Three Sheet

SUSPICION
(1951R - RKO) Cary Grant, Joan Fontaine, Dir: Alfred Hitchcock
One Sheet: $125 - $250   *Re-release.*

SUSPIRIA
(1977 - 20th Century Fox) Jessica Harper, Joan Bennett
One Sheet: $7 - $15   *Dir: Dario Argento.*

SUTTER'S GOLD
(1936 - Universal) Edward Arnold, Binnie Barnes
One Sheet: $100 - $200

One Sheet

SUTURE
(1994 - Goldwyn) Dennis Haysbert, Michael Harris
One Sheet: $3 - $5

SUZANNA
(1922 - Allied) Mabel Normand, George Nichols
One Sheet: $600 - $1,000

SUZY
(1936 - MGM) Jean Harlow, Franchot Tone, Cary Grant
One Sheet: $800 - $1,500

SVENGALI
(1931 - Warner Bros.) John Barrymore, Marian Marsh
One Sheet: $1,600 - $2,500   *Graven Images, pg. 52.*

SVENGALI
(1955 - MGM) Hildegarde Neff, Terence Morgan
One Sheet: $30 - $50

SWAMP FIRE
(1946 - Paramount) Buster Crabbe, Johnny Weissmuller
One Sheet: $40 - $75

SWAMP THING
(1982 - Embassy) Louis Jourdan, Adrienne Barbeau
One Sheet: $7 - $15

SWAMP WATER
(1941 - 20th Century Fox) Dana Andrews, Walter Brennan, Anne Baxter
One Sheet: $75 - $150

One Sheet

SWAMP WOMAN
(1941 - PRC) Ann Corio, Jack LaRue
One Sheet: $40 - $75

SWAMP WOMEN
(1956 - Woolner Bros.) Beverly Garland, Marie Windsor
One Sheet: $30 - $50

SWAN, THE
(1956 - MGM) Grace Kelly, Alec Guinness
One Sheet: $40 - $75

SWAN LAKE
(1960 - Columbia) M. Plisetskaya, N. Fadeychev
One Sheet: $30 - $50   *Dancing (Ballet).*

SWAN PRINCESS, THE
(1994 - New Line) -
One Sheet: $3 - $5   *Cartoon.*

SWANEE RIVER
(1931 - Sono Art/World Wide) Grant Withers, Thelma Todd
One Sheet: $100 - $200

SWANEE RIVER
(1939 - 20th Century Fox) Don Ameche, Andrea Leeds, Al Jolson
One Sheet: $250 - $600

SWANEE SHOWBOAT
(1949 - Ajax) Nina McKinney, Pigmeat Markham
One Sheet: $250 - $500   *Black cast. Separate Cinema, pg. 132.*

SWAPPERS, THE
(1970 - Trans American) James Donnelly, Larry Taylor, Valerie St. John
One Sheet: $7 - $15

SWARM, THE
(1978 - Warner Bros.) Michael Caine, Katherine Ross
One Sheet: $7 - $15

SWASHBUCKLER
(1976 - Universal) Robert Shaw, James Earl Jones
One Sheet: $3 - $5

SWAT THE CROOK
(1919 - Pathe) Harold Lloyd, Bebe Daniels
One Sheet: $1,600 - $2,500

SWEATER GIRL
(1942 - Paramount) Eddie Bracken, June Preisser
One Sheet: $30 - $50

SWEDEN HEAVEN AND HELL
(1969 - Avco Embassy) Narrated by Edmund Purdom
One Sheet: $5 - $10

SWEDISH FLY GIRLS
(1972 - TransAmerican) Birte Tove, Susan Hurley
One Sheet: $5 - $10   *Sexploitation.*

SWEENEY TODD THE DEMON BARBER OF FLEET STREET
(1939 - -) Tod Slaughter, Stella Rho
One Sheet: $150 - $300   *Graven Images, pg. 95.*

SWEEPINGS
(1933 - RKO) Lionel Barrymore, Gloria Stuart
One Sheet: $250 - $500

One Sheet

SWEEPSTAKES
(1931 - RKO/Pathe) Eddie Quillan, James Gleason
One Sheet: $100 - $200

SWEEPSTAKES ANNIE
(1935 - Liberty) Tom Brown, Marian Nixon
One Sheet: $75 - $150

SWEEPSTAKES WINNER
(1939 - Warner Bros.) Marie Wilson, Allen Jenkins
One Sheet: $75 - $125

SWEET & SOUR
(1977? - Jeffrey Michaels) Mary Margaret, Jamie Gillis
One Sheet: $5 - $10   *XXX.*

SWEET ADELINE
(1935 - Warner Bros.) Irene Dunne, Donald Woods
One Sheet: $100 - $200

SWEET AND LOWDOWN
(1944 - 20th Century Fox) Benny Goodman Orch., Linda Darnell
One Sheet: $125 - $250   *Big Band musical.*

SWEET BIRD OF YOUTH
(1962 - MGM) Paul Newman, Geraldine Page
One Sheet: $30 - $50   *Academy Award Movie Posters #211.*

SWEET BODY OF DEBORAH, THE
(1969 - Warner Bros.) Carroll Baker, Jean Sorel, Evelyn Stewart
One Sheet: $7 - $15

SWEET CHARITY
(1969 - Universal) Shirley MacLaine, Sammy Davis, Jr., Ricardo Montalban
One Sheet: $20 - $40   *Two styles.*

SWEET DREAMS
(1985 - TriStar) Jessica Lange, Ed Harris
One Sheet: $7 - $15

SWEET GENEVIEVE
(1947 - Columbia) Jean Porter, Jimmy Lydon
One Sheet: $15 - $35

SWEET HEARTS DANCE
(1988 - -) Don Johnson, Susan Sarandon
One Sheet: $5 - $10

SWEET JESUS, PREACHER MAN
(1973 - MGM) Roger E. Morley, William Smith

One Sheet: $15 - $30   *Blaxploitation.*

SWEET KITTY BELLAIRS
(1930 - Warner Bros.) Claudia Dell, Ernest Torrence, Walter Pidgeon
One Sheet: $125 - $250

SWEET LIBERTY
(1985 - Universal) Alan Alda, Michael Caine
One Sheet: $3 - $5

SWEET LORRAINE
(1987 - -) Maureen Stapleton, Lee Richardson
One Sheet: $3 - $5

SWEET MAMA
(1930 - First National) Alice White, David Manners
One Sheet: $150 - $300

SWEET MUSIC
(1935 - Warner Bros.) Rudy Vallee, Ann Dvorak
One Sheet: $100 - $200

SWEET NOVEMBER
(1968 - Warner Bros.) Sandy Dennis, Anthony New.ey
One Sheet: $5 - $10

SWEET REVENGE
(1976 - MGM/UA) Stockard Channing, Sam Waterston
One Sheet: $10 - $20   *AKA: DANDY, THE ALL AMERICAN GIRL.*

SWEET RIDE, THE
(1968 - 20th Century Fox) Tony Franciosa, Jacqueline Bisset
One Sheet: $15 - $30   *Bisset's film debut Surfing graphics and full-length photo image of bikini-clad Bisset standing in the ocean.*

SWEET ROSIE O'GRADY
(1943 - 20th Century Fox) Betty Grable, Robert Young
One Sheet: $150 - $300

One Sheet

SWEET SMELL OF SUCCESS
(1957 - United Artists) Burt Lancaster, Tony Curtis
One Sheet: $30 - $60

SWEET SUGAR
(1972 - Dimension) Phyllis Elizabeth Davis, Ella Edwards
One Sheet: $7 - $15   *AKA: CHAINGANG GIRLS.*

SWEET SURRENDER
(1935 - Universal) Frank Parker, Tamara
One Sheet: $75 - $150

SWEET SWEETBACK'S BAADASSSSS SONG
(1971 - Cinemation) Dir:Melvin Van Peebles
One Sheet: $75 - $150   *Blaxploitation.*

One Sheet

SWEETHEART OF SIGMA CHI, THE
(1933 - Monogram) Mary Carlisle, Betty Grable
One Sheet: $200 - $400

SWEETHEART OF SIGMA CHI, THE
(1946 - Monogram) Phil Regan, Elyse Knox
One Sheet: $30 - $50

SWEETHEART OF THE CAMPUS
(1941 - Columbia) Ruby Keeler, Ozzie Nelson
One Sheet: $50 - $100

SWEETHEART OF THE FLEET
(1942 - Columbia) Joan Davis, Jinx Falkenburg
One Sheet: $15 - $35

SWEETHEART OF THE NAVY
(1937 - Grand National) Eric Linden, Cecilia Parker
One Sheet: $40 - $75

SWEETHEARTS
(1938 - MGM) Jeanette McDonald, Nelson Eddy
One Sheet: $350 - $750

SWEETHEARTS
(1962R - MGM) Jeanette McDonald, Nelson Eddy
One Sheet: $15 - $25   *Re-release.*

SWEETHEARTS AND WIVES
(1930 - First National) Billie Dove, Sidney Blackmer
One Sheet: $125 - $250

SWEETHEARTS OF RHYTHM
(195? - -) Black all-girl orchestra
One Sheet: $75 - $150   *Black cast. Big Band musical.*

SWEETHEARTS OF THE U.S.A.
(1944 - Monogram) Una Merkel, Donald Lewis
One Sheet: $15 - $35

SWEETHEARTS ON PARADE
(1930 - Columbia) Alice White, Marie Prevost, Lloyd Hughes
One Sheet: $150 - $300

SWEETHEARTS ON PARADE
(1952 - Republic) Ray Middleton, Lucille Norman
One Sheet: $15 - $25

SWEETIE
(1929 - Paramount) Nancy Carroll, Helen Kane
One Sheet: $350 - $750

SWELL GUY
(1946 - Universal) Sonny Tufts, Ann Blyth
One Sheet: $15 - $35

SWELLHEAD
(1930 - Tiffany) James Gleason, Johnny Walker
One Sheet: $125 - $250

SWELL-HEAD
(1935 - Columbia) Wallace Ford, Dickie Moore
One Sheet: $75 - $150

SWIFTY
(1935 - Diversion) Hoot Gibson, June Gale
One Sheet: $150 - $350

SWIMMER, THE
(1968 - Columbia) Burt Lancaster, Janice Rule
One Sheet: $10 - $20

SWIMMING POOL, THE
(1970 - Avco/Embassy) Alain Delon, Romy Schneider
One Sheet: $5 - $10

SWIMMING TO CAMBODIA
(1987 - -) Spalding Gray
One Sheet: $5 - $10

SWIMMING WITH SHARKS
(1995 - Trimark) Kevin Spacey, Frank Whaley, Michelle Forbes
One Sheet: $5 - $12

SWING
(1938 - Micheaux) Cora Green, Carman Newsome
One Sheet: $250 - $600   *Black cast. Separate Cinema, pg. 19.*

SWING FEVER
(1943 - MGM) Kay Kyser & Orch., Marilyn Maxwell, Lena Horne

One Sheet: $75 - $150   *Big Band musical.*

SWING HIGH
(1930 - Pathe Exchange) Helen Twelvetrees, Fred Scott
One Sheet: $250 - $500

SWING HIGH, SWING LOW
(1937 - Paramount) Carole Lombard, Fred MacMurray
One Sheet: $250 - $600

SWING HOSTESS
(1944 - PRC) Martha Tilton, Iris Adrian
One Sheet: $15 - $35

SWING IN THE SADDLE
(1944 - Columbia) Jane Frazee, Jimmy Wakely Orch., Red River Dave
One Sheet: $75 - $150   *Country musical.*

SWING IT PROFESSOR
(1937 - Marks & Malcolm Trading) Pinky Tomlin, Paula Stone
One Sheet: $40 - $75

SWING IT SAILOR!
(1937 - Grand National) Wallace Ford, Isabel Jewell
One Sheet: $75 - $150

SWING IT SOLDIER
(1941 - Universal) Ken Murray, Frances Langford
One Sheet: $30 - $50

SWING KIDS
(1993 - Buena Vista) Robert Sean Leonard, Christian Bale
One Sheet: $3 - $5

SWING OUT SISTER
(1945 - Universal) Rod Cameron, Arthur Treacher
One Sheet: $30 - $50

SWING OUT THE BLUES
(1944 - Columbia) Bob Haymes & Orch., Lynn Merrick
One Sheet: $40 - $75   *Big Band musical.*

SWING PARADE OF 1946
(1946 - Monogram) Gale Storm, Phil Regan, Three Stooges (Curly)
One Sheet: $150 - $300

SWING SHIFT
(1984 - Warner Bros.) Goldie Hawn, Kurt Russell
One Sheet: $5 - $10

SWING SHIFT MAISIE
(1943 - MGM) Ann Sothern, James Craig
One Sheet: $30 - $50

SWING SISTER SWING
(1938 - Universal) Ken Murray, Ernest Truex
One Sheet: $75 - $150   *Big Band musical.*

SWING THAT CHEER
(1938 - Universal) Tom Brown, Andy Devine
One Sheet: $50 - $100

SWING THE WESTERN WAY
(1947 - Columbia) The Hoosier Hotshots
One Sheet: $50 - $100   *Country musical.*

SWING TIME
(1936 - RKO) Fred Astaire, Ginger Rogers
One Sheet: $3,500 - $5,000   *Price is for Style A (Astaire/Rogers dancing). One Sheet(Style B):$2,500-$3,500.*

SWING VACATION
(1939 - RKO) Charles "Buddy" Rogers & Orchestra
One Sheet: $100 - $200

SWING YOUR LADY
(1937 - Warner Bros.) Humphrey Bogart, Penny Singleton
One Sheet: $200 - $400

SWING YOUR PARTNER
(1943 - Republic) Esther Dale, Dale Evans, Roger Clark
One Sheet: $40 - $75   *Country musical.*

SWINGER, THE
(1966 - Paramount) Ann-Margret, Tony Franciosa
One Sheet: $15 - $35

SWINGERS PARADISE
(1965 - AIP) Cliff Richard, Susan Hampshire
One Sheet: $10 - $20

SWINGIN' ALONG
(1962 - 20th Century Fox) Tommy Noonan, Barbara Eden
One Sheet: $15 - $25

SWINGIN' IN THE BARN
(1940 - Universal) -
One Sheet: $50 - $100

SWINGIN' MAIDEN, THE
(1964 - Columbia) Michael Craig, Anne Helm
One Sheet: $5 - $10

SWINGIN' ON A RAINBOW
(1945 - Republic) Jane Frazee, Brad Taylor
One Sheet: $20 - $40

SWINGIN' SUMMER, A
(1965 - United Screen Arts) James Stacy, William Wellman, Jr.
One Sheet: $15 - $30

SWINGING CHEERLEADERS
(1974 - Centaur) Jo Johnston, Rainbeaux Smith
One Sheet: $7 - $15   *Sexploitation.*

SWINGING STEWARDESSES, THE
(1972 - Hemisphere) Ellen Traeger, Inga Steeger
One Sheet: $5 - $10   *Sexploitation.*

SWINGSHIFT CINDERELLA
(1945 - MGM) Dir: Tex Avery
One Sheet: $250 - $600   *Cartoon. Cartoon Movie Posters #295.*

SWINGTIME JOHNNY
(1943 - Universal) The Andrews Sisters, Mitch Ayres Orch.
One Sheet: $75 - $175   *Big Band musical.*

SWISS CHEESE FAMILY ROBINSON
(1943 - 20th Century Fox) Mighty Mouse
One Sheet: $250 - $600   *Cartoon. Full color stock poster with printed title. Huge image of Mighty Mouse on yellow background.*

SWISS FAMILY ROBINSON
(1940 - RKO) Thomas Mitchell, Edna Best
One Sheet: $100 - $200

SWISS FAMILY ROBINSON
(1948R - RKO) Thomas Mitchell, Edna Best
One Sheet: $20 - $40   *Re-release.*

SWISS FAMILY ROBINSON
(1960 - Buena Vista) John Mills, Dorothy McGuire
One Sheet: $15 - $25

SWISS FAMILY ROBINSON
(1969R - Disney) John Mills, Dorothy McGuire
One Sheet: $7 - $15   *Re-release.*

SWISS FAMILY ROBINSON
(1972R - Buena Vista/Disney) John Mills, Dorothy McGuire
One Sheet: $5 - $10

SWISS FAMILY ROBINSON
(1975R - Buena Vista/Disney) John Mills, Dorothy McGuire
One Sheet: $4 - $8   *Re-release.*

SWISS MISS
(1938 - MGM) Stan Laurel, Oliver Hardy, Della Lind
One Sheet: $1,300 - $2,000

SWISS MISS
(194?R - Favorite Films) Stan Laurel, Oliver Hardy, Della Lind
One Sheet: $100 - $200   *Re-release.*

SWITCHBLADE SISTERS
(1975 - Centaur) Robbie Lee, Joanne Mail
One Sheet: $10 - $20   *Sexploitation.*

SWITCHING CHANNELS
(1988 - Columbia) Kathleen Turner, Burt Reynolds, Christopher Reeve
One Sheet: $7 - $15

SWORD AND THE DRAGON
(1960 - Valiant) Boris Andreyev, Andrei Abrikosou
One Sheet: $30 - $50   *Russian.*

SWORD AND THE ROSE, THE
(1953 - RKO) Richard Todd, Glynis Johns
One Sheet: $30 - $50

SWORD AND THE SORCERER, THE
(1982 - Group 1) Lee Horsley, Kathleen Beller
One Sheet: $5 - $10

SWORD IN THE DESERT
(1949 - Universal) Dana Andrews, Marta Toren
One Sheet: $30 - $50

SWORD IN THE STONE, THE
(1963 - Buena Vista/Disney) -
One Sheet: $75 - $125   *Cartoon.*

SWORD IN THE STONE, THE
(1973R - Buena Vista/Disney) -
One Sheet: $10 - $20   *Re-release. Cartoon. Full color.*

SWORD IN THE STONE/WINNIE THE POOH COMBO
(1983R - Disney) -
One Sheet: $10 - $20   *Re-release double feature poster. Cartoon.*

SWORD OF ALI BABA, THE
(1965 - Universal) Peter Mann, Jocelyn Lane
One Sheet: $5 - $10

SWORD OF DOOM
(1967 - Toho) Tatsuya Nakadai, Toshiro Mifune
One Sheet: $15 - $35

SWORD OF EL CID, THE
(1964 - -) Roland Carey, Chantal Deberg
One Sheet: $3 - $5

SWORD OF MONTE CRISTO, THE
(1951 - 20th Century Fox) George Montgomery, Paula Corday
One Sheet: $15 - $30

SWORD OF SHERWOOD FOREST
(1961 - Columbia) Richard Greene, Peter Cushing
One Sheet: $7 - $15

SWORD OF THE AVENGER
(1948 - Eagle-Lion) Ramon Delgado, Sigrid Gurie
One Sheet: $15 - $35

SWORD OF THE CONQUEROR
(1962 - United Artists) Jack Palance, Eleonora Rossi-Drago
One Sheet: $5 - $10

SWORD OF VENUS
(1952 - RKO) Robert Clarke, Catherine McLeod
One Sheet: $15 - $25

SWORD POINTS
(1928 - Educational) Lupino Lane Comedies
One Sheet: $125 - $250

SWORDSMAN, THE
(1947 - Columbia) Larry Parks, Ellen Drew
One Sheet: $15 - $35

SWORDSMAN OF SIENA, THE
(1962 - MGM) Stewart Granger, Sylva Koscina
One Sheet: $15 - $25

SWORN ENEMY
(1936 - MGM) Robert Young, Florence Rice
One Sheet: $100 - $200

SYLVESTER
(1985 - Columbia) Richard Farnsworth, Melissa Gilbert
One Sheet: $2 - $3

SYLVIA
(1965 - Paramount) Carroll Baker, George Maharis
One Sheet: $15 - $25

SYLVIA SCARLETT
(1936 - RKO) Katharine Hepburn, Cary Grant (their 1st film together)
One Sheet: $1,600 - $2,500

SYMPATHY FOR THE DEVIL
(1970 - New Line Cinema) The Rolling Stones
One Sheet: $150 - $300   *Special poster (34"x47"): $1,500-$2,500.*

SYMPHONIE PASTORALE
(1948 - Pathe) Michele Morgan, Pierre
Blancher
One Sheet: $15 - $25   *French.*

SYMPHONY HOUR
(1942 - RKO/Disney) Mickey Mouse
One Sheet: $4,000 - $6,000   *Cartoon. Full
color. Cartoon Movie Posters #149.*

SYMPHONY IN SLANG
(1951 - MGM) Tex Avery
One Sheet: $250 - $600   *Cartoon. Full
color stone litho. Cartoon Movie Posters #310.*

SYMPHONY IN TWO FLATS, A
(1931 - Sono Art/World Wide) Ivor Novello,
Jaqueline Logan
One Sheet: $75 - $150

SYMPHONY OF LIVING
(1935 - Chesterfield) Evelyn Brent, Al Shean
One Sheet: $50 - $100

SYMPHONY OF SIX MILLION
(1932 - RKO) Ricardo Cortez, Irene Dunne
One Sheet: $100 - $200

SYMPOSIUM ON POPULAR SONGS
(1962 - Disney) Ludwig Von Drake
One Sheet: $40 - $75   *Cartoon.*

SYNANON
(1965 - Columbia) Edmond O'Brien, Chuck
Connors
One Sheet: $10 - $20

SYNCOPATION
(1929 - RKO) Barbara Bennett, Bobby Watson
One Sheet: $800 - $1,500   *RKO's first
musical.*

SYNCOPATION
(1942 - RKO) Adolphe Menjou, Jackie Cooper,
All star jazz cast
One Sheet: $250 - $600   *Jazz musical.*

SYNTHETIC SIN
(1929 - First National) Colleen Moore
One Sheet: $150 - $350

SYSTEM, THE
(1953 - Warner Bros.) Frank Lovejoy, Jerome
Cowan, Joan Weldon
One Sheet: $10 - $20

TABLE FOR FIVE
(1983 - CBS) John Voight, Richard Crenna
One Sheet: $3 - $5

TABOOS OF THE WORLD
(1965 - AIP) Vincent Price
One Sheet: $20 - $40   *Documentary.*

TABU
(1931 - Paramount) Anna Chevalier, Matahi
One Sheet: $150 - $300

TAFFY AND THE JUNGLE HUNTER
(1965 - Allied Artists) Jacques Bergerac,
Manuel Padilla
One Sheet: $3 - $5

TAG: THE ASSASSINATION GAME
(1982 - -) Robert Carradine, Linda Hamilton
One Sheet: $2 - $3

TAGGART
(1965 - Universal) Tony Young, Dan Duryea
One Sheet: $10 - $20   *Story by Louis
L'Amour.*

TAHITI HONEY
(1943 - Republic) Simone Simon, Dennis
O'Keefe, Lionel Stander
One Sheet: $50 - $100

TAHITI NIGHTS
(1944 - Columbia) Dave O'Brien, Jinx
Falkenburg
One Sheet: $40 - $75

TAIL SPIN
(1939 - 20th Century Fox) Alice Faye,
Constance Bennett
One Sheet: $125 - $250

TAILOR, THE
(1923 - Fox) Al. St. John
One Sheet: $600 - $1,000

TAILOR-MADE MAN, A
(1931 - MGM) William Haines, Dorothy Jordan
One Sheet: $100 - $200

TAILSPIN TOMMY
(1934 - Universal) Maurice Murphy, Patricia
Farr
One Sheet: $800 - $1,500   *Serial.
Aviation. 12 Chapters.*

**TAILSPIN TOMMY IN THE GREAT AIR
MYSTERY**
(1935 - Universal) Clark Williams, Noah Beery,
Jr., Jean Rogers
One Sheet: $600 - $1,000   *Serial.
Aviation. 12 Chapters.*

TAI-PAN
(1986 - DeLaurentiis) Bryan Brown, Joan Chen
One Sheet: $3 - $5

TAKE, THE
(1974 - Columbia) Billy Dee Williams, Eddie
Albert, Frankie Avalon
One Sheet: $7 - $15   *Blaxploitation.*

TAKE A CHANCE
(1918 - Pathe) Harold Lloyd
One Sheet: $1,600 - $2,500

TAKE A CHANCE
(1927R - Pathe) Harold Lloyd
One Sheet: $200 - $400   *Re-release.*

TAKE A CHANCE
(1933 - Paramount) James Dunn, Lillian Roth
One Sheet: $125 - $250

Mini Window Card

TAKE A CHANCE
(1992 - Touchtone) Jason Gedrich, Stephen
Baldwin
One Sheet: $3 - $5

TAKE A GIANT STEP
(1960 - United Artists) Johnny Nash, Estelle
Hemsley, Ruby Dee
One Sheet: $30 - $50   *Black Cast.
Separate Cinema, pg. 119.*

TAKE A GIRL LIKE YOU
(1970 - Columbia) Hayley Mills, Oliver Reed
One Sheet: $5 - $10

TAKE A HARD RIDE
(1975 - 20th Century Fox) Jim Brown, Lee Van
Cleef, Fred Williamson, Jim Kelly
One Sheet: $7 - $15   *Sports Movie
Posters #360.*

TAKE A LETTER, DARLING
(1942 - Paramount) Rosalind Russell, Fred
MacMurray
One Sheet: $40 - $75

TAKE CARE OF MY LITTLE GIRL
(1951 - 20th Century Fox) Jeanne Crain, Jean
Peters
One Sheet: $15 - $35

TAKE HER SHE'S MINE
(1963 - 20th Century Fox) James Stewart,
Sandra Dee
One Sheet: $15 - $25

TAKE IT ALL
(1966 - Lopert) Johanne, Claude Jutra
One Sheet: $7 - $15

TAKE IT BIG
(1944 - Paramount) Jack Haley, Ozzie Nelson,
Harriet Hilliard(Nelson)
One Sheet: $50 - $100

TAKE IT OR LEAVE IT
(1944 - 20th Century Fox) Phil Baker, Phil
Silvers, Marjorie Massow
One Sheet: $40 - $75   *Based on the*

popular radio show.

Window Card

TAKE ME BACK TO OKLAHOMA
(1940 - Monogram) Tex Ritter, Bob Wills & his
Texas Playboys
One Sheet: $100 - $200   *Country
musical. Full color stone litho.*

TAKE ME NAKED
(1966 - -)
One Sheet: $15 - $35

TAKE ME OUT TO THE BALL GAME
(1949 - MGM) Frank Sinatra, Esther Williams,
Gene Kelly
One Sheet: $100 - $200   *Sports
(Baseball). Sports Movie Posters #58.*

One Sheet

TAKE ME TO TOWN
(1953 - Universal) Ann Sheridan, Sterling
Hayden
One Sheet: $15 - $25

TAKE MY LIFE
(1942 - Toddy) Harlem Tuff Kids
One Sheet: $150 - $300   *Black cast.
Separate Cinema, pg. 118.*

TAKE MY LIFE
(1947 - Eagle-Lion) Hugh Williams, Greta Gynt
One Sheet: $15 - $25

TAKE NEXT CAR
(1922 - Pathe) Paul Parrott, Jobyna Ralston
One Sheet: $100 - $200

TAKE ONE FALSE STEP
(1949 - Universal) William Powell, Shelley
Winters
One Sheet: $40 - $75

TAKE THE HEIR
(1930 - Screen Story Syndicate) Guy Kibbee,
Cora Witherspoon
One Sheet: $100 - $200

TAKE THE HIGH GROUND
(1953 - MGM) Richard Widmark, Karl Malden
One Sheet: $15 - $35

TAKE THE MONEY AND RUN
(1969 - Cinerama) Woody Allen, Janet Margolin
One Sheet: $20 - $40   *Allen's first
film as writer, director, and star.*

TAKE THE STAND
(1934 - Liberty) Jack LaRue, Thelma Todd
One Sheet: $100 - $200

TAKE THIS JOB AND SHOVE IT
(1981 - -) Robert Hays, Art Carney
One Sheet: $3 - $5

TAKEN BY FORCE

**(1989 - Manson Int'l) Michelle Johnson,
Christen Kauffman**
One Sheet: $5 - $10

TAKING CARE OF BUSINESS
(1990 - -) Charles Grodin, James Belushi
One Sheet: $3 - $5

TAKING OF PELHAM ONE TWO THREE, THE
(1974 - United Artists) Walter Matthau, Robert
Shaw, Martin Balsam
One Sheet: $5 - $10

TAKING OFF
(1971 - Universal) Buck Henry, Lynn Carlin
One Sheet: $3 - $5

TAKING THE COUNT
(1937 - Vitaphone) Robert Norton (Joe
Palooka), Shemp Howard, Beverly Phalon
One Sheet: $800 - $1,500   *Sports
(Boxing). Sports Movie Posters #140.*

TALE OF FIVE WOMEN, A
(1951 - United Artists) Bonar Colleano, Gina
Lollobrigida
One Sheet: $7 - $15

TALE OF TWO CITIES, A
(1917 - Fox) William Farnum, Jewel Carmen
One Sheet: $500 - $800

TALE OF TWO CITIES, A
(1935 - MGM) Ronald Colman, Elizabeth Allan,
Basil Rathbone
One Sheet: $3,500 - $5,000

TALE OF TWO CITIES, A
(1958 - Rank) Dirk Bogarde, Dorothy Tutin,
Christopher Lee
One Sheet: $15 - $30

TALE OF TWO CITIES, A
(1962R - MGM) Dirk Bogarde, Dorothy Tutin,
Christopher Lee
One Sheet: $20 - $40   *Re-release.*

TALENT SCOUT
(1937 - Warner Bros.) Donald Woods, Jeanne
Madden
One Sheet: $40 - $75

TALES FROM THE CRYPT
Also see DEMON KNIGHT

TALES FROM THE CRYPT
(1972 - Cinerama) Joan Collins, Peter Cushing
One Sheet: $20 - $40

One Sheet

**TALES FROM THE CRYPT PRESENTS
BORDELLO OF BLOOD**
(1996 - Universal) Dennis Miller, Erika Eleniak,
Angie Everhart
One Sheet: $5 - $12   *Horror.*

TALES FROM THE CRYPT/VAULT OF HORROR
(1973R - Cinerama) -
One Sheet: $7 - $15   *Re-release
double feature poster.*

TALES FROM THE DARKSIDE: THE MOVIE
(1990 - Paramount) Deborah Harry, Christian
Slater
One Sheet: $7 - $15

TALES FROM THE HOOD
(1995 - Savoy) Corbin Bernsen, David Alan
Grier
One Sheet: $5 - $12

TALES FROM THE TUBE
(197? - Bob Cording & Jerry Humpries) -
One Sheet: $50 - $100   *Surfing
documentary.*

TALES OF HOFFMANN, THE
(1951 - Lopert) Moira Shearer, Robert Helpmann
One Sheet: $10 - $20

TALES OF MANHATTAN
(1942 - 20th Century Fox) Charles Boyer, Rita Hayworth
One Sheet: $250 - $600

TALES OF ROBIN HOOD
(1951 - Lippert) Robert Clarke, Mary Hatcher
One Sheet: $15 - $25

TALES OF TERROR
(1962 - AIP) Vincent Price, Basil Rathbone
One Sheet: $40 - $75

TALES THAT WITNESS MADNESS
(1973 - Paramount) Kim Novak, Joan Collins
One Sheet: $5 - $10

TALK ABOUT A LADY
(1946 - Columbia) Jinx Falkenburg, Joe Besser
One Sheet: $30 - $50

TALK ABOUT A STRANGER
(1952 - MGM) George Murphy, Nancy Davis
One Sheet: $15 - $25

TALK OF HOLLYWOOD, THE
(1930 - Sono Art/World Wide) Nat Carr, Fay Marbe
One Sheet: $200 - $400

TALK OF THE DEVIL
(1937 - Gaumont) Ricardo Cortez, Sally Eilers
One Sheet: $75 - $150

TALK OF THE TOWN, THE
(1942 - Columbia) Cary Grant, Jean Arthur, Ronald Colman
One Sheet: $600 - $1,000

TALK RADIO
(1988 - -) Eric Bogosian, Alec Baldwin
One Sheet: $7 - $15

TALKING SCREEN SNAPSHOTS
(1932 - Columbia) Various Stars
One Sheet: $150 - $300

TALL DARK AND HANDSOME
(1941 - 20th Century Fox) Cesar Romero, Virginia Gilmore
One Sheet: $30 - $50

TALL GUY, THE
(1990 - -) Jeff Goldblum, Emma Thompson
One Sheet: $3 - $5

TALL IN THE SADDLE
(1944 - RKO) John Wayne, Ella Raines
One Sheet: $250 - $600

TALL IN THE SADDLE
(1949R - RKO) John Wayne, Ella Raines
One Sheet: $75 - $150   Re-release.

TALL IN THE SADDLE
(1952R - RKO) John Wayne, Ella Raines
One Sheet: $40 - $75   Re-release.

TALL MAN RIDING
(1956 - Warner Bros.) Randolph Scott, Dorothy Malone
One Sheet: $30 - $50

TALL MEN, THE
(1955 - 20th Century Fox) Clark Gable, Jane Russell
One Sheet: $30 - $60

TALL STORY
(1960 - Warner Bros.) Anthony Perkins, Jane Fonda
One Sheet: $20 - $40   Fonda's film debut.

TALL STRANGER, THE
(1957 - Allied Artists) Joel McCrea, Virginia Mayo
One Sheet: $15 - $25

TALL T, THE
(1957 - Columbia) Randolph Scott, Richard Boone
One Sheet: $40 - $75   Cowboy Movie Posters #305.

TALL TALE
(1995 - Buena Vista) Nick Stahl, Patrick Swayze, Scott Glenn

One Sheet: $3 - $5

TALL, TAN AND TERRIFIC
(1946 - Astor) Mantan Moreland, Francine Everett
One Sheet: $125 - $250   Black cast.

TALL TARGET, THE
(1951 - MGM) Dick Powell, Adolphe Menjou, Ruby Dee
One Sheet: $30 - $60

TALL TEXAN, THE
(1953 - Lippert) Lloyd Bridges, Marie Windsor
One Sheet: $15 - $30

TALL WOMEN, THE
(1967 - Allied Artists) Anne Baxter, Maria Perschy
One Sheet: $7 - $15

TAMAHINE
(1964 - MGM) Nancy Kwan, John Fraser
One Sheet: $7 - $15

TAMALE VENDOR, THE
(1931 - Educational) Tom Patricola, Charles Judels
One Sheet: $100 - $200

TAMANGO
(1959 - Hal Roach) Dorothy Dandridge, Curt Jurgens
One Sheet: $75 - $125   Cinemascope. Separate Cinema, pg. 84.

TAMARIND SEED, THE
(1974 - Avco Embassy) Julie Andrews, Omar Sharif, Dir: Blake Edwards
One Sheet: $15 - $25

T.A.M.I. SHOW, THE
(1964 - AIP) Rolling Stones, All Star Rock cast
One Sheet: $75 - $125   Rock and R&B awards documentary.

TAMING OF THE SHREW, THE
(1929 - United Artists) Mary Pickford, Douglas Fairbanks
One Sheet: $800 - $1,500

TAMING OF THE SHREW, THE
(1967 - Columbia) Elizabeth Taylor, Richard Burton
One Sheet: $30 - $50

One Sheet

TAMING OF THE WEST, THE
(1939 - Columbia) Bill Elliott, Iris Meredith
One Sheet: $75 - $125

TAMING SUTTON'S GAL
(1957 - Republic) John Lupton, Gloria Talbott
One Sheet: $10 - $20

TAMING THE EAST
(1924 - Universal) Buddy Messinger
One Sheet: $250 - $600

TAMING THE WILD
(1936 - Victory) Rod La Rocque, Maxine Doyle
One Sheet: $75 - $150

TAMMY AND THE BACHELOR
(1957 - Universal) Debbie Reynolds, Leslie Nielsen
One Sheet: $20 - $40

TAMMY AND THE DOCTOR
(1963 - Universal) Sandra Dee, Peter Fonda
One Sheet: $15 - $35

TAMMY AND THE MILLIONAIRE
(1967 - Universal) Debbie Watson, Frank McGrath

One Sheet: $15 - $25

TAMMY TELL ME TRUE
(1961 - Universal) Sandra Dee, John Gavin
One Sheet: $15 - $35

TAMPICO
(1944 - 20th Century Fox) Edward G. Robinson, Lynn Bari, Victor McLaglen
One Sheet: $50 - $100

TANGANYIKA
(1954 - Universal) Van Heflin, Ruth Roman
One Sheet: $20 - $40

TANGIER
(1946 - Universal) Maria Montez, Preston Foster, Sabu
One Sheet: $100 - $200

TANGIER INCIDENT
(1953 - Monogram) George Brent, Mari Aldon
One Sheet: $10 - $20

TANGLED HERDS
(1926 - -) Buddy Roosevelt
One Sheet: $250 - $500

TANGLED TRAILS
(1922 - -) Neal Hart, Violet Palmer
One Sheet: $250 - $500

TANGLED WEB, THE
(1912 - Reliance) Rosemary Theby
One Sheet: $250 - $600

TANGO
(1936 - Invincible) Marian Nixon, Chick Chandler
One Sheet: $75 - $150

TANGO AND CASH
(1989 - Warner Bros.) Sylvester Stallone, Kurt Russell, Teri Hatcher
One Sheet: $7 - $15

TANGO AND POKER
(1920 - Unicorn) -
One Sheet: $200 - $375

TANGO TANGLE, THE
(1914 - Keystone) Charlie Chaplin, Roscoe "Fatty" Arbuckle
One Sheet: $10,000 - $15,000   Price assumes Chaplin is pictured on the poster. Beware stock re-release posters. See next listing.

TANGO TANGLE, THE
(192?R - -) Charlie Chaplin, Roscoe "Fatty" Arbuckle
One Sheet: $200 - $400   Re-release.

TANGO-BAR
(1935 - Paramount) Carlos Gardel, Rosita Moreno
One Sheet: $100 - $200

TANK
(1984 - Lorimar) James Garner, G. D. Spradlin
One Sheet: $3 - $5

TANK BATTALION
(1958 - AIP) Don Kelly, Marjorie Hellen
One Sheet: $15 - $25

TANK COMMANDOS
(1959 - AIP) Robert Barron, Maggie Lawrence
One Sheet: $15 - $25

TANK FORCE
(1958 - Columbia) Victor Mature, Leo Genn
One Sheet: $7 - $15

TANK GIRL
(1995 - United Artists) Lori Petty, Malcolm McDowell, Naomi Watts
One Sheet: $10 - $20   Advance (Daylgo): $20-$40.

TANKS A MILLION
(1941 - United Artists) William Tracy, Elyse Knox
One Sheet: $30 - $50

TANKS ARE COMING, THE
(1951 - Warner Bros.) Steve Cochran, Mari Aldon
One Sheet: $10 - $20

TANNED LEGS
(1929 - RKO) Ann Pennington, Arthur Lake, June Clyde
One Sheet: $800 - $1,500

TAP
(1989 - -) Gregory Hines, Suzanne Douglas
One Sheet: $3 - $5

TAP ROOTS
(1948 - Universal) Susan Hayward, Boris Karloff, Dir: Walter Wanger
One Sheet: $75 - $150

TAP ROOTS/KANSAS RAIDERS
(1956R - Universal) Susan Hayward, Boris Karloff/Audie Murphy
One Sheet: $30 - $60   Re-release double feature poster.

TAPEHEADS
(1988 - De Laurentis) John Cusack, Tim Robbins
One Sheet: $5 - $10

TAPS
(1981 - 20th Century Fox) Timothy Hutton, George C. Scott
One Sheet: $7 - $15

TARANTULA
(1955 - Universal) John Agar, Mara Corday
One Sheet: $250 - $500   Graven Images, pg. 168.

Title Card

TARANTULA
(1964R - Universal) John Agar, Mara Corday
One Sheet: $40 - $75   Re-release.

TARAS BULBA
(1962 - United Artists) Tony Curtis, Yul Brynner
One Sheet: $15 - $30

TARAWA BEACHHEAD
(1958 - Columbia) Kerwin Mathews, Julie Adams
One Sheet: $15 - $30

TARGET
(1952 - RKO) Tim Holt, Richard Martin
One Sheet: $15 - $35

TARGET
(1985 - CBS) Gene Hackman, Matt Dillon
One Sheet: $3 - $5

TARGET EARTH
(1954 - Allied Artists) Virginia Grey, Richard Denning
One Sheet: $250 - $600   Graven Images, pg. 179.

TARGET FOR TONIGHT
(1941 - Warner Bros.) Documentary
One Sheet: $15 - $35

TARGET: HARRY
(1980 - Corman/ABC) Vic Morrow, Suzanne Pleshette
One Sheet: $7 - $15   AKA: HOW TO MAKE IT.

TARGET HONG KONG
(1953 - Columbia) Richard Denning, Nancy Gates
One Sheet: $15 - $25

TARGET OF AN ASSASSIN
(1978 - Pro International) Anthony Quinn, John Philip Law
One Sheet: $5 - $10

TARGET SEA OF CHINA
(1954 - -) Harry Lanter, Lyle Talbot
One Sheet: $10 - $20   Feature version of TRADER TOM OF THE CHINA SEAS.

TARGET UNKNOWN
(1951 - Universal) Mark Stevens, Robert

Douglas
One Sheet: $15 - $30

TARGET ZERO
(1955 - Warner Bros.) Richard Conte, Peggie Castle
One Sheet: $15 - $30

TARGETS
(1968 - Paramount) Boris Karloff, Tim O'Kelly, Nancy Hsueh
One Sheet: $15 - $30

TARNISHED
(1950 - Republic) Dorothy Patrick, Arthur Franz
One Sheet: $15 - $30

TARNISHED ANGEL
(1938 - RKO) Sally Eilers, Ann Miller
One Sheet: $75 - $150

TARNISHED ANGELS, THE
(1957 - Universal) Rock Hudson, Robert Stack
One Sheet: $20 - $40

TARNISHED LADY
(1931 - Paramount Publix) Tallulah Bankhead, Clive Brook
One Sheet: $500 - $900

TARS AND SPARS
(1946 - Columbia) Alfred Drake, Janet Blair
One Sheet: $30 - $50

One Sheet

TARTARS, THE
(1962 - MGM) Victor Mature, Orson Welles
One Sheet: $15 - $30

TARZAN AND HIS MATE
(1934 - MGM) Johnny Weissmuller, Maureen O'Sullivan
One Sheet: $4,000 - $6,500   *Sports Movie Posters #373.*

One Sheet

TARZAN AND THE AMAZONS
(1945 - RKO) Johnny Weissmuller, Brenda Joyce, Johnny Sheffield
One Sheet: $200 - $400

TARZAN AND THE GOLDEN LION
(1927 - -) James Pierce
One Sheet: $1,900 - $3,000

TARZAN AND THE GREAT RIVER
(1967 - Paramount) Mike Henry, Jan Murray
One Sheet: $20 - $40

TARZAN AND THE GREEN GODDESS
(1938 - Principal) Herman Brix
One Sheet: $350 - $750

TARZAN AND THE HUNTRESS
(1947 - RKO) Johnny Weissmuller, Brenda Joyce

One Sheet: $250 - $600

TARZAN AND THE JUNGLE BOY
(1968 - Paramount) Mike Henry, Rafer Johnson
One Sheet: $15 - $30

TARZAN AND THE LEOPARD WOMAN
(1945 - RKO) Johnny Weissmuller, Brenda Joyce, Acquanetta
One Sheet: $200 - $400

One Sheet

TARZAN AND THE LOST SAFARI
(1957 - MGM) Gordon Scott, Yolande Donlan
One Sheet: $30 - $50

TARZAN AND THE MERMAIDS
(1948 - RKO) Johnny Weissmuller, Brenda Joyce, Linda Christian
One Sheet: $150 - $350

TARZAN AND THE SHE-DEVIL
(1953 - RKO) Lex Barker, Joyce MacKenzie
One Sheet: $40 - $75

TARZAN AND THE SLAVE GIRL
(1950 - RKO) Lex Barker, Vanessa Brown
One Sheet: $50 - $100

TARZAN AND THE TRAPPERS
(1958 - -) Gordon Scott, Eve Brent
One Sheet: $20 - $40

TARZAN AND THE VALLEY OF GOLD
(1966 - AIP) Mike Henry, Nancy Kovack
One Sheet: $15 - $25

TARZAN ESCAPES
(1936 - MGM) Johnny Weissmuller, Maureen O'Sullivan, John Buckler
One Sheet: $1,900 - $3,000

TARZAN ESCAPES
(1954R - MGM) Johnny Weissmuller, Maureen O'Sullivan, John Buckler
One Sheet: $75 - $125   *Re-release.*

TARZAN FINDS A SON!
(1939 - MGM) Johnny Weissmuller, Maureen O'Sullivan
One Sheet: $1,300 - $2,000

TARZAN GOES TO INDIA
(1962 - MGM) Jock Mahoney, Mark Dana
One Sheet: $15 - $35

TARZAN OF THE APES
(1918 - National) Elmo Lincoln, Enid Markey
One Sheet: $7,500 - $12,000   *First Tarzan film.*

TARZAN THE APE MAN
(1932 - MGM) Johnny Weissmuller, Maureen O'Sullivan, Neil Hamilton
One Sheet: $10,000 - $15,000   *Weissmuller's film debut. Sports Movie Posters #372.*

Title Card

TARZAN THE APE MAN
(1954R - MGM) Johnny Weissmuller, Maureen O'Sullivan, Neil Hamilton
One Sheet: $30 - $60   *Re-release.*

TARZAN THE APE MAN
(1959 - MGM) Dennis Miller, Joanna Barnes
One Sheet: $30 - $50

TARZAN THE APE MAN
(1981 - MGM) Bo Derek, Richard Harris
One Sheet: $7 - $15   *Advance:$15-$25.*

One Sheet

TARZAN THE FEARLESS
(1933 - Principal) Buster Crabbe, Jacqueline Wells
One Sheet: $800 - $1,500   *Serial. 15 Chapters.*

TARZAN THE MAGNIFICENT
(1960 - Paramount) Gordon Scott, Betta St. John, Jock Mahoney
One Sheet: $30 - $50

TARZAN THE MIGHTY
(1928 - Universal) Frank Merrill
One Sheet: $1,600 - $2,500   *Serial. 15 Chapters.*

TARZAN THE TIGER
(1929 - Universal) Frank Merrill, Natalie Kingston
One Sheet: $1,600 - $2,500   *Serial. 10 Chapters.*

TARZAN TRIUMPHS
(1943 - RKO) Johnny Weissmuller, Frances Gifford, Johnny Sheffield
One Sheet: $250 - $500

TARZAN'S DEADLY SILENCE
(1970 - National General) Ron Ely, Jock Mahoney
One Sheet: $15 - $25

TARZAN'S DESERT MYSTERY
(1943 - RKO) Johnny Weissmuller, Nancy Kelly, Johnny Sheffield
One Sheet: $250 - $600

TARZAN'S DESERT MYSTERY
(1948R - RKO) Johnny Weissmuller, Nancy Kelly, Johnny Sheffield
One Sheet: $75 - $150   *Re-release.*

TARZAN'S FIGHT FOR LIFE
(1958 - MGM) Gordon Scott, Eve Brent
One Sheet: $30 - $50

TARZAN'S GREATEST ADVENTURE
(1959 - Paramount) Gordon Scott, Sara Shane
One Sheet: $30 - $50

TARZAN'S HIDDEN JUNGLE
(1955 - RKO) Gordon Scott, Vera Miles
One Sheet: $40 - $75

TARZAN'S JUNGLE REBELLION
(1970 - National General) Ron Ely, Manuel Padilla, Jr.
One Sheet: $15 - $25

TARZAN'S MAGIC FOUNTAIN
(1948 - RKO) Lex Barker, Brenda Joyce, Albert Dekker
One Sheet: $75 - $125

TARZAN'S NEW YORK ADVENTURE
(1942 - MGM) Johnny Weissmuller, Maureen O'Sullivan
One Sheet: $700 - $1,200

TARZAN'S NEW YORK ADVENTURE
(1948R - MGM) Johnny Weissmuller, Maureen O'Sullivan
One Sheet: $100 - $200   *Re-release.*

TARZAN'S PERIL
(1951 - RKO) Lex Barker, Virginia Huston, Dorothy Dandridge
One Sheet: $100 - $200   *Separate Cinema, pg. 124.*

TARZAN'S REVENGE
(1938 - Principal) Glenn Morris, Eleanor Holm
One Sheet: $250 - $500

TARZAN'S SAVAGE FURY
(1952 - RKO) Lex Barker, Dorothy Hart
One Sheet: $50 - $100

TARZAN'S SECRET TREASURE
(1941 - MGM) Johnny Weissmuller, Maureen O'Sullivan, Johnny Sheffield
One Sheet: $600 - $1,000

One Sheet

TARZAN'S SECRET TREASURE
(1948R - MGM) Johnny Weissmuller, Maureen O'Sullivan, Johnny Sheffield
One Sheet: $100 - $200   *Re-release.*

TARZAN'S THREE CHALLENGES
(1963 - MGM) Jock Mahoney, Woody Strode
One Sheet: $30 - $50

TASK FORCE
(1949 - Warner Bros.) Gary Cooper, Jane Wyatt
One Sheet: $50 - $100

TASSELS IN THE AIR
(1938 - Columbia) The Three Stooges (Curly)
One Sheet: $7,500 - $12,000   *Comedy short. Duotone.*

TASTE OF BLOOD, A
(1967 - Creative Film Enterprises) Dir: Herschell Gordon Lewis
One Sheet: $50 - $100

TASTE OF HONEY, A
(1962 - Continental) Dora Bryan, Rita Tushingham
One Sheet: $5 - $10

TASTE THE BLOOD OF DRACULA
(1970 - Warner Bros.) Christopher Lee
One Sheet: $30 - $60

TATTERED DRESS, THE
(1957 - Universal) Jeff Chandler, Jeanne Crain
One Sheet: $20 - $40

TATTOO
(1981 - -) Maud Adams, Bruce Dern
One Sheet: $3 - $5

TATTOO CONNECTION, THE
(197? - -) Jim Kelly
One Sheet: $7 - $15   *Blaxploitation martial arts.*

TATTOOED POLICE HORSE, THE
(1964 - Buena Vista) Sandy Sanders, Charles Seel
One Sheet: $5 - $10

TATTOOED STRANGER, THE
(1950 - RKO Pathe) John Miles, Patricia White
One Sheet: $15 - $25

TAWNY PIPIT
(1947 - Universal-International) Bernard Miles, Rosamund John
One Sheet: $15 - $25

TAXI
(1932 - Warner Bros.) James Cagney, Loretta Young
One Sheet: $2,200 - $3,500

TAXI
(1953 - 20th Century Fox) Dan Dailey, Constance Smith
One Sheet: $30 - $50

TAXI BLUES
(1990 - -) Piotr Zaitchenko, Piotr Mamonov
One Sheet: $7 - $15   *Russian.*

TAXI DANCER, THE
(1927 - MGM) Joan Crawford
One Sheet: $1,600 - $2,500

TAXI DRIVER
(1976 - Columbia) Robert De Niro, Jodie Foster
One Sheet: $75 - $125   *Price is for full color style. One Sheet(Style B, B&W):$35-$50.*

One Sheet

TAXI DRIVER
(1996R - Columbia) Robert DeNiro
One Sheet: $15 - $25   *Re-release.*

TAXI FOR TOBRUK
(1965 - Seven Arts) Charles Aznavour, Lino Ventura
One Sheet: $15 - $25

TAXI, MISTER
(1943 - United Artists) William Bendix, Grace Bradley
One Sheet: $50 - $100

TAZA, SON OF COCHISE
(1953 - Universal) Rock Hudson, Barbara Rush
One Sheet: $40 - $75   *Originally filmed in 3-D.*

T-BIRD GANG
(1959 - Film Group) Ed Nelson, Jon Brinkley, Dir:Roger Corman
One Sheet: $50 - $100   *Teenage gangs.*

TCHAIKOVSKY
(1971 - Tiomkin) Innokenti Smoktunovsky, Antonina Shuranova
One Sheet: $5 - $10   *Russian.*

TEA AND SYMPATHY
(1956 - MGM) Deborah Kerr, John Kerr
One Sheet: $50 - $100

TEA FOR TWO
(1950 - Warner Bros.) Doris Day, Gordon MacRae
One Sheet: $15 - $35

TEA WITH A KICK!
(1923 - Associate Exhibitors) Doris May, Creighton Hale
One Sheet: $600 - $1,000

TEACHER, THE
(1974 - Crown) Angel Tompkins, Jay North
One Sheet: $3 - $5

TEACHER'S PEST
(1939 - Columbia) Charley Chase, Richard Fiske, Ruth Skinner
One Sheet: $75 - $150   *Comedy short. Duotone.*

TEACHER'S PET
(1957 - Paramount) Clark Gable, Doris Day
One Sheet: $30 - $60

TEACHERS
(1984 - MGM/United Artists) Nick Nolte, JoBeth Williams
One Sheet: $3 - $5

TEACHERS ARE PEOPLE
(1952 - RKO/Disney) Goofy
One Sheet: $250 - $600   *Cartoon. Full color.*

TEAHOUSE OF THE AUGUST MOON, THE
(1956 - MGM) Marlon Brando, Glenn Ford
One Sheet: $30 - $50

TEAR GAS SQUAD
(1940 - Warner Bros.) Dennis Morgan, John Payne, Gloria Dickson
One Sheet: $40 - $75

TEARS FROM SIMON
(1956 - Republic) David Farrer, David Knight
One Sheet: $15 - $25

TEASER, THE
(1923 - Universal) Laura La Plante
One Sheet: $150 - $350

TEASERAMA
(1950 - Klaw) Betty Page, Tempest Storm
One Sheet: $100 - $200   *Sexploitation.*

One Sheet

TECHNO-CRAZY
(1933 - Educational) Billy Bevan
One Sheet: $75 - $150

TECKMAN MYSTERY, THE
(1955 - Associated Artists) Margaret Leighton, John Justin
One Sheet: $10 - $20

TEE FOR TWO
(1945 - MGM) Tom & Jerry
One Sheet: $250 - $600   *Cartoon. Sports (Golf). Cartoon Movie Posters #273. Sports Movie Posters #225.*

TEEN WOLF
(1985 - Atlantic) Michael J. Fox, James Hampton
One Sheet: $7 - $15

TEEN WOLF TOO
(1987 - -) Jason Bateman, Kim Darby
One Sheet: $3 - $5

TEENAGE
(1943 - Continental) Exploitation
One Sheet: $50 - $100

TEENAGE BAD GIRL
(1957 - DCA) Anna Neagle, Sylvia Syms
One Sheet: $30 - $50

TEENAGE CAVEMAN
(1958 - AIP) Robert Vaughn, Leslie Bradley
One Sheet: $50 - $100

TEENAGE CRIME WAVE
(1955 - Columbia) Tommy Cook, Mollie McCart
One Sheet: $20 - $40

TEENAGE DEVIL DOLLS
(196? - -) Robert Sherry, Barbara Marks
One Sheet: $15 - $25

TEENAGE DOLL
(1957 - Howco) June Kenney, Fay Spain
One Sheet: $40 - $75   *Teen girl gangs.*

TEENAGE HITCH HIKERS
(1975 - -) Kathie Christopher, Sandra Peabody
One Sheet: $10 - $20

TEENAGE INTIMACIES
(1975 - Mishkin) Sally Stroke
One Sheet: $5 - $10

One Sheet: $3 - $5

TEENAGE MILLIONAIRE
(1961 - United Artists) Jimmy Clanton, Rocky Graziano, various artists
One Sheet: $15 - $35   *Rock 'n' Roll.*

TEENAGE MONSTER
(1958 - Howco) Anne Gwynne, Gloria Castillo
One Sheet: $30 - $60

TEENAGE MOTHER
(1967 - Jerry Gross) Arlene Sue Farber, Frederick Ricco
One Sheet: $20 - $40   *Sexploitation. B&W poster w/ super-exploitation graphics.*

TEENAGE MUTANT NINJA TURTLES
(1990 - New line) -
One Sheet: $5 - $10

TEENAGE MUTANT NINJA TURTLES II: THE SECRET OF THE OOZE
(1991 - New Line) -
One Sheet: $5 - $10

TEENAGE MUTANT NINJA TURTLES III
(1993 - New Line) Elias Koteas, Paige Turco
One Sheet: $3 - $5

TEENAGE REBEL
(1956 - 20th Century Fox) Ginger Rogers, Michael Rennie
One Sheet: $20 - $40

TEENAGE STRANGLER
(1967 - Ajay) Bill Bloom, Jo Canterbury
One Sheet: $15 - $30   *Red & black duotone.*

TEENAGE THUNDER
(1959 - Howco) Charles Courtney, Melinda Byron, Robert Fuller
One Sheet: $30 - $50   *Hot Rods.*

TEENAGE WOLFPACK
(1957 - DCA) -
One Sheet: $15 - $35

TEENAGE ZOMBIES
(1960 - Governor) Don Sullivan, Katherine Victor
One Sheet: $50 - $100

TEENAGER
(1974 - WorldWide) Joe Warfield, Andrea Cagan
One Sheet: $5 - $10

TEENAGERS FROM OUTER SPACE
(1959 - Warner Bros.) David Love, Dawn Anderson
One Sheet: $40 - $75

TEETH
(1924 - Fox) Tom Mix, Lucy Fox
One Sheet: $500 - $800

TEETH OF THE TIGER, THE
(1919 - Paramount-Artcraft) An Arsene Lupin Story
One Sheet: $100 - $200

TELEFON
(1977 - MGM) Charles Bronson, Lee Remick
One Sheet: $7 - $15

TELEGRAPH TRAIL, THE
(1933 - Vitagraph) John Wayne, Frank McHugh
One Sheet: $2,500 - $4,000

One Sheet

TELEPHONE, THE
(1988 - -) Whoopi Goldberg, Severn Darden
One Sheet: $5 - $10

TELEPHONE GIRL, THE
(1927 - Paramount) Madge Bellamy, Holbrook Blinn
One Sheet: $250 - $600

TELEPHONE OPERATOR
(1938 - Monogram) Judith Allen, Grant Withers
One Sheet: $100 - $200

TELEVISION SPY
(1939 - Paramount) Judith Barret, William Henry
One Sheet: $50 - $100

TELL 'EM NOTHING
(1926 - Pathe) Charley Chase
One Sheet: $350 - $750

TELL IT TO A POLICEMAN
(1925 - Pathecomedy) Glenn Tryon
One Sheet: $250 - $500

TELL IT TO A STAR
(1945 - Republic) Robert Livingston, Ruth Terry
One Sheet: $30 - $50

TELL IT TO THE JUDGE
(1949 - Columbia) Rosalind Russell, Robert Cummings
One Sheet: $30 - $50

TELL IT TO THE MARINES
(1926 - MGM) Lon Chaney, William Haines
One Sheet: $1,600 - $2,500

TELL ME IN THE SUNLIGHT
(1967 - Movie-Rama) Steve Cochran, Shary Marshall
One Sheet: $5 - $10

TELL ME THAT YOU LOVE ME JUNIE MOON
(1970 - Paramount) Liza Minnelli, Robert Moore, Ken Howard
One Sheet: $7 - $15

TELL NO TALES
(1939 - MGM) Melvyn Douglas, Louise Platt
One Sheet: $50 - $100

TELL THEM WILLIE BOY IS HERE
(1970 - Universal) Robert Redford, Robert Blake, Katharine Ross
One Sheet: $7 - $15

TELL-TALE HEART, THE
(1941 - MGM) Joseph Schildkraut, Roman Bohneu
One Sheet: $75 - $150

TELL-TALE HEART, THE
(1961 - Brigadier) Laurence Payne, Adrienne Corri
One Sheet: $30 - $50

TEMBO
(1951 - RKO) Howard Hill
One Sheet: $15 - $30

TEMP, THE
(1993 - Paramount) Timothy Hutton, Lara Flynn Boyle
One Sheet: $3 - $5

TEMPEST
(1928 - United Artists) John Barrymore
One Sheet: $600 - $1,000

TEMPEST
(1958 - Paramount) Van Heflin, Silvana Mangano
One Sheet: $15 - $30

TEMPEST
(1982 - Columbia) John Cassavetes, Gena Rowland
One Sheet: $3 - $5

TEMPEST CODY RIDES WILD
(1919 - Universal) Marie Walcamp
One Sheet: $300 - $700   *Cowboy Movie Posters #19.*

TEMPEST CODY RIDES WILD
(1923 - Universal) Marie Walcamp
One Sheet: $150 - $350

TEMPLE OF VENUS, THE
(1923 - William Fox) Mary Philbin
One Sheet: $500 - $800

TEMPLE TOWER
(1930 - Fox) Kenneth MacKenna, Marceline Day
One Sheet: $125 - $250

TEMPTATION
(1930 - Columbia) Lawrence Gray, Eileen Percy
One Sheet: $125 - $250

TEMPTATION
(1936 - Micheaux) Andrew S. Bishop
One Sheet: $2,500 - $4,000 *Black cast. Separate Cinema, pg. 17.*

TEMPTATION
(1946 - Universal) Merle Oberon, Paul Lukas
One Sheet: $40 - $75

Window Card

TEMPTATION HARBOR
(1947 - Monogram) Robert Norton, Simone Simon
One Sheet: $15 - $30

TEMPTATION'S WORKSHOP
(1934 - Mayfair) Tyrrell Davis, Helen Foster
One Sheet: $125 - $250

TEMPTRESS, THE
(1926 - MGM) Greta Garbo, Lionel Barrymore
One Sheet: $2,200 - $3,500

10
(1979 - Warner Bros.) Dudley Moore, Julie Andrews, Bo Derek
One Sheet: $7 - $15

TEN CENTS A DANCE
(1931 - Columbia) Barbara Stanwyck, Ricardo Cortez
One Sheet: $2,500 - $4,000

TEN CENTS A DANCE
(1945 - Columbia) Jimmy Lloyd, Jane Frazee, Robert Scott
One Sheet: $30 - $50

TEN COMMANDMENTS, THE
(1923 - Paramount) Richard Nix, Nita Naldi
One Sheet: $3,500 - $5,000

TEN COMMANDMENTS, THE
(1956 - Paramount) Charlton Heston, Yul Brynner
One Sheet: $100 - $200

One Sheet

TEN COMMANDMENTS, THE
(1960R - Paramount) Charlton Heston, Yul Brynner
One Sheet: $30 - $50 *Re-release.*

TEN COMMANDMENTS, THE
(1966R - Paramount) Charlton Heston, Yul Brynner
One Sheet: $30 - $50 *Re-release.*

TEN COMMANDMENTS, THE
(1972R - Paramount) Charlton Heston, Yul

Brynner
One Sheet: $15 - $25 *Re-release.*

TEN DAYS TO TULARA
(1958 - United Artists) Sterling Hayden, Grace Raynor
One Sheet: $5 - $10

TEN DAYS WONDER
(1972 - Levitt/Pickman) Orson Welles, Anthony Perkins
One Sheet: $15 - $25

TEN DOLLAR RAISE
(1935 - Fox) Edward Everett Horton, Karen Morley
One Sheet: $100 - $200

TEN FROM YOUR SHOW OF SHOWS
(1972 - Walter Reade) Sid Caesar, Imogene Coca
One Sheet: $10 - $20 *TV tie-in.*

TEN GENTLEMEN FROM WEST POINT
(1942 - 20th Century Fox) George Montgomery, Maureen O'Hara
One Sheet: $40 - $75

TEN LAPS TO GO
(1938 - States Rights) Rex Lease, Muriel Evans
One Sheet: $200 - $400 *Sports (Auto racing).*

TEN LITTLE INDIANS
(1966 - Seven Arts) Hugh O'Brian, Shirley Eaton
One Sheet: $7 - $15

TEN LITTLE INDIANS
(1975 - Avco) Oliver Reed, Elke Sommer
One Sheet: $3 - $5

TEN LITTLE INDIANS
(1989 - Warner Bros.) Donald Pleasence, Frank Stallone
One Sheet: $5 - $10

TEN MODERN COMMANDMENTS
(1927 - Paramount) Esther Ralston
One Sheet: $500 - $900

TEN NIGHTS IN A BAR-ROOM
(1930S - Kent) William Farnum
One Sheet: $100 - $200 *Exploitation.*

TEN NIGHTS IN A BEDROOM
(1930 - Roadshow) -
One Sheet: $100 - $200 *Exploitation.*

TEN NORTH FREDERICK
(1958 - 20th Century Fox) Gary Cooper, Diane Varsi
One Sheet: $30 - $50

TEN OF DIAMONDS
(1917 - Triangle) Dorothy Dalton, Jack Livingston
One Sheet: $300 - $700

10 RILLINGTON PLACE
(1971 - Columbia) Richard Attenborough, Judy Geeson
One Sheet: $5 - $10

TEN SECONDS TO HELL
(1959 - United Artists) Jeff Chandler, Jack Palance
One Sheet: $15 - $25

TEN TALL MEN
(1951 - Columbia) Burt Lancaster, Jody Lawrance
One Sheet: $15 - $30

10:30 P.M. SUMMER
(1966 - Lopert) Melina Mercouri, Romy Schneider
One Sheet: $3 - $5

TEN THOUSAND BEDROOMS
(1957 - MGM) Dean Martin, Anna Maria Alberghetti
One Sheet: $15 - $30 *Martin's first film without Lewis.*

TEN TO MIDNIGHT
(1983 - Golan-Globus) Charles Bronson, Andrew Stevens
One Sheet: $7 - $15

TEN WANTED MEN
(1955 - Columbia) Randolph Scott, Jocelyn Brando, Richard Boone

---

One Sheet: $15 - $35

TEN WHO DARED
(1960 - Buena Vista) Brian Keith, John Beal
One Sheet: $15 - $25

TENANT, THE
(1976 - Paramount) Roman Polanski, Isabelle Adjam
One Sheet: $10 - $20

TENDER COMRADE
(1943 - RKO) Ginger Rogers, Robert Ryan
One Sheet: $125 - $250

TENDER IS THE NIGHT
(1962 - 20th Century Fox) Jennifer Jones, Jason Robards, Jr.
One Sheet: $15 - $35

TENDER MERCIES
(1982 - Universal) Robert Duvall, Tess Harper
One Sheet: $7 - $15 *Academy Award: Best Actor(Duvall). Academy Award Movie Posters #330.*

TENDER TRAP, THE
(1955 - MGM) Frank Sinatra, Debbie Reynolds
One Sheet: $30 - $50

TENDER YEARS, THE
(1947 - 20th Century Fox) Joe E. Brown, Richard Lyon, Josephine Hutchinson
One Sheet: $30 - $50

TENDERFOOT, THE
(1932 - First National) Joe E. Brown, Ginger Rogers
One Sheet: $250 - $500

TENNESSEE CHAMP
(1953 - MGM) Shelley Winters, Dewey Martin
One Sheet: $40 - $75 *Sports (Boxing).*

TENNESSEE JAMBOREE
(1964 - Columbia Roadshows) Jim Reeves, Marty Robbins
One Sheet: $40 - $75 *Country musical.*

TENNESSEE JOHNSON
(1942 - MGM) Van Heflin, Ruth Hussey, Lionel Barrymore
One Sheet: $30 - $50

TENNESSEE'S PARTNER
(1955 - RKO) John Payne, Ronald Reagan
One Sheet: $75 - $125

TENNIS CHUMPS
(1949 - MGM) Tom and Jerry
One Sheet: $250 - $500 *Cartoon. Sports (Tennis). Cartoon Movie Posters #279. Sports Movie Posters #331.*

TENNIS RACQUET
(1949 - RKO/Disney) Goofy
One Sheet: $500 - $800 *Cartoon. Sports (Tennis). Full color. Sports Movie Posters #332.*

TENSION
(1949 - MGM) Richard Basehart, Audrey Totter
One Sheet: $15 - $35

TENSION AT TABLE ROCK
(1956 - RKO) Richard Egan, Dorothy Malone
One Sheet: $15 - $30

TENTACLES
(1977 - AIP) Henry Fonda, Shelly Winters
One Sheet: $7 - $15

TENTH AVENUE ANGEL
(1947 - MGM) Margaret O'Brien, Angela Lansbury, George Murphy
One Sheet: $30 - $50

TENTH AVENUE KID
(1938 - Republic) Bruce Cabot, Beverly Roberts
One Sheet: $75 - $125

TENTH MAN, THE
(1937 - Gaumont) John Lodge, A. Cellier
One Sheet: $50 - $100

TENTH VICTIM, THE
(1965 - Embassy) Marcello Mastroianni, Ursula Andress
One Sheet: $15 - $25

TENTING TONIGHT ON THE OLD

CAMPGROUND
(1942 - Universal) Johnny Mack Brown
One Sheet: $40 - $75

TEQUILA SUNRISE
(1988 - -) Michelle Pfeiffer, Mel Gibson
One Sheet: $15 - $25

TERESA
(1950 - MGM) Pier Angeli, John Ericson, Rod Steiger (film debut)
One Sheet: $20 - $40

TERM OF TRIAL
(1963 - Warner Bros.) Laurence Olivier, Simone Signoret
One Sheet: $15 - $30

TERMINAL CHOICE
(1985 - -) Joe Spano, Diana Venora
One Sheet: $3 - $5

TERMINAL MAN, THE
(1974 - Warner Bros.) George Segal, Joan Hackett
One Sheet: $7 - $15

TERMINAL VELOCITY
(1994 - Buena Vista) Charlie Sheen, Nastassja Kinski
One Sheet: $5 - $10

TERMINATOR, THE
(1984 - -) Arnold Schwarzenegger, Linda Hamilton, Michael Biehn
One Sheet: $30 - $50

TERMINATOR II
(1991 - Carolco) Arnold Schwarzenegger, Linda Hamilton
One Sheet: $7 - $15

TERMITES OF 1938
(1938 - Columbia) The Three Stooges (Curly)
One Sheet: $7,500 - $12,000 *Comedy short. Duotone.*

TERMS OF ENDEARMENT
(1983 - Paramount) Shirley MacLaine, Debra Winger, Jack Nicolson
One Sheet: $10 - $20 *Academy Award: Best Picture, Best Actress (MacLaine), Best Director(Brooks), Best Supporting Actor(Nicolson). Academy Award Movie Posters #329, #331 & #332.*

TERRIBLE DISCOVERY, A
(1912 - Biograph) Dir: D.W. Griffith
One Sheet: $250 - $500

TERRIBLE PEOPLE, THE
(1928 - Pathe) Allene Ray, Walter Miller
One Sheet: $150 - $300 *Serial. 10 Chapters.*

TERRIFIED!
(1963 - Crown) Rod Lauren, Steve Drexel
One Sheet: $5 - $10

TERROR, THE
(1920 - Fox) Tom Mix, Francelia Billington
One Sheet: $600 - $1,000

TERROR, THE
(1926 - Blue Streak Western) Art Acord, Velma Connor
One Sheet: $250 - $500 *Cowboy Movie Posters #58.*

TERROR, THE
(1928 - Warner Bros.) May McAvoy, Louise Fazenda, Edward Everett Horton
One Sheet: $1,600 - $2,500 *Warner Bros. first talking horror film. Graven Images, pg. 38.*

TERROR, THE
(1941 - Alliance) Wilfrid Lawson, Bernard Lee
One Sheet: $50 - $100

TERROR, THE
(1963 - AIP) Boris Karloff, Jack Nicholson, Dir: Roger Corman
One Sheet: $75 - $150

TERROR
(1979 - Crown International) John Nolan, Carolyn Courage
One Sheet: $5 - $10

TERROR ABOARD
(1933 - Paramount) John Halliday, Charlie Ruggles
One Sheet: $100 - $200

TERROR AT BLACK FALLS
(1962 - Beckman) House Peters, Jr., Sandra Knight
One Sheet: $10 - $20

TERROR AT MIDNIGHT
(1956 - Republic) Scott Brady, Joan Vohs
One Sheet: $15 - $25

TERROR AT THE RED WOLF INN
(1972 - -) Linda Gillin, Arthur Space
One Sheet: $3 - $5

TERROR BY NIGHT
(1946 - Universal) Basil Rathbone, Nigel Bruce, Alan Mowbray
One Sheet: $200 - $400   *Sherlock Holmes series.*

TERROR CREATURES FROM THE GRAVE
(1965 - Pacemaker) Barbara Steele, Richard Garret
One Sheet: $15 - $35

TERROR FROM THE YEAR 5,000
(1958 - AIP) Joyce Holden, Ward Costello
One Sheet: $150 - $300

TERROR HOUSE
(1942 - Pathe) James Mason, Wilfred Lawson
One Sheet: $100 - $200   *AKA: THE NIGHT HAS EYES.*

TERROR IN A TEXAS TOWN
(1958 - United Artists) Sterling Hayden, Sebastian Cabot
One Sheet: $15 - $25

TERROR IN THE AISLES
(1984 - Universal) Donald Pleasence, Nancy Allen
One Sheet: $5 - $10   *Compilation of film clips.*

TERROR IN THE CRYPT
(1963 - -) -
One Sheet: $15 - $25

TERROR IN THE HAUNTED HOUSE
(1959 - Howco) Gerald Mohr, Cathy O'Donnell
One Sheet: $30 - $60   *AKA: MY WORLD DIES SCREAMING.*

TERROR IN THE JUNGLE
(1969 - Crown) Robert Burns, Fawn Silver
One Sheet: $10 - $20

TERROR IN THE WAX MUSEUM
(1973 - Cinerama) Ray Milland, Elsa Lanchester
One Sheet: $15 - $25

TERROR IS A MAN
(1959 - Valiant) Francis Lederer, Richard Derr
One Sheet: $15 - $35

TERROR ISLAND
(1920 - Paramount Artcraft) Harry Houdini
One Sheet: $7,500 - $12,000

TERROR MOUNTAIN
(1928 - -) Tom Tyler, Frankie Darro
One Sheet: $250 - $600

TERROR OF GODZILLA
(1973 - UPA (Bob Comm Ent.)) Katsuhiko Sasaki
One Sheet: $40 - $75   *AKA: MONSTERS FROM THE UNKNOWN PLANET*

TERROR OF SHEBA
(1974 - Fanfare) Lana Turner, Trevor Howard
One Sheet: $20 - $40   *AKA: PERSECUTION.*

TERROR OF THE TONGS
(1961 - Columbia) Christopher Lee, Geoffrey Toone
One Sheet: $15 - $30

TERROR OF TINY TOWN, THE
(1938 - Principal) Billy Curtis, Yvonne Moray
One Sheet: $600 - $1,000   *Only film with an all midget cast.*

TERROR ON A TRAIN
(1952 - MGM) Glenn Ford, Anne Vernon
One Sheet: $15 - $35

TERROR SHIP
(1954 - Lippert) William Lundigan
One Sheet: $15 - $30

TERROR STREET

(1953 - Lippert) Dan Duryea, Alsy Albgin
One Sheet: $15 - $25

TERROR TRAIL
(1933 - Universal) Tom Mix, Naomi Judge
One Sheet: $1,300 - $2,000

TERROR TRAIL
(1946 - Columbia) Charles Starrett, Smiley Burnette
One Sheet: $30 - $50

TERROR TRAIN
(1980 - 20th Century Fox) Jamie Lee Curtis, David Copperfield
One Sheet: $5 - $10

TERROR WITHIN, THE
(1988 - -) Andrew Stevens, Starr Andreeff
One Sheet: $5 - $10

TERRORISTS, THE
(1975 - 20th Century Fox) Sean Connery, Ian McShane
One Sheet: $5 - $10

TERRORNAUTS, THE
(1969 - Avco/Embassy) Simon Oates, Zena Marshall
One Sheet: $15 - $30

TERRORS ON HORSEBACK
(1946 - PRC) Buster Crabbe, Al "Fuzzy" St. John, Kermit Maynard
One Sheet: $30 - $50

TERRY AND THE PIRATES
(1940 - Columbia) William Tracy, Granville Owen
One Sheet: $1,300 - $2,000   *Serial. 15 Chapters.*

TERRY OF THE TIMES
(1930 - Universal) Reed Howes, Lotus Thompson
One Sheet: $125 - $250

TERRYTOONS STOCK
(1933C - Educational) Paul Terry-Toons
One Sheet: $200 - $400   *Cartoon. Giraffe and other jungle animals in red against yellow background, bearded man in hat with paintbrush. Cartoon MoviePosters #80.*

TERRYTOONS STOCK
(1935 - Educational) Paul Terry Toons
One Sheet: $250 - $500   *Cartoon. Characters in marching band below title. Yellow background, red characters.*

TERRYTOONS STOCK
(1937 - Educational) Terry-Toons
One Sheet: $200 - $400   *Cartoon. Kangaroo conducting a dog and old man playing drums and fiddle below title. Orange background. Cartoon Movie Posters #82.*

TERRYTOONS STOCK
(1938 - 20th Century Fox) Terry-Toons
One Sheet: $250 - $500   *Cartoon. Artist's hands sketching two-headed character below space for paste on title snipe. Cartoon Movie Posters #85.*

TERRYTOONS STOCK
(1938B - Educational) Terry-Toons
One Sheet: $200 - $400   *Cartoon. Kangaroo, dog, and old man singing below space for paste on title snipe. Orange, yellow and black.*

TERRYTOONS STOCK
(1939 - 20th Century Fox) Terry-Toons
One Sheet: $125 - $250   *Cartoon. Two-headed giant (holding Gandy Goose) and circle of characters below blank space for paste on title snipe. Cartoon MoviePosters #84.*

TERRYTOONS STOCK
(1940 - 20th Century Fox) Terry-Toons
One Sheet: $100 - $200   *Cartoon. Dinky Duck (lower left) and other characters below & right of blank space for titles, "Terry-Toons" on music staff in redletters across top. Cartoon Movie Posters #86.*

TERRYTOONS STOCK
(1942 - 20th Century Fox) Mighty Mouse, Gandy Goose
One Sheet: $250 - $500   *Cartoon. Mighty Mouse & Gandy Goose (with rifle and helmet) beneath blank title space. Cartoon Movie Posters #88.*

TERRYTOONS STOCK

(1944 - 20th Century Fox) Terry-Toons
One Sheet: $200 - $400   *Cartoon. Characters standing in line across middle of poster, Mighty Mouse in blue costume at lower right, "Paul Terry" in yellowletters across top, blue star background. Cartoon Movie Posters #87.*

TERRYTOONS STOCK
(1950 - 20th Century Fox) Mighty Mouse
One Sheet: $150 - $300   *Cartoon. Characters (Mighty Mouse upper right) surround theater notice. Cartoon Movie Posters #94.*

TERRYTOONS STOCK
(1955 - 20th Century Fox) Mighty Mouse, Heckle and Jeckle
One Sheet: $150 - $300   *Cartoon. Mighty Mouse carrying characters on tray. Cartoon Movie Posters #93.*

TERRYTOONS STOCK
(1957 - 20th Century Fox) Mighty Mouse, Dinky Duck, Heckle and Jeckle
One Sheet: $150 - $300   *Cartoon. Characters against a checkerboard background. Cartoon Movie Posters #92.*

TERRYTOONS STOCK
(1960 - 20th Century Fox) Heckle & Jeckle, Mighty Mouse
One Sheet: $40 - $75   *Cartoon. Characters around a film projector.*

TESS
(1981 - Columbia) Nastassia Kinski, Leigh Lawson
One Sheet: $10 - $20

TESS OF THE D'URBERVILLES
(1924 - Metro-Goldwyn) Blanche Sweet, Conrad Nagel
One Sheet: $300 - $700

TESS OF THE STORM COUNTRY
(1922 - Famous Players) Mary Pickford, W.R. Walters
One Sheet: $600 - $1,000

TESS OF THE STORM COUNTRY
(1932 - Fox) Janet Gaynor, Charles Farrell
One Sheet: $250 - $500

Mini Window Card

TESS OF THE STORM COUNTRY
(1960 - 20th Century Fox) Diane Baker, Lee Philips
One Sheet: $5 - $10

TEST PILOT
(1938 - MGM) Clark Gable, Myrna Loy, Spencer Tracy
One Sheet: $300 - $600

TESTAMENT
(1983 - -) Jane Alexander, William DeVane
One Sheet: $5 - $10

TESTAMENT OF DR. MABUSE, THE
(1933 - Nero) Otto Wernicke, Rudolf Klein-Rogge, Dir: Fritz Lang
One Sheet: $6,500 - $10,000   *German. Price is for original Austrian poster (German posters are not known as movie was banned prior to premiere). German re-release poster is worth $300-$500. Also see: THE LAST WILL OF DR. MABUSE. Graven Images, pg. 56.*

TESTAMENT OF ORPHEUS, THE
(1962 - Cinedis) Jean Cocteau, Edouard Dermit
One Sheet: $700 - $1,200   *French. Price is for French one panel.*

TESTING BLOCK, THE
(1920 - Paramount) William S. Hart
One Sheet: $1,300 - $2,000

TEX
(1982 - -) Matt Dillon, Jim Metzler, Meg Tilly
One Sheet: $5 - $10

TEX GRANGER
(1948 - Columbia) Robert Kellard, Peggy Stewart
One Sheet: $40 - $75   *Serial. Western. 15 Chapters.*

TEX RIDES WITH THE BOY SCOUTS
(1937 - Grand National) Tex Ritter, Marjorie Reynolds
One Sheet: $150 - $300

TEXAN, THE
(1920 - Fox) Tom Mix, Gloria Hope
One Sheet: $600 - $1,000

TEXAN, THE
(1930 - Paramount Publix) Gary Cooper, Fay Wray
One Sheet: $800 - $1,500

TEXAN, THE
(1931 - Principal) Buffalo Bill Jr., Lucille Brown
One Sheet: $250 - $600   *Cowboy Movie Posters # 117.*

TEXAN MEETS CALAMITY JANE, THE
(1950 - Columbia) Evelyn Ankers, James Ellison
One Sheet: $15 - $35

TEXANS, THE
(1938 - Paramount) Randolph Scott, Joan Bennett
One Sheet: $350 - $750   *Cowboy Movie Posters #s 227, 228.*

TEXANS NEVER CRY
(1951 - Columbia) Gene Autry, Gail Davis
One Sheet: $50 - $100

TEXAS
(1941 - Universal) William Holden, Glenn Ford
One Sheet: $75 - $150

TEXAS ACROSS THE RIVER
(1966 - Universal) Dean Martin, Alain Delon
One Sheet: $10 - $20

TEXAS BAD MAN, THE
(1932 - Universal) Tom Mix, Lucille Powers
One Sheet: $1,300 - $2,000

TEXAS BAD MAN
(1953 - Monogram) Wayne Morris, Elaine Riley
One Sheet: $15 - $35

TEXAS, BROOKLYN AND HEAVEN
(1948 - United Artists) Guy Madison, Diana Lynn
One Sheet: $30 - $50

TEXAS BUDDIES
(1932 - World-Wide) Bob Steele, Nancy Drexel, Gabby Hayes
One Sheet: $250 - $500

One Sheet

TEXAS CARNIVAL
(1951 - MGM) Esther Williams, Red Skelton
One Sheet: $50 - $100

TEXAS CHAINSAW MASSACRE
(1974 - New Line) Marilyn Burns, Gunner Hansen
One Sheet: $40 - $75

TEXAS CHAINSAW MASSACRE
(1980R - New Line) Marilyn Burns, Gunner Hansen
One Sheet: $15 - $30   *Re-release.*

Beware, this poster is commonly sold as original release. Check date.

TEXAS CHAINSAW MASSACRE 2, THE
(1986 - Cannon) Dennis Hopper, Caroline Williams
One Sheet: $15 - $35 *One Sheet(Leatherface):$40. One Sheet(Entire Family):$50.*

TEXAS CITY
(1952 - Monogram) Johnny Mack Brown
One Sheet: $15 - $35

TEXAS COWBOY, A
(1929 - -) Bob Steele
One Sheet: $250 - $500

TEXAS CYCLONE
(1932 - Columbia) Tim McCoy, Walter Brennan, Wheeler Oakman, John Wayne (bit)
One Sheet: $800 - $1,500 *Cowboy Movie Posters #131.*

TEXAS DYNAMO
(1950 - Columbia) Charles Starrett, Smiley Burnette
One Sheet: $15 - $35

TEXAS GUINAN
(1920 - Texas Guinan Productions) Texas Guinan
One Sheet: $250 - $500 *Cowboy Movie Posters #26.*

TEXAS GUN FIGHTER
(1932 - Quadruple) Ken Maynard
One Sheet: $200 - $400

TEXAS JACK
(1935 - -) Jack Perrin, Jayne Regan
One Sheet: $250 - $600

TEXAS KID, THE
(1943 - Monogram) Johnny Mack Brown
One Sheet: $30 - $50

TEXAS LADY
(1955 - RKO) Claudette Colbert, Barry Sullivan
One Sheet: $15 - $35

TEXAS LAWMEN
(1951 - Monogram) Johnny Mack Brown
One Sheet: $15 - $35

TEXAS MANHUNT
(1942 - PRC) Bill Boyd
One Sheet: $20 - $40 *Not Bill "Hopalong Cassidy" Boyd.*

TEXAS MARSHAL, THE
(1941 - PRC) Tim McCoy, Kay Leslie
One Sheet: $75 - $125

TEXAS MASQUERADE
(1943 - United Artists) William Boyd
One Sheet: $125 - $250 *Hopalong Cassidy series.*

TEXAS PANHANDLE
(1945 - Columbia) Charles Starrett, Tex Harding
One Sheet: $30 - $50

TEXAS PIONEERS
(1932 - Monogram) Bill Cody, Andy Shuford
One Sheet: $125 - $250

TEXAS RAMBLER, THE
(1934 - Spectrum) Bill Cody
One Sheet: $100 - $200

TEXAS RANGER, THE
(1934 - Columbia) Buck Jones, Carmelita Geraghty
One Sheet: $250 - $600

TEXAS RANGERS, THE
(1936 - Paramount) Fred MacMurray, Jack Oakie
One Sheet: $100 - $200

TEXAS RANGERS, THE
(1951 - Columbia) George Montgomery, Gale Storm
One Sheet: $20 - $40

TEXAS RANGERS RIDE AGAIN
(1940 - Paramount) John Howard, Ellen Drew
One Sheet: $50 - $100

TEXAS RENEGADES
(1940 - PRC) Tim McCoy, Nora Lane
One Sheet: $100 - $200

TEXAS STAGECOACH
(1940 - Columbia) Charles Starrett, Iris Meredith
One Sheet: $50 - $100

TEXAS STAMPEDE
(1939 - Columbia) Charles Starrett, Iris Meredith
One Sheet: $50 - $100

TEXAS STREAK, THE
(1926 - Universal) Hoot Gibson, Blanche Mehaffey
One Sheet: $250 - $600

TEXAS TERROR
(1935 - Monogram) John Wayne, Lucile Brown
One Sheet: $1,600 - $2,500

One Sheet

TEXAS TERROR
(1945R - Monogram) John Wayne, Lucile Brown
One Sheet: $75 - $150 *Re-release.*

TEXAS TERRORS
(1940 - Republic) Don Barry, Julie Duncan
One Sheet: $30 - $50

TEXAS TERRORS
(1950R - Republic) Don Barry
One Sheet: $15 - $25 *Re-release.*

TEXAS TO BATAAN
(1942 - Monogram) Range Busters
One Sheet: $30 - $50

TEXAS TOM
(1950 - MGM) Tom & Jerry
One Sheet: $350 - $750 *Cartoon. Full color stone litho.*

TEXAS TRAIL
(1937 - Paramount) William Boyd, George "Gabby" Hayes
One Sheet: $600 - $1,000 *Hopalong Cassidy series.*

TEXAS TROUBLE SHOOTERS
(1942 - Monogram) Range Busters
One Sheet: $20 - $40

TEXAS WILDCATS
(1939 - Victory) Tim McCoy
One Sheet: $75 - $150

TEXASVILLE
(1990 - Columbia) Jeff Bridges, Cybill Shepherd
One Sheet: $3 - $5

TEXICAN, THE
(1966 - Columbia) Audie Murphy, Broderick Crawford
One Sheet: $15 - $35

THANK GOD IT'S FRIDAY
(1978 - Columbia) Jeff Goldblum, Donna Summers, The Commodores
One Sheet: $7 - $15 *Rock 'n' Roll.*

THANK YOU ALL VERY MUCH
(1969 - Columbia) Sandy Dennis, Ian McKellen
One Sheet: $5 - $10

THANK YOU, JEEVES!
(1936 - 20th Century Fox) Arthur Treacher, David Niven
One Sheet: $125 - $250

THANK YOU, MR. MOTO
(1937 - 20th Century Fox) Peter Lorre, Pauline Frederick, Sidney Blackmer
One Sheet: $250 - $600

THANK YOUR LUCKY STARS
(1943 - Warner Bros.) Eddie Cantor, Joan Leslie, All star cast
One Sheet: $75 - $150

One Sheet

THANKS A MILLION
(1935 - 20th Century Fox) Dick Powell, Fred Allen, Ann Dvorak
One Sheet: $200 - $400

THANKS FOR EVERYTHING
(1938 - 20th Century Fox) Adolphe Menjou, Jack Oakie
One Sheet: $75 - $150

THANKS FOR LISTENING
(1937 - -) Pinky Tomlin, Maxine Doyle
One Sheet: $30 - $50

THANKS FOR THE MEMORY
(1938 - Paramount) Bob Hope, Shirley Ross
One Sheet: $150 - $300

THAR SHE BLOWS
(1969 - David Friedman) -
One Sheet: $15 - $25

THAT BRENNAN GIRL
(1946 - Republic) Mona Freeman, James Dunn
One Sheet: $15 - $35

THAT CERTAIN AGE
(1938 - Universal) Deanna Durbin, Jackie Cooper, Melvyn Douglas
One Sheet: $100 - $200

THAT CERTAIN FEELING
(1956 - Paramount) Bob Hope, Eva Marie Saint, Pearl Bailey
One Sheet: $30 - $50

THAT CERTAIN WOMAN
(1937 - Warner Bros.) Bette Davis, Henry Fonda
One Sheet: $250 - $500

THAT CHAMPIONSHIP SEASON
(1982 - Cannon) Bruce Dern, Stacy Keach, Robert Mitchum
One Sheet: $7 - $15 *Sports (Basketball). Sports Movie Posters #98.*

One Sheet

THAT COLD DAY IN THE PARK
(1969 - Commonwealth United) Sandy Dennis, Michael Burns, John Garfield, Jr.
One Sheet: $7 - $15

THAT DARN CAT
(1965 - Buena Vista/Disney) Hayley Mills, Dean Jones
One Sheet: $15 - $30

THAT DARN CAT

THAT DARN CAT
(1973R - Disney) Hayley Mills, Dean Jones
One Sheet: $5 - $10 *Re-release.*

THAT DARN CAT
(1997 - Disney) Christina Ricci, Doug E. Doug
One Sheet: $3 - $5

THAT FORSYTE WOMAN
(1949 - MGM) Errol Flynn, Greer Garson, Walter Pidgeon
One Sheet: $50 - $100

THAT FUNNY FEELING
(1965 - Universal) Sandra Dee, Bobby Darin
One Sheet: $15 - $30

THAT GANG OF MINE
(1940 - Monogram) East Side Kids
One Sheet: $75 - $125

THAT GIRL FROM PARIS
(1936 - RKO) Lily Pons, Gene Raymond, Lucille Ball
One Sheet: $125 - $250

One Sheet

THAT HAGEN GIRL
(1947 - Warner Bros.) Ronald Reagan, Shirley Temple
One Sheet: $75 - $150

THAT HAMILTON WOMAN
(1941 - United Artists) Vivien Leigh, Laurence Olivier
One Sheet: $700 - $1,200

One Sheet

THAT I MAY LIVE
(1937 - 20th Century Fox) Rochelle Hudson, Robert Kent
One Sheet: $100 - $200

THAT KIND OF WOMAN
(1958 - Paramount) Sophia Loren, Tab Hunter
One Sheet: $20 - $40

THAT LADY
(1955 - 20th Century Fox) Olivia de Havilland, Gilbert Roland
One Sheet: $15 - $30

THAT LADY IN ERMINE
(1948 - 20th Century Fox) Betty Grable, Douglas Fairbanks Jr., Cesar Romero
One Sheet: $125 - $250

THAT MAN BOLT
(1973 - Universal) Fred Williamson, Byron Webster
One Sheet: $7 - $15 *Blaxploitation.*

THAT MAN FROM RIO
(1964 - Lopert) Jean-Paul Belmondo, Francoise Dorleac
One Sheet: $15 - $25

THAT MAN FROM TANGIER
(1955 - United Artists) Nils Asther, Nancy Coleman
One Sheet: $10 - $20

THAT MAN GEORGE
(1967 - Allied Artists) George Hamilton, Claudine Auger
One Sheet: $7 - $15

THAT MAN IN ISTANBUL
(1966 - Columbia) Horst Buchholz, Sylvia Koscina
One Sheet: $7 - $15

THAT MAN OF MINE
(1947 - -) Ruby Dee
One Sheet: $75 - $150   *Black cast.*

THAT MAN'S HERE AGAIN
(1937 - Warner Bros.) Mary Maguire, Tom Brown
One Sheet: $40 - $75

THAT MIDNIGHT KISS
(1949 - MGM) Kathryn Grayson, Jose Iturbi, Ethel Barrymore, Mario Lanza
One Sheet: $30 - $50

THAT NATZY NUISANCE
(1943 - United Artists) Bobby Watson
One Sheet: $50 - $100

THAT NIGHT
(1957 - Universal International) John Beal, Augusta Dabney
One Sheet: $7 - $15

THAT NIGHT
(1993 - Warner Bros.) Juliette Lewis, C. Thomas Howell
One Sheet: $3 - $5

THAT NIGHT IN RIO
(1941 - 20th Century Fox) Alice Faye, Don Ameche
One Sheet: $300 - $700

THAT NIGHT IN RIO
(1972R - 20th Century Fox) Alice Faye, Don Ameche
One Sheet: $7 - $15   *Re-release.*

THAT NIGHT WITH YOU
(1945 - Universal) Franchot Tone, Susanna Foster
One Sheet: $30 - $50

THAT OLD FEELING
(1997 - Universal) Bette Midler, Dennis Farina
One Sheet: $3 - $5

THAT OTHER WOMAN
(1942 - 20th Century Fox) Virginia Gilmore, James Ellison, Dan Duryea
One Sheet: $30 - $50

THAT ROYLE GIRL
(1926 - Paramount) W.C. Fields, Carol Dempster
One Sheet: $1,600 - $2,500

THAT SPLENDID NOVEMBER
(1971 - United Artists) Gina Lollobrigida, Paolo Turco
One Sheet: $7 - $15

THAT TENNESSEE BEAT
(1966 - 20th Century Fox) Sharon DeBord, Minnie Pearl
One Sheet: $20 - $40   *Country musical.*

One Sheet

THAT TEXAS JAMBOREE

(1946 - Columbia) Carolina Cotton, Hoosier Hotshots, The Plainsmen
One Sheet: $40 - $75   *Country musical.*

THAT THING YOU DO!
(1996 - 20th Century Fox) Tom Hanks, Jonathon Schaech, Liv Tyler
One Sheet: $5 - $10   *Hanks directorial debut.*

THAT TOUCH OF MINK
(1962 - Universal) Cary Grant, Doris Day
One Sheet: $30 - $60   *Sports (Baseball). Lobby card (baseball players in dugout scene):$75-$125. Sports Movie Posters #67.*

THAT TOUCH OF MINK/TO KILL A MOCKINGBIRD
(1967R - Universal) Cary Grant, Doris Day/ Gregory Peck, Mary Badham
One Sheet: $20 - $40   *Re-release double feature poster.*

THAT UNCERTAIN FEELING
(1941 - United Artists) Merle Oberon, Melvyn Douglas
One Sheet: $40 - $75

THAT WAS THEN, THIS IS NOW
(1985 - Paramount) Emilio Estevez, Kim Delaney, Craig Shefferr
One Sheet: $7 - $15

THAT WAY WITH WOMEN
(1947 - Warner Bros.) Dane Clark, Martha Vickers, Sydney Greenstreet
One Sheet: $15 - $35

THAT WONDERFUL URGE
(1948 - 20th Century Fox) Tyrone Power, Gene Tierney
One Sheet: $40 - $75

THAT'S A GOOD GIRL
(1934 - United Artists) Jack Buchanan, Elsie Randolph
One Sheet: $75 - $150

THAT'S DANCING
(1985 - MGM/UA) Gene Kelly, Sammy Davis, Jr., Mikhail Barishnikov
One Sheet: $15 - $25   *Dance compilation.*

THAT'S ENTERTAINMENT
(1974 - MGM) All-Star cast
One Sheet: $15 - $25   *Highlights from MGM's musical past.*

THAT'S ENTERTAINMENT II
(1976 - MGM) All-Star Cast
One Sheet: $7 - $15

THAT'S GRATITUDE
(1934 - Columbia) Frank Craven, Mary Carlisle
One Sheet: $75 - $125

THAT'S LIFE
(1986 - Columbia) Jack Lemmon, Julie Andrews
One Sheet: $3 - $5

THAT'S MY BABY
(1944 - Republic) Richard Arlen, Ellen Drew
One Sheet: $15 - $30

THAT'S MY BOY
(1932 - Columbia) Richard Cromwell, Mae Marsh, USC Football team
One Sheet: $200 - $400   *Sports (Football). Sports Movie Posters #185.*

THAT'S MY BOY
(1951 - Paramount) Dean Martin, Jerry Lewis, Polly Bergen
One Sheet: $50 - $100   *Sports (Football, Track).*

THAT'S MY DADDY
(1928 - -) Reginald Denny
One Sheet: $150 - $300

THAT'S MY GAL
(1947 - Republic) Lynne Roberts, Donald Barry, Pinky Lee
One Sheet: $15 - $35

THAT'S MY MAN
(1947 - Republic) Don Ameche, Catherine McLeod
One Sheet: $15 - $35

THAT'S MY PUP

(1953 - MGM) Tom & Jerry
One Sheet: $250 - $500   *Cartoon. Full color.*

THAT'S MY STORY
(1937 - Universal) Claudia Morgan, William Lundigan
One Sheet: $75 - $125

THAT'S MY WIFE
(1929 - MGM) Laurel & Hardy
One Sheet: $3,500 - $5,000

THAT'S PICTURES
(1936 - Vitaphone Broadway Brevity) J. C. Flippen
One Sheet: $50 - $100   *Short Subject. Duotone.*

THAT'S RIGHT - YOU'RE WRONG
(1939 - RKO) Kay Kyser, Adolphe Menjou, Lucille Ball
One Sheet: $200 - $400

One Sheet

THAT'S THE SPIRIT
(1945 - Universal) Jack Oakie, Peggy Ryan, Buster Keaton (cameo)
One Sheet: $30 - $50

THAT'S THE WAY IT IS
(1971 - MGM) Elvis Presley
One Sheet: $40 - $75   *Rock 'n' Roll concert film.*

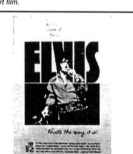

One Sheet

THEATRE D'OMBRES
(1897 - -) -
One Sheet: $2,200 - $3,500   *French.*

THEATRE OF BLOOD
(1973 - United Artists) Vincent Price, Diana Rigg
One Sheet: $30 - $50

THEATRE OF DEATH
(1967 - Hemisphere) Christopher Lee, Julian Glover
One Sheet: $15 - $35   *AKA: BLOOD FIEND.*

THEFT OF THE MONA LISA, THE
(1932 - RKO) Willy Forst, Trude von Molo
One Sheet: $150 - $300

THEIR BIG MOMENT
(1934 - RKO) ZaSu Pitts, Slim Summerville
One Sheet: $75 - $150

THEIR FIRST MISTAKE
(1932 - MGM) Laurel & Hardy
One Sheet: $1,900 - $3,000

THEIR LAST BEAN
(1938 - 20th Century Fox) Terry-toons
One Sheet: $100 - $200   *Cartoon. Full*

---

color stone litho. Stock poster with inset title.

THEIR MAD MOMENT
(1931 - Fox) Warner Baxter, Dorothy Mackaill
One Sheet: $250 - $500

THEIR OWN DESIRE
(1930 - MGM) Norma Shearer, Lewis Stone
One Sheet: $200 - $400

THEIR PURPLE MOMENT
(1928 - MGM) Laurel & Hardy
One Sheet: $3,500 - $5,500

THELMA AND LOUISE
(1991 - MGM/Pathe) Susan Sarandon, Geena Davis
One Sheet: $20 - $40

THELONIOUS MONK: STRAIGHT, NO CHASER
(1988 - -) Thelonius Monk
One Sheet: $20 - $40   *Jazz documentary.*

THEM!
(1954 - Warner Bros.) James Whitmore, Edmund Gwenn
One Sheet: $500 - $800   *Graven Images, pg. 5, 168.*

One Sheet

THEM THAR HILLS
(1934 - MGM) Laurel & Hardy, Mae Busch
One Sheet: $150 - $350

THEN CAME THE WOMAN
(1926 - ACA) Frank Mayo
One Sheet: $150 - $350

THEN THERE WERE THREE
(1961 - Parade) Alex Nicol, Frank Latimore
One Sheet: $7 - $15

THEODORA GOES WILD
(1936 - Columbia) Irene Dunne, Melvyn Douglas
One Sheet: $600 - $1,000   *Dunne's first starring comedy.*

THERE AIN'T NO JUSTICE
(1939 - Ealing) Jimmy Hanley, Edward Rigby
One Sheet: $50 - $100

THERE ARE NO VILLIANS
(1919 - Metro) Viola Dana
One Sheet: $125 - $250

THERE GOES KELLY
(1945 - Monogram) Jack Moran, Wanda McKay
One Sheet: $15 - $30

THERE GOES MY GIRL
(1937 - RKO) Gene Raymond, Ann Sothern
One Sheet: $75 - $150

THERE GOES MY HEART
(1938 - United Artists) Fredric March, Virginia Bruce
One Sheet: $100 - $200

THERE GOES THE BRIDE
(1933 - Gaumont) Owes Nares, Jessie Matthews
One Sheet: $150 - $300

THERE GOES THE BRIDE
(1980 - Vanguard) Tom Smothers, Twiggy
One Sheet: $15 - $30

THERE GOES THE GROOM
(1937 - RKO) Ann Sothern, Burgess Meredith
One Sheet: $75 - $150

THERE HE GOES
(1925 - Pathecomedy) Harry Langdon

One Sheet: $250 - $500

THERE IS NO 13
(1977 - Film Ventures) Mark Damon
One Sheet: $5 - $10

THERE WAS A CROOKED MAN
(1970 - Warner Bros.) Kirk Douglas, Henry Fonda
One Sheet: $7 - $15

THERE'S A GIRL IN MY HEART
(1949 - Allied Artists) Lee Bowman, Elyse Knox
One Sheet: $15 - $25

THERE'S A GIRL IN MY SOUP
(1970 - Columbia) Peter Sellers, Goldie Hawn
One Sheet: $7 - $15

THERE'S ALWAYS A WOMAN
(1938 - Columbia) Joan Blondell, Melvyn Douglas
One Sheet: $75 - $150

THERE'S ALWAYS TOMORROW
(1934 - Universal) Binnie Barnes, Frank Morgan
One Sheet: $75 - $150

THERE'S ALWAYS TOMORROW
(1955 - Universal) Barbara Stanwyck, Fred MacMurray
One Sheet: $30 - $55

THERE'S ALWAYS VANILLA
(1972 - Cambist) Roy Laine, Judith Streiner
One Sheet: $3 - $5

THERE'S MAGIC IN MUSIC
(1941 - Paramount) Alan Jones, Susanna Foster
One Sheet: $40 - $75   *Classical music. AKA: THE HARD-BOILED CANARY.*

THERE'S NO BUSINESS LIKE SHOW BUSINESS
(1954 - 20th Century Fox) Marilyn Monroe, Dan Dailey, Ethel Merman
One Sheet: $200 - $400

THERE'S NO PLACE LIKE HELL
(1980 - ABC) Michael Moriarity, William Devane
One Sheet: $5 - $10

THERE'S ONE BORN EVERY MINUTE
(1942 - Universal) Hugh Herbert, Guy Kibbee, Elizabeth Taylor
One Sheet: $50 - $100   *Taylor's film debut.*

THERE'S SOMETHING ABOUT A SAILOR
(1943 - Columbia) Evelyn Keyes, Tom Neal
One Sheet: $30 - $50

THERE'S THAT WOMAN AGAIN
(1938 - Columbia) Melvyn Douglas, Virginia Bruce
One Sheet: $50 - $100

THERESE AND ISABELLE
(1968 - -) Essy Persson, Anna Gael
One Sheet: $10 - $20

THESE ARE THE DAMNED
(1964 - Columbia) Macdonald Carey, Shirley Anne Field
One Sheet: $7 - $15

THESE GLAMOUR GIRLS
(1939 - MGM) Lew Ayres, Lana Turner
One Sheet: $125 - $250   *Turner's first starring role.*

THESE THOUSAND HILLS
(1958 - 20th Century Fox) Don Murray, Richard Egan
One Sheet: $7 - $15

THESE THREE
(1936 - United Artists) Miriam Hopkins, Merle Oberon, Joel McCrea
One Sheet: $250 - $500

THESE WILDER YEARS
(1956 - MGM) James Cagney, Barbara Stanwyck
One Sheet: $30 - $50

THEY ALL COME OUT
(1939 - MGM) Rita Johnson, Tom Neal
One Sheet: $50 - $100

THEY ALL DIED LAUGHING
(1964 - Continental) Leo McKern, Janet Munro

One Sheet: $7 - $15

THEY ALL KISSED THE BRIDE
(1942 - Columbia) Joan Crawford, Melvyn Douglas
One Sheet: $100 - $200

THEY ALL KISSED THE BRIDE
(1955R - Columbia) Joan Crawford, Melvyn Douglas
One Sheet: $15 - $35   *Re-release.*

THEY ALL LAUGHED
(1981 - Time-Life) Audrey Hepburn, Ben Gazzara, Dorothy Stratton
One Sheet: $15 - $25

THEY ASKED FOR IT
(1939 - Universal) Michael Whalen, Joy Hodges
One Sheet: $50 - $100

THEY CALL IT SIN
(1932 - First National) Loretta Young, George Brent
One Sheet: $250 - $500

THEY CALL ME BRUCE
(1982 - -) Johnny Yune, Ralph Mauro
One Sheet: $2 - $3

THEY CALL ME MISTER TIBBS
(1970 - United Artists) Sidney Poitier, Martin Landau, Barbara McNair
One Sheet: $10 - $20

THEY CALL ME TRINITY
(1971 - Avco) Terence Hill
One Sheet: $10 - $20

THEY CAME FROM BEYOND SPACE
(1967 - Embassy) Robert Hutton, Jennifer Jayne
One Sheet: $15 - $25

THEY CAME FROM WITHIN
(1976 - Transamerican) Paul Hampton, Joe Silver, Dir:David Cronenberg
One Sheet: $15 - $30

THEY CAME TO BLOW UP AMERICA
(1943 - 20th Century Fox) George Sanders, Anna Sten
One Sheet: $150 - $300

THEY CAME TO CORDURA
(1959 - Columbia) Gary Cooper, Rita Hayworth
One Sheet: $30 - $50

THEY CAME TO ROB LAS VEGAS
(1968 - Warner Bros.) Gary Lockwood, Elke Sommer
One Sheet: $15 - $25

THEY DARE NOT LOVE
(1941 - Columbia) George Brent, Martha Scott, Paul Lukas
One Sheet: $30 - $50

THEY DIED WITH THEIR BOOTS ON
(1942 - Warner Bros.) Errol Flynn, Olivia de Havilland
One Sheet: $600 - $1,000   *Teams final film together.*

One Sheet

THEY DRIVE BY NIGHT
(1940 - Warner Bros.) George Raft, Ann Sheridan, Humphrey Bogart
One Sheet: $200 - $400

THEY DRIVE BY NIGHT
(1948R - Warner Bros.) George Raft, Humphrey Bogart
One Sheet: $50 - $100   *Re-release.*

THEY DRIVE BY NIGHT
(1956R - Warner Bros.) George Raft, Ann Sheridan, Humphrey Bogart
One Sheet: $50 - $100   *Re-release.*

THEY GAVE HIM A GUN
(1937 - MGM) Spencer Tracy, Franchot Tone
One Sheet: $100 - $200

THEY GO BOOM
(1929 - MGM) Laurel & Hardy
One Sheet: $3,500 - $5,000

THEY GOT ME COVERED
(1942 - RKO) Bob Hope, Dorothy Lamour
One Sheet: $125 - $250

THEY GOT ME COVERED
(1951R - RKO) Bob Hope, Dorothy Lamour
One Sheet: $40 - $75   *Re-release.*

THEY HAD TO SEE PARIS
(1929 - Fox) Will Rogers
One Sheet: $600 - $1,000   *Roger's first talkie.*

Insert

THEY KNEW WHAT THEY WANTED
(1940 - RKO) Carole Lombard, Charles Laughton
One Sheet: $150 - $300

THEY LEARNED ABOUT WOMEN
(1930 - MGM) Joseph T. Schenck, Gus Van, Bessie Love
One Sheet: $250 - $500   *Sports (Baseball).*

THEY LIVE
(1988 - -) Roddy Piper, Keith David, Meg Foster
One Sheet: $5 - $10

THEY LIVE BY NIGHT
(1948 - RKO) Cathy O'Donnell, Farley Granger
One Sheet: $40 - $75

THEY LIVE IN FEAR
(1944 - Columbia) Cliff Seuern, Otto Kruger
One Sheet: $50 - $100   *Nazis.*

THEY MADE HER A SPY
(1939 - RKO) Sally Eilers, Allan Lane
One Sheet: $50 - $100

THEY MADE ME A CRIMINAL
(1939 - Warner Bros.) John Garfield, Ann Sheridan, Claude Rains
One Sheet: $250 - $500   *Sports Movie Posters #143.*

THEY MADE ME A FUGITIVE
(1947 - Warner Bros.) Trevor Howard, Sally Gray
One Sheet: $40 - $75   *AKA: I BECAME A CRIMINAL; THEY MADE ME A CRIMINAL.*

THEY MADE ME A KILLER
(1946 - Paramount) Barbara Britton, Robert Lowery
One Sheet: $30 - $50

THEY MEET AGAIN
(1941 - Paramount) Jean Hersholt, Dorothy Lovett
One Sheet: $30 - $50

THEY MET AT MIDNIGHT
(1948 - -) See PICADILLY INCIDENT

THEY MET IN A TAXI
(1936 - Columbia) Chester Morris, Fay Wray
One Sheet: $125 - $250

THEY MET IN ARGENTINA
(1941 - RKO) Maureen O'Hara, Buddy Ebsen
One Sheet: $50 - $100

THEY MET IN BOMBAY
(1941 - MGM) Clark Gable, Rosalind Russell, Peter Lorre
One Sheet: $150 - $350

THEY MIGHT BE GIANTS
(1971 - Universal) George C. Scott, Joanne Woodward
One Sheet: $5 - $10

THEY ONLY KILL THEIR MASTERS
(1972 - MGM) James Garner, Katharine Ross
One Sheet: $5 - $10

THEY RAID BY NIGHT
(1942 - PRC) Lyle Talbot, June Duprez
One Sheet: $15 - $35

THEY RAN FOR THEIR LIVES
(1969 - Masterpiece) John Payne, Luana Patten
One Sheet: $5 - $10

THEY RODE WEST
(1954 - Columbia) Robert Francis, Donna Reed
One Sheet: $15 - $25

THEY SAVED HITLER'S BRAIN
(1963 - Crown) Walter Stocker, Audrey Caine
One Sheet: $15 - $25   *AKA: MADMEN OF MANDORAS; THE RETURN OF DR. H.*

THEY SHALL HAVE MUSIC
(1939 - United Artists) Jascha Heifetz, Gene Reynolds, Walter Brennan, Joel McCrea
One Sheet: $75 - $150   *Classical music.*

THEY SHOOT HORSES, DON'T THEY?
(1969 - Cinerama) Jane Fonda, Michael Sarrazin
One Sheet: $15 - $30   *Academy Award Movie Posters #256.*

THEY STILL CALL ME BRUCE
(1987 - -) James Orr, Johnny Yune
One Sheet: $2 - $3

THEY STOOGE TO CONGA
(1943 - Columbia) The Three Stooges (Curly)
One Sheet: $2,500 - $4,000   *Comedy short. Duotone.*

THEY WANTED TO MARRY
(1937 - RKO) Gordon Jones, Betty Furness
One Sheet: $75 - $150

THEY WENT THAT-A-WAY AND THAT-A-WAY
(1978 - International) Tim Conway, Chuck McCann
One Sheet: $5 - $10

THEY WERE EXPENDABLE
(1945 - MGM) Robert Montgomery, John Wayne, Donna Reed
One Sheet: $125 - $250

THEY WERE NOT DIVIDED
(1950 - Eagle Lion Classics) Edward Underdown, Ralph Clanton
One Sheet: $10 - $20

THEY WERE SISTERS
(1946 - Universal) James Mason, Phyllis Calvert, Dulcie Gray
One Sheet: $15 - $30

THEY WERE SO YOUNG
(1954 - Lippert) Scott Brady, Raymond Burr
One Sheet: $15 - $30

THEY WON'T BELIEVE ME
(1947 - RKO) Robert Young, Susan Hayward
One Sheet: $100 - $200

THEY WON'T FORGET
(1937 - Warner Bros.) Claude Rains, Gloria Dickson, Lana Turner
One Sheet: $75 - $150   *Turner's first starring role.*

THEY'RE OFF
(1947 - RKO/Disney) Goofy
One Sheet: $250 - $500   *Cartoon. Full color. Cartoon Movie Posters #182.*

THICKER THAN WATER

(1935 - MGM) Laurel & Hardy
One Sheet: $1,600 - $2,500

THIEF, THE
(1920 - Fox) Pearl White
One Sheet: $600 - $1,000

THIEF, THE
(1952 - United Artists) Ray Milland, Rita Gam
One Sheet: $40 - $75   *Unusual non-speaking film.*

THIEF
(1981 - United Artists) James Caan, Tuesday
Weld, Willie Nelson
One Sheet: $5 - $10

THIEF CATCHER, A
(1914 - Keystone) -
One Sheet: $150 - $300

THIEF CATCHER, THE
(1920 - -) Charlie Chaplin
One Sheet: $350 - $750

THIEF IN THE DARK, A
(1928 - Fox) George Meeker, Marjorie Beebe
One Sheet: $1,600 - $2,500   *Graven
Images, pg. 32.*

THIEF OF BAGDAD, THE
(1924 - United Artists) Douglas Fairbanks,
Anna May Wong
One Sheet: $5,000 - $7,500   *Price is for all
styles except those listed below. Graven Images,
pg. 26. Prices vary widely. Eight different one
sheet styles exist. One Sheet (Flying
Horse):$12,000-$20,000. One Sheet (Flying
Carpet): $9,000-$15,000.*

One Sheet (Flying Carpet)

THIEF OF BAGDAD, THE
(1940 - United Artists) Conrad Veidt, Sabu
One Sheet: $800 - $1,500   *Graven
Images, pg. 119, 230.*

One Sheet

THIEF OF BAGDAD, THE
(1947R - Film Classics) Conrad Veidt, Sabu
One Sheet: $100 - $200   *Re-release.*

THIEF OF BAGDAD, THE
(1961 - MGM) Steve Reeves, Georgia Moll
One Sheet: $15 - $35

THIEF OF BAGDAD, THE
(1978 - -) Roddy McDowall, Peter Ustinov
One Sheet: $7 - $15

THIEF OF DAMASCUS
(1952 - Columbia) Paul Henreid, Jeff Donnell
One Sheet: $15 - $30

THIEF OF HEARTS
(1984 - Paramount) Steven Bauer, Barbara
Williams

One Sheet: $3 - $5

THIEF OF VENICE
(1952 - 20th Century Fox) Maria Montez, Paul
Christian
One Sheet: $15 - $35

THIEF WHO CAME TO DINNER, THE
(1972 - Warner Bros.) Ryan O'Neal, Jacqueline
Bisset
One Sheet: $5 - $10   *Two styles.*

THIEVES
(1977 - Paramount) Marlo Thomas, Charles
Grodin
One Sheet: $7 - $15

THIEVES FALL OUT
(1941 - Warner Bros.) Eddie Albert, Joan Leslie
One Sheet: $30 - $50

THIEVES' HIGHWAY
(1949 - 20th Century Fox) Richard Conte,
Valentina Cortese
One Sheet: $15 - $35

THIEVES' HIGHWAY
(1955R - 20th Century Fox) Richard Conte,
Valentina Cortese
One Sheet: $7 - $15   *Re-release.*

THIEVES' HOLIDAY
(1946 - United Artists) George Sanders, Signe
Hasso, Carole Landis
One Sheet: $40 - $75   *AKA:
SCANDAL IN PARIS.*

THIN AIR
(1969 - Tigon) George Sanders, Maurice Evans
One Sheet: $10 - $20   *AKA: THE
BODY STEALERS*

THIN BLUE LINE, THE
(1988 - -) -
One Sheet: $7 - $15   *Crime
Documentary.*

THIN ICE
(1937 - 20th Century Fox) Sonja Henie, Tyrone
Power
One Sheet: $300 - $700

THIN LINE BETWEEN LOVE & HATE, A
(1996 - New Line) Martin Lawrence, Lynn
Whitfield
One Sheet: $5 - $10

THIN MAN, THE
(1934 - MGM) William Powell, Myrna Loy
One Sheet: $5,000 - $7,500

One Sheet

THIN MAN, THE
(1962R - MGM) William Powell, Myrna Loy
One Sheet: $15 - $25   *Re-release.*

THIN MAN GOES HOME, THE
(1944 - MGM) William Powell, Myrna Loy
One Sheet: $250 - $500

THIN RED LINE, THE
(1964 - Allied Artists) Keir Dullea, Jack Warden
One Sheet: $7 - $15

THING, THE
(1982 - Universal) Kurt Russell, A. Wilford
Brimley
One Sheet: $15 - $30   *Advance:$75-
$125.*

THING (FROM ANOTHER WORLD), THE
(1951 - RKO) Kenneth Tobey, Margaret
Sheridan, James Arness
One Sheet: $250 - $500   *One Sheet
and Three Sheet are text without graphics. Half*

Sheet:$400-800. Insert(best poster on this
title):$600-$1,200. Graven Images, pg. 153.

THING CALLED LOVE, THE
(1993 - Paramount) River Phoenix, Samantha
Mathis
One Sheet: $7 - $15

THING THAT COULDN'T DIE, THE
(1958 - Universal) William Reynolds, Andra
Martin
One Sheet: $40 - $75

THING WITH TWO HEADS, THE
(1972 - AIP) Ray Milland, Rosie Grier
One Sheet: $15 - $35   *Sports Movie
Posters #364.*

THINGS ARE TOUGH ALL OVER
(1982 - -) Cheech Marin, Tommy Chong
One Sheet: $5 - $10

THINGS CHANGE
(1988 - -) Don Ameche, Joe Mantegna
One Sheet: $3 - $5

THINGS TO COME
(1936 - United Artists) Raymond Massey,
Cedric Hardwicke
One Sheet: $4,000 - $6,000   *Graven
Images, pg. 44, 78-79. Early futuristic science
fiction film.*

Insert

THINGS TO COME
(1947R - United Artists) Raymond Massey,
Cedric Hardwicke
One Sheet: $200 - $400   *Re-release.*

**THINGS TO DO IN DENVER WHEN YOU'RE
DEAD**
(1995 - Miramax) Andy Garcia, Christopher
Walken
One Sheet: $3 - $5

THINK FAST, MR. MOTO
(1937 - 20th Century Fox) Peter Lorre, Virginia
Field
One Sheet: $300 - $700   *First Moto
title.*

THIRD ALARM, THE
(1922 - FBO) Ralph Lewis, Johnnie Walker
One Sheet: $200 - $400

THIRD ALARM, THE
(1930 - Tiffany) Anita Louise, Jean Hersholt
One Sheet: $125 - $250

THIRD DAY, THE
(1965 - Warner Bros.) George Peppard,
Elizabeth Ashley
One Sheet: $5 - $10

THIRD DEGREE, THE
(1913 - Lubin) Bernard Siegel, Gaston Bell
One Sheet: $600 - $1,000

THIRD EYE, THE
(1920 - Pathe) Eileen Percy, Warner Oland
One Sheet: $200 - $400   *Serial. 15
Chapters.*

THIRD FINGER, LEFT HAND
(1940 - MGM) Myrna Loy, Melvyn Douglas
One Sheet: $75 - $150

THIRD KEY, THE
(1957 - Rank) Jack Hawkins, John Stratton
One Sheet: $15 - $35

3RD MAN, THE
(1949 - Alexander Korda) Joseph Cotten, Valli,
Orson Welles, Trevor Howard
One Sheet: $800 - $1,500

3RD MAN, THE
(1956R - -) Joseph Cotten, Valli, Orson Welles,
Trevor Howard
One Sheet: $50 - $100   *Re-release.*

THIRD MAN ON THE MOUNTAIN, THE
(1959 - Buena Vista/Disney) Michael Rennie,
James MacArthur
One Sheet: $15 - $25

THIRD OF A MAN
(1962 - United Artists) James Drury, Jan
Shepard
One Sheet: $10 - $20

THIRD SECRET, THE
(1964 - 20th Century Fox) Stephen Boyd, Jack
Hawkins
One Sheet: $5 - $10

THIRD VOICE, THE
(1960 - 20th Century Fox) Edmond O'Brien,
Julie London
One Sheet: $7 - $15

THIRTEEN FIGHTING MEN
(1960 - 20th Century Fox) Grant Williams, Brad
Dexter
One Sheet: $10 - $20

13 FRIGHTENED GIRLS
(1963 - Columbia) Kathy Dunn, Murray
Hamilton
One Sheet: $20 - $45

13 GHOSTS
(1960 - Columbia) Charles Herbert, Jo Morrow
One Sheet: $20 - $40   *Graven
Images, pg. 206.*

THIRTEEN HOURS BY AIR
(1936 - Paramount) Fred MacMurray, Joan
Bennett
One Sheet: $100 - $200

THIRTEEN LEAD SOLDIERS
(1948 - 20th Century Fox) Tom Conway, Marla
Palmer
One Sheet: $20 - $40   *Bulldog
Drummond series.*

13 RUE MADELEINE
(1947 - 20th Century Fox) James Cagney,
Annabella
One Sheet: $150 - $300

13 WEST STREET
(1962 - Columbia) Alan Ladd
One Sheet: $15 - $25

THIRTEEN WOMEN
(1932 - RKO) Irene Dunne, Myrna Loy
One Sheet: $300 - $500

THIRTEENTH CHAIR, THE
(1929 - MGM) Conrad Nagel, Leila Hyams
One Sheet: $3,500 - $5,000   *Graven
Images, pg. 10.*

THIRTEENTH CHAIR, THE
(1937 - MGM) Madge Evans, Henry Daniell
One Sheet: $50 - $100

THIRTEENTH GUEST, THE
(1932 - Monogram) Ginger Rogers, Lyle Talbot
One Sheet: $200 - $400

THIRTEENTH HOUR, THE
(1947 - Columbia) Richard Dix, Karen Morley
One Sheet: $50 - $100

13TH LETTER, THE
(1951 - 20th Century Fox) Charles Boyer, Linda
Darnell
One Sheet: $50 - $100

THIRTEENTH MAN, THE
(1937 - Monogram) Weldon Heyburn, Inez
Courtney
One Sheet: $50 - $100

30-
(1959 - Warner Bros.) Jack Webb, William
Conrad, David Nelson
One Sheet: $15 - $30

30 BELOW ZERO
(1926 - Fox) Buck Jones, Eva Novak
One Sheet: $250 - $600

THIRTY DAY PRINCESS
(1934 - Paramount) Sylvia Sidney, Cary Grant,
Edward Arnold

One Sheet: $700 - $1,200

30 FOOT BRIDE OF CANDY ROCK, THE
(1959 - Columbia) Lou Costello, Dorothy
Provine
One Sheet: $30 - $60

30 IS A DANGEROUS AGE, CYNTHIA
(1968 - Columbia) Dudley Moore, Suzy Kendall
One Sheet: $7 - $15

39 STEPS, THE
(1935 - Gaumont-British) Robert Donat,
Madeleine Carroll, Dir: Alfred Hitchcock
One Sheet: $7,500 - $12,000

One Sheet

39 STEPS, THE
(1938R - Gaumont-British) Robert Donat,
Madeleine Carroll, Dir: Alfred Hitchcock
One Sheet: $250 - $500   *Re-release.*

39 STEPS, THE
(1960 - 20th Century Fox) Kenneth More, Taina
Elg
One Sheet: $15 - $25

THIRTY SECONDS OVER TOKYO
(1944 - MGM) Van Johnson, Robert Walker,
Spencer Tracy
One Sheet: $75 - $150

36 HOURS
(1965 - MGM) James Garner, Eva Marie Saint
One Sheet: $15 - $25

THIRTY SIX HOURS TO KILL
(1936 - 20th Century Fox) Brian Donlevy,
Gloria Stuart
One Sheet: $75 - $150

**THIRTY-TWO SHORT FILMS ABOUT GLENN
GOULD**
(1994 - Goldwyn) Colm Feore
One Sheet: $5 - $10

30 YEARS OF FUN
(1963 - 20th Century Fox) Laurel & Hardy,
Chaplin, Keaton
One Sheet: $15 - $30   *Compilation.*

THIS ABOVE ALL
(1942 - 20th Century Fox) Tyrone Power, Joan
Fontaine
One Sheet: $600 - $1,000

THIS ABOVE ALL
(1952R - 20th Century Fox) Tyrone Power,
Joan Fontaine
One Sheet: $75 - $125   *Re-release.*

THIS ANGRY AGE
(1958 - Columbia) Anthony Perkins, Silvana
Mangano
One Sheet: $15 - $30

THIS BOY'S LIFE
(1993 - Warner Bros.) Robert DeNiro, Ellen
Barkin
One Sheet: $3 - $5

THIS COULD BE THE NIGHT
(1957 - MGM) Jean Simmons, Paul Douglas
One Sheet: $20 - $40

THIS DAY AND AGE
(1933 - Paramount) Charles Bickford, Richard
Cromwell
One Sheet: $150 - $300

THIS EARTH IS MINE
(1959 - Universal-International) Rock Hudson,
Jean Simmons
One Sheet: $20 - $40

THIS GUN FOR HIRE
(1942 - Paramount) Alan Ladd, Veronica Lake,
Robert Preston
One Sheet: $3,500 - $5,000

One Sheet

THIS GUN FOR HIRE
(1945R - Paramount) Alan Ladd, Veronica Lake
One Sheet: $600 - $1,000   *Re-release.*
*Lobby cards are dated 1945 but otherwise not
indicated as re-release.*

THIS HAPPY BREED
(1947 - Universal) Robert Newton, Celia
Johnson, John Mills
One Sheet: $15 - $30

THIS HAPPY FEELING
(1958 - Universal-International) Debbie
Reynolds, Curt Jurgens
One Sheet: $15 - $30

THIS IS A HIJACK
(1973 - Fanfare Corp.) Adam Roarke, Neville
Brand
One Sheet: $3 - $5

THIS IS CHINA
(1935 - Guaranteed) -
One Sheet: $100 - $225

THIS IS CINERAMA
(1973R - Cinerama) -
One Sheet: $15 - $35   *Re-release.*
Documentary.

THIS IS ELVIS
(1981 - -) David Scott, Paul Biensh III
One Sheet: $30 - $50   *DocuDrama.*

THIS IS MY AFFAIR
(1937 - 20th Century Fox) Robert Taylor,
Barbara Stanwyck
One Sheet: $250 - $500   *Two styles.*

THIS IS MY ALASKA
(1969 - -) Leroy "Buster" Shebal
One Sheet: $3 - $5

One Sheet

THIS IS MY LIFE
(199? - 20th Century Fox) -
One Sheet: $3 - $5

THIS IS MY LOVE
(1954 - RKO) Linda Darnell, Dan Duryea
One Sheet: $30 - $50

THIS IS RUSSIA
(1957 - Universal-International) -
One Sheet: $20 - $40   *Documentary.*

THIS IS SPINAL TAP
(1984 - Embassy) Michael McKean,
Christopher Guest, Harry Shearer
One Sheet: $40 - $75   *Rock 'n' Roll.*

Pseudo-rockumentary.

THIS IS THE ARMY
(1943 - Warner Bros.) George Murphy, Ronald
Reagan, Joan Leslie
One Sheet: $15 - $35   *Duotone One
Sheet(all text). Half Sheet/Insert:$50-$100.
Lobby Card (Reagan shown):$25-$50.*

One Sheet

THIS IS THE BOWERY
(1941 - MGM) John Nesbitts
One Sheet: $150 - $300

THIS IS THE LIFE
(1935 - 20th Century Fox) Jane Withers, John
McGuire
One Sheet: $75 - $150

One Sheet

THIS IS THE LIFE
(1943 - Universal) Susanna Foster, Patric
Knowles
One Sheet: $15 - $35

THIS IS THE NIGHT
(1932 - Paramount) Lily Damita, Charlie
Ruggles, Cary Grant
One Sheet: $250 - $600   *Grant's film
debut.*

THIS IS YOUR ARMY
(1954 - -) -
One Sheet: $15 - $35

THIS ISLAND EARTH
(1955 - Universal) Jeff Morrow, Rex Reason,
Faith Domergue
One Sheet: $600 - $1,000   *Graven
Images, pg. 174-175.*

One Sheet

THIS ISLAND EARTH
(1960R - Universal) Jeff Morrow, Rex Reason,
Faith Domergue
One Sheet: $50 - $100   *Re-release.*

THIS ISLAND EARTH
(1964R - Universal) Jeff Morrow, Rex Reason,
Faith Domergue
One Sheet: $50 - $100   *Re-release.*

THIS LAND IS MINE
(1943 - RKO) Charles Laughton, Maureen
O'Hara
One Sheet: $40 - $75

THIS LOVE OF OURS
(1945 - Universal) Merle Oberon, Charles
Korvin
One Sheet: $30 - $50

One Sheet

THIS MAD WORLD
(1930 - MGM) Basil Rathbone, Kay Johnson
One Sheet: $150 - $300

THIS MAN IS MINE
(1934 - RKO) Irene Dunne, Ralph Bellamy
One Sheet: $250 - $500

THIS MAN IS NEWS
(1939 - Paramount) Barry Barnes, Valerie
Hobson
One Sheet: $40 - $75

THIS MAN'S NAVY
(1945 - MGM) Wallace Berry, James Gleason
One Sheet: $30 - $50

THIS MARRIAGE BUSINESS
(1938 - RKO) Victor Moore, Vicki Lester
One Sheet: $50 - $100

THIS MODERN AGE
(1931 - MGM) Joan Crawford, Marjorie
Rambeau
One Sheet: $1,300 - $2,000

THIS PROPERTY IS CONDEMNED
(1966 - Paramount) Natalie Wood, Robert
Redford, Charles Bronson
One Sheet: $15 - $35

THIS REBEL AGE
(1961R - Cinema Associates) Steve Cochran,
Mamie Van Doren
One Sheet: $15 - $30   *Retitled, Re-
release of THE BEAT GENERATION.*

THIS REBEL BREED
(1960 - Warner Bros.) Rita Moreno, Mark
Damon
One Sheet: $15 - $30

THIS RECKLESS AGE
(1932 - Paramount Publix) Buddy Rogers,
Peggy Shannon
One Sheet: $150 - $300

THIS SAVAGE LAND
(1969 - Universal) Barry Sullivan, Brenda Scott,
George C. Scott
One Sheet: $15 - $25

THIS SIDE OF HEAVEN
(1934 - MGM) Lionel Barrymore, Fay Bainter
One Sheet: $100 - $200

THIS SIDE OF THE LAW
(1949 - Warner Bros.) Viveca Lindfors, Kent
Smith
One Sheet: $15 - $30

THIS SPORTING AGE
(1932 - Columbia) Jack Holt, Evalyn Knapp
One Sheet: $125 - $250   *Sports Movie
Posters #290.*

THIS SPORTING LIFE
(1963 - Continental) Richard Harris, Rachel
Roberts

One Sheet: $3 - $5

THIS THING CALLED LOVE
(1941 - Columbia) Rosalind Russell, Melvyn Douglas
One Sheet: $40 - $75

THIS TIME FOR KEEPS
(1942 - MGM) Robert Sterling, Ann Rutherford
One Sheet: $30 - $50

THIS TIME FOR KEEPS
(1947 - MGM) Esther Williams, Jimmy Durante, Lauritz Melchior
One Sheet: $40 - $75   *Sports Movie Posters #327.*

THIS WAS A WOMAN
(1949 - 20th Century Fox) Sonia Dresdel, Barbara White
One Sheet: $15 - $25

THIS WAS PARIS
(1942 - Warner Bros.) Ann Dvorak, Ben Lyon
One Sheet: $40 - $75

THIS WAY PLEASE
(1937 - Paramount) Charles (Buddy)Rogers, Betty Grable
One Sheet: $150 - $350

THIS WOMAN IS DANGEROUS
(1952 - Warner Bros.) Joan Crawford, Dennis Morgan
One Sheet: $40 - $75

THIS WOMAN IS MINE
(1935 - Paramount) Gregory Ratoff, John Loder, Benita Hume
One Sheet: $75 - $150

THIS WOMAN IS MINE
(1941 - Universal) Franchot Tone, Carol Bruce
One Sheet: $30 - $60

THIS'LL MAKE YOU WHISTLE
(1938 - C & M) Jack Buchanan
One Sheet: $50 - $100

THOMAS CROWN AFFAIR, THE
(1968 - United Artists) Steve McQueen, Faye Dunaway, Paul Burke
One Sheet: $30 - $50

THOMASINE & BUSHROD
(1974 - Columbia) Max Julien, Vonetta McGee, Dir: Gordon Parks, Jr.
One Sheet: $10 - $20   *Blaxploitation.*

THOROUGHBRED, THE
(1916 - Triangle) Frank Keenan
One Sheet: $250 - $500

THOROUGHBRED, THE
(1930 - Tiffany) Wesley Barry
One Sheet: $125 - $250

THOROUGHBREDS
(1944 - Republic) Roger Pryor, Tom Neal
One Sheet: $20 - $40

THOROUGHBREDS DON'T CRY
(1937 - MGM) Judy Garland, Mickey Rooney
One Sheet: $250 - $600   *Team's first film together.*

THOROUGHLY MODERN MILLIE
(1967 - Universal) Julie Andrews, Mary Tyler Moore, Carol Channing
One Sheet: $15 - $25

THOSE ATHLETIC GIRLS
(1918 - Paramount) Louise Fazenda
One Sheet: $800 - $1,500   *Sports Movie Posters #31.*

THOSE CALLOWAYS
(1964 - Buena Vista/Disney) Brian Keith, Vera Miles
One Sheet: $15 - $25

THOSE DARING YOUNG MEN IN THEIR JAUNTY JALOPIES
(1969 - Paramount) Peter Cook, Tony Curtis, Susan Hampshire
One Sheet: $10 - $20   *Sports (Auto racing). Sports Movie Posters #20.*

THOSE ENDEARING YOUNG CHARMS
(1945 - RKO) Robert Young, Laraine Day
One Sheet: $30 - $50

THOSE FANTASTIC FLYING FOOLS
(1967 - AIP) Burl Ives, Troy Donahue

One Sheet: $10 - $20   *AKA: BLAST-OFF.*

THOSE HIGH GREY WALLS
(1939 - Columbia) Walter Connolly, Iris Meredith
One Sheet: $50 - $100

THOSE LOVE PANGS
(1914 - Keystone) Charlie Chaplin
One Sheet: $7,500 - $12,000

THOSE MAGNIFICENT MEN IN THEIR FLYING MACHINES
(1965 - 20th Century Fox) Stuart Whitman, Sarah Miles, Red Skelton
One Sheet: $15 - $25

THOSE REDHEADS FROM SEATTLE
(1953 - Paramount) Rhonda Fleming, Gene Barry
One Sheet: $30 - $50   *3-D.*

THOSE THREE FRENCH GIRLS
(1930 - MGM) Fifi D'Orsay, Reginald Denny
One Sheet: $150 - $300

THOSE WE LOVE
(1932 - World Wide) Mary Astor, Lilyan Tashman
One Sheet: $100 - $200

THOSE WERE THE DAYS
(1940 - Paramount) William Holden, Bonita Granville
One Sheet: $40 - $75

THOSE WERE THE HAPPY TIMES
(1969 - 20th Century Fox) Julie Andrews, Richard Crenna
One Sheet: $15 - $25

THOSE WHO DANCE
(1930 - Warner Bros.) Monte Blue, Lila Lee
One Sheet: $150 - $300

THOU SHALT NOT KILL
(1939 - Republic) Charles Bickford, Owen Davis Jr.
One Sheet: $40 - $75

THOUSAND AND ONE NIGHTS, A
(1945 - Columbia) Cornel Wilde, Evelyn Keyes
One Sheet: $30 - $50

THOUSAND CLOWNS, A
(1966 - United Artists) Jason Robards, Barbara Harris
One Sheet: $15 - $25   *Academy Award Movie Posters #232.*

THOUSAND EYES OF DR. MABUSE, THE
(1960 - Ajay) Dawn Addams, Peter Van Eyck, Dir: Fritz Lang
One Sheet: $15 - $30

THOUSANDS CHEER
(1943 - MGM) Kathryn Grayson, Gene Kelly, Mickey Rooney, Judy Garland
One Sheet: $75 - $150

Window Card

THRASHIN'
(1986 - -) Josh Brolin, Robert Rusler
One Sheet: $3 - $5   *Skateboarding.*

THREAT, THE
(1949 - RKO) Michael O'Shea, Virginia Grey
One Sheet: $15 - $30

THREAT, THE
(1960 - Warner Bros.) Robert Knapp, Linda Lawson
One Sheet: $5 - $10

THREE
(1969 - United Artists) Charlotte Rampling, Robie Porter, Sam Waterston
One Sheet: $3 - $5

THREE AGES, THE
(1923 - Metro) Buster Keaton, Wallace Beery, Oliver Hardy
One Sheet: $6,500 - $10,000

THREE AMIGOS, THE
(1986 - Orion) Steve Martin, Chevy Chase, Martin Short
One Sheet: $5 - $10

THREE ARABIAN NUTS
(1951 - Columbia) The Three Stooges (Shemp)
One Sheet: $200 - $400   *Comedy short. Duotone.*

3 BAD MEN
(1926 - Fox) George O'Brien, Dir: John Ford
One Sheet: $600 - $1,000

THREE BAD SISTERS
(1955 - United Artists) Marla English, Kathleen Hughes
One Sheet: $15 - $30

THREE BEARS, THE
(1935 - Celebrity) By Ub Iwerks
One Sheet: $700 - $1,200   *Cartoon. A ComiColor Cartoon. Cartoon Movie Posters #115.*

THREE BEARS, THE
(1938 - 20th Century Fox) Terry-toons
One Sheet: $100 - $200   *Cartoon. Full color stone litho. Stock poster with inset title.*

THREE BITES OF THE APPLE
(1967 - MGM) David McCallum, Sylva Koscina
One Sheet: $3 - $5

THREE BLIND MICE
(1938 - 20th Century Fox) Loretta Young, Joel McCrea
One Sheet: $100 - $200

THREE BLONDES IN HIS LIFE
(1961 - Cinema Association) Jock Mahoney, Greta Thyssen
One Sheet: $7 - $15

THREE BRAVE MEN
(1957 - 20th Century Fox) Ernest Borgnine, Ray Milland
One Sheet: $10 - $20

THREE CABALLEROS, THE
(1944 - RKO/Disney) Donald Duck
One Sheet: $300 - $700   *Cartoon. The Disney Poster, pg. 85. Cartoon Movie Posters #376.*

Window Card

THREE CABALLEROS, THE
(1977R - Disney) Donald Duck
One Sheet: $15 - $35   *Re-release. Cartoon.*

THREE CAME HOME
(1950 - 20th Century Fox) Claudette Colbert, Patric Knowles
One Sheet: $15 - $35

THREE CAME TO KILL
(1960 - United Artists) Cameron Mitchell, John Lupton
One Sheet: $10 - $20

THREE CASES OF MURDER
(1954 - Wessex) Alan Badel, Elizabeth Sellars, Orson Welles.
One Sheet: $15 - $30

THREE CHEERS FOR LOVE
(1936 - Paramount) Ray Cummings, Eleanor Whitney
One Sheet: $75 - $150

THREE CHEERS FOR THE IRISH
(1940 - Warner Bros.) Thomas Mitchell, Priscilla Lane, Dennis Morgan
One Sheet: $50 - $100

One Sheet

THREE COCKEYED SAILORS
(1940 - United Artists) Tommy Trinder, Claude Hulbert
One Sheet: $15 - $25

THREE COINS IN THE FOUNTAIN
(1954 - 20th Century Fox) Clifton Webb, Dorothy McGuire
One Sheet: $20 - $40

THREE COMRADES
(1938 - MGM) Robert Taylor, Margaret Sullavan
One Sheet: $75 - $125

THREE CORNERED MOON
(1933 - Paramount) Claudette Colbert, Richard Arlen
One Sheet: $200 - $400

THREE DARING DAUGHTERS
(1948 - MGM) Jeanette MacDonald, Jose Iturbi
One Sheet: $30 - $60

THREE DARK HORSES
(1952 - Columbia) The Three Stooges (Shemp)
One Sheet: $150 - $350   *Comedy short. Duotone.*

THREE DAY PASS
(1968 - Sigma III) Harry Baird, Nicole Berger
One Sheet: $3 - $5

3 DAYS OF THE CONDOR
(1975 - Paramount) Robert Redford, Faye Dunaway
One Sheet: $15 - $30

THREE DESPERATE MEN
(1951 - Lippert) Preston Foster, Virginia Grey
One Sheet: $15 - $25

THREE DUMB CLUCKS
(1937 - Columbia) The Three Stooges (Curly)
One Sheet: $8,500 - $14,000   *Comedy short. Duotone.*

THREE FACES EAST
(1926 - -) Jetta Goudal, Robert Ames
One Sheet: $200 - $400

THREE FACES EAST
(1930 - Warner Bros.) Constance Bennett, Erich von Stroheim
One Sheet: $500 - $800

THREE FACES OF EVE, THE
(1957 - 20th Century Fox) Joanne Woodward, David Wayne
One Sheet: $15 - $30   *Academy Award Movie Posters #177.*

THREE FACES WEST
(1940 - Republic) John Wayne, Charles Coburn
One Sheet: $200 - $450

THREE FACES WEST
(1948R - Republic) John Wayne, Charles Coburn
One Sheet: $40 - $75   *Re-release.*

THREE FAT MEN, THE
(19?? - Sovexport) Lina Brankite

One Sheet: $50 - $100

3:15
(1986 - -) Adam Baldwin, Deborah Foreman
One Sheet: $2 - $3

3 FOR BEDROOM "C"
(1952 - Warner Bros.) Gloria Swanson, James Warren
One Sheet: $30 - $50

THREE FOR BREAKFAST
(1948 - RKO/Disney) Donald Duck, Chip N' Dale
One Sheet: $800 - $1,500   *Cartoon. The Disney Poster, pg. 48.*

THREE FOR JAMIE DAWN
(1956 - Allied Artists) Laraine Day, Ricardo Montalban
One Sheet: $15 - $25

THREE FOR THE ROAD
(1987 - -) Charlie Sheen, Kerri Green
One Sheet: $3 - $5

THREE FOR THE SHOW
(1954 - Columbia) Betty Grable, Marge & Gower Champion
One Sheet: $40 - $75

THREE FUGITIVES
(1989 - -) Nick Nolte, Martin Short, Sarah Rowland
One Sheet: $3 - $5

THREE GIRLS ABOUT TOWN
(1941 - Columbia) Joan Blondell, Janet Blair, Binnie Barnes
One Sheet: $40 - $75

THREE GIRLS DOWN
(1973 - New World) Robert Collins, Isabel Jewel
One Sheet: $3 - $5

THREE GIRLS LOST
(1931 - Fox) Loretta Young, John Wayne, Lew Cody, Joyce Compton
One Sheet: $600 - $1,000

3 GODFATHERS
(1936 - MGM) Chester Morris, Lewis Stone, Walter Brennan
One Sheet: $200 - $400

3 GODFATHERS
(1949 - MGM) John Wayne, Harry Carey, Jr., Dir: John Ford
One Sheet: $200 - $400

3 GOLD COINS
(1920 - Fox) Tom Mix
One Sheet: $600 - $1,000   *Cowboy Movie Posters #21.*

THREE GUNS FOR TEXAS
(1968 - Universal) Neville Brand, Peter Brown
One Sheet: $15 - $25

THREE GUYS NAMED MIKE
(1950 - MGM) Jane Wyman, Van Johnson
One Sheet: $15 - $30

THREE HAMS ON RYE
(1950 - Columbia) The Three Stooges (Shemp)
One Sheet: $200 - $400   *Comedy short. Duotone.*

THREE HEARTS FOR JULIA
(1943 - MGM) Ann Sothern, Lee Bowman
One Sheet: $30 - $50

365 NIGHTS IN HOLLYWOOD
(1934 - Fox) Alice Faye, James Dunn
One Sheet: $600 - $1,000

300 SPARTANS, THE
(1962 - 20th Century Fox) Richard Egan, Sir Ralph Richardson
One Sheet: $10 - $20

THREE HOURS TO KILL
(1954 - Columbia) Dana Andrews, Donna Reed
One Sheet: $15 - $30

THREE HUSBANDS
(1950 - United Artists) Emlyn Williams, Eve Arden
One Sheet: $15 - $25

THREE IN A ROW
(1919 - Exhibitors Mutual) Elinor Field
One Sheet: $150 - $300

THREE IN EXILE
(1925 - Truart) Louise Lorraine, Art Acord, Rex the Wonder Dog
One Sheet: $150 - $300

THREE IN THE ATTIC
(1968 - AIP) Yvette Mimieux, Christopher Jones
One Sheet: $15 - $25

3 IN THE CELLAR
(1970 - AIP) Joan Collins, Larry Hagman
One Sheet: $7 - $15

THREE IN THE SADDLE
(1945 - PRC) Tex Ritter, Dave O'Brien
One Sheet: $30 - $60

THREE INTO TWO WON'T GO
(1969 - Universal) Claire Bloom, Rod Steiger, Judy Geeson
One Sheet: $7 - $15

THREE IS A FAMILY
(1944 - United Artists) Marjorie Reynolds, Fay Bainter
One Sheet: $30 - $50

THREE JUMPS AHEAD
(1923 - Fox) Tom Mix, Alma Bennett
One Sheet: $500 - $800

THREE KIDS AND A QUEEN
(1935 - Universal) May Robson, Frankie Darro
One Sheet: $100 - $200

THREE KINDS OF HEAT
(1987 - -) Robert Ginty, Victoria Barrett
One Sheet: $2 - $3

THREE LITTLE BEERS
(1935 - Columbia) The Three Stooges (Curly)
One Sheet: $13,000 - $20,000   *Comedy short. Duotone.*

THREE LITTLE GIRLS IN BLUE
(1946 - 20th Century Fox) June Haver, George Montgomery, Vivian Blaine, Celeste Holm
One Sheet: $50 - $100

THREE LITTLE PIGS, THE
(1933 - Disney) Silly Symphony
One Sheet: $10,000 - $15,000   *Cartoon. Cartoon Movie Posters #69.*

THREE LITTLE PIGSKINS
(1934 - Columbia) The Three Stooges (Curly), Lucille Ball
One Sheet: $16,000 - $25,000   *Comedy short. Sports (Football). Duotone.*

THREE LITTLE PIRATES
(1946 - Columbia) The Three Stooges (Curly)
One Sheet: $2,500 - $4,000   *Comedy short. Duotone.*

THREE LITTLE SEW AND SEWS
(1939 - Columbia) The Three Stooges (Curly)
One Sheet: $7,500 - $12,000   *Comedy short. Duotone.*

THREE LITTLE SISTERS
(1944 - Republic) Mary Lee, Ruth Terry
One Sheet: $20 - $40

THREE LITTLE TWERPS
(1943 - Columbia) The Three Stooges (Curly)
One Sheet: $2,500 - $4,000   *Comedy short. Duotone.*

THREE LITTLE WORDS
(1950 - MGM) Fred Astaire, Red Skelton
One Sheet: $75 - $150

THREE LIVE GHOSTS
(1936 - MGM) Richard Arlen, Beryl Mercer
One Sheet: $75 - $150

THREE LIVES OF THOMASINA, THE
(1963 - Buena Vista) Patrick McGoohan, Susan Hampshire
One Sheet: $15 - $30

THREE LOAN WOLVES
(1946 - Columbia) The Three Stooges (Curly)
One Sheet: $2,500 - $4,000   *Comedy short. Duotone.*

THREE LOVES HAS NANCY
(1938 - MGM) Janet Gaynor, Robert Montgomery, Franchot Tone
One Sheet: $50 - $100

THREE MARRIED MEN
(1936 - Paramount) Lynne Overman, William Frawley
One Sheet: $75 - $150

THREE MEN AND A BABY
(1987 - Touchstone) Tom Selleck, Steve Guttenberg, Ted Danson
One Sheet: $3 - $5

THREE MEN AND A LITTLE LADY
(1990 - Touchstone) Tom Selleck, Steve Guttenberg, Ted Danson
One Sheet: $5 - $10

THREE MEN FROM TEXAS
(1940 - Paramount) William Boyd, Russell Hayden
One Sheet: $150 - $350   *Hopalong Cassidy series.*

THREE MEN IN THE TUB
(1938 - MGM) Our Gang
One Sheet: $600 - $1,000   *Separate Cinema, pg. 115.*

THREE MEN IN THE TUB
(1952R - Monogram) Little Rascals
One Sheet: $50 - $100   *Re-release. Separate Cinema, pg. 115.*

THREE MEN IN WHITE
(1944 - MGM) Lionel Barrymore, Van Johnson, Ava Gardner
One Sheet: $50 - $100

THREE MEN ON A HORSE
(1936 - Warner Bros.) Joan Blondell, Frank McHugh, Sam Levene
One Sheet: $75 - $150

THREE MESQUITEERS, THE
(1936 - Republic) Bob Livingston, Ray Corrigan, Max Terhune
One Sheet: $75 - $150

THREE MISSING LINKS
(1938 - Columbia) The Three Stooges (Curly)
One Sheet: $7,500 - $12,000   *Comedy short. Duotone.*

THREE MURDERESSES
(1960 - 20th Century Fox) Alain Delon, Mylene Demongeot
One Sheet: $7 - $15

THREE MUSKETEERS, THE
(1921 - United Artists) Douglas Fairbanks
One Sheet: $4,000 - $6,000

THREE MUSKETEERS, THE
(1933 - Mascot) John Wayne, Ruth Hall
One Sheet: $700 - $1,200   *Serial. 12 Chapters. Beware 2-color re-issue.*

THREE MUSKETEERS, THE
(1935 - RKO) Walter Abel, Paul Lukas
One Sheet: $250 - $500

THREE MUSKETEERS, THE
(1939 - 20th Century Fox) Don Ameche, The Ritz Brothers
One Sheet: $250 - $600

One Sheet

THREE MUSKETEERS, THE
(1943R - Mascot) John Wayne, Ruth Hall
One Sheet: $250 - $500   *Re-release. Serial.*

THREE MUSKETEERS, THE
(1948 - MGM) Lana Turner, Gene Kelly, Van Heflin
One Sheet: $100 - $200

THREE MUSKETEERS, THE
(1956R - MGM) Lana Turner, Gene Kelly, Van Heflin
One Sheet: $30 - $50   *Re-release.*

THREE MUSKETEERS, THE
(1974 - 20th Century Fox) Oliver Reed, Raquel Welch
One Sheet: $15 - $25

THREE MUSKETEERS, THE
(1993 - Buena Vista) Charlie Sheen, Kiefer Sutherland, Chris O'Donnell
One Sheet: $5 - $10

3 NINJAS
(1992 - Touchstone) Victor Wong
One Sheet: $3 - $5

3 NINJAS KICK BACK
(1994 - TriStar) Victor Wong, Max Elliot Slade
One Sheet: $3 - $5

3 NINJAS KNUCKLE UP
(1995 - TriStar) Victor Wong, Charles Napier
One Sheet: $3 - $5

THREE O'CLOCK HIGH
(1987 - -) Casey Siemaszko, Anne Ryan
One Sheet: $3 - $5

THREE OF A KIND
(1936 - Invincible) Chick Chandler, Evalyn Knapp
One Sheet: $50 - $100

THREE OF A KIND
(1944 - Astor) Billy Gilbert, Shemp Howard
One Sheet: $75 - $150

THREE OF HEARTS
(1993 - New Line) William Baldwin, Kelly Lynch, Sherilyn Fenn
One Sheet: $3 - $5

THREE ON A COUCH
(1966 - Columbia) Jerry Lewis, Janet Leigh
One Sheet: $15 - $25

THREE ON A HONEYMOON
(1934 - Fox) Sally Eilers, ZaSu Pitts, Charles Starrett
One Sheet: $100 - $200

THREE ON A MATCH
(1932 - First National) Joan Blondell, Bette Davis, Humphrey Bogart(cameo)
One Sheet: $1,600 - $2,500   *Lobby Card(Bogart):$300-$500.*

THREE ON A SPREE
(1961 - United Artists) Jack Watling, Carole Lesley
One Sheet: $3 - $5

THREE ON A TICKET
(1947 - PRC) Hugh Beaumont, Cheryl Walker
One Sheet: $15 - $25

THREE ON A WEEKEND
(1938 - Gaumont) John Lodge, Margaret Lockwood
One Sheet: $50 - $100

THREE ON THE TRAIL
(1936 - Paramount) William Boyd, Jimmy Ellison
One Sheet: $350 - $750   *Hopalong Cassidy series.*

THREE OUTLAWS, THE
(1956 - Associated) Neville Brand, Bruce Bennett
One Sheet: $15 - $25

THREE PASSIONS, THE
(1929 - St. George) Alice Terry, Ivan Petrovitch
One Sheet: $150 - $300

THREE PESTS IN A MESS
(1945 - Columbia) The Three Stooges (Curly)
One Sheet: $2,500 - $4,000   *Comedy short. Duotone.*

THREE RING CIRCUS
(1954 - Paramount) Dean Martin, Jerry Lewis, Zsa Zsa Gabor
One Sheet: $40 - $75

THREE RUSSIAN GIRLS
(1944 - United Artists) Anna Sten, Kent Smith
One Sheet: $40 - $75

THREE SAILORS AND A GIRL

(1953 - Warner Bros.) Jane Powell, Gordon
MacRae, Gene Nelson
One Sheet: $15 - $30

THREE SAPPY PEOPLE
(1939 - Columbia) The Three Stooges (Curly)
One Sheet: $7,500 - $12,000   *Comedy short.*
Duotone.

THREE SECRETS
(1950 - Warner Bros.) Eleanor Parker, Patricia
Neal, Ruth Roman
One Sheet: $15 - $30

THREE SISTERS
(1930 - Fox) Louise Dresser, Tom Patricola
One Sheet: $150 - $300

THREE SISTERS
(1974 - American Film Theatre) Jeanne Watts,
Joan Plowright, Louise Purnell
One Sheet: $5 - $10

THREE SMART GIRLS
(1936 - Universal) Deanna Durbin, Nan Gray,
Barbara Read
One Sheet: $200 - $400   *Durbin's film*
debut.

THREE SMART GIRLS GROW UP
(1939 - Universal) Deanna Durbin, Nan Grey,
Helen Parrish
One Sheet: $125 - $250

THREE SMART SAPS
(1942 - Columbia) The Three Stooges (Curly)
One Sheet: $3,500 - $5,000   *Comedy short.*
Duotone.

THREE SONS
(1939 - RKO) Edward Ellis, William Gargan
One Sheet: $40 - $75

THREE SONS O' GUNS
(1941 - Warner Bros.) Wayne Morris, Tom
Brown
One Sheet: $20 - $40

THREE STEPS NORTH
(1951 - United Artists) Lloyd Bridges, Lea
Padovani
One Sheet: $15 - $25

**THREE STOOGES GO AROUND THE WORLD IN
A DAZE, THE**
(1963 - Columbia) The Three Stooges (Curly
Joe)
One Sheet: $40 - $75

THREE STOOGES IN ORBIT, THE
(1962 - Columbia) The Three Stooges (Curly
Joe)
One Sheet: $50 - $100

THREE STOOGES MEET HERCULES, THE
(1961 - Columbia) The Three Stooges (Curly
Joe), Vicki Trickett
One Sheet: $50 - $100

THREE STRANGERS
(1946 - Warner Bros.) Sydney Greenstreet,
Peter Lorre, Geraldine Fitzgerald
One Sheet: $40 - $75

THREE STRIPES IN THE SUN
(1955 - Columbia) Aldo Ray, Phil Carey
One Sheet: $15 - $25

3:10 TO YUMA
(1957 - Columbia) Glenn Ford, Van Heflin
One Sheet: $20 - $40

THREE TEXAS STEERS
(1939 - Republic) The 3 Mesquiteers (John
Wayne, Ray Corrigan, Max Terhune)
One Sheet: $600 - $1,000

THREE TEXAS STEERS
(1953R - Republic) The 3 Mesquiteers (John
Wayne, Ray Corrigan, Max Terhune)
One Sheet: $40 - $75   *Re-release.*

THREE THE HARD WAY
(1974 - Allied Artists) Jim Brown, Fred
Williamson
One Sheet: $15 - $25   *Blaxploitation.*

THREE TOUGH GUYS
(1974 - Paramount) Fred Williamson, Isaac
Hayes, Lino Ventura
One Sheet: $7 - $15   *Blaxploitation.*

THREE TROUBLEDOERS, THE
(1946 - Columbia) The Three Stooges (Curly)

One Sheet: $2,500 - $4,000   *Comedy short.*
Duotone.

THREE VIOLENT PEOPLE
(1957 - Paramount) Charlton Heston, Anne
Baxter
One Sheet: $15 - $30

THREE WARRIORS
(1977 - United Artists) Randy Quaid, McKee
"Kiki" Red Wing
One Sheet: $5 - $10

THREE WEEKENDS
(1928 - -) Clara Bow
One Sheet: $1,300 - $2,000

THREE WEEKS OFF
(1922 - Century) Lee Moran
One Sheet: $150 - $300

THREE WHO LOVED
(1931 - RKO) Betty Compson, Conrad Nagel
One Sheet: $125 - $250

THREE WISE FOOLS
(1946 - MGM) Margaret O'Brien, Lewis Stone,
Lionel Barrymore
One Sheet: $40 - $75

THREE WISE GIRLS
(1931 - Columbia) Jean Harlow, Mae Clarke,
Marie Prevost
One Sheet: $800 - $1,500

THREE WISE GUYS, THE
(1936 - MGM) Robert Young, Bruce Cabot
One Sheet: $75 - $150

THREE WISHES
(1995 - Savoy) Patrick Swayze, Mary Elizabeth
Mastrantonio
One Sheet: $5 - $10

THREE WOMEN
(1977 - Fox) Shelley Duvall, Sissy Spacek,
Janice Rule
One Sheet: $7 - $15

THREE WORD BRAND
(1921 - -) William S. Hart
One Sheet: $250 - $500

THREE WORLDS OF GULLIVER, THE
(1960 - Columbia) Kerwin Mathews, Jo Morrow
One Sheet: $40 - $75   *Harryhausen*
effects.

THREE YOUNG TEXANS
(1954 - 20th Century Fox) Mitzi Gaynor, Keefe
Brasselle
One Sheet: $15 - $25

THREE'S A CROWD
(1945 - Republic) Gertrude Michael, Charles
Gordon
One Sheet: $15 - $25

THREEPENNY OPERA, THE
(1931 - -) Lotte Lenya, Rudolph Forster
One Sheet: $250 - $500   *German.*

THREEPENNY OPERA
(1963 - Embassy) Sammy Davis Jr., Curd
Jurgens
One Sheet: $30 - $50   *French/*
German.

THREESOME
(1994 - TriStar) Lara Flynn Boyle, Stephen
Baldwin, Josh Charles
One Sheet: $5 - $10

THRILL HUNTER, THE
(1933 - Columbia) Buck Jones, Dorothy Revier
One Sheet: $350 - $750

THRILL KILLERS, THE
(1965 - Hollywood Star) Cash Flagg, Liz Renay
One Sheet: $30 - $50

THRILL OF A LIFETIME
(1938 - Paramount) Betty Grable, Leif
Erickson, Dorothy Lamour
One Sheet: $125 - $250

THRILL OF A ROMANCE
(1945 - MGM) Esther Williams, Van Johnson
One Sheet: $75 - $150

THRILL OF BRAZIL, THE
(1946 - Columbia) Evelyn Keyes, Ann Miller
One Sheet: $15 - $35

THRILL OF IT ALL, THE
(1963 - Universal) Doris Day, James Garner
One Sheet: $20 - $40

THRILL OF YOUTH, THE
(1932 - Invincible) June Clyde, Allen Vincent
One Sheet: $100 - $200

THRILL SEEKERS
(196? - -) -
One Sheet: $15 - $30   *Sexploitation.*
AKA: GUTTER GIRLS.

THRONE OF BLOOD
(1961 - Brandon Films) Toshiro Mifume,
Takashi Shimura
One Sheet: $250 - $500   *Japanese.*
Kurosawa's classic adaptation of Macbeth. Exists
as a Japanese poster with english stickers
attached.Original Japanese poster (w/o
stickers):$500-$800.

THRONE OF THE GODS, THE
(1933 - Imperial) -
One Sheet: $50 - $100

THROUGH A GLASS DARKLY
(1962 - Janus) Harriet Andersson, Dir: Ingmar
Bergman
One Sheet: $30 - $60

THROUGH THE BACK DOOR
(1921 - United Artists) Mary Pickford
One Sheet: $700 - $1,200

THROUGH THE DARK
(1924 - Goldwyn/Cosmopolitan) Colleen Moore,
Forrest Stanley
One Sheet: $200 - $400

THROW A SADDLE ON A STAR
(1946 - Columbia) Ken Curtis, Adele Roberts
One Sheet: $20 - $40

THROW MOMMA FROM THE TRAIN
(1987 - Orion) Danny DeVito, Billy Crystal,
Anne Ramsey
One Sheet: $5 - $10

THROWBACK, THE
(1935 - Universal) Buck Jones, Muriel Evans
One Sheet: $500 - $800

THROWN OUT OF JOINT
(1933 - RKO) -
One Sheet: $100 - $200

THRU DIFFERENT EYES
(1929 - Fox) Mary Duncan, Warner Baxter
One Sheet: $350 - $750

THRU DIFFERENT EYES
(1942 - 20th Century Fox) Frak Craven, Mary
Howard
One Sheet: $40 - $75

THUMB TRIPPING
(1972 - Avco/Embassy) Michael Burns, Meg
Foster
One Sheet: $3 - $5

THUMBELINA
(1994 - Warner Bros.) Thumbelina
One Sheet: $5 - $10   *Cartoon.*

THUMBS UP
(1943 - Republic) Brenda Joyce, Richard
Fraser
One Sheet: $15 - $35

THUNDER
(1929 - MGM) Lon Chaney
One Sheet: $800 - $1,500

THUNDER AFLOAT
(1939 - MGM) Wallace Beery, Chester Morris
One Sheet: $40 - $75

THUNDER ALLEY
(1967 - AIP) Annette Funicello, Fabian
One Sheet: $30 - $50   *Sports (Auto*
racing).

THUNDER AND LIGHTNING
(1977 - 20th Century Fox) David Carradine,
Kate Jackson
One Sheet: $7 - $15

THUNDER BAY
(1953 - Universal) James Stewart, Joanne Dru
One Sheet: $40 - $75

THUNDER BELOW
(1932 - Paramount Publix) Tallulah Bankhead,

Charles Bickford, Paul Lukas
One Sheet: $250 - $500

THUNDER BIRDS
(1942 - 20th Century Fox) Gene Tierney,
Preston Foster, John Sutton
One Sheet: $75 - $150

Window Card

THUNDER BIRDS
(1952 - Republic) Mona Freeman, John
Barrymore, Jr.
One Sheet: $15 - $25

THUNDER IN CAROLINA
(1960 - Howco International) Rory Calhoun,
Alan Hale
One Sheet: $40 - $75   *Sports (Auto*
Racing).

THUNDER IN GOD'S COUNTRY
(1951 - Republic) Rex Allen, Mary Ellen Kay
One Sheet: $15 - $35

THUNDER IN THE CITY
(1937 - Columbia) Edward G. Robinson, Nigel
Bruce
One Sheet: $100 - $200

THUNDER IN THE CITY
(1940R - Columbia) Edward G. Robinson, Nigel
Bruce
One Sheet: $50 - $100   *Re-release.*

THUNDER IN THE DESERT
(1938 - Republic) Bob Steele, Louise Stanley
One Sheet: $150 - $350

THUNDER IN THE EAST
(1935 - United Artists) Charles Boyer, John
Loder
One Sheet: $75 - $150

THUNDER IN THE EAST
(1953 - Paramount) Alan Ladd, Deborah Kerr
One Sheet: $20 - $40

THUNDER IN THE NIGHT
(1935 - 20th Century Fox) Edmund Lowe,
Karen Morley
One Sheet: $125 - $250

THUNDER IN THE PINES
(1948 - Screen Guild) George Reeves, Marian
Martin
One Sheet: $30 - $50

THUNDER IN THE SUN
(1959 - Paramount) Susan Hayward, Jeff
Chandler
One Sheet: $15 - $35

THUNDER IN THE VALLEY
(1947 - 20th Century Fox) Lon McCallister,
Peggy Ann Garner
One Sheet: $30 - $50

THUNDER ISLAND
(1963 - 20th Century Fox) Gene Nelson, Fay
Spain
One Sheet: $10 - $20

THUNDER MOUNTAIN
(1925 - William Fox) Madge Bellamy, Zasu
Pitts, Leslie Fenton
One Sheet: $250 - $600

THUNDER MOUNTAIN
(1935 - Fox) George O'Brien
One Sheet: $125 - $250

THUNDER MOUNTAIN
(1947 - RKO) Tim Holt
One Sheet: $15 - $35

THUNDER OF DRUMS, A
(1961 - MGM) George Hamilton, Richard Boone
One Sheet: $10 - $20

THUNDER ON THE HILL
(1951 - Universal) Claudette Colbert, Ann Blyth
One Sheet: $15 - $35

THUNDER OVER ARIZONA
(1956 - Republic) Skip Homeier, Kristine Miller
One Sheet: $10 - $20

THUNDER OVER HAWAII
(1957 - AIP) Richard Denning, Beverly Garland
One Sheet: $30 - $50   *AKA: NAKED PARADISE.*

THUNDER OVER HAWAII
(1960R - AIP) Richard Denning, Beverly Garland
One Sheet: $15 - $25   *Re-release.*

THUNDER OVER MEXICO
(1933 - Mexican Picture Trust) -
One Sheet: $30 - $50

THUNDER OVER SANGOLAND
(1954 - Lippert) Jon Hall, Marjorie Lord
One Sheet: $15 - $35

THUNDER OVER THE PLAINS
(1954 - Warner Bros.) Randolph Scott, Phyllis Kirk
One Sheet: $15 - $35

THUNDER OVER THE PRAIRIE
(1941 - Columbia) Charles Starrett
One Sheet: $30 - $50

THUNDER PASS
(1954 - Lippert) Dane Clark, Dorothy Patrick
One Sheet: $15 - $30

THUNDER RIVER FEUD
(1942 - Monogram) Range Busters
One Sheet: $40 - $75

THUNDER ROAD
(1958 - United Artists) Robert Mitchum, Gene Barry
One Sheet: $100 - $200

THUNDER ROCK
(1944 - MGM) Michael Redgrave, Barbara Mullen
One Sheet: $20 - $40

THUNDER TOWN
(1946 - PRC) Bob Steele, Syd Saylor
One Sheet: $75 - $150

THUNDER TRAIL
(1937 - Paramount) Gilbert Roland, Marsha Hunt
One Sheet: $100 - $200   *Cowboy Movie Posters #s 221, 224.*

THUNDER TRAIL
(1945R - Paramount) Gilbert Roland, Marsha Hunt
One Sheet: $40 - $75   *Re-release.*

THUNDER TRAIL
(1951R - Paramount) Gilbert Roland, Marsha Hunt
One Sheet: $20 - $40   *Re-release.*

THUNDERBALL
(1965 - United Artists) Sean Connery, Claudine Auger
One Sheet: $200 - $450

British Quad

THUNDERBALL/FROM RUSSIA WITH LOVE
(1968R - United Artists) Sean Connery

One Sheet: $30 - $50   *Re-release double feature poster.*

THUNDERBALL/YOU ONLY LIVE TWICE
(1971R - United Artists) Sean Connery
One Sheet: $15 - $30   *Re-release double feature poster. One sheet is red/black duotone.*

THUNDERBIRD 6
(1969 - -) -
One Sheet: $7 - $15

THUNDERBIRDS
(1952 - Republic) John Derek, John Barrymore Jr.
One Sheet: $15 - $30

THUNDERBIRDS ARE GO
(1968 - Century) Voices: Sylvia Anderson, Ray Barrett
One Sheet: $40 - $75   *Marionettes.*

THUNDERBOLT
(1929 - Paramount) George Bancroft, Fay Wray, Richard Arlen
One Sheet: $600 - $1,000

THUNDERBOLT
(1936 - Regal) Lobo The Marvel Dog
One Sheet: $75 - $150

THUNDERBOLT
(1947 - Monogram) -
One Sheet: $20 - $40   *Documentary.*

THUNDERBOLT AND LIGHTFOOT
(1974 - United Artists) Clint Eastwood, Jeff Bridges
One Sheet: $15 - $30   *Advance (Eastwood with cannon):$20-$30. Style B (bullet holes in car door):$30-$50.*

THUNDERBOLT STRIKES, THE
(1926 - Rayart) Jack Perrin
One Sheet: $250 - $600

THUNDERBOLT'S TRACKS
(1927 - Rayart) Jack Perrin, Pauline Curley
One Sheet: $250 - $500

THUNDERGAP OUTLAWS
(1947R - PRC) Dave (Tex) O'Brien, Jim Newill
One Sheet: $15 - $25   *Re-titled re-release of BAD MEN OF THUNDER GAP.*

THUNDERGATE
(1923 - First National) Owen Moore, Virginia Brown Faire
One Sheet: $200 - $400

THUNDERHEAD, SON OF FLICKA
(1945 - 20th Century Fox) Roddy McDowall, Preston Foster
One Sheet: $50 - $100

Window Card

THUNDERHEART
(1992 - TriStar) Val Kilmer, Sam Shepard
One Sheet: $5 - $10

THUNDERHOOF
(1948 - Columbia) Preston Foster, Mary Stuart
One Sheet: $20 - $40

THUNDERING CARAVANS
(1950 - Republic) Allan "Rocky" Lane
One Sheet: $15 - $35

THUNDERING FLEAS
(1926 - Pathe) Our Gang, Oliver Hardy, Charley Chase
One Sheet: $700 - $1,200

THUNDERING FRONTIER

(1940 - Columbia) Charles Starrett, Iris Meredith
One Sheet: $50 - $100

THUNDERING GUN SLINGERS
(1944 - PRC) Buster Crabbe, Al St. John
One Sheet: $20 - $40

THUNDERING HERD, THE
(1933 - Paramount) Randolph Scott, Buster Crabbe
One Sheet: $200 - $400

THUNDERING HOOFS
(1942 - RKO) Tim Holt
One Sheet: $40 - $75

THUNDERING JETS
(1958 - 20th Century Fox) Audrey Dalton, Rex Reason
One Sheet: $15 - $25

THUNDERING LANDLORDS
(1925 - Pathe) Glenn Tryon
One Sheet: $125 - $250

THUNDERING TRAIL, THE
(1951 - -) Lash LaRue, Fuzzy St. John
One Sheet: $20 - $40

THUNDERING TRAILS
(1943 - Republic) Three Mesquiteers
One Sheet: $40 - $75

THUNDERING WEST
(1939 - Columbia) Charles Starrett, Iris Meredith
One Sheet: $75 - $125

THUNDERSTORM
(1956 - Allied Artists) Linda Christian, Carlos Thompson
One Sheet: $15 - $25

THX - THE AUDIENCE IS LISTENING
(1980S - Lucas) -
One Sheet: $30 - $50   *Sound System promo.*

THX-1138
(1971 - Warner Bros.) Robert Duvall, Donald Pleasence, Dir: George Lucas
One Sheet: $40 - $75   *Nudity Style:$100-$150.*

THY NAME IS WOMAN
(1924 - Metro) Ramon Navarro
One Sheet: $250 - $500

THY NEIGHBOR'S WIFE
(1953 - 20th Century Fox) Hugo Haas, Cleo Moore
One Sheet: $20 - $40

TIARA TAHITI
(1963 - Zenith) James Mason, John Mills
One Sheet: $7 - $15

TICKET TO HELL
(1930? - -) Warner Baxter
One Sheet: $1,900 - $3,000   *One sheet poster to never released film - see "50 Years Of Movie Posters", pg. 87".*

TICKET TO PARADISE
(1936 - Republic) Roger Pryor, Wendy Barrie
One Sheet: $50 - $100

TICKET TO TOMAHAWK, A
(1950 - 20th Century Fox) Dan Dailey, Anne Baxter, Marilyn Monroe
One Sheet: $125 - $250   *Half Sheet(Monroe shown):$150-$300. Lobby Card(Monroe):$75-$125.*

TICKLE ME
(1965 - Allied Artists) Elvis Presley, Jocelyn Lane
One Sheet: $40 - $75

TICKLISH AFFAIR, A
(1963 - MGM) Shirley Jones, Gig Young
One Sheet: $10 - $20

TICK...TICK...TICK
(1970 - MGM) Jim Brown, George Kennedy, Frederic March
One Sheet: $15 - $30   *Blaxploitation. Price is for full-color Style C one sheet. One Sheet (Style A, B&W): $10-$20.*

TIDAL WAVE
(1975 - New World) Lorne Greene, Kenji Kobayashi

One Sheet: $7 - $15

TIE ME UP! TIE ME DOWN!
(1990 - Miramax) Victoria Abril, Antonio Banderas
One Sheet: $15 - $25   *Spanish.*

TIE THAT BINDS, THE
(1995 - Hollywood) Daryl Hannah, Keith Carradine
One Sheet: $3 - $5

TIE-DIED: ROCK 'N ROLL'S MOST DEADICATED FANS
(1995 - ISA) The Grateful Dead
One Sheet: $15 - $30   *Rock 'n' Roll documentary.*

One Sheet

TIGER AND THE FLAME, THE
(1955 - United Artists) Sohrab Modi, Mehtab
One Sheet: $15 - $25

TIGER AND THE PUSSYCAT, THE
(1967 - Embassy) Vittorio Gassman, Ann-Margret
One Sheet: $15 - $35

TIGER BAY
(1933 - Wyndham) Anna May Wong, Henry Victor
One Sheet: $200 - $400

TIGER BAY
(1959 - -) John Mills, Hayley Mills
One Sheet: $15 - $30   *Hayley Mills' film debut.*

TIGER BY THE TAIL
(1970 - Commonwealth United) Christopher George, Tippi Hedren
One Sheet: $3 - $5

TIGER FANGS
(1942 - PRC) Frank Buck, June Duprey
One Sheet: $50 - $100

TIGER FORCE
(1975 - -) -
One Sheet: $5 - $10

TIGER MAKES OUT, THE
(1967 - Columbia) Eli Wallach, Anne Jackson, Dustin Hoffman
One Sheet: $15 - $35   *Hoffman's film debut.*

TIGER ROSE
(1923 - Warner Bros.) Lenore Ulric, Forrest Stanley
One Sheet: $150 - $300

TIGER ROSE
(1929 - Warner Bros.) -
One Sheet: $150 - $300

TIGER SHARK
(1932 - First National) Edward G. Robinson, Richard Arlen, Dir: Howard Hawks
One Sheet: $600 - $1,000   *Hawks' directorial debut.*

TIGER SHARK
(1942R - First National) Edward G. Robinson, Richard Arlen, Dir: Howard Hawks
One Sheet: $50 - $100   *Re-release.*

TIGER SHARK
(1956R - Warner Bros.) Edward G. Robinson, Richard Arlen, Dir: Howard Hawks
One Sheet: $30 - $50   *Re-release.*

TIGER TROUBLE
(1945 - RKO/Disney) Goofy
One Sheet: $1,300 - $2,000   *Cartoon. Full*

color. The Disney Poster, pg. 77.

TIGER TRUE
(1921 - -) Frank Mayo, Fritzi Brunette
One Sheet: $200 - $400

TIGER WALKS, A
(1964 - Buena Vista/Disney) Brian Keith, Vera
Miles
One Sheet: $10 - $20

One Sheet

TIGER WARSAW
(1988 - -) Patrick Swayze, Piper Laurie
One Sheet: $5 - $10

TIGER WOMAN, THE
(1917 - Fox) Theda Bara, E.F. Roseman, Mary
Martin
One Sheet: $600 - $1,000

TIGER WOMAN, THE
(1944 - Republic) Allan Lane, Linda Stirling
One Sheet: $125 - $250   *Serial. 12
Chapters.*

TIGER WOMAN, THE
(1945 - Republic) Adele Mara, Kane Richmond
One Sheet: $125 - $250

TIGER'S CLAW
(1957 - -) -
One Sheet: $15 - $25

TIGER'S CLAW
(197? - Trans Continental) Bruce Lo, Jiro
Yabuki
One Sheet: $5 - $10

TIGER'S CUB
(1920 - Fox) Pearl White
One Sheet: $800 - $1,500

TIGER'S TALE, A
(1987 - Atlantic) Ann-Margret, C. Thomas
Howell
One Sheet: $5 - $10

TIGHT LITTLE ISLAND
(1949 - Universal-International) Basil Radford,
Joan Greenwood
One Sheet: $10 - $20

TIGHT REIN
(1919 - Pathe) Anna Nilsson, Tom Moore
One Sheet: $150 - $350

TIGHT SHOES
(1941 - Universal) Broderick Crawford, Shemp
Howard
One Sheet: $75 - $125

TIGHT SPOT
(1955 - Columbia) Ginger Rogers, Edward G.
Robinson
One Sheet: $30 - $50

TIGHTROPE
(1984 - Warner Bros.) Clint Eastwood,
Genevieve Bujold
One Sheet: $15 - $30

TIGRESS, THE
(1975 - Mount Everest) Dyanne Thorne
One Sheet: $3 - $5

TIJUANA STORY, THE
(1957 - Columbia) Rodolfo Acosta, James
Darren
One Sheet: $15 - $35

TIKO AND THE SHARK
(1963 - MGM) Marlene Among, Al Kauwe
One Sheet: $5 - $10

TIL THERE WAS YOU
(1997 - Paramount) Jeanne Tripplehorn, Dylan
McDermott
One Sheet: $4 - $8

TIL WE MEET AGAIN
(1940 - Warner Bros.) Merle Oberon, George
Brent
One Sheet: $40 - $75

TILL THE CLOUDS ROLL BY
(1946 - MGM) Robert Walker, Lucille Bremer,
All Star Cast
One Sheet: $125 - $250

TILL THE END OF TIME
(1946 - RKO) Guy Madison, Dorothy McGuire
One Sheet: $30 - $50

TILL WE MEET AGAIN
(1936 - Paramount) Herbert Marshall, Gertrude
Michael
One Sheet: $50 - $100

TILL WE MEET AGAIN
(1944 - Paramount) Ray Milland, Barbara
Britton
One Sheet: $40 - $75

Window Card

TILLIE AND GUS
(1933 - Paramount) W. C. Fields, Alison
Skipworth, Baby LeRoy
One Sheet: $1,600 - $2,500

TILLIE THE TOILER
(1927 - MGM) Marion Davies, Matt Moore
One Sheet: $700 - $1,200

TILLIE THE TOILER
(1941 - Columbia) William Tracy, Kay Harris
One Sheet: $50 - $100

TILLIE'S PUNCTURED ROMANCE
(1914 - Keystone) Charlie Chaplin, Marie
Dressler
One Sheet: $5,000 - $8,000   *Chaplin's first
feature film. Chaplin probably not pictured on the
one sheet.*

TILLIE'S PUNCTURED ROMANCE
(1927 - Paramount) W.C. Fields, Chester
Conklin, Louise Frazenda
One Sheet: $1,600 - $2,500

TILT
(1979 - Warner Bros.) Brooke Shields, Ken
Marshall, Joan Crawford
One Sheet: $5 - $10   *Advance:$10-
$20.*

TIM
(1979 - Pisces) Mel Gibson, Piper Laurie
One Sheet: $5 - $10   *Gibson's film
debut.*

TIM TYLER'S LUCK
(1937 - Universal) Frankie Thomas, Frances
Robinson
One Sheet: $200 - $400   *Serial. 12
Chapters.*

TIMBER
(1941 - RKO) Donald Duck
One Sheet: $3,500 - $5,000   *Cartoon.
Cartoon Movie Posters #161.*

TIMBER
(1942 - Universal) Leo Carrillo, Andy Devine
One Sheet: $30 - $50

TIMBER COUNTRY TROUBLE
(1955 - Newhall) Guy Madison, Andy Devine
One Sheet: $15 - $25   *From the Wild
Bill Hickok Adventure Series.*

TIMBER FURY
(1950 - Eagle-Lion) David Bruce, Laura Lee
One Sheet: $15 - $25

TIMBER QUEEN
(1944 - Paramount) Richard Arlen, Mary Beth
Hughes
One Sheet: $30 - $50

TIMBER STAMPEDE
(1939 - RKO) George O'Brien, Marjorie
Reynolds
One Sheet: $75 - $125

TIMBER TRAIL, THE
(1948 - Republic) Monte Hale, Lynne Roberts
One Sheet: $15 - $35

TIMBER TRAMPS
(1977 - -) Leon Ames
One Sheet: $5 - $10

TIMBER WAR
(1936 - Ambassador) Kermit Maynard
One Sheet: $75 - $150

One Sheet

TIMBER WOLF
(1925 - Fox) Buck Jones, Elinor Fair, David
Dyas
One Sheet: $200 - $400

TIMBERESQUE
(1938 - Consolidated) -
One Sheet: $40 - $75

TIMBERJACK
(1954 - Republic) Sterling Hayden, Vera
Ralston
One Sheet: $15 - $25

TIMBUKTU
(1958 - United Artists) Victor Mature, Yvonne
De Carlo
One Sheet: $15 - $25

TIME AFTER TIME
(1979 - Warner Bros.) Malcolm McDowell,
David Warner
One Sheet: $5 - $10

TIME BANDITS
(1981 - Avco) Sean Connery, Shelley Duvall,
John Cleese, Michael Palin
One Sheet: $7 - $15

TIME BOMB
(1961 - Allied Artists) Curt Jurgens, Mylene
Demongeot
One Sheet: $7 - $15

TIME FOR DYING, A
(1970 - Fipco) Richard Lapp, Anne Randall,
Audie Murphy
One Sheet: $7 - $15

TIME FOR KILLING, A
(1967 - Columbia) Glenn Ford, Inger Stevens
One Sheet: $10 - $20

TIME IS MY ENEMY
(1954 - Republic) Dennis Price, Renee
Asherson
One Sheet: $7 - $15

TIME LIMIT
(1957 - United Artists) Richard Widmark,
Richard Basehart
One Sheet: $10 - $20

TIME LOST AND TIME REMEMBERED
(1966 - Continental) Sarah Miles, Cyril Cusack
One Sheet: $5 - $10

TIME MACHINE, THE
(1960 - MGM) Rod Taylor, Yvette Mimieux
One Sheet: $150 - $350   *Graven
Images, pg. 220.*

TIME MACHINE, THE
(1972R - MGM) Rod Taylor, Yvette Mimieux
One Sheet: $15 - $30   *Re-release.*

TIME OF DESTINY, A
(1988 - -) William Hurt, Timothy Hutton
One Sheet: $3 - $5

TIME OF INDIFFERENCE
(1965 - Continental) Rod Steiger, Claudia
Cardinale
One Sheet: $5 - $10

TIME OF THEIR LIVES, THE
(1946 - Universal) Bud Abbott, Lou Costello,
Marjorie Reynolds
One Sheet: $100 - $200

TIME OF YOUR LIFE, THE
(1948 - United Artists) James Cagney, William
Bendix
One Sheet: $50 - $100

TIME OUT FOR MURDER
(1938 - 20th Century Fox) Gloria Stuart,
Michael Whalen
One Sheet: $50 - $100

TIME OUT FOR RHYTHM
(1941 - Columbia) Rudy Vallee, Ann Miller, The
Three Stooges (Curly)
One Sheet: $75 - $150   *Price
assumes Stooges not pictured on the poster.*

TIME OUT FOR ROMANCE
(1937 - 20th Century Fox) Claire Trevor,
Michael Whalen
One Sheet: $75 - $150

TIME OUT OF MIND
(1947 - Universal) Phyllis Calvert, Robert
Hutton
One Sheet: $15 - $25

TIME, THE PLACE AND THE GIRL, THE
(1946 - Warner Bros.) Dennis Morgan, Jack
Carson
One Sheet: $30 - $50

TIME TO KILL
(1942 - 20th Century Fox) Lloyd Nolan,
Heather Angel
One Sheet: $40 - $75

One Sheet

TIME TO KILL, A
(1996 - Warner Bros.) Sandra Bullock, Matthew
McConaughey, Samuel L. Jackson
One Sheet: $7 - $15   *Drama.*

TIME TO LOVE AND A TIME TO DIE, A
(1958 - Universal) John Gavin, Jock Mahoney
One Sheet: $15 - $25

TIME TO SING, A
(1968 - MGM) Hank Williams, Jr., Shelley
Fabares
One Sheet: $30 - $50   *Country
musical.*

TIME TRACKERS
(1989 - -) Ned Beatty, Wil Shriner
One Sheet: $5 - $10

TIME TRAVELERS, THE
(1964 - AIP) Preston Foster, Philip Carey
One Sheet: $30 - $50

TIME WALKER
(1982 - -) Ben Murphy, Nina Axelrod

One Sheet: $4 - $8

TIMECOP
(1994 - Universal) Jean-Claude Van Damme, Ron Silver
One Sheet: $5 - $10

TIMES HAVE CHANGED
(1923 - Fox) William Russell
One Sheet: $250 - $500

TIMES SQUARE
(1929 - Gotham) Alice Day, Arthur Lubin
One Sheet: $700 - $1,200

TIMES SQUARE
(1980 - AFD) Tim Curry, Trini Alvarado
One Sheet: $7 - $15

TIMES SQUARE LADY
(1935 - MGM) Robert Taylor, Virginia Bruce
One Sheet: $250 - $500

TIMES SQUARE PLAYBOY
(1936 - Warner Bros.) Warren William, Gene Lockhart
One Sheet: $125 - $250

TIMETABLE
(1956 - United Artists) Mark Stevens, King Calder, Jack Klugman
One Sheet: $15 - $25 *Klugman's film debut.*

TIMID GHOST, THE
(1937 - Educational) Kemper, Gilbert
One Sheet: $150 - $300

TIMID YOUNG MAN, THE
(1935 - Educational) Buster Keaton
One Sheet: $250 - $500

TIMOTHY'S QUEST
(1936 - Paramount) Virginia Weidler, Dickie Moore
One Sheet: $75 - $125

TIN CUP
(1996 - Warner Bros.) Kevin Costner, Rene Russo, Don Johnson
One Sheet: $7 - $15 *Sports (Golf).*

One Sheet

TIN HATS
(1927 - MGM) Conrad Nagel, Claire Windsor
One Sheet: $125 - $250

TIN MEN
(1987 - Touchstone) Richard Dreyfuss, Danny DeVito
One Sheet: $7 - $15

TIN PAN ALLEY
(1940 - 20th Century Fox) Alice Faye, Betty Grable, John Payne
One Sheet: $250 - $500

One Sheet

TIN STAR, THE
(1957 - Paramount) Henry Fonda, Anthony Perkins
One Sheet: $40 - $75

TIN STAR, THE
(1965R - Paramount) Henry Fonda, Anthony Perkins
One Sheet: $15 - $25 *Re-release.*

TINGLER, THE
(1959 - Columbia) Vincent Price, Judith Evelyn
One Sheet: $75 - $150 *Graven Images, pg. 190.*

TIOGA KID, THE
(1948 - PRC) Eddie Dean, Jennifer Holt
One Sheet: $15 - $35

TIP ON A DEAD JOCKEY
(1957 - MGM) Robert Taylor, Dorothy Malone
One Sheet: $15 - $30

TIPOFF, THE
(1931 - RKO) Ginger Rogers, Robert Armstrong
One Sheet: $500 - $800

TIPOFF GIRLS
(1938 - Paramount) Lloyd Nolan, Mary Carlisle
One Sheet: $100 - $200

TIRE TROUBLE
(1923 - Pathe) Our Gang
One Sheet: $1,600 - $2,500

TIRE TROUBLE
(1940 - 20th Century Fox) Terry-toons
One Sheet: $100 - $200 *Cartoon. Full color stone litho. Stock poster with inset title.*

TISH
(1942 - MGM) Marjorie Main, Lee Bowman
One Sheet: $20 - $40

TIT FOR TAT
(1935 - MGM) Laurel & Hardy
One Sheet: $1,900 - $3,000

TITAN - STORY OF MICHELANGELO, THE
(1950 - -) Narrated by Fredric March
One Sheet: $20 - $40 *Documentary. Academy Award: Best Documentary.*

TITANIC
(1953 - 20th Century Fox) Clifton Webb, Barbara Stanwyck
One Sheet: $125 - $250

TITANICA
(1995 - Imax) Dir: Stephen Law
One Sheet: $5 - $10

TITFIELD THUNDERBOLT, THE
(1952 - Universal International) Stanley Holloway, George Relph
One Sheet: $7 - $15

T-MEN
(1948 - Eagle-Lion) Dennis O'Keefe, Mary Meade, Alfred Ryder
One Sheet: $30 - $60

TO A FINISH
(1921 - Fox) Buck Jones, Helen Ferguson
One Sheet: $200 - $400

TO BE OR NOT TO BE
(1942 - United Artists) Carole Lombard, Jack Benny
One Sheet: $250 - $500 *Lombard's final film.*

TO BE OR NOT TO BE
(1983 - 20th Century Fox) Mel Brooks, Anne Bancroft
One Sheet: $7 - $15

TO BEAT THE BAND
(1935 - RKO) Hugh Herbert, Roger Pryor, The Fred Keating Orchestra
One Sheet: $75 - $150 *Big Band musical.*

TO CATCH A THIEF
(1955 - Paramount) Cary Grant, Grace Kelly, Dir: Alfred Hitchcock
One Sheet: $250 - $500

TO CATCH A THIEF
(1963R - Paramount) Cary Grant, Grace Kelly, Dir: Alfred Hitchcock
One Sheet: $30 - $50 *Re-release.*

TO CATCH A THIEF/VERTIGO COMBO
(1963R - Paramount) Dir: Alfred Hitchcock
One Sheet: $40 - $75 *Double feature re-release.*

TO COMMIT A MURDER
(1970 - Cinerama) Louis Jourdan, Senta Berger, Edmond O'Brien
One Sheet: $5 - $10

TO DIE FOR
(1989 - Skouras) Brendan Hughes, Sydney Walsh
One Sheet: $3 - $5

TO DIE FOR
(1995 - Columbia) Nicole Kidman, Matt Dillon
One Sheet: $5 - $10

TO DIE OF LOVE
(1972 - MGM) Annie Girardot, Bruno Pradal
One Sheet: $7 - $15

TO EACH HIS OWN
(1946 - Paramount) Olivia de Havilland, John Lund
One Sheet: $125 - $250 *Lund's film debut. Academy Award: Best Actress(de Havilland). Academy Award Movie Posters #106.*

TO FIND A MAN
(1972 - Columbia) Pamela Sue Martin, Darren O'Connor
One Sheet: $5 - $10

TO GILLIAN ON HER 37TH BIRTHDAY
(1996 - Triumph) Kathy Baker, Claire Danes
One Sheet: $4 - $8

TO HAVE AND HAVE NOT
(1945 - Warner Bros.) Humphrey Bogart, Lauren Bacall, Walter Brennan
One Sheet: $250 - $500 *First pairing of Bogart and Bacall. Bacall's film debut.*

One Sheet

TO HAVE AND HAVE NOT
(1954R - Warner Bros.) Humphrey Bogart, Lauren Bacall, Walter Brennan
One Sheet: $75 - $150 *Re-release.*

TO HAVE AND TO HOLD
(1994 - Buena Vista) Meg Ryan, Andy Garcia
One Sheet: $5 - $10

TO HELL AND BACK
(1955 - Universal) Audie Murphy, Marshall Thompson
One Sheet: $75 - $150

TO KILL A CLOWN
(1972 - 20th Century Fox) Alan Alda, Blythe Danner
One Sheet: $7 - $15

TO KILL A MOCKINGBIRD
(1962 - Universal) Gregory Peck, Mary Badham, Robert Duvall
One Sheet: $200 - $400 *Academy Award: Best Actor(Peck). Duvall's film debut. Academy Award Movie Posters #209.*

TO KILL A MOCKINGBIRD/THAT TOUCH OF MINK
(1967R - Universal) -
One Sheet: $40 - $75 *Re-release double feature .*

TO LIVE
(1994 - Goldwyn) Ge You, Gong Li, Niu Ben
One Sheet: $5 - $10

TO LIVE AND DIE IN L.A.
(1985 - MGM/UA) William Petersen, Willem Dafoe

One Sheet: $10 - $20

TO LOVE AND CHERISH
(1913 - Lubin) -
One Sheet: $250 - $500

TO MARY - WITH LOVE
(1936 - 20th Century Fox) Warner Baxter, Myrna Loy
One Sheet: $250 - $500

TO PARIS WITH LOVE
(1955 - Continental) Alec Guinness, Odile Versois
One Sheet: $40 - $75

TO PLEASE A LADY
(1950 - MGM) Clark Gable, Barbara Stanwyck
One Sheet: $40 - $75

TO SIR WITH LOVE
(1967 - Columbia) Sidney Poitier, Judy Geeson
One Sheet: $30 - $50

TO SLEEP WITH ANGER
(1990 - -) Danny Glover, Sheryl Lee
One Sheet: $5 - $10

TO THE DEVIL A DAUGHTER
(1976 - Hammer) Christopher Lee, Nastassja Kinski
One Sheet: $30 - $50

TO THE ENDS OF THE EARTH
(1948 - Columbia) Dick Powell, Signe Hasso
One Sheet: $40 - $75

TO THE LAST MAN
(1923 - Paramount) Lois Wilson, Richard Dix
One Sheet: $250 - $600

TO THE LAST MAN
(1933 - Paramount) Randolph Scott
One Sheet: $200 - $400

TO THE SHORES OF TRIPOLI
(1942 - 20th Century Fox) John Payne, Maureen O'Hara
One Sheet: $40 - $75

TO THE VICTOR
(1938 - Gaumont) Will Fyffe, John Loder, Margaret Lockwood
One Sheet: $40 - $75

TO THE VICTOR
(1948 - Warner Bros.) Dennis Morgan, Viveca Lindfors
One Sheet: $15 - $35

TO TRAP A SPY
(1966 - MGM) Robert Vaughn, David McCallum
One Sheet: $30 - $50 *MAN FROM U.N.C.L.E. TV tie-in.*

TO WONG FOO, THANKS FOR EVERYTHING, JULIE NEWMAR
(1995 - Universal) Wesley Snipes, Patrick Swayze
One Sheet: $10 - $20

TOAST OF NEW ORLEANS, THE
(1950 - MGM) Kathryn Grayson, Mario Lanza
One Sheet: $20 - $40

TOAST OF NEW YORK, THE
(1937 - RKO) Edward Arnold, Frances Farmer, Cary Grant
One Sheet: $300 - $700

TOBACCO ROAD
(1941 - 20th Century Fox) Charley Grapewin, Marjorie Rambeau, Gene Tierney
One Sheet: $600 - $1,000

TOBACCO ROAD
(1956R - 20th Century Fox) Charley Grapewin, Marjorie Rambeau, Gene Tierney
One Sheet: $50 - $100 *Re-release.*

TOBOR THE GREAT
(1954 - Republic) Charles Drake, Karin Booth
One Sheet: $300 - $700 *Graven Images, pg. 180.*

TOBRUK
(1967 - Universal) Rock Hudson, George Peppard
One Sheet: $10 - $20

TOBY TYLER
(1960 - Buena Vista) Kevin Corcoran, Henry Calvin
One Sheet: $15 - $35

TODAY
(1930 - Majestic) Conrad Nagel, Catherine
Dale Owen
One Sheet: $100 - $200

TODAY I HANG
(1942 - PRC) Walter W. King, Mona Barrie
One Sheet: $30 - $50

TODAY WE KILL, TOMORROW WE DIE
(1971 - Cinerama) Montgomery Ford, Bud
Spencer
One Sheet: $5 - $10

TODAY WE LIVE
(1933 - MGM) Joan Crawford, Gary Cooper
One Sheet: $800 - $1,500

Title Card

TODD KILLINGS, THE
(1971 - National General) Robert F. Lyons,
Richard Thomas
One Sheet: $10 - $20

TODDLES
(1927 - Paramount) -
One Sheet: $100 - $200

TOGETHER
(1979 - -) Maximilian Schell, Jacqueline Bisset
One Sheet: $3 - $5

TOGETHER AGAIN
(1944 - Columbia) Irene Dunn, Charles Boyer
One Sheet: $40 - $75

TOGETHER BROTHERS
(1974 - -) Ahmad Nurradin, Anthony Wilson
One Sheet: $7 - $15   *Blaxploitation.*

TOGETHER WE LIVE
(1935 - Columbia) Willard Mack, Ben Lyon,
Esther Ralston
One Sheet: $75 - $150

TOKYO AFTER DARK
(1958 - Paramount) Richard Long, Michi Kobi
One Sheet: $15 - $25

TOKYO FILE
(1951 - RKO) Florence Marly, Robert Payton
One Sheet: $15 - $25

TOKYO JOE
(1949 - Columbia) Humphrey Bogart, Alexander
Knox, Sessue Hayakawa
One Sheet: $100 - $200

TOKYO OLYMPIAD
(1964 - -) Bob Hayes, Valery Brumel, Abebe
Bikila
One Sheet: $50 - $100   *Sports Movie
Posters #283.*

TOKYO ROSE
(1945 - Paramount) Osa Massen, Keye Luke
One Sheet: $30 - $50

TOKYO STORY
(1972 - Ofuna/New Yorker) Chiyeko
Higashiyama, Setsuko Hara
One Sheet: $30 - $50

TOL'ABLE DAVID
(1921 - First National) Richard Barthelmess,
Gladys Hulette
One Sheet: $800 - $1,500

TOL'ABLE DAVID
(1930 - Columbia) John Carradine
One Sheet: $250 - $500

TOLL GATE, THE
(1920 - Paramount-Artcraft) William S. Hart,

Anna Q. Nilsson
One Sheet: $1,600 - $2,500

TOM & JERRY
(1931 - RKO) Dizzy Whirl of Brand New Laughs
One Sheet: $1,900 - $3,000   *Cartoon.*
Cartoon Movie Posters #142.

TOM & VIV
(1995 - Miramax) Willem Dafoe, Rosemary
Harris
One Sheet: $5 - $12

TOM AND HUCK
(1995 - Buena Vista) Jonathan Taylor Thomas,
Brad Renfro
One Sheet: $5 - $10

TOM AND JERRY FESTIVAL
(1962 - MGM) Tom & Jerry
One Sheet: $40 - $75   *Cartoon.*

TOM AND JERRY IN THE HOLLYWOOD BOWL
(1950 - MGM) Tom & Jerry
One Sheet: $800 - $1,500   *Cartoon.*
Cartoon Movie Posters #280.

TOM AND JERRY STOCK POSTER
(1940S - MGM) Tom & Jerry
One Sheet: $150 - $300   *Cartoon.*

TOM AND JERRY STOCK POSTER
(1956 - MGM) Tom & Jerry
One Sheet: $150 - $300   *Cartoon.*

TOM BROWN OF CULVER
(1932 - Universal) Tom Brown, Andy Devine,
Sidney Toler, Tyrone Power
One Sheet: $200 - $400   *Power's film
debut.*

TOM BROWN'S SCHOOLDAYS
(1940 - RKO) Freddie Bartholomew, Jimmy
Lydon, Cedric Hardwicke
One Sheet: $50 - $100

TOM BROWN'S SCHOOLDAYS
(1950 - United Artists) John Howard Davies,
Robert Newton
One Sheet: $15 - $30

TOM CATS
(1977 - -) Chris Mulkey, Scott Lawrence
One Sheet: $15 - $25

TOM, DICK AND HARRY
(1941 - RKO) Ginger Rogers, George Murphy,
Burgess Meredith
One Sheet: $100 - $200

TOM HORN
(1979 - Warner Bros.) Steve McQueen, Linda
Evans
One Sheet: $15 - $30

TOM JONES
(1963 - Lopert) Albert Finney, Susannah York,
Lynn Redgrave
One Sheet: $30 - $60   *Academy
Award: Best Picture, Best Direction(Tony
Richardson). Redgrave's film debut. Academy
Award Movie Posters #213& #214.*

TOM JONES/IRMA LA DOUCE
(1965R - United Artists) Albert Finney,
Susannah York/Shirley MacLaine, Jack
Lemmon
One Sheet: $7 - $15   *Re-release
double feature poster.*

TOM SAWYER
(1930 - Paramount Publix) Jackie Coogan,
Mitzi Green
One Sheet: $250 - $500

TOM SAWYER
(1973 - United Artists) Johnny Whitaker,
Celeste Holm
One Sheet: $7 - $15

TOM SAWYER, DETECTIVE
(1938 - Paramount) Donald O'Connor, Billy
Cook
One Sheet: $75 - $150

TOM THUMB
(1936 - Celebrity) Ub Iwerks
One Sheet: $800 - $1,500   *Cartoon. Full
color stone litho. Cartoon Movie Posters #120.*

TOM THUMB
(1958 - MGM) Russ Tamblyn, Alan Young,
Peter Sellers
One Sheet: $20 - $40

TOM THUMB
(1967 - Childhood) Maria Elena Marquez, Jose
Elias Moreno
One Sheet: $2 - $3

TOM THUMB
(1970R - MGM) Russ Tamblyn, Alan Young,
Peter Sellers
One Sheet: $5 - $10   *Re-release.*

TOM TILLING'S BABY
(1912 - -) -
One Sheet: $500 - $800   *French.*

TOMAHAWK
(1951 - Universal) Van Heflin, Yvonne De Carlo
One Sheet: $15 - $30

TOMAHAWK TERRITORY
(1952 - -) Clayton Moore
One Sheet: $30 - $60

TOMAHAWK TRAIL
(1956 - United Artists) Chuck Connors, Susan
Cummings
One Sheet: $15 - $25

TOMB OF LIGEIA, THE
(1965 - AIP) Vincent Price, Elizabeth Shepherd
One Sheet: $30 - $50

**TOMB OF TORTURE/CAVE OF THE LIVING
DEAD**
(1966 - Trans-Lux) -
One Sheet: $15 - $25   *Double
feature poster.*

TOMBOY, THE
(1921 - -) Eileen Percy, Hal Cooley
One Sheet: $200 - $400

TOMBOY
(1940 - Monogram) Jack Morgan, Marcia Mae
Jones
One Sheet: $40 - $75

TOMBOY
(1985 - Crown Int.) Betsy Russell, Jerry
Dinome
One Sheet: $3 - $5

TOMBOY AND THE CHAMP
(1961 - Universal) Candy Moore, Ben Johnson
One Sheet: $7 - $15

TOMBSTONE
(1993 - Hollywood) Kurt Russell, Val Kilmer
One Sheet: $40 - $75   *Price is for
double-sided poster. One Sheets with white backs
are second printings worth $20-$30. One Sheet
(Advance): $50-$100.*

One Sheet

TOMBSTONE CANYON
(1932 - K.B.S.) Ken Maynard, Cecilia Parker
One Sheet: $200 - $400

TOMBSTONE TERROR
(1935 - Supreme) Bob Steele, Gabby Hayes
One Sheet: $150 - $350

TOMBSTONE, THE TOWN TOO TOUGH TO DIE
(1942 - Paramount) Richard Dix, Rex Bell
One Sheet: $75 - $150

TOMMY BOY
(1995 - Paramount) Chris Farley, David Spade,
Bo Derek
One Sheet: $3 - $5

TOMMY THE MOVIE
(1975 - Columbia) Ann Margret, Roger Daltrey,
Elton John, Eric Clapton
One Sheet: $40 - $75   *Rock 'n' Roll.*

TOMMY THE TOREADOR
(1960 - Warner Bros.) Tommy Steele, Janet
Munro
One Sheet: $10 - $20

TOMORROW
(1972 - Filmgroup) Robert Duvall, Olga Bellin
One Sheet: $5 - $10

TOMORROW AND TOMORROW
(1932 - Paramount) Ruth Chatterton, Robert
Ames
One Sheet: $150 - $350

TOMORROW AT SEVEN
(1933 - RKO) Chester Morris, Vivienne
Osborne
One Sheet: $250 - $600

TOMORROW AT TEN
(1964 - Governor) John Gregson, Robert Shaw
One Sheet: $3 - $5

TOMORROW IS ANOTHER DAY
(1951 - Warner Bros.) Ruth Roman, Steve
Cochran
One Sheet: $15 - $30

TOMORROW IS FOREVER
(1945 - RKO) Claudette Colbert, Orson Welles
One Sheet: $100 - $200

TOMORROW IS TOO LATE
(1952 - MGM) Pier Angeli
One Sheet: $250 - $600

TOMORROW NEVER COMES
(1978 - Rank) Oliver Reed, Raymond Burr
One Sheet: $5 - $10

TOMORROW THE WORLD
(1944 - United Artists) Fredric March, Skippy
Homeier, Betty Field
One Sheet: $50 - $100

TOMORROW WE LIVE
(1936 - Associated British Film) Godfrey
Tearle, Renee Gadd
One Sheet: $150 - $300

TOMORROW WE LIVE
(1942 - PRC) Jean Parker, Ricardo Cortez
One Sheet: $30 - $50

TOMORROW'S YOUTH
(1934 - Monogram) Dickie Moore, Martha
Sleeper
One Sheet: $100 - $200

TONG MAN, THE
(1919 - Haworth) Sessue Hayakawa
One Sheet: $800 - $1,500

TONGA ISLES, THE
(1916 - Paramount) -
One Sheet: $125 - $250   *From the
Paramount Travel Pictures series.*

TONGUE MARK, THE
(1913 - Majestic) -
One Sheet: $250 - $600

TONGUES OF FLAME
(1924 - Paramount) Thomas Meighan, Bessie
Love
One Sheet: $150 - $350

TONIGHT AND EVERY NIGHT
(1945 - Columbia) Rita Hayworth, Lee Bowman
One Sheet: $150 - $300

TONIGHT FOR SURE
(1963 - Searchlight) Don Kenney, Karl
Schanzer, Dir: Francis Ford Coppola
One Sheet: $50 - $100   *Coppola's first
film, pre-dating DEMENTIA 13.*

TONIGHT IS OURS
(1933 - Paramount) Claudette Colbert, Fredric
March
One Sheet: $250 - $500

TONIGHT OR NEVER
(1931 - Feature) Gloria Swanson, Boris Karloff
One Sheet: $250 - $600

TONIGHT WE RAID CALAIS
(1943 - 20th Century Fox) John Sutton,
Annabella
One Sheet: $30 - $50

TONIGHT WE SING
(1953 - 20th Century Fox) David Wayne, Ezio

Pinza
One Sheet: $15 - $25

TONIGHTS THE NIGHT
(1954 - Allied Artists) David Niven, Yvonne DeCarlo
One Sheet: $15 - $25

TONKA
(1958 - Buena Vista) Sal Mineo, Jerome Courtland
One Sheet: $15 - $30

TONTO BASIN OUTLAWS
(1941 - Monogram) Range Busters
One Sheet: $30 - $50

TONTO KID, THE
(1935 - Resolute) Rex Bell, Ruth Mix, Buzz Barton
One Sheet: $150 - $350

TONY ROME
(1967 - 20th Century Fox) Frank Sinatra, Jill St. John
One Sheet: $15 - $25

TONY THE WONDERHORSE APPEARING IN TOM MIX SCREEN SPECIALS
(1925 - Fox) -
One Sheet: $250 - $500

TOO BAD SHE'S BAD
(1955 - Gala) Sophia Loren, Virrorio De Sica, Marcello Mastrianni
One Sheet: $30 - $50

TOO BUSY TO WORK
(1932 - Fox) Will Rogers, Marian Nixon
One Sheet: $500 - $800

TOO BUSY TO WORK
(1939 - 20th Century Fox) Jed Prouty, Spring Byington
One Sheet: $30 - $50

TOO HOT TO HANDLE
(1938 - MGM) Clark Gable, Myrna Loy
One Sheet: $250 - $600

TOO HOT TO HANDLE
(1962 - Topaz) Jayne Mansfield, Christopher Lee
One Sheet: $40 - $75

TOO HOT TO HANDLE
(1976 - Topaz) Cheri Caffaro, Vic Diaz
One Sheet: $10 - $20

TOO LATE BLUES
(1962 - Paramount) Bobby Darin, Stella Stevens
One Sheet: $15 - $25

TOO LATE FOR TEARS
(1949 - United Artists) Lizabeth Scott, Don DeFore
One Sheet: $30 - $50

TOO LATE THE HERO
(1970 - Cinerama) Michael Caine, Cliff Robertson
One Sheet: $3 - $5

TOO MANY BLONDES
(1941 - Universal) Rudy Vallee, Helen Parrish, Humberto Herpera & his Orchestra
One Sheet: $30 - $50   *Big Band musical.*

TOO MANY COOKS
(1931 - RKO) Bert Wheeler, Dorothy Lee
One Sheet: $150 - $300

TOO MANY CROOKS
(1958 - British Lion) Terry-Thomas, George Cole
One Sheet: $10 - $20

TOO MANY GIRLS
(1940 - RKO) Lucille Ball, Richard Carlson, Desi Arnaz
One Sheet: $200 - $400   *Arnaz's film debut. Film where Desi & Lucy first met.*

TOO MANY GIRLS
(1952R - RKO) Lucille Ball, Richard Carlson, Desi Arnaz
One Sheet: $50 - $100   *Re-release.*

TOO MANY HUSBANDS
(1940 - Columbia) Jean Arthur, Fred MacMurray
One Sheet: $75 - $125

TOO MANY KISSES
(1925 - Paramount) Richard Dix, Frances Howard, William Powell
One Sheet: $250 - $500

TOO MANY PARENTS
(1936 - Paramount) Frances Farmer, Billy Lee
One Sheet: $150 - $300

TOO MANY WINNERS
(1942 - PRC) Hugh Beaumont, Trudy Marshall
One Sheet: $50 - $100

TOO MANY WIVES
(1937 - RKO) Anne Shirley, John Morley
One Sheet: $75 - $150

TOO MUCH HARMONY
(1933 - Paramount) Bing Crosby, Jack Oakie
One Sheet: $150 - $300

TOO MUCH TOO SOON
(1958 - Warner Bros.) Dorothy Malone, Errol Flynn
One Sheet: $20 - $40

TOO SOON TO LOVE
(1960 - Universal) Jennifer West, Richard Evans, Jack Nicholson
One Sheet: $15 - $25

TOO TOUGH TO KILL
(1935 - Columbia) Victor Jory, Ward Bond
One Sheet: $100 - $200

TOO YOUNG TO KISS
(1951 - MGM) June Allyson, Van Johnson
One Sheet: $15 - $30

TOO YOUNG TO KNOW
(1945 - Warner Bros.) Joan Leslie, Robert Hutton
One Sheet: $30 - $50

TOO YOUNG TO MARRY
(1931 - First National) Loretta Young
One Sheet: $250 - $500

TOOT, WHISTLE, PLUNK, AND BOOM
(1953 - RKO/Disney) -
One Sheet: $500 - $800   *Cartoon. Academy Award: Best Cartoon Short.*

TOOTH WILL OUT, THE
(1951 - Columbia) The Three Stooges (Shemp)
One Sheet: $200 - $400   *Comedy short. Duotone.*

TOOTSIE
(1982 - Columbia) Dustin Hoffman, Jessica Lange
One Sheet: $7 - $15   *Academy Award: Best Supporting Actress (Lange). Academy Award Movie Posters #328.*

TOP BANANA
(1953 - United Artists) Phil Silvers, Rose Marie
One Sheet: $30 - $50   *Filmed in 3-D.*

TOP DOG
(1995 - MGM/UA) Chuck Norris
One Sheet: $5 - $10

TOP GUN
(1955 - United Artists) Sterling Hayden, William Bishop
One Sheet: $15 - $25

TOP GUN
(1986 - Paramount) Tom Cruise, Kelly McGillis
One Sheet: $30 - $50

TOP HAT
(1935 - RKO) Fred Astaire, Ginger Rogers
One Sheet: $5,000 - $8,000

One Sheet (Style A)

TOP HAT
(1953R - RKO) Fred Astaire, Ginger Rogers
One Sheet: $200 - $400   *Re-release.*

TOP MAN
(1943 - Universal) Donald O'Connor, Susanna Foster, Lillian Gish
One Sheet: $30 - $50

TOP O' THE MORNING
(1949 - Paramount) Bing Crosby, Ann Blyth
One Sheet: $30 - $50

TOP OF NEW YORK, THE
(1922 - Paramount) May McAvoy
One Sheet: $250 - $600

TOP OF THE HEAP
(1972 - Fanfare) Christopher St. John
One Sheet: $15 - $25   *Blaxploitation.*

TOP OF THE TOWN
(1937 - Universal) George Murphy, Doris Nolan
One Sheet: $75 - $150

One Sheet

TOP OF THE WORLD
(1925 - Paramount) Anna Q. Nilsson, James Kirkwood
One Sheet: $250 - $600

One Sheet

TOP OF THE WORLD
(1955 - United Artists) Don Terry, Leo Carrillo
One Sheet: $15 - $25

TOP SECRET
(1984 - Paramount) Val Kilmer, Lucy Gutteridge
One Sheet: $7 - $15

TOP SECRET AFFAIR
(1957 - Warner Bros.) Kirk Douglas, Susan Hayward
One Sheet: $20 - $40

TOP SERGEANT
(1942 - Universal) Don Terry, Leo Carrillo
One Sheet: $40 - $75

TOP SERGEANT MULLIGAN
(1941 - Monogram) Sterling Holloway, Nat Pendleton
One Sheet: $30 - $50

TOP SPEED
(1930 - First National) Joe E. Brown, Jack Whiting
One Sheet: $200 - $400

TOPAZ
(1970 - Universal) Frederick Stafford, John Forsythe, Dir: Hitchcock
One Sheet: $20 - $40

TOPAZE
(1933 - RKO) John Barrymore, Myrna Loy
One Sheet: $1,300 - $2,000

TOPEKA
(1953 - Monogram) Bill Elliott
One Sheet: $15 - $35

TOPEKA TERROR, THE
(1945 - Republic) Allan "Rocky" Lane, Linda Stirling
One Sheet: $30 - $50

TOPEKA TERROR, THE
(1954R - Republic) Allan "Rocky" Lane, Linda Stirling
One Sheet: $7 - $15   *Re-release.*

TOPKAPI
(1964 - United Artists) Melina Mercouri, Maximilian Schell, Peter Ustinov
One Sheet: $10 - $20   *Academy Award Movie Posters #225.*

TOPPER
(1937 - MGM) Roland Young, Cary Grant, Constance Bennett
One Sheet: $600 - $1,000

TOPPER
(1944R - MGM) Roland Young, Cary Grant, Constance Bennett
One Sheet: $50 - $100   *Re-release.*

TOPPER RETURNS
(1941 - United Artists) Roland Young, Joan Blondell, Eddie "Rochester" Anderson
One Sheet: $100 - $200

TOPPER TAKES A TRIP
(1939 - United Artists) Roland Young, Constance Bennett, Billie Burke
One Sheet: $200 - $400

TOPSY AND EVA
(1927 - United Artists) Rosetta Duncan, Vivian Duncan
One Sheet: $250 - $600

TORA! TORA! TORA!
(1970 - 20th Century Fox) Jason Robards, Martin Balsam
One Sheet: $10 - $20

TORCH, THE
(1950 - Eagle-Lion) Paulette Goddard, Pedro Armendariz
One Sheet: $15 - $30

TORCH SINGER
(1933 - Paramount) Claudette Colbert, Ricardo Cortez
One Sheet: $600 - $1,000

TORCH SONG
(1953 - MGM) Joan Crawford, Michael Wilding
One Sheet: $75 - $150

TORCH SONG TRILOGY
(1988 -) Anne Bancroft, Matthew Broderick
One Sheet: $3 - $5

TORCHY BLANE - PLAYING WITH DYNAMITE
(1939 - Warner Bros.) Jane Wyman, Allen Jenkins
One Sheet: $40 - $75

TORCHY BLANE IN CHINATOWN
(1939 - Warner Bros.) Glenda Farrell, Barton MacLane
One Sheet: $40 - $75

TORCHY BLANE IN PANAMA
(1938 - Warner Bros.) Paul Kelly, Lola Lane
One Sheet: $50 - $100

TORCHY GETS HER MAN
(1938 - Warner Bros.) Glenda Farrell, Barton MacLane
One Sheet: $50 - $100

TORCHY RUNS FOR MAYOR
(1939 - Warner Bros.) Glenda Farrell, Barton MacLane
One Sheet: $40 - $75

TORERO!
(1957 - Columbia) Louis Precuna
One Sheet: $5 - $10

TORMENTED
(1960 - Allied Artists) Richard Carlson, Susan Gordon
One Sheet: $15 - $25

TORN CURTAIN
(1966 - Universal) Paul Newman, Julie Andrews, Dir: Alfred Hitchcock
One Sheet: $30 - $60

TORNADO
(1943 - Paramount) Chester Morris, Nancy Kelly
One Sheet: $30 - $50

Window Card

TORNADO IN THE SADDLE
(1942 - Columbia) Russell Hayden, Bob Wills
One Sheet: $30 - $50   *Country music western.*

TORNADO RANGE
(1948 - PRC) Eddie Dean, Roscoe Ates
One Sheet: $15 - $35

TORPEDO ALLEY
(1952 - Allied Artists) Mark Stevens, Dorothy Malone
One Sheet: $15 - $25

TORPEDO BAY
(1964 - AIP) James Mason, Lilli Palmer
One Sheet: $10 - $20

TORPEDO BOAT
(1942 - Paramount) Richard Arlen, Jean Parker
One Sheet: $30 - $50

TORPEDO RUN
(1958 - MGM) Glenn Ford, Ernest Borgnine
One Sheet: $20 - $40

TORRENT, THE
(1926 - MGM) Ricardo Cortez, Greta Garbo
One Sheet: $3,500 - $5,000   *Garbo's first American film.*

TORRID ZONE
(1940 - Warner Bros.) James Cagney, Ann Sheridan, Pat O'Brien
One Sheet: $200 - $400   *Duotone.*

One Sheet

TORRID ZONE
(1949R - Warner Bros.) James Cagney, Ann Sheridan, Pat O'Brien
One Sheet: $50 - $100   *Re-release.*

TORRID ZONE
(1957R - Warner Bros.) James Cagney, Ann Sheridan, Pat O'Brien
One Sheet: $30 - $50   *Re-release.*

TORSO
(1974 - Champion) Suzy Kendall, Tina Aumont
One Sheet: $3 - $5

TORTILLA FLAT
(1942 - MGM) Spencer Tracy, John Garfield, Hedy Lamarr

TORTURE GARDEN
(1967 - Columbia) Jack Palance, Burgess Meredith
One Sheet: $10 - $20

TOTAL RECALL
(1990 - TriStar) Arnold Schwarzenegger, Rachel Ticotin
One Sheet: $7 - $15

TOTO THE HERO
(1993 - Triton) -
One Sheet: $5 - $10   *Cartoon.*

TOUCH, THE
(1971 - Cinerama) Elliott Gould, Bibi Andersson, Max von Sydow
One Sheet: $3 - $5

TOUCH
(1997 - MGM/UA) Skeet Lurich, Bridget Fonda
One Sheet: $3 - $5

TOUCH AND GO
(1955 - Universal International) Jack Hawkins, Margaret Johnston
One Sheet: $10 - $20

TOUCH AND GO
(1984 - -) Michael Keaton, Maria Conchita Alonso
One Sheet: $3 - $5

TOUCH OF CLASS, A
(1973 - Avco/Embassy) Glenda Jackson, George Segal
One Sheet: $7 - $15   *Academy Award: Best Actress(Jackson). Academy Award Movie Posters #277.*

One Sheet

TOUCH OF EVIL
(1958 - Universal) Charlton Heston, Janet Leigh, Orson Welles
One Sheet: $200 - $400

TOUCH OF HELL, A
(1964 - Governor) Anthony Quayle, Sarah Churchill
One Sheet: $7 - $15

TOUCH OF LARCENY, A
(1960 - Paramount) James Mason, George Sanders
One Sheet: $7 - $15

TOUCHABLES, THE
(1968 - 20th Century Fox) Judy Huxtable, Esther Anderson
One Sheet: $7 - $15

TOUCHDOWN
(1931 - Paramount Publix) Richard Arlen, Jack Oakie
One Sheet: $200 - $400   *Sports (Football).*

TOUCHDOWN, ARMY
(1938 - Paramount) John Howard, Robert Cummings
One Sheet: $100 - $200   *Sports (Football).*

TOUCHDOWN DEMONS
(1940 - 20th Century Fox) Terry-toons
One Sheet: $100 - $200   *Cartoon. Sports (Football). Full color stone litho. Stock poster with inset title.*

TOUCHDOWN MICKEY
(1932 - United Artists/Disney) Mickey Mouse
One Sheet: $40,000 - $50,000   *Cartoon. Sports (Football).*

TOUCHDOWN MICKEY
(1974R - Buena Vista/Disney) Mickey Mouse
One Sheet: $15 - $30   *Re-release. Cartoon. Sports (Football). One Sheet is black and white.*

TOUCHED BY LOVE
(1988 - Columbia) Deborah Raffin, Diane Lane
One Sheet: $3 - $5

TOUGH
(1974 - -) Dion Gossett, Dir: Horace Jackson
One Sheet: $15 - $25   *Blaxploitation. "He's bad, he's black, he's beautiful!"*

TOUGH AS THEY COME
(1942 - Universal) Billy Halop, Bernard Punsley, Dead End Kids
One Sheet: $75 - $125

TOUGH ASSIGNMENT
(1949 - Lippert) Don Barry, Marjorie Steele
One Sheet: $15 - $25

TOUGH ENOUGH
(1983 - 20th Century Fox) Dennis Quaid, Stan Shaw
One Sheet: $3 - $5

TOUGH GIRL
(1953 - -) -
One Sheet: $15 - $25

TOUGH GUY
(1935 - MGM) Jackie Cooper, Jean Hersholt, Rin-Tin-Tin Jr.
One Sheet: $125 - $250

TOUGH GUYS
(1986 - Touchstone) Burt Lancaster, Kirk Douglas
One Sheet: $5 - $10

TOUGH GUYS DON'T DANCE
(1987 - Cannon) Ryan O'Neal, Isabella Rossellini
One Sheet: $3 - $5

TOUGH KID
(1939 - Monogram) Frankie Darro, Dick Purcell
One Sheet: $40 - $75

TOUGH LITTLE GUY
(1938 - Universal) -
One Sheet: $50 - $100

TOUGH TO HANDLE
(1937 - Conn) Frankie Darro, Kane Richmond
One Sheet: $40 - $75

One Sheet

TOUGHER THEY COME, THE
(1950 - Columbia) Wayne Morris, Preston Foster
One Sheet: $15 - $30

TOUGHEST GUN IN TOMBSTONE
(1958 - United Artists) George Montgomery, Beverly Tyler
One Sheet: $15 - $35

TOUGHEST MAN ALIVE, THE
(1955 - Allied Artists) Dane Clark, Lita Milan
One Sheet: $15 - $30

TOUGHEST MAN IN ARIZONA, THE
(1952 - Republic) Vaughn Monroe, Joan Leslie
One Sheet: $15 - $30

TOURIST, THE
(1925 - Educational) Johnny Arthur
One Sheet: $250 - $500

TOURIST TRAP, THE

(1979 - Band Compass) Chuck Connors, Jon Van Ness, Tanya Roberts
One Sheet: $7 - $15

TOURNAMENT TEMPO
(1957 - -) -
One Sheet: $30 - $50

TOVARICH
(1937 - Warner Bros.) Claudette Colbert, Charles Boyer
One Sheet: $200 - $400

TOW SERVICE
(1926 - Universal) Joe Murphy, Fay Tincher
One Sheet: $200 - $400   *From THE GUMPS series.*

TOWARD THE UNKNOWN
(1956 - Warner Bros.) William Holden, Lloyd Nolan, James Garner
One Sheet: $20 - $40   *Garner's film debut.*

TOWED IN A HOLE
(1933 - MGM) Laurel & Hardy
One Sheet: $1,900 - $3,000

TOWER OF LONDON
(1939 - Universal) Basil Rathbone, Boris Karloff
One Sheet: $500 - $900   *Graven Images, pg. 101.*

One Sheet

TOWER OF LONDON
(1948R - Realart) Boris Karloff, Basil Rathbone
One Sheet: $75 - $150

TOWER OF LONDON
(1962 - United Artists) Vincent Price, Dir:Roger Corman
One Sheet: $50 - $100

TOWERING INFERNO, THE
(1974 - 20th Century Fox) Steve McQueen, Paul Newman
One Sheet: $30 - $60

TOWN CALLED HELL, A
(1971 - Scotia International) Robert Shaw, Stella Stevens
One Sheet: $7 - $15

TOWN ON TRIAL
(1956 - Columbia) Charles Coburn, Barbara Bates
One Sheet: $15 - $25

TOWN TAMER
(1965 - Paramount) Dana Andrews, Terry Moore
One Sheet: $15 - $25

TOWN THAT DREADED SUNDOWN, THE
(1977 - AIP) Ben Johnson, Dawn Wells, Dir: Charles B. Pierce
One Sheet: $15 - $25

TOWN WENT WILD, THE
(1944 - PRC) Freddie Bartholomew, James Lydon
One Sheet: $30 - $50

TOWN WITHOUT PITY
(1961 - United Artists) Kirk Douglas, E.G. Marshall
One Sheet: $15 - $30

TOXIC AVENGER, THE
(1985 - Troma) Andree Maranda, Mitchell Cohen
One Sheet: $10 - $20

TOXIC AVENGER PART II, THE
(1989 - Troma) Lloyd Kaufman, Ron Fazio

One Sheet: $5 - $10

TOXIC AVENGER PART III, LAST TEMPTATION OF TOXIE, THE
(1989 - Troma) Lloyd Kaufman, Ron Fazio
One Sheet: $3 - $5

TOY, THE
(1982 - Columbia) Richard Pryor, Jackie Gleason
One Sheet: $5 - $10

TOY SOLDIERS
(1991 - TriStar) Louis Gossett, Jr., Sean Astin, Wil Wheaton
One Sheet: $3 - $5

TOY STORY
(1995 - Buena Vista) Voice of Tom Hanks, Tim Allen
One Sheet: $10 - $20   *Animation. 1st computer generated feature film. Advance Style: $15-$25.*

One Sheet

TOY TIGER
(1956 - Universal) Jeff Chandler, Laraine Day
One Sheet: $10 - $20

TOY TINKERS
(1948 - Disney) Donald Duck
One Sheet: $1,600 - $2,500   *Cartoon.*

TOY WIFE, THE
(1938 - MGM) Luise Rainer, Robert Young, Melvyn Douglas
One Sheet: $150 - $300

TOYS
(1992 - 20th Century Fox) Robin William, L. L. Cool J.
One Sheet: $5 - $10

TOYS IN THE ATTIC
(1963 - United Artists) Dean Martin, Geraldine Page
One Sheet: $15 - $25

TOYS OF FATE
(1918 - Metro) Alla Nazimova, Charles Bryant
One Sheet: $350 - $750

T.R. BASKIN
(1971 - Paramount) Candice Bergen, Peter Boyle
One Sheet: $3 - $5

TRACES OF RED
(1992 - Samuel Goldwyn) James Belushi, Lorraine Bracco
One Sheet: $3 - $5

TRACK 29
(1988 - -) Theresa Russell, Gary Oldman, Christopher Lloyd
One Sheet: $7 - $15

TRACK OF THE CAT
(1954 - Warner Bros.) Robert Mitchum, Diana Lynn
One Sheet: $30 - $60

TRACK OF THUNDER
(1969 - United Artists) Tom Kirk, Ray Stricklyn
One Sheet: $15 - $25   *Sports (Stock car racing).*

TRACK THE MAN DOWN
(1956 - Republic) Kent Taylor, Petula Clark
One Sheet: $15 - $35

TRACKDOWN
(1976 - United Artists) Jim Mitchum, Karen Lamm, Erik Estrada, Anne Archer
One Sheet: $5 - $10

TRACKED BY THE POLICE
(1927 - Warner Bros.) Rin Tin Tin, Jason Robards
One Sheet: $250 - $600

TRACKED TO EARTH
(1922 - Universal) Frank Mayo, Virginia Valli
One Sheet: $150 - $300

TRACKS
(1922 - Playgoers) Bill Patton, George Berrell
One Sheet: $600 - $1,000

TRACY RIDES
(1934 - William Steiner) Tom Tyler
One Sheet: $200 - $400

TRADE WINDS
(1938 - United Artists) Fredric March, Joan Bennett
One Sheet: $75 - $150

TRADER HORN
(1931 - MGM) Harry Carey, Duncan Renaldo
One Sheet: $1,300 - $2,000

TRADER HORN
(1938R - MGM) Harry Carey, Duncan Renaldo
One Sheet: $75 - $150   *Re-release.*

TRADER HORN
(1953R - MGM) Harry Carey, Duncan Renaldo
One Sheet: $50 - $100   *Re-release.*

TRADER HORN
(1973 - MGM) Rod Taylor, Anne Heywood
One Sheet: $7 - $15

TRADER MICKEY
(1932 - United Artists) Mickey Mouse
One Sheet: $25,000 - $40,000   *Cartoon. The Disney Poster, pg. 17.*

TRADER TOM OF THE CHINA SEAS
(1954 - Republic) Harry Lauter, Aline Towne
One Sheet: $30 - $50   *Serial. 12 Chapters.*

TRADING PLACES
(1982 - Paramount) Dan Aykroyd, Eddie Murphy
One Sheet: $5 - $10

TRAFFIC
(1973 - Columbia) Jacques Tati, Maria Kimberly, Dir: Jacques Tati
One Sheet: $15 - $25

TRAFFIC IN CRIME
(1946 - Republic) Kane Richmond, Adele Mara
One Sheet: $15 - $35

TRAFFIC IN SOULS
(1913 - Universal) Matt Moore, Jane Gail, William Welsh
One Sheet: $1,300 - $2,000   *Price is for Style A(see Christies,12/90,lot#250). One Sheet(other style):$400-$800.*

TRAGEDY AT MIDNIGHT, A
(1942 - Republic) Margaret Lindsay, John Howard
One Sheet: $20 - $40

TRAIL BEYOND, THE
(1934 - Lone Star) John Wayne
One Sheet: $1,600 - $2,500

TRAIL BEYOND, THE
(194?R - Lone Star) John Wayne
One Sheet: $75 - $150   *Re-release.*

TRAIL BLAZERS, THE
(1940 - Republic) Three Mesquiteers, Pauline Moore
One Sheet: $40 - $75

TRAIL BLAZERS
(1953 - Monogram) Alan Hale Jr., Richard Tyler
One Sheet: $15 - $25

TRAIL DRIVE, THE
(1933 - Universal) Ken Maynard, Cecilia Parker
One Sheet: $200 - $400   *Cowboy Movie Posters #160.*

TRAIL DUST
(1936 - Paramount) William Boyd, James Ellison
One Sheet: $250 - $500   *Hopalong Cassidy series.*

TRAIL GUIDE
(1951 - RKO) Tim Holt, Linda Douglas
One Sheet: $15 - $25

TRAIL MIX-UP
(1990 - Disney) Roger Rabbit, Baby Herman, Jessica Rabbit
One Sheet: $7 - $15   *Cartoon.*

One Sheet

TRAIL OF '98, THE
(1929 - MGM) Dolores Del Rio, Ralph Forbes
One Sheet: $600 - $1,000   *Cowboy Movie Posters #70.*

TRAIL OF KIT CARSON
(1945 - Republic) Allan Lane, Helen Talbot
One Sheet: $20 - $40

TRAIL OF ROBIN HOOD
(1950 - Republic) Roy Rogers, Penny Edwards
One Sheet: $100 - $200

TRAIL OF TERROR
(1935 - Supreme) Bob Steele, Beth Marion
One Sheet: $125 - $250

TRAIL OF TERROR
(1943 - PRC) Dave O'Brien, Jim Newill
One Sheet: $30 - $50

TRAIL OF THE ARROW
(1952 - Monogram) Guy Madison, Andy Devine
One Sheet: $10 - $20   *Wild Bill Hickok series.*

TRAIL OF THE LONESOME PINE
(1916 - Lasky) Charlotte Walker, Theodore Roberts, Thomas Meighan
One Sheet: $150 - $300

TRAIL OF THE LONESOME PINE
(1936 - Paramount) Henry Fonda, Sylvia Sidney, Fred MacMurray
One Sheet: $700 - $1,200

TRAIL OF THE LONESOME PINE
(1955R - Paramount) Henry Fonda, Sylvia Sidney, Fred MacMurray
One Sheet: $40 - $75   *Re-release.*

TRAIL OF THE LOST CHORD, THE
(1913 - American Film Mfg.) Ed Coxen
One Sheet: $250 - $500

TRAIL OF THE MOUNTIES
(1947 - Screen Guild) Russell Hayden, Jennifer Holt
One Sheet: $20 - $40

TRAIL OF THE OCTOPUS, THE
(1919 - Hallmark) Ben Wilson, Neva Gerber
One Sheet: $150 - $350   *Serial. 15 Episodes.*

TRAIL OF THE PINK PANTHER, THE
(1982 - MGM/United Artists) Peter Sellers, David Niven
One Sheet: $5 - $10

TRAIL OF THE ROYAL MOUNTED
(1938 - Goodwill) Kermit Maynard
One Sheet: $75 - $150   *Serial. Western.*

TRAIL OF THE RUSTLERS
(1950 - Columbia) Charles Starrett, Smiley Burnette
One Sheet: $15 - $35

TRAIL OF THE SILVER SPURS, THE
(1941 - Monogram) John King, Ray Corrigan
One Sheet: $30 - $50

TRAIL OF THE VIGILANTES
(1940 - Universal) Franchot Tone, Warren

William
One Sheet: $40 - $75

TRAIL OF THE YUKON
(1949 - Monogram) Kirby Grant, Suzanne Dalbert
One Sheet: $20 - $40

TRAIL OF VENGEANCE
(1937 - Republic) Johnny Mack Brown
One Sheet: $75 - $150

TRAIL RIDER, THE
(1925 - Fox) Buck Jones, Nancy Deaver
One Sheet: $500 - $900

TRAIL RIDERS
(1942 - Monogram) Range Busters
One Sheet: $20 - $40

TRAIL STREET
(1947 - RKO) Randolph Scott, Robert Ryan
One Sheet: $30 - $50

TRAIL TO GUNSIGHT
(1944 - Universal) Eddie Dew, Maris Wrixon
One Sheet: $15 - $35

TRAIL TO LAREDO
(1948 - Columbia) Charles Starrett, Smiley Burnette
One Sheet: $20 - $40

TRAIL TO MEXICO
(1946 - Monogram) Jimmy Wakely, Lee "Lasses" White
One Sheet: $20 - $40

TRAIL TO SAN ANTONE
(1947 - Republic) Gene Autry, Peggy Stewart
One Sheet: $75 - $150

TRAIL TO SAN ANTONE
(1953R - Republic) Gene Autry, Peggy Stevens
One Sheet: $30 - $50   *Re-release.*

TRAIL TO VENGEANCE
(1945 - Universal) Kirby Grant, Fuzzy Knight
One Sheet: $20 - $40

TRAIL TO YESTERDAY, THE
(1918 - Metro) Bert Lytell, Anna Q. Nilsson
One Sheet: $150 - $300

TRAIL'S END
(1949 - Monogram) Johnny Mack Brown, Max Terhune
One Sheet: $15 - $35

TRAILED BY THREE
(1920 - Pathe) Stuart Holmes
One Sheet: $150 - $300   *Serial. 15 Chapters.*

TRAILIN'
(1921 - Fox) Tom Mix, Ava Novak
One Sheet: $500 - $800

TRAILIN' TROUBLE
(1930 - Universal) Hoot Gibson
One Sheet: $150 - $300

TRAILIN' TROUBLE
(1937 - Grand National) Ken Maynard
One Sheet: $150 - $300

TRAILIN' WEST
(1936 - Warner Bros.) Dick Foran, Paula Stone
One Sheet: $50 - $100

TRAILIN' WEST
(1949 - Warner Bros.) Chill Wills, Elaine Riley
One Sheet: $20 - $40

TRAILING DANGER
(1947 - Monogram) Johnny Mack Brown, Raymond Hatton
One Sheet: $20 - $40

TRAILING DOUBLE TROUBLE
(1940 - Monogram) John King, Ray Corrigan
One Sheet: $30 - $50

TRAILING NORTH
(1933 - Monogram) Bob Steele, Gabby Hayes
One Sheet: $150 - $300   *Cowboy Movie Posters # 150.*

TRAILING THE KILLER
(1932 - World-Wide) Francis McDonald, Heinie Conklin
One Sheet: $75 - $125

TRAILS OF ADVENTURE

(1935 - American) Buffalo Bill, Jr., Edna Aslin

TRAILS OF THE WILD
(1935 - Ambassador) Kermit Maynard
One Sheet: $75 - $125

TRAIN, THE
(1965 - United Artists) Burt Lancaster, Paul Scofield
One Sheet: $15 - $25   *Price is for style A one sheet. One Sheet (style B): $25-$50.*

TRAIN FOR DURANGO, A
(1973 - Stellar IV) Anthony Steffen, Mark Damon
One Sheet: $3 - $5

TRAIN ROBBERS, THE
(1973 - Warner Bros.) John Wayne, Ann-Margret
One Sheet: $40 - $75   *Advance:$50-$100.*

TRAIN TO ALCATRAZ
(1948 - Republic) Donald Barry, Janet Martin
One Sheet: $20 - $40

TRAIN TO TOMBSTONE
(1950 - Lippert) Don Barry, Tom Neal
One Sheet: $15 - $35

TRAINSPOTTING
(1996 - Miramax) Ewan McGregor, Ewen Bremner
One Sheet: $7 - $15   *Heroin Addiction.*

TRAITOR WITHIN, THE
(1942 - Republic) Don "Red" Barry, Jean Parker
One Sheet: $20 - $40

TRAITOR'S GATE
(1966 - Columbia) Albert Lieven, Gary Raymond
One Sheet: $7 - $15

TRAITORS, THE
(1963 - Universal) Patrick Allen, James Maxwell
One Sheet: $5 - $10

TRAMP, THE
(1915 - Essanay) Charlie Chaplin, Edna Purviance
One Sheet: $16,000 - $25,000

TRAMP, TRAMP, TRAMP
(1926 - First National) Joan Crawford, Harry Langdon
One Sheet: $2,500 - $4,000

TRAMP, TRAMP, TRAMP
(1942 - Columbia) Jackie Gleason, Jack Durant
One Sheet: $50 - $100

TRAMP TROUBLE
(1937 - RKO) Edgar Kennedy
One Sheet: $100 - $200   *One sheet is full color. Lobby Card set is duotone.*

TRAMPLERS, THE
(1966 - Embassy) Jospeh Cotten, Gordon Scott
One Sheet: $5 - $10

TRANSATLANTIC
(1931 - Fox) Edmund Lowe, Lois Moran
One Sheet: $150 - $300

TRANSATLANTIC MERRY-GO-ROUND
(1934 - Reliance) Jack Benny, Nancy Carroll
One Sheet: $250 - $600

TRANSATLANTIC TUNNEL
(1935 - Gaumont) Richard Dix, Leslie Banks
One Sheet: $250 - $500   *Graven Images, pg. 75.*

TRANSGRESSION
(1931 - RKO) Kay Francis, Ricardo Cortez
One Sheet: $150 - $300

TRANSIENT LADY
(1935 - Universal) Gene Raymond, Henry Hull
One Sheet: $100 - $200

TRANSYLVANIA 6-5000
(1985 - New World) Jeff Goldblum, Joseph Bologna, Carol Kane
One Sheet: $5 - $10

TRAP, THE
(1946 - Monogram) Sidney Toler, Mantan

Moreland
One Sheet: $75 - $150   *Charlie Chan series.*

TRAP, THE
(1959 - Paramount) Richard Widmark, Lee J. Cobb
One Sheet: $15 - $25

TRAP FOR SANTA CLAUS, A
(1909 - Biograph) -
One Sheet: $1,900 - $3,000

TRAP HAPPY
(1946 - MGM) Tom & Jerry
One Sheet: $300 - $700   *Cartoon. Full color stone litho. Cartoon Movie Posters #275.*

TRAPEZE
(1956 - United Artists) Burt Lancaster, Gina Lollobrigida
One Sheet: $30 - $50

TRAPEZE/VIKINGS
(1962R - United Artists) -
One Sheet: $15 - $25   *Re-release double feature poster.*

TRAPP FAMILY, THE
(1961 - 20th Century Fox) Ruth Leuwerick, Hans Holt
One Sheet: $3 - $5

TRAPPED
(1931 - Big 4) Nick Stuart, Priscilla Dean
One Sheet: $75 - $125

TRAPPED
(1937 - Columbia) Charles Starrett, Peggy Stratford
One Sheet: $50 - $100

TRAPPED
(1949 - Eagle-Lion) Lloyd Bridges, Barbara Paxton
One Sheet: $15 - $30

TRAPPED BY A BLONDE
(1949 - Columbia) Hugh Herbert
One Sheet: $20 - $40

TRAPPED BY BOSTON BLACKIE
(1948 - Columbia) Chester Morris, June Vincent
One Sheet: $30 - $50

TRAPPED BY G-MEN
(1937 - Columbia) Jack Holt, Wayne Gibson
One Sheet: $75 - $150

TRAPPED BY TELEVISION
(1936 - Columbia) Mary Astor
One Sheet: $250 - $500

TRAPPED IN PARADISE
(1994 - 20th Century Fox) Nicholas Cage, Jon Lovitz, Dana Carvey
One Sheet: $3 - $5

TRAPPED IN TANGIERS
(1960 - 20th Century Fox) Edmund Purdom, Genevieve Page
One Sheet: $7 - $15

TRAPPED IN THE SKY
(1939 - Columbia) Jack Holt, Katherine DeMille
One Sheet: $50 - $100

TRASH
(1970 - -) Joe Dellesandro, Holly Woodlawn, Prod: Andy Warhol
One Sheet: $30 - $50

TRAUMA
(1962 - Parade) John Conte, Lynn Bari
One Sheet: $7 - $15

TRAUMA
(1976 - Ent. Int'l) Fiona Richmond
One Sheet: $5 - $10

TRAVELIN' ON
(1922 - Paramount) William S. Hart, James Farley
One Sheet: $250 - $600

TRAVELING EXECUTIONER, THE
(1970 - MGM) Stacy Keach, Marianna, Hill, Bud Cort
One Sheet: $5 - $10

TRAVELING HUSBANDS
(1931 - RKO) Frank Albertson, Constance Cummings

One Sheet: $75 - $150

TRAVELING SALESLADY
(1935 - First National) Joan Blondell, William Gargan
One Sheet: $75 - $150

Mini Window Card

TRAVELING SALESMAN, THE
(1921 - Paramount) Roscoe "Fatty" Arbuckle
One Sheet: $1,600 - $2,500

TRAVELING SALESWOMAN, THE
(1950 - Columbia) Joan Davis, Andy Devine
One Sheet: $15 - $30

TRAVELS WITH MY AUNT
(1972 - MGM) Maggie Smith, Alec McCowen
One Sheet: $30 - $50   *Outstanding art.*

TREACHERY RIDES THE RANGE
(1936 - Warner Bros.) Dick Foran
One Sheet: $75 - $150   *Cowboy Movie Posters #206.*

TREACHERY RIDES THE TRAIL
(1949 - Warner Bros.) Narration by Art Gilmore
One Sheet: $15 - $35

TREAD SOFTLY STRANGER
(1959 - Bentley) Diana Dors, George Baker
One Sheet: $10 - $20

TREASON
(1933 - Columbia) Buck Jones
One Sheet: $350 - $750   *Cowboy Movie Posters # 145.*

TREASURE ISLAND
(1919 - Paramount) Lon Chaney, Shirley Mason
One Sheet: $1,300 - $2,000

TREASURE ISLAND
(1934 - MGM) Wallace Beery, Jackie Cooper
One Sheet: $800 - $1,500

TREASURE ISLAND
(1950 - RKO/Disney) Bobby Driscoll, Robert Newton
One Sheet: $50 - $100

TREASURE ISLAND
(1970 - -) K. Gordon Murray
One Sheet: $3 - $5

TREASURE ISLAND
(1972 - National General) Orson Welles, Kim Burfield
One Sheet: $15 - $25

TREASURE ISLAND
(1975R - RKO/Disney) Bobby Driscoll, Robert Newton
One Sheet: $5 - $10   *Re-release.*

TREASURE JEST
(1943 - Columbia) Fox & Crow
One Sheet: $250 - $500   *Cartoon. Full color poster with scene inset.*

TREASURE OF LOST CANYON, THE
(1951 - Universal) William Powell, Julie Adams
One Sheet: $15 - $30

TREASURE OF MATECUMBE
(1976 - Disney) Robert Foxworth, Joan Hackett, Peter Ustinov
One Sheet: $5 - $10

TREASURE OF MONTE CRISTO
(1949 - Screen Guild) Glenn Langan, Adele Jergens
One Sheet: $15 - $35

One Sheet: $75 - $150

TREASURE OF PANCHO VILLA, THE
(1955 - RKO) Shelley Winters, Rory Calhoun
One Sheet: $15 - $35

TREASURE OF RUBY HILLS
(1955 - Allied Artists) Zachary Scott, Carole Matthews
One Sheet: $10 - $20

TREASURE OF SILVER LAKE, THE
(1965 - Columbia) Lex Barker, Gotz George
One Sheet: $15 - $30

TREASURE OF THE FOUR CROWNS
(1983 - -) Tony Anthony, Ana Obregon
One Sheet: $3 - $5   *Filmed in 3-D.*

TREASURE OF THE GOLDEN CONDOR
(1953 - 20th Century Fox) Cornel Wilde, Constance Smith
One Sheet: $15 - $30

TREASURE OF THE SIERRA MADRE, THE
(1948 - Warner Bros.) Humphrey Bogart, Walter Huston
One Sheet: $600 - $1,000   *Academy Award: Best Direction(John Huston), Best Supporting Actor(Walter Huston). Academy Award MoviePosters#116 & #120.*

TREASURE OF THE SIERRA MADRE, THE
(1953R - Warner Bros.) Humphrey Bogart, Walter Huston
One Sheet: $50 - $100   *Re-release.*

TREAT 'EM ROUGH
(1942 - Universal) Peggy Moran, Eddie Albert
One Sheet: $20 - $40

TREE FOR TWO
(1943 - Columbia) -
One Sheet: $100 - $200   *Cartoon.*

TREE GROWS IN BROOKLYN, A
(1945 - 20th Century Fox) Dorothy McGuire, Peggy Ann Garner, James Dunn
One Sheet: $100 - $200   *Academy Award Movie Posters #102.*

TREE IN A TEST TUBE
(1943 - -) Stan Laurel, Oliver Hardy
One Sheet: $200 - $400

TREE SURGEON, THE
(1944 - MGM) -
One Sheet: $250 - $500   *Cartoon. Full color stone litho. Cartoon Movie Posters #251.*

TREK
(1985 - Down Under) -
One Sheet: $3 - $5

TREMORS
(1990 - Universal) Kevin Bacon, Fred Ward
One Sheet: $5 - $10

TRENCHCOAT
(1983 - -) Margot Kidder, Robert Hays
One Sheet: $3 - $5

TRENT'S LAST CASE
(1929 - Fox) Donald Crisp, Raymond Griffith
One Sheet: $500 - $900

TRENT'S LAST CASE
(1952 - Republic) Michael Wilding, Margaret Lockwood, Orson Welles
One Sheet: $15 - $35

TRESPASS
(1992 - Universal) Bill Paxton, Ice-T, Ice Cube
One Sheet: $5 - $10

TRESPASSER, THE
(1929 - United Artists) Gloria Swanson
One Sheet: $700 - $1,200   *Her first all-talking picture.*

TRESPASSER, THE
(1947 - Republic) Dale Evans, Douglas Fowley
One Sheet: $15 - $35

TRIAL
(1955 - MGM) Glenn Ford, Dorothy McGuire
One Sheet: $15 - $25

TRIAL, THE
(1963 - Europa) Anthony Perkins, Orson Welles
One Sheet: $50 - $100

TRIAL AND ERROR
(1962 - MGM) Peter Sellers, Richard Attenborough

One Sheet: $7 - $15

TRIAL AND ERROR
(1997 - New Line) Michael Richards, Jeff
Daniels
One Sheet: $3 - $5

TRIAL BY TRIGGER
(1944 - Warner Bros.) Robert Shayne, Cheryl
Walker
One Sheet: $15 - $30

TRIAL OF BILLY JACK
(1974 - Warner Bros.) Delores Taylor, Tom
Laughlin
One Sheet: $5 - $10

TRIAL OF DONALD DUCK, THE
(1948 - RKO/Disney) Donald Duck
One Sheet: $1,300 - $2,000   *Cartoon. The
Disney Poster, pg. 52.*

TRIAL OF LEE HARVEY OSWALD, THE
(1964 - Falcon) Arthur Nations, George
Russell, George Mazyrack
One Sheet: $20 - $40

TRIAL OF MARY DUGAN, THE
(1941 - MGM) Laraine Day, Robert Young
One Sheet: $50 - $100

TRIAL OF VIVIENNE WARE, THE
(1932 - Fox) Joan Bennett, ZaSu Pitts
One Sheet: $125 - $250

TRIALS OF OSCAR WILDE, THE
(1960 - Kingsley) Peter Finch, James Mason
One Sheet: $20 - $40   *AKA: THE
GREEN CARNATION.*

TRIALS WITHOUT JURY
(1950 - Republic) Robert Rockwell, Kent Taylor
One Sheet: $15 - $25

TRIBES
(1970 - Fox) Darren McGavin, Earl Holliman,
Jan-Michael Vincent
One Sheet: $5 - $10

TRIBUTE
(1980 - 20th Century Fox) Jack Lemmon,
Robby Benson
One Sheet: $3 - $5

TRIBUTE TO A BAD MAN
(1956 - MGM) James Cagney, Stephen
McNally, Don Dubbins
One Sheet: $40 - $75

TRICK BABY
(1973 - Universal) Kiel Martin, Mel Stewart
One Sheet: $10 - $20   *Blaxploitation.*

TRICK FOR TRICK
(1933 - Fox) Ralph Morgan, Victor Jory
One Sheet: $100 - $200

TRICK OR TREAT
(1952 - RKO/Disney) Donald Duck
One Sheet: $1,000 - $1,800   *Cartoon.
Cartoon Movie Posters #177.*

TRICK OR TREAT
(1986 - -) Marc Price, Tony Fields
One Sheet: $5 - $10

TRICK OR TREATS
(1982 - Lone Star) Jackelyn Giroux, Peter
Jason
One Sheet: $3 - $5

TRICKY BUSINESS
(1940 - 20th Century Fox) Terry-toons
One Sheet: $100 - $200   *Cartoon. Full
color stone litho. Stock poster with inset title.*

TRICKY DICKS
(1953 - Columbia) The Three Stooges (Shemp)
One Sheet: $150 - $350   *Comedy short.
Duotone.*

TRIGGER EFFECT, THE
(1996 - Gramercy) Kyle MacLachlan, Elisabeth
Sue
One Sheet: $3 - $5

TRIGGER FINGERS
(1939 - Victory) Tim McCoy, Ben Corbett
One Sheet: $100 - $200

TRIGGER FINGERS
(1946 - Monogram) Johnny Mack Brown,
Raymond Hatton
One Sheet: $30 - $50

TRIGGER JR.
(1950 - Republic) Roy Rogers, Dale Evans
One Sheet: $75 - $175

TRIGGER LAW
(1944 - Monogram) Art Jarrett, Al St. John
One Sheet: $20 - $40

TRIGGER PALS
(1939 - Grand National) Art Jarrett, Lee Powell,
Al St. John
One Sheet: $40 - $75

TRIGGER SMITH
(1939 - Monogram) Jack Randall, Joyce Bryant
One Sheet: $30 - $50

TRIGGER TRAIL
(1944 - Universal) Rod Cameron, Fuzzy Knight
One Sheet: $20 - $40

TRIGGER TRICKS
(1930 - Universal) Hoot Gibson
One Sheet: $150 - $300

TRIGGER TRIO, THE
(1937 - Republic) The Three Mesquiteers
e
One Sheet: $50 - $100

TRIGGERMEN
(1948 - Monogram) Johnny Mack Brown,
Virginia Carroll
One Sheet: $30 - $60

TRILOGY
(1969 - Allied Artists) Mildred Natwick,
Maureen Stapleton, Martin Balsam
One Sheet: $3 - $5

TRIMMED
(1922 - Universal) Hoot Gibson, Patsy Ruth
Miller
One Sheet: $250 - $500

TRIMMED IN GOLD
(1926 - Pathe) -
One Sheet: $150 - $300

TRIMMED IN SCARLET
(1923 - Universal) Kathlyn Williams, Roy
Stewart
One Sheet: $250 - $500

TRINITY IS STILL MY NAME
(1972 - Avco/Embassy) Terence Hill, Bud
Spencer
One Sheet: $7 - $15

TRIO
(1950 - Paramount) Jean Simmons, Michael
Rennie
One Sheet: $20 - $40

TRIP, THE
(1967 - AIP) Peter Fonda, Susan Strasberg
One Sheet: $30 - $50   *Drug film.*

TRIP TO BOUNTIFUL, THE
(1985 - Island) Geraldine Page, John Heard,
Rebecca De Mornay
One Sheet: $7 - $15   *Academy
Award: Best Actress(Page). Academy Award
Movie Posters #344.*

TRIP TO PARADISE, A
(1921 - -) Bert Lytell, Virginia Valli
One Sheet: $200 - $400

TRIP TO PARIS, A
(1938 - 20th Century Fox) Jed Prouty, Shirley
Deane
One Sheet: $40 - $75

TRIPLE CROSS
(1967 - Warner Bros.) Christopher Plummer,
Romy Schneider
One Sheet: $7 - $15

TRIPLE CROSSED
(1958 - Columbia) The Three Stooges (Joe
Besser)
One Sheet: $75 - $125   *Comedy short.
Duotone. Remake of HE COOKED HIS GOOSE.*

TRIPLE DECEPTION
(1957 - Rank) Michael Craig, Julia Arnall
One Sheet: $10 - $20

TRIPLE JUSTICE
(1940 - RKO) George O'Brien, Virginia Vale
One Sheet: $50 - $100

TRIPLE THREAT
(1948 - Columbia) Richard Crane, Gloria Henry
One Sheet: $75 - $150   *Sports
(Football).*

TRIPLE TROUBLE
(1918 - Essanay) Charlie Chaplin, Edna
Purviance
One Sheet: $5,000 - $8,000

TRIPLE TROUBLE
(1950 - Monogram) Leo Gorcey, Huntz Hall
One Sheet: $40 - $75

TRIPLET TROUBLE
(1952 - MGM) Tom & Jerry
One Sheet: $250 - $600   *Cartoon. Full
color stone litho.*

TRIPOLI
(1950 - Paramount) John Payne, Maureen
O'Hara
One Sheet: $20 - $40

TRIUMPH
(1934 - Paramount) Leatrice Joy, Rod La
Rocque
One Sheet: $100 - $200

TRIUMPH OF SHERLOCK HOLMES, THE
(1935 - Olympic) Arthur Wonter, Ian Fleming
One Sheet: $500 - $800

TRIUMPH OF THE SPIRIT
(1990 - New Line) Willim Dafoe, Edward James
Olmos
One Sheet: $7 - $15   *Sports
(Boxing). Sports Movie Posters #166.*

TRIUMPH OF THE WILL
(1935 - UFA) Dir: Leni Riefenstahl
One Sheet: $11,000 - $18,000   *German. Rare
Hitler propaganda documentary. Price is for
original German poster measuring 56"x38".*

TRIUMPH OF VENUS, THE
(1918 - General) Betty Lee
One Sheet: $250 - $500

TRIUMPHS OF A MAN CALLED HORSE
(1983 - Hesperia) Richard Harris, Michael Beck
One Sheet: $5 - $10

TROCADERO
(1944 - Republic) Rosemary Lane, Johnny
Downs
One Sheet: $15 - $35

TROG
(1970 - Warner Bros.) Joan Crawford (her last
film), Michael Gough
One Sheet: $15 - $30

TROJAN HORSE, THE
(1943 - 20th Century Fox) Mighty Mouse
One Sheet: $250 - $500   *Cartoon. Title
on stock poster.*

TROJAN HORSE, THE
(1962 - Europa) Steve Reeves, John Drew
Barrymore
One Sheet: $30 - $50

TROJAN WOMEN, THE
(1971 - Cinerama) Katharine Hepburn,
Vanessa Redgrave
One Sheet: $10 - $20

TROLL
(1986 - Empire) Michael Moriarty, Shelly Hack
One Sheet: $7 - $15

TROMBA THE TIGER MAN
(1947 - Lippert) Rene Deltgen, Angelika Hauff
One Sheet: $30 - $50

TRON
(1982 - Disney) Jeff Bridges, Bruce Boxleitner
One Sheet: $7 - $15

TROOP BEVERLY HILLS
(1989 - -) Shelley Long, Craig T. Nelson
One Sheet: $3 - $5

TROOPER 77
(1925 - Ray Art) Herbert Rawlinson
One Sheet: $150 - $300   *Serial. 12
Chapters.*

TROOPER HOOK
(1957 - United Artists) Joel McCrea, Barbara
Stanwyck
One Sheet: $15 - $35

TROOPERS THREE
(1930 - Tiffany) Rex Lease, Dorothy Gulliver
One Sheet: $100 - $200

TROPIC FURY
(1939 - Universal) Richard Arlen, Andy Devine
One Sheet: $50 - $100

TROPIC HOLIDAY
(1938 - Paramount) Dorothy Lamour, Ray
Milland, Martha Raye
One Sheet: $150 - $300

Mini Window Card (Trimmed)

TROPIC OF CANCER
(1970 - Paramount) Rip Torn, James Callahan
One Sheet: $3 - $5

TROPIC ZONE
(1952 - Paramount) Ronald Reagan, Rhonda
Fleming
One Sheet: $50 - $100

TROPICAL HEAT WAVE
(1952 - Republic) Estelita, Robert Hutton
One Sheet: $15 - $30

TROUBLE
(1922 - First National) Jackie Coogan, Wallace
Beery
One Sheet: $250 - $600

TROUBLE ALONG THE WAY
(1953 - Warner Bros.) John Wayne, Donna
Reed
One Sheet: $75 - $150

One Sheet

TROUBLE AT MIDNIGHT
(1937 - Universal) Noah Beery Jr., Catherine
Hughes
One Sheet: $75 - $150

TROUBLE BUSTERS
(1933 - Majestic) Jack Hoxie
One Sheet: $100 - $200

TROUBLE CHASERS
(1945 - Monogram) Maxie Rosenbloom, Billy
Gilbert
One Sheet: $15 - $35

TROUBLE FOR TWO
(1936 - MGM) Rosalind Russell, Robert
Montgomery
One Sheet: $75 - $150

TROUBLE IN MIND
(1985 - -) Kris Kristofferson, Keith Carradine
One Sheet: $5 - $10

TROUBLE IN MOROCCO
(1937 - Columbia) Jack Holt, Mae Clarke
One Sheet: $50 - $100

TROUBLE IN PARADISE

(1932 - Paramount Publix) Miriam Hopkins, Kay Francis
One Sheet: $3,500 - $5,000

Mini Window Card (Trimmed)

TROUBLE IN STORE
(1955 - Republic) Norman Wisdom, Margaret Rutherford
One Sheet: $15 - $25

TROUBLE IN SUNDOWN
(1939 - RKO) George O'Brien, Rosalinda Keith
One Sheet: $75 - $150

TROUBLE IN TEXAS
(1937 - Grand National) Tex Ritter, Rita Cansino(Hayworth)
One Sheet: $200 - $400   *Cowboy Movie Posters #223.*

TROUBLE IN THE GLEN
(1954 - Republic) Margaret Lockwood, Forrest Tucker
One Sheet: $15 - $25

TROUBLE IN THE SKY
(1961 - Universal) Michael Craig, Peter Cushing
One Sheet: $10 - $20

TROUBLE MAKERS
(1948 - Monogram) Leo Gorcey, Huntz Hall, Lionel Stander
One Sheet: $40 - $75

TROUBLE MAN
(1972 - 20th Century Fox) Robert Hooks, Paul Winfield
One Sheet: $10 - $20   *Blaxploitation.*

TROUBLE ON THE TRAIL
(1952 - Allied Artists) Guy Madison, Andy Devine
One Sheet: $15 - $35   *Wild Bill Hickok series.*

TROUBLE PREFERRED
(1948 - 20th Century Fox) Peggy Knudsen, Lynne Roberts
One Sheet: $15 - $25

TROUBLE SHOOTER, THE
(1924 - Fox) Tom Mix, Kathleen Key
One Sheet: $250 - $600

TROUBLE WITH ANGELS, THE
(1966 - Columbia) Rosalind Russell, Binnie Barnes, Hayley Mills
One Sheet: $15 - $25

TROUBLE WITH GIRLS, THE
(1969 - MGM) Elvis Presley, Marlyn Mason
One Sheet: $30 - $60

One Sheet

TROUBLE WITH HARRY, THE

(1954 - Paramount) John Forsythe, Edmund Gwenn, Dir: Alfred Hitchcock
One Sheet: $100 - $200   *Shirley MacLaine's film debut.*

Half Sheet

TROUBLE WITH HARRY, THE
(1983R - Paramount) John Forsythe, Edmund Gwenn, Dir: Alfred Hitchcock
One Sheet: $7 - $15   *Re-release.*

TROUBLE WITH WIVES, THE
(1925 - Paramount) Florence Vidor, Tom Moore, Esther Ralston
One Sheet: $150 - $300

TROUBLE WITH WOMEN, THE
(1947 - Paramount) Ray Milland, Teresa Wright
One Sheet: $15 - $35

TROUBLEMAKER, THE
(1964 - Janus) Thomas Aldredge, Joan Darling
One Sheet: $3 - $5

TROUBLES OF A BRIDE
(1924 - Fox) Robert Agnew, Mildred June
One Sheet: $250 - $600

TRUANT OFFICER DONALD
(1941 - RKO/Disney) Donald Duck
One Sheet: $3,500 - $5,000   *Cartoon. Cartoon Movie Posters #163.*

TRUCK BUSTERS
(1943 - Warner Bros.) Richard Travis, Virginia Christine
One Sheet: $30 - $50

TRUCK STOP WOMEN
(1974 - LT) Claudia Jennings, Lieux Dressler
One Sheet: $15 - $35   *Sexploitation.*

TRUCK TURNER
(1974 - AIP) Isaac Hayes, Nichelle Nichols, Yaphet Kotto
One Sheet: $10 - $20   *Black cast.*

TRUE BELIEVER
(1988 - Columbia) James Woods, Robert Downey, Jr.
One Sheet: $3 - $5

TRUE COLORS
(1991 - Paramount) John Cusack, James Spader
One Sheet: $3 - $5

TRUE CONFESSION
(1937 - Paramount) Carole Lombard, Fred MacMurray, John Barrymore
One Sheet: $75 - $150

TRUE CONFESSIONS
(1981 - United Artists) Robert DeNiro, Robert Duvall
One Sheet: $5 - $10

TRUE GLORY
(1945 - Columbia) Gen. Dwight D. Eisenhower, WWII documentary
One Sheet: $75 - $150

TRUE GRIT
(1969 - Paramount) John Wayne, Glen Campbell
One Sheet: $75 - $150   *Academy Award: Best Actor(Wayne). Academy Award Movie Posters #253.*

TRUE HEART SUSIE
(1919 - Artcraft) Lillian Gish, Robert Harron
One Sheet: $1,300 - $2,000

TRUE IDENTITY
(1991 - Disney) Lenny Henry

One Sheet: $3 - $5

TRUE LIES
(1994 - 20th Century Fox) Arnold Schwarzenegger, Jamie Lee Curtis
One Sheet: $7 - $15

TRUE LOVE
(1989 - -) Annabella Sciorra, Ron Eldard
One Sheet: $3 - $5

TRUE ROMANCE
(1993 - Warner Bros.) Christian Slater, Patricia Arquette, all star cast
One Sheet: $7 - $15

TRUE STORIES
(1986 - Warner Bros.) David Byrne, John Goodman
One Sheet: $10 - $20

TRUE STORY OF JESSE JAMES, THE
(1957 - 20th Century Fox) Robert Wagner, Jeffrey Hunter
One Sheet: $15 - $25

TRUE STORY OF LYNN STUART, THE
(1958 - Columbia) Betsy Palmer, Jack Lord
One Sheet: $7 - $15

TRUE TO LIFE
(1943 - Paramount) Mary Martin, Franchot Tone
One Sheet: $75 - $150   *Half Sheet(all Hirschfeld art):$600-$1000.*

One Sheet

TRUE TO THE ARMY
(1942 - Paramount) Allan Jones, Ann Miller, Judy Canova
One Sheet: $50 - $100

TRUE TO THE NAVY
(1930 - Paramount Publix) Fredric March, Clara Bow
One Sheet: $800 - $1,500

TRUE-LIFE ADVENTURES
(1975 - Disney/Buena Vista) Narrators: James Algar, Winston Hibler
One Sheet: $7 - $15

TRUMPET BLOWS, THE
(1934 - Paramount) George Raft, Francis Drake
One Sheet: $100 - $200

TRUMPET ISLAND
(1920 - Vitagraph) Marguerite de la Motte, Wallace MacDonald
One Sheet: $250 - $500

TRUNK, THE
(1961 - Columbia) Phil Carey, Julia Arnall
One Sheet: $5 - $10

TRUNK TO CAIRO
(1967 - AIP) Audie Murphy, George Sanders
One Sheet: $15 - $25

TRUST
(1991 - -) Adrienne Shelly, Martin Donovan
One Sheet: $5 - $10

TRUSTED OUTLAW, THE
(1937 - Republic) Bob Steele
One Sheet: $100 - $200

TRUTH, THE
(1961 - Kingsley) Brigitte Bardot
One Sheet: $50 - $100   *French Title: LA VERITE. Price is for U.S. poster. Original French:$150-$300.*

TRUTH ABOUT CATS AND DOGS, THE

One Sheet: $3 - $5

(1996 - Fox) Janeane Garofalo, Uma Thurman
One Sheet: $7 - $15   *Romantic Comedy.*

TRUTH ABOUT MURDER, THE
(1946 - RKO) Bonita Granville, Morgan Conway
One Sheet: $30 - $50

TRUTH ABOUT SPRING, THE
(1965 - Universal) Hayley Mills, John Mills
One Sheet: $15 - $30

TRUTH ABOUT WOMEN, THE
(1958 - Continental) Laurence Harvey, Julie Harris
One Sheet: $10 - $20

TRUTH ABOUT YOUTH, THE
(1930 - First National) Loretta Young, Myrna Loy
One Sheet: $350 - $750

TRUTH JUGGLER, THE
(1922 - Pathe) Paul Parrott
One Sheet: $150 - $300

TRUTH OR DARE
(1991 - -) Documentary: Madonna
One Sheet: $15 - $25   *AKA: IN BED WITH MADONNA. Advance $20-$40.*

TRUTHFUL TULLIVER
(1927R - Triangle) -
One Sheet: $150 - $300   *Re-release.*

TRYGON FACTOR, THE
(1969 - Warner Bros.) Stewart Granger, Susan Hampshire
One Sheet: $3 - $5

TSAR'S BRIDE, THE
(1966 - Artkino) Raissa Medashkovskaya, Natalya Rudava
One Sheet: $5 - $10   *Russian.*

TUBBY THE TUBA
(1977 - New York Institute of Technology) Voice of Dick Van Dyke
One Sheet: $5 - $10   *Cartoon. Full color.*

TUCKER: THE MAN AND HIS DREAM
(1988 - Lucasfilm) Jeff Bridges, Joan Allen
One Sheet: $7 - $15

TUCSON
(1949 - 20th Century Fox) Jimmy Lydon, Penny Edwards
One Sheet: $15 - $35

TUCSON RAIDERS
(1944 - Republic) Bill Elliott
One Sheet: $30 - $50

TUFF TURF
(1985 - New World) James Spader, Kim Richards
One Sheet: $3 - $5

TUGBOAT ANNIE
(1933 - MGM) Marie Dressler, Wallace Beery, Maureen O'Sullivan
One Sheet: $300 - $700   *Price is for style A (see Sothebys, 9/92).*

TUGBOAT ANNIE SAILS AGAIN
(1940 - Warner Bros.) Marjorie Rambeau, Jane Wyman, Ronald Reagan
One Sheet: $100 - $200

TUGBOAT MICKEY
(1940 - RKO/Disney) Mickey Mouse
One Sheet: $4,000 - $6,000   *Cartoon. The Disney Poster, pg. 28.*

TUGBOAT PRINCESS
(1936 - Columbia) Edith Fellows, Walter C. Kelly
One Sheet: $50 - $100

TULIPS
(1981 - Avco) Gabe Kaplan, Bernadette Peters
One Sheet: $3 - $5

TULSA
(1949 - PRC) Susan Hayward, Robert Preston
One Sheet: $30 - $50

TULSA
(1951R - PRC) Susan Hayward, Robert Preston
One Sheet: $15 - $30   *Re-release. Duotone.*

TULSA KID, THE

(1940 - Republic) Don "Red" Barry, Noah Beery
One Sheet:　$30 - $50

TULSA KID, THE
(1948R - Republic) Don "Red" Barry, Noah Beery
One Sheet:　$7 - $15　　*Re-release.*

TUMBLEDOWN RANCH IN ARIZONA
(1941 - Monogram) Ray Corrigan, John King
One Sheet:　$30 - $50

TUMBLEWEED
(1953 - Universal) Audie Murphy, Lori Nelson
One Sheet:　$30 - $50

TUMBLEWEED TRAIL
(1942 - PRC) Bill Boyd, Art Davis
One Sheet:　$20 - $40　　*Not William "Hopalong Cassidy" Boyd.*

TUMBLEWEED TRAIL
(1946 - PRC) Eddie Dean, Shirley Patterson
One Sheet:　$15 - $30

TUMBLEWEEDS
(1925 - United Artists) William S. Hart, Lucien Littlefield
One Sheet:　$800 - $1,400

TUMBLEWEEDS
(1939R - United Artists) William S. Hart, Lucien Littlefield
One Sheet:　$100 - $200　　*Re-release.*

TUMBLING RIVER
(1927 - Fox) Tom Mix, Dorothy Dwan
One Sheet:　$250 - $600

TUMBLING TUMBLEWEEDS
(1935 - Republic) Gene Autry, Smiley Burnette
One Sheet:　$800 - $1,500　　*Gene Autry's first feature film.*

TUMBLING TUMBLEWEEDS
(1940R - Republic) Gene Autry, Smiley Burnette
One Sheet:　$125 - $250　　*Re-release.*

TUMBLING TUMBLEWEEDS
(1943R - Republic) Gene Autry, Smiley Burnette
One Sheet:　$75 - $125　　*Re-release.*

TUMMY TROUBLE
(1989 - Touchstone/Amblin) Roger Rabbit
One Sheet:　$15 - $25　　*Cartoon.*

TUNA CLIPPER
(1949 - Monogram) Roddy McDowall, Elena Verdugo
One Sheet:　$15 - $30

TUNES OF GLORY
(1960 - United Artists) Alec Guinness, John Mills
One Sheet:　$15 - $30

TUNISIAN VICTORY
(1944 - MGM) North Africa liberation documentary
One Sheet:　$50 - $100

TUNNEL, THE
(1940 - Supreme) Paul Robeson, Rachel Thomas, Edward Chapman
One Sheet:　$800 - $1,500　　*Separate Cinema, pg.46, 47 (Danish).*

TUNNEL OF LOVE, THE
(1958 - MGM) Doris Day, Richard Widmark
One Sheet:　$20 - $40

TUNNELVISION
(1976 - -) Chevy Chase, Howard Hesseman, Laraine Newman
One Sheet:　$20 - $40

TURBO: A POWER RANGERS MOVIE
(1997 - 20th Century Fox) Jason David Frank, Catherine Sutherland
One Sheet:　$7 - $15

TURBULENCE
(1996 - MGM) Ray Liotta, Lauren Holly
One Sheet:　$5 - $10

TURK 182
(1985 - 20th Century Fox) Timothy Hutton, Robert Urich, Kim Cattrall
One Sheet:　$3 - $5

TURN BACK THE CLOCK
(1933 - MGM) Lee Tracy, Mae Clarke, Ted

Healy & His Stooges (Curly)
One Sheet:　$250 - $600　　*Price assumes Three Stooges not pictured on the one sheet.*

TURN OFF THE MOON
(1937 - Paramount) Charlie Ruggles, Eleanore Whitney
One Sheet:　$50 - $100

Mini Window Card (Trimmed)

TURN TO THE RIGHT
(1922 - -) Alice Terry, Jack Mulhall
One Sheet:　$150 - $300

TURN TO THE RIGHT
(1927 - -) -
One Sheet:　$125 - $250

TURNABOUT
(1940 - United Artists) Carole Landis, John Hubbard, Adolphe Menjou, Mary Astor
One Sheet:　$50 - $100

TURNER AND HOOCH
(1989 - Touchstone) Tom Hanks, Mare Winningham
One Sheet:　$5 - $10

TURNING POINT, THE
(1952 - Paramount) William Holden, Alexis Smith
One Sheet:　$15 - $35

TURNING POINT, THE
(1977 - 20th Century Fox) Anne Bancroft, Shirley MacLaine, Mikhail Baryshnikov
One Sheet:　$15 - $25　　*Baryshnikov's film debut.*

TURNING THE TABLES
(1919 - Paramount-Artcraft) Dorothy Gish
One Sheet:　$700 - $1,200

TURTLE DIARY
(1985 - CBS) Glenda Jackson, Ben Kingsley
One Sheet:　$3 - $5

TUTTLES OF TAHITI, THE
(1942 - RKO) Charles Laughton, Jon Hall
One Sheet:　$40 - $75

TUXEDO JUNCTION
(1941 - Republic) Weaver Bros., Frankie Darro, Clayton Moore
One Sheet:　$40 - $75　　*Country musical.*

TV OF TOMORROW
(1953 - MGM) Stock
One Sheet:　$30 - $50

TWELVE ANGRY MEN
(1956 - United Artists) Henry Fonda, Lee J. Cobb
One Sheet:　$50 - $100

TWELVE CHAIRS, THE
(1970 - UMC) Ron Moody, Frank Langella, Dom DeLuise
One Sheet:　$15 - $25

TWELVE CROWDED HOURS
(1939 - RKO) Richard Dix, Lucille Ball
One Sheet:　$100 - $200

TWELVE HOURS TO KILL
(1960 - 20th Century Fox) Nico Minardos, Barbara Eden
One Sheet:　$10 - $20

TWELVE MILES OUT
(1927 - MGM) Joan Crawford, John Gilbert
One Sheet:　$600 - $1,000

---

12 MONKEYS
(1995 - Universal) Bruce Willis, Brad Pitt
One Sheet:　$7 - $15　　*Advance Style: $12-$16.*

12 O'CLOCK AND ALL AIN'T WELL!
(1940' - 20th Century Fox) Terry Toons
One Sheet:　$100 - $200　　*Cartoon.*

TWELVE O'CLOCK HIGH
(1949 - 20th Century Fox) Gregory Peck, Hugh Marlowe
One Sheet:　$250 - $500　　*Academy Award Movie Posters #124.*

TWELVE O'CLOCK HIGH
(1955R - 20th Century Fox) Gregory Peck, Hugh Marlowe
One Sheet:　$30 - $50　　*Re-release.*

12 TO THE MOON
(1960 - Columbia) Ken Clark
One Sheet:　$15 - $30

20TH CENTURY
(1934 - Columbia) John Barrymore, Carole Lombard
One Sheet:　$13,000 - $20,000

25TH HOUR, THE
(1967 - MGM) Anthony Quinn, Virna Lisi
One Sheet:　$5 - $10

25 YEARS AGO
(1960 - Universal) -
One Sheet:　$15 - $35　　*Documentary.*

24 HOUR ALERT
(1955 - Warner Bros.) -
One Sheet:　$5 - $10

24 HOURS
(1931 - Paramount) Clive Brook, Kay Francis
One Sheet:　$75 - $150

20 MILLION MILES TO EARTH
(1957 - Columbia) William Hopper, Joan Taylor
One Sheet:　$125 - $250　　*Ray Harryhausen effects. One Sheet(rare overseas release):$800-$1,500. Graven Images, pg. 177.*

20 MILLION SWEETHEARTS
(1934 - First National/Vitaphone) Dick Powell, Pat O'Brien, Ginger Rogers
One Sheet:　$500 - $800　　*Big Band musical. Ted Fiorito and His Band.*

TWENTY MINUTES OF LOVE
(1914 - Keystone) Charlie Chaplin
One Sheet:　$7,500 - $12,000

TWENTY MINUTES OF LOVE
(1916R - -) Charlie Chaplin
One Sheet:　$250 - $500　　*Re-release.*

20 MULE TEAM
(1940 - MGM) Wallace Beery, Leo Carrillo
One Sheet:　$30 - $60

21 DAYS TOGETHER
(1940 - Columbia) Vivien Leigh, Laurence Olivier
One Sheet:　$600 - $1,000

TWENTY PLUS TWO
(1961 - Allied Artists) David Janssen, Jeanne Crain
One Sheet:　$10 - $20

27TH DAY
(1957 - Columbia) Valerie French, Gene Barry
One Sheet:　$40 - $75

20,000 EYES
(1962 - 20th Century Fox) -
One Sheet:　$7 - $15

20,000 LEAGUES UNDER THE SEA
(1954 - Buena Vista/Disney) Kirk Douglas, James Mason
One Sheet:　$150 - $350　　*Graven Images, pg. 149, 176.*

20,000 LEAGUES UNDER THE SEA
(1963R - Disney) Kirk Douglas, James Mason
One Sheet:　$40 - $75　　*Re-release.*

20,000 LEAGUES UNDER THE SEA
(1971R - Walt Disney) Kirk Douglas, James Mason
One Sheet:　$15 - $35　　*Re-release.*

20,000 MEN A YEAR
(1939 - 20th Century Fox) Randolph Scott,

Preston Foster
One Sheet:　$125 - $250

20,000 YEARS IN SING SING
(1932 - First National) Spencer Tracy, Bette Davis
One Sheet:　$250 - $600　　*One Sheet is text without graphics.*

TWENTY THREE AND A HALF HOURS' LEAVE
(1919 - Paramount Artcraft) Douglas MacLean, Doris May
One Sheet:　$150 - $300

23 1/2 HOURS LEAVE
(1937 - Grand National) James Ellison, Terry Walker
One Sheet:　$50 - $100

23 PACES TO BAKER STREET
(1956 - 20th Century Fox) Van Johnson, Vera Miles
One Sheet:　$15 - $25

TWICE BLESSED
(1945 - MGM) Preston Foster, Gail Patrick, Lee and Lynn Wilde
One Sheet:　$15 - $35

TWICE DEAD
(1988 - -) Tom Breznahan, Jill Whitlow
One Sheet:　$3 - $5

TWICE IN A LIFETIME
(1985 - Bud Yorkin) Gene Hackman, Ann-Margret
One Sheet:　$3 - $5

TWICE TWO
(1933 - MGM) Laurel & Hardy
One Sheet:　$2,500 - $4,000

TWICE UPON A TIME
(1983 - Warner Bros.) -
One Sheet:　$7 - $15　　*Cartoon.*

TWICE-TOLD TALES
(1963 - United Artists) Vincent Price, Sebastian Cabot
One Sheet:　$40 - $75

TWILIGHT FOR THE GODS
(1958 - Universal) Rock Hudson, Cyd Charisse
One Sheet:　$20 - $40

TWILIGHT IN THE SIERRAS
(1950 - Republic) Roy Rogers, Dale Evans
One Sheet:　$100 - $200

TWILIGHT IN THE SIERRAS
(1956R - Republic) Roy Rogers, Dale Evans
One Sheet:　$50 - $100　　*Re-release.*

TWILIGHT OF HONOR
(1963 - MGM) Richard Chamberlain, Nick Adams
One Sheet:　$10 - $20

TWILIGHT ON THE PRAIRIE
(1944 - Universal) Eddie Quillan, Vivian Austin
One Sheet:　$20 - $40

TWILIGHT ON THE RIO GRANDE
(1947 - Republic) Gene Autry, Adele Mara
One Sheet:　$75 - $150

TWILIGHT ON THE RIO GRANDE
(1953R - Republic) Gene Autry, Adele Mara
One Sheet:　$40 - $75　　*Re-release.*

TWILIGHT ON THE TRAIL
(1941 - Paramount) Bill Boyd, Andy Clyde
One Sheet:　$150 - $300　　*Hopalong Cassidy series.*

One Sheet

TWILIGHT PEOPLE
(1972 - Dimension) John Ashley, Pam Grier
One Sheet: $7 - $15

TWILIGHT TIME
(1983 - MGM) Karl Malden
One Sheet: $3 - $5

TWILIGHT WOMEN
(1953 - Lippert) Freda Jackson, Lois Maxwell
One Sheet: $15 - $30

TWILIGHT ZONE - THE MOVIE
(1983 - Warner Bros.) Dan Aykroyd, Vic Morrow
One Sheet: $10 - $20   *TV tie-in.*

TWILIGHT'S LAST GLEAMING
(1977 - Allied Artists) Burt Lancaster, Richard Widmark
One Sheet: $5 - $10

TWIN BEDS
(1942 - United Artists) Joan Bennett, George Brent
One Sheet: $30 - $50

TWIN HUSBANDS
(1934 - Chesterfield) John Miljan, Shirley Grey
One Sheet: $75 - $150

TWIN PEAKS: FIRE WALK WITH ME
(1992 - New Line) Kyle Maclachlan, Sheryl Lee
One Sheet: $7 - $15   *TV tie-in.*

TWIN TRIPLETS
(1935 - MGM) Thelma Todd, Patsy Kelly
One Sheet: $250 - $500

TWINKLE AND SHINE
(1959 - -) Doris Day, Jack Lemmon
One Sheet: $15 - $25   *Re-title of IT HAPPENED TO JANE.*

TWINKLE IN GOD'S EYE, THE
(1955 - Republic) Mickey Rooney, Coleen Gray
One Sheet: $15 - $25

TWINKLETOES
(1926 - First National) Colleen Moore
One Sheet: $200 - $400

TWINS
(1988 - Universal) Arnold Schwarzenegger, Danny DeVito
One Sheet: $5 - $10

TWINS OF EVIL
(1972 - Universal) Peter Cushing, Dennis Price
One Sheet: $20 - $40

TWINS OF EVIL/HANDS OF THE RIPPER COMBO
(1972 - Universal) -
One Sheet: $15 - $25   *Double feature poster.*

TWIST ALL NIGHT
(1962 - AIP) Louis Prima, June Wilkinson
One Sheet: $30 - $50   *Rock 'n' Roll.*

TWIST AND SHOUT
(1986 - -) Adam Tonsberg, Lars Simonsen
One Sheet: $5 - $10

TWIST AROUND THE CLOCK
(1961 - Columbia) Chubby Checker, Dion
One Sheet: $40 - $75   *Rock 'n' Roll.*

One Sheet

TWIST OF FATE
(1954 - British-Lion) Ginger Rogers, Herbert Lam
One Sheet: $30 - $50   *AKA: THE BEAUTIFUL STRANGER.*

TWIST OF SAND, A
(1968 - United Artists) Richard Johnson, Honor Blackman, Jeremy Kemp
One Sheet: $3 - $5

TWISTED NERVE
(1969 - National General) Hayley Mills, Hywell Bennet, Billie Whitelaw
One Sheet: $10 - $20

TWISTER
(1996 - Warner Bros.) Bill Paxton, Helen Hunt, Jamie Gertz
One Sheet: $7 - $15

TWO AGAINST THE WORLD
(1932 - Warner Bros.) Constance Bennett, Neil Hamilton
One Sheet: $125 - $250

TWO AGAINST THE WORLD
(1936 - Warner Bros.) Humphrey Bogart, Beverly Roberts
One Sheet: $350 - $750

TWO ALONE
(1934 - RKO) ZaSu Pitts, Jean Parker, Tom Brown
One Sheet: $100 - $200

TWO AND ONE TWO
(1934 - Fox) Rosita Moreno, Valentine Parera
One Sheet: $125 - $250

TWO ARABIAN KNIGHTS
(1927 - United Artists) William Boyd, Mary Astor
One Sheet: $250 - $500   *Academy Award Movie Posters #6.*

TWO ARE GUILTY
(1964 - MGM) Anthony Perkins, Jean-Claude Brialy
One Sheet: $10 - $20

TWO BEFORE ZERO
(1963 - Ellis) -
One Sheet: $3 - $5

TWO BITS
(1995 - Miramax) Al Pacino, Jerry Barone
One Sheet: $5 - $10

TWO BLONDES AND A REDHEAD
(1947 - Columbia) Jean Porter, Jimmy Lloyd, June Preisser
One Sheet: $20 - $40

TWO BRIGHT BOYS
(1939 - Universal) Jackie Cooper, Freddie Bartholomew
One Sheet: $75 - $150

2 DAYS IN THE VALLEY
(1996 - MGM/UA) Danny Aiello, James Spader, Teri Hatcher
One Sheet: $5 - $10

TWO DOLLAR BETTOR
(1951 - Realart) John Litel, Marie Windsor
One Sheet: $15 - $25

TWO ENGLISH GIRLS
(1971 - Janus) Jean-Pierre Leaud, Kika Markham, Dir: Troufee
One Sheet: $30 - $50   *French.*

TWO EVIL EYES
(1990 - -) Harvey Keitel, Adrienne Barbeau, Dirs: Romero & Argento
One Sheet: $15 - $25

TWO FACES OF DR. JEKYLL, THE
(1961 - AIP) See HOUSE OF FRIGHT

TWO FLAGS WEST
(1950 - 20th Century Fox) Linda Darnell, Joseph Cotten
One Sheet: $15 - $35

TWO FLAMING YOUTHS
(1927 - Paramount) W.C. Fields, Chester Conklin, Mary Brian
One Sheet: $1,600 - $2,500

TWO FOR THE ROAD
(1967 - 20th Century Fox) Audrey Hepburn, Albert Finney
One Sheet: $40 - $75

TWO FOR THE SEESAW
(1962 - United Artists) Robert Mitchum, Shirley MacLaine
One Sheet: $15 - $35

TWO FOR TONIGHT
(1935 - Paramount) Bing Crosby, Joan Bennett
One Sheet: $150 - $350

TWO GALS AND A GUY
(1951 - United Artists) Janis Paige, Robert Alda
One Sheet: $15 - $25

TWO GENTLEMEN SHARING
(1969 - AIP) Robin Phillips, Hal Frederick, Judy Geeson
One Sheet: $5 - $10

TWO GIRLS AND A SAILOR
(1944 - MGM) Gloria DeHaven, June Allyson, Van Johnson
One Sheet: $30 - $50

TWO GIRLS ON BROADWAY
(1940 - MGM) Lana Turner, Joan Blondell, George Murphy
One Sheet: $50 - $100

TWO GROOMS FOR A BRIDE
(1957 - 20th Century Fox) Virginia Bruce, John Carroll
One Sheet: $10 - $20

TWO GUN BETTY
(1918 - Pathe) Bessie Barriscale
One Sheet: $250 - $500

TWO GUN GINSBURG
(1929 - RKO) -
One Sheet: $150 - $300

TWO GUN LADY
(1956 - Associated) Peggie Castle, William Talman
One Sheet: $15 - $25

TWO GUN MAN
(1914R - W.H. Production) William S. Hart
One Sheet: $200 - $400   *Re-release.*

TWO GUNS AND A BADGE
(1954 - Allied Artists) Wayne Morris, Beverly Garland
One Sheet: $15 - $30

TWO GUYS FROM MILWAUKEE
(1946 - Warner Bros.) Dennis Morgan, Jack Carson, Joan Leslie
One Sheet: $15 - $35

TWO GUYS FROM TEXAS
(1948 - Warner Bros.) Dennis Morgan, Jack Carson, Dorothy Malone
One Sheet: $30 - $50

TWO HEADS ON A PILLOW
(1934 - Liberty) Neil Hamilton, Miriam Jordan
One Sheet: $75 - $150

200 MOTELS
(1971 - United Artists) Frank Zappa's Mothers Of Invention, Ringo Starr
One Sheet: $75 - $125

TWO IF BY SEA
(1995 - Warner Bros.) Denis Leary, Sandra Bullock, Yaphet Kotto
One Sheet: $4 - $8

TWO IN A CROWD
(1936 - Universal) Joan Bennett, Joel McCrea
One Sheet: $75 - $150

TWO IN A TAXI
(1941 - Columbia) Anita Louise, Dick Purcell
One Sheet: $50 - $100

TWO IN REVOLT
(1936 - RKO) Louise Latimer, John Arledge
One Sheet: $50 - $100

TWO IN THE DARK
(1936 - RKO) Walter Abel, Margaret Grahame
One Sheet: $75 - $125

TWO JAKES, THE
(1990 - Paramount) Jack Nicholson
One Sheet: $7 - $15

TWO KINDS OF LOVE
(1920 - -) George McDaniels, Ted Brooks, Jimsy Maye
One Sheet: $200 - $400

TWO KINDS OF WOMEN
(1932 - Paramount Publix) Miriam Hopkins

MacLaine
One Sheet: $15 - $35

TWO LATINS FROM MANHATTAN
(1941 - Columbia) Joan Davis, Jinx Falkenburg
One Sheet: $40 - $75

TWO LAZY CROWS
(1949R - Columbia) Scrappy
One Sheet: $30 - $60   *Cartoon. Re-release.*

TWO LITTLE BEARS, THE
(1961 - 20th Century Fox) Eddie Albert, Jane Wyatt
One Sheet: $7 - $15

TWO LOST WORLDS
(1950 - Eagle Lion) Laura Elliott, Jim Arness
One Sheet: $30 - $50

TWO LOST WORLDS
(1957R - Eagle Lion) Laura Elliott, Jim Amess
One Sheet: $15 - $20   *Re-release.*

TWO LOST WORLDS/UNKNOWN ISLAND
(1950S - Classic Pictures) -
One Sheet: $15 - $30   *Double feature poster.*

TWO LOVES
(1961 - MGM) Shirley MacLaine, Laurence Harvey
One Sheet: $15 - $30

TWO MINUTE WARNING
(1976 - Universal) Charlton Heston, John Cassavetes
One Sheet: $10 - $20   *Sports (Football). Sports Movie Posters #204.*

TWO MOONS
(1920 - Fox) Buck Jones, Carol Holloway
One Sheet: $500 - $800   *Cowboy Movie Posters #23.*

TWO MOUSEKETEERS, THE
(1952 - MGM) Tom & Jerry
One Sheet: $250 - $600   *Cartoon. Academy Award: Best Cartoon Short. Full color stone litho. Cartoon Movie Posters #281.*

TWO MRS. CARROLLS, THE
(1947 - Warner Bros.) Humphrey Bogart, Barbara Stanwyck
One Sheet: $125 - $250

TWO MUCH
(1996 - Touchstone) Antonio Banderas, Melanie Griffith, Daryl Hannah
One Sheet: $7 - $15

TWO MUGS FROM BROOKLYN
(1942 - United Artists) William Bendix, Joe Sawyer, Grace Bradley
One Sheet: $30 - $50

TWO MULES FOR SISTER SARA
(1970 - Universal) Shirley MacLaine, Clint Eastwood
One Sheet: $30 - $50

TWO NIGHTS WITH CLEOPATRA
(1953 - Ultra) Sophia Loren
One Sheet: $30 - $50

TWO O'CLOCK COURAGE
(1945 - RKO) Tom Conway, Ann Rutherford
One Sheet: $20 - $40

TWO OF A KIND
(1951 - Columbia) Lizabeth Scott, Edmond O'Brien
One Sheet: $30 - $50

TWO OF A KIND
(1983 - 20th Century Fox) John Travolta, Olivia Newton-John
One Sheet: $15 - $25

TWO OF US, THE
(1936 - Gaumont) Jack Hulbert, Gina Malo
One Sheet: $50 - $100

TWO ON A GUILLOTINE
(1965 - Warner Bros.) Connie Stevens, Dean Jones
One Sheet: $15 - $25

TWO PEOPLE
(1973 - Universal) Peter Fonda, Lindsay Wagner (her 1st major role)
One Sheet: $7 - $15

TWO RODE TOGETHER

(1961 - Columbia) James Stewart, Richard Widmark
One Sheet: $20 - $40

TWO SAPLINGS
(1943 - Columbia) -
One Sheet: $40 - $75 *Comedy short. Duotone.*

TWO SECONDS
(1932 - First National) Edward G. Robinson, Preston Foster
One Sheet: $150 - $350

TWO SENORITAS FROM CHICAGO
(1943 - Columbia) Jinx Falkenburg, Joan Davis
One Sheet: $30 - $50

TWO SINNERS
(1935 - Republic) Otto Kruger, Martha Sleeper
One Sheet: $75 - $150

TWO SISTERS FROM BOSTON
(1946 - MGM) Kathryn Grayson, June Allyson
One Sheet: $20 - $40

Window Card

TWO SMART PEOPLE
(1946 - MGM) Lucille Ball, John Hodiak
One Sheet: $75 - $125

TWO SOLITUDES
(1976 - Compass) Jean Pierre Armont, Stacey Keach
One Sheet: $3 - $5

TWO TARS
(1928 - MGM) Laurel & Hardy, Edgar Kennedy
One Sheet: $4,000 - $6,000

TWO THOROUGHBREDS
(1939 - RKO) Jimmy Lydon, Joan Brodell
One Sheet: $30 - $50

2001: A SPACE ODYSSEY
(1968 - MGM) Keir Dullea, Dir: Stanley Kubrick
One Sheet: $150 - $300 *Price is for Style A (space wheel) one sheet. One Sheet(Style B, men on moon):$150-$300; One Sheet(Style C,centrifuge):$800-$1500; One Sheet (star child):$1200-$1800; One Sheet (Eve style): $1200-$2000; One Sheet (hologram):$2500.*

An epic drama of adventure and exploration

One Sheet

2001: A SPACE ODYSSEY
(1971R - MGM) Keir Dullea, Dir: Stanley Kubrick
One Sheet: $75 - $125 *Re-release. Starchild poster.*

2001: A SPACE ODYSSEY
(1974R - MGM) Keir Dullea, Dir: Stanley Kubrick
One Sheet: $30 - $50 *Re-release.*

2001: A SPACE ODYSSEY

(1980R - MGM) Keir Dullea, Dir: Stanley Kubrick
One Sheet: $15 - $30 *Re-release.*

2000 B.C.
(1931 - Educational) Terry-toons
One Sheet: $800 - $1,500 *Cartoon. Cartoon Movie Posters #77.*

TWO THOUSAND MANIACS
(1964 - -) Connie Mason, Thomas Wood, Dir: Herschell Gordon Lewis
One Sheet: $75 - $150

2010
(1984 - MGM) Roy Scheider, John Lithgow, Helen Mirren
One Sheet: $15 - $25

2000 YEARS LATER
(1969 - Warner Bros.) Terry Thomas, Edward Horton
One Sheet: $7 - $15

TWO TICKETS TO BROADWAY
(1951 - RKO) Tony Martin, Janet Leigh
One Sheet: $20 - $40

TWO TICKETS TO LONDON
(1943 - Universal) Michele Morgan, Alan Curtis
One Sheet: $30 - $50

TWO TICKETS TO PARIS
(1962 - Columbia) Joey Dee, Gary Crosby
One Sheet: $15 - $25

TWO TOUGH TENDERFEET
(1918 - Mack Sennett) Polly Moran, Ben Turpin, Charlie Lynn
One Sheet: $200 - $400 *Cowboy Movie Posters #15.*

TWO TOUGH TENDERFEET
(1923 - Paramount) Ben Turpin, Polly Moran
One Sheet: $250 - $600

TWO WEEKS IN ANOTHER TOWN
(1962 - MGM) Kirk Douglas, Edward G. Robinson
One Sheet: $15 - $30

TWO WEEKS IN SEPTEMBER
(1967 - Paramount) Brigitte Bardot, Laurent Terzieff
One Sheet: $20 - $40

TWO WEEKS TO LIVE
(1943 - RKO) Lum 'n' Abner
One Sheet: $75 - $125

TWO WEEKS VACATION
(1952 - RKO/Disney) Goofy
One Sheet: $500 - $800 *Cartoon. The Disney Poster, pg. 62.*

TWO WEEKS WITH LOVE
(1950 - MGM) Jane Powell, Ricardo Montalban
One Sheet: $20 - $40

TWO WEEKS WITH PAY
(1921 - Realart) Bebe Daniels, Jack Mulhall
One Sheet: $250 - $500

TWO WHO DARED
(1937 - Grand National) Anna Sten, Henry Wilcoxon
One Sheet: $50 - $100

TWO WISE MAIDS
(1937 - Republic) Alison Skopworth, Polly Moran
One Sheet: $40 - $75

TWO WOMEN
(1961 - Champion) Sophia Loren
One Sheet: $75 - $150 *Academy Award: Sophia Loren. Academy Award Movie Posters #204. Price is for U.S. release poster.*

TWO WORLDS
(1930 - British International) Norah Baring, John Longden
One Sheet: $100 - $200

TWO YANKS IN TRINIDAD
(1942 - Columbia) Pat O'Brien, Brian Donlevy
One Sheet: $30 - $50

TWO YEARS BEFORE THE MAST
(1946 - Paramount) Brian Donlevy, Alan Ladd
One Sheet: $75 - $150

TWO-FACED WOMAN
(1941 - MGM) Greta Garbo (last film),

Constance Bennett
One Sheet: $500 - $800 *One Sheet(Style C):$200-$400.*

One Sheet

TWO-FISTED
(1935 - Paramount) Lee Tracy, Gail Patrick
One Sheet: $75 - $150

TWO-FISTED GENTLEMEN
(1936 - Columbia) James Dunn, June Clayworth
One Sheet: $100 - $200

TWO-FISTED JUSTICE
(1930 - Monogram) Tom Tyler, Barbara Weeks
One Sheet: $150 - $300

TWO-FISTED JUSTICE
(1942 - Monogram) Range Busters
One Sheet: $20 - $40

TWO-FISTED LAW
(1932 - Columbia) Tim McCoy, John Wayne
One Sheet: $150 - $300 *Cowboy Movie Posters #s 123, 126. Wayne had a bit part and is probably not shown on any posters.*

TWO-FISTED RANGERS
(1939 - Columbia) Charles Starrett, Lorna Gray
One Sheet: $50 - $100

TWO-FISTED SHERIFF
(1937 - Columbia) Charles Starrett, Barbara Weeks
One Sheet: $75 - $150

TWO-FISTED STRANGER
(1946 - Columbia) Charles Starrett, Smiley Burnette
One Sheet: $30 - $50

TWO-GUN CABALLERO, THE
(1931 - Imperial) Robert Fraser, Bobby Nelson
One Sheet: $50 - $100

TWO-GUN JUSTICE
(1938 - Monogram) Tim McCoy, Betty Compson
One Sheet: $150 - $300

TWO-GUN LAW
(1937 - Columbia) Charles Starrett, Peggy Stratford
One Sheet: $75 - $150

TWO-GUN MAN, THE
(1931 - Tiffany) Ken Maynard
One Sheet: $150 - $350

TWO-GUN MAN FROM HARLEM
(1938 - Sack) Herbert Jeffrey, Clarence Brooks
One Sheet: $150 - $300 *Black cast. Separate Cinema, pg. 50.*

TWO-GUN MARSHAL
(1953 - United Artists) Guy Madison, Andy Devine
One Sheet: $15 - $35 *Wild Bill Hickok series.*

TWO-GUN MICKEY
(1934 - United Artists) Mickey Mouse
One Sheet: $19,000 - $30,000 *Cartoon.*

TWO-GUN MICKEY
(1974R - Disney) Mickey Mouse
One Sheet: $15 - $30 *Re-release. Cartoon.*

TWO-GUN SHERIFF
(1941 - Republic) Don Barry
One Sheet: $30 - $50

TWO-GUN TEACHER, THE

(1952 - Allied Artists) Guy Madison, Andy Devine
One Sheet: $15 - $35 *Wild Bill Hickok series.*

TWO-HEADED SPY, THE
(1958 - Columbia) Jack Hawkins, Gia Scala, Michael Caine
One Sheet: $7 - $15

TWO-LANE BLACKTOP
(1971 - Universal) James Taylor, Warren Oates
One Sheet: $30 - $50 *Sports (Auto Racing).*

TWO-MAN SUBMARINE
(1944 - Columbia) Ann Savage, Tom Neal
One Sheet: $30 - $50

TWO-MOON JUNCTION
(1988 - -) Sherilyn Fenn, Richard Tyson
One Sheet: $7 - $15

TWONKY, THE
(1952 - United Artists) Hans Conried, Gloria Blondell
Ore Sheet: $50 - $100 *Sci-fi.*

TWO-TIME MAMA
(1926 - Pathecomedy) Glenn Tryon, Vivien Oakland
One Sheet: $200 - $400

TYCOON
(1947 - RKO) John Wayne, Laraine Day
One Sheet: $125 - $250

TYPHOON
(1940 - Paramount) Dorothy Lamour, Robert Preston
One Sheet: $200 - $400

TYRANT OF THE SEA
(1950 - Columbia) Ron Randell, Rhys Williams
One Sheet: $7 - $15

TYSON VS. HOLYFIELD
(1991 - -) Mike Tyson, Evander Holyfield
One Sheet: $30 - $50 *Sports (Boxing). Advance poster for match that never took place.*

U2: RATTLE AND HUM
(1988 - -) U2
One Sheet: $15 - $30 *Rock 'n' Roll documentary. Advance(Bono):$35-$60. Advance(Edge):$30-$50. Advance(Regular):$25-$40.*

U-238 AND THE WITCH DOCTOR
(1953 - Republic) Clayton Moore, Phyllis Coates
One Sheet: $50 - $100 *Feature version of JUNGLE DRUMS OF AFRICA.*

U-BOAT 29
(1939 - Columbia) Conrad Veidt, S. Shaw, Valerie Hobson
One Sheet: $75 - $150

U-BOAT PRISONER
(1944 - Columbia) Bruce Bennett, John Abbott
One Sheet: $20 - $40

UFO
(1956 - United Artists) -
One Sheet: $40 - $75 *Documentary.*

UFO: TARGET EARTH
(1974 - Centrum) Nick Plakias, Cythia Cline, Phil Erickson
One Sheet: $7 - $15

UGETSU
(1953 - -) Machiko Kyo, Masayuki Mori
One Sheet: $50 - $100

UGLY AMERICAN, THE
(1963 - Universal) Marlon Brando, Eiji Okada
One Sheet: $30 - $50

UGLY DACHSHUND, THE
(1966 - Buena Vista) Suzanne Pleshette, Dean Jones
One Sheet: $15 - $25

UGLY DUCKLING, THE
(1949R - RKO/Disney) -
One Sheet: $200 - $400 *Re-release. Cartoon. Duotone.*

UGLY ONES, THE
(1968 - United Artists) Richard Wyler, Tomas Milian, Ella Karin

One Sheet: $3 - $5   *Spaghetti western.*

UHF
(1989 - -) "Weird Al" Yankovic, Victoria Jackson
One Sheet: $5 - $10

ULTIMATE WARRIOR, THE
(1975 - Warner Bros.) Yul Brynner, Max von Sydow
One Sheet: $7 - $15

ULYSSES
(1954 - Paramount) Kirk Douglas, Silvana Mangano
One Sheet: $40 - $75

ULYSSES
(1960R - Paramount) Kirk Douglas, Silvana Mangano
One Sheet: $15 - $25   *Re-release.*

ULYSSES
(1967 - Continental) Barbara Jefford, Milo O'Shea
One Sheet: $10 - $20

ULZANA'S RAID
(1972 - Universal) Burt Lancaster, Richard Jaeckel
One Sheet: $7 - $15

UMBERTO D
(1955 - Amato-Rizzoli) Carlo Battisti, Maria Pia Casilio
One Sheet: $30 - $50   *Italian.*

UMBRELLAS OF CHERBOURG, THE
(1964 - Allied Artists) Catherine Deneuve, Nino Castelnuovo
One Sheet: $20 - $40

UM-PA
(1933 - Columbia) Jack Osterman, Gloria Shea
One Sheet: $150 - $300

UNACCUSTOMED AS WE ARE
(1929 - MGM) Laurel & Hardy, Edgar Kennedy, Mae Busch
One Sheet: $4,000 - $6,000   *The team's first sound comedy.*

UNASHAMED
(1932 - MGM) Helen Twelvetrees, Robert Young
One Sheet: $100 - $200

UNASHAMED
(1940S - -) -
One Sheet: $40 - $75   *Exploitation.*

UNBEARABLE LIGHTNESS OF BEING, THE
(1987 - Saul Zaentz) Daniel Day-Lewis, Juliette, Binoche
One Sheet: $15 - $30

UNBORN SOULS
(1939 - Del Frazier) -
One Sheet: $50 - $100   *Exploitation.*

UNCANNY, THE
(1977 - Rank) Peter Cushing, Ray Millard, Donald Pleasence
One Sheet: $15 - $35

UNCENSORED
(1944 - 20th Century Fox) Eric Portman, Phyllis Calvert
One Sheet: $40 - $75

UNCERTAIN GLORY
(1944 - Warner Bros.) Errol Flynn, Paul Lukas
One Sheet: $150 - $300

One Sheet

UNCERTAIN LADY
(1934 - Universal) Edward Everett Horton, Genevieve Tobin
One Sheet: $75 - $150

UNCHAINED
(1954 - Warner Bros.) Elroy Hirsch, Barbara Hale
One Sheet: $20 - $40

UNCHAINED GODDESS, THE
(1958 - N. W. Ayer & Son) -
One Sheet: $5 - $10

UNCHAINED SEAS
(1921 - -) Rudolph Valentino
One Sheet: $800 - $1,500

UNCIVIL WAR BIRDS
(1946 - Columbia) The Three Stooges (Curly)
One Sheet: $2,500 - $4,000   *Comedy short. Duotone.*

UNCIVIL WARRIORS
(1935 - Columbia) The Three Stooges (Curly)
One Sheet: $13,000 - $20,000 *Comedy short. Duotone.*

UNCLE, THE
(1966 - Lenart) Rupert Davies, Brenda Bruce
One Sheet: $3 - $5

UNCLE BUCK
(1989 - Universal) John Candy, Amy Madigan
One Sheet: $3 - $5

UNCLE DONALD'S ANTS
(1952 - RKO/Disney) Donald Duck
One Sheet: $500 - $800   *Cartoon. The Disney Poster, pg. 61.*

UNCLE HARRY
(1945 - Universal) George Sanders, Geraldine Fitzgerald
One Sheet: $30 - $60

UNCLE SILAS
(1951 - Two Cities) Jean Simmons, Derek Bond
One Sheet: $30 - $50   *AKA: THE INHERITANCE.*

UNCLE TOM'S CABANA
(1947 - MGM) Tex Avery
One Sheet: $800 - $1,500   *Cartoon. Separate Cinema, pg. 9. Cartoon Movie Posters #303.*

UNCLE TOM'S CABIN
(1918 - Paramount Famous Lasky) -
One Sheet: $250 - $600

UNCLE TOM'S CABIN
(1927 - Universal) James B. Lowe, Virginia Grey
One Sheet: $600 - $1,000   *Separate Cinema, pg. 8.*

UNCLE TOM'S CABIN
(1940S - -) -
One Sheet: $50 - $100   *Price is for orange/black or red/black duotone posters.*

UNCLE TOM'S CABIN
(1958R - Colorama) Narrated by Raymond Massey
One Sheet: $30 - $50   *Re-release of 1927 silent film.*

UNCLE TOM'S CABIN
(1969 - Kroger Babb) John Kitzmiller, O.W. Fischer, voice of Ella Fitzgerald
One Sheet: $15 - $25   *Separate Cinema, pg. 9.*

UNCLE TOM'S CABOOSE
(1920 - Universal) Lois Dorety, Harry Keaton
One Sheet: $200 - $400

UNCLE WAS A VAMPIRE
(1959 - -) -
One Sheet: $15 - $25

UNCOMMON VALOR
(1983 - Paramount) Gene Hackman, Robert Stack
One Sheet: $3 - $5

UNCONQUERED
(1947 - Paramount) Gary Cooper, Paulette Goddard, Boris Karloff
One Sheet: $500 - $800

UNCONQUERED
(1955R - Paramount) Gary Cooper, Paulette

Goddard, Boris Karloff
One Sheet: $40 - $75   *Re-release.*

UNCROWNED KING, THE
(192? - Mercury) Carlyle Blackwell
One Sheet: $200 - $400

UNDEAD, THE
(1957 - AIP) Allison Hayes, Richard Garland, Dir:Roger Corman
One Sheet: $100 - $200

UNDEFEATED, THE
(1969 - 20th Century Fox) John Wayne, Rock Hudson
One Sheet: $40 - $75

UNDER A TEXAS MOON
(1930 - Warner Bros.) Frank Fay, Myrna Loy
One Sheet: $200 - $400

UNDER AGE
(1941 - Columbia) Nan Grey, Alan Baxter, Mary Anderson
One Sheet: $40 - $75

UNDER ARIZONA SKIES
(1946 - Monogram) Johnny Mack Brown, Raymond Hatton
One Sheet: $30 - $50

UNDER CALIFORNIA STARS
(1948 - Republic) Roy Rogers, Jane Frazee
One Sheet: $100 - $200

UNDER CAPRICORN
(1949 - Warner Bros.) Ingrid Bergman, Joseph Cotten, Dir: Alfred Hitchcock
One Sheet: $100 - $200

One Sheet

UNDER COLORADO SKIES
(1947 - Republic) Monte Hale, Adrian Booth
One Sheet: $20 - $40

UNDER COVER MAN
(1932 - Paramount Publix) George Raft, Nancy Carroll
One Sheet: $500 - $800

UNDER COVER MAN
(1936 - Republic) Johnny Mack Brown
One Sheet: $100 - $200

UNDER COVER OF NIGHT
(1937 - MGM) Edmund Lowe, Florence Rice
One Sheet: $100 - $200

UNDER EIGHTEEN
(1931 - Warner Bros.) Warren William, Marian Marsh
One Sheet: $100 - $200

UNDER FIESTA STARS
(1941 - Republic) Gene Autry, Smiley Burnette
One Sheet: $150 - $300   *Cowboy Movie Posters #269.*

UNDER FIESTA STARS
(194?R - Republic) Gene Autry, Smiley Burnette
One Sheet: $50 - $100   *Re-release.*

UNDER FIRE
(1957 - 20th Century Fox) Rex Reason, Harry Morgan
One Sheet: $15 - $25

UNDER FIRE
(1983 - Orion) Nick Nolte, Gene Hackman, Joanna Cassidy
One Sheet: $3 - $5

UNDER MEXICALI STARS
(1950 - Republic) Rex Allen, Dorothy Patrick

One Sheet: $15 - $35

UNDER MILK WOOD
(1973 - Timon) Richard Burton, Elizabeth Taylor
One Sheet: $10 - $20

UNDER MONTANA SKIES
(1930 - Tiffany) Kenneth Harlan, Dorothy Gulliver
One Sheet: $75 - $150

UNDER MY SKIN
(1950 - 20th Century Fox) John Garfield, Micheline Presle
One Sheet: $40 - $75

UNDER NEVADA SKIES
(1946 - Republic) Roy Rogers, Dale Evans
One Sheet: $125 - $250

UNDER PRESSURE
(1935 - Fox) Edmund Lowe, Victor McLaglen
One Sheet: $100 - $200

UNDER SECRET ORDERS
(1943 - Guaranteed) John Loder, Erich Von Stroheim
One Sheet: $30 - $50

One Sheet

UNDER SIEGE
(1992 - Warner Bros.) Steven Segal, Tommy Lee Jones
One Sheet: $7 - $15

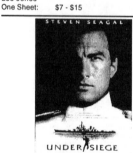
One Sheet

UNDER SIEGE 2: DARK TERRITORY
(1995 - Warner Bros./New Regency) Steven Seagal, Eric Bogosian
One Sheet: $5 - $12

UNDER STRANGE FLAGS
(1938 - Victory) Tom Keene, Luana Walters
One Sheet: $75 - $125

UNDER SUSPICION
(1930 - Fox) Lois Moran, J. Harold Murray
One Sheet: $150 - $300

UNDER SUSPICION
(1937 - Columbia) Jack Holt, Katherine DeMille
One Sheet: $50 - $100

UNDER SUSPICION
(1991 - Columbia) Liam Neeson, Laura San Giacoma
One Sheet: $7 - $15

UNDER TEN FLAGS
(1960 - Paramount) Van Heflin, Charles Laughton
One Sheet: $15 - $30

UNDER TEXAS SKIES
(1940 - Republic) Three Mesquiteers, Lois

Ranson
One Sheet: $40 - $75

UNDER THE BIG TOP
(1938 - Monogram) Marjorie Main, Anne Nagel
One Sheet: $75 - $150

UNDER THE BOARDWALK
(1989 - -) Richard Joseph Paul, Danielle Von Zerneck
One Sheet: $5 - $10

UNDER THE CHERRY MOON
(1986 - -) Prince, Jerome Benton, Kristin Scott-Thomas
One Sheet: $15 - $30

UNDER THE GUN
(1950 - Universal) Richard Conte, Audrey Totter
One Sheet: $15 - $30

UNDER THE LASH
(1921 - Paramount) Gloria Swanson
One Sheet: $500 - $800

UNDER THE PAMPAS MOON
(1935 - Fox) Warner Baxter, Rita Cansino (Hayworth)
One Sheet: $200 - $400

UNDER THE RAINBOW
(1981 - Warner Bros.) Chevy Chase, Carrie Fisher
One Sheet: $3 - $5

UNDER THE RED ROBE
(1937 - 20th Century Fox) Conrad Veidt, Annabella
One Sheet: $500 - $900

UNDER THE RED ROBE
(1940R - 20th Century Fox) Conrad Veidt, Annabella
One Sheet: $100 - $200   *Re-release.*

UNDER THE RED SEA
(1952 - RKO) -
One Sheet: $15 - $35   *Documentary.*

UNDER THE ROOFS OF PARIS
(1930 - Tobis) Albert Prejean, Pola Illery, Gaston Modot
One Sheet: $150 - $300   *French.*

UNDER THE TONTO RIM
(1928 - Paramount) Richard Arlen, Mary Brian
One Sheet: $250 - $600

UNDER THE TONTO RIM
(1933 - Paramount) Richard Arlen, Mary Brian
One Sheet: $350 - $750   *Cowboy Movie Posters # 162.*

UNDER THE TONTO RIM
(1947 - RKO) Tim Holt, Nan Leslie
One Sheet: $30 - $50

UNDER THE VOLCANO
(1984 - 20th Century Fox) Albert Finney, Jacqueline Bisset
One Sheet: $3 - $5

UNDER THE YOKE
(1918 - Fox) Theda Bara
One Sheet: $250 - $600

UNDER THE YUM-YUM TREE
(1963 - Columbia) Jack Lemmon, Carol Lynley
One Sheet: $15 - $30

UNDER TWO FLAGS
(1936 - 20th Century Fox) Ronald Colman, Claudette Colbert
One Sheet: $1,600 - $2,500

One Sheet

UNDER TWO FLAGS
(1943R - 20th Century Fox) Ronald Coleman, Claudette Colbert
One Sheet: $100 - $200   *Re-release.*

UNDER WESTERN SKIES
(1926 - Universal) Norman Kerry
One Sheet: $250 - $500

UNDER WESTERN SKIES
(1945 - Universal) Martha O'Driscoll, Noah Beery Jr.
One Sheet: $15 - $35

UNDER WESTERN STARS
(1938 - Republic) Roy Rogers
One Sheet: $800 - $1,500   *Cowboy Movie Posters #226. Roy Rogers first starring role. Two styles.*

UNDER YOUR SPELL
(1936 - 20th Century Fox) Lawrence Tibbett, Wendy Barrie
One Sheet: $75 - $150

UNDERCOVER
(1943 - Ealing) Michael Wilding, John Clements
One Sheet: $20 - $40

UNDERCOVER
(1987 - Cannon) David Neidorf, Jennifer Jason Leigh
One Sheet: $3 - $5

UNDERCOVER AGENT
(1939 - Monogram) Russell Gleason, Shirley Beane
One Sheet: $40 - $75

UNDERCOVER BLUES
(1993 - MGM) Dennis Quaid, Kathleen Turner
One Sheet: $3 - $5

UNDERCOVER DOCTOR
(1939 - Paramount) Lloyd Nolan, J. Carroll Naish
One Sheet: $50 - $100

UNDERCOVER GIRL
(1950 - Universal) Alexis Smith, Scott Brady
One Sheet: $15 - $30

UNDERCOVER MAISIE
(1947 - MGM) Ann Sothern, Barry Nelson
One Sheet: $40 - $75   *AKA: UNDERCOVER GIRL.*

UNDERCOVER MAN, THE
(1936 - Republic) Johnny Mack Brown
One Sheet: $75 - $150

UNDERCOVER MAN, THE
(1942 - United Artists) William Boyd, Andy Clyde
One Sheet: $125 - $250   *Hopalong Cassidy series.*

UNDERCOVER MAN, THE
(1949 - Columbia) Glenn Ford, Nina Foch
One Sheet: $30 - $50

UNDERCOVER MAN, THE
(1955R - Columbia) Glenn Ford, Nina Foch
One Sheet: $15 - $25   *Re-release.*

UNDERCOVER WOMAN, THE
(1946 - Republic) Stephanie Batchelor, Robert Livingston
One Sheet: $15 - $35

UNDERCOVERS HERO
(1975 - United Artists) Peter Sellers
One Sheet: $5 - $10

UNDERCURRENT
(1946 - MGM) Katharine Hepburn, Robert Taylor, Robert Mitchum
One Sheet: $100 - $200   *Superb stone litho.*

UNDERDOG, THE
(1943 - PRC) Barton MacLane, Charlotte Wynters
One Sheet: $20 - $40

UNDERGROUND
(1941 - Warner Bros.) Jeffrey Lynn, Philip Dorn
One Sheet: $30 - $50

UNDERGROUND
(1970 - United Artists) Robert Goulet, Daniele Gaubert
One Sheet: $5 - $10   *WW II spies.*

UNDERGROUND AGENT
(1942 - Columbia) Bruce Bennett, Leslie Brooks
One Sheet: $30 - $50

UNDERGROUND GUERILLAS
(1944 - Columbia) John Clement, Mary Morris
One Sheet: $20 - $40

UNDERGROUND RUSTLERS
(1941 - Monogram) Range Busters
One Sheet: $30 - $50

UNDERNEATH, THE
(1995 - Gramercy) Peter Gallagher, Alison Elliott
One Sheet: $5 - $10

UNDER-PUP, THE
(1939 - Universal) Gloria Jean, Nan Grey, Robert Cummings
One Sheet: $50 - $100   *Jean's film debut.*

UNDERSEA GIRL
(1957 - Allied Artists) Mara Corday, Pat Conway
One Sheet: $15 - $30

UNDERSEA KINGDOM
(1936 - Republic) Ray "Crash" Corrigan
One Sheet: $1,300 - $2,000   *Serial. 12 Chapters. Graven Images, pg. 99.*

One Sheet

UNDERSEA KINGDOM
(1950R - Republic) Ray "Crash" Corrigan
One Sheet: $100 - $200   *Re-release. Serial.*

UNDERSTANDING HEART, THE
(1927 - MGM) Joan Crawford
One Sheet: $1,300 - $2,000

UNDERTOW
(1930 - Universal) Mary Nolan, Johnny Mack Brown
One Sheet: $100 - $200

UNDERTOW
(1949 - Universal) Scott Brady, John Russell, Rock Hudson (film debut)
One Sheet: $30 - $50

UNDERWATER!
(1954 - RKO) Jane Russell, Gilbert Roland
One Sheet: $75 - $150

Window Card

UNDERWATER CITY, THE
(1962 - Columbia) William Lundigan, Julie Adams
One Sheet: $15 - $30

UNDERWATER WARRIOR

(1957 - MGM) Dan Dailey, Claire Kelly
One Sheet: $15 - $35

UNDERWORLD
(1927 - Paramount) George Bancroft, Evelyn Brent, Clive Brook
One Sheet: $1,300 - $2,000

Title Card

UNDERWORLD
(1937 - Micheaux) Bee Freeman, Sol Johnson
One Sheet: $1,600 - $2,500   *Black cast. Full color. Separate Cinema, pg. 14.*

UNDERWORLD STORY, THE
(1950 - United Artists) Dan Duryea, Gale Storm
One Sheet: $15 - $35

UNDERWORLD, U.S.A.
(1961 - Columbia) Cliff Robertson, Dolores Dorn
One Sheet: $15 - $35

UNDYING MONSTER, THE
(1942 - 20th Century Fox) James Ellison, Heather Angel, John Howard
One Sheet: $125 - $250   *Graven Images, pg. 129.*

One Sheet

UNE RAVISSANTE IDIOTE
(1964 - Imperia) Brigitte Bardot, Anthony Perkins
One Sheet: $75 - $125   *French. Price is for original French poster. American title: AGENT 38-24-36.*

UNEARTHLY, THE
(1957 - Republic) John Carradine, Allison Hayes
One Sheet: $50 - $100

UNEARTHLY STRANGER, THE
(1964 - AIP) John Neville, Jean Marsh
One Sheet: $20 - $40

UNEASY THREE, THE
(1925 - Pathe) Charley Chase, Katherine Grant, Bull Montana
One Sheet: $300 - $700

UNEXPECTED FATHER, THE
(1931 - Universal) Slim Summerville, ZaSu Pitts
One Sheet: $100 - $200

UNEXPECTED FATHER, THE
(1939 - Universal) Baby Sandy, Mischa Auer
One Sheet: $30 - $50

UNEXPECTED GUEST
(1947 - United Artists) Bill Boyd, Rand Brooks
One Sheet: $75 - $125   *Hopalong Cassidy series.*

UNEXPECTED UNCLE

(1941 - RKO) Charles Coburn, Anne Shirley
One Sheet: $30 - $50

UNFAITHFUL
(1931 - Paramount Publix) Ruth Chatterton,
Paul Lucas
One Sheet: $100 - $200

UNFAITHFUL, THE
(1947 - Warner Bros.) Ann Sheridan, Lew
Ayres
One Sheet: $15 - $35

UNFAITHFULLY YOURS
(1948 - 20th Century Fox) Rex Harrison, Linda
Darnell
One Sheet: $125 - $250

UNFAITHFULLY YOURS
(1984 - 20th Century Fox) Dudley Moore,
Nastassja Kinski
One Sheet: $3 - $5

UNFAITHFULS, THE
(1960 - Allied Artists) Gina Lollobrigida, Mai
Britt
One Sheet: $15 - $30

UNFINISHED BUSINESS
(1941 - Universal) Irene Dunne, Robert
Montgomery
One Sheet: $50 - $100

UNFINISHED DANCE, THE
(1947 - MGM) Margaret O'Brien, Cyd Charisse
One Sheet: $30 - $50

UNFORGETTABLE
(1996 - MGM) Linda Fiorentino, Ray Liotta
One Sheet: $5 - $10

UNFORGIVEN, THE
(1960 - United Artists) Burt Lancaster, Audrey
Hepburn, Audie Murphy
One Sheet: $50 - $100   *Cowboy
Movie Posters #309.*

UNFORGIVEN
(1992 - Warner Bros.) Clint Eastwood, Gene
Hackman, Morgan Freeman
One Sheet: $15 - $35   *Academy
Award: Best Picture, Best Director (Eastwood),
Best Supporting Actor (Hackman). Advance One
Sheet:$40-$80. Cowboy Movie Posters #361.*

UNGUARDED HOUR, THE
(1936 - MGM) Franchot Tone, Loretta Young
One Sheet: $150 - $350

UNGUARDED MOMENT, THE
(1956 - Universal) Esther Williams, George
Nader
One Sheet: $15 - $30

UNHOLY, THE
(1988 - -) Ben Cross, Hal Holbrook
One Sheet: $7 - $15

UNHOLY FOUR, THE
(1954 - Lippert) Paulette Goddard, William
Sylvester
One Sheet: $15 - $35

UNHOLY GARDEN, THE
(1931 - Universal) Ronald Colman, Fay Wray
One Sheet: $250 - $500

UNHOLY GARDEN, THE
(1941R - Universal) Ronald Colman, Fay Wray
One Sheet: $75 - $125   *Re-release.*

UNHOLY NIGHT, THE
(1929 - MGM) Ernest Torrence, Lionel
Barrymore, Boris Karloff
One Sheet: $800 - $1,500   *Graven
Images, pg. 11.*

UNHOLY PARTNERS
(1941 - MGM) Edward G. Robinson, Edward
Arnold
One Sheet: $50 - $100

UNHOLY ROLLERS
(1972 - AIP) Claudia Jennings, Roberta Collins
One Sheet: $15 - $25   *Sports (Roller
Derby).*

UNHOLY THREE, THE
(1925 - MGM) Lon Chaney, Victor McLaglen
One Sheet: $2,500 - $4,000

UNHOLY THREE, THE
(1930 - MGM) Lon Chaney, Lila Lee, Elliott
Nugent

One Sheet: $3,500 - $5,000   *Chaney's only
talkie and last film.*

UNHOLY WIFE, THE
(1957 - Universal International) Diana Dors,
Rod Steiger
One Sheet: $30 - $50

UNIDENTIFIED FLYING OBJECTS
(1956 - -) See UFO

UNIDENTIFIED FLYING ODDBALL
(1979 - Disney) Dennis Dugan
One Sheet: $5 - $10

UNINVITED, THE
(1944 - Paramount) Ray Milland, Gail Rusell,
Ruth Hussey
One Sheet: $200 - $400   *Graven
Images, pg. 128.*

One Sheet

UNINVITED GUEST, THE
(1923 - Walker) Steward Rome, Madge Stuart
One Sheet: $200 - $400

UNINVITED PEST, THE
(1949 - MGM) Barney Bear
One Sheet: $250 - $600   *Cartoon.
Cartoon Movie Posters #256.*

UNION DEPOT
(1932 - First National) Joan Blondell, Douglas
Fairbanks Jr.
One Sheet: $150 - $300

UNION PACIFIC
(1939 - Paramount) Joel McCrea, Barbara
Stanwyck
One Sheet: $500 - $800   *Cowboy
Movie Posters #253.*

One Sheet (Advance)

UNION PACIFIC
(1943R - Paramount) Joel McCrea, Barbara
Stanwyck
One Sheet: $75 - $150   *Re-release.*

UNION PACIFIC
(1950R - Paramount) Joel McCrea, Barbara
Stanwyck
One Sheet: $40 - $75   *Re-release.*

UNION STATION
(1950 - Paramount) William Holden, Nancy
Olson
One Sheet: $30 - $50

UNITED WE STAND
(1942 - 20th Century Fox) -
One Sheet: $50 - $100   *Documentary.*

UNIVERSAL CITY CALIFORNIA
(1915 - Universal)
One Sheet: $1,900 - $3,000   *Promotional
poster for "Grand Opening of the World's Only

Movie City."*

UNIVERSAL SOLDIER
(1992 - TriStar) Dolph Lundgren, Jean-Claude
Van Damme
One Sheet: $5 - $10

UNIVERSAL SPECIAL ATTRACTIONS
(192? - Universal) Marie Prevost Publicity
One Sheet: $150 - $300

UNKNOWN, THE
(1927 - MGM) Lon Chaney, Norman Kerry,
Joan Crawford
One Sheet: $4,000 - $6,000

Lobby Card

UNKNOWN, THE
(1946 - Columbia) Karen Morley, Jim Bannon
One Sheet: $15 - $30

UNKNOWN CAVALIER
(1926 - First National) Ken Maynard
One Sheet: $250 - $600

UNKNOWN GUEST
(1943 - Monogram) Victor Jory, Pamela Blake
One Sheet: $30 - $50

UNKNOWN GUEST
(1949 - -) Virginia Grey, Philip Reed
One Sheet: $15 - $25

UNKNOWN ISLAND
(1948 - United Artists) Richard Denning, Barton
MacLane, Virginia Grey
One Sheet: $30 - $50

UNKNOWN MAN, THE
(1951 - MGM) Walter Pidgeon, Ann Harding
One Sheet: $30 - $50

UNKNOWN RANGER, THE
(1936 - Columbia) Bob Allen
One Sheet: $75 - $125

UNKNOWN SOLDIER, THE
(1926 - -) Charles Emmett Mack
One Sheet: $150 - $300

UNKNOWN TERROR, THE
(1957 - 20th Century Fox) John Howard, Mala
Powers
One Sheet: $30 - $50

UNKNOWN VALLEY
(1933 - Columbia) Buck Jones
One Sheet: $500 - $800   *Cowboy
Movie Posters #'s 146, 149.*

UNKNOWN WOMAN, THE
(1935 - Columbia) Richard Cromwell, Marian
Marsh
One Sheet: $125 - $250

UNKNOWN WORLD
(1951 - Lippert) Bruce Kellogg, Marilyn Nash
One Sheet: $50 - $100

UNLAWFUL ENTRY
(1992 - 20th Century Fox) Ray Liotta, Kurt
Russell, Madeleine Stowe
One Sheet: $4 - $8

UNMAN, WITTERING AND ZIGO
(1971 - Paramount) David Hemmings, Carolyn
Seymour
One Sheet: $5 - $10

UNMARRIED
(1939 - Paramount) Buck Jones, Helen
Twelvetrees
One Sheet: $100 - $200

UNMARRIED WOMAN, AN

(1978 - 20th Century Fox) Jill Clayburgh, Alan
Bates
One Sheet: $7 - $15

UNMASKED
(1950 - Republic) Barbara Fuller, Robert
Rockwell
One Sheet: $15 - $30

UNNATURAL
(1956 - DCA) Hildegarde Neff, Eric Von
Stroheim
One Sheet: $30 - $60

UNO CONTRO TUTI
(19?? - -) Charlie Chaplin
One Sheet: $250 - $500   *Italian.*

UNSANE
(1982 - -) Tony Franciosa, John Saxon
One Sheet: $7 - $15

UNSEEN, THE
(1945 - Paramount) Joel McCrea, Gail Russell
One Sheet: $75 - $150

UNSEEN, THE
(1981 - Triune) Barbara Bach, Sydney Lassick
One Sheet: $5 - $10

UNSEEN FORCES
(1921 - First National) Sylvia Breamer, Conrad
Nagel
One Sheet: $250 - $600

UNSINKABLE MOLLY BROWN, THE
(1964 - MGM) Debbie Reynolds, Harve
Presnell
One Sheet: $15 - $30

UNSTOPPABLE MAN, THE
(1961 - Sutton) Cameron Mitchell, Marius
Goring
One Sheet: $10 - $20

UNSTRAP ME
(1968 - Hawk) Walter Gutman, George Segal
One Sheet: $5 - $10

UNSTRUNG HEROES
(1995 - -) Nathan Watt, Andie MacDowell, John
Turturro
One Sheet: $5 - $10

UNSUITABLE JOB FOR A WOMAN, AN
(1982 - Goldcrest) Billie Whitelaw
One Sheet: $3 - $5

UNSUSPECTED, THE
(1947 - Warner Bros.) Claude Rains, Joan
Caulfield
One Sheet: $30 - $50

UNTAMED
(1929 - MGM) Joan Crawford, Robert
Montgomery
One Sheet: $800 - $1,500

UNTAMED
(1940 - Paramount) Ray Milland, Patricia
Morison
One Sheet: $50 - $100

UNTAMED
(1955 - 20th Century Fox) Tyrone Power,
Susan Hayward
One Sheet: $30 - $50

UNTAMED AFRICA
(1933 - Warner Bros.) -
One Sheet: $75 - $150

UNTAMED BREED, THE
(1948 - Columbia) Sonny Tufts, Barbara Britton
One Sheet: $15 - $30

UNTAMED FRONTIER
(1952 - Universal) Joseph Cotten, Shelley
Winters
One Sheet: $15 - $25

UNTAMED FURY
(1947 - Pathe Industries) Gaylord Pendleton,
Mikel Conrad
One Sheet: $15 - $30

UNTAMED HEART
(1993 - MGM) Christian Slater, Marisa Tomei
One Sheet: $3 - $5

UNTAMED HEIRESS
(1954 - Republic) Judy Canova, Don Barry
One Sheet: $15 - $25

UNTAMED MISTRESS
(1960 - Brenner) Allan Nixon, Jacqueline Fontaine
One Sheet: $40 - $75

UNTAMED WOMEN
(1952 - United Artists) Mark Lowell, Doris Merrick
One Sheet: $50 - $100

UNTAMED YOUTH
(1957 - Warner Bros.) Mamie Van Doren, Lori Nelson
One Sheet: $40 - $75

One Sheet

UNTIL THEY SAIL
(1957 - MGM) Jean Simmons, Paul Newman
One Sheet: $15 - $30

UNTOUCHABLES, THE
(1987 - Paramount) Kevin Costner, Sean Connery
One Sheet: $15 - $35   *Academy Award: Best Supporting Actor(Connery). Academy Award Movie Posters #356.*

UNUSUAL OCCUPATIONS
(1941 - Paramount) -
One Sheet: $40 - $75   *Documentary.*

UNWED MOTHER
(1958 - Allied Artists) Norma Moore, Robert Vaughn
One Sheet: $20 - $40

UNWELCOME GUEST, THE
(1945 - MGM) Barney Bear
One Sheet: $250 - $600   *Cartoon.*

UNWELCOME STRANGER, THE
(1935 - Columbia) Jackie Searle, Jack Holt
One Sheet: $100 - $200

UNWRITTEN CODE, THE
(1944 - Columbia) Ann Savage, Tom Neal
One Sheet: $15 - $35

UNWRITTEN LAW, THE
(1932 - Majestic) Greta Nissen, Skeets Gallagher
One Sheet: $150 - $300

UNZIPPED
(1995 - Miramax) Issac Mizrahi, Cindy Crawford, Naomi Campbell
One Sheet: $5 - $10   *Behind-the-scenes look at high fashion.*

UP!
(1972 - -) Dir: Russ Meyer
One Sheet: $15 - $30

UP 'N' ATOM
(1941 - Columbia) Color Rhapsodies
One Sheet: $150 - $350   *Cartoon. Full color semi-stock poster with inset of title.*

UP A TREE
(1955 - RKO/Disney) Donald Duck, Chip and Dale
One Sheet: $350 - $750   *Cartoon.*

UP CLOSE AND PERSONAL
(1996 - Touchstone) Robert Redford, Michelle Pfeiffer
One Sheet: $5 - $10

UP FOR MURDER
(1931 - Universal) Lew Ayres, Genevieve Tobin
One Sheet: $150 - $300

UP FROM THE BEACH
(1965 - 20th Century Fox) Cliff Robertson, Red Buttons

One Sheet: $10 - $20

UP FRONT
(1951 - Universal) David Wayne, Tom Ewell
One Sheet: $15 - $25

UP GOES MAISIE
(1945 - MGM) Ann Sothern, George Murphy
One Sheet: $20 - $40

UP IN ARMS
(1944 - RKO) Danny Kaye, Constance Dowling
One Sheet: $75 - $125   *Kaye's film debut.*

UP IN CENTRAL PARK
(1948 - Universal) Deanna Durbin, Dick Haymes, Vincent Price
One Sheet: $50 - $100

UP IN DAISY'S PENTHOUSE
(1953 - Columbia) The Three Stooges (Shemp)
One Sheet: $150 - $350   *Comedy short. Duotone. Remake of THREE DUMB CLUCKS.*

UP IN MABEL'S ROOM
(1944 - United Artists) Dennis O'Keefe, Marjorie Reynolds
One Sheet: $15 - $30

UP IN SMOKE
(1957 - Allied Artists) Huntz Hall, Stanley Clements
One Sheet: $40 - $75

UP IN SMOKE
(1978 - -) See CHEECH & CHONG'S ...

UP IN THE AIR
(1940 - Monogram) Frankie Darro, Marjorie Reynolds, Mantan Moreland
One Sheet: $40 - $75

UP JUMPED THE DEVIL
(1940 - -) Mantan Moreland
One Sheet: $100 - $200   *Black cast.*

UP PERISCOPE
(1959 - Warner Bros.) James Garner, Edmond O'Brien
One Sheet: $15 - $25

UP POPS THE DEVIL
(1931 - Paramount) Carole Lombard, Norman Foster
One Sheet: $250 - $600

UP ROMANCE ROAD
(1918 - -) William Russell, Charlotte Burton
One Sheet: $125 - $250

UP THE CREEK
(1959 - Dominant) David Tomlinson, Peter Sellers
One Sheet: $7 - $15

UP THE CREEK
(1984 - -) Tim Matheson, Jennifer Runyon
One Sheet: $5 - $10   *Sports (River rafting). Sports Movie Posters #295.*

UP THE DOWN STAIRCASE
(1967 - Warner-Bros.- Seven Arts) Sandy Dennis, Patrick Bedford
One Sheet: $10 - $20

UP THE JUNCTION
(1968 - Paramount) Suzy Kendall, Dennis Waterman
One Sheet: $3 - $5

UP THE MACGREGORS
(1967 - Columbia) David Bailey, Leo Anchoriz
One Sheet: $3 - $5

UP THE RIVER
(1930 - Fox) Spencer Tracy, Humphrey Bogart
One Sheet: $800 - $1,500

UP THE RIVER
(1938 - 20th Century Fox) Preston Foster, Phyllis Brooks
One Sheet: $40 - $75

UP THE SANDBOX
(1972 - National General) Barbra Streisand, David Selby
One Sheet: $30 - $60   *Price is for style A one sheet with Amsel art. Non-Amsel art style: $20-$40.*

UP TO HIS EARS
(1966 - Lopert) Jean-Paul Belmondo, Ursula Andress

One Sheet: $10 - $20

UP YOUR ALLEY
(1972 - Group 1) Frank Corsentino, Haji
One Sheet: $3 - $5

UPHILL ALL THE WAY
(1985 - -) Roy Clark, Mel Tillis
One Sheet: $15 - $25   *Country musical.*

UPON THIS ROCK
(1950 - Preferred) -
One Sheet: $15 - $35

UPPER HAND, THE
(1967 - Paramount) Jean Gabin, George Raft
One Sheet: $7 - $15   *AKA: RIFIFI IN PARIS; RIFIFI INTERNAZIONALE.*

UPPER WORLD
(1934 - Warner Bros.) Ginger Rogers, Mary Astor
One Sheet: $300 - $700

UPSTAIRS AND DOWNSTAIRS
(1961 - 20th Century Fox) Mylene Demongeot, Michael Craig
One Sheet: $5 - $10

UPTIGHT
(1968 - Paramount) Raymond St. Jacques, Ruby Dee, Frank Silvera
One Sheet: $10 - $20

UPTOWN NEW YORK
(1932 - World-Wide) Jack Oakie, Shirley Grey
One Sheet: $100 - $200

Mini Window Card (Trimmed)

UPTOWN SATURDAY NIGHT
(1974 - Warner Bros.) Sidney Poitier, Bill Cosby
One Sheet: $15 - $25   *Black cast.*

UPTURNED GLASS, THE
(1947 - Universal) James Mason, Rosamund John, Pamela Kellino
One Sheet: $20 - $40

URANIUM BOOM
(1956 - Columbia) Dennis Morgan, Patricia Medina
One Sheet: $10 - $20

URBAN COWBOY
(1980 - Paramount) John Travolta, Debra Winger
One Sheet: $15 - $35   *Advance (Mylar):$30-$50..*

USED CARS
(1980 - Columbia) Kurt Russell, Gerrit Graham
One Sheet: $3 - $5

USED PEOPLE
(1992 - 20th Century Fox) Shirley Maclaine, Kathy Bates
One Sheet: $4 - $8

USUAL SUSPECTS, THE
(1995 - Gramercy) Gabriel Byrne, Kevin Spacey
One Sheet: $40 - $80   *Academy Award: Best Supporting Actor (Spacey). Price is for double-sided poster only. One-sided poster:$15-$25. Two-sided posters are scarce.*

UTAH
(1945 - Republic) Roy Rogers, Dale Evans
One Sheet: $150 - $300   *Cowboy Movie Posters #272.*

UTAH BLAINE
(1957 - Columbia) Rory Calhoun, Angela

Stevens
One Sheet: $15 - $25

UTAH KID, THE
(1930 - Tiffany) Rex Lease
One Sheet: $150 - $300

UTAH KID
(1944 - Monogram) Hoot Gibson, Bob Steele
One Sheet: $50 - $100

UTAH TRAIL
(1936 - Grand National) Tex Ritter
One Sheet: $125 - $250

UTAH WAGON TRAIN
(1951 - Republic) Rex Allen, Penny Edwards
One Sheet: $15 - $35

UTOPIA
(1954 - Exploitation) Stan Laurel, Oliver Hardy
One Sheet: $100 - $200   *Laurel & Hardy's final film.*

VACATION DAYS
(1947 - Monogram) Freddie Stewart, June Preisser
One Sheet: $10 - $20

VACATION FROM LOVE
(1938 - MGM) Dennis O'Keefe, Florence Rice
One Sheet: $40 - $75

VACATION FROM MARRIAGE
(1945 - MGM) Robert Donat, Deborah Kerr
One Sheet: $30 - $60

VACATION IN RENO
(1946 - RKO) Jack Haley, Anne Jeffreys
One Sheet: $30 - $50

VAGABOND, THE
(1916 - Mutual) Charlie Chaplin, Edna Purviance
One Sheet: $8,000 - $13,000

VAGABOND ADVENTURES
(1930S - RKO) -
One Sheet: $100 - $200

VAGABOND KING, THE
(1930 - Paramount Publix) Dennis Roth, Jeanette MacDonald
One Sheet: $150 - $350

VAGABOND KING, THE
(1955 - Paramount) Kathryn Grayson, Oreste
One Sheet: $10 - $20

VAGABOND LADY
(1935 - MGM) Robert Young, Evelyn Venable
One Sheet: $100 - $200

VAGABOND LOAFERS
(1949 - Columbia) The Three Stooges (Shemp)
One Sheet: $350 - $750   *Comedy short. Duotone. Remake of A-PLUMBING WE WILL GO.*

VAGABOND LOVER
(1929 - RKO) Rudy Vallee, Sally Blane
One Sheet: $250 - $500

VAGABOND LUCK
(1919 - -) Albert Ray, Elinor Fair
One Sheet: $200 - $400

VAGRANT, THE
(1927 - Educational) Lloyd "Ham" Hamilton
One Sheet: $150 - $300

VALACHI PAPERS, THE
(1972 - Columbia) Charles Bronson, Jill Ireland
One Sheet: $5 - $10

VALDEZ IS COMING
(1971 - United Artists) Burt Lancaster, Susan Clark
One Sheet: $7 - $15

VALENTINO
(1951 - Columbia) Eleanor Parker, Anthony Dexter
One Sheet: $20 - $40

VALENTINO
(1977 - United Artists) Rudolf Nureyev, Leslie Caron, Michelle Phillips
One Sheet: $10 - $20

VALENTINO RETURNS
(1987 - -) Frederick Forrest, Veronica Cartwright
One Sheet: $1 - $2

VALENTINO RETURNS
(1987 - -) Frederick Forrest, Veronica Cartwright
One Sheet: $3 - $5

VALERIE
(1957 - United Artists) Sterling Hayden, Anita Ekberg
One Sheet: $15 - $25

VALIANT, THE
(1929 - Fox) Paul Muni, Marguerite Churchill
One Sheet: $350 - $750

VALIANT, THE
(1962 - United Artists) John Mills, Ettore Manni
One Sheet: $3 - $5

VALIANT HOMBRE
(1949 - United Artists) Duncan Renaldo, Leo Carrillo
One Sheet: $20 - $40   *Cisco Kid series.*

VALIANT IS THE WORD FOR CARRIE
(1936 - Paramount) Gladys George, Arline Judge
One Sheet: $100 - $200

VALIANT TAILOR, THE
(1934 - Celebrity) Ub Iwerks
One Sheet: $600 - $1,000   *Cartoon. Full color stone litho. Cartoon Movie Posters #107.*

VALLEY GIRL
(1983 - -) Nicolas Cage, Deborah Foreman
One Sheet: $15 - $25

VALLEY OBSCURED BY CLOUDS, THE
(1975 - Lagoon) Valerie Lagrange, Bulle Ogier
One Sheet: $40 - $75

VALLEY OF DECISION, THE
(1945 - MGM) Greer Garson, Gregory Peck
One Sheet: $30 - $60

VALLEY OF FEAR
(1947 - Monogram) Johnny Mack Brown, Raymond Hatton
One Sheet: $30 - $50

VALLEY OF FIRE
(1951 - Columbia) Gene Autry, Pat Buttram
One Sheet: $40 - $75

VALLEY OF GWANGI
(1969 - Warner Bros./7 Arts) James Franciscus, Gila Golan, Richard Carlson
One Sheet: $30 - $60   *Ray Harryhausen effects.*

VALLEY OF HEADHUNTERS
(1953 - Columbia) Johnny Weissmuller, Christine Larson
One Sheet: $75 - $150

VALLEY OF HUNTED MEN
(1942 - Republic) Three Mesquiteers (Tom Tyler, Bob Steele, Jimmie Dodd)
One Sheet: $50 - $100

VALLEY OF MYSTERY
(1967 - Universal) Peter Graves, Richard Egan
One Sheet: $5 - $10

VALLEY OF SILENT MEN
(1922 - Paramount) Alma Rubens, Lew Cody
One Sheet: $150 - $300

VALLEY OF TERROR
(1937 - Ambassador) Kermit Maynard
One Sheet: $100 - $200

VALLEY OF THE DOLLS
(1967 - 20th Century Fox) Barbara Parkins, Patty Duke, Sharon Tate
One Sheet: $40 - $75

VALLEY OF THE DRAGONS
(1961 - Columbia) Cesare Danova, Sean McClory
One Sheet: $7 - $15

VALLEY OF THE EAGLES
(1951 - Lippert) Jack Warner, Nadia Gray
One Sheet: $15 - $30

VALLEY OF THE GIANTS
(1938 - Warner Bros.) Wayne Morris, Claire Trevor
One Sheet: $75 - $125

VALLEY OF THE KINGS
(1954 - MGM) Eleanor Parker, Robert Taylor

One Sheet: $20 - $40

VALLEY OF THE LAWLESS
(1936 - Supreme) Johnny Mack Brown
One Sheet: $75 - $150

VALLEY OF THE REDWOODS
(1960 - 20th Century Fox) John Hudson, Lynn Bernay
One Sheet: $5 - $10

VALLEY OF THE SUN
(1942 - RKO) Lucille Ball, James Craig
One Sheet: $150 - $300

Window Card

VALLEY OF THE SUN
(1952R - RKO) Lucille Ball, James Craig
One Sheet: $50 - $100   *Re-release.*

VALLEY OF THE ZOMBIES
(1946 - Republic) Bob Livingston, Ian Keith
One Sheet: $150 - $300   *Graven Images, pg. 135.*

VALLEY OF VANISHING MEN, THE
(1942 - Columbia) Bill Elliott, Slim Summerville
One Sheet: $75 - $150   *Serial. Western. 15 Chapters.*

VALLEY OF VENGEANCE
(1944 - PRC) Buster Crabbe, Al St. John
One Sheet: $30 - $50

VALLEY OF WANTED MEN
(1935 - -) Frankie Darro, Grant Withers
One Sheet: $75 - $150

VALMONT
(1989 - Orion) Colin Firth, Meg Tilly
One Sheet: $7 - $15

VALUE FOR MONEY
(1957 - Rank) John Gregson, Diana Dors
One Sheet: $10 - $20

VAMP
(1986 - -) Grace Jones, Chris Makepeace
One Sheet: $7 - $15

VAMPING VENUS
(1928 - First National) Thelma Todd
One Sheet: $250 - $500

VAMPIRE, THE
(1957 - United Artists) John Beal, Coleen Gray
One Sheet: $40 - $75

VAMPIRE AND THE BALLERINA, THE
(1962 - United Artists) Helene Remy, Maria L. Rolando
One Sheet: $30 - $50

VAMPIRE BAT, THE
(1933 - Majestic) Lionel Atwill, Fay Wray, Melvyn Douglas
One Sheet: $700 - $1,200   *Graven Images, pg. 67.*

VAMPIRE BEAST CRAVES BLOOD, THE
(1969 - Eastman) Peter Cushing, Robert Fleming
One Sheet: $15 - $35   *AKA: THE BLOOD BEAST TERROR.*

VAMPIRE BEAST CRAVES BLOOD/CURE OF THE BLOOD GHOULS
(1969 - -) -
One Sheet: $10 - $20   *Double feature poster.*

VAMPIRE CIRCUS
(1972 - 20th Century Fox) John Moulder Brown, Lynne Frederick
One Sheet: $15 - $30

VAMPIRE CIRCUS/COUNTESS DRACULA COMBO
(1972 - 20th Century Fox) -
One Sheet: $10 - $20   *Double feature poster.*

VAMPIRE IN BROOKLYN
(1995 - Paramount) Eddie Murphy, Angela Bassett
One Sheet: $3 - $5

VAMPIRE LOVERS, THE
(1971 - Hammer) Ingrid Pitt, Pippa Steele
One Sheet: $15 - $35

VAMPIRE'S GHOST, THE
(1945 - Republic) John Abbott, Peggy Stewart
One Sheet: $125 - $250

VAMPIRE'S GHOST, THE
(1957R - Republic) John Abbott, Peggy Stewart
One Sheet: $20 - $45   *Re-release.*

VAMPIRE'S KISS
(1989 - Hemdale) Nicolas Cage
One Sheet: $10 - $20

VAMPIRE/DINOSAURUS/THE BLOB COMBO
(1965R - -) -
One Sheet: $15 - $30   *Triple feature re-release poster. Duotone.*

VAMPIRES NIGHT ORGY, THE
(1973 - IAC) Jack Taylor, Charo Soriano
One Sheet: $15 - $35   *AKA: ORGY OF THE VAMPIRES.*

VAMPYR
(1932 - Black Cat) Julian West, Henriette Gerard, Dir: Carl Theodor Dreyer
One Sheet: $6,500 - $10,000   *French. Graven Images, pg. 56.*

VAN, THE
(1977 - Crown) Stuart Getz, Harry Moses
One Sheet: $5 - $10

VAN, THE
(1997 - Fox Searchlight) Colm Meany, Donal O'Kelly
One Sheet: $3 - $5

VAN GOGH
(1992 - -) Jacques Dutronc, Bernard Le Coq
One Sheet: $7 - $15   *French.*

VAN NUYS BLVD.
(1979 - Crown) Bill Adler, Cythia Wood
One Sheet: $15 - $25

VANESSA
(1935 - MGM) Helen Hayes, Robert Montgomery
One Sheet: $100 - $200

VANISHING, THE
(1993 - 20th Century Fox) Jeff Bridges, Kiefer Sutherland, Nancy Travis
One Sheet: $3 - $5

VANISHING AMERICAN, THE
(1925 - Paramount) Richard Dix, Noah Beery
One Sheet: $800 - $1,500   *Cowboy Movie Posters #55.*

VANISHING AMERICAN, THE
(1955 - Republic) Scott Brady, Audrey Totter
One Sheet: $15 - $30

VANISHING BODY, THE
(1953R - Realart) Boris Karloff, Bela Lugosi
One Sheet: $100 - $200   *Re-titled re-release of THE BLACK CAT (1934).*

VANISHING DAGGER, THE
(1920 - Universal) Eddie Polo
One Sheet: $200 - $400   *Serial. 18 Chapters.*

VANISHING FRONTIER, THE
(1932 - Paramount Publix) Johnny Mack Brown
One Sheet: $125 - $250

VANISHING LEGION, THE
(1931 - Mascot) Harry Carey, Edwina Booth
One Sheet: $150 - $350   *Serial.*

VANISHING LEGION, THE
(1937R - -) Harry Carey, Edwina Booth
One Sheet: $50 - $100   *Re-release. Serial.*

VANISHING OUTPOST, THE
(1951 - Realart) Lash LaRue, Fuzzy St. John
One Sheet: $30 - $50

VANISHING POINT
(1971 - 20th Century Fox) Barry Newman, Cleavon Little
One Sheet: $15 - $25

VANISHING PRAIRIE, THE
(1954 - Walt Disney) -
One Sheet: $30 - $50   *Documentary.*

VANISHING PRIVATE, THE
(1942 - RKO/Disney) Donald Duck
One Sheet: $2,500 - $4,000   *Cartoon. Cartoon Movie Posters #167.*

VANISHING SHADOW, THE
(1934 - Universal) Onslow Stevens, Ada Ince
One Sheet: $250 - $500   *Serial. 12 Chapters.*

VANISHING TRAILS, THE
(1920 - Canyon) Franklyn Farnum, Mary Anderson
One Sheet: $150 - $350   *Serial. Western. 15 Chapters.*

VANISHING VIRGINIAN, THE
(1941 - MGM) Frank Morgan, Kathryn Grayson
One Sheet: $40 - $75

VANISHING WESTERNER, THE
(1950 - Republic) Monte Hale, Paul Hurst
One Sheet: $15 - $35

VANITY
(1927 - PDC) Leatrice Joy, Charles Ray
One Sheet: $200 - $400

VANITY FAIR
(1932 - Hollywood Exchange) Myrna Loy, Conway Tearle
One Sheet: $600 - $1,000

VANITY STREET
(1932 - Columbia) Charles Bickford, Helen Chandler
One Sheet: $250 - $500

VANQUISHED, THE
(1953 - Paramount) John Payne, Jan Sterling
One Sheet: $15 - $25

VANYA ON 42ND STREET
(1994 - Sony Classics) Wallace Shawn, Julianne Moore
One Sheet: $3 - $5

VARAN THE UNBELIEVABLE
(1962 - Crown) Myron Healy, Tsuruko Kobayashi
One Sheet: $40 - $75

VARIETY
(1925 - Famous Players) Emil Jannings, Lya De Putti
One Sheet: $1,900 - $3,000   *German.*

VARIETY GIRL
(1947 - Paramount) Bing Crosby, Bob Hope, Gary Cooper, Mary Hatcher
One Sheet: $100 - $200

VARIETY LIGHTS
(1950 - -) Peppino DeFilippo
One Sheet: $250 - $600   *Italian. Fellini's first Co-Direction.*

VARIETY TIME
(1948 - RKO) Jack Paar, Edgar Kennedy, Leon Errol
One Sheet: $30 - $50

VARSITY SHOW
(1937 - Waner Bros.) Dick Powell, Fred Waring
One Sheet: $75 - $150

VARSITY VANITIES
(1940 - Universal) Tilton, Six Hits & a Miss
One Sheet: $100 - $200

VASECTOMY
(1986 - -) Abe Vigoda, Paul Sorvino
One Sheet: $3 - $5

VAULT OF HORROR
(1973 - Cinerama) Terry-Thomas, Glynis Johns, Daniel Massey
One Sheet: $15 - $30

VEILED MYSTERY, THE
(1920 - Vitagraph) Antonio Moreno
One Sheet: $250 - $500   *Serial. 15*

Chapters.

VEILS OF BAGDAD, THE
(1953 - Universal) Victor Mature, Mari Blanchard
One Sheet: $15 - $25

VELVET SMOOTH
(197? - -) Johnny Hill, Emerson Boozer
One Sheet: $15 - $25   *Blaxploitation.*

VELVET TOUCH, THE
(1948 - Independent Artists Ltd.) Rosalind Russell, Leo Genn, Sydney Greenstreet
One Sheet: $40 - $75

VELVET VAMPIRE, THE
(1971 - New World) Michael Blidgett, Sherry Mills
One Sheet: $15 - $35   *AKA: THROUGH THE LOOKING GLASS.*

VENDETTA
(1914 - Kleine) -
One Sheet: $700 - $1,200

VENDETTA
(1950 - RKO) Faith Domergue, George Dolenz
One Sheet: $50 - $100

VENDETTA
(1986 - Concorde) Karen Chase, Cindy Martin
One Sheet: $3 - $5

VENETIAN AFFAIR
(1967 - MGM) Robert Vaughn, Elke Sommer, Boris Karloff
One Sheet: $15 - $30

VENETIAN NIGHTS
(1934 - Gaumont) Matheson Lang, Joseph Schildkraut
One Sheet: $100 - $200

VENGEANCE
(1918 - Sun) Eileen Sedgwick, "Lightning" the Police Dog
One Sheet: $150 - $300

VENGEANCE
(1930 - Columbia) Jack Holt, Dorothy Revier
One Sheet: $125 - $250

VENGEANCE
(1937 - Rialto) Lyle Talbot, Wendy Barrie
One Sheet: $50 - $100   *AKA: WHAT PRICE VENGEANCE?.*

VENGEANCE AND THE WOMAN
(1917 - Vitagraph) Dir: William Duncan
One Sheet: $200 - $400   *Serial. 15 Chapters.*

VENGEANCE IS MINE!
(1916 - -) Crane Wilbur, Carl von Schiller
One Sheet: $350 - $750

VENGEANCE MINE
(1918 - -) Irene Castle, Frank Sheridan
One Sheet: $250 - $500

VENGEANCE MINE
(1929 - -) Richard Arlen, Mary Brian
One Sheet: $150 - $300

VENGEANCE MINE
(1948 - Eros) Valentine Dyall, Anne Firth, Dir: Alan Cullimore
One Sheet: $100 - $200

VENGEANCE OF FU MANCHU, THE
(1968 - Warner Bors.-Seven Arts) Christopher Lee, Douglas Wilmer
One Sheet: $15 - $25

VENGEANCE OF SHE, THE
(1968 - 20th Century Fox) John Richardson, Olinka Berova
One Sheet: $15 - $30

VENGEANCE OF THE HANGED, THE
(1958 - -) -
One Sheet: $30 - $50   *Mexican.*

VENGEANCE OF THE WEST
(1942 - Columbia) Bill Elliott, Tex Ritter
One Sheet: $40 - $75

VENGEANCE VALLEY
(1951 - MGM) Burt Lancaster, Robert Walker, Joanne Dru
One Sheet: $30 - $50

VENGEANCE VALLEY

(1962R - MGM) Burt Lancaster, Robert Walker, Joanne Dru
One Sheet: $7 - $15   *Re-release.*

VENICE/VENICE
(1993 - International Rainbow) -
One Sheet: $3 - $5

VENOM
(1982 - -) Klaus Kinski, Nicol Williamson, Sterling Hayden
One Sheet: $5 - $10

VENTRILOQUIST CAT
(1950 - MGM) Tex Avery
One Sheet: $500 - $900   *Cartoon. Full color stone litho. Cartoon Movie Posters #311.*

VENUS IN FURS
(1970 - AIP) James Darren, Barbara McNair
One Sheet: $10 - $20

VENUS MAKES TROUBLE
(1937 - Columbia) James Dunn, Patricia Ellis
One Sheet: $200 - $400

VENUS OF VENICE
(1927 - First National) Constance Talmadge
One Sheet: $250 - $600

VERA CRUZ
(1954 - United Artists) Gary Cooper, Burt Lancaster
One Sheet: $40 - $75

VERBOTEN
(1959 - Columbia) James Best, Susan Cummings
One Sheet: $7 - $15

VERDICT, THE
(1946 - Warner Bros.) Peter Lorre, Sydney Greenstreet
One Sheet: $75 - $150

VERDICT, THE
(1982 - 20th Century Fox) Paul Newman, Charlotte Rampling
One Sheet: $5 - $10

VERMILION PENCIL, THE
(1922 - R.C. Pictures) Sessue Hayakawa
One Sheet: $250 - $600

VERONICA LAKE PERSONALITY POSTER
(1946? - Paramount) Veronica Lake
One Sheet: $150 - $300

One Sheet

VERONIKA VOSS
(1982 - Maura) Rosel Zech, Hilmar Thate
One Sheet: $20 - $40   *German.*

VERTIGO
(1958 - Paramount) James Stewart, Kim Novak, Dir: Alfred Hitchcock
One Sheet: $500 - $800   *Saul Bass art.*

VERTIGO
(1963R - Paramount) James Stewart, Kim Novak, Dir: Alfred Hitchcock
One Sheet: $50 - $100   *Re-release. Saul Bass art.*

VERTIGO
(1983R - Paramount) James Stewart, Kim Novak, Dir: Alfred Hitchcock
One Sheet: $10 - $20   *Re-release.*

VERTIGO
(1996 - Paramount) James Stewart, Kim Novak, Dir: Alfred Hitchcock
One Sheet: $15 - $25   *Re-release. Restored version. Saul Bass art.*

VERY BRADY SEQUEL, A
(1996 - Paramount) Shelley Long, Gary Cole, Tim Matheson
One Sheet: $5 - $12   *TV tie-in.*

VERY CURIOUS GIRL, A
(1971 - Regional) Bernadette La Font, Georges Geret
One Sheet: $3 - $5

VERY HONORABLE GUY, A
(1934 - First National) Joe E. Brown, Alice White
One Sheet: $100 - $200

VERY PRIVATE AFFAIR, A
(1962 - MGM) Brigitte Bardot, Marcello Mastroianni
One Sheet: $40 - $75

VERY SPECIAL FAVOR, A
(1965 - Universal) Rock Hudson, Leslie Caron
One Sheet: $15 - $30

VERY THOUGHT OF YOU, THE
(1941 - Warner Bros.) Dennis Morgan, Eleanor Parker
One Sheet: $30 - $60

VERY YOUNG LADY, A
(1941 - 20th Century Fox) Jane Withers, Nancy Kelly
One Sheet: $40 - $75

VIA PONY EXPRESS
(1933 - Majestic) Jack Hoxie, Lane Chandler
One Sheet: $150 - $350

VIBES
(1988 - Columbia) Cyndi Lauper, Jeff Goldblum
One Sheet: $5 - $10

VICE AND VIRTUE
(1965 - MGM) Annie Girardot, Catherine Deneuve
One Sheet: $15 - $30

VICE RAID
(1960 - United Artists) Mamie Van Doren, Richard Coogan
One Sheet: $40 - $75

VICE SQUAD
(1931 - Paramount Publix) Paul Lukas, Kay Francis
One Sheet: $125 - $250

VICE SQUAD
(1953 - United Artists) Edward G. Robinson, Paulette Goddard
One Sheet: $50 - $100

VICE SQUAD
(1982 - Avco/Embassy) Season Hubley, Gary Swanson
One Sheet: $5 - $10

VICE VERSA
(1988 - -) Judge Reinhold, Fred Savage
One Sheet: $3 - $5

VICIOUS BREED, THE
(1957 - Coronet) -
One Sheet: $15 - $25

VICIOUS CIRCLE
(1948 - United Artists) Conrad Nagel, Lyle Talbot
One Sheet: $30 - $50

VICIOUS YEARS, THE
(1950 - Film Classics) Tommy Cook, Gan Moore
One Sheet: $15 - $30

VICKI
(1953 - 20th Century Fox) Jeanne Crain, Jean Peters
One Sheet: $15 - $25

VICTIM
(1961 - Pathe) Dirk Bogarde, Sylvia Syons
One Sheet: $7 - $15

VICTOR/VICTORIA
(1982 - MGM) Julie Andrews, James Garner
One Sheet: $7 - $15

VICTORIA THE GREAT
(1937 - RKO) Anna Neagle, Anton Walbrook
One Sheet: $100 - $200

VICTORS, THE
(1963 - Columbia) Vincent Edwards, George

Hamilton
One Sheet: $10 - $20

VICTORY
(1919 - Paramount/Artcraft) Jack Holt, Seena Owen, Wallace Beery
One Sheet: $350 - $750

VICTORY
(1940 - Paramount) Fredric March, Betty Field
One Sheet: $40 - $75

VICTORY
(1980 - Paramount) Sylvester Stallone, Michael Caine, Pele
One Sheet: $10 - $20   *Sports (Soccer). Sports Movie Posters #316.*

VICTORY AT SEA
(1954 - United Artists) -
One Sheet: $30 - $50   *Documentary.*

VICTORY THROUGH AIR POWER
(1943 - Disney) Disney Aviation Feature
One Sheet: $200 - $400

VICTORY VEHICLES
(1943 - Disney) Goofy
One Sheet: $800 - $1,500   *Cartoon.*

VIDEODROME
(1983 - Filmplan International) James Woods, Sonja Smits
One Sheet: $10 - $20

VIE PRIVEE
(1962 - Cocinor) Brigitte Bardot
One Sheet: $100 - $200   *French. Price is for original French 47x63 poster.*

VIENNESE NIGHTS
(1930 - Warner Bros.) Alexander Gray, Vivienne Segal
One Sheet: $125 - $250

VIEW FROM POMPEY'S HEAD, THE
(1955 - 20th Century Fox) Richard Egan, Dana Wynter
One Sheet: $7 - $15

VIEW FROM THE BRIDGE, A
(1962 - Continental) Raf Vallone, Jean Sorel
One Sheet: $3 - $5

VIEW TO A KILL, A
(1985 - MGM/UA) Roger Moore, Christopher Walken, Tanya Roberts
One Sheet: $10 - $20   *Advance(Style A):$15-$25. Advance(Style B):$10-$20.*

One Sheet (Advance)

VIGIL IN THE NIGHT
(1940 - RKO) Carole Lombard, Brian Aherne
One Sheet: $150 - $300

VIGILANTE, THE
(1947 - Columbia) Ralph Byrd, Ramsay Ames
One Sheet: $75 - $150   *Serial. 15 Chapters.*

VIGILANTE
(1983 - Magnum) Robert Forster, Fred Williamson, Mr. "T"
One Sheet: $5 - $10   *Blaxploitation.*

VIGILANTE FORCE
(1976 - United Artists) Kris Kristofferson, Jan-Michael Vincent
One Sheet: $3 - $5

VIGILANTE HIDEOUT
(1950 - Republic) Allan "Rocky" Lane, Eddy Waller
One Sheet: $15 - $35

VIGILANTE TERROR
(1953 - Monogram) Bill Elliott, Mary Ellen Kay
One Sheet: $15 - $35

VIGILANTES ARE COMING, THE
(1936 - Republic) Bob Livingston, Kay Hughes
One Sheet: $150 - $300   *Serial.*
Western. 12 Episodes. Cowboy Movie Posters
#195.

VIGILANTES OF BOOMTOWN
(1947 - Republic) Allan Lane, Bobby Blake
One Sheet: $30 - $50   *Red Ryder*
series.

VIGILANTES OF BOOMTOWN
(1951R - Republic) Allan Lane, Bobby Blake
One Sheet: $5 - $10   *Re-release.*

VIGILANTES OF DODGE CITY
(1944 - Republic) Bill (Red Ryder) Elliott
One Sheet: $40 - $75

VIGILANTES RETURN, THE
(1947 - Universal) Jon Hall, Maragret Lindsay
One Sheet: $15 - $30

VIGILANTES RIDE, THE
(1943 - Columbia) Russell Hayden, Shirley
Patterson
One Sheet: $20 - $40

VIKING, THE
(1931 - Newfoundland Labrador) -
One Sheet: $200 - $400

VIKING QUEEN, THE
(1967 - 20th Century Fox) Don Murray, Carita
One Sheet: $7 - $15

VIKING WOMEN AND THE SEA SERPENT
(1958 - AIP) Abby Dalton, Susan Cabot,
Dir:Roger Corman
One Sheet: $75 - $125

Half Sheet

VIKINGS, THE
(1958 - United Artists) Kirk Douglas, Janet
Leigh, Tony Curtis
One Sheet: $50 - $100

VILLA!
(1958 - 20th Century Fox) Brian Keith, Cesar
Romero
One Sheet: $15 - $25

VILLA RIDES!
(1968 - Paramount) Yul Brynner, Robert
Mitchum, Charles Bronson
One Sheet: $15 - $25

VILLAGE
(1953 - United Artists) John Justin, Eva
Dahibeck
One Sheet: $10 - $20

VILLAGE BARN DANCE
(1940 - Republic) Richard Cromwell, Doris Day
(not Que Sera Sera)
One Sheet: $30 - $50   *Country*
musical.

VILLAGE BLACKSMITH, THE
(1922 - Fox) Dir: Jack Ford
One Sheet: $200 - $400

VILLAGE BLACKSMITH
(1938 - -) Terry Toons
One Sheet: $50 - $100   *Cartoon.*

VILLAGE OF THE DAMNED
(1961 - MGM) George Sanders, Barbara
Shelley
One Sheet: $40 - $75   *Graven*
Images, pg. 224.

VILLAGE OF THE DAMNED
(1995 - Universal) Christopher Reeve, Kirstie
Alley, Dir:John Carpenter
One Sheet: $5 - $10

VILLAGE OF THE GIANTS
(1965 - Embassy) Tommy Kirk, Johnny
Crawford
One Sheet: $30 - $50

VILLAGE SMITHY
(1941 - Disney) Donald Duck
One Sheet: $4,000 - $6,000   *Cartoon.*

VILLAGE TALE
(1935 - RKO) Randolph Scott, Kay Johnson
One Sheet: $100 - $200

VILLAIN
(1971 - MGM) Richard Burton, Nigel Davenport
One Sheet: $5 - $10

VILLAIN, THE
(1979 - Columbia) Kirk Douglas, Ann-Margret,
Arnold Schwarzenegger
One Sheet: $10 - $20

VILLAIN STILL PURSUED HER, THE
(1940 - RKO) Anita Louise, Alan Mowbray,
Buster Keaton
One Sheet: $75 - $125

VINCENT & THEO
(1990 - -) Dir: Robert Altman
One Sheet: $15 - $25   *Van Gogh*
border art.

VINE, WOMEN, AND SONG
(1945 - Columbia) -
One Sheet: $15 - $35

VINTAGE, THE
(1957 - MGM) Mel Ferrer, Pier Angeli, John
Kerr
One Sheet: $15 - $30

VIOLATORS, THE
(1957 - Universal International) Arthur
O'Connell, Nancy Malone
One Sheet: $15 - $30

VIOLENCE
(1947 - Monogram) Nancy Coleman, Michael
O'Shea
One Sheet: $15 - $25

VIOLENT FOUR
(1968 - Paramount) Gian Maria Volonte, Tomas
Milian
One Sheet: $5 - $10

VIOLENT IS THE WORD FOR CURLY
(1938 - Columbia) The Three Stooges (Curly)
One Sheet: $7,500 - $12,000   *Comedy short.*
Duotone.

VIOLENT MEN, THE
(1954 - Columbia) Glenn Ford, Barbara
Stanwyck
One Sheet: $30 - $50

VIOLENT ROAD
(1958 - Warner Bros.) Brian Keith, Dick Foran
One Sheet: $15 - $25

VIOLENT SATURDAY
(1955 - 20th Century Fox) Victor Mature, Sylvia
Sidney
One Sheet: $15 - $25

VIOLENT YEARS, THE
(1956 - Headliner) Jean Moorehead, Barbara
Weeks
One Sheet: $40 - $75   *AKA:*
FEMALE. Scripted by Ed Wood, Jr.

VIOLET RAY, THE
(1916 - Kalem) George Larkin, Ollie Kirkby
One Sheet: $250 - $500

VIOLETS ARE BLUE...
(1986 - -) Sissy Spacek, Kevin Kline
One Sheet: $3 - $5

VIOLETS IN SPRING
(1936 - MGM) George Murphy, Virginia Grey
One Sheet: $100 - $200

V.I.P'S, THE
(1963 - DGM) Elizabeth Taylor, Richard Burton
One Sheet: $30 - $60

VIRGIN AND THE GYPSY, THE

(1970 - Chevron) Joanna Shimkus, Franco
Nero, Honor Blackman
One Sheet: $20 - $40

VIRGIN IN HOLLYWOOD, A
(1952 - Sonney Amusement) -
One Sheet: $15 - $30   *Sexploitation.*

VIRGIN OF STAMBOUL
(1920 - -) Priscilla Dean, Wallace Beery, Dir:
Tod Browning
One Sheet: $600 - $1,000

VIRGIN OF THE SEMINOLE, THE
(1923 - -) Shingzie Howard, William E.
Fontaine
One Sheet: $250 - $600

VIRGIN PARADISE, A
(1921 - -) Pearl White, Robert Elliott, Jr.
One Sheet: $150 - $300

VIRGIN QUEEN, THE
(1955 - 20th Century Fox) Bette Davis, Richard
Todd
One Sheet: $50 - $100

VIRGIN SOLDIERS, THE
(1970 - Columbia) Lynn Redgrave, Hywel
Bennett, Nigel Davenport
One Sheet: $5 - $10

VIRGIN SPRING, THE
(1960 - Janus) Max von Sydow, Drigitta
Pettersson, Dir: Ingmar Bergman
One Sheet: $50 - $120   *Swedish.*
Academy Award: Best Foreign film. Price is for
original Swedish sheet. One Sheet(non-review
American release). $40-$75.

VIRGINIA
(1941 - Paramount) Madeleine Carroll, Fred
MacMurray
One Sheet: $75 - $150

One Sheet

VIRGINIA CITY
(1940 - Warner Bros.) Errol Flynn, Humphrey
Bogart, Miriam Hopkins
One Sheet: $600 - $1,000

One Sheet

VIRGINIA CITY
(1956R - Warner Bros.) Errol Flynn, Humphrey
Bogart
One Sheet: $30 - $50   *Re-release.*

VIRGINIA JUDGE, THE
(1935 - Paramount) Walter C. Kelly, Marsha
Hunt, Stepin Fetchit
One Sheet: $125 - $250

VIRGINIAN, THE
(1929 - Paramount) Gary Cooper, Richard
Arlen, Walter Huston
One Sheet: $4,000 - $6,000   *Cowboy*

Movie Posters #'s 74, 76, 77. Silent and sound
one sheets exist.

VIRGINIAN, THE
(1946 - Paramount) Joel McCrea, Brian
Donlevy
One Sheet: $50 - $100

One Sheet

VIRGINIAN, THE
(1956R - Paramount) Joel McCrea, Brian
Donlevy
One Sheet: $15 - $25   *Re-release.*

VIRGINS OF BALI
(1932 - Imperial)
One Sheet: $75 - $150

VIRIDIANA
(1961 - Columbia) Silvia Pinal, Fernando Rey,
Francisco Rabal
One Sheet: $150 - $350   *Spanish.*

VIRTUE
(1932 - Columbia) Carole Lombard, Pat O'Brien
One Sheet: $600 - $1,000

VIRTUOSITY
(1995 - Paramount) Denzel Washington,
Russell Crowe
One Sheet: $5 - $12

VIRTUOUS HUSBAND, THE
(1931 - Universal) Elliott Nugent, Jean Arthur
One Sheet: $150 - $300

VIRTUOUS LIARS
(1924 - -) David Powell, Maurice Costello
One Sheet: $200 - $400

VIRTUOUS SIN, THE
(1930 - Paramount Publix) Walter Huston, Kay
Francis
One Sheet: $500 - $800

VIRTUOUS SINNERS
(1919 - Pioneer) Rudolph Valentino
One Sheet: $800 - $1,500

VISCOUNT, THE
(1967 - Warner Bros) Kerwin Mathews,
Edmond O'Brien
One Sheet: $7 - $15

VISION QUEST
(1984 - Warner Bros.) Matthew Modine, Linda
Fiorentino
One Sheet: $3 - $5

VISIONS OF LIGHT
(1993 - Kino) -
One Sheet: $7 - $15

VISIT, THE
(1964 - 20th Century Fox) Ingrid Bergman,
Anthony Quinn
One Sheet: $15 - $25

VISIT TO A SMALL PLANET
(1960 - Paramount) Jerry Lewis, Joan
Blackman
One Sheet: $20 - $40

**VISIT TO A SMALL PLANET/THE BELLBOY
COMBO**
(1966R - Paramount) Jerry Lewis
One Sheet: $10 - $20   *Double*
feature poster.

VISITING HOURS
(1982 - Filmplan International) Michael
Ironside, Lee Grant
One Sheet: $5 - $10

VISITOR, THE

(1979 - International Picture Show) Mel Ferrer, John Huston, Sam Peckinpah
One Sheet: $15 - $25

VISITORS, THE
(1972 - United Artists) Patrick McVey, Patricia Joyce
One Sheet: $3 - $5

VISITORS, THE
(1995 - Miramax) Christian Clavier, Jean Reno
One Sheet: $3 - $5

VITAL SIGNS
(1990 - -) Adrian Pasdar, Diane Lane
One Sheet: $3 - $5

VIVA CISCO KID
(1940 - 20th Century Fox) Cesar Romero, Jean Rogers
One Sheet: $100 - $200

VIVA JAMES BOND
(1970 - -) -
One Sheet: $15 - $30

VIVA KNIEVEL!
(1977 - Warner Bros.) Evel Knievel, Leslie Nielsen
One Sheet: $10 - $20   *Sports*
(Motorcycle stunts). Sports Movie Posters #274.

One Sheet

VIVA LAS VEGAS
(1964 - MGM) Elvis Presley, Ann-Margret
One Sheet: $250 - $500   *Price is for style A one sheet. One Sheet (Style B): $300-$600. One Sheet (Style C, rare):$400-$800.*

VIVA MARIA!
(1966 - United Artists) Brigitte Bardot, Jeanne Moreau
One Sheet: $30 - $50

VIVA MAX!
(1969 - Commonwealth United) Peter Ustinov, Pamela Tiffin, Jonathan Winters
One Sheet: $15 - $25

VIVA VILLA!
(1934 - MGM) Wallace Beery, Leo Carrillo
One Sheet: $600 - $1,000

VIVA ZAPATA!
(1952 - 20th Century Fox) Marlon Brando, Jean Peters, Anthony Quinn
One Sheet: $250 - $500   *Academy Award Movie Posters #146.*

VIVACIOUS LADY
(1938 - RKO) Ginger Rogers, James Stewart
One Sheet: $500 - $800

One Sheet

VOGUES
(1937 - United Artists) Warner Baxter, Joan

Bennett
One Sheet: $75 - $150   *AKA: VOGUES OF 1938.*

VOICE FROM MINARET, THE
(1923 - First National) Norma Talmadge
One Sheet: $500 - $800

VOICE IN THE MIRROR, THE
(1958 - Universal-International) Richard Egan, Julie London, Walter Matthau
One Sheet: $15 - $35

VOICE IN THE NIGHT
(1934 - Columbia) Tim McCoy
One Sheet: $150 - $350

VOICE IN THE NIGHT, THE
(1941 - Columbia) Clive Brook, Diana Wynyard
One Sheet: $40 - $75

VOICE IN THE WIND, A
(1943 - United Artists) Francis Lederer,Sigrid Gurie
One Sheet: $50 - $100

VOICE OF BUGLE ANN, THE
(1936 - MGM) Lionel Barrymore, Eric Linden, Maureen O'Sullivan
One Sheet: $125 - $250

VOICE OF HOLLYWOOD
(1931 - -) -
One Sheet: $250 - $500   *Short.*

VOICE OF THE HURRICANE
(1964 - Selected) Muriel Smith, David Cole
One Sheet: $5 - $10

VOICE OF THE TURTLE, THE
(1947 - Warner Bros.) Ronald Reagan, Eleanor Parker, Eve Arden
One Sheet: $50 - $100

VOICE OF THE WHISTLER
(1945 - Columbia) Richard Dix, Lynn Merrick
One Sheet: $30 - $60

VOLCANO
(1997 - 20th Century Fox) Tommy Lee Jones, Anne Heche
One Sheet: $4 - $8

VOLERE/VOLARE
(1993 - Fine Line) Maurizio Nichetti, Angela Finocchia
One Sheet: $3 - $5   *Italian.*

VOLGA BOATMAN, THE
(1926 - PRC) William Boyd, Elinor Fair, Dir: Cecil B. DeMille
One Sheet: $250 - $500

VOLTAIRE
(1933 - Warner Bros.) George Arliss, Doris Kenyon
One Sheet: $150 - $300

VOLUNTEERS
(1985 - Tristar) Tom Hanks, John Candy
One Sheet: $5 - $10

VOLUPTUOUS GRADUATES
(197? - SRC) Sally Marshall, Penny Warden
One Sheet: $7 - $15   *Sexploitation.*

VOLUPTUOUS VIXENS '76
(1975 - -) -
One Sheet: $15 - $35   *Sexploitation.*

VON RICHTHOFEN AND BROWN
(1971 - United Artists) John Phillip Law, Dir: Roger Corman(last film)
One Sheet: $15 - $30

VON RYAN'S EXPRESS
(1965 - 20th Century Fox) Frank Sinatra, Trevor Howard
One Sheet: $15 - $30

VOODOO DEVIL DRUMS
(1940 - Toddy) -
One Sheet: $75 - $150   *Black cast. Separate Cinema, pg. 122.*

VOODOO ISLAND
(1957 - United Artists) Boris Karloff, Beverly Tyler
One Sheet: $40 - $75

VOODOO MAN
(1944 - Monogram) Bela Lugosi, George Zucco, John Carradine
One Sheet: $150 - $300   *Graven*

Images, pg. 133.

VOODOO TIGER
(1952 - Columbia) Johnny Weissmuller, Jean Byron
One Sheet: $30 - $50

VOODOO WOMAN
(1956 - AIP) Marla English, Tom Conway
One Sheet: $40 - $75

Half Sheet

VOYAGE, THE
(1974 - Champion) Sophia Loren, Richard Burton
One Sheet: $5 - $10

VOYAGE
(1993 - 20th Century Fox) Eric Roberts, Rutger Hauer
One Sheet: $3 - $5

VOYAGE OF SILENCE
(1968 - Lopert) Marco Pico, Ludmila Mikael
One Sheet: $5 - $10

VOYAGE OF THE DAMNED
(1976 - Avco/Embassy) Faye Dunaway, Max von Sydow
One Sheet: $7 - $15

VOYAGE OF THE ROCK ALIENS
(1987 - -) Pia Zadora, Jermaine Jackson
One Sheet: $7 - $15

VOYAGE TO THE BOTTOM OF THE SEA
(1961 - 20th Century Fox) Walter Pidgeon, Joan Fontaine
One Sheet: $50 - $100

VOYAGE TO THE EDGE OF THE WORLD
(19?? - -) Jacques Cousteau
One Sheet: $5 - $10   *Documentary.*

VOYAGE TO THE END OF THE UNIVERSE
(1964 - AIP) Dennis Stephens, Francis Smolen
One Sheet: $15 - $35

VULTURE, THE
(1966 - Paramount) Robert Hutton, Akim Tamiroff
One Sheet: $15 - $25

W PLAN, THE
(1930 - RKO) Brian Aherne, Madeleine Carroll
One Sheet: $150 - $300

W. W. AND THE DIXIE DANCE KINGS
(1975 - 20th Century Fox) Burt Reynolds, Art Carney
One Sheet: $7 - $15   *Two styles.*

WABASH AVENUE
(1950 - 20th Century Fox) Betty Grable, Victor Mature
One Sheet: $250 - $500   *Price is for style "B" one sheet. One Sheet(other style):$150-$300.*

WAC FROM WALLA WALLA, THE
(1952 - Republic) Judy Canova, Stephen Dunne
One Sheet: $15 - $30

WACKIEST SHIP IN THE ARMY, THE
(1960 - Columbia) Jack Lemmon, Ricky Nelson
One Sheet: $15 - $30

WACKO
(1983 - Jensen Farley) Joe Don Baker, Stella Stevens, George Kennedy
One Sheet: $5 - $10

WACKY WIGWAM
(1937 - Columbia) -

One Sheet: $100 - $200   *Cartoon.*

WACKY WORLD OF MOTHER GOOSE, THE
(1967 - Embassy) -
One Sheet: $3 - $5   *Cartoon.*

WACO
(1952 - Monogram) "Wild Bill" Elliott
One Sheet: $15 - $35

WACO
(1966 - Paramount) Howard Keel, Jane Russell
One Sheet: $10 - $20

WAGES FOR WIVES
(1925 - Fox) Jacqueline Logan, Zasu Pitts
One Sheet: $150 - $300

WAGES OF FEAR
(1955 - DCA) Yves Montand, Vera Clouzot, Dir: H. G. Clouzot
One Sheet: $50 - $100   *French/Italian.*

WAGES OF SIN, THE
(1929 - -) Lorenzo Tucker, Katherine Noisette
One Sheet: $600 - $1,000

WAGES OF SIN, THE
(1938 - Real Life Dramas) -
One Sheet: $50 - $100   *Exploitation. AKA: SKID ROW.*

WAGES OF VIRTUE
(1924 - Paramount) Gloria Swanson
One Sheet: $1,300 - $2,000

WAGON MASTER
(1950 - RKO) Ben Johnson, Joanne Dru
One Sheet: $75 - $150

WAGON SHOW
(1928 - First National) Ken Maynard
One Sheet: $600 - $1,000   *Cowboy Movie Posters #62.*

WAGON TEAM
(1952 - Columbia) Gene Autry
One Sheet: $40 - $75

WAGON TRACKS
(1919 - -) William S. Hart, Jane Novak
One Sheet: $800 - $1,500

WAGON TRACKS WEST
(1943 - Republic) Bill Elliott, Gabby Hayes
One Sheet: $30 - $50

WAGON TRACKS WEST
(1952R - Republic) Bill Elliott, Gabby Hayes
One Sheet: $10 - $20   *Re-release.*

WAGON TRAIL, THE
(1927R - Aywon) -
One Sheet: $150 - $300   *Re-release.*

WAGON TRAIL, THE
(1935 - Ajax) Harry Carey, Gertrude Messinger
One Sheet: $125 - $250

WAGON TRAIN
(1940 - RKO) Tim Holt, Ray Whitley
One Sheet: $40 - $75

WAGON WHEELS
(1934 - Paramount) Randolph Scott
One Sheet: $150 - $300   *Cowboy Movie Posters # 164.*

WAGON WHEELS WEST
(1943 - Warner Bros.) Robert Shayne, Nina Foch
One Sheet: $20 - $40

WAGON WHEELS WESTWARD
(1945 - Republic) "Wild Bill" Elliott, Bobby Blake
One Sheet: $30 - $50

WAGONS EAST
(1994 - TriStar) John Candy, Richard Lewis
One Sheet: $7 - $15

WAGONS ROLL AT NIGHT, THE
(1941 - Warner Bros.) Humphrey Bogart, Sylvia Sidney, Eddie Albert
One Sheet: $250 - $500

WAGONS WEST
(1952 - Monogram) Peggie Castle, Rod Cameron
One Sheet: $15 - $30

WAGONS WESTWARD
(1940 - Republic) Chester Morris, Anita Louise,

Buck Jones
One Sheet: $75 - $150

WAIKIKI WEDDING
(1937 - Paramount) Bing Crosby, Bob Burns, Martha Raye
One Sheet: $100 - $200

Mini Window Card (trimmed)

WAIT 'TIL THE SUN SHINES NELLIE
(1952 - 20th Century Fox) Jean Peters, David Wayne
One Sheet: $10 - $20

WAIT UNTIL DARK
(1967 - Warner-Bros.-Seven Arts) Audrey Hepburn, Alan Arkin
One Sheet: $30 - $50

WAITING FOR CAROLINE
(1969 - Lopert) Alexandria Stewart, Francoise Tasse
One Sheet: $3 - $5

WAITING FOR GUFFMAN
(1997 - Sony) Christopher Guest, Eugene Levy
One Sheet: $3 - $5

WAITING FOR THE MOON
(1987 - -) Linda Hunt, Linda Bassett
One Sheet: $5 - $10

WAITING TO EXHALE
(1995 - 20th Century Fox) Whitney Houston, Angela Bassett
One Sheet: $7 - $15

WAITRESS!
(1982 - Troma) Carol Drake, Jim Harris
One Sheet: $5 - $10

WAJAN-SON OF THE WITCH
(1937 - Mutual) -
One Sheet: $500 - $800   *Documentary.*

WAKE ISLAND
(1942 - Paramount) Brian Donlevy, Macdonald Carey
One Sheet: $75 - $150

WAKE ME WHEN IT'S OVER
(1960 - 20th Century Fox) Ernie Kovacs, Margo Moore
One Sheet: $5 - $10

WAKE OF THE RED WITCH
(1949 - Republic) John Wayne, Gail Russell
One Sheet: $150 - $300

WAKE UP AND DREAM
(1934 - Universal) Russ Columbo, Roger Pryor, June Knight
One Sheet: $100 - $200

WAKE UP AND DREAM
(1946 - 20th Century Fox) June Haver, John Payne
One Sheet: $30 - $50

WAKE UP AND LIVE
(1937 - 20th Century Fox) Walter Winchell, Ben Bernie, Jack Haley, Alice Faye
One Sheet: $100 - $200

WAKEFIELD CASE, THE
(1921 - -) Herbert Rawlinson, John P. Wade
One Sheet: $150 - $300

WALK A CROOKED MILE
(1948 - Columbia) Louis Hayward, Dennis O'Keefe, Louise Allbritton
One Sheet: $15 - $35

WALK A TIGHTROPE
(1964 - Paramount) Dan Duryea, Patricia

Owens
One Sheet: $7 - $15

WALK, DON'T RUN
(1966 - Columbia) Cary Grant, Samantha Eggar
One Sheet: $10 - $20   *Two styles. Grant's final film.*

WALK EAST ON BEACON
(1952 - Columbia) George Murphy, Virginia Gilmore
One Sheet: $10 - $20

WALK IN THE CLOUDS, A
(1995 - 20th Century Fox) Keanu Reeves, Anthony Quinn
One Sheet: $7 - $15

WALK IN THE SPRING RAIN
(1970 - Columbia) Ingrid Bergman, Anthony Quinn
One Sheet: $7 - $15

WALK IN THE SUN, A
(1945 - 20th Century Fox) Dana Andrews, Richard Conte
One Sheet: $30 - $60

One Sheet

WALK IN THE SUN, A
(1951R - 20th Century Fox) Dana Andrews, Richard Conte
One Sheet: $10 - $20   *Re-release.*

WALK LIKE A DRAGON
(1960 - Paramount) Jack Lord, Nobu McCarthy
One Sheet: $15 - $25

WALK LIKE A MAN
(1986 - MGM) Howie Mandel, Christopher Lloyd
One Sheet: $3 - $5

WALK ON THE WILD SIDE
(1962 - Columbia) Laurence Harvey, Capucine
One Sheet: $20 - $40   *Saul Bass art.*

WALK PROUD
(1979 - Universal) Robby Benson, Sarah Holcomb
One Sheet: $3 - $5

WALK SOFTLY, STRANGER
(1949 - RKO) Joseph Cotton, Valli
One Sheet: $50 - $100

WALK TALL
(1960 - 20th Century Fox) Willard Parker, Joyce Meadows
One Sheet: $7 - $15

WALK THE DARK STREET
(1956 - Associated Artists) Chuck Connors, Don Ross
One Sheet: $15 - $25

WALK THE PROUD LAND
(1956 - Universal) Audie Murphy, Pat Crowley
One Sheet: $30 - $50

WALK THE WALK
(1970 - Woolner) (Kroger Babb), Bernie Hamilton, Honor Lawrence
One Sheet: $15 - $35

WALK WITH LOVE AND DEATH, A
(1969 - 20th Century Fox) Anjelica Huston, Assaf Dayan
One Sheet: $7 - $15   *Huston's film debut.*

WALKABOUT
(1971 - 20th Century Fox) Jenny Agutter, David

Gulpilil
One Sheet: $7 - $15

WALKER
(1988 - -) Ed Harris, Marlee Matlin
One Sheet: $7 - $15

WALKING AND TALKING
(1996 - Miramax) Catherine Keener, Anne Heche
One Sheet: $5 - $10   *Comedy.*

WALKING DEAD, THE
(1936 - Warner Bros.) Boris Karloff, Dir: Michael Curtiz
One Sheet: $4,000 - $6,000   *Graven Images, pg. 86.*

WALKING DEAD, THE
(1941R - Warner Bros.) Boris Karloff, Dir: Michael Curtiz
One Sheet: $250 - $600   *Re-release.*

WALKING DEAD, THE
(1995 - Savoy) Joe Morton, Allen Payne
One Sheet: $5 - $10

WALKING DOWN BROADWAY
(1938 - 20th Century Fox) Claire Trevor, Michael Whalen
One Sheet: $75 - $150

WALKING HILLS, THE
(1949 - Columbia) Randolph Scott, Ella Raines
One Sheet: $20 - $40

WALKING MY BABY BACK HOME
(1953 - Universal) Donald O'Connor, Janet Leigh
One Sheet: $15 - $30

WALKING ON AIR
(1936 - RKO) Gene Raymond, Ann Sothern
One Sheet: $75 - $150

WALKING STICK, THE
(1970 - MGM) David Hemmings, Samantha Eggar, Emlyn Williams
One Sheet: $5 - $10

WALKING TALL
(- - -) Also see FINAL CHAPTER - WALKING TALL

WALKING TALL
(1973 - Cinerama) Joe Don Baker, Elizabeth Hartman
One Sheet: $15 - $25

WALKING TALL, PART II
(1975 - AIP) Bo Svenson, Luke Askew
One Sheet: $5 - $10

WALKING TALL: THE FINAL CHAPTER
(1977 - -) See FINAL CHAPTER-WALKING TALL

WALKING TARGET
(1960 - United Artists) Joan Evans, Ronald Foster
One Sheet: $5 - $10

WALL OF NOISE
(1963 - Warner Bros.) Suzanne Pleshette, Ty Hardin
One Sheet: $10 - $20

WALL STREET
(1930 - Columbia) Aileen Pringle, Ralph Ince
One Sheet: $150 - $300

WALL STREET
(1987 - 20th Century Fox) Michael Douglas, Charlie Sheen
One Sheet: $15 - $30   *Academy Award: Best Actor(Douglas). Academy Award Movie Posters #354.*

WALL STREET COWBOY
(1939 - Republic) Roy Rogers, Gabby Hayes
One Sheet: $250 - $500

WALLABY JIM OF THE ISLANDS
(1937 - Grand National) George Huston, Ruth Coleman
One Sheet: $40 - $75

WALLFLOWER
(1948 - Warner Bros.) Joyce Reynolds, Robert Hutton
One Sheet: $15 - $25

WALLS CAME TUMBLING DOWN, THE
(1946 - Columbia) Lee Bowman, Marguerite

Chapman
One Sheet: $40 - $75

WALLS OF GOLD
(1933 - 20th Century Fox) Sally Eilers, Norman Foster
One Sheet: $125 - $250

WALLS OF HELL, THE
(1964 - Hemisphere) Jock Mahoney, Fernando Poe, Jr.
One Sheet: $5 - $10

WALLS OF JERICHO, THE
(1948 - 20th Century Fox) Cornel Wilde, Linda Darnell, Kirk Douglas
One Sheet: $40 - $75

WALT DISNEY ALL-CARTOON FESTIVAL
(1953 - RKO/Disney) Mickey Mouse, Donald Duck, etc
One Sheet: $100 - $200   *Cartoon.*

WALT DISNEY CARTOON SHORT SUBJECTS
(1965 - Buena Vista) Mickey Mouse, Donald Duck, Goofy
One Sheet: $75 - $125   *Cartoon.*

One Sheet

WALT DISNEY SHORT SUBJECTS
(1950S - Beuna Vista/Disney) Mickey Mouse, etc
One Sheet: $100 - $200   *Cartoon.*

WALT DISNEY STOCK
(1947 - Disney) -
One Sheet: $125 - $275   *Cartoon.*

WALT DISNEY'S MICKEY MOUSE CARTOON
(1935 - United Artists/Disney) Mickey Mouse
One Sheet: $13,000 - $20,000   *Cartoon. Stock poster. Lobby Card known to exist. Cartoon Movie Posters #64.*

WALTER LANTZ CARTUNE STOCK
(1939 - Universal) -
One Sheet: $250 - $600   *Cartoon. Full color stock w/all characters. Cartoon Movie Posters #53.*

WALTER LANTZ CARTUNE STOCK
(1942 - Universal) Andy Panda, Woody Woodpecker
One Sheet: $800 - $1,500   *Cartoon. Full color stock poster featuring first image of Woody Woodpecker.*

WALTER LANTZ CARTUNE STOCK
(1948 - Universal) Cartoon Stars
One Sheet: $100 - $200   *Cartoon. Full color stock poster blank at center surrounded by cartoon stars including Woody Woodpecker.*

WALTER WANGER'S VOGUES OF 1938
(1937 - United Artists) Warner Baxter, Joan Bennett
One Sheet: $100 - $200

WALTZ ACROSS TEXAS
(1982 - Aster) Anne Archer, Noah Beery
One Sheet: $5 - $10

WALTZ DREAM, THE
(1926 - MGM) Dir: Ludwig Berger
One Sheet: $250 - $600   *German.*

WALTZ OF THE TOREADORS
(1962 - Continental) Peter Sellers, Dany Robin
One Sheet: $7 - $15

WALTZ TIME IN VIENNA
(1933 - UFA) -
One Sheet: $150 - $300   *German.*

WANDA

(1971 - Bardene International) Barbara Loden, Michael Higgins
One Sheet: $3 - $5

WANDA NEVADA
(1979 - United Artists) Peter Fonda, Brooke Shields
One Sheet: $5 - $10

WANDERER, THE
(1920' - -) Harry Carey
One Sheet: $200 - $400

WANDERER, THE
(1923 - Paramount) Butch Collier
One Sheet: $150 - $300

WANDERER, THE
(1926 - Paramount) Ernest Torrence, Greta Nissen
One Sheet: $800 - $1,500

WANDERER OF THE WASTELAND, THE
(1924 - Paramount) Jack Holt, Noah Beery
One Sheet: $250 - $500

WANDERER OF THE WASTELAND, THE
(1935 - Paramount) Dean Jagger, Buster Crabbe
One Sheet: $75 - $175

Mini Window Card (Trimmed)

WANDERER OF THE WASTELAND, THE
(1945 - RKO) James Warren, Audrey Long
One Sheet: $15 - $35

WANDERERS OF THE WEST
(1941 - Monogram) Tom Keene
One Sheet: $50 - $100

WANDERING PAPAS
(1926 - Pathecomedy) Clyde Cook
One Sheet: $150 - $350

WANDERING TWO, THE
(1923 - Universal) See THE LEATHER PUSHERS (SERIAL)

WANING SEX, THE
(1926 - MGM) Conrad Nagel, Sally O'Neill
One Sheet: $250 - $500

WANTED BY THE POLICE
(1938 - Monogram) Frankie Darro, Robert Kent
One Sheet: $50 - $100

WANTED: DEAD OR ALIVE
(1951 - Monogram) Whip Wilson
One Sheet: $20 - $40

WANTED: DEAD OR ALIVE
(1987 - -) Rutger Hauer, Gene Simmons
One Sheet: $7 - $15

WANTED FOR MURDER
(1946 - 20th Century Fox) Eric Portman, Dulcie Gray, Derek Farr
One Sheet: $15 - $35

WANTED! JANE TURNER
(1936 - RKO) Lee Tracy, Gloria Stuart
One Sheet: $100 - $200

WAR, THE
(1994 - Universal) Elijah Wood, Kevin Costner
One Sheet: $5 - $10

WAR AGAINST MRS. HADLEY, THE
(1942 - MGM) Van Johnson, Fay Bainter, Edward Arnold
One Sheet: $30 - $50

WAR AND PEACE
(1956 - Paramount) Audrey Hepburn, Henry Fonda

One Sheet: $75 - $150

WAR AND PEACE
(1963R - Paramount) Audrey Hepburn, Henry Fonda
One Sheet: $20 - $40 *Re-release.*

WAR AND PEACE
(1968 - Continental) Ludmila Savelyeva, Sergei Bondarchuk
One Sheet: $5 - $10

WAR ARROW
(1954 - Universal) Jeff Chandler, Maureen O'Hara
One Sheet: $15 - $30

One Sheet

WAR AT HOME, THE
(1996 - Touchstone) Emilio Estevez, Kathy Bates, Martin Sheen
One Sheet: $3 - $5

WAR BETWEEN MEN AND WOMEN, THE
(1972 - National General) Jack Lemmon, Barbara Harris
One Sheet: $5 - $10

WAR BETWEEN THE PLANETS
(1971 - Mercury) Jack Stuart, Amber Collins
One Sheet: $15 - $35

WAR BRIDES
(1916 - Selznick) Nazimoua
One Sheet: $600 - $1,000

WAR CORRESPONDENT
(1932 - Columbia) Jack Holt, Ralph Graves, Lila Lee
One Sheet: $150 - $300

WAR DEVIL
(1970 - -) -
One Sheet: $7 - $15

WAR DOGS
(1942 - Monogram) Billy Lee, Addison Richards
One Sheet: $15 - $30

WAR DOGS
(1943 - MGM) -
One Sheet: $250 - $500 *Cartoon. Full color stone litho.*

WAR DRUMS
(1957 - United Artists) Lex Barker, Joan Taylor
One Sheet: $15 - $30

WAR HORSE, THE
(1927 - William Fox) Buck Jones, Lola Todd
One Sheet: $250 - $600

WAR HUNT
(1962 - United Artists) John Saxon, Robert Redford (film debut)
One Sheet: $15 - $25

WAR IS A RACKET
(1934 - Eureka) Col. Harry K. Eustace, Gertrude Clemens
One Sheet: $150 - $300

WAR IS HELL
(1964 - Allied Artists) Tony Russell, Baynes Barron
One Sheet: $5 - $10

WAR ITALIAN STYLE
(1967 - AIP) Buster Keaton, Franco and Ciccio
One Sheet: $15 - $30

WAR LORD, THE
(1965 - Universal) Charlton Heston, Richard Boone
One Sheet: $15 - $30

WAR LOVER, THE
(1962 - Columbia) Steve McQueen, Robert Wagner
One Sheet: $15 - $30

WAR NURSE
(1930 - MGM) Robert Montgomery, June Walker
One Sheet: $75 - $150

WAR OF THE BUTTONS
(1963 - Comet) Martin Lartique, Andre Treton
One Sheet: $10 - $20 *French.*

WAR OF THE COLOSSAL BEAST
(1958 - AIP) Sally Fraser, Roger Pace
One Sheet: $150 - $300 *Sequel to THE AMAZING COLOSSAL MAN. Graven Images, pg. 188.*

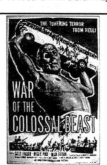

One Sheet

WAR OF THE GARGANTUAS, THE
(1966 - UPA Release) Russ Tamblyn, Kumi Mizuno
One Sheet: $50 - $100 *Price is for UPA release one sheet. International Style (full color):$100-$150.*

WAR OF THE GARGANTUAS/GODZILLA'S REVENGE
(1970 - Maron Films) Russ Tamblyn, Kumi Mizuno
One Sheet: $40 - $75

WAR OF THE GARGANTUAS/MONSTER ZERO
(1966 - Maron Films) Russ Tamblyn, Kumi Mizuno
One Sheet: $40 - $75 *Double feature poster.*

WAR OF THE PLANETS
(1966 - -) Tony Russel, Lisa Gastoni
One Sheet: $15 - $25

WAR OF THE PLANETS
(1977 - Toho) Kensaku Morita, William Ross
One Sheet: $15 - $25 *AKA: WAR IN SPACE; COSMOS.*

WAR OF THE RANGE
(1933 - Monarch) Tom Tyler, Slim Whitaker
One Sheet: $150 - $300

WAR OF THE ROSES
(1989 - 20th Century Fox) Michael Douglas, Kathleen Turner
One Sheet: $7 - $15

WAR OF THE SATELLITES
(1958 - Allied Artists) Susan Cabot, Dick Miller
One Sheet: $40 - $75

WAR OF THE WILDCATS
(1959R - -) John Wayne, Martha Scott
One Sheet: $30 - $50 *Re-titled re-release of IN OLD OKLAHOMA.*

WAR OF THE WIZARDS
(1983 - 21st Century) Richard Kiel, Charles Lang
One Sheet: $5 - $10

WAR OF THE WORLD-NEXT CENTURY, THE
(1981 - Zespoly) Roman Wilhemi
One Sheet: $5 - $12

WAR OF THE WORLDS
(1953 - Paramount) Gene Barry, Ann Robinson
One Sheet: $700 - $1,200 *Half Sheet (Saucers attacking):$3000-$5000. Graven Images, pg. xiv, 151, 156-157.*

WAR OF THE WORLDS
(1965R - Paramount) Gene Barry, Ann Robinson

One Sheet: $100 - $200 *Re-release. Graven Images, pg. 146.*

WAR OF THE WORLDS
(1977R - Paramount) Gene Barry, Ann Robinson
One Sheet: $10 - $20 *Re-release.*

WAR OF THE WORLDS/WHEN WORLDS COLLIDE COMBO
(1977R - Paramount) -
One Sheet: $15 - $30 *Re-release double feature poster.*

WAR OF THE ZOMBIES
(1965 - AIP) John Drew Barrymore, Ida Galli
One Sheet: $30 - $50

WAR PAINT
(1953 - United Artists) Robert Stack, Joan Taylor
One Sheet: $15 - $25

One Sheet

WAR PARTY
(1965 - 20th Century Fox) Michael T. Miker, Davey Davidson
One Sheet: $5 - $10

WAR PARTY
(1989 - Hemdale) Billy Wirth, Kevin Dillon
One Sheet: $3 - $5

WAR ROOM, THE
(1993 - October Films) George Stephanopaulos
One Sheet: $3 - $5 *Documentary.*

WAR WAGON, THE
(1967 - Universal) John Wayne, Kirk Douglas
One Sheet: $40 - $75

WARE CASE,THE
(1939 - Fox) Clive Brook, Jane Baxter
One Sheet: $100 - $200

WARGAMES
(1983 - MGM) Matthew Broderick, Dabney Coleman
One Sheet: $5 - $10

WAR-GODS OF THE DEEP
(1965 - AIP) Vincent Price, Tab Hunter
One Sheet: $30 - $50

WARKILL
(1968 - Universal) George Montgomery, Tom Drake
One Sheet: $7 - $15

WARLOCK
(1959 - 20th Century Fox) Richard Widmark, Henry Fonda
One Sheet: $15 - $25

WARLOCK: THE ARMAGEDDON
(1993 - TriMark) Julian Sands, Lori Singer
One Sheet: $3 - $5

WARLORDS OF ATLANTIS
(1978 - Columbia) Doug McClure, Peter Gilmore
One Sheet: $10 - $20

WARLORDS OF THE 21ST CENTURY
(1982 - New World) Michael Beck, Annie McEnroe
One Sheet: $7 - $15 *AKA: BATTLETRUCK.*

WARM CORNER
(1938 - Gainsborough) Leslie Henson, Heather Thatcher
One Sheet: $75 - $150

WARM DECEMBER, A
(1973 - National General) Sidney Poitier,
Esther Anderson
One Sheet: $10 - $20

WARM IN THE BUD
(1970 - Filmmakers) Robert Mont, Dean
Strickland
One Sheet: $5 - $12

WARMING UP
(1928 - Paramount) Richard Dix
One Sheet: $250 - $600   *Sports
(Baseball). Sports Movie Posters #39.*

WARN LONDON
(1934 - British Lion) Edmund Gwenn, John
Loder
One Sheet: $75 - $150

WARN THAT MAN
(1943 - Pathe) Gordon Harker, Raymond Lovell
One Sheet: $15 - $25

WARNER BROS. CARTOON STOCK
(1946 - Warner Bros) -
One Sheet: $700 - $1,200   *Cartoon. Full
color, stock poster showing Bugs Bunny standing
at ticket counter holding a cane in the air,
surrounded by various cartoonstars. Cartoon
Movie Posters #104.*

WARNER BROS. CARTOON STOCK
(1948 - Warner Bros.) Bugs Bunny, Elmer
Fudd, Porky Pig
One Sheet: $250 - $600   *Cartoon.*

WARNER BROS. CARTOON STOCK
(1952 - Warner Bros.) Bugs Bunny and others
One Sheet: $250 - $600   *Cartoon. "A
Warner Bros. Cartoon" Bugs Bunny at drawing
table sitting on can of carrots. Cartoon Movie
Posters #105.*

WARNING SHOT
(1967 - Paramount) David Janssen, Ed Begley
One Sheet: $3 - $5

WARNING SIGN
(1985 - -) Sam Waterston, Kathleen Quinlan,
Yaphet Kotto
One Sheet: $7 - $15

WARNING TO WANTONS, A
(1949 - GFD) Harold Warrender
One Sheet: $10 - $20

WARPATH
(1951 - Paramount) Edmond O'Brien, Dean
Jagger
One Sheet: $15 - $25

WARREN CASE, THE
(1934 - Pathe) Richard Bird, Nancy Burne
One Sheet: $150 - $300

WARRENDALE
(1968 - Grove Press) -
One Sheet: $3 - $5

WARRENS OF VIRGINIA, THE
(1915 - Paramount) Blanche Sweet, James
Neill
One Sheet: $800 - $1,500

WARRING CLANS
(1963 - Toho) Yuzo Kayama, Yuriko Hoshi
One Sheet: $15 - $30

WARRIOR AND THE SLAVE GIRL, THE
(1959 - Columbia) Gianna Maria Canale,
Georges Marchal
One Sheet: $15 - $25

WARRIOR AND THE SORCERESS, THE
(1984 - New Horizons) David Carradine, Luke
Askew
One Sheet: $7 - $15

WARRIOR EMPRESS, THE
(1961 - Columbia) Kerwin Mathews, Tina
Louise
One Sheet: $15 - $30

WARRIOR QUEEN
(1987 - -) Sybil Danning, Donald Pleasence
One Sheet: $15 - $25

WARRIOR'S FAITH, A
(1912 - Bison) -
One Sheet: $1,600 - $2,500

WARRIOR'S HUSBAND, THE
(1933 - Fox) Elissa Landi

One Sheet: $150 - $300

WARRIORS, THE
(1955 - Allied Artists) Errol Flynn, Joanne Dru
One Sheet: $30 - $50

WARRIORS, THE
(1979 - Paramount) Michael Beck, James
Remar
One Sheet: $15 - $25

WARRIORS FIVE
(1962 - Italian Interntional) Jack Palance,
Giovanna Ralli
One Sheet: $7 - $15   *French/Italian.*

WARRIORS OF VIRTUE
(1997 - MGM) Angus MacFadyen, Mario
Yedidia
One Sheet: $3 - $5

WASHINGTON CROSSING THE DELAWARE
(1912 - Edison) -
One Sheet: $600 - $1,000

WASHINGTON MASQUERADE, THE
(1932 - MGM) Lionel Barrymore, Karen Morley
One Sheet: $100 - $200

WASHINGTON MELODRAMA
(1941 - MGM) Frank Morgan, Lee Bowman,
Ann Rutherford
One Sheet: $40 - $75

WASHINGTON MERRY-GO-ROUND
(1932 - Columbia) Lee Tracy, Constance
Cummings
One Sheet: $75 - $150

WASHINGTON STORY
(1952 - MGM) Van Johnson, Patricia Neal
One Sheet: $15 - $25

WASP WOMAN, THE
(1959 - The Filmgroup) Susan Cabot, Fred
Eisley
One Sheet: $300 - $700   *Graven
Images, pg. 186.*

WASTREL, THE
(1963 - Lux Film) Van Heflin
One Sheet: $5 - $10

WATCH BEVERLY
(1932 - Butcher) Henry Kendall
One Sheet: $100 - $200

WATCH DOG, THE
(1940 - 20th Century Fox) Terry-toons
One Sheet: $100 - $200   *Cartoon. Full
color stone litho. Stock poster with inset title.*

WATCH IT, SAILOR
(1961 - Columbia) Dennis Price, Marjorie
Rhodes
One Sheet: $5 - $12

WATCH ON THE RHINE
(1943 - Warner Bros.) Paul Lukas, Bette Davis
One Sheet: $150 - $300   *Academy
Award: Best Actor.*

One Sheet

WATCH THE BIRDIE
(1950 - MGM) Red Skelton, Arlene Dahl
One Sheet: $40 - $75

WATCHED
(1974 - Penthouse) Stacy Keach, Harris Yulin
One Sheet: $4 - $8

WATCHER IN THE WOODS, THE
(1981 - Disney) Bette Davis
One Sheet: $15 - $25

WATCHERS
(1988 - -) Corey Haim, Barbara Williams
One Sheet: $5 - $10

WATCHERS 2
(1990 - -) -
One Sheet: $3 - $5

WATER
(1985 - -) Michael Caine, Brenda Vaccaro
One Sheet: $2 - $3

WATER BABIES, THE
(1979 - Ariadne) James Mason, Tommy Pender
One Sheet: $5 - $10   *Partial
Animation.*

WATER GYPSIES, THE
(1932 - RKO) Ann Todd, Ian Hunter
One Sheet: $100 - $200

WATER HOLE, THE
(1928 - -) Jack Holt, Nancy Carroll
One Sheet: $250 - $500

WATER RUSTLERS
(1939 - Grand National) Dave O'Brien, Dorothy
Page
One Sheet: $40 - $75

WATER, WATER, EVERYWHERE
(1920 - Samuel Goldwyn) Will Rogers
One Sheet: $250 - $600

WATERDANCE, THE
(1992 - Columbia/TriStar) Eric Stoltz, Wesley
Snipe, Helen Hunt
One Sheet: $2 - $3

WATERFRONT
(1939 - Warner Bros.) Gloria Dickson, Dennis
Morgan
One Sheet: $50 - $100

WATERFRONT
(1944 - PRC) J. Carroll Naish, John Carradine
One Sheet: $30 - $50

WATERFRONT AT MIDNIGHT
(1948 - Paramount) William Gargan, Mary Beth
Hughes, Richard Travis
One Sheet: $30 - $50

WATERFRONT LADY
(1935 - Mascot) Ann Rutherford, Frank
Albertson
One Sheet: $75 - $150

WATERHOLE #3
(1967 - Paramount) James Coburn, Margaret
Blye
One Sheet: $7 - $15

WATERLAND
(1993 - Fine Line) Jeremy Irons, Ethan Hawke
One Sheet: $3 - $5

WATERLOO
(1971 - Paramount) Rod Steiger, Christopher
Plummer
One Sheet: $7 - $15

WATERLOO BRIDGE
(1931 - Universal) Mae Clark, Kent Douglas,
Bette Davis
One Sheet: $500 - $800   *One Sheet
does not show Davis. Lobby Card(Davis
shown):$300-$600.*

WATERLOO BRIDGE
(1940 - MGM) Vivien Leigh, Robert Taylor
One Sheet: $600 - $1,000

WATERLOO ROAD
(1945 - Eagle-Lion) John Mills, Stewart
Granger
One Sheet: $20 - $40

WATERMELON MAN
(1970 - Columbia) Godfrey Cambridge, Dir:
Melvin Van Peebles (debut)
One Sheet: $10 - $20   *Black cast.*

WATERSHIP DOWN
(1978 - Avco/Embassy) Voices of John Hurt,
Richard Briers
One Sheet: $15 - $30   *Cartoon.*

WATERWORLD
(1995 - Universal) Kevin Costner, Dennis
Hopper
One Sheet: $7 - $15

WATTSTAX

(1973 - Columbia) Isaac Hayes, Carla Thomas,
Richard Pryor
One Sheet: $15 - $30   *Black cast.
Soul Music Concert film.*

WATUSI
(1958 - MGM) George Montgomery, Taina Elg
One Sheet: $15 - $25   *Separate
Cinema, pg. 127.*

WAVE, A WAC AND A MARINE, A
(1944 - Monogram) Elyse Knox, Henny
Youngman
One Sheet: $15 - $35

WAVELENGTH
(1983 - Wavelength Film) Robert Carradine,
Cherie Currie, Keenan Wynn
One Sheet: $3 - $5

WAXWORK
(1988 - -) Zach Galligan, Deborah Foreman
One Sheet: $5 - $10

WAY AHEAD, THE
(1945 - Two Cities) David Niven, Huntley
Raymond
One Sheet: $30 - $50   *AKA: THE
IMMORTAL BATTALION.*

WAY BACK HOME
(1931 - RKO) Phillips Lord, Bette Davis (bit
part)
One Sheet: $200 - $400   *Davis not
shown on one sheet.*

WAY DOWN EAST
(1920 - United Artists) Richard Barthelmess,
Lillian Gish, Dir: D.W. Griffith
One Sheet: $2,200 - $3,500

WAY DOWN EAST
(1935 - 20th Century Fox) Rochelle Hudson,
Henry Fonda
One Sheet: $200 - $400

One Sheet

WAY DOWN SOUTH
(1939 - RKO) Bobby Breen, Sally Blane
One Sheet: $75 - $125

WAY FOR A SAILOR
(1930 - MGM) John Gilbert, Wallace Beery
One Sheet: $100 - $200

WAY OF A GAUCHO
(1952 - 20th Century Fox) Gene Tierney, Rory
Calhoun
One Sheet: $20 - $40

WAY OF A MAN, THE
(1923 - Pathe) -
One Sheet: $250 - $500   *Serial. 10
Chapters.*

WAY OF A WOMAN, THE
(1919 - Select) Norman Talmadge
One Sheet: $150 - $300

WAY OF ALL FLESH, THE
(1928 - Paramount) Emil Jannings
One Sheet: $800 - $1,500   *Academy
Award: Best Actor. Academy Award Movie
Posters #10.*

WAY OF ALL FLESH, THE
(1940 - Paramount) Akim Tamiroff, Gladys
George
One Sheet: $30 - $50

WAY OF ALL MEN, THE
(1930 - Warner Bros.) Douglas Fairbanks,Jr.,
Dorothy Revier
One Sheet: $200 - $400

WAY OF LOST SOULS, THE
(1929 - Warner Bros.) Pola Negri
One Sheet: $500 - $800

WAY OF THE WEST
(1934 - Superior) Wally Wales, Bobby Nelson, Marla Bratton
One Sheet: $75 - $150

WAY OF YOUTH, THE
(1934 - British/Dominions) Irene Vanburgh, Sebastian Shaw
One Sheet: $50 - $100

WAY OUT, THE
(1955 - RKO) Gene Nelson, Mona Freeman
One Sheet: $10 - $20

WAY OUT
(1966 - Premiere) Frank Rodriguez, James Dunleavy
One Sheet: $7 - $15

WAY OUT WEST
(1930 - MGM) William Haines
One Sheet: $125 - $250

WAY OUT WEST
(1937 - MGM) Laurel & Hardy
One Sheet: $3,500 - $5,000

WAY OUT WEST
(1947R - Film Classics) Laurel & Hardy
One Sheet: $50 - $100   *Re-release.*

WAY TO LOVE, THE
(1933 - Paramount) Maurice Chevalier, Ann Dvorak
One Sheet: $150 - $350

WAY TO THE GOLD, THE
(1957 - 20th Century Fox) Sheree North, Jeffrey Hunter
One Sheet: $5 - $10

WAY TO THE STARS, THE
(1945 - Two Cities) Michael Redgrave, John Mills
One Sheet: $40 - $75

WAY WE LIVE NOW, THE
(1970 - United Artists) Nicholas Pryor, Linda Simon, Joanna Miles
One Sheet: $3 - $5

WAY WE WERE, THE
(1973 - Columbia) Barbra Streisand, Robert Redford
One Sheet: $15 - $25

One Sheet

WAY WE WERE, THE
(1975R - Columbia) Barbra Streisand, Robert Redford
One Sheet: $7 - $15   *Re-release.*

WAY WEST, THE
(1967 - United Artists) Kirk Douglas, Robert Mitchum, Sally Field
One Sheet: $10 - $20   *Field's film debut. Cowboy Movie Posters #321.*

WAYNE'S WORLD
(1992 - Paramount) Dana Carvey, Mike Myers
One Sheet: $5 - $10

WAYNE'S WORLD 2
(1993 - Paramount) Mike Myers, Dana Carvey
One Sheet: $5 - $10

WAYWARD
(1932 - Paramount Publix) Nancy Carroll, Richard Arlen
One Sheet: $75 - $150

WAYWARD BUS, THE
(1957 - Republic) Jayne Mansfield, Dan Dailey
One Sheet: $30 - $50

WAYWARD CANARY, THE
(1932 - United Artists) Mickey Mouse
One Sheet: $25,000 - $40,000   *Cartoon. The Disney Poster, pg. 22.*

WAYWARD GIRL, THE
(1957 - Republic) Marcia Henderson, Peter Walker
One Sheet: $20 - $40

WAY...WAY OUT
(1966 - 20th Century Fox) Jerry Lewis, Connie Stevens
One Sheet: $15 - $25

W.C. FIELDS AND ME
(1976 - Universal) Rod Steiger, Valerie Perrine
One Sheet: $5 - $10

WE ARE NOT ALONE
(1939 - Warner Bros.) Paul Muni, Jane Bryan
One Sheet: $75 - $125

WE ARE THE MARINES
(1942 - 20th Century Fox) -
One Sheet: $75 - $125

WE DIVE AT DAWN
(1943 - Gainsborough) Eric Portman, John Mills
One Sheet: $40 - $75

WE FAW DOWN
(1928 - MGM) Laurel & Hardy
One Sheet: $4,000 - $6,000

WE GO FAST
(1941 - 20th Century Fox) Lynn Bari, Alan Curtis
One Sheet: $40 - $75

WE HAVE OUR MOMENTS
(1937 - Universal) Sally Eilers, James Dunn
One Sheet: $75 - $150

WE LIVE AGAIN
(1934 - United Artists) Fredric March, Anna Sten
One Sheet: $250 - $600

WE SHALL RETURN
(1963 - United International) Cesar Romero, Tony Ray
One Sheet: $5 - $10

WE THINK THE WORLD OF YOU
(1988 - -) Alan Bates, Gary Oldman, Frances Barber
One Sheet: $5 - $10

WE WANT A CHILD
(1953 - Lippert) -
One Sheet: $30 - $50

WE WANT OUR MUMMY
(1939 - Columbia) The Three Stooges (Curly)
One Sheet: $7,500 - $12,000   *Comedy short. Duotone.*

WE WENT TO COLLEGE
(1936 - MGM) Walter Abel, Una Merkel
One Sheet: $100 - $200

WE WERE DANCING
(1942 - MGM) Norma Shearer, Melvyn Douglas
One Sheet: $100 - $200

WE WERE STRANGERS
(1949 - Columbia) Jennifer Jones, John Garfield
One Sheet: $50 - $100

WE WHO ARE ABOUT TO DIE
(1937 - RKO) Preston Foster, Ann Dvorak
One Sheet: $75 - $125

WE WHO ARE YOUNG
(1940 - MGM) Lana Turner, John Shelton
One Sheet: $50 - $100

WE'LL BURY YOU
(1962 - -) Khrushcev
One Sheet: $30 - $50

WE'RE BACK: A DINOSAUR'S STORY
(1993 - Universal) -
One Sheet: $7 - $15   *Cartoon.*

WE'RE GOING TO BE RICH
(1938 - 20th Century Fox) Gracie Fields, Brian

Donlevy, Victor McLaglen
One Sheet: $75 - $125

WE'RE IN THE LEGION NOW
(1937 - Grand National) Reginald Denny, Esther Ralston
One Sheet: $75 - $125

WE'RE IN THE MONEY
(1935 - Warner Bros.) Joan Blondell, Glenda Farrell
One Sheet: $100 - $200

WE'RE IN THE NAVY NOW
(1926 - Paramount) Wallace Beery, Raymond Hatton
One Sheet: $600 - $1,000

WE'RE NO ANGELS
(1955 - Paramount) Humphrey Bogart, Aldo Ray, Peter Ustinov
One Sheet: $50 - $100

WE'RE NO ANGELS
(1989 - Paramount) Robert De Niro, Sean Penn
One Sheet: $5 - $10

WE'RE NOT DRESSING
(1934 - Paramount) Carole Lombard, George Burns, Gracie Allen, Bing Crosby
One Sheet: $250 - $500

WE'RE NOT MARRIED
(1952 - 20th Century Fox) Ginger Rogers, David Wayne, Marilyn Monroe
One Sheet: $150 - $300

WE'RE ON THE JURY
(1937 - RKO) Helen Broderick, Victor Moore
One Sheet: $75 - $150

One Sheet

WE'RE ONLY HUMAN
(1935 - RKO) Preston Foster, Jane Wyatt
One Sheet: $75 - $150

WE'RE RICH AGAIN
(1934 - RKO) Edna May Oliver, Billie Burke
One Sheet: $100 - $200

WE'VE NEVER BEEN LICKED
(1943 - Universal) Richard Quine, Robert Mitchum, Noah Beery, Jr.
One Sheet: $75 - $150

WEAK AND THE WICKED, THE
(1954 - Allied Artists) Glynis Johns, John Gregson
One Sheet: $10 - $20

WEAKER SEX, THE
(1948 - Rank) Ursula Jeans, Derek Bond
One Sheet: $50 - $100

WEAPON, THE
(1956 - Alliance) Steve Cochran, Lizabeth Scott
One Sheet: $10 - $20

WEARY RIVER
(1929 - First National) Richard Barthelmess, Betty Compson, Dir: Frank Lloyd
One Sheet: $200 - $400

WEATHER IN THE STREETS, THE
(1984 - -) Michael York, Lisa Eichlorn
One Sheet: $3 - $7

WEB, THE
(1947 - Universal) Edmond O'Brien, Ella Raines, Vincent Price
One Sheet: $100 - $200

WEB OF DANGER, THE
(1947 - Republic) Bill Kennedy, Damian

O'Flynn
One Sheet: $15 - $30

WEB OF EVIDENCE
(1959 - Columbia) Van Johnson, Vera Miles
One Sheet: $10 - $20

WEB OF SUSPICION
(1959 - Paramount) Philip Friend, Susan Beaumont
One Sheet: $10 - $20

WEBSTER BOY, THE
(1962 - Regal) John Cassavetes, Elizabeth Sellars
One Sheet: $10 - $20

WEDDING, A
(1978 - 20th Century Fox) Desi Arnaz, Jr., Carol Burnett
One Sheet: $5 - $10

WEDDING AT MONACO, THE
(1956 - MGM) Grace Kelly and Prince Rainier
One Sheet: $40 - $75   *Documentary.*

WEDDING BANQUET, THE
(1993 - Samuel Goldwyn) -
One Sheet: $3 - $5

WEDDING BELLS
(1933 - Columbia) Krazy Kat
One Sheet: $1,300 - $2,000   *Cartoon. Cartoon Movie Posters #32.*

WEDDING IN WHITE
(1973 - Avco/Embassy) Donald Pleasence, Carol Kane
One Sheet: $3 - $5

WEDDING MARCH, THE
(1928 - Paramount) Erich von Stroheim, Fay Wray
One Sheet: $3,500 - $5,000

WEDDING NIGHT, THE
(1935 - Samuel Goldwyn) Gary Cooper, Anna Sten, Walter Brennan
One Sheet: $250 - $600

WEDDING NIGHT, THE
(1970 - AIP) Dennis Waterman, Tessa Wyatt
One Sheet: $3 - $5

WEDDING PARTY, THE
(1969 - Ondine) Jill Clayburgh, Robert De Niro
One Sheet: $15 - $25   *Film debut of both stars.*

WEDDING PRESENT
(1936 - Paramount) Cary Grant, Joan Bennett
One Sheet: $300 - $700

One Sheet

WEDDING REHEARSAL
(1932 - London) Roland Young, John Loder
One Sheet: $75 - $150

WEDDING RINGS
(1930 - First National) H.B. Warner, Lois Wilson
One Sheet: $150 - $300

WEDDING WORRIES
(1941 - MGM) Our Gang
One Sheet: $250 - $600

WEDDINGS AND BABIES
(1960 - 20th Century Fox) Viveca Lindfors, John Myers
One Sheet: $7 - $15

WEDDINGS ARE WONDERFUL
(1938 - RKO) June Clyde
One Sheet: $75 - $125

WEDNESDAY CHILDREN, THE
(1973 - Venture) Tom Kelly, Al Miskell
One Sheet: $5 - $10

WEDNESDAY'S CHILD
(1934 - RKO) Edward Arnold, Shirley Gray
One Sheet: $125 - $250

WEDNESDAY'S CHILD
(1972 - Cinema) Sandy Ratcliff, Bill Dean
One Sheet: $3 - $5

WEE GEORDIE
(1956 - Argonaut) Bill Travers, Alistair Sim
One Sheet: $15 - $30   *AKA:*
GEORDIE.

WEE WEE MONSIEUR
(1938 - Columbia) The Three Stooges (Curly)
One Sheet: $7,500 - $12,000   *Comedy short.*
Duotone.

WEE WILLIE WINKIE
(1937 - 20th Century Fox) Shirley Temple,
Victor McLaglen
One Sheet: $1,300 - $2,000   *One*
Sheet(Style B):$600-$1,200.

One Sheet

WEEDS
(1987 - -) Nick Nolte, Rita Taggart
One Sheet: $5 - $10

WEEK END MILLIONAIRE
(1936 - Gaumont) Buddy Rogers, Mary Brian
One Sheet: $100 - $200

One Sheet

WEEKEND AT BERNIE'S
(1989 - 20th Century Fox) Andrew McCarthy,
Jonathan Silverman
One Sheet: $3 - $5

WEEKEND AT BERNIE'S 2
(1993 - TriStar) Andrew McCarthy, Jonathan
Silverman
One Sheet: $3 - $5

WEEKEND AT DUNKIRK
(1966 - 20th Century Fox) Jean-Paul
Belmondo, Catherine Spaak
One Sheet: $5 - $10

WEEKEND AT THE WALDORF
(1945 - MGM) Ginger Rogers, Walter Pidgeon
One Sheet: $75 - $150

WEEKEND FOR THREE
(1941 - RKO) Dennis O'Keefe, Jane Wyatt,
Philip Reed
One Sheet: $30 - $50

WEEKEND IN HAVANA
(1941 - 20th Century Fox) Alice Faye, Carmen
Miranda, John Payne

One Sheet: $200 - $400

WEEKEND MARRIAGE
(1932 - First National) Loretta Young, George
Brent
One Sheet: $150 - $300

WEEKEND PASS
(1944 - Universal) Martha O'Driscoll, Noah
Beery, Jr.
One Sheet: $20 - $40

WEEKEND PASS
(1984 - -) Partick Hauser, D. W. Brown
One Sheet: $3 - $5

WEEKEND WARRIORS
(1986 - -) Chris Lemmon, Lloyd Bridges, Vic
Tayback
One Sheet: $3 - $5

WEEKEND WITH FATHER
(1951 - Universal) Van Heflin, Patricia Neal
One Sheet: $10 - $20

WEEKEND WITH LULU
(1961 - Columbia) Bob Monkhouse, Leslie
Phillips
One Sheet: $5 - $10

WEEKEND WITH THE BABYSITTER
(1970 - Crown) George E. Carey, Susan
Romen
One Sheet: $10 - $20

WEEKEND WIVES
(1929 - World Wide) Monty Banks, Estelle
Brody
One Sheet: $250 - $500

WEEKENDS ONLY
(1932 - Fox) Joan Bennett
One Sheet: $125 - $250

WEIRD ONES, THE
(1962 - Crescent) Mike Braden, Rudy Duran
One Sheet: $7 - $15

WEIRD SCIENCE
(1984 - Universal) Anthony Michael Hall, Kelly
LeBrock
One Sheet: $5 - $10   *Advance:$10-*
$20.

WEIRD WOMAN
(1944 - Universal) Lon Chaney Jr., Anne
Gwynne
One Sheet: $100 - $200

WEIRD WOMAN
(1952R - Realart) Lon Chaney Jr., Anne
Gwynne
One Sheet: $30 - $50   *Re-release.*

WEIRD WORLD OF LSD, THE
(1960S - -) -
One Sheet: $30 - $50   *Drug*
exploitation.

WELCOME DANGER
(1929 - Paramount) Harold Lloyd
One Sheet: $250 - $600

WELCOME HOME
(1935 - Fox) Arline Judge, James Dunn
One Sheet: $100 - $200

WELCOME HOME
(1989 - Columbia) Kris Kristofferson, Sam
Waterston
One Sheet: $2 - $3

WELCOME HOME, BROTHER CHARLES
(1975 - Crown International) Marlo Monte,
Reatha Grey, Tiffany Peters
One Sheet: $10 - $20   *Blaxploitation.*

WELCOME HOME, ROXY CARMICHAEL
(1990 - Paramount) Winnona Ryder, Jeff
Daniels
One Sheet: $5 - $12

WELCOME HOME, SOLDIER BOYS
(1972 - 20th Century Fox) Joe Don Baker, Alan
Vint
One Sheet: $5 - $10

WELCOME LITTLE STRANGER
(1940 - 20th Century Fox) Terry-toons
One Sheet: $100 - $200   *Cartoon. Full*
color stone litho. Stock poster with inset title.

WELCOME STRANGER
(1947 - Paramount) Bing Crosby, Joan

Caulfield, Barry Fitzgerald
One Sheet: $40 - $75

WELCOME TO 18
(1987 - -) Courney Thorne-Smith, Mariska
Hargitay
One Sheet: $2 - $3

WELCOME TO BLOOD CITY
(1977 - EMI) Jack Palance, Keir Dullea
One Sheet: $5 - $10

WELCOME TO HARD TIMES
(1967 - MGM) Henry Fonda, Janice Rule
One Sheet: $5 - $10

WELCOME TO L.A.
(1976 - United Artists) Keith Carradine, Harvey
Keitel
One Sheet: $7 - $15

WELCOME TO MY NIGHTMARE
(1975 - Key) Alice Cooper
One Sheet: $40 - $75   *Rock 'n' Roll.*

One Sheet

WELCOME TO THE CLUB
(1971 - Columbia) Brian Foley, Jack Warden
One Sheet: $3 - $5

WELCOME TO THE DOLLHOUSE
(1996 - Sony Classics) Heather Matarazzo, Dir:
Todd Solondz
One Sheet: $5 - $12   *Comedy.*

WELL, THE
(1951 - United Artists) Harry Morgan, Barry
Kelley
One Sheet: $5 - $10

WELL-DIGGER'S DAUGHTER, THE
(1946 - Pagnol) Raimu, Fernandel, Joesette
Day
One Sheet: $50 - $100   *French.*

WELL-GROOMED BRIDE, THE
(1946 - Paramount) Olivia de Havilland, Ray
Milland, Sonny Tufts
One Sheet: $40 - $75

WELLS FARGO
(1937 - Paramount) Joel McCrea, Frances Dee,
Johnny Mack Brown
One Sheet: $500 - $800   *Cowboy*
Movie Posters #214.

WELLS FARGO
(1958R - Paramount) Joel McCrea, Frances
Dee, Johnny Mac Brown
One Sheet: $20 - $40   *Re-release.*
Full color.

WELLS FARGO DAYS
(1944 - Warner Bros.) Dennis Moore, Louise
Stanley
One Sheet: $15 - $30

WELLS FARGO GUNMASTER
(1951 - Republic) Allan"Rocky"Lane, Chubby
Johnson
One Sheet: $15 - $35

WENCH, THE
(1948 - Spalter) Marla Casares, Roger Piquat
One Sheet: $15 - $25

WEREWOLF, THE
(1956 - Columbia) Steve Ritch, Joyce Holden
One Sheet: $75 - $125

WEREWOLF IN A GIRL'S DORMITORY
(1963 - MGM) Barbara Lass, Carl Schell, Curt
Lowens
One Sheet: $20 - $40   *AKA: THE*
GHOUL IN SCHOOL.

WEREWOLF OF LONDON
(1935 - Universal) Henry Hull, Valerie Hobson,
Warner Oland
One Sheet: $10,000 - $15,000   *Graven*
Images, pg. 42, 89.

One Sheet

WEREWOLF OF LONDON
(1951R - Realart) Henry Hull, Valerie Hobson,
Warner Oland
One Sheet: $250 - $500   *Re-release.*

WEREWOLF VS. THE VAMPIRE WOMAN, THE
(1970 - Plate-Ellman) Paul Naschy, Gaby
Fuchs
One Sheet: $40 - $75   *Spanish/*
German.

WEREWOLVES ON WHEELS
(1971 - Fanfare) Steven Oliver, Barry McGuire
One Sheet: $15 - $30   *Biker/horror*
film.

WEST BOUND LIMITED
(1937 - Universal) Lyle Talbot, Polly Rowles
One Sheet: $75 - $125

WEST BOUND MAIL
(1937 - Columbia) Charles Starrett, Rosalind
Keith
One Sheet: $75 - $150

WEST IS WEST
(1920 - Universal) Harry Carey
One Sheet: $500 - $900

WEST OF ABILENE
(1940 - Columbia) Charles Starrett, Marjorie
Cooley
One Sheet: $40 - $75

WEST OF BROADWAY
(1931 - MGM) John Gilbert, El Brendel, Lois
Moran
One Sheet: $150 - $300

WEST OF CARSON CITY
(1939 - Universal) Johnny Mack Brown, Bob
Baker
One Sheet: $75 - $125

WEST OF CHEYENNE
(1938 - Columbia) Charles Starrett, Iris
Meredith
One Sheet: $50 - $100

WEST OF CHICAGO
(1922 - Fox) Charles Jones, Renee Adoree
One Sheet: $150 - $300

WEST OF CIMARRON
(1942 - Republic) Tom Tyler, Bob Steele
One Sheet: $40 - $75

WEST OF DODGE CITY
(1947 - Columbia) Charles Starrett
One Sheet: $15 - $35

WEST OF ELDORADO
(1949 - Monogram) Johnny Mack Brown, Max
Terhune
One Sheet: $15 - $35

WEST OF HOT DOG
(1924 - Standard) Stan Laurel
One Sheet: $250 - $600

WEST OF LARAMIE
(1949 - Universal) Tex Williams, Smokey
Rogers
One Sheet: $15 - $35

WEST OF PINTO BASIN
(1940 - Monogram) Ray Corrigan, John King

One Sheet: $30 - $50

WEST OF RAINBOW'S END
(1926 - Rayart) Jack Perrin, Pauline Curley, Starlight & Rex
One Sheet: $250 - $500

WEST OF RAINBOW'S END
(1938 - Monogram) Tim McCoy, Nora Lane
One Sheet: $200 - $400

WEST OF SHANGHAI
(1937 - Warner Bros.) Boris Karloff, Ricardo Cortez
One Sheet: $100 - $200

WEST OF SINGAPORE
(1933 - Monogram) Betty Compson, Weldon Heyburn
One Sheet: $125 - $250

WEST OF SONORA
(1948 - Columbia) Charles Starrett
One Sheet: $20 - $40

WEST OF TEXAS
(1943 - PRC) Dave O'Brien, Jim Newill
One Sheet: $20 - $40

WEST OF THE ALAMO
(1946 - Monogram) Jimmy Wakely, Lee"Lasses"White
One Sheet: $15 - $35

WEST OF THE BRAZOS
(1950 - Lippert) James Ellison, Russell Hayden
One Sheet: $7 - $15

WEST OF THE DIVIDE
(1934 - Monogram) John Wayne
One Sheet: $2,500 - $4,000

WEST OF THE LAW
(1942 - Monogram) Buck Jones, Tim McCoy
One Sheet: $100 - $200

WEST OF THE PECOS
(1935 - RKO) Richard Dix, Martha Sleeper
One Sheet: $75 - $150

WEST OF THE PECOS
(1945 - RKO) Robert Mitchum, Barbara Holt
One Sheet: $75 - $150

WEST OF THE RIO GRANDE
(1944 - Monogram) Johnny Mack Brown
One Sheet: $20 - $40

WEST OF THE ROCKIES
(1941 - Warner Bros.) William Travis, Rufe Davis
One Sheet: $15 - $35

WEST OF THE SANTE FE
(1938 - Columbia) Charles Starrett, Iris Meredith
One Sheet: $50 - $100

WEST OF THE WATER TOWER
(1924 - -) Glenn Hunter, May McAvoy
One Sheet: $125 - $250

WEST OF TOMBSTONE
(1942 - Columbia) Charles Starrett, Russell Hayden
One Sheet: $30 - $50

WEST OF WYOMING
(1950 - Monogram) Johnny Mack Brown, Milburn Merante
One Sheet: $15 - $30

WEST OF ZANZIBAR
(1928 - MGM) Lon Chaney, Lionel Barrymore
One Sheet: $700 - $1,200

WEST OF ZANZIBAR
(1954 - Universal-International) Anthony Steel, Sheila Sim
One Sheet: $7 - $15

WEST POINT
(1928 - MGM) Joan Crawford, William Haines
One Sheet: $800 - $1,500   *Price is valid only if Crawford is pictured.*

WEST POINT OF THE AIR
(1935 - MGM) Robert Young, Maureen O'Sullivan, Wallace Beery
One Sheet: $250 - $600

WEST POINT STORY, THE
(1950 - Warner Bros.) James Cagney, Virginia Mayo, Doris Day

One Sheet: $40 - $75

WEST POINT WIDOW
(1941 - Paramount) Richard Carlson, Anne Shirley
One Sheet: $75 - $150

WEST SIDE KID, THE
(1943 - Republic) Donald Barry, Dale Evans, Henry Hull
One Sheet: $30 - $50

WEST SIDE STORY
(1961 - United Artists) Natalie Wood, Richard Beymer
One Sheet: $75 - $150   *Academy Award: Best Picture, Best Supporting Actor(George Chakiris), Best Supporting Actress(Rita Moreno), BestDirection(Robert Wise, Jerome Robbins). Price is for Style A one sheet w/ Bass art. One Sheet (AA, not Bass style):$30-$50*

Window Card (Trimmed)

WEST SIDE STORY
(1968R - United Artists) Natalie Wood, Richard Beymer
One Sheet: $30 - $50   *Re-release.*

WEST TO GLORY
(1947 - Pathe) Eddie Dean, Roscoe Ates
One Sheet: $15 - $35

WESTBOUND
(1959 - Warner Bros.) Randolph Scott, Virginia Mayo
One Sheet: $15 - $25

WESTBOUND STAGE
(1940 - Monogram) Tex Ritter
One Sheet: $75 - $150

WESTERN CARAVANS
(1939 - Columbia) Charles Starrett, Iris Meredith
One Sheet: $50 - $100

WESTERN CODE, THE
(1932 - Columbia) Tim McCoy, Nora Lane
One Sheet: $250 - $600

WESTERN COURAGE
(1935 - Columbia) Ken Maynard
One Sheet: $250 - $500

WESTERN CYCLONE
(1943 - PRC) Buster Crabbe
One Sheet: $30 - $50

WESTERN DAZE
(1941 - Paramount) George Pal's Puppetoons
One Sheet: $200 - $400   *Duotone.*

WESTERN ENGAGEMENT, A
(1925 - Arrow) Dick Hatton, Marilyn Mills
One Sheet: $150 - $350   *Cowboy Movie Posters #51.*

WESTERN FRONT 1918
(1930 - Nero) -
One Sheet: $250 - $500   *Swedish.*

WESTERN FRONTIER
(1935 - Columbia) Ken Maynard
One Sheet: $150 - $300

WESTERN GOLD
(1937 - Principal) Smith Ballew, Heather Angel
One Sheet: $40 - $75

WESTERN HERITAGE
(1948 - RKO) Tim Holt
One Sheet: $20 - $40

WESTERN HONOR
(1930 - Syndicate) Bob Steele, Ione Reed

One Sheet: $200 - $400   *AKA: THE MAN FROM NOWHERE.*

WESTERN JAMBOREE
(1938 - Republic) Gene Autry, Smiley Burnette
One Sheet: $200 - $400

WESTERN JUSTICE
(1935 - -) -
One Sheet: $75 - $150

WESTERN LUCK
(1924 - Fox) Buck Jones
One Sheet: $200 - $400

One Sheet

WESTERN MAIL
(1942 - Monogram) Jean Trent, Tom Keene
One Sheet: $40 - $75

WESTERN PACIFIC AGENT
(1950 - Lippert) Kent Taylor, Sheila Ryan
One Sheet: $15 - $25

WESTERN RENEGADES
(1949 - Monogram) Johnny Mack Brown, Max Terhune
One Sheet: $15 - $35

WESTERN TRAILS
(1938 - Universal) Bob Baker, Marjorie Reynolds
One Sheet: $50 - $100

WESTERN UNION
(1941 - 20th Century Fox) Robert Young, Randolph Scott
One Sheet: $500 - $800   *Cowboy Movie Posters #266.*

WESTERN WELCOME
(1938 - RKO) Ray Whitley, Diana Gibson
One Sheet: $40 - $75

WESTERN WHOOPEE
(1948 - Universal) Tex Williams, Patricia Alphin
One Sheet: $30 - $50

WESTERNER, THE
(1934 - Columbia) Tim McCoy
One Sheet: $250 - $600

WESTERNER, THE
(1940 - United Artists) Gary Cooper, Walter Brennan, Forrest Tucker
One Sheet: $700 - $1,200   *Academy Award: Best Supporting Actor(Brennan, his 3rd Oscar). Tucker's film debut. Academy Award MoviePosters #71. Cowboy Movie Posters #258.*

One Sheet

WESTERNER, THE
(1946R - Film Classics) Gary Cooper, Walter Brennan, Forrest Tucker
One Sheet: $50 - $100   *Re-release.*

WESTERNER, THE
(1954R - Film Classics) Gary Cooper, Walter Brennan, Forrest Tucker
One Sheet: $40 - $75   *Re-release.*

WESTLAND CASE, THE
(1937 - Universal) Preston Foster, Carol Hughes
One Sheet: $75 - $150

WESTWARD BOUND
(1943 - Monogram) Ken Maynard, Hoot Gibson
One Sheet: $75 - $125

WESTWARD HO
(1935 - Republic) John Wayne
One Sheet: $4,000 - $6,000

WESTWARD HO
(1942 - Republic) Bob Steele, Tom Tyler
One Sheet: $75 - $125

WESTWARD HO THE WAGONS
(1956 - Walt Disney) Fess Parker, Kathleen Crowley
One Sheet: $20 - $40

WESTWARD PASSAGE
(1932 - RKO) Laurence Olivier, Ann Harding
One Sheet: $350 - $750

WESTWARD THE WOMEN
(1951 - MGM) Robert Taylor, Denise Darcel
One Sheet: $15 - $30

WESTWARD TRAIL, THE
(1948 - Pathe) Eddie Dean, Phyllis Blanchard
One Sheet: $15 - $35

WESTWORLD
(1973 - MGM) Yul Brynner, Richard Benjamin, James Brolin
One Sheet: $7 - $15   *Cowboy Movie Posters #340.*

WET GOLD
(1921 - Goldwyn) Ralph Ince, Aleen Burr
One Sheet: $150 - $300

WET PAINT
(1926 - Paramount) Raymond Griffith, Helene Costello
One Sheet: $150 - $300

WET PARADE, THE
(1932 - MGM) Walter Huston, Robert Young, Jimmy Durante
One Sheet: $100 - $200

WETBACKS
(1956 - Banner) Lloyd Bridges, Nancy Gates
One Sheet: $15 - $30

WHALERS, THE
(1938 - RKO/Disney) -
One Sheet: $3,500 - $5,000   *Cartoon. Price is for 14x28 full color silkscreen card used with lobby standee. Cartoon Movie Posters #143A.*

WHALERS, THE
(1953R - RKO/Disney) -
One Sheet: $50 - $100   *25th Anniversary Re-release. Cartoon.*

WHALES OF AUGUST, THE
(1987 - Alive) Bette Davis, Lillian Gish, Vincent Price, Ann Sothern
One Sheet: $15 - $25

WHAM BAM SLAM
(1955 - Columbia) The Three Stooges (Shemp)
One Sheet: $150 - $300   *Comedy short. Duotone.*

WHARF ANGEL, THE
(1934 - Paramount) Victor McLaglen, Dorothy Dell
One Sheet: $100 - $200

WHAT!
(1965 - Francinor) Daliah Lavi, Christopher Lee
One Sheet: $15 - $25

WHAT A BLONDE
(1945 - RKO) Leon Errol, Elaine Riley
One Sheet: $30 - $60

WHAT A CHASSIS!
(1963 - D'Art-Panarama) Robert Dhery, Colette Brosset
One Sheet: $15 - $25   *French. AKA: THE AMERICAN BEAUTY.*

WHAT A GUY

(194? - -) Mantan Moreland
One Sheet: $75 - $150   *Black cast.*

WHAT A LIFE
(1939 - Paramount) Jackie Cooper, Betty Field
One Sheet: $40 - $75

WHAT A MAN
(1930 - Sono-Art) Reginald Denny, Miriam Seegar
One Sheet: $125 - $250

WHAT A MAN!
(1939 - British Lion) Sidney Howard
One Sheet: $50 - $100

WHAT A MAN!
(1944 - Monogram) Johnny Downs, Wanda McKay
One Sheet: $15 - $30

WHAT A WAY TO GO!
(1964 - 20th Century Fox) Shirley MacLaine, Paul Newman
One Sheet: $15 - $25

WHAT A WIDOW
(1930 - United Artists) Gloria Swanson, Owen Moore
One Sheet: $600 - $1,000

WHAT A WIFE LEARNED
(1923 - First National) John Bowers, Evelyn McCoy
One Sheet: $800 - $1,500

WHAT A WOMAN
(1943 - Columbia) Rosalind Russell, Brian Aherne
One Sheet: $30 - $60

WHAT ABOUT BOB?
(1991 - Touchstone) Bill Murray, Richard Dreyfuss
One Sheet: $5 - $10

WHAT BECAME OF JACK AND JILL?
(1972 - 20th Century Fox) Vanessa Howard, Mona Washbourne
One Sheet: $7 - $15

WHAT BECAME OF JACK AND JILL?/STRANGE VENGEANCE OF ROSALIE COMBO
(1972 - 20th Century Fox) -
One Sheet: $5 - $10   *Double feature poster.*

WHAT BECOMES OF THE CHILDREN?
(1918 - -) Cora Beach, Morgan Jones
One Sheet: $250 - $600

WHAT BECOMES OF THE CHILDREN?
(1930S - Puritan) Joan Marsh, Robert Fraser
One Sheet: $150 - $300   *Exploitation.*

WHAT DID YOU DO IN THE WAR, DADDY?
(1966 - United Artists) James Coburn, Dick Shawn
One Sheet: $5 - $10

WHAT DO MEN WANT?
(1921 - Lois Weber/Wid Gunning) Claire Windsor, J. Frank Glendon
One Sheet: $1,600 - $2,500

WHAT DO YOU SAY TO A NAKED LADY?
(1970 - United Artists) Allen Funt comedy
One Sheet: $7 - $15

WHAT EVER HAPPENED TO BABY JANE?
(1962 - Warner Bros.) Bette Davis, Joan Crawford
One Sheet: $75 - $125   *Graven Images, pg. 205.*

WHAT EVER HAPPENED TO BABY JANE?
(1977R - Warner Bros.) Bette Davis, Joan Crawford
One Sheet: $15 - $30   *Re-release.*

WHAT EVERY GIRL SHOULD KNOW
(1927 - Warner Bros.) Patsy Ruth Miller
One Sheet: $350 - $750

WHAT EVERY WOMAN KNOWS
(1934 - MGM) Helen Hayes, Brian Aherne
One Sheet: $150 - $300

WHAT GOES UP
(1939 - -) Eddie Green, Babe Matthews, Honey-boy Johnson
One Sheet: $75 - $150   *Black cast.*

WHAT HAPPENED TO JONES

(1926 - Universal) Reginald Denny, Marian Nixon
One Sheet: $150 - $300

WHAT HAPPENED TO ROSA
(1920 - Goldwyn) Mabel Normand, Hugh Thompson
One Sheet: $100 - $200   *Duotone.*

WHAT HAPPENS AT NIGHT
(1940 - 20th Century Fox) Terry-toons
One Sheet: $100 - $200   *Cartoon. Full color stone litho. Stock poster with inset title.*

WHAT HAVE I DONE TO DESERVE THIS?
(1985 - -) Carmen Maura
One Sheet: $20 - $40   *Spanish.*

WHAT MEN WANT
(1930 - Universal) Pauline Stark, Ben Lyon
One Sheet: $100 - $200

WHAT NEXT, CORPORAL HARGROVE?
(1945 - MGM) Robert Walker, Keenan Wynn
One Sheet: $15 - $30

WHAT! NO BEER?
(1933 - MGM) Jimmy Durante, Buster Keaton
One Sheet: $1,600 - $2,500

WHAT PRICE DECENCY
(1933 - Equitable) Dorothy Burgess
One Sheet: $125 - $250

WHAT PRICE GLORY?
(1926 - Fox) Victor McLaglen, Edmund Lowe
One Sheet: $1,300 - $2,000

WHAT PRICE GLORY?
(1952 - 20th Century Fox) James Cagney, Dan Dailey
One Sheet: $40 - $75

WHAT PRICE HOLLYWOOD?
(1932 - RKO Pathe) Constance Bennett, Lowell Sherman
One Sheet: $4,000 - $6,000

WHAT PRICE INNOCENCE?
(1933 - Columbia) Betty Grable
One Sheet: $600 - $1,000

WHAT THE PEEPER SAY
(1972 - Leisure/Media) Mark Lester, Britt Ekland
One Sheet: $3 - $5

WHAT WIVES WANT
(1923 - Universal) Ethel Grey Terry, Vernon Steele
One Sheet: $150 - $300

WHAT WOMEN DID FOR ME
(1927 - Pathe) -
One Sheet: $250 - $500

WHAT'S BUZZIN' COUSIN?
(1943 - Columbia) Ann Miller, John Hubbard, Freddy Martin's Orchestra
One Sheet: $75 - $150   *Big Band musical.*

WHAT'S COOKIN'?
(1942 - Universal) Andrews Sisters, Gloria Jean
One Sheet: $75 - $150

WHAT'S EATING GILBERT GRAPE?
(1993 - Paramount) Johnny Depp, Juliette Lewis
One Sheet: $5 - $10

WHAT'S GOOD FOR THE GOOSE
(1969 - National Showmanship) Norman Wisdom, Sally Geeson
One Sheet: $3 - $5

WHAT'S HIS NAME
(1914 - Paramount) Max Figman, Lolita Robertson
One Sheet: $250 - $600

WHAT'S LOVE GOT TO DO WITH IT
(1993 - Touchstone) Angela Basset, Larry Fishburne
One Sheet: $7 - $15

WHAT'S NEW PUSSYCAT?
(1965 - United Artists) Peter Sellers, Peter O'Toole, Woody Allen
One Sheet: $30 - $60   *Frazetta art. Allen's first feature as actor and writer.*

WHAT'S SO BAD ABOUT FEELING GOOD?

(1968 - Universal) George Peppard, Mary Tyler Moore, Dom DeLuise
One Sheet: $5 - $10

WHAT'S THE MATADOR
(1942 - Columbia) Three Stooges (Curly)
One Sheet: $3,500 - $5,000   *Comedy short. Duotone.*

WHAT'S THE MATTER WITH HELEN?
(1971 - United Artists) Debbie Reynolds, Shelley Winters
One Sheet: $5 - $10

WHAT'S THE WORLD COMING TO?
(1926 - Pathe) Clyde Cook
One Sheet: $250 - $600

WHAT'S UP, DOC?
(1972 - Warner Bros.) Barbra Streisand, Ryan O'Neal
One Sheet: $15 - $30   *Two styles.*

WHAT'S UP FRONT
(1964 - Delta) Tommy Holden, Marilyn Manning
One Sheet: $7 - $15

WHAT'S UP TIGER LILY?
(1966 - AIP) Woody Allen, China Lee
One Sheet: $30 - $50

WHAT'S YOUR HURRY?
(1920 - Paramount) Wallace Reid, Lois Wilson
One Sheet: $250 - $500

WHAT'S YOUR RACKET
(1934 - Mayfair) J. Carroll Naish, Regis Toomey
One Sheet: $100 - $200

WHATEVER HAPPENED TO AUNT ALICE?
(1969 - Cinerama) Geraldine Page, Ruth Gordon
One Sheet: $7 - $15

WHEELER DEALERS, THE
(1963 - MGM) James Garner, Lee Remick
One Sheet: $7 - $15

WHEELS OF DESTINY
(1934 - Universal) Ken Maynard, Dorothy Dix
One Sheet: $250 - $600

WHEN A FELLOW NEEDS A FRIEND
(1932 - MGM) Jackie Cooper, Ralph Graves
One Sheet: $100 - $200

WHEN A GIRL'S BEAUTIFUL
(1947 - Columbia) Stephen Dunne, Adele Jergens
One Sheet: $50 - $100

WHEN A MAN LOVES A WOMAN
(1995 - Touchstone) Andy Garcia, Meg Ryan
One Sheet: $3 - $5

WHEN A MAN RIDES ALONE
(1919 - American) William Russell, Lule Warrenton
One Sheet: $200 - $400

WHEN A MAN RIDES ALONE
(1933 - Monarch) Tom Tyler, Adele Lacey
One Sheet: $150 - $300

WHEN A MAN SEES RED
(1917 - Fox) William Farnum, Jewel Carmen
One Sheet: $250 - $500

WHEN A MAN SEES RED
(1934 - Universal) Buck Jones, Dorothy Revier
One Sheet: $800 - $1,500   *Cowboy Movie Posters #169.*

One Sheet

WHEN A MAN SEES RED
(1947R - Universal) Buck Jones, Dorothy Revier
One Sheet: $75 - $150   *Re-release.*

WHEN A MAN'S A MAN
(1935 - Fox) George O'Brien
One Sheet: $125 - $250

WHEN A MAN'S A PRINCE
(1926 - Pathe) -
One Sheet: $200 - $400

WHEN A STRANGER CALLS
(1979 - Columbia) Carol Kane, Charles Durning
One Sheet: $3 - $5

WHEN COMEDY WAS KING
(1960 - 20th Century Fox) Charlie Chaplin, Buster Keaton
One Sheet: $20 - $40   *Silent comedy compilation by Robert Youngson.*

WHEN DINOSAURS RULED THE EARTH
(1971 - Warner Bros.) Victoria Vetri, Robin Hawdon
One Sheet: $20 - $40

WHEN DRAGONS COLLIDE
(1983 - Elmark) Pei Lng, Ping Pei, Chang Li
One Sheet: $10 - $20   *Martial arts.*

WHEN EIGHT BELLS TOLL
(1971 - Cinerama) Anthony Hopkins, Robert Morley
One Sheet: $5 - $10

WHEN FALSE TONGUES SPEAK
(1917 - -) Virginia Pearson, Carl Harbaugh
One Sheet: $125 - $250

WHEN GANGLAND STRIKES
(1956 - Republic) Raymond Greenleaf, Marjie Millar
One Sheet: $15 - $25

WHEN G-MEN STEP IN
(1938 - Columbia) Don Terry, Jacqueline Wells
One Sheet: $75 - $150

WHEN HARRY MET SALLY
(1989 - Castle Rock) Billy Crystal, Meg Ryan
One Sheet: $30 - $50

WHEN HELL BROKE LOOSE
(1958 - Paramount) Charles Bronson, Richard Jaeckel
One Sheet: $15 - $25

WHEN I GROW UP
(1951 - Eagle Lion Classics) Bobby Driscoll, Robert Preston
One Sheet: $15 - $30

WHEN IN ROME
(1951 - MGM) Van Johnson, Paul Douglas
One Sheet: $15 - $25

WHEN JOHNNY COMES MARCHING HOME
(1942 - Universal) Jane Frazee, Allan Jones, Donald O'Connor
One Sheet: $30 - $50

WHEN KNIGHTHOOD WAS IN FLOWER
(1922 - Paramount) Marion Davies
One Sheet: $1,300 - $2,000

WHEN LADIES MEET
(1933 - MGM) Ann Harding, Myrna Loy
One Sheet: $200 - $400

WHEN LADIES MEET
(1941 - MGM) Joan Crawford, Robert Taylor, Greer Garson
One Sheet: $100 - $200

WHEN LIGHTNING STRIKES
(1934 - -) Francis X. Bushman
One Sheet: $100 - $200

WHEN LONDON SLEEPS
(1932 - Twickenham) Harold French, Francis L. Sullivan
One Sheet: $500 - $800

WHEN LONDON SLEEPS
(1934 - Reunion) Victor Varconi, Joan Maude
One Sheet: $250 - $500

WHEN LOVE IS BLIND
(1919 - -) Ben Turpin
One Sheet: $150 - $300

WHEN LOVE IS YOUNG
(1937 - Universal) Virginia Bruce, Kent Taylor, Walter Brennan
One Sheet: $75 - $150

WHEN MAGOO FLEW
(1954 - Columbia) Mr. Magoo
One Sheet: $125 - $250   *Cartoon.*
Cartoon Movie Posters #45.

WHEN MEN ARE MEN
(1921 - -) William Duncan, Edith Johnson
One Sheet: $150 - $300

WHEN MY BABY SMILES AT ME
(1948 - 20th Century Fox) Betty Grable, Dan Dailey
One Sheet: $75 - $150

WHEN NIGHT IS FALLING
(1995 - October) Pascale Bussieres, Rachel Crawford
One Sheet: $5 - $12

WHEN STRANGERS MARRY
(1933 - Columbia) Jack Holt, Lillian Bond
One Sheet: $200 - $400

WHEN STRANGERS MARRY
(1944 - Monogram) Dean Jagger, Kim Hunter, Robert Mitchum
One Sheet: $125 - $250   *Mitchum's first major role.*

WHEN STRANGERS MEET
(1934 - Liberty) Richard Cromwell, Arline Judge
One Sheet: $75 - $150

WHEN THE BOYS MEET THE GIRLS
(1965 - MGM) Connie Francis, Harve Presnell
One Sheet: $30 - $50

WHEN THE CLOCK STRIKES
(1961 - United Artists) James Brown, Merry Anders
One Sheet: $7 - $15   *AKA: THE CLOCK STRIKES THREE.*

WHEN THE CLOUDS ROLL BY
(1919 - United Artists) Douglas Fairbanks
One Sheet: $700 - $1,200   *Two styles.*

WHEN THE DALTONS RODE
(1940 - Universal) Randolph Scott, Kay Francis
One Sheet: $50 - $100

WHEN THE DOOR OPENED
(1925 - Fox) Jacqueline Logan
One Sheet: $150 - $300

WHEN THE LEGENDS DIE
(1972 - 20th Century Fox) Richard Widmark, Frederic Forrest
One Sheet: $7 - $15

WHEN THE LIGHTS GO ON AGAIN
(1944 - PRC) James Lydon
One Sheet: $15 - $30

WHEN THE REDSKINS RODE
(1951 - Columbia) Jon Hall, Mary Castle
One Sheet: $15 - $30

WHEN THE WHALES CAME
(1989 - 20th Century Fox) Paul Scofield
One Sheet: $5 - $10

WHEN THE WIFE'S AWAY
(1946 - Columbia) Hugh Herbert, Christine McIntyre
One Sheet: $20 - $40

WHEN THIEF MEETS THIEF
(1937 - Criterion) Douglas Fairbanks Jr., Valerie Hobson
One Sheet: $150 - $300

WHEN TIME RAN OUT
(1980 - Warner Bros.) William Holden, Paul Newman
One Sheet: $5 - $10

WHEN TOMORROW COMES
(1939 - Universal) Irene Dunne, Charles Boyer
One Sheet: $100 - $200

WHEN WE WERE KINGS
(1997 - Gramercy) Muhammad Ali, George Foreman
One Sheet: $15 - $30   *Documentary of RUMBLE IN THE JUNGLE fight.*

WHEN WERE YOU BORN

(1938 - Warner Bros.) Anna May Wong, Margaret Lindsay
One Sheet: $100 - $200

WHEN WILLIE COMES MARCHING HOME
(1950 - 20th Century Fox) Dan Dailey, Corinne Calvet
One Sheet: $15 - $30

WHEN WOMEN HAD TAILS
(1970 - Film Ventures) Senta Berger, Frank Wolff
One Sheet: $15 - $25

WHEN WORLDS COLLIDE
(1951 - Paramount) Richard Derr, Barbara Rush
One Sheet: $500 - $800   *Graven Images, pg. 156.*

WHEN YOU'RE IN LOVE
(1937 - Columbia) Grace Moore, Cary Grant
One Sheet: $250 - $600

WHEN YOU'RE MARRIED
(1916R - Maco Comedies) Charlie Chaplin
One Sheet: $1,300 - $2,000   *Re-release*

WHEN YOU'RE SMILING
(1950 - Columbia) Jerome Courtland, Lois Albright
One Sheet: $15 - $25

WHEN'S YOUR BIRTHDAY?
(1937 - RKO) Joe E. Brown, Marian Marsh
One Sheet: $100 - $200

Mini Window Card (trimmed)

WHERE ANGELS FEAR TO TREAD
(1992 - New Line) Helena Bonham-Carter, Judy Davis
One Sheet: $3 - $5

WHERE ANGELS GO...TROUBLE FOLLOWS
(1968 - Columbia) Rosalind Russell, Stella Stevens, Milton Berle
One Sheet: $15 - $25

WHERE ARE YOUR CHILDREN?
(1944 - Monogram) Jackie Cooper, Patricia Morison
One Sheet: $30 - $60

WHERE BRAINS ARE NEEDED
(1915 - Universal) Murdock MacQuarrie, Agnes Vernon
One Sheet: $250 - $600

WHERE DANGER LIVES
(1950 - RKO) Robert Mitchum, Faith Domergue
One Sheet: $75 - $175

WHERE DID YOU GET THAT GIRL?
(1940 - Universal) Leon Errol, Helen Parrish, Charles Lang
One Sheet: $40 - $75

WHERE DO WE GO FROM HERE?
(1945 - 20th Century Fox) Fred MacMurray, Joan Leslie, June Haver
One Sheet: $50 - $100

WHERE DOES IT HURT?
(1972 - Cinerama) Peter Sellers, Jo Ann Pflug
One Sheet: $5 - $10

WHERE EAGLES DARE
(1969 - MGM) Richard Burton, Clint Eastwood
One Sheet: $40 - $75   *One Sheet(Style B):$50-$100.*

WHERE EAGLES DARE
(1975R - MGM) Richard Burton, Clint Eastwood
One Sheet: $15 - $25   *Re-release.*

WHERE EAST IS EAST
(1929 - MGM) Lon Chaney, Lupe Velez
One Sheet: $800 - $1,500

WHERE IS MY CHILD?
(1937 - Menorah) Celia Adler, Samuel Steinberg
One Sheet: $50 - $100

WHERE IS MY WANDERING BOY TONIGHT?
(1922 - Equity) Cullen Landis, Carl Stockdale
One Sheet: $150 - $300

WHERE IS THIS WEST?
(1923 - Universal) Jack Hoxie, Mary Philbin
One Sheet: $150 - $350   *Cowboy Movie Posters #31.*

WHERE IT'S AT
(1969 - United Artists) David Janssen, Robert Drivas, Rosemary Forsyth
One Sheet: $7 - $15

WHERE LOVE HAS GONE
(1964 - Paramount) Susan Hayward, Bette Davis, Jane Greer
One Sheet: $15 - $30

WHERE SINNERS MEET
(1934 - RKO) Diana Wynyard, Clive Brook
One Sheet: $200 - $400

WHERE THE BOYS ARE
(1961 - MGM) Dolores Hart, George Hamilton, Yvette Mimieux
One Sheet: $30 - $50

WHERE THE BOYS ARE '84
(1984 - TriStar) Lisa Hartman, Lorna Luft
One Sheet: $3 - $5

WHERE THE BUFFALO ROAM
(1938 - Monogram) Tex Ritter, Dorothy Scott
One Sheet: $75 - $150

WHERE THE BULLETS FLY
(1966 - Embassy) Tom Adams, Dawn Addams
One Sheet: $7 - $15

WHERE THE DAY TAKES YOU
(1992 - Columbia) Sean Astin, Lara-Flynn Boyle, Dermot Mahoney
One Sheet: $3 - $5

WHERE THE GREEN ANTS DREAM
(1984 - Orion Classics) Bruce Spence, Ray Barrett
One Sheet: $15 - $25

WHERE THE HEART IS
(1990 - Touchstone) Dabney Coleman, Uma Thurman
One Sheet: $5 - $10

WHERE THE HOT WIND BLOWS
(1960 - MGM) Gina Lollobrigida, Yves Montand
One Sheet: $20 - $40

WHERE THE NORTH BEGINS
(1947 - Bali) Russell Hayden, Jennifer Holt
One Sheet: $15 - $35

WHERE THE PAVEMENT ENDS
(1923 - Metro) Ramon Novarro, Alice Terry
One Sheet: $250 - $500

WHERE THE RIVER RUNS BLACK
(1986 - -) Charles Durning, Alessandro Rabelo
One Sheet: $3 - $5

WHERE THE SIDEWALK ENDS
(1950 - 20th Century Fox) Dana Andrews, Gene Tierney
One Sheet: $150 - $350

WHERE THE SIDEWALK ENDS
(1955R - 20th Century Fox) Dana Andrews, Gene Tierney
One Sheet: $30 - $50   *Re-release.*

WHERE THE SPIES ARE
(1966 - MGM) David Niven, Francoise Dorleac
One Sheet: $5 - $10

WHERE THE TRAIL DIVIDES
(1914 - Lasky) Robert Edeson, Winifred Kingston
One Sheet: $500 - $900

WHERE THE TRUTH LIES
(1962 - Paramount) Juliette Greco, Jean Marc Bory
One Sheet: $3 - $5

WHERE THE WEST BEGINS
(1938 - Monogram) Jack Randall
One Sheet: $40 - $75

WHERE THERE'S A WILL
(1937 - Gaumont) Will Hay, Hartley Power
One Sheet: $50 - $100

WHERE THERE'S LIFE
(1947 - Paramount) Bob Hope, Signe Hasso, William Bendix
One Sheet: $50 - $100

WHERE TRAILS DIVIDE
(1937 - Monogram) Tom Keene
One Sheet: $50 - $100

WHERE TRAILS END
(1942 - Monogram) Tom Keene
One Sheet: $30 - $60

WHERE WERE YOU WHEN THE LIGHTS WENT OUT?
(1968 - MGM) Doris Day, Robert Morse, Terry-Thomas
One Sheet: $7 - $15   *Two styles.*

WHERE'S CHARLEY?
(1952 - Warner Bros.) Ray Bolger, Allyn Ann McLerie
One Sheet: $15 - $25

WHERE'S JACK?
(1969 - Paramount) Tommy Steele, Stanley Baker, Fiona Lewis
One Sheet: $3 - $5

WHERE'S MY MAN TO-NITE?
(1950S - Sack)
One Sheet: $75 - $150   *Black cast.*
Re-titled, re-release of MARCHING ON!.

WHERE'S MY WANDERING BOY THIS EVENING?
(1923 - Pathe) Ben Turpin
One Sheet: $500 - $800

WHERE'S POPPA?
(1970 - United Artists) George Segal, Ruth Gordon
One Sheet: $3 - $5

WHICH IS WHICH?
(1926 - Stern Bros.) -
One Sheet: $150 - $300

WHICH WAY TO THE FRONT?
(1970 - Warner Bros.) Jerry Lewis, Jan Muray
One Sheet: $15 - $25

WHIFFS
(1975 - 20th Century Fox) Elliott Gould, Eddie Albert
One Sheet: $5 - $10

WHILE NEW YORK SLEEPS
(1920 - Fox) Estelle Taylor, William Locke
One Sheet: $350 - $750

WHILE NEW YORK SLEEPS
(1938 - 20th Century Fox) Michael Whalen, Jean Rogers
One Sheet: $100 - $200

WHILE PARIS SLEEPS
(1932 - Fox) Victor McLaglen
One Sheet: $100 - $200

WHILE SATAN SLEEPS
(1922 - Paramount) Jack Holt, Wade Boteler
One Sheet: $100 - $200

WHILE THE CITY SLEEPS
(1928 - MGM) Lon Chaney, Anita Page
One Sheet: $800 - $1,500   *Gangster film.*

Window Card (trimmed)

WHILE THE CITY SLEEPS
(1956 - RKO) Dana Andrews, Ida Lupino, Rhonda Fleming
One Sheet: $40 - $75   *Dir: Fritz Lang.*

WHILE THE PATIENT SLEPT
(1935 - First National) Aline MacMahon, Lyle Talbot
One Sheet: $75 - $150

WHILE THOUSANDS CHEER
(1940 - Million Dollar) Kenny Washington, Mantan Moreland
One Sheet: $1,000 - $1,800   *Black cast. Washington was the first African-American to play in the NFL after WWII. He is featured prominently on the posters in a football setting. Sports Movie Posters #196.*

WHILE YOU WERE SLEEPING
(1995 - Buena Vista) Sandra Bullock, Bill Pullman, Peter Gallagher
One Sheet: $7 - $15

WHIP, THE
(1928 - First National) Dorothy Mackaill, Ralph Forbes
One Sheet: $250 - $500

WHIP AND FLESH
(1967 - -)
One Sheet: $15 - $25

WHIP HAND, THE
(1951 - RKO) Elliott Reid, Lurene Tuttle
One Sheet: $10 - $20

WHIPLASH
(1949 - Warner Bros.) Dane Clark, Alexis Smith
One Sheet: $30 - $50

WHIPSAW
(1935 - MGM) Myrna Loy, Spencer Tracy
One Sheet: $250 - $500

WHIRLPOOL
(1934 - Columbia) Jack Holt, Jean Arthur
One Sheet: $150 - $300

WHIRLPOOL
(1950 - 20th Century Fox) Gene Tierney, Jose Ferrer, Richard Conte
One Sheet: $100 - $200

WHIRLPOOL
(1970 - Cinemation) Karl Launchburg, Vivian Neves
One Sheet: $3 - $5

WHIRLWIND
(1933 - Columbia) Tim McCoy
One Sheet: $350 - $750

One Sheet

WHIRLWIND
(1951 - Columbia) Gene Autry, Smiley Burnette
One Sheet: $50 - $100

WHIRLWIND HORSEMAN
(1938 - Grand National) Ken Maynard, Joan Barclay
One Sheet: $100 - $200   *Duotone.*

WHIRLWIND RAIDERS
(1948 - Columbia) Charles Starrett, Smiley Burnette
One Sheet: $15 - $35

WHIRLWIND WESTERNS
(1925 - Rayart) Jack Perrin
One Sheet: $200 - $400

WHISKEY MOUNTAIN

(1977 - -) Christopher George, Preston Pierce
One Sheet: $7 - $15

WHISPERERS, THE
(1967 - Lopert) Dame Edith Evans, Eric Portman
One Sheet: $3 - $5

WHISPERING CITY
(1947 - Eagle Lion) Helmut Dantine, Mary Anderson
One Sheet: $15 - $25

WHISPERING ENEMIES
(1939 - Columbia) Jack Holt, Dolores Costello
One Sheet: $40 - $75

WHISPERING FOOTSTEPS
(1943 - Republic) John Hubbard, Rita Quigley
One Sheet: $15 - $35

WHISPERING GHOSTS
(1942 - 20th Century Fox) Milton Berle, Brenda Joyce, John Carradine
One Sheet: $50 - $100

WHISPERING SHADOW, THE
(1933 - Mascot) Bela Lugosi, Henry B. Walthall
One Sheet: $800 - $1,500   *Serial. 12 Chapters.*

WHISPERING SKULL, THE
(1944 - PRC) Dave O'Brien, Tex Ritter
One Sheet: $40 - $75

WHISPERING SMITH
(1949 - Paramount) Alan Ladd, Robert Preston, Brenda Marshall
One Sheet: $100 - $200

WHISPERING SMITH
(1956R - Paramount) Alan Ladd, Robert Preston, Brenda Marshall
One Sheet: $15 - $30   *Re-release.*

WHISPERING SMITH SPEAKS
(1936 - Fox) George O'Brien,
One Sheet: $125 - $250

WHISPERING SMITH VERSUS SCOTLAND YARD
(1952 - RKO) Richard Carlson, Greta Gynt
One Sheet: $15 - $25

WHISPERING WIRES
(1926 - Fox) Anita Stewart
One Sheet: $200 - $400

WHISPERS IN THE DARK
(1992 - Paramount) Annabella Sciorra, Alan Alda
One Sheet: $3 - $5

WHISTLE AT EATON FALLS, THE
(1951 - Columbia) Lloyd Bridges, Dorothy Gish
One Sheet: $15 - $30

WHISTLE DOWN THE WIND
(1962 - Pathe) Hayley Mills, Alan Bates
One Sheet: $15 - $25

WHISTLE STOP
(1946 - United Artists) Ava Gardner, George Raft, Victor McLaglen
One Sheet: $75 - $125

WHISTLER, THE
(1944 - Columbia) Richard Dix, J. Carroll Naish
One Sheet: $50 - $100

WHISTLIN' DAN
(1932 - Tiffany) Ken Maynard
One Sheet: $150 - $300

WHISTLING BULLETS
(1937 - Ambassador) Kermit Maynard, Jack Ingram
One Sheet: $50 - $100

WHISTLING HILLS
(1951 - Monogram) Johnny Mack Brown
One Sheet: $15 - $35

WHISTLING IN BROOKLYN
(1943 - MGM) Red Skelton, Ann Rutherford, Brooklyn Dodgers
One Sheet: $150 - $300   *Sports (Baseball). Dodgers shown on some posters.*

WHISTLING IN DIXIE
(1942 - MGM) Red Skelton, Ann Rutherford
One Sheet: $75 - $150

WHISTLING IN THE DARK

(1933 - MGM) Ernest Truex, Una Merkel
One Sheet: $75 - $150

WHISTLING IN THE DARK
(1941 - MGM) Red Skelton, Ann Rutherford, Conrad Veidt
One Sheet: $100 - $200

WHITE AND UNMARRIED
(1921 - Paramount) Thomas Meighan, Jacqueline Logan
One Sheet: $250 - $500

WHITE ANGEL, THE
(1936 - Warner Bros.) Kay Francis, Ian Hunter
One Sheet: $50 - $100

WHITE BALLOON, THE
(1996 - October) Aida Mohammadkhani, Dir: Jafar Panahi
One Sheet: $5 - $12

WHITE BANNERS
(1938 - Warner Bros.) Claude Rains, Fay Bainter
One Sheet: $50 - $100

WHITE BONDAGE
(1937 - Warner Bros.) Jean Muir, Gordon Oliver
One Sheet: $50 - $100   *Duotone.*

WHITE BUFFALO, THE
(1977 - United Artists) Charles Bronson, Jack Warden
One Sheet: $7 - $15

WHITE CARGO
(1942 - MGM) Hedy Lamarr, Walter Pidgeon
One Sheet: $125 - $250

WHITE CHRISTMAS
(1954 - Paramount) Bing Crosby, Danny Kaye, Rosemary Clooney, Vera-Ellen
One Sheet: $125 - $250

WHITE CHRISTMAS
(1961R - Paramount) Bing Crosby, Danny Kaye, Rosemary Clooney, Vera-Ellen
One Sheet: $20 - $40   *Re-release.*

WHITE CLIFFS OF DOVER, THE
(1944 - MGM) Irene Dunne, Alan Marshal
One Sheet: $30 - $60

WHITE COCKATOO, THE
(1935 - Warner Bros.) Ricardo Cortez, Jean Muir
One Sheet: $100 - $200

WHITE DAWN, THE
(1974 - Paramount) Warren Oates, Timothy Bottom, Lou Gossett
One Sheet: $3 - $5

WHITE DESERT, THE
(1925 - MGM) Claire Windsor, Pat O'Malley
One Sheet: $200 - $400

WHITE DEVIL, THE
(1929 - UFA) Ivan Mosjoukine, Lil Dagover
One Sheet: $150 - $300

One Sheet

WHITE EAGLE
(1921 - Pathe) Ruth Roland
One Sheet: $250 - $500   *Serial. Western. 15 Chapters.*

WHITE EAGLE
(1932 - Columbia) Buck Jones, Barbara Weeks
One Sheet: $1,900 - $3,000   *Cowboy Movie Posters #'s 124, 127.*

WHITE EAGLE

(1941 - Columbia) Buck Jones, Dorothy Fay
One Sheet: $150 - $350   *Serial. Western. 15 Chapters.*

WHITE FANG
(1936 - 20th Century Fox) Michael Whalen, Jean Muir
One Sheet: $75 - $150

One Sheet

WHITE FANG
(1991 - Disney) Klaus Maria Brandauer, Ethan Hawke
One Sheet: $3 - $5

WHITE FEATHER
(1955 - 20th Century Fox) Robert Wagner, Debra Paget, Jeffrey Hunter
One Sheet: $15 - $35

WHITE FIRE
(1953 - Lippert) Scott Brady, Mary Castle
One Sheet: $5 - $10

WHITE GODDESS
(1953 - Lippert) Jon Hall, M'Liss McClure
One Sheet: $15 - $30

WHITE GORILLA, THE
(1945 - Louis Weiss) Ray Corrigan
One Sheet: $75 - $150

WHITE HEAT
(1934 - Pinnacle) Virginia Cherrill, Mona Maris, Hardie Albright
One Sheet: $150 - $300

One Sheet

WHITE HEAT
(1949 - Warner Bros.) James Cagney, Virginia Mayo, Edmond O'Brien
One Sheet: $150 - $300

WHITE HEAT
(1956R - -) James Cagney, Virginia Mayo, Edmond O'Brien
One Sheet: $40 - $75   *Re-release.*

WHITE HELL OF PITZ PALU
(1930 - Universal)
One Sheet: $250 - $600

WHITE HORSEMAN, THE
(1921 - Universal) Art Acord
One Sheet: $250 - $500   *Serial. Western. 18 Chapters.*

WHITE HUNTER
(1936 - 20th Century Fox) Warner Baxter, June Lang
One Sheet: $75 - $150

WHITE HUNTER, BLACK HEART
(1990 - Warner Bros.) Clint Eastwood
One Sheet: $10 - $20

WHITE HUNTRESS
(1957 - AIP) Susan Stephan, John Bentley
One Sheet: $5 - $10

WHITE KNIGHTS
(1985 - Columbia) Mikhail Baryshnikov,
Gregory Hines
One Sheet: $7 - $15   *Two styles.*

WHITE LEGION
(1936 - Grand National) Ian Keith, Tala Birell
One Sheet: $50 - $100

WHITE LIES
(1934 - Columbia) Walter Connolly, Fay Wray
One Sheet: $150 - $350

WHITE LIGHTNING
(1953 - Allied Artists) Stanley Clements, Steve
Brodie, Lee Van Cleef
One Sheet: $40 - $75   *Sports
(Hockey). Sports Movie Posters #233.*

WHITE LIGHTNING
(1973 - United Artists) Burt Reynolds, Jennifer
Billingsley
One Sheet: $10 - $20

WHITE LINE FEVER
(1975 - Columbia) Jan-Michael Vincent, Kay
Lenz
One Sheet: $5 - $10

WHITE MAN
(1924 - Preferred) Alice Joyce, Kenneth Harlan
One Sheet: $200 - $400

WHITE MAN'S LAW, THE
(1918 - Paramount) Sessue Hayakawa,
Florence Vidor, Jack Holt
One Sheet: $250 - $600

WHITE MANE
(1954 - United Artists) Alain Emery, Frank
Silvera
One Sheet: $7 - $15

WHITE MEN CAN'T JUMP
(1992 - 20th Century Fox) Wesley Snipes,
Woody Harrelson
One Sheet: $5 - $10   *Sports
(Basketball). Sports Movie Posters #101.*

WHITE MISCHIEF
(1988 - -) Sarah Miles, Joss Ackland, Greta
Scacchi
One Sheet: $5 - $10

WHITE MOTH, THE
(1924 - -) Barbara La Marr, Conway Tearle
One Sheet: $150 - $300

WHITE OAK
(1921 - Paramount) William S. Hart, Vola Vale
One Sheet: $1,900 - $3,000

WHITE OF THE EYE, THE
(1987 - -) David Keith, Cathy Moriarty
One Sheet: $5 - $10

WHITE ORCHID, THE
(1954 - United Artists) William Lundigan,
Peggie Castle
One Sheet: $15 - $25

WHITE PALACE
(1990 - Universal) Susan Sarandon, James
Spader
One Sheet: $5 - $10

WHITE PARADE, THE
(1934 - Fox) Loretta Young, John Boles
One Sheet: $150 - $300

WHITE PONGO
(1945 - PRC) Richard Fraser, Lionel Royce
One Sheet: $75 - $150

WHITE ROSE, THE
(1923 - United Artists) Mae Marsh, Carol
Dempster
One Sheet: $600 - $1,000

WHITE SANDS
(1992 - Warner Bros.) Willem Dafoe, Mickey
Rourke, Mary Elizabeth Mastrantonio
One Sheet: $3 - $5   *Advance:$10-
$20.*

WHITE SAVAGE
(1943 - Universal) Maria Montez, Jon Hall,
Sabu
One Sheet: $150 - $300

WHITE SAVAGE
(1948R - Universal) Maria Montez, Jon Hall,
Sabu
One Sheet: $30 - $50   *Re-release.*

WHITE SAVAGE WOMEN
(1953R - -) Maria Montez, Sabu
One Sheet: $30 - $50   *Re-titled re-
release of WHITE SAVAGE.*

WHITE SHEIK, THE
(1956 - -) See SCEICCO BIANCO (ITALIAN)

WHITE SHOULDERS
(1931 - RKO) Sydney Toler, Mary Astor
One Sheet: $150 - $350

WHITE SISTER
(1923 - Metro) Ronald Colman, Lillian Gish
One Sheet: $1,600 - $2,500

WHITE SISTER
(1928R - MGM) Ronald Colman, Lillian Gish
One Sheet: $600 - $1,000   *Re-release.*

WHITE SISTER
(1933 - MGM) Helen Hayes, Clark Gable
One Sheet: $1,300 - $2,000

Title Card

WHITE SISTER
(1973 - Columbia) Sophia Loren, Fernando Rey
One Sheet: $5 - $10

WHITE SLAVE GIRLS
(1965 - -) -
One Sheet: $15 - $25   *Sexploitation.*

WHITE SLAVE SHIP
(1962 - AIP) Pier Angeli, Edmond Purdom
One Sheet: $15 - $25

WHITE SLAVERY
(1950S - -) -
One Sheet: $75 - $125   *Sexploitation.*

WHITE SQUALL
(1996 - Hollywood) Jeff Bridges
One Sheet: $5 - $12

WHITE SQUAW, THE
(1956 - Columbia) David Brian, May Wynn
One Sheet: $7 - $15

WHITE THUNDER
(1925 - FBO) Yakima Canutt, William H. Turner
One Sheet: $600 - $1,000

WHITE TIE AND TAILS
(1946 - Universal) Dan Duryea, Ella Raines,
William Bendix
One Sheet: $30 - $50

WHITE TOWER, THE
(1950 - RKO) Glenn Ford, Valli, Claude Rains
One Sheet: $15 - $30

WHITE VOICES
(1965 - Franla Rizzoli) Paolo Ferrari, Sandra
Milo
One Sheet: $3 - $5

WHITE WARRIOR
(1961 - Warner Bros.) Steve Reeves, Giorgia
Moll
One Sheet: $15 - $25

WHITE WATER SUMMER
(1987 - -) Kevin Bacon, Sean Austin
One Sheet: $3 - $5

WHITE WILDERNESS
(1958 - Disney) Narrated by Winston Hibler
One Sheet: $15 - $30   *Documentary.*

WHITE WINGS
(1923 - Pathe) Stan Laurel, James Finlayson
One Sheet: $250 - $600

WHITE WITCH DOCTOR
(1953 - 20th Century Fox) Susan Hayward,
Robert Mitchum
One Sheet: $75 - $125

WHITE WOMAN
(1933 - Paramount) Carole Lombard, Charles
Laughton
One Sheet: $500 - $800

WHITE ZOMBIE
(1932 - United Artists) Bela Lugosi, Madge
Bellamy
One Sheet: $2,500 - $4,000   *Graven
Images, pg. 61.*

WHITE ZOMBIE
(1940R - United Artists) Bela Lugosi, Madge
Bellamy
One Sheet: $100 - $200   *Re-release.*

WHO ARE MY PARENTS?
(1922 - Fox) Roger Lytton, Peggy Shaw
One Sheet: $500 - $800

WHO DONE IT?
(1942 - Universal) Abbott & Costello, Patric
Knowles
One Sheet: $150 - $350

WHO DONE IT?
(1949 - Columbia) The Three Stooges (Shemp)
One Sheet: $350 - $750   *Comedy short.
Duotone.*

WHO DONE IT?
(1956 - Rank) Benny Hill, David Kossoff
One Sheet: $40 - $75

WHO FRAMED ROGER RABBIT
(1988 - Disney) Roger Rabbit
One Sheet: $15 - $30   *Cartoon. Two
styles. One Sheet(Mylar Jessica):$150-$300.*

One Sheet

WHO IS GUILTY?
(1940 - Monogram) Ben Lyon
One Sheet: $40 - $75

WHO IS HARRY KELLERMAN
(1971 - National General) Dustin Hoffman,
Barbara Harris
One Sheet: $5 - $10

WHO IS HOPE SCHUYLER?
(1942 - 20th Century Fox) Sheila Ryan, Joseph
Allen Jr., Ricardo Cortez
One Sheet: $30 - $50

**WHO IS KILLING THE GREAT CHEFS OF
EUROPE?**
(1978 - Warner Bros.) George Segal,
Jacqueline Bisset
One Sheet: $5 - $10

WHO KILLED AUNT MAGGIE?
(1940 - Republic) John Hubbard, Wendy Barrie
One Sheet: $30 - $50

WHO KILLED DOC ROBBIN?
(1948 - United Artists) Virginia Grey, Don
Castle
One Sheet: $15 - $30

WHO KILLED GAIL PRESTON?
(1937 - Columbia) Robert Paige, Don Terry,
Rita Hayworth
One Sheet: $125 - $250

WHO KILLED MARY WHAT'S 'ERNAME?
(1971 - Cannon) Red Buttons, Sylvia Miles

WHO KILLED TEDDY BEAR?
(1965 - Magna) Juliet Prowse, Sal Mineo
One Sheet: $7 - $15

WHO KILLED WHO?
(1943 - MGM) Tex Avery
One Sheet: $1,300 - $2,000   *Cartoon.
Cartoon Movie Posters #287.*

WHO SAYS I CAN'T RIDE A RAINBOW?
(1971 - Transvue) Jack Klugman, Norma
French
One Sheet: $3 - $5

WHO SLEW AUNTIE ROO?
(1971 - AIP) Shelley Winters, Mark Lester
One Sheet: $5 - $10

WHO WAS THAT LADY?
(1960 - Columbia) Tony Curtis, Dean Martin,
Janet Leigh
One Sheet: $10 - $20

WHO'LL STOP THE RAIN?
(1978 - United Artists) Nick Nolte, Tuesday
Weld
One Sheet: $7 - $15

WHO'S AFRAID OF VIRGINIA WOOLF?
(1966 - Warner Bros.) Elizabeth Taylor,
Richard Burton, Sandy Dennis
One Sheet: $30 - $50   *Academy
Award: Best Actress. Academy Award Movie
Posters #236.*

WHO'S BEEN SLEEPING IN MY BED?
(1964 - Paramount) Dean Martin, Elizabeth
Montgomery, Carol Burnett
One Sheet: $15 - $25   *Burnett's film
debut.*

WHO'S GOT THE ACTION?
(1963 - Paramount) Dean Martin, Lana Turner
One Sheet: $15 - $25

WHO'S GUILTY?
(1945 - Columbia) Robert Kent, Amelita Ward
One Sheet: $75 - $150   *Serial. 15
Chapters.*

WHO'S HARRY CRUMB
(1989 - -) John Candy, Annie Potts, Jeffrey
Jones
One Sheet: $3 - $5

WHO'S MINDING THE MINT?
(1967 - Columbia) Jim Hutton, Dorothy Provine
One Sheet: $5 - $10

WHO'S MINDING THE STORE?
(1963 - Paramount) Jerry Lewis, Jill St. John
One Sheet: $15 - $30

WHO'S THAT GIRL
(1987 - Warner Bros.) Madonna, Griffin Dunne
One Sheet: $10 - $20

WHO'S THAT KNOCKING AT MY DOOR?
(1968 - Brenner) Zina Bethune, Harvey Keitel
One Sheet: $7 - $15   *Keitel's film
debut.*

WHO'S THE MAN?
(1993 - New Line) Doctor Dre, Ed Lover
One Sheet: $3 - $5

WHOLE TOWN'S TALKING, THE
(1926 - Universal) Edward Everett Horton,
Virginia Lee Horton
One Sheet: $250 - $600

WHOLE TOWN'S TALKING, THE
(1935 - Columbia) Edward G. Robinson, Jean
Arthur, Dir: John Ford
One Sheet: $250 - $500

WHOLE TRUTH, THE
(1958 - Columbia) Stewart Granger, Donna
Reed
One Sheet: $10 - $20

WHOLLY MOSES!
(1980 - Columbia) Dudley Moore, Larraine
Newman
One Sheet: $3 - $5

WHOM THE GODS DESTROY
(1934 - Columbia) Robert Young, Walter
Connolly
One Sheet: $100 - $200

WHOOPEE

(1930 - United Artists) Eddie Cantor, Eleanor Hunt
One Sheet: $800 - $1,500   *Early Technicolor process.*

WHOOPEE BOYS, THE
(1986 - -) Michael O'Keefe, Paul Rodriguez
One Sheet: $3 - $5

WHOOPEE PARTY, THE
(1932 - United Artists) Mickey Mouse
One Sheet: $25,000 - $40,000   *Cartoon. The Disney Poster, pg. 23.*

WHOOPS I'M AN INDIAN
(1936 - Columbia) The Three Stooges (Curly)
One Sheet: $10,000 - $16,000   *Comedy short. Duotone.*

WHORE
(1991 - -) Theresa Russell, Benjamin Mouton, Dir: Ken Russell
One Sheet: $5 - $10

WHOSE BABY
(1917 - RKO) Gloria Swanson
One Sheet: $600 - $1,000

WHOSE LIFE IS IT ANYWAY
(1981 - MGM/United Artists) Richard Dreyfuss, John Cassavetes
One Sheet: $5 - $10

WHY
(1972 - Hallmark) Alberto Sordi, Elga Andersen
One Sheet: $2 - $3

WHY BOTHER TO KNOCK
(1964 - Seven Arts) Richard Todd, Nicole Maurey, Elke Sommer
One Sheet: $3 - $5

WHY BRING THAT UP
(1929 - Paramount) Moran & Mack
One Sheet: $250 - $500

WHY CHANGE YOUR WIFE?
(1920 - Paramount-Artcraft) Dir: Cecil B. DeMille
One Sheet: $600 - $1,000

WHY GIRLS LEAVE HOME
(1945 - PRC) Pamela Blake, Sheldon Leonard, Lola Lane
One Sheet: $75 - $150

WHY GIRLS LOVE SAILORS
(1927 - Pathe) Laurel & Hardy
One Sheet: $4,000 - $6,000

WHY IS A PLUMBER?
(1929 - MGM) Jean Harlow, Ed Kennedy
One Sheet: $500 - $800

WHY LEAVE HOME?
(1929 - Fox) Walter Catlett, Sue Carol
One Sheet: $500 - $800

WHY MEN WORK
(1924 - Pathe) Charlie Chase
One Sheet: $800 - $1,500

WHY MUST I DIE?
(1960 - AIP) Terry Moore, Debra Paget
One Sheet: $15 - $25

WHY PLAY LEAP FROG?
(1950 - MGM) -
One Sheet: $200 - $400   *Cartoon. Full color stone litho.*

WHY SAILORS GO WRONG
(1928 - -) Sally Phipps, Sammy Cohen
One Sheet: $150 - $300

WHY WOMEN REMARRY
(1923 - Associated Photoplays) Milton Sills, Ethel Grey Terry
One Sheet: $100 - $200

WHY WORRY?
(1923 - Pathecomedy) Harold Lloyd
One Sheet: $1,300 - $2,000

WICHITA
(1955 - Allied Artists) Joel McCrea, Vera Miles
One Sheet: $15 - $25

WICKED
(1931 - Fox) Victor McLaglen
One Sheet: $200 - $400

WICKED AS THEY COME
(1956 - Columbia) Arlene Dahl, Phil Carey

One Sheet: $20 - $40

WICKED CITY, THE
(1951 - Eagle Lion Classics) Maria Montez, Lilli Palmer
One Sheet: $30 - $50

WICKED DREAMS OF PAULA SCHULTZ
(1968 - United Artists) Elke Sommer, Bob Crane
One Sheet: $7 - $15

WICKED LADY, THE
(1946 - Universal) James Mason, Margaret Lockwood
One Sheet: $30 - $50

WICKED LADY, THE
(1983 - MGM/United Artists) Faye Dunaway, Alan Bates
One Sheet: $5 - $10

WICKED STEPMOTHER
(1988 - -) Bette Davis, Barbara Carrera
One Sheet: $10 - $20   *Davis' final film.*

WICKED, WICKED
(1973 - MGM) Tiffany Bolling, Scott Brady
One Sheet: $3 - $5

WICKED WIFE
(1955 - Allied Artists) Nigel Patrick, Moira Lister
One Sheet: $40 - $75

WICKED WOLF, THE
(1943 - 20th Century Fox) Mighty Mouse
One Sheet: $250 - $500   *Cartoon. Full color stock poster with printed title. Huge image of Mighty Mouse on yellow background.*

WICKED WOMAN, A
(1934 - MGM) Mady Christians, Jean Arthur
One Sheet: $100 - $200

WICKED WOMAN
(1953 - United Artists) Beverly Michaels, Richard Egan
One Sheet: $20 - $40

WICKER MAN, THE
(1973 - Warner Bros.) Edward Woodward, Christopher Lee, Britt Ekland
One Sheet: $15 - $25

WICKY-WACKY ROMANCE, A
(1939 - 20th Century Fox) Terry-toons
One Sheet: $100 - $200   *Cartoon. Full color stone litho. Stock poster with inset title.*

WIDE AWAKE
(1997 - Miramax) Denis Leary, Dana Delaney, Rosie O'Donnell
One Sheet: $4 - $8

WIDE OPEN
(1930 - Warner Bros.) Louise Fazenda, Edward Everett Horton
One Sheet: $200 - $400

WIDE OPEN FACES
(1938 - Columbia) Joe E. Brown, Jane Wyman
One Sheet: $100 - $200

WIDE OPEN FACES
(194?R - Trinity) Joe E. Brown
One Sheet: $40 - $75   *Re-release.*

WIDE OPEN SPACES, THE
(1932 - RKO/Pathe) Ned Sparks, Dorothy Sebastian, William Farnum
One Sheet: $150 - $300

WIDE OPEN SPACES
(1947 - RKO/Disney) Donald Duck
One Sheet: $1,300 - $2,000   *Cartoon. Full color.*

WIDE OPEN TOWN
(1941 - Paramount) William Boyd, Russell Hayden
One Sheet: $125 - $250

WIDE, WIDE WORLD
(1965 - -) -
One Sheet: $5 - $10   *Documentary.*

WIDOW FROM CHICAGO, THE
(1930 - Warner Bros.) Edward G. Robinson, Neil Hamilton
One Sheet: $150 - $300

WIDOW FROM MONTE CARLO, THE

(1936 - Warner Bros.) Dolores Del Rio, Warren William
One Sheet: $75 - $150

WIDOW IN SCARLET
(1932 - Mayfair) Dorothy Revier, Lloyd Whitlock
One Sheet: $200 - $400

WIDOWS' PEAK
(1994 - Fine Line) Mia Farrow, Natasha Richardson, Joan Plowright
One Sheet: $5 - $10

WIFE, DOCTOR AND NURSE
(1937 - 20th Century Fox) Loretta Young, Warner Baxter, Virginia Bruce
One Sheet: $100 - $200

One Sheet

WIFE, HUSBAND AND FRIEND
(1939 - 20th Century Fox) Loretta Young, Warner Baxter
One Sheet: $100 - $200

WIFE OF GENERAL LING, THE
(1938 - Gaumont) Griffith Jones, Adrienne Renn
One Sheet: $75 - $125

WIFE OF MONTE CRISTO, THE
(1946 - Pathe) John Loder, Eva Gabor
One Sheet: $15 - $25

WIFE SWAPPERS
(1970 - Trans-American) James Donnelly, Valerie St.John
One Sheet: $10 - $20   *AKA: THE SWAPPERS.*

WIFE TAKES A FLYER, THE
(1942 - Columbia) Franchot Tone, Joan Bennett
One Sheet: $40 - $75

WIFE TAMERS
(1926 - Pathe) Lionel Barrymore, Clyde Cook
One Sheet: $300 - $700

WIFE VS. SECRETARY
(1936 - MGM) Clark Gable, Jean Harlow, Myrna Loy
One Sheet: $800 - $1,500

WIFE WANTED
(1946 - Monogram) Kay Francis, Paul Cavanaugh
One Sheet: $30 - $50   *Francis' final film.*

WIFE'S RELATIONS, THE
(1928 - Columbia) Shirley Mason, Ben Turpin
One Sheet: $300 - $600

One Sheet

WIGSTOCK: THE MOVIE
(1995 - Goldwyn) RuPaul, The Lady Bunny

One Sheet: $7 - $15

One Sheet

WILBY CONSPIRACY, THE
(1975 - United Artists) Sidney Poitier, Michael Caine
One Sheet: $5 - $10

WILD AND DIRTY, THE
(1978 - -) -
One Sheet: $15 - $25

WILD AND THE INNOCENT, THE
(1959 - Universal) Audie Murphy, Joanne Dru
One Sheet: $30 - $50

WILD AND WONDERFUL
(1964 - Universal) Tony Curtis, Christine Kaufmann
One Sheet: $10 - $20

WILD AND WOOLFY
(1945 - MGM) Droopy, Barney Bear
One Sheet: $1,600 - $2,500   *Cartoon. Cartoon Movie Posters #294.*

WILD AND WOOLFY
(1952R - MGM) Droopy, Barney Bear
One Sheet: $150 - $300   *Re-release. Cartoon. Full color stone litho. Stock poster with title inset.*

WILD AND WOOLFY
(1990R - MGM) Barney Bear
One Sheet: $10 - $20   *Re-release. Cartoon.*

WILD AND WOOLLY
(1937 - 20th Century Fox) Jane Withers, Walter Brennan, Lon Chaney Jr.
One Sheet: $100 - $200   *Cowboy Movie Posters #222.*

One Sheet

WILD ANGELS, THE
(1966 - AIP) Peter Fonda, Nancy Sinatra, Dir: Roger Corman
One Sheet: $40 - $75   *Biker film.*

WILD AT HEART
(1990 - Goldwyn) Laura Dern, Nicolas Cage
One Sheet: $5 - $10

WILD BEAUTY
(1946 - Universal) Don Porter, Lois Collier
One Sheet: $20 - $40

WILD BILL
(1995 - United Artists) Jeff Bridges, Ellen Barkin
One Sheet: $5 - $12

WILD BILL HICKOK
(1923 - -) William S. Hart, Ethel Grey Terry
One Sheet: $1,600 - $2,500

WILD BILL HICKOK RIDES
(1942 - Warner Bros.) Constance Bennett, Bruce Cabot
One Sheet: $50 - $100

WILD BILL HICKOK RIDES
(1946R - Warner Bros.) Constance Bennett, Bruce Cabot
One Sheet: $30 - $50   *Re-release.*

WILD BLUE YONDER, THE
(1951 - Republic) Wendell Corey, Vera Ralston
One Sheet: $40 - $75

WILD BOYS OF THE ROAD
(1933 - First National) Frankie Darro, Rochelle Hudson
One Sheet: $200 - $400

WILD BRIAN KENT
(1936 - Principal) Ralph Bellamy, Mae Clarke
One Sheet: $100 - $200

WILD BUNCH, THE
(1969 - Warner Bros.) William Holden, Ernest Borgnine, Dir: Sam Peckinpah
One Sheet: $150 - $350   *Cowboy Movie Posters #326.*

WILD BUNCH, THE
(1970R - Warner Bros.) William Holden, Ernest Borgnine, Dir: Sam Peckinpah
One Sheet: $40 - $75   *Re-release.*

WILD BUNCH, THE
(1995R - Warner Bros.) William Holden, Ernest Borgnine, Dir: Sam Peckinpah
One Sheet: $7 - $15   *Re-release. Restored version.*

WILD CARGO
(1934 - Radio) Frank Buck, native cast
One Sheet: $250 - $500

WILD CHILD
(1970 - United Artists) Francois Truffaut, Jean Gruault
One Sheet: $5 - $10

WILD COMPANY
(1930 - Fox) H.B. Warner, Frank Albertson, Bela Lugosi
One Sheet: $300 - $700

WILD COUNTRY, THE
(1947 - Pathe) Eddie Dean
One Sheet: $15 - $35

WILD COUNTRY, THE
(1971 - Walt Disney) Steve Forrest, Ronny Howard
One Sheet: $7 - $15

WILD DAKOTAS, THE
(1956 - American Releasing) Bill Williams, Coleen Gray
One Sheet: $10 - $20

WILD FRONTIER, THE
(1947 - Republic) Allan Lane
One Sheet: $20 - $40

WILD GEESE
(1978 - Rank) Roger Moore, Richard Harris, Richard Burton
One Sheet: $10 - $20

WILD GEESE CALLING
(1941 - 20th Century Fox) Henry Fonda, Joan Bennett
One Sheet: $75 - $150   *One Sheet(stone litho style):$300-$500.*

Mini Window Card (trimmed)

WILD GEESE II

(1985 - -) Scott Glenn, Barbara Carrera
One Sheet: $3 - $5

WILD GIRL
(1932 - Fox) Joan Bennett
One Sheet: $150 - $300

WILD GOLD
(1934 - Fox) John Boles, Claire Trevor
One Sheet: $100 - $200

WILD HARVEST
(1947 - Paramount) Alan Ladd, Dorothy Lamour, Robert Preston
One Sheet: $40 - $75

WILD HEART, THE
(1951 - RKO) Jennifer Jones, David Farrar
One Sheet: $15 - $30

WILD HEARTS CAN'T BE BROKEN
(1991 - Disney) -
One Sheet: $3 - $5

WILD HERITAGE
(1958 - Universal) Will Rogers, Jr., Maureen O'Sullivan
One Sheet: $10 - $20

WILD HONEY
(1942 - MGM) Barney Bear
One Sheet: $600 - $1,000   *Cartoon. Cartoon Movie Posters #255.*

WILD HORSE
(1931 - Allied) Hoot Gibson, Stepin Fetchit
One Sheet: $500 - $900

WILD HORSE AMBUSH
(1952 - Republic) Michael Chapin, Eilene Janssen
One Sheet: $15 - $25

WILD HORSE CANYON
(1939 - Monogram) Jack Randall, Dorothy Short
One Sheet: $40 - $75

WILD HORSE MESA
(1925 - Paramount) Jack Holt, Noah Beery
One Sheet: $250 - $600   *Cowboy Movie Posters #50.*

WILD HORSE MESA
(1932 - Paramount Publix) Randolph Scott
One Sheet: $500 - $800

WILD HORSE MESA
(1947 - RKO) Tim Holt
One Sheet: $30 - $60

WILD HORSE PHANTOM
(1944 - PRC) Buster Crabbe
One Sheet: $30 - $50

WILD HORSE RANGE
(1940 - Monogram) Jack Randall, Phyllis Ruth
One Sheet: $40 - $75

WILD HORSE RODEO
(1937 - Republic) Three Mesquiteers
One Sheet: $50 - $100

WILD HORSE RUSTLERS
(1943 - PRC) Bob Livingston
One Sheet: $30 - $50

WILD HORSE STAMPEDE
(1926 - Universal) Jack Hoxie
One Sheet: $250 - $500   *A Blue Streak Western.*

WILD HORSE STAMPEDE
(1943 - Monogram) Ken Maynard, Hoot Gibson
One Sheet: $50 - $100

WILD HORSES
(1982 - Satori) Keith Aberdein, John Bach
One Sheet: $5 - $10

WILD IN THE COUNTRY
(1961 - 20th Century Fox) Elvis Presley, Hope Lange
One Sheet: $75 - $150

WILD IN THE STREETS
(1968 - AIP) Shelley Winters, Christopher Jones
One Sheet: $15 - $25   *Drugs.*

WILD INNOCENCE
(1937 - Herman Garfield) Wendy Munro
One Sheet: $75 - $125

WILD IS THE WIND
(1957 - Paramount) Anna Magnani, Anthony Quinn
One Sheet: $15 - $25

WILD JUSTICE
(1925 - United Artists) George Sherwood, Peter the Great (a dog)
One Sheet: $125 - $250

WILD LIFE, THE
(1984 - Universal) Eric Stolz, Christopher Penn
One Sheet: $3 - $5

WILD MAN OF BORNEO, THE
(1941 - MGM) Frank Morgan, Mary Howard
One Sheet: $75 - $125

WILD MONEY
(1937 - Paramount) Edward Everett Horton, Louise Campbell
One Sheet: $75 - $125

WILD MUSTANG
(1935 - Ajax) Harry Carey, Barbara Fritchie
One Sheet: $150 - $300

WILD NORTH, THE
(1952 - MGM) Stewart Granger, Cyd Charisse
One Sheet: $15 - $30

WILD ON THE BEACH
(1965 - 20th Century Fox) Frankie Randall, Sherry Jackson, Sonny and Cher
One Sheet: $30 - $50   *Rock 'n' Roll.*

WILD ONE, THE
(1953 - Columbia) Marlon Brando, Mary Murphy
One Sheet: $500 - $800   *Price is for Style A One Sheet. One Sheet(Style B):$250-$500.*

WILD ONE, THE
(1960R - Columbia) Marlon Brando
One Sheet: $75 - $150   *Re-release. Duotone. Closeup portrait of Brando.*

WILD ORCHID
(1990 - -) Mickey Rourke, Carre Otis, Jacqueline Bisset
One Sheet: $7 - $15

WILD ORCHIDS
(1929 - MGM) Greta Garbo, Lewis Stone
One Sheet: $2,500 - $4,000

WILD PACK, THE
(1972 - AIP) Kent Lane
One Sheet: $3 - $5   *Teenqage gangs. AKA: THE SANDPIT GENERALS*

WILD PARTY, THE
(1929 - Paramount) Clara Bow, Fredric March
One Sheet: $1,600 - $2,500

WILD PARTY, THE
(1956 - United Artists) Anthony Quinn, Carol Ohmart
One Sheet: $15 - $25

WILD PARTY, THE
(1974 - AIP) Raquel Welch, James Coco
One Sheet: $10 - $20

WILD RACERS, THE
(1968 - AIP) Fabian, David Landers
One Sheet: $15 - $30   *Sports (Stock car racing).*

WILD REBELS
(1967 - Crown) Steve Alaimo, Bobbie Byers, Willie Pastrano
One Sheet: $20 - $40   *Biker film.*

WILD RIDE, THE
(1960 - Filmgroup) Jack Nicholson, Georgianna Carter
One Sheet: $40 - $80   *Sports (Auto racing). Sports Movie Posters #16.*

WILD RIDERS
(1971 - Crown International) Alex Rocco, Elizabeth Knowels, Sherry Bain
One Sheet: $20 - $40   *Biker film.*

WILD RIVER
(1960 - 20th Century Fox) Lee Remick, Montgomery Clift, Bruce Dern
One Sheet: $30 - $50   *Dern's film debut.*

WILD ROVERS
(1971 - MGM) William Holden, Ryan O'Neal

One Sheet: $5 - $10

WILD SEASON
(1968 - Universal) Gert Van Den Bergh, Marie Du Toit
One Sheet: $5 - $10

WILD STALLION
(1952 - Monogram) Ben Johnson, Edgar Buchanan, Martha Hyer
One Sheet: $15 - $30

WILD STRAWBERRIES
(1959 - Janus) Victor Sjostrom, Bibi Anderson
One Sheet: $75 - $150   *Swedish.*

WILD THING
(1987 - -) Rod Knepper, Kathleen Quinlan
One Sheet: $5 - $10

WILD WAVES
(1929 - Columbia) Mickey Mouse
One Sheet: $16,000 - $25,000   *Cartoon. Duotone. The Disney Poster, pg. 18.*

WILD WEST
(1946 - PRC) Eddie Dean, Al LaRue
One Sheet: $15 - $35

WILD WEST
(1977 - Filmways) Charles Bronson, Clint Eastwood, Steve McQueen, John Wayne
One Sheet: $20 - $40   *Documentary.*

WILD WEST
(1993 - Samuel Goldwyn) David Atwood
One Sheet: $3 - $5

WILD WEST DAYS
(1937 - Universal) Johnny Mack Brown, George Shelley
One Sheet: $150 - $350   *Serial. Western. 13 Chapters.*

WILD WEST WHOOPEE
(1931 - Cosmos) Jack Perrin, Josephine Hill
One Sheet: $150 - $300

WILD WESTERNERS, THE
(1962 - Columbia) James Philbrook, Nancy Kovack
One Sheet: $15 - $25

WILD WHEELS
(1969 - Fanfare) Don Epperson, Robert Dix
One Sheet: $15 - $25   *Biker gangs.*

WILD, WILD PLANET, THE
(1967 - MGM) Tony Russel, Lisa Gastoni
One Sheet: $15 - $35

WILD, WILD WINTER
(1966 - Universal) Gary Clarke, Chris Noel
One Sheet: $15 - $25

WILD, WILD WOMEN
(1918 - -) Hugh Fay, Harry McCoy
One Sheet: $250 - $500   *Featuring the Hall Room Boys.*

WILD, WILD WORLD
(1965 - Sokoler)
One Sheet: $3 - $5

WILD, WILD WORLD OF JAYNE MANSFIELD, THE
(1968 - -) Jayne Mansfield
One Sheet: $30 - $50   *Documentary.*

WILD WOMEN OF BORNEO
(1932 - First Anglo) Narrated by Gordon Roberts
One Sheet: $50 - $100

WILD WOMEN OF WONGO, THE
(1959 - Tropical) Jean Hawkshaw, Johnny Walsh
One Sheet: $40 - $80

WILD WORLD OF BATWOMAN, THE
(1966 - ADP) Katherine Victor, George Andre, Dir: Jerry Warren
One Sheet: $50 - $100

WILDCAT, THE
(1915 - Lubin Mfg.) Texas Guinan
One Sheet: $800 - $1,500

WILDCAT
(1942 - Paramount) Richard Arlen, Buster Crabbe
One Sheet: $30 - $50

WILDCAT BUS

(1940 - RKO) Fay Wray, Charles Lang
One Sheet: $75 - $150

WILDCAT OF TUCSON, THE
(1940 - Columbia) Bill Elliott, Evelyn Young
One Sheet: $40 - $75

WILDCAT SAUNDERS
(1936 - Atlantic) Jack Perrin, Blanche Mehaffey
One Sheet: $125 - $250

WILDCATS
(1986 - Warner Bros.) Goldie Hawn, Swoosie
Kurtz, James Keach
One Sheet: $5 - $10

WILDCATTER, THE
(1937 - Universal) Scott Colton, Jean Rogers
One Sheet: $50 - $100

WILDER NAPALM
(1993 - TriStar) Dennis Quaid, Debra Winger
One Sheet: $3 - $5

WILDERNESS FAMILY PART 2
(1978 - Pacific International) Roberto Logan,
Susan Shaw
One Sheet: $3 - $5   *AKA:
FURTHER ADVENTURES OF THE WIDERNESS
FAMILY-PART TWO.*

WILDERNESS MAIL
(1935 - Ambassador) Kermit Maynard
One Sheet: $100 - $200

WILD-WEST
(1926 - Bray Productions) Dinky Doodle
One Sheet: $250 - $600   *Cartoon.
Cartoon Movie Posters #12.*

WILL ANY GENTLEMAN?
(1954 - Stratford) George Cole, Veronica Hurst
One Sheet: $7 - $15

WILL IT HAPPEN AGAIN?
(1948 - American) -
One Sheet: $5 - $10

WILL PENNY
(1968 - Paramount) Charlton Heston, Joan
Hackett
One Sheet: $15 - $25

WILL SUCCESS SPOIL ROCK HUNTER?
(1957 - 20th Century Fox) Jayne Mansfield,
Tony Randall
One Sheet: $40 - $75

WILLARD
(1971 - Cinerama) Bruce Davison, Ernest
Borgnine
One Sheet: $7 - $15

WILLIAM S. HART CLASSIC
(192?R - Enterprising Dist. Corp.) -
One Sheet: $600 - $1,000   *Re-release.
Scene cards announce upcoming films.*

WILLIAM S. HART STOCK POSTER
(1916? - -) -
One Sheet: $800 - $1,500

**WILLIAM SHAKESPEARE'S ROMEO AND
JULIET**
(1996 - 20th Century Fox) Leonardo DiCaprio,
Claire Danes
One Sheet: $5 - $10

WILLIE AND JOE BACK AT THE FRONT
(1952 - Universal) Tom Ewell, Harvey Lembeck
One Sheet: $10 - $20

WILLIE BOY
(1975R - Universal) Robert Redford, Robert
Blake
One Sheet: $3 - $5   *Re-release*

WILLIE DYNAMITE
(1974 - Universal) Roscoe Orman, Diana
Sands
One Sheet: $10 - $20   *Blaxploitation.*

WILLIE McBEAN & HIS MAGIC MACHINE
(1965 - Magna) Rankin/Bass Stop-Motion
Animation
One Sheet: $15 - $25

WILLIE WHOPPER
(1933 - MGM) UB Iwerks
One Sheet: $1,900 - $3,000   *Cartoon.*

WILLIES, THE
(1990 - -) James Karen, Sean Astin
One Sheet: $3 - $5

WILLOW
(1988 - Lucasfilm) Val Kilmer, Joanne Whalley
One Sheet: $10 - $20   *Advance:$20-
$35*

**WILLY WONKA AND THE CHOCOLATE
FACTORY**
(1971 - Paramount) Gene Wilder, Jack
Albertson
One Sheet: $30 - $50

**WILLY WONKA AND THE CHOCOLATE
FACTORY**
(1974R - Paramount) Gene Wilder, Jack
Albertson
One Sheet: $15 - $35   *Re-release.*

WILSON
(1944 - 20th Century Fox) Alexander Knox,
Charles Coburn
One Sheet: $40 - $75

WIMMEN IS A MYSTERY
(1940 - Paramount) Popeye, Fleischer Studio
One Sheet: $1,600 - $2,500   *Cartoon.
Duotone. Great image of Olive Oyl & Nephews.*

WINCHESTER '73
(1950 - Universal) James Stewart, Shelley
Winters
One Sheet: $150 - $300   *Cowboy
Movie Posters #289.*

WINCHESTER '73
(1958R - Universal) James Stewart, Shelley
Winters
One Sheet: $50 - $100   *Re-release.*

WIND, THE
(1928 - MGM) Lillian Gish, Lara Hanson
One Sheet: $1,900 - $3,000

WIND
(1992 - TriStar) Matthew Modine, Jennifer Grey
One Sheet: $3 - $5

WIND ACROSS THE EVERGLADES
(1958 - Warner Bros.) Burl Ives, Christopher
Plummer, Peter Falk
One Sheet: $10 - $20   *Falk's film
debut.*

WIND AND THE LION, THE
(1975 - MGM) Sean Connery, Candice Bergen
One Sheet: $15 - $25

WIND CANNOT READ, THE
(1960 - 20th Century Fox) Dirk Bogarde, Yoko
Tani
One Sheet: $5 - $10

WIND IS MY LOVER, THE
(1950 - Film Classics) -
One Sheet: $15 - $25

WINDJAMMER
(1937 - RKO) George O'Brien, Constance
Worth
One Sheet: $75 - $150

One Sheet

WINDOM'S WAY
(1958 - Rank) Peter Finch, Mary Ure
One Sheet: $100 - $200

WINDOW, THE
(1949 - RKO) Bobby Driscoll, Barbara Hale
One Sheet: $100 - $200

WINDS OF AUTUMN, THE
(1976 - Howco) Andrew Prine, Jack Elam
One Sheet: $3 - $5

WINDS OF CHANGE

(1979 - -) -
One Sheet: $7 - $15

WINDS OF JARRAH, THE
(1983 - Castle Hill) Terence Donovan, Susan
Lyons
One Sheet: $3 - $5

WINDS OF THE WASTELAND
(1936 - Republic) John Wayne, Phyllis Fraser
One Sheet: $1,600 - $2,500   *Cowboy
Movie Posters #199.*

WINDWALKER
(1980 - Pacific International) Trevor Howard
One Sheet: $5 - $10

WINE
(1924 - Universal) Clara Bow, Robert Agnew,
Myrtle Stedman
One Sheet: $1,600 - $2,500

WINE OF MORNING
(1955 - Bob Jones University) -
One Sheet: $15 - $25

WINE OF YOUTH
(1924 - Metro-Goldwyn) Eleanor Boardman
One Sheet: $150 - $300

WINE, WOMEN, AND HORSES
(1937 - Warner Bros.) Barton MacLane, Ann
Sheridan
One Sheet: $75 - $150   *Sports (Horse
Racing). Sports Movie Posters #248.*

WINE, WOMEN, AND SAUERKRAUT
(1927 - William Fox) -
One Sheet: $250 - $600

WINE, WOMEN AND SONG
(1934 - Chadwick) Lilyan Tashman, Lew Cody
One Sheet: $75 - $150

One Sheet

WING AND A PRAYER
(1944 - 20th Century Fox) Don Ameche, Dana
Andrews
One Sheet: $50 - $100

WING TOY
(1921 - Fox) Shirley Mason, Raymond McKee
One Sheet: $150 - $300

WINGED VICTORY
(1944 - 20th Century Fox) Pvt. Lon McCallister,
Jeanne Crain
One Sheet: $50 - $100

WINGS
(1927 - Paramount) Clara Bow, Charles
Rogers, Gary Cooper
One Sheet: $4,500 - $7,000   *Academy
Award: Best Picture. First film to win Best Picture
award. Price is for original, first release one sheet.
One Sheet(Roadshow):$2500-$4000. Academy
Award Movie Posters #1, #2, & #3.*

WINGS AND THE WOMAN
(1942 - RKO) Anna Neagle, Robert Newton
One Sheet: $40 - $75

WINGS FOR THE EAGLE
(1942 - Warner Bros.) Ann Sheridan, Dennis
Morgan
One Sheet: $30 - $50

WINGS IN THE DARK
(1934 - Paramount) Myrna Loy, Cary Grant
One Sheet: $500 - $800

WINGS OF ADVENTURE
(1930 - Tiffany) Rex Lease, Armida, Clyde
Cook
One Sheet: $125 - $250

WINGS OF CHANCE
(1961 - Universal) Jim Brown, Frances Rafferty
One Sheet: $5 - $10

WINGS OF DANGER
(1952 - Lippert) Zachary Scott, Robert Beatty
One Sheet: $15 - $25

WINGS OF DESIRE
(1988 - -) Bruno Ganz, Peter Falk, Dir: Wim
Wenders
One Sheet: $30 - $50   *German/
French.*

WINGS OF EAGLES, THE
(1957 - MGM) John Wayne, Dan Dailey,
Maureen O'Hara
One Sheet: $40 - $75   *Red/black
duotone.*

One Sheet

WINGS OF THE HAWK
(1953 - Universal) Van Heflin, Julia Adams
One Sheet: $30 - $50   *Filmed in 3-D.*

WINGS OF THE MORNING
(1937 - 20th Century Fox) Annabella, Henry
Fonda, Leslie Banks
One Sheet: $125 - $250   *England's first
technicolor film.*

WINGS OF THE NAVY
(1939 - Warner Bros.) George Brent, Olivia de
Havilland
One Sheet: $50 - $100

WINGS OVER HONOLULU
(1937 - Universal) Ray Milland, Wendy Barrie
One Sheet: $75 - $150

WINGS OVER THE PACIFIC
(1943 - Monogram) Inez Cooper, Edward Norris
One Sheet: $15 - $30

WINK OF AN EYE
(1958 - United Artists) Doris Dowling, Jonathan
Kidd
One Sheet: $5 - $10

WINKING IDOL, THE
(1926 - Universal) William Desmond, Eileen
Sedgwick
One Sheet: $200 - $400   *Serial. 10
Chapters.*

WINNER, THE
(1965 - Gilmore/Kinglsey) Abdoulaye Faye,
Marcel Brucherd
One Sheet: $3 - $5

WINNER TAKE ALL
(1932 - Warner Bros.) James Cagney, Virginia
Bruce
One Sheet: $1,300 - $2,000   *Sports
(Boxing). Sports Movie Posters #130.*

WINNER TAKE ALL
(1939 - 20th Century Fox) Tony Martin, Gloria
Stuart
One Sheet: $125 - $250

WINNER TAKE ALL
(1948 - Monogram) Joe Kirkwood, Elyse Knox
One Sheet: $50 - $100   *Sports
(Boxing). Joe Palooka series.*

WINNER'S CIRCLE, THE
(1948 - 20th Century Fox) Jean Willes, Morgan
Garley
One Sheet: $15 - $30

WINNERS OF THE WEST
(1921 - Universal) Art Acord
One Sheet: $300 - $600   *Serial. 18*

chapters.

WINNERS OF THE WEST
One Sheet

WINNERS OF THE WEST
(1940 - Universal) Dick Foran, Anne Nagel
One Sheet: $75 - $125   *Serial. Western. 13 chapters.*

WINNERS OF THE WEST
(195?R - Universal) Dick Foran, Anne Nagel
One Sheet: $15 - $35   *Re-release. Serial. Western.*

WINNERS OF THE WILDERNESS
(1927 - MGM) Joan Crawford
One Sheet: $800 - $1,500

WINNIE THE POOH AND THE BLUSTERY DAY
(1968 - Buena Vista/Disney) Winnie the Pooh
One Sheet: $75 - $125   *Cartoon. Academy Award: Best Cartoon Short. Full color.*

WINNIE THE POOH AND THE HONEY TREE
(1964 - Disney) Winnie The Pooh
One Sheet: $75 - $125   *Cartoon.*

WINNIE THE POOH AND TIGGER TOO
(1974 - Buena Vista/Disney) Winnie the Pooh, Tigger
One Sheet: $40 - $75   *Cartoon. Full color.*

WINNIE THE POOH/HORSE IN THE GREY FLANNEL SUIT
(1969 - Buena Vista/Disney) -
One Sheet: $30 - $50   *Cartoon. Double feature poster.*

WINNING
(1969 - Universal) Paul Newman, Joanne Woodward, Robert Wagner
One Sheet: $30 - $50   *Sports (Auto Racing). Sports Movie Posters #19.*

WINNING
(1973R - Universal) Paul Newman, Joanne Woodward, Robert Wagner
One Sheet: $15 - $30   *Re-release. Sports (Auto Racing).*

WINNING OF BARBARA WORTH, THE
(1926 - United Artists) Ronald Colman, Vilma Banky, Gary Cooper(film debut)
One Sheet: $250 - $600   *Cowboy Movie Posters #57.*

WINNING OF THE WEST
(1953 - Columbia) Gene Autry
One Sheet: $50 - $100

WINNING TEAM, THE
(1952 - Warner Bros.) Ronald Reagan (as G.C. Alexander), Doris Day
One Sheet: $100 - $200   *Sports (Baseball). Sports Movie Posters #60.*

WINNING TEAM, THE
(1957R - Warner Bros.) Ronald Reagan (as G.C. Alexander)
One Sheet: $40 - $75   *Re-release. Sports (Baseball).*

WINNING THE WEST
(1943 - 20th Century Fox) Mighty Mouse
One Sheet: $250 - $500   *Cartoon. Full color stock poster with printed title. Huge image of Mighty Mouse on yellow background.*

WINNING TICKET, THE
(1935 - MGM) Leo Carrillo, Irene Hervey
One Sheet: $75 - $150

WINSLOW BOY, THE
(1948 - London) Robert Donat, Margaret Leighton

One Sheet: $15 - $35

WINSOR MCCAY
(1911 - Vitagraph) McCay
One Sheet: $2,500 - $4,000   *Cartoon. Price is for original French 47x63. "Le Dernier Cri Des Dessins Animes"-The Latest Thing In Drawn Animation. French poster to Little Nemo.Cartoon Movie Posters #1.*

WINTER A GO-GO
(1965 - Columbia) James Stacy, William Wellman, Jr.
One Sheet: $15 - $30   *Rock 'n' Roll.*

WINTER CARNIVAL
(1939 - United Artists) Ann Sheridan, Richard Carlson
One Sheet: $50 - $100   *Sports (Skiing). Sports Movie Posters #310.*

WINTER HILARITIES
(1953R - RKO/Disney) -
One Sheet: $75 - $150   *Re-release. Cartoon. Duotone.*

WINTER KILLS
(1979 - Avco/Embassy) Jeff Bridges, John Huston
One Sheet: $5 - $10

WINTER MEETING
(1948 - Warner Bros.) Bette Davis, Janis Paige, James Davis
One Sheet: $40 - $75

WINTER PEOPLE
(1989 - Columbia) Kurt Russell, Kelly McGillis
One Sheet: $3 - $5

WINTER SPORTS IN SWITZERLAND
(1914 - Pathe) -
One Sheet: $150 - $300

WINTER WONDERLAND
(1947 - Republic) Lynne Roberts, Charles Drake
One Sheet: $20 - $40

WINTERSET
(1936 - RKO) Burgess Meredith (film debut), Margo, John Carradine
One Sheet: $100 - $200

WINTERTIME
(1943 - 20th Century Fox) Sonja Henie, Cornel Wilde
One Sheet: $150 - $300

One Sheet

WIRED
(1989 - Taurus) Michael Chiklis, Ray Sharkley
One Sheet: $7 - $15

WIRETAPPERS
(1956 - Embassy) Bill Williams, Georgie Lee
One Sheet: $5 - $10

WISDOM
(1987 - 20th Century Fox) Emilio Estevez, Demi Moore
One Sheet: $2 - $3

WISE GIRL
(1937 - RKO) Miriam Hopkins, Ray Milland
One Sheet: $75 - $125

WISE GIRLS
(1930 - MGM) Elliott Nugent, Norma Lee, Marion Shilling
One Sheet: $100 - $200   *AKA: KEMPY.*

WISE GUYS, THE
(1969 - Universal) Bourvil, Lino Ventura
One Sheet: $3 - $5

WISE GUYS
(1986 - MGM/United Artists) Danny DeVito, Joe Piscopo
One Sheet: $5 - $10

WISE GUYS PREFER BRUNETTES
(1926 - Pathe) Helene Chadwick, Jimmie Finlayson
One Sheet: $125 - $250

WISER SEX, THE
(1932 - Paramount) Claudette Colbert
One Sheet: $500 - $800

One Sheet

WISH YOU WERE HERE
(1987 - Film Four) Emily Lloyd, Tom Bell
One Sheet: $2 - $3

WISHBONE CUTTER
(1978 - Howco) Joe Don Baker, Sondra Locke
One Sheet: $3 - $5

WISHING MACHINE, THE
(1974 - Paramount) -
One Sheet: $5 - $10

WISTFUL WIDOW OF WAGON GAP, THE
(1947 - Universal) Bud Abbott, Lou Costello, Marjorie Main
One Sheet: $75 - $150

WITCH, THE
(1969 - Arco) Rosanna Schiaffino, Richard Johnson
One Sheet: $20 - $40

WITCH FROM BENEATH THE SEA, THE
(1962 - Diamond) John Sutton, Zygmunt Sulistrowski
One Sheet: $7 - $15   *Duotone.*

WITCH WITHOUT A BROOM, A
(1967 - PRC) Jeff Hunter, Maria Perschy
One Sheet: $5 - $10

WITCHBOARD
(1985 - -) Todd Allen, Tawny Kitaen
One Sheet: $5 - $10

WITCHCRAFT
(1964 - 20th Century Fox) Lon Chaney, Jack Hedley
One Sheet: $15 - $35

WITCHCRAFT '70
(1970 - Transamerican) -
One Sheet: $10 - $20   *Documentary.*

WITCHCRAFT/HORROR OF IT ALL
(1964 - 20th Century Fox) -
One Sheet: $10 - $20   *Double feature poster.*

WITCHES, THE
(1969 - Dino De Laurentiis) Silvana Mangano, Clint Eastwood, Annie Girardot
One Sheet: $50 - $100   *Price is for Style A one sheet showing Eastwood. Insert (Eastwood shown): $50-$100.*

WITCHES, THE
(1990 - -) Anjelica Huston, Jasen Fisher, Mai Zetterling
One Sheet: $5 - $10

WITCHES OF EASTWICK, THE
(1987 - Warner Bros.) Jack Nicholson, Cher, Michelle Pfeiffer
One Sheet: $7 - $15

WITCHFINDER GENERAL
(1968 - Tigon) Vincent Price, Ian Ogilvy
One Sheet: $15 - $30   *AKA: THE*

CONQUEROR WORM. *Price is for British Quad. Graven Images, pg. 217.*

WITCHING HOUR, THE
(1934 - Paramount) Sir Guy Standing, John Halliday, Judith Allen
One Sheet: $150 - $300

WITCHMAKER, THE
(1969 - Escelsior) Anthony Eisley, Thordis Brandt
One Sheet: $5 - $10

WITH A SONG IN MY HEART
(1952 - 20th Century Fox) Susan Hayward, David Wayne
One Sheet: $40 - $75

WITH BYRD AT THE SOUTH POLE
(1930 - Paramount) Narrated by Floyd Gibbons
One Sheet: $600 - $1,000   *Documentary.*

WITH LOVE AND HISSES
(1927 - Pathe) Laurel & Hardy
One Sheet: $4,000 - $6,000

WITH LOVE AND KISSES
(1936 - Melody) Pinky Tomlin, Kane Richmond
One Sheet: $75 - $150

WITH SIX YOU GET EGGROLL
(1968 - National General) Doris Day, Brian Keith, Pat Carroll
One Sheet: $15 - $25   *Day's final film.*

WITH STANLEY IN AFRICA
(1922 - Universal) George Walsh, Louise Lorraine
One Sheet: $150 - $300   *Serial. 18 Chapters.*

WITH THE AID OF PHRENOLOGY
(1913 - Biograph) -
One Sheet: $250 - $600

WITH WILLIAMSON BENEATH THE SEA
(1932 - Principal) -
One Sheet: $100 - $200

WITH WINGS OUTSPREAD
(1922 - Aywon) Fred Terry, Walter Franklin
One Sheet: $250 - $600

WITHIN THE LAW
(1923 - First National) Norma Talmadge
One Sheet: $250 - $600

WITHIN THE LAW
(1939 - MGM) Ruth Hussey, Paul Kelly
One Sheet: $50 - $100

WITHIN THE ROCK
(1934 - Showmen's) -
One Sheet: $50 - $100

WITHIN THESE WALLS
(1945 - 20th Century Fox) Thomas Mitchell, Mark Stevens
One Sheet: $30 - $50

One Sheet

WITHNAIL AND I
(1986 - -) Richard E. Grant, Paul McGann
One Sheet: $40 - $85   *Ralph Steadman art.*

WITHOUT A CLUE
(1988 - Orion) Michael Caine,Ben Kingsley
One Sheet: $5 - $10

WITHOUT A TRACE
(1983 - 20th Century Fox) Kate Nelligan, Judd Hirsch
One Sheet: $2 - $3

WITHOUT APPARENT MOTIVE
(1972 - 20th Century Fox) Jean-Louis
Trintignant, Dominique Sanda
One Sheet: $3 - $5

WITHOUT CHILDREN
(1934 - Liberty) Marguerite Churchill, Bruce
Cabot
One Sheet: $75 - $150

WITHOUT HONOR
(1949 - United Artists) Laraine Day, Dane
Clark, Franchot Tone
One Sheet: $15 - $30

WITHOUT HONORS
(1932 - Weiss) Harry Carey, George "Gabby"
Hayes
One Sheet: $250 - $500

One Sheet

WITHOUT LIMIT
(1921 - Metro) Anna Q. Nilsson, Robert Frazer
One Sheet: $150 - $350

WITHOUT LOVE
(1945 - MGM) Spencer Tracy, Katharine
Hepburn
One Sheet: $100 - $200

WITHOUT ORDERS
(1936 - RKO) Robert Armstrong, Sally Eilers
One Sheet: $100 - $200

WITHOUT PITY
(1948 - Lux) John Kitzmiller, Carla Del Poggio
One Sheet: $75 - $150   *Italian. AKA:*
SENZA PIETA. Separate Cinema, pg. 148.

WITHOUT REGRET
(1935 - Paramount) Ellisa Landi, Kent Taylor
One Sheet: $75 - $150

WITHOUT RESERVATIONS
(1946 - RKO) Claudette Colbert, John Wayne,
Don Defore
One Sheet: $150 - $300

WITHOUT WARNING
(1952 - United Artists) Adam Williams, Meg
Randall
One Sheet: $15 - $25

WITNESS
(1985 - Paramount) Harrison Ford, Kelly
McGillis
One Sheet: $5 - $10

WITNESS CHAIR, THE
(1936 - RKO) Ann Harding, Walter Abel
One Sheet: $100 - $200

WITNESS FOR THE PROSECUTION
(1957 - United Artists) Tyrone Power, Marlene
Dietrich, Charles Laughton
One Sheet: $75 - $175

WITNESS TO MURDER
(1954 - United Artists) Barbara Stanwyck,
George Sanders
One Sheet: $30 - $50

WITNESS VANISHES, THE
(1939 - Universal) Edmund Lowe, Wendy
Barrie
One Sheet: $75 - $150

WITTGENSTEIN
(1993 - Zeitgeist) Tilda Swinton, Karl Johnson
One Sheet: $3 - $5   *Documentary.*

WIVES AND LOVERS
(1963 - Paramount) Janet Leigh, Van Johnson
One Sheet: $15 - $25

WIVES NEVER KNOW
(1936 - Paramount) Charles Ruggles, Mary
Boland, Adolphe Menjou
One Sheet: $75 - $150

WIVES UNDER SUSPICION
(1938 - Universal) Warren William, Gail Patrick
One Sheet: $75 - $125

WIZ, THE
(1978 - Universal) Diana Ross, Michael
Jackson, Richard Pryor
One Sheet: $15 - $25   *Black cast.*

WIZARD, THE
(1927 - William Fox) Edmund Lowe, Leila
Hyams
One Sheet: $1,600 - $2,500   *Graven*
Images, pg. 30.

WIZARD, THE
(1989 - Universal) Fred Savage, Beau Bridges,
Christian Slater
One Sheet: $3 - $5

WIZARD OF BAGHDAD, THE
(1960 - 20th Century Fox) Dick Shawn, Diane
Baker
One Sheet: $5 - $10

WIZARD OF GORE, THE
(1971 - Mayflower) Ray Sager, Judy Cler, Dir:
H.G. Lewis
One Sheet: $40 - $75

WIZARD OF LONELINESS, THE
(1988 - -) Lukas Haas, Lea Thompson
One Sheet: $5 - $10

WIZARD OF MARS
(1964 - American General) John Carradine,
Roger Gentry
One Sheet: $15 - $30

WIZARD OF OZ, THE
(1925 - Chadwick) Larry Semon, Dorothy
Dwan, Oliver Hardy
One Sheet: $6,500 - $10,000   *Hardy played*
the Tin Man.

WIZARD OF OZ, THE
(1939 - MGM) Judy Garland, Ray Bolger, Jack
Haley, Bert Lahr, F. Morgan
One Sheet: $10,000 - $15,000   *Prices vary*
widely. One Sheet(all text):$3000-$5000. Graven
Images, pg. 105.

One Sheet

WIZARD OF OZ, THE
(1949R - MGM) Judy Garland, Ray Bolger,
Jack Haley, Bert Lahr, F. Morgan
One Sheet: $600 - $1,000   *Re-release.*

WIZARD OF OZ, THE
(1951R - MGM) Judy Garland, Ray Bolger,
Jack Haley, Bert Lahr, F. Morgan
One Sheet: $200 - $400   *Re-release.*

WIZARD OF OZ, THE
(1955R - MGM) Judy Garland, Ray Bolger,
Jack Haley, Bert Lahr, F. Morgan
One Sheet: $150 - $300   *Re-release.*

WIZARD OF OZ, THE
(1964R - MGM) Judy Garland, Ray Bolger,
Jack Haley, Bert Lahr, F. Morgan
One Sheet: $75 - $150   *Re-release.*
Silver Anniversary.

WIZARD OF OZ, THE
(1972R - MGM) Judy Garland, Ray Bolger,
Jack Haley, Bert Lahr, F. Morgan
One Sheet: $30 - $50   *Re-release.*

WIZARD OF OZ, THE
(1989R - MGM) Judy Garland, Ray Bolger,
Jack Haley, Bert Lahr, F. Morgan
One Sheet: $15 - $30   *Re-release.*
50th Anniversary poster.

WIZARDS
(1977 - 20th Century Fox) Ralph Bakshi
animation
One Sheet: $30 - $50   *Cartoon.*
William Stout art. One Sheet(Style B with butterfly
lady):$40-$60.

One Sheet

WOLF
(1994 - TriStar) Jack Nicholson, Michelle
Pfeiffer
One Sheet: $7 - $15

WOLF AT THE DOOR, THE
(1933 - Columbia) Scrappy
One Sheet: $800 - $1,500   *Cartoon.*
Cartoon Movie Posters #35.

WOLF CALL
(1939 - Monogram) Movita, John Carroll
One Sheet: $75 - $125

WOLF DOG, THE
(1933 - Mascot) Rin-Tin-Tin, Jr., Frankie Darro
One Sheet: $100 - $200   *Serial.*
Western. 12 Chapters.

WOLF DOG
(1958 - 20th Century Fox) Jim Davis, Allison
Hayes
One Sheet: $15 - $25

WOLF HUNTERS, THE
(1949 - Monogram) Kirby Grant, Jan Clayton
One Sheet: $15 - $35

WOLF LARSEN
(1958 - Allied Artists) Barry Sullivan, Gita Hall
One Sheet: $10 - $20

WOLF LOWRY
(1917 - Triangle) William S. Hart, Margery
Wilson
One Sheet: $1,300 - $2,000

WOLF LOWRY
(192?R - -) William S. Hart, Margery Wilson
One Sheet: $200 - $400   *Re-release.*

WOLF MAN, THE
(1924 - Fox) John Gilbert
One Sheet: $800 - $1,500

WOLF MAN, THE
(1941 - Universal) Lon Chaney Jr., Claude
Rains
One Sheet: $6,500 - $10,000   *Graven*
Images, pg. viii, 106, 115.

Insert

WOLF MAN, THE
(1951R - Realart) Lon Chaney, Jr., Claude
Rains
One Sheet: $250 - $600   *Re-release.*

WOLF OF NEW YORK
(1940 - Republic) Edmund Lowe, Rose Hobart
One Sheet: $50 - $100

WOLF OF WALL STREET, THE
(1929 - Paramount) George Bancroft, Olga
Baclanova
One Sheet: $1,300 - $2,000

WOLF SONG
(1929 - Paramount) Gary Cooper, Lupe Valez
One Sheet: $800 - $1,500

WOLF! WOLF!
(1943 - 20th Century Fox) Mighty Mouse
One Sheet: $250 - $500   *Cartoon. Full*
color stock poster with printed title. Huge image of
Mighty Mouse on yellow background.

WOLF'S SIDE OF THE STORY, THE
(1938 - 20th Century Fox) Terry-toons
One Sheet: $100 - $200   *Cartoon. Full*
color stone litho. Stock poster with inset title.

WOLFEN
(1981 - Warner Bros.) Albert Finney, Diane
Venora
One Sheet: $7 - $15

WOLFMAN
(1979 - Omni) Earl Owensby, Julian Morton
One Sheet: $5 - $15

WOLVES OF THE DESERT
(1926 - -) Ben Wilson
One Sheet: $200 - $400

WOLVES OF THE NIGHT
(1924 - Fox) William Farnum
One Sheet: $200 - $450

WOLVES OF THE RANGE
(1943 - PRC) Bob Livingston
One Sheet: $15 - $35

WOLVES OF THE SEA
(1937 - Jay Dee Kay) Hobart Bosworth
One Sheet: $40 - $75

WOMAN, A
(1915 - Essanay) Charlie Chaplin, Edna
Purviance
One Sheet: $7,500 - $12,000

WOMAN
(1918 - Maurice Tourneur) Florence Billings,
Ethel Hallor
One Sheet: $250 - $500   *Burton Rice*
art.

One Sheet

WOMAN ACCUSED, THE
(1933 - Paramount) Nancy Carroll, Cary Grant
One Sheet: $500 - $800

WOMAN AGAINST THE WORLD
(1938 - Columbia) Ralph Forbes, Alice Moore
One Sheet: $100 - $200

WOMAN AGAINST WOMAN
(1938 - MGM) Virginia Bruce, Herbert Marshall
One Sheet: $50 - $100

WOMAN ALONE, THE
(1936 - Gaumont British) Sylvia Sidney, Oscar
Homolka, Dir: Alfred Hitchcock
One Sheet: $800 - $1,500

WOMAN BETWEEN, THE

(1931 - RKO) Lili Damita, Anita Louise
One Sheet: $100 - $200

WOMAN CHASES MAN
(1937 - United Artists) Miriam Hopkins, Joel McCrea
One Sheet: $150 - $300

WOMAN CHASES MAN
(1956R - United Artists) Miriam Hopkins, Joel McCrea
One Sheet: $15 - $25   *Re-release.*

WOMAN COMMANDS, A
(1932 - RKO) Basil Rathbone, Pola Negri
One Sheet: $350 - $750

WOMAN DISPUTED
(1928 - United Artists) Norma Talmadge, Gilbert Roland
One Sheet: $250 - $500

WOMAN DOCTOR
(1939 - Republic) Frieda Inescort, Henry Wilcoxon
One Sheet: $30 - $60

WOMAN EATER
(1959 - Columbia) George Coulouris, Norman Claridge
One Sheet: $40 - $75

WOMAN FROM MONTE CARLO, THE
(1932 - First National) Lil Dagover, Walter Huston
One Sheet: $100 - $200

WOMAN FROM MOSCOW, THE
(1928 - Paramount Famous Lasky) Pola Negri, Norman Kerry
One Sheet: $250 - $600

WOMAN FROM TANGIER, THE
(1947 - Columbia) Adele Jergens, Stephen Dunne, Ian MacDonald
One Sheet: $15 - $35

WOMAN HATER
(1948 - Universal) Stewart Granger, Edwige Feuillere
One Sheet: $30 - $50

WOMAN HATERS
(1934 - Columbia) Moe Howard, Larry Fine, Curly Howard
One Sheet: $5,000 - $7,500   *Comedy short. The "Stooges" first Columbia short, appearing separately (not as a team).*

WOMAN HUNGRY
(1930 - First National) Sidney Blackmer, Lila Lee
One Sheet: $150 - $300

WOMAN HUNT
(1972 - New World) John Ashley, Pat Woodell
One Sheet: $5 - $10

WOMAN I LOVE, THE
(1937 - RKO) Paul Muni, Miriam Hopkins
One Sheet: $150 - $300

One Sheet

WOMAN I STOLE, THE
(1933 - Columbia) Jack Holt, Fay Wray, Noah Beery, Sr.
One Sheet: $150 - $300

WOMAN IN A DRESSING GOWN
(1957 - Warner Bros.) Yvonne Mitchell, Sylvia Syms
One Sheet: $5 - $10

WOMAN IN BONDAGE
(1943 - Monogram) Gail Patrick, Nancy Kelly

One Sheet: $40 - $75

WOMAN IN DISTRESS
(1937 - Columbia) May Robson, Irene Harvey
One Sheet: $75 - $150

WOMAN IN GREEN, THE
(1945 - Universal) Basil Rathbone, Nigel Bruce, Hillary Brooke
One Sheet: $250 - $600   *Sherlock Holmes series.*

WOMAN IN HIDING
(1950 - Universal) Ida Lupino, Howard Duff
One Sheet: $15 - $35

WOMAN IN QUESTION, THE
(1950 - Columbia) Jean Kent, Dirk Bogarde
One Sheet: $15 - $30

WOMAN IN RED
(1935 - First National) Barbara Stanwyck, Gene Raymond
One Sheet: $1,300 - $2,000

WOMAN IN RED, THE
(1984 - Orion) Gene Wilder, Kelly LeBrock
One Sheet: $7 - $15

One Sheet

WOMAN IN ROOM 13, THE
(1920 - Goldwyn) Pauline Frederick, Charles Clary
One Sheet: $250 - $500

WOMAN IN ROOM 13, THE
(1932 - Fox) Myrna Loy
One Sheet: $200 - $400

WOMAN IN THE DARK, THE
(1934 - RKO) Fay Wray, Ralph Bellamy, Melvyn Douglas
One Sheet: $150 - $300

WOMAN IN THE DARK
(1951 - Republic) Penny Edwards, Ross Elliott
One Sheet: $15 - $25

WOMAN IN THE HALL
(1948 - Eagle-Lion) Ursula Jeans, Jean Simmons
One Sheet: $15 - $25

WOMAN IN THE MOON
(1929 - UFA) Fritz Rasp, Klans Pohl, Dir: Fritz Lang
One Sheet: $6,500 - $10,000   *German. AKA: BY ROCKET TO THE MOON; GIRL IN THE MOON. Price is for original German one sheet. A German three sheet isknown to exist in a Berlin archive.*

WOMAN IN THE WINDOW, THE
(1944 - International) Edward G. Robinson, Joan Bennett, Dir: Fritz Lang
One Sheet: $150 - $350

WOMAN IN WHITE, THE
(1948 - Warner Bros.) Alexis Smith, Eleanor Parker, Sydney Greenstreet
One Sheet: $30 - $50

WOMAN IS THE JUDGE, A
(1939 - Columbia) Frieda Inescort, Rochelle Hudson, Otto Kruger
One Sheet: $50 - $100

WOMAN LIKE SATAN, A
(1959 - Lopert) Brigitte Bardot
One Sheet: $40 - $75

WOMAN OBSESSED
(1959 - 20th Century Fox) Susan Hayward, Stephen Boyd
One Sheet: $15 - $35

WOMAN OF AFFAIRS, A
(1928 - MGM) Greta Garbo, John Gilbert
One Sheet: $3,500 - $5,500

WOMAN OF DISTINCTION, A
(1950 - Columbia) Rosalind Russell, Ray Milland
One Sheet: $15 - $35

WOMAN OF EXPERIENCE, A
(1931 - RKO) Helen Twelvetrees, Lew Cody
One Sheet: $150 - $300

WOMAN OF MYSTERY, THE
(1914 - Blanche) Claire Whitney, Vinnie Burns
One Sheet: $250 - $500

WOMAN OF PARIS, A
(1923 - United Artists) Dir: Charlie Chaplin (Cameo), Edna Purviance, Adolph Menjou
One Sheet: $2,500 - $4,000

WOMAN OF SIN
(1961 - Ellis Films) Dany Carrel, Pierre Vaneck
One Sheet: $15 - $25   *Sexploitation exposing the photo model racket! Duotone.*

WOMAN OF STRAW
(1964 - United Artists) Gina Lollobrigida, Sean Connery
One Sheet: $15 - $30

WOMAN OF THE NORTH COUNTRY
(1952 - Republic) Ruth Hussey, Rod Cameron, Gale Storm(last film)
One Sheet: $15 - $35

WOMAN OF THE RIVER
(1957 - Columbia) Sophia Loren, Gerard Oury
One Sheet: $30 - $50

WOMAN OF THE TOWN, THE
(1943 - United Artists) Claire Trevor, Albert Dekker
One Sheet: $30 - $50

WOMAN OF THE YEAR
(1942 - MGM) Spencer Tracy, Katharine Hepburn
One Sheet: $600 - $1,000   *Team's first film.*

WOMAN ON PIER 13, THE
(1951 - RKO) Robert Ryan, Laraine Day
One Sheet: $30 - $50

WOMAN ON THE BEACH, THE
(1947 - RKO) Joan Bennett, Robert Ryan
One Sheet: $75 - $125

WOMAN ON THE RUN
(1950 - Universal) Ann Sheridan, Dennis O'Keefe
One Sheet: $15 - $35

WOMAN ON TRIAL, THE
(1927 - Paramount) Pola Negri
One Sheet: $350 - $750

WOMAN RACKET, THE
(1930 - MGM) Tom Moore, Blanche Sweet
One Sheet: $100 - $200

WOMAN REBELS, A
(1936 - RKO) Katharine Hepburn, Herbert Marshall
One Sheet: $800 - $1,500

WOMAN THEY ALMOST LYNCHED, THE
(1953 - Republic) John Lund, Audrey Totter
One Sheet: $15 - $30

WOMAN TIMES SEVEN
(1967 - Embassy) Shirley MacLaine, Alan Arkin, Peter Sellers
One Sheet: $15 - $25

WOMAN TO WOMAN
(1923 - Tiffany) Betty Compson, Clive Brook
One Sheet: $200 - $400

WOMAN TRAP
(1929 - Paramount) Hal Skelly, Evelyn Brent
One Sheet: $125 - $250

WOMAN TRAP
(1936 - Paramount) Gertrude Michael, George Murphy
One Sheet: $50 - $100

WOMAN UNDER THE INFLUENCE, A
(1974 - Faces) Peter Falk, Gena Rowlands
One Sheet: $15 - $25

WOMAN WANTED
(1935 - MGM) Maureen O'Sullivan, Joel McCrea
One Sheet: $75 - $150

WOMAN WHO CAME BACK, THE
(1945 - Republic) Nancy Kelly, John Loder
One Sheet: $15 - $35

WOMAN WHO COULDN'T DIE, THE
(1964 - Warner Bros.) Gary Merrill, Jane Merrow
One Sheet: $10 - $20

WOMAN WHO WOULDN'T DIE, THE
(1965 - Warner Bros.) Raymond Garth, Alice Taylor
One Sheet: $7 - $15

WOMAN WITH NO NAME, THE
(1951 - Souvaine Selective) Phyllis Calvert, Edward Underdown
One Sheet: $10 - $20

WOMAN'S A FOOL
(1943 - -) Ida Cox, Ardella
One Sheet: $150 - $300

WOMAN'S ANGLE, THE
(1952 - Stratford) Edward Underdown, Cathy O'Donnell
One Sheet: $10 - $20

WOMAN'S DEVOTION, A
(1956 - Republic) Ralph Meeker, Janice Rule
One Sheet: $7 - $15

WOMAN'S FACE, A
(1941 - MGM) Joan Crawford, Melvyn Douglas, Conrad Veidt
One Sheet: $200 - $400

WOMAN'S JUSTICE, A
(1931 - Major)
One Sheet: $250 - $500

WOMAN'S MAN, A
(1934 - Monogram) Wallace Ford, Kitty Kelly
One Sheet: $75 - $150

WOMAN'S SECRET, A
(1949 - RKO) Maureen O'Hara, Melvyn Douglas, Gloria Grahame
One Sheet: $30 - $50

WOMAN'S VENGEANCE, A
(1948 - Universal) Charles Boyer, Ann Blyth, Jessica Tandy
One Sheet: $50 - $100

WOMAN'S WOMAN, A
(1922 - XL) Mary Alden, Louise Lee
One Sheet: $150 - $300

WOMAN'S WORLD, A
(1954 - 20th Century Fox) Clifton Webb, June Allyson
One Sheet: $15 - $30

WOMAN-WISE
(1937 - 20th Century Fox) Rochelle Hudson, Michael Whalen
One Sheet: $100 - $200

WOMEN, THE
(1939 - MGM) Norma Shearer, Joan Crawford, Rosalind Russell
One Sheet: $800 - $1,500

One Sheet

WOMEN ARE LIKE THAT
(1937 - Warner Bros.) Kay Francis, Pat O'Brien
One Sheet: $75 - $125

WOMEN ARE TROUBLE
(1936 - MGM) Paul Kelly, Stu Erwin
One Sheet: $75 - $150

WOMEN EVERYWHERE
(1930 - Fox) J. Harold Murray, Fifi D'Orsay
One Sheet: $125 - $250

WOMEN FROM HEADQUARTERS
(1950 - Republic) Virginia Huston, Robert Rockwell
One Sheet: $15 - $25   *AKA: WOMAN FROM HEADQUARTERS.*

WOMEN IN BONDAGE
(1943 - Monogram) Gail Patrick, Nancy Kelly, Anne Nagel
One Sheet: $100 - $200

WOMEN IN CAGES
(1971 - New World) Pam Grier, Judy Brown
One Sheet: $15 - $25   *Sexploitation/ Blaxploitation.*

WOMEN IN HIS LIFE, THE
(1933 - MGM) Otto Kruger, Ben Lyon
One Sheet: $100 - $200

WOMEN IN LOVE
(1970 - United Artists) Alan Bates, Oliver Reed, Glenda Jackson
One Sheet: $20 - $40   *Academy Award: Best Actress. Price is for Style B one sheet showing Bates and Reed wrestling. Academy Award Movie Posters #261.*

WOMEN IN PRISON
(1937 - Columbia) Wyn Cahoon, Scott Colton
One Sheet: $150 - $300

WOMEN IN THE NIGHT
(1947 - Film Classics) Tala Birell, William Henry
One Sheet: $15 - $30

WOMEN IN THE WIND
(1939 - Warner Bros.) Kay Francis, Victor Jory, William Gargan
One Sheet: $50 - $100

One Sheet

WOMEN IN WAR
(1940 - Republic) Elsie Janis, Wendy Barrie, Patric Knowles
One Sheet: $30 - $50

WOMEN LOVE ONCE
(1931 - Paramount Publix) Paul Lukas, Virginia Boardman
One Sheet: $100 - $200

WOMEN MEN MARRY, THE
(1922 - Truart) Elmo Lincoln, Hedda Hopper
One Sheet: $250 - $500

WOMEN MEN MARRY, THE
(1931 - Headline) Randolph Scott, Natalie Moorhead
One Sheet: $125 - $250

WOMEN MEN MARRY, THE
(1937 - MGM) George Murphy, Claire Dodd
One Sheet: $50 - $100

WOMEN MUST DRESS
(1935 - Monogram) Minna Gombell, Gavin Gordon
One Sheet: $75 - $150

WOMEN OF ALL NATIONS
(1931 - Fox) Humphrey Bogart, Bela Lugosi, Greta Nissen, Fifi D'Orsay
One Sheet: $800 - $1,500

WOMEN OF PITCAIRN ISLAND, THE

(1956 - 20th Century Fox) James Craig, Lynn Bari
One Sheet: $15 - $25

WOMEN OF THE PREHISTORIC PLANET
(1965 - Feature Film) Wendell Corey, Keith Larsen
One Sheet: $15 - $35

WOMEN ON THE VERGE OF A NERVOUS BREAKDOWN
(1988 - -) Carmen Maura, Antonio Banderas
One Sheet: $7 - $15

WOMEN WITHOUT NAMES
(1940 - Paramount) Robert Paige, Ellen Drew
One Sheet: $150 - $300

WOMEN WITHOUT NAMES
(1950 - Lopert) -
One Sheet: $15 - $25

WOMEN'S PRISON
(1936 - -) Sylvia Sydney
One Sheet: $150 - $300

WOMEN'S PRISON
(1954 - Columbia) Ida Lupino, Howard Duff
One Sheet: $30 - $50

WON TON TON, THE DOG WHO SAVED HOLLYWOOD
(1975 - Paramount) Bruce Dern, Madelind Kahn
One Sheet: $3 - $5

WONDER BAR
(1934 - Warner Bros.) Al Jolson, Kay Francis
One Sheet: $800 - $1,500

WONDER DOG, THE
(1950 - RKO/Disney) Pluto
One Sheet: $500 - $850   *Cartoon. The Disney Poster, pg. 31.*

WONDER KID
(1951 - London) Bobby Henry, Oskar Werner
One Sheet: $10 - $20

WONDER MAN
(1945 - RKO) Danny Kaye, Virginia Mayo
One Sheet: $50 - $100

WONDERFUL ADVENTURES OF PINOCCHIO
(1945R - -) See 1945 PINOCCHIO Re-release

WONDERFUL CHANCE, THE
(1920 - -) Rudolph Valentino
One Sheet: $600 - $1,000

WONDERFUL COUNTRY, THE
(1959 - United Artists) Robert Mitchum, Julie London
One Sheet: $20 - $40

WONDERFUL LAND OF OZ, THE
(1969 - Childhood) -
One Sheet: $15 - $25   *Cartoon.*

WONDERFUL TO BE YOUNG
(1962 - Paramount) Cliff Richard, Robert Morley
One Sheet: $7 - $15

WONDERFUL WORLD OF THE BROTHERS GRIMM, THE
(1962 - MGM) Laurence Harvey, Claire Bloom
One Sheet: $15 - $25   *Cinerama One Sheet: $225.*

WONDERFUL WORLD OF THOSE CUCKOO CRAZY ANIMALS, THE
(1976R - United Artists) -
One Sheet: $7 - $15   *Re-titled, re-release of IT'S SHOWTIME.*

WONDERS OF ALADDIN, THE
(1961 - MGM) Donald O'Connor, Noelle Adam
One Sheet: $15 - $30

WOODLAND CAFE
(1937 - Disney) Silly Symphony
One Sheet: $3,500 - $5,000   *Cartoon.*

WOODLAND CAFE
(1948R - Disney) Silly Symphony
One Sheet: $250 - $500   *Re-release. Cartoon.*

WOODSTOCK
(1970 - Warner Bros.) Joan Baez, Joe Cocker, The Who, Jimi Hendrix, etc.
One Sheet: $75 - $150   *Rock 'n' Roll. Price is for style A one sheet showing artwork of*

bird on guitar. *One Sheet (StyleB):$100-$200.*

WOODSTOCK
(1994 - -) -
One Sheet: $7 - $15   *Documentary.*

WOODY WOODPECKER CARTUNE STOCK
(1950 - Universal-International) Woody Woodpecker
One Sheet: $500 - $800   *Cartoon Movie Posters #55.*

WOODY WOODPECKER CARTUNE STOCK
(196? - Universal) Woody Woodpecker
One Sheet: $40 - $75   *"Walter Lantz's Famous Funny Bird".*

WORDS AND MUSIC
(1948 - MGM) June Allyson, Mickey Rooney, Judy Garland, Tom Drake
One Sheet: $75 - $175

WORDS AND MUSIC
(1962R - MGM) June Allyson, Mickey Rooney, Judy Garland, Tom Drake
One Sheet: $15 - $30   *Re-release.*

WORK
(1915 - Essanay) Charlie Chaplin, Edna Purviance
One Sheet: $8,000 - $13,000

WORKING FOR PEANUTS
(1953 - RKO/Disney) Donald Duck, Chip N' Dale
One Sheet: $600 - $1,000   *Cartoon. The Disney Poster, pg. 47.*

WORKING GIRL
(1988 - 20th Century Fox) Harrison Ford, Sigourney Weaver, Melanie Griffith
One Sheet: $7 - $15

WORKING GIRLS
(1931 - Paramount) Paul Lukas, Frances Dee
One Sheet: $125 - $250

WORKING GIRLS
(1986 - -) Louise Smith, Ellen McElduff
One Sheet: $3 - $5

WORKING MAN, THE
(1933 - Warner Bros.) George Arliss, Bette Davis
One Sheet: $600 - $1,000

WORLD ACCORDING TO GARP, THE
(1981 - Warner Bros.) Robin Williams, Mary Beth Hurt
One Sheet: $7 - $15

WORLD ACCUSES, THE
(1934 - Chesterfield) Vivian Tobin, Dickie Moore
One Sheet: $125 - $250

WORLD AND THE FLESH, THE
(1932 - Paramount Publix) George Bancroft, Miriam Hopkins
One Sheet: $200 - $400

WORLD APART, A
(1988 - Film Four) Barbara Hershey, Jodhi May
One Sheet: $5 - $10

WORLD CHANGES, THE
(1933 - First National) Paul Muni, Mary Astor
One Sheet: $150 - $350

WORLD DANCES, THE
(1953 - Festival) -
One Sheet: $7 - $15

WORLD FOR RANSOM
(1954 - Monogram) Dan Duryea, Patric Knowles
One Sheet: $15 - $25

WORLD GONE MAD, THE
(1933 - Majestic) Pat O'Brien, Evelyn Brent
One Sheet: $250 - $500   *AKA: THE PUBLIC BE HANGED; PUBLIC BE DAMNED.*

WORLD GONE WILD
(1988 - -) Bruce Dern, Michael Pare
One Sheet: $3 - $5

WORLD IN FLAMES
(1940 - Paramount) -
One Sheet: $40 - $75

WORLD IN HIS ARMS
(1952 - Universal) Gregory Peck, Ann Blyth
One Sheet: $30 - $50

WORLD IN HIS ARMS
(1958R - Universal-International) Gregory Peck, Ann Blyth
One Sheet: $15 - $25   *Re-release.*

WORLD IN MY CORNER, THE
(1956 - Universal) Audie Murphy, Barbara Rush
One Sheet: $30 - $50   *Sports (Boxing).*

WORLD IN MY POCKET, THE
(1962 - MGM) Rod Steiger, Nadja Tiller
One Sheet: $10 - $20

WORLD MOVES ON, THE
(1934 - Fox) Madeleine Carroll, Franchot Tone
One Sheet: $150 - $300

WORLD OF ABBOTT & COSTELLO, THE
(1965 - Universal) Bud Abbott, Lou Costello, All-star cast
One Sheet: $30 - $50

WORLD OF HENRY ORIENT, THE
(1964 - United Artists) Peter Sellers, Paula Prentiss
One Sheet: $15 - $25

WORLD OF SUZIE WONG, THE
(1961 - Paramount) William Holden, Nancy Kwan
One Sheet: $15 - $25

WORLD PREMIERE
(1941 - Paramount) John Barrymore, Frances Farmer
One Sheet: $200 - $400

One Sheet

WORLD, THE FLESH, AND THE DEVIL, THE
(1958 - MGM) Harry Belafonte, Inger Stevens
One Sheet: $40 - $75   *Separate Cinema, pg. 153.*

WORLD WAS HIS JURY, THE
(1957 - Columbia) Edmond O'Brien, Mona Freeman
One Sheet: $15 - $30

WORLD WITHOUT END
(1955 - Allied Artists) Hugh Marlowe, Nancy Gates
One Sheet: $100 - $200   *First sci-fi in Cinemascope.*

WORLD WITHOUT SUN
(1965 - Columbia) Jacques Cousteau documentary
One Sheet: $15 - $25

WORLD'S APART
(1921 - Selznick) Eugene O'Brien, Olive Tell
One Sheet: $150 - $300

WORLD'S APPLAUSE, THE
(1923 - -) Bebe Daniels, Lewis Stone
One Sheet: $250 - $500

WORLD'S GREATEST ATHLETE, THE
(1973 - Buena Vista) Jan-Michael Vincent, Tim Conway, John Amos
One Sheet: $7 - $15   *Sport (Track and field).*

WORLD'S GREATEST ATHLETE, THE
(1974R - Buena Vista) Jan-Michael Vincent, Tim Conway, John Amos
One Sheet: $5 - $10   *Sport (Track and field). Re-release.*

WORLD'S GREATEST LOVER, THE
(1977 - 20th Century Fox) Gene Wilder, Dom DeLuise Dir: Gene Wilder
One Sheet: $10 - $20

WORLDLY GOODS
(1930 - Continental) James Kirkwood, Merna Kennedy
One Sheet: $100 - $200

WORST WOMAN IN PARIS, THE
(1933 - Fox) Adolphe Menjou, Helen Chandler, Benita Hume
One Sheet: $250 - $500

One Sheet

WORTH WINNING
(1989 - -) Mark Harmon, Madeleine Stowe
One Sheet: $5 - $10

WOTTA NIGHTMARE
(1939 - Paramount) Popeye
One Sheet: $1,900 - $3,000   *Cartoon. Duotone. Cartoon Movie Posters #214.*

WRAITH, THE
(1986 - -) Charlie Sheen, Nick Cassavetes
One Sheet: $3 - $5

WRANGLER'S ROOST
(1941 - Monogram) Ray Corrigan, John King
One Sheet: $30 - $60

WRATH OF GOD, THE
(1972 - MGM) Robert Mitchum, Rita Hayworth Frank Langella
One Sheet: $15 - $30   *Hayworth's final film.*

One Sheet

WRECK OF THE HESPERUS, THE
(1943 - 20th Century Fox) Mighty Mouse, Terry-toons
One Sheet: $500 - $800   *Cartoon. First time referred to as Mighty Mouse. Full color stock poster with printed title. Huge image of Mighty Mouse on yellow background.*

WRECK OF THE HESPERUS, THE
(1948 - Columbia) Williard Parker, Edgar Buchanan, Patricia White
One Sheet: $20 - $40

WRECK OF THE MARY DEARE
(1959 - MGM) Gary Cooper, Charlton Heston
One Sheet: $20 - $40

WRECKER, THE
(1933 - Columbia) Jack Holt, Genevieve Tobin
One Sheet: $150 - $300

WRECKING CREW, THE
(1942 - Paramount) Richard Arlen, Chester Morris
One Sheet: $30 - $60

WRECKING CREW, THE
(1969 - Columbia) Dean Martin, Elke Sommer, Sharon Tate, Nancy Kwan
One Sheet: $15 - $35

WRESTLER, THE
(1974 - Entertainment Ventures) Ed Asner, Elaine Giftos, Verne Gagne
One Sheet: $15 - $25   *Sports (Wrestling).*

One Sheet

WRESTLING ERNEST HEMINGWAY
(1993 - Warner Bros.) Shirley MacLaine
One Sheet: $7 - $15

WRESTLING QUEEN, THE
(1973 - Harnell) Vivian Vachon, Bill Watts
One Sheet: $15 - $25   *Great graphics.*

WRESTLING WOMEN VS. THE AZTEC APE
(1962 - -) Elizabeth Campbell, Lorena Velasquez
One Sheet: $40 - $75   *Mexican.*

WRESTLING WOMEN VS. THE AZTEC MUMMY
(1964 - -) Lorena Velasquez, Armando Silvestri
One Sheet: $50 - $100   *Mexican.*

WRITTEN ON THE WIND
(1956 - Universal) Rock Hudson, Lauren Bacall, Robert Stack, Dorothy Malone
One Sheet: $50 - $100   *Academy Award Movie Posters #173.*

WRONG AGAIN
(1929 - MGM) Laurel & Hardy
One Sheet: $3,500 - $5,000

WRONG ARM OF THE LAW
(1963 - Continental) Peter Sellers, Lionel Jeffries
One Sheet: $7 - $15

WRONG BOX, THE
(1966 - Columbia) John Mills, Ralph Richardson, Michael Caine, Peter Sellers
One Sheet: $7 - $15

WRONG GUYS, THE
(1988 - -) Louie Anderson, Richard Lewis
One Sheet: $3 - $5

WRONG IS RIGHT
(1982 - Columbia) Sean Connery, George Grizzard
One Sheet: $5 - $10

WRONG MAN, THE
(1956 - Warner Bros.) Henry Fonda, Vera Miles, Dir: A. Hitchcock
One Sheet: $100 - $200

One Sheet

WRONG ROAD, THE
(1937 - Republic) Richard Cromwell, Helen Mack
One Sheet: $40 - $75

WUSA
(1970 - Paramount) Paul Newman, Joanne Woodward
One Sheet: $10 - $20

WUTHERING HEIGHTS
(1939 - United Artists) Merle Oberon, Laurence Olivier
One Sheet: $500 - $800

WUTHERING HEIGHTS
(1955R - Merle Oberon, Laurence Olivier) United Artists
One Sheet: $40 - $75   *Re-release.*

WUTHERING HEIGHTS
(1971 - AIP) Timothy Dalton, Anna Calder-Marshall
One Sheet: $7 - $15

WYATT EARP
(1994 - Warner Bros.) Kevin Costner, Dennis Quaid, Gene Hackman
One Sheet: $7 - $15   *Cowboy Movie Posters #362.*

WYNKEN, BLYNKEN AND NOD
(1948R - RKO/Disney) -
One Sheet: $150 - $350   *Re-release. Cartoon. Duotone.*

WYOMING
(1940 - MGM) Wallace Beery, Ann Rutherford
One Sheet: $40 - $75

WYOMING
(1947 - Republic) William Elliott, Vera Ralston
One Sheet: $30 - $50

WYOMING BANDIT, THE
(1949 - Republic) Allan "Rocky" Lane, Eddy Waller
One Sheet: $20 - $40

WYOMING HURRICANE, THE
(1944 - Columbia) Russell Hayden, Bob Wills
One Sheet: $20 - $40   *Country western musical.*

WYOMING MAIL
(1950 - Universal) Stephen McNally, Alexis Smith
One Sheet: $15 - $30

WYOMING OUTLAW
(1939 - Republic) Three Mesquiteers(John Wayne, Ray Corrigan, Raymond Hatton)
One Sheet: $500 - $800

WYOMING OUTLAW
(1953R - Republic) -
One Sheet: $50 - $100   *Re-release.*

WYOMING RENEGADES
(1955 - Columbia) Phil Carey, Martha Hyer
One Sheet: $15 - $25

WYOMING ROUNDUP
(1952 - Monogram) Whip Wilson
One Sheet: $20 - $40

WYOMING WILDCAT
(1941 - Republic) Don "Red" Barry, Julie Duncan
One Sheet: $30 - $50

X - THE MAN WITH THE X-RAY EYES
(1963 - AIP) Ray Milland, Dir: Roger Corman
One Sheet: $50 - $100

X MARKS THE SPOT
(1931 - Tiffany) Lew Cody, Sally Blane, Wallace Ford
One Sheet: $100 - $200

X MARKS THE SPOT
(1942 - Republic) Damian O'Flynn, Helen Parish
One Sheet: $20 - $40

X THE UNKNOWN
(1957 - RKO) Dean Jagger, Edward Chapman
One Sheet: $40 - $75

X Y AND ZEE
(1972 - Columbia) Elizabeth Taylor, Michael Caine
One Sheet: $15 - $25

X-15
(1961 - United Artists) David McLean, Charles Bronson
One Sheet: $30 - $50

XANADU
(1980 - Universal) Olivia Newton-John, Gene Kelly
One Sheet: $15 - $25

XTRO
(1983 - New Line) Philip Sayer, Bernice Stegers
One Sheet: $7 - $15

YAKUZA
(1975 - Warner Bros.) Robert Mitchum, Takakura Ken
One Sheet: $5 - $10

YANCO
(1964 - Hoffman) Richardo Ancons, Maria Bustamente
One Sheet: $3 - $5

YANK AT ETON, A
(1942 - MGM) Mickey Rooney, Edmund Gwenn
One Sheet: $50 - $100

One Sheet

YANK AT OXFORD, A
(1938 - MGM) Robert Taylor, Lionel Barrymore, Maureen O'Sullivan
One Sheet: $125 - $250

YANK IN INDO-CHINA, A
(1952 - Columbia) John Archer, Jean Willes
One Sheet: $10 - $20

YANK IN KOREA, A
(1951 - Columbia) Lon McCallister, William Phillips
One Sheet: $15 - $25

YANK IN LIBYA, A
(1942 - PRC) Joan Woodbury
One Sheet: $15 - $30

YANK IN LONDON, A
(1945 - 20th Century Fox) Anna Neagle, Rex Harrison, Dean Jagger
One Sheet: $30 - $50

One Sheet

YANK IN THE R.A.F., A
(1940 - 20th Century Fox) Tyrone Power, Betty Grable
One Sheet: $250 - $500

YANK IN THE R.A.F., A
(1953R - -) Tyrone Power, Betty Grable
One Sheet: $75 - $125   *Re-release. Full color.*

YANK IN VIET-NAM, A
(1964 - Allied Artists) Marshall Thompson, Enrique Magalona
One Sheet: $15 - $25

YANK ON THE BURMA ROAD, A
(1942 - MGM) Barry Nelson, Loraine Day

One Sheet: $30 - $60

YANKEE BUCCANEER
(1952 - Universal) Jeff Chandler, Scott Brady
One Sheet: $15 - $25

YANKEE CLIPPER
(1926 - PDC) William Boyd
One Sheet: $200 - $400

YANKEE DON, THE
(1931 - Capital) Richard Talmadge, Lupita Tovar
One Sheet: $125 - $250

YANKEE DOODLE DANDY
(1943 - Warner Bros.) James Cagney, Joan Leslie
One Sheet: $250 - $600   *Academy Award: Best Actor(Cagney). Duotone. Academy Award Movie Posters #84.*

YANKEE DOODLE DANDY
(1957R - Warner Bros.) James Cagney, Joan Leslie
One Sheet: $50 - $100   *Re-release.*

YANKEE DOODLE MOUSE, THE
(1943 - MGM) Tom & Jerry
One Sheet: $600 - $1,000   *Cartoon. Academy Award: Best Cartoon Short. Cartoon Movie Posters #265.*

YANKEE DOODLE MOUSE, THE
(1949R - MGM) Tom & Jerry
One Sheet: $150 - $350   *Re-release. Cartoon. Full color stone litho.*

YANKEE FAKIR
(1947 - Republic) Douglas Fowley, Joan Woodbury
One Sheet: $15 - $30

YANKEE PASHA
(1953 - Universal) Jeff Chandler, Rhonda Fleming
One Sheet: $15 - $25

YANKEE SENOR, THE
(1926 - Fox) Tom Mix, Olive Borden
One Sheet: $500 - $800

YANKS
(1979 - Universal) Richard Gere, Vanessa Redgrave
One Sheet: $3 - $5

YANKS AHOY
(1942 - United Artists) Joe Sawyer, William Tracy
One Sheet: $30 - $50

Half Sheet

YANKS ARE COMING, THE
(1943 - PRC) Maxie Rosenbloom, Mary Healy
One Sheet: $15 - $25

YAQUI DRUMS
(1956 - Allied Artists) Rod Cameron, Mary Castle
One Sheet: $15 - $30

YARN ABOUT YARN, A
(1940 - 20th Century Fox) Terry-toons
One Sheet: $150 - $300   *Cartoon. Full color stone litho. Stock poster with inset title.*

YE OLDEN DAYS
(1933 - United Artists) Mickey Mouse
One Sheet: $45,000 - $60,000   *Cartoon. The Disney Poster, pg. 24. Cartoon Movie Posters #63.*

YEAR OF LIVING DANGEROUSLY, THE
(1983 - MGM) Mel Gibson, Sigourney Weaver,

Linda Hunt
One Sheet: $10 - $20   *Academy Award: Best Supporting Actress (Hunt). Academy Award Movie Posters #333.*

YEAR OF THE CANNONBALLS
(1971 - -) -
One Sheet: $10 - $20

YEAR OF THE COMET
(1992 - Columbia) Penelope Ann Miller, Tim Daly
One Sheet: $5 - $10

YEAR OF THE DRAGON
(1985 - MGM/UA) Mickey Rourke, John Lone
One Sheet: $7 - $15

YEAR OF THE GUN
(1991 - Triumph) Andrew McCarthy, Valeria Golino, Sharon Stone
One Sheet: $5 - $10

YEARLING, THE
(1946 - MGM) Gregory Peck, Jane Wyman, Claude Jarman, Jr.
One Sheet: $75 - $150

YEARLING, THE
(1956R - MGM) Gregory Peck, Jane Wyman, Claude Jarman, Jr.
One Sheet: $20 - $40   *Re-release.*

YEARS BETWEEN, THE
(1947 - Universal) Michael Redgrave, Valerie Hobson
One Sheet: $15 - $35

YELLOW BALLOON, THE
(1953 - Allied Artists) Andrew Ray, Kenneth More
One Sheet: $10 - $20

YELLOW CAB MAN, THE
(1949 - MGM) Red Skelton, Gloria De Haven
One Sheet: $50 - $100

YELLOW CANARY, THE
(1944 - RKO) Anna Neagle, Richard Greene
One Sheet: $50 - $100

YELLOW CANARY, THE
(1963 - 20th Century Fox) Pat Boone, Barbara Eden
One Sheet: $15 - $30

YELLOW CARGO
(1936 - Grand National) Conrad Nagel
One Sheet: $75 - $150

YELLOW DOG CATCHER, THE
(1919 - Fox) -
One Sheet: $150 - $350

YELLOW DUST
(1936 - RKO) Richard Dix, Leila Hyams
One Sheet: $150 - $300

YELLOW FIN
(1951 - Monogram) Wayne Morris, Adrian Booth
One Sheet: $15 - $30

YELLOW HAIRED KID, THE
(1952 - Monogram) Guy Madison, Andy Devine
One Sheet: $20 - $40   *Wild Bill Hickok series.*

YELLOW JACK
(1938 - MGM) Robert Montgomery, Virginia Bruce
One Sheet: $50 - $100

YELLOW MASK, THE
(1930 - BIP) Dorothy Seacombe, Warwick Ward
One Sheet: $125 - $250

YELLOW MENACE, THE
(1916 - Unity) Edwin Stevens
One Sheet: $250 - $500   *Serial. 16 Chapters.*

YELLOW MOUNTAIN, THE
(1954 - Universal) Lex Barker, Mala Powers
One Sheet: $15 - $35

YELLOW ROLLS ROYCE, THE
(1965 - MGM) Rex Harrison, Shirley MacLaine, Ingrid Bergman
One Sheet: $20 - $40

YELLOW ROSE OF TEXAS, THE
(1944 - Republic) Roy Rogers, Dale Evans
One Sheet: $150 - $350

YELLOW SKY
(1948 - 20th Century Fox) Gregory Peck, Anne Baxter
One Sheet: $75 - $150

YELLOW STAIN, THE
(1922 - Fox) John Gilbert, Claire Anderson
One Sheet: $250 - $500

YELLOW SUBMARINE
(1968 - United Artists) The Beatles
One Sheet: $250 - $600   *Cartoon. Rock 'n' Roll. Peter Maxx art. Cartoon Movie Posters #387.*

YELLOW TICKET, THE
(1931 - Fox) Boris Karloff, Laurence Olivier, Lionel Barrymore
One Sheet: $600 - $1,000

YELLOW TOMAHAWK, THE
(1954 - United Artists) Rory Calhoun, Peggie Castle
One Sheet: $15 - $30

YELLOWBEARD
(1983 - Orion) Graham Chapman, Peter Boyle
One Sheet: $3 - $5

YELLOWNECK
(1955 - Republic) Lin McCarthy, Stephen Courtleigh
One Sheet: $15 - $25

YELLOWSTONE
(1936 - Universal) Andy Devine, Ralph Morgan
One Sheet: $75 - $150

YELLOWSTONE CUBS
(1963 - Disney) Narrated by Rex Allen
One Sheet: $15 - $25   *Cartoon.*

YELLOWSTONE KELLY
(1959 - Warner Bros.) Clint Walker, Edward Byrnes
One Sheet: $15 - $35

YENTL
(1983 - MGM/United Artists) Barbra Streisand, Mandy Patinkin
One Sheet: $5 - $10

YES!
(1970S - Cannon) Gunilla Ivansson, Gun Flack
One Sheet: $3 - $5

YES, GIORGIO
(1982 - MGM) Luciano Pavarotti, Kathryn Harrold
One Sheet: $4 - $8

YES, MR. BROWN
(1933 - British/Dominions) Jack Buchanan, Elsie Randolph
One Sheet: $50 - $100

YES, MY DARLING DAUGHTER
(1939 - Warner Bros.) Priscilla Lane, Jeffrey Lynn
One Sheet: $40 - $75

One Sheet

YES OR NO?
(1920 - First National) Norma Talmadge
One Sheet: $250 - $500

YES SIR, MR. BONES
(1951 - Lippert) Sally Anglin, Pete Daley
One Sheet: $40 - $75

YES SIR, THAT'S MY BABY
(1949 - Universal) Donald O'Connor, Charles Coburn
One Sheet: $30 - $50

YES, WE HAVE NO BONANZA
(1939 - Columbia) The Three Stooges (Curly)
One Sheet: $7,500 - $12,000   *Comedy short. Duotone.*

YES, YES, NANETTE
(1925 - Pathe) Jimmy Finlayson, "Babe" (Oliver) Hardy, Dir: Stan Laurel
One Sheet: $700 - $1,200

YESSONGS
(1975 - Ellman) Yes
One Sheet: $30 - $50   *Rock 'n' Roll.*

YESTERDAY AND TODAY
(1953 - United Artists) -
One Sheet: $10 - $20

YESTERDAY MACHINE, THE
(1962 - -) Tim Holt, Jack Herman
One Sheet: $10 - $20

YESTERDAY, TODAY AND TOMORROW
(1964 - Embassy) Sophia Loren, Marcello Mastroianni
One Sheet: $20 - $40

YESTERDAY'S ENEMY
(1959 - Columbia) Stanley Baker, Leo McKern
One Sheet: $10 - $20

YESTERDAY'S HEROES
(1940 - 20th Century Fox) Robert Sterling, Jean Rogers
One Sheet: $50 - $100

YIP YIP YIPPY
(1939 - Paramount) Betty Boop, Fleischer Studio
One Sheet: $600 - $1,000   *Cartoon. Duotone. Betty is not on poster. Cartoon Movie Posters #207.*

YODELIN' KID FROM PINE RIDGE
(1937 - Republic) Gene Autry, Betty Bronson
One Sheet: $250 - $500

YOG - MONSTER FROM SPACE
(1970 - AIP) Akira Kubo
One Sheet: $30 - $60

YOJIMBO
(1961 - Toho) Toshiro Mifune, Dir: Akira Kurosawa
One Sheet: $100 - $200   *Price is for original Japanese poster.*

YOKE'S ON ME, THE
(1944 - Columbia) The Three Stooges (Curly)
One Sheet: $2,500 - $4,000   *Comedy short. Duotone.*

YOKEL BOY
(1942 - Republic) Albert Dekker, Joan Davis
One Sheet: $15 - $30

YOKEL DUCK MAKES GOOD
(1942 - 20th Century Fox) Terry-toons
One Sheet: $125 - $250   *Cartoon. Full color stock poster with inset title. Large image of Supermouse and Gandy Goose.*

YOLANDA
(1924 - MGM) Marion Davies, Lyn Harding
One Sheet: $350 - $750

YOLANDA AND THE THIEF
(1945 - MGM) Fred Astaire, Lucille Bremer
One Sheet: $100 - $200

YOLANTA
(1964 - Artkino) Natalya Rudnaya, Yuri Petrov
One Sheet: $3 - $5

YOR
(1983 - Columbia) Reb Brown, Corrine Clery
One Sheet: $5 - $10

YOU AND ME
(1938 - Paramount) Sylvia Sidney, George Raft
One Sheet: $150 - $300

YOU ARE WHAT YOU EAT
(1968 - PRC) Tiny Tim, Paul Butterfield, Peter Yarrow
One Sheet: $50 - $100   *Tim's only film.*

YOU BELONG TO ME
(1934 - Paramount) Lee Tracy, Helen Mack
One Sheet: $150 - $300

YOU BELONG TO ME

(1941 - Columbia) Barbara Stanwyck, Henry Fonda
One Sheet: $200 - $400

YOU CAME ALONG
(1945 - Paramount) Robert Cummings, Lizabeth Scott
One Sheet: $50 - $100

YOU CAN'T BEAT LOVE
(1937 - RKO) Preston Foster, Joan Fontaine
One Sheet: $75 - $150

YOU CAN'T BEAT THE IRISH
(1952 - Stratford) Jack Warner, Michael Dolan
One Sheet: $30 - $50

YOU CAN'T BEAT THE LAW
(1943 - Monogram) Edward Norris, Joan Woodbury
One Sheet: $20 - $40

YOU CAN'T BUY EVERYTHING
(1934 - MGM) May Robson, Lewis Stone
One Sheet: $100 - $200

YOU CAN'T BUY LUCK
(1937 - RKO) Vinton Haworth, Helen Mack
One Sheet: $100 - $200

YOU CAN'T CHEAT AN HONEST MAN
(1939 - Universal) W.C. Fields, Edgar Bergen, Charlie McCarthy
One Sheet: $800 - $1,500

YOU CAN'T CHEAT AN HONEST MAN
(1948R - Realart) W.C. Fields, Edgar Bergen, Charlie McCarthy
One Sheet: $100 - $200   *Re-release.*

YOU CAN'T DO WITHOUT LOVE
(1945 - Columbia) Vera Lynn, Donald Stewart
One Sheet: $15 - $30

YOU CAN'T ESCAPE FOREVER
(1942 - Warner Bros.) George Brent, Brenda Marshall
One Sheet: $20 - $40

YOU CAN'T FOOL A FOOL
(1946 - Columbia) Andy Clyde
One Sheet: $75 - $150   *Comedy short. Duotone.*

YOU CAN'T FOOL YOUR WIFE
(1923 - Paramount) Leatrice Joy
One Sheet: $700 - $1,200

YOU CAN'T FOOL YOUR WIFE
(1940 - RKO) Lucille Ball, James Ellison
One Sheet: $125 - $250

YOU CAN'T GET AWAY WITH MURDER
(1939 - Warner Bros.) Humphrey Bogart, Gale Page
One Sheet: $250 - $500

YOU CAN'T HAVE EVERYTHING
(1937 - 20th Century Fox) Alice Faye, The Ritz Brothers
One Sheet: $200 - $400

One Sheet

YOU CAN'T RATION LOVE
(1944 - Paramount) Betty Jane Rhodes, Johnnie Johnston
One Sheet: $15 - $35

YOU CAN'T RUN AWAY FROM IT
(1956 - Columbia) June Allyson, Jack Lemmon
One Sheet: $15 - $25

YOU CAN'T TAKE IT WITH YOU
(1938 - Columbia) Jean Arthur, Lionel Barrymore, James Stewart D: Frank Capra

One Sheet: $1,300 - $2,000   *Academy Award: Best Picture, Best Direction(Frank Capra). Academy Award MoviePosters #57 & #59.*

One Sheet

YOU CAN'T WIN 'EM ALL
(1970 - Columbia) Tony Curtis, Charles Bronson
One Sheet: $7 - $15

YOU FOR ME
(1952 - MGM) Peter Lawford, Jane Greer
One Sheet: $15 - $30

YOU GOTTA STAY HAPPY
(1948 - Universal) Joan Fontaine, James Stewart, Eddie Albert
One Sheet: $40 - $75

YOU KNOW WHAT SAILORS ARE
(1953 - United Artists) Akim Tamiroff, Donald Sinden
One Sheet: $15 - $25

YOU LIGHT UP MY LIFE
(1977 - Columbia) Didi Conn, Joe Silver
One Sheet: $3 - $5

YOU MAY BE NEXT
(1936 - Columbia) Ann Sothern, Lloyd Nolan
One Sheet: $75 - $150

YOU MUST BE JOKING
(1966 - Columbia) Michael Callan, Lionel Jeffries
One Sheet: $3 - $5

YOU NAZTY SPY
(1940 - Columbia) The Three Stooges (Curly)
One Sheet: $5,000 - $7,500   *Comedy short. Duotone.*

YOU NEVER CAN TELL
(1951 - Universal) Dick Powell, Peggy Dow
One Sheet: $15 - $25

YOU ONLY LIVE ONCE
(1937 - United Artists) Sylvia Sidney, Henry Fonda, Dir: Fritz Lang
One Sheet: $600 - $1,000

YOU ONLY LIVE TWICE
(1967 - United Artists) Sean Connery, Bernard Lee
One Sheet: $200 - $400   *Price is for Style A one sheet. One Sheet (Advance)$150-$300. One Sheet(Style B or C):$150-$300.*

One Sheet (Advance)

YOU ONLY LIVE TWICE
(1980R - United Artists/Transamerica) Sean Connery, Bernard Lee
One Sheet: $15 - $30   *Re-release. Looks identical to original but has Transamerica logo.*

YOU SAID A MOUTHFUL
(1932 - First National) Joe E. Brown, Ginger Rogers
One Sheet: $250 - $600

One Sheet

YOU SO CRAZY
(1994 - Goldwyn) Martin Lawrence
One Sheet: $5 - $12   *Concert film.*

YOU WERE MEANT FOR ME
(1948 - 20th Century Fox) Jeanne Crain, Dan Dailey, Oscar Levant
One Sheet: $30 - $50

YOU WERE NEVER LOVELIER
(1942 - Columbia) Fred Astaire, Rita Hayworth
One Sheet: $500 - $800

YOU'LL FIND OUT
(1940 - RKO) Kay Kyser, Peter Lorre, Boris Karloff, Bela Lugosi
One Sheet: $200 - $400   *Graven Images, pg. 131.*

YOU'LL LIKE MY MOTHER
(1972 - Universal) Patty Duke, Richard Thomas
One Sheet: $5 - $10

YOU'LL NEVER GET RICH
(1941 - Columbia) Fred Astaire, Rita Hayworth
One Sheet: $250 - $600   *Price is for Style A One Sheet.*

YOU'RE A BIG BOY NOW
(1967 - Seven Arts) Elizabeth Hartman, Geraldine Page
One Sheet: $5 - $10

YOU'RE A LUCKY FELLOW, MR. SMITH
(1943 - Universal) Allan Jones, Evelyn Ankers
One Sheet: $30 - $50

YOU'RE A SWEETHEART
(1937 - Universal) Alice Faye, George Murphy, Ken Murray
One Sheet: $200 - $400

YOU'RE DARN TOOTIN'
(1928 - MGM) Laurel & Hardy
One Sheet: $3,500 - $5,000

YOU'RE IN THE ARMY NOW
(1941 - Warner Bros.) Phil Silvers, Jimmy Durante
One Sheet: $50 - $100

Window Card

YOU'RE IN THE NAVY NOW
(1951 - 20th Century Fox) Gary Cooper, Jane Greer
One Sheet: $40 - $75

YOU'RE MY EVERYTHING
(1949 - 20th Century Fox) Dan Dailey, Anne Baxter

One Sheet: $30 - $50

YOU'RE NEVER TOO YOUNG
(1955 - Paramount) Dean Martin, Jerry Lewis
One Sheet: $30 - $50

YOU'RE NEVER TOO YOUNG
(1964R - Paramount) Dean Martin, Jerry Lewis
One Sheet: $5 - $10   *Re-release.*

YOU'RE NOT SO TOUGH
(1940 - Universal) The Dead End Kids, Nan Grey
One Sheet: $75 - $150

YOU'RE ONLY YOUNG ONCE
(1938 - MGM) Lewis Stone, Mickey Rooney
One Sheet: $50 - $100

YOU'RE OUT OF LUCK
(1941 - Monogram) Frankie Darro, Mantan Moreland, Kay Sutton
One Sheet: $30 - $50

YOU'RE TELLING ME
(1934 - Paramount) W.C. Fields, Joan Marsh
One Sheet: $1,300 - $2,000

YOU'RE TELLING ME
(1942 - Universal) Hugh Herbert, Anne Gwynne
One Sheet: $20 - $40

YOU'RE THE ONE
(1941 - Paramount) Bonnie Baker, Orrin Tucker & His Orchestra
One Sheet: $40 - $75   *Big Band musical.*

YOU'VE GOT TO BE SMART
(1967 - World-Cine) Tom Stern, Roger Perry, Mamie Van Doren
One Sheet: $15 - $25

YOUNG AMERICA
(1932 - Fox) Spencer Tracy, Doris Kenyon
One Sheet: $300 - $700

YOUNG AMERICA
(1942 - 20th Century Fox) Jane Withers, William Tracy
One Sheet: $40 - $75

YOUNG AMERICANS
(1967 - Columbia) The Young Americans
One Sheet: $10 - $20   *Rock 'n' Roll.*

YOUNG AND BEAUTIFUL
(1934 - Mascot) William Haines, Judith Allen
One Sheet: $75 - $150

YOUNG AND DANGEROUS
(1957 - 20th Century Fox) Lili Gentle, Mark Damon
One Sheet: $15 - $25

YOUNG AND INNOCENT
(1937 - Gaumont) Derrick de Marney, Nova Pilbeam, Dir: Alfred Hitchcock
One Sheet: $1,900 - $3,000   *British. U.S. title: THE GIRL WAS YOUNG.*

YOUNG AND THE BRAVE, THE
(1963 - MGM) Rory Calhoun, William Bendix
One Sheet: $10 - $20

YOUNG AND THE WILLING
(1964 - Universal) Ian McShane, Virginia Maskell
One Sheet: $7 - $15

YOUNG AND WILD
(1958 - Republic) Gene Evans, Scott Marlowe
One Sheet: $30 - $50

YOUNG AND WILLING
(1942 - United Artists) William Holden, Eddie Bracken
One Sheet: $30 - $50

YOUNG AND WILLING
(1964 - Universal) Virginia Maskell, Paul Rogers
One Sheet: $7 - $15

YOUNG ANIMALS, THE
(1968 - AIP) Tom Nardini, Patty McCormack, David Macklin
One Sheet: $7 - $15   *AKA: BORN WILD.*

YOUNG APRIL
(1926 - -) Joseph Schildkraut, Bessie Love
One Sheet: $150 - $300

YOUNG AS YOU FEEL
(1931 - Fox) Will Rogers, Fifi D'Orsay
One Sheet:　$200 - $400

YOUNG AS YOU FEEL
(1940 - 20th Century Fox) Jed Prouty, Spring Byington
One Sheet:　$30 - $50

YOUNG AT HEART
(1954 - Warner Bros.) Doris Day, Frank Sinatra
One Sheet:　$50 - $100

YOUNG BESS
(1953 - MGM) Jean Simmons, Stewart Granger
One Sheet:　$30 - $50

YOUNG BILL HICKOK
(1940 - Republic) Roy Rogers, George "Gabby" Hayes
One Sheet:　$250 - $500

YOUNG BILL HICKOK
(1949R - Republic) Roy Rogers, George "Gabby" Hayes
One Sheet:　$40 - $75　　*Re-release.*

YOUNG BILLY YOUNG
(1969 - United Artists) Robert Mitchum, Angie Dickinson, Robert Walker
One Sheet:　$15 - $25

YOUNG BLOOD
(1933 - Monogram) Bob Steele
One Sheet:　$125 - $250　　*Cowboy Movie Posters # 151.*

YOUNG BRIDE
(1932 - RKO) Helen Twelvetrees, Eric Linden
One Sheet:　$150 - $300

YOUNG BUFFALO BILL
(1940 - Republic) Roy Rogers, George "Gabby" Hayes
One Sheet:　$250 - $600

YOUNG CAPTIVES, THE
(1958 - Paramount) Steven Marlo, Luana Patten
One Sheet:　$10 - $20

YOUNG CASSIDY
(1965 - MGM) Rod Taylor, Flora Robson
One Sheet:　$5 - $10

YOUNG DANIEL BOONE
(1950 - Monogram) David Bruce, Kristine Miller
One Sheet:　$30 - $50

YOUNG DESIRE
(1930 - Universal) Mary Nolan, William Janney
One Sheet:　$150 - $300

YOUNG DIANA, THE
(1922 - Paramount) Marion Davies
One Sheet:　$500 - $900

YOUNG DILLINGER
(1965 - Allied Artists) Nick Adams, Robert Conrad
One Sheet:　$15 - $30

YOUNG DIVORCEES, THE
(1977? - Monarch) Tom Fielding
One Sheet:　$3 - $5

YOUNG DOCTORS, THE
(1961 - United Artists) Fredric March, Ben Gazzara
One Sheet:　$15 - $25

YOUNG DOCTORS IN LOVE
(1982 - 20th Century Fox) Michael McKean, Sean Young
One Sheet:　$3 - $5

YOUNG DON'T CRY, THE
(1957 - Columbia) Sal Mineo, James Whitmore
One Sheet:　$15 - $25

YOUNG DONOVAN'S KID
(1931 - RKO) Boris Karloff, Jackie Cooper, Richard Dix
One Sheet:　$200 - $400

YOUNG DR. KILDARE
(1938 - MGM) Lew Ayres, Lionel Barrymore
One Sheet:　$75 - $150

YOUNG DYNAMITE
(1937 - Conn) Frankie Darro, Kane Richmond
One Sheet:　$40 - $75

YOUNG EAGLES

(1930 - Paramount) Charles "Buddy" Rogers, Jean Arthur
One Sheet:　$150 - $300

YOUNG EAGLES, THE
(1934 - First Division) Bobby Cox, Jim Vance
One Sheet:　$200 - $400　　*Serial. Western. 12 Episodes.*

YOUNG EINSTEIN
(1989 - Warner Bros.) Yahoo Serious, Odile Le Clezio
One Sheet:　$3 - $5

YOUNG FRANKENSTEIN
(1974 - Fox) Gene Wilder, Peter Boyle, Marty Feldman, Dir: Mel Brooks
One Sheet:　$30 - $60

One Sheet

YOUNG FUGITIVES
(1938 - Universal) Robert Wilcox, Dorothea Kent
One Sheet:　$50 - $100

YOUNG FURY
(1965 - Paramount) Rory Calhoun, Virginia Mayo, William Bendix
One Sheet:　$15 - $25　　*Bendix's final film.*

YOUNG GO WILD, THE
(1962 - Ultra) Peter Van Eyck, Christian Wolff
One Sheet:　$15 - $25　　*Teenage crime.*

YOUNG GRADUATES, THE
(1971 - Crown) Patricia Wymer
One Sheet:　$3 - $5

YOUNG GUNS, THE
(1956 - Allied Artists) Russ Tamblyn, Gloria Talbott
One Sheet:　$10 - $20

YOUNG GUNS
(1988 - Morgan Creek) Emilio Estevez, Kiefer Sutherland
One Sheet:　$10 - $20

YOUNG GUNS II
(1990 - 20th Century Fox) Emilio Estevez, Lou Diamond Phillips
One Sheet:　$5 - $10

YOUNG GUNS OF TEXAS
(1963 - 20th Century Fox) Jim Mitchum, Jody McCrea
One Sheet:　$5 - $10

YOUNG IDEAS
(1943 - MGM) Susan Peters, Herbert Marshall
One Sheet:　$30 - $50

YOUNG IN HEART, THE
(1938 - United Artists) Douglas Fairbanks, Jr, Janet Gaynor
One Sheet:　$75 - $150

YOUNG JESSE JAMES
(1960 - 20th Century Fox) Ray Stricklyn, Merry Anders
One Sheet:　$15 - $25

YOUNG KING COLE
(1922 - Universal-Jewel) Reginald Denny
One Sheet:　$250 - $500

YOUNG LAND, THE
(1959 - Columbia) Pat Wayne, Yvonne Craig
One Sheet:　$15 - $25

YOUNG LIONS, THE
(1958 - 20th Century Fox) Marlon Brando, Montgomery Clift, Dean Martin

One Sheet:　$50 - $100

YOUNG LOVERS, THE
(1949 - Filmmakers) Keefe Brasselle, Sally Forrest
One Sheet:　$15 - $30

YOUNG LOVERS, THE
(1964 - MGM) Peter Fonda, Sharon Hugueny, Nick Adams
One Sheet:　$7 - $15

YOUNG MAN OF MANHATTAN
(1930 - Paramount Publix) Ginger Rogers, Claudette Colbert, Norman Foster
One Sheet:　$500 - $800

YOUNG MAN WITH A HORN
(1949 - Warner Bros.) Kirk Douglas, Lauren Bacall
One Sheet:　$50 - $100

YOUNG MAN WITH IDEAS
(1951 - MGM) Glenn Ford, Ruth Roman
One Sheet:　$15 - $25

YOUNG MR. LINCOLN
(1939 - 20th Century Fox) Henry Fonda, Alice Brady
One Sheet:　$600 - $1,000

YOUNG MR. PITT, THE
(1942 - 20th Century Fox) Robert Donat, Phyllis Calvert
One Sheet:　$50 - $100

YOUNG ONE, THE
(1961 - Olmec) Zachary Scott
One Sheet:　$5 - $10

YOUNG PEOPLE
(1940 - 20th Century Fox) Shirley Temple, Jack Oakie, Charlotte Greenwood
One Sheet:　$250 - $500

YOUNG PHILADELPHIANS, THE
(1959 - Warner Bros.) Paul Newman, Barbara Rush
One Sheet:　$20 - $40

YOUNG POISONER'S HANDBOOK, THE
(1996 - Cinepix) Hugh O'Conor
One Sheet:　$5 - $12　　*Comedy.*

YOUNG RACERS, THE
(1963 - AIP) Mark Damon, William Campbell
One Sheet:　$15 - $35　　*Sports (Auto racing).*

YOUNG RAJAH, THE
(1922 - Paramount) Rudolph Valentino
One Sheet:　$1,900 - $3,000

YOUNG ROMANCE
(1915 - Paramount) Edith Taliaferro, Tom Forman
One Sheet:　$350 - $750

YOUNG ROUNDERS, THE
(197? - -) Joel McCrea, Slim Pickens, Marty Robbins
One Sheet:　$15 - $30　　*Country musical.*

YOUNG RUNAWAYS, THE
(1968 - MGM) Brooke Bundy, Kevin Coughlin, Lloyd Bochner
One Sheet:　$7 - $15

YOUNG SAVAGES, THE
(1961 - United Artists) Burt Lancaster, Shelley Winters, Telly Savalas
One Sheet:　$10 - $20　　*Teenage gangs. Savalas' film debut.*

YOUNG SHERLOCK HOLMES
(1985 - Paramount) Nicholas Rowe, Alan Cox
One Sheet:　$5 - $10

YOUNG SINNERS
(1931 - Fox) Thomas Meighan, Hardie Albright, Dorothy Jordan
One Sheet:　$125 - $250

YOUNG SINNERS
(1965 - United Screen Arts) Tom Laughlin, Stephanie Powers
One Sheet:　$7 - $15

YOUNG STRANGER, THE
(1957 - RKO) Kim Hunter, James McArthur
One Sheet:　$15 - $25

YOUNG SWINGERS, THE

(1964 - 20th Century Fox) Rod Lauren, Molly Bee
One Sheet:　$15 - $30

YOUNG, THE EVIL, AND THE SAVAGE, THE
(1968 - AIP) Michael Rennie, Mark Damon
One Sheet:　$10 - $20

YOUNG TOM EDISON
(1940 - MGM) Mickey Rooney, Fay Bainter
One Sheet:　$75 - $125

YOUNG TORLESS
(1968 - Kanawha) Matthieu Carriere, Bernd Tischer, Marian Seidowsky
One Sheet:　$5 - $10

YOUNG WARRIORS, THE
(1966 - Universal) James Drury, Steve Carlson
One Sheet:　$5 - $10

YOUNG WHIRLWIND
(1928 - FBO) Buzz Baron, Edmund Cobb
One Sheet:　$150 - $350

YOUNG WIDOW
(1946 - United Artists) Jane Russell, Louis Hayward
One Sheet:　$50 - $100

YOUNG, WILLING, AND EAGER
(1962 - Brenner Association) Jess Conrad, Hermione Baddeley
One Sheet:　$7 - $15

YOUNG WINSTON
(1972 - Columbia) Simon Ward, Robert Shaw, Anne Bancroft
One Sheet:　$3 - $5

YOUNG WIVES' TALE
(1952 - Stratford) Audrey Hepburn, Nigel Patrick
One Sheet:　$75 - $150

YOUNG WOODLEY
(1930 - British International) Madeleine Carroll, Frank Lawton
One Sheet:　$100 - $200

YOUNGBLOOD
(1978 - AIP) Lawrence-Hilton Jacobs, Bryan O'Dell
One Sheet:　$15 - $25　　*Blaxploitation.*

YOUNGBLOOD
(1986 - United Artists) Rob Lowe, Cynthia Gibb, Patrick Swayze
One Sheet:　$7 - $15

YOUNGBLOOD HAWKE
(1964 - Warner Bros.) James Franciscus, Suzanne Pleshette
One Sheet:　$10 - $20

YOUNGER BROTHERS, THE
(1918 - Long Horn) -
One Sheet:　$250 - $600

YOUNGER BROTHERS, THE
(1949 - Warner Bros.) Wayne Morris, Janis Paige, Bruce Bennett
One Sheet:　$15 - $25

YOUNGER GENERATION, THE
(1929 - -) Jean Hersholt, Rex Lease, Dir: Frank Capra
One Sheet:　$800 - $1,500　　*Silent film with talking sequences.*

YOUNGEST PROFESSION, THE
(1943 - MGM) Virginia Weidler, Edward Arnold
One Sheet:　$30 - $50

YOUR CHEATIN' HEART
(1965 - MGM) George Hamilton, Susan Oliver
One Sheet:　$15 - $30　　*Based on the life of Hank Williams.*

YOUR PAST IS SHOWING
(1958 - Rank) Terry-Thomas, Peter Sellers
One Sheet:　$15 - $30

YOUR SHADOW IS MINE
(1963 - Continental) Jill Haworth, Michael Ruhl
One Sheet:　$5 - $10

YOUR THREE MINUTES ARE UP
(1973 - Cinerama) Beau Bridges, Ron Leiberman
One Sheet:　$3 - $5

YOUR UNCLE DUDLEY
(1935 - 20th Century Fox) Edward Everett

Horton, Lois Wilson
One Sheet: $100 - $200

YOURS, MINE AND OURS
(1968 - United Artists) Lucille Ball, Henry
Fonda
One Sheet: $15 - $30   *Frazetta art.*

YOUTH AFLAME
(1945 - Continental) Joy Reese, Warren Burr
One Sheet: $30 - $50   *Exploitation.*

YOUTH ON PARADE
(1942 - Republic) John Hubbard, Martha
O'Driscoll
One Sheet: $20 - $40

YOUTH ON PAROLE
(1937 - Republic) Marian Marsha
One Sheet: $40 - $75

YOUTH ON TRIAL
(1945 - Columbia) Cora Sue Collins, Eric
Sinclair
One Sheet: $40 - $75

YOUTH RUNS WILD
(1944 - RKO) Kent Smith, Bonita Granville
One Sheet: $50 - $100

YOUTH TAKES A FLING
(1938 - Universal) Joel McCrea, Andrea Leeds
One Sheet: $200 - $400

YOUTH TO YOUTH
(1922 - Metro) Billie Dove
One Sheet: $150 - $350

YOUTH WILL BE SERVED
(1940 - 20th Century Fox) Jane Withers, Jane
Darwell, Robert Conway
One Sheet: $50 - $100

YOUTH'S DESIRE
(1920 - -) Joseph Bennett, Doris Baker
One Sheet: $125 - $250

YUKON FLIGHT
(1940 - Monogram) James Newill, Louise
Stanley
One Sheet: $50 - $100   *RENFREW
series.*

YUKON GOLD
(1952 - Monogram) Kirby Grant
One Sheet: $20 - $40

YUKON JAKE
(1924 - Pathe) Ben Turpin
One Sheet: $600 - $1,000

One Sheet

YUKON MANHUNT
(1951 - Monogram) Kirby Grant, Margaret Field
One Sheet: $15 - $35

YUKON PATROL, THE
(1942 - Republic) Allan Lane, Lita Conway
One Sheet: $30 - $50   *Feature-length
version of the serial KING OF THE ROYAL
MOUNTED.*

YUKON VENGEANCE
(1954 - Monogram) Kirby Grant, Mary Ellen
Kay
One Sheet: $15 - $35

YUMPIN' YIMINY
(1941 - Columbia) El Brendel
One Sheet: $75 - $150   *Comedy short.
Duotone.*

Z
(1969 - Cinema 5) Yves Montand, Irene Papas
One Sheet: $40 - $75   *Academy*

Award: Best Foreign film.

ZABRISKIE POINT
(1970 - MGM) Mark Frechette, Daria Halprin,
Rod Taylor
One Sheet: $20 - $40   *Dir:
Michelangelo Antonioni.*

ZACHARIAH
(1971 - Cinerama) John Rubinstein, Patricia
Quinn, Don Johnson
One Sheet: $15 - $25   *Rock 'n' Roll.
First "electric western."*

ZAMBA
(1949 - Eagle-Lion) Jon Hall, June Vincent,
George Cooper
One Sheet: $10 - $20

ZAMBOANGA
(1937 - Grand National) -
One Sheet: $50 - $100

ZANDER THE GREAT
(1925 - MGM) Marion Davis, Hedda Hopper
One Sheet: $200 - $400

ZANDY'S BRIDE
(1974 - Warner Bros.) Gene Hackman, Liv
Ullmann
One Sheet: $5 - $10

ZANZABUKU
(1956 - Republic) -
One Sheet: $15 - $30   *Documentary.*

ZANZIBAR
(1940 - Universal) James Craig, Eduardo
Cilanneli, Lola Lane
One Sheet: $30 - $50

ZANZIBAR
(1948R - Universal) James Craig, Eduardo
Cilanneli, Lola Lane
One Sheet: $15 - $25   *Re-release.*

ZAPPED!
(1982 - Embassy) Scott Baio, Heather Thomas
One Sheet: $3 - $5

ZARAK
(1956 - Columbia) Victor Mature, Anita Ekberg,
Michael Wilding
One Sheet: $10 - $20

ZARDOZ
(1974 - 20th Century Fox) Sean Connery,
Charlotte Rampling
One Sheet: $30 - $60   *Cult classic.*

ZAZA
(1924 - Paramount) Gloria Swanson
One Sheet: $1,300 - $2,000

ZAZA
(1938 - Paramount) Claudette Colbert, Herbert
Marshall
One Sheet: $500 - $800

ZEB'S MUSICAL CAREER
(1913 - Edison) -
One Sheet: $500 - $800

ZEBRA FORCE
(1977 - -) Mike Lane
One Sheet: $3 - $5

ZEBRA IN THE KITCHEN
(1965 - MGM) Jay North, Martin Milner
One Sheet: $7 - $15

ZEBRA IN THE KITCHEN
(1972R - MGM) Jay North, Martin Milner
One Sheet: $3 - $5   *Re-release.*

ZEBRAHEAD
(1993 - Triumph) Michael Rappaport, N'Bushe
Wright
One Sheet: $3 - $5

ZED & TWO NOUGHTS, A
(1985 - -) Andrea Ferreol, Brian Deacon
One Sheet: $5 - $10

ZELIG
(1983 - Warner Bros.) Woody Allen, Mia Farrow
One Sheet: $5 - $10   *Two styles,
full-color style worth 50% more.*

ZELLY AND ME
(1988 - -) Glynis Johns
One Sheet: $3 - $5

ZENOBIA

(1939 - United Artists) Oliver Hardy, Harry
Langdon, Billie Burke
One Sheet: $250 - $500

ZENTROPA
(1992 - Miramax) Jean Marc Barr, Barbara
Sukowa
One Sheet: $3 - $5   *Partial
German.*

ZEPPELIN
(1971 - Warner Bros.) Elke Sommer, Michael
York
One Sheet: $15 - $25

ZERO
(1928 - Pathe) Stewart Rome, Fay Compton
One Sheet: $150 - $300

ZERO FOR CONDUCT
(1933 - -) Jean Daste, Robert Le Flon
One Sheet: $150 - $300   *French.*

ZERO HOUR
(1940 - Republic) Otto Kruger, Frieda Inescort
One Sheet: $40 - $75

ZERO HOUR
(1957 - Paramount) Dana Andrews, Linda
Darnell
One Sheet: $15 - $35

ZERO TO SIXTY
(1978 - First Artists) Darren McGavin, Joan
Collins
One Sheet: $7 - $15

ZEUS AND ROXANNE
(1996 - MGM) Steve Guttenberg, Kathleen
Quinlan
One Sheet: $3 - $5

ZEX - THE ELECTRONIC MONSTER
(1959 - -) -
One Sheet: $50 - $100

ZIEGFELD FOLLIES
(1946 - MGM) William Powell, Fred Astaire,
Lucille Ball, All-star cast
One Sheet: $600 - $1,000   *George Petty
art.*

Six Sheet

ZIEGFELD GIRL
(1941 - MGM) James Stewart, Judy Garland,
Lana Turner, Hedy Lamarr
One Sheet: $350 - $750

**ZIGGY STARDUST AND THE SPIDERS FROM
MARS**
(1983 - -) David Bowie
One Sheet: $30 - $60   *Rock 'n' Roll.*

ZIGZAG
(1970 - MGM) George Kennedy, Anne Jackson,
Eli Wallach
One Sheet: $5 - $10

ZINA
(1985 - -) Domiziana Giordano
One Sheet: $3 - $5

ZIS BOOM BAH
(1941 - Monogram) Grace Hayes, Peter Lind
Hayes
One Sheet: $15 - $35   *Big Band
musical.*

ZITA
(1968 - -) Joanne Shimkus
One Sheet: $5 - $10

ZOMBIE
(1979 - Gross) Tisa Farrow, Ian McCulloch
One Sheet: $15 - $25

ZOMBIE HIGH
(1987 - -) Richard Cox
One Sheet: $5 - $10

ZOMBIE ISLAND MASSACRE
(1984 - -) David Broadnax
One Sheet: $7 - $15

ZOMBIES OF MORA TAU
(1957 - Columbia) Allison Hayes, Gregg Palmer
One Sheet: $40 - $75

ZOMBIES OF THE STRATOSPHERE
(1952 - Republic) Judd Holdren, Aline Towne,
Leonard Nimoy
One Sheet: $75 - $125   *Serial. 12
Chapters. Leonard Nimoy's first film. Graven
Images, pg. 181.*

ZOMBIES ON BROADWAY
(1945 - RKO) Wally Brown, Alan Carney, Bela
Lugosi
One Sheet: $100 - $200

ZONTAR, THE THING FROM VENUS
(1968 - Azalea) John Agar, Anthony Houston
One Sheet: $15 - $35

ZOO IN BUDAPEST
(1933 - Fox) Loretta Young, Gene Raymond
One Sheet: $350 - $750

ZOOT CAT, THE
(1944 - MGM) Tom & Jerry
One Sheet: $1,000 - $1,800   *Cartoon.
Cartoon Movie Posters #266.*

ZOOT SUIT
(1981 - Universal) Daniel Valdez, Edward
James Olmos
One Sheet: $5 - $10

ZORBA THE GREEK
(1965 - International Classics) Anthony Quinn,
Alan Bates, Irene Papas
One Sheet: $30 - $60   *Academy
Award Movie Posters #226.*

ZORRO RIDES AGAIN
(1937 - Republic) Duncan Renaldo, John
Carroll, Helen Christian
One Sheet: $200 - $400   *Serial.
Western. 12 Chapters. One Sheet(Chapter
1):$300-$600.*

ZORRO RIDES AGAIN
(1959 - Republic) Duncan Renaldo, John
Carroll
One Sheet: $50 - $100   *Feature-length
version of the serial.*

ZORRO THE GAY BLADE
(1981 - 20th Century Fox) George Hamilton,
Lauren Hutton
One Sheet: $3 - $5

ZORRO'S BLACK WHIP
(1944 - Republic) George J. Lewis, Linda
Stirling
One Sheet: $125 - $250   *Serial.
Western. 12 Chapters.*

ZORRO'S FIGHTING LEGION
(1939 - Republic) Reed Hadley, Sheila Darcy
One Sheet: $200 - $400   *Serial.
Western. 12 Chapters. One Sheet(Chapter
One):$400-$600.*

ZOTZ
(1962 - Columbia) Tom Poston, Julia Meade
One Sheet: $5 - $10

ZOU ZOU
(1934 - Marc Allegret Films) Josephine Baker,
Jean Gabin
One Sheet: $4,000 - $6,000   *Price is for
Original French 47x63. Belgian(24x33):$1000-
$2000. Separate Cinema, pg. 78.*

Z.P.G.
(1972 - Paramount) Oliver Reed, Geraldine
Chaplin, Diane Cilento
One Sheet: $5 - $10

ZULU
(1964 - Embassy) Stanley Baker, Michael
Caine, Jack Hawkins
One Sheet: $30 - $50

ZULU DAWN
(1979 - Warner Bros.) Burt Lancaster, Peter
O'Toole
One Sheet: $5 - $10

Collecting
Hollywood
magazine

The MOVIE POSTER Marketplace!

Whether you're new to the hobby, or have been around for years, Collecting Hollywood is THE magazine for you!

SAMPLE COPY $5

Brought to you by the publishers of this Price Guide!!!

JOIN THE FUN! GET SIX ISSUES OF COLLECTING HOLLYWOOD DELIVERED TO YOUR MAILBOX FOR ONLY $13.95!

SUBSCRIPTION ORDER FORM

TO USE YOUR CREDIT CARD CALL 1-423-265-5515
Monday - Friday until 5 PM Eastern Time. We accept Mastercard or Visa

☐ New Subscription   ☐ Renewal

USA   **6 issues**
☐ **3RD CLASS MAIL** $13.95
   Standard delivery inside the 50 States.
   Takes 10-14 days to arrive.
☐ **PRIORITY MAIL** $31.95
   2 Day delivery hot off the press.
CANADA
☐ **Airmail** $31.95
   Fastest delivery to the Provinces.
   Takes 7-10 days to arrive.
OVERSEAS
☐ **Airmail** $49.95

PAYMENT METHOD

Please start my subscription immediately.

I'll pay by ( ) check ( ) money order ( ) credit card

If paying by credit card:

Credit Card #: _____

Exp. Date: _____

Signature: _____

REMIT PAYMENT WITH ORDER TO: Collecting Hollywood, P.O. Box 2512, Chattanooga, TN 37409

Name: _____

Address: _____

City/State/Zip: _____

Telephone: _____

☐ Dealer   ☐ Collector   ☐ Other

WHAT DO YOU COLLECT?

EMAIL SUBS: JONRWARREN@AOL.COM

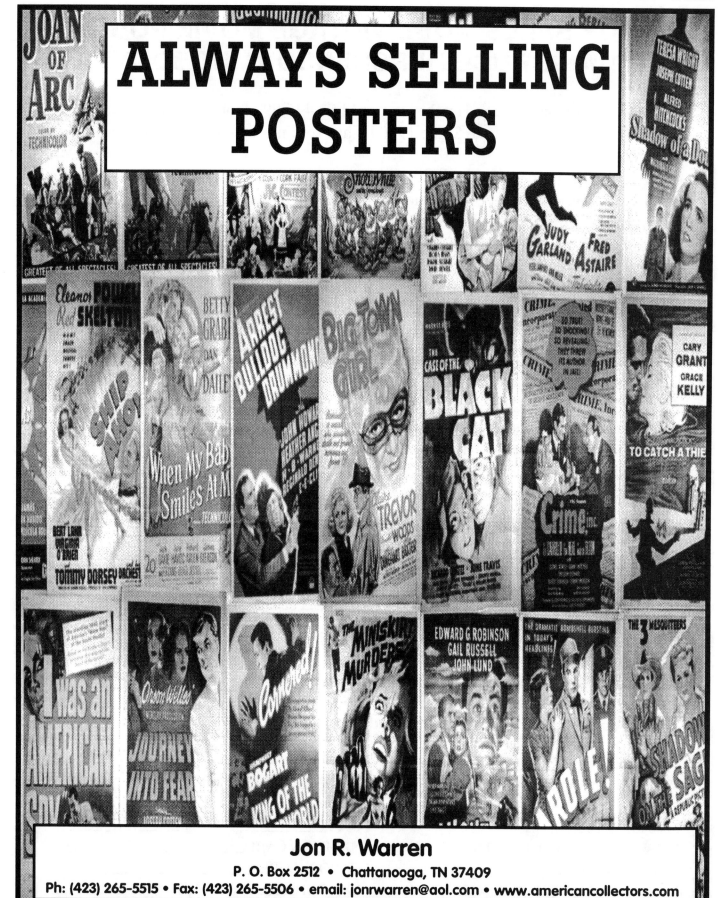

ALWAYS SELLING POSTERS

Jon R. Warren

P. O. Box 2512 • Chattanooga, TN 37409

Ph: (423) 265-5515 • Fax: (423) 265-5506 • email: jonrwarren@aol.com • www.americancollectors.com

ALWAYS BUYING
POSTERS

Jon R. Warren

P. O. Box 2512 • Chattanooga, TN 37409

Ph: (423) 265-5515 • Fax: (423) 265-5506 • email: jonrwarren@aol.com • www.americancollectors.com

Your Posters are Slowly Dying!!!
Don't Gamble with their Futures!!!

Preserve Your Movie Memorabilia with R-Kival™ Quality Mylar® D

Movie Poster Size Sleeves & Boards

Avoid protective sleeves made of polyethylene, polypropylene and polyvinyl chloride (PVC). Most of these plastics are coated with chemicals and contain additives that migrate into paper and cause premature aging. Even uncoated polypropylene emits gases that seep into paper. The only material which can actually preserve paper is uncoated, archival quality polyester film such as Mylar® D or Melinex® 516. BCE's Movie Gards™ are made entirely from Mylar® D. This exceptionally strong transparent film will resist moisture, pollutants, oils and acids, and has a life expectancy of hundreds of years.

4 Mil Mylar® Movie-Gards™ for Movie Posters

CAT#	SIZE IN INCHES Plus 3/4" tab	TO FIT	PRICE EACH	wt. lbs.	PRICE PER 25	wt. lbs.	PRICE PER 50	wt. lbs.	PRICE PER 100	wt. lbs.	PRICE PER 500	wt. lbs.	PRICE PER 1,000	wt. lbs.
65	11 1/2" x 14 1/2"	Lobby Card					133.00	4	228.00	8	995.00	35	1,730.00	71
71*	27 3/4" x 41 3/4"	One Sheet Size (w/o tab)	13.35	3	290.00	15	504.00	24	874.00	48	3,795.00	240	6,620.00	480
72*	14 3/4" x 36 3/4"	Insert Poster (w/o tab)	6.40	3	140.00	9	242.00	12	420.00	22	1,825.00	111	3,170.00	222
73*	28 3/4" x 22 3/4"	Half Sheet Poster (w/o tab)	7.50	3	165.00	10	286.00	14	496.00	27	2,150.00	135	3,740.00	270
74*	14 3/4" x 22 3/4"	Window Card Poster (w/o tab)	4.65	3	100.00	7	176.00	8	305.00	14	1,325.00	69	2,300.00	137

* Indicates no corner cut tab.
Note: In order to obtain the higher quantity discount, mix and match in increments of 50 only. All products are sold only in quantities, and multiples of quantities, shown on pricing chart.

Start with Mylar®
Movie Gards™

- Heavy-duty (4 mil thick) true archival protective sleeve
- Made entirely of crystal clear, archival Mylar® D
- Heat sealed with our exclusive Ultra-Weld™ for the strongest seams in the industry

Add an Acid-Free Backing Board
Time-X-Tenders™

- The original, true acid free, R-Kival™ backing boards
- Heavy weight, 42 mil thick
- 8.5 pH with a 3% calcium carbonate buffer throughout

42 Mil Acid Free Time-X-Tenders™ Backing Boards for Movie Posters

CAT #	SIZE	FOR USE WITH	PRICE PER 25	wt. lbs.	PRICE PER 50	wt. lbs.	PRICE PER 100	wt. lbs.	PRICE PER 500	wt. lbs.
35	11 1/4" x 14 1/4"	Lobby Cards	$21.00	4	$37.00	8	$61.00	16	$242.00	80
36	27 1/4" x 41 1/4"	One Sheet Size	190.00	30	345.00	60	575.00	120	2,300.00	600
37	14 1/4" x 36 1/4"	Insert Poster	66.00	15	118.00	30	196.00	60	782.00	300
38	28 1/4" x 22 1/4"	Half Sheet Size	118.00	18	213.00	36	355.00	72	1,415.00	360
39	14 1/4" x 22 1/4"	Window Card Poster	59.00	16	107.00	32	177.00	64	710.00	320

Mix and match in increments of 50 only.

Combination Special

Get a set of 10 Mylar® Movie-Gards™
& 10 Acid-Free Time-X-Tenders™

Cat #	To Fit	Price per set	Wt. (lbs.)
6535	Lobby Cards	39.00	3
7136	One Sheet Size	279.00	13
7237	Insert Poster	83.00	7
7338	Half Sheet Poster	115.00	8
7439	Window Card Poster	66.50	5

GENERAL SHIPPING AND HANDLING CHART

TOTAL SHIPPING WEIGHT	IF YOUR ZIP CODE BEGINS WITH:				APO, FPO, AK, HI & ALL U.S. TER. via Parcel Post	ALL FOREIGN COUNTRIES via Parcel Post
	0,1	2,3 or 4	5,6 or 7	8,9		
0-2	5.75	6.75	7.25	7.75	7.00	12.50
3-5	7.25	7.75	8.25	8.75	9.50	14.50
6-10	8.75	10.00	10.50	11.50	16.75	29.25
11-15	10.00	11.50	12.25	14.25	22.00	37.75
16-20	11.50	13.50	14.50	17.75	25.50	48.75
21-25	14.00	15.25	17.75	19.25	28.50	65.50
26-30	15.25	17.00	19.75	22.00	29.00	75.00
31-35	17.50	19.75	22.00	25.75	30.00	84.50
36-40	18.50	20.50	23.25	26.25	33.00	94.50
41-45	19.50	22.50	25.75	29.50	34.00	103.75
46-50	21.00	25.00	27.75	32.50	35.00	116.50

Note: If weight is above 50 lbs., add together additional amounts. (Example: 60 lbs. in Zip 1 would be $21.00 plus $8.75, or $29.75 total.)

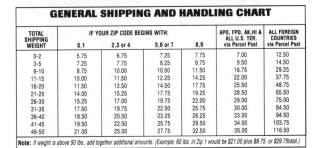

Bill Cole Enterprises, Inc.

P.O. Box 60, DEPT. MPG, Randolph, MA 02368-0600
(617) 986-2653   Fax (617) 986-2656
e-mail: BCEmylar@internetmci.com
web site: http://www. neponset.com/bcemylar

Time-X-Tenders™, Movie Gards™ Ultra-Weld™, and R-Kival™ are trademarks of Bill Cole Enterprises, Inc. All references to Mylar® refer to archival quality polyester film such as Mylar® type D by Dupont Co., or equivalent material such as Melinex® 516 by ICI Corp.

PLEASE HELP!
Corrections & Additions Form

Please contribute to the efforts of fellow movie poster collectors by adding titles or other information found missing from this edition. Are there errors, typos, mis-listings, mis-prices, or omissions that need to be corrected? Fill out this form and mail it to the address below. You will become eligible for one of the free copies sent out to contributors to next year's edition.

PRICE CHANGES

Title	Year	Price

NEW TITLES

Title	Year	Price

Please use other sheets and list title, year, main stars, releasing company, and one sheet value (if known)

ERRORS/TYPOS

Title	Year	Page#

Your Name:

Address:
City: State:
Zip:

Phone:

Mail to:
Warren's Movie Poster Price Guide
P. O. Box 2512
Chattanooga, TN 37409
(423) 265-5515 or FAX: (423) 265-5506